MINING ENGINEERS' HANDBOOK

MINING ENGINEERS' HANDBOOK

WRITTEN BY A STAFF OF FORTY-SIX SPECIALISTS
UNDER THE EDITORSHIP OF

ROBERT PEELE
LATE PROFESSOR EMERITUS OF MINING ENGINEERING IN
THE SCHOOL OF MINES, COLUMBIA UNIVERSITY

WITH THE COLLABORATION OF

JOHN A. CHURCH
MINING AND METALLURGICAL ENGINEER

THIRD EDITION
SECOND PRINTING

IN TWO VOLUMES
VOL. I

NEW YORK
JOHN WILEY & SONS, INC.
LONDON: CHAPMAN & HALL, LIMITED

PUBLISHER'S PREFACE

In making plans for new editions of our handbooks in mechanical engineering and in electrical engineering, it soon became clear that engineering science and practice had developed to such an extent that handbooks were growing beyond all practical bounds. They had become both bulky and inconvenient and contained much duplicated material. In order to solve the problems presented by these conditions, the editors of our various handbooks were asked to serve as an advisory editorial board.

This board recommended, first, that the fundamental material underlying all engineering be published in a separate volume, and, second, that the existing handbooks as they are revised be issued in several volumes containing material closely related to the specialized branches of engineering. As a result of these recommendations, the Wiley Engineering Handbook Series has been initiated, which in the beginning will comprise the following: Eshbach's "Handbook of Engineering Fundamentals"; Kent's "Mechanical Engineers' Handbook" in two volumes, viz., "Power" and "Design and Shop Practice"; Pender's "Electrical Engineers' Handbook" in two volumes, viz., "Electric Power" and "Communication and Electronics"; Peele's "Mining Engineers' Handbook."

This division has also made it possible to devote more space to the various topics so that the entire new series of handbooks contains more complete information on all topics than heretofore has been possible. It is our hope that this new plan will give engineers information that is more useful, more complete, and in more convenient form.

JOHN WILEY & SONS, INC.

PREFACE TO THIRD EDITION

The first edition of this book was published early in 1918. In preparing the second edition, issued in 1927, many changes in subject matter were found necessary, as set forth in the preface to that edition, and references to them need not be repeated here. Most of these alterations were called for by the progressive modifications of mining methods and appliances, and the development of new methods. Much new matter was added, some of the older text omitted, and some sections of the book were almost entirely rewritten.

Rewriting the present edition made necessary the radical revision of text and illustrations of Sections 3, 4, 5, 8, 10, 10A, 12, 14, 15, 16, 22, 24, 26, 27, 32, 33, 35 and 40, together with minor changes in many other parts of the book.

Especial attention is called to the following: (a) important new matter throughout Section 10, on further changes in practice in "Methods of Mining," by James F. McClelland, Vice President of Phelps Dodge Corp; (b) new articles 24 to 28 of renumbered Section 45; (c) a valuable new Section 44, on "Petroleum Production," by S. F. Shaw, has been added; (d) the marked advance of "Geophysical Prospecting" during the past decade has made advisable the addition of an entirely new Section 10A, on that subject, by Frederick W. Lee, of the U. S. Geological Survey. This Section replaces, in greatly expanded form, the data formerly contained in Articles 3 and 4 of Section 10; (e) Section 14, on "Mine Ventilation," has been almost wholly rewritten by George E. McElroy, of the U. S. Bureau of Mines; (f) radical revisions have also been made in Section 12, "Hoisting Plant, Shaft Pockets and Ore Bins," by Professor Philip B. Bucky, of the Columbia School of Mines, and of Section 15, "Compressed Air Practice," by A. W. Loomis, of the Ingersoll-Rand Co; (g) the wide development of methods and devices for underground handling and conveying of mineral has led to the transfer of most of the data, formerly in Article 92 of Section 10, to Section 27, the first part of which has been rewritten and expanded by Walter M. Dake, Research Manager of the McGraw-Hill Publishing Co.

The preparation of this edition has further required resetting the entire book. A larger format was necessary, since the two volumes of the Third Edition are Nos VI and VII of the new Wiley Engineering Handbook Series. This change, together with the extensive revisions of text already referred to, has consumed much more time and labor than were required for the second edition.

To the list of deaths of the original Associate Editors, noted in the preface to the second edition, the following names must now be added: Edwin S. Jarrett (Sec. 8), F. Ernest Brackett (Sec. 14), Richard T. Dana (Sec. 15) T. R. Woodbridge (Sec. 29), E. J. Hall (Sec. 30), and Charles H. Burnside (Sec. 36).

For various reasons, a number of associate editors of the second edition were unable to serve again. Their places have been taken by: Clinton L. Bogert (Sec. 3), Samuel R. Russell (Sec. 5), Charles F. Jackson (Sec. 6), Ralph H. Chambers (Sec. 8), Philip B. Bucky (Sec. 12), George E. McElroy (Sec. 14), A. W. Loomis (Sec. 15), Walter M. Dake (Sec. 27), J. B. Morrow and staff (part I of Sec. 35), and Theodore Baumeister, Jr. (Sec. 40). For further information as to these accessions to the list of Associate Editors, see the Table of Contents.

It is a pleasure to acknowledge the efficient collaboration of my friend John A. Church, in connection with this new edition. Besides being the Associate Editor of Section 7, on "Shaft Sinking in Rock," he has done a large amount of work in revising manuscripts, as received from the contributors to the book, and in the preparation of illustrations for the engraver.

ROBERT PEELE

NEW YORK,
March, 1941

PREFACE TO FIRST EDITION

There is a considerable literature of mining, comprising treatises, textbooks, monographs, papers published in the transactions of engineering societies, and the contents of the mining periodicals. The treatises and textbooks are largely descriptive, and are intended chiefly for students. Among the best known are those of Foster, Hughes, Haton de la Goupillière, Köhler, Cambessédès, Callon, Ponson, Bulman and Redmayne, Bailes, Boulton, and Pamely. Though many of these books are antiquated in their engineering features, some of the older ones (as those of Callon and Haton) contain much that is still of value, and mining engineers would do well to have acquaintance with them. Besides the general treatises there are the more recent monographs of Truscot, Hatch and Chalmers, and Denny, on the Witwatersrand goldfields, Charleton's "Tin Mines of the World," Hoover's "Principles of Mining," Finlay's "Cost of Mining," and a number of useful books on specific subjects relating to mining, or to the mechanical engineering of mines.

A valid reason for bringing out a new Mining Engineers' Handbook may be found in the fact that the two already in existence either omit, or treat too briefly, many subjects which constitute important parts of the professional equipment of the present day mining engineer. It will be apparent, even on a cursory examination of the following pages, that a handbook of mining must include a greater variety of subject matter than books on other branches of engineering, and that the field to be covered is too wide to be dealt with satisfactorily by a single writer within any reasonable period of time.

In February and March, 1913, the Editor of this book outlined the table of contents, and invited a number of Associate Editors to contribute sections on their respective specialties. Besides those sections dealing with mineralogy, ore deposits, methods of prospecting, exploration and mining, and mining plant of all kinds, there are others on certain branches of civil, electrical and mechanical engineering. It may be thought by some that this collateral material occupies too much space in a book on mining. But, in view of the important part played by the allied branches of engineering in equipping and operating modern mines, the Editor believes the allotment of space is reasonable. He has endeavored to meet the demands not only of engineers concerned with the development and management of mines, but also of the large number of those who have more to do with, and greater interest in, the construction details involved in the installation of plant. Therefore, the aim has been to supply such data on machinery, power plant, electric transmission and structural design, as the mining engineer may need when in the field and out of reach of his personal notes and technical library. For office use, there is at the end of each section a bibliography of the more important books and papers on the subjects dealt with.

In practice, no well-defined boundary exists between the fields of work of the mining engineer and the metallurgist. While, under some conditions and in some regions, the mining engineer's functions end with the winning of the ore and its delivery to a custom reduction works (mill or smelter), in other cases the mining company's plant includes a concentrating mill, amalgamating or cyaniding works (as at many gold and silver mines), or even a smelting establishment. In planning the book, the question arose as to how much space should properly be given to the processes of ore treatment. To cover any considerable part of the great field of modern metallurgy would be impracticable, without extending the work beyond the limits of a single volume. Realizing that the urgent need of a companion Handbook of Metallurgy must soon be supplied, it was decided, as a compromise, to furnish condensed summaries of those processes of treatment which are frequently carried on by mining companies themselves. The book, therefore, contains sections on ore-dressing, ore-testing, gold amalgamation, an outline of the cyanide process, the preparation of anthracite, bituminous coal and coke, and a brief résumé of certain facts respecting the selling, purchasing, and metallurgical treatment of ores, that are of immediate interest to the engineer in control of mining operations.

The relatively small space allotted to coal mining is due chiefly to three considerations: first, a Coal-mining Pocketbook is already in existence; second, metal-mining methods are more varied than those for coal, due to the greater diversity in form and occurrence of metalliferous deposits; third, having discussed in Section 10, under Metal-mining Methods, the operations common to nearly all mining, the articles on coal mining are properly confined to the methods and data peculiar to that branch of the industry.

The question of supplying cost data is difficult. A large number of itemized tables are included in the sections on Cost of Mining, Exploitation of Mineral Deposits, Boring, and other subjects, but costs of machines and apparatus are given sparingly throughout the book. This has been judged best, because of frequent price changes, and the great diversity of types of mechanical plant. In any case, to make close estimates, the engineer must apply to the makers for current prices. In some parts of the book, the names of machinery builders have been used freely, but without intention to indicate a preference for the product of any particular maker.

While the Editor has aimed to make the style and arrangement uniform, he has had good reason to realize the difficulty of securing consistency in these matters, considering the heterogeneous nature of the subject matter, and the fact that it has been written or compiled by so large a corps of Associate Editors. In these circumstances, unity and evenness of treatment can hardly be expected, but an endeavor has been made to observe a reasonable proportion between the length of each section and its relative importance. To save space, abbreviations are employed for a few words in common use by engineers, and chemical elements and compounds are generally represented by their symbols.

The thanks of the Editor are due to members of the staff for their painstaking work, in many cases carried on in the intervals between pressing professional engagements in the field, and to the Publishers for their liberal spirit of coöperation in facilitating the preparation of the book. The Editor desires to express his especial appreciation of the valuable suggestions and assistance in revising manuscript and correcting proof, of Professor Edward K. Judd, of the Columbia School of Mines. It was planned to publish this book in 1916. The breaking out of the Great War, about one year after the work was begun, is responsible in large measure for the delay.

ROBERT PEELE

COLUMBIA SCHOOL OF MINES,
NEW YORK, *December*, 1917

LIST OF CONTRIBUTORS

Arthur P. Ackerman.—*Rock Excavation.*

Theodore Baumeister, Jr, Associate Professor of Mechanical Engineering, Columbia University; Consulting Engineer.—*Power and Power Machinery.*

Clinton L. Bogert, Consulting Engineer.—*Earth Excavation.*

Charles B. Breed, Professor of Railway and Highway Engineering, Massachusetts Institute of Technology.—*Surveying.*

Philip B. Bucky, E.M., Associate Professor of Mining, School of Mines, Columbia University.—*Hoisting Plant, Shaft Pockets, and Ore Bins.*

C. H. Burnside, Late Associate Professor of Mechanics, Columbia University.—*Engineers' Tables* and *Mathematics and Mechanics.*

F. Ernest Brackett, Late Mining Engineer.—*Mine Ventilation.*

Ralph H. Chambers, D.Eng., Consulting Civil Engineer.—*Shaft Sinking in Unstable and Waterbearing Ground.*

Homer L. Carr, Mining Engineer.—*Shaft Sinking in Rock.*

John A. Church, Jr., Mining Engineer.—*Shaft Sinking in Rock.*

Walter M. Dake, Research Manager, Mining Publications, McGraw–Hill Publishing Company.—*Underground Mechanical Loading, Conveying, and Handling.*

Richard T. Dana, C.E., Late Consulting Engineer.—*Compressed Air Practice, Earth Excavation* and *Rock Excavation.*

D. H. Davis, Chief Chemist, Pittsburgh Coal Co.—*Preparation and Coking of Bituminous Coal.*

John V. N. Dorr, Metallurgical Engineer, New York City.—*Gold Amalgamation and Cyanidation.*

Archibald Douglas of Douglas & Armitage, Counsellors at Law, New York City.—*Mining Laws.*

Edward L. Dufourcq, Late Consulting Engineer.—*Gold Amalgamation and Cyanidation.*

Edward B. Durham, Mining Engineer.—*Aerial Tramways and Cableways.*

Howard N. Eavenson, Mining Engineer.—*Coke.*

J. K. Finch, Renwick Professor of Civil Engineering, Columbia University.—*Elements of Hydraulics* and *Elements of Structural Design.*

J. R. Finlay, Consulting Mining Engineer.—*Cost of Mining* and *Mine Organization and Accounts.*

Halbert P. Gillette, C.E.—*Earth Excavation* and *Rock Excavation.*

E. J. Hall, Late Professor of Assaying, School of Mines, Columbia University.—*Assaying.*

V. D. Hanson, Preparation Engineer, Pittsburgh Coal Co.—*Preparation and Coking of Bituminous Coal.*

H. G. Haskell, E.M.—*Explosives.*

Robert E. Hobart, Mechanical Superintendent, Lehigh Navigation Coal Co.—*Drainage of Mines.*

Edwin C. Holden, Consulting Mining Engineer.—*Underground Transport.*

Fletcher B. Holmes, A.B.—*Explosives.*

Charles F. Jackson, Mining Engineer.—*Tunneling.*

Edwin S. Jarrett, C.E. (The Late).—*Shaft Sinking in Unstable and Waterbearing Ground.*

Edward K. Judd, E.M., Formerly Assistant Professor of Mining, School of Mines, Columbia University.—*Chemical and Physical Notes and Tables; Prospecting, Develop-*

xi

ment and Exploitation of Mineral Deposits; Underground Surveying; and *Wages and Welfare.*

James Furman Kemp, Late Professor of Geology, Columbia University.—*Geology and Mineral Deposits.*

Edward F. Kern, Formerly Professor of Metallurgy, School of Mines, Columbia University.—*Assaying.*

Paul F. Kerr, Professor of Mineralogy, Columbia University.—*Geology and Mineral Deposits* and *Mineralogy.*

Arthur LaMotte, Ph.G., B.Sc.—*Explosives.*

Frederick W. Lee, Chief, Section of Geophysics, U S Geological Survey.—*Geophysical Prospecting.*

F. J. LeMaistre, Ph.G., B.Sc.—*Explosives.*

Robert S. Lewis, Professor of Mining, University of Utah.—*Boring.*

A. W. Loomis, Mechanical Engineer, Ingersoll-Rand Co.—*Compressed Air Practice.*

W. W. Lynch, E.M.—*Prospecting, Development, and Exploitation of Mineral Deposits.*

James F. McClelland, E.M., Vice President, Phelps Dodge Corporation.—*Prospecting, Development, and Exploitation of Mineral Deposits* and *Engineers' Tables.*

George E. McElroy, Senior Mining Engineer, U S Bureau of Mines.—*Mine Ventilation.*

Charles M. Means, Consulting Engineer, Pittsburgh.—*Electric Power for Mine Service.*

Alfred J. Moses, Late Professor of Mineralogy, Columbia University.—*Mineralogy.*

Arthur Notman, Consulting Engineer.—*Cost of Mining* and *Mine Organization and Accounts.*

Robert Van Arsdale Norris, Late Consulting Mining Engineer.—*Drainage of Mines.*

S. M. Parmley, Preparation Engineer, Pittsburgh Coal Co.—*Preparation and Coking of Bituminous Coal.*

H. L. Parr, Professor of Mechanical Engineering, Columbia University.—*Mechanical Engineering Miscellany.*

Robert Peele, Professor Emeritus of Mining Engineering, School of Mines, Columbia University.—*Chemical and Physical Notes and Tables* and *Engineers' Tables.*

George S. Rice, Formerly Chief Mining Engineer, U S Bureau of Mines.—*Mine Air, Gases, Dusts, Hygiene, Explosions, and Accidents.*

Samuel R. Russell, Explosives Dept, E. I. DuPont de Nemours & Co.—*Rock Excavation.*

Reno H. Sales, Geologist to the Anaconda Copper Mining Co, Butte, Mont.—*Mine Geologic Maps and Models.*

Walter I. Slichter, Professor of Electrical Engineering, Columbia University.—*Electrical Engineering.*

S. F. Shaw, E.M., Consulting Engineer, Westgate Oil Co, Anglo-Canadian Oil Co, Ltd, etc.—*Petroleum Production Methods.*

Paul Sterling, Mechanical Engineer, Lehigh Valley Coal Co.—*Preparation and Storage of Anthracite Coal.*

Arthur F. Taggart, Professor of Mineral Dressing, School of Mines, Columbia University.—*Boring; Breaking, Crushing, and Sorting of Ores*; and *Testing of Ores.*

Edward D. Thurston, Jr, Formerly Associate Professor of Mechanical Engineering, Columbia University.—*Engineering Thermodynamics.*

Arthur L. Walker, Formerly Professor of Metallurgy, School of Mines, Columbia University.—*Selling, Purchasing, and Treatment of Ores.*

William M. Weigel, E.M.—*Hoisting Plant, Shaft Pockets, and Ore Bins.*

William Young Westervelt, Consulting Mining Engineer.—*Mine Examinations, Valuations, and Reports.*

Horace V. Winchell, Late of the California Bar.—*Mining Laws.*

George R. Wood, Electrical Engineer.—*Electric Power for Mine Service.*

T. R. Woodbridge, Late Consulting Metallurgical Chemist, U S Bureau of Mines.—*Ore Sampling.*

TABLE OF CONTENTS FOR VOLUME I

Detailed tables of contents are given at the beginning of each section. An alphabetical index appears following Section 14.

For contents of other handbooks of this series, see pages following Index of this volume.

SECTION 1

MINERALOGY

BY

ALFRED J. MOSES

LATE PROFESSOR OF MINERALOGY, COLUMBIA UNIVERSITY

REVISED BY

PAUL F. KERR

PROFESSOR OF MINERALOGY, COLUMBIA UNIVERSITY

IDENTIFICATION AND STUDY OF MINERALS

1. DEFINITIONS

On the basis of several thousand analyses the crust of the earth for a depth of about ten miles is estimated by Clarke, " *Data of Geochemistry*," to be composed almost entirely of compounds of fourteen elements:

	Per cent		Per cent		Per cent
Oxygen...............	49.78	Sodium...............	2.33	Chlorine..............	0.21
Silicon...............	26.08	Potassium............	2.28	Carbon...............	0.19
Aluminum............	7.34	Magnesium............	2.24	Phosphorus...........	0.11
Iron.................	4.11	Hydrogen............	0.95	Sulphur..............	0.11
Calcium..............	3.19	Titanium.............	0.37		
				Total..............	99.29

These great elements, and the sixty or so others which form the remaining fraction of 1%, occur in approximately 1500 different chemical combinations, known as minerals; that is, as *homogeneous substances of definite chemical composition, found ready-made in nature, and not directly a product of the life or decay of an organism.*

The two conditions in which minerals may occur. A mineral, like other chemical substances, usually occurs either in crystals of characteristic shapes or in masses made up of many crystals so crowded together that the shapes are not evident, although in each grain of the aggregation the crystalline structure will be shown by the constancy of the properties in parallel directions and their variation in directions not parallel.

Any mineral may in solidifying fail to assume a crystalline structure, because of too great viscosity, or too rapid cooling, or other cause. If this condition is invariable, the mineral is said to be *amorphous*. Opal is the best example. Amorphous minerals are few in number.

2. IDENTIFICATION BY AID OF CRYSTALS

The forms of crystals are often a great aid in mineral identification. Symmetry, interfacial angles and crystal habit are also of value. Cleavage and markings on crystal faces are significant.

Symmetry. In every complete crystal there is some repetition of angles and similarly grouped faces. By considering this so-called " symmetry " crystals may be grouped in divisions, and as all crystals of any one mineral have the same grade of " symmetry," they belong to the same symmetry division.

In identifying an axis of symmetry imagine or actually cause the crystal to revolve about some prominent line through its centre. Note the groupings of faces at the initial position. Note whether at any stage of the revolution the crystal faces appear to be all coincident (rarely), or all parallel to the initial positions of other faces. Or, in other words, note whether groups of faces are replaced during the revolution by other groups containing just as many faces at exactly the angles of the first set. If so, a probable axis of symmetry has been determined. If by measurement the angles of one set correspond in value and order with those of the other sets, then the existence of the symmetry axis is confirmed. According to the number of times corresponding groups or faces recur during a complete revolution about a symmetry axis the axis is known as two-fold, three-fold, four-fold, or six-fold. These are the ordinary axes of symmetry.

If a plane so divides the crystal that on each side of that plane there are grouped the same number of faces at the same angles to it and to each other, this plane is called a Plane of Symmetry.

Divisions or "systems" based on symmetry. The following seven divisions result readily from this partial determination of symmetry, the statements not implying the absence of other symmetry elements:

1. Isometric........ { More than one axis of three-fold symmetry. (Often also more than one of four-fold.)
2. Tetragonal....... One axis of four-fold symmetry and one only.
3. Hexagonal....... { Rhombohedral division—one axis of three-fold symmetry and one only.
4. Hexagonal....... Hexagonal division—one axis of six-fold symmetry.
5. Orthorhombic.... { Three axes of two-fold symmetry, but nothing higher than two-fold; or one axis of two-fold symmetry at the intersection of two planes of symmetry.
6. Monoclinic....... { One axis of two-fold symmetry and one only, or one plane of symmetry, or both.
7. Triclinic......... Without axes or planes of symmetry.

Distinguishing species by angles. Although different crystals of the same substance may differ in shape, angles, and number of faces, the angles between *corresponding* faces are constant and characteristic.

Corresponding faces on the same crystal, or on different crystals of the same substance, occupy corresponding or analogous positions with reference to the symmetry axes and usually correspond in lustre and markings. They frequently do not correspond in shape.

The measuring of a few selected angles will, therefore, usually serve to differentiate the crystal from others in the same symmetry division.

Angles may be determined within one or two degrees by a very simple apparatus, such as the Penfield No. 2 goniometer, consisting of a cardboard on which is printed a graduated semicircle, with an arm of celluloid swiveled by an eyelet in the centre of the semicircle, or better a similar apparatus of metal with removable and adjustable arms. In using, the crystal is placed so that the card edge and the swinging arm, or the two metal arms, are each in contact with a face and perpendicular to the edge of intersection of the two faces, and the mean of at least three readings is used.

The "cleavage" directions, obtained as described later, are of great service in orientating the crystal. These and the angles between them are used in the lists which follow each system.

Zones are composed of faces all parallel to the same line. Their intersections are therefore parallel to this line and to each other.

Isometric crystals. If a crystal shows more than one axis of three-fold symmetry it is an isometric crystal, and not otherwise. There will always be present, also, axes of two-fold or four-fold symmetry. The faces are often squares and equilateral triangles, or these modified by cutting off corners. The dimensions are usually approximately equal in several directions, the forms approaching sometimes to the sphere. Repetitions in any crystal of equal angles and "corresponding" faces are more frequent than in other crystal systems.

Angles. These are of the same series whatever the species. The important species may be classed by their "habit"; that is, the dominant forms of the crystals, as follows:

Tetrahedral. (Tetrahedron angles, 70° 31') boracite, sphalerite, tetrahedrite.

Cubic. *With easy cubic cleavage:* cobaltite, galena, halite; *with octahedral cleavage:* fluorite, smaltite; *without marked cleavage:* argentite, boracite, cerargyrite, cuprite, pyrite.

Octahedral. (Octahedron angles, 109° 29') chromite, cobaltite, cuprite, fluorite, franklinite, galena, gold, linnæite, magnetite, pyrite, spinel. Cleavages: galena, cubic; fluorite, octahedral. Partings: franklinite and magnetite, octahedral.

Dodecahedral. (Dodecahedron angles, 120°) boracite, cuprite, garnet, magnetite, sphalerite.

Trapezohedral. (24-faced trapezohedra, approximating spheres; common angles, 131° 19', 146° 27') analcite, garnet, leucite.

Pyritohedral. (12-faced pyritohedra; most common angles, 126° 53' and 113° 35') cobaltite, pyrite, smaltite.

Tetragonal crystals. If the crystal shows one axis of four-fold symmetry, and only one, it is a tetragonal crystal, and not otherwise. A section taken at right angles to the four-fold axis is usually square or octagonal, or more rarely the angles are again truncated. The dimension in direction of the four-fold axis is usually notably greater or less than in directions at right angles thereto.

Angles. In the zone of faces parallel to the four-fold axis there are no variations in angle dependent on the species. Between prominent *corresponding* faces the angles are almost always

90°, and between prominent *adjacent* faces either 90° or 135°. The characterizing angles lie in other zones.

The principal tetragonal minerals may be classified by angles and cleavage as follows: Angles between corresponding faces *oblique to the four-fold axis:* chalcopyrite, 71° 20′; wulfenite, 99° 38′; scheelite, 100° 5′; apophyllite, 105°; braunite, 109° 53′; cassiterite, 121° 41′; rutile, 123° 8′; zircon, 123° 19′; vesuvianite, 129° 21′; wernerite, 136° 15′.

Braunite, scheelite, and wulfenite cleave at the angles mentioned. Wernerite and rutile cleave parallel to the four-fold axis, giving angles of 90° and 135°. Apophyllite cleaves at right angles to the four-fold axis.

Hexagonal crystals. If the crystal shows one and only one axis of three-fold symmetry it is a hexagonal crystal, rhombohedral division. If the crystal shows one and only one axis of six-fold symmetry it is a hexagonal crystal, hexagonal division. A section taken at right angles to the axis of three-fold or six-fold symmetry is usually a hexagon, or its most prominent edges form a hexagon or at least an equiangular triangle. Not infrequently each angle is replaced by one or two smaller edges. The dimension parallel to this axis is usually notably greater or less than the dimensions at right angles thereto.

Angles. In the zone of faces parallel to the three-fold (or six-fold) axis there are no variations in angle dependent on the species. The angles between prominent corresponding faces are chiefly 120° or 60°. Other angles in this zone are usually large and their occurrence leads to an apparently rounded, often nearly circular, cross-section. The characterizing angles lie in other zones.

The crystals of important hexagonal minerals may be classified by angles between corresponding faces and by cleavage as follows:

I. With evident axis of three-fold symmetry and usually rhombohedral habit:

Angles which are both interfacial and between cleavage directions. Soda nitre, 73° 30′; chabazite, 85° 14′; hematite, 86°; calcite, 105° 5′; dolomite, 106° 15′; rhodochrosite, 107°; siderite, 107°; magnesite, 107° 24′; smithsonite, 107° 40′; proustite, 107° 58′.

Angles which are interfacial only. Ilmenite, 85° 31′; alunite, 90° 50′; cinnabar, 92° 37′; willemite, 115° 30′; phenacite, 116° 36′; tourmaline, 133° 8′ or 103°.

II. With real or apparent axis of six-fold symmetry, and usually prismatic habit:

Prisms capped by faces oblique to axis and at angles, for example, corundum, 86° 4′ or 128° 2′; quartz, 94° 14′ or 133° 44′; apatite, 142° 15′.

Prisms usually capped by single face at right angles to axis. Beryl, iodyrite, mimetite, nephelite, pyrargyrite, pyromorphite, vanadinite.

Tabular. Graphite, molybdenite, iridosmine.

Orthorhombic crystals. If a crystal shows either three axes of two-fold symmetry or one axis with two planes of symmetry, and nothing of higher symmetry, it belongs to the orthorhombic system. Cross-sections taken at right angles to the axes of symmetry are unlike in angles, and tend to rectangles and rhombs or to these combined.

Angles. There is no zone of faces which has a constant series of angles for all species. The interfacial angles in the zones parallel to the axes of symmetry are unlike (except when 90°) and vary with the species. The orientation is best obtained by reference to cleavages, and on this basis the important species may be tabulated as follows:

I. With one direction of cleavage which bisects prominent angles, for example: stibnite, 90° 26′; sillimanite, 91° 45′; goethite, 94° 52′; manganite, 99° 40′; brochantite, 104° 32′; atacamite, 113° 03′; staurolite, 129° 20′. Topaz, with one direction of cleavage, has prominent angles 124° 17′ and 90° 11′, not bisected by the cleavage.

II. Crystals with two directions of cleavage or more than two in one zone, and common angles between faces parallel to two such directions: columbite and olivine, 90°; andalusite, 90° 48′; natrolite, 91° 15′; enargite, 97° 53′; hemimorphite, 103° 51′; arsenopyrite, 112° 27′; cerussite, 117° 14′; strontianite, 117° 19′; aragonite, 118° 12′; chalcocite, 119° 35′.

III. Crystals with three or more directions of cleavage not in one zone, and common angles between faces parallel to such directions: anhydrite, 90°; barite 90° and 101° 38′; anglesite, 90° and 103° 44′; celestite, 90° and 104° 10′; stephanite, 90° and 107° 44′.

Monoclinic crystals. If a crystal shows one and only one axis of two-fold symmetry, or one and only one plane of symmetry, or both, it is a monoclinic crystal. Any face in the zone of the symmetry axis makes a 90° angle with the symmetry plane (or a face parallel to it). No other 90° angles occur. The cross-section of the zone of the symmetry axis is never rectangular, rarely rhombic and usually markedly unsymmetrical.

Angles. No zone has a constant series of angles for each species. In this system the one symmetry plane, the one symmetry axis and the cleavages, all assist in the orientation leading to the following tabulation:

Easiest cleavage	Species	Angles in zone of symmetry axis	Angles bisected by symmetry plane
Parallel to symmetry plane............	Colemanite..........	110° 9', 111° 36'	107° 56', 140° 12', 126° 9'
	Gypsum..............	....	131° 30', 143° 48', 138° 40'
	Realgar..............	....	74° 26', 132° 3'
	Vivianite.............		108° 2'
	Wolframite..........	118° 6', 124° 18', 117° 6'	100° 37', 98° 6', 117° 49'
Perpendicular to symmetry plane........	Azurite..............	135° 14', 137° 10', 132° 45'	99° 19', 119° 13', 90° 53'
	Borax...............	106° 35'	87°, 122° 33', 96° 32'
	Cryolite.............	124° 58', 124° 43'	91° 58', 71° 32'
	Epidote..............	115° 23', 128° 19', 155° 11'	70° 4', 70° 29', 63° 5'
	Monazite.............	140° 48', 87° 17', 126° 29'	93° 26'
	Orthoclase...........	99° 42', 129° 44'	118° 47', 90° 7'
	Polybasite...........	90°	119° 58'
Angle between easiest cleavages bisected by plane of symmetry..	Amphibole...........	130° 6'	124° 11', 148° 28'
	Crocoite.............	....	93° 41', 119° 10'
	Pyroxene............	105° 50', 148° 40'	87° 10', 120° 49', 131° 31'
	Spodumene..........	110° 20'	87°, 91° 26
	Sphene..............	140° 43', 159°	113° 31', 136° 11', 67° 57'
No cleavage...........	Datolite..............	90° 9', 135°	115° 13', 120° 56', 115° 21

The micas and chlorites are usually pseudo-hexagonal.

Triclinic crystals. If the crystal shows no axes nor planes of symmetry it is a triclinic crystal. There will be no right angles either between faces or edges. The only corresponding faces will be opposite (parallel) faces. The crystals of some of the most prominent triclinic minerals, however, approximate in angles monoclinic crystals but are usually distinguishable by the occurrence of faces which have no symmetrically placed associates.

Angles. No angle will occur more than twice in any crystal. There are comparatively few common triclinic species. The following table records a few of their most important angles.

Angles between the two easiest cleavages or the faces parallel to the cleavages		Other angles between common adjacent faces
The Plagioclases:		
Albite...........................	93° 36'	127° 44', 120° 46'
Anorthite.!......................	94° 10'	116° 3', 98° 46', 120° 31'
Labradorite.....................	93° 56'	....
Oligoclase......................	93° 28'	128° 3', 98° 8', 120° 54'
Amblygonite....................	104° 30'	120° 54'
Chalcanthite....................	123° 10'	110° 10', 70° 22', 103° 27'
Cyanite.........................	101° 30'	74° 16', 131° 42', 78° 58'
Rhodonite......................	87° 32'	107° 24'

Cleavage and its value as a test. In any crystal, whether with characteristic external form or not, the cohesion varies in different directions. Under strain there is frequently a tendency to split or cleave perpendicular to the directions of weakest cohesion *in definite* planes, which are always parallel to possible faces of simple crystals characteristic of the substance. All crystals of the same substance yield like cleavages. The number of directions of cleavage and the angles between the cleavage planes are characteristic; moreover the cleavages serve to orientate the crystals in many cases. If the individual crystals are large enough, cleavage is obtained by placing the edge of a knife or chisel upon the crystal and striking it a sharp, quick blow. If the individual crystals are very small the cleavage directions can usually be developed by crushing with pressure or a blow, and examining the fragments with a hand glass. In pyroxene, spodumene, corundum, magnetite, and some other species, some specimens break easily in definite planes, while others do not. This is not true cleavage, but a secondary phenomenon due to pressure, and is called " parting."

Cleavage and parting shapes may be microscopically determined. To do this, sieve the crushed material through a 100-mesh screen upon a 120-mesh screen. Crushed fragments of transparent minerals may be placed on a slide, covered with a transparent liquid, and examined by the petrographic microscope, as described by E. S. Larsen and H. Berman, USGS, *Bull*. 848 (1934) (Bib). Thin sections of massive, transparent minerals or rocks may be examined as described in *Thin-section Mineralogy*, by A. F. Rogers and P. F. Kerr, McGraw-Hill, N Y, 1933.

3. IMPORTANT PHYSICAL TESTS NOT DIRECTLY DEPENDENT ON CRYSTALLINE STRUCTURE

The most important of these tests or characters are Luster, Color and Streak, Hardness, and Specific Gravity.

Lustre. The luster of a mineral is dependent upon its refractive power, its transparency, and its structure. It may be called the *kind* of brilliancy or shine of the mineral.

In determinative work minerals are broadly divided into Metallic and Non-metallic. Metallic luster is the luster of metals. It is exhibited only by opaque minerals, and these, *with the exception of the native metals, have a black or nearly black streak.* Opaque dark-colored minerals not distinctly non-metallic are said to be sub-metallic. Non-metallic luster is exhibited by all transparent or translucent minerals. It may be vitreous or glassy, adamantine like the cut diamond, resinous like sphalerite, pearly like mother of pearl, silky like fibrous serpentine, greasy like nephelite, or waxy like chalcedony.

Hardness. The resistance of a *smooth* plane surface to abrasion is called its hardness and is recorded in terms of the following scale:

1.0	Talc	6.0	Orthoclase	8.5	Chrysoberyl
2.0	Gypsum	7.0	Quartz	9.0	Sapphire
3.0	Calcite	7.5	Zircon	9.5	Carborundum
4.0	Fluorite	8.0	Topaz	10.0	Diamond
5.0	Apatite				

Approximations may be reached by use of finger nail ($2\,1/2$), copper coin (3) and knife ($5\,1/2$). Some smooth surface of the mineral to be tested is selected, on which a point of the standard is pressed and moved back and forth several times one-eighth of an inch or less. If the mineral is scratched it is softer than the standard. Two minerals of equal hardness will scratch each other. Pulverulent or splintery minerals are " broken down " by the test and yield an " apparent " hardness often much lower than the true hardness. Rough surfaces also yield doubtful results.

Color and streak. The color of minerals of metallic luster and the color of the powder, or streak, when not white, are very much used in sight recognition. Minerals with non-metallic luster often vary greatly in color. The color is most safely obtained on a fresh surface. The streak is usually obtained by rubbing the mineral on a smooth but not glazed white or black surface, such as a porcelain " streak plate " or a piece of touchstone (black quartz). The excess of powder should be brushed away and the thin adhering layer considered.

Specific gravity. The specific gravity of a substance is equal to its weight divided by the weight of an equal volume of distilled water at 4° C. Ordinarily room temperature is used. Pure compact material is needed. The most accurate results are obtained by a delicate chemical balance, but for determinative purposes the following are more rapid and sufficiently accurate.

The Jolly balance. Two scale pans are attached, one below the other, to a spiral spring, parallel to which is a mirror with a graduated scale. The lower scale pan is kept submerged in distilled water. The coincidence of a bead on the wire and its image in the mirror give:

A = Reading with nothing in either scale pan.
B = " " mineral in upper scale pan.
C = " " same fragment in lower scale pan.

$$\text{Sp Gr} = (B - A) \div (B - C)$$

The Westphal balance. More accurate results are obtained by substituting for the thermometer float of a Westphal balance a double scale pan, the lower pan of which must be immersed in distilled water.

A = Weight needed to balance apparatus.
B = " " " " " with mineral in upper scale pan.
C = " " " " " " " " lower scale pan.

$$\text{Sp Gr} = (A - B) \div (C - B)$$

Special specific-gravity balance. An improved form, suitable for non-porous solids, has been described by Kerr. It is useful for rapid and accurate determinations. Though based upon the usual chemical balance, it has a notched beam with rollers for weighing.

Heavy liquids. If a fragment of a mineral is floating in a liquid of higher specific gravity and a diluent is stirred in, drop by drop, until the fragment if pushed down will neither sink nor rise but stay where pushed, the specific gravity of the liquid as determined by a Westphal balance will be the specific gravity of the mineral. The heavy liquids most used are: clerici solution, a mixture of thallium malonate and thallium formate (4.25), diluent, water; methylene iodide (3.32), diluent, benzol; bromoform (2.90), diluent, xylol or benzol; solution of mercuric iodide and potassic iodide (3.2), diluent, water.

4. TESTING WITH THE BLOWPIPE

Apparatus. The *essential* pieces of apparatus for all the tests given are:

1. Either a gas blowpipe, or some form of burner for gas or heavy oil and a plain blowpipe.
2. Platinum wire about 0.25 mm diameter. Six inches of it will make four wires. A holder is needed.
3. Platinum-pointed forceps.
4. Charcoal in convenient sizes and with smooth surfaces (say 4 by 1 by $5/8$ in).
5. Tubes of hard glass about 3 by $3/16$ in, closed at one end.
6. Pocket lens of good quality.
7. Simple goniometer.
8. Merwin Color Screen (G. M. Flint, Cambridge, Mass).

For the other apparatus considerable latitude is possible and substitutes can be improvised for the regular stock article. The needed list would be: watch glasses, bottles (1 oz) for reagents, hammer, anvil, and magnet.

About ten reagents are used, the principal being borax, salt of phosphorus, sodic carbonate, potassic bisulphate, cobaltic nitrate, and hydrochloric acid. Two others are needed in preparing the bismuth flux and there will be needed occasionally metallic tin and nitric or sulphuric acid.

A continuous blowpipe blast is obtained by distending the cheeks and using the mouth as an air reservoir, breathing regularly through the nose and from time to time admitting more air from the lungs through the throat to the mouth.

Any luminous flame may be used and, by regulating the relative amounts of air and flame, may be " blown " as a clear blue flame or a yellow flame, both of which owe their color to incomplete combustion (CO or C) and therefore tend to *reduce*, that is, to take oxygen from substances placed therein. Hereafter this flame is designated by the letters R.F. A practically non-luminous colorless envelope surrounds the blue flame and less distinctly the yellow flame. In this there is an excess of oxygen and it therefore tends to *oxidize* substances placed therein. Hereafter this flame is designated by the letters O.F.

Fusion or fusibility. The ease of fusibility and the phenomena during fusion are convenient tests. The hottest portion of the flame is just beyond the tip of the blue flame. Some substances, noticeably certain iron ores, which are infusible in the oxidizing flame are fusible in the reducing flame.

The test is most safely made by first heating on charcoal a fragment of the substance the size of a pin's head, to prove presence or absence of volatile or easily-reducible elements, which are likely to alloy with platinum. If these are present the fusion test must be limited to the test on charcoal. If reducible metals or volatile constituents are absent, a small sharp-edged fragment is heated in the platinum forceps, at the tip of the blue flame, directing the flame upon the point. Fragments long enough to project beyond the platinum should be used and it is always well to examine the splinter with a magnifying glass, before and after heating. *Fragments for comparison must be approximately of same size and shape.*

The degree of fusibility is stated either in terms of a scale of fusibility, suggested by von Kobell, or more simply as easily fusible, fusible, fusible with difficulty, or infusible:

Easily fusible:
1. *Stibnite*, coarse splinters fuse in a candle flame.
2. *Chalcopyrite*, small fragments fuse in the Bunsen burner flame.

Fusible:
3. *Garnet (almandite)*, coarse splinters easily fuse before the blowpipe. Not fusible in Bunsen burner.
4. *Actinolite*, fine splinters fuse easily before the blowpipe.

Fusible with difficulty:
5. *Orthoclase*, fused only in fine splinters or on thin edges before the blowpipe.
6. *Hemimorphite*, finest edge only rounded in hottest part of flame.

Infusible:
7. *Quartz*, infusible, retaining the edge in all its sharpness.

The result of the fusion may be a glass or slag, which is clear and transparent, or white and opaque, or of some color, or filled with bubbles; during the fusion there may be a frothing or intumescence, or a swelling and splitting (exfoliation). In certain instances the color and form may change without fusion, or the substance may take fire and burn, or fusion may follow the loss of some volatile constituent.

Solubility. Acids, especially dilute (1 : 1) hydrochloric acid, are used not only to determine composition but also to determine the ease or degree of solubility. This test fails only from carelessness. The substance must be selected as nearly pure as possible, finely ground and added to the acid in successive small quantities. A clear solution should be aimed at, acid being added if more is needed until everything has dissolved. If complete solution cannot be obtained, the liquid must be filtered and the clear filtrate slowly and partially evaporated until separation commences. If doubt exists as to solubility the *liquid must be evaporated to dryness*, a residue proving solution to have taken place. Solubility may be accompanied by effervescence with or without odor in cold acid, or only on heating. The evaporation may be difficult and incomplete, or there may be separation of a perfect jelly, or of separate lumps of jelly, or of powder, or of crystals. The solution may be of a characteristic color.

Testing for chemical components. The tests used are described in place in the determinative tables following Art 14. The manipulations and precautions are briefly as follows:

I. Testing in closed tubes. A narrow tube of hard glass, about 3 in by $3/16$ in and closed at one end, is best. Enough of the substance is slid down a narrow strip of paper, previously inserted in the tube, to fill it to the height of about $1/4$ in; the paper is withdrawn, and the inclined tube heated gradually at the lower end to a red heat. Soda or other reagents are sometimes mixed with the substance. The results may be: evolution of water, odorous or non-odorous vapors, sublimates of various colors, decrepitation, phosphorescence, fusion, charring, change of color, and magnetization.

II. Testing on charcoal. A shallow cavity, to prevent the substance from slipping, is bored at one end of the charcoal, and a small fragment of the mineral is placed in it. The charcoal is held in the left hand, the surface tipped at about 120° to the direction in which the flame is blown, and a gentle O.F. is blown on the substance. If no sublimate forms the heat is increased, still keeping the flame oxidizing. Another fragment is tested in the R.F., the substance being kept covered for several minutes with the yellow flame.

The sublimates, their color, position on the charcoal, ease of removal by heating in the O.F. or R.F., and the colors imparted to the flame are all noted. Chemical changes may also be indicated by reduced metal, magnetic residues, alkalinity, etc.

III. Testing with soda on charcoal. Sodic carbonate (" Soda "), heated on charcoal, acts as a flux; it also exerts a reducing action, attributed to the formation of sodic cyanide, nascent sodium, and carbon monoxide. It combines with many substances, forming both fusible and infusible compounds. The most satisfactory general method is to mix one part of the substance to be tested with three parts of moistened soda and a little borax, and treat with a good R.F. on charcoal until everything that can be absorbed has disappeared.

IV. Testing with bismuth flux on charcoal and on plaster tablets. Sublimates of brilliantly colored iodides and sulpho-iodides are obtained if bismuth flux (two parts sulphur, one part potassium iodide, and one part acid potassium sulphate) is mixed with certain powdered minerals, placed on charcoal, or a plaster tablet, and heated gently. The larger series of tests are obtained on plaster, the sublimates differing in position and to some extent in color from those obtained on charcoal. Plaster tablets are prepared by spreading a thick paste of plaster of Paris and water upon a sheet of oiled glass, and smoothing to a uniform thickness ($1/8$ in to $1/4$ in). While still soft, the paste is cut with a knife into uniform slabs, 4 in by $1 1/2$ in. It is then dried, after which the tablets are easily detached from the glass.

V. Flame coloration. A number of minerals when heated color the flame, some at a gentle heat, some only at the highest heat attainable. Repeated dipping of the mineral in hydrochloric acid usually assists by forming volatile chlorides. A good method to cover all cases is as follows: Arrange a black background, such as a piece of charcoal, powder the substance finely, flatten the end of a clean platinum wire and dip it in dilute acid, then in the powder, and hold it first just touching the flame near the blowpipe and then at the tip of the blue flame; again dip in the acid and again heat as before.

Concentrated sulphuric acid, and also a paste made of water, $4 1/2$ parts acid potassium sulphate and 1 part of calcium fluoride, are also used to release certain flame-coloring constituents, especially boron, phosphorus and lithium.

Red flames of calcium, strontium, lithium, and the violet flames of potassium in the presence of sodium, are most conveniently studied by Merwin's Color Scale (*Science*,

Vol 30, p 571), consisting of three colored strips of celluloid; No. 1, blue, No. 2, overlapping blue and violet, No. 3, violet.   These absorb different portions of the spectrum as follows:

	No. 1	No. 2	No. 3
Sodium	Absorbed	Absorbed	Absorbed
Potassium	Blue-violet	{ Violet and { Violet-red	{ Violet and { Violet-red
Calcium	Greenish yellow	Absorbed	Faint crimson
Strontium or lithium	Absorbed	Absorbed	Crimson

These elements are still more exactly distinguished by use of a small pocket spectroscope.   The mineral is moistened with hydrochloric acid and brought on a platinum wire into the non-luminous flame of the Bunsen burner.   This is viewed through the spectroscope and bright lines are seen.   The yellow sodium line is almost invariably present and the position of the other lines is best fixed by their situation relative to this bright yellow line.

VI. Bead tests with borax and with salt of phosphorus.   The oxides of certain elements dissolve in borax and salt of phosphorus and impart characteristic colors to the mass, which may differ when hot and cold and according to the degree of oxidation or reduction. Preliminary to bead tests, sulphides, arsenides, arsenates, etc, may be converted into oxides by treating in a shallow cavity on charcoal at a dull red heat; first with a feeble oxidizing flame, then a feeble reducing flame, then again an oxidizing flame, and so on as long as odors or fumes are noticeable.

To make a bead.   Make a loop in platinum wire by bending it around a pencil point so that the end meets but does not cross the straight part.   Heat the loop, dip it into the flux, and fuse to a clear bead the portion that adheres.   Add more flux until the bead is of full rounded shape.   With salt of phosphorus the bead should be held a little above the flame so that the ascending hot gases will help to retain the flux upon the wire.   Touch the warm bead to the substance, place it in the O.F., and treat until clear.   Note the colors, hot and cold.   Then treat in the R.F. and note colors as before.

Flaming.   Some substances heated with a strong flame will give clear glasses until saturated; but if heated slowly and gently or intermittently, will yield opaque or enamel-like beads *before* saturation.

VII. Testing with cobalt solution.   Certain substances become colored, when moistened with a solution of cobalt nitrate in ten parts of water and then heated to a white heat. The test is usually made on charcoal.   Certain other substances yield colors if strongly heated, cooled, and then moistened with the cobalt solution without reheating.   Certain minerals boiled with cobalt solution are colored thereby.

5.   X-RAY METHODS OF STUDY

Recent years have witnessed the development of X-ray methods of mineral study. X-ray powder photographs may be used to aid in identifying many minerals.   Clays, bauxite, fine micaceous silicates, poorly crystallized metallics and other natural products, not readily identified in other ways, are often readily identified by comparison of X-ray diffraction photographs with known standards.   The methods of X-ray study applicable to minerals have been described by Hull, Davey, Wyckoff, Bragg, and others.

Single crystals are most frequently used for X-ray studies, to yield information regarding internal structures.   The earliest to be developed was the method of Laue, making use of a pinhole beam of X-rays passing through a small crystal.   The Braggs later developed the X-ray spectrometer, which depends upon the reflection of X-rays from single crystal faces.   Lately, students of crystal structure have found the Weissenberg X-ray goniometer especially useful.

6.   POLISHED SURFACES OF METALLIC ORES

Many textures and mineral combinations, not readily visible to the unaided eye, may be observed with the reflecting microscope.   Polished surfaces must be prepared in advance with considerable care to produce flat, nearly uniform surfaces, as free from scratches as possible.   Such surfaces may be etched and observed under the microscope and also examined by reflected polarized light.

Microchemical technique is also applied to small fragments of metallic minerals, removed from a polished surface with a needle while the surface is under microscopic observation. Among the comprehensive treatments of microscopic examination of metallic ores are the works of Van der Veen, Schneiderhöhn and Ramdohr, and Short.

7. EXAMINATION OF FRAGMENTS OF NON-OPAQUE MINERALS

Fragments of non-opaque minerals, about 100 to 120 mesh in size, may often be studied and identified by the polarizing microscope. The fragments are placed on a glass slide and immersed in an inert liquid of known refractive index, the indices of the mineral being compared with the index of the immersion liquid. Repeated mounts, made with liquids of different indices, by comparison yield the indices of refraction of a mineral with a fair degree of precision. Other optical properties may be determined at the same time. The methods may often be applied to examination of non-opaque constituents of tailings. The optical properties of many minerals observable with the microscope have been listed by Larsen and Berman.

8. EXAMINATION OF THIN SECTIONS

The structures and textures of non-opaque minerals are best examined in thin sections beneath the microscope. The polarizing microscope of the types manufactured by E. Leitz, Zeiss-Winkel, Bausch and Lomb, or the Spencer Lens Co, are useful for this purpose. Many optical criteria not obvious in ordinary specimens may be used in such an examination. The methods have been outlined by Winchell, Johannsen, and Rogers and Kerr.

OCCURRENCE AND ASSOCIATION OF MINERALS

9. MINERALS OF ROCKS AND VEINS

Associates. Most minerals are found under a variety of conditions, and with different groups of associates. The most probable associates of any mineral in any particular occurrence are: 1. The common minerals of that deposit. 2. Minerals containing some prominent element or elements of the given mineral. In the following lists, which include the rock-forming minerals, common minerals, and those of economic importance, the species in italics are relatively rare.

Minerals of the igneous rocks. These minerals in general have either separated from a fusion solution or " magma " (each separating whenever for the existing temperature and pressure the magma is supersaturated with it), or they have formed later, as secondary minerals, by the decomposition or alteration of the primary minerals.

Principal primary minerals of igneous rocks. Amphibole (hornblende), biotite, chrysolite (olivine), enstatite, hypersthene, leucite, muscovite, nepheline (elaeolite), orthoclase, plagioclase, pyroxene (augite), quartz, sodalite.

Minor primary minerals of igneous rocks. Analcite, apatite, *chalcopyrite, chrysoberyl,* chromite, *cinnabar,* corundum, *epidote, garnet* (almandine, andradite, pyrope), *goethite, gold, graphite,* hematite, ilmenite, *lepidolite,* magnetite, *millerite, molybdenite,* monazite, pyrite, pyroxene (diopside), pyrrhotite, rutile.

Secondary minerals in igneous rocks. *Albite,* alunite, analcite, apophyllite, aragonite, *azurite, barite,* calcite, chabazite, chalcedony, *chalcanthite, chalcopyrite,* chlorite, *chrysocolla,* copper, datolite, epidote, kaolin, lepidolite, limonite, magnetite, *malachite,* muscovite, natrolite, opal, *pyrargyrite,* quartz, serpentine, siderite, *sphalerite,* stibnite, talc, *tetrahedrite, turquois,* wernerite.

Minerals of pegmatite veins. Vein-like portions of granites or other igneous rocks in which the minerals of the rock are found in much larger crystals and in which many other minerals occur not noticed in the adjoining rocks.

Albite, *amblygonite,* apatite, beryl, biotite, *cassiterite, chabazite, chlorite, chrysoberyl, columbite,* cryolite, *diamond, galena, garnet* (almandite and spessartite), graphite, lepidolite, magnetite, micro-cline, *molybdenite, monazite,* muscovite, nepheline, orthoclase, *pyrite, pyrrhotite,* quartz, spodumene, topaz, tourmaline, uraninite, zircon.

Minerals of ore veins. For convenience these have been listed under two headings: Minerals in zone of weathering or oxidation, and minerals of unoxidized zone. **In zone of oxidation.** Anglesite, azurite, brochantite, calamine, celestite, cerargyrite, cerussite, *chalcanthite,* chrysocolla, copper, crocoite, cuprite, embolite, erythrite, goethite, gold, iodyrite, limonite, malachite, manganite, mimetite, pyromorphite, rhodochrosite, siderite, silver, smithsonite, *strontianite, sulphur,* vanadinite, *vivianite,* wulfenite. **In unoxidized**

zone. Antimony, argentite, *arsenic*, arsenopyrite, barite, bornite, braunite, calcite, calaverite, chalcocite, chalcopyrite, cobaltite, copper, dolomite, fluorite, galena, gold, graphite, jamesonite, linnæite, marcasite, millerite, niccolite, orpiment, orthoclase, pentlandite, proustite, pyrargyrite, pyrite, pyrrhotite, quartz, realgar, smaltite, sphalerite, stannite, stephanite, stibnite, sylvanite, tetrahedrite, uraninite.

Minerals of tin veins. Albite, amblygonite, apatite, arsenopyrite, bismuth, calcite, cassiterite, chlorite, columbite, fluorite, galena, kaolin, lepidolite, *molybdenite*, pyrite, pyroxene, quartz, scheelite, wernerite, wolframite.

Minerals of apatite veins. Albite, amphibole, apatite, biotite, calcite, *enstatite*, hematite, ilmenite, magnetite, oligoclase, pyrite, quartz, rutile, sphene, tourmaline, wernerite.

Minerals due to volcanic exhalations. Alunite, sassolite, sulphur, and relatively small quantities of other species, as amphibole, hematite, sal-ammoniac, etc, occur as the result of gases given off during volcanic action.

10. MINERALS FOUND IN SALINE RESIDUES

These exist as sediments precipitated from solution in natural waters, springs, rivers, marshes, lakes, seas, and oceans.

From springs. Alunogen, aragonite, barite, bauxite (?), calcite, celestite, chalcedony, cinnabar, fluorite, hydrozincite, kalinite, limonite, pyrite, sassolite, siderite, sulphur.

From soda and borax lakes and lagoons. Anhydrite, calcite, borax, celestite, *cerargyrite*, colemanite, dolomite, *embolite*, *gold*, gypsum, halite, mirabilite, sassolite, *soda nitre*, *sulphur*, *trona*, ulexite.

From oceans, seas, lakes, and marshes. Apatite, anhydrite, bauxite, boracite, *calcite*, carnallite, *celestite*, *cerargyrite*, *dolomite*, *epsomite*, gypsum, halite, kainite, kieserite, limonite, siderite, wad.

Local saline residues (often incrustations or efflorescences). Alunite, alunogen, chalcanthite, copiapite, epsomite, kalinite, mirabilite.

11. MINERALS IN GRAVELS, SANDS, CLAYS, AND MARLS

Minerals common to all. Biotite, calcite, chlorite, *garnet*, hematite, kaolinite, limonite, *magnetite*, muscovite, orthoclase, plagioclase, pyrite, *pyrophyllite*, *pyroxene*, rutile, siderite, sphene, *tourmaline*.

Gem minerals and ores in gravels and sands. Cassiterite, chrysoberyl, chrysolite, corundum, diamond, gold, ilmenite, monazite, platinum, spinel, tourmaline, topaz, zircon.

Minor minerals in gravels and sands. *Amphibole*, *andalusite*, apatite, cyanite, *dolomite*, enstatite, epidote, *hypersthene*, *microcline*, sepiolite, serpentine, *sillimanite*.

Ores in clays. Galena, limonite, manganite, psilomelane, pyrolusite, wad.

Minor minerals in clays and marls. Amphibole, aragonite, barite, *celestite*, gypsum, halloysite, *orpiment*, realgar, strontianite, *vivianite*.

Minerals in sandstones. Chiefly quartz, orthoclase, plagioclase, limonite, muscovite. *Minor minerals are carnotite*, galena, *gold*, marcasite, manganite, pyrite, pyrolusite, siderite, sphalerite.

Minerals in sedimentary limestone. Aragonite, calcite, dolomite, fluorite, galena, limonite (bog ore), *nitre*, opal, *oidorite*, *soda nitre*, sulphur, sphalerite.

In serpentine and soapstones. *Amphibole*, *aragonite*, *arsenopyrite*, calcite, chlorite, chromite, chrysolite, cinnabar, diamond, dolomite, enstatite, epidote, garnet (pyrope), garnierite, ilmenite, magnesite, magnetite, phlogopite, *platinum*, *pyroxene*, pyrophyllite, quartz, *sepiolite*, serpentine, talc.

12. CONTACT MINERALS

When an igneous rock penetrates a preëxisting rock the heat, pressure, and evolved vapors frequently produce new minerals at and near the surface of contact.

Contacts with limestone. Amphibole (tremolite), anorthite, biotite, bornite, chondrodite, *clinozoisite*, corundum, *danburite*, *enstatite*, epidote, *fluorite*, garnet (grossular and andradite), graphite, *lazurite*, molybdenite, phlogopite, pyrite, pyroxene (diopside), *scheelite*, spinel, tourmaline, *vesuvianite*, wernerite, wollastonite and *zoisite*.

Contacts with silicate rocks (clay, shale, slate, or crystalline schists). Amphibole (hornblende), andalusite (chiastolite), biotite, chlorite, corundum, kyanite, epidote, garnet, ilmenite, magnetite, pyroxene (augite), quartz, rutile, sillimanite, spinel, staurolite, sphene, tourmaline, topaz, wernerite, zircon.

Minerals of Metamorphic Rocks

The minerals of the metamorphic rocks include many species of the original rocks, and many species already listed under contact minerals. A partial list follows: In *Crystalline limestones, and dolomites*: amphibole (tremolite), apatite, aragonite, calcite, *chondrodite*, corundum, dolomite, franklinite, *molybdenite*, phlogopite, pyroxene, pyrrhotite, rhodonite, serpentine, smithsonite, spinel, *talc*, willemite, zincite, zircon. In *Gneisses and Schists*: the contact minerals of the second list (contacts with silicate rocks). Also actinolite, apatite, beryl, biotite, calcite, chalcopyrite, chrysoberyl, *datolite, fluorite, gibbsite*, graphite, hematite, molybdenite, monazite, muscovite, orthoclase, plagioclase, pyrite, pyrophyllite, pyrrhotite, talc, *tetrahedrite*, vesuvianite, zeolites.

THE USES OF MINERALS

This list includes only the principal uses of the minerals as such, and their uses as the material from which other substances are directly extracted or manufactured. The secondary products derived from these primary products are not mentioned.

13. USES OF MINERALS IN THEIR NATURAL STATE

Abrasives. Quartz, garnet, opal (tripolite and diatomaceous earth), corundum and emery, diamond (bort), orthoclase. Leucite and alunite rocks have been used as millstones.

Building stones. Quartz, orthoclase, plagioclase, muscovite, biotite, pyroxene and amphibole in varying proportions, forming igneous rocks commercially known as granite and trap; talc and pyrophyllite (soapstones), serpentines, calcite and dolomite (limestones and marbles), quartz (sandstone).

Electrical insulators. Muscovite, phlogopite, calcite (marble), andalusite, kyanite, sillimanite, and dumortierite.

Fertilizers. Carnallite and kainite for potash; soda nitre for nitrogen; gypsum and calcite for lime; apatite (phosphate rock) for phosphoric acid. Muscovite and biotite as retainers of moisture.

Fluxes. Calcite, fluorite, borax, pyrolusite.

Glass. Chiefly quartz (sand and sandstone) and calcite (limestone); to a less extent orthoclase, plagioclase, cryolite, and pyrolusite.

Lubricants. Graphite, talc, muscovite.

Paints and pigments. Hematite and limonite as "metallic paint"; the same minerals associated with clay, "ocher." Calcite (chalk) as "whiting"; wad, barite, gypsum, asbestos, muscovite, talc, kaolin, quartz, magnesite, azurite, graphite, asphaltum, rutile.

Paper manufacture. Talc (fibrous), gypsum (selenite), as constituents of sheets. Barite, calcite, kaolin, magnesite, bauxite, muscovite, for weight and glaze.

Porcelain, pottery, etc. Kaolin and other clays, quartz, orthoclase, albite, halite, gypsum and pyrophyllite.

Precious stones. Diamond, beryl, emerald, corundum (sapphire and ruby), chrysoberyl (alexandrite), garnet (demantoid), spinel (ruby spinel). **Semi-precious stones.** Other varieties of beryl, corundum, chrysoberyl, spinel, and garnet. Also opal, chrysolite (peridot), quartz (amethyst and yellow), topaz, tourmaline, turquoise, zircon, spodumene (kunzite, hiddenite), orthoclase (moonstone). **Ornamental stones.** Amber, chalcedony (onyx, carnelian, sard, agate, etc), quartz (rose cat's eye, aventurine, smoky, etc), orthoclase (amazon stone), plagioclase (labradorite and sunstone). Amphibole (jade), lazurite (lapis lazuli), malachite, azurite, calamine, smithsonite, chrysocolla, fluorite, gypsum (satin spar), serpentine, hematite, pyrite, rhodonite, talc. Occasional faceted stones are cut from apatite, andalusite, cassiterite, chondrodite, cyanite, pyroxene (diopside), enstatite, epidote, prehnite, staurolite, sphene and vesuvianite.

Refractory materials and heat insulators. Asbestos, bauxite, chromite, dolomite, graphite, ilmenite, kaolin, magnesite, muscovite, opal (diatomaceous earth), serpentine (chrysotile), quartz, pyrophyllite, talc (soapstone), sillimanite, andalusite, kyanite and vermiculite.

Rubber manufacture. Sulphur, stibnite, barite, calcite, talc, pyrophyllite.

Soap and washing powders, toilet articles. Borax, opal (diatomaceous earth), talc, quartz, magnesite, orthoclase.

Sundries. *Coloring or decolorizing:* pyrolusite, psilomelane, rutile. *Condiments:* halite. *Explosives:* nitre, sulphur. *Filters:* opal (tripolite). *Enamels:* fluorite, borax. *Matches:* stibnite sulphur. *Optical:* quartz, calcite, fluorite, gypsum, muscovite. *Pencils:* graphite, talc, pyrophyllite. *Pipes:* sepiolite (meerschaum), succinite (amber).

14. PRODUCTS EXTRACTED OR MANUFACTURED DIRECTLY FROM MINERALS

Aluminum from bauxite, possibly gibbsite, with cryolite as flux.

Alundum (Al_2O_3) from bauxite.

Aluminium sulphate and alum from alunite, cryolite, bauxite, kaolin.

Antimony from stibnite and its alteration products and lead ores carrying antimony.

Arsenic from arsenopyrite and sometimes from smaltite, cobaltite, enargite, etc.

Barium hydroxide and barium sulphide from barite.

Beryllium and beryllium oxide from beryl.

Bismuth from native bismuth, bismutite, and bismite.

Borax and boric acid, from colemanite, ulexite, borax, and sassolite.

Bromine from halite (salt brine).

Cadmium from sphalerite and smithsonite containing greenockite.

Calcium oxide (*lime*) from calcite (limestone).

Calcium sulphate (*hemi-hydrate*) *or plaster* from gypsum.

Calcium superphosphate from apatite.

Cements from calcite and clays.

Carbonic acid from magnesite and calcite.

Chlorine from hydrochloric acid and pyrolusite, the former being derived from halite.

Chromium alloys, especially ferrochrome from chromite.

Cobalt oxide and cobalt arsenate (*zaffre*) from smaltite, cobaltite, and cobaltiferous limonite.

Copper principally from chalcocite, native copper, chalcopyrite, bornite, cuprite, malachite, and azurite, although enargite, tetrahedrite, atacamite, brochantite, chalcanthite, and chrysocolla are all sources of copper in certain districts. In addition to these the iron sulphides often carry copper which is extracted after burning for sulphuric acid.

Copper sulphate from chalcopyrite.

Gold from gold and the gold tellurides (sylvanite, calaverite, petzite), from silver and copper ores and from pyrite, arsenopyrite and pyrrhotite, and sphalerite and other sulphides or tellurides.

Hydrochloric acid from halite.

Hydrofluoric acid from fluorite and cryolite.

Iodine from sodium iodate obtained from soda nitre.

Iridium from iridosmine.

Iron from hematite, limonite, magnetite, and siderite, goethite, and turgite (commercially included with limonite), some ilmenite, and rarely residues from the roasting of pyrites.

Iron sulphate (*ferrous*) or "*copperas*" from pyrite and chalcopyrite.

Iron manganese alloy from franklinite and certain manganiferous hematites and siderites; also from pyrolusite, psilomelane, manganite and other manganese oxides.

Lead, chiefly from galena and cerussite. Anglesite and pyromorphite sometimes occur in quantity.

Lead sulphate (sublimed white lead and blue lead) from galena.

Lithium carbonate from spodumene, lepidolite, and amblygonite.

Magnesium from carnallite.

Magnesium carbonate from dolomite. Basic carbonate from kieserite.

Magnesium oxide from magnesite, and indirectly kieserite.

Magnesium chloride from carnallite.

Magnesium sulphate (epsom salts) from kieserite and less often from magnesite and dolomite.

Manganese alloys from pyrolusite, psilomelane and braunite, or with intermixed rhodochrosite and rhodonite.

Manganese salts from pyrolusite.

Mercury from cinnabar.

Molybdenum and ammonic molybdate from molybdenite.

Nickel from pentlandite, garnierite, nickeliferous pyrrhotite, and to a less extent from millerite, niccolite and the cobalt minerals, cobaltite and linnæite.

Nitric acid from soda-nitre and nitre.

Palladium from copper ores and platinum.

Phosphorus from an impure calcium phosphate (sombrerite), or from bone ash.

Platinum from native platinum and sperrylite, and from some gold and copper ores.

Potassium from carnallite.

Potassium dichromate from chromite.

Potassium sulphate from kainite.

Potassium nitrate from soda nitre and carnallite.

Radium chloride from uraninite, carnotite, and autunite.

Rhodium from platinum.

Selenium from sulphur, chalcopyrite, and pyrite.

Silicon carbide (carborundum) from quartz and coke.

Silicon alloys (ferro-silicon) from quartz.

Silver from native silver, argentite, cerargyrite, embolite, proustite, pyrargyrite, and less important, hessite, polybasite, and iodyrite. Included in other minerals, notably, galena and cerussite, but also in copper ores, manganese ores and with gold in pyrite and arsenopyrite.

Sodium borate (borax) from colemanite, ulexite, sassolite, kernite, and native borax.

Sodium stannate from cassiterite.

Sodium sulphate (salt-cake) from halite, and from this, caustic soda, carbonate, bicarbonate.

Strontium nitrate and chloride from strontianite.

Sulphuric acid, sulphurous acid, from native sulphur, pyrite, marcasite, chalcopyrite, sphalerite, pyrrhotite, and other sulphide ores.

Tantalum from columbite.

Thorium nitrate and thorium oxide from monazite, thorite, thorianite.

Tin and sodium stannate from cassiterite.

Titanium, titanium oxide, and ferro-titanium from ilmenite.

Titanium carbide from rutile.

Tungsten, ferro-tungsten, from wolframite and scheelite.

Tungstate of soda from wolframite.

Uranium yellow or sodium diuranate from uraninite, carnotite.

Vanadium, and ferro-vanadium from carnotite, patronite, roscoelite, vanadinite, descloizite.

Vanadic oxide from mottramite.

Zinc, "*zinc dust,*" *and zinc oxide* from sphalerite, smithsonite, and calamine; and in New Jersey, willemite and zincite.

Zinc sulphate from sphalerite.

Zirconium oxide from zircon.

DESCRIPTIVE AND DETERMINATIVE TABLES

Rare species without economic value are omitted. Their inclusion would greatly increase the complexity of the tables and also increase the difficulty of determination.

Rare minerals require special methods beyond the scope of a simple set of mineral tables; chemical analyses, optical, and X-ray determinations are usually necessary.

Due to the limited space the species are described only in the tables, and the accompanying diagrammatic index will enable the user to find a brief description of any species. (For example, scheelite. A reference to 22 in the diagram will give composition, crystal system, hardness, specific gravity, colors, solubility, flame coloration, behavior with fluxes and general appearance.)

The uses and occurrence of minerals are summarized in separate tables. In using the tables the customary precautions are understood to be taken:

1. Tests must be made upon homogeneous materials, and lusters and colors observed on fresh fractures.

2. Classifying tests must be decided; not weak, nor indefinite. If undecided, the species on both sides of the dividing line must be considered.

3. Hardness tests should be assumed to be within say one half; that is, a determination H = 5 should for safety be taken as 4.5 to 5.5.

As shown by the accompanying key, the principal subdivision is between metallic and non-metallic luster. The blowpipe test is made subordinate for minerals of metallic luster and minerals of non-metallic luster with colored streaks; but, for minerals of non-metallic luster with white streaks, experience proves that the blowpipe or the microscope lead to a determination with less repetition than such qualities as color and hardness.

A novel feature of the tables is the "scheme within a scheme," by which the order of testing may be varied. For instance, in 16, 17, 18 the arrangement is by blowpipe tests in order of hardness, but the parallel columns permit color to be used as the classifying test; that is, the order of testing may be color and hardness or blowpipe test and hardness.

Similarly in 5, 6 the arrangement of the metallic white and gray minerals is by streak and hardness, but the parallel columns permit the behavior on charcoal in oxidizing and reducing flame to be used as the classifying test; that is, the order of testing may be color, streak and hardness, or color and behavior on charcoal.

Chemical symbols are used only for the formulas of the species and for the common solvents, HCl, H_2SO_4, HNO_3, KOH, etc. Aside from these a few abbreviations are used, the principal being:

Systems of crystallization are indicated by the letters: I (Isometric), T (Tetragonal), O (Orthorhombic), M (Monoclinic), Tri (Triclinic), H (Hexagonal).

Terms in blowpipe tests. Soda for sodic carbonate, S. Ph. for salt of phosphorus, O. F. and R. F. for oxidizing and reducing flame, Co. Sol. for cobalt solution, coal for charcoal.

The + sign in any column opposite any mineral indicates that the quality indicated is a character of that mineral.

The following diagram furnishes at a glance the procedure to be followed in identifying an unknown mineral:

OUTLINE OF DETERMINATIVE TABLES

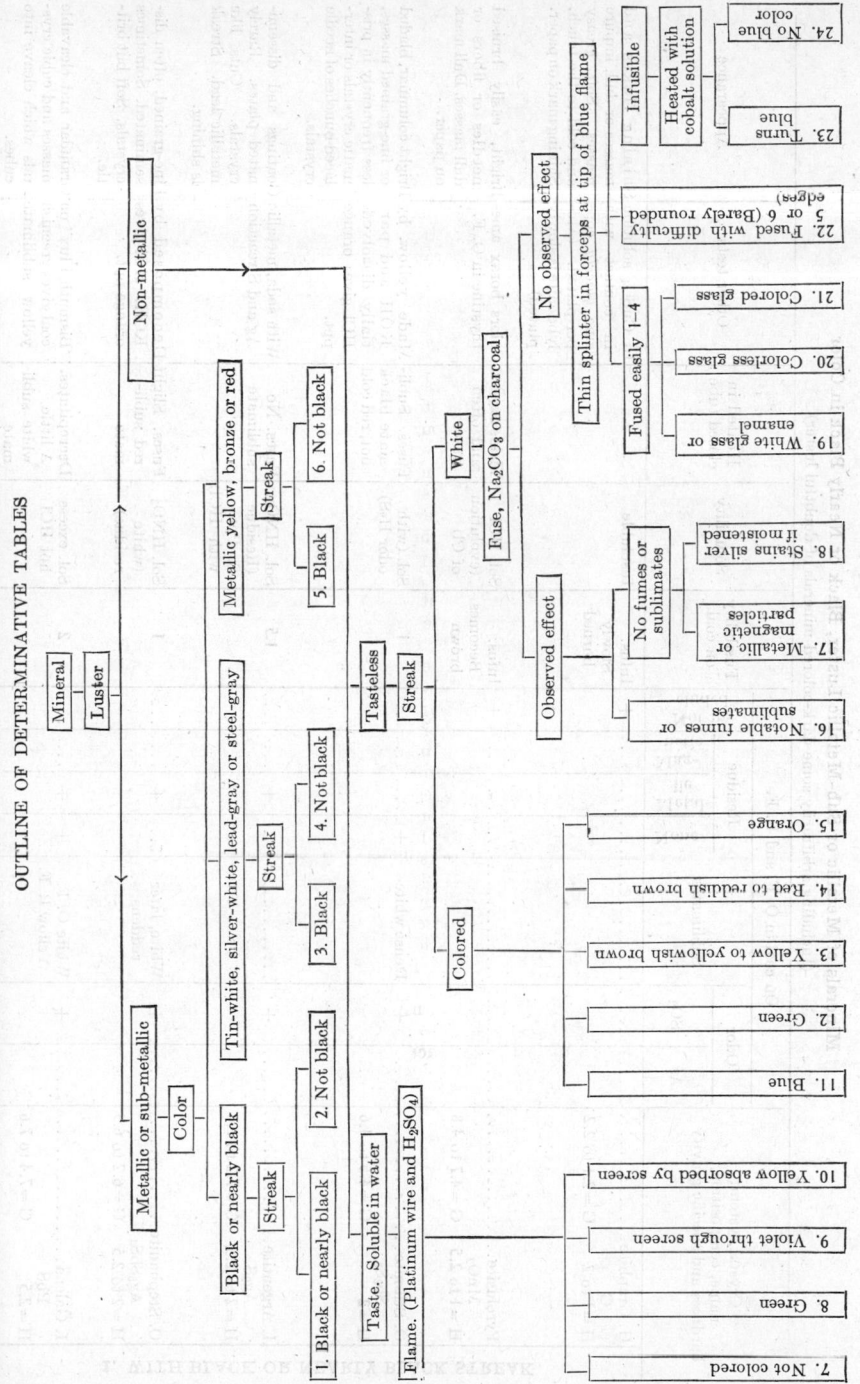

Minerals of Metallic or Sub-Metallic Luster, Black or Nearly Black in Color

(Including arbitrarily some dark-colored minerals of doubtful luster)

1. WITH BLACK OR NEARLY BLACK STREAK

Crystal system: name, composition, hardness and specific gravity	Odor As	Odor SO_2	Sublimates	Residue None	Residue Metallic	Residue Magnetic	Residue Not included	Fusibility on coal	Solubility	Heated in closed tube	Other tests	Appearance
H. Graphite. C H = 1 to 2　G = 2.1 to 2.2	....	....					+	Infus. Slowly burned	Insoluble	......	In $CuSO_4$ solution in contact with zinc *quickly* copper-plated. (Molybdenite is slowly plated)	Shining flakes and masses or dull, impure masses. Soft, greasy and cold to the touch. Shining mark on paper.
Pyrolusite. MnO_2 H = 1 to 2.5　G = 4.7 to 4.8	....	....					+	Infus. Becomes brown	Sol. HCl (evolution of Cl)	Yields oxygen and often water	Colors borax amethystine in O. F.	Bright, easily bruised needles or fibers or dull masses. Dull mark on paper.
O. Stibnite. Sb_2S_3 H = 2　G = 4.5 to 4.6	....	+	Dense white	+				1	Sol. (with odor H_2S)	Fuses. Sublimate black hot, red cold	Made yellow by KOH and partially dissolved. HCl gives orange ppt.	Bright columnar, bladed or fine-grained masses, less frequently in prismatic crystals or interlaced bunches of needle crystals.
I. Argentite. Ag_2S H = 2 to 2.5　G = 7.2 to 7.6	....	+			+			1.5	Sol. HNO_3. (Residue S. Ppt. with HCl)	Fuses. No sublimate	With soda, metallic Ag and S reaction	Coatings and disseminated plates. Rarely crystals. Cuts like metallic lead. Streak is shining.
O. Stephanite. Ag_5SbS_4 H = 2 to 2.5　G = 6.2 to 6.3	....	+	White, later reddens		+			1	Sol. HNO_3 (white residue)	Fuses. Slight red sublimate	Decomposed by KOH. HCl gives orange ppt.	Fine-grained, often disseminated. Sometimes crystals. Soft but brittle.
I. Galena. PbS H = 2.5　G = 7.4 to 7.6	....	+	White O. F. Yellow R. F.	+	+			2	Sol. excess hot HCl	Decrepitates. A little white sublimate	"Bismuth Flux" on coal gives greenish yellow sublimate	Granular and cleavable masses and cubic crystals which cleave into cubes.

1. WITH BLACK OR NEARLY BLACK STREAK

Mineral (composition, H, G)	Charcoal globule	Charcoal sublimate	+	Fusibility	Magnetic	Solubility	On heating	Flame / bead reaction	Crystal form and remarks
O. Jamesonite. $Pb_2Sb_2S_5$ H=2.5 G=5.5 to 6	+	Dense white. Some yellow	+	1		Sol. (with odor H_2S)	Brownish red sublimate	"Bi. Flux" on coal gives greenish yellow sublimate	Needle crystals, or hair-like or felted; also compact and fibrous massive.
O. Polybasite. $(Ag \cdot Cu)_9SbS_6$ H=2 to 3 G=6 to 6.2	+	Dense white		1		Sol. HNO_3. (Ppt. with HCl)	Fuses. No sublimate	Metallic residue ignited with HCl gives azure blue flame	Best known in six-sided plates. In thin splinters is cherry red by transmitted light.
O. Chalcocite. Cu_2S H=2.5 to 3 G=5.5 to 5.8	+			2 to 2.5		Sol. HNO_3 (residue S)	Fuses. No sublimate	Emerald green flame made azure blue by HCl	Compact masses, nodules and disseminated. Often coated with the green carbonate. Rarely crystals.
O. Enargite. Cu_3AsS_4 H=3 G=4.4	+	Volatile white	+	1		Sol. HNO_3	Decrepitates. Yellow subl. then fuses and gives red subl.	Metallic residue ignited with HCl gives azure blue flame	Columnar, granular and compact masses and prisms, sometimes radiating.
Tenorite. CuO H=3 G=5.8 to 6.2	+		+	Infus. O.F. Fus. R.F.		Soluble		Like enargite	Dull earthy masses, powder and shining scales.
I. Tetrahedrite. $Cu_8Sb_2S_7$ H=3 to 4.5 G=4.5 to 5.1	+	Dense white	+	1.5	Sometimes	Sol. HNO_3	Decrepitates. Fuses. Dark red sublimate	Like enargite	Fine-grained masses and "tetrahedral" crystals. Sometimes coated with chalcopyrite.
Psilomelane. MnO_2, BaO, H_2O, etc. H=5 to 6 G=4.5 to 5				Infus.	+	Sol. HCl (evolution Cl)	Oxygen and water	Colors borax amethystine O.F. Solutions usually give white ppt. with H_2SO_4	Massive with smooth rounded surfaces, or stalactitic. Never crystallized.
H. Ilmenite. $FeTiO_3$ H=5 to 6 G=4.5 to 5				Infus. O.F. Fus. diff. R.F.	+	Sol. (boiled with tin is violet)		S. Ph. bead. O.F. red. R.F. violet.	Thin plates, imbedded grains, sand and tabular hexagonal crystals.
I. Uraninite. $UO_3 \cdot UO_2$, PbO, etc. H=5.5 G=9 to 9.7				Infus.	Sometimes	Sol HNO_3 (yellow)		Solutions give yellow ppt. with ammonia. Borax O.F. "flames" yellow enamel near saturation	Massive botryoidal or granular. Pitch-like luster. Rarely small crystals.

Minerals of Metallic or Sub-Metallic Luster, Black or Nearly Black in Color—*Continued*

Crystal system: name, composition, hardness and specific gravity	On coal in O. F. and R. F.							Fusibility on coal	Solubility	Heated in closed tube	Other tests	Appearance
	Odor		Sublimates	Residue								
	As	SO₂		None	Metal-lic	Mag-netic	Not in-cluded					
2. STREAK BLACK OR NEARLY BLACK												
I. Magnetite. Fe₃O₄ H = 5.5 to 6.5 G = 4.9 to 5.2						+		5.5 in R. F.	Sol. HCl		Magnetic before heating but loses magnetism in O. F.	Coarse- and fine-grained masses and sand and octrahedral crystals. Strongly attracted by a steel magnet. Sometimes itself a magnet (lodestone).
O. Columbite. Fe(CbTa)₂O₆ H = 6 G = 5.4 to 6.5							+	Infusible	Insoluble		Fused KHSO₄ and boiled HCl and tin give deep blue O. F.	Prismatic crystals, often iridescent, in pegmatite dikes. Also massive.
T. Braunite. Mn₂O₃ H = 6 to 6.5 G = 4.7 to 4.8							+	Infusible	Sol. HCl (evolution Cl)	A little water no oxygen	Colors borax amethystine in O. F. Solution often yields silica jelly	Fine-grained masses and occasional small pyramids almost isometric.
WITH STREAK NOT BLACK												
H. Pyrargyrite. Ag₃SbS₃ H = 2.5 G = 5.7 to 5.8		+	Dense white		+			1	Sol. HNO₃. White residue	Subl. black hot, red cold	Decomposed by KOH. HCl produces orange ppt.	Veins or crusts with a brilliant adamantine luster showing red tint. In thin layers. Rare crystals. Streak purplish-red.
I. Sphalerite. ZnS H = 3.5 to 4 G = 3.9 to 4.1		+	Yellow hot, White cold	+				Infusible (or fus. with difficulty)	Effervesces. Gives odor H₂S	No sublimate	Sublimate on coal made bright green by ignition with cobalt solution	Black and gray crystals and cleavable to fine-grained masses. Streak pale brown.
O. Manganite. MnO (OH) H = 4 G = 3.7 to 4.7							+	Infusible. (Becomes brown)	Sol. HCL. (Evolves Cl)	Much water. A little oxygen	Borax O. F. amethystine	Crystals often grouped in bundles, rarely massive, granular or stalactitic. Streak dark brown.

Mineral	Fusibility			Soluble	Reddens / Water	Reactions	Remarks
$Fe_2(OH)_6 \cdot Fe_2O_3$ H = 5 to 5.5 G = 3.6 to 4	5 to 5.5 to slag	+	+	Soluble	Reddens. Yields much water	Often reacts for manganese and may give jelly residue	Cellular and pulverulent or as compact masses often radiated or stalactitic and with varnish-like surfaces. Never crystallized. Streak yellowish-brown.
O. Goethite $FeO(OH)$ H = 5 to 5.5 G = 4 to 4.4	5 to 5.5 to slag	+	+	Soluble	Reddens. Yields water	Often reacts for manganese. (Soda bead O. F. bluish green)	Occurs massive but is best known as crystals, often flattened like scales, or needle-like, or in parallel position. These shade into feather-like and velvety crusts.
T. Hausmannite Mn_3O_4 H = 5 to 5.5 G = 4.7 to 4.8	Infusible	+	+ (if fused)	Sol. HCl. (Evolves Cl)		Borax O. F. amethystine	Granular masses occasionally in twinned pyramids. Streak chestnut brown.
M. Wolframite $(FeMn)WO_4$ H = 5 to 5.5 G = 7.1 to 7.5	3 to 4 (crystalline bead)	+		Partial		Solutions become deep blue on addition of tin. Solution of S. Ph. bead in HCl best	Heavy monoclinic crystals and cleavable, bladed and granular masses. Streak brownish black.
Ilmenite $FeTiO_3$ H = 5 to 6 G = 4.5 to 5	Infus. O. F. Slightly R. F.	+	+	Partial		Filtered solution boiled with tin becomes violet	Usually compact masses, often thin plates or imbedded grains or as sand. Rarely in tabular hexagonal crystals. Streak brownish red.
I. Uraninite $UO_3 \cdot UO_2$, etc H = 5.5 G = 9 to 9.7	Infusible (or fused with difficulty)	+		Sol. HNO_3 (to yellow liquid)		Solution gives yellow ppt. with ammonia. Borax R. F. green, near saturation blackens	Botryoidal or granular with pitch-like luster. Rarely in small isometric crystals. Streak dark green.
I. Chromite $FeCr_2O_4$ H = 5.5 G = 4.3 to 4.6	Infusible O. F. Slightly R. F.	+		Insoluble		Borax or S. Ph., O.F. or R.F., emerald green cold	Granular or compact or rarely in small octahedral crystals. Pitch-like luster. Often with serpentine. Streak dark brown.

2. WITH STREAK NOT BLACK

Minerals of Metallic or Sub-Metallic Luster, Black or Nearly Black in Color—*Continued*

2, WITH STREAK NOT BLACK

Crystal system: name, composition, hardness and specific gravity	On coal in O. F. and R. F.							Fusibility on coal	Solubility	Heated in closed tube	Other tests	Appearance
	Odor		Sublimates	Residue								
	As	SO$_2$		None	Metallic	Magnetic	Not included					
H. Hematite. Fe_2O_3 H = 5.5 to 6.5 G = 4.9 to 5.3						+		Infusible	Soluble			Coarse to fine micaceous masses and tabular or coarser crystals with brilliant luster. Occasionally kidney-shaped. Streak brownish red.
O. Columbite. Fe (CbTa)$_2$O$_6$ H = 6 G = 5.4 to 6.5							+	Infusible	Insoluble		Fused with KOH and boiled with HCl and tin gives blue solution.	Masses and brilliant, often iridescent, prismatic crystals. Streak dark red.
I. Franklinite. (FeMnZn) O (FeMn)$_2$O$_3$ H = 6 to 6.5 G = 5 to 5.2			Slight white			+		Infusible	Slowly in HCl evolving Cl		Soda bead O.F bluish green	Compact masses, rounded grains and octahedral crystals. Slightly magnetic. Red zincite and yellow to green willemite are associates. Streak dark brown.
T. Rutile. TiO$_2$ H = 6 to 6.5 G = 4.1 to 4.2							+	Infusible	Insoluble		S. Ph. bead in R. F. violet	Masses and crystals with considerable luster. Streak pale yellow.
T. Cassiterite. SnO$_2$ H = 6 to 7 G = 6.8 to 7.1			Some varieties give white sublimate				+	Infusible	Insoluble		With soda or sulphur on coal in strong heat a subl. yellow hot, white cold, made bluish green by ignition with cobalt solution	Brilliant crystals, usually with brown tinge. Streak pale yellow.

Minerals of Metallic Luster, Tin-White, Silver-White, Lead-Gray or Steel-Gray in Color

Crystal system: name, composition, hardness and specific gravity	Odor (On coal in O. F. and R. F.)		Sublimates	Residue			Fusibility	Solubility	Heated in closed tube	Other tests	Appearance
	As	SO₂		None	Metallic	Magnetic					
O.Stibnite. Sb₂S₃ H=2 G=4.5	.....	+	Dense white. Volatile	+	.....	.....	1	Sol. HCl hot (odor H₂S)	Fuses, yields black subl. hot, brownish red cold	Solution in upper part test tube reppt. as orange by H₂S from dissolving portion	Lead-grey columnar or fine-grained masses or prisms. Cleaves into lath-shaped fragments.
I. Galenite. PbS H=2.5 G=7.4 to 7.6	.....	+	White, O. F. Yellow R. F.	+	+	.....	2	Sol. HCl hot. (Crystals on cooling)	Decrepitates. A little white sublimate	Greenish yellow subl. on coal with Bi flux	Lead-grey granular and cleavable masses and cubic crystals which cleave into cubes.
O. Jamesonite. Pb₂Sb₂S₅ H=2.5 G=5.5 to 6	.....	+	Dense white. Some yellow, volatile	+	+	.....	1	Sol. (with odor H₂S)	Subl. brownish red cold	Like galenite	Steel-gray to dark-gray needle crystals, or hair-like or felted; also compact and fibrous massive.
I. Tetrahedrite. Cu₈Sb₂S₇ H=3 to 4.5 G=4.5 to 5.1	Sometimes	+	Dense white	.....	+	.....	1.5	Sol. HNO₃	Fuses. Dark-red sublimate	Metallic residue ignited with HCl gives azure blue flame	Steel-gray fine-grained masses and tetrahedral crystals.
I. Stannite. (Cu·Sn·Fe) S H=4 G=4.5	.....	+	Non-volatile white sublimate (yellow hot)	.....	+	.....	1.5	Sol. HNO₃ (green with white residue)	....	Subl. on coal becomes bluish green by ignition with cobalt solution	Steel-gray, massive, granular. Often intermixed with yellow chalcopyrite.
I. Linnæite. (Co·Ni)₃S₄ H=5.5 G=4.8 to 5	.....	+	....	.....	.....	+	2	Sol. HNO₃ (red with sulphur residue)	Slight yellow sublimate	Borax deep blue O. F. and R. F.	Steel-gray granular or compact masses, or small octahedral crystals.
I. Cobaltite. CoAs₂ H=5.5 G=6 to 6.1	+	+(weak)	Volatile white sublimate	.....	.....	+(weak)	Easy	Sol. HNO₃ (red with white residue)	Unaltered	Like linnæite	Gray masses and tin-white crystals. Often a red tarnish.

3. WITH BLACK STREAK

Minerals of Metallic Luster, Tin-White, Silver-White, Lead-Gray or Steel-Gray in Color—*Continued*

4. WITH STREAK NOT BLACK

Crystal system: name, composition, hardness and specific gravity	On coal in O. F. and R. F.						Fusibility	Solubility	Heated in closed tube	Other tests	Appearance
	Odor		Sublimates	Residue							
	As	SO₂		None	Metal-lic	Mag-netic					
I. Smaltite. CoAsS H=5 to 6 G=6.4 to 6.6	+		Volatile white sublimate			+	Easy	Sol. HNO₃ (red to green)	Mirror and black sublimate	Like linnæite	Steel-gray masses and tin-white crystals usually cubes, often with erythrite.
O. Arsenopyrite. FeAsS H=5.5 to 6 G=6 to 6.2	+	+	Volatile white sublimate			+	2	Sol. HNO₃ (sulphur residue)	Brownish red subl. Later mirror and black	After short ignition on coal, dissolves in HCl with odor of H₂S and yellow ppt.	Tin-white to gray masses or crystals often striated, the sections of which are rhombic and rectangular.
I. Sperrylite. PtAs₂ H=6 to 7 G=10.6	+		Slight vol. sublimate		+		Easy	Insoluble	......	In open tube white subl. and spongy residue	Tin-white grains and minute crystals
Mercury. Hg H=— G=13.6				+			Volatilizes	Sol. HNO₃	Subl. of small metallic globules	With Bi flux on plaster, volatile, scarlet and yellow subl.	A tin-white liquid found in scattered globules or in cavities with cinnabar.
H. Molybdenite. MoS H=1 to 1.5 G=4.6 to 4.9		+	Slight white and bronze				Infus.	Sol. conc. HNO₃ (luminous)	......	Colors flame yellowish green and is reddened	Bluish gray scales and foliated masses cleaving to flexible non-elastic plates. Streak greenish-gray on glazed porcelain.
Gold tellurides. (Au·Ag)Te₂ H=1.5 to 2.5 G=7.9 to 9			Grayish white		+		1	Sol. HNO₃ (gold residue). In hot H₂SO₄ purple.	......	The sublimate placed on porcelain moistened with conc. H₂SO₄ and warmed is violet	Steel gray to silver white, sometimes inclined to yellow. Incrusting or in small veins. Streak silver white to gray.
H. Bismuth. Bi (often with As) H=2 to 2.5 G=9.7 to 9.8	Sometimes		Yellow and white sublimates	+			1	Sol. HNO₃ (white ppt. by water)	......	Chocolate brown and red subl. with Bi flux on plaster tablet	Silver white with reddish tinge, often "branching," or in isolated grains. Streak silver white.

4. WITH STREAK NOT BLACK

Mineral			Sublimate		Fusibility	Solubility		Flame / chemical test	Description
I. Hessite. (Au·Ag)Te H = 2 to 2.5 G = 8.3 to 8.6	……	+	Slight gray sublimate	……	Easy	Sol. HNO$_3$. In hot H$_2$SO$_4$ purple	……	Like gold telluride	Gray, fine-grained to coarse-grained or in isometric crystals. Streak gray.
H. Tellurium. Te with Se·S H = 2 to 2.5 G = 6.1 to 6.3	……	+	Slight gray sublimate	……	Easy	In hot H$_2$SO$_4$ is purple	……	Like gold telluride	Tin-white, fine-grained or minute hexagonal prisms. Streak tin-white.
I. Silver. Ag H = 2.5 to 3 G = 10.1 to 11.1	……	……	……	+	2	Sol. HNO$_3$ or H$_2$SO$_4$	……	Solutions plate copper and give curdy white ppt. with HCl	Pale "silver" white branching crystals, wire flakes and masses. Tarnishes brown to black. Malleable. Streak silver-white.
Antimony Sb H = 3 to 3.5 G = 6.5 to 6.7	Sometimes	……	Dense white volatile	+	1	Soluble	……	Burns with yellow-green flame	Tin-white, fine-grained or radiated. Very brittle.
H. Arsenic. As H = 3.5 G = 5.6 to 5.7	+	……	Volatile white	+	Volatilizes	Sol. HNO$_3$	Mirror	Burns with light-blue flame	Tin-white, tarnishing almost black. Usually massive, with rounded surfaces. Sometimes in concentric layers. Streak tin white.
I. Tetrahedrite. Cu$_8$Sb$_2$S$_7$ H = 3 to 4.5 G = 4.5 to 5.1	Sometimes	+	White volatile	+	1.5	Sol. HNO$_3$ (green with white residue)	Decrepitates brownish red sublimate	Solutions blue with ammonia. Roasted residue ignited with HCl azure blue flame	Steel-gray fine-grained masses and tetrahedral crystals. Streak cherry red.
I. Platinum. Pt (Fe) H = 4 to 4.5 G = 14 to 19	……	+	……	+	Infus.	Sol. aqua regia only	……	……	Steel-gray to tin-white grains, scales and nuggets. Malleable and sometimes attracted by the magnet. Streak shining steel-gray.
H. Iridosmine. (Ir·Os) H = 6 to 7 G = 19 to 21	……	+	……	+	Infus. (Unpleasant odor)	Insoluble	Open tube, pungent, unpleasant odor	……	Tin-white or gray, very hard flat grains and hexagonal plates. Streak steel gray.

Minerals of Metallic Luster, Metallic Yellow, Bronze or Red in Color

Crystal system: name, composition, hardness and specific gravity	Odor As	Odor SO₂	Sublimates	Residue None	Residue Metallic	Residue Magnetic	Fusibility	Solubility	Heated in closed tube	Other tests	Appearance
I. Bornite...... Cu_5FeS_4 H=3 G=4.9 to 5.4		+				+	2.5	Sol. HNO_3 (residue S)	Blackens	Magnetic globule is brittle with red fracture and ignited with HCl gives azure blue flame	Red bronze on fresh fracture. Tarnishes in blue, purple and black tints. Very brittle and usually massive.
H. Millerite..... NiS H=3 to 3.5 G=5.3 to 5.6		+				+	1.5 to 2	Sol. aqua. regia	....	Roasted colors borax O.F. red hot, brown cold	Brass colored in hair-like or needle crystals. Crusts made up of radiating needles.
T. Chalcopyrite.. $CuFeS_2$ H=3.5 to 4.1 G=4.1 to 4.3		+				+	2 to 2.5	Sol. HNO_3 (residue S)	Darkens, may give yellow sublimate	Like bornite except gray "fracture"	Bright-yellow brassy masses and crystals, tarnishing in peacock colors.
I. Pentlandite... (Fe·Ni) S H=3.5 to 4 G=4.6 to 5		+				+	1.5 to 2	....	....	Fused globule yellow on fracture. Borax O.F. reddish brown	Light bronze-yellow masses resembling pyrrhotite but not attracted by a steel magnet. Cleavage octahedral.
H. Pyrrhotite.... FeS H=3.5 to 4.5 G=4.5 to 4.6		+				+	Easy	Effervesces (odor H_2S)	A little S	Slightly magnetic before fusion	Bronze-yellow masses, tarnishing brown. Powder attracted by a steel magnet.
H. Niccolite..... NiAs H=5 to 5.5 G=7.2 to 7.7	+		Volatile, white			+	2	Partial	Mirror sublimate	Borax and roasted material give blue, green, brown, successively as borax is changed	Pale copper-red masses sometimes enclosed in white metallic crust.
I. Pyrite........ FeS_2 H=6 to 6.5 G=4.9 to 5.2		+				+	2.5 (burns)	Sol. HNO_3 (residue S)	Fusible sublimate red hot, yellow cold	Fused mass effervesces in HCl with odor H_2S	Pale brass-yellow cubes or other crystals, isolated or grouped in crusts or bounding a mass. Also massive globular, nodular stalactitic.
O. Marcasite.... FeS_2 H=6 to 6.5 G=4.6 to 4.9		+				+	2.5 (burns)	Sol. HNO_3 (residue S)	Fusible sublimate red hot, yellow cold	Like pyrite	Pale brass-yellow "spear," "cockscomb" and simple tabular crystals. Often radiated. Fresh fracture whiter than that of pyrite.

5. WITH BLACK STREAK

6. WITH STREAK NOT BLACK

Crystal system: name, composition, hardness and specific gravity				Solubility				Appearance
I. Gold.......... Au $H=2.5$ to 3 $G=15.6$ to 19.3	2.5	+	.....	Sol. aqua regia	....	....	The fused mass is yellow low	Golden yellow to pale yellow nuggets, grains and scales or distorted crystals, passing into wire, fern and leaf forms. Malleable. Streak golden yellow to pale yellow.
I. Copper.......... Cu $H=2.5$ to 3 $G=8.8$ to 8.9	3	+	.....	Sol. HNO_3 (green)	....	....	Fused mass is red and ignited with HCl gives azure blue flame	Copper-ed, disseminated grains, sheets and irregular masses or groups of extended and branching crystals. Malleable. Streak copper red and shining.

Minerals of Non-Metallic Luster and with Decided Taste (Soluble in Water)

Crystal system: name, composition, hardness and specific gravity	Taste	Heated on charcoal	Heated in closed tube	Recrystallization in a drop of water	Appearance
M. Alunogen.......... $Al_2(SO_4)_3$ $18\ H_2O$ $H=1.5$ to 3 $G=1.6$ to 1.8	Astringent	Fuses, loses water becomes infusible. Deep blue with Co. sol.	Much water, SO_2 and SO_3 at high heat	Feathery	White efflorescence or fibrous crusts.
O. Epsomite.......... $MgSO_4$ $7\ H_2O$ $G=1.7$ $H=2$ to 2.5	Bitter	Like alunogen but pink with Co. sol.	Water. Acid at high temperature	Lath shaped	White fibers or crusts.
M. Copiapite.......... $Fe_3(OH)_2(SO_4)_5$ $18\ H_2O$ $H=2.5$ $G=3.1$	Metallic, nauseous	Fuses, becomes magnetic	Much acid water	No recrystallization	Yellow scales or granular masses.
M. Borax.......... $Na_2B_4O_7$ $10\ H_2O$ $H=2$ to 2.5 $G=1.7$	Sweetish alkaline	$F.=1$ to 1.5. Swells and gives clear glass	Puffs up. Gives much water	Unsymmetrical polygons	Snow white crystals, crusts or porous masses.
M. Kernite.......... $Na_2B_4O_7$ $4\ H_2O$ $H=3$ $G=1.953$	Trace of sweetish taste	$F.=1$. Swells and gives a clear glass	Puffs up; gives much water	Unsymmetrical polygons	Transparent, cleavable, colorless crystals, resembling selenite.
Tri. Sassolite.......... H_3BO_3 $G=1.4$ $H=1$	Acid	$F.=2$. With intumescence to clear glass	Water and a little ammonia	Six-sided plates and threads	White pearly scales or plates.
Tri. Chalcanthite.......... $CuSO_4$ $5\ H_2O$ $H=2.5$ $G=2.1$ to 2.3	Metallic, nauseous	Fuses. Reduces with effervescence to copper button	Swells, whitens. Yields water	Blue crystals	Blue glassy crystals, veins and crusts.

7. FLAME NOT COLORED

8. FLAME GREEN

FUSED, POWDERED, MOISTENED WITH CONC. H_2SO_4, AND IGNITED ON PLATINUM WIRE

Minerals of Non-Metallic Luster and with Decided Taste (Soluble in Water)—Continued

Crystal system: name, composition, hardness and specific gravity	Taste	Heated on charcoal	Heated in closed tube	Recrystallization in a drop of water	Appearance
9. FLAME VIOLET THROUGH COLOR SCREEN					
O. Carnallite......... $KCl.MgCl.6H_2O$ H=1 G=1.6	Salty and bitter	F.=1 to 1.5. Ignited with Co. sol, pink	Much water	Rectangles	White to reddish granular masses. Very deliquescent.
O. Nitre......... KNO_3 H=2 G=2.1	Salty and cooling	F.=1. Deflagrates	With $KHSO_4$ brown vapor	Lath shaped	White needles or thin crusts.
I. Kalinite......... $KAl(SO_4)_2+12H_2O$ H=2.5 G=1.7	Astringent	F.=1. Swells, froths, will stain silver	Much water. Acid at high heat	Octahedron. (Three-six- and four-sided polygons)	White fibers or mealy efflorescence.
M. Kainite......... $MgSO_4.KCl+3H_2O$ H=2.5 to 3 G=2 to 2.2	Salty and bitter	Fuses easily and if fused with soda will stain silver	Water	Rectangles	White to brownish red granular masses.
I. Sylvite......... KCl H=2 G=1.97 to 1.99	Bitter	F.=1.5	Residue alkaline on moist test paper	Square (cubes)	White or colorless. May be bluish or yellowish red.
10. FLAME YEL., ABSORBED BY COLOR SCREEN					
H. Soda nitre......... $NaNO_3$ H=1.5 to 2 G=2.2	Cooling	F.=1. Deflagrates	With $KHSO_4$ brown vapor	Rhombic outlines	White, pale red or pale yellow masses and crystals with forms and angles of calcite.
M. Mirabilite......... $Na_2SO_4+10H_2O$ H=1.5 to 2 G=1.5	Bitter	Fuses and will stain silver	Water	Lath shaped	White efflorescence or powdery crust.
I. Halite......... $NaCl$ H=2.5 G=2.4 to 2.6	Salty	F.=1.5	A little water	Square (cubes)	White or colorless or impure brown, yellow or red masses and crystals with cubic cleavage.
M. Trona... $NaCO_3.NaHCO_3+2H_2O$ H=2.5 to 3 G=2.1	Alkaline	Fuses easily	Water	Spherulitic	White glistening crusts.

FUSED, POWDERED, MOISTENED WITH CONC. H_2SO_4, AND IGNITED ON PLATINUM WIRE

Minerals of Non-Metallic Luster, Tasteless and with Colored Streak

Crystal system: name, composition, hardness and specific gravity	In powder boiled with hydrochloric acid				Fusibility on coal	Heated in closed tube	Other tests	Appearance
	There is effervescence	There is a residue of jelly	Simple solution	Insoluble				
11. WITH BLUE STREAK								
M. Vivianite. $Fe_3(PO_4)_2 + 8\,H_2O$ H = 1.5 to 2 G = 2.6 to 2.7	......	......	+	......	2 to 2.5 (Magnetic)	Water. Turns brown	Momentary blue flame with H_2SO_4 (conc.). Yellow pt. with ammonic molybdate	Bluish-green to dark blue, often earthy and filling shells, horn, etc. Rarely as colorless or glassy crystals, gradually becoming blue.
—. Chrysocolla. $CuSiO_3 \cdot 2\,H_2O$ H = 2 to 4 G = 2 to 2.3	......	......	+ (Separation of silica)	......	Infusible. (Blackens)	Blackens. Yields water	....	Enamel-like crusts, veins, or masses.
M. Azurite. $Cu_3(OH)_2(CO_3)_2$ H = 3.5 to 4 G = 3.8	+	......	......	......	3 (Black)	Blackens. Yields water	Emerald-green flame. Solutions blue with ammonia	Dark-blue glassy crystals, lighter blue crusts, velvety, dull or earthy masses.
I. Lazurite. $Na_4(NaS,Al)Al_2(SiO_2)_3$ H = 5 to 5.5 G = 2.6 to 2.9	+ (Odor H_2S)	+	......	......	3.5 (White)	Water. Green glow	Yellow flame	Deep-blue fine-grained masses, usually spangled with pyrite and intermixed with other minerals.
12. WITH GREEN STREAK								
Chlorite group. H = 1 to 2.5 G = 2.6 to 2.9 (Micaceous dark-green minerals such as clinochlore $H_8Mg_5Al_2Si_3O_{18}$)	......	......	......	+	Fuses. (Colored)	Much water	Milky solutions with concentrated H_2SO_4	Dark-green masses of coarse to very fine scales. Tabular and curiously twisted six-sided crystals and fan-shaped groups which cleave into thin soft pliable but not elastic plates. Also as a pigment in other minerals.
Garnierite. $H_3(Ni \cdot Mg)SiO_4 + H_2O$ H = 2 to 3 G = 2.3 to 2.8	......	......	+ (Separation of silica)	......	Infusible. (Magnetic)	Blackens. Yields water	Borax O.F. violet hot, brown cold	Dark emerald-green masses, often cellular and very crumbly and paler-green masses and crusts. Luster dull.
O. Atacamite. $Cu_2(OH)_3Cl$ H = 3 to 3.5 G = 3.7 to 3.8	......	......	+ (Green)	......	3 to 4 (Copper)	Acid water	Azure blue flame. White and red sublimates	Deep emerald-green, confused aggregates and slender prisms. Formerly found as a sand.

Minerals of Non-Metallic Luster, Tasteless and with Colored Streak—*Continued*

Crystal system: name, composition, hardness and specific gravity	In powder boiled with hydrochloric acid				Fusibility on coal	Heated in closed tube	Other tests	Appearance
	There is effervescence	There is a residue of jelly	Simple solution	Insoluble				
12. WITH GREEN STREAK								
M. Malachite. $Cu_2(OH)_2CO_2$ H = 3.5 to 4 G = 3.9 to 4	+				3. (Black)	Blackens. Much water	Green flame, blue with HCl	Bright-green radiating fibers or crusts, often banded in shades of green, sometimes stalactitic. Also dull green and earthy. Rarely, slender crystals.
O. Brochantite. $CuSO·3Cu(OH)_2$ H = 3.5 to 4 G = 3.9			+		Fuses. (Copper)	Water. May blacken. Acid at high temperature	Green flame, blue with HCl. Fused with soda, stains silver	Emerald-green needle crystals. Fibrous veins and crusts.
Turquois. $Al_2(OH)_3PO_4H_2O$ H = 6 G = 2.6 to 2.8			+		Infusible. (Brown)	Blackens. Yields water	Yellow ppt. as in vivianite. Green flame, blue with HCl	Sky-blue to green nearly opaque nodules or veins, with luster of wax.
13. WITH YELLOW TO YELLOWISH-BROWN STREAK								
H. Iodlyte. AgI H = 1 G = 5.6 to 5.7				+	Fuses. (Silver)	Fuses, orange hot, yellow cold	Closed tube with $KHSO_4$ violet vapor and globule deep red hot, yellow cold. Unchanged by sun	Yellow or yellowish-green, thin veins or flexible plates or crystals. Cuts like wax and is not affected by sunlight. Streak yellow.
Sulphur, S. H = 1.5 to 2.5 G = 2.0 to 2.1				+	| (SO_2 odor. Blue flame)	Fusible subl. brown hot, yellow cold	....	Sulphur yellow to brown, translucent crystals, irregular masses, crusts, stalactites and powder. Streak pale yellow.
O. Orpiment. As_2S_3 H = 1.5 to 2 G = 3.4 to 3.6				+	| (Arsenical odor. Blue flame)	Boils. Transparent yellow sublimate	Soluble in nitric acid with separation of sulphur	Lemon yellow, foliated and cleavable to flexible scales, also granular, and as small crystals. Streak lemon yellow.
O. Autunite. $Ca(UO_2)_2(PO_4)_2+8H_2O$ H = 2 to 2.5 G = 3 to 3.2			+ (Green)		Easy (Black and crystalline)	Fades. Yields water	Yellow ppt. as in vivianite. Borax colorless O. F., green R. F.	Yellow tabular nearly square crystals and scales and foliated aggregates. Streak pale yellow.
H. Greenockite. CdS H = 3 to 3.5 G = 4.9 to 5	+ (Odor H_2S)				Infusible but brown sublimate	Carmine hot, yellow cold	The coal may show also a variegated tarnish	Bright yellow coating or inclusion with zinc minerals. Streak orange yellow.

13. WITH YELLOW TO YELLOWISH-BROWN STREAK

Species					Fusibility	Reagent test	B.B. on coal	Crystallography, color, streak
$Pb_5Cl(VO_4)_3$ $H = 3$ $G = 6.6$ to 7.8	+	+ (Residue)			1.5 (Black)	With $KHSO_4$. Red hot, yellow cold	On coal greenish yellow subl. with Bi flux. With S. Ph. O. F. amber, R. F. green	Red, yellow or brown. Sharp hexagonal prisms, sometimes hollow. Also globular masses. Streak pale yellow.
H. Pyromorphite. $Pb_5Cl(PO_4)_3$ $H = 3.5$ to 4 $G = 5.9$ to 7.1		+ (Residue)			2 (Recrystallizes)		Yellow ppt. as in vivianite. Greenish yellow subl. on coal with Bi flux	Green, brown or gray. Hexagonal prisms and tapering groups in parallel position. Also rounded and moss-like aggregations.
H. Siderite. $FeCO_3$ $H = 3.5$ to 4 $G = 3.8$ to 3.9		+ (Slowly in cold acid)			5 (Black and magnetic)	Blackens, becomes magnetic	Solution gives dark-blue ppt. with potassic ferricyanide (ferrous iron)	Brown crusts of curved (rhombohedral) crystals, or massive with cleavage at 107° or granular. Streak pale yellow.
I. Sphalerite ZnS $H = 3.5$ to 4 $G = 3.9$ to 4.1		+ (Odor H_2S)			Infusible or with difficulty	No sublimate	On coal subl. yellow hot, white cold, bright green if ignited with cobalt solution	Yellow-brown or black transparent to translucent crystals and cleavable masses with strong resinous luster, and compact fine-grained masses or alternate concentric layers with galena. Streak pale brown.
O. Goethite. $FeO(OH)$ $H = 5$ to 5.5 $G = 4$ to 4.4			+		5 to 5.5 (Black. Magnetic)	Water. Reddens	On coal R. F. strongly magnetic	Occurs massive but is best known as yellowish to brown and red needles, scales and velvety crusts. Streak yellow to yellowish brown.
Limonite. $Fe_2O_3 \cdot Fe_2(OH)_6$ $H = 5$ to 5.5 $G = 3.6$ to 4			+		5 to 5.5 (Black. Magnetic)	Much water. Reddens	Like goethite	Brown dull-lustered heterogeneous bog ore, cellular stalactitic and pipe-like concretions of rusty brown to nearly black, often fibrous smooth masses.
T. Rutile. TiO_2 $H = 6$ to 6.5 $G = 4.1$ to 4.2				+	Infusible		S. Ph. O. F. slowly to yellow, made violet R. F.	Brownish red to nearly black crystals with brilliant luster often parallel or netted. More rarely massive. Streak pale brown.
T. Cassiterite. SnO_2 $H = 6$ to 7 $G = 6.8$ to 7.1				+	Infusible		On coal strongly heated and aided by soda or sulphur gives button and subl. yellow hot, white, cold, bluish green if ignited with cobalt solution	Brown to red and nearly black. Dull, kidney-shaped and roundel pebbles. Brilliant crystals, and disseminated grains. Streak pale brown.

Minerals of Non-Metallic Luster, Tasteless and with Colored Streak—*Continued*

Crystal system: name, composition, hardness and specific gravity	In powder boiled with hydrochloric acid				Fusibility on coal	Heated in closed tube	Other tests	Appearance
	There is effervescence	There is a residue of jelly	Simple solution	Insoluble				
14. WITH RED TO REDDISH-BROWN STREAK								
M. Erythrite.......... $Co_3(AsO_4)_2 \cdot 8 H_2O$ $G = 2.9$ $H = 1.5$ to 2.5	......	......	+ (Light red)	......	Fuses. (Garlic odor)	Water	Borax deep blue, O. F. and R. F.	Pink earthy crusts or powder or crimson fibers. Streak pink to crimson.
H. Cinnabar........... HgS $H = 2$ to 2.5 $G = 8$ to 8.2				+	Volatilizes without fusion	Black subl., red if rubbed	Closed tube with soda metallic mirror which can be collected into visible globules. Soluble aqua regia	Vermilion, scarlet and dark brownish-red fine-grained masses. Crystalline crusts. Streak scarlet.
H. Proustite........... Ag_3AsS_3 $H = 2$ to 2.5 $G = 5.6$ to 5.7				+	— (Garlic odor. Silver)	Fuses. Slight red subl., yellow cold	Soluble HNO_3. Decomposed by boiling KOH and a yellow ppt. by HCl	Scarlet to vermilion crusts or masses. Rare six-sided prisms with brilliant adamantine luster. Streak scarlet.
H. Pyrargyrite........... Ag_3SbS_3 $G = 5.8$ $H = 2.5$				+	— (White subl. Silver)	Fuses. Subl. black hot, red cold	As with proustite but ppt. is orange	Blackish red veins or crusts with a brilliant adamantine luster. Red tint stronger in thin layers. Rare red crystals. Streak purplish red.
Bauxite........... $Al_2O(OH)_4$ $G = 2.4$ to 2.5 $H = 1$ to 3	......	......	+	......	Infusible	Water at high heat	Deep blue if ignited with cobalt solution	Red to reddish-brown masses of rounded grains or clay-like. Dull in luster. Streak reddish brown.

Mineral			Fusibility	Closed tube	Reaction	Color and Streak
14. WITH RED TO REDDISH-BROWN STREAK						
I. Cuprite. Cu_2O H = 3.5 to 4 G = 5.8 to 6.1		+ (Brown)	3 (Copper)		Ignited with HCl, azure-blue flame	Dark-red to brick-red masses, Deep-red to crimson isometric crystals, sometimes hair-like. Streak brownish red, shining.
H. Ilmenite. $FeTiO_3$ H = 5 to 6 G = 4.5 to 5		+ (Slowly)	Infusible O. F. with difficulty R. F.		Solution boiled with tin becomes violet. Fused with soda is magnetic	Brownish-black to rusty-brown plates, grains and masses and thin tabular crystals. Streak brownish red.
H. Hematite. Fe_2O_3 H = 5.5 to 6.5 G = 4.9 to 5.3		+	Infusible (Magnetic)		Dark-blue ppt. with potassic ferrocyanide	Dull dark red, massive, oölitic, or earthy, sometimes kidney-shaped and fibrous. Streak brownish red.
15. WITH ORANGE STREAK						
M. Realgar. As_2S_2 H = 1.5 to 2 G = 3.4 to 3.6	+		1 (Burns blue flame)	Boils, gives subl. black hot, red cold	Soluble KOH. HCl ppts. yellow flakes. Soluble HNO_3	Orange-red granular masses of resinous luster and transparent crystals. Streak orange red.
M. Crocoite. $PbCrO_4$ H = 2.5 to 3 G = 5.9 to 6.1		+	1.5 (Lead)	With $KHSO_4$ dark violet hot, greenish cold	In S. Ph. O. F. and R. F. bright green. On coal Bi flux greenish yellow	Hyacinth red prisms. Streak orange yellow.
O. Descloizite. $(PbOH)VO_4 (Pb, Zn)$ H = 3.5 G = 5.9 to 6.2		+	Fuses (Lead)	Some water	In S. Ph. O. F. amber, R. F. green. On coal with Bi flux greenish yellow	Black, brown or red crusts of minute crystals. Streak brownish orange.
H. Zincite. ZnO H = 4 to 4.5 G = 5.4 to 5.7		+	Infusible (Sublimate)	Blackens	Sublimate ignited with cobalt solution is bright green	Deep red to brick-red adamantine masses. Granular or cleavable. Very rare crystals. Streak orange yellow.

Minerals of Non-Metallic Luster, Tasteless and with White Streak, and Yielding Reactions on Charcoal with Sodic Carbonate

Crystal system: name, composition, hardness and specific gravity	Blue	Green	Yellow	Brown	Red	Gray	Colorless or white	Black	Solubility	Flame coloration	Heated in closed tube	Other tests	Appearance
O. Sulphur. S H = 1.5 to 2.5 G = 2 to 2.1		+	−	+					Insoluble	Blue	Yellow fusible. Sublimate brown hot	Takes fire and burns with odor SO_2	Bright translucent crystals and masses or powder with resinous or dull luster.
—Hydrozincite. $Zn_3CO_3(OH)_4$ H = 2 to 2.5 G = 3.6 to 3.8							+		Sol. with effervescence		Water. Yellow hot	On coal R. F. heavy white subl. made bright green by ignition with cobalt solution	Chalk-like masses or crusts on other zinc minerals.
O. Valentinite. Sb_2O_3 H = 2.5 to 3 G = 5.6							+		Soluble	Yellow green (Coal R. F.)	Fuses, partly sublimes	Volatile white subl. on coal	White silky minute crystals or radiating fibers.
O. Anglesite. $PbSO_4$ H = 3 G = 6.1 to 6.4						+	+		Insoluble		Decrepitates	Bright yellow subl. on coal with Bi flux	Simple crystals, often transparent and colorless. White brittle masses and compact granular masses of gray color from intermixed galena.
T. Wulfenite. $PbMoO_4$ H = 3 G = 6.7 to 7			+	+	+	+			Partial to green solution		Darkens. Decrepitates	Like anglesite. Also solution, cooled, diluted boiled with tin is blue	Tabular square crystals of resinous luster.

16. NOTABLE FUMES OR SUBLIMATES

FUSED ON CHARCOAL WITH SODIC CARBONATE YIELDS:

Mineral			Solubility	With	S.Ph. O.F. / R.F.	Remarks
16. NOTABLE FUMES OR SUBLIMATES						
FUSED ON CHARCOAL WITH SODIC CARBONATE YIELDS:						
H. Vanadinite. $Pb_5Cl(VO_4)_3$ H=3 G=6.6 to 7.2	+	+ + +	Sol. HNO_3 to yellow solution	With $KHSO_4$ yellow to red hot, yellow cold	S.Ph. O.F. amber, R.F. green	Sharp hexagonal prisms, sometimes hollow. Also parallel groups and globular masses.
O. Cerussite. $PbCO_3$ H=3 to 3.5 G=6.5 to 6.6	+ +	+ + +	Sol. with effervescence in hot HCl. Crystals on cooling	Turns yellow then red, cools yellow	Like anglesite	Twinned crystals or interlaced fibers or granular masses, often with galena.
H. Pyromorphite. $Pb_5Cl(PO_4)_3$ H=3.5 to 4 G=5.9 to 7.1	+ + +	+ + +	Sol. HNO_3		Like anglesite. Also fuses O. F. and on cooling has facets	Hexagonal prisms and tapering groups in parallel position. Also rounded and moss-like aggregations.
I. Sphalerite. ZnS H=3.5 to 4 G=3.9 to 4.1	+ +	+ + +	Sol. with effervescence and odor H_2S		On coal R.F. heavy white subl. made bright green by ignition with cobalt solution	Transparent to translucent crystals and cleavable masses with strong resinous luster. Compact masses or alternate layers with galena. Rarely a white powder.
Heminorphite (calamine) $(ZnOH)_2SiO_3$ H=4.5 to 5 G=4.3 to 4.5	+ +	+ + + +	Sol. with jelly	Water	Like sphalerite (best if soda and borax added in ignition)	White masses, the cavities lined with crystals, often showing only ends, usually parallel, forming ridges. The fracture shows the crystals like parallel fibers.
H. Smithsonite. $ZnCO_3$ H=5 G=4.3 to 4.5	+ +	+ + + +	Sol. with effervescence	Yellow hot, if pure	Like sphalerite	Porous, cellular masses. Crusts with smooth rounded surfaces. Occasional drusy surfaces, the crystal ends being three-faced.

Minerals of Non-Metallic Luster, Tasteless and with White Streak, and Yielding Reactions on Charcoal with Sodic Carbonate—*Continued*

FUSED ON CHARCOAL WITH SODIC CARBONATE YIELDS:

Group	Crystal system: name, composition, hardness and specific gravity	Blue	Green	Yellow	Brown	Red	Gray	Colorless or white	Black	Solubility	Flame coloration	Heated in closed tube	Other tests	Appearance
16, NOTABLE FUMES OR SUBLIMATES	H. Willemite. Zn_2SiO_4 H=5.5 G=3.9 to 4.2		+	+	+	+				Sol. with jelly			Like sphalerite	Granular masses intermixed usually with black and red grains. Rarely large reddish or brownish crystals. Luster resinous.
	T. Cassiterite. SnO_2 H=6 to 7 G=6.8 to 7.1			+	+				+	Insoluble			On coal with soda non-volatile subl. made bluish green by ignition with cobalt solution	Crystals with brilliant adamantine luster, disseminated grains and rounded heavy pebbles dull and often with radiating structure.
17, NO FUMES OR SUBLIMATES BUT IS REDUCED TO METALLIC OR MAGNETIC PARTICLES	I. Cerargyrite. AgCl H=1 to 1.5 G=5 to 5.5		+		+		+			Insoluble		With $KHSO_4$ yellow hot, white cold, violet in sun	On coal acrid odor and silver button	Thin crusts which darken in sunlight and cut like wax with shining surface after cutting.
	I. Embolite. Ag(Cl·Br) H=1 to 1.5 G=5.3 to 5.8									Insoluble		With $KHSO_4$ dark red hot, dark yellow cold, dark green in sun	Like cerargyrite	Like cerargyrite.
	Chrysocolla. $CuSiO_3 \cdot 2H_2O$ H=2 to 4 G=2 to 2.3	+	+							Sol. with residue	Emerald green	Blackens. Yields water	With soda on coal, a copper button	Enamel-like crusts, veins or compact masses. Never crystals.
	H. Siderite. $FeCO_3$ H=3.5 to 4 G=3.8 to 3.9				+		+			Slow effervescence in cold acid		Black and magnetic	On coal becomes black and magnetic	Compact, fine-grained and cleavable masses and rhombohedral curved crystals. Cleavage angles 107°.

18. NO FUMES, SUBLIMATES OR REDUCED PARTICLES, BUT IF MOISTENED WILL STAIN SILVER

FUSED ON CHARCOAL WITH SODIC CARBONATE YIELDS:

Mineral							Solubility	Flame color	Heating / tube	Ignition test	Description
M. Gypsum. $CaSO_4\,2H_2O$, H = 1.5 to 2, G = 2.3	+	+	+	+		+	Soluble. Recrystallizes on evaporation	Yellowish red	Whitens. Yields water		Soft, colorless or slightly tinted masses, which may be scaly, silky fibrous or compact or may be masses and crystals, cleaving in three directions to a rhombic plate of 66°.
O. Barite. $BaSO_4$, H = 2.5 to 3.5, G = 4.3 to 4.6	+	+	+	+		+	Insoluble	Yellowish green			Granular, cleavable and fibrous. Crystals common. Cleaves in three directions to rhombic plates of 78½°.
O. Celestite. $SrSO_4$, H = 3 to 3.5, G = 4	+	+	+	+		+	Insoluble	Crimson			Colorless to white crystals and fibrous, lamellar and granular masses. Cleaves in three directions to rhombic plates of 76°.
O. Anhydrite. $CaSO_4$, H = 3 to 3.5, G = 2.9 to 3	+	+	+			+	Soluble. White ppt. with $BaCl_2$	Yellowish red			Cleavable and fine-grained masses. Cleaves in three directions at 90°.
H. Alunite. $K(AlO_2)_2(SO_4)_2 + 3H_2O$, H = 3.5 to 4.5, G = 2.6 to 2.7				+			Partial	Violet. (Color Screen)	Water at high heat	Blue by ignition with Co. solution	Fibrous or lamellar or small cuboids, usually mixed with hard, siliceous material.
I. Lazurite (Lapis Lazuli) $Na_4(NaS_3Al)$ $Al_2(SiO_4)_3$, H = 5 to 5.5, G = 2.4						+	Sol. with jelly and odor H_2S	Yellow	Water and green glow	Blue in fine powder	Fine-grained, usually spangled with pyrite and intermixed with other minerals.

Minerals of Non-Metallic Luster, Tasteless and with White Streak, and Yielding No Tests with Sodic Carbonate

Crystal system: name, composition, hardness and specific gravity	Purple or violet	Blue	Green	Yellow	Brown	Red	Gray	Colorless or white	Solubility	Flame coloration	Heated in closed tube	Other tests	Appearance
M. Lepidolite. $(KLi)_3Al(SiO_3)_3$ H = 2 to 2.5 G = 2.8 to 3.2	+					+	+		Slight in HCl	Crimson			Masses of coarse or fine scales with easy cleavage into thinner plates.
M. Cryolite. $AlNa_3F_6$ H = 2.5 G = 2.9 to 3							+	+	Soluble	Yellow	Etches tube	Blue if ignited with Co. solution	Translucent masses resembling watery snow. Rarely small six-sided monoclinic crystals nearly cubes.
I. Fluorite. CaF_2 H = 4 G = 3 to 3.3	+	+	+	+	+	+		+	Soluble	Red to orange	Phosphorescent. With $KHSO_4$ etches tube		Transparent cubes and masses of glassy luster which cleave in four directions at angles 70° 31′. Color usually brilliant. Sometimes banded.
M. Stilbite. $H_4R_2Al_2(SiO_2)_6 + 4H_2O$ H = 3.5 to 4 G = 2.1 to 2.2					+			+	Soluble with residue		Water	Swells greatly during fusion	Sheaf-like groups or many small crystals forming a crust or lining. One easy cleavage giving symmetrical pearly face.
H. Chabazite. $(CaNa_2)Al(SiO_4)_3\ 6H_2O$ H = 4.5 G = 2.0 to 2.1						+		+	Soluble with lumps jelly		Much water	Intumescence during fusion	Groups of small rhombohedral crystals which are nearly cubes.
T. Apophyllite. $H_{14}K_2Ca_8(SiO_3)_{16}\ 9H_2O$ H = 4.5 to 5 G = 2.3 to 2.4						+		+	Soluble with lumps jelly	Pale violet (Color Screen)	Much water	Exfoliates during fusion	Tabular or "cubic" or pointed crystals with internal opalescence. Occasionally lamellar. One easy cleavage.

19. FUSES EASILY (1 to 4) TO WHITE GLASS OR ENAMEL

A THIN FRAGMENT HEATED IN PLATINUM FORCEPS AT TIP OF BLUE FLAME

19. FUSES EASILY (1 TO 4) TO A WHITE GLASS OR ENAMEL

THIN FRAGMENT HEATED IN PLATINUM FORCEPS AT TIP OF BLUE FLAME

Mineral	Blowpipe behavior	Closed tube	Flame	Cleavage / Solubility	Crystal form and remarks
T. Wernerite Group. Silicates of NaCaAl $H = 5$ to 6 $G = 2.7$	Bubbles in fused material		Yellow	Imperfect	Coarse thick crystals with octagonal or square cross-section. Cleavage angles 135° or 90°. Cleavages faintly fibrous. More rarely massive columnar or fine-grained aggregates.
Tri Plagioclase. $n\mathrm{NaAlSi_3O_8} + m\mathrm{CaAl_2Si_2O_8}$ (Albite) (Labradorite) $H = 5$ to 7 $G = 2.6$ to 2.7			Yellow	Insoluble Partial	Masses and crystals with two easy cleavages, nearly but not exactly 90°. Often show parallel striations. Sometimes opalescent.
Tri. Amblygonite. Li (AlF) $\mathrm{PO_4}$ $H = 6$ $G = 3$ to 3.1	Momentary blue-green flame with $\mathrm{H_2SO_4}$	Water and etching of tube	Crimson to yellowish red	Insoluble	Cleavable masses and rough crystals. One easy cleavage.
O. Prehnite. $\mathrm{H_2Ca_2Al_2 (SiO_4)_3}$ $H = 6$ to 6.5 $G = 2.8$ to 2.9	After fusion dissolves leaving jelly	A little water		Soluble	Lining cavities as smooth rounded crusts or as sheaf-like groups of tabular crystals. Sometimes in barrel-shaped crystals.
H. Tourmaline. $\mathrm{R_{18}B_2 (SiO_4)_4}$ $H = 6$ to 6.5 $G = 2.8$ to 2.9	After ignition dissolves leaving jelly		Green with $\mathrm{KHSO_4 + CaF_2}$	Insoluble	Prismatic crystals often hemimorphic and roughly triangular in cross-section.
I. Boracite. $H = 7$ $G = 2.9$ to 3	Violet if ignited with cobalt solution		Yellowish green	Soluble	Minute glassy crystals.

Minerals of Non-Metallic Luster, Tasteless and with White Streak, and Yielding No Tests with Sodic Carbonate—*Continued*

THIN FRAGMENT HEATED IN PLATINUM FORCEPS

20. FUSES EASILY (1 TO 4) TO COLOR-LESS GLASS

Crystal system: name, composition, hardness and specific gravity	The color of the mineral is:								Solubility	Flame coloration	Heated in closed tube	Other tests	Appearance
	Purple or violet	Blue	Green	Yellow	Brown	Red	Gray	Colorless or white					
Ulexite. $CaNaB_5O_9 \cdot 8H_2O$ $H=1$ $G=1.65$								+	Soluble	Reddish yellow	Much water	Green flame with $KHSO_4$ and CaF_2	Nodular masses of silky fibers.
M. Colemanite. $Ca_2B_6O_{11} \cdot 5H_2O$ $H=4$ to 4.5 $G=2.2$ to 2.3								+	Soluble (with crystals on cooling)	Green	Water	Decrepitates before fusing	Highly modified crystals with one easy cleavage, cleavable or fine-grained compact "porcelain-like" or loose, chalk-like masses.
O. Natrolite. $Na_2Al_2Si_3O_{10}+2H_2O$ $H=5$ to 5.5 $G=2.2$				+				+	Soluble with jelly	Yellow	Water		Slender prisms with square cross-section and flat pyramid at end.
I. Analcime. $NaAl(SiO_2)_2 \cdot H_2O$ $H=5$ to 5.5 $G=2.2$ to 2.3						+		+	Soluble with lumps jelly	Yellow	Water, but keeps luster	Becomes opaque before fusion	Trapezohedral crystals usually forming a lining. Rarely granular.
M. Datolite. $Ca(BOH)SiO_4$ $H=5$ to 5.5 $G=2.9$ to 3								+	Soluble with jelly	Green	Water at high heat		Brilliant small highly modified glassy crystals lining a cavity, also porcelain masses. No easy cleavage.

THIN FRAGMENT, HEATED IN PLATINUM FORCEPS AT TIP OF BLUE FLAME

20. FUSES EASILY (1 TO 4) TO A COLORLESS GLASS

Mineral	Tests	Solubility	Flame	Special reaction	Remarks
H. Nephelite. $Na_2Al_2Si_2O_8$ $H=5.5$ to 6 $G=3.2$ to 3.6	+ + +	Soluble with jelly	Yellow	Blue if ignited with cobalt solution	Translucent masses and coarse hexagonal crystals with peculiar greasy luster. More rarely highly modified small white crystals.
Pyroxene (diopside). $CaMg(SiO_3)_2$ $H=5$ to 6 $G=3.2$ to 3.6	+ +	Insoluble			Usually prismatic crystals with eight-sided cross-section and angles between alternate faces 90° or 87°. Cleavage angle of 87°.
M. Amphibole (tremolite). $CaMg_3(SiO_3)_4$ $H=5$ to 6 $G=2.9$ to 3.4	+ + +	insoluble			Fibrous and columnar, often radiating. Also crystals with cross-section, a rhomb of 124° or six-sided section. Cleavage at 124°.
Tri. Plagioclase. $nNaAlSi_3O_8 + mCaAl_2$ Si_2O_8 $H=5$ to 7 $G=2.6$ to 2.7	+				Masses and crystals with two easy cleavages, nearly but not exactly 90°. Often show parallel striations. Sometimes opalescent.
(Albite) $NaAlSi_3O_8$	+ +	Insoluble	Yellow		Usually pure white, often granular with curved cleavage surfaces.
(Anorthite) $CaAl_2Si_2O_8$	+ + +	Soluble with jelly		White ppt. with H_2SO_4	Highly modified glassy crystals or grayish-white larger crystals
(Oligoclase) Ab_2 to $_6$ An	+ +	Insoluble	Yellow		Broad cleavages. Good striations. Sometimes spangled (Sunstone).
(Labradorite) $AbAn_1$ to $_3$	+ +	Partial	Crimson		Good striations. Beautiful play of color.
M. Spodumene. $LiAl(SiO_3)_2$ $H=6.5$ to 7 $G=3.1$ to 3.2	+ +	Insoluble		Sprouts and becomes opaque during fusion	Coarse, flattened prisms with cleavage at 87°. Often separate in broad plates (bisecting cleavage angle). Often striated and etched or roughened.

Minerals of Non-Metallic Luster, Tasteless and with White Streak, and Yielding No Tests with Sodic Carbonate—*Continued*

Crystal system: name, composition, hardness and specific gravity	The color of the mineral is:								Solubility	Flame coloration	Heated in closed tube	Other tests	Appearance
	Blue	Green	Yellow	Brown	Red	Gray	Colorless or white	Black					
M. Sphene. $CaSiTiO_5$ $G=3.4$ to 3.5 $H=5$ to 5.5		+	+	+					Soluble slowly		May become yellow	S. Ph. O. F. slowly soluble. Undissolved portion milk white, R. F. violet	Wedge-shaped or tabular crystals, with adamantine luster. Also massive. Easy cleavages give monoclinic shapes.
Pyroxene. $RSiO_3$. Many varieties (Augite) ($R=CaMgFeAl$) $H=5$ to 6 $G=3.2$ to 3.6		+		+				+	Insoluble or nearly				Usually eight-sided prisms with angles between alternate faces 90° and 87°. Cleavage angle 87°.
M. Amphibole $RSiO_3$ (Actinolite) $Ca (MgFe)_3 (SiO_2)_4$ $H=5$ to 6 $G=2.9$ to 3.4		+							Insoluble				Bladed non-terminated crystals, divergent fibers and granules.
(Hornblende). $CaMgFeAl$, etc		+						+	Insoluble or nearly				Crystals six-sided cross-section, with angles 124° and 116°, also fibrous and compact masses. Sometimes with luster of horn.
O. Hypersthene. $(Mg \cdot Fe) SiO_3$ $H=5$ to 6 $G=3.4$ to 3.5		+						+	Partially soluble			After fusion attracted by magnet	Foliated aggregates sometimes with peculiar "Schiller," or pearly effect.
Tri. Rhodonite. $MnSiO_3$ $H=6$ to 6.5 $G=3.4$ to 3.7				+	+				Soluble with white residue			Borax, O. F. amethystine	Fine-grained or cleavable masses and disseminated grains, often coated with a black oxide. Sometimes in crystals.
M. Epidote. $Ca_2 (Al \cdot Fe)_2 (AlOH) (SiO_4)_3$ $H=6$ to 7 $G=3.2$ to 3.5		+			+				Insoluble or nearly		Water at high heat	After fusion will gelatinize	A secondary mineral often with the original mineral as grains or needles. Less frequently in distinct crystals.

21. FUSES EASILY (1 TO 4) TO A COLORED GLASS

THIN FRAGMENT HEATED IN PLATINUM FORCEPS AT TIP OF BLUE FLAME

THIN FRAGMENT HEATED IN PLATINUM FORCEPS AT TIP OF BLUE FLAME

21. FUSES EASILY (1 TO 4) TO COLORED GLASS

Mineral						Solubility	Color reaction	Water at high heat	After fusion	Remarks
T. Idocrase (vesuvianite)…… $Ca_6Al_3(OH \cdot F)(SiO_4)_6$ $H=6.5$ $G=3.3$ to 3.4		+	+	+		Insoluble or nearly		Water at high heat	After fusion will gelatinize	Square and octagonal prisms and radiated columnar or granular masses or compact masses resembling jade.
I. Garnet…… $R_3R_2(SiO_4)_3$ $H=6.5$ to 7.5 $G=3.1$ to 4.3 (most varieties)	+	+	+		+	Insoluble			After fusion will gelatinize	Imbedded crystals, often nearly spherical or in druses and granular, lamellar and compact masses. Also found in alluvial material as rounded grains.
H. Tourmaline…… $R_{13}B_3(SiO_5)_4$ $H=7$ to 7.5 $G=3$ to 3.2	+		+		+	Insoluble	Green with $KHSO_4 \cdot CaF_2$		After fusion will gelatinize	Prismatic crystals, the cross-section often showing a triangular prism. Often the color is different at opposite ends or center and outer shell. Also radiating aggregates and in compact masses.

22. FUSES WITH DIFFICULTY (5 TO 6) SOMETIMES BARELY ROUNDING EDGES

Mineral						Solubility	Color reaction	Water at high heat	After fusion	Remarks
Pyrophyllite…… $HAl(SiO_3)_2$ $H=1$ to 2 $G=2.8$ to 2.9	+	−	+	+		Partial		Water	Blue if ignited with cobalt solution	Radiated folie or fibers and compact masses. Smooth and soft like talc.
O. Talc…… $H_2Mg_3(SiO_2)_4$ $H=1$ to 1.5 $G=2.5$ to 2.9	+		+	+		Insoluble		Water	Pink if ignited with cobalt solution	Foliaced compact and fibrous masses with soapy feeling. The foliated talc cleaves into non-elastic plates.
M. Chlorite Group (Prochlorite)…… $H_9(Mg,Fe)_5Al_2Si_3O_{10}$ $H=1$ to 2 $G=2.8$ to 2.9	+		+			Milky solution with conc. H_2SO_4		Much water		Masses of coarse to very fine scales. Tabular and curiously twisted six-sided crystals and fan-shaped groups which cleave into thin, soft pliable but not elastic plates. Also as a pigment in other minerals.
(Clinochlore)…… $(H_8Mg_5Al_2Si_3O_{18})$ $H=1$ to 2.5 $G=2.6$ to 2.9	+			+		Like prochlorite		Much water		
Sepiolite…… $H_4Mg_2Si_3O_{10}$ $H=2$ to 2.5 $G=1$ to 2	+		+		+	Sol. with jelly		Water	Pink if ignited with cobalt solution	Soft, compact, smooth feeling masses of very light weight. Rarely fibrous.

Minerals of Non-Metallic Luster, Tasteless and with White Streak, and Yielding No Tests with Sodic Carbonate—*Continued*

Crystal system: name, composition, hardness and specific gravity	Blue	Green	Yellow	Brown	Red	Gray	Colorless or white	Black	Solubility	Flame coloration	Heated in closed tube	Other tests	Appearance
M. Muscovite. $(HK)AlSiO_4$ H = 2 to 2.5 G = 2.8 to 3		+	+	+		+			Insoluble even in H_2SO_4		Water at high heat		Plates and masses of scales and crystals, often large and rough, with rhombic or hexagonal cross-section. Luster pearly, cleavage very easy into thin elastic plates.
M. Biotite. $(H\cdot K)_2(Mg\cdot Fe)_2\,Al_2(SiO_4)_3$ H = 2.5 to 3 G = 2.7		+	+	+	+			+	Like prochlorite		Water at high heat		Scales or aggregates. Rarely large sheets or pseudo hexagonal crystals cleaving easily into thin elastic plates. Luster pearly.
M. Phlogopite. $(K\cdot H)_3 Mg_3 Al\,(SiO_4)_3$ H = 2.5 to 3 G = 2.8				+					Like prochlorite		Water at high heat		Rough prisms with hexagonal or rhombic scales. Also disseminated scales. Cleaves easily into thin elastic plates.
Serpentine. $H_4Mg_3Si_2O_9$ H = 3 to 4 G = 2.5 to 2.6		+	+	+	+		+	+	Soluble with residue		Water	Pink or brownish red if powder ignited with cobalt solution	Compact masses with little luster and smooth somewhat greasy feel, often with veins of silky fibers or foliated.
O. Strontianite. $SrCO_3$ H = 3 to 3.5 G = 3.7							+		Effervesces in cold dilute acids	Crimson		Sprouts and glows intensely during fusion	Masses of parallel or radiating imperfect needle crystals. More rarely fine granular.
M. Wollastonite. $CaSiO_3$ H = 4 to 5 G = 2.8 to 2.9						+	+		Soluble with jelly	Pale red			Fibrous to compact masses. Rarely tabular crystals. Usually intermixed with calcite.
T. Scheelite. $CaWO_4$ H = 4.5 to 5 G = 5.9 to 6.1				+		+	+		Soluble with yellow residue made blue by tin	Pale red		S. Ph. O. F. colorless to milk white. R. F. deep blue	Very heavy masses with resinous luster. Square pyramids and drusy crusts.

22. FUSES WITH DIFFICULTY (5 TO 6) SOMETIMES BARELY ROUNDING EDGES

THIN FRAGMENT HEATED IN PLATINUM FORCEPS AT TIP OF BLUE FLAME

22. FUSES WITH DIFFICULTY (5 TO 6) SOMETIMES BARELY ROUNDING EDGES

THIN FRAGMENT HEATED IN PLATINUM FORCEPS AT TIP OF BLUE FLAME

Mineral								Solubility	Flame color	Reagent	Solution added to	Form
H. Apatite........ $Ca_5(Cl \cdot F)(PO_4)_3$ $H = 4.5$ to 5 $G = 3.2$	+	·	+	+	+	+	+	Soluble	Yellowish red. Momentary green with H_2SO_4	·········	Solution added to nitric solution of ammonium molybdate gives bright yellow ppt.	Usually hexagonal prisms. Luster of oiled glass, dull if altered. Also compact, dull, massive bone phosphate.
Collophane (amorphous)..... essentially $Ca_3P_2O_8 \cdot H_2O$ with $CO_2 \cdot F \cdot SO_4$ $H = 2$–5 $G = 2.6$–2.9	+	+	+	+	+	+	+	Soluble	Yellowish red. Momentary green with H_2SO_4	Water	Yellow ppt. with HNO_3 and ammonium molybdate	Usually massive and without form. May be oölitic or show bone structure.
O. Enstatite....... $(Mg \cdot Fe)SiO_3$ $H = 5.5$ $G = 3.1$ to 3.3	·	·	+	·	·	·	+	Insoluble or nearly	·········		Like serpentine	Lamellar to fibrous masses, often with pearly luster.
Orthoclase...... $KAlSi_3O_8$ $H = 6$ to 6.5 $G = 2.5$ to 2.6	·	+	+	·	·	·	+	Insoluble	Violet (Color screen)			Masses and crystals which cleave in two directions at exactly 90°. Except in the variety microcline the surfaces resulting are not grooved. Sometimes opalescent.
H. Tourmaline...... $R_{18}B_2(SiO_5)_4$ $H = 7$ to 7.5 $G = 3$ to 3.2	+	·	+	+	+	+	+	Insoluble	Green with $KHSO_4$ CaF_2		After fusion will gelatinize	Prismatic crystals, often showing a triangular prism. The color may differ at opposite ends or center and outer shell. Also radiating aggregates and in compact masses.
H. Beryl...... $Be_3Al_2(SiO_2)_6$ $H = 7.5$ to 8 $G = 2.6$ to 2.8	·	+	+	·	·	·	+	Insoluble			Often becomes white on fusion	Hexagonal prisms, from mere threads to several feet in length. Sometimes also in columnar or granular masses.

Minerals of Non-Metallic Luster, Tasteless and with White Streak, and Yielding No Tests with Sodic Carbonate—*Continued*

Crystal system: name, composition, hardness and specific gravity	Purple or violet	Blue	Green	Yellow	Brown	Red	Gray	Colorless or white	Black	Solubility	Flame coloration	Heated in closed tube	Other tests	Appearance
M. Aluminite. Al_2SO_{11} $9H_2O$ H=1 to 2 G=1.6								+		Soluble		Much acid water. Odor SO_2	Infusible with soda but mass will stain silver	Rounded chalky masses with peculiar, harsh (meager) feel.
—Bauxite. $Al_2O(OH)_4$ H=1 to 3 G=2.4 to 2.5				+	+	+		+		Soluble slowly		Water at high heat	May become magnetic in R. F.	Masses of rounded grains (pisolites or oölites) or earthy or clay-like. No luster.
M. Kaolinite. $H_4Al_2Si_2O_9$ H=2 to 2.5 G=2.6			+	+	+	+		+		Insoluble		Water	Often plastic with water	Dull clay-like or mealy masses. Greasy feel.
M. Montmorillonite. $(Mg,Ca)O, Al_2O_3·5SiO_2·NH_2O$ H=1 to 2 G=2+				+	+	+	+	+		Insoluble		Water	Often swells in water	Often occurs in soapy or wax-like masses of clay.
M. Gibbsite. $Al(OH)_3$ H=2.5 to 3.5 G=2.4								+		Soluble		Water	Exfoliates on heating	Small stalactites or thin, smooth crusts, with internally fibrous structure. Rarely in small crystals.
O. Andalusite. (Chiastolite) Al_2SiO_5 H=4 to 5 G=2.1							+	+·	+	Insoluble				Coarse, rounded prisms. Often superficially black. Cross-sections show a cross or checked figure.

THIN FRAGMENT HEATED IN PLATINUM FORCEPS AT TIP OF BLUE FLAME

23. INFUSIBLE BUT IN POWDER IS MADE DEEP BLUE BY IGNITION WITH COBALT SOLUTION

THIN FRAGMENT HEATED IN PLATINUM FORCEPS AT TIP OF BLUE FLAME

23. INFUSIBLE BUT IN POWDER IS MADE DEEP BLUE BY IGNITION WITH COBALT SOLUTION

Mineral			Solubility / Test	Description
Tri. Kyanite Al_2SiO_5 H = 5 to 7 G = 3.6 to 3.7	+	+	Insoluble	Triclinic blade-like crystals and blade-like masses, cleaving parallel largest face. Color or deeper along center.
Leucite $KAl(SiO_2)_2$ H = 5.5 to 6 G = 2.4 to 2.5	+	+	Soluble with residue · Violet (Color screen)	Translucent nearly spherical crystals and grains in volcanic rocks.
O. Sillimanite Al_2SiO_5 H = 6 to 7 G = 3.2	+	+	Insoluble	Thin, almost fibrous prisms and tough fibrous aggregates.
O. Andalusite $Al(AlO)SiO_4$ H = 7 to 7.5 G = 3.1 to 3.2	+	+	Insoluble	Coarse, nearly square prisms or tough, columnar or granular masses.
O. Dumortierite $8 Al_2O_3 \cdot B_2O_3 \cdot 6 SiO_2 \cdot H_2O$ H = 7 G = 3.26 to 3.36	+	+	Insoluble · Water	Blade-like or fibrous crystals.
Topaz $Al_2Si_6O_{25}F_{10}$ H = 8 G = 3.4 to 3.6	+	+	Insoluble · Heated in open tube with fused S. Ph, etches glass	Glassy crystals with one easy cleavage. Also columnar aggregates, and water-worn crystals in alluvial deposit.

Minerals of Non-Metallic Luster, Tasteless and with White Streak, and Yielding No Tests with Sodic Carbonate—*Continued*

Crystal system: name, composition, hardness and specific gravity	The color of the mineral is:									Solubility	Flame coloration	Heated in closed tube	Other tests	Appearance
	Purple or violet	Blue	Green	Yellow	Brown	Red	Gray	Colorless or white	Black					
I. Spinel. $MgAl_2O_4$ H = 8 G = 3.5 to 4.5			+			+	+		+	Insoluble			Often changes color on heating	Simple or twinned octahedral crystals and rolled pebbles.
O. Chrysoberyl. $BeAl_2O_4$ H = 8.5 G = 3.5 to 3.8			+	+						Insoluble				Usually pseudohexagonal crystals or pebbles. Emerald green crystals by transmitted light are purplish red; some pebbles show an internal opalescence.
H. Corundum. Al_2O_3 H = 9 G = 3.9 to 4.1		+			+	+	+		+	Insoluble				Coarse crystals or masses with partings in four directions at 86° and 57°, or granular, slightly translucent.
(Sapphire) or (Ruby)	+	+	+	+		+	+	+		Insoluble			Color changed by heating	Transparent to translucent, usually in crystals and of fine colors.
(Emery)							+		+					Opaque, granular corundum, intimately mixed with hematite or magnetite.

THIN FRAGMENT HEATED IN PLATINUM FORCEPS AT TIP OF BLUE FLAME

23. INFUSIBLE BUT IN POWDER IS MADE DEEP BLUE BY IGNITION WITH COBALT SOLUTION

24. INFUSIBLE AND IS *NOT* MADE DEEP BLUE BY IGNITION WITH COBALT SOLUTION

THIN FRAGMENT HEATED IN PLATINUM FORCEPS AT TIP OF BLUE FLAME

Mineral	Cobalt solution	Flame	Acid test	Description
H. Calcite...... $CaCO_3$ H=3 G=2.7	Unchanged when boiled with cobalt solution	Orange red	Lumps rapidly, effervesces in cold dilute acid	Crystals of many shapes which cleave in three directions to rhombohedron of 105°. Cleavable, coarse and fine-grained, fibrous and loosely coherent masses. Crusts, stalactites.
O. Aragonite...... $CaCO_3$ H=3.5 to 4 G=2.9	Becomes lilac if boiled with cobalt solution	Orange red	Like calcite	Simple or pseudohexagonal crystals. Also columnar and needle masses, oölitic, stalactitic and coral-like. Two easy cleavages with angles near 120° (116°, 122°).
H. Dolomite...... $CaMg(CO_3)_2$ H=3.5 to 4 G=2.8 to 2.9	Pink if ignited with cobalt solution	Orange red	Lumps slowly, effervesces in cold dilute acid	Curved rhombohedral crystals, or coarse to fine-grained masses. Cleaves in three directions to rhombohedron of 106°.
H. Magnesite...... $MgCO_3$ H=3.5 to 4.5 G=3 to 3.1	Like dolomite		Effervesces only in warm acid	Compact, dull nodules or veins in serpentine. Shell-like fracture. Rarely cleavable.
H. Rhodochrosite...... $MnCO_3$ H=4.5 G=3.5 to 4.5	Darkens on ignition. Borax, O.F. amethystine		Like dolomite	Rhombohedral crystals often with curved edges cleavable and granular masses. Sometimes as a crust.
M. Monazite...... $(Ce \cdot La \cdot Di)\,PO_4$ H=5 to 5.5 G=4.9 to 5.3	Yellow ppt. if solution added to nitric solution of ammonic molybdate.	Momentary green with H_2SO_4	Soluble white residue	Translucent grains in some sands and small imbedded resinous crystals.

Minerals of Non-Metallic Luster, Tasteless and with White Streak, and Yielding No Tests with Sodic Carbonate—*Continued*

Crystal system: name, composition, hardness and specific gravity	Purple or violet	Blue	Green	Yellow	Brown	Red	Gray	Colorless or white	Black	Solubility	Flame coloration	Heated in closed tube	Other tests	Appearance
Turquois. $Al_2(OH)_3PO_4H_2O$ H=5 to 6 G=2.6		+	+							Sol. HNO_3	Green (Cu)		Like monazite	Nearly opaque material with wax-like luster found filling cracks and cavities in igneous rocks.
M. Chondrodite. $H_2Mg_{19}Si_8O_{34}F_4$ H=6.5 G=3.1 to 3.2				+	+	+				Sol. with jelly			Heated in open tube with fused S. Ph. etches glass	Compact masses, disseminated grains and crystals of great complexity.
O. Chrysolite. $(MgFe)_2SiO_4$ H=6.5 7 G=3.3 to 3.6			+	+						Sol. with jelly			Whitens on heating	Transparent to translucent granular masses or glassy grains, or sand.
Opal. SiO_2nH_2O H=5.5 to 6.5 G=2.1 to 2.2		+	+	+	+	+	+	+		Insoluble		A little water; becomes opaque	Slowly soluble in caustic alkali	Translucent veins or lining with internal color reflections, or without "opalescence" and with waxy luster, and shell-like fracture. Also dull like pumice and like drops of melted glass.
T. Rutile. TiO_2 H=6 to 6.5 G=4.1 to 4.2					+	+			+	Insoluble			In S. Ph. R. R. F. gives violet	Crystals with brilliant luster often parallel or netted. More rarely massive.
Chalcedony. SiO_2 H=6.5 G=2.6		+				+	+	+	+	Insoluble.				Translucent crusts and cavity linings with smooth rounded surfaces, often in concentric layers with wax-like luster. Never in crystals.

The color of the mineral is:

24. INFUSIBLE AND IS *NOT* MADE DEEP BLUE, BY IGNITION WITH COBALT SOLUTION

THIN FRAGMENT HEATED IN PLATINUM FORCEPS AT TIP OF BLUE FLAME

THIN FRAGMENT HEATED IN PLATINUM FORCEPS AT TIP OF BLUE FLAME

24. INFUSIBLE AND *NOT* MADE DEEP BLUE BY IGNITION WITH COBALT SOLUTION

Mineral	Tests	Solubility	+ marks	Remarks
H. Quartz, SiO_2, $H=7$, $G=2.6$		Insoluble	+ + + + + + + +	Glassy hexagonal crystals and glassy shapeless material between crystals of other minerals. Also nearly opaque material, containing much iron and alumina.
I. Garnet (Ouvarovite), $Ca_3Cr_2(SiO_4)_3$, $H=7$, $G=3.1$ to 4.3		Insoluble	+	Crystals only.
T. Zircon, $ZrSiO_4$, $H=7.5$, $G=4.7$	Glows intensely on heating	Insoluble	+ + + + +	Sharp-cut square prisms, long or short, usually imbedded in the associated mineral. Luster usually adamantine or greasy. Also rounded pebbles.
O. Staurolite, $Fe(AlO)_4(AlOH)(SiO_4)$, $H=7.5$, $G=3.6$ to 3.7	A little water	Insoluble	+	Prisms often twinned, or in threes, crossing at 90° and 120°. Surfaces bright if unaltered.
H. Tourmaline, $R_{13}B_2(SiO_5)_4$, $H=7$ to 7.5, $G=3$ to 3.2	Green with $KHSO_4$ CaF_2	Insoluble	+ + + + +	Glassy hexagonal prisms differently faced at the two ends. Cross-section often suggests a triangle.
I. Diamond, C, $H=10$, $G=3.5$	In powder is burned to CO_2	Insoluble	+ + + + + +	Crystals often rounded with luster suggesting oiled glass, and cleavage in four directions at 70° 31'.

MINERAL SUBSTANCES NOT EASILY DETERMINABLE BY A SCHEME

The following mineral substances of economic importance have not been included in the determinative tables, some because they lack fixed characters, others because their characters are lost in those of their associated substances and others because they occur only in one known locality.

Amber, once the most prized of gems, now used sometimes in jewelry, oftener as a mouthpiece for pipes, is a name given to those fossil resins which contain succinic acid and were derived from a particular extinct species of pine. The amber of the Baltic Sea and the Sicilian amber are the most valued. Color, garnet red, reddish, yellow, brownish, sometimes with bluish fluorescence. Luster resinous, streak white, $H = 2$ to 2.5. $G = 1.096$. Melts quietly at $125°$ to $150°$ C. and gives off a choking vapor.

Asphalts are rather indefinite mixtures of hydrocarbons and their oxidized products. They vary from thick, highly viscous liquids to solids, are generally black in color with pitch-like luster, and burn easily with a pitchy odor. They are slightly heavier than water. Examples: the pitch lakes of Trinidad and of Bermudez, Venzuela; the manjak of Barbados; the elastic elaterite of Derbyshire, England; the albertite of New Brunswick, and the gilsonite of Utah. Sandstones and limestones impregnated with asphalt occur in many localities.

Brucite $Mg(OH)_2$. A white, compact, finely-crystalline mineral, with slightly greenish tint. Soluble in dilute HCl, yielding tests for Mg; also yields water in closed tube. Found in a large deposit on western side of Paradise Range, Nevada, associated with magnesite and dolomite, along a contact of granite with a magnesite-dolomite series. Other forms, of non-commercial importance, sometimes associated with serpentine, are apt to be micaceous or fibrous.

Carnotite, $2UO_3V_2O_5K_2O \cdot 3 H_2O$ (?). A canary yellow, pulvurulent mineral, in minute scales, filling the interstices of sandstone in several counties in Colorado. Rarely compact and wax-like. It contains radium, and is an impure vanadate of uranium and potassium, or uranium and lime, or both. Is a commercial source of radium, uranium, and vanadium.

Clays are mixtures of mineral fragments, due to rock decay. They are usually plastic when wet, can be molded, and harden on heating. By analysis they are principally silica and alumina, with some iron oxide and small amounts of other elements. Mineralogically they contain hydrous silicates of alumina, free quartz, and varying amounts of many other minerals. In origin they may have resulted from decay in place (residual clays) or may have been transported by water, ice, or wind (sedimentary clays). The most important clays are:

Kaolins. White-burning, residual clays, often not plastic, approaching kaolinite in composition, but not necessarily composed chiefly of that mineral. They are the basis of white wares and porcelain, etc.

Ball clays. White-burning sedimentary clays. They are highly plastic and are added to kaolin to give plasticity.

Fire clays. Either sedimentary or residual clays, which stand high degrees of heat without fusion. Composition very variable and apparently best with little free silica, lime, magnesia, or alkalis.

Fuller's earth. A montmorillonite-bearing clay, greenish in color when moist. Is a natural adsorbent for coloring matter in oil.

Stoneware clays. Clays sufficiently plastic and tough to be turned on a potter's wheel.

Terra-cotta clays. Usually buff-burning clays, with low shrinkage and dense-burning character.

Sewer pipe and paving-brick clays. Vitrifiable, high in fluxes.

Brick clays. Low-grade clays, with considerable plasticity, which harden at a comparatively low temperature.

Slip clays. Melt at a comparatively low temperature and form a glaze.

Paper clays. White clays free from sand; used for mixing with pulp fiber.

Bentonite. Composed essentially of the mineral montmorillonite, usually formed by alteration of volcanic ash. Many bentonites swell in water. Some bentonitic clays extensively used for clarifying oil.

Diatomite. An extremely light porous, white, mass of microscopic, opaline, organisms (diatoms), chiefly silica, but yielding much water in the closed tube. Used as a heat insulator, also for brick or in filtration.

Gilsonite. An asphaltite. Sp gr $= 1.01$ to 1.10; melting point, $230°$ to $400°$ F; found in veins in NE Utah. Was probably distilled by heat from the underlying Green River shale. Used for varnishes and japans, printing and rotogravure inks, and in various commercial products; 32 227 tons reported mined in 1935.

Grahamite or Glance Pitch. An asphaltite. Sp gr of about 1.15 or more. Largely mined in Cuba, where found in sedimentary and serpentinous rocks. Formerly mined in Pushmatoka Co, Okla, and Ritchie Co, W Va.

Kieserite $(MgSO_4 + H_2O)$ is the source of Epsom salts, and an important source of magnesium oxide and basic carbonate (magnesia alba). It occurs at Stassfurt, Prussia, as about one-fifth of a layer 190 ft thick, chiefly halite and carnallite, and as one of the constituents of the overlying mixed salts. Exposed to the air it becomes epsomite. After removal of associates there remains a mass slowly soluble in water and easily fusible. $H = 3$ to 3.5, $G = 2.5$. Rarely orthorhombic crystals.

Livingstonite $(HgSb_4S_7)$. Found in Mexico at Huitzuco and Guadalcazar and said to have been used as a source of mercury. It resembles stibnite in appearance, has metallic luster, lead-gray color, red streak, $H = 2$, $G = 4.81$, and occurs in groups of slender prismatic crystals.

Mottramite ($(CuPb)_5V_2O_{10} \cdot 2\ H_2O$). The vanadium of commerce was formerly obtained from thin, blackish incrustations of mottramite upon the Keuper sandstone, Cheshire, England. Streak yellow, H = 3, G = 5.9.

Ocher, commercially, is a golden-yellow intimate mixture of clay with 20% or more of hydrated ferric oxide. Mineralogists use the name also for pulverulent yellow iron oxide (xanthosiderite) and for pulverulent red hematite.

Ozocerite, or mineral wax, is essentially a paraffine, colorless to white when pure, but oftener greenish or brown, and possessing all the properties of beeswax except its stickiness. A little is mined in Utah and about 3 000 tons are imported annually from Galicia and Moldavia. Used in crude state as insulation for electric wires. By distilling it yields ceresine, used for candles, burning oils, paraffine, a product like vaseline and a residuum which, with india-rubber, constitutes the insulating material called okonite.

Patronite (vanadium sulphide). At the one locality of Cerro de Pasco, Peru, there is a vein 7 or 8 ft thick of a nearly black material resembling slaty coal. About two-thirds of this is patronite and one-third metallic sulphides and free sulphur. Below it is 1 to 2 ft of coke-like material, chiefly carbon, which blends into a lustrous black material 4 to 6 ft thick, containing more sulphur than carbon, but known as asphaltite. The ashes of these two associates are also rich in vanadium, and the roasted or burned material is exported.

Petroleum is a mixture of hydrocarbons, obtained from the earth. It varies from a light, easily flowing liquid, to a thick viscous oil, and is usually of a dark brown or greenish color, with a distinct fluorescence. Chemically the American petroleum consists principally of hydrocarbons of the paraffine series C_nH_{2n+2}, with smaller amounts of the series C_nH_{2n} and C_nH_{2n-6}. The oils from Baku, on the Caspian, Rangoon, Galicia, and the Caucasus, contain more of the C_nH_{2n} or olefin series.

Roscoelite (vanadium mica). A mica of brown to brownish-green color, long known as an associate of gold in certain mines of California, and containing approximately 25% V_2O_3, is now commercially obtained from a soft Colorado sandstone of greenish color, in which the roscoelite fills the interstices between the grains.

Thorianite ($ThO_2U_3O_8$). Small water-worn blackish cubic crystals found in the Ceylon gem gravels and used as a source of thoria. H = 5.5 to 6, G = 9.3. It is radioactive.

Thorite ($ThSiO_4$). Black or orange-yellow, zircon-like crystals and masses, occurring in Norway in small quantity; used as a source of thoria. H = 4.5 to 5, G = 4.8 to 5.2. Infusible; gelatinizes with acids.

Tripoli. A fine, siliceous powder, containing chalcedony or opal; used as abrasive; clay-like in appearance, but quite gritty.

Umber is drab-colored mixture of iron and aluminum silicates, containing manganese oxide. It becomes reddish brown on burning. Sienna is similar, but with less manganese and lighter in color.

Vermiculite. Various forms of soft, pliable or inelastic mica; when heated, slowly expanded material useful in heat insulation.

Wad. Earthy to compact indefinite mixtures of oxides, especially of manganese, cobalt or copper, are known as wad. They have no constant characters, but may be valuable ores. Usually dark brown to black in color.

INDEX TO DETERMINATIVE TABLES *

(Numbers indicate the sections in the tables)

* Mineral names correspond with recommendations of Committee on Nomenclature, of Mineralogical Soc of America.

I—3

BIBLIOGRAPHY

Descriptive Mineralogy. Treatises

Dana, J. D.   System of Mineralogy, 6th ed, with three appendices.   John Wiley & Sons, N Y, 1892
Hintze, Carl.   Handbuch der Mineralogie.   Bd 1, 1897; Bd 2, 1904.   von Veit & Co, Leipzig

Descriptive and Determinative Mineralogy. Text Books and Treatises

Cahern and Wooton.   The Mineralogy of the Rarer Metals.   2nd ed.   Charles Griffin & Co, Ltd, London, 1920
Dana-Ford.   Textbook of Mineralogy.   4th ed.   John Wiley & Sons, N Y, 1932
Kraus, E. H., Hunt, W. F. and Ramsdell, L. S.   Mineralogy.   Introduction to the study of minerals and crystals.   McGraw-Hill Book Co, N Y, 3rd ed, 1936
Miers, H. A.   Mineralogy.   An Introduction to the Scientific Study of Minerals.   Macmillan & Co, London, 1902
Rogers, A. F.   Introduction to the Study of Minerals.   3rd ed.   McGraw-Hill Book Co, N Y, 1937
Brush-Penfield.   Manual of Determinative Mineralogy.   16th ed.   John Wiley & Sons, N Y, 1906
Frazer-Brown.   Tables for the Determination of Minerals.   6th ed.   J. B. Lippincott Co, Philadelphia, 1910
Kraus-Hunt.   Tables for the Determination of Minerals.   2nd ed.   McGraw-Hill Book Co, N Y, 1930
Lewis, J. V.   Determinative Mineralogy.   4th ed.   Revised by A. C. Hawkins.   John Wiley & Sons, N Y, 1931
Plattner-Kolbeck.   Probierkunst mit der Lötrohre.   7th ed.   Johann Barth, Leipzig, 1907
Warren, C. H.   Determinative Mineralogy.   McGraw-Hill Book Co, N Y, 1921

Crystallography

Bayley, W. S.   Elementary Crystallography.   McGraw-Hill Book Co, N Y, 1910
Groth-Jackson.   The Optical Properties of Crystals.   Translated from 4th ed.   John Wiley & Sons, N Y, 1910
Groth-Marshall.   Introduction to Chemical Crystallography.   John Wiley & Sons, N Y, 1906
Lewis, W. J.   A Treatise on Crystallography.   Univ Press, Cambridge, England, 1899
Tutton, A. E. H.   Crystallography and Practical Crystal Measurement.   2 vols.   Macmillan & Co, London, 1922

Minerals in Thin Section

Iddings, J. P.   Rock Minerals.   2nd ed.   John Wiley & Sons, N Y, 1912
Johannsen, A.   Essentials for the Microscopic Determination of Rock Forming Minerals and Rocks.   Univ of Chicago Press, 1922
Johannsen, A.   Manual of Petrographic Methods.   McGraw-Hill Book Co, N Y, 1914
Pirsson, L. V.   Rocks and Rock Minerals.   John Wiley & Sons, N Y, 1908
Rogers, A. F., and Kerr, P. F.   Thin Section Mineralogy.   McGraw-Hill Book Co, N Y, 1933
Weinschenck-Clark.   Petrographic Methods.   McGraw-Hill Book Co, N Y, 1912

Microscopic Study of Mineral Fragments

Larsen, E. S., and Berman, H.   Microscopic Determination of the Non-opaque Minerals.   U S G S, *Bull* 848, 1934
Schroeder van de Kolk, J. L. C.   Tabellen zur mikroskopischen Bestimmung der Mineralien nach ihren Brechnungs-exponenten.   2nd ed.   Wiesbaden, 1906
Winchell, A. N.   Elements of Optical Mineralogy.   Part I.   5th ed.   John Wiley & Sons, N Y, 1937

Microscopic Study of Opaque Ore-minerals

Davy-Farnham.   Microscopic Examination of Ore Minerals.   McGraw-Hill Book Co, N Y, 1920
Murdoch, J.   Microscopic Determination of Opaque Minerals.   John Wiley & Sons, N Y, 1916
Schneiderhöhn, H. and Ramdohr, P.   Lehrbuch der Erzmikroskopie.   Berlin, 1934
Short, M. N.   Microscopic Determination of Ore Minerals.   U S G S *Bull* 825, 1931
Van der Veen, R. W.   Mineragraphy and Ore-deposition.   G. Naeff, The Hague, 1925

Occurrence, Association and Origin of Minerals

Byschlag-Krusch-Vogt.   Die Lagerstätten der nutzbaren Mineralien und Gesteine.   Ferdinand Enke, Stuttgart, 1909
Clarke, F. W.   The Data of Geochemistry.   Bulletin 770, U S G S, 1924
Merrill, G. P.   The Non-metallic Minerals.   2nd ed.   John Wiley & Sons, N Y
Van Hise, C. R.   A Treatise on Metamorphism.   Monograph 47, U S G S, 1904

Uses of Minerals

Ladoo, R. B.   Non-metallic Minerals.   McGraw-Hill Book Co, N Y, 1925
Mineral Resources of the United States.   Annually since 1883, U S G S; from 1932, Bur Mines
The Mineral Industry.   Annually since 1892, McGraw-Hill Book Co, N Y
Spurr-Wormser.   Marketing of Metals and Minerals.   McGraw-Hill Book Co, 1925
Mineral Raw Materials.   U S Bur Mines Staff, 1937

Gems and Precious Stones

Bauer, Max.   Precious Stones.   Trans by L. J. Spencer.   1904
Bauer, Max.   Edelsteinkunde.   Revised by Schlossmacher.   Leipzig, 1932
Cattelle, W. R.   Precious Stones.   J. B. Lippincott Co, Philadelphia, 1903
Eppler, A.   Die Schmuck- und Edelsteine.   Felix Krais, Stuttgart, 1912
Kraus-Holden.   Gems and Gem Minerals.   2nd ed   McGraw-Hill Book Co, N Y, 1931
Smith, G. F. H.   Gem Stones.   Methuen & Co, Ltd, London

SECTION 2

GEOLOGY AND MINERAL DEPOSITS

BY

JAMES FURMAN KEMP

LATE PROFESSOR OF GEOLOGY, COLUMBIA UNIVERSITY

REVISED BY

PAUL F. KERR

PROFESSOR OF MINERALOGY, COLUMBIA UNIVERSITY

Note.—Numbers in parentheses in text refer to Bibliography at end of this section.

GEOLOGY

1. INTRODUCTION

A rock is a mineral or aggregate of minerals, forming an essential part of the earth; but many important mineral bodies, such as ores of metals, are not to be considered as rocks. Of about 1 500 species of minerals, only 20 or 30 are important as rock constituents.

The three great classes of rocks are: IGNEOUS, solidified from fusion; SEDIMENTARY, deposited in water or air; METAMORPHIC, recrystallized or otherwise altered igneous and sedimentary rocks, such that their original character has been obscured. Igneous rocks are believed to have been the predecessors and source of all others (1, 2, 3).

An analysis, illustrating GROSS COMPOSITION of the outer 10 miles of the earth, is given in Sec I, Art 1. Compared with the percentages there stated, nickel and iron probably become increasingly abundant toward the earth's center.

Most abundant elements of rock-forming minerals are: silicon, oxygen, aluminum, iron, magnesium, calcium, sodium, potassium, and hydrogen; secondarily, carbon, chlorine, phosphorus, titanium, manganese, and sulphur. All other elements, even the familiar copper, lead and zinc, and the precious metals, or an abundant atmospheric gas, as nitrogen, are small in amount.

2. CHEMICAL COMPOSITION OF ROCK-FORMING MINERALS

Rock-forming minerals comprise silicates, oxides, carbonates, sulphates, chlorides, phosphates, sulphides, and native elements.

Silicates are the most important, whence silicic acid, in various forms, is the foremost acid in Nature. Three principal forms of silicic acid are represented in the rock-making minerals: H_2SiO_3 (metasilicic), H_4SiO_4 (orthosilicic), and $H_4Si_3O_8$. Pyroxenes, amphiboles, and leucite are salts of metasilicic acid. Micas, olivine, anorthite, nephelite, garnet, and many minor minerals are orthosilicates. Orthoclase and albite are salts of $H_4Si_3O_8$. Some silicates have only the usual bases, aluminum, iron, magnesium, calcium, and the alkalies, and are called ANHYDROUS; others, usually formed by weathering or alteration of the first, contain hydrogen and oxygen in such proportions as to be driven off as water, and are called HYDRATED SILICATES. This distinction is rendered important by the general secondary character of hydrated silicates. The chief anhydrous silicates in igneous rocks embrace the following mineral groups: feldspars and feldspathoids, pyroxenes, amphiboles, micas, and olivine. Rarer and less important are: zircon, sphene, tourmaline, and analcime. On weathering or other alteration, the hydrated silicates, kaolinite, chlorite, and serpentine, usually result. Metamorphic rocks contain a few characteristic silicates, besides the common ones of igneous rocks, viz: staurolite, sillimanite, kyanite, andalusite, scapolite, and epidote.

Oxides are next important, of which quartz (SiO_2) stands first, being abundant in the great classes of rocks. The related forms of silica, chalcedony, cristobalite and tridymite, and the hydrated variety, opal, should also be noted. Next are the oxides of iron, magnetite and hematite, and the hydrated form, limonite. With magnetite are associated chromite and ilmenite ($FeO \cdot TiO_2$). Water, whether liquid or ice, is technically a mineral.

Carbonates are calcite, dolomite, and siderite, with their intermediate mixtures. They are of chief importance in sedimentary and metamorphic rocks, occurring rarely in igneous rocks, except as products of weathering. There are two common SULPHATES, anhydrite and gypsum. One CHLORIDE, common salt, alone merits attention. The PHOSPHATES are apatite and collophane. Two SULPHIDES, pyrite and pyrrhotite, are widely distributed. The one NATIVE rock-forming element is graphite.

3. ROCK-FORMING MINERALS (1, 2, 3)

Minerals of the igneous rocks are grouped according to their usual order of crystallization into: 1. Iron ores and minute associates. 2. Ferromagnesian silicates (olivine, pyroxenes, amphiboles, and micas). 3. Feldspars and feldspathoids (plagioclase, orthoclase, nephelite, leucite, and analcime). 4. Quartz, in acidic and higher medium rocks only. For descriptions, see Sec I, Determinative Tables.

Minerals of the sedimentary rocks are ordinarily fragments of minerals from igneous rocks. Quartz is most resistant to solution, alteration, and abrasion, and therefore appears in almost all sands and sandstones. The others are less frequent. After quartz, carbonates are of chief interest. Calcite and dolomite constitute the limestones, sometimes with slight admixture of siderite. Kaolinite, montmorillonite and hydromica enter the fine sediments. The two sulphates, gypsum, the more abundant, and anhydrite, appear only in sedimentary rocks. The same is true of the chloride, rock salt.

Minerals of the metamorphic rocks. The components of both sedimentary and igneous rocks, when deeply buried, with attendant heat and pressure, recrystallize at times to distinctively metamorphic minerals. Silica, being omnipresent, survives as quartz. The aluminous components afford andalusite, sillimanite, and kyanite. Magnesian, iron, and aluminous compounds yield abundant biotite and occasional epidote. Lime, in association with ferric iron or alumina, makes garnet possible, but orthoclase may become muscovite. The feldspars are important components. The ferromagnesian minerals (chlorite and serpentine) are derived from magnesium- and iron-bearing originals.

Summary of Rock-forming Minerals

Igneous Rocks. QUARTZ
  FELDSPARS: orthoclase, plagioclase
  FELDSPATHOIDS: nepheline, leucite, analcime, melilite
  PYROXENES: hypersthene, diopside, augite, soda-pyroxenes
  AMPHIBOLES: hornblende, soda-amphiboles
  MICAS: biotite, muscovite
  OTHER MINERALS: olivine, magnetite, ilmenite, apatite, zircon
Sedimentary Rocks. Fragments from igneous rocks, especially quartz and feldspars; kaolinite, montmorillonite, hydromica, calcite, dolomite, siderite, limonite
Metamorphic Rocks. Quartz, feldspars, biotite, muscovite, hornblende, epidote, garnet, sillimanite, andalusite, calcite, dolomite, serpentine, talc, chlorite

4. IGNEOUS ROCKS

Structures and textures. In a broad way, igneous rocks, as contrasted with sedimentary and metamorphic, have a massive structure; that is, their minerals are not arranged in parallel or distinct layers. Massive is in many respects a synonym of igneous. Examined more in detail, as in hand-specimens, they have 4 common textures. Where the molten mass has been too quickly chilled to crystallize, the texture is GLASSY. This texture appears on outer borders of thin masses, on upper surfaces of lava flows, and, in relatively infusible varieties, it may extend through an entire flow. It is most frequent in siliceous rocks, which have high fusing points; it is rare in the medium, and scarcely known in the basic. Where molten masses have cooled rather rapidly, and yet not so quickly as to prevent crystallization, very fine-grained textures result, called FELSITIC. But, if older, larger, and already well-formed crystals at the time be swimming in the magma, which then crystallizes in relatively small components, the texture is called PORPHYRITIC. The large crystals are called PHENOCRYSTS and the matrix the GROUND-MASS. Phenocrysts of acidic rocks are chiefly quartz and feldspars; the dark ferromagnesian silicates are much less common. In medium rocks, quartz practically fails, and feldspars are associated with more of the ferromagnesian minerals. In basic porphyritic rocks, feldspars decline, while augite and olivine, and very rarely biotite and hornblende, gradually replace them. When a molten magma crystallizes into an aggregate of fairly coarse components of about the same size, the texture is GRANITOID (like granite). Rarely, in these coarsely crystalline rocks, the feldspars become unusually large and stand out in contrast with the rest.

As a result of explosive outbreaks at volcanic vents, igneous rocks are sometimes blown out as fragments of all sizes, from impalpable dust to large bombs. The fragments settle down on the sides of the cone or at greater distances, and yield rocks with marked fragmental texture, allied to sediments. If coarse, they are called BRECCIAS; if fine, TUFFS.

Chemical composition of igneous rocks. SILICA ranges from about 80% to a theoretical minimum of 0% in certain igneous iron ores; only in rare cases does it fall below 40%. Igneous rocks containing above 65% silica are called ACIDIC; those with 55 to 65%, MEDIUM; below 50%, BASIC. Of ALUMINA the superior limit is 25 to 30%; general range, 12 to 18%; minimum, nearly 0. IRON OXIDES are low, 1% or less, in the most acidic rocks, but increase in the basic to 10 to 20%; in rare extremes, 90 to 95%. MAGNESIA sinks to a mere trace in the acidic, rising with fall of silica to 30% in the extremely basic. LIME is low in the acidic, gradually increasing to about 15% maximum in certain basic rocks. POTASH is highest in the rare leucite rocks, reaching 10 or 12%; it ranges from

4 to 7% in medium rocks with much orthoclase, and disappears in basic types. SODA has a similar maximum in the rare nepheline rocks, and the same range in medium rocks rich in albite, approaching extinction in the extremely basic. WATER, of 0.5 or 1%, usually indicates weathered rocks.

It is important to connect chemical compositions with the resultant minerals and vice versa. Chemical composition obviously determines the minerals, and, in so far as extremely acidic rocks have relatively high fusing points and chill more easily, it also influences texture.

Classification of igneous rocks shown in Table 1 has general acceptance by geologists. Rocks range from acidic on left of table to basic on right; from quickly-chilled rocks above to slowly-cooled rocks below, a still lower line of fragmentals marking transition to sediments. The forms assumed in Nature are in extreme left-hand column; to be defined after the descriptions. The rocks are further subdivided in vertical columns on basis of mineralogy. Feldspars and feldspathoids are the fundamental basis of subdivision; other minerals are subordinate.

The table gives a general view of the igneous rocks and defines those commonly met in mining. For close determination greater refinement may be desirable. In some mining districts in the western U S are found the GRANO-DIORITES (intermediate between granites and quartz-diorites), not mentioned in the table; they have about the same amounts of orthoclase and plagioclase. Intermediate between syenites and diorites are the MONZONITES. If they have a little quartz, but not as much as grano-diorites, they are termed quartz-monzonites. Butte granite, containing the copper veins, is usually described as quartz-monzonite. Several great bodies of "porphyry coppers" are in monzonite-porphyries. The varieties of gabbro containing hypersthene instead of common augite are called NORITE; important because they contain the nickel-copper ores at Sudbury, Ont. (For meaning of names of other rare igneous rocks, sometimes appearing in reports, see glossary in later editions of Kemp's "Handbook of Rocks.")

Glassy rocks are the most evident results of cooling from fusion. They are almost always acidic and are represented by the rhyolites and dacites, described later. More basic varieties are known, but are less frequent. Commonest glasses are the OBSIDIANS, black, red, and brown, with 0.5 to 1% water. They may be assumed to be quickly-chilled rhyolites or dacites. PUMICE is an excessively cellular obsidian. A rarer glass, which chills into an aggregate of shot-like spheroids, is PEARLITE or PEARL-STONE, usually containing 2 to 4% water. The last glass deserving mention is the rare, resinous PITCH-STONE, having 5 to 10% water and is more easily fusible with blowpipe than the others.

Rhyolite-granite series embraces igneous magmas containing: silica, 65 to 80%; alumina, 12 to 15%; iron oxides, 1 to 3%; magnesia, less than 1%; lime, 1 to 2%; potash and soda, 5 to 8%. They are common in Nature, and on crystallizing yield finely to coarsely crystalline rocks, consisting chiefly of orthoclase, acidic plagioclase, and quartz, together with relatively small amounts of the dark silicates, biotite, hornblende, and augite, stated in order of frequency. Light-colored minerals are in great excess.

Rocks of this series are: RHYOLITE (syn, liparite), felsitic or partly glassy texture, few phenocrysts; RHYOLITE-PORPHYRY (syn, quartz-porphyry), felsitic ground-mass, abundant phenocrysts; GRANITE-PORPHYRY, predominant phenocrysts, subordinate ground-mass; GRANITE, granitoid texture, components of about the same size, but feldspars sometimes abnormally large. PEGMATITES: crystallization of granite is often accompanied by separation of portions of the magma, in association with abnormally large admixtures of dissolved gases. These portions pass outward into wall-rocks as dikes, often for great distances and in large size; on crystallizing, they yield very coarse aggregates of same minerals as appear in granite itself, with many rare elements concentrated in them, and are called pegmatite. In this series the prominent minerals are feldspars and quartz; dark silicates are subordinate. They are closely related to the dacite-quartz-diorite series, from which to distinguish them microscopic examination may be necessary. The distinction is practically of small moment. This series is very abundant and widely distributed. Its tuffs and breccias are also frequent.

Trachyte-syenite series embraces igneous magmas containing: silica, 55 to 65%; alumina, 15 to 20%; iron oxides, 1 to 3%; magnesia, 1 to 2%; lime, 1 to 3%; potash and soda, 7 to 12%. They are much less common than the rhyolite-granite series. On crystallizing they yield finely to coarsely crystalline rocks, consisting of orthoclase, acidic plagioclase, and usually notable proportions of the dark silicates, biotite, hornblende, and augite, one or several. Quartz fails, or, at most, is extremely subordinate. Light-colored minerals are in excess.

Rocks of this series are: TRACHYTE, felsitic texture, few phenocrysts; TRACHYTE-PORPHYRY (syns, porphyry, orthoclase-porphyry), felsitic ground-mass, abundant phenocrysts; SYENITE-PORPHYRY, predominant phenocrysts, subordinate ground-mass; SYENITE, granitoid texture, sometimes varied by abnormally large feldspars. Syenitic-pegmatites are known, but are less frequent than granitic.

Table 1. Igneous Rocks

Acidic ← Excess of Light-colored Minerals   Excess of Dark-colored Minerals → Basic

Occurrence / Texture	Glassy	Chief Feldspar, Orthoclase — +Quartz	−Quartz	Nepheline or Leucite	Chief Feldspar, Plagioclase / Andesite-Obsidian — Biotite (or)(and) Hornblende +Quartz	−Quartz	Pyroxenes −Olivine	Pyroxenes +Olivine	No Feldspar — Nepheline, Leucite Pyroxenes −Olivine / +Olivine	No Feldspar — Augite (or)(and) Hornblende (or)(and) Biotite −Olivine	+Olivine	Ultrabasic rocks
(Glasses)		Acid Glasses, Obsidian, Pearlite, Pumice, Pitchstone			Andesite-Obsidian				Basic Glasses, Scorias, Trachylyte, Basalt-Obsidian			
Surface Flows. Cellular, Glassy or Felsitic. Phenocrysts few		Rhyolite (Felsite)	Trachyte (Felsite)	Phonolite (rare), Leucite rocks (very rare)	Dacite (Felsite)	Andesite (Felsite)	Augite-andesite	Basalt	Basalt Group	Augitite	Limburgite	Basic segregations in normal magmas
Dikes, Intrusive Sheets, Laccoliths. Porphyritic. Phenocrysts prominent		Rhyolite-porphyry (Quartz-porphyry)	Trachyte-porphyry	Phonolite-porphyry	Dacite-porphyry	Andesite-porphyry	Augite-andesite-porphyry	Basalt-porphyry	A series of rare basaltic rocks with nepheline (or)(and) leucite, seldom melilite or analcite. Not readily distinguished from basalt without the microscope. Extremely rare in America	Augitite-porphyry	Limburgite-porphyry	
Laccoliths. Porphyritic. Phenocrysts predominate		Granite-porphyry	Syenite-porphyry	Nepheline-syenite-porphyry	Quartz-diorite-porphyry	Diorite-porphyry	Gabbro-porphyry	Olivine-gabbro-porphyry		Pyroxenite-porphyry	Peridotite-porphyry	Meteorites / Water
Laccoliths, Batholiths. Granitoid		Granite	Syenite	Nepheline-syenite	Quartz-diorite	Diorite	Gabbro	Olivine-gabbro		Pyroxenite	Peridotite	Ice
Beds, Strata. Fragmental		Rhyolite tuffs and breccias	Trachyte tuffs and breccias	Phonolite tuffs and breccias	Dacite tuffs and breccias	Andesite tuffs and breccias	Andesite tuffs and breccias	Basaltic tuffs and breccias	Basaltic tuffs and breccias	Basaltic tuffs and breccias		
SiO_2		80–65%	65–55%	60–50%	70–60%	65–50%	65–50%	55–45%	50–40%	55–30%		30–0%

In this series, feldspars are most prominent; dark silicates, subordinate. Lack of quartz is the chief distinction from rhyolites and granites. Tuffs and breccias are known.

Phonolite-nepheline-syenite series embraces igneous magmas containing: silica, 50 to 60%; alumina, 18 to 22%; iron oxides, 1 to 3%; magnesia, 1 to 2%; lime, 1 to 2%; potash and soda, 10 to 15%. They occur infrequently. On crystallizing they yield finely to coarsely crystalline rocks, consisting of orthoclase, less abundant plagioclase, nepheline (more rarely leucite), and pyroxene. Though rare, they are of great scientific interest.

Rocks of this series are: PHONOLITE, felsitic or porphyritic, with few phenocrysts; PHONOLITE-PORPHYRY, felsitic ground-mass, abundant phenocrysts, of which orthoclase is chief, nepheline being usually confined to ground-mass; NEPHELINE-SYENITE-PORPHYRY, predominant phenocrysts, subordinate ground-mass; NEPHELINE-SYENITE, granitoid texture, from rather fine to extremely coarse varieties, shading into pegmatites.
In most of these rocks, orthoclase is most prominent, but in the last-named, nepheline is at times abundant. Many varieties have been recognized, depending on entrance of minerals less usual than those named, and the decline of normal components. Sodalite is sometimes very prominent. Biotite and hornblende are not so frequent as pyroxene. Rocks with leucite are known, but are far less common than those with nepheline.

Dacite-quartz-diorite series embraces igneous magmas containing: silica 60 to 70%; alumina, 12 to 15%; iron oxides, 1 to 3%; magnesia, 1 to 3%; lime, 2 to 4%; soda and potash (soda in excess), 4 to 7%. They are common in eruptive centers. On crystallizing they yield finely to coarsely crystalline rocks, consisting of plagioclase, less orthoclase, and quartz, as the most prominent minerals, with biotite, hornblende, and pyroxene, one or several. The light-colored minerals are in excess.

Rocks of this series are: DACITE, felsitic or partly glassy textures, few phenocrysts; DACITE-PORPHYRY, felsitic ground-mass, with abundant phenocrysts; QUARTZ-DIORITE PORPHYRY, predominant phenocrysts, subordinate ground-mass; QUARTZ-DIORITE, granitoid texture.

Andesite-diorite series embraces igneous magmas containing: silica, 50 to 65%; alumina, 15 to 18%; iron oxides, 4 to 9%; magnesia, 2 to 7%; lime, 3 to 8%; soda, 3 to 5%; potash, 2 to 3%. They are very widespread. On crystallizing, they yield finely to coarsely crystalline rocks, consisting of plagioclase, a little orthoclase, and biotite, hornblende, or augite, one or several. The light-colored minerals are in excess and are the chief phenocrysts. The rocks have usually light gray colors.

Rocks of this series are: ANDESITE (varieties, mica-andesite, hornblende-andesite, augite-andesite), felsitic textures, few phenocrysts; ANDESITE-PORPHYRY, felsitic ground-mass, with abundant phenocrysts; DIORITE-PORPHYRY, predominant phenocrysts, ground-mass subordinate; DIORITE, granitoid texture. Andesites are important in many western mining districts; in the recently extinct and active volcanoes along Pacific coast, in Mexico, and in other parts of world.

Basalt-gabbro series embraces igneous magmas containing: silica, 40 to 55%; alumina, 16 to 20%; iron oxides, 6 to 15%; magnesia, 5 to 10%; lime, 6 to 12%; soda, 2 to 4%; potash, 1 to 2%. They are very widespread. On crystallizing they yield finely to coarsely crystalline heavy rocks, consisting of plagioclase, little or no orthoclase, and large proportions of pyroxene, olivine, and magnetite. The dark silicates are in excess and give rocks dark gray or black colors.

Rocks of this series are: BASALT, felsitic textures, few phenocrysts; BASALT-PORPHYRY, felsitic ground-mass, abundant phenocrysts; GABBRO-PORPHYRY, predominant phenocrysts, subordinate ground-mass; DIABASE, granitoid texture, feldspars long rectangular, pyroxene irregular, in spaces among the well-crystallized feldspars; GABBRO, granitoid, components as broad as long.
Basalt-gabbro rocks are very abundant. Phenocrysts are almost entirely olivine and pyroxene. The peculiar texture of diabase, due to feldspars completing their crystallization before the pyroxenes, contrary to rule, gives it a special place. Varieties of pyroxene afford special varieties of both basalts and gabbros. Hornblende and biotite are rarely observed; nepheline, leucite, analcite, and melilite sometimes appear and may displace the plagioclase. All feldspars and feldspathoids may fail, giving the rare basalts, limburgite and augitite, and the rare gabbros, peridotite and pyroxenite (Table 1).
Ultra-basic rocks. There are a few rare igneous rocks with less than 40% silica and correspondingly high bases. The most important are the igneous magnetites, often titaniferous; in some places they are independent dikes and sheets, in others, segregations in igneous rocks.
Determination of igneous rocks. Their crystalline, massive character usually serves to identify them as igneous, but a warning may be given respecting certain dense contact-products, called HORNFELS. First decide on predominance of light- or dark-colored minerals; next, on texture. If light-colored minerals are in excess, feldspar is determined as orthoclase (no striations on cleavage faces), or plagioclase (striated). Quartz is looked for. Having thus decided general name, the dark silicate is determined. If dark-colored minerals are in excess, and phenocrysts are also dark, the rock is placed in the basalt-gabbro series and identified more sharply by its textures. A rock so

finely crystalline that no minerals can be identified is called felsite, if light-colored; or basalt, if dark. Microscopic examination is necessary for further refinement. Greatly altered rocks, such as are commonly adjacent to mineral veins, can often be determined through surviving characters only discernible with microscope. If stained with chlorite, they are called GREENSTONES.

5. SEDIMENTARY ROCKS

There are 4 groups (Table 2): (a) Breccias and mechanical sediments, not limestones; (b) Limestones; (c) Organic remains, not limestones; (d) Precipitates from solution.

Table 2. Sedimentary Rocks

Breccias		Fragmentals, not Limestones		Transition to Limestone	Limestones			Organic Rocks, not Limestones	Precipitates from Solution
		Loose	Consolidated	Consolidated	Loose	Consolidated			
Fault-breccias / Talus-breccias	Coarse	Gravel	Conglomerate	Calcareous conglomerate	Limestone-rubble Gravel Coral heads, etc	Rubble-limestone Calcirudites	Alkaline	....	Rock salt, gypsum, stalactites, stalagmites, "Mexican onyx," travertine
	Fine to Medium	Sands	Sandstone	....	Shell or coral sands	Sand-lime-stones Coquina Calcarenites	Siliceous	Infusorial or diatomaceous earth Some cherts Some sinters	Silicified wood Some cherts Some sinters
Eruptive-breccias		Mud	Argillaceous sandstone Shale	Calcareous sandstone Calcareous shale	Shell or coral muds	Mud limestones Calcilutites	Ferruginous	Some limonite	Some limonite
		Silt	Clay	Marl	Calcareous slimes or ooze	Lithographic limestone	Carbonaceous	Peat Lignite Bituminous coal Anthracite	Asphaltites

Determination of sedimentary rocks. Almost all may be recognized on sight. It is important to make effervescing tests with acid, to identify limestones, calcareous shales, etc. Scraping up a little heap of powdered rock favors effervescence. Warming a corner or edge of the rock even in flame of a match does the same, and may make stubborn dolomite yield to acid.

The rocks of group (a) may be arranged from coarse to fine, as follows:

	Coarse		to		Fine
Breccia	Gravel and Conglomerate	Sand and Sandstone	Argillaceous sandstone, Calcareous sandstone	Silt and Shale, Calcareous shale	Clay, Marl

Breccias consist of angular fragments and are of 3 kinds: fault, talus, and eruptive, the names being equivalent to definitions. Mechanical sediments, or gravels, contain rounded or water-worn fragments, and when consolidated are CONGLOMERATES. They pass into SANDS as the boulders or pebbles disappear; and when consolidated, SANDSTONES

Table 3. Metamorphic Rocks

Contact			Regional							Products of Weathering
Internal	External	(Contact effects)	Gneisses corresponding in Mineralogy to the Granitoid Igneous Rocks. A few others — Derived from Igneous	Derived from Sedimentary or others	Crystalline Schists		Quartzites and Slates	Crystalline Limestones	Ophicalcites, Serpentines, Soapstones	
Glasses	Conglomerates and sandstones	Effects relatively slight. Quartzites (Buchite)	Granite gneiss or gneiss proper	Granitic gneiss or gneiss proper	Mica	Mica schists often with garnet, staurolite, etc. Phyllites	Quartzites (Quartz schists)	Marbles often with mica, tremolite, etc	Serpentinous marble or ophicalcite, verd-antique	Residual soils
Felsites	Shales and clays	Andalusite hornfels, Lime-silicate hornfels, Spotted slates	Syenite gneiss	Syenitic gneiss	Horn-blende	Hornblende schists often with garnet, epidote, scapolite. Amphibolites	Graywackes Slates (Phyllites)		Serpentine often with chromite, garnet, etc	Subsoil
			Diorite gneiss	Dioritic gneiss, etc						Saprolites in general
Porphyries	Limestones	Garnet, diopside, vesuvianite, epidote, wollastonite, scapolite, ores	Gabbro gneiss	Conglomerate gneiss	Various schists	Chlorite schist or green schists. Talc schists. Eclogite. Glaucophane schists. Quartz schists		Dolomites often with mica, tremolite, etc.	Soapstone or steatite	Laterites, especially from basalt
			Pyroxenite gneiss	Gneisses with a prominent mineral, such as biotite-gneiss, etc.						
	Coals	Natural coke, Anthracite	Peridotite gneiss							

result. Sands, with admixture of clay or mud, become SHALES; as the sand disappears, SILTS and CLAYS; if calcareous, they are calcareous sandstone, calcareous shale, and MARL. Limestones may be coarsely or finely fragmental, but are almost always derived from remains of organisms. **Other organic remains** yielding rocks are the siliceous diatoms and sponges, and carbonaceous plants in coal seams. **Precipitates** are rock salt, gypsum, and stalagmitic marbles. Certain ferruginous rocks also are probably of this nature.

6. METAMORPHIC ROCKS

These are of 3 great classes: CONTACT ROCKS, produced by intrusive igneous rocks from their immediate walls; REGIONALLY METAMORPHIC TYPES, which extend over great areas; and PRODUCTS OF WEATHERING.

Contact rocks embrace both the chilled border facies of intrusive (internal or ENDOMORPHIC), and the recrystallized products from shales, slates, or limestones (external or EXOMORPHIC). Other rocks, such as sandstones and regionally metamorphic varieties, are much less influenced by intrusives. The general name for densely crystalline, altered shales is HORNFELS. From limestones a series of lime-silicates results; among them, garnet, pyroxene, epidote, and vesuvianite are commonest. Copper ores and magnetite often occur with them.

Regionally metamorphic rocks embrace representatives of both igneous and sedimentary types, mineralogically resembling sometimes one, sometimes the other. They include gneisses, mica-, hornblende-, and chlorite-schists, quartz-schists, quartzites, slates, marbles, ophicalcites, serpentines, and soapstones. GNEISSES are banded or foliated rocks of the granitoid-igneous types, but are most commonly like the granites. MICA-SCHISTS are more finely foliated, and richer in mica than the gneisses. HORNBLENDE-SCHISTS are finely foliated, roughly parallel aggregates of prismatic hornblende, with relatively few other minerals. CHLORITE-SCHISTS, QUARTZ-SCHISTS, etc, are finely foliated, with the characteristic mineral prominently developed. QUARTZITES are sandstones hardened and solidified with newly deposited silica. SLATES are derived from shales and clays, with a new cleavage produced by pressure, but having no definite relation to original bedding. Irregularly breaking, metamorphosed, sandy shales, and volcanic tuffs and breccias, are called GRAYWACKE. MARBLES are recrystallized limestones, often dolomites mineralogically. They may be mottled with serpentine, forming OPHICALCITES. SERPENTINES are usually metamorphosed peridotites. SOAPSTONES are higher in silica, and consist of talc. They may be old pyroxenites or siliceous magnesian limestones.

Products of weathering constitute the mantle of decomposition products, resting upon fresh bedrock to a greater or less degree, which is due partly to mechanical breaking up of the original rock, partly to alteration and disintegration by removal of soluble ingredients. Quartz and aluminous hydrated silicates, with ferric hydrate, become relatively enriched, while the other oxides go off in solution. Soils and subsoils result, and sediments are afforded for making sedimentary rocks. General names for the mantle of weathered products are: SAPROLITE or rotten rock; LATERITE, residual soils, etc. Laterization is most pronounced in tropical climates.

Determination of metamorphic rocks is rarely difficult. Definitions convey the idea of characters. Dense hornfelses sometimes resemble felsites, and may require microscopic determination. Gneisses, with increasingly fine foliation, shade into mica-schists and mica-schists into slates, so that distinctions may be matters of judgment. The other rocks of this series give little difficulty.

7. FORMS ASSUMED BY IGNEOUS ROCKS

In the field, igneous rocks are found in dikes, necks, bosses, stocks, surface flows, intrusive sheets or sills, laccoliths, and batholiths. The size and shape of these bodies exercise an important influence on texture of the component rock. Small bodies chill quickly and are glassy or felsitic; large bodies cool slowly and are porphyritic or granitoid. Designating one horizontal dimension as length (L), the horizontal dimension at right angles to L as breadth (B), and the vertical dimension as depth (D), a mathematical expression can be roughly formulated for each type.

Dikes are long, narrow bodies of igneous rock, filling fissures in older rocks, into which it has entered in molten condition. In dikes, L and D are great, B relatively small; they vary from less than 1 in wide and a few yards long, to fractions of a mile in width and many miles in length. They usually have steep dips; are often intimately associated with orebodies, and in one place or another embrace all varieties of igneous rocks. They may mark the last outbreaks in a series of eruptions in a particular district, and are then usually very basic, as at Cripple Creek, Colo.

Dikes may radiate from an igneous center for miles into the surrounding strata, as in the Crazy Mts, Mont, or the Trinidad coal region, Colo. They may appear hundreds of miles from other known igneous rocks, as in the coal measures of S W Pennsylvania. A dike derived from solidified molten rock, even though a magma be regarded as a solution, practically all of which crystallizes *in situ*, is contrasted with a vein, similar in shape and in relations to the walls, but which is deposited from solution, the solvent passing on. Yet, in the case of pegmatites, it is not clear whether the term dike or vein should be used; they may be considered the result of aqueo-igneous processes of fusion.

Neck is the solidified mass of lava that remains in the throat of a volcano after its last outbreak. When first congealed, it connects the lava that has poured from the crater with the unerupted residue in depth, just as a human neck connects head and trunk. As seen in the field, it is usually a decapitated neck, in that it is exposed to view only after removal of the lava flow and much of the cone by erosion. *L* and *B* are small, *D* great.

In volcanoes, which yield both lavas and explosive products, the neck may be part solid lava and part breccia. Necks project in a rudely columnar manner from remnants of the old crater and from débris furnished by their own disintegration.

Bosses are roughly cylindrical masses of igneous rock, projecting above surrounding wall rocks like the boss on an old-time circular shield. Coarse granite or pegmatite, because of its relative resistance to erosion, often projects from surrounding mica-schists or other softer rocks. Bosses differ from necks in not being due to volcanic activity. As in case of necks, however, *L* and *B* are relatively small, *D* great.

Stocks are large, roughly cylindrical masses of intrusive porphyritic or granitoid rock in the midst of older walls. They do not necessarily stand in relief, but otherwise resemble bosses; *L* and *B* are small with respect to *D*, although absolutely rather large.

The name "stock" is the German word for floor or story in a house, and was applied to masses of igneous rock of cylindrical shape, because certain granite bodies of rounded outline, containing disseminated cassiterite, were formerly mined in horizontal slices or floors. Finally the mass of rock itself came to be called a stock. For good illustrations, see Telluride folio of U S Geol Surv.

Surface flows are produced when lava wells out from a vent, and flows over surface in a relatively thin sheet; *L* and *B* are large, *D* small. In upper and under portions are many cavities, caused by expanding gases; the middle part is usually dense, and in a thick flow may be comparatively coarse-grained. The cavities are flattened and rounded like an almond, whence, from the Greek, they are called AMYGDALOIDS.

The top of a flow may be rough, slaggy scoria, even consisting of cakes of chilled and broken crust. Where dissolved gases have all escaped before consolidation and while lava is yet molten, the final chilled surface may be comparatively smooth. Surface flows may bury one another in succession, or be covered with later sediments. They are distinguished from intrusive sheets, because their heat can at most affect only underlying rocks, not those formed above them after cooling; whereas intrusive sheets bake both walls. More than 100 successive surface flows of basalt have been cut by deep shafts in the Lake Superior copper district.

Intrusive sheets or sills are masses of igneous rock which have been forced between strata of older rocks, and have solidified parallel with them. *L* and *B* are great, *D* small. The shape resembles that of a surface flow, and when a surface flow resting on sediments is buried under subsequent beds the result is much the same. The heat of intrusive sheets, however, always affects the sediments above and below them, and sometimes produces important contact zones.

Intrusive sheets vary from a few feet thick, and of no great known extent, to such a sill as the Palisades of Hudson River, visible 50 miles, traceable by drill 25 miles more; its thickness reaches 600 ft, but is usually less. Intrusive sheets doubtless rise from the depths along fissures, like dikes, but then turn sidewise between strata along a line of least resistance. They are sometimes associated with ore-deposits, as at Leadville, Colo, and Mercur, Utah.

Laccoliths are a variation of the intrusive sheet and are lenticular in shape. If a sill be supposed to start from its feeding dike, sidewise between strata, and to find it easier to raise the overlying beds of a limited area than to force its way with uniform thickness far and wide, a lenticular mass will result, tapering from a central maximum thickness to a thin edge. Hence, *L* and *B* are relatively large, *D* smaller but variable. Laccoliths which are fed outwardly from a central supply fissure are symmetrical; but this fissure is sometimes a fault, with hard strata opposite soft ones, so that the intrusive can penetrate outwardly only on one side. Unsymmetrical masses, practically half-laccoliths, result. Laccoliths heave up overlying strata in domes, and when these are eroded the laccolith is exposed in midst of outwardly dipping beds. The entrance of laccoliths may have been aided by incipient folding or arching of beds under compression. Laccoliths are widespread in the western states. The name was coined by G. K. Gilbert from the Greek word for cistern, as the shape suggested the ancient dome-covered vaults for storing water.

Chonoliths are irregular intrusive bodies, either filling a pre-existing cavity, or rending apart the rocks to make a way for itself. The name was coined by R. A. Daly from the Greek word for a mould in which metal is cast. No definite expression in terms of *L*, *B*, and *D* is possible.

Batholiths are huge masses of intrusive rock, of irregular shape and great extent; *L*, *B*, and *D* are all great. Granite masses, square miles in area and sometimes cubic miles in volume, are illustrations. They are specially abundant in pre-Cambrian strata.

8. FORMS ASSUMED BY SEDIMENTARY AND METAMORPHIC ROCKS

The distinguishing feature of sedimentary rocks is their arrangement in parallel layers, during formation. Variations in deposition of sediment from high and low tides, storms and calms, floods and droughts, produce contrasts in coarseness and fineness. At the outset they are flat, except for the slight inclination of the sea bottom, and irregularities due to delta formation and swift currents. The inclined position often seen in exposures today is due to subsequent disturbances.

Stratification. The smallest division of a sedimentary rock is a LAYER or LAMINA. It may be a fraction of an inch thick and marks one period of especially abundant deposit. Layers go together to form BEDS, the natural units of sedimentary rocks. Bedding planes are recognizable and thick- and thin-bedded sedimentaries are distinguished. Beds combine to constitute a STRATUM, or tabular mass of one kind of sedimentary rock between others which are different. A stratum may range from 1 to 1 000 ft thick. Thin strata are called SEAMS, as of coal. Limestones, shales, and sandstones afford thick strata. In geological mapping, a thick and persistent stratum is often called a FORMATION.

Sedimentary rocks present all the features of the bottom, or of the strand between high and low water: as ripple marks, tracks, stranded shells, rill-marks, mud-cracks, flow and plunge from swift currents, irregular beddings, and cross-bedding in individual layers, as in deltas. Since the greatest thickness of sediments gathers along subsiding shore lines, with attendant advances of sea over land, there are found in normal succession: conglomerates, which represent old shore shingle, followed by sandstones, representing off-shore shallows; next shales, corresponding to deeper, quieter water; lastly, as representing still deeper water, free of mechanical sediments, are limestones, consisting largely of organic remains. This normal succession is not always found, since estuaries and rivers destroy uniformity, but it is not infrequent. There are also desert accumulations, wherein wind-blown particles are important, and are associated with beds from temporary streams, lakes, and floods. Land accumulations are characteristically red, from oxidation of iron.

9. ROCK DISTURBANCES

World-wide observation has shown that the rocky outer portion of the earth has been subject to many disturbances. Great masses may rise or sink without changing the local attitude of the rocks. These continental movements are of scientific interest, but seldom of importance to the engineer. Localized movements, due to elevation of a long and relatively narrow belt in a mountain chain, and disturbances incident to intrusive entrance of bodies of igneous rock, are more important. The results of these movements are termed FOLDS and FAULTS.

Folds are bendings in strata, whereby each layer assumes a curved form, approximating a portion of a cylinder. When classified in order from least to greatest, folds embrace MONOCLINES, ANTICLINES, and SYNCLINES of several types, also DOMES AND BASINS.

Monoclines (Fig 1) are terrace-like bendings of strata, with inclination varying in amount, but always in same direction, as the name implies. A roll at top of the terrace marks a belt of especial strain in the strata affected, and may be accompanied by numerous cracks. At foot of the terrace is a second roll in reversed direction, with attendant strains and cracks. In the upper roll, overlying beds are subject to tension, underlying to compression; in the lower roll, the upper beds are compressed, the lower tense. Between these areas is necessarily a surface of no strain.

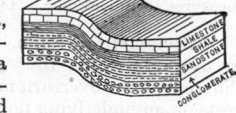

Fig 1. Monocline, in a Succession of Beds

Monoclines which involve porous beds, such as open-textured sandstones between tight shales, are sometimes important places for accumulation and storage of natural gas and petroleum. The search for these is essentially an endeavor to locate, with the drill, favorable monoclines or gentle anticlines. Monoclines have been described as arrested anticlines. In a series of sediments comprising shales or other soft strata, monoclines or even more violent folds in stiffer strata may at depth disappear entirely in the adjustment of soft underlying shales, the plastic movement of which takes up and distributes the fold until it is diffused and lost. The name monocline (or monoclinal structure) is sometimes applied to a remaining half of an eroded anticline or syncline, the other half of which is not apparent; inclination of the beds is all in one direction.

Anticline and syncline (Fig 2) are complementary terms; one rarely appears without the other.   An anticline is an arch-like bend, a syncline a corresponding trough.   The upper part of an anticline is called the CREST; its sloping sides, LIMBS or LEGS; the central portion, running parallel with the axis of the concentric partial cylinders, the surfaces of which are represented by each folded bed, is the AXIS.   The bottom of a syncline is the trough.   Beneath anticlinial crest and synclinal trough the beds are especially strained and cracked; the cracks tending to gape upward in the anticline and downward in the syncline.   The limbs of each type of fold are less strained than crest or trough.   Thus, good building stone will be found on the limbs rather than at crest or in trough.   On the contrary, veins and mineral deposits from circulating waters find natural resting places in crest and trough.

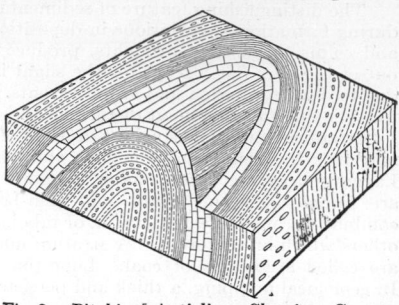

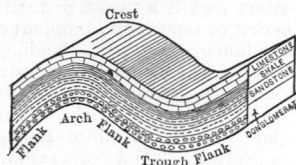

Fig 2.   Anticline and Syncline, with Horizontal Axis

Fig 3.   Pitching Anticline, Showing Concentrically Curving Outcrops of Eroded Beds

Anticlines and synclines, when followed for a mile or more, seldom have horizontal axes as shown in Fig 2.   The axes usually pitch downward (Fig 3), though they may afterward rise again. In Fig 2, the component beds, if eroded, would appear at surface in parallel bands.   When pitching folds are eroded, the several beds appear at surface as concentric curves (Fig 3).   In anticlines the upper or later beds are outside, the under or older, inside; in synclines the under or older beds are outside, the upper or later, inside.   Because of these relations, geologic structure may sometimes be inferred from a colored geologic map.

Anticlines received their name because the observer was assumed to stand at the crest, from which the beds inclined outwardly in opposite directions; hence the prefix "anti," for "opposed."   Standing in the trough of the syncline the observer sees the inclined beds sloping toward him, hence the prefix "syn," for "together."   Anticlines and synclines of which the inclination is the same on both sides of axis (see diagrams) are called SYMMETRICAL. Symmetrical folds may vary from those of comparatively slight disturbance to tightly compressed folds. In the former, where the limbs of a bed are separated by other beds, the fold is called OPEN; but where from extreme compression the limbs of a single bed are brought tightly together, the fold is CLOSED.   Fig 2 shows open symmetrical folds; Fig 4 closed symmetrical folds.   A limiting case of the anticline, speaking mathematically, is the DOME, in which the beds pitch radially in all directions from a central point.   The variable direction of the inclination has suggested the name QUAQUAVERSAL.   A dome is an anticline of which the axis is reduced to a point. Domes are chiefly developed above laccoliths; seldom in other relations.   A BASIN is a syncline the axis of which is a point, toward which the strata converge.   Basins in this strict sense are rare, and result from local removal of support and collapse of strata.   The term is also used in the geology of coal for a synclinal arrangement of strata, wherein a rising pitch of the axis in opposite directions brings the measures to the surface.   The seams thus form concentric canoe-shaped or spoon-bowl synclines.

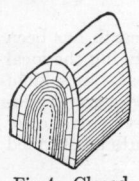

Fig 4.   Closed Fold

Unsymmetrical folds.   Strains which caused a fold may have pushed one limb under or over the other, thus producing unsymmetrical inclinations.   From relatively slight differences, the overturn may increase until the overturned portion rests on an underlying portion.   Such folds may even be S-shaped (SIGMOID) or RECUMBENT.   On a small scale, these often occur in metamorphic districts; on a large scale they occur mainly in regions of violent disturbance.

Type names may be used, such as the Jura type for symmetrical folds; Appalachian type for those steeper on one side than the other (Fig 5).   Closed folds are those of which the limbs are squeezed so tightly at one spot as to cause a great bulge of an upper or under core of rock.   When the surrounding strata incline away radially from the compressed area, like ribs of a fan, the fold is called a fan-fold.

Folds vary in size from small wrinkles and puckers, as in schists, to arcs having chords of yards, miles, or hundreds of miles.   Folds are sometimes designated as of the first, second, third, or higher orders.   A mountain range, consisting of an anticline or a syncline, is respectively called an ANTICLINORIUM or SYNCLINORIUM, the Greek

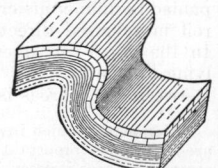

Fig 5.   Overturned Fold of Appalachian Type

word for mountain being added to type of fold. When great flat folds occupy an appreciable part of earth's surface, they are called respectively GEANTICLINES and GEOSYNCLINES, prefixing Greek word for earth to name of fold. Folds are of great importance in engineering work, not only in mining bedded minerals like coal, salt, and some iron ores, or in the discovery of petroleum and gas, but also in connection with railway tunnels, aqueducts, and other engineering work.

Dip and strike. DIP is the angle of inclination of a vein or bed below horizontal. STRIKE (course or bearing) is the direction of line of intersection of an inclined vein or bed with a horizontal plane.

The dip angle is the angle between two perpendiculars, one in the inclined plane, the other in the horizontal, let fall from a common point on their line of intersection (the strike). The strike is stated in degrees and minutes, E or W of N or S, for example N 25° 30′ E. Since plane of dip is at right angles to line of strike, it is recorded in degrees E or W of strike; thus, a strike of N 25° E and dip of 50° N W signifies that the plane in which dip is measured runs 65° west of north. Some observers note exact direction and amount of dip, leaving strike to be inferred. Thus, a record of a sandstone bed dipping 50° in a direction N 65° W, implies a strike of N 25° E. First mode of statement is customary in America. A GEOLOGIST'S COMPASS has one flat side, and usually a pendulum, swinging around a graduated semi-circle, so as to give direct dip reading. In plotting, each observation of strike may be corrected for variation of needle, or, in more elaborate compasses, the graduated circle may be turned to read directly observations referred to true north.

10. FAULTS

A fault is a dislocation in otherwise continuous strata or masses. It results when rocks are so excessively strained that they yield along a crack or series of cracks, one side altering its position with respect to other. One side may rise, sink, move laterally, or (as resultant of all 3 movements) diagonally, with respect to other side. In nearly all cases the fault plane or planes are inclined to horizontal, the upper and under sides being designated by the miner's terms, HANGING WALL and FOOT WALL. Limiting cases are vertical and horizontal faults.

Classification of faults (11, 12). The commonest are: normal, reverse and shift faults (Fig 6, 7 and 8). In NORMAL FAULT ("normal" here meaning "usual" or "common") the hanging wall has slipped down with reference to foot wall. The movement is rarely directly down line of dip of fault plane, but usually on a diagonal. The position of any point in dislocated portion is referred to the 3 axes of solid geometry: the vertical

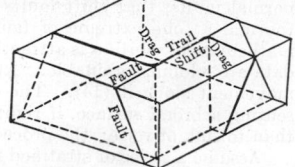

Fig 8. Shift Fault in Vein Dipping 50°. Same Effect would be Produced by Normal Fault, with Diagonal Displacement Involving Shift Component Away from Observer; or by a Large Throw, Straight Down the Dip

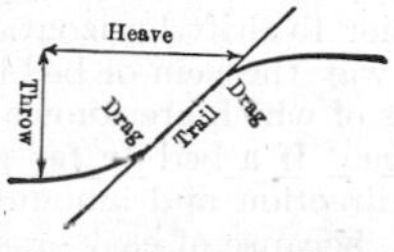

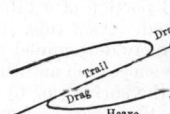

Fig 6. Normal Fault, Displacing Flat Coalseam. Cross-section

Fig 7. Reverse Fault, Begun as an Overturned Fold. Cross-section

component is the THROW; horizontal component perpendicular to the strike of the fault plane is the HEAVE; and horizontal component in fault plane is the SHIFT. These mathematical factors assist in determining direction and amount of movement, the line of which is the diagonal of the rectangular prism the edges of which are the heave, throw, and shift.

Fault-breccia. Movement of fault walls, or of one wall on the other, often crushes adjacent rock to a mass of angular fragments, mixed with more finely comminuted material. Circulating waters may cement the whole into a solid mass, by depositing new minerals, sometimes producing valuable ore. This mass is a FAULT-BRECCIA. Fragments of any bed, dike, or vein, involved in the fault movement, will be dragged along from stationary side in direction of movement; or will be left behind by moving side; and if followed along fault plane, will indicate direction of movement. Such fragments furnish valuable evidence and by F. T. Freeland have been aptly termed the TRAIL OF THE FAULT. Should a vein be cut off by a fault, with attendant breccia, fragments of the vein should be sought in the breccia and the trail followed to pick up continuation of vein.

Drag. Faults often cut relatively soft beds, as shales or shaly sandstones. Friction of the walls upon each other causes a downward bend in the beds of stationary or lifted side and an upward bend in those of the moving or dropped side. These bends, called DRAG, show the direction of movement (Fig 6). Drag is not found in strong rocks, like granites or heavily-bedded limestones.

Slickensides are polished and usually grooved surfaces, often caused by movement of walls of a fault or vein. Upon the wall-rock the grooves indicate direction of movement, but do not necessarily show which side has gone up, or down, or laterally.

Some observers have thought that by scraping finger nail or finger across the grooves, one side of them will be found steeper than the other. If the grooves are tested in slickensides on underside of plane of movement, such steep ridge is considered to be the lower side of groove, or the side which resisted bearing down of hanging wall while moving diagonally downward in fault plane. It will thus indicate the actual direction of movement. Should the steep ridge be on upper side of grooves, an upward movement of hanging wall is indicated. Others have thought that when the finger is moved along the groove the greater roughness is felt in the direction of movement of the part felt. Slickensides on fragments in fault-breccia are of little significance, since they are not *in situ.*

Horses are large disconnected masses of wall rock, involved in faults, or produced by forking of a fault fissure around a split-off fragment, and especially when related to subsequent vein-formation along fault.

Shear-zones. When a fault movement is distributed along a number of parallel planes not widely spaced, the wall rocks are broken into parallel tabular masses, and are said to be SHEETED. The resulting fault is "distributed," and the sheeted strip is a SHEAR-ZONE. GOUGE is a sheet of clay, often occurring along the outer edge of fault breccias, especially those subsequently mineralized by circulating waters. Other names are: SELVAGE and FLUCAN.

Fault-scarp. If a fault involves an appreciable vertical component, the relatively lifted side may stand out as a terrace or escarpment, the fault-scarp. Erosion soon wears it down, so that fresh fault-scarps are rarely recognizable. Faults have sometimes aided the deposition of ore bodies by furnishing waterways. When they are developed across an older mineral deposit, serious displacement may be caused.

Rules for solving faults have been formulated by Schmidt (13), Zimmermann (15), Freeland (9) and others. In studying a fault, observe trail, drag and slickensides. Stratigraphical succession, if known, will reveal amount of displacement. Bore-holes are useful. Models assist, and are sometimes superior to projections on paper. If there be no evidence to contrary, the assumption that fault is normal is justified, because most faults are such. Nevertheless, experience shows that a reverse fault occasionally appears in a series of normal faults, that shift faults may occur, and that fault movement may be rotational (normal at one extreme of fault plane, reverse at other). On encountering a fault, a mathematical solution is attractive, but, despite many text-book discussions, the necessary data are seldom obtainable. Attention should be concentrated on the fault plane and the movement along it (14). The dislocated portion of a tabular body is to be sought, presenting a broad surface, if rightly attacked. As a rule, it is easier to drift horizontally, than to sink or raise; the procedure is largely determined by the way the vein or bed lies.

Assume a series of stratified rocks, the succession and thickness of which are known by previous mining operations, by study of the surface, or by borings. If a bed on far side of fault is recognizable, and its place in the series known, the direction and amount of movement may be determined. As gulches often occur on faults, because of easy erosion of crushed rock, faults may sometimes be solved more readily by study of surface exposures than by observation solely underground. Directions of slickensides, drag, and trail, commonly found in faulted stratified rocks, are highly significant. If none of these evidences is decisive in dealing with a mineral deposit cut by a fault, there is strong probability that the fault is normal. On this assumption, if a fault be encountered on its under side the rule is to cross it and sink; if on its upper side, to cross it and raise. This is expressed in the old rule: " follow the obtuse angle." But, if the fault happens to be reverse, the rule would lead in wrong direction.

In dealing with steeply dipping veins in massive rocks, or steeply dipping stratified rocks containing coal seams or other interstratified deposits, the succession of strata must be known to determine the movement. Then, solving tentatively as a normal fault, due weight must be given to throw and shift, as possible components of diagonal movement. That is, besides the heave and throw of a normal fault, a large shift-component might cause displacement opposite to that anticipated, instead of straight down the dip. The occurrence of slickensides, trail, and drag may then be essential to correct solution.

Zimmermann's rule (15), for steep faults, cutting steeply dipping veins. Suppose (Fig 9), in driving a level on vein *so*, striking N 30° W and dipping 60° W, a fault *ff* is met, striking N 80° E and dipping 45° S. At intersection *o*, draw *ob* perpendicular to strike of fault, and prolong it toward *l*, beyond the fault. Project upon plane of level the intersection *og* of fault and vein. Line *og* is horizontal, and passes obliquely through *o*, into unexplored ground, toward *h*, on one side or other of *ol*. Then, if exploratory drift on far side of fault be turned from *oh* toward *ol*, and parallel to strike of fault, the displaced segment *xy* of vein will in most cases be found.

The horizontal projection *og* is found as in small diagram of Fig 9. Draw horizontal line *mn,* lay off *ma* and *mb* to represent dips of vein and fault; draw *mo* perpendicular and *ob* parallel to *mn*. Then *oa* and *ob* are the distances by which, in descending a vertical distance *mo*, the planes of vein and fault depart horizontally from vertical.   In main part of Fig 9, *oa* and *ob* are drawn respectively perpendicular to strikes of vein and fault; and *ac* and *de*, passing through *g*, are parallel to those strikes.   Whence *g* lies in the horizontal projection of intersection of vein and fault.

In Fig 10 is shown a similar relation of vein and fault, except that the vein lies east and exploratory drift should turn east, as shown.   Both solutions depend on assumption that the hanging wall of fault (*i e*, its south wall) has slipped down with little shift down on its foot wall.   With strongly diagonal movement the fault might still be normal, but the solution might lead miner in wrong direction. Therefore check all rules by trail, drag, slickensides, etc.

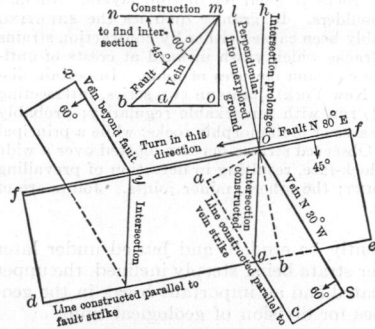

Fig 9.   Zimmermann's Solution of a Fault
(Projection on Horizontal Plane)

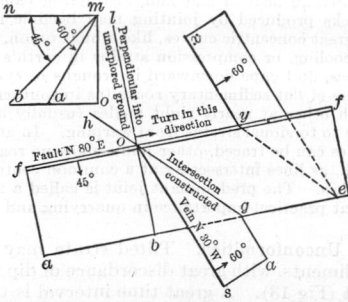

Fig 10. Zimmermann's Solution of a Fault.
Construction as in Fig 9, but Vein Dips
East, whence Exploratory Drift Turns
East

The following additional terms apply to faults.   In tilted, stratified rocks, faults striking parallel with the strata are STRIKE-FAULTS, often resulting when folds pass into faults.   Faults running across strike and parallel with line of dip are DIP-FAULTS.   STEP-FAULTS are series of parallel faults, dipping in same direction.   The HADE is the angle made by a fault plane with a vertical plane; hence, hade is the complement of dip, and is a superfluous term.

Various puzzling cases of faulting have become classic.   Fig 11 shows a Cornish case, from de la Beche; Fig 12, a case of two contrasted pegmatites in Sweden, observed by A. G. Högbom.   Two parallel veins may be so faulted as to bring dislocated part of one opposite sundered end of another, and temporarily conceal the existence of a fault.   In a certain shift fault, cutting a vein at right angles to vein's strike, the amount of shift was observed to grow gradually less in depth, leading to inference of a HINGE-FAULT, or possibly a ROTATIONAL FAULT.

Normal faults are often explained as due to tension strains in earth's crust, leading to drawing apart of the two sides of fault, and the slipping down of upper portion on lower; hence, they have been called tension or gravity faults.   Reverse faults, by contrast, are called compression or THRUST faults; they often begin as overturned folds.   If these stresses do produce their respective faults, then reverse faults should customarily have low dips, since, on approaching the perpendicular, friction would increase prohibitively.   But, if tensional stress were relieved by a series of parallel faults, and one fault block were to drop below its neighbors, there would be a normal fault on one side of dropped block and a reverse fault on the other.

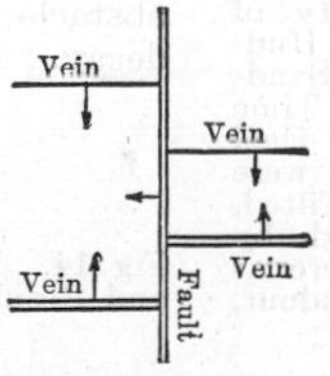

Fig 11. Two Veins, with Converging Dips, Normally Faulted

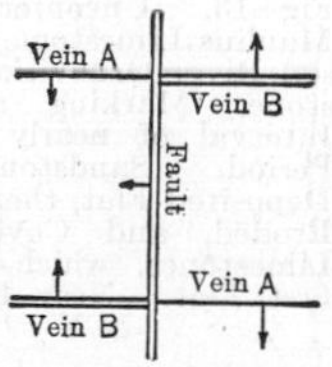

Fig 12. Two Veins, with Converging Dips, Dropped Below their Intersection by a Normal Fault

Compressive strains along the strike can easily develop normal faults by downward bulge of hanging wall and upward bulge of foot.   Where comparatively short faults die out at each end, this explanation has weight.   Again, assuming that in depth rocks are capable of viscous flow and transfer, pressure transmitted upward from such moving masses may cause faults from stresses wholly different from any previously mentioned.   Where faults are inclined, fault blocks with the larger base would be relatively lifted, as compared with those having smaller base.   Foot-walls would therefore rise relatively, causing normal faults (6, 7, 8, 10).

11. JOINTS, UNCONFORMITIES, OUTCROPS, EROSION

Joints are cracks which cross strata and masses, without producing dislocation of walls. Notwithstanding absence of dislocation, there may be difficulty in discriminating between joints and distributed faults of slight displacement, which produce sheeted structure.

All joints are due to easing of some kind of strain; as contractions in cooling of igneous rock, expansion of cold rock under the sun's heat, shrinkage from drying of water-soaked sediments, tensional strains at crests of anticlines or in outer layers in bottoms of synclines, and torsional stresses produced over wide areas by warping of earth's crust. As a result rocks break into polygonal columns of greater or less regularity. In joints produced by contraction of igneous magmas during consolidation, the long axes of the prisms are theoretically perpendicular to cooling surface. If the magma be homogeneous and transfer of heat uniform, regular hexagonal columns result, parted also across their axes by cup-shaped joints. Occasionally, as at Giant's Causeway, theoretical perfection is almost attained; usually, the columns are of all numbers of sides, from 3 to 8. Similar forms result from drying.

Strong heat of sun and weathering cause massive rocks to shell off in thin layers. Angular blocks produced by jointing may become rounded boulders. In granite quarries the SHEETING in great concentric curves, like a huge onion, has probably been caused either by contraction strains in cooling, or compression strains in earth's crust. Cracks which yawn upward at crests of anticlines, and gape downward in troughs of synclines, are common features of folds. In certain districts of flat sedimentary rocks (as in southern central New York), joints in two series, intersecting each other at nearly right angles (usually about 80°), run with remarkable regularity; probably due to torsional strains from warping. In areas of massive or metamorphic rocks, while a principal series can be traced, other joints show no regularity. Observed strikes may be plotted over a wide area, as lines intersecting at a common center like a clock-face, resulting in detection of prevailing strikes. The predominant joint is called a MASTER JOINT; the others, minor joints. Joints are of great practical importance in quarrying and in mining.

Unconformities. Tilted strata may subsequently be eroded, and buried under later sediments, with great discordance of dip; the lower strata being steeply inclined, the upper flat (Fig 13). A great time interval is thus indicated and an important break in the geological record. Unconformities are the best bases for division of geological time.

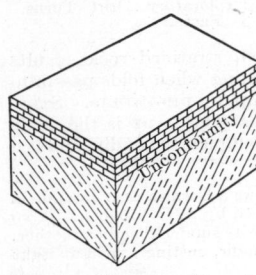

Practically flat strata may be carved by erosion into gorges of narrow valleys; which, if again submerged, may be filled with new, flat sediments, showing no discordance of dip with older strata, but perhaps bringing sandstones sharply against limestones or other strata. This relation is a DISCONFORMITY (Fig 14). Should the sea, because of gradual submergence of shore, creep gradually upward and bring younger flat strata on top of much older ones, a SEDIMENTARY OVERLAP is formed.

Outcrops are portions of solid rock IN PLACE, projecting at surface. By observations upon them questions are solved regarding structure and stratigraphic relations. Regions without outcrops must be explored by trenches, pits, or bore-holes; in northern latitudes glacial drift is the chief obstacle; in southern, the products of rock weathering or decay. Heavy vegetation may increase difficulty.

Fig 13. Unconformity of Manlius Limestone on Hudson River Ordovician Sandstone, Marking a Time Interval of nearly a Geol Period. Sandstones were Deposited Flat, then Tilted, Eroded, and Covered by Limestones, which were at first Flat. Near Rondout, N Y

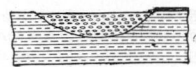

Fig 14. Disconformity, Vert Sec. Older Sandstones Eroded, and Resulting Valley Filled with Conglomerate, with no Discordance of Dip

Erosion, the wearing down of land and transfer of loose particles by water, wind, or ice, to places of deposition at lower altitudes, is in one sense destructive; in another, constructive, for sedimentary rocks are thereby composed.

Water erosion by streams, waves, or currents along shore lines, is the most important. Matter carried in suspension facilitates wear of rock masses exposed to moving grit. Of the same substance, larger particles require swifter currents for their removal than do the smaller, the surfaces of which are relatively greater compared to their masses. Small particles of high specific gravity may require as great velocity of current as large particles of low specific gravity. As velocity decreases, sorting action takes place; the large and the heavy small particles sink first, small particles remaining in suspension, though presence of solutions of mineral salts or of acids facilitates clearing of fresh water emulsions. The transporting ability of a current increases with sixth power of velocity. Thus, if a current can move a 1-in cube of quartz, by doubling its velocity it can move a 4-in cube, or 64 cu in; because, twice as much water strikes the cube, with twice the velocity.

Competence of a stream refers to the maximum size of particle of given sp gr which, at a given velocity, the stream will move. Thus, a small, rapid stream can move a relatively large particle. Its competence is great, but total transported material will be small. Conversely, a large, slow-moving stream might carry in suspension a great quantity of small particles. Its competence is small, but its capacity is great. These principles are important in the development of placers; they also underlie the artificial concentration of ores.

Waves on a shore line batter cliffs, and with the ammunition provided by boulders do great execution during storms. In creeping across a subsiding shore they may ultimately level every eminence in their way. Off-shore currents are vehicles of transport, building up bars, spits, etc. In association with sedimentation by rivers, such currents wear away points and fill coastal bays.

Winds are specially effective in desert regions, the loose surface materials lacking protection of vegetation. Small particles as dust are carried by milder winds; while by storms even gravel may be swept along. The march of sand dunes is one of the results.

Glaciers are powerful agents in carrying away loosened pieces from cliffs, and grinding smaller particles from rocks on their sides and bottoms. Deposited products of glacial action are called MORAINES, with terminal, lateral, and ground moraines as varieties. The material is rarely sorted, so that very coarse and very fine are mingled. Unsorted glacial deposits are usually associated with others worked over by water.

12. SUMMARY OF STRATIGRAPHIC GEOLOGY

Definite periods of time are assignable for the formation of strata of earth's crust, and each period is characterized by presence of remains of distinctive organisms. During the 19th century, geologists succeeded in classifying according to geological age nearly all strata of earth's surface, however remote the region, provided properly preserved organic remains or fossils were present. Strata without fossils, or so metamorphosed as to destroy their fossils, were either classified by their relations to determined strata, or else proved insoluble problems. Recognizing the importance of uniformity of usage in time divisions and their corresponding strata, the International Geological Congress, Paris, 1900, adopted the following:

TIME	STRATA	TIME	STRATA
1. Era	No equivalent	4. Age	Stage
2. Period	System	5. Phase	Zone
3. Epoch	Series		

This table signifies that, during a period, strata constituting a system were formed; during the shorter epoch, a series, and so on. A system may embrace several series, each of which has stages, in turn divisible into zones. In the geological mapping of a district it is customary to work primarily on basis of periods-systems, and then under each to apply a local, geographical name to any stratum sufficiently persistent and well defined to be recognizable over an extensive area. The following table summarizes the generally accepted conclusions. For periods the older names are given, but it is now common to terminate periodic names in " ic "; thus, Carbonic for Carboniferous, etc.

Eras	Periods	Eras	Periods
Quaternary or Psychozoic	Recent Pleistocene, or Glacial	Paleozoic	Permian Carboniferous Devonian Silurian Ordovician Cambrian
Tertiary or Cenozoic	Pliocene Miocene Oligocene Eocene		
Mesozoic	Cretaceous Comanchean Jurassic Triassic	Pre-Cambrian or Archean	Keweenawan Huronian Laurentian Keewatin

Pre-Cambrian. Igneous rocks and metamorphic sediments predominate; including gneisses, schists, quartzites, slates, and marbles, with associated deep-seated and volcanic igneous rocks. In North America the most extensive exposures are in Canada, constituting a vast V-shaped area, with Hudson's Bay in the opening and the point at the Great Lakes. Underlying the entire continent, they also appear in backbones of the Appalachian and Rocky Mountains, and occasionally project elsewhere in small patches. Though almost devoid of fossil remains, sponges, algæ, and trails of moving organisms have in recent years been discovered in the Huronian, in Lake Superior region and Montana. Pre-Cambrian strata are very productive of metals, especially iron. KEEWATIN greenstones contain the gold veins at Porcupine, some of the Cobalt silver veins, and iron ore of Vermilion Range, Minn. LAURENTIAN consists of intrusive igneous rocks, poor in ore deposits. HURONIAN embraces a great series of metamorphosed sediments, with some igneous rocks, and yields the chief American iron ores in the Lake region. It has also most of the silver veins at

Cobalt, Ont. KEWEENAWAN is largely a succession of basaltic rocks and minor sediments; it contains the copper mines of Keweenaw Point, Mich.

Paleozoic. Around the edges of pre-Cambrian areas are the earliest Paleozoic strata (unless from overlap later ones have crept inward over the earlier). The successive strata of the 6 periods are often marked off by unconformities, upturned by disturbances, and are sometimes missing in individual cases, where land conditions prevailed. In North America they are in greatest development in the U S, east of the Mississippi, and in states just west of it. In the Cordilleran region the areas are smaller and scattered. The Clinton iron ores appear in the east in the SILURIAN; the eastern coal supply comes from the CARBONIFEROUS; the eastern oil and gas are mainly in the ORDOVICIAN, DEVONIAN, and CARBONIFEROUS.

Mesozoic strata are chief components of western half of North America; are of vast development in the Great Plains, the Cordillera, and Mexico. The western coals are chiefly in CRETACEOUS strata, but appear also in EOCENE beds of next era. The mountain upheavals at close of CRETACEOUS, with attendant igneous outbreaks, are largely reponsible for the western ore deposits.

Cenozoic strata appear in the east in a coastal fringe. In the west they are represented by old land or lake deposits in the Great Plains, and marine strata along the Pacific. Because of the great development of mammals, the fossil remains are of great interest, especially in their bearings on doctrine of evolution.

Quaternary (sometimes called PSYCHOZOIC) is the era of man's especial development. It is marked by the continental ice sheet in its early portion in the north; in the south, by products of weathering and recent sediments. The strata of the closing GLACIAL or PLEISTOCENE (Pleistocene is term especially used for regions south of glacial drift) pass gradually into coastal deposits now forming.

Note.—For full discussion of eras and periods, see Bibliog, numbers 17 to 22.

MINERAL DEPOSITS: ORES

13. INTRODUCTION, DEFINITIONS OF ORE

Mineral deposits include both ores and non-metallic minerals. In earlier years the metals were chiefly mined, but in recent time non-metallic minerals have greatly increased in relative importance. Metalliferous minerals only are included under the head of "ore deposits," non-metallics being treated separately.

Scientifically, the word "ore" comprehends all metal-bearing minerals which are commercial sources of the metals, percentages not being considered. Technically, an ore is a metal-bearing mineral, or aggregate of such minerals, mixed with barren matter, called "gangue," and capable of being mined at a profit. By contrast, where the element of profit is uncertain or impossible, the term "mineral deposit" may be used instead of "ore deposit." Thus, pay ore or commercial ore is contrasted with an orebody of uncertain yield. The richer part of an ore deposit is the "pay-streak" or "ore-shoot;" very rich parts, "bonanzas." The phrase "the ores" is sometimes employed by students of the microscopic characters of igneous rocks, to designate the group of minute minerals which first crystallize in the cooling of a molten magma. Magnetite is its most conspicuous member (25).

14. METALS IN THE EARTH'S CRUST

Ore deposits are portions of earth's crust enormously enriched with metals as compared with the rest. On basis of composition of the crust given in Sec 1, Art 1 (fuller details in Bull 491, U S Geol Surv, pp 27, 33), it is seen that among percentages down to a minimum of 0.03, a few common metals are named, viz: aluminum, 7.28; iron, 4.12; manganese, 0.08. In igneous rocks, considered alone, nickel, 0.023, and chromium, 0.033, are also found. Copper may reach 0.01%, but all others, lead, zinc, silver, gold, quicksilver, tin, etc, are expressed in very small decimals of 1%. An ore deposit, therefore, is a relatively enormous local concentration of metals, from a minimum of 4 times for low-grade aluminum ores, 7 times for low-grade iron ores, and 200 times for low-grade copper ores, to a concentration which, for the other metals, may reach thousands or hundreds of thousands. Ore deposits are largely produced by concentration by circulating waters in earth's crust.

15. CAVITIES IN ROCKS; GROUND-WATERS

Cavities in rocks. From the point of view of physics, the smallest cavities are those below capillaries, i e, below tubes 0.0002 mm diam, or tabular spaces 0.0001 mm across. In these, under ordinary conditions, adhesion prevents circulation. Capillaries range from the above dimensions to 0.5 mm for tubes and 0.25 mm for tabular spaces. In rocks these small cavities, called voids, appear as surviving and unfilled pores of crystals, contact spaces between minerals or grains, and cleavage cracks. They are expressed in tenths of

1% of the volume in dense rocks, up to 10% or more in porous sandstones. Cavities of larger size are found in pumice, amygdaloids, jointed rocks, faults, and caves.

Ground-waters, or waters which are below the earth's surface, are of 3 kinds: meteoric, connate, and magmatic. METEORIC water descends as rain and snow, in part soaking into the ground, and forming the standing body of water which requires pumping in mines, etc. CONNATE water is contained in sediments deposited beneath sea or lakes, having been carried down with the sediments as they were buried beneath later strata. MAGMATIC water is set free in the cooling and consolidation of molten masses of igneous rock, becoming manifest at volcanic vents and presumably in hot springs, which nearly always accompany expiring vulcanism.

Formerly, in discussing the formation of orebodies by underground circulation, only meteoric waters were considered. They were believed to descend to the general limit of cavities, to migrate extensively through small cavities in rocks; and, when heated from below and charged with ore and gangue, to return by larger channels towards the surface, forming veins and other orebodies. Connate waters were recognized in brines, often pumped to surface for salt. But, as experience in deep mines proved that meteoric water is almost always limited to the upper zone of about 1 000 ft, geologists have attributed more and more importance to magmatic waters to which the primary introduction of ore and gangue can be referred with fewer difficulties. This view is strengthened by the common association of ore deposits with intrusive igneous rocks, by study of contact zones and pegmatites, and by observations upon volcanic emissions. Apparently, magmatic waters or vapors or gases emerge from the igneous mass charged with the components of ores and gangue; but in subsequent circulation, they make take up more minerals, and bring all to a place of precipitation. The heat of an intrusive, igneous mass is a powerful agent in promoting underground circulations. It is more efficient than the normal increase of temperature with depth, or than natural head from high points of entrance and low points of emergence, the friction of small passages being considered (29).

16. MINERALS AND LOCALIZATION OF ORE DEPOSITS

Ore minerals are primary and secondary. The PRIMARY are those originally deposited in forming an orebody; the SECONDARY are produced by alteration of primary minerals under certain conditions. Except aluminum, iron, manganese, chromium, platinum and tin, all primary ore minerals are sulphides, arsenides, sulpharsenides, sulphantimonides, or similar compounds. Sulphides are of chief importance. Though secondary minerals are largely oxidized compounds, they also comprise a few very important sulphides.

The importance of the distinction lies in the following relations to the surface. Ground-waters stand at varying depths, depending on local rainfall, rock texture and local geological structure. Between ground-water level and the surface, is a zone called by Posepny the vadose zone, by Van Hise the zone of weathering, through which the oxidizing and dissolving rain waters freely descend. Within this vertical range, sulphides become oxidized to sulphates, and pass extensively into solution. Migrating downward, the solutions merge into the standing and protecting ground-waters, and often precipitate their dissolved metals in a zone of SECONDARY ENRICHMENT, at or near ground-water level. The reaction is especially important in copper mines.

Gangue minerals comprise quartz, calcite, fluorite, barite, rhodochrosite, rhodonite, and admixed minerals of the country rock. Decomposition or alteration under influence of thermal waters gives rise to much sericite, kaolinite, and related species.

Localization of ore deposits. Ore deposits resulting from processes outlined above are developed where circulating mineral-bearing solutions find favorable places to precipitate their contents. One method of classification is to arrange in a logical scheme the favorable geological places for this reaction. For the formation of some kinds of ore deposit, however, circulating solutions are not required. Ores may crystallize directly from molten magmas, and, either by sinking in the fluid mass because of higher specific gravity, or for some reason not well understood, may enrich the rock mass to the requirements of mining. Again, and in contrast with the reactions above indicated, moving waters in streams, or by wave action, may liberate and concentrate heavy minerals in sedimentary deposits, to the point of profitable mining. Again, in residual deposits, heavy and resistant minerals may be left behind in a concentrated condition by removal of products of weathering. In a few cases, chiefly iron ores, the processes of sedimentation, or associated precipitation, have given rise to bedded ore deposits. Experience shows, therefore, that it is difficult consistently to classify orebodies on any one of these subordinate principles. But, as compared with old-time schemes, based on shape, the broad principle of MODE OF ORIGIN has become increasingly important. In the following classification, the endeavor has been to pass from igneous phenomena, pure and simple, to surface reactions not connected with igneous phenomena, emphasizing especially the PLACE where orebodies originate.

Zonal distribution. Closer study of mining regions in the Cordilleran region of North America leads to following conclusions: (a) Ore deposition follows intrusions of igneous rocks, most frequently those related to granites or species intermediate between granites and diorites (as, granodiorites and quartz-monzonites). The ores are products of the cooling stages, precipitated in largest part from magmatic waters (30). (b) Ore and gangue minerals are distributed outwardly from the igneous center, in a series beginning with those requiring high temperatures and high pressures for their formation, and passing through varieties precipitated under diminishing temp and press until surface conditions are reached (31). Some persistent minerals, as pyrite, have a wide range of conditions. (c) It results that around an igneous source, both vertically and laterally, when the original magma produced several metals, zones characteristically containing certain ores may be recognized. In the igneous intrusive may be magmatic segregations (Art 17). Next come pegmatic dikes and contact zones; then, gold-bearing quartz veins related to pegmatites, dike-veins; then copper-bearing pyrite-quartz veins, passing into zinc-blende bearing phases in which zinc replaces copper, while pyrite persists. Farther out, galena replaces zinc-blende, and yields in succession to high-grade silver ores, gold tellurides, antimony ores, and others. Finally, gangue minerals alone survive (32). This principle is called the zonal distribution of metals, and in many districts has proved of great value as a guide to mine development.

17. CLASSIFICATION OF ORE DEPOSITS (37)

I. Primary magmatic origin.

(a) Masses produced by crystallization and segregation in cooling and solidifying igneous magmas: titaniferous and non-titaniferous magnetites, chromite, corundum, platinum, and probably sulphides of iron, nickel, and copper. A few dikes and sheets of igneous magnetite are known.

II. Deposited by emissions from cooling and solidifying magmas.

(b) Veins of nature of pegmatites, varying from the mineralogy of granite to fairly pure quartz; often with tourmaline, fluorite and minerals containing boron or fluorine; productive of tin, rare elements, and exceptionally gold, and intermediate in nature between dikes and veins; sometimes described as aqueo-igneous. (c) Contact deposits, produced from limestones by emissions from adjoining igneous magma, and consisting of lime-silicates, as: garnet, diopside, wollastonite, vesuvianite, epidote; also, magnetite, specular hematite, sulphides of iron, copper, and other metals.

III. Deposited by circulating ground-waters.

(d) Deposits in or along faults, with replacement and impregnation of the walls; often called "true fissure" veins. They vary from the filling of an open and clean-cut fissure, to impregnation and replacement of closely spaced faults of small individual displacement. (e) Saddle-reefs: precipitations of quartz or other minerals, at crest and between layers of an anticline, and extending with diminishing thickness for varying but usually moderate distances down its flanks. Inverted saddles appear in synclines. Apparently arching of the strata has aided precipitation. (f) Deposits in joints with greater or less replacement and impregnation of the walls; often called "gash veins," because limited to a single stratum or sheet. (g) Impregnations of volcanic agglomerates in the conduits of extinct explosive volcanoes. (h) Impregnations with greater or less replacement of permeable rocks, as: amygdaloids, volcanic tuffs and breccias, open-textured sandstones and conglomerates, autoclastics, etc. Supply conduit may be obscure. (i) Replacements of limestones, calcareous shales or other beds, which have yielded to circulating ground-waters. Supply conduit may be obscure.

IV. Deposited or concentrated by aid of surface waters.

(j) Surface precipitations, which may later be involved in stratified series. Bog iron ores. (k) Resistant or insoluble minerals, concentrated as a residuum by weathering and removal of the matrix. Residual deposits; Cuban brown hematites. (l) Placers or concentrations of heavy minerals in sands and gravels by action of moving water. Gold placers; stream tin.

18. IRON ORES

Four minerals are chiefly productive of iron: limonite (brown hematite, brown ore) $2 Fe_2O_3 \cdot 3 H_2O$, Fe 59.8%; siderite (carbonate, spathic ore) $FeCO_3$, Fe 48.3%; hematite (red and specular) Fe_2O_3, Fe 70.0%; magnetite (magnetic ore) $FeO \cdot Fe_2O_3$, Fe 72.4%.

Associated with limonite, but less common, are other ferric hydrates, as: turgite ($2 Fe_2O_3 \cdot H_2O$); goethite ($Fe_2O_3 \cdot H_2O$). Hydrated silicates may also occur, as: chamoisite (hydrated ferrous aluminum silicate); thuringite (hydrated ferrous or ferric aluminum silicate); greenalite (hydrated ferrous silicate). Siderite may have its iron partly replaced by magnesium and calcium. With brown hematites, manganese minerals are not uncommon. Pyrite (FeS_2) may appear with all the ores, and, when largely freed of its sulphur, may yield a residue possible of utilization for poor grades of iron. Pyrrhotite (Fe_7S_8) is frequent with magnetites. Ilmenite ($FeO \cdot TiO_2$) is mechanically mingled with many magnetites. Objectionable ingredients of iron ores are S and P; definite limits of these for merchantable grades of ore are variable, due to possible admixtures in furnace practice; in general, the less the better. In ores for acid bessemer pig, permissible phosphorus max is 0.001 part of the percentage of iron. Roughly, therefore, about 0.06% is max with richest ores.

Magnetites and specular hematites are the richest iron ores. In America lump magnetite ores have in the past exceeded 65% iron, but today practically only magnetically concentrated ore reaches this figure. Kiruna, Swedish Lapland, however, can furnish a great tonnage of this grade, even to American furnaces. Average of all iron ore mined in the U S in 1925 was not far from 50% iron. The grade will doubtless gradually decline. Alabama Clinton red hematites run 36 to 37%. Some crude ore is even lower. The principal local supply of continental Europe, from the minette ores, averages about 30%. The nearness of good fuels, markets, mixtures, etc, determine limiting percentages.

In the U S about four-fifths of the ore comes from Lake Superior region. Next in order are the red hematites of Alabama and Tennessee, the brown hematites and the magnetites of Appalachian belt. Individual mines in Wyoming, Colorado, and New Mexico have fed the iron and steel plant at Pueblo, Colo. Magnetites will be produced in time on the Pacific coast for a future industry to be located presumably in the Puget Sound region.

Lake Superior iron districts. In order of productiveness in the Lake Superior region are Minnesota, Michigan, and Wisconsin. Ontario has one productive range, and possibility of developing others. The ores of this region are all in pre-Cambrian strata:

Keweenawan: sandstones, basalt flows. Copper. Huronian. Upper, Middle and Lower: sedimentary and some igneous rocks. Iron ores in the sediments. Laurentian: granites. Keewatin: green schists, from ancient basic eruptives. Some sediments with iron ores.

As now mined the ores are chiefly soft, partially hydrated hematites, their percentage of water not reaching that of limonite. They have been produced by alteration of great beds of cherty carbonates of iron, of hydrated ferrous silicate, and of associated pyrite, under the general processes of weathering. Soft earthy masses of ore have thus resulted; of enormous volume, accessible, cheaply mined, and of relative purity as regards phosphorus and sulphur. They occupy synclinal basins, troughs produced by intersection of igneous dikes with each other or with impervious strata, or other minor places where circulating and oxidizing meteoric ground-waters have been temporarily obstructed in their flow. Besides soft ores there are lenticular bodies of hard specular hematite, produced by metamorphism of ancient soft-ore bodies; also great bodies of jaspery or siliceous iron-bearing strata, of 35% and above in iron, which, partly as concentrating ore, partly as low-grade lump ores, with the gradual exhaustion of better grades, will be available for a long time to come. The grade is well above that of present European ores. These ores originally formed beds precipitated at surface (Art 17, IV, *j*). They became buried in a stratified series, and afterward by weathering yielded residual deposits (Art 17, IV, *k*), some of which extend to great depths and are cases of secondary enrichment. Some have been metamorphosed to specular hematite, and even magnetite. In northeastern Minnesota gabbros occur with igneous titaniferous magnetites, not yet shown to be valuable (Art 17, I, *a*) (38).

Clinton red hematites are next in productiveness. They appear as beds of oölitic, often fossiliferous ore, associated with olive-green shales and subordinate limestones of the Clinton stage, at base of Silurian system. They outcrop in S E Wisconsin, western Ohio, central Kentucky, western New York, south of Lake Ontario, and farther east at town of Clinton (whence their name); in Pennsylvania, Virginia, eastern Tennessee, Georgia, and Alabama. Their greatest development is in Alabama, where they form an inner terrace, called Red Mountain, in the Birmingham anticlinal valley. Good coking coals and limestone are near, so that low-cost pig can be produced even from 35 and 40% ores. At outcrops the ores are siliceous; below ground-water level, they become basic. All are moderately high in phosphorus. They are probably oölitic beds, precipitated in shallow estuaries, fed by iron-bearing drainage (C. H. Smyth). Although utilized in Tennessee and Georgia, they are most important in Alabama. In time those in New York, Kentucky and Wisconsin are destined to be of greater moment than now.

Brown hematites ("brown ores") of the U S are produced chiefly along that portion of the Appalachian mountains formed by early Paleozoic strata, and just west of the earlier crystallines. They are products of weathering of ferruginous rocks, especially limestones. In almost all the mines they must be freed of ochers and clays by washing.

Magnetites occur in two chief types of deposits. The commoner is a lenticular or pod-shaped mass, in gneisses, parallel with the foliation. They appear widely in the ancient Appalachian crystallines, but are most productive in the Adirondacks. The second type appears in the contact zones (Art 17, II, *c*), produced by intrusive igneous rocks on limestones or limey shales. The greatest deposit of this type in the East is at Cornwall, Penn. The igneous rock is diabase and the limestone, Cambro-Ordovician. In the West many such deposits are known, in Utah (Iron Springs Dist), Nevada, California, and along the northwest coast.

In Europe, Germany, England, and France follow the U S in order of production of iron ores, the greatest single source being found in a series of Jurassic beds in and near Luxemburg, and in the northeast of England. The ores (called "minette") are of 30% or a little higher, and are brown hematites, carbonates, and various silicates.   Minor orebodies are in veins, of carbonates, and in beds of clay iron-stone and black-band.   Spain ships from Bilbao great quantities of partially hydrated hematite, the weathered product of spathic ores in depth.   Sweden is a heavy exporter of magnetites, especially from the igneous sheet of magnetite at Kiruna, Lapland.   Many lenticular magnetites have been worked in middle Sweden.   Great bodies of igneous magnetites exist in the Urals.   Algiers ships important amounts of red, partly hydrated hematites.

Large orebodies have recently been developed in N E Cuba, where ancient serpentines have weathered for ages, leaving a residual soil, rich enough in iron to form ore.   Great reserves of specular hematite, of ancient geological age, occur in eastern Brazil, state of Minas Geraes.   With the opening of the Panama canal, iron ores reached American furnaces from Chile.   In S E Newfoundland, at Wabana, extensive beds of red hematite have been developed in recent years (39).

19.   COPPER ORES

The minerals in Table 4 constitute the common ores of copper:

Table 4.   Copper Ores

Sulphides	% Cu	Sulphates	% Cu
Chalcopyrite,		Chalcanthite, $CuSO_4 \cdot 5H_2O$	25.38
$\quad CuFeS_2(Cu_2S \cdot Fe_2S_3)$	34.60	Brochantite, $Cu_4(OH)_6SO_4$	56.10
Bornite, $Cu_3FeS_3(2\,Cu_2S \cdot Fe_2S_3)$	55.50	Carbonates	
Covellite, CuS	66.48		
Chalcocite, Cu_2S	79.80	Malachite, $CuCO_3 \cdot Cu(OH)_2$	57.27
		Azurite, $2\,CuCO_3 \cdot Cu(OH)_2$	55.10
Sulpharsenides and Sulphantimonides		Silicate	
Enargite, $Cu_3AsS_4(3\,Cu_2S \cdot As_2S_5)$	48.40		
Tetrahedrite,		Chrysocolla, $CuSiO_3 \cdot 2H_2O$	36.00
$\quad Cu_8Sb_2S_7(4\,Cu_2S \cdot Sb_2S_3)$	52.06	Oxychloride	
Oxides		Atacamite, $Cu_2Cl \cdot (OH)_3$	59.29
Melaconite, CuO	78.86	Native Metal	
Cuprite, Cu_2O	88.80	Native copper, Cu	100.00

The distinction between primary and secondary minerals is more important with copper than with any other metal.   Some copper minerals appear in both groups.   PRI-MARY: chalcopyrite, bornite, chalcocite, enargite, tetrahedrite (some native copper in Lake Superior mines).   SECONDARY: chalcocite, covellite, melaconite, cuprite, chalcanthite, brochantite, malachite, azurite, chrysocolla, atacamite, and native copper.   Possibly chalcopyrite and bornite are secondary in some cases.   As a primary mineral lean copper-bearing pyrite is very important, especially in intrusive rocks.   When oxidized by meteoric waters in the vadose zone (belt of weathering), all copper-bearing sulphides yield some form of sulphate.   This soluble salt, in deposits in siliceous rocks, trickles downward until, in contact with some reducing agent, like pyrite, the copper is precipitated as chal-cocite.   This causes great concentration of copper, at or near ground-water level, termed SECONDARY ENRICHMENT.   From bodies of copper-bearing sulphides, in regions of abun-dant rainfall, as at Ducktown, Tenn, an upper zone or GOSSAN of brown hematite results, which may form an iron ore.   Below this, near ground-water level, a belt of rich chalcocite (black ore) appears, containing most of the copper once distributed throughout upper part of deposit.   Still lower are unaltered, primary sulphides.   In a comparatively arid region, when copper-bearing sulphides, usually in form of cupriferous pyrite, are disseminated in intrusive igneous rocks, or quartzites, or schists (which may be crushed or rendered open-textured along a zone of movement), descending waters of the vadose zone develop an upper leached belt, underlain by a chalcocite-bearing section of maximum richness; and below this is a belt of slight secondary enrichment.   Thus have originated the disseminated copper ores, now being extensively mined in the southwest.   If oxidizing reactions occur in open-textured tuffs, or contact lime silicates, chrysocolla often results, instead of chal-cocite; if in presence of limestone, the blue and green carbonates and cuprite are characteristic products.   In North America most of the copper produced comes from chalcocite.   The region of Northern Rhodesia, with adjacent portions of Katanga, con-tains the largest copper-bearing area known.

Examples of copper deposits (letters in parentheses refer to Classification, Art 17).

A. Bodies of copper-bearing sulphides, chiefly chalcopyrite or lean, copper-bearing pyrite in igneous rocks (a).   Chalcopyrite may be associated with a nickel-bearing sul-phide, pentlandite, and with pyrrhotite, in basic intrusives (Sudbury, Ontario).   Lean copper-bearing pyrite of igneous intrusive masses, usually monzonites, requires secondary enrichment for profitable operation (Bingham Canyon, Utah, and near Ely, Nevada).

B. Irregular masses of copper-bearing sulphides in contact zones (*c*) and associated with lime silicates. Secondary enrichment, incident to oxidation, may be necessary to increase percentage to mining requirements. Various minor forms of deposit may be associated. Bisbee and Morenci, Ariz, are best illustrations.

C. Veins along faults, with greater or less replacement and impregnation of the walls (*d*), as at Butte, Mont, where walls are granite. Innumerable other veins are known in all parts of world.

D. Lenticular or pod-shaped bodies of pyrite or pyrrhotite, with chalcopyrite (usually of later introduction). The lenses favor schists or slates, and lie parallel with the foliation. These rocks may be sheared eruptives, or may be sediments (Ducktown, Tenn, and many orebodies along Appalachians). Other examples appear in foot-hills of Sierra Nevadas, Cal. Rio Tinto, Spain, is one of the largest bodies yet discovered.

These orebodies were probably originally veins (*d*) parallel to structural planes of wall-rocks, and subsequently pinched into lenses by pressure. The type called "Kieslager" may be of sedimentary origin, or introduced as veins and pinched by pressure. Some have been considered igneous intrusives, as at Sulitelma, Norway, and Bodenmais, Bavaria.

E. Native copper in nodules, sheets, minute scales, and sometimes large branching masses, in amygdaloidal basalts, and associated conglomerates (*h*). Keweenaw Point, Michigan, is chief example. Introduction of the copper is a disputed subject, whether a product of expiring igneous activity, or of circulating meteoric and connate waters.

F. Impregnations of sedimentary rocks with sulphides or their oxidized products, often deposited on organic remains (*h*). Mansfeld, Germany, is best known example, where a black shale, with abundant organic remains, is impregnated with copper minerals for a width less than 1 ft, but over a great area. It is uncertain whether the copper was precipitated from Permian sea-water along with the sediments, or introduced by circulating ground-waters long after sediments were deposited. Triassic strata of the U S have many copper impregnations, mostly small.

The percentage of copper for successful mining depends on widely varying conditions. Native copper rock, on Keweenaw Point, Mich, yielding only 0.65% (13 lb per ton), has been treated successfully. The disseminated chalcocite of Bingham Canyon, Utah, has yielded average assays over 3 months' periods as low as 1%, with approx a seven-eighths recovery. Raw smelting ores, of slightly above 2% and with little aid from precious metals, have been worked at Ducktown, Tenn. In early days in western U S, ores of 10 to 20% were frequent in oxidized and enriched parts of deposits. Vast quantities of 10% ore are now reported from S E Congo State, Central Africa. To be valuable, all low-grade deposits must be of great size (40).

20. LEAD AND ZINC ORES

Lead. Following minerals constitute the common ores of lead: galena, PbS, 86.6% lead; anglesite, $PbSO_4$, 68.3%; cerussite, $PbCO_3$, 77.5%; pyromorphite, 3 $(PbO \cdot P_2O_5)$ $PbCl_2$, 76.2% (much rarer than the others). Other compounds sometimes appear in small amount, as wulfenite, crocoite and vanadinite.

Galena is the chief primary lead ore, of which others are oxidation products. It is frequently associated with zinc blende and pyrite. All lead ores are commoner in limestones than with other wall rocks. Many lead ores carry silver in commercial amounts, especially in regions characteristically productive of precious metals. Gold is a rarer associate. The oxidized product of galena is oftener cerussite than anglesite. All oxidized ores are mingled with limonite in varying degree, and with silica and earthy minerals from alteration of wall rocks. Lead and zinc can best be discussed together.

Zinc. Following minerals constitute the common ores of zinc: sphalerite or zinc blende, ZnS, 67% zinc, hemimorphite (calamine), 2 $ZnO \cdot H_2O \cdot SiO_2$, 54.2%; smithsonite, $ZnCO_3$, 52.1%; willemite, 2 $ZnO \cdot SiO_2$, 58.6%; zincite, ZnO, 80.3%; franklinite, $(Fe,Mn,Zn)O(Fe,Mn)_2O_3$, variable, about 6.0%. Willemite, zincite and franklinite, exceptional in their occurrence in northern New Jersey, form a group by themselves.

Zinc blende is the almost universal primary mineral; calamine and smithsonite are its oxidation products. The latter two are often inseparably mixed, and together are known as "galmei" in Europe. "Dry-bone" is a local name in Mississippi Valley, the oxidation products suggesting old bones. (The significance of the names calamine and smithsonite in England is the exact reverse of the American meaning, smithsonite being used for the hydrated silicate.) The oxidized compounds are characteristic of the vadose zone. They may coat bedrock beneath a cap of residual products. The deposits are summarized from those with lead alone to those with zinc alone. Intimate mixtures of both ores afford one of the great metallurgical problems today. Neither lead nor zinc deposits have been found in immediate association with igneous rocks, such that a direct igneous origin could be ascribed to them. They reach their places of precipitation in solution.

Examples of lead and zinc deposits.   (Letters in parentheses refer to Art 17.)
A. Disseminated and sometimes coalescing deposits of galena with associated sulphides, in sedimentary strata.   The galena impregnates the older sediment; believed to have been introduced in solution, and to have replaced preëxisting minerals; source is conjectural (*h* and *i*).   In S E Missouri, the chief American source of lead for lead alone, Cambrian limestones are impregnated.

Near Laurium, Greece, galena replaces limestones involved with mica schists.   At Leadville, Colo, Carboniferous limestone has been replaced with silver-bearing galena, pyrite, manganese compounds and sometimes zinc blende, along under sides of sills of rhyolite-porphyry ("white porphyry").   Extensive oxidation developed carbonate ores for the early miners.   Galena may yield to zinc blende in amount.   In Belgium, Luxemburg, and near Aix-la-Chappelle, huge amounts of subordinate lead ores have been mined in Devonian and Carboniferous limestone along great faults.   Zinc blende was doubtless the original mineral.   In Silesia the zinc and lead ores are in Triassic limestones.

At Commern, Germany, knots of galena are disseminated in Triassic sandstone.   In Cœur d'Alene district, Idaho, silver-bearing galena, with siderite, appears in great bodies in pre-Cambrian quartzite, along or near extensive faults.   Zinc blende has been met in some mines; copper ores in a few others.   Siderite seems to have first replaced the quartzite, and then yielded to galena.   The reaction is much the same as with original limestones.

In S W Missouri zinc blende and subordinate galena impregnate breccias of chert, interbedded in Lower Carboniferous limestones.
B. Galena, zinc blende and associated sulphides in joints (" gash veins ") and related cavities (*f*).   In S W Wisconsin and neighboring states of Upper Mississippi Valley the Ordovician " Galena " limestone has numerous vertical gash veins, with horizontal " runs " and inclined " pitches," containing galena, zinc blende, marcasite, and calcite.
C. Galena and zinc blende in fissure veins, often together, often separate, usually with other sulphides (*d*).   Precious metals are frequently associated.   Such deposits are world-wide, and in all kinds of wall-rocks.
D. Lenticular deposits containing willemite, franklinite, subordinate zincite and many lime silicates, are folded in pitching synclinal troughs in pre-Cambrian limestones.   It is difficult to classify these deposits.   Their zinc-bearing minerals are unique.   The mineralogy suggests contact zones (*c*), but the actual metamorphosing igneous rock is not apparent.

21. SILVER AND GOLD ORES

Though deposits are known containing either gold or silver alone, these metals are generally associated and must be discussed together.   Both are extensively obtained in connection with copper and lead.   Lead ores are often called " wet ores," because metallic lead, freed in smelting, acts as a solvent for the precious metals, the distinctive ores of which are called " dry ores."   Zinc desilverization for base bullion, electrolytic refining for copper, and the substitution of cyanidation for amalgamation, have greatly facilitated treatment of silver and gold ores.
Silver-bearing minerals: argentite ("silver glance"), Ag_2S, 87.1% silver; hessite, Ag_2Fe, 62.8%; proustite ("light ruby ore"), Ag_3S_3As or $3 Ag_2S \cdot As_2S_3$, 65.5%; pyrargyrite ("dark ruby ore"), Ag_3S_3Sb, or $3 Ag_2S \cdot Sb_2S_3$, 59.8%; stephanite ("brittle silver ore"), Ag_5S_4Sb or $5 Ag_2S \cdot Sb_2S_3$, 68.5%; cerargyrite ("horn silver"), $AgCl$, 75.3%; native silver, Ag, 100%.
Galena almost always contains at least a trace of silver, which probably occurs as an isomorphous sulphide, but not appearing separately in polished plates.   Silver is a component of certain varieties of tetrahedrite, and in this form is often found in copper ores.

Galena is probably a base for other copper minerals.   Silver is sometimes found in zinc blende, but rarely in pyrite.   Modern silver production is chiefly in connection with base metals. Cerargyrite and native silver are habitually secondary minerals, resulting from alteration in the vadose zone of other minerals mentioned above, or from silver-bearing, base-metal minerals.   Argentite is sometimes secondary; it certainly is also primary.   The others are generally primary.

Gold-bearing minerals: calaverite, $AuTe_2$, 44.5% gold; sylvanite (" graphic tellurium "), $(AuAg) Te_3$, variable; native gold, alloyed with silver, etc, variable.   Gold most commonly occurs in quartz veins, both as native, and as scales and wires mechanically mixed in pyrite.   It may be set free by oxidation and removal of the pyrite.   It also accompanies mispickel, chalcopyrite, and rarely galena.   In some of these minerals, when the ores are refractory, it may exist as an involved telluride, or as a bismuth compound (Richard Pearce).   The tellurides of gold (a number of rare mixed tellurides of gold and other metals are not mentioned above) are primary minerals.   On oxidizing and losing tellurium, they yield extremely fine particles, not readily panned and resisting amalgamation; called " rusty " gold. Gold, presumably as chloride, sometimes descends in solution from oxidized portions of veins containing manganese minerals, and is reprecipitated at or near water level. Presence of calcite may interfere with the reaction. The high sp gr and resistance of gold to natural solvents greatly favor the formation of placer deposits.

German writers sometimes classified precious metal deposits into an older series, in geological age, and a later series. The great silver-gold veins associated with mountain upheaval and igneous outbreaks, at close of the Cretaceous and in the opening Tertiary periods, can thus be distinguished from older ones. Each group can then be subdivided on associated minerals, of which a series of subtypes can be established. Other writers have placed less emphasis on variations in time and mineralogy. Admitting some characteristic mineral associations, which might make possible finer subdivision, the following large types are permissible (see Classification, Art 17).

Predominant silver. A. Fissure veins, with distinctively silver minerals in quartz gangue, often amethystine and associated with manganese minerals and some calcite. Galena, zinc blende, pyrite and copper minerals, are very subordinate. Many great veins of Mexico, as at Pachuca, Real del Monte, and Guanajuato, exhibit these characters. The Butte silver veins are similar, but now, in instances, have developed copper in depth. In general, argentite is the chief source of silver (d).

B. Fissure veins yielding silver with little gold, in association with galena, zinc blende, copper minerals, and pyrite, in gangue of quartz, calcite, barite, fluorite, one or several (d). Veins of this mineralogy are world-wide in distribution.

C. Native silver and minor silver minerals, with arsenides of cobalt and nickel, in shrinkage cracks or fissures involving slight displacement (d and f). Cobalt, Ont., is best example, where veins are predominantly in Huronian conglomerate, associated with a diabase sill, which has some veins, and Keewatin green schists, which contain a few.

D. Impregnations of porous rocks, sandstones, tuffs, etc., with argentite, cerargyrite, and native silver; supply fissures obscure; some copper minerals may occur. (Silver Reef, Utah, Silver Cliff, Colo.)

E. Impregnations and replacements of crushed rocks along faults (silver-bearing galena in Cœur d'Alene, Idaho, Art 20, A).

F. Replacements of calcareous rocks with silver-bearing galena and associated sulphides. Leadville, Colo. (See Art 20, A, for other cases.)

Predominant gold. A. Fissure veins containing native gold, alone, or mechanically mixed in pyrite and much rarer base-metal sulphides, in quartz gangue. Gray, greasy-looking quartz seems to accompany best values. The common association of quartz with gold makes this type of world-wide distribution. Veins appear most frequently in schists, slates, or other metamorphic rocks, and in association with intrusive rocks, of which granite is commonest.

B. Impregnations and replacements of open-textured rocks with gold-bearing pyrite. The "banket" of gold-bearing conglomerates of Transvaal, the chief producers today, is the best example.

C. Saddle-reefs, or arch-like deposits of gold-bearing quartz at crests of anticlines (e) (Bendigo, Victoria, and gold reefs of Nova Scotia). Saddle-reefs may succeed one another in depth. Slates or slaty schists are common wall-rocks.

D. Veins carrying gold tellurides. At Cripple Creek, Colo, they are associated with an eroded Eocene volcano, often favoring neighborhood of minor dikes of phonolite and basaltic rocks, with which volcanic activity closed. Purple fluorite is a characteristic associate. In Boulder Co, Colo, veins are in gneisses; at Kalgoorlie, Western Australia, in amphibolites; in Hungary, altered andesitic rocks, called propylites. Once considered extremely rare, tellurides have been very productive in Cripple Creek and Kalgoorlie.

E. Lateral impregnations and replacements of calcareous shales, with tellurides along supply fissures, called verticals. Example, so-called " Potsdam " or " refractory ores," of the Black Hills, S Dak, the walls of which are of Cambrian age.

F. Contact zones, on the border of intrusive igneous rock and limestone, containing gold-bearing mispickel in lime silicates (Nickel Plate mine, B C). The usual contact zone of this type carries copper sulphides with a little gold (Art 19, B).

G. Placer deposits of gold-bearing gravels, which may be: residual, from weathering of rocks *in situ;* river gravels in active streams; river gravels in abandoned and often buried channels; alluvial fans; sea-beaches with active surf; sea-beaches now elevated and inland. Gold in streams favors places where current has been checked, as the inside of bends; junctions of tributaries; heads of quiet reaches. Gold favors gravel next the bedrock, or next a "false bedrock" of clay, but fine particles may be generally distributed in a thick vertical section. Magnetite, zircon, garnet, and various resistant, heavy minerals are characteristic associates, yielding "black sands" (42).

22. MINOR METALS

Aluminum is obtained today from bauxite, hydrous aluminum oxide, which is treated electrolytically in a bath of cryolite ($3 NaF \cdot AlF_3$). Bauxite is developed by weathering of aluminous rocks, and may appear as a residual product. It may also be produced by solvent action of sulphuric acid, from oxidizing pyrite, upon aluminous rocks, such as shales. The resulting acid solution of aluminum sulphate may be neutralized by limestone, with precipitation of aluminum hydrate, which may then form concretionary masses. In America bauxite is largely produced in Georgia, where the last named reaction is believed to explain its occurrence. In Arkansas, it is associated with syenitic eruptives, to the alteration of which its formation is attributed. Cryolite is commercially obtained only on west coast of Greenland, where it constitutes a large, flat vein in gneiss. Siderite, galena, zinc blende, and a few other minerals are sparingly mingled with it.

Antimony is obtained from its sulphide, stibnite (Sb_2S_3); sometimes from the oxide, senarmontite (Sb_2O_3); and as an alloy from antimonial lead ores. Characteristic occurrence of stibnite is in quartzose veins, but less regular deposits in sandstone are recorded. The industry is small.

Arsenic is produced largely as a by-product in smelting arsenical lead, copper, gold or cobalt ores, chiefly enargite (Cu_3AsS_4). It is sold as oxide, but much more could be saved were there a better market for it.

Barium is chiefly consumed as the sulphate ($BaSO_4$). Barite characteristically appears in veins in limestones; is also a frequent gangue with lead and copper ores, regardless of nature of vein walls. Chief output in U S comes from deposits in Georgia, Missouri, and California.

Bismuth is a rare by-product in lead-silver refining. A few districts, as Leadville, Colo, and Cobalt, Canada, produce bismuth ore.

Cadmium is a minor associate of zinc, and whenever separated is a small by-product in zinc metallurgy, or in treatment of zinc-bearing lead ores. Greenockite (CdS) is the chief mineral.

Cæsium is a rare alkaline element of much the same associations as rubidium.

Cerium, with didymium, erbium, lanthanum, thorium, and yttrium, constitutes a group called the cerium group of rare earths. Their compounds, especially those of thorium, have incandescent properties when heated, for which purpose they are sought. They are obtained as phosphates in monazite and xenotime, and are characteristic of pegmatites. They may appear in normal granite. Being resistant and heavy, monazite and xenotime have accumulated in placers in the drainage of pegmatite and granite areas of the Carolinas; also on sea coast of Bahia, Brazil.

Chromium ($FeO \cdot Cr_2O_3$), sometimes $(Fe \cdot Mg)O \cdot (Cr \cdot Al \cdot Fe)_2O_3$, is a characteristic associate of richly magnesian, basic igneous rocks, usually altered to serpentine. The chromite is believed to be a direct crystallization from molten magma. It forms irregular, sometimes large, distributed masses, and being extremely resistant may be freed and concentrated as a residual product in weathering. Commercial chromite should contain at least 40% Cr_2O_3. Rhodesia is a great producer of chromite ore.

Cobalt forms a variety of arsenides and sulphides, practically always in association with nickel. Linnæite (Co_3S_4), smaltite ($CoAs_2$), cobaltite ($CoAsS$), and the oxidized product erythrite or "cobalt bloom" ($Co_3As_2O_8 \cdot 8 H_2O$). Cobalt has long been derived from the ores of Cobalt, Ont; Belgian Congo, Rhodesia, and French Morocco are also important producers.

Didymium (see Cerium).

Erbium (see Cerium).

Iridium (see Platinum).

Lanthanum (see Cerium).

Lithium is obtained from amblygonite $Li(AlF)PO_4$, lepidolite, the lithia-mica $LiK[Al(OH, F)_2]Al(SiO_3)_3$, with lithia ($Li_2O$) 2 to 5%; and spodumene ($LiO \cdot Al_2O_3 \cdot 4 SiO_2$) with lithia 7.5%. Both are pegmatite minerals, occurring mainly in Black Hills, S Dak. The commercial importance of lithium has increased in recent years.

Magnesium is chiefly used as the earthy carbonate, magnesite, a refractory material. In Washington, magnesite lenses are found in metamorphosed dolomite. Magnesite also favors association with serpentines, in the alteration of which it is formed in veins in California. Russia, Austria and the U S have recently been the chief producers.

Manganese. The chief minerals are pyrolusite (MnO_2), psilomelane ($MnO_2 \cdot NH_2O$, plus K, Ba, etc), wad (an earthy Mn mineral), manganite ($Mn_3O_4 \cdot H_2O$), rhodochrosite ($MnCO_3$) and franklinite ($FeZnMn)O \cdot (Fe Mn)_2O_3$. Russia, Gold Coast, India, Brazil and Cuba supply most of the manganese used in the U S. In geological relations of its ores, manganese is similar to the brown hematites (Art 6). The ores are usually residual products of weathering, and are found as nodules in clay or as masses on surface. They should be relatively low in phosphorus, for use in spiegeleisen, and not too high in silica (43).

Mercury has one chief ore, cinnabar (HgS_2), with which a little native mercury may be associated. Cinnabar appears in veins with quartz, calcite, altered wall-rock and bitumen. It may also impregnate porous beds, such as sandstones. In practice mercury is called quicksilver or "quick." In the U S, cinnabar is mined in Calif, Nev, Ark, and Texas.

Molybdenum is obtained from molybdenite (MoS_2). Wulfenite ($PbMoO_4$) has attracted some attention. The molybdenite deposits at Climax, Colo, are among the largest known in the world. The ore occurs in a large circular stock of granite. The bottom of the mineralization has not been determined.

Nickel has 3 varieties of ores: (a) sulphides and arsenides (millerite, NiS, niccolite, NiAs) and related minerals, all of small moment today; (b) pentlandite, (Fe Ni)S, the nickel, iron and sulphur being each about one third. (Although nickel was formerly thought to replace iron in pyrrhotite, it is now considered to be in mechanically intermingled pentlandite); (c) a series of hydrated silicates of nickel and magnesium, somewhat analogous to serpentine in general composition and forming veins in serpentine, or produced in the alteration of very basic igneous rocks.

The nickel industry today is practically limited to 2 localities. At Sudbury, Ont, and vicinity, pentlandite with pyrrhotite and chalcopyrite are concentrated at bottom of a huge intrusive sheet, which varies from norite at the base, where the ores appear, to acid, micrographic granite at its upper surface. The sheet is folded into a huge basin, 40 miles across, and is buried in center beneath overlying sediments and volcanics. The ores favor embayments in the underlying older rocks, and one offsetting dike at the outer periphery. The underside of sheet dips inward at 60°, and is impregnated with nickel and copper ores up to widths of 100 or 150 ft. The gangue is self-fluxing. The ore bodies are generally classed under a, Art 17, but the 3 sulphides seem to have crystallized in serial order, and at times to have undergone some redeposition. The hydrated silicates of nickel are found, in workable richness, in the serpentinous district of New Caledonia. They constitute veins, and are the second but much smaller factor in the world's supply (44).

Osmium is a characteristic associate of platinum, in the placers of which its one source, iridosmine, is found, in scales or scaly nuggets and "colors."

Palladium is a characteristic associate of platinum in placers, and in the few cases where platinum has been discovered in copper ores. In latter case careful assays are necessary to avoid mistaking palladium for platinum.

Platinum appears in metallic grains and nuggets, more or less alloyed with iron, palladium, and rarer metals of the platinum group. It is characteristically associated with peridotites and pyroxenites, in which it is a direct crystallization from the original fused magma. Platinum is frequently intergrown with chromite. Aside from natural alloys, its one compound is sperrylite (PtAs$_2$), a minute associate of the Sudbury nickel-copper ores, and rarely elsewhere (45). Russia, Canada, Colombia and So Africa are the chief producers.

Potassium is treated as a saline (see Non-Metallic Minerals).

Radium is an extremely rare associate of the more abundant uranium, from the minerals of which it is separated (see Uranium).

Rhodium is a minor associate of platinum.

Rubidium is a rare alkaline element, associated in minute amounts with lithium in lepidolite and other lithium minerals.

Ruthenium is an extremely rare associate of platinum.

Sodium is treated as a saline (see Non-Metallic Minerals).

Strontium is obtained from the sulphate, celestite (SrSO$_4$), occurring like barite, but less abundant (see Barium).

Thorium (see Cerium). Thorianite is also found commercially in Ceylon and Australia.

Tin has one ore, cassiterite (SnO$_2$), and one rare sulphide, stannite. Cassiterite is almost always associated with granites and pegmatites, or veins closely akin to pegmatites. In weathering and erosion of these, being heavy and resistant, it is concentrated in placers as pebbles and finer particles, called stream tin. Cassiterite is obtained both by deep mining and placer working. It has been observed associated with rhyolites. Tin is also obtained in important quantities from Bolivian silver veins. Bolivia is now one of the largest producers of tin.

Titanium appears in the titaniferous magnetites, in which it has hitherto been a disadvantage to the iron. The nelsonite rocks of Virginia furnish titanium oxide in the form of rutile. Large amounts of ilmenite, (FeTi)O$_3$, are found in the sands of Travancore, India.

Tungsten, now an important metal in steel manufacture, is obtained from several tungstates, viz: wolframite, (FeMn)WO$_4$; huebnerite, MnWO$_4$; scheelite, CaWO$_4$. In the U S it is found chiefly in contact metamorphic deposits, where scheelite occurs associated with garnet and epidote, as at Mill City, Nev. The quartz veins at Atolia, Calif, have had an important history of scheelite production. The wolframite ores of China are extensively produced.

Uranium has gained great prominence as the associate of radium, but has also uses of its own. Pitchblende or uraninite, (UPb$_2$)$_3$U$_2$O$_2$, the earlier and still prized source, is a rare but characteristic mineral of pegmatites and related veins. A series of phosphates, torbernite, autunite, etc, have similar geological relations. Carnotite, a vanadate, K$_2$O·2 U$_2$O$_3$·V$_2$O$_5$·3 H$_2$O, with 15 to 18% vanadium oxide, is found impregnating sandstones in western Colorado and eastern Utah. The uranium-bearing veins of Katanga, Belgian Congo, are an important source of radium. The Great Bear Lake district of Canada is also important.

Vanadium is a minor component of titaniferous iron ores, and of the uranium-bearing carnotite, and, in a series of vanadium sulphides and their oxidized derivatives, appears in asphaltite veins in Perú. Vanadium is also found in the carnotite ores of western Colo and Utah.

Yttrium (see Cerium).

Zirconium has one mineral, zircon (ZrSiO$_4$), an associate of granites and other feldspathic rocks and pegmatites, from which on weathering it is freed and concentrated in placers.

NON-METALLIC MINERALS

Here is included a miscellaneous series with no fundamental relations; hence, arranged alphabetically. The carbon series is the most important (46).

23. ABRASIVES; ASBESTOS; ASPHALT

Abrasives. Corundum and emery (emery is a mixture of corundum, spinel, magnetite and other hard and heavy minerals) are found in two principal geological relations: CORUNDUM crystallizes from rare igneous magmas containing excess of Al_2O_3 above requirements of ordinary rockmaking minerals. Most of the world's supply of corundum comes from the Transvaal, where the mineral is found in syenite pegmatites. EMERY is commonly found at igneous contacts or where inclusions of aluminous sediments are involved and partly digested in igneous rocks. A vein or bed at Chester, Mass, containing emery in metamorphic rocks, is still different. GARNET, either in hornblende schist, as in the Adirondacks, or in mica schist, as at Reading, Conn, is a minor abrasive. Crushed, angular fragments of QUARTZ are used for sand-paper. DIATOMACEOUS EARTH and decomposed chert (TRIPOLI) are soft abrasives. WHETSTONES are made of gritty slates, which sometimes owe their "tooth" to minute garnets or other hard minerals; or of novaculite, a fine-grained siliceous rock in which the solution and removal of minute rhombs of calcite have left sharp-edged cavities. Coarse varieties are sandstones, or sandy schists, in which are set rutile, garnet, etc. GRINDSTONES are made of sandstones sufficiently friable not to wear smooth (50).

Asbestos of commerce, a variety of serpentine, called chrysotile, appears as veins with cross-fibers in some serpentine districts (most important is in southern Quebec). Poorer grades appear along slips in the serpentine and in the mass of the rock. Some believe the Canadian asbestos to be a deep-seated alteration product of basic igneous rocks; others, that it is developed from serpentine in fissures near intrusive dikes of aplite, a variety of granite (51).

Asphalt (see Carbon Minerals).

24. BUILDING STONE, CLAY, LIMES, CEMENTS

The granite industry is mainly developed along Atlantic seaboard; secondarily, in Wisconsin, Missouri, and California. Among igneous rocks, granite breaks best in the quarry. When of good grade, it is homogeneous in texture, though sometimes suffering from black inclusions, local coarse crystallizations, and development of gneissoid structure. SANDSTONES are widely quarried. The "brownstone" of eastern U S is a Triassic sandstone, from Longmeadow, Mass; Portland, Conn; Avon, N J; Hummelstown, near Harrisburg, Penn. "Bluestone," of Hudson River region, is a Devonian argillaceous sandstone, specially adapted to flagstones, curbing, sills, and lintels. Potsdam red sandstone or quartzite is Cambrian; quarried on western side of Adirondacks. A softer stone of nearly the same geological horizon is produced on south shore of Lake Superior. Medina pink sandstone of the Silurian is extensively obtained along the Erie Canal, between Rochester and Lockport, N Y. Cleveland or Ohio sandstone is a gray or pale-blue stone, of Mississippian (Lower Carboniferous) age, developed in outskirts of Cleveland. LIMESTONES. Preëminent is the Indiana or Bedford oölitic stone, of Mississippian (Lower Carboniferous) age, which outcrops in an extended N and S belt in S W Indiana. MARBLES, of Cambrian and Ordovician age, are extensively developed along the border of Western Vermont, Eastern Tennessee, and Georgia; of other age, in Colo. SLATES appear in S W Vermont and neighboring parts of N Y, and in the Lehigh Valley, Penn. They are in less degree produced in Virginia, the Lake Superior region, and Newfoundland. Wales is a famous source of slate and of skilled workers in slate. SERPENTINE is quarried in southeastern Pennsylvania and the neighboring parts of Maryland (52).

Clays belong to three general groups: (1) kaolin group, in which the chief mineral is kaolinite, $Al_2O_2 \cdot 2\ SiO_2 \cdot 2\ H_2O$; (2) montmorillonite group, in which the chief mineral in montmorillonite, $CaO \cdot MgO$, $Al_2O_3 \cdot 3\ SiO_2 \cdot nH_2O$; (3) alkali-bearing clay mineral group. Kaolin is chiefly of two kinds, residual, or transported, which are the finest sediments of still water. Residual clays are commonest south of the terminal moraine of Glacial epoch. They are impure and variable. Transported clays were extensively deposited by the floods which followed the melting of the continental glacier. They are very abundant in the valleys of the Connecticut and Hudson rivers, and are the basis of a great brick industry. Fireclay for refractory materials should be as free as possible from other ingredients than SiO_2, Al_2O_3, and H_2O. It is often found beneath coal seams. In these relations fireclays are mined in Pennsylvania, Maryland, Ohio, and at Cheltenham, Mo. Other fireclays of Cretaceous age are developed at Woodbridge and its neighborhood, N J, and near Golden, Colo (53). Clays of the montmorillonite group are extensively derived by the alteration of volcanic ash and find an important application in the purification of petroleum products.

Shales often possess properties which fit them for vitrified brick. They are then ground, moulded, and hard-burned. They are useful for pavements, especially where no good rock is available for macadam.

Limes and cements. For quicklime, calcium carbonate should be pure, free from coloring ingredients, such as iron compounds, and is preferred with little mgnesium carbonate. Silica and alumina together develop hydraulic properties, and injure "fat" limes. Kilns are widespread and, for local use, any reasonably pure limestone answers. Rockland, Me, is the principal American producing district. As limestones contain increasing amounts of alumina and silica, they develop hydraulic properties when burned, and in varieties of special excellence afford natural rock cement. The crude stone is called a "water-lime." Although important in former years, the natural cements have given way to "Portland" cement, which is an artificial mixture of limestone and clay or shale, entirely under control of the chemist, and being therefore more uniform in properties. In Portland cement magnesia is kept very low, not over 2 or 3%. The Lehigh Valley, Penn, is chief center of manufacture in U S, but plants are widely distributed (54).

25. THE CARBON MINERALS

These embrace Coals and their relatives, and the Petroleum series, including Natural Gas, Maltha, Asphalt, and Asphaltites.

Coals and their relatives are vegetable remains so preserved in sedimentary strata as to become progressively enriched in carbon. They begin as some form of woody tissue, perhaps also in part spores, algæ, and resins; under conditions of retarded oxidation they pass toward a theoretical limit of nearly pure carbon, and finally to mineral ash. Cellulose, the principal original contributor, is $C_6H_{10}O_5$ (approx, C 50%, H 6%, and O 44%), but there was always also a little N, S, and mineral matter in original deposit. If vegetable tissue accumulates under a protecting layer of water, oxidation is retarded and relative enrichment in carbon ensues. On subsidence of the land, or, in case of lakes and swamps, as result of heavy floods, sediments bury the accumulated vegetable tissue. The complete process comprises several stages. PEAT is still brown; a visible aggregate of stems, leaves, etc; high in O and H and relatively low in C. LIGNITE is firmer, often black, but has a brown streak, and usually still shows evidence of vegetable tissue; has less O and H than peat and relatively more C. Sub-bituminous coals or black lignites are a stage beyond typical lignite, but are not typically bituminous. BITUMINOUS COALS (Sec 35) are black, solider, lower in O, higher in C, and at times possess coking properties. SEMI-BITUMINOUS and SEMI-ANTHRACITE mark passages to ANTHRACITE (Sec 34) in which the C is greatly enriched and the coal hard and firm. Still further stages toward graphite are known.

Table 5. Characteristic Chemical Composition of Coal Series

Cellulose	Peat	Lignite	Bituminous	Anthracite
C 50	59	69.0	82.0	95.0
H 6	6	5.5	4.5	2.5
O 43	33	25.0	13.0	2.5
N 1	2	0.5	0.5	trace

Sulphur is also present in varying percentages, up to several units, and mineral ash never fails.

Coals are analyzed commercially in 2 ways, proximate and elementary. In PROXIMATE ANALYSIS, moisture, volatile matter, fixed carbon, ash and sulphur are usually determined. Sample is dried, weighed, ignited until flames cease or for a standard time over a standard Bunsen burner, weighed, ignited again to consume the carbon; after which residue is weighed for ash. Sulphur is determined in a separate sample. This analysis shows if the coal is high or low in water; is high or low in volatiles; has a long or short flame; cokes or not; is high or low in ash; is sulphurous or not. These are the most important points regarding a fuel. Dividing the percentage of fixed carbon by the percentage of volatiles gives the "fuel ratio," characteristic for each particular coal. Anthracites give high, and richly bituminous coals low ratios. Ratios vary from less than 1, to about 30. ELEMENTARY ANALYSIS of a dried sample gives the C, H, O, N, S, and ash. It affords a better idea of the heat units in the coal, a matter of growing importance each year, but does not indicate coking properties nor qualities. It is known that the O in coals is already combined with C or H, and is as inert as ash, besides reducing the available C and H. Since H has a high calorific value, the necessary proportion to yield H_3O with the O present is often called combined hydrogen; the excess, disposable hydrogen. Relatively high values of the latter are esteemed.

Table 6. Characteristic Proximate Analyses

	Moisture	Volatiles	Fixed carbon	Ash	Sulphur
Peat..............................	20.22	52.31	24.52	2.95	....
Lignite...........................	17.75	37.85	37.40	6.20	0.80
Sub-bituminous....................	13.43	37.15	45.57	3.85	....
Bituminous........................	1.26	30.11	59.62	8.23	0.78
Semi-bituminous...................	1.23	15.47	73.51	9.09	0.70
Semi-anthracite...................	1.29	8.10	83.35	6.23	1.03
Anthracite........................	4.12	3.08	86.38	5.92	0.50

Table 7.　Characteristic Elementary Analyses

	Moisture	C	H	O	N	S	Ash
Peat (air dried)	13.60	40.78	5.55	30.95	1.40	0.58	20.74
Lignite	22.63	54.91	6.39	32.59	1.02	0.59	4.50
Sub-bituminous	11.05	59.08	5.37	21.52	1.33	1.73	10.97
Bituminous	3.36	68.69	4.84	11.49	1.54	1.01	12.43
Semi-bituminous	1.53	82.87	4.76	4.99	1.68	0.65	5.05
Anthracite	1.97	91.40	2.81	1.83	0.21	0.71	3.04

Heat units are expressed as British thermal units (B t u), or as French (calories). High ash or high-oxygen coals give low thermal values. The usual range is as follows, the peat being exceptionally good (Sussex Co, N J):

Peat	Lignite		Bituminous coal		Anthracite	
High	Low	High	Low	High	Low	High
8 260	7 204	10 143	10 242	13 790	12 047	14 686

Moisture in coal is a serious drawback, and varies so much in unprotected samples, especially of lignites and sub-bituminous coals, that the sample, as soon as cut in the mine, should be put into an air-tight glass jar, and analyzed as soon as possible after top is unscrewed.

Classification. Many attempts have been made to classify coals, but for eastern coals the scheme suggested by H. D. Rogers, State Geologist of Penn, about 1855, is still widely current:

Bituminous	Volatiles, greater than 18
Semi-bituminous	" 18 to 12
Semi-anthracite	" 12 to 8
Anthracite	" less than 8

More recent schemes are those of: M. R. Campbell, based on $C \div H$ ratio, as shown by elementary analysis; F. G. Grout, who employs ratios based on sum of volatiles and fixed carbon of a proximate analysis, and the elementary carbon of ultimate analysis; and D. B. Dowling, who employs what he calls the split-volatile ratio. All these give greater attention to western lignites and sub-bituminous coals, which in earlier years were practically unknown. Elaborate classifications are unimportant commercially. The B t u's and the physical and coking properties are the essentials.

Geological associates of coal seams are almost always shales and sandstones. They often have a fireclay floor; are seldom associated with limestones. A seam may be broken up into benches by a " parting " of shale, called " slate " by miners. A parting may increase in thickness and separate a seam into 2 distinct seams. Seams may be cut out by old drainage channels, either contemporaneous with the old swamp, or later and long after coal was formed. Pot-holes and channels in Carboniferous coals were developed even in the Glacial epoch and filled with gravel. Coal seams may be pinched by the upward bulge of a relatively plastic clay floor, and may have cracks filled with clay gouge.

Coal seams are subject to faults and folds; are very often in synclines (" basins "), left disconnected by erosion of intervening anticlines. Folds may be violent, as in middle anthracite fields of Penn, and in Belgian and French areas. Coal seams are of all thicknesses from a fraction of an inch to many feet. The thickest single seam, reasonably free from thick partings, recorded in America, is at Adaville, Western Wyoming, with 86 ft of clean coal (except for one parting of 1 in of sandstone). A thickness of 1 ft is ordinarily considered the minimum of workability.

With increase of ash (20% ash is the usual commercial maximum) coals pass into " bony " coals, then into " bone " and into bituminous shale or slate. Foreign matter may be minutely interstratified with thin layers of relatively pure coal; or be invisibly mingled. If the layers are sufficiently coarse, crushing and washing may greatly reduce the ash (Sec 34 and 35). In a cross-section of a good seam can be recognized: bright lustrous " glance " coal and dull, lusterless " splint " coal. The proportions vary; one variety may be in great excess. There is a third variety, porous, tender, and often showing plant structure, called " mother of coal " or " mineral charcoal." It affords an unfortunate place of precipitation for gypsum, pyrite, and other undesirables. The sulphur in coal is partly in pyrite, when half passes off in burning; partly in gypsum, when all passes into the ash; and partly in sulphurous hydrocarbons. In coking or other combustion, roughly one-half the sulphur passes off.

In geological age coal ranges practically from Carboniferous period through Tertiary. Anthracite is even reported in remote pre-Cambrian strata of Finland, but no seams of importance are yet known older than Carboniferous. The oldest seam in America is in the Pocono sandstone series, of the Mississippian (Lower Carboniferous) strata of S W Virginia (Altona and elsewhere). The really important coals begin with the Pennsylvanian. In eastern half of North America, they range up into the Permian and even Triassic (in Va and N C). In the western U S, coals range from early Cretaceous to Pliocene. The Laramie of Cretaceous and Eocene Tertiary are most productive. The later coals are often lignitic, especially if in relatively undisturbed strata (55).

Petroleum series. Coals are residual accumulations; petroleums are evolved, and move from their sources elsewhere for storage. The petroleum series embraces gases, liquids, and solids. The chemistry is very complex, but most of the members belong to the marsh-gas or paraffine series of compounds, C_nH_{2n+2}. Up to C_4H_{10} they are gases at ordinary temperatures; from $C_{20}H_{42}$ up they are solids. The gases are called natural gas; the liquids, petroleum; the thick, black, tarry liquids, maltha; the solids at ordinary temperatures, of tough leathery character, asphalt; the brittle, coal-like substances, asphaltite; the natural paraffines, ozocerite. Shales impregnated with bituminous matter are called oil shales. They may be rich in paraffines. (See Sec 44.)

Natural gases are chiefly CH_4, but have some higher members, with a little of the olefine series C_nH_{2n}, more or less of H_2S, N, O, CO_2, and others rarer.

Petroleums include the liquids at ordinary temperatures. Some are of low sp gr, some high. These characters are expressed in degrees Beaumé, a scale in which 10° Beaumé is sp gr 1. Others are calculated by the formula: $(140 \div sp\ gr) - 130$. Light petroleums range from 35° B up; the heavy drop below 20° B. Lighter oils give higher percentages of illuminants and are the most valuable. Heavy oils have an asphalt base. Some oils contain sulphur compounds. Malthas are much rarer than petroleums, and have different uses; asphalts are employed for paving; asphaltites for varnishes, etc.

Origin of petroleums. There are two radically different views: the inorganic (now discarded) and the organic. There is some support for the theory attributing hydrocarbons to igneous sources, but most geologists favor the organic explanations. These assume original plant or animal matter in the sediments, by decomposition in the rock (T. S. Hunt); or distillation from internal heat (J. S. Newberry); or, the modern view, by bacterial decomposition while freshly deposited, the hydrocarbons being later squeezed out of the shales and mud-rocks, by pressure of overlying accumulations, into porous beds for storage. The latter genesis certainly applies to CH_4, but has not been proved for oils.

Storage in the rocks is better understood. The most extensive pools are found under low anticlinal folds, in which an impervious shale rests upon a porous sandstone or limestone, so as to imprison the gas and oil; which, from some source of the hydrocarbons rise through the heavier ground-waters and are finally caught beneath the crest. Theoretically, and sometimes actually, there is an uppermost layer of gas, a layer beneath of oil, and a bottom layer of water or connate brine. Usually either gas or oil rests on brine. Other deposits favor lenticular or pod-like bodies of sandstone in shales, apparently old sand-bars, or similar accumulations. Prospecting is usually guided in recent years by the anticlinal view. The axes of anticlines rise and fall, and pools are thus non-continuous along their trend. A very gentle anticline or even a slight monocline may suffice. Pools sometimes seem to lie to one side of the observed anticlinal crest (Sec 44).

Geologically, the oldest gases and oils are tapped from Ordovician (or Lower Silurian) strata, of which the Trenton limestone is very productive in Ohio and Indiana. Higher in the Paleozoic, the Silurian (or Upper Silurian), Devonian and Carboniferous strata are all productive in the Eastern States. A sandstone at base of the Coal Measures (Carboniferous) is very productive in Illinois, Kansas, and Oklahoma. Cretaceous sandstones carry oil in Wyoming; and Cretaceous limestones are the apparent source of Mexican petroleum, even though tapped from overlying Tertiary beds. Various Tertiary horizons yield oils in different parts of the world, but the Miocene is especially rich. In America are the following fields: Appalachian; Lima-Indiana (western Ohio and Indiana); Illinois; Mid-Continental, in Kansas, Oklahoma and northern Texas; Gulf, in Louisiana and Texas; Mexican, in the coastal plain or tierra caliente, west of Tampico and farther south; and California. There are many smaller areas in Colorado, Wyoming, Alberta, and Alaska. Trinidad is productive, also Venezuela. Abroad, Rumania, Baku on the Caspian Sea, Dutch East Indies, and Japan are the chief producers, but some oil has also been found in Germany (56).

Maltha is a rather unusual product, but appears at times where oils with an asphaltic base rise to surface and lose their more volatile constituents. Maltha may impregnate porous sandstone.

Asphalt, a further stage in the process, may accumulate in pools, or impregnate porous sandstones or limestones. Sometimes oils have risen in fissures and have changed with loss of volatiles to brittle substances, suggesting coal. Illustrations: albertite, of N B; grahamite, of West Va; uintaite and wurtzilite, of Utah. Oils with a paraffine base have left behind the natural paraffine, ozocerite, in fissures in sandstone (57).

Graphite is the final metamorphic stage of all carbon minerals. It appears sometimes in pegmatite veins, but more often impregnates sandstones, schists, and crystalline limestones, from which it may be separated by concentrating the light components (58).

26. MISCELLANEOUS NON-METALLIC MINERALS

Gems are objects of mining, but the geological relations are very diverse. Diamonds seem to be original crystallizations in very basic igneous rocks, in South Africa and in western Arkansas. They are elsewhere obtained from placer deposits. Sapphires may be in contact zones, or components of an igneous dike, as at Yogo, Mont. Beryls are pegmatite minerals, but the variety emerald may be in contact zones. Turquoise appears in small veinlets in various rocks, where copper salts have circulated. No brief summary can include more than a few of the widely contrasted associations (59).

Graphite (see Carbon Minerals).

Gums (see Carbon Minerals).

Gypsum (see Salines).

Mica, in commercial quantities, occurs as a constituent of coarsely crystallized pegmatites; both muscovite (white) and phlogopite (amber) are utilized, the former produced mainly in India and N Carolina the latter in Ontario and Quebec provinces, Canada. Market requirements are: (a) minimum size of rectangular trimmed sheet, 2 sq in (larger sizes bring higher prices). Demand for pulverized mica is amply supplied by trimmings from sheet-mica mines. (b) Softness; the softer the mica the better adapted it is for electric commutator insulation. (c) Freedom from inclusions, which are generally iron minerals and diminish insulating properties. (d) Flexibility. Value of a given mica can be ascertained only by submitting samples to a dealer. Electrical manufacturers are the largest consumers.

Limes (see Building Stone).

Natural Gas (see Carbon minerals).

Ozocerite (see Carbon Minerals).

Paints (mineral paints, pigments), or the bases for them, are sometimes the objects of mining. Practically all are minerals of iron. Limonite, deposits containing iron carbonate, and red hematite, are all utilized. The crude product is usually calcined to insure uniformity of color or shade. Fine clays stained with limonite yield ochers. Barite and even refuse slate are ground for "fillers."

Petroleum (see Carbon Minerals).

Phosphates are dug or quarried for fertilizers. They are of 2 kinds: (a) Crystalline apatite, which generally appears on borders of igneous intrusive rocks and is especially associated with pre-Cambrian limestones, along the Ottawa River in Ontario and Quebec. Apatite in different geological relations is obtained as tailings in magnetic concentration of richly phosphatic magnetites, at Mineville, N Y. (b) Earthy phosphates, such as fossil bones, coprolites, and replacements of $CaCO_3$ in limestones by phosphate of lime.

Along the seacoast of South Carolina, Tertiary beds have long been dug for fossil phosphates and replaced limestone nodules. More recent discoveries of Florida rock phosphates, and of pebble phosphates in deltas in the drainage of rock-phosphate areas, have afforded very low-cost product. In the Peace River, Fla, is done much dredging and concentration similar to that in placer gold deposits. Beds of rock phosphate in sedimentary series have been still more recently discovered and utilized in Tennessee. Other beds have been discovered by prospectors in N E Utah, but have been withdrawn from location by the Federal Government. These phosphates form interstratified beds, probably produced by reaction upon limestone of phosphoric acid from organic remains. Guano, formed by the droppings of wild-fowl in regions of slight rainfall, is now practically exhausted (60).

Resins (fossil) (see Carbon Minerals).

Salines. When circulating ground-waters have traversed rocks containing alkali salts, and have afterwards been impounded and evaporated to dryness, or when bodies of sea water are isolated and evaporated, the dissolved salts are precipitated in the inverse order of solubility. From sea water, gypsum precipitates first, then common salt, and then rarely the less abundant potassium salts. In general, potassium-bearing final mother-liquors seem to have escaped, or else their very soluble precipitates were removed in next inrush of salt water.

From isolated bodies of the ocean, cut off perhaps by a barrier cast up during a storm, relatively thin beds of salt and their associates have been derived. Thick beds of hundreds of feet in section are difficult to explain in this way. A substitute explanation is the "Bar Theory" of Ochsenius. A deep estuary is assumed to be isolated by a broad bar from the open sea. Evaporation on the bar leads to the passage down inner side of bar, of heavy concentrated brine, until salt is deposited in the estuary's depths. Thick beds may also be precipitated in salt lakes, in deep depressions without outlet, yet so situated as to be fed by salt-bearing streams. Great Salt Lake is an illustration. Salt deposits at Petite Anse, Louisiana, and elsewhere along Gulf of Mexico, appear in columnar or chimney-like form, crossing sedimentary strata as great cylindrical masses, above which are domes or mounds, and around which the beds turn up. These are best explained by uprising salt springs and the expansive force of growing crystals, which may have thrust the strata aside and upward. Important beds of potassium salts occur in the Stassfurt region, western Germany, and large deposits have been found in the Permian rocks of New Mexico and Texas. Beds of Na_2SO_4 are not infrequent in arid regions, and less often waters or even beds charged with Na_2CO_3 and sodium and calcium borates, likewise occur in a few districts (as southern California and western Nevada), where local drainage contains these rare salts. The soils of the northern Chilean desert have become charged with sodium nitrate; also in a few other arid localities (61)

Borax is obtained, by chemical treatment, mainly from 2 minerals: boracite, occurring in fumaroles in northern Italy, and in dry-lake deposits in many desert regions of the world; and colemanite (borate of lime) occurring as beaded saline deposits in southern California. More recently, Kernite ($Na_2B_4O_7 \cdot 4H_2O$), has been found in great quantities in tabular deposits in the Mojave desert region of Calif.

Sulphur. In native state, sulphur is found in 2 types of deposit: (a) In or near volcanic craters, expiring or largely dormant. Emitted as vapor, sulphur condenses on walls of cavities and impregnates porous tuffs and breccias. It is possible, but not highly probable, that SO_2 and H_2S when mingled hot react to deposit sulphur. (b) In association with gypsum in sedimentary strata, as in Sicily, Louisiana, and Texas. The sulphur was formerly believed to result from reduction of gypsum ($CaSO_4 \cdot 2 H_2O$), by organic matter in circulating ground-waters. There is at present a disposition to refer it to minute organisms now known to secrete elementary sulphur, and to favor its precipitation amid deposits of decaying organic matter, at bottom of certain bodies of water. Gypsum is a universal associate (62). The sulphur deposits in Louisiana and Texas occur with limestone, in the capping above salt domes.

BIBLIOGRAPHY

Rocks and their Minerals All good treatises on geology have chapters on rocks
1. Harker, A. Petrology for Students. Longmans, Green & Co, London and N Y. Revised ed. (Based on microscopic study)
2. Kemp, J. F. Handbook of Rocks. 5th ed. D. Van Nostrand Co, N Y
3. Pirsson, L. V. Rocks and Rock Minerals. John Wiley & Sons, Inc, N Y. Iddings, J. P. Igneous Rocks. 2 vol. John Wiley & Sons, Inc, N Y, 1913
4. Alling, H. L. Interpretative Petrology of the Igneous Rocks. McGraw-Hill, 1936
5. Grout, F. F. Petrography and Petrology. McGraw-Hill, 1932

Faults Current textbooks on ore deposits, mining and geology, usually have a chapter on faults
6. Church, J. A. Cause of Faulting. *Trans A I M E*, Vol 21, p 782
7. Dannenberg, Robert. Ueber Verwerfungen. Freiberg, 1884
8. Emmons, S. F. Faulting in Veins. *E & M Jour*, Vol 53, p 548
9. Freeland, F. T. Fault rules. *Trans A I M E*, Vol 21, p 491. A clear exposition
10. Koehler, G. Die Störungen der Gänge, Flötze und Lager. Leipzig, 1886. Trans by W. B. Phillips, as: Irregularities of Lodes, Veins and Beds. *E & M Jour*, June 25, 1887, p 454; July 2, 1887, p 4
11. Ransome, F. L. Directions of Movement and the Nomenclature of Faults. *Econ Geol*, Vol 1, p 777; discussion in Vol 2
12. Read, H. F., W. M. Davis, A. C. Lawson and F. L. Ransome, Committee on Proposed Nomenclature of Faults. *Bull* Geol Soc Amer, Vol 24, pp 163–181
13. Schmidt, J. C. L. Theorie der Verschiebung älterer Gänge. Frankfurt, 1810
14. Tolman, C. F., Jr. Graphical Solution of Fault Problems. *Min & Sci Pr*, 1911. A pamphlet
15. Zimmermann, C. Die Wiederausrichtung verworfener Gänge, Lager und Flötze.
16. Stoces and White. Structural Geology. Von Nostrand, 1935

Stratigraphic Geology
17. Chamberlin and Salisbury. Geology. 3 vol. Henry Holt & Co, N Y, 1906
18. Chamberlin and Salisbury. College Geology. 1 vol, 1909
19. Dana, J. D. Manual of Geology, American Book Co, N Y, 1895
20. Geikie, A. Textbook of Geology. 2 vol. Macmillan, London and N Y, 1913
21. Le Conte, J. Elements of Geology, revised by H. L. Fairchild. D. Appleton Co, N Y
22. Scott, W. B. Introduction to Geology. Macmillan, N Y
23. Moore, R. C. Historical Geology. Wiley, 1932
24. Schuchert and Dunbar. Historical Geology. McGraw-Hill, 1932

Mineral Deposits: Ores
25. Kemp, J. F. What is an Ore? *Min & Sci Pr*, Mar 20, 1909, pp 419–423
26. Lindgren, Waldemar. Mineral Deposits. McGraw-Hill, 1933
27. Lilley, E. Economic Geology of Mineral Deposits. Holt & Co, 1936
28. Ore Deposits of the Western United States. *Trans A I M E*, 1933
29. Kemp, J. F. The Ground Waters. *Trans A I M E*, Vol 45, p 3. Van Hise, C R. Some Principles Governing the Deposition of Ores. *Idem*, Vol 30, p 27
30. Kemp, J. F. Role of the Igneous Rocks in Formation of Veins. *Trans A I M E*, Vol 31, p 163; Vol 33, p 699
31. Lindgren, W. Relation of Ore Deposition to Physical Conditions. Internat Geol Cong, Vol X, Mexico, 1906; *Econ Geol*, Vol 2, p 195 (1907)
32. Spurr, J. E. A Theory of Ore Deposition. *Econ Geol*, Vol 2, p 781; Vol 7, p 485; The Ore Magmas. 2 vols, N Y (1923)
33. Billingsley, P. and Grimes, J. W. Ore Deposits of the Boulder Batholith of Montana. *Trans A I M E*, Vol 51, p 31
34. Textbook of Mining Geology. James Park. 4th ed
35. Outlines of Occurrence and Geology of Petroleum. I. A. Stigand
36. Tolman, C. F. Ground Water. McGraw-Hill, 1937

37. Beck, R. Lehre von den Erzlagerstätten. Berlin, 1909, 3rd ed. Trans of 2nd ed, " The Nature of Ore Deposits," by W. H. Weed, 1905. Beyschlag, Krusch und Vogt. Die Lagerstätten der nutzbaren Mineralien und Gesteine. 2 vol, 1909. Trans by S. J. Truscott, Macmillan, 1914, 3 vol. von Cotta, B. Die Lehre von den Erzlagerstätten. Freiberg, 1859–61. Trans by F. Prime, Jr, as Cotta's Treatise on Ore Deposits, N Y, 1870. De Launay, L. Traite de Métallogenie, Paris, 1912, 3 vol. Fuchs et De Launay. Traite des Gites Minéraux et Métalliferes, Paris, 1893, 2 vol. von Groddeck A. Die Lehre von Lagerstätten der Erze. Leipzig, 1879. Kemp, J. F. Ore Deposits of United States and Canada. N Y, 1901. Krusch, P. Die Untersuchung und Bewertung von Erzlagerstätten. Berlin, 1911. Lindgren, W. Mineral Deposits, N Y, 1913. Ries. Economic Geology of United States. N Y, 1911. Stelzner, B. Die Erzlagerstätten. Leipzig, 1906, 3 vol. Thomas and MacAlister. The Geology of Ore Deposits. London, 1909. Whitney, J. D. Metallic Wealth of United States, 1854. For occurrence, technology, and statistics of ores and minerals, see Mineral Industry (ann), McGraw-Hill, N Y; also Mineral Resources (ann) U S Geol Surv, Washington
38. Geology of Lake Superior Region. Monograph 52, U S Geol Surv, 1912
39. Iron Ore Resources of the World. Tenth Internat Geol Cong, Stockholm, 1910. 2 vol and atlas (Greatest single work on iron ores)
40. Weed, W. H. Copper Mines of the World. McGraw-Hill Book Co. N Y, 1907
41. Copper Resources of the World. XVI Internat Geol Congress, 1935
42. Day, D. T. and Richards, R. H. Investigations of Black Sands from Placer Mines. Bull 285, U S Geol Surv, pp 150–164, 1906. Emmons, W. H. Agency of Manganese in Superficial Alteration and Secondary Enrichment of Gold Deposits in the U S. Trans A I M E, Vol 42, p 3
43. Penrose, R. A. F., Jr. Manganese, its Uses, Ores, and Deposits. Arkansas Geol Surv, 1890, 1892
44. Argall, P. Nickel, Occurrence, Geology, Distribution and Genesis of its Ore Deposits. Proc Colo Sci Soc, Vol 4, p 395
45. Kemp, J. F. Geological Relations and Distribution of Platinum and Associated Metals. Bull 193, U S Geol Surv

Mineral Deposits: Non-metallic Minerals

46. Merrill, G. P. The Non-Metallic Minerals. John Wiley & Sons, Inc. Ries, H. Economic Geology of the United States, Macmillan & Co. Stutzer, O. Die Nichterze. Berlin, 1911–14
47. Ries, H. Economic Geology. 7th ed. Wiley, 1937
48. Industrial Minerals & Rocks. Trans A I M E, 1937
49. Ladoo, R. B. Non-metallic minerals, Occurrence, Preparation, Utilization. McGraw-Hill, 1925
50. Griswold, L. R. On Whetstones, etc. Ann Rep Ark Geol Surv, 1890, Vol III. King, F. P. Corundum in Georgia. Ga Geol Surv, Bull 2, 1894. Pratt, J. H. and Lewis, J. V. Corundum and the Peridotites of Western N C. Geol Surv of N C, 1905
51. Cirkel, F. Asbestos. Dept of Mines, Canada. Bull No 69, 1910
52. Merrill, G. P. Stones for Building and Decoration. John Wiley & Sons, Inc, N Y. Merrill, G. P. and Hawes, G. S. Rept on Building Stones. Tenth Census U S, Vol 10. Local Reports of State Geol Survs
53. Ries, H. Clays, their Occurrence, Properties and Uses. John Wiley & Sons, Inc, 1906. Ries, H. and Leighton, H. History of the Clay-Working Industry in the U S. John Wiley & Sons, Inc, 1909. See State Geol Survs, notably of New Jersey; 1880, by J. C. Smock, and 1904, by H. Ries
54. Eckel, E. C. Cements, Limes and Plasters. John Wiley & Sons, Inc, 1905. Literature on cement is extensive
55. Coal Resources of the World. Eleventh Internat Geol Cong, Toronto, Can, 1913, 3 vol and atlas (important work). Campbell, M. R. and others. Methods of Testing, Sampling and Classifying Coals. Prof Paper 48, U S Geol Surv, 1906. Dowling, D. B. Classification of Coals on Split-volatile Ratio. Jour Can Min Inst, Vol 11, p 220. Grout, F. F. On Classification of Coals. Econ Geol Vol 2, p 225. Porter, J. B. Investigation of the Coals of Canada. Ottawa, Govt Printing Office, 1912. Stevenson, J. J. Proc Amer Phil Soc, Vol 50, pp 1 and 519; Vol 51, p 423; Vol 52, p 376 (Best review of geology of coal extant)
56. Engler, C. and Hoefer, H. Das Erdöl, seine Physik, Chemie, Geologie. Leipzig, 1909. Hoefer, H. Das Erdöl und seine Verwandten. Braunschweig, 3rd ed, 1912. Orton, E. Geol Surv of Ohio, Econ Geol, Vol 6; Geol Surv Ky, 1892; Bull 30, N Y State Museum, 1899; Bull Geol Soc Amer, Vol 9, p 85, 1898. Thompson, A. B. Petroleum Mining. D. Van Nostrand, 1910. Peckham, S. F. Tenth Census, U S, Vol 10, Rept on Petroleum
57. Eldredge, G. H. Asphalt and Bituminous Rock Deposits of the U S. 22nd Ann Rept, U S Geol Surv, Part I, p 209
58. Cirkel, F. Graphite, its Properties, Occurrence Refining and Uses. Can Dept Mines, Bull No 18, 1907. Stutzer, O. Nichterze. Part I, p 1, 1911
59. Kunz, G. F. Gems and Precious Stones of North America. McGraw-Hill Book Co
60. Eldredge, G. H. Sketch of Phosphates of Florida. Trans A I M E, Vol 21, p 196. Hayes, C. W. Tennessee Phosphates. 17th Ann Rept; U S Geol Surv, Part II, 1896. Trans A I M E, Vol 25, p 19. Stutzer, O. On Phosphates. Nichterze, Part I, p 265, 1911
61. Clarke, F. W. Data of Geochemistry. Bull 770, U S Geol Surv, 1924. Hahn, F. F. The Form of Salt Deposits. Econ Geol, Vol 7, p 120, 1912
62. Stutzer, O. On sulphur. Nichterze, Part I, p 185, 1911

SECTION 3

EARTH EXCAVATION

FIRST EDITION BY
HALBERT P. GILLETTE, C.E.

SECOND EDITION BY
RICHARD T. DANA, C.E.

THIRD EDITION LARGELY REWRITTEN BY
CLINTON L. BOGERT, CONSULTING ENGINEER

Note.—Numbers in parentheses in text refer to Bibliography at end of this section.

This section deals only with open-cut excavation, embankment and dredging. For earthwork in tunnels, shafts or caissons, see Sec 6, 7, 8. Mechanical details, methods of work and equipment are given only to the extent that their usefulness to the project may be judged. Horse-drawn vehicles for moving earth have been largely replaced by mechanical equipment; for data on this subject, see Art 5 of the Second Edition; also, Sec 27.

EARTH EXCAVATION

1. ECONOMICS

Factors in economical handling of earth: (1) organization and management; (2) effic of workmen; (3) type, condition and interchangeability of equipment; (4) lost time; (5) weather conditions. Wet or freezing weather adds to costs of handling and transport; freezing may convert loose earth into a solid mass, and thawing, into sloppy mud. Liberal allowances should always be made for LOST TIME.

Management. LABOR-UNION RESTRICTIONS. Examples: a truck driver can do no other work, an oiler is paid for double time if he must wait until a power shovel is idle after 5 P M; these and similar regulations add greatly to costs and must be provided for in estimates (For.extent of unionization, see *Eng News Record*, Jan 24, 1937, p 943). Coordination between loading, transport and dumping is essential to effic. Much small-scale work must still be done by hand or minor equipment, at relatively high unit cost. It is important that sizes of shovels are economically correct, that picks are sharp, and that rest periods are coordinated with work of equipment units.

Costkeeping. Much equipment used in earth moving is utilized also for moving rock, handling concrete, etc. The cost of equipment should be apportioned to its several uses. **Comparative cost data** of other jobs should be used cautiously; allowances should be made for date, locality, length of haul, horse or motor equipment, labor conditions and unionization, delays due to rock, structures or traffic, and the character of material. Soils differ greatly in wt, cohesiveness, capacity for holding water, natural slope under quiescent loads, and final slope under moving loads.

Lost time. Construction may be discontinued in winter, only because it costs more. Rain and mud, next to winter idleness, are the chief causes of lost time, due to storms and waiting for ground to dry. Water-soaked soil hampers work by increasing weights to be handled, and hindering movement of men and machinery.

Saturation affects soils differently; sand and gravel give a firmer footing when wet; clayey soils, gumbo and alluvial silt become mud. Drainage should be provided to divert surface water from workings, or dispose quickly of that which enters. Employ machines capable of traveling over soft ground; provide equipment that can operate say a third of the time in rainfall, or in water-soaked material.

Machinery maintenance. Failure of any one machine may mean stoppage of others. One man should be in sole charge of maintenance. With a dozen or more machines, he should have a special repair and blacksmith shop, welding equipment and all necessary tools and spare parts; for small tools, duplicates should be kept on hand. In the Culebra cut of Panama Canal, machine shops mounted on cars were highly profitable in keeping a large fleet of steam shovels in repair. Inspection of machinery, oiling and other routine servicing may well be done at lunch time, between shifts, or at night; if not done in working hours, unions demand payment for overtime. Motor trucks may be required to report regularly to gasolene stations having water, compressed air, oil and tires. For less mobile machines, as power shovels and cableways, supplies should be delivered by trucks on regular trips. Road maintenance is especially important now that rubber tires are widely used. Roads should be kept well surfaced (19).

Economics of power shovels (1). In earthwork handled by machinery the following principles are fundamental: (*a*) the shorter the time required to fill dipper and the longer the arc of swing to dumping point, the more important is size of dipper or bucket, width of cutting edge, and ability to fill it properly; (*b*) effort should be made to increase both number and size of bucket loads; (*c*) OPERATING CYCLE comprises: loading time, swinging and dumping time, time to return bucket to loading point. Time losses can be reduced by moving trucks or cars forward during cycle of dipper or bucket operation; (*d*) height of lift should be minimized. In bucket-crane work, the shortest feasible length of boom should be used, with minimum arc of swing; (*e*) if digging is hard, blasting is done whenever its cost is less than that which would be due to delays to shovel and hauling equipment, plus extra repairs to shovel; (*f*) every organization should determine its output multiplier (Art 5), which depends upon management of work, placing, handling and upkeep of equipment, balance maintained between the types of equipment used, effic and coordination of personnel.

Choice of equipment. No definite rule applies. Equipment for doing work at lowest cost depends upon: investment for capac sought; labor and operating cost; facility of instructing operating men; adaptability to future work (ignored if equipment will not survive the job). To minimize loading cost, use self-loading machines where soil conditions permit. Self-loaders cannot be operated in rocky or sticky soil, in soils with stumps and roots, or below water line. Scarifying certain hard soils (Art 4) prior to loading may be required, especially for large self-loading scrapers (2). For data on DEPRECIATION OF EQUIPMENT, see *Contractors & Engineers Monthly*, July, 1931.

Time losses of power-shovels. Studies by Keystone Driller Co list as UNAVOIDABLE LOSSES: checking grade, moving, blasting, broken cable, mechanical trouble, stumps and roots, frozen material; as AVOIDABLE LOSSES: insufficient supply and inefficient operation of hauling units, inefficient operator, refueling.

2. SOIL PHYSICS AND MECHANICS

Recent studies (3–6) are of value respecting: (*a*) slopes for unsheeted excavations; (*b*) closeness to which excavation can be carried to a building; (*c*) distance or width of berm between working face and spoil bank; (*d*) water required for backfilling; (*e*) degree of compacting and settlement to be expected in rolled earth embankments; (*f*) suitability of material for hydraulic fill dams; (*g*) design of sheeted trenches. "Soil mechanics in present stage of development can be more a liability than an asset to an engineer, unless he has initiative and opportunity to keep abreast of latest developments by personal contact" (6).

Classification of soils by U S Bur Public Roads is based on plasticity, moisture equivalent, grain size, shrinkage and swell.

Aver increase of vol of earth when first loosened: clean sand and gravel, 14%; loam, loamy sand or gravel, 20%; dense clay and dense mixtures of gravel and clay, 35%; unusually dense gravel and clay, as from river beds, 50%.

Voids. If hard spherical grains are thoroughly compacted, the voids amount to 26%; if massed as loosely as possible, the voids are 48%. When measured loose, pit sand or gravel has 35 to 40% voids. Sand of uniform size has 45% voids, measured loose, but only 36% when watered and rammed. Uniform pebbles have 44% voids measured loose; 39% when watered and rammed. Clay allowed to settle in water has 50 to 79% voids; measured loose in the ordinary state, the voids are about 50% (1).

Table 1. Voids in Different Soils

(D. C. Henny)

Soil	Percentage of voids		
	Loose	Compact	Wet-rammed
Surface (organic)..	59	49	44
Fine subsoil.......	54	43	45
Gravel...........	42	37	34
Coarse subsoil.....	55	49	46

Quicksand is a hydraulic condition of granular material, where there is sufficient movement of ground water through it to lift the particles, so that they tend to flow upon one another. Fine-grained sand becomes "quicksand" much more readily than a coarse sand.

Table 2. Average Weights of Soils

Soil	Condition	Lb per cu ft	Lb per cu yd	Soil	Condition	Lb per cu ft	Lb per cu yd
Sand...........	Wet	122	3 294	Clay...........	Loose, dry	70	1 890
Sand...........	Dry	100	2 700	Clay...........	In place	116	3 132
Sand...........	Packed	110	2 970	Clay...........	Compressed	130	3 510
Gravel.......	Wet	125	3 375	Clayey earth.....	Rolled dry	110	2 970
Gravel........	Dry	112	3 024	Mud...........		112	3 024

Angle of repose. The face of a mass of earth when exposed for a time to the elements assumes a NATURAL SLOPE, the angle of which with the horizontal is called the ANGLE OF REPOSE. Values in Table 3 are average; in cohesive materials, they may change markedly when the water level against a saturated slope is rapidly lowered (7). Slopes may slough due to seepage toward an open cut, and may change when height and wt of bank become great enough to displace underlying materials.

Table 3. Slopes and Angles of Repose

Kind of earth	Slope of repose	Angle of repose	Kind of earth	Slope of repose	Angle of repose
Sand, clean, loose............	1.5 : 1	34°	Clay, wet.................	3.5 : 1	16°
Sand and clay, loose.........	1.33 : 1	37°	Rock, hard (riprap)........	1 : 1	45°
Sand, wet.................	2.5 : 1	22°	Sand, clay, gravel (suction-dredged)...............	2 : 1	26°
Gravel, clean, loose.........	1.33 : 1	37°			
Gravel and clay, loose.......	1.33 : 1	37°	River mud (suction-dredged).	3 : 1	18°
Clay, dry, loose.............	1.33 : 1	37°	Gravel and sand on shores,		
Clay, dry, natural..........	1 : 1	45°	exposed to waves........	7.5 : 1	7.5°

Stability of cohesionless materials (6). There is a rather wide range of uncertain behavior between the loose unstable and the compact stable state. SHEARING RESISTANCE OF SOILS, important in all problems of stability, is influenced largely by water content (Fig 1, 2). In general, it depends upon combined effect of cohesion and internal friction, the cohesive resistance being independent of any applied pressure. Tests to measure shear resistance may be made by the Krey shearing box, obtaining values for cohesion and angle of internal friction (8).

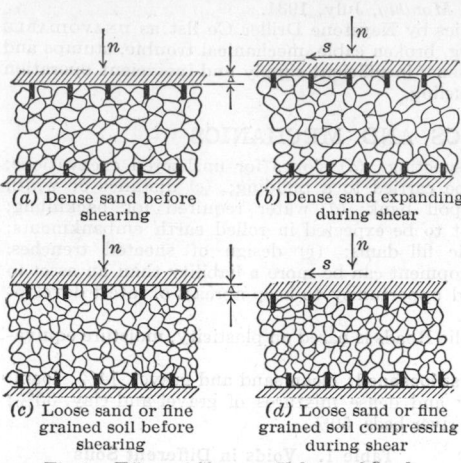

(*a*) Dense sand before shearing

(*b*) Dense sand expanding during shear

(*c*) Loose sand or fine grained soil before shearing

(*d*) Loose sand or fine grained soil compressing during shear

Fig 1.　Effect of Shear on Volume of Sand, Shown by Grain Rearrangement

Landslides and slips are often due to geological causes, such as unfavorable strata with moist surfaces. Conditions leading to landslides: (1) cuts in tilted strata on downdipping side of sandstone, limestone and solid shale beds; nearly vert face left in cut in shale or sandstone, from which material is precipitated by frost action, or slippage on interbedded seams of water-softened clay; (2) accumulations on hillsides of clay silt from decomposed rocks which become fluid when wet; (3) beds of plastic clay not far below surface; (4) plastic clay coatings formed on slopes beneath detritus by wetting and softening of shales. Water lubricates surfaces and increases wt of materials. A homogeneous soil may slide when geometric shape of the mass becomes unstable, as when a trench reaches a certain depth. For each angle of slope there is a max height where part of the mass slides along a surface, which is always curved, never plane (5).

Slips in embankments resemble landslides. The principal soil properties governing safety of embankments are: shearing resistance; coef of permeability; difference in consistency between undisturbed and remolded states; and extent of stratification and fissures, which influence creation of hydrostatic pressure (6). Compaction is aimed to control shearing resistance, stratification and permeability (Art 9).

Corrective measures against landslides. Ordinarily, removal of the shifting material is too costly. Good drainage is first preventive. Landslides have been halted by draining away the water; more effective than piling, blasting or rock-facing slopes (9, 11). From 1931 to 1934, slides and slips of embankments caused 3 000 deaths in 13 major disasters, and cost millions of dollars (13).

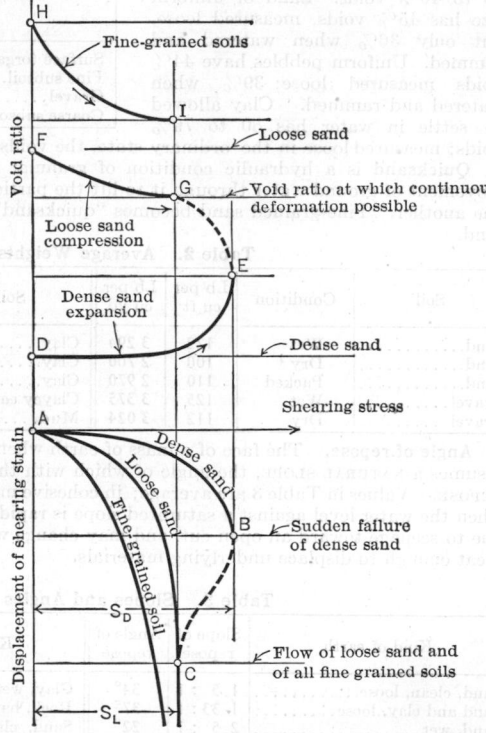

Fig 2.　Displacement and Volume Change, as Functions of Shearing Stress of Sands

Shrinkage of embankments has long been a subject of discussion, due to lack of experimental data and of an accepted meaning of the term. Shrinkage may be expressed as the relation of: vol of fresh fill to that of the same fill after settlement; or, as the vol of an excavation to that of the settled fill made from it. A cu yd of earth measured in place will occupy less space ultimately in compacted embankment. The usual allowance for shrinkage, 8–12%, does not apply to gumbo, cemented gravel, or materials from beds of streams, all of which are dense, and their shrinkage can be determined only by actual measurement. Investigations by "Bur of Valuation," of Interstate Commerce Comm, indicate that 9.1% is a minimum, and 14.4% is a closer final aver. These figures were modified by a Comm of the "Railroad Presidents' Conference" whieh, on basis of 12 million cu yd of earth embankment, found an aver of 10.4% initial shrinkage (Table 4), and, after complete settlement, 14.4% (see *Eng News-Rec*, Mch 10, 1921, p 434).

Table 4. Shrinkage of Earth in R R Fills, as Determined by Measurement and by the Rule of "Bur of Valuation," Interstate Commerce Comm (18)

Railway	State	Material	Shrinkage by measurement, %	Shrinkage by the rule, %	Method of construction	Vol. of excavation, cu yd
Ill Cent.....	Ill	Dune sand, fine and dry....	8.81	9.1	A	256 408
Nor & West..	....	Light clay, considerable sand, some mica..............	8.8–9.7	9.1	C, D	124 059
Cent Vt.....	R I	Fine, dry sand.............	7.77	9.1	A	96 767
Nor & West..	....	Some quicksand...........	10.3	9.1	C, D	77 120
So Pac......	Ore	Silt and coarse gravel, bottom of large fill..........	10.3	9.1	B, C, D	64 160
Nor & West..	....	60% dry sand.............	6.1	9.1	C, D	44 360
So Pac......	Ore	Clayey silt, gravelly in spots.	10.1	9.1	B	31 660
So Pac......	Ore	Cemented material, clayey, mostly cuts; 2.5% rock in fill....................	15.1	8.6	E	26 781
So Pac......	Ore	Borrow-pit earth, very clayey	1.8	9.1	B	11 016
So Pac......	Ore	Clayey silt................	11.1	8.7	A, C	9 648
So Pac......	Ore	Very clayey..............	3.5	9.1	C, D	5 572
Cent Vt.....	R I	Stiff blue clay.............	12.27	9.1	A	3 047

A. Unloaded from trestle. B. Teams and scrapers. C. Steam shovels. D. Dump wagons.
E. Carts and horse-drawn cars, dumped from sides and ends of fills.

3. EARTH-MOVING EQUIPMENT (17)

Operations: (1) loosening surface; (2) loading; (3) transport and dumping; sometimes (4) compacting. FOR LOOSENING hard ground: scarifiers, rippers, rooters, dipper shovels, backhoes and skimmers, pneumatic spades, dredges, steam jets, explosives, and hydraulic sluicing. FOR LOADING: mechanical shovels with clamshell or dragline dippers, push shovels, backhoes, elevating graders, cableways, belt conveyers. FOR TRANSPORT: wheelbarrows, carts, trucks, cars, graders and scrapers, cableways, conveyers, hydraulic sluicing. FOR COMPACTING: rollers, vibrators and drainage operations.

Hand labor and horse-drawn vehicles have been generally superseded by mechanical equipment, except for minor operations. For large-scale work, the trend is toward complete mechanization. Cars and trucks are usually mounted on low-press pneumatic tires, involving more attention to haulage roads. Power scrapers are more used on short-haul work, and their radius may be extended. Diesel is supplanting gasolene power for all except very small units (17).

Hand work. Few soils can be shoveled without picking or plowing. Light blasting is often advantageous.

Table 5. Rates of Picking, Cu Yd per Hour

Stiff clay or cemented gravel.....	1.4
Strong heavy soils..............	2.5
Loam.........................	4
Light sandy soils..............	6

Picking is costly. Table 5 shows fair aver duty per man-hr (19).

A man shoveling 1.4 cu yd per hr of the loosened material mentioned in Table 7 can handle only about half that amount if he does his own picking. Advantage of cheaper means of loosening is obvious.

Plowing is satisfactory for preceding shovel or smaller scraper work. Table 6 shows fair aver duty of horse-drawn plows.

Table 6.   Rates of Plowing

Soil	Labor	Cu yd per hr
Loam................................	1 driver, 1 holder, 2 horses............	50
Gravel and loam.....................	1 " 1 " 2 "	35
Fairly tough clay...................	1 " 1 " 2 "	25
Very hard soil......................	1 " 1 " 4–6 "	15–20
Ordinary soil	{ 2 men on plow beam of rooter plow } { 1 driver, 6 horses, on gang plow... }	40

Wheelbarrows, of wood, steel or aluminum alloy, generally have steel wheels, sometimes pneumatic tires; the latter, with large-diam wheels, reduce traction on soft ground. Loads are 2–2.5 cu ft.   The lightest barrows weigh 35 lb, empty; the larger, over 90 lb. The man holds $1/5$ to $1/3$ of the load (17).

Carts.   One-horse, 2-wheeled, dump carts hold 0.3–0.5 cu yd.   On ordinary road loads seldom exceed 0.4 cu yd (place measure).   With hauls of 300 ft or less, 1 driver can attend 2 carts by taking one to the dump while the other is being loaded.   Cost of cart work per cu yd = $1/20$ hr wages of team, driver and helper on plow; + $2/3$ hr wages of labor shoveling; + $1/4$ hr wages of cart horse and driver for "lost time"; + $1/20$ hr wages of cart horse and driver for each 100 ft of haul.

Wagons.   Horse-drawn, bottom-dump wagons have nominal capac of 1–2.5 cu yd. Speed of travel per min (not including delays and rests): poor roads, 130 ft; fair dirt roads. 175 ft; best roads, 220 ft.

Table 7.   Loading by Shoveling

Method	Cu yd per man-hr	Authority
Mud into wheelbarrows...............	0.8	M. Ancelin
Gravel " "	1.7–2.7	"
Earth " "	1.6–4.8	"
" " " , aver.........	2.2	"
" " "	2.8	Gillespie
Earth (all kinds) into wagons..........	2.1	Cole (a)
"	2.0	D. K. Clark
Sand into cars from high face..........	1.8	Gillette (b)
Plowed gravelly soil into wagons........	1.3	" (c)
Iowa soil.............................	1.5–2.0	J. M. Brown
" "	2.8	" (d)
Clay and gravel into carts.............	1.0	E. Morris
Loam into carts.......................	1.2	"
Sandy earth into carts.................	1.4	"
Loose sand into carts..................	2.0	G. A. Parker
Clay, tenacious, Chicago...............	1.25	" (e)
Hardpan into low dump cars..........	1.5	Gillette
Aver earth " " " "	1.75	"

(a) 10 miles, Erie Canal.   (b) 10 000 cu yd bank measurement.   (c) 20 000 cu yd in embankment.   (d) A rush job.   (e) Spaded out and handled with forks.

Railroad cars.   Air-dump cars must discharge their loads quickly, with as small air press and consumption as possible, and leave dumped material so that the cars can be righted and backed promptly, with minimum labor for track shifting and incidental work at dump.   Car should be simple in design, rugged in construction, with few operating parts, all easily accessible (19).

Industrial railways are for extensive hauling over a long fixed route, as for R R construction, highways, dams, tunnels, aqueducts, large ditches and canals.   Greater flexibility is obtained by use of locomotives, though grades of over a few per cent seriously limit wt of cars hauled.   Track gage is usually 18, 24 or 36 in; some 42 in.   Rails weigh 8–20 lb per yd, and are in 20, 30 or 33-ft lengths.   Second-hand rails and ties often serve for short job.   Portability of track is important where there is much shifting and relaying.   Light track is economical, in which ties and rails are assembled in lengths of 15–20 or even 30 ft, that can be carried by 2 or 3 men; with curved sections, switches and turntables, and joints readily fastened and unfastened.   Units can be laid on firm ground with little if any grading.   Ties may be of wood, but steel saves shifting time (19).

Track grades.   If a locomotive alone can operate on 8% grade, it will haul a train of its own wt on only a 4% grade.   Hence, practicable grades are determined by the relation (grade % × wt loco) ÷ (wt loco + wt of loaded train). Under favorable track conditions, the operation of locomotives may approach theoret fric coef, but a little water or grease on rails seriously reduce its tractive power (see Sec 11).

Tractors (see Sec 27) are mounted on caterpillars or rubber tires; draw-bar pull, up to 22 000 lb in first gear. Rubber tracks, claimed to be good for 5 000 miles, are offered in place of metal. Principal tractors (1939): International, Caterpillar, Cletrac and Allis Chalmers. Horsepower, 22–96; the smaller sizes have gas or Diesel drives; the larger, Diesel only. Wt, 5 000 to over 30 000 lb, but unit ground loads for crawler-traction are limited to 6 lb per sq in. Draw-bar pull varies with speed, grade and ground conditions. Load should not exceed 75% of max draw-bar pull of tractor in second gear (2). Allis Chalmers, Model I-U, is a fast, powerful wheel tractor for hauling and road building at low cost. Speeds, $2^1/_3$–25 miles per hr. ˙ OPERATING COSTS. Studies of Dept of Agriculture, Cornell Univ (1935), on about 70 machines, of 16–30 brake h p, showed costs from 25¢ to $1.12 per hr; aver 50–70¢ (19).

Motor trucks for earthwork are power-dumping. Nominal capac, 1.5–18 cu yd. The rear end may have wheels or caterpillar traction.

Dump trucks. Speeds were formerly kept down by governors to about 15 miles per hr, but are now generally unrestricted. Wt, 11 000–14 500 lb; h p, 75–100. Recent special types ("dumptors" and "iron mules") have a short wheel-base, making possible quick turns within 15 ft; driver sits behind body and has unobstructed view to rear for reverse running; speed, 10–13 miles per hr in high gear and 3.5–4 in low, in both forward and reverse gear (19). POWER. Steam has been mostly replaced by gasolene and Diesel engines. Diesels have higher first cost and more complicated mechanism, but use cheaper fuel and $1/_2$–$1/_3$ the quantity required by gasolene machines. Elec operation is sometimes employed for large-scale work.

Crawler wagons, developed since 1920, are desirable in soft, wet ground, where soil is sticky. They roll and smooth the road surface, instead of cutting it into ruts, as is done by motor trucks. As many variable factors affect wagon operation, cost estimates must be conservative. Skill of operators of the loading machines, and the wide variations in character of the material excavated, directly affect yardage output. For crawlers hauled by tractors, costs are: 5-cu yd wagon, 45¢ per hr; 10 to 13-cu yd wagon, 69¢ per hr, excluding deprec (2).

Pneumatic-tired, bottom-dump wagons, of 20, 25 or 30-cu yd capac, will haul greater distances, at lower cost, than crawlers or other equipment, providing scale of work justifies the investment, and road surfaces are good, with grades less than 5%. A Cletrac No 80 tractor, with 25-yd wagon, will haul an aver of about 72 cu yd per hr to a distance of 2 000 ft, the rate of work being affected by size of shovel, skill of operator, extent of swing, vert lift, and soil conditions. A 25-yd wagon costs about $8 750 f o b; cost of operation, about 84¢ per hr, including deprec (2). Two wagons are sometimes hauled in tandem.

Scrapers drawn by tractors can dig economically to depth of 24 in and transport several hundred ft, provided ground has been cleared and grubbed (Art 4) and is free of boulders. There are many forms: as wheeled and carryall scrapers, bulldozers, trailbuilders, self-loading wheelers. Limit of haul, 200 to about 1 400 ft (2) (see also Sec 27).

Graders have a cutting blade between front and rear wheels. Capac, 1–12 cu yd. They may be pulled by tractors of 15–80 h p, or propelled by their own power (usually about 50 h p). Mounted on 4 steel wheels, or 4, 6 or 8 rubber-tired wheels. Blade or moldboard, 7–16 ft long, 12 ft being usual, with a height of about 18 in, is adjustable in height and tip. Wt, from 1 400 lb for towed graders, to 17 000 lb for power machines. Speeds of power graders, usually 2 miles per hr in low gear, 19 miles in high gear, with two intermediate gears and reverse (2).

Bulldozers are tractor scrapers with a very strong blade, arranged to be lifted 3–3.5 ft, and lowered 5–6 ft below ground level. Wt, 3 500–6 000 lb. Capac when loaded for shoving, 2–4 cu yd; h p, 30–70. Speeds, 120–240 ft per min. After depositing load, return is made with blade raised, at about 240 ft per min. Cost, $750–$1 825, f o b. The blade is movable only up and down. "TRAILBUILDER" blade can be angled horiz, vert or moved up and down (2). Cost, $900–$2 750.

Carryall scrapers, on pneumatic tires, pick up loads singly or in tandem, and travel at high-gear speeds. They are operated by a power-control unit, which obtains power from tractor drive shaft and transmits it by cable to the working parts. Single carryall scrapers require 2 drums; cable from one drum raises or lowers bowl in loading and unloading, the other operates front apron and tailgate in unloading and spreading. For tandem operation, a 4-drum unit is needed (2). LE TOURNEAU CARRYALL is mounted on large pneumatic tires, and has Timken bearings. Alloy steels of great strength and resiliency are used, minimizing the wt. Capac is large because: (a) the expanding bowl carries the soil back into the bucket during loading, so that the tractor can put more effort into cutting;

(b) entire wt of body can be applied to the cutting edge; (c) front apron, tailgate and telescoping bucket facilitate loading; (d) the operator can instantaneously adjust cutting depth, or raise the blade to avoid stumps or rocks, or avoid stalling motor in deep cuts.

Self-loading, single-unit scraper will load seamed rocky material without blasting. It is adapted to hauls of 500–2 000 ft. Sizes, 5, 6, 10 and 12 cu yd when heaped. Cost, $2 400 for 5-yd size to $5 225 for 12 yd, f o b.

Self-loading wheel scrapers are adapted to longer hauls than ordinary scrapers; up to 200–1 000 ft. Capac is small, 1.5 and 2 cu yd. They are hauled singly, in tandem, or, under favorable conditions, in threes. Cost, $800–$1 150, f o b (2).

Fresno scraper, the oldest type of wheel scraper, was formerly drawn by horses, now usually by tractors. Capac, 0.75–3.5 cu yd. Cost (1938), $130–$450.

Spreaders. Western spreader car is hauled on 36-in track by locomotive. Designed for spreading material dumped from R R cars. Body and frame are of wood, strongly braced and ironed; trucks, of I-beams. It has steel-faced oak wings or blades, 15.5 ft long, with removable cutting edges, and will spread 7 ft from outside of rail. Long wheelbase of Model U carryall, with split-second cable control, gives great accuracy in spreading.

Belt conveyers (see Sec 27 for details of construction and applications). For earth work they are important as accessories to dredges, trench excavators and elevating graders.

Power shovels (Fig 3) were first mounted on crawlers instead of R R trucks in 1911. In 1939 practically all except those for R R service have crawler mountings, which exert bearing press on ground of only 0.72–1.08 ton per sq ft, and require no auxiliary mats. DIPPERS usually have capac of 2–3.8 cu yd; occasionally up to 15 yd. Manganese steel is largely used for lips and dipper teeth. By welding to the teeth hard wearing surfaces of stellite, or an alloy of cobalt, chromium and tungsten, life is increased more than ten times. BUCKETS are self-filling (clamshell or orangepeel); or hand filled (turnover or bottom-dump). The orangepeel may exert more digging force and is heavier than the clamshell. Capac, 0.5–3 cu yd; corresponding weights 2 000 and 7 000 lb. Clamshells of 16.5 cu yd have been built. Turn-over buckets hold 0.5–1.5 cu yd; shape, cylindrical or cubical. Exact placing of material is impossible with them. Bottom-dump buckets are of 1–3 cu yd; seldom used. Dredge buckets can be used with any type of engine having 2 drums. Advantage of orangepeel or clamshell bucket on a crane over a dipper shovel is that there is practically no limit to digging depth; whereas the depth for dipper shovel is limited (Fig 3).

Excavators with booms. Most power shovels with dippers smaller than 2.5 yd have interchangeable booms, so that with delay of a few hours they can be converted in the field to plunger shovel, a backhoe, dragline, or clamshell. Plungers are lighter than dippers of same capac and hence have greater cycle speed. Dipper shovels fill buckets by a "crowding" (pushing) motion; backhoes (backdiggers, pullscoops, ditchers), by pulling toward the machine, the bucket being thrust forward by an auxiliary handle. Skimmers, plungers and scoops fill bucket by pulling it away from shovel under the boom by a cable, and carry load to dumping point by raising and swinging the boom. Operations are more restricted than those of a dipper shovel. See Sec 27.

Table 8. Operating Speeds, in Seconds, of Dipper Shovel

	Loading	Swinging	Dumping	Returning	Total
Maximum..	16	7.5	5.75	7.25	36.5
Average....	9.6	6.0	2.4	6.2	24.2
Minimum ..	7	5.25	2	5.5	19.75

Minimum may be expected in poorly blasted rock and max in dry earth (21).

Table 9. Digging Radius of Revolving Shovel, 24-ft Boom; 14-ft Dipper Handle; Caterpillar Tread; 1 yd Dipper (Fig 3)

Boom angle with horiz, deg	Height of dump, dipper door open A	Radius of dump C	Digging radius D	Radius floor level cut E	Center rotation to point to boom G
45	14′ 2″	23′ 6″	26′ 11″	19′ 9″	21′ 11″
55	17′ 2″	21′ 3″	25′ 3″	16′ 7″	18′ 9″
60	18′ 6″	19′ 11″	24′ 5″	15′ 0″	17′ 0″

Clamshells and orangepeels, suspended from a crane, fill the buckets solely by dead wt

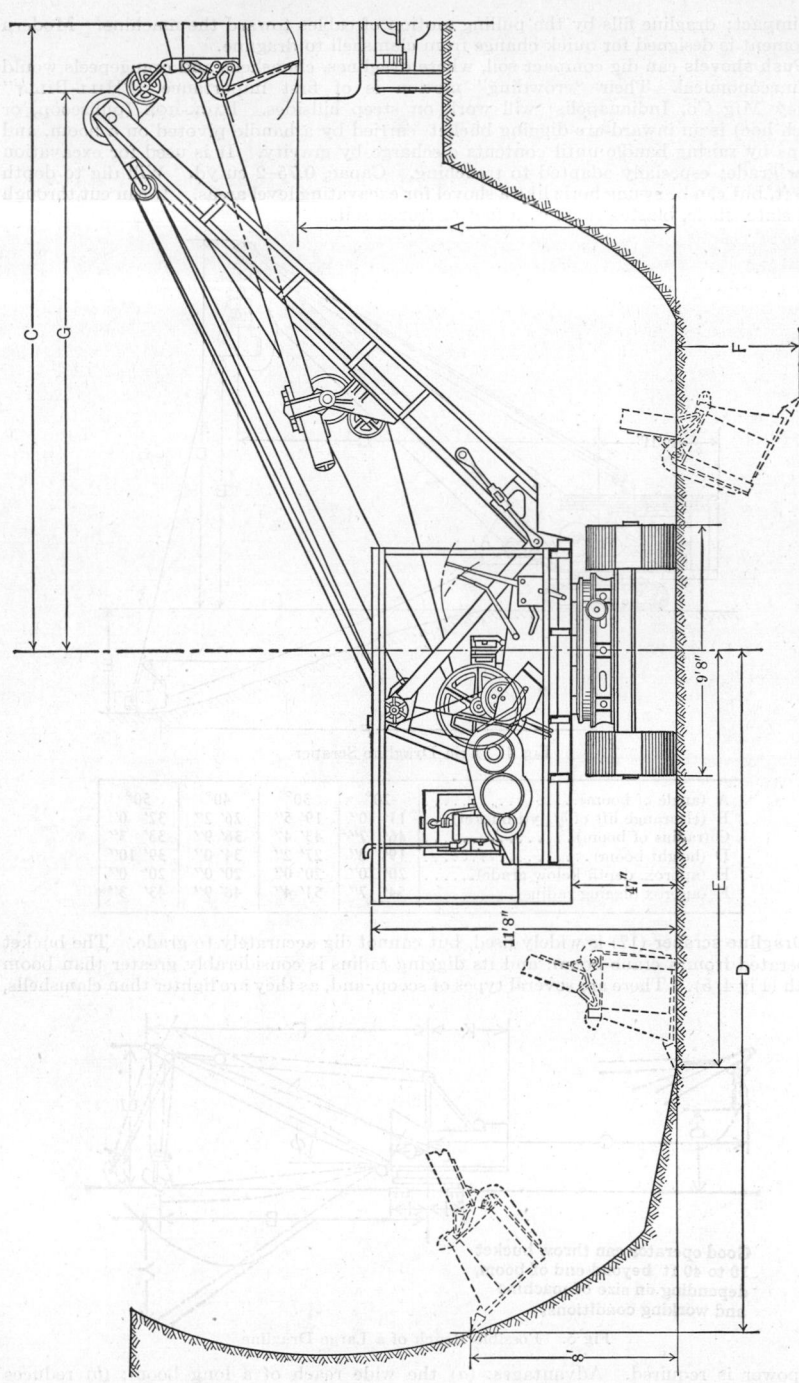

Fig 3.   Power-shovel with Dipper

and impact; dragline fills by the pulling motion of cables toward the machine. Modern equipment is designed for quick change from clamshell to dragline.

Push shovels can dig compact soil, where draglines, clamshells and orangepeels would be uneconomical. Their "crowding" motion is of first importance. "HILL-BILLY" (Insley Mfg Co, Indianapolis) will work on steep hillsides. BACK-HOE (pullscoop, or trench hoe) is an inward-arc digging bucket, carried by a handle pivoted on a boom, and dumps by raising handle until contents discharge by gravity. It is used for excavation below grade; especially adapted to trenching. Capac, 0.75–2 cu yd. Will dig to depth of 25 ft, but can be swung horiz like a shovel for excavating level areas. It can cut through hard slate, shale, blasted rock, or a foot of frozen soil.

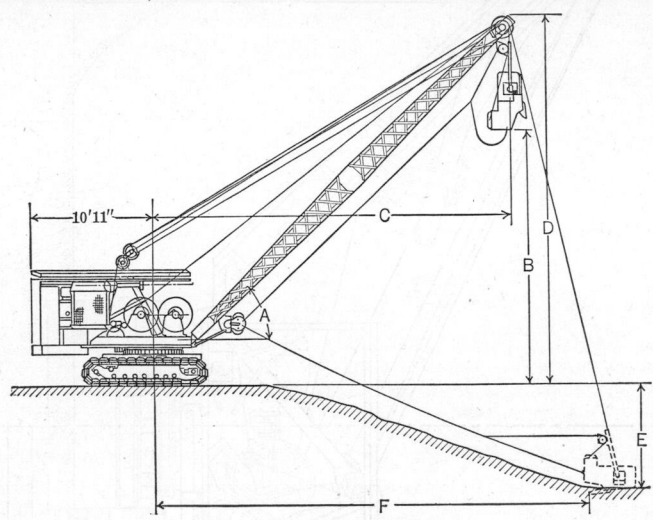

Fig 4.   Erie Dragline Scraper

	20°	30°	40°	50°
A (angle of boom)	20°	30°	40°	50°
B (clearange lift of 3/4 yd bucket)	11' 10''	19' 5''	26' 2''	32' 0''
C (radius of boom)	46' 7''	43' 4''	38' 9''	33' 3''
D (height boom)	19' 8''	27' 2''	34' 0''	39' 10''
E (approx. depth below grade)	20' 0''	20' 0''	20' 0''	20' 0''
F (approx digging radius)	54' 7''	51' 4''	48' 9''	43' 3''

Dragline scraper (17) is widely used, but cannot dig accurately to grade. The bucket is operated from a crane boom, and its digging radius is considerably greater than boom length (Fig 4, 5). There are several types of scoop, and, as they are lighter than clamshells,

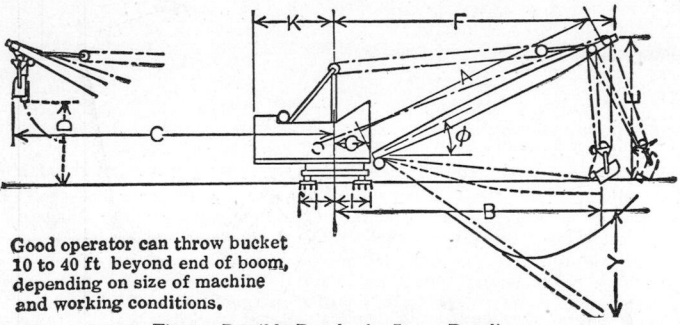

Good operator can throw bucket 10 to 40 ft beyond end of boom, depending on size of machine and working conditions.

Fig 5.   Possible Reach of a Large Dragline

less power is required. Advantages: (*a*) the wide reach of a long boom; (*b*) reduces amount of labor and equipment by combining digging, elevating and conveying in a single machine controlled by one operator; (c) small lifting force needed while bucket is filling, power for loading being applied in a nearly straight line from winding drum; (d) nearly all the engine power is available for cutting through obstructions while filling the bucket. Range of digging with 0.75-yd bucket is about 14 ft horiz and 17 ft vert; dumping height, about 18 ft. Booms up to 160 ft have been used. Draglines are especially useful for moving soils say 500 ft, with a tower excavator, or belt or other conveyer, close behind. Under aver conditions, a 150-ft boom dragline can excavate and place for 10¢ per cu yd on 300-ft max movements; for 500 ft, 14¢. With belt conveyer, cost is a little more to excavate and place, but less to haul. Cable replacement is a large item of expense; may be 50–80% of total; careful handling is essential. Plow-steel cable, 6 × 19 Lang lay (see Sec 12) is recommended. Drum diam is 400–500 times that of individual wires.

Table 10. Dimensions of Dragline Scrapers
(Averages from catalogs of well-known mfrs) Trautwine, 1937 Ed

Capac, cu yd	0.5	0.75	1	1.25	2.5	5	10
Boom length, ft	30	38	40	40	85	155	160
Dumping reach of boom at 25°, ft	32	39	42	42	92	164	......
Added throw beyond dumping reach, ft	13	13	13	13	......	......	40
Dumping reach of boom at 40°, ft	15	20	21	22	45	71	......
Max height, boom lowered, ft	11.5	12	12	15	......	......	......
Depth of cut, ft	16	18	19	21	58	75	......
Pull on bucket, ton	6	8	10.5	12.5	......	......	......
Dragline speed, ft per min	110	100	116	110	......	......	......
Rotating speed, rev per min	5.25	3.5	3.5	2.25	......	......	0.85

Trenching machines are of wheel or ladder type, the buckets in both revolving towards the machine. Buckets deliver to belt conveyer, discharging on one side of trench. Depth of trench for bucket-wheel machines is 8–12 ft max; width, 12 in up. Speed in ordinary soil is claimed by makers as 1.25–4 ft of trench per min; in exceptional cases, 5 ft; partly frozen ground may slow it to 0.5 ft. Depth of trench for ladder trenches is 12–20 ft; width, same as for bucket-wheel machines. Trenching machines are especially suitable for widths to 4 ft (see Art 5).

Cableways for trenching are strung over line of trench, handling a number of buckets loaded by men in trench. Formerly much used, and are still useful for deep digging, and where excavated material cannot be stored alongside.

Elevating grader (17) is a combination of plow and belt or bucket conveyer, on frame carried by wheels or caterpillars. Plow cuts a furrow about 1 ft wide, and 6–7 in deep. Moldboard delivers material onto lower end of a small conveyer or elevator of changeable inclination, 14–25 ft long, belt being usually 42 or 48 in wide. Conveyer is at right angles to direction of motion, extending to right or left, and upward for loading wagons moving alongside and keeping pace with it. The machine may be hauled by tractor, and conveyer operated either by separate power unit, making belt speed control easier, or by a "power-take-off" from wheels or tractor, which is simpler and lighter (for details, see Sec 27).

4. METHODS OF EXCAVATION

(For dredging, embankments, trenching, ditching and hydraulic handling, see Art 7–9)

Clearing, grubbing and stripping. CLEARING is the cutting of trees (generally leaving 2.5-ft stumps) and their disposal, together with brush. Pulling stumps and roots is termed GRUBBING. STRIPPING is the shallow excavation and removal of top-soil containing organic matter; where backfilling follows laying of pipes, etc, top-soil may be stored nearby for use as dressing on barren backfill. Clearing and grubbing are especially necessary where graders and scrapers are to be used. Roots and small brush interfere with all machines except power shovels and dragline excavators, which do their own grubbing. Cost of grubbing is difficult to estimate, as local conditions are extremely variable.
Methods of grubbing: (a) by tractors and bulldozers; (b) burning, blasting and pulling stumps; (c) by scarifiers. Grubbing by hand is uneconomical, but still practiced. In cold regions, if large roots are cut in fall, winter frosts may heave stumps and lessen work of removal. If standing trees are pulled over after partial grubbing, their wt in falling will break roots difficult to reach, and lift stump out of hole.
Blasting stumps (16): (a) expose tap root to depth of say 18 in and bore a hole in it with wood auger, more than half through; split a dynamite cartridge, pack well into the

hole, and tamp with moist clay; (b) place 2 or more cartridges at least 2 ft below surface of ground, and close against the tap root. To place a heavy charge for a large stump, the bottom of the hole alongside the stump may be enlarged by "springing" it with a light charge of one-quarter cartridge. For more than one hole, a blasting machine should be used to explode all simultaneously. A charge under middle of a stump having large lateral roots may merely split the stump. For large stumps, charges are often placed under each heavy root. Single charges under small stumps should be placed considerably below the butt, so that the cushion of earth will distribute the force, and prevent splitting the stump. Fresh, fibrous-rooted stumps are harder to blast than those that are decayed or have tap roots. For sound stumps, charges of 40% dynamite are given in Table 11; for green stumps, multiply these by 1.5–2; for decayed stumps, use less than shown.

Table 11. Dynamite Required to Blast Stumps

Diam of stump, in.....	12	18	24	30	36	48	60	72
40% dynamite, lb.....	0.56	0.75	1.12	1.50	2.25	3.75	5.25	8.25

For western fir, pine and cedar stumps, in firm deep soil, use 1.5 lb of Judson (contractor's powder) per ft diam of stump, up to 4 ft; for larger diam, 2–2.5 lb per ft; in gravel or loose ground, 2.5–3.5 lb per ft. For stumps 8 ft or more in diam, the charge of Judson powder in lb = diam of stump, ft.

Burning stumps. Soil is dug away, partly exposing largest roots. Brush and logs are piled about stump, and kept burning until it and larger roots are consumed. This method is good for rotten stumps, difficult to blast or pull. CHAR-PIT method consists in placing brush or kindling around stump and covering all with clay and sod, leaving small openings for admission of air; stumps should first be split, by exploding dynamite in ship-auger hole in center of stump. A portable gasolene engine and blower are useful in burning large stumps, and may be more economical than grubbing or blasting.

Pulling stumps is done by hand, or horse-drawn machines, but chiefly by tractors. Though slower, pulling may be cheaper for a single stump than grubbing or blasting. Pulling is facilitated if stump is first shattered with small blast. Small trees, singly or in groups, can be torn out by tractors; such trees should not be cut, as it is more difficult to make fast to small stumps.

Disposal of stumps in cut-over forest land costs as much as grubbing. It is best to blast first, using only enough powder to shatter stumps and loosen their hold, and then pull and collect them with a winding engine; 1 200–1 500 ft of rope will reach all stumps on 5 acres at one set-up. Rope is carried over a gin pole, about which stumps are piled and then burned. Brush land may be cleared by heavy, tractor-hauled plows, but considerable hand labor is necessary to gather and remove debris.

Loosening. Efficiency is gained by blasting frozen crust, particularly in dragline work, and it is generally best to "dig in," and have a good working face before frost comes. For winter blasting, non-freezing explosives are essential. It is economical to loosen heavy soils by scarifiers (see below); their use ahead of scraper shortens loading time. On aver hauls, one tractor and scarifier can keep ahead of 2 or 3 tractor and scraper units (2).

Scarifiers have a series of vert teeth, side by side on a bar; may be used instead of blade of grader or attached to rear of a road roller. Types: RIPPER is useful for breaking hard-surfaced roads and general surface work, in conjunction with large scrapers. ROOTER resembles a harrow with 3 to 9 teeth, and digs to depth of 2 ft. It is mounted on 2 wheels, 2–3 ft diam, and pulled by tractor. Wt, 2 500–8 000 lb. Valuable in preparing hard ground for graders, dislodging stumps, or breaking up concrete; they frequently obviate blasting frozen ground (2).

Loosening by explosives. Hardpan is economically loosened by charges of low-grade dynamite, or Judson (contractor's) powder. Holes, except in high banks, should be at 45° to the vert. Horiz holes in face of a bank are effective. For details of chamber and coyote-hole blasting, see Sec 5.

Thawing frozen ground may be done by burning gasolene or coal oil, or by use of lime, steam jets, or wood fires. Ground frozen too hard to be excavated by a trench machine, can be softened by spreading small pieces of lime along the line of proposed trench, covering them with manure or straw, and pouring on hot water to slack the lime and liberate the heat. Clay, frozen so hard to depth of 34 in that stones embedded in it could be sheared off without loosening them, has been thawed by jetting holes with a 1/2-in pipe connected by hose to a boiler. In each hole was inserted a 1/2-in capped pipe, with 4 1/8-in holes bored in it, and steam forced in to thaw out the surrounding ground (10).

Hot water thawing is more economical than steam for working frozen gold-bearing gravels. In the Yukon district, Alaska, a 30-hp pump, with 4-in intake and 3-in discharge, delivered water at

40 lb press through a 1-in nozzle; 6 000 gal of water were used over and over. The water was kept at a temp of 150° Fah by discharging the pump exhaust into the suction sump. In 10 hr this thawed and broke down 175 cu yd gravel (see also Sec 10). Cold water has also been used.

Bank blasting. In hard, cemented material, dynamite is better than black powder; in soft ground, the latter is more economical. With very high banks the bottom should be blown out and the top allowed to drop. Charges should be placed so that the line of least resistance is horiz. With banks 50 to 150 ft high in cemented gravel, the length of main drift should generally equal $2/3$ the height of bank. Cross drifts are driven parallel to the bank face, their length depending on length of face to be blasted. Powder charge for aver conditions is about 0.4 lb per cu yd of ground. (For further details, see Sec 5.)

Blasting at the property of the Milton Mining and Water Co, Sweetland, Cal, during 3 years, required an aver of 0.382 lb Judson powder per cu yd. The top gravel had been washed off, leaving banks (usually hard and cemented for 50 ft, but soft above) from 50 to 150 ft high. In some parts, 8.3 to 8.5 cu yd were shattered per lb of powder.

In soils difficult to pick, blasting may be economical. Excavate by picks until a face is formed, and make vert 1.5 to 2.25-in holes in a line back of the face with pointed bar, churn drill, or auger. Depth of holes should be a little less than the height of bank, distance between them being 1.5 times line of least resistance (Sec 5, Art 5). In the formula $B = CR^3$, $B =$ charge in oz, and $R =$ line of least resistance in ft; the "rock coeff" C should be determined by trial. For loam, conglomerates, and ordinary soil, using 30% dynamite, C is usually nearly 0.6. Holes in frozen ground should be "chambered" (Sec 4, Art 8).

Loading. Elevating graders and power shovels, with dipper or backhoe equipment, are favored for large-scale work. For earth cuts the tractor-wheeled scrapers are used. Elevating grader will load for about 5¢ and power shovel for 7¢ per cu yd, not including waiting time of hauling equipment. Cost of spreading, watering and rolling is about 7¢; of hauling, 0.75¢ per cu yd in place, not including road maintenance. The dragline scraper is always economical for excavating large, shallow areas.

Influence of depth of cut on power-shovel costs (23). Unit cost of excavating with dipper shovel in shallow cuts may be 2 or 3 times more than for medium depths. Output is greatest in cuts between 4 and 12 ft deep, where full dipper loads can be taken by each crowding and hoisting movement. Latest type of plunger shovel also works best at depths of 4–12 ft, but has an advantage in working speed, because the boom and scoop assembly, size for size, weighs nearly 6 000 lb less than standard boom and dipper. Time studies indicate 10–14% faster work than dipper shovel. For depths exceeding 12 ft, it is generally best to resort to benching. Power-shovel delays on 51 highway operations: hauling equipment, 9.9%; moving shovel and repairs, 18.6%; weather, 14.9%; misc, 20.2%. Effect of material on time for loading dipper: good earth, 5.6 sec; earth and some rock, cemented material, 8.4 sec; poorly-blasted rock, 10.3–16.7 sec.

Following figures are for work of Bucyrus steam shovels under favorable conditions. No. 20-B, loading blue clay and sand into trucks, 93.5 cu yd per hr; road grading, overcasting, digging clay, roots, stumps and rocks, 50 yd per hr; road work in solid limestone, poorly blasted, 34 yd per hr. No. 30-B on road work, loading earth, rock and some shale, 130 cu yd per hr; partly loading in cars, partly overcasting, clay and laminated limestone, 70 yd per hr. Loading in wagons, very stiff clay, 60 yd per hr.

On R R grading in West Va (22), 4 Lorain gasolene crawler shovels with 1.25-cu yd dipper, loaded trains of four 4-cu yd dump cars in 3 min, dumping at height of 17–18 ft. Output per 10-hr shift, 1 000–3 000 cu yd; distance hauled on each side of cut, about 1 000 ft. Much of excavation was in rock or hard shale, requiring blasting.

Power-shovel costs for general grading: $5/8$-cu yd dipper, 23.3¢ per yd; $7/8$-cu yd dipper, 17.7–19.2¢ per cu yd.

Selection of hauling equipment. For short hauls and large-scale work, the combined excavating, hauling and placing unit, like the elevating grader and dragline scraper, are desirable. For long hauls, bottom or side-dump crawler wagons, and especially tractor-drawn pneumatic-tired wagons holding 3–25 cu yd, are economical. New developments are the 24-cu yd wagon, mounted on 16 large low-press tires, and the pneumatic-tire tractor unit, with trailer wagon. They are speedy, but require solid roads; can not run on very wet earth surfaces (17). Apply to makers for tables of economic hauls for the different machines.

Elevating grader. If soil is free from rocks and stumps, a motor-driven, 48-in grader, pulled by a Cletrac tractor, will load on aver a 7-cu yd wagon per min, where the plow can work to its full depth and loading is done without turning; or a 10–13 yd wagon in 1.5–2 min (2).

Fresno scraper (sliding), in absence of ledge rock or boulders larger than scraper opening, will haul more dirt per dollar invested and at lower cost than any other excavator, within a distance of 200–300 ft, and is widely used for removing overburden, stripping, and cutting down grades. The 0.75-yd size can handle 15 cu yd per hr on 200-ft haul, at about 39¢ per yd; a 3.5-yd Fresno will handle 70 cu yd 200 ft at about 13.5¢ per cu yd, all including deprec (2).

Bulldozer, in leveling dumps or moving dirt on short hauls, is a closer competitor of the Fresno, within the same distances, and is useful for similar work. Hard material must first be loosened. Experiment determines best speed to avoid spilling. They are effective for scraping down slopes as steep as 35%; and, if gear is right, they can back up the grade for next load. On 200-ft haul, capac is 13–40 cu yd firm dirt per hr, at cost of 20–47¢ per yd for bulldozer and Cletrac motor, including deprec. These figures are conservative for good soil and level grades; capac increases on down grades, and decreases on up grades (2).

Observations in 1934 indicate that aver load transported from cut to fill under ordinary conditions varies with length and shape of blade, and grade and character of soil. Loads on the 4 bulldozers in Table 12 often fluctuated as much as 100%; smallest loads, about 2 cu yd, largest 4 cu yd (16). Recent improvements, permitting independent vert movements of either end of bulldozer and also lateral movement, make it easier to keep excavation in proper condition, and to shape slopes at proper angle.

Table 12.   Operation of Tractor-powered Bulldozers (16)

	1	2	3	4
Number of trips timed	3 731	511	800	560
Cu yd placed in fill	11 741	1 655	1 822	1 352
Rate, cu yd per hr	68.4	57	35.2	44.1
Load, cu yd	3.15	3.24	2.3	2.41
Loading distance, ft	30	40	28	39
Loading speed, ft per sec	2.4	2.4	1.4	2.7
Haul distance, ft	168	216	309	232
Haul speed, ft per sec	3.7	3.2	3.2	3.1
Return distance, ft	200	260	340	275
Return speed, ft per sec	2.3	2.5	4.7	2.5
Average down grade, per cent	26	17	11	20

Table 13.   Operation of Large, Self-loading Wheeled Scrapers

	1	2	3	4	5	6	7	8
Rated capac, cu yd	3	6	8	4	5	4	4	5
Condition of equipment	Good	Very good	Very good	Very good	Very good	Fair	Good	Fair
Number of trips timed	212	269	132	145	54	56	3 200	963
Loading distance, ft	75	116	144	80	86	92	100	38
Loading speed, ft per sec	2.3	1.8	2.0	2.1	2.	1.8	2.0	2.3
Hauling distance, ft	180	327	290	210	372	1 400	300	237
Hauling speed, ft per sec	2.9	3.5	2.8	3.0	3.2	3	2.5	3.3
Return distance, ft	254	405	449	280	450	1 450	400	275
Return speed, ft per sec	3.2	3.8	3.8	3.7	3.8	4.7	5.5	2.7
Dumping time, sec	10.4	......	......	......	46	34	11	10.4
Turning time, sec	18	22	20	24	27	22	20	......
Load carried to dump, in percentage of full load	95	75	50	90	61	75	90	......
Aver pay yardage, in percentage of rated load capac	57	45	35	54	37	45	53	44

NOTE.—Scrapers 1 to 5 were on same job; and 1, 5, 6 and 7 were of same make, but working under different conditions. Scraper No 7 worked in winter, when materials were wet and sticky. For such soils, crawler wagons are preferable.

Cost of excavation by self-loading wheeled scrapers, hauled by tractor, is 13–18¢ per cu yd, including deprec, but exclusive of hand labor. Tandem scrapers have been largely replaced by single units of greater capac (2). They are especially adapted to cut-and-fill work on hauls of less than 2 000 ft.

Cableways (17) are suitable for large-scale work. Except where movable towers are used, irregular topography, swamps and bodies of water are no obstacles. They require no earthwork, no bridges, and their operation is unaffected by weather. On some recent gov't projects, single loads of 15 tons or more have been handled. For design and details of construction, see Sec 26.

5. TRENCHING AND DITCHING

Hand labor is still used for small-scale jobs. Cost depends on character of soil, number of boulders or other obstructions, presence of water, and depth and (somewhat) on the width of trench. In trenches over 4 ft deep, some soil must be shoveled twice: first, to surface; then, as spoil pile grows, back from edge of trench. In trenches 6–12 ft deep, soil must first be thrown to a staging about halfway up, thence to surface and finally, back from edge. For depths of 12–18 ft, the soil must be handled 4 times. Timbering of deep trenches slows up rate of work.

Trenching machine, resembling a very small chain-bucket dredge, can operate satisfactorily in narrow trenches, where soil is free from large stones; always leaving vert walls, and therefore applicable only to stable, dry soils (24).

Power shovels for trenching (with dipper, plunger, backhoe, or clamshell) are supported on timbers spanning the trench (Fig 6). As their wt comes directly on the banks, they can not be used in soft ground unless the walls are sheeted and braced. The shovel must usually be stopped while the trench is being sheeted, and the consequent delays materially decrease the output. Trenching machines, though not subject to this delay, cannot dig in such difficult soil as power shovels.

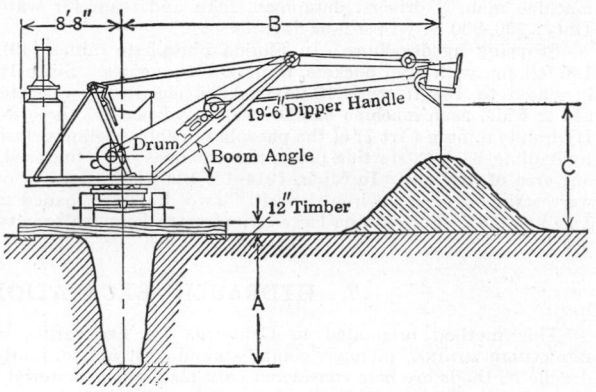

Fig 6. Trenching with Power Shovel

Dragline can dig trenches and ditches to depth of about 20 ft, and to any width greater than about 30 in; best adapted to wider work. Sloping banks are readily made, thus eliminating need of shoring and bracing. In soft, wet soils, as when the ground-water level is very near the surface, draglines can operate at about the same cost as in dryer ground. In wide ditching, it is far cheaper to use dragline and slope the banks, than to use trenching machine or clamshell, and shore the sides; added cost of moving a larger vol of earth to obviate need for shoring or bracing is negligible. Under bad soil conditions the dragline can deposit the spoil far enough from edge of trench to insure stability, which can not be done by trenching machine (24).

Trench sheeting. All deep trenches left open more than say a day should be sheeted. In fluid sands, cross bracing follows theory. In other soils, many practical shorers place heaviest braces near top rather than at bottom; for, if a wedge starts to slide from surface its center of thrust is 1/3 depth below surface.

Cableways (See Sec 26) can be used to advantage for trenches 6 ft and wider. A cableway on 30-ft towers, 300 to 400 ft apart, handling 1-cu yd tub at a time, is good in either soft digging or rock, as no part of the machine is carried on the side banks. Tubs can be loaded at any point and swung as much as 10 ft to the side. Engine and 1 tower stand on a car or rails; the other tower stands on the ground, and must be lowered for removal to a new position but can be readily shifted as work advances. Outfit, weighing about 19 tons, can be loaded on 1 R R car.

Backfilling is generally done by bulldozers or backhoes. Cost depends on: condition of soil (whether frozen, wet, packed, or dry); means employed; amount of tamping required. When back-filling and tamping are done by hand, work per man-hr is 1–3 cu yd, aver 1.5 cu yd; most compact tamping (clay excepted) is obtained by casting soil into water; for thorough dry tamping on large-scale work, use power tampers.

Ditching by explosives, if properly done, will excavate and spread the material over a distance, and is economical in dry or wet ground, or soil under water. The flow of water is depended upon to clean out the bottom. In stiff clay or hardpan, holes should be 26 in apart, in loose mucky soil, 30 in apart, and are punched or bored to within 6 in of desired depth of ditch. Strongly sodded soil is cut with a spade along side lines. For methods of charging and firing dynamite, see Sec 4, 5. Holes are best blasted simultaneously with a magneto; or placed 18 to 24 in apart and exploded by concussion from a middle hole, detonated by fuse and cap; 20% dynamite is ordinarily used, or 40% in stiff, tenacious soil. For soils soft at top, hard at bottom, use 40% dynamite in bottom of charge and 20% above.

6. STRIPPING (37–40)

For stripping and other opencut work economic methods are of utmost importance. More effective excavating machinery is now making opencut mining possible where underground methods only were formerly feasible.

Elevating grader for coal stripping in Kansas (33). Overburden, 16.5 ft aver depth, was removed in strips 60–75 ft wide, alternate strips 40 ft wide being temporarily left untouched. One side of cut was kept vert; the other sloped 1 : 2. Intervening strips were excavated after the coal first stripped was mined, and as much as possible of the material from them filled into adjoining excavations. Equipment: elevating grader and tractor, and 8 3-horse, 1.5-cu yd dump wagons. Crew: engineer, steersman for tractor, machine man, 8 drivers, dumpman, man and team for water wagon, and stableman. Duty: 750–800 cu yd per 9-hr day.

Stripping by draglines. In Florida phosphate mines (49), the booms were at first 136 ft long, with 8-yd buckets, using Diesel engines. Since 1920, boom length has been increased to 168 ft, with 10-yd buckets, electrically operated. In excavations about 210 ft wide, each machine handles 600 cu yd per hr; three 8-hr shifts, 3 men per shift. Hydraulic mining (Art 7) of the phosphate pebbles follows close behind draglines, so that, by hauling back to starting point, the draglines place material from second cut in mined out area of first cut. In Mich, 1914–15, 1 200 000 cu yd of overburden 60–100 ft deep, were stripped from an iron deposit. Two draglines loaded 206 000 cu yd into cars in 1 month (38). For data on large strippings in Penn anthracite district, see Bib (42) and Sec 10.

7. HYDRAULIC EXCAVATION

This method originated in California for excavating gold-bearing gravels. For HYDRAULIC MINING, piping, "giants" (monitors), and ground sluices, see Sec 10. Hydraulic methods are here considered only for moving material in ordinary excavation, as for hydraulic-fill dams, embankments, and grading (33).

Hydraulicking is essentially a loosening operation, attacking the material on a nearly vert face, with high-press hydraulic nozzles, and is obviously suitable only where earth is moved downgrade. Ample water supply, either gravity or pumped, is essential. Centrifugal pumps (Sec 40) are generally used. For gravity supply the head may be several hundred ft. A head of 80–100 ft may remove the material, but 200–600 ft heads are often needed for effic cutting. Quantity of water is determined by head, size of nozzle and rate of work. Water delivered by hydraulic giants is approx:

Diam of nozzle, in	1	3	6	9
Flow under 200-ft head, cu ft per min	33	250	1 500	2 700

One 8-in nozzle, using 3 600 cu ft per min, has excavated 800 cu yd per hr; but, a number of small nozzles are sometimes more effective than a single large one. Sluices for transporting mixture of water and earth usually require a grade of 4%. Proportion of solids that water will carry is from 6 to 20%; aver, 11–12% (Sec 10).

Stripping by sluicing and hydraulicking (35). Fig 7 shows layout for an ore deposit in Mesabi district, Minn. Overburden was sluiced into a nearby river so long as the difference in elevation permitted. Afterward, a hydraulic giant undercut the overburden, washing it through a rough sluiceway to sump, whence a centrifugal sand pump delivered it 1 000 ft through 12-in pipe to river (Fig 7). Giant was supplied by pumps of 3 500 gal per min rated capac, pumping through 1 500 ft of 12-in pipe. The centrifugal pump (capac 5 000 gal) required care to keep it at proper speed to deal with sump inflow. Overburden, of unconsolidated glacial drift, washed easily and work was done cheaply. In another case (35), from 3 to 6 ft of loam, sand and gravel were washed off a shale deposit by 2 giants, with normal water press of 115 lb. Crew: engineer, fireman, and 2 men on the giants. Aver duty, 2 000 cu yd per 10 hr. Cost, 2¢ per cu yd.

Hydraulic-fill dams. With enough water, a sufficiently high working face and grade to convey mixed earth and water, dams can be built more cheaply (and as well) by hydraulicking than by ordinary methods of embankment with rolling and tamping. Water is delivered by pump or gravity to a HYDRAULIC GIANT or MONITOR; press at nozzle, 75–300 lb per sq in; veloc, 100 to 200 ft per sec; vol 8–20 cu ft per sec. When water is scarce waste may be led to sump or clarifying basin, and used again. Soil, after being loosened by monitor, is carried by sluices to pipes or flumes and thence to dam. Bank from which earth is washed must be at higher elevation than crest of dam, grade to dam being at least 2% for fine materials, and 6 to 8% for coarse, heavy stuff. Design and construction of hydraulic-fill dams should be under expert supervision (52). There have been conspicuous failures.

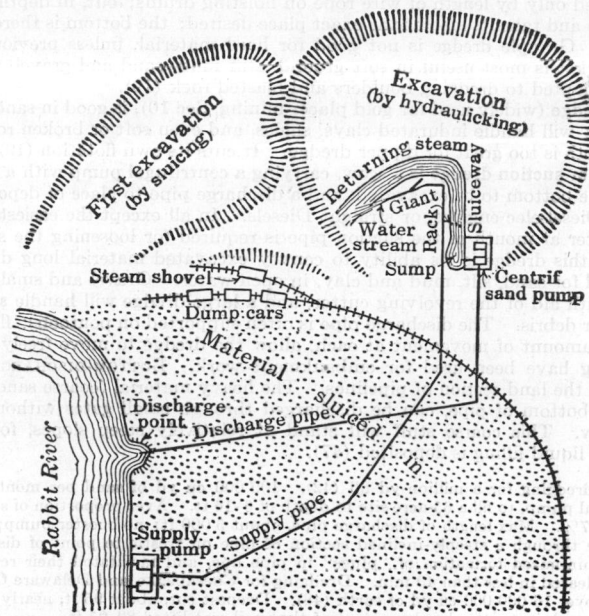

Fig 7. Layout for Hydraulic Stripping (35)

Northern Pacific R R embankment. A number of trestles were filled by the hydraulic method. In 8 cases, where there was a gravity supply of water, the cost was 4.79¢ per cu yd. In one case, pumping was necessary, making a cost of 13.5¢, which included clearing of dense forest growth.

8. DREDGING

Dredging is required to deepen waterways for navigation or flood control, and to procure sub-aqueous material for land filling and levees. It is done by a floating equipment, except on narrow channels, where draglines or walking dredges are used. Mud, silt and sand are easiest materials to excavate, but, if mingled with much water, repetition of work is sometimes needed; or, with disproportionately large quantities of water, subsequent separation may be troublesome. Sand, silt and gravels are easy to dredge; sticky clays will adhere to buckets, and may clog suction orifice or pipe line; indurated clays or hardpans may have to be blasted before dredging (17).

Depth and width of cut determine type of dredge. Distance of transport of dredged material is important, often requiring long pipe-lines, or use of scows and tugs. Sometimes material must be rehandled at an intermediate point. Permanence of work is a controlling factor. Isolated jobs may justify use of any available dredge that can do the work, even if poorly suited to it. But, in general, the plant should be closely adapted to work in hand, and have high operating effic (19).

Types of dredges: dipper; grapple or grab-bucket; ladder or bucket-elevator; hydraulic or suction. Those having bunkers or hoppers for carrying dredged material are "hopper dredges" (35).

Dipper dredge is essentially a power shovel mounted on a scow. There are 3 classes: for drainage and irrigation ditches; for deep water and harbor improvements; and for canal work. Ditching dredges are small, with narrow hulls and telescopic bank spuds; canal dredges have narrow hulls and side floats; deep-water dredges, for depths to 50 ft, are generally of large size, with spuds operated by independent engines. Wooden hulls are common, but steel hulls are now favored (Sec 10).

Grapple dredge is a floating derrick, with clamshell, orangepeel, or other type of grab bucket. It serves for very deep water or in confined places. The largest have 6-yd buckets, 225-ft booms and can dump 400 ft from digging point. Under suitable conditions they are very economical, requiring only a lever man, oiler and fireman per shift. Digging depth is limited only by length of wire rope on hoisting drums; but, in depth, the bucket may not settle and take its load at the exact place desired; the bottom is therefore usually very uneven. Grapple dredge is not good for hard material, unless previously broken. Clamshell bucket is most useful in soft ground, stiff mud, sand and gravel. Orangepeel buckets are adapted to dredging boulders and blasted rock (19).

Ladder dredge (widely used for gold placer mining, Sec 10), is good in sand and gravel, if not too fine; will handle indurated clays, shales, and even soft or broken rock and hard pan, when depth is too great for dipper dredge. It cuts its own flotation (19).

Hydraulic or suction dredge is a scow, carrying a centrifugal pump with a suction pipe reaching to the bottom to be excavated, and a discharge pipe to place of deposit. Usually powered by Diesel-elec engines, or straight Diesels. In all except the easiest materials, a revolving cutter at mouth of the suction pipe is required for loosening the soil. Special advantage of this dredge is its ability to convey excavated material long distances. It is largely used for sand, silt, mud and clay, in open water. Gravel and small stones may be dredged with aid of the revolving cutter, and a large dredge will handle stumps, loose rock and other debris. The discharge pipe is often supported on pontoons; flexible joints, with a small amount of movement at each, allow the dredge to move freely. Pipe lines 10 000 ft long have been used for embankment work. BOTTOM-DISCHARGE GATES are important for the land section of pipelines. The heavy material (coarse sand and stones) rolling along bottom of pipe, can be discharged through small gates without disturbing the main flow. This coarse stuff will stand at relatively steep slopes, forming dikes, behind which liquid filling is deposited (47).

Hydraulic dredging for a million-yd fill (42). 100 000 cu yd of sand per month pumped by 15-in centrifugal pump, to fill a 65-acre site to depth of 6–16 ft. Aver proportion of solids to water, 12.5%; max, 27%. Max length of discharge pipe, about 5 000 ft; no booster pump; total lift was close to dredge through a steeply-inclined section of pipe on trestle to point of discharge. This arrangement minimized formation of "plugs" in pipe line, and facilitated their removal; nearly all stoppages cleared in less than 40 min. Dredging for Chesapeake and Delaware Canal involved excavation of over 16 000 000 cu yd of earth (48). Deepest cut, about 95 ft, nearly all by suction dredges, with revolving cutter heads. Most of the spoil was lifted 80–95 ft.

9. EMBANKMENTS AND DAMS
(See Art 7 for hydraulic-fill dams)

Railroad embankments are generally made by filling from old trestles. A ditching machine, with 16-yd dump cars may be used for jobs to 5 000 cu yd; steam shovel for larger work. Shrinkage is usually 12% when fill is placed by wagons; to 15% when dumped from cars. Embankments are often compacted by wetting, harrowing, and rolling in thin layers. Unstable material beneath embankments may be removed by blasting, to hasten settlement (see du Pont Co's circular on this subject).

Embankment placed hydraulically (41). In 160 days, 821 000 cu yd of fine sand were placed by a suction dredge with cutting head, pumping through 24-in pipe. Pump, operated by two 500-hp elec motors, gave discharge veloc of 12–15 ft per sec; volume at times reached 1 000 cu yd per hr. Total runoff of sand from embankment was about 250 000 cu yd, adding 30% to vol handled. Length of discharge pipe was 4 000 ft, working from dredge alone; booster pump used for an additional 9 000 ft; an exceptionally long distance. Pipe carried on pontoons was No 7 gage, riveted, with slip joints; No 10 gage elsewhere.

Compacting earth-fill dams (14). For sand and silt, rolling is usually better than tamping. Best moisture content is just below saturation; layer thickness; 12 in; best rolling equipment, a heavy crawler tractor, followed by a "sheepsfoot" tamper (2), or a disk roller; 6–8 passes of the tractor over a layer produce desired density.

Vibrating machines, sometimes used, are expensive (*Eng News-Record*, July 23, 1936). For a recent (1937) Western dam, a central impervious core was built in 6-in layers, sprinkled to maintain moisture content at about 16%. Core compacted by 12 or more passes of "sheepsfoot" roller, giving a press of 250 lb per sq in.

Change in volume by compacting. On an earth dam, where a mixture of earth and gravel was hauled in wagons and sprinkled and rolled in 6-in layers, it was found that material weighing 116.5 lb per cu ft in its natural bank, weighed only 79.6 lb per cu ft as dumped loosely by wagons; that is, it swelled 46%; after consolidation by rolling in thin layers, it weighed 133 lb per cu ft, a shrinkage of 12%. An exception to the general proposition that earth can be compacted to less than its original volume is dry clay, particularly when taken from deep pits; it absorbs moisture from the air, and occupies more space in embankment than in its original bed (33).

BIBLIOGRAPHY

(A) *Trans* Amer Soc Civ Engrs. (B) *Eng News-Record.* (C) *Eng & Min Jour*
1. Holcomb. *Civil Eng'g*, Oct, 1930, p 26
2. Milligan, D. A.   Modern Methods of Moving Earth. Pub Cleveland Tractor Co, 1938
3. Teraghi.   (A) Vol 93, 1929, p 270
4. Gilboy.   (A) Vol 98, 1935, p 218.   (B) Feb 10, 1938, p 241
5. Hogentogler.   Engineering Properties of Soils. McGraw-Hill Book Co, 1937
6. Casagrande, *Proc* Internat Conf on Soil Mechanics and Foundations, 1936, p 37
7. Taylor, *Jour* Boston Civ Engrs, July, 1937
8. Cooling & Smith, *Proc* Internat Conf on Soil Mechanics and Foundations, 1936
9. *Public Works*, Mch, 1936, p 14
10. (B), 1917, p 519
11. (B) Feb 11, 1937, p 213
12. (B) July 1, 1937, p 32
13. Ladd.   (B) Mch 8, 1934, p 324
14. (B) June 11, 1938, p 850
15. (B) July 7, 1938, p 9
16. Powers.   Road and Street Data Book. Gillette Pub Co, 1936, p 223
17. Knappe, T. T.   Development of Earth Moving Equipment. *Civil Eng'g*, Mch, 1936, p 143
18. (B) Aug 28, 1919, p 417
19. Trautwine. Civ Engr's Pocket Book, 1937 edn
20. (B) Aug 26, 1920, p 419
21. Keystone Driller Co, *Research Bull* No 2
22. *Eng'g and Contract'g*, July, 1929, p 269
23. (B) June 5, 1924, p 977
24. *Pacific Builder and Engr*, Sep 5, 1936

25. (B) Aug 2, 1923, p 185
26. *Water Works*, Jan, 1929, p 113
27. (B) Jan 23, 1919, p 183
28. (B) May 19, 1927, p 812
29. (B) May 30, 1935, p 775
30. (B) Dec 22, 1927, p 996
31. (B) Dec 22, 1927, p 1013
32. (B) Aug 11, 1921, p 227
33. (B) Sep 4, 1924, p 384
34. (B) May 14, 1931, p 813
35. Earthwork and Its Cost. Gillette, H. P. McGraw-Hill Book Co
36. (B) Nov 8, 1928, p 697
37. Stripping with Hydraulic Giant. L. O. Kellogg. (C) Vol 97, p 166
38. Stripping with Dragline, L. E. Ives.   (C) Vol 98, p 941
39. Stripping an Anthracite Bed with Dragline.   *Coal Age*, Vol 18, p 63
40. Coal Mine Stripping with Power Shovels. Shurick and Toenniges. (B) May 5, 1932, p 642
41. *Civil Eng'g*, July, 1938, p 465
42. (B) Oct 21, 1920, p 791
43. (B) July 17, 1930, p 84
44. *Eng News*, Jan 27, 1916, p 145
45. Internat Cong of Navigation. Saunders, W. L. 1931
46. Robinson, A. W.   (A) Vol 54, part C
47. (B) Apl 3, 1930, p 55
48. (B) Oct 29, 1925, p 705
49. *Civil Eng'g*, July, 1938, p 465
50. (B) Dec 2, 1926, p 899
51. (B) Apr 23, 1931, p 687
52. Hydraulic-fill Dams. C. D. Hazen.   (A) Vol 83, pp 1701–1800

SECTION 4

EXPLOSIVES

BY

H. G. HASKELL, E.M., FLETCHER B. HOLMES, A.B., ARTHUR LA MOTTE,

AND F. J. LEMAISTRE, PH.G., B.Sc.

REVISED FOR THE SECOND AND THIRD EDITIONS BY

ARTHUR LA MOTTE, FLETCHER B. HOLMES AND F. J. LEMAISTRE

Note. Numbers in parentheses in text refer to Bibliography at end of this section.

EXPLOSIVES

1. CHEMISTRY OF EXPLOSIVES

Underlying principles. The power of an explosive to do work depends upon the facts: (a) that a small volume of explosive is capable, under certain conditions, of changing into a large volume of gas at high temperature, and (b) that this change takes place almost instantaneously, resulting in the development of great expansive force at the moment of detonation. In the case of black blasting powder, a mixture of sulphur, charcoal and sodium or potassium nitrate, the nitrate supplies oxygen for combustion of the sulphur and charcoal. The decomposition of black powder, once started, therefore proceeds without need of oxygen from the air. The case is somewhat different with nitroglycerin, a compound of carbon, hydrogen, and nitrogen, which is explosive in itself without requiring admixture with other substances. When detonated, it is decomposed into CO_2, nitrogen, and water, which at the high temperature of explosion occupies at atmospheric pressure about 1 000 times the volume of the original nitroglycerin.

Ingredients and their properties. The common ingredients of high explosives are given in Table 1. The term " explosive base " in column 3 covers, besides compounds explosive in themselves, certain compounds which are not explosive alone, but become so when sensitized by some such substance as nitroglycerin.

Note. Throughout this section, nitroglycerin will generally be designated by N G, and other ingredients of explosives by their chemical symbols.

Reactions. When carbon burns in presence of an excess of oxygen CO_2 is formed; if there be insufficient oxygen for complete combustion, CO also is formed. When carbon in lumps burns in air, combustion is slow; but if in form of dust the reaction is very rapid, and may result in explosion. The ingredients of black blasting powder (S, charcoal and niter) are finely ground, and thoroughly incorporated, to bring all parts of the combustibles into close contact with the oxidizing ingredient, thus favoring rapid and complete combustion.

When black powder explodes, the reaction is:

$$20\,KNO_3 + 30\,C + 10\,S = 6\,K_2CO_3 + K_2SO_4 + 3\,K_2S_3 + 14\,CO_2 + 10\,CO + 10\,N_2$$

Potass nitrate	Char- coal	Sul- phur	Potass carbon- ate	Potass sul- phate	Potass trisul- phide	Carbon dioxide	Carbon mon- oxide	Nitro- gen
Solid	Solid	Solid	Solid	Solid	Solid	Gas	Gas	Gas

The explosion is accompanied by evolution of heat, which expands the gases to a very large volume, resulting in high pressure.

When nitroglycerin explodes, the reaction is:

$$4\,C_3H_5(NO_3)_3 = 12\,CO_2 + 10\,H_2O + 6\,N_2 + O_2$$

N G		Carbon dioxide	Water	Nitro- gen	Oxygen
Liquid		Gas	Vapor	Gas	Gas

The intense rapidity of this change is illustrated by the fact that, if a pipe 5 miles long were filled with N G, and a blasting cap were detonated at one end, the entire column would be converted into gas within about one second.

Dynamite consists essentially of a mixture of $NaNO_3$, wood meal, and N G. The $NaNO_3$ may be replaced by KNO_3, the wood meal by flour or sawdust, and even a portion of the N G by other organic compounds or by NH_4NO_3. The solid ingredients are not so finely divided as those of black powder, nor so thoroughly incorporated; hence, the mixture would not burn so rapidly except for the N G, the extremely rapid explosion of which so accelerates combustion of the other ingredients that the whole mixture explodes much faster than black powder. Taking a dynamite of the composition: N G, 40%; $NaNO_3$, 46%; wood meal, 14%; and assuming that wood meal has same ultimate composition as pure cellulose $(C_6H_{10}O_5)_x$, the reaction of explosion is:

$$2\,C_3H_5(NO_3)_3 + 6\,NaNO_3 + C_6H_{10}O_5 = 9\,CO_2 + 6\,N_2 + 10\,H_2O + 2\,O_2 + 3\,Na_2CO_3$$

Table 1. Ingredients of High Explosives

Ingredient	Chem symbol	Function	Remarks
Nitroglycerin.............	$C_3H_5(NO_3)_3$......	Explosive base	Liquid, highly explosive
Tetranitro-di-glycerin......	$C_6H_{10}N_4O_{13}$......	Explosive base	Viscous liquid, highly explosive, practically non-freezing
Ethylene glycol dinitrate...	$C_2H_4(NO_3)_2$......	Explosive base, and to reduce freezing point	Liquid, highly explosive, somewhat volatile, non-freezing
Nitrocellulose (guncotton)..	$(C_6H_7(NO_3)_3O_2)_x$	Explosive base and gelatinizing agent	Solid, highly inflammable, and explosive when dry
Nitrostarch..............	$(C_6H_7(NO_3)_3O_2)_x$	Explosive base	White powder, highly inflammable and explosive when dry
Organic nitro-compounds...	....	Explosive base, but used primarily to reduce freezing point	Some solid, others liquid; the higher nitro-compounds explosive, the lower non-explosive in themselves
Ammonium nitrate........	NH_4NO_3.........	⎫	Solid, not explosive alone, very soluble in water
Potassium chlorate........	$KClO_3$..........	Explosive bases and oxygen carriers	Soluble in water, highly explosive when mixed with combustible matter
Potassium perchlorate......	$KClO_4$..........	⎭	Difficultly soluble in water, highly explosive when mixed with combustible matter
Liquid oxygen.............	....	Highly volatile	Carbonaceous matter in contact becomes highly inflammable. Most sensitive when absorbed by lampblack
Sodium nitrate............	$NaNO_3$..........	Oxygen carrier	Soluble in water, not explosive alone, deliquescent
Potassium nitrate..........	KNO_3...........	Oxygen carrier	Soluble in water, not explosive alone, not deliquescent
Wood pulp...............	....	Absorbent and combustible	Best combustible absorbent; in highest grades equal to kieselguhr in absorbent capacity
Wood meal...............	....	Absorbent and combustible	Fairly high absorbent capacity
Ground coal..............	....	Combustible	....
Charcoal.................	....	Combustible	....
Flour....................	....	Combustible	....
Sulphur..................	S...............	Combustible	....
Chalk....................	$CaCO_3$..........	Antacid	....
Zinc oxide...............	ZnO.............	Antacid	....
Kieselguhr...............	SiO_2............	Absorbent	Has no value except as absorbent

Gaseous products of explosion. When explosives detonate, they usually form a mixture of solid, liquid, and gaseous products. The solid products may include sodium or potassium carbonate, sodium or potassium sulphate or sulphite, where sulphur is present in the explosive, and calcium carbonate, etc. Nearly all explosives, except black powder, form large quantities of water, becoming vapor at moment of detonation. Smoke consists of the solid products in a finely divided state. Gaseous products are of most importance to the miner, since they determine character of fumes after a blast, and provide the ruptive force. (For products of different explosives, see Sec 23, Mine Air.)

With the **Bichel pressure gage** (1) it is possible to detonate an explosive in a closed chamber, to withdraw a sample of the gases formed by the explosion, and to determine their composition. The gases produced by a 40% straight gelatin under these conditions have approximately the following composition, as determined experimentally: CO_2, 57%; N_2, 42%; O_2, 1%. Fumes given off by any explosive fired in a vacuum do not correspond with those fired under strong confinement. The material blasted may greatly change the character of fumes, either by entering into the reaction, or by exercising a cooling effect on the explosion. Presence of water or high humidity also may alter the fumes produced. The composition of the gases varies with different explosives. In some cases there is a small amount of free O_2, as in example cited above; in others, no free O_2 but varying amounts of CO and H_2. CO is poisonous, and serious or even fatal consequences may result from the use of explosives which produce large amounts of this gas in places where ventilation is poor. See Table 2.

Table 2. Fumes, Special Gelatin 60%

Tested in Bichel Bomb; no confinement other than bomb itself. Total gas = 5.35 cu ft per lb.

	By %	Cu ft per lb	Cu ft per $1 \frac{1}{4}'' \times 8''$ cartridge		By %	Cu ft per lb	Cu ft per $1 \frac{1}{4}'' \times 8''$ cartridge
CO_2	47.1%	2.52	1.23	CH_4	0.7%	0.04	0.02
CO	1.5	0.08	0.04	H_2S	1.2	trace	trace
O_2	nil	nil	nil	NO_2	nil ·	nil	nil
H_2	3.6	0.19	0.10	N_2	45.9	2.46	1.20
						5.35	2.62

Some states have passed regulations requiring makers of explosives to mark their containers according to the fume class, which refers to amount of poisonous gas (CO and H_2S) in cu ft per $1\frac{1}{4}'' \times 8''$ cartridge, when tested according to standard procedure of U S Bur of Mines. Fume Class 1, less than 0.16 cu ft; Fume Class 2, 0.16 to 0.33 cu ft; Fume Class 3, 0.33 to 0.67 cu ft.

Fume Class 1 includes: Straight Gelatins, 20% to 60%; Ammonia Gelatins, 30% to 75%; Ammonia Semi-gelatins (less than 128 cartridges).

Fume Class 2 includes: Permissible gelatins and Semi-gelatins; Ammonia Dynamites, 15% to 60%; Low-density Ammonia Dynamites (not dipped); Class A Ammonia Permissibles; Straight Dynamites, 10% to 30%.

Fume Class 3 includes: Low-density Ammonia Dynamites (dipped); Class B Ammonia Permissibles.

Explosives complying with the requirements of Fume Class 1 may be used in underground workings free from combustible gases and/or combustible dust without specific application by the operator to the Industrial Accident Commission. The Commission also provides that the explosive: (1) has not deteriorated by prolonged or improper storage; (2) is properly charged and stemmed with non-combustible stemming; (3) does not have a burden so heavy that it will be liable to blow out; (4) is not overloaded; and (5) that the mine is properly ventilated.

Before blasting, men must be removed to a safe distance from the face, and shall not return until the poisonous gases have been cleared. Explosives complying with the requirements of Fume Classes 2 and 3 shall not be used underground unless the operator has made specific application to, and shown to the satisfaction of, Industrial Accident Commission that ventilation is adequate.

Character of fumes from an explosive is affected by conditions under which explosive is used. When dynamite BURNS instead of detonating the fumes are entirely different from those formed by detonation, and contain large amounts of oxides of nitrogen and CO, both poisonous. Burning of dynamite in a drill-hole may result from improper mode of charging; for example, if the fuse be passed through a cartridge, the dynamite may be ignited by side-spit of fire from fuse. Blown-out shots are apt to produce noxious fumes; well-tamped shots are least apt to yield them. When dynamite is so charged that maximum amount of useful work is done, the fumes are least harmful.

Ammonia gelatins, straight gelatins and semi-gelatins give the least vol of noxious fumes per lb of explosive. The ammonia dynamites are next in order and the straight dynamites are the worst. All of these give off much worse fumes when fired unconfined than when tamped with adequate stemming.

2. HIGH EXPLOSIVES

General classification of explosives. There are two general classes: (*a*) the different types of black blasting powder, and (*b*) high explosives. Black powder is a mixture of combustible and oxidizing ingredients, no one of which is explosive alone; high explosives always contain an ingredient which is explosive in itself, at least when sensitized by proper means. Because of this difference in composition, high explosive detonates with much greater rapidity than black powder; hence, the great rending and shattering effect of high explosive, even when unconfined. It is a common idea that high explosives " shoot down," while black powder " shoots up." This fallacy arises from the fact that the slow black powder, when exploded unconfined on top of a rock or other object, does no damage to the rock, but dissipates into the air; while the quicker high explosive, under same conditions may break the rock beneath it, even without confinement other than that of the atmosphere. All explosives exert equal pressure in all directions.

Table 3. Classification of High Explosives

Principal types	Essential ingredients
1. Straight dynamite............................	Nitroglycerin, sodium nitrate, and wood pulp or other combustible material
2. Ammonia dynamite............................	Like 1, with addition of ammonium nitrate
3. Straight gelatin.............................	Nitroglycerin, nitrocotton, sodium nitrate, and wood pulp or other combustible material
4. Ammonia gelatin.............................	Like 3, with addition of ammonium nitrate
5. Blasting gelatin.............................	Nitroglycerin and nitrocotton
6. Granulated dynamite.........................	Sodium nitrate, sulphur, and coal, sensitized by nitroglycerin
7. Special explosives for coal mines.. { Gelatin permissibles. Used in very wet work, especially for "lifters" where coal is cut at roof	Similar to 3 and 4, containing ammonium chloride and sodium chloride to reduce the temp of detonation
Ammonium nitrate class.....	High percentage of ammonium nitrate, with low percentages of nitroglycerin and wood pulp
8. Explosives not containing nitroglycerin......... { Ammonium nitrate class.....	Ammonium nitrate, with small amount of organic nitro-compounds
Nitrostarch class...........	Nitrostarch, sodium nitrate, ammonium nitrate and combustible material
Chlorate class..............	Potassium chlorate or perchlorate, with organic substances
9. Liquid-oxygen explosives.....................	Liquid oxygen and finely divided carbon

Note. Low-freezing modifications of nearly all dynamites and gelatins are also on the market. They have same essential composition as the above, with additional ingredients which cause them to remain unfrozen for a long time at temp far below freezing point of other N G explosives.

Properties. The different types of high explosives (Table 3) vary widely in their properties. Some are exceedingly quick, others relatively slow, still others intermediate in quickness. They also vary in density, from the heavy gelatins to some of the coalmine powders, which are very light. High explosives are graded according to their strength compared with straight dynamite, the only type in which the grade strength corresponds to actual percentage of nitroglycerin contained in the explosive. The other types make up their strength by use of nitro-substitution compounds, explosive salts and guncotton. High explosives containing no N G are graded as for "40%."

Straight dynamite containing only N G, $NaNO_3$, wood meal, and an antacid (Table 1), is taken as standard because it is the simplest and best known type of high explosive in the U S. It is more or less pulpy, easily crumbled when wrapper is removed, obtainable in different strengths up to 60%, very quick, fairly waterproof, and the most sensitive of the dynamites. A 50-lb case contains 100 $1\frac{1}{4}$ by 8-in sticks. Straight dynamites are suitable for work requiring strength and quickness, where water conditions are not too severe; not recommended where ventilation is poor. High explosives made from tetranitro-diglycerol have a freezing point of −35° F.

Ammonia dynamites have explosive base consisting of N G and NH_4NO_3. They are of same strengths as straight dynamites, but slightly slower and less sensitive; are not easily ignited by flame, and, hence, not liable to be lighted by side-spit of fuse. Because of the solubility of NH_4NO_3 in water, they require more care in wet work than straight dynamites.

Straight gelatins are distinguished by plasticity, high density, imperviousness to water, and comparative freedom of their explosion products from noxious fumes; good for wet work, or where ventilation is poor and where a "permissible explosive" is unnecessary. They contain guncotton dissolved in N G, making a jelly which coats the soluble ingredients, and imparts to latter its own characteristics.

Ammonia gelatins are somewhat similar to the straight gelatins in plasticity, density and fumes, but they do not stand water quite so well.

Blasting gelatin is a tough, elastic, jelly-like mass which, except for 1% of antacid, consists entirely of N G and nitro-cotton. It is the strongest and most water-resisting of all explosives.

When loaded to fill drill-hole completely it is excellent for hard rock, especially where large holes can not be drilled. Owing to its elasticity it is difficult to make it fill the holes completely; whence, a loss of efficiency. Best results are obtained if explosive is charged with wrappers on; it can then be pressed in to fill the hole, without so much tendency to spring back and leave unfilled spaces. When soft and plastic, blasting gelatin is no more dangerous than other explosives, but when frozen it should be handled very carefully. It is dangerous to break frozen sticks of blasting gelatin. Use of a proportion of ethylene glycol with the glycerin, nitrated, makes a satisfactory low-freezing Blasting Gelatin.

Granular dynamites are mixtures of $NaNO_3$ and combustible dope in form of hard grains, with a small percentage of N G. They are free running, especially the lowest grade, known as R R P, containing 5% N G, which is in grains nearly corresponding in size to FF blasting powder. R R P dynamite is usually packed in paraffined bags, containing 12 1/2 lb. Granular dynamites are slowest of all dynamites, approaching black powder more nearly than other high explosives; not well adapted for wet work, but resist water better than black powder; especially useful for stripping work in sprung holes and for loosening sand and earth.

Trinitrotoluene (TNT) is a brownish, yellow powder, the higher grades melting at about 80° C. It is chiefly used in commercial explosives for making Cordeau fuse; has sometimes been used as an explosive ingredient. TNT is about as strong as 50% Straight Dynamite, but, owing to very great oxygen deficiency, its explosion produces so much CO that it can not be used underground where ventilation is poor.

Picric acid has been used as an explosive. It acts somewhat like TNT, but is uncertain in its behavior and has the added disadvantage of staining everything with which it comes in contact a bright yellow. Neither TNT nor picric acid stands water very well.

Coal mining explosives. Permissible explosives, formerly called short-flame or safety explosives, should be used in mines containing dangerous amounts of inflammable gas or dust. They have been used in the U S since 1902, when 11 300 lb were sold. In 1913, 27 685 771 lb of permissibles were sold, and in 1936, 47 859 019 lb.

"Permissibles." At the Pittsburgh testing station of U S Bureau of Mines, coal-mining explosives are tested to determine whether they meet definite requirements for safety in "fiery" mines. Those which pass the prescribed physical and chemical tests are classed as "permissible" explosives (27), lists of which are published at intervals.

The tests include firing "blown-out" shots into explosive mixtures of gas and air, coal dust and air, or gas and dust with air, in a steel gallery. Explosives which do not cause ignition of such mixtures, and are also satisfactory as to chemical composition, stability, sensitiveness, and volume of poisonous gases evolved, are considered "permissible," when used under prescribed conditions. These explosives are recommended by U S Bureau of Mines for use in collieries, and in some states are required by law for dangerous mines. Bureau of Mines bulletins describe methods of testing, results, and fees for testing explosives (21, 27, 30, 43).

Classification of permissible explosives in the U S: (a) ammonium-nitrate explosives, containing NH_4NO_3 as chief ingredient, are insensitive to shock, free from liability to ignition from side-spit of fuse, and produce small amount of noxious fumes; (b) hydrated explosives (now obsolete), in which the desired reduction of temperature results chiefly from water of crystallization of salts included in their composition; (c) explosives of the organic-nitrate (other than N G class) include nitrostarch explosives; (d) nitroglycerin class comprises those containing N G which are not included in the other classes, and are now obsolete, the gelatin permissibles being far superior as to water resistance and freedom from fumes. In each class are explosives of widely varying properties, and the selection of a suitable "permissible" depends largely upon local conditions (24, 27, 43).

High explosives not containing N G usually contain no liquid ingredient which can freeze, a decided advantage in cold climates. They are usually lacking in plasticity, are often somewhat dusty, and have the disadvantages of low density, low strength, and low sensitiveness. They can not be used indiscriminately instead of N G explosives, but are useful for special purposes.

Low-freezing explosives, made from tetra-nitro-di-glycerin and ethylene glycol dinitrate, are similar in properties to other nitroglycerin explosives, but will resist freezing at temperatures considerably below the freezing point of nitroglycerin and may remain unfrozen for days or weeks at temperatures as low as $-35°$ F. They are much superior to dynamites, having the freezing point lowered by the addition of nitro-aromatic compounds and have practically done away with the necessity of thawing explosives anywhere in the United States.

Liquid-oxygen explosives have not been successful in underground work in the U S, although used in the iron mines in Lorraine. They are also used extensively in coal stripping in the Middle West, where large blasts are made in the overburden. They are fired with electric blasting caps, or Cordeau. Great care must be taken in their use, as the oxygen causes the grass or other combustible material around the operation to become extremely inflammable. Their principal advantage is cheapness; disadvantages are that they must be fired in a relatively short time after the cartridges of finely divided carbon, lamp black or gas black are dipped in the liquid oxygen, and strength of the cartridges is extremely variable. They are more sensitive to impact than any other commercial high explosive.

They are fired with either fuse or electric blasting cap, but care must be taken that the liquid oxygen does not run down the fuse, as it is liable to explode prematurely. They have been used with some success in very large cartridges in well drill-holes for quarrying, and in Lorraine, France, in the iron mines, largely owing to the fact that for a time they escaped the government tax on explosives (14, 15). Chlorate of potash or sodium with a liquid nitro-aromatic ("Rack-a-Rock") is still used in some parts of the world. It has to be prepared immediately before using and it becomes unstable with age.

Testing high explosives. While laboratory tests, however elaborate, can not entirely replace practical field tests, in determining relative value of different explosives for any particular work, they can aid in selection, if carried out with suitable apparatus and by competent persons. No single apparatus or test is sufficient, since the practical value of an explosive depends upon many factors. Some of the more important factors, determinable in a well-equipped laboratory, are: STRENGTH: determined in the ballistic mortar (5, 10) or in the Druckmesser. QUICKNESS, or velocity of detonation: determined by the Bichel (1) or the Dautriche method (10). STRENGTH AND QUICKNESS combined: determined by the Trauzl lead block test (2). (Note. For a discussion of the Druckmesser, Trauzl, and ballistic mortar tests, with comparison of results, see Rep Eighth International Cong Applied Chem, N Y, Vol 25, p 217). SAFETY in gaseous and dusty mines: determined by means of a testing gallery, as at the testing plant of the U S Bureau of Mines, Pittsburgh (63). OTHER FACTORS are: propagating power, density, resistance to water, resistance to freezing, stability, and sensitiveness to impact. Density of high explosives is generally expressed in number of 1 1/4 by 8-in cartridges per 50-lb case. Fig 1 and Table 4 show the relation.

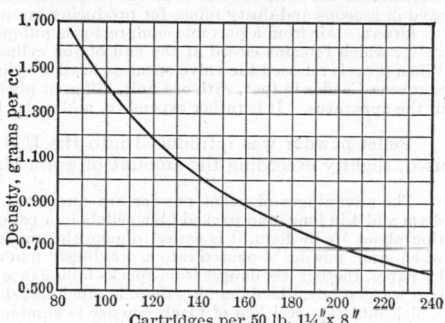

Fig 1. Stick Count of Cartridges *vs* Density

Table 4. Approximate Number Cartridges per 50-lb Case

Size of ctge, in	Straight dynamite	Ammonia dynamite	35% gelatin	60% gelatin	Semi-gelatin (high density)	Semi-gelatin (low density)
7/8 × 8	205	220	167	178	204	234
1 × 8	155	167	132	142	156	178
1 1/8 × 8	127	137	111	118	130	148
1 1/4 × 8	102	110	89	96	105	120
1 1/2 × 8	75	79	59	63	75	86
2 × 8	42	45	34	37	42	48

3. BLACK BLASTING POWDER

" A " blasting powder (saltpeter) is made from KNO_3, charcoal, and sulphur, in the approximate proportions of 75, 15, and 10. It is used mainly in quarrying, for blasting hard dimension stone, and for work in damp climates.

" B " blasting powder (soda) is made from $NaNO_3$, charcoal, and sulphur, in the approximate proportions of 72, 16, and 12. Because of its lower cost " B " powder is more commonly used than "A" powder, and is sufficiently strong for most of the purposes for which black powders are used. Owing to deliquescent property of soda niter, "B" powder is less desirable for use in damp climates, and for long transportation or storage.

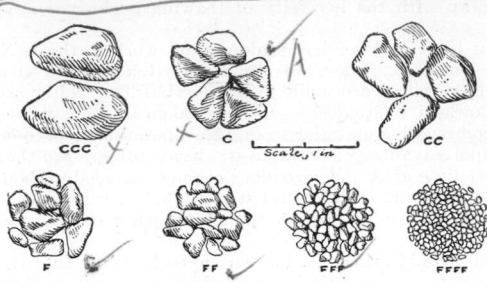

Fig 2. Standard Sizes of Black Powder Grains

Important properties. Black powder is not made in different strengths like dynamite, but varies in quickness, depending upon size of grain. Classes "A" and "B" are of different granulations. For "A" powder the common sizes are C, F, FF, and FFF; for "B" powder, CCC, CC, C, F, FF, FFF, FFFF. The CCC grains, representing largest size and rarely used, are about $1/2$ in diameter; FFFF grains, the smallest, are about $1/16$ in diameter. Fig 2 shows the sizes to scale.

The finer granulations are quicker than the coarser, and are used for blasting rock, coking coal, etc; the coarser granulations are slow and are used for other coals, shale and earthwork, or wherever it is desirable to heave out the material in large pieces, instead of shattering it (see Art 9). Blasting powder is either glazed (polished) or unglazed. Glazed powder is brighter, and more free-running than unglazed, and is more generally used. Glazing does not increase effic and produces more smoke. The sp gr of black powder varies from 1.5 to 1.9, usually about 1.8. High sp gr results from compressing the powder to smaller bulk, with consequent reduction of air-spaces in the grain. Black powder is unaffected by cold, but has little resistance to water, since niter is readily soluble.

Cardox depends for its action on rupture of the disk at one end of a steel cylinder, filled with liquid CO_2 and containing a heating agent somewhat similar to Thermite. This gasifies the liquid CO_2, breaks the disk and emits gas at end of the cylinder at bottom of the borehole. Cardox is used in gaseous and dusty mines for producing lump coal.

Airdox. Air from a portable compressor is pumped into a steel cylinder having a double-acting valve, which remains closed at the end of the cylinder as long as press is applied inside cylinder. When press is released the valve opens at head of cylinder, releasing the air. Airdox has the advantage over Cardox in that, with one unit, different pressures can be applied to the coal without change in the apparatus. It is rather expensive, and so far has had limited application.

Pellet powder was introduced into the U S in 1928, and in 1936, 40 933 550 lb were used, slightly exceeding the amount of grain blasting powder.

The advantages of pellet powder are numerous. Being made in cylinders of $1 1/4$ to $2 1/2$ in diam and 4 in long, and packed four pellets in a paper wrapper, each pellet having an axial perforation about $3/8$ in diam, it is easier to gage the amount of explosive needed for a certain shot than when grain powder is poured into a previously made paper tube. As the cartridges are protected by paper, there is less danger from sparks falling into the explosive, and the cartridges being packed in a wooden box, like dynamite, there is much less danger from handling, and the hazard of driving a pick into the steel keg of black powder is eliminated. Pellet powder can be used in somewhat wet holes, provided the charge is fired immediately after tamping. It is best fired by an electric squib, a miner's squib or safety fuse.

Composition of Explosives Listed in Table 5

" *Hi-Velocity* " *Blasting gelatin* is a modification of Blasting gelatin, by which the explosive reaches its maximum velocity at once, regardless of the water pressure under which it is used. Not suitable for close work underground.

Du Pont " *Extra* " has high ammonia content and low nitroglycerin, excellent fumes, but a very slow, heaving action; 135 to 170 cartridges, $1 1/4$ in by 8 in, per 50-lb case.

" *Gelex* " *No 2* is a low density, high ammonia, semi-gelatin, having a cartridge count of about 120; is fairly plastic, sticks well in uppers, and is one of the best explosives for close work; also one of the most economical.

" *Red Cross* " *blasting* is a free running, granular high explosive, especially designed for sprung-holes, although successful in certain kinds of work where there is little moisture.

" *Gelobel* " *No 4*, a permissible of the semi-gelatin type; resists water well and has good fumes. Much used for rock work in gaseous and dusty mines and for producing lump coal where hard-rock bands are encountered.

" *Monobel* " is a permissible made in 5 grades, designated by letters A, B, C, D and E, running from 135 to 205, $1 1/4$ in by 8 in, cartridges per 50-lb case. They have much lower velocities than the Duobels, and with the latter comprise a series of permissibles adapted to every type of coal mining where the work is dry.

Table 5. Brands of Explosives and Uses to Which They Are Adapted

Class of work				Explosive recommended	Class of Work				Explosive recommended
Artesian wells.........				Hi-velocity 80% blasting gelatin	Ore mines...........				Gelex 1 and 2
Boulders	Block-holes..			Du Pont Extra D-H	Quarries	Coyote tunnels ...			Nitramon Red Cross 40%
	Mud-caps...			Straight 40–60%		Block-holes.......			Du Pont Extra D-H
	Snake-holes..			Gelatin 40–60%		Air-hammer holes	Sprung..		Red cross blasting
Clay mining	Open-pit.....	Wet		Gelex 2			Not sprung..		Du Pont Extra
		Dry		Pellet powder Red Cross blasting		Well-drill holes....			Nitramon
	Under-ground	Wet		Gelex 2	Salamanders.........				Blasting gelatin
		Dry		Pellet powder	Salt mining..........				LV Du Pont Extra
Coal mining	Non-gaseous...			Pellet powder	Scrapping old machy..				Straight 40-60%
	Gaseous	Wet		Gelobel 4	Shaft sinking.........				Du Pont gelatin 40–60%
		Dry		Monobel or Duobel Lump Coal C	Stripping	Well drills........			Nitramon
Concrete and masonry..				Red Cross 40%		Hammer drills	Wet...		Gelatin 40%
Foundation excavations.				Special gelatin 30–40%			Dry....		Red Cross Extra
Gullies...............				Red Cross blasting 2		Horizontal holes...			Red Cross blasting 2-4
Gypsum mining	Open-pit.....			Gelex 2	Springing............				Straight 40–60%
	Underground.			Du Pont Extra E–1, G–1	Sprung holes.........				Red Cross blasting 2-3-5
Ice blasting...........				Gelatin 40%	Submarine blasting....				Hi-velocity gelatin Straight 60%
Log jams.............				Straight 40–60%	Tunneling and drifting.				Gelatin, Du Pont or Special 40-60%
Lime-stone mining	Hand-loaded...			Du Pont Extra D-E					
	Machine loaded.......			Du Pont Extra C-1 to F-1					
Open-pit mining	Sprung holes...	Wet.		Gelatin 30%					
		Dry.		Red Cross blasting					
	Airhammer holes.......			Gelex 2					
	Well-drill holes.			Gelatin and Du Pont Extras					

"Duobel" is the name of high-velocity permissibles, lettered from A to G and running from 135 cartridges, 1 1/4 in by 8 in, per 50-lb case for Duobel A, to 250 for Duobel G.

"Lump Coal" C is a new permissible having medium density and extremely low velocity. At present made only in cartridges 1 1/2 in diam. It runs 118, 1 1/2 in by 8 in, cartridges per 50-lb case, or 160, 1 1/4 in by 8 in diam per case, although it is, at present, not made of 1 1/4 in diam.

"Red Cross" Extra dynamite is an ammonia dynamite of high density, averaging 102 to 106 cartridges, 1 1/4 in by 8 in, per 50-lb case. Strengths are from 15 to 60% and suited to a wide variety of work.

"Special" gelatin is an ammonia gelatin similar in most respects to du Pont gelatin, but not quite so water resisting and not adapted for very wet work, like submarine blasting. Its fumes are considered slightly better than straight du Pont gelatin; not quite so dense as the latter.

" *Seismogel* " A and B are 60% Special Ammonia dynamites, A being packed very hard, and B grade medium hard, providing the rigidity necessary in certain phases of shooting in seismic prospecting.

Straight dynamite consists of N G, nitrate of soda, wood pulp and a small amount of chalk. It is the only explosive at present in which the grade corresponds to actual percentage of N G. Has very poor fumes and should not be used underground. Very quick in its action and especially adapted where little or no tamping can be used.

Du Pont "Extras" D-1, E-1, F-1 and G-1 are of considerably lower velocity than the regular du Pont Extras, but in other respects are similar.

" *Nitramon* " is a new blasting agent, not of itself explosive; that is, it is so insensitive that it can not be detonated by a blasting cap or impact of a rifle bullet. Requires a primer of T N T or of dynamite to explode it. It is put up in tin cans from 4 in to 8 in diam, and 21 in to 24 in long, the 21-in being the length of the 8-in diam can. Has been used very successfully in quarry work, well-drill holes and tunnels, and, when used with Cordeau or Primacord, is the safest blasting agent now known.

Blasting gelatin consists of N G and nitrocotton only, and is the strongest explosive known. Used where greatest strength is required, regardless of expense.

4. TRANSPORT OF EXPLOSIVES AND BLASTING SUPPLIES

Transport by rail. A shipper of explosives should be familiar with local ordinances, state and federal laws, and the regulations of the Interstate Commerce Commission. By Act of Congress, March 4, 1909, effective Jan 1, 1910, and as amended March 4, 1921, the Interstate Commerce Commission has power to regulate interstate transport of explosives. These regulations specify that explosives to be shipped by rail must pass certain tests for stability and sensitiveness, that containers shall stand specified tests for strength, and that cases and contents be packed in a prescribed way. Nearly all makers of explosives doing R R business pack their products to comply with the regulations. Copies of regulations are obtainable from Bureau of Explosives (17, 33).

Explosives which can not be shipped by rail include: 1. Liquid nitroglycerin. 2. Dynamite containing over 60% N G (except gelatins); see Table 2, No 3, 4, and 5. 3. Dynamite having an unsatisfactory absorbent, or showing signs of leakage of N G. 4. Nitro-cellulose in a dry condition, in quantities over 10 lb, in one outside package. 5. Dry fulminates in bulk.

The matter of forbidden explosives is of interest to the user mainly in connection with condition of his stock, in case of reshipment; then item 3 above becomes important. Dynamite stored for a great length of time, or under adverse temperature conditions, may exude N G, and become unfit for rail transport. With proper storage, reasonably rapid movement of stock, and care to use old stocks first, this condition should not arise. If necessary to ship by rail explosives not acceptable under Interstate Commerce Commission regulations, these explosives must be repacked only when authorized by Bureau of Explosives. No explosives in broken or damaged packages should be offered for rail shipment. The aforementioned Act of Congress makes it a criminal offense to ship explosives on common carriers carrying passengers for hire, or to offer for shipment any explosive under deceptive markings.

Explosives which must not be shipped together. The Bureau of Explosives publishes a chart showing the explosives and other inflammable articles which must not be shipped together. A specially important regulation is that blasting caps must not be shipped or stored with high explosives.

Condition of cars. R R cars in which explosives are shipped must be carefully inspected, and must comply with certain specifications. They must also be certified and placarded in uniform manner, as well as loaded and braced in a specified way.

Carload shipments. The Interstate Commerce Commission regulations permit shipment in one car of not more than 70 000 lb gross weight of explosives. The minimum quantity taken at carload prices varies with different railroads and in different parts of the country, ranging from 17 500 to 40 000 lb. Consignee must remove shipment of explosives from carriers' property within 48 hr after notice of arrival at destination; many railroads allow only 24 hr.

Shipment by boat. Navigation laws must be complied with, also all local regulations as to authorized docks and quantities which may be unloaded. Regulations prohibiting transport of caps with dynamite apply whether the vessel is under Interstate Commerce Commission jurisdiction or not; but it is permissible on large vessels, in certain cases, to carry caps in special compartments, entirely separate from the cargo of high explosives and at safe distance therefrom.

Shipment by wagons or trucks. Special care should be taken that vehicles used for transport of explosives are in good condition and preferably provided with springs, free from excess grease and oil, and that any exposed metal on the inside of vehicle is protected, to prevent its coming in contact with the explosives. Never overload vehicles. Put no metal or metal tools in the bed or body of vehicle carrying explosives. See that explosives transported in open-body vehicles are well covered, to protect them from sun and weather.

5. SHIPPING CONTAINERS

Black blasting powder for general use is shipped in kegs of two sizes, known as kegs and half-kegs, containing 25 and 12 1/2 lb of powder, or in 5-lb cans usually packed 20 in a box. Much of the black powder for anthracite coal fields is packed in paper cartridges or "skins," of 12 1/2 lb of powder. Two " skins " (25 lb of powder) are packed together in a long can. Approx gross weights of packages of black powder are:

25-lb keg with contents, 27 1/4 lb; 12 1/2-lb keg with contents, 13 3/4 lb; 20 5-lb cans, with contents and shipping box, 135 lb; 25-lb can, with contents in two cartridges, 29 lb.

High explosives are contained in cylindrical cartridges, about 8 in long by 7/8 to 2 in diameter. Cartridges are usually packed in wooden boxes or cases, 25 or 50 lb to the case.

Table 6. Distances for Magazines, American Practice (16)

Blasting and electric blasting caps		Other explosives		Inhabited buildings, barricaded * (Feet)	Public railway, barricaded * (Feet)	Public highway, barricaded * (Feet)
Number over	Number not over	Pounds over	Pounds not over			
1 000	5 000	....	....	15	10	5
5 000	10 000	....	....	30	20	10
10 000	20 000	....	....	60	35	18
20 000	25 000	....	50	73	45	23
25 000	50 000	50	100	120	70	35
50 000	100 000	100	200	180	110	55
100 000	150 000	200	300	260	155	75
150 000	200 000	300	400	320	190	95
200 000	250 000	400	500	360	215	110
250 000	300 000	500	600	400	240	120
300 000	350 000	600	700	430	260	130
350 000	400 000	700	800	460	275	140
400 000	450 000	800	900	490	295	150
450 000	500 000	900	1 000	510	305	155
500 000	750 000	1 000	1 500	530	320	160
750 000	1 000 000	1 500	2 000	600	360	180
1 000 000	1 500 000	2 000	3 000	650	390	195
1 500 000	2 000 000	3 000	4 000	710	425	210
2 000 000	2 500 000	4 000	5 000	750	450	225
2 500 000	3 000 000	5 000	6 000	780	470	235
3 000 000	3 500 000	6 000	7 000	805	485	245
3 500 000	4 000 000	7 000	8 000	830	500	250
4 000 000	4 500 000	8 000	9 000	850	510	255
4 500 000	5 000 000	9 000	10 000	870	520	260
5 000 000	7 500 000	10 000	15 000	890	535	265
7 500 000	10 000 000	15 000	20 000	975	585	290
10 000 000	12 500 000	20 000	25 000	1 055	635	315
12 500 000	15 000 000	25 000	30 000	1 130	680	340
15 000 000	17 500 000	30 000	35 000	1 205	725	360
17 500 000	20 000 000	35 000	40 000	1 275	765	380
		40 000	45 000	1 340	805	400
		45 000	50 000	1 400	840	420
		50 000	55 000	1 460	875	440
Note: Distances for 125 000		55 000	60 000	1 515	910	455
to 225 000 lb: from inhabited		60 000	65 000	1 565	940	470
bldgs, 1 900–2 095 ft; from		65 000	70 000	1 610	970	485
R Rs, 1 140–1 260 ft; from		70 000	75 000	1 655	995	500
highways, 570–630 ft. The		75 000	80 000	1 695	1 020	510
full schedule prescribes dis-		80 000	85 000	1 730	1 040	520
tances for quantities up to		85 000	90 000	1 760	1 060	530
500 000 lb.		90 000	95 000	1 790	1 075	540
		95 000	100 000	1 815	1 090	545
		100 000	125 000	1 835	1 100	550

* Barricaded, as here used, signifies that the building containing explosives is screened from other buildings, railways, or from highways by either natural or artificial barriers. *Where such barriers do not exist, the distances should be doubled.*

Character of cases, as to strength, thickness of wood and construction, is regulated by Interstate Commerce Commission. The number of cartridges of each size in a 50-lb case is fairly regular for any given kind of dynamite. (See Table 4.)

Approx wt per cu in: Gelatin (straight and ammonia), 0.97 oz; Dynamite (straight, ammonia, and granulated), 0.85 oz; Colliery powders, 0.63 oz. (*Note.* There are some exceptions; also a few explosives, such as the low granulated dynamites, which are packed in 12 1/2-lb paper bags, 4 bags to a case.)

Blasting supplies. Caps are packed in tin boxes, containing 100 caps, and the boxes in wooden cases of 500, 1 000, 2 000, 3 000, or 5 000 caps. Electric caps and electric squibs are packed in cardboard boxes containing 25 or 50 each, and these are packed in wooden cases of from 250 to 500 caps or squibs. Safety fuse is in coils of two 50-ft lengths; shipped in wooden boxes containing from 1 000 to 6 000 ft.

6. STORAGE OF EXPLOSIVES AND BLASTING SUPPLIES

Explosives should be stored in well-ventilated buildings, erected for the purpose. Buildings for storage of black powder or blasting supplies should be fireproof; those for dynamite, both bullet-proof and fireproof.

Location of magazine. In selecting a magazine site the local topography should be considered, and advantage taken of such natural protection as is afforded by hills and areas of timber. The magazine should be far enough from adjacent buildings to minimize danger to life or property through an accidental explosion.

Table 6 gives distances depending upon quantity of explosives required, 1919, to be maintained between magazines and inhabited buildings, public railways, and public highways.

It is the result of an investigation of a committee appointed by the explosives manufacturers of the U S, and represents conclusions reached after prolonged study of available data. The Bureau of Explosives of American Railway Association has approved and applies the distances specified to be maintained between magazines and public railways. When there are specific state laws and local regulations, they must be complied with, but if there be none, the table of distances gives the accepted practice. Where explosives are distributed among several magazines the distances between magazines should comply with the following formula (distances given are for magazines fully protected from each other by natural or artificial barriers; lacking such protection, distance should be doubled). For magazines containing 25 000 lb or under, not less than 100 ft; for magazines containing over 25 000 lb, add 1 1/3 ft for each 1 000 lb of explosives added. When applying Table 6 for location, if *magazines are nearer* than the above distances, they should be *classed as one magazine* containing total quantity of explosives stored in all. Magazines containing blasting caps should never be nearer than 50 ft to any other magazine, and if quantity is over 20 000 caps, distance should be at least 100 ft.

Construction of magazines. Dimensions of magazine without aisles:

Capacity	Dimensions	Capacity	Dimensions
5 000 lb	8 ft × 8 ft	25 000 lb	12 ft × 12 ft
10 000	8 × 10	30 000	12 × 14
15 000	8 × 12	40 000	14 × 16
20 000	10 × 12	50 000	14 × 18

These capacities are based on sizes of dynamite cases (Art 5). If permissibles or the more bulky powders are stored, capacities will be comewhat reduced.

Magazines of these sizes are for temporary use, and should therefore be as small as possible for quantity of explosives stored. They are for consumers using explosives in 2 or 3 sizes or grades; dimensions are therefore minimum for given quantities, leaving floor space sufficient only for a man to enter magazine when filled to capacity.

Dimensions of magazine with aisle from front to back and cross aisle through center:

Capacity	Dimensions	Capacity	Dimensions
5 000 lb	8 ft × 9 ft	25 000 lb	12 ft × 18 ft
10 000	10 × 12	30 000	12 × 20
15 000	12 × 12	40 000	14 × 22
20 000	12 × 16	50 000	14 × 24

In constructing a magazine consideration should be given to permanency of storage, variety of explosives, quantities in which shipments to magazine will be made, and ease of replenishing stock from distributing magazines.

Construction specifications. Stone and concrete magazines are undesirable, because of danger from missiles in case of accident. Brick or sand-filled magazines may be used for dynamite, black powder, or blasting caps. Wood and iron magazines without sand filling are suitable for black powder; other types may be used, but this is the most inexpensive construction; it is not recommended for dynamite, because it is not bullet-proof. The nature and thickness of walls varies with the kind of small arms in general use in region where magazine is situated. Tests show that it requires 10 in of sand, between walls of 1-in boards, to stop the bullet from a U S Govt Springfield rifle. Where ordinary sporting rifles, such as 30–30 Winchester, are used, 8 in of sand is sufficient. A 9-in brick wall is bullet-proof against the strongest small arms in use in U S. In the case of doors it is found that $3/8$-in boilerplate, backed with 3 thickness of $7/8$-in hardwood, will stop the

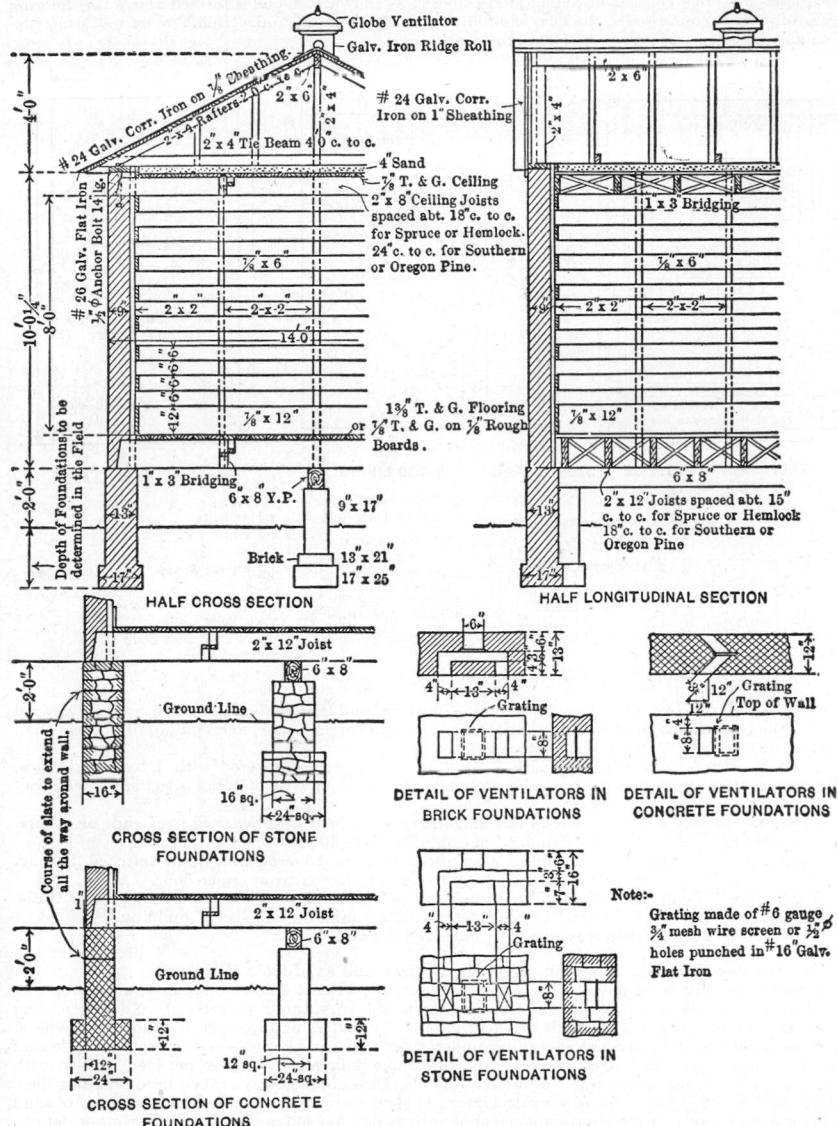

Fig 3.   Brick Dynamite Magazine

bullet from a U S Springfield rifle. This combination of iron and wood seems to be the most practicable, as any increase in thickness of either the wood or iron, with corresponding reduction of the other, adds materially to weight of the door.

Magazines of various widths may be designed along lines indicated below, size and spacing of material being revised accordingly.

(a) **Dynamite magazine of brick.** Fig 3 shows a brick dynamite magazine 14 ft wide and of any desired length consistent with this width.

Foundations may be of brick, stone, or concrete. They should reach below frost line, or to a good bearing material.

Walls are 9 in thick, laid in cement mortar. Use as soft a brick as possible, consistent with good quality and durability.

Bullet-proof roof consists of ceiling-joists, floored as shown. A box is formed above this flooring by a 6-in strip around walls, the box being filled with 4 to 6 in of sand. Bullet-proof roof construction also helps to maintain a uniform temperature.

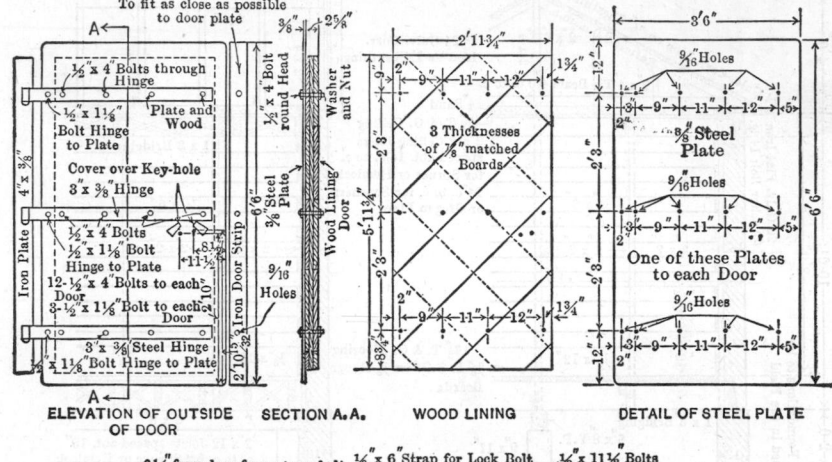

ELEVATION OF OUTSIDE OF DOOR   SECTION A.A.   WOOD LINING   DETAIL OF STEEL PLATE

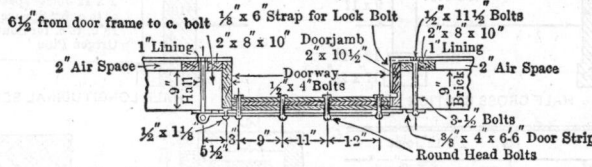

Fig 4.   Bullet-proof Door for Magazine shown in Fig 3

Roof. Rafters covered with rough boards or ship-lap, and then with No 24 corrugated galvanized iron. The iron should have side lap of not less than two corrugations, and end lap of not less than 6 in. Tin roof may be used, but is more expensive.

Lining. Brick walls are lined with 2 by 2-in nailing strips, covered with 1 by 6-in boards, forming a lattice work. Nails should be countersunk. The purpose of lining is to keep stock away from walls and assist ventilation.

Cornice. Merely a strip of No 24 flat galvanized iron, bent and fastened over ends of rafters. All iron should be put on with galvanized nails and lead washers.

Floors. 1 3/8-in matched flooring, or a sub-floor of 7/8 in, covered with 7/8-in matched flooring. Note that floor stops 2 in from brick wall, to provide ventilation from under floor.

Ventilation. Foundation is ventilated as shown in Fig 3. Roof vents should be Star or Globe ventilators, or equivalent, size and number depending on climate, and size of building.

Doors. Fig 4 shows details of door for magazine shown in Fig 3.

(b) **Wooden dynamite magazine,** covered with iron and sand-filled (Fig 5).

Foundation may be of posts, brick, stone, or concrete, as best suited to local conditions.

Walls are of two rows of 2 by 4-in studs, spaced as shown, desired quantity of sand determining spacing of studs across wall. Studs are held parallel by nailers at top, bottom, and intermediate, in number sufficient to prevent spreading under weight of sand. Studs are covered outside and inside by 7/8-in matched boards, to prevent sand from leaking away. Space between is filled with coarse sand (never use coarse gravel or broken stone because of possibility of their becoming missiles). Lower foot of filling to consist of a weak mixture of sand and cement, to prevent remainder of sand from leaking away. Outer sheating is covered with No 24 flat galvanized iron. For other details, the specifications for brick magazine apply. When post foundations are used the board apron should be ventilated by holes, 8 by 4 in, covered with punched sheet steel.

(c) **Black blasting powder magazine.** Fig 6 shows a wood and iron magazine for black powder or blasting supplies.

Walls. Of 2 by 4-in or 2 by 6-in studding, covered on outside with 7/8-in boards and No 24 flat galvanized iron; on inside, by 1 by 6-in lattice work.

Roof, cornice and floors (see specifications for brick magazine).

Foundation and ventilation (see specifications for sand-filled magazine).

Door. Standard door for this type magazine consists of two thicknesses of 7/8-in boards, covered with iron of any desired weight, No 22 being considered the lightest for security. Either a mortise lock or padlock may be used.

(d) **Iron storage magazine.** A "knock-down" iron magazine is manufactured, which is satisfactory for northern or temperate climates. Obtainable in sizes from 6 by 8 ft to 15 by 30 ft.

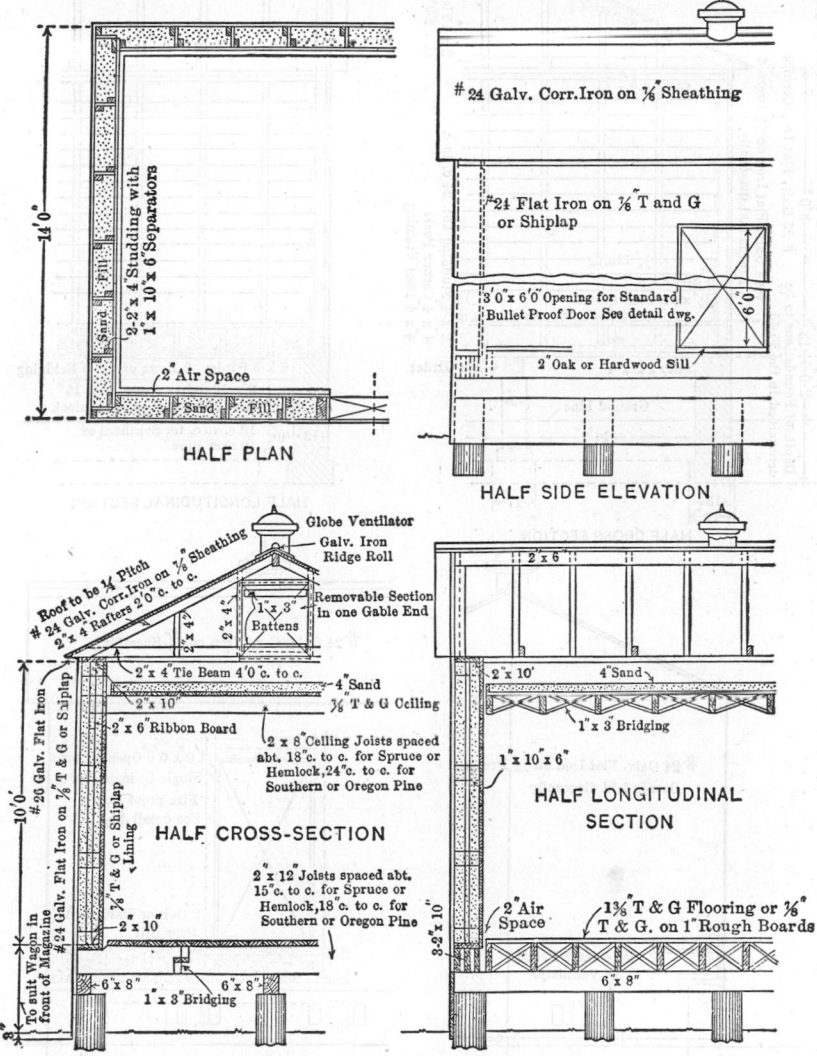

Fig 5. Wooden Dynamite Magazine

When used for dynamite storage, it should be made bullet-proof by lining with 3 or 4 in of hard wood, or with studs and sheathing, sand-filled, or with brick.

(e) **Small portable magazine,** for storage of small quantities of explosives within mine or quarry, or at stores, or within city limits. A box may be made of 2-in oak, or other hard wood and covered with sheet iron. For dynamite, iron should be at least 1/16 in thick. Top of box, of like material, should be on hinges. Inside metal should be countersunk. Box should be kept locked and marked to indicate contents.

Care of stock in magazines. Magazines should be so constructed and located that they will not be brought to high temperatures by rays of sun. N G becomes less viscous

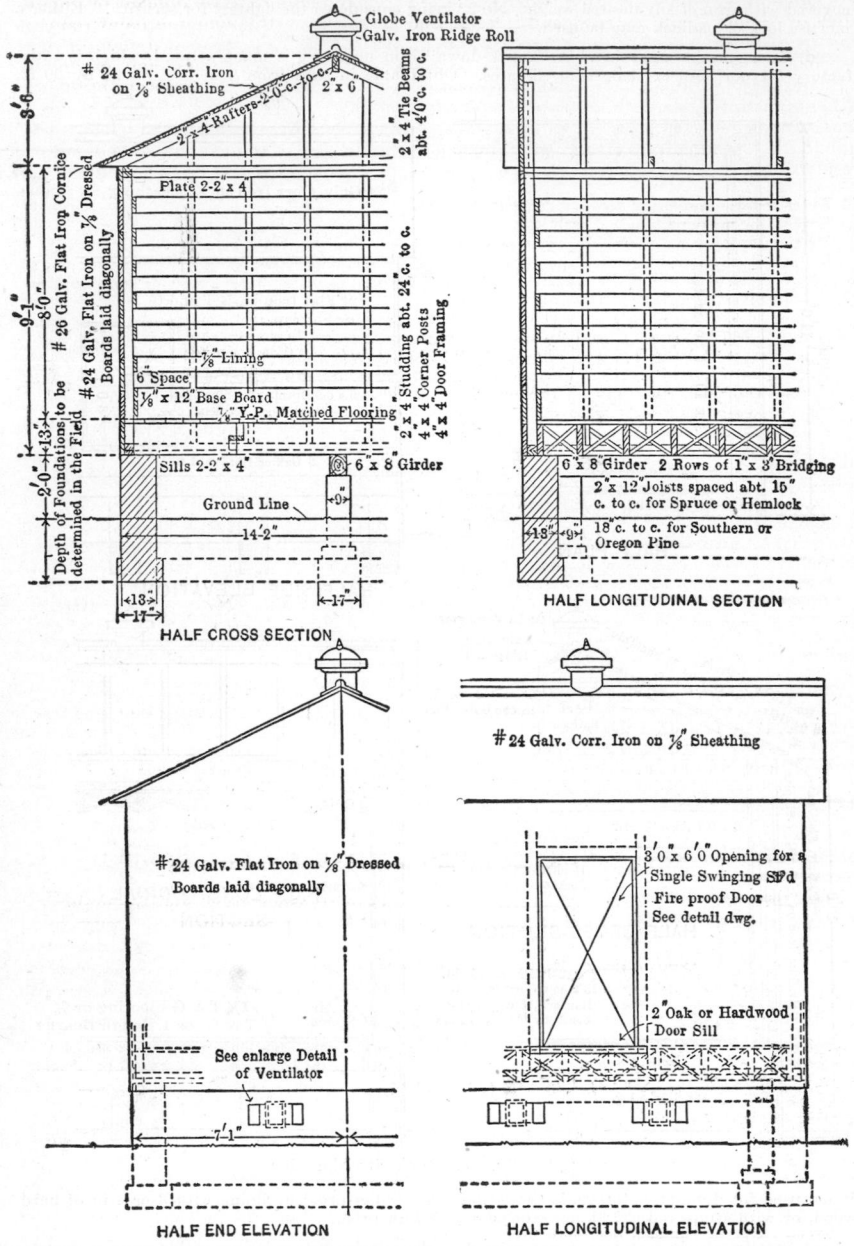

Fig 6. Black Powder Magazine

at high temperatures, which may cause the dynamite to leak. In hot climates metal magazines should be protected by double roof and sides, with good ventilation between, so that temperature in magazine will not rise above outside temperature. Dynamites containing large proportions of nitrate of ammonia, such as the ammonia permissibles, are liable to become set, so that, when subjected to high temp, they are difficult or impossible to prime. Painting roofs and sides of iron magazines with aluminum paint reduces the temp when magazine is exposed to sun's rays. Take care to keep dynamite dry, especially the ammonia dynamites, as they contain hygroscopic salts, and in humid climates may eventually attract enough moisture to impair their sensitiveness and strength. When dynamite is shipped in winter at very low temperatures, it should not be sent down immediately into the mine, as cold dynamite may condense enough moisture in the warm humid mine to impair its efficiency. Magazines should always be in charge of one person, responsible for condition of magazine and stocks, and their proper and safe handling.

Rules for dynamite and powder magazines.
Explosives must be handled carefully.
Do not throw down boxes of explosives violently, nor drag them along the floor.
Do not open boxes of dynamite or powder kegs in or near magazine.
Do not have in or about the magazine loose cartridges, open boxes of dynamite, or loose powder.
Do not make up primers in the magazine.
Do not smoke, have matches, oil-burning lamps or lanterns, fire-arms or cartridges in, or near, magazine. If artificial light be needed, use electric flashlight or electric lantern.
Do not store blasting caps nor electric blasting caps in this magazine.
Store dynamite and black powder separately. Store dynamite boxes flat, top side up, grades and brands showing; store powder kegs on sides with seams down, or on ends, bungs down.
Powder kegs should be rolled over and contents shaken every 2 or 3 months.
Always use old stocks first.
Keep magazine floor clean.
Keep the ground immediately around magazine clear of leaves, grass, trees, stumps, and débris, to prevent fire from reaching it.
Do not allow any shooting in neighborhood of magazine.
Keep the door locked. No unauthorized person should be admitted to magazine.
Do not keep any steel, or metallic tools or other implements, in the magazine.
See that good ventilation is maintained during all seasons of year.
When repairs have to be made to interior of magazine, all stocks of explosives should be removed to safe distance and carefully protected from weather during progress of repairs. Before starting repairs in a black-powder magazine scrub floor with water. If dynamite has been stored in a magazine, any stains on floor should be carefully scrubbed with solution consisting of: 1/2 gal water, 1 gal denatured alcohol, 1/4 gal acetone, 1 lb sodium sulphide (fused) or potassium sulphide.

Rules for blasting-supply magazines.
Store blasting supplies only in this magazine, i e, blasting caps, electric blasting caps, and fuse.
Do not store powder or dynamite in this magazine.
Do not have loose blasting caps, electric blasting caps, nor coils of fuse lying around magazine, nor take them out of original packages until required for use. Keep packages closed.
Open boxes with a wooden mallet, except when lids are screwed on; then use a screw driver. Do not keep any other metallic tools in magazine.

7. HANDLING OF EXPLOSIVES AND BLASTING SUPPLIES

The Interstate Commerce Commission in matters of transportation, and the majority of states in framing their laws, recognize that explosives are a commercial necessity, and furthermore that they can be handled with reasonable safety. Nevertheless, one must always recognize their nature; their function is to explode. All owners of explosives should require employes to observe rigidly the rules and regulations which experience has shown will best conserve safety of the men themselves, as well as of the public.

From cars or boats to magazine. Use only wooden or non-sparking metal tools in breaking the bracing in cars. Wooden wedges and mallets answer all practical purposes. Damaged or broken cases or kegs found in shipment should be set aside, and not taken to magazine with undamaged stock. If damage is slight, the cases or kegs should be taken to a safe distance from magazine, or from car, and repaired. If damage is too great for repair, take explosives to point of consumption and use immediately. If broken cartridges or loose grains of powder are scattered in the car, they should be carefully swept up and removed before proceeding with unloading, and afterwards destroyed. If there is a railroad siding to magazine, and runways and trucks are used, there should be no exposed metal on runways, and trucks should be rubber-tired. If an inclined chute is used, make of 1-in planed boards, with 4-in side guards throughout its length, fastened with brass screws. D-shaped strips or runners, not more than 6 in apart and running lengthwise of chute, should be fastened by wooden pegs to upper surface of bottom board. When dynamite packages are being handled, wipe down chutes with waste moistened with machine oil. A mattress, 4 by 6 ft, and not less than 4 in thick, or a heavy jute or hemp mat of like dimensions, should be placed under discharge end of chute. Chute must not be so steep that packages slide too rapidly. With a long chute, station men at frequent intervals along it, to check speed of packages and prevent bumping together. Do not rehandle or switch the car to other points after the bracing has been removed; in case part of shipment is to go to another point, the part remaining in car should be rebraced (according to Interstate Commerce Commission regulations) before car is offered for shipment. The load on any vehicle should be braced. Always protect explosives from weather.

Within mine or quarry. Same rules and regulations should be adopted as apply around magazines and elsewhere above ground. Never bring exposed lights close to explosives. Only the smallest possible quantity for economic handling or operation should be taken underground at one time. In transporting into the mine by cage or tram-car, only the man in charge should be permitted to ride in same cage or car with explosives. Primers should be made up at a point entirely separated from regular stock of dynamite. If made up above ground, they should be taken into mine at a separate time and in separate car from other explosives. In opening dynamite cases, use no metal tools other than those made of non-sparking materials; wooden wedges and mallets are best. Blasting-powder kegs should be opened by turning back the four clips at the bung and lifting the cap and paper washer with the fingers. Never drive a hole in a powder keg even with a wooden pin. The rather common practice of driving a pick or other tool through the keg is dangerous. If possible, avoid leaving dynamite or powder in mine over night. If this can not be avoided, the explosive should be left in a place set aside for that purpose, protected from dampness, and posted so that all persons will know nature of material stored.

Thawing frozen dynamite. Practically all high explosives now made in the U S are formulated on the low-freezing or non-freezing basis, so that thawing dynamite, with its attendant hazards and expense, has ceased to be a factor.

Disposition of damaged explosives. Dynamite to be destroyed should be removed from magazine in quantities not exceeding 100 lb, to a safe place 400 to 500 ft distant from any magazine, and 1 000 ft or more from any dwelling, building, public road, or railroad; where, in event of its exploding while burning, no damage will be done. Lids of boxes should be carefully removed with wooden wedge and mallet, each cartridge slit, and the opened cartridges spread upon the ground over as large a space as practicable. To insure proper burning of the dynamite, spread a quantity of straw, paper shavings, or excelsior on ground first, on which dynamite is placed. A chain of straw paper, or other material, is then led away from the dynamite to such a distance that it may be lighted without danger of flame reaching the dynamite before operator reaches a position of safety, which should be 400 or 500 ft distant. Explosions sometimes occur, even with care, and operator should never remain near the burning explosive. Black powder may be destroyed by pouring it into a stream or large body of water; the greater part quickly dissolves and remainder becomes harmless. Cases which have contained dynamite are dangerous; they should not be used again for any purpose, but should be burned, using same precautions as described above for destroying damaged dynamite.

To destroy damaged blasting caps, place them, not more than 100 at a time, in a paper bag containing a small dynamite cartridge, with a good electric blasting cap in the middle, or in contact with the damaged caps; put the bag in a hole in the ground, cover it with sand, and fire with a blasting machine from a distance not less than 200 ft. Fuse and cap can be used with care when the bag and damaged caps are completely covered. If it is impossible to dig a hole, the caps may be drowned in deep water, but not in rivers, ponds or creeks. Before being destroyed, electric blasting caps should have their wires cut off an inch or two from capsule, as the wires are liable to cushion the shock and prevent complete explosion of all the caps. Observe utmost caution in handling blasting caps, as they are extremely sensitive to shock, friction, heat, and sparks.

Precautionary Rules:

Don't forget the nature of explosives; but remember that with proper care they can be handled with comparative safety.

Don't smoke while handling explosives, and don't handle them near an open flame.

Don't leave explosives in a field where cattle can get at them. Cattle like taste of soda and saltpeter in explosives, but the other ingredients may make them sick or kill them.

Don't carry loose caps in the clothing. Keep them in their boxes.

Don't tap or attempt to open a blasting cap or electric blasting cap.

Don't try to withdraw wires from an electric blasting cap.

Don't attempt to take caps from the box by inserting a wire, nail, or other sharp metallic instrument.

Don't store or transport blasting caps or electric blasting caps with high explosives.

Don't store fuse in a hot place, as this may dry it out so that uncoiling will break it.

Don't allow priming (the placing of the detonator in dynamite) to be done in thawing-house or magazine.

Don't leave explosives, caps, or blasting machines in a wet or damp place. Keep in a suitable, dry place, under lock and key, and where children or irresponsible persons can not get at them.

Don't use frozen or chilled explosives; it is dangerous and wasteful.

Don't thaw dynamite on heated stoves, rocks, sand, bricks, or metal, nor in an oven; don't thaw dynamite in front of, near, or over, a steam boiler, forge, or fire of any kind.

Don't heat thawing-house with pipes containing steam under pressure; high temperature is dangerous and escaping steam may spoil the explosive.

Don't place a hot-water thawer over a fire; never put dynamite into hot water, nor allow it to come in contact with steam.

8. CHARGING AND FIRING EXPLOSIVES (See also Sec 5, 6)

Priming is the placing of a detonator, electric blasting cap or blasting cap attached to fuse, in a dynamite cartridge, or placing an electric squib in a cartridge of blasting powder or pellet powder. For high explosives, place detonator so that its closed end points toward bulk of the explosive. For rotation shots it is advisable to put primer at or near bottom of hole, with the detonator pointing toward the collar, to prevent the primer from being thrown out in case the collar of the hole is cut off by a previously fired shot. If primer is inserted last, place the detonator so that its closed end points toward bottom of hole.

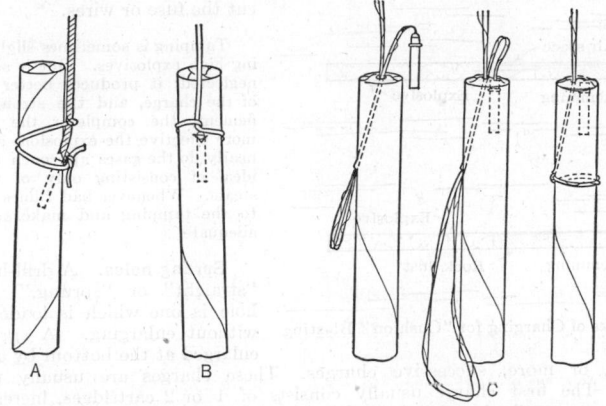

Fig 7. Methods for Priming Dynamite. A and C are recommended; B, often used

Fig 7 shows methods for priming dynamite, (A) with cap and fuse, (B) with electric blasting cap, in cartridges of 1 1/8 in diam or less, (C) with electric cap, in cartridges of 1 1/4 in diam or more.

The detonator should be so secured that it will not change its position, nor jam against sides of hole, nor come in contact with tamping stick. The wires of an electric blasting cap should not be secured in a half hitch; for, when tension is applied, the current may be short-circuited where wires cross each other. In priming dynamite with cap and fuse, the fuse should never be " laced " or run through the cartridge, because " side-spit " of fuse will often ignite dynamite, a part of which will burn, decreasing efficiency of charge and producing noxious fumes. Top of cap should be imbedded 1/2 in deep in the dynamite, to cushion it from tamping stick. This small length of fuse will not side-spit before cap explodes.

Charging. Eliminate all air spaces by slitting cartridges lengthwise with a sharp knife and pressing them firmly home, so that they expand and entirely fill the hole. Exceptions to this are: (a) Blasting gelatin should not be slit, as it is so elastic that it can not be rammed solidly like other dynamites; (b) in certain veins of coal an air space is purposely left to cushion action of explosive and so prevent undue shattering.

There are 4 methods of "cushion" blasting (Fig 8): (a) leaving an air space of 4 to 6 in or more at bottom of hole; (b) using cartridges of much smaller diam than the hole and not expanding them; (c) leaving a spacer at the end of the cartridge and tamping up solid to the spacer; (d) putting in the first and second dummy of tamping very lightly, or using rock dust for the first dummy.

Dynamite cartridges, especially gelatins, should never be broken, if there is a possibility that some portion of the explosive is frozen. They may appear soft on outside and yet have a frozen core. Breaking such a cartridge may explode it; accidents due to this practice have led to legislation in many foreign countries.

Tamping is required in practically all work except springing a hole (see below). The word "tamping" is now used to designate the act of compacting the explosive or the stemming in the drill holes, while "stemming" designates the material used for confining the explosive. Stemming is necessary for all explosives to develop their full power, to minimize amount of poisonous gases evolved, and to do the work at least cost. The only possible excuse for not using stemming is if misfires are expected, and these can generally be avoided by careful priming. It is easy to insert another primer and explode the missed charge if no stemming is used. Clay, sand, and loam make best stemming. Broken rock, screenings, and ore dust serve fairly well, but are liable to break or cut the fuse or wires.

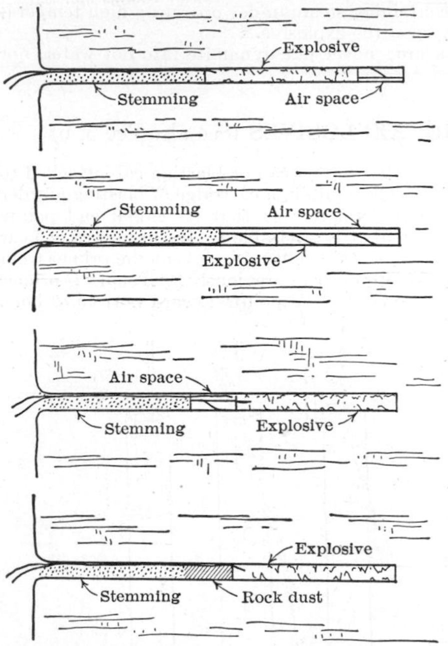

Tamping is sometimes slighted in charging high explosives. But it should not be neglected; it produces better confinement of the charge, and the stronger the confiement, the completer the reaction, the more effective the explosion, and the more nearly do the gases approach the chemist's ideal of consisting only of CO_2, N and steam. Whenever bad fumes appear, look to the tamping and make sure that it is adequate.

Sprung holes. A drill-hole may be "straight" or "sprung." A straight hole is one which is loaded and fired without enlarging. A sprung hole is enlarged at the bottom by exploding in it one, two, or more, successive charges. These charges are usually not tamped (stemmed). The first charge usually consists of 1 or 2 cartridges, increased in subsequent charges until the chamber is large enough to hold the required quantity of explosive. This operation is known as "springing," "chambering," or "squibbing."

Fig 8. Modes of Charging for "Cushion" Blasting

Springing is done to concentrate a large amount of explosive in the bottom of the hole, thereby saving cost of drilling a number of holes. Sufficient time should elapse between successive springings to allow hole to cool completely; there is great danger in charging a freshly sprung hole. Except in soft rocks, slow-acting dynamites are better for springing than the quick-acting, as more of the rock is thrown out of the hole and there is less liability to cave and choke up. If sides of hole are very rough, final charge may be loaded through a tube of brass, tin, or galvanized iron, about 2 ft longer than the hole and as large as will fit into it. This prevents cartridges from being caught on or smeared along sides of hole. Where a loading tube is not available, the cartridges are usually attached to a sharpened stick, lowered to bottom of hole and shaken off. *Never spring* a hole adjacent to a loaded one.

Wiring for electric blasting. There are three general methods: series, parallel, and parallel series connection.

In series connection (Fig 9) one of the wires from first drill-hole is connected to the leading or firing line. The other wire is then connected to one of the wires from second hole and the other wire of that to one of the wires of third hole, and so on to the last hole; the remaining free wire from that is connected to the leading or firing line. Series connection is necessary when firing with ordinary blasting machine. The current required for series connection is at least 1.5 amperes, and the voltage sufficient to overcome resistance of electric caps. Resistance varies with length of wires. About one volt is required for each cap connected in series, although an excess, up to about 440 volts, is not harmful. Too high voltage may cause misfires from short circuits across the cap wires, especially when more than one cap is used in a hole. Direct current is generally used but alternating current is equally efficient when of a frequency of 60 cycles or more, and can be used down to 25 cycles. Alternating currents of lower frequency may cause trouble from misfires of the less sensitive caps in the circuit.

In parallel wiring (Fig 10) one wire from each cap is connected to one leading line, and the second cap wire to the other leading line. This method can be used only where a power or lighting current is available, having 1.5 amperes for each cap so connected. Thus, with 20 caps, firing circuit must have at least 30 amperes. The voltage required is very low. The greater the number of caps in circuit, the lower the resistance. Assuming resistance of leading wire at 3 ohms and resist-

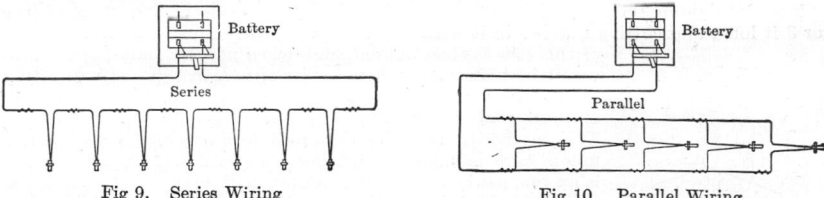

Fig 9. Series Wiring   Fig 10. Parallel Wiring

ance of each cap at 1 ohm, the resistance of 20 caps in parallel is $(1 \div 20) + 3$ ohms or 3.05 ohms. Parallel connections of ordinary electric caps are not often used on account of large volume of current required.

In parallel-series wiring (Fig 11) the caps are first connected in series of say from 4 to 10, and each series thus connected is in turn attached at its two free ends to the leading wires. The current required is found by multiplying the number of series by 1.5, which gives the current in amperes. To determine required voltage, multiply resistance of each cap by number of caps in each series, and divide that by total number of series. This system is used frequently for firing a large number of charges, where power or lighting current is available.

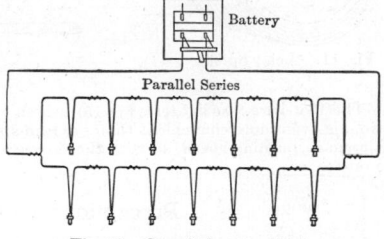

Fig 11. Parallel-series Wiring

Electric firing may be done with a blasting machine, or a power or lighting circuit. It is generally best and simplest to use a blasting machine, with the caps connected in series; but with modern, shunt-wound machines, having a capacity of 50 caps, parallel series connections have been used successfully, provided not more than four series, with 50 caps in each are connected to the machine. Ends of wires should be scraped bright and clean and twisted tightly together, and, if much water be present, covered with insulating tape. The two remaining free wires from the two caps at ends of series are then connected to the leading wires, which should be bent or hooked at end, to prevent the smaller wire from slipping if leading wires are subjected to strain. Test circuit with a

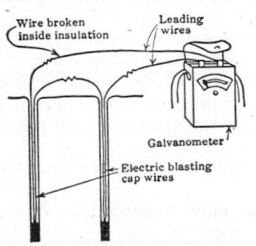

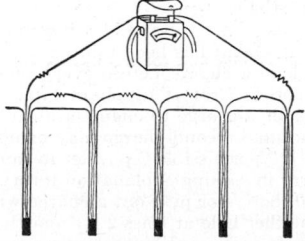

Fig 12.   Testing Circuit with   Fig 13.   Detecting Poor Contacts in
          Galvanometer   Electric Circuit

circuit tester (galvanometer) at ends of leading wires which are to be attached to battery (Fig 12). This is to be sure there are no broken connections or short circuits. Poor contacts and connections give abnormally *high resistance* readings. Looped connections of wires may show *no circuit* one moment and *normal resistance* the next. When spliced wires touch each other and make a short circuit, *no resistance* is shown (Fig 13). The ends of leading wires are inserted into the binding posts of blasting machine and firmly secured by thumb nuts. Place blasting machine on a level spot (a dry board or plank is best), to prevent its tipping over, and operate handle with both hands and full force.

If firing is by means of a power or lighting circuit, use a special switch of such design as to show at a glance whether circuit is open or closed. Avoid complicated switches, especially those having springs. The switch should be so constructed that it can be locked in the open position. The cut-out on switches should be of ample capacity and, when delay electric caps are used, the switch should be closed and opened again as quickly as possible to prevent the wires in the holes from becoming heated, sometimes sufficiently to ignite the dynamite.

Mode of lighting for cap and fuse firing. Often done by taking an extra piece of fuse 2 or 3 ft long, and cutting notches in it with a knife at intervals of about 2 in. The end of this fuse is then lighted, and, when powder train burns up to a notched place, the flame spits out vigorously. By directing each of these flames against end of the fuse to be lighted a round of shots may be lighted with certainty, in a few seconds. This method may inflict disagreeable burns on blaster's hands unless care is taken. Lighting fuse with hot lamp or candle is unsafe, as the spit of the ignited fuse may extinguish flame and leave blaster in the dark. One of the surest and safest methods is to slit the fuse at the end to expose powder train, and light it by means of a LEAD SPITTER, which consists of a piece of lead tube $1/8$ in diam, filled with meal powder (Fig 14). It burns at about same speed as fuse, but emits a strong shower of sparks, even in wet dripping mines and tunnels.

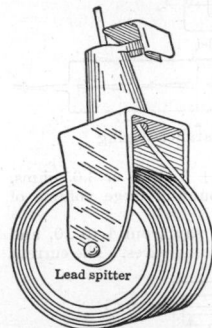

Fig 14. Lead Spitter

Fig 15. Hot-wire Fuse Lighter

The Hot-wire fuse lighter (Fig 15), which consists of an iron wire covered with a powder composition, is even more convenient than the lead spitter. They are in lengths from 7 to 12 in, and quite uniform in burning speed, so that they serve as a safety signal, showing the blaster when it is time to retire.

Precautions in Charging and Firing

Don't tamp with iron or steel bars. Use a wooden tamping stick, with no metal parts.

Don't force a primed cartridge into a drill-hole. Drill hole of ample size for cartridge.

Don't prime dynamite cartridges, nor charge nor connect drill-holes for electric firing during immediate approach or progress of a thunderstorm.

Don't fasten cap to fuse with the teeth, nor by flattening it with a knife; use a crimper.

Don't attempt to use electric blasting caps with ordinary insulation in very wet work. For this purpose secure waterproof caps.

Don't handle fuse carelessly in cold weather; when cold it is stiff and cracks easily.

Don't " lace " fuse through dynamite cartridges. This practice is frequently responsible for burning the charge.

Don't cut fuse short to save blasting time. It is dangerous economy.

Don't use fuse that has been injured by falling rock or in other manner.

Don't explode a charge before every one is well beyond danger zone and protected from flying débris. Protect supply of explosives also from this source of danger.

Don't explode a charge to chamber a drill-hole and then immediately reload it, as the hole will be hot and second charge may explode prematurely.

Don't use a " permissible " powder in same drill-hole with another explosive.

Don't hurry in seeking explanation for a misfire.

Don't drill, bore, nor pick out a charge which has failed to explode. Where safe, drill and charge another hole at least 2 ft from the missed one.

Don't expect high explosives to do good work if you try to explode them with a detonator weaker than No 6.

9. SPECIAL USES FOR EXPLOSIVES

High explosives in coal mining. Use of the "permissible explosives," as defined by testing station of the Bureau of Mines (21), is increasing in both anthracite and bituminous fields. They were used at first in gaseous and dusty mines solely as a safety precaution, because of their comparative freedom from liability to ignite gas and dust mixtures. It is now recognized that, by intelligent use of these explosives, the softest coal is shattered as slightly as with slowest grades of black powder (30). Permissible explosives are used for rock work in hard-coal mines, and in bituminous mines, where gas pockets may be encountered. Different kinds of permissible explosives should never be used in same hole.

Ore mining. The best type of explosive for a given case can be determined only by experience. It depends not only on character of ore, but on ventilation and class of labor. It is often feasible to substitute with satisfactory results a less expensive explosive for a more costly one, in mines where the miners may be made to adopt methods of drilling, charging, and firing other than those to which they are accustomed. Thus, in soft hematite, a slow-acting ammonia powder properly primed, loaded, and confined, will often break more ore per pound than a more expensive dynamite handled unintelligently. The use of short fuse, lacing fuse through cartridge, and insufficient tamping are dangerous and extravagant practices, often difficult to eradicate (24, 28).

Drifting or tunneling. It is desirable to "pull the cut" at the first shot; hence, it often pays to use a stronger explosive for firing the cut than is required for the relief, rib, and lifter holes. The effectiveness of a charge in the cut-holes can not be increased by increasing amount of explosive beyond a certain point, because a definite depth of tamping is required to prevent charge from blowing out.

Generally, cut-holes require an explosive having strength and density of 60% gelatin. Blasting gelatin is sometimes the most economical for this purpose, in spite of its relatively high cost. In refractory rock, or one with unfavorable stratification, cut-holes are often blasted more satisfactorily by electricity than with cap and fuse. Delay electric caps (Art 10) are advantageous where cut-holes bottom up well; but they should not be used in same circuit with cut-hole shots, if latter require to be loaded and fired a second time (6, 20, 25).

Stoping. Every mine is an individual problem. The principal point regarding the explosive is the size to which it is desired to break the material. For soft ore, ammonia dynamite breaks fine enough for easy handling without undue pulverizing. Where ventilation is poor, gelatin, semi-gelatin or ammonia dynamites are necessary, regardless of their other properties, and with much water, gelatin is best. Gelatin dynamite has added advantage that it will "stick" in "uppers." If necessary to blast out dry timbers in old stopes, to allow the top to cave and fill worked-out spaces, a permissible explosive should be used, to avoid possibility of fire.

When firing with cap and fuse, the LEAD (difference in length of fuse in holes designed to fire in succession) should never be less than 10%. For instance, if the first of such a round of holes has a 5-ft fuse, the hole to be fired next should have a fuse at least 6 in longer. With less "lead" than this, variation in burning speed of even the best fuse may cause holes to fire out of order, generally spoiling the shot. When fuses are not lighted in their proper order, the necessity for increased "lead" is apparent. When firing holes in rotation the priming cartridge is sometimes placed at or near bottom of hole, so as to have all fuses burning at a safe distance inside the holes, when first shot explodes; then, if the collar of a hole is shot off, its fuse will not be cut, causing misfire. This practice is good with ammonia dynamite or gelatin dynamite, but never with straight dynamites, which are readily ignited by the least side-spit from a fuse and are therefore liable to burn in the hole. EFFICIENT TAMPING SHOULD BE INSISTED UPON; it produces greater effect, and the more complete the detonation, the less noxious will be the fumes. Ready-made paper tamping bags are a convenience and their use leads miners to exercise more care in tamping.

Tunnel driving. The most satisfactory explosives are the gelatins, which have maximum density and water resistance, and produce minimum of fumes. In firing the heading, the charges must be concentrated in the bottom of the holes, to leave room for sufficient tamping to insure a clean break. The holes are usually wet, especially in the bench, and in dry holes or uppers, gelatin is desirable because it can be relied upon to "stick." Ventilation in tunnels is generally poor and the fumes from gelatins are the least noxious of all high explosives. For heading cut-holes, 60 or 75% gelatin is generally used; for relief, rib roof, floor, and bench shots, 40% gelatin is usually strong enough (48).

Shaft sinking. Gelatin dynamite is usually best for shaft sinking, due to its water resistance, plasticity, and freedom from noxious gases. Strength depends on hardness and toughness of the rock. This must be determined in each case, and sometimes a change in rock as shaft deepens necessitates a change in strength of explosive. Strong caps are essential, to insure max velocity and strength from the explosive, minimum of fumes, and to offset possible lack of sensitiveness in the explosive due to low temperature. When the shaft is not wet enough to require use of gelatin dynamite, considerable economy can be had by using semi-gelatins, which are also suitable in the same conditions where rock is comparatively soft. These explosives give off a minimum of obnoxious fumes.

Quarrying dimension stone; also stone for fills, rip-rapping, and cribbing, as well as for building. Use slow-acting explosives; the more powerful, quick-acting explosives shatter the stone. Granular, and other slow-acting powders, such as the low-freezing ammonia grades, may be used in holes where an air space is left for starting a line of fracture. For subsequent blasting, black powder is best, fired by electric squib, ordinary fuse, or electricity. For large charges, blasting powder is fired with advantage by a dynamite primer.

Quarrying small stone (for crushers, cement works, kilns, etc) (29, 32). High explosive may be used, the one best adapted to be determined by experience. Quick-acting explosives are best for rock which readily transmits shock of explosion to a considerable distance. Hard limestone, trap, granite, etc, usually require dynamites of 50% strength and upwards. In very wet holes, where explosive is immersed several hours, gelatin dynamites must be used. In dry work, and in rock which absorbs much of shock of explosion, slow-acting explosives, like granular powder and low-freezing ammonia powders, are usually best. Quick-acting explosives should not be used in rocks like sandstone and marl, nor slow-acting explosives in flint, granite, or the like. Low-freezing explosives of all grades, especially low-freezing gelatins, are preferable in cold weather, because they do not suffer loss in efficiency as noted with the straight grades.

Straight nitroglycerin dynamites are not recommended for quarrying, as the gelatins have every advantage possessed by the straight powders and are much safer to handle. The only exception to this is that, for mudcapping, straight powders are much more effective than gelatins. In well drill holes good results are obtained by using 50% or 60% gelatin in the bottom and 50% or 40% ammonia dynamite as a top charge, and firing with Cordeau. A special gelatin has been recently developed, known as Quarry Gelatin, made on an unbalanced formula and suitable for open work only. It gives excellent results in hard rock quarries. It must never be used underground.

Stripping. The slowest-acting high explosives are best; granulated dynamites and low grades of low-freezing ammonia dynamites (20 to 30%) being generally used. In heavy stripping, holes should be sprung and fired with slowest-acting explosive. For dry work, free-running dynamite or a mixed granulation of blasting powder is most economical. For moist ground use granular dynamite; if very wet, a low-grade straight dynamite. High-grade dynamite, such as 40% straight, is good for springing charges, but not for final charge except when holes are full of water.

Well sinking; quickest method. Small V-cut, of 4 or 6 holes, drilled by hand and loaded with 60% gelatin dynamite; subsequently trimmed up with vertical holes of same depth and blasted with well-tamped charges of same explosive. Even if holes are under water, always tamp with sand to secure best results.

Scrapping old machinery. When work warrants the expense, best explosive for breaking iron is blasting gelatin. It can be molded into shape as required, strung out to produce a break at point desired, and will "stick" where no other explosive will do so. If blasting gelatin is not obtainable, or is too expensive, use high-grade straight dynamite (50% or 60%). Charges should be well covered with wet mud, or wet clay free from particles of stone or rock; with clean, fine mud, shots are made with slight danger to surrounding objects. Scrapping old machinery in buildings may frequently be done without breaking any glass, if windows are open at top and bottom when shot is fired. High explosive may be used for driving out keys from shafting, driving a wheel from an axle, or loosening spindle from a crushing roll, by using plenty of mud with small charges, placed where blow is to be struck.

Road building. Explosives are used in road building principally for rock excavation, or loosening sand, loam, or clay. In dry work, 40% straight dynamite, and in wet work, 40% gelatin are best for hard rock, and 40% low-freezing ammonia for soft rock. For loosening soil, the weakest and slowest explosives are best, since their effect extends farther than that of quicker-acting explosives. Low-freezing 20% ammonia dynamite, granular dynamite, and railroad black blasting powder are economical for this work. In loosening earth, make holes not deeper than 30 in, and 4 to 6 ft center to center, loading each with not more than two cartridges of 1 1/4 by 8-in dynamite. This charge will not make deep pot holes and material can be handled with horse scraper without miring the animals. For blasting boulders, block-holing is most economical, and 40% low-freezing dynamite is suitable. If time is more important than economy of explosive, boulders can be broken quicker by mud-capping or "adobe shots," with 40 to 60% straight dynamite. Free-running high explosives have been developed to a point recently where they are used extensively in road building, and in general blasting where holes are sprung, or where it is undesirable to use blasting powder on account of the proximity of steam shovels and dinkeys, as they are not so inflammable as black powder. They are made in 4 or 5 strengths, are usually packed in bags, and can be poured into the holes, making for rapidity of the loading operation.

Submarine blasting. Though gelatin dynamites withstand action of water better than other high explosives (blasting gelatin stands water almost indefinitely), straight N G dynamites are usually preferred for submarine excavation because of their greater sensitiveness. The temperature of the water is usually so low that gelatins, less sensitive than straight dynamite under the best conditions, are very difficult to explode completely. Hence, holes are spoiled, rock is not broken, and unexploded gelatin is found by the dredges. Straight 60% dynamite is sufficiently sensitive to explode by concussion from an adjacent hole, if holes are not more than 4 or 5 ft apart. Consequently, in case of failure of one of the electric caps or connections, all the holes will be exploded by concussion. In submarine work, holes are generally untamped, except by water, and the quicker-acting straight dynamite therefore does better work. The cartridges should just fit the holes; especially necessary for shallow holes. Where range firing is not practiced and gelatin is used (usually 90%), a 2 by 8-in cartridge of 60% straight dynamite is often used as a booster for the electric cap.

Quite recently a high-velocity gelatin has been developed which is well suited to submarine blasting. It picks up its full velocity at once, thus differing from other gelatins which take from 4 to 8 inches to reach full velocity. High-velocity gelatin also detonates with full strength and velocity under water pressure where any other high explosive would fail. It is much less likely to propagate from hole to hole than the straight nitroglycerin dynamites.

Miscellaneous uses: clearing land of stumps and boulders; ditching and draining swamps; breaking log and ice jams; destroying wrecks; cutting off pilings; breaking soil for tree planting; hardpan and subsoil blasting; digging holes for posts and poles; excavating for foundations and cellars; trenching for tiling and pipe lines; breaking frozen ore and other materials; loosening frozen material in railroad cars; tearing down old buildings; splitting logs for railroad ties, fence rails, etc; cutting off large fires; starting snow slides; breaking old building foundations; blasting old mine timbers; controlling forest fires.

Black blasting powder in coal mining has so long been used that, as regards execution only, it is considered best for this work. Most coal miners are so familiar with its use, and good miners can judge it so accurately, that excellent results are usually obtained with it (10). The slow heaving action of black powder produces a large percentage of lump coal. Because of its bulk, it can be charged advantageously and estimated so closely that it can generally be used more economically than other powders. But, as black powder is loose, care and judgment are required to get best results.

Black powder is made up by the miner in paper cartridges or shells, observing following points: Make cartridge of proper diam to slip into the hole without too much waste space, and of proper length to hold just the quantity of powder necessary. Shake the powder down into the shell, to compact it, to minimize air-space and get the full force. After cartridge is placed in hole it must be well pushed back, unless an air-space is desired to cushion force of explosion (Fig 19).

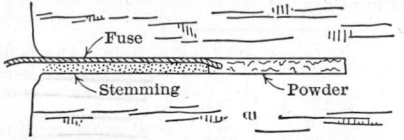

Fig 16. Blasting in Coal with Black Powder and Fuse

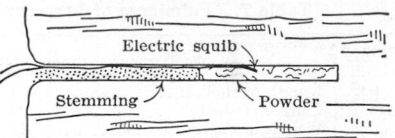

Fig 17. Blasting in Coal with Black Powder; Middle Cartridge Primed with Electric Squib

Fuse or electric squib (Fig 16 and 17) is fastened in cartridge to ignite powder, or a "needle" (Fig 18) or a "blasting barrel" (if hole is wet) is inserted into the powder, and the stemming compacted firmly around it. The more securely charge is confined, the greater the force developed. When unconfined it will simply burn (23, 39).

If a miner's squib (Art 10) is used, pull out needle and insert squib, large end first, into hole made by needle, or in the blasting barrel, and ignite small end of squib. The squib burns for a few seconds, and then shoots back into the powder, igniting it. Use right kind of stemming, so that needle-hole will be smooth, or, if barrel is used (1/4-in iron pipe), see that the hole in

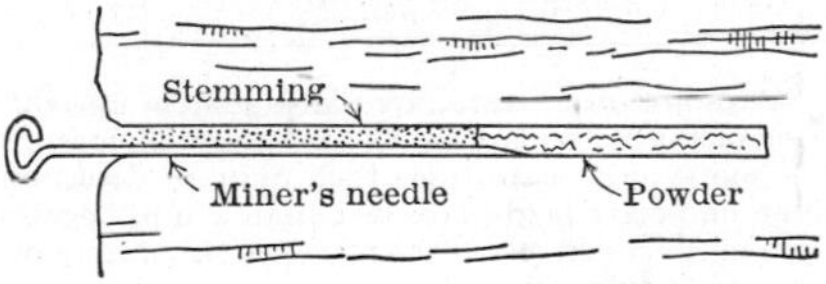

Fig 18. Miner's Needle, for Squib

it is clear and clean.

When black powder is ignited with squib or fuse, the force seems to spread through seams of the coal, displacing it forcibly. It does not exert a sharp shock and therefore does not produce much fines, if proper granulation of powder and correct quantity be used. When very slow action is desired an air-space is left, either between powder and stemming or around cartridge (Fig 19). The proper granulation of black powder is determined only by knowledge of the powder and the coal, and by trial. A test is necessary to determine

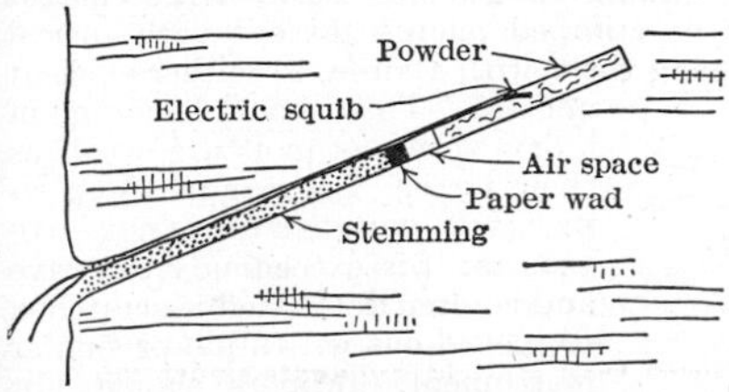

Fig 19. Blasting in Coal. Air Space between Charge and Stemming

conclusively which size of grain is best for any particular coal.

Earth-work and soft-ore mining. In blasting soft iron ore in open-pit work, holes are drilled by a well drill, operated by steam, electricity or gasolene, or by piston or hammer drills. Where there is unusual danger in using black powder, due to sparks from steam shovels and locomotives, special high explosives may be employed. These are somewhat similar to permissibles, and are difficult or impossible to ignite by a spark. But they are not, as a rule, so economical as black powder.

Railroad work. In cutting through fairly solid rock, the holes are usually 18 or 20 ft deep, spaced 8 ft apart; they are sprung with 50% straight dynamite until each hole will hold sufficient explosive to break material small enough to be handled by steam shovel. Roughly, from 25 to 75 lb explosive per hole is used in rock of average hardness.

As it is economical to fire simultaneously as many holes as possible, a large-size blasting machine, or a power or lighting circuit, should be used for firing. For soft rock, shale, clay, loam, or sand, it is economical to use a power churn drill. This makes a 4 to 6-in hole, of any required depth, usually 40 to 100 ft; holes usually spaced 15 or 20 ft apart. The holes are often sprung with dynamite, and after thorough cooling, usually overnight, are charged with black powder, sometimes several tons in a blast. Black powder or granulated dynamites can be used only when holes are dry, and with great care when working near steam shovels, locomotives, etc, as many accidents have occurred from sparks dropping into black powder. If work is wet and sparks can not be avoided, use a fairly low-grade low-freezing ammonia dynamite. In firing simultaneously a large number of holes (50 to 100), use waterproof electric caps, to prevent leakage of current through rock, with attendant chance of misfires.

10. BLASTING SUPPLIES

Blasting caps. A cap is a copper cylinder, closed at one end, containing a pressed charge of detonating composition, and is fired by a fuse. Caps are graded according to quantity of detonating composition contained (Table 7).

Table 7. Fulminate of Mercury Blasting Caps.

	Grade	No 6	No 7	No 8
For Fuse Firing	Length of shell, in	1.375	1.625	1.875
	Calibre of shell "	0.234	0.234	0.234
	Weight of charge, grains	15.430	23.150	30.860
	" " " grams	1.000	1.500	2.000

	Grade	No 6	No 7	No 8
For Electric Firing	Length of shell, in	1.562	1.750	2.000
	Calibre of shell "	0.273	0.273	0.273
	Weight of charge, grains	15.430	23.150	30.860
	" " " grams	1.000	1.500	2.000

Note. The table refers only to caps charged with fulminate of mercury composition (consisting usually of 80% fulminate of mercury and 20% chlorate of potash), which is the standard against which other detonating compounds are graded.

Caps are often tested by placing them upright on a square lead plate, and noting size and character of the hole made in the plate by exploding the cap. This is only applicable for comparison of same type of caps, and then only to determine if caps have deteriorated. No 8 caps usually make no better lead-plate test than No 6, because only a small part of charge in contact with the plate produces effect on the plate itself. Many other materials have been tried, some of them much superior to fulminate of mercury.

For high explosives, the stronger the cap the better the execution, as a rule. No 6 detonators should be used for tunneling, shaft-sinking and similar work; large charges sometimes require No 8. Caps should never be crimped on fuse except with special crimpers made for purpose; biting them, or nicking them with a knife, is neither efficient nor safe. They should be stored in a dry place, as moisture weakens their force. DO NOT ATTEMPT TO EXTRACT COMPOSITION FROM CAP SHELLS; it is exceedingly sensitive and is often detonated if scratched or picked out with a pin or similar instrument. Miners should not wear oil or paraffine hat-lamps when handling caps; many accidents have occurred from sparks falling into a box of caps.

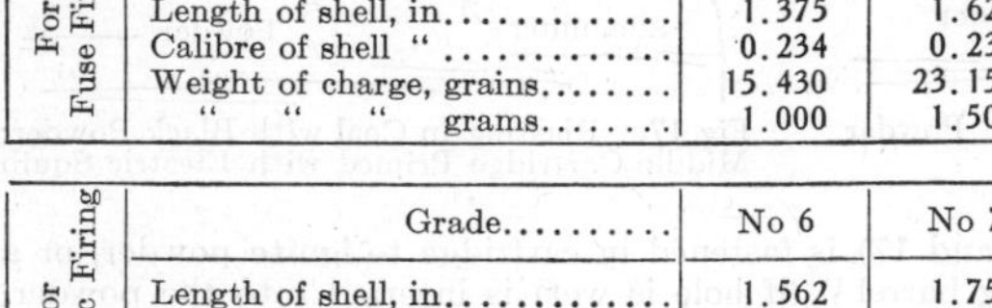

Pressed Fulminate
Asphalt
Asphalt & Sulphur
Loose Fulminate
Sulphur

Fig 20. Electric Blasting Cap

Electric blasting caps (fuzes) (Fig 20). An electric cap consists of a copper shell 1 9/16 to 2 in long by 0.273 in diameter, closed at one end. It contains a charge of detonating composition, in which is embedded a fine platinum wire, connecting the two copper wires. These copper wires are held in place and insulated from each other by three plugs: of mixed asphalt and sulphur, asphalt alone, the latter being retained by corrugations in the shell. Electric caps are used for safety in gaseous and dusty collieries, and for firing charges simultaneously, thus economizing explosive. ONLY ONE KIND OR BRAND OF ELECTRIC CAPS SHOULD BE CONNECTED IN ONE SERIES. Different brands vary in sensitiveness, and if the caps in a series are not uniform, the least sensitive will probably misfire.

Delay electric blasting caps are for firing blasts in 2 or more volleys with one application of electric current. They are used in series with ordinary electric caps. When current is transmitted, about one second elapses before first-delay caps detonate, and same period between these and second-delay. These detonators are useful in tunnel driving and are

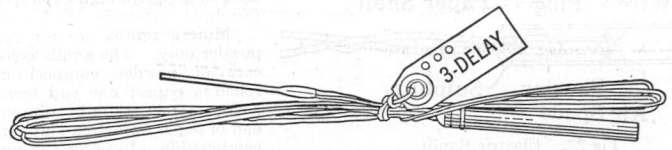

Fig 21. Ventless Delay Electric Cap. (Aluminum foil shunt)

especially recommended for shaft-sinking, often enabling blaster to fire entire round without returning to the face. Fig 21 shows the recently introduced "Ventless Delay Electric Cap."

This new development, has a uniform diam shell, in which the delay element gives off no gas in burning. This permits making various periods of delay, regardless of the pressure under which the cap is placed. Being completely sealed and waterproof, delay is uniform, regardless of the confinement or amount of press developed in water strata from firing previous adjacent holes.

The holes of a round are best connected in parallel and fired with power current, if available. The best way to make a parallel connection is to drive stakes into two end holes at each end of shaft section, stretch number 16 bare copper wire tight across the face between each pair of stakes, and connect one wire from each cap to each of these buss wires. Then, if one leading wire is connected to one end of a buss wire, the other leading wire to the other end of the other buss wire, a balanced parallel connection results, which will minimize trouble. The number of connections on each buss wire should equal the total number of holes.

Electric fuse igniters (Fig 22) are devices for igniting a fuse, usually of high-grade waterproof quality, by electric current. When shipped they are not attached to fuses, but are crimped on when used. The interval between the operation of blasting machine (or turning on of current) and the firing of the cap, depends on length of the fuse attached.

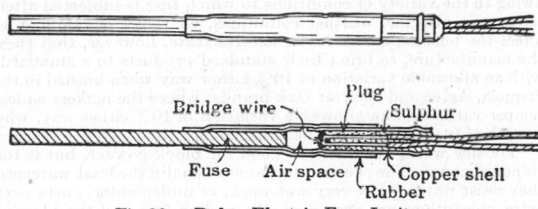

Bridge wire

Plug

Sulphur

Fuse   Air space   Copper shell

Rubber

Fig 22. Delay Electric Fuse Igniter

Special electric blasting caps. For very wet work, and where sludge and water possess high conductivity, special insulation of cap wires is necessary to prevent current leaking from wires at one end of series to wires at other end, thus forming a shunt around wires at middle of circuit. This condition can be detected by making resistance readings of firing circuit on a direct-reading ohmmeter. If reading is the same, there is no leakage; if there is a drop in resistance, after loading in wet holes, there is liability of electric leakage, indicating necessity for special waterproof cap wires. For firing charges in deep water, a special, highly waterproof electric cap is made. There are other modifications for various purposes, such as having wires of larger gage than ordinary to decrease resistance in deep-hole blasting. Electric caps are also made with iron wires; used where only 2 or 3 shots are fired simultaneously. These have much higher electrical resistance than caps with copper wires, and are not recommended for lengths over 8 ft. Electric caps with tin-coated copper wires are used in certain mines where it is objectionable to have particles of bare copper in material mined, and where number of charges fired simultaneously makes use of iron wires impracticable.

Electric squibs (Fig 23) are somewhat similar to electric caps, except that the shell is aluminum instead of copper, and cap filling is fine-grained black powder instead of a detonating compound. They are for black powder only; can not be used for high explosives. They possess advantage of simultaneously firing several charges, and permit more perfect confinement of charge than with miner's squibs; also, the charge can be ignited in middle, giving a little quicker and stronger action and insuring explosion of entire charge before any portion can be cut off by fall of surrounding material. Fig 24 shows an electric squib with twisted shunt.

Electric squibs are safer than fuse or ordinary squibs, because shots are not fired until every one, including blaster, is at a safe distance, and hang-fires are entirely prevented. They are made with iron or copper wires; iron wire is cheaper but requires stronger current (see above).

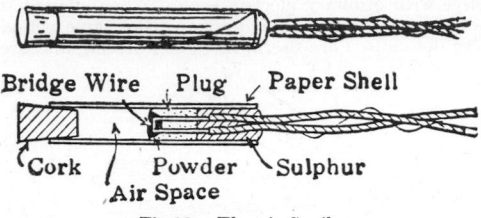

Bridge Wire   Plug   Paper Shell

Cork   Powder   Sulphur
Air Space

Fig 23.   Electric Squib

Delay electric squibs for rotation firing with pellet or black blasting powder are similar in construction to delay electric blasting caps, but can not be used to detonate high explosives as they merely shoot out a small, hot flame.

Miners' squibs are for firing black powder only. The squib consists of a core of powder composition tightly rolled in paper; one end terminates in a slow match, made by dipping twisted end of paper in melted sulphur or other combustible. In using, the squib is laid in mouth of hole formed by withdrawal of needle, or in the blasting barrel (Art 9). The other end of hole so formed terminates in the charge. Outer end of squib is lighted, and burns several seconds until its powder core is ignited, whereupon it shoots down into the charge and ignites that. Time between lighting of fuse and firing of charge can be varied to a certain extent by position of tail of squib: when turned up it burns more slowly; when turned down, much faster. The squib is very cheap, but not so safe as ordinary fuse. Since it requires an opening through which to travel, the charge is not confined so effectually as with fuse or electric squib.

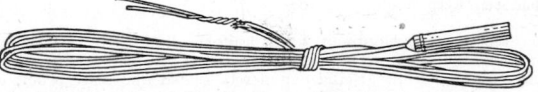

Fig 24.   Electric Squib, Closed Shell.   Twisted Shunt

Safety fuse consists of a train or core of a special kind of powder, tightly wrapped in successive turns of hemp, jute, or cotton yarn, and tape, made more or less waterproof by addition of asphalt or other varnish, or gutta-percha. When tightly tamped, so that gases from burning powder train can not escape, the pressure causes fuse to burn faster.

The manufacturers make no warrant or representations as to the burning speed of their product, owing to the variety of conditions to which fuse is subjected after leaving the factory, including differences in altitude, weather conditions, character of tamping, and mishandling, all of which may affect the burning speed. The makers state, however, that they use every care and precaution in the manufacture, to bring their standard products to a standard burning speed of 90 sec per yard, with an allowable variation of 10% either way when burned in the open at sea level; except Clover, Sequoia, Aztec and Charter Oak brands, where the makers endeavor to approach a standard of 120 sec per yard, with an allowable variation of 10% either way, when burned in the open at sea-level. Length of fuse must always be sufficient for the blaster to reach a place of safety.

For dry work, hemp fuse is good for black powder, but is too small in diameter properly to fit standard caps. The cheaper grades are usually the least waterproof; the more expensive, the better they resist water. For very wet work, or under water, gutta-percha fuse will usually serve. When extra precautions are necessary, the end of fuse and the blasting cap may be dipped into asphalt paint and dried, or joint between cap and fuse covered with tallow or soft soap. Do not use oil or grease, which is liable to affect powder train by dissolving the asphalt paint. As the powder in core of fuse absorbs moisture always cut off an inch or two from end, before inserting in cap. Cut off end square across, push into cap without twisting until it just touches the cap charge. If fuse is cut at an angle, pointed end may bend over, and by covering end of powder train, cause misfire. Nearly every kind of fuse spits out of sides more or less in burning, and therefore should not be buried in the dynamite. When necessary to have priming cartridge at bottom of hole, a fuse should be selected that will spit from the sides as little as possible, and cartridge shells must not be slit; fuse is less likely to ignite dynamite through the paper wrapper.

Detonating fuses are of two different kinds: the older, known as Cordeau, consists of a lead tube about 1/4 in diam filled with TNT (trinitrotoluene). It detonates at a veloc of 17 060 ft per sec, and is used principally in deep-well drill holes, in quarries and large open-pit mining. The extreme violence with which it explodes is sufficient to detonate high explosives lying alongside it in a bore-hole, and therefore the charge detonates almost instantaneously throughout its entire length. Primacord, a newer development, comprises an explosive core of penta-erythrite-tetranitrate (PETN), contained in a waterproof coat and a textile covering. It is little if any more sensitive than Cordeau, but has superior initiating power, although it does not carry the detonation across as large an air gap as Cordeau, owing to the latter's lead sheath. Speed of Primacord is approx 20 341 ft per sec. Its principal advantage over Cordeau is the ease of handling, light weight, and assurance of propagating from the trunk lines to the branch lines. Fig 25 and 26 show the proper method of connecting branch lines to trunk line, and the proper knot for splicing trunk line. Neither Primacord nor Cordeau is much used underground, except for shooting out props in iron mines where stray electric currents are prevalent.

In all cases, the end of the fuse must be cut square across and seated directly on the cap filling, as any air space is likely to cause misfires.

Cap crimpers are of 3 types (Fig 27): (1) sleeve-type (a) leaves a vent between the fuse and copper shell, and in wet work must be dipped in some cap sealing compound to

Fig 25. Primacord; Connecting Branch Line   Fig 26. Primacord; Splicing Trunk Line

exclude water; (2) sleeve-type crimper (b) has an efficient fuse-cutter which cuts the fuse square across, but while this is desirable, it does not make a water-tight crimp; (3) type c makes an air-tight crimp on smooth-surface fuse and will resist water well enough in ordinary wet holes. If there is much water, any kind of crimp should be further protected by sealing the joint between fuse and cap.

Blasting machines. The usual form is a small dynamo, the armature of which is rotated by a downward thrust of the rack-bar transmitted by a pinion. There are two

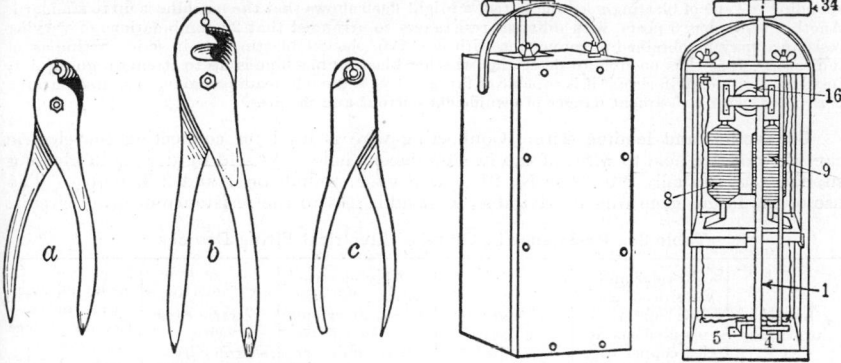

Fig 27. Cap Crimpers   Fig 28. Blasting Machine

types; one (Fig 28), which is series-wound, uses the entire current generated during descent of the rack-bar, to excite the field magnets. At end of stroke, this current is transmitted to the binding posts and firing circuit. In shunt-wound type, the dynamo is fully enclosed and part of the current is shunted through the field magnets until the end of stroke, when a contact is made, sending the entire current out on the line. Shunt type is easier to operate than the other, and having a greater volume of current, is better adapted to firing more than one series of holes at a time. Place machine in a firm, level position, and operate with both hands and full force; an attempt to operate it with one hand, or in a half-hearted way, will often result in misfires from insufficient current. Keep blasting machines in dry, cool place. The commutator, brushes, and circuit-breaking contact points should be kept clean, bright, and free from oil. Oil bearings and gears occasionally.

Single-shot blasting machines (also called pocket, or permissible machines) are employed, usually in coal mines, where it is necessary or desirable to fire one shot at a time (Fig 29). They are capable of firing up to 3 shots simultaneously. Constructed on the magneto principle, they are operated by a quick twist of the handle, which is removable and acts as a lock to prevent premature or accidental operation. Dry cells also are sometimes used for single-shot firing, usually consisting of 3 carbon-zinc elements, connected in series; but, as the contact points are always alive, they are not as safe as the magneto machines, the binding posts of which are dead except at end of stroke.

Circuit testers (galvanometers) are of two general types: one merely indicates whether circuit is open or closed; the other is essentially a small direct-reading ohm-meter, indicating by movement of a needle across graduated scale the approximate resistance of blasting circuit in ohms. With the latter, it may be determined whether a given blasting circuit is complete, or broken, or short-circuited. By a table, given below, showing resistance of electric caps with different lengths and sizes of connecting and leading wire, the exact condition of blasting circuit at moment of firing may be determined fairly accurately. The circuit-tester is a valuable adjunct, and, where a considerable amount of electric blasting is done, should form part of blaster's equipment. In addition to breaks and short circuits, it also detects leakage of current through ground, rails, air pipes, steam pipes, and imperfect connections. The instrument is furnished with a silver chloride cell, which is constant in its current output. The current thereby generated is so weak that the danger of firing an electric cap while testing is remote; but, as a matter of precaution, tests should be made from a safe distance. The ordinary type of direct-reading ohm-meter and battery tester, containing carbon-zinc dry-cell batteries, is liable to send sufficient current through a blasting circuit to explode an electric cap, and greater caution is therefore necessary in using them, especially for testing one cap at a time.

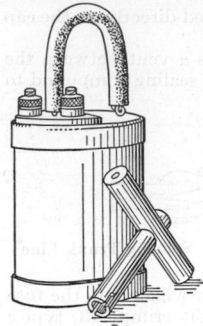

Fig 29. Single-shot (Pocket) Blasting Machine

Blasting machine testers (rheostats). These are for determining inexpensively the capacity and condition of a blasting machine. There are several types. One provides a means of sending a current through different resistances and a small lamp, so that, when connected to the poles corresponding to type of blasting machine tested, a bright flash shows that the machine is up to standard. Another tester has 6 posts, with different resistances so arranged that 20 combinations of varying resistance may be obtained in connection with use of an electric blasting cap in series, acting as an indicator. It is thus possible to determine whether blasting machine is up to strength, and if not, just how many caps in circuit it is capable of firing. By its use overloading a given blasting machine is avoided, with consequent danger of insufficient current and misfires.

Connecting and leading wire. Connecting wire is used for connecting the electric cap wires of one hole to wires of cap in an adjacent hole. As sold by dealers in blasting supplies, it is usually No 20 or No 21 B & S gage, wound on 1 and 2-lb spools. The use of the larger gage wire is advisable, as it adds less to the resistance of firing circuit.

Table 8. Resistance in Ohms of Electrical Firing Devices *

Length of wires, ft	Regular and waterproof electric caps with plain or enameled copper wire (includes duplex wrap)	Seismograph electric caps	Delay electric caps, delay electric igniters and electric squibs with plain or enameled copper wires	Electric caps with iron wire	Delay electric caps, delay electric igniters and electric squibs with iron wire
4	1.25	0.99	1.03	1.99	1.73
5	1.29	1.01	1.07	2.19	1.93
6	1.32	1.03	1.10	2.39	2.14
7	1.35	1.05	1.13	2.59	2.33
8	1.38	1.07	1.16	2.80	2.55
9	1.42	1.10	1.20	3.00	2.75
10	1.45	1.12	1.23	3.22	2.95
12	1.51	1.16	1.29	....	....
14	1.58	1.20	1.35	....	....
16	1.64	1.25	1.42	....	....
18	1.71	1.29	1.49	....	....
20	1.79	1.33	1.57	....	....
22	1.86	1.37	1.64	....	....
24	1.93	1.41	1.71	....	....
26	2.00	1.46	1.78	....	....
28	2.07	1.50	1.85	....	....
30	2.14	1.54	1.92	....	....
40	2.48	1.75	2.26	....	....
50	2.83	1.96	2.61	....	....
60	3.17	2.18	2.95	....	....

* These figures, from E. I. duPont de Nemours Powder Co, apply to products made by that concern. They are approx correct for most other makes of caps.

This wire should not be used for connecting a line of holes to blasting machine; for that purpose LEADING WIRE should be used, of No 14 gage or larger. No 14 B & S gage wire, in coils of 500 ft, is satisfactory for all kinds of dry work. For wire gages, see Sec 42, Art 3.

Resistance tables. The resistance of copper wire, B & S gage, per 1 000 ft, of sizes usually employed in electric blasting, is:

Gage No	Ohms		Wires of electric caps
8	0.6271 ⎫		have a resistance of 0.032
10	0.9972 ⎬ Power and lighting circuit		ohm per ft (doubled). The
12	1.586 ⎭		resistance of the bridge wire
14	2.521	Leading wire	in the cap varies from 0.859
16	4.009 ⎫ Sometimes used for leading wire, but not		to 1.1 ohm, depending on
18	6.374 ⎭ recommended for firing large circuits		the manufacture; it does
20	10.14 ⎫ Connecting wire		not necessarily indicate the
21	12.78 ⎭		sensitiveness of the cap.
22	16.12	Size attached to electric caps	

Resistance of electrical firing devices. These include electric blasting caps, electric squibs, delay electric blasting caps and delay electric igniters, with both copper and iron wires. Enameled copper wires have same resistance as plain wires, but much better resistance to electrical leakage.

BIBLIOGRAPHY

1. Bichel, C. E.   New Methods of Testing Explosives.   J. B. Lippincott Co, Phila, 1905
2. Brunswick, H.   Explosives.   Trans by C. E. Munroe and A. L. Kibler.   John Wiley & Sons, N Y, 1912
3. Bureau for Sale Transportation of Explosives.   General Information Respecting Explosives.   Bur of Explosives, N Y, Pamphlet No 7
4. Callen, A. C.   Extension Study Course in Coal Mining Explosives.   Burton Pub Co, Chicago, 1924
5. Comey, A. M.   Safety Blasting Explosives.   International Text Book Co, Scranton, Pa, 1908
6. Daw, A. W. and Z. W.   Blasting of Rock in Mines, Quarries and Tunnels.   Spon, London, 1898
7. Farmer R. C.   Manufacture and Use of Explosives.   Pitman, London, 1921
8. Hercules Powder Co, Wilmington, Del: Modern Blasting in Quarries and Open Pits, 1927; Rock Tunnel Methods, 1931
9. Levy, S. I.   Modern Explosives.   Pitman, London, 1920
10. Marshall, A.   Explosives, History, Manufacture, Properties and Tests.   Churchill, London, 1917
11. Marshall, A.   Dictionary of Explosives.   Churchill, London, 1917; Vol III, 1932
12. Martin, G, and Barbour, W.   Industrial Nitrogen Compounds and Explosives (2nd ed).   Crosby, Lockwood & Co, London, 1917
13. Naoum, P.   Nitroglycerine and Nitroglycerine Explosives.   Williams & Wilkins, Balto, Md, 1928
14. Perrott, G. St. J.   Properties of Liquid Oxygen Explosives.   *Trans* A I M E, Vol 71, p 1248
15. O'Neil, F. W., and Van Fleet, H.   Liquid Oxygen as an Explosive.   *Trans* A I M E, 1926
16. American Table of Distances to be Maintained between Storage Magazines for Explosives.   Inst of Makers of Explosives, N Y
17. Commercial Explosives.   National Safety Council, Safe Practices, No 28
18. La Motte, A.   Safety in the Use of Explosives.   *Proc* National Safety Council, p 1115–1132 (1918)
19. Schwartz, Von.   Fire and Explosion Risk.   Griffin, London, 1917
20. Snelling, W. O.   Safety Factors in the Use of Explosives in Cement Rock Quarrying.   *Proc* National Safety Council, p 405–429 (1919)

Publications of U S Bureau of Mines
   Bulletins
21. No   10.   Use of Permissible Explosives
22. "   15.   Investigations of Explosives Used in Coal Mines
23. "   17.   Primer on Explosives for Coal Miners
24. "   48.   Selection of Explosives for Engineering and Mining Operations
25. "   57.   Safety and Efficiency in Mine Tunneling
26. "   59.   Investigation of Detonators and Electric Detonators
27. "   66.   Tests of Permissible Explosives
28. "   80.   Primer on Explosives for Metal Miners and Quarrymen
29. "   124.   Sandstone Quarrying in the United States
30. "   137.   Use of Permissible Explosives in Illinois Mines
31. "   154.   Mining and Milling of Lead and Zinc Ore in Missouri-Kan-Okla Dist
32. "   160.   Rock Quarrying for Cement Manufacture
33. "   198.   Regulation of Explosives in the United States
34. "   219.   Explosives: Their Materials, Constitution and Analysis
35. "   287.   Gases from Blasting in Tunnels and Metal-mine Drifts
36. "   311.   Drilling and Blasting in Metal-mine Drifts and Crosscuts
37. "   346.   Physical Testing of Explosives at the Bur of Mines Explosives Experiment Station, Bruceton, Pa.

Technical Papers

38. No   7. Investigations of Fuse and Miner's Squibs
39. "   17. Effect of Stemming on Efficiency of Explosives
40. " 162. Initial Priming Substances for High Explosives
41. " 210. Analytical Method for Detonating Blown-out Shots in Coal Mines
42. " 234. Sensitiveness of Explosives to Frictional Impact
43. " 364. Permissible Explosives, Mining Equipment and Apparatus, Approved Prior to January 1, 1924
44. " 383. Blasting to Lessen Boulders in Hard-ore Stopes
45. " 429. Permissible Single-shot Blasting Units
46. " 482. Toxic Gases from 60% Gelatin Explosives
47. " 567. Preventing Accidents by Proper Use of Permissibles

Miner's Circulars

48. No 13. Safety in Tunneling
49. "   19. The Prevention of Accidents from Explosives in Metal Mines
50. "   21. What a Miner Can Do to Prevent Explosions of Gas and Coal Dust
51. "   22. Dangerous and Safe Practices in Bituminous Coal Mines
52. "   27. Causes and Prevention of Fires and Explosions in Bituminous Coal Mines

Reports of Investigations

53. No 2147. Dangers from Explosives' Fumes in Metal Mining
54. " 2156. Misfires in Metal Mining
55. " 2384. Failure of Center Shots in Blasting
56. " 2436. Effect of Cartridge Diameter on Strength and Sensitiveness of High Explosives
57. " 2528. Transport of Explosives in and about Mines
58. " 2739. Gases from Blasting in Heavy Sulphides
59. " 2789. Charging Explosives in Drift Rounds in Metal Mines
60. " 2975. Dynamites: Their Strength, Rate of Detonation, and Poisonous Gases Evolved
61. " 3235. Some Physical Properties and Characteristics of Fuse
62. " 3269. Special Multiple-shot Blasting Units

Miscellaneous

63. Schedule 17. Procedure in Testing Explosives for Permissibility for Use in Gaseous and Dusty Coal Mines
64. Information Circular No 6871. How to Use Permissible Explosives Properly
65. Schedule 17C. Procedure for Testing Explosives for Permissibility in Coal Mines, with Test Requirements, Tolerance Limits and Schedule of Fees (supersedes 17A and 17B)

SECTION 5

ROCK EXCAVATION

BY

HALBERT P. GILLETTE

REVISED AND LARGELY REWRITTEN FOR THE SECOND EDITION BY

RICHARD T. DANA and ARTHUR P. ACKERMAN

AND NOW REVISED FOR THE THIRD EDITION BY

SAMUEL R. RUSSELL

EXPLOSIVES DEPT, E. I. DU PONT DE NEMOURS & CO

Note.—Numbers in parentheses in text refer to Bibliography at end of this section.

ROCK EXCAVATION

This section contains data on blasting in general, and surface excavation of rock, as in open-cut mining, quarrying, railroad and highway through-cuts and side-hill cuts, and trenching. Related subjects are: Explosives (Sec 4), Tunneling (Sec 6), Shaft Sinking (Sec 7) and Machine Drills and Compressors (Sec 15).

In this revision, much material of the first edition has been retained, including many cost figures when accompanied by sufficient information for converting them to present-day values.

1. FACTORS AFFECTING METHODS AND COSTS

Open-cut methods depend upon size, location and purpose of the work. Costs vary greatly with the method adopted, together with the character of rock.

Character and formation of rock affect drilling speed, amount of explosive, size into which the rock breaks, mode of breaking, and tonnage handled. DRILLING SPEED. In hard, tough rocks this is generally much lower than in soft, though, in some shales and other friable rocks, accumulation of sludge in the hole prevents the drill from striking an effective blow and retards drilling. This is especially true with solid steel, and may be remedied by using a water jet, Art 4. In soft rocks a heavy blow may seat the bit so that it sticks. Seamy, blocky rock also causes sticking or FITCHERING; overcome by withdrawing the bit and dropping into the hole a handful of quartz or C-I fragments. Hard, friable minerals may make easy-drilling rock, as some pyrites and sandstone. Grains of soft sandstone easily break loose and are blown from the hole, whereas sandstone cemented with SiO_2 may drill as hard as solid quartz. AMOUNT AND KIND OF EXPLOSIVE (Sec 4) is determined only by test or experience (Table 1). SIZE OF PIECES INTO WHICH ROCK BREAKS depends somewhat

Table 1. Relative Toughness of Rocks, Tested with Drop Hammer (23)

Kind of rock	Tough- ness. Lime- stone = 1	Ft lb per sq ft of fracture	Kind of rock	Tough- ness. Lime- stone = 1	Ft lb per sq ft of fracture
Fresh diabase	3.0	624.9	Feldspathic sandstone	1.7	354.1
Pyroxene quartzite	2.7	562.4	Gabbro	1.6	333.2
Sandstone	2.6	541.6	Chert	1.5	312.4
Altered diabase	2.4	499.9	Calcareous sandstone	1.5	312.4
Fresh basalt	2.3	479.1	Granite	1.5	312.4
Hornblende-schist	2.1	437.4	Slate	1.2	249.9
Diorite	2.1	437.4	Granite-gneiss	1.2	249.9
Hornblende granite	2.1	437.4	Andesite	1.1	229.1
Rhyolite	2.0	416.6	Limestone	1.0	208.3
Quartzite	1.9	395.7	Mica-schist	1.0	208.3
Biotite gneiss	1.9	395.7	Dolomite	1.0	208.3
Augite-diorite	1.9	395.7	Biotite-granite	1.0	208.3
Altered basalt	1.7	354.1	Hornblende-gneiss	1.0	208.3

on toughness, but more on presence or absence of joint planes. Pieces too large to load require blockholing, which is costly and delays loading (Art 7; also see Sec 10). MANNER OF BREAKING is affected by position of joint planes and the dip of strata. As rock can not be excavated to neat lines by blasting, more must be removed than required; this excess is called OVERBREAKAGE. Unit of measurement of open-cut excavation is the cu yd. Table 2 gives weights of rocks.

Overbreakage for 8 months during 1909 in open-cut work on the Livingstone improvement of the Detroit River was 14.7%; 273 750 cu yd of limestone excavation was paid for, and 314 000 cu yd loosened (12). Overbreakage in open cuts (mostly in granite), on Grand Trunk Pacific R R, was 10 to 40% (20). Overbreakage in the approaches to a tunnel near Peekskill was 10%, the strata dipping at a high angle (20).

Voids in hard rock, when broken by a crusher, amount to about 35% if all sizes are mixed and the stone slightly shaken, but, if screened, each size has 45 to 48% voids. Soft, friable rocks, as shales, break into widely varying sizes and therefore have a lower percentage of voids. Hard rock blasted in large pieces and thrown into cars has about 40 to 45% voids, 1 cu yd of solid rock making 1.67 to 1.82 cu yd broken.

Voids	30%	35%	40%	45%	50%	55%
No of cu yd, loose measure, from 1 cu yd of solid rock	1.43	1.54	1.60	1.90	2.00	2.22

Table 2. Weight of Rocks

For weights of minerals and ores, see Sec 25, Table 3; Sec 1, Descriptive Tables

Material	Wt per cu ft, lb		Cu ft per ton		Tons per cu yd	
	In place	Broken	In place	Broken	In place	Broken
Dolomite................	160	....	12.5	....	2.16	1.30
Gneiss..................	168	96	11.9	20.8	2.27	1.30
Granite and porphyry......	170	97	11.8	20.6	2.30	1.31
Greenstone and trap.......	187	107	10.7	18.7	2.52	1.39
*Hematite................	267	....	7.5	....	3.60	....
Limestone...............	168	96	11.9	20.8	2.27	1.30
*Limestone ores..........	154	....	13.0	....	2.08	....
Quartz..................	165	94	12.1	21.3	2.23	1.27
*Quartzose ores..........	138	....	14.5	....	1.86	....
Sandstone...............	151	86	13.2	23.3	2.08	1.16
Slate...................	175	95	11.4	21.1	2.36	1.28
*Vein quartz.............	148	....	13.5	....	2.00	....
*Vein quartz, 15% PbS.....	164	....	12.2	....	2.21	....
*Vein quartz, 15% FeS2.....	160	....	12.5	....	2.16	....

* Refers to possible wt of ores; pure minerals, usually weigh more.

Swelling in fill. On excavating a mixture of solid and loose rock and earth, 1 cu yd in place makes about 1.4 cu yd in fill. If rock be first stripped of earth, and then blasted and dumped by itself, the percentage of voids is larger. At Boulder, Colo, 3 600 cu yd of solid rock made a 5 340 cu yd embankment; a ratio of 1 : 1.51. In Virginia, 50 000 cu yd of limestone and mica schist, broken and put in embankment, made 90 000 cu yd, an increase of 80%. In subaqueous excavation, Ashtabula Harbor, O, 62 869 cu yd (place measure) gave 103 537 cu yd measured in scows, an increase of 65%.

2. DRILL STEEL AND BITS

Shape and temper of bits greatly influence efficiency of drilling. While quality of drill steel has in late years approached standardization, its proper heat treatment for given working conditions is still debatable, notwithstanding much research and experimentation (2, 4).

Types of bit in common use (Fig 1). For machine drills in general, usual shapes of cutting edge are: right-angle cross, X and Z, and modifications, like the Carr bit and others. For HAMMER DRILLS, the 6-point bit is common, but its advantages are not apparent, except for the smaller machines, like sinkers. There is little difference between cross and 6-point bits in respect of ease of sharpening. Z bit is less readily made, and difficult to temper for standing up under high air press, due to weakness of tips of cutting edges. Carr bit is easiest of all to make and readily takes a hard temper.

Bit wings should be thick enough (usually 0.5-0.75 in) to stand up well, but as thin as consistent with strength, to leave space for free ejection of cuttings; the bit then "muds" well and cuts faster. Gage and shape of bit must permit of free rotation in the hole. Cutting edge must be symmetrical, to equalize wear and prevent RIFLING, with consequent FITCHERING of the bit; which causes abnormal strains, with danger of breaking bit or machine.

Angle of cutting edge (angle between its sides) averages about 90°; if much greater, the bit crushes rather than fractures the rock; if less, it cuts faster, but also dulls faster and is more liable to break. In soft rock, a slender cutting edge tends to penetrate past the point of fracture, thus wasting energy in crushing and wedging out the rock. Outside taper of the wings of a cross bit is measured by their angle with the axis. This angle, in a bit good for rapid cutting, long wear and ease of resharpening, begins at about 14° and, near cutting edge, ends at 5°. Diam of bit's outer guiding surfaces then nearly equals that of the cutting edge, which is thus well supported, increasing life of the gage, and minimizing tendency to rifle.

Comparative tests of hammer-drill bits, by Forbes and Barton (4), in drilling very hard granite, led to the following conclusions: (a) in down holes, cutting speed varies inversely as $diam^2$, at least for small gages; (b) drilling speed increases almost uniformly with increase of air press. About 85 lb seems best adapted to all bits for drilling in the granite used for tests; (c) speed of drilling appears proportional to coarseness of cuttings, as shown by screen analysis and study of bottoms of drill holes; (d) considering its cutting qualities, small loss in gage, and ease of making and tempering, the Carr bit is excellent for rock of aver hardness; (e) at low air press and in soft rock, Z bit may surpass the Carr bit in cutting speed; but, due to difficulty of forging and tempering, it is less desirable; (f) 6-point bit is apparently inferior for ordinary work, but may be useful for starting holes and shallow drilling; (g) for high air press and very hard rock, the cross bit, with a 5° outer taper on the wings, seems superior to all others.

While tests in other rocks might show different results, the relative cutting quality of different bits would probably be the same in all rocks. Other characteristics, as mudding freely and freedom from fitchering, may make one bit better than another for soft rocks.

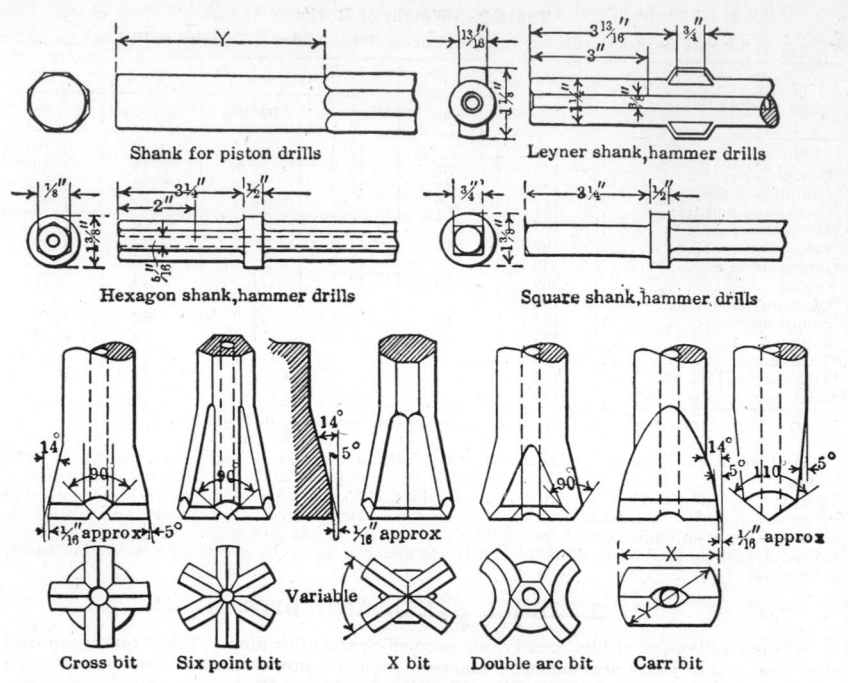

Fig 1.   Types of Drill Bits and Shanks

Table 3.   Weights and Diam of Drill Steel

Nominal size A, in	Solid Wt, lb per ft	Hollow Hole diam B, in	Hollow Wt, lb per ft
Hexagon*			
7/8	2.24	17/64	2.05
1	2.92	17/64	2.73
1 1/8	3.71	11/32	3.39
1 1/4	4.58	11/32	4.26
Round			
7/8	2.04	17/64	1.85
1	2.66	17/64	2.47
1 1/8	3.36	11/32	3.04
1 1/4	4.15	11/32	3.83
1 3/8	5.02	3/8	4.65
Octagon			
3/4	1.58	......	......
7/8	2.15	......	......
1	2.81	......	......
1 1/8	3.55	......	......
1 1/4	4.38	......	......
1 3/8	5.31	......	......
1 1/2	6.32	......	......

a , *c* , *d*

Quarter octagon*

Nominal size A, in	Diag C, in	Solid Wt, lb per ft	Hollow Hole diam B, in	Hollow Wt, lb per ft
7/8	1 1/16	2.49	17/64	2.30
1	1 7/32	3.25	17/64	3.06
1 1/8	1 23/64	4.10	11/32	3.78
1 1/4	1 1/2	5.04	11/32	4.72

b

Solid cruciform†

Nominal size A, in	Inner diag B, in	Rib C, in	Radius R, in	Wt, lb per ft
Light section				
1	3/4	7/16	3/32	2.31
1 1/8	25/32	7/16	1/8	2.76
1 1/4	13/16	7/16	1/8	3.19
Heavy section				
1	25/32	1/2	3/64	2.43
1 1/8	29/32	9/16	3/32	3.09
1 1/4	29/32	9/16	1/8	3.55

e

* All sizes have a corner radius of 1/32 in   † All sizes have a radius at outer corners of 1/16 in

Table 4. Length of Bar Stock Required to Form Shank and Bit of Drill Steels

Section: hollow and solid hex, round, oct, or cruc; size, in	Length of stock for forging shank, in					
	3 1/4" Jack-hamer-shank	4 1/4" Jack-hamer-shank	Leyner lug-shank	Stoper steel, allow for shank	Piston-drill steel	
					With shank	Without shank
7/8	7	8	....	6	4 3/4	5
1	6 3/4	7 3/4	8	6	5 1/4	5 1/2
1 1/8	....	7 5/8	7 5/8	6	5 3/4	6
1 1/4	....	....	7 1/2	6	5 3/4	6

Cross and Carr bits
Diam of bit, in; length of stock for forging bit, in

	1 1/2	1 5/8	1 3/4	1 7/8	2	2 1/8	2 1/4	2 3/8	2 1/2	2 5/8	2 3/4	2 7/8	3
1 7/8	1 1/2	2	2 1/2	3 3/8	4 1/8	5 1/4	6 1/4	8 1/4	10 1/4	12 1/4	14 1/4	16	17
1	7/8	1 1/8	1 3/8	1 3/4	2	2 3/8	3 1/4	4 1/4	4 3/4	6	7 1/4	8 1/4	9
1 1/8	3/4	1	1 1/4	1 1/2	1 3/4	2	2 1/2	3 1/8	3 5/8	4 3/8	5 1/2	7 1/2	8 1/4
1 1/4	....	1/2	5/8	3/4	1	1 1/4	1 1/2	1 3/4	2 1/4	3 1/4	4	5	5 3/4

6-Point Rose bit; length of stock for forging bit, in

7/8	1 7/8	2 1/8	3 1/4	4 1/4	5 1/4	6 5/8	8 1/4	9 1/2	12	15 1/8	17 1/4	......	......
1	1 1/8	1 1/2	1 3/4	2 1/4	3	3 3/4	4 1/4	5 3/4	7	8 5/8	9 5/8	10 3/4	11 1/2
1 1/8	7/8	1 1/8	1 1/2	1 7/8	2 3/8	2 5/8	3 1/4	3 7/8	4 3/4	6 1/2	7 1/2	8 1/4	9

To find length of bar required for any length of steel, add to the length given in table for shank and bit, the "drilling length" (depth of hole).

Hints on drill steel (Sullivan Mach'y Co), that may well be posted in blacksmith shop:

Don't use poor or dull drill steel, nor steel with a soft striking or shank end; don't use steels if shank end is not properly squared, or if shank is not of correct length; don't attempt to use a steel the shank of which will not enter the chuck bushing freely; don't overheat the steel; don't forge a bit and use only the regular dolly, as it will result in a very short upset, which does not give cutting edges any support while drilling, resulting in broken wings; don't leave round corners after sharpening. Make them square; resulting in faster drilling speed, and prolonging life of bit; don't forget that the bit tips are hotter than the center when heated hurriedly, and that they cool quicker; don't hammer cold steel; it is hard work, and injures the steel.

Be sure that: drill steel is straight and bit and shank are formed in alinement with the steel body; shank is of proper length and shape; lugs or collar at base of shank are of proper diam and length; hole throughout the steel is of proper size and free from obstruction; striking end of shank is flat and square, with inner and outer edges slightly rounded; bit is of proper shape, with cutting and reaming edges formed full and to required size; gage of bit is of correct size for the length of steel; reaming edges are concentric with axis of steel; angle of reaming side corresponds to the standard established for existing conditions; there are no sharp corners at shoulder, where bit blends into the steel body; drill steel is free from cracks and other imperfections that might result in breakage; steels are of proper length to correspond with the established length of steel change; hole in hollow steel used with air-tube and water-tube drills is punched out at shank end, to a diam of 3/8 in, for at least 3 in.

Hand sharpening. Bits should be constantly turned in the fire, removed when cherry red and dressed. The edge of a badly-worn chisel bit is first upset to give it proper width. The bit is then held on the anvil at a slope of about 1 rise to 2 horiz, with its edge even with edge of the anvil. While hammering it is turned after each half-dozen blows. A file may be used on the hot bit for final dressing. Blows should be light and glancing, to draw the fibers of the steel towards the edge, thus toughening the metal. There are 2 methods of sharpening machine-drill bits: SET-HAMMER and FULLER-AND-DOLLY. In the first, a set-hammer is placed on the bevels for driving the steel back. After being sharpened a few times a drill bit must be reformed. In the second method the steel is first drawn sharp at the corners with a fuller and then set back in the center with a dolly.

Machine sharpeners (Sec 15) should be used except for small work, where cost of a machine would be prohibitive. Large saving results from proper heat treatment, starting with the initial forging heat. Unless this is correct, later heat treatment is useless.

Physical properties of the bit depend upon the temperature of the steel preceding both forging and quenching, and the care exercised in forging. The finest grain exists as the steel passes through the critical range on the rising heat. Further heating coarsens the grain, which effect remains in the steel if allowed to cool undisturbed. Hammering produces a finer grain if continued until the critical temp is reached; if it be stopped while the steel is above the critical temp, coarse crystallization again sets in; if continued below that temp, distortions and internal strains are caused, resulting in brittleness and breakage. Steel should not be allowed to "soak" in the furnace, as it increases coarseness of structure.

Critical temperature can be practically understood by watching the slow heating of a piece of steel. It brightens in color with rising heat, until a point is reached where it apparently becomes a trifle darker than the furnace. The darkening is due to absorption of heat, and the temp at which this absorption takes place is the DECALESCENT or CRITICAL POINT. If heating continues, the steel again assumes the same brilliance as the furnace. If the furnace is now allowed to cool slowly, a point is reached where the steel remains visibly brighter than the furnace, but in a few seconds it assumes color of the furnace and darkens with it. The brightening, due to throwing off heat, occurs at the RECALESCENT POINT.

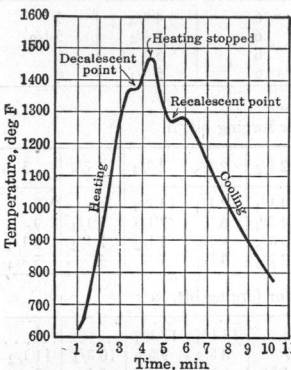

Fig 2. Critical Temperatures for High-carbon Steel (Steel and its Treatment, E. F. Houghton & Co.)

Fig 2 shows the critical temp for high-carbon steel, heated slowly to about 1 500° F, and then allowed to cool slowly. The critical point varies according to the carbon contents; for steel containing 0.6–0.9% carbon, the range is 1 420°–1 350° F. As steel becomes non-magnetic at about the critical temp, that point can be determined for a given steel by bringing the heated bit close to an ordinary magnet; if the magnet is attracted the temp is below the critical point. Magnetic indicators for blacksmiths' use display a lighted lamp to show that the steel is still magnetic and requires further heating.

Cooling bath for quenching heated steel may be of water, brine, rape-seed oil, tallow, or coal tar. Brine is the fastest quenching medium, but is difficult to keep at constant temp; tar is slowest. Oil is used when a high degree of hardness is not necessary. Circulating cold water is best; for uniform results its temp must be fairly constant. When the steel reaches proper temp, quenching should be rapid; its object being to retain the characteristics of the metal as produced by proper heating.

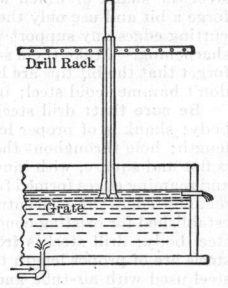

Fig 3. Drill-tempering Tank

Important points for heat treatment of drill steel (2). (*a*) Use only best grade of steel. (*b*) Use oil, gas or elec furnace, which permit close regulation of temp, impossible with coal or coke. (*c*) For both forging and tempering, heat in a non-oxidizing furnace atmosphere. Oxidizing action causes scaling and decarbonization. Indirect (reflected) heat is desirable. (*d*) Forge bits at a temp above the critical point, but never above 1 600° F. Never forge bit or shank when steel is too cold; forging should stop at or just above the critical point; if necessary, reheat. Forge by rapid hammering, not by squeezing or bulldozing, (*e*) For tempering, heat to 1 450–1 500°, quenching on a rising heat, never after temp has fallen below 1 375°. The lower the temp, while still above the critical range, the greater the density, hardness, and toughness of steel. (*f*) Always quench the steel by holding it vertically. (*g*) Temper bits only as far back from cutting edge as will give desired results. (*h*) After forging, anneal by heating to 1 550°, covering with powdered lime if possible; better tempering is thus obtained. (*i*) Never forge and temper on same heat. (*j*) Keep quenching bath cool; if necessary, agitate the bath to prevent its heating too rapidly. (*k*) Heat-treat cutting end of bit to insure a core of max density and hardness, and that all surfaces subject to wear are supported by a toughened core. (*l*) Chemical composition of drill steel should be within following limits: C, 0.85–0.90%; Mn, 0.30–0.40%; Si, 0.10–0.20%; P, not over 0.03%; S, not over 0.03%.

Reclaiming short lengths of steel by welding (6). For 1.25-in hollow steel, time required is: grinding ends square and removing scale, 2 min; countersuiting, 1 min; welding by elec butt method, 0.25–0.35 min, total, 3.3 min. Power consumption; about 0.25 kw-hr per weld of open circuit; voltage, about 4 volts to insure ease in flashing. One man can prepare and weld 2 pieces of steel of aver size in about 5 min. Subsequent heat treating may be done in the welder, by increasing the opening between dies to 3 or 4 in, again clamping the welded steel in the dies, heating to proper temp and slowly cooling in lime. Tests by Sullivan Mach'y Co on steels thus welded gave satisfactory results, as compared to those of original steels.

Sectional drill rods (Fig 4) have been used for holes to 270 ft depth, with hammer drills like Waugh Models 31 and 34, of Denver Rock Drill Mfg Co, which makes and heat-

treats the special steel sleeves for joining the sections.
drill's rotating mechanism in deep holes requires
use of the independent rotation type (7, 8). Deep
holes can thus be drilled at any reasonable angle, for
exploring and sampling orebodies (42).

Table 5 gives cost of such work by Chief Consol
Mining Co, Utah, in 1924. The figures include charging
off deprec of equipment in 2 years; sleeves and steel
were taken at 10¢ per ft drilled, other charges being
direct distributed. Wages: driller, $5.25, helper, $4.75.
Monthly costs, 28–90¢ per ft of hole; monthly aver
drilled per shift, 12.2–34 ft; deepest hole, 272 ft. About
$1 per ft covered all costs of actual drilling. During 8
months' use of diamond drills for same work, cost averaged
$4.94 per ft. It was considered that, to depth of 250 ft,
hammer drills had a 5 to 1 advantage over diamond drills.

The heavy duty thrown on the

Table 5. Cost of Deep-hole Hammer Drilling (8)

	Per ft
Labor....................	$0.44
Misc labor and supplies	0.13
Air charge, bit sharpening, and making up new steel..	0.11
Deprec of equipment......	0.17
Supervision..............	0.07
Blasting out for set-up room	0.05
Total.................	$0.97

Detachable rock-drill bits. Use of detachable bits has greatly increased in recent
years. Many regular steel and drill manufacturers
supply them in various bit gages from $1\frac{1}{4}$ to 4 in.
Chief types are the 4-point cross bit, 6-point or
rose bit and Carr bit with either side or center
hole; the commonest is the 4-point cross bit.
The bits are threaded to the drill shank, and are
easily changed. They are especially advantageous
for scattered or isolated work, such as rock excavation in road construction. A number of
large metal mines have adopted them and reports
indicate savings of 10% to 35% over the conventional type. In the U S Bureau of Mines Inform
Circ 6911 the following advantages are listed:
(1) saving in transport between shop and working
face (nipping); (2) faster drilling; (3) reduction
in loss of steel from all causes; (4) more inches
drilled per bit; (5) less stock of steel required,
hence less investment; (6) smaller gage loss per
bit; (7) smaller gage changes, due to precision
and uniformity of factory shaping; (8) lower total
cost per ft of hole.

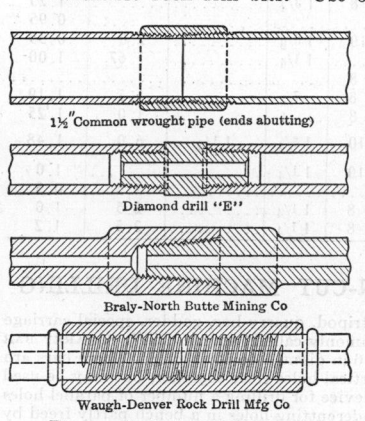

1⅛″ Common wrought pipe (ends abutting)

Diamond drill "E"

Braly-North Butte Mining Co

Waugh-Denver Rock Drill Mfg Co

Fig 4. Evolution of Sectional Drill Rods (7)

Bits can be reground 3 times in most cases to
next following gage; and then rehardened and reground 2 or 3 times more, making in all
an aver use of 5 or 6 times per bit.

3. METHODS OF HAND DRILLING

Methods. SINGLE-HAND DRILLING is usually practicable in the softer rocks to depth
of about 3 ft; wt of hammer, 3.5 to 4.5 lb. DOUBLE-HAND drilling is good for deep holes
or very hard rock; 2 strikers may be employed; wt of hammer, 10 lb. For 6 to 8-ft holes,
the starting bit is usually 1.25 to 1.5-in gage. CHURN DRILL, well handled, is effective for
deep vertical holes. It is raised and dropped by one or more men. (See Sec 9.)

Effect of diam of hole on the speed of drilling has never been fully determined. In general,
doubling the diam divides the speed by from 2 to 4.

Direction of hole. A horiz hole is drilled at about 0.5 the speed of a vertical down hole; in
"uppers" the speed is materially less. Horiz and up holes are usually dry, and the cuttings prevent
the bit from striking the rock effectively; water in down holes keeps the cuttings in suspension,
permitting the bit to strike against a relatively clean face.

Hardness of rock as affecting speed of drilling. In vertical holes (1.5-in starting bit), 1 man
holding and 2 men striking can in 10 hr drill 6-ft holes at following rates: granite, 7 ft; trap, 11 ft;
limestone, 16 ft.

Hand churn drilling. 30-ft holes in blue sandstone, 2.75-in diam at start and 1.5-in at
bottom, can be made in 10 hr; 3 men working at about 0.5 the speed on first 18 ft, 4 men on last 12 ft; brown
sandstone is slightly harder to drill. On Mesabi Range, Minn, 4 men drill 40 ft of 1.5-in
hole in stripping overburden and 96 ft in iron ore.

Hand-power auger drills are sometimes used for prospecting and boring blast holes in soft
ground, as coal, slate, shale, salt, gypsum, and talc. They vary from simple hand augers to elaborate machines with tripod or post mountings. Mounted machines weigh 80 to 100 lb (Sec 9).

Table 6. Rate of Hand-hammer Drilling (Original)

Kind of work	Kind of rock	Men per drill	Hr per day	Diam of bit, in Starting	Diam of bit, in Finishing	Depth of hole, ft	Ft per hr
Railroad cut..	Hard limestone..............	3	10	.....	1 1/2	....	1.7
Open cut.....	Mica schist.................	3	.....	1 7/8	1 1/4	7.5	1.5
Open cut.....	Mica schist.................	3	10	1 7/8	1 1/4	7.5	1.5
Side-hill cut...	Gneiss.....................	3	10	2	1 1/4–1 1/2	6–16	1.41
Open cut.....	Hard porphyry..............	3	.....	.....	.....	20	0.6–0.8
Railroad cut..	Very hard granite...........	3	10	.....	.....	.....	1.4
Railroad cut..	Dark hornblende............	3	10	1 3/8	....	12	2.9
Railroad cut..	Red granite.................	3	10	1 3/8	....	12	2.0
Railroad cut..	Trap, diabase...............	3	10	1 3/8	....	12	1.85
Block holes...	Red granite.................	3	10	1 3/8	.... {	0.5–4 av 1.25	} 1.04
Trench.......	Limestone..................	1	8	1 3/4	....	......	1.25
Trench.......	Shale......................	.....	.....	.....	.....	......	0.95
Tunnel.......	Gneiss, tough schist.........	1	10	1 3/8	....	2.0	0.35
Tunnel.......	Very hard mica schist........	2–3	.....	1 1/4	....	1.67	1.00
Tunnel.......	Conglomerate, shale.........	.....	8	.....	.....	......	.....
Tunnel.......	Tough sandstone...........	1	8	7/8	....	1.5	1.19
Tunnel.......	Very hard syenite, quartzite...	2	8	.....	.....	1.0	1.25
Mine....... {	Augite diorite, firm red } porphyry	2	10	1 3/4	1 1/4	6.0	1.48
Mine.........	Chalcopyrite, limestone......	2	10	1 1/4	....	......	1.0
Mine.........	Medium rock...............	1	.....	.....	.....	2.5	0.5
Tunnel.......	Compact phonolite dike......	1	8	1 1/4	....	2.5	1.0
Shaft........	Compact phonolite dike......	1	8	1 1/4	....	2.5	1.2

4. METHODS AND COST OF OPEN-CUT MACHINE DRILLING

Drill mountings (Sec 15) for open-cut work are the tripod, quarry-bar, gadder, special carriage for deep holes, and the derrick or wagon mounting, commonly called "wagon drill". QUARRY BAR is a horiz bar supported at each end by legs. It is 3 to 6 in diam, 8 to 12 ft long. These bars are primarily for drilling in quarries a number of rows of vertical holes close together, but may be used for similar work in trenches, etc. GADDER is a quarry device for drilling a number of parallel holes in a plane at any angle, from horiz to vertical, as the undercutting holes in a bench partly freed by channeling. A heavy carriage, running on a track, has hinged to it a standard, adjustable at different angles, on which slides a saddle carrying the drill. Wagon mounting is a steel frame and derrick, on 3 or 4 wheels either all steel or with pneumatic tires; or on steel skids. Various type drills can be used. The whole mounting is easily moved by hand. In some types the derrick can be canted, for drilling at angles other than vertical. Holes to 40 ft deep can be drilled with steel changes of 6 to 10 ft. Some drills are equipped with air motors and automatic feed. In larger types for down holes, say to 40 ft, the drill is fed by its own weight, plus a slab-back with adjustable weights. Drill is raised by hand or air hoist. Speeds of 25 to 70 ft per hour are possible, depending on hardness of rock, depth and diam of hole and air press. For cost of mountings, see Sec 15.

Drill trucks are used to some extent for deep-hole drilling, and for trench work. They are operated from a central compressed-air or steam plant, or may carry their own boiler. The drill may be stationary, or mounted on a turn-table. The cuttings are removed from the hole by a water jet or by special steels. There are other devices for mounting one or more ordinary machine drills on a bar. A special device for sewer work is described in Art 10. Respecting drill carriages, see also Sec 6, 15 (11, 20).

Cost of machine drilling comprises: (a) wages of drill crew; (b) proportion of wages of power-plant crew; (c) fuel; (d) drill sharpening; (e) repairs and renewals; (f) oil and water; (g) interest on plant; (h) depreciation of plant; (i) proportion of general expense including taxes; (j) erecting, dismantling, and moving plant.

Factors affecting speed of drilling: (a) character of rock, as hardness, stickiness, seams, sludge, and dust-forming qualities; (b) time for changing bits; (c) time for taking down, moving, and setting up machine; (d) depth of hole; (e) direction of hole; (f) diam of hole; (g) use of air or water, or both, in the hole; (h) shape of bit; (i) quality of black-smithing; (j) percentage of time lost by blasting, breakdowns, delays; (k) size, weight, and type of drill and mounting; (l) air or steam press at the drill; (m) skill of crew.

Time occupied by the different operations in drilling may be classed under CUTTING TIME and DELAYS, the sum of which gives total CYCLE TIME for drilling one hole. Delays comprise time to (a) raise drill, (b) loosen bit, (c) remove it, (d) get bailer and bail, (e) get bit, (f) insert bit in chuck, (g) tighten chuck, and (h) get started. Besides the cycle time, there is the time required to move the drill to other holes, set it up, start it, and miscellaneous delays. For time studies of work with piston drills see (12), where drills were mounted on tripods for holes 7 to 24 ft deep and 2.5 to 5.5 in diam at start, in granite, limestone, and slate. From these records, cutting time averages 58.2% of cycle time; cycle time, 74.7% of total time; time for moving and starting a drill, 12.5% of total time; time lost in delays, 12.8% of total time. Cutting speed: in granite, 0.18 ft per min; limestone, 0.13 ft per min; slate, 0.17 ft per min.

Table 7. Average Time Drilling Vertical Holes (Tripod-mounted Drill)

Kind of rock	Lm	S	Sd	Gr	Tr
Length of shift, hr	10	10	10	10	10
Air pressure, lb per sq in	70	70	70	80	70
Diam drill cylinder, in	3.25	3.25	3.25	3.25	3.25
Diam starting bit, in	2.5	2.5	2	3.5	2.5
Diam finishing bit, in	1.75	1.5	1.25	1.25	2
Depth of hole, ft	12	6	12	20	6
Drilling first 2 ft, min	9	10.5	8	12	14
Cranking out, removing bit, min	1	3.5	1.25	1	1.5
Cleaning out hole, min	1	3	1.25	1	1.5
Putting in new bit, cranking, min	1	2.5	1	1.5	1.5
Drilling second 2 ft, min	13	10.5	1	1.5	14
Drilling last 2 ft, min	12	10.5	6	11	14
Moving machine, setting up, min	15	35	12	11	36
Ft drilled per shift	....	....	96	48	36

Note.— Lm = limestone; S = sandstone (hard); Sd = sandstone (soft); Gr = granite; Tr = trap (diabase).
Rate of drilling. Formula for estimating number of ft drilled per shift (20): $N = S \div \left(r + \dfrac{m}{f} + \dfrac{s}{D} \right)$; where, N = ft drilled per shift; S = working time per shift, min = 600 per 10-hr shift, if no time is lost by blasts, breakdowns, etc; r = actual time to drill 1 ft, min; m = time to crank up, change drills, clean out hole, and crank down = 3 to 4 min ordinarily; f = length of feed = 2 ft in ordinary percussion drills; s = time to shift machine and set it up = 5 to 60 min, usually 12 to 20 min; D = depth of hole, ft.

Records of work with $3\frac{1}{8}$-in piston drills, at 70 lb air or steam press, starting bit about 2.75 in, finishing bit 1.5 in, gave following speeds for 1 ft of hole (20): soft sandstone and limestone, 3 min; medium sandstone and limestone, 4 min; hard granite and sandstone, 5 min; very hard trap and granite, 6–8 min; soft rocks that sludge rapidly, 8–10 min. (For other drilling records, see Sec 15; also " Compressed Air Plant," Peele, 5th Ed, Chap 20.)

Drilling rate is not significant without specification of diam and direction of hole, air press, type of machine, method of removing cuttings, and nature of the rock. Hard, tough rocks have been drilled at 12 in per min; softer rocks faster, especially in down holes. As long as a bit retains its cutting edge it will maintain its initial drilling rate. As depth of hole increases, the drilling rate of hammer drills decreases less than that of piston drills. Theoretically, as follower bits are of smaller gage, drilling rate should increase in inverse proportion to square of diam of hole, but the tightness and sludge in small diam holes keep the rate approx constant (1).

Hammer drills. Speed of cutting. A Sullivan, Class D-19 drill, 1.25-in cylinder, hollow steel, and air at 100 lb, drilled in granite 1.25-in holes, 1 ft deep, in an aver of 1.75 min, using 25 cu ft free air per min. A Class D-15 drill, in same granite, drilled $\frac{5}{8}$-in holes at rate of 1 4 $\frac{5}{8}$-in hole in 10 sec, and a 5.25-in hole in 15 sec. In trench work in oölitic limestone, 12 DB-15 drills averaged 40 1.5-ft holes per drill per 10-hr shift for 12 mo work. Best record was 100 1.5-ft holes in 10 hr and 36 3.5-ft holes in 7 hr. In dark green granite, a DB-15 drill in 16 hr made 47 ft in 25 holes, from 19 to 36 in deep; a DB-19 drill made 19 ft in 5 holes, from 32 to 60 in deep. A DC-19 drill in soft sandstone, made 20 holes 18 in deep, at rate of 25 sec per hole.
Sets of drill steel, comprising a starter and 1 or more follower bits, generally have length increments of 1 to 2 ft. For hard, tough rock the increment is usually 1 ft; for softer rocks, 2 ft. Tests should be made to determine max and aver distances drilled per bit in the different rocks encountered. The fewer the changes, the shorter the drilling time for a given depth of hole.
Starting diam of hole depends upon its depth, reduction in gage of follower bits, depth drilled per bit, and diam of cartridges.

Commonest sizes of cartridge are $1\frac{1}{8}$ and $1\frac{1}{4}$ in, more rarely 1 in; the size being generally constant in any one mine. Bottom diam of hole is thus $1\frac{1}{8} - 1\frac{3}{8}$ in. Gage of bits composing a set varies by $\frac{1}{8}$ or $\frac{1}{16}$ in; for hammer drills, $\frac{1}{16}$ in is satisfactory. With 12 steels, a 12-ft hole requires a starting diam of 2 in for $1/16$-in change in gage. The smaller the starting diam, the higher the aver drilling rate. Depth of hole is determined by blasting conditions.

Fitchering or sticking of the bit is caused by: poor alinement of steel in the hole, bent steel, improper type or poorly sharpened bit, too much or too little feed water, worn or broken shanks, seamy rock, pebbles or spalls falling alongside of bit and jamming, mud collar behind the bit, hard nodules in the rock causing poor alinement of hole and bending of drill shank.

In soft rock a bull bit may penetrate so far that the drill's lifting force on up stroke is insufficient to withdraw it. Remedy is to use a cross or X bit, which is less likely to jam. Sludge is washed out of the hole by the rising stream of water, or blown out by the air or water jet, the larger cuttings falling back and jamming when the drill shank is too small relatively to diam of hole. If hollow steel is not used, a good jet can be made by a 0.5-in pipe, connected to a hose through which water is pumped. Where water is not available in quantity, a fair substitute is a narrow barrel-hoop shoved down the hole; in rotating slowly around the bit, it stirs up the sludge.

Cable, well, or churn drills (Sec 9) are extensively used for deep holes for blasting in quarries and open-cut excavation. Advantages, as compared with machine drills: any depth can be drilled, to the possible limit of blasting; no stripping of the overlying earth is necessary; holes in high faces are drilled to full depth, instead of working in benches; the large-diam holes hold larger charges, hence wider spacing of fewer holes, and saving of time; smaller consumption of fuel for power.

Size of churn-drill holes. Bits are 4 to 9 or 10 in diam, the smaller sizes best for low faces and soft material (but where bank is low, machine drills on wagon mounting are more economical). Common sizes are $5 \, 5/8$ and 6 in; best adapted to limestone formations where drilling cost per ft is not high and relatively closer spacing permits better distribution of explosive. However, use of 8- and 9-in holes has much increased, especially in deep faces and hard rock, where cost per ft is always high. The larger bits permit wider spacing of holes, and greater weight of tools prevents excessive drifting and seems to compensate for greater area of rock cut, so that the cost per ft is no more (often less) than for 6-in bits, while drilling cost per ton or yd is less, with little difference in cost of explosive.

Following are comparative costs of 6- and 9-in drills at Tilden Pit, Cleveland Cliffs Iron Co, using Bucyrus-Armstrong 29 T, 9-in bit (*E & M Jour*, Nov, 1937):

	6-in bit	9-in bit		6-in bit	9-in bit
No of holes................	14	14	Total explosive, lb..........	9 300	20 040
Total footage drilled.........	1 416	1 377	Tons per lb explosive.......	3.8	3.04
Aver depth of hole..........	105	100	Drilling cost per ton........	$0.074	$0.0334
Spacing of holes.............	15×22	20×30	Operating cost per ft........	$1.95	$1.69
Burden per ft of hole, cu yd....	12.2	22.2	Drilling rate, ft in 8 hr.......	13.7	15.6
Total tons blasted...........	35 400	62 000			

N Y Trap Rock Corp, on Hudson River, aver of 4 years' operation in 4 quarries, based on 5 000–35 000 ft drilled per yr:

Kind of rock	Aver depth of hole, ft	Diam of hole, in	Spacing, ft	Ft per hr elapsed time	Cost per ft
Dolomite, hard.............................	70	8	17 × 24	2.03	$1.13
Limestone, soft.............................	35	6	14 × 18	2.75	0.64
Limestone, medium........................	110	10	15 × 27	3.11	1.06
Basalt, hard...............................	120	8	22 × 30	1.4	2.12

Cost of operating churn drills (see Sec 9 for tabulated data). For steam power about 10 or 12 bbl of water and 500 to 650 lb of coal per day are required; for gasolene power (gasolene @ 12¢ per gal), cost is from 70¢ to $1.20 per day; with electric power at 2¢ per kw-hr, cost is about $1.25 per day. A compressed-air operated churn drill uses about as much air as a 3.25-in piston drill. About 2 gal wash water are required per ft of hole. If necessary, it can be collected and used repeatedly. SHARPENING BITS costs much less than for machine drilling; one bit, drilling 10 to 50 ft of hole, requires 1 hr to dress.

Comparative cost of churn and machine drilling. A Cyclone drill, making 3-in holes, 24 ft deep, in solid brown sandstone in Ohio, put down 692 ft in 14 days of 10 hr, or 50 ft per day (20). A 3.25-in machine drill, making 1.75-in holes, 20 ft deep, put down 28 holes in 8 days, or 70 ft per day.

Table 8. Speed of Blast-hole Drilling with Churn or Cable Drills (Original)

Kind of material	Ft per hr	Diam hole, in	Depth, ft	Machine	Remarks
Clay, soapstone................	10	5 5/8	18	....	Railroad work
Limestone....................	9	5 1/2	30	Cyclone	Cement quarry
Limestone....................	8	5	34	Cyclone	Lime, crushed-rock quarry
Shale........................	6	5 5/8	20	Cable drill	....
Overburden, porphyry ore......	5.7	....	55	Keystone	Open-cut mining
Limestone....................	5.5	5 5/8	....	Keystone	Crushed stone
Hard basalt..................	1.6	8	120	Cyclone	Crushed stone
Soil, gravel..................	5.2	2 1/2	23	Cyclone	....
Brown sandstone..............	5.0	3	24	Cyclone	....
Brown sandstone..............	5.0	5 1/2	50	....	Crushed stone
Shale........................	4.8	5 5/8	75	Star	....
Hard, seamy limestone........	4.7	5	22–30	Loomis	....
Half earth, half slate..........	4.4	....	12	Keystone	Aqueduct
Limestone....................	4.0	....	50	Keystone	Lime quarry
Iron ore.....................	2.33	9	95	Armstrong	Ore mining
Copper ore, porphyry.........	3.5	6 1/2	60	Keystone	Mining
Shale........................	2–8	4 1/2–6	20–80	Star	....
Limestone....................	3.2	10	110	Armstrong	Crushed stone
Copper ore...................	1.5–2.5	6	30–35	Star	Mining
Limestone....................	3.0	6	200	Loomis	Cement quarry
Limestone, sandstone.........	1.0	5 5/8	20	Cable drill	....
Hard limestone...............	2.1	8	70	Armstrong	Crushed stone

Daily field costs (exclusive of sharpening) of the above work were: Churn drill. Runner, $3; helper (and fireman), $2; water, 60¢; coal @ 10¢ per bushel, 60¢; total, $6.20; cost per ft, $12.54. Machine drill. Runner, $3; helper, $1.50; fireman, $2; water, 75¢; coal, $1; total, $8.25; cost per ft, 11.8¢. The larger diam of the churn-drill holes saved dynamite, as each hole was sprung but 3 times, whereas the machine-drill holes had to be sprung 4 or 5 times. See also Sec 9.

5. THEORY AND PRACTICE OF BLASTING

Conditions influencing results of blasting: size and number of free faces; cohesive strength of the rock; structure of rock (massive, jointed, laminated, stratified, or fissured); strength and nature of the explosive; character of fuse and stemming; whether the shot acts alone or simultaneously with others; whether the broken rock falls or must be lifted by the blast; form and size of chamber containing the explosive; proportion of length of line of least resistance to length of the hole, and to height of free face (3, 11, 20). See also Sec 4.

Rules for blasting. Many have been formulated, but all neglect some of the conditions stated above. Also, most published rules are applicable to black powder only and are valueless for high

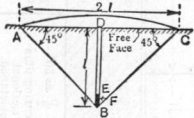

Fig 5. Theoretical Crater, Normal Hole

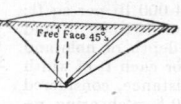

Fig 6. Theoretical Crater, Oblique Hole

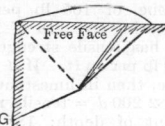

Fig 7. Hole with Two Free Faces

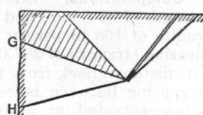

Fig 8. Hole with Two Free Faces

explosives; and practically all ignore the use to which the blasted rock is to be put. Hence, experience and judgment are more useful in determining proper methods than the theories and rules summarized below. Theory of blasting is discussed in detail in (5). According to the CRATER THEORY, a charge in a mass of earth or rock with horiz surface will blow out a funnel-shaped crater, the sides of which have a slope of 1 to 1 to the FREE FACE (Fig 5). Distance DB (more exactly, DF) is the LINE OF LEAST RESISTANCE = l; hence, volume of crater is $V = 0.33\ l \times \pi l^2 = l^3$ (nearly). Hence, general formula for volume of rock loosened is $V = ml^3$. According to Schoen (5), $m = 0.4$ for tough, soft rock, and 0.9 for hard, brittle rock.

Direction of hole. If vertical (normal, as in Fig 5), the charge may blow out stemming and fail to break; hence, hole should be inclined (Fig 6), to reduce chances of a blow-out, as well as to incease area of free face and volume of rock broken. Limiting inclination of drill hole is 45°.

Effect of free faces. The greater the area of free face, the easier can rock be blasted. Fig 7 shows area of volume broken when there are 2 free faces (point G being uncertain). Fig 8 shows area when charge is at unequal distances from the 2 faces; shaded area will probably not be removed by the direct force of the blast, but may be broken indirectly. When 2 or more free faces are exposed, the longest line of resistance should not exceed 1.5 l. To obtain the aid of gravity, l should be horiz, and the longest line of resistance vertical.

Relation of factors. Length l should be proportioned to size and diam of the hole. In general, in open-cut work the depth of holes should approximate 1.5 l.

Table 9. Relations of Diam and Depth of Hole, and Line of Least Resistance

Diam of hole, in	Depth of hole, ft	l, ft	Diam of hole, in	Depth of hole, ft	l, ft
1.25	3.50	3.50	1.5	12.00	6.00
1.25	5.75	3.75	1.75	5.00	5.00
1.25	10.00	5.00	1.75	9.00	6.00
1.5	4.00	4.00	1.75	14.00	7.00
1.5	7.50	5.00			

Holes blasted simultaneously. Fig 9 shows the effect. If a and b are blasted separately, c would not break out; when blasted together c is broken, if x is not too great. In aver hard rock $x = 1.5\ l$ to $2\ l$; in weak rock, x should be about equal to l.

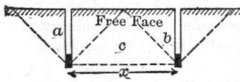

Fig 9.   Effect of Holes Fired Simultaneously

Rock coefficient. To obtain it, select a homogeneous bench 2 ft wide by 3 ft high. In this drill several vertical holes, so spaced that the blasting of one will not crack nor start the rock around another. Charge each with different weighed amounts of the explosive to be used, beginning with a small quantity. Fire the holes separately. If C = rock coeff, P = wt of powder, lb, l = line of least resistance, ft; then $C = P \div l^3$, and $P = Cl^3$. For 3 free faces, use 0.66 P; for 4 faces, 0.5 P; for 5, 0.4 P; for 6, 0.25 P.

Size of drill hole for charge. If P = wt of explosive, lb; g = sp gr of explosive, and d = diam of hole, ft; then, $P = 0.34\ gd^3$.

Spacing holes in open-cut work. Much depends on depth of cut, character of rock and diam of hole. In aver size machine-drilled holes for shallow cuts, 6 ft and less, vert holes in most rocks should be set back from face a distance equal to depth, and spaced apart a distance 0.85 of depth. With holes to 12 ft deep, spacing and burden should be about 0.65 of depth; to 20 or 25 ft, spacing and burden should not exceed 0.5 depth (usually less in hard rock) unless holes are sprung, in which case spacings may be wider.

Deep holes for quarry blasting (22). In homogeneous rock having a vert face, 3 resistances tend to counteract the explosive force (Fig 10): (A) resistance distributed along the hole, caused by the rock's tensile strength. This may be resolved into a single force acting midway between top and bottom of face, and of a magnitude equal to total distributed resistance; (B) shearing resistance across the horiz line between the hole and bottom of face, represented by the rock's shearing strength; (C) frictional resistance to sliding at the bottom.

Computations. Limestone of 165 lb per cu ft has tensile strength of 82 000 lb and shearing strength of 184 000 lb per sq ft; granite of 168 lb per cu ft has tensile strength of 101 500 lb and shearing strength of 287 000 lb per sq ft. If d is depth of hole and b its distance back from face, then in limestone for each ft of width of spacing between holes: 82 200 d = tensile resistance, considered as concentrated at midpoint of depth; 187 000 b = shearing resistance concentrated at bottom; and $165 \times b \times d$ = wt of the block. Assuming coeff of fric = 0.65, 107 bd = fric resistance to sliding at bottom. For granite, the computations are similar. Values of shearing resistance apply to homogeneous rock; not where there is a parting line at the quarry face.

Ideal method would be to concentrate enough explosive in bottom of hole to overcome shearing and frictional resistances, and distribute enough explosive throughout the hole to overcome tensile resistance.

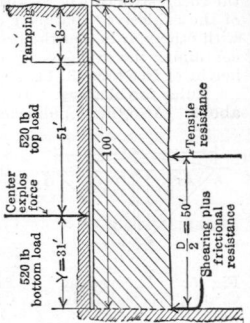

Fig 10.   Forces to be Overcome in Deep-hole Blasting (22)

In practice this is rarely feasible; if the charge be distributed throughout the hole, its total force may be considered as concentrated at a given point, half above and half below. For max effect, this point should be so located as to balance opposing resistances. In Fig 10 it is at a distance Y above the bottom, proportional to the rock resistances. That is,

$$Y = \frac{d}{2} \times \frac{\text{Tensile resistance}}{\text{Tensile resistance} + (\text{shearing resistance} + \text{frictional resistance})}.$$

For limestone (see above), $Y = \dfrac{d}{2} \times \dfrac{82\ 200\ d}{82\ 200\ d + 187\ 000\ b + 107\ bd}$.

Similarly for granite. Thus, for practical purposes, Y is the dividing point of the charge, half the total being below this point and half above.

To find the wt of explosive required, the depth of hole, its distance from the face, and the spacing between holes, must be known. From these factors the BURDEN in cu ft and tons on each hole is computed. Location of holes to give best fragmentation at low cost must be determined for each case by trial. If there is no parting at the quarry floor, the holes must go below floor line to insure breaking to bottom (Table 10).

Table 10. Aver Spacing of Deep Holes in Quarry with Vert Face (22)

Depth of hole, ft	Height of face, ft	Distance back, ft	Spacing, ft	Height of bottom charge, ft	Diam hole at bottom, in	Depth of top tamping, ft
20	18	13	10.5	3.5	4	9
30	28	14.5	12	6.5	4.25	10
40	37	16	13	10	4.5	12
50	47	17.5	14	13	4.75	13
60	56	19	15.5	16	5	14
70	66	20.5	16.5	20	5.25	15
80	75	22	18	23	5.5	16
90	85	23.5	19	27	5.75	17
100	94	25	20	30	6	18
160	152	35	20	52	8	25

Height of bottom charge given in Table 10 is an aver between limestone and granite. Assuming aver duty of explosive to be 4 ton of rock broken per lb of explosive, and spacing as shown, a 100-ft hole in limestone would have a burden of $\dfrac{100 \times 25 \times 20 \text{ ft}}{12 \text{ cu ft per ton}} = 4\ 166$ ton, requiring a charge of 1 040 lb. Applying previous formula,

$$y = \frac{82\ 200 \times 100}{(82\ 200 \times 100) + (187\ 000 \times 25) + (107 \times 25 \times 100)} \times (100 \div 2) = 31.4 \text{ ft.}$$

Thus, half the charge (520 lb) should be in the lower 31 ft of hole. Wt of explosive contained in a given depth of hole depends on diam of hole and density of explosive. In Table 11, cartridges are assumed to be slit and well tamped to fill the hole completely, with no air spaces.

Table 11. Approx Weight (Lb) of Explosive Contained in 1 Ft of Hole

Diam of hole, in	Straight N G	Gelex type	Red Cross Extra	Quarry Gelatin	B Blasting Powder	Du Pont Extra D
4	6.60	6.1	6.33	7.35	5.28	5.46
4 1/2	8.40	7.7	8.06	9.35	6.72	6.95
5	10.50	9.7	10.08	11.69	8.40	8.71
5 1/2	12 6	11.3	12.1	14.0	10.1	9.80
6	15.0	13.8	14.4	16.7	12.0	12.55
7	20.4	19.0	19.6	22.7	16.3	17.09
8	26.7	24.5	25.6	29.7	21.4	21.85
9	33.7	31.2	32.4	37.6	27.0	27.68

Depth of lift. In deep open cuts or pits, rock is usually excavated in 2 or more benches or lifts. Depth for economical drilling, size into which the rock breaks on blasting, and presence or absence of seams or of horiz drill holes (called toe holes) which might assist breaking, all determine economic height of lift. 3 1/8 and 3 1/2-in machine drills are good to depths of 16 to 24 ft. Churn drills are efficient for almost any depth, and where they are used lifts of 100 ft are common. Max depth for hand drilling is usually about 8 ft with hand hammer, and for machine drills, 18 ft. As a rule, the higher the bench, the farther back from the face may the holes be located; but, the farther back the holes, the coarser will the rock break. In deep holes, the explosive should be separated into several charges with stemming between; for, if the entire charge is at the bottom of the hole, the bottom of the bench may be blown out and the top left overhanging. If 2 rows of horiz holes are drilled in the face, besides the vert holes, height of bench may be increased.

Examples of open-cut blasting indicating that 4–6 ton of rock can be broken per lb explosive (25). Limestone quarry in Tenn, stone used for R R ballast, etc. Blast was of 16 5/8-in holes; aver depth, 75 ft; spaced 18 ft apart; aver face burden, 22 ft. Charge of 3 750 lb 60% and 3 700 lb 40% low-freezing dynamite broke 5.7 ton per lb.

Blast in cement rock, in Penn, of 14 5 5/8-in holes; aver depth, 86 ft, spaced 18 ft; face burden, 30 ft. Charge of 4 850 lb 60% and 3 250 lb 40% dynamite broke 55 000 ton, or 6.8 ton per lb.

Kentucky limestone quarry, for R R ballast; 9 holes, aver depth, 50 ft, spaced 18 ft apart and 25 ft back; 3 250 lb 40% dynamite broke 16 200 ton, or 5 ton per lb.

Table 12.   Spacing of Holes, Charges, and Results of Machine-drill Blasts (Original)

Rock	Kind of work	Aver depth of hole, ft	Aver dist of rows from face, ft	Aver dist apart of holes, ft	Ft of hole per cu yd	Grade of explosive, % Ngl	Kind of explosive	Explosive per cu yd of rock, lb	Diam of hole, in
Limestone....	Canal..........	12	8	8	0.40	40	A	0.75	......
Limestone....	Crushed stone....	6	5	6	1.00	40	A	0.70	......
Limestone....	Cement.........	20	....	....	....	50	A	0.37	.
Hard dolomite	R R thro'-cut (a).	20	7	7	0.42	60	A (b)	1.05	.
Limestone....		15·	....	....	0.43	50	A	0.26 (c)	......
Limestone....	Canal..........	14	4	6	....	40 60	A A	0.38 0.38	....
Limestone....	Canal (d)........	13	8	6	0.56	40 60	A A	0.38 0.44	 4.5
Hard lime-stone	Crushed stone	26 (e) 12 (f)	9	6.5 6	0.47	60 60	A } A }	1.35	5.5 4.5
Sandstone....	R R side-cut.....	20	12–18	12–18	0.10	40 {	B A	1.00 0.10	....
Sandstone....	R R thro'-cut....	20	12–18	12–18	0.20	40 {	B A	2.00 0.20	....
Sandstone....	R R cut.........	20	18	14	0.15	......	B	0.15 (g)	......
Soft shale.....	R R side-cut.....	24	12–18	12–18	0.08	40 {	B A (c)	0.70 0.03	....
Hard shale....	R R thro'-cut....	24	12–18	12–18	0.20	40 {	B A (c)	1.50 0.10	....
Granite......	Rubble..........	16	5	5	1.36	60	A	0.20	......
Hard granite..	Crushed, rubble..	(h)	......	5	......	75 60	A } A }	......	2.5
Gneiss.......	....	12	....	....	1.33	40	A	0.60	......
Gneiss.......	....	14	....	....	0.63	40	A	0.50	......
Syenite.......	Mine...........	12	2.5	6 (i)	1.70	40	A	0.67	......
Iron ore......	Mine...........	12.5	....	....	0.32	52	A	0.44	......
Seamy trap...	Crushed.........	14	....	....	0.35	75	A	0.20	......
Massive trap..	....	16	....	....	1.00	40	A	0.70	......
Seamy slate...	R R thro'-cut....	12 (j)	10	10	0.27	60	A	1.11	4.5
Seamy rock...	Dam filling......	18	....	....	0.13	......	B	1.85	......

A. Dynamite. B. Black powder. (a) 35 holes. (b) Holes sprung with 2 lb dynamite. (c) Holes sprung. (d) 45 holes. (e) 60 holes; top holes, vertical, 26 ft deep. (f) 75 holes; 2 toe holes, one at 15° and one at 60° with vertical, 10 to 14 ft deep, the former being 6 ft away from & 2.5 ft in front of latter. (g) Sprung 3 times. (h) 1st row 6 to 15 ft, from face; 2nd row, 7 to 10 ft from first row; about 2.5 lb of 75% dynamite & 6.25 lb of 60% per hole. (i) Holes staggered. (j) 30 holes; holes at angle of 15° with vertical. Sprung with 3 lb of dynamite.

Oklahoma quarry, for R R ballast; 8 holes, 95 ft deep, spaced 28 ft; aver face burden, 33 ft. Charge of 2 200 lb gelatin, 3 350 lb 60% and 1 250 lb 40% dynamite broke 62 000 ton, or 9 ton per lb. Blast badly balanced, requiring very strong explosive at bottom. Cost per ton was as high or higher than a well-balanced blast.

Blast in iron ore of 26 5⅝-in holes; aver depth, 84 ft; spaced 15 by 15 ft; triple loaded; 8 500 lb 40% dynamite broke 50 000 ton, or 5 ton per lb.

Blast in cement rock, in N J, of 11 holes; aver depth, 102 ft; spaced 20 by 22 ft; 2 040 lb 60% and 4 475 lb 40% gelatin broke 40 000 ton, or 6 ton per lb.

A 75 000-ton blast, West Va, cost 3.3¢ per ton (1915). Of 15 6-in holes, 13 were 125 ft deep, drilled about 5 ft below quarry floor; 2 holes were 72 and 85 ft. Aver spacing, 15 ft; top burden of 8–12 ft; bottom burden 25–35 ft. Charge per hole, 400–500 lb 60% gelatin, on top of which were 150–600 lb du Pont quarry powder. Cordeau fuse was held taut while cartridges were dropped down the holes. In 10 holes, charges were split near middle by 10–20 ft clay tamping; 5 holes were loaded solid, with 30 ft tamping. On each line of Cordeau was 1 No 6 du Pont electric cap. Caps were connected in series and tested. About 50% of the stone was broken to 1-man size; none thrown over 100 yd from face. Aver burden per hole, 2 000 cu yd; aver charge, 900 lb. Total rock broken, 60 500 loose yd (75 000 ton), or 5.5 ton per lb. Cost per ton: explosives, fuse and caps, 2.2¢; drilling and charging, 1.1¢.

6.   CHARGING AND FIRING

For facts respecting ordinary methods of charging black powder and dynamite, including data on fuse, detonators, squibs, tamping, and electric firing, see Sec 4, 6 (14, 20). *Note.—* Stemming is the tamping material; tamping, the act of inserting stemming.

Table 13. Spacing of Holes, Charges, and Results of Churn-Drill Blasts (Original)

Kind of rock	Character of work	No of holes	Diam of hole, in	Aver depth, ft	Aver dist holes from face, ft	Aver dist apart of holes, ft	Total explosive used, lb	Grade of explosive, %	Kind of explosive	Rock blasted, cu yd	Explosive per cu yd, lb
E	Crushed stone..	4	5 5/8	66	....	....	5 500	....	A	20 000	0.275
E	Crushed stone..	8	5	50	12	12	1 200	40	A	....	....
E	Cement quarry.	12	6	204	32	16.5 {	7 700	....	B }	47 000	0.483
							15 000	....	A }		
E	Cement quarry.	8	6	65	20	20	4 000	40	A	....	....
E {	Open-pit iron mine........ }	...	6	20	15	15	65(b)	40	A	....	....
E	R R ballast....	8	6	48	19	18	3 300	40	A	5 720	0.578
E	Cement quarry.	9	6	62	32	20 {	1 800	40 }	A	12 320	0.349
							2 500	60 60 }			
E	Cement quarry.	12	8	140	30	30 {	17 000	....	B }	59 000	0.55
							16 000	....	A }		
E {	Hard R R ballast }	8	6	95	33	28 {	2 200	....	B	27 300	0.249
							3 350	60	A }		
							1 250	40	A }		
E	Lime quarry....	3	6	100	24	17 {	1 200	60 }	A	5 720	0.315
							600	40 }			
E	Cement quarry.	9	6	52.5	36	20 {	1 720	60 }	A	13 660	0.309
							2 500	40 }			
F	Hard granite...	16	6	115	16	32	18 597	....	C	34 000	0.5
G	Copper mine...	1	....	80	....	....	4 000(e)	40	A	12 000	0.333
H	R R thro'-cut...	578	4	25–40	(f)	(f) {	1 200	60 }	B	35 000	0.814
							27 275	35 }			
I } J }	Open-pit mine..	....	{ 5 5/8 { 5 5/8	60 60	40 15	35 15	100(g) 625	40	A D	3 100 500	0.323 1.250
K	Placer dredge...	....	....	30	20	50	30(i)	80	A	....	....
.....	R R thro'-cut...	8	4.5	32–37	(h)	22	50 300	2F–3F	D	16 113	0.311
E	Open-pit iron ore	14	9	100	30	20	23 000	....	B	30 500	0.575

A. Dynamite.   *B.* Gelatin.   *C.* Nitramon.   *D.* Black blasting powder.   *E.* Limestone.
F. Sandstone.   *G.* Porphyry.   *H.* Basalt.   *I.* Copper porphyry.   *J.* Tough carbonate.   *K.* Gravel.
L. Ore and capping.   (*b*) Per hole.   (*e*) Sprung with 150 lb of 40% dynamite.   (*f*) Holes in 5 parallel lines: 1 center line, 2 lines 10 ft away; 2 lines 24 ft from center line. Holes staggered, 14 ft apart, and chambered with 60% dynamite. Loading required 8 days. (*g*) Per hole. (*h*) Holes on center line, the first being 18 ft from face. Holes sprung with 15 sticks 60% dynamite, then 55 sticks, then 275 sticks. Tamping, after springing, cost $12 to drill out. (*i*) Per hole; cost of blasting about 5¢ per cu yd.

Deep-hole blasting. For this it is often advisable to place the dynamite in several distinct charges separated by stemming, each charge having its own primer, or all connected by a line of Cordeau fuse or Primacord. If the rock consists of hard and soft layers, charges should be placed in the hard layers. Contractor's powder and free-running high explosive grades are charged like black powder, but are exploded by a dynamite primer. Other grades and all dynamites are exploded with detonators. If black powder and dynamite are charged in the same hole, explosion of the powder will detonate the dynamite.

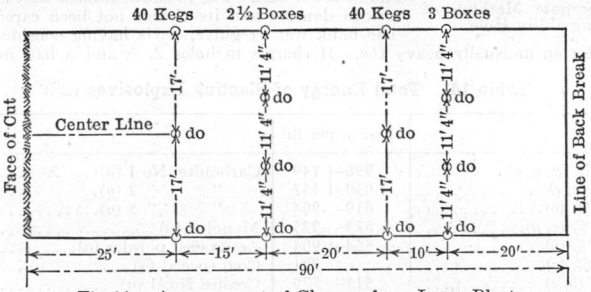

Fig 11. Arrangement of Charges for a Large Blast

Dynamite and black powder in one blast. In blue sandstone large charges of black powder and dynamite in alternate rows of holes were found effective (20). In Fig 11, the 24-ft holes were made with churn drill, with 3-in bit. Holes marked "kegs" were loaded with 25-lb kegs of black powder; and those marked "boxes" were loaded to within 4 ft of the top with 40% dynamite, as shown. Before loading holes with black powder, each one was sprung (see below); first with 15 sticks of 1.25 by 8-in size dynamite, second with 40 sticks, third with 80 sticks, and a final charge of 130 sticks of 40% dynamite per hole. The dynamite and powder were fired together, on the theory that the powder would lift the rock and the dynamite would shatter it. About 2 700 cu yd of rock were broken in one blast, with 800 lb of dynamite for springing and 6 000 lb of black powder and 1 100 lb of dynamite for the final charges.

Springing deep holes (26) (Sec 4, Art 8, 9). By starting with a small charge, followed by gradually increased charges, the chamber at bottom of hole can be made nearly spherical, giving best concentration of explosive. First springing charge should not occupy more than 0.05 of total depth of hole.

Gelatin dynamite is best for springing; it is safe, its plasticity and density eliminate air spaces, and, though slow in action when shot in the open, it has max quickness when confined, except in hardpan, clay and similar material; in these soft materials, ammonia dynamite is preferable. Charge should be packed solidly, to exclude air; stemming free from broken rock and small in amount, so the springing charge will drive it out of the hole. Water stemming has advantages due to ease of application; it reduces amount of rock blown out and keeps the hole cool, which is necessary before making the main charge. Springing shots should be fired electrically. After study of bore-hole temperatures, the du Pont Co recommends that no explosive be placed in a sprung hole if a tamping stick left in the hole about 5 min feels warm to the hand. When holes are left to cool naturally, it is well to regulate the intervals between charges as follows: after first spring, 1 hr; second, 2 hr; third, 3 hr; fourth, 4 hr; fifth, 5 hr. After last springing, wait until next day before charging. Heavy springing is not advisable in soft shales, as it may fill the chamber with debris. In highly inclined strata, the shock of springing may cause a slip and close the hole.

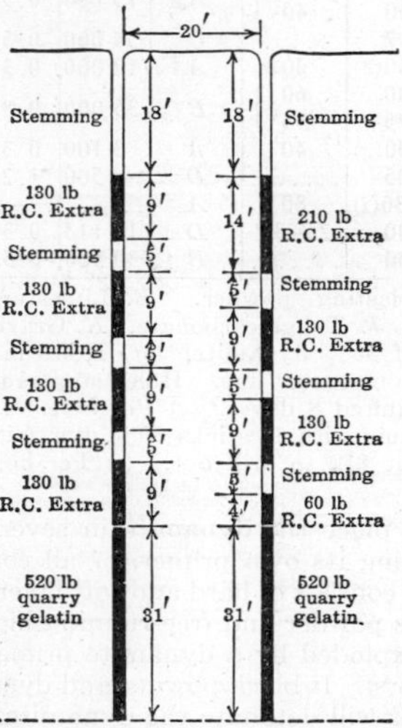

Fig 12. Alternate Methods of Charging a 6-in Hole

Charging deep holes. If the rock is seamed and cracked, the charge should not extend to upper part of hole; there must be ample space for stemming.

Referring to Table 10, for 6-in holes of depth and spacing as in Fig 12, 18 ft of stemming is recommended; leaving 51 ft between bottom charge and stemming for second half of charge. 520 lb of Red Cross Extra would fill 36 ft of the hole, leaving 15 ft for stemming. For max effect, it would be best to divide the charge into 4 sections, with 5 ft of stemming between them. For electric blasting, it is unwise to split the charge into so many sections, due to difficulty of wiring. Where there are both hard and soft strata above bottom charge, the explosive is placed in the hard strata and stemming in the weaker. In uniform rock, broken charges are placed in adjoining holes so that explosive and stemming alternate along the line of holes.

Length of bottom charge is worked out as above for the different depths and spacings of holes in Table 13. When the face slopes, causing heavy toe resistance, explosive can be concentrated at the bottom by drilling larger diam holes, or decreasing the spacing; a row of staggered holes at the toe assists in such cases. With a well-defined parting line at the quarry floor, it is rarely necessary to drill below grade; and, as the shearing resistance is then reduced, less explosive is required near the floor.

Separate calculations for each hole (38) give best results and at lower cost. Fig 13 shows a blast that might have done serious damage had its charge not been carefully computed. The bank was irregular; parts having considerable overhang, and some holes an unusually heavy toe. If charges in holes 2, 7, and 8 had not been broken

Table 14.   Total Energy of Blasting Explosives (23)

	Ft-ton per lb		Ft-ton per lb
Blasting gelatin (a, b, c)............	996–1 149	Carbonite No 1 (a)............	421–539
Nitroglycerin (b, c)...............	1 030–1 157	" " 2 (a)............	465–498
Dynamite, 75% (b)...............	819– 904	" " 3 (a)............	494
" 65% (c, d)............	879– 925	Monobel (a)...................	796
" 40% (b)...............	864– 904	Aetna coal powder (a).........	517–533
" 30% (c)...............	721	Coal special (a)...............	525–564
Nitrocellulose (b, c).............	511– 770	Coalite No. 1 (a)...............	502
Fulminate mercury (b, c)........	287– 288	" " 2 (a)...............	553
Black powder (a, b).............	402– 553		

a = U S Bur Mines.   b = Brunswig.   c = Heise.   d = Bichel.

near the bottom, where the bank sloped inward, fragments of rock might have damaged buildings and plant, which were within 300 ft of the face. By care in computing each charge, no rock was thrown more than 150 ft.

Force of explosives (23). Total energy of an explosive (Table 14) is the sum of its shattering (percussive) and propellent forces; for practical results, the relative shattering and propellent values must be known (Table 15).

If for a given case an explosive is not sufficiently shattering, use one of equal total energy but greater percussive value. For throwing broken rock farther, use an explosive of greater propellent force; or, if in this case, the rock was breaking to desired size, use explosive of greater total energy.

Table 15. Explosives in Order of Decreasing Shattering and Increasing Propellent Force (23)

HIGH SHATTERING FORCE

Nitroglycerin
Blasting gelatin
75% gelatin dynamite
60% dynamite, active dope
50%   "   "   "
40%   "   "   "
30%   "   "   "
"40%" ammonia dynamite
"40%" gelatin   "
Granular nitroglycerin powder
Black powder (fine grained)
   "   "   (coarse grained)
HIGH PROPELLENT FORCE

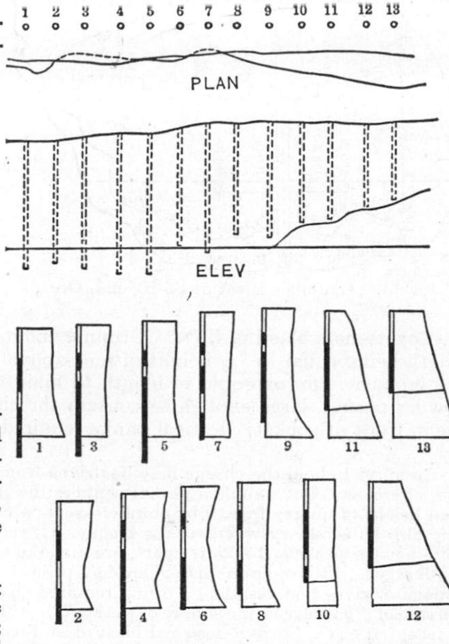

Fig 13. Different Loadings for Varying Conditions of Quarry Face

Blasting formulas are inaccurate, because of difficulty in measuring the actual force developed, uncertainty as to the BURDEN on the charge, and varying rock characteristics. Tests are always necessary, but empirical formulas and all available data are useful as guides.

General remarks on explosives: shattering effect increases with speed of explosion; effic varies with degree of confinement of charge; excessive noise means wasted energy. Useful effect depends upon suitability of an explosive for its work, as well as upon its strength, i c, upon the force it develops. Straight dynamites are rated on percentage by weight of nitroglycerin (NG) contained; a 40% straight dynamite contains 40% NG, and any other kind (regardless of content) which develops the same force, weight for weight, is rated as 40%, the rating of straight dynamites serving as a reference. A dynamite of 40% *bulk strength* develops the same force *volume for volume*, as a 40% straight dynamite. Some high explosives, as the permissibles, the du Pont "Extras" and certain others for special work, are not rated by percentage, but marked by numbers or letters designating strength. Force developed is not in direct ratio to percentage rating; a 40% dynamite does not develop twice the force of a 20%, because ingredients other than NG and ammonium nitrate have some explosive effect of their own, altering the ratio. True ratios are shown in Table 16; 1 cartridge of 40% is equal in force to 0.87 cartridge of 60% or 1.31 cartridges of 20%, except that in soft material the ratios may be lowered by greater spreading and heaving effect of the lower grades of explosive.

Table 16. Equivalents of Dynamite of Different Strengths

One cartridge % N G	60%	50%	45%	40%	35%	30%	25%	20%	15%
60	**1.00**	1.06	1.09	1.15	1.21	1.29	1.38	1.50	1.64
50	0.94	**1.00**	1.02	1.08	1.14	1.21	1.30	1.41	1.55
45	0.92	0.98	**1.00**	1.05	1.12	1.19	1.27	1.38	1.51
40	0.87	0.93	0.95	**1.00**	1.06	1.13	1.20	1.31	1.43
35	0.82	0.87	0.89	0.94	**1.00**	1.06	1.13	1.23	1.35
30	0.77	0.82	0.84	0.89	0.94	**1.00**	1.07	1.16	1.27
25	0.73	0.77	0.79	0.83	0.88	0.94	**1.00**	1.09	1.19
20	0.67	0.71	0.73	0.76	0.81	0.86	0.92	**1.00**	1.10
15	0.61	0.65	0.66	0.70	0.74	0.79	0.84	0.91	**1.00**

Chamber blasting is done by driving a small tunnel or sinking a shaft, at the end of which chambers are excavated for the main charges of explosive. For black powder the chamber may be below the floor of the drifts, for convenience in pouring loose powder into large wooden boxes, built in the chambers. The tramping of the men packs it tightly, and the solid sides of the excavation offer greater resistance to the explosion. COYOTE HOLES are one-man tunnels or drifts (Fig 15).

Chamber blast, St. Helena, Ore (Fig 14). The rock was basaltic, weighing 175 lb per cu ft. Explosive was No 2, MV Trojan powder; charge, 3 500 lb. The tunnels were tamped to the portal with muck. The rock was sufficiently broken to be handled by steam shovel, little bulldozing (sledging) being necessary. Vol broken, 14 280 cu yd.

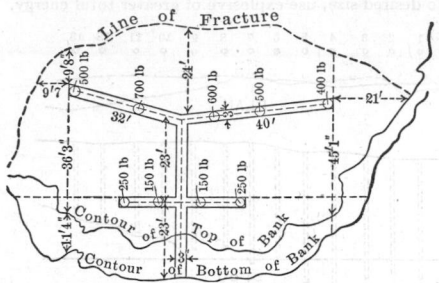

Fig 14.　Chamber Blast at St Helena, Ore

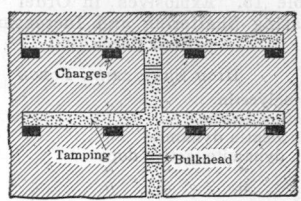

Fig 15. Tunnel, Crosscuts and Powder Pockets for Coyote Blasting (27)

Coyote-hole blasting (27). A tunnel about 2.5 by 3.5 ft section is driven into the face, length being equal to $^2/_3$ height of face above tunnel. At end of tunnel and forming a T is a crosscut, approx equal in length to main tunnel. At each end of crosscut is sunk a powder pocket, large enough to contain the charge; their depth = 1 ft for each 10 ft of toe in front of pocket; vertical banks required less depth (Fig 15).

An offset to hold the charge may be driven from the crosscut, or the charge is simply placed on floor of crosscut, but a sunken pocket confines the charge better. When length of tunnel is greater than height of quarry face, 2 or more crosscuts are driven to distribute the charges properly; this may also be necessary when rock is blocky. If rock is hard and high fragmentation desired, 2 or more powder pockets, 15–25 ft apart, are made in each crosscut.

Charges. Coarse-grain black powder, primed with 5–10% of its wt of 40 or 60% straight dynamite, gives best results. To find required charge, first compute the cu yd of material above the tunnel ("yardage in the square of the shot") = (length of tunnel × length crosscut × aver height of face, ft) ÷ 27. A well-designed blast often breaks twice the yardage in square of shot, but the above is conservative. For road-surfacing rock, the charge is 0.3–1.5 lb per cu yd in square of shot. To throw rock clear of right of way, as in sidehill road making, the charge may be 1.75–3.5 lb per cu yd; for this purpose, better err on side of over-charging; a good blast will throw 60–80% clear of right of way.

Charging (27). One 50-lb case 40% straight dynamite is placed in bottom of each powder pocket; 3 cartridges being primed with electric caps. Electric blasting cap wires are connected in series, if a blasting machine is used, or in parallel if fired by a power current (Fig 16). Free ends of wires are connected to No 14 gage duplex leading wire, running out to the face. All joints well taped and leading wire wrapped in roofing paper or gunny sacking to protect from injury.

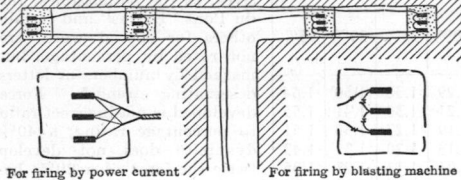

For firing by power current　For firing by blasting machine

Fig 16. Modes of Wiring for Coyote-hole Blasting (27)

Computed charge is placed in the pockets on top of primer. Loading explosive in original packages saves time, and is safer; but, in charging blasting powder in sidehill work, for wasting the rock, it is best to pour it into the pockets. The charge is covered with dry earth or rock screenings. One wire from right-hand pocket is connected with a wire from left-hand pocket, and the 2 free wires are connected through the leading wires to the blasting machine. For max detonating effect, run a line of countered Cordeau fuse from unit to unit, with a coil on bottom of each pocket. When any one charge explodes, the Cordeau detonates the others.

Crosscuts and tunnel are finally tamped with broken stone. Logs are often used to aid in confining filling; a row being laid crosswise on floor at end of tunnel, their ends projecting into the crosscuts. Spaces between the logs are filled with clay. Other layers of logs follow, to the roof of tunnel. Main tunnel is then tamped, and blast is ready for firing.

Best theoretical length of tunnel (27) is equal to about $^2/_3$ the height of face; but, with only 1 crosscut, a tunnel more than 60 ft long is impracticable. A shorter tunnel and 1 crosscut generally give best results at least cost; for high banks and large charges several crosscuts may be driven.

Table 17.   Charges Used in Chamber and Coyote Blasts (Original)

Case	Rock	Rock loosened, cu yd	Dynamite, lb	Black powder, lb	Judson powder, lb	Lb per cu yd Dynamite	Lb per cu yd Black powder	Lb per cu yd Judson powder	
I......	Granite......	110 000	144	35 000	....	0.001	0.320	....	
II.....	Porphyry....	50 000	100	....	1 200	0.002	....	0.024	
III....	Granite......	00 000	5 400	29 050(a)	....	0.067	0.374(a)	....	
IV.....	Limestone...	....	....	....	12 000	....	....	....	
V......	Sandstone....	220 000	1 250	43 100	....	0.006	0.195	....	
VI.....	Rock........	350 000	11 400	....	114 000(b)	0.033	....	0.326	
VII....	Basalt.......	14 280	....	....	3 500	....	....	0.245(b)	
VIII..	Black trachyte	250 000	3 000	....	30 000	0.012	....	0.120	
IX.....	Limestone....	1 700	26	2 775	....	0.015	1.632	....	
X......	Trap........	150 000	7 000	....	....	0.047	....	....	
XI....	Granite......	440 000	32	18 250	....	0.0001	0.042	....	
XII....	Gravel......	....	....	17 500	....	....	....	....	
XIII...	Gravel......	150 000	....	50 000	....	....	0.333	....	
XIV.	Cemented gravel	500 000	....	....	36 400	....	....	0.072	
XV.....	Gravel.......	200 000	3 500	....	....	0.018	....	....	
XVI....	Rock........	10 000	500	7 500	....	0.050	0.750	....	
XVII...	Basalt.......	40 000	....	35 000	....	....	0.875	....	
XVIII..	Basalt.......	90 000	....	34 625	....	....	0.385	....	
XIX....	Basalt.......	40 600	....	....	10 000	....	....	0.247	
XX....	Basalt.......	110 000	....	....	21 000	....	....	0.191	
XXI....	Basalt.......	56 000	....	....	10 000	....	....	0.179	
XXII...	Hard basalt..	400 000	20 000	431 000	....	0.050	1.078	....	
XXIII..	Basalt.......	54 800	....	....	8 000(b)	....	....	0.146(b)	
XXIV	Cemented gravel	180 000	....	30 025	....	....	0.167	....	

(a) Champion powder, 7 and 9% Ngl.   (b) Trojan powder.

Notes on Table 17 (20).   I. West Beaver Creek dam, Col. Tunnel 75 ft below apex of rock, 135 ft long, with several bends. Cross drifts, 35 ft long, each way from end of tunnel. Charges at ends of cross drifts, with 3 000 lb of powder along outer wall of remainder of cross drift. Stemming: rock, earth, timber. II. Otay, Cal. Tunnel, 4 by 5.5 ft, 50 ft long. 18-ft Y-branches at end for chambers. Charges: 4 000 lb Judson powder and 50 lb dynamite in one chamber; 8 000 lb powder and 50 lb dynamite in other. Cost: drifting, $645; powder, $960; charging, $75; total, 3.6¢ per cu yd. Further breaking by powder in seams made total cost 5¢ per cu yd. III. San Diego, Cal. Morena dam. Open cut perpendicular to face, with 4 by 5-ft drift, 115 ft long, parallel to and 100 ft from cut. Chambers sunk beneath floor at end and 70 ft from face. Face chamber contained 500 lb 7% Champion powder and 1 500 lb 40% dynamite; end chamber, 28 550 lb 7 and 9% powder, 1 900 lb 40%, and 2 000 lb 60% dynamite. Stemming: earth, timber. Cost: opencut, $3 500; drifting and charging, $2 478; explosives, $3 116; total, 5.05¢ per ton. IV. Northampton, Pa. Quarry. Face, 135 ft high. Drift, 3 ft wide and 238 ft long, along a fault 50 to 100 ft from face. 4 chambers below tunnel, 45 ft apart, and 3 crosscuts each way, 25 to 56 ft long. Total cost, $3 825. V. Ferrino, Wash. Quarry. 65-ft face. Two 3.5 by 4-ft drifts, 200 ft apart; one 150 ft long, with 3 crosscuts 50 ft apart, each 80 to 100 ft long; the other 180 ft long, with 4 crosscuts, each 70 to 100 ft long. 60% dynamite. Stemming: muck, timber, and cement bulkheads. VI. Piedra, Cal. Quarry. Aver height of face, 91 ft; aver overburden, 68 ft. 6 drifts, each 80 ft long, with 2 crosscuts each side. Crosscuts 40 ft apart, 40 ft long. Pits at ends of cuts. 60% dynamite and Judson R R P. Cost of explosives, 2.6¢ per cu yd. VII. St Helena, Ore. Quarry. Drift, 3 ft wide by 46 ft long, with crosscuts at end, one 32 ft, the other 40 ft long. Halfway from face, a crosscut in each side, 32 ft long. No 2 Trojan powder in 4 charges of 150 to 250 lb in short cut and 5 charges of 400 to 700 lb in long cut. Cost: explosives, $359; loading, $58. VIII. Corona, Cal. Quarry. Overburden, 80 ft. Drift, 110 ft long, with side drift 60 ft from face, 15 ft long to left and 40 ft to right; diagonal drift 80 ft from face, 40 ft to left, and at the end a diagonal drift 50 ft to left and a straight drift 50 ft long to right. End of drifts charged with Judson R R P and 60% dynamite. IX. U P R R. 18-ft cut. 2 pits charged with 26 lb dynamite and 2 775 lb of powder. Cost, about $1.10 per cu yd. X. Hudson River. 200-ft face. 1 drift at bottom, 65 ft deep; other drift, 60 ft from top of face, 80 ft deep. Two 25-ft shafts at top; also drill holes. XI. Long Cove, Me. Shaft, 4 by 4 ft, 64 ft deep, with 2 drifts at bottom, each 27 ft long. Crosscuts from ends of drifts, 26 ft long. Explosives in crosscuts. Estimate of 1 000 000 tons broken seems too high. XII. Paragon hydraulic mine. Face, 150 ft high. Drift, 110 ft long. Crosscut at right, 70 ft long, with drift at end, parallel to main drift, 55 ft long. Crosscut at left, 60 ft long, with drift at end, 30 ft long. Much space left untamped for expansion of gases. Cost: drifting, $300; explosives, $2 700. XIII. Blue Point hydraulic mine. Drift, 3 by 4 ft, 275 ft long. 6 crosscuts, each 120 ft long on left; 6 on right, each 80 ft long. First drift on right, 75 ft from portal, and at end a 15-ft drift, parallel to main drift. XIV. Dardanelles mine. Face, 175 ft high, 1 200 ft long. 5 parallel drifts, across each of which were 2 or more crosscuts. Total length of drifts, 1 200 ft. XV. Hydraulic mine. Giant powder No 2. XVI. Colorado. Dam. Coyote. or one-man tunnel, 40 ft long. 2 crosscuts from end, each 12 ft long, with pits at end. Explosive, FFB powder and 40% dynamite, charged in pits. Stemming: earth. Cost: labor, $384; dynamite, $155; powder, $1 140; caps and fuse, $11. Total, 16.9¢ per cu yd. XVII. Oregon. R R. Coyote hole, 2.5 by 3 ft in hillside, 50 ft deep. Crosscuts at end, 75 and 45 ft. Charges in the 3 openings. XVIII. Crooks Landing. R R. 4 or 5 coyote holes, 80 ft long, with Ts 40 to 60 ft long at ends. XIX. Oregon. R R. 165 ft breast. XX and XXI. Oregon. R R. XXII. Snake River, Wash. R R. 75 coyote holes, 2.5 by 3 ft, each averaging 89 ft long, run into and then parallel to sidehill face. 3 500 ft of cliff mined by 6 177 ft of coyote holes. 20 000 lb of dynamite used in preparing for main blast of F to 5 F black powder. XXIII. Oregon. Coyote holes. No 2 Trojan powder. XXIV. Smartsville, Cal. Hydraulic mine. Shaft, 74 ft deep, with main drift 185 ft long from bottom. 3 crosscuts, 70, 120, and 170 ft from shaft, 40 ft long on either side. 10 lifter drifts from crosscuts, each 15 ft long, parallel to main drift. Total drifts, 570 ft long by 2.5 ft wide by 3.5 ft high. Material moved, 270 by 180 by 100 ft. *Note.*—Above costs are pre-war.

Gophering is a mode of blasting used in breaking the overburden in the Mesabi, Minn, mining districts, and elsewhere, in sandy, loose ground, where vertical holes can not be kept open (20). (See *Eng & Min Jour*, Vol 88, p 696.) A hole is bored with a pointed bar, at a down angle of 15° to 20° in the side of the bank. Dynamite cartridges, placed end to end, are pushed into the hole and exploded. The muck is removed with a long-handle shovel, the hole deepened further, and the process repeated until a hole 10 or 12 in diam and deep enough is obtained. A chamber is made at the end by springing with 2 or 3 cartridges. A long-handle box filled with powder is pushed in and overturned.

Boulder blasting is done by: mudcapping or bulldozing; blockholing; and undermining or snakeholing. Other cheaper methods are: by sledging; by drop-hammer or drop weights; by heating with fire and then cracking by applying cold water; by a combination of 2 or more of these methods. Heating can not be used with boulders larger than 0.5 to 0.75 cu yd. Mudcapping consists in exploding a charge of dynamite on the surface of a rock, after covering it with earth (Fig 17); it is most effective when a depression is selected for the explosive, if the cap is laid on the dynamite and not shoved into it, and if wet clay is used as a covering. Snakeholing consists in boring a hole beneath a boulder and firing a charge in it (Fig 18). It is more efficient, but not so rapid as mudcapping. Blockholing consists in drilling a shallow hole in the boulder for small charge of dynamite.

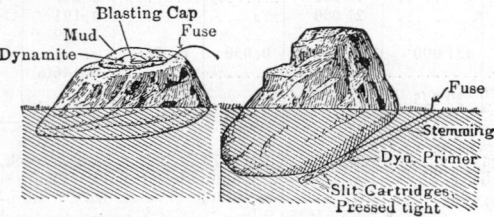

Fig 17. Mudcapping   Fig 18. Snakeholing

Relative costs per cu yd of breaking boulders, from a number of pre-war records (20) was: sledging, 4.3¢; drop-hammer, 6.5¢; heating, 14.9¢; blockholing, 16.8¢; undermining, 17.5¢; mudcapping, 31¢; mudcapping and sledging, 32.1¢.

Table 15.   Charges for Boulder Blasting (du Pont Co)

Weight of boulder, lb	Approx No of 1.25 by 8-in cartridges (40–60% dynamite)			Weight of boulder, lb	Approx No of 1.25 by 8-in cartridges (40–60% dynamite)		
	Mud-capping	Snake-holing	Block-holing		Mud-capping	Snake-holing	Block-holing
500	1.5	1	0.25	4 000	4	3.5	1.25
1 000	2	1.5	0.5	5 000	4.5	4	1.75
2 000	3	2.5	0.67	7 500	6	5	2.5
3 000	3.5	3	1	10 000	8	6	3.5

Details of charging, tamping and firing (see Sec 4, Art 8–10). In general, a charge should not occupy more than 0.3–0.5 the depth of hole (24). The wasteful practice of nearly filling the hole with explosive should be prohibited. In close-spaced holes, the primer is sometimes placed at bottom, as the fuses are then less liable to be cut off by adjacent shots; but this position of primer may cause side-spitting of fuses; primer is best inserted last. Complete detonation being essential for max force, use only strong caps in good condition.

Burning speed of fuse is affected by differences in atmos press. A fuse burning at 30 sec per ft at sea level burns at 40 sec per ft at 5 000 ft, and 50 sec at 10 000 ft. Fuse in a hole full of water burns faster than in a dry hole. For firing holes in sequence, at least 2-in difference in length of fuses is essential; thus, in a 6-hole round, shortest fuse is 12 in shorter than longest.

For electric firing, delay electric blasting caps, electric igniters, wiring of holes, and circuit testers, see Sec 4, Art 10.   Switches for taking current from power lines should be enclosed in a box that can not be closed or locked unless switch is open.

Results of tamping experiments by U S Bur of Mines, Trauzl lead-block method (28): (*a*) for black powder, the best tamping is requisite for max effect; (*b*) for 40% dynamite, even small amounts of good stemming show, by lead-block tests, at least 50% increase in effic (other tests, in actual

Table 19. Characteristics of Modes of Firing Dynamite

	Cap and fuse	Electric cap	Delay elec cap	Delay elec igniter and cap
Full energy from explosive...............	1st	1st	1st	1st
Freedom from misfire...................	3d	1st	1st	2d
Relative safety to blaster................	3d	1st	1st	2d
First cost............................	1st	2d	4th	3d

Summary: electric firing is best, for both black powder and dynamite, in everything but first cost, which may be greatly increased by misfires or a single major accident.

rock, 20–25%), rate of effic decreasing with more tamping; (*c*) good tamping diminishes danger of ignition of coal gas or dust from blow-out shots; (*d*) considering effic only, the length of stemming should be at least 3 times that of explosive.   If safety be the prime factor, as in gaseous or dusty mines, holes should be completely filled with best stemming; (*e*) more stemming is necessary for old or frozen dynamite; (*f*) the larger the diam of hole, the greater the length of stemming required; (*g*) well-stemmed holes produce most perfect detonation, with smallest evolution of poisonous gases; (*h*) moist fine clay or other plastic material makes best stemming for all explosives; dry powdery material is least effic.   Wooden tamping bars should always be used.

Use of paper tamping bags (30), containing specially mixed stemming, increases blasting effic; breakage is improved, with possibility of using lower-grade explosive or smaller charges.   Cartridge-shaped bags of different sizes, obtainable from makers of explosives, are now widely used.

Anaconda Copper Mining Co has developed a machine for filling tamping bags.   At a Virginia coal mine the filling apparatus consists of an inclined receiving table for the screened clay, set on a pitch of 35°, with a horiz shelf at its base.   In the shelf is a row of holes 4 in apart, each with a brass tube 1.25 in diam by 10 in long, extending below the shelf.   A hinged drop table underneath the shelf supports a series of 1.5-in tamping bags, which are slipped over the tubes and filled.   With this device, 1 man fills 4 000 bags in 8 hr.

Avoiding waste of explosives (31).   Blasters should be taught to think in terms of cost of explosive, and to figure tonnage of rock broken per ft of hole in number of shots, hole spacing, etc; all of which leads to economy.

Prevention of misfires (33).   Use good explosive materials.   Keep explosives in dry storage (Sec 4, Art 6).   Carefully prepare cap and fuse; cut off 0.25 in of all fuse exposed to air for any length of time; cut fuse squarely across, and push it without twisting motion into the cap (Sec 4, Art 8).

Note.—Table 4 of Sec 4 contains data for making preliminary determinations of the character, grade and strength of explosive for different kinds of rock and of excavation. It is advisable, however, for large-scale operations, and particularly for underground coal and metal mining, to supplement the recommendations given in the table by actual blasting tests and data of work in similar ore or rock (see Art 4, 5; also Sec 6, 7 and, in Sec 10, the data on drifting, crosscutting, stoping, etc).

7. HAND AND MECHANICAL LOADING AND HAULING

Hand work.   One man can load 2 to 20 cu yd of rock (place measure) in 10 hr, depending mainly on size of pieces and height to be lifted.

On Chicago Drainage Canal the aver per man in 10 hr was about 7 cu yd loaded into dump cars. Sledging took about 14% of the time.   Aver per man loading into low cableway skips, 10 cu yd; LARGE STONES were rolled into the skips, very little sledging being required.   In loading wagons with high sides, 1 man will average 10 cu yd solid measure (17 cu yd loose) of easily-lifted stones per 10 hr.   Stones handled singly can be thrown off a wagon twice as fast.   Stones can be loaded on wagons having stone racks at rate of about 13 cu yd per 10 hr, and rolled off at 50 cu yd per hr (20). CRUSHED STONE can be shoveled from smooth boards or steel sheets at the rate of 13 cu yd solid measure (22 cu yd loose) in 10 hr; in shoveling from the ground or hopper-bottom cars, 1 man will handle only 7 to 8 cu yd solid measure (12 to 14 cu yd loose).

Steam shovel work. Cost of rock excavation varies greatly. In the soft iron ore of Mesabi range, under fair conditions, a steam shovel easily loads 250 cu yd per hr; but, in poorly drilled and blasted rock, broken in large pieces, it may do as little as 17 cu yd per hr.

Table 20. Output of Steam Shovels, Loading Blasted Rock. One 10-hr day's work (13)

Material....	Iron ore		Stock pile		Limestone			Slate, lime-stone	Por-phyry, granite	Por-phyry	Sand-stone
Work........	In bank		Stock pile		Quarry	R R cut		R R	R R	R R	Canal
Conditions....	Good	Fair	Fair	Good	Fair	Low face		Good	Hard	Hard	Bad drilling
No of shovels.	1	1	av of 5	1	av of 2	1	1	av of 2	av of 2	1	1
Size, tons.....	70	95	70	90	95	65	70	70	70	65	70
Dipper, cu yd.	2.5	2.5	2.5	2.5	2.4	......	......	2.5	2.5	2.5	2.25
Coal, tons....	1.75	3	2.35	4.5	3.5	2.8	2.3	2.8	2.2	2.2	3
Oil, gal.......	1.4	3.25	1.45	8.5	......	......	......	......	......	......	5
Water, gal....	3,000	5 000	3 500	7 700	......	......	......	......	......	......	4 500
Cu yd loaded..	892	1 350	1 251	2 728	917	358	205	1 126	799	447	379, 8 hr

In N Y mica schist, broken large, a 65-ton, 2.25-cu yd dipper shovel averaged for several weeks about 280 cu yd solid measure per day into cars; part loaded by the dipper, part lifted by a chain hooked over the dipper teeth (20). On Chicago Drainage Canal, 2 Bucyrus 55-ton shovels, with broad shallow 2.25 cu-yd dippers, loaded limestone on one section (Table 20). The rock was in large pieces, much of which had to be lifted with chains. Combined output of the 2 shovels was 118 650 cu yd (solid measure) during 406 10-hr shifts, or an aver of 296 cu yd per shovel per shift (20).

Steam shovels for rock excavation are now largely of the revolving type, with 0.75-4 cu yd dippers and caterpillar treads. They have greater mobility than R R type on car trucks and can always be kept within the most effective range of work. Bucyrus 120B revolving shovel for rock work is in 3 sizes: STANDARD, 4-cu yd dipper, 29.5-ft boom, 20-ft dipper handle; HIGH-LIFT, 3.5-cu yd dipper, 32-ft boom, 22-ft dipper handle; EXTRA HIGH-LIFT, 3-cu yd dipper, 36-ft boom, 25-ft dipper handle. Makers report 260 cu yd blasted rock handled per hr; under favorable conditions, 300 cu yd possible (see Sec 3, Art 8 and Sec 27).

Loading with derricks, and bucket or skip. A horse-operated derrick, with a crew of 1 foreman, 1 hooker, 6 shovelers, 2 tagmen, and 1 dumpman, water boy and team and driver, unloaded 120 cu yd loose measure in 1 day. In using an engine-operated derrick, with a bullwheel for slewing, tagmen (for slewing the boom) and team are eliminated, and an engineman and coal are required. A crew of 1 engineer, 1 signal man, 1 dumpman, and 7 loaders, unloaded from a scow 21.3 cu yd of 3/8-in crushed stone per hr. Clamshell buckets are good for unloading cars and scows.

Cableways (Sec 26) are frequently used in quarry work, canal and trench excavation, and in open-pit mining.

Table 21. Output of 4 Chicago Drainage Canal Cableways (1 month)

	1	2	3	4
No of 10-hr shifts......................	49	35	52	49
Total cu yd rock.......................	12 633	8 632	16 162	14 535
No of skip-loads, day shift..............	5 111	5 327	5 435	4 369
No of skip-loads, night shift............	4 087	1 201	5 467	4 468
Cu yd solid rock per skip..............	1.44	1.32	1.48	1.65
Cu yd solid rock per shift..............	258	247	311	297
No of laborers.........................	27	27	32	32
No of foremen.........................	2	2	2	2
Total labor, hr........................	12 861	9 608	17 075	15 227
Cu yd rock loaded per man per shift........	9.82	8.98	9.46	9.54
Tons coal per shift....................	1.83	1.83	2.28	2.28

Chicago Drainage Canal (20) employed 19 cableways with spans of 550 to 725 ft, traveling towers 73 to 93 ft high, and equipped with aerial dumps. Main cables, 2.25-in, hauling and hoisting cables, 0.75-in, button and dumping cables, 5/8-in. A 70-hp boiler and 10 by 12-in engine gave a hoisting speed of 250 ft, and a traveling speed of 1 000 ft per min. A complete outfit, with 2 by 7 by 7-ft skips, weighed 225 tons. Crew: engineman, fireman, signalman, rigger and laborers for loading. Capac of cableways, 300 to 450 cu yd solid measure per 10 hr.

Arrowrock Dam, Boise irrigation project, Idaho. Two Lidgerwood cableways handled 101 263 cu yd of blasted rock, boulders, gravel and sand. Span, 1 300 ft; aver traveling distance, 500 ft; aver hoisting distance, 300 ft. Hoisting load, 8 tons, at 300 ft per min; conveying speed, 1 200 ft per min. Skips, 8 by 8 by 2 ft. In July, 1912, 2-shift work; in Aug, Sept, and Oct, 3 shifts. Output for 4 mo, 40 624 loads, averaging 2.49 cu yd, practically all handled in 2 shifts. Cost of operation (not including loading), 37¢ per cu yd, as follows: labor, 11.1¢; power, 4¢; supplies, 1.5¢; repairs, 4.7¢; deprec, 6.4¢; preparatory expense, 9.2¢. Wages: laborers, $2.40 per 8 hr; cableway operators, $4 to $5; riggers, $3 to $4. Power cost, 1.5¢ per kw-hr. Deprec was figured on charging off 75% of first cost and all the installation cost (20).

Canal work. On St Mary's Channel Improvement, 4 cableways handled 1 700 000 cu yd of limestone in 2.5 yr. Rock was loaded into skips by 4 60-ton traction-mounted steam shovels. Skips held 6 cu yd each, but sometimes 8 cu yd (18 tons) were handled. 2 cableways had spans of 1 100 ft and 2 of 800 ft. Aver haul, 300 ft. Best month's record for all, 22 000 cu yd each; best month's record for one cableway, 30 000 cu yd (20).

Stone-boats are wooden or sheet-iron platforms, best mounted on runners, for hauling large stones short distances. If the runners are greased, 1 ton can be pulled by a team weighing 2 400 lb. A SKID ROAD is formed of partly imbedded round sticks of timber set like ties of a track 3 to 6 ft apart. A stone-boat holding 0.5 cu yd (solid measure) of rock can be drawn over such a road. A LIFTER or DEVIL is a wooden stretcher on which 2 men can carry as much as 0.5 cu yd. On the Grand Trunk Pac R R (20), rock was cheaply hauled by stone-boats on pole tracks in summer for hauls less than 600 ft, and in winter any distance. Track was of 2 lines of 20 to 30-ft poles, 4 to 8 in diam, 5.5 ft apart for 2-horse team and 3 ft apart for 3-horse team. Poles were joined by 2-in hardwood pins. Boats were of 10 or 12 logs, 7 in diam by 8 ft long, fastened together by 2 1.25-in rods. In winter the track was iced; in summer, greased (1 gal per 100 ft per day). In winter, a team could haul 3 yd rock; in summer, 1.5 yd; aver load, 7/8 cu yd. On a 500-ft haul a team and 6 men took 40 to 60 loads per 10 hr. Aver yardage per man loading, 7.3 cu yd; many rocks were large and had to be blockholed. The excavation comprised: 20% shovel dirt, 30% easily lifted stones, and 50% pieces 1 to 5 yd in volume. Cost of loading, 31¢ per cu yd; cost of transport, 17¢. Wages: muckers, $2.00 to $2.25; foremen, $3.75; maintenance of each horse, 75¢ per day.

Wheelbarrows hold about 0.04 cu yd solid rock; loaded by 1 man in 2 min, and wheeled at 180 to 250 ft per min, losing 0.75 min per round trip.

Carts and wagons. In aver rock, 1 cu yd solid equals 1.75 cu yd broken, and weighs about 2.2 tons. Over poor dirt roads, with occasional steep rises, 0.5 cu yd (1 ton) solid rock may be hauled by 2 horses; on hard, level road, 1.5 cu yd; aver load on good roads, 1 cu yd (2 ton). Aver speed of haul, 220 ft per min. A 1-horse cart, on short, downhill hauls, takes an aver load of 0.25 cu yd solid rock; under favorable conditions, 1/3 cu yd aver. For short hauls, 1 driver can run 2 carts. With wagons, 2 men and a driver can load 1 cu yd on a stone rack in 15 min and 1 man and driver can unload it in 7 min, or total lost time of 22 min. Aver of each loader, 7.5 cu yd in 10 hr (Sec 27).

Cars on track. For tractive power of horses and resistance of ordinary dump cars see Sec 3. On level track, a team will haul 2 cars, each of 3 cu yd solid rock; on slight down grade, 1 horse will haul 2 cars holding 1 to 1.5 cu yd. On good track, at slight down grade, 1 horse can haul 4 light rocker-dump cars holding 4 cu yd, if assisted by laborers in starting. If rock be broken into sizes that 1 or 2 men can lift, 6 to 7.5 cu yd can be loaded per man in 10 hr. About 4 min are lost in changing teams from empty to loaded cars, provided the track arrangement is good. Speed should be 200 ft per min.

Steam-shovel loading. In loading rock by steam shovel, the output of the attendant train and locomotive is limited chiefly by the shovel output, not by the speed at which a train can be handled. Following work was done in a quarry of hard crystalline limestone, by 2 Bucyrus 95-ton, 2.5-cu yd dipper, shovels (13). SHOVEL A. First day: Working time, 691.5 min; lost time, 59 min, of which 41 min were for blasting, clearing track, and tightening jacks, 13 min waiting for cars to be spotted, and 5 min idling. Second day: 138 min were lost waiting for cars, of which 87 min were spent in drilling, blasting, leveling, and preparing to move, and 55 min idling. On 2 days, 197 min, or 15.5% of the time, was lost waiting for cars, while cars lost on account of shovel, for no apparent reason, 7 min; moving forward, 107 min; drilling, 125 min; blasting, 67 min; clearing track, 9 min; total, 315 min, or 25%. SHOVEL B in 2 days worked 1 290 min. A total of 266 min or 20.6% was spent waiting for cars, of which 87 min was in idling. On same days, 327 min (25.4%) was lost to the trains by the shovel, as follows: oiling, 10 min; getting up steam, 42; repairs, 5; waiting for cars to be loaded, 52; blasting, 81; moving forward, 113; coaling and miscellaneous, 25 min. There were 5 35-ton dinkey locomotives, 4 working and 1 being overhauled. They hauled 10-car trains. Cars held 5 cu yd and weighed 4 tons. While moving, the engines averaged 527 ft per min; minimum speed, 156 ft; maximum, 1 000 ft per min (see also Sec 27).

8. QUARRYING (see also Open-cut Excavation, Art 9)

Kinds of stone. DIMENSION STONE is quarried and split to assigned dimensions ready for dressing. RUBBLE STONE is in rough slabs or blocks of irregular sizes. For dimension stone, there must be a good WORKING FACE and usually a CHANNEL at each end, to expose 3 faces. Then, by wedging or careful blasting, long blocks are secured, which are split into short blocks for handling by derricks. To get a cushioning effect in blasting dimension stone, several inches of hole above the charge may be filled with hay; called "expansion tamping." For rubble or backing stone, but little channeling is done; the rock is shaken up by light blasts and irregular slabs barred and wedged out.

Joints and cleavage planes must be carefully considered. All sedimentary rocks and some others, as granite, have 3 perpendicular cleavage planes called the GRAIN, RIFT, and HEAD. Trap rocks, diabase, diorite, porphyry, etc, often have no rift and are unfit for dimension stone. Cost of quarrying depends partly on thickness of beds and their DIP (slope) to the horizontal. With steep dips, both thick and thin-bedded stone must usually be removed simultaneously; as the quarry deepens, the depth soon becomes too great for profitable work. If joints are irregular a quarry is a BOULDER QUARRY; if vertical and at right angles, BLOCK QUARRY; where there is practically no vertical joint, but a series of horiz joints, a SHEET QUARRY.

Plug and feathering consists of splitting rocks by shallow holes, in which 2 FEATHERS or shims (pieces of half-round iron, the sides of which are curved to fit the hole) are forced apart by hammering a wedge plug between them (Fig 19).

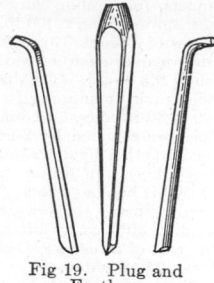

Fig 19. Plug and Feathers

Holes required. A granite block 6 ft thick may be split with a row of plug holes 5 in deep and 6 to 8 in apart; for a 3-ft block, holes are 2.5 to 3 in deep. Marbles and sandstones require deep holes. For sandstone, holes are 1.25 to 2 in diam, 4 to 16 in apart, depth being $2/3$ the thickness of the block.

Drilling methods. Plug holes are drilled by hand, pneumatic hammer drill, or reciprocating drill. For shallow holes, the hammer drill is cheapest; hand hammer next. For deep holes, a reciprocating drill on a quarry bar, or a hammer drill, is most economical. HAND PLUG-HOLE DRILLING. In granite, 1 man can drill in 8 hr 80 $5/8$-in holes, 2.5 in deep; total, 17 ft. With holes 24 to 30 in apart, and wages at 30¢ per hr, cost of splitting a block is 2.5 to 3¢ per sq ft. PNEUMATIC HAMMER DRILLS. In granite, 1 man can drill in 8 hr 250 $5/8$-in holes, 3 in deep, if the driller does not drive the plugs. In sand stone, 4-ft holes have been drilled in 18 min, and 20 holes, 18 in deep, were drilled at rate of 1 hole in 25 sec. BABY DRILL, on quarry bar, will drill a 3- or 4-in hole in 0.75 min, averaging about 100 holes per day.

Special quarry methods. BROACHING or broach channeling consists in drilling a row of holes very close together, and then, with a BROACH or chisel, cutting out the rock between them. One drill on a quarry bar (Sec 15) will broach per day: in granite, 10–20 sq ft; marble, 20–30; limestone, 15–35; sandstone, 20–40 sq ft. GADDER is for drilling rows of horiz holes near the quarry floor, or a vertical or inclined row in the face. One drill has made 350 ft of 2-ft holes in marble in 10 hr. TRACK CHANNELER is a self-propelling machine, traveling back and forth on a 10 to 30-ft section of track, and cutting a narrow groove with a single bit, or one or more GANGS of bits. See "Compressed Air Plant," Peele, 5th edn, Chap XXII.

Some channelers cut vertical grooves, others can be swung at varying angles, or are arranged for undercutting. Ingersoll "Broncho" channeler is mounted on 2 parallel bars, resembling a quarry bar. Channelers may carry a boiler, or be operated by steam or compressed air from an independent plant. Ingersoll-Rand Co builds an air-electric channeler, similar in operation to their air-elec drill. Channelers cost $2 500-$4 500 (pre-war). In dimension-stone quarries (other than granite) they are economic necessities, because fully 20% of the stone quarried without channeling is lost in subsequent cutting. In granite, broaching or wedging is usually cheaper. Cost of running a channeler is about the same as of a steam drill; 2 men and 0.5 ton coal per day are required. COST OF CHANNELING LIMESTONE, N Y State Barge Canal, for 16 consecutive months follows: Sullivan Y-8 channelers, costing $2 800 each, were used. Operating crew per channeler: 0.16 to 0.5 of the time of a foreman @ $4 per day, 1 runner @ $3.50, 1 fireman @ $2, 1 helper @ $1.75, 1 laborer @ $1.50. Cost per sq ft for 126 544 sq ft: labor, 22¢; coal, 2.3¢; water, 0.2¢; repairs, 0.1¢; int and deprec, 2.4¢; total, 27¢ (1908–9).

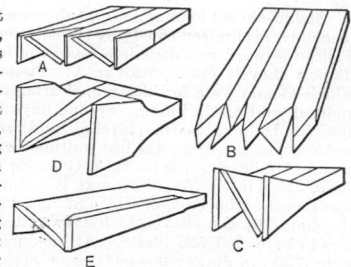

Fig 20. Channeler Bits

Standard or rigid-back channelers cut to depths of 10 to 16 ft; swing-back and bar channelers, 6 to 12 ft; undercutting channelers, 7 ft. Max inclinations of swing-back channeler having boiler or reheater, 24°; other types, 28°. The bits do not rotate. In Fig 20: A shows the gang used in marble or rocks which chip freely; B, that used for tough rocks which do not chip freely; C, for slate; D is used in both quarry and contract work for sharp, gritty stones; E is the sold Z-bit, common in contract work in rough broken stone.

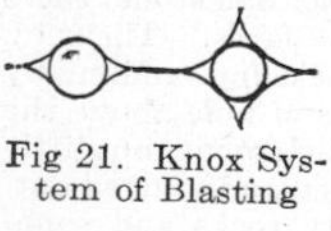

Knox system of blasting. A number of round holes are drilled, and then reamed by hand to the shape shown in Fig 21. In medium sandstone, holes should be 10 to 15 ft apart; in limestone, about 4 ft apart. Black powder or contractor's powder will split the rock in the direction of the angles (20).

Fig 21. Knox System of Blasting

Quarrying by compressed air is practiced at Mt Airy, N C, where the granite has few joints, and splits readily in almost any direction. A centrally located hole, 2 to 3 in diam and 6 to 8 ft deep, is sprung with dynamite. Then, repeated charges of black powder, beginning with a handful and gradually increasing in size, start and extend horiz cleavage cracks. When the cleavage reaches 75 or 100 ft in all directions, air at 70 lb press is admitted through a pipe cemented into the hole. In say 0.5 hr, the cleavage reaches the surface 250 ft ± from the drill hole, and the large flat slab is split into blocks by plugs and feathers.

Table 22. Rate of Cutting with Sullivan Channelers (from Sullivan bulletins)

Location	Kind of rock	Sq ft cut	Time	Location	Kind of rock	Sq ft cut	Time
Day's work				*Day's work*			
Philipsburg, Que....	A	63	10 hr	Pennsylvania.....	G	60	Aver day
W Rutland, Vt......	{ A	100	10 hr	Vermont.........	G	75	Aver day
	{ A	2 509	Aver mo	Virginia..........	H	200	Aver day
Tennessee..........	A	80	Aver day	Virginia..........	H	262	Aver day
Vermont...........	A	219	High day	*Contract work*			
Georgia...........	A	200	Aver day				
Tennessee..........	A	150	Good day	Lockport, Ill......	C	210	Aver 10 hr
Brandon, Vt........	B	1 485	Aver mo	Lockport, Ill......	C	382	High 10 hr
Brandon, Vt........	B	1 677	Aver mo	Sault Ste Marie....	D	75–100	Aver day
Bloomington, Ill.....	C	6 000	10 days	Keokuk, Ia.......	D	80	10 hr
Batesville, Ark......	D	130	Aver day	Sault Ste Marie....	E	70–80	8 hr
Carthage, Mo.......	D	137.5	Aver day	Sault Ste Marie....	I	60–75	8 hr
Amherst, O.........	E	225	Day	New York City....	J	60–75	8 hr
Florida Keys.......	F	750	Aver 10 hr	Panama Canal....	K	120	8 hr

A. Marble. *B.* Hard marble. *C.* Limestone. *D.* Hard limestone. *E.* Sandstone. *F.* Coral rock. *G.* Slate. *H.* Soft soapstone. *I.* Tough sandstone. *J.* Gneiss. *K.* Medium broken rock.

For quarrying a granite dome at Lithonia, Ga (34), free from joints and sheeting planes, an artificial sheeting plane was necessary. For this, 2 3-in holes about 8 ft deep were drilled close together, each charged with a spoonful of black blasting powder, tamped with clay, and fired simultaneously. The "rift" being horiz, the light blasts started a horiz fracture from the bottom of the holes, which were cleaned out and refired repeatedly with gradually increasing charges, never large enough to disturb the stemming. Care was taken to avoid making vert cracks, through which the compressed air subsequently used would be dissipated. Solar heat is said to assist this process; during the hottest weather the fracture extended without explosives. The light blasting was continued until the boundary of the horiz fracture roughly formed a circle with a radius of 160–180 ft. An iron pipe was then set in each hole with sand and melted sulphur, to make an air-tight joint. Air at 100 lb was forced through the pipes into the horiz fracture, which widened with a rending noise until it reached the surface on the flank of the rock dome; the sheeting plane thus formed having an area of 1–2 acres.

Quarrying broken stone (36, 37). Size of crusher (which depends on character of rock) affects size of shovel dipper. If the rock can not be easily broken with sledges at the crusher, secondary blasting is necessary before loading on cars; use of a small shovel dipper prevents feeding excessively large pieces to crusher. Height of quarry face has some effect on size of shovel, but more on type of drilling equipment and mode of working. To prevent injury to shovel, combined working length of boom and dipper handle should equal the height of face, which should generally be less than 40 ft for any size of shovel. Though high faces are more cheaply drilled and blasted, the stone may break too large, with greater cost of secondary blasting.

Quarrying flux for blast furnaces in western Penn (36). The strata are horiz, faces 7–22 ft high. Drilling is done on top and at such distance back from face that large shovels can clean up a blast on 1 passage. With higher faces, or smaller shovels, 2 or more passages are necessary. The face is developed with a gradual spiraling, causing highly effic operation.

R R shovels on track, with 2.5 to 4-yd dippers, deliver 1 200–1 500 ton a day; smaller sizes undesirable. Small shovels on traction wheels may serve for: (a) say, less than 800 ton per day; (b) splitting up total tonnage into several units; (c) where a light-weight track is used: (d) where quarry conditions prevent adoption of spiral faces.

Transport systems for quarries (36) depend upon relative size of shovel, car and crusher, and unit of train movement. For R R type shovels, the quarry track should be at least 42 in gage; standard gage (4 ft 8.5 in) is preferable, for cars to 15-ton capac.

High cars are cheaper to load than low, because, when the shovel completes its working stroke, the dipper is usually elevated, ready for dumping. Large cars save time in spotting the dipper; hence, faster dumping with less spill. Capacity of train unit on 1 movement should equal at least 20 min nominal shovel duty. A 1 200-ton R R shovel should load a 40-ton train in 10–15 min, 5–10 min being allowed for moving shovel, shifting trains, hard digging, etc; 300-ton traction shovel requires at least a 10-ton train.

In many quarries, especially where length of haul is moderate, motor trucks are used from shovel to crusher. Advantages over track and car are greater flexibility of operation, elimination of track and usually lower cost. Truck bodies vary from 5 to 10 cu yd capac, either side or end dump;

penumatic tires are common (Sec 27). Aver transport cost, on 36 trucks, based on 3-yr records in four different quarries in N Y, Conn, and No Carolina, is 2.5 to 5¢ per ton mile.

Quarry blasting problems (38). At a sandstone quarry, when the holes were in straight lines, the rock broke large, the explosive force being mainly expended in shearing from the face. This was largely overcome by staggering the holes (Fig 22). In another case, in very tough rock, holes rarely broke to the bottom. Drilling as in Fig 23 improved the work. In hard limestone, better

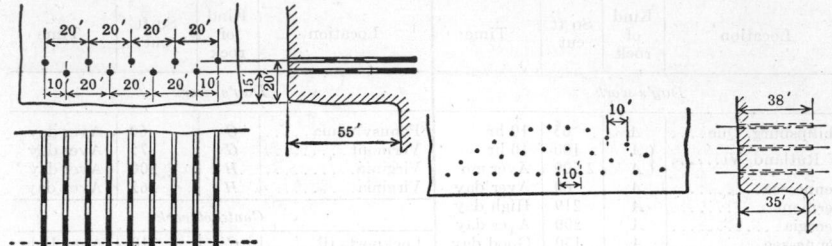

Fig 22. Staggered Holes to Increase Shattering Effect

Fig 23. Arrangement of Holes for Breaking Hard Bottom

results were obtained by drilling as in Fig 24. The rows farthest from face were made with well drills, and charges concentrated near bottom. Two rows in front of these were tripod-drilled and charged from a point halfway up to within 5 ft of surface; this greatly reduced secondary blasting. At a quarry in hard, stratified limestone, ordinary methods failed to break rock small enough for handling. Fig 25 shows the remedy. Holes in back row were 60 ft deep; in front, 35 ft. The deep holes were charged with 150 lb 40% straight dynamite and 40% gelatin; front holes, with 50 lb of 40% straight dynamite.

Secondary blasting (39), required when main blast breaks too large for shovel or crusher, is done by blockholing or mudcapping (Art 6); blockholing is usually the cheaper. Holes are 1 1/8 in,

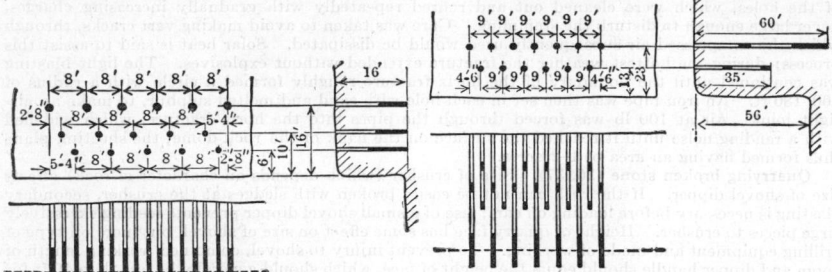

Fig 24. Arrangement of Holes to Reduce Secondary Blasting

Fig 25. Arrangement of Holes on High Face to Reduce Secondary Blasting

for 1-in cartridges; with small diam cartridges there is less waste in cutting them for small charges. Mudcapping requires only a few min to prepare, and saves shovel time in waiting for boulders to be drilled. Large boulders, which can not be handled by the shovel are rolled and nosed out of the way, to be broken later.

Underground quarries (35) avoid cost of removing deep over-burden, and permit year-round operation. When topography is suitable, they are opened by tunnels.

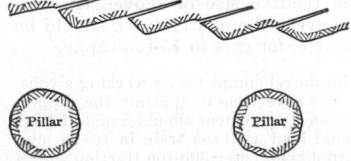

Fig 26. Saw-tooth Method of Working Quarry Faces

The methods often resemble breast and bench stoping for mining flat deposits (see Sec 10, under details of Open Stopes, showing bottom headings, suitable for faces 16–24 ft high; also see bench work for 24-ft faces and over). Due to low value of the material, the quarry stratum should usually be at least 16 ft thick. Fig 26 shows saw-tooth method of slabbing off in horiz strata, leaving pillars to support roof; it resembles rill stoping, Sec 10. Sectional steel (Art 2) has been used in benches 12–24 ft high, so that entire bench can be shot at one time. An 8-ft heading is first cut; then, with sectional rods, holes can be drilled to bottom.

9. OPEN-CUT ROCK EXCAVATION

For this work are used many of the methods and machines considered in preceding Articles. It resembles some kinds of quarrying, and is similar in nearly all respects to stripping operations and open-cut mining, detailed in Sec 10. For machine drills, see Sec 15; churn drilling, for deephole blasting, Sec 9; for steam shovels, Sec 3 and Sec 5, Art 7.

Side-hill cuts, where rock is wasted directly in front of the excavation, are usually the least expensive type of open cut. Ratio of the propulsive effect of black powder to its shattering effect is about 8.6, while that of dynamite is about 1; hence, it is often desirable in side-hill work to use black powder, so that the rock may be thrown as far as possible from its bed.

Side-hill cuts (20) on Watauga and Yadkin Valley R R, N C, were made by blasting rock clear of right of way in one operation; about 0.5 cu yd being thrown out per lb of explosive. In a cut of 8 000 cu yd (95% hard mica schist), 23 holes were drilled in 2 rows; upper holes approx 20 ft deep, to 2 ft below grade; lower holes, 16 ft deep, to 6 ft below grade. They were sprung twice, first by 5–6 sticks of dynamite, then by 25–30 sticks. Experience showed that 1 springing, with 10–12 sticks, would have chambered the holes better. Main charge of 7 925 lb powder broke 7 000 cu yd.
A small side-hill cut in hard rock, made by hand-drilled holes, 7–11 ft deep, contained 1 300 cu yd. Cost, including $126 for removing loose rock after blasting and dressing the face, was (in 1913) 34.3¢ per cu yd. About 320 ft of holes were drilled at about 40¢ per ft; 0.24 ft of hole per cu yd blasted. Springing required 0.12 lb dynamite per cu yd; main blast, black powder, 2.3 lb per cu yd.

Through cuts occur oftenest in canal and R R work. Depth and width of cut, and mode of removal, determine the plan of attack. Excavation in through cuts generally costs more than in side-hill cuts.

Excavating rock in open cuts, Grand Trunk Pac R R (20). Cuts, 20 ft wide at bottom, sloped 3 in to 1 ft. Overbreakage, usually paid for, was 10 to 40%. Rock was granite, trap, and diabase. Steam drills used in large cuts, hand drills in small. HAND DRILLS (1-in steel, 1 3/8-in bit) made holes as deep as 30 ft. To depths of 6 ft, 2 men struck and 1 held the drill; below 6 ft, all used hammers, the drill rotating automatically on the rebound; wages, $2.25 per 10 hr (day's work), or 45¢ per ft, sharpening and nippering furnished. 3 men, drilling 10 to 14-ft holes, averaged in dark hornblende 29 ft per day, in red granite, 20 ft, and in trap and diabase 18.5 ft. In drilling block holes, 1 gang made 49 holes, averaging 15 in each, in 6 days. Drill sharpening for one month, for 5 gangs who drilled 2 142 ft, cost: blacksmith @ $3.50, $87.50; helper @ $2, $48; nipper @ $2, $48; coal, $12; total, $195.50, or 9¢ per ft. Average cost by 5 gangs, each drilling 18 ft per day: drilling, 37¢; sharpening, 9¢; total, 46¢ per ft.
Holes to 30 or 35 ft deep were made by 3.25 and 3.5-in steam drills; holes to 25 ft deep, by 3-in drills. Starting bits, 3.5 in; finishing bits, about 1.25 in. Cost of running 1 drill per 10-hr day: runner, $3.75; helper, $2.25; fireman, $2.50; 0.5 blacksmith, $1.87; 0.5 helper, $1.13; 1 cord wood, $2.25; coal, 30¢; repairs and oil, 38¢; total, $14.43. Aver, 30 ft drilled per day, costing 48¢ per ft. When 2 drills were run from 1 boiler, cost was about 38¢ per ft.
Cuts over 25 ft deep were made in 2 lifts. In bottom benches, 1 ft of hole and in top benches, 2 or 3 ft of hole, were chambered. A 26-ft hole, 14 ft from face, was sprung by: (a) 2 sticks 60% dynamite, water-tamped; (b) 5 sticks, water-tamped; (c) 12 sticks, water-tamped; (d) 30 sticks, sand-tamped; (e) 70 sticks, sand-tamped; total, 119 sticks. Another similar hole: (a) 2 sticks, water-tamped; (b) 5 sticks, water-tamped; (c) 12 sticks, water-tamped; (d) 35 sticks, sand-tamped; (e) 100 sticks, sand-tamped; total, 154 sticks. First hole was charged with 275 sticks of 40% dynamite; second, with 150 sticks of 60% and 175 sticks of 40% dynamite. (1 stick = 0.35 lb.) These holes broke 450 cu yd of rock. Cost: drilling, 4.8¢; springing, 6.3¢; blasting, 9.3¢; total, 20.4¢ per cu yd. Blaster, 37.5¢, and powder monkey, 22.5¢ per hr. Dynamite, 18¢ per lb for 40% 22¢ for 60%, about 0.4 lb of 40% being used per cu yd for the main blasts, and 0.38 lb of 60% for springing. About 75 lb black powder equaled 50 lb 40% dynamite. Cost of excavating 7 024 cu yd red granite from a tunnel approach on same R R was $1.019 per cu yd.

10. TRENCHING

Overbreakage. Specifications should name a minimum width of trench, beyond which NEAT LINES the rock removed shall not be paid for. Depth should also be named. Overbreakage in rock sometimes exceeds the specified cross-section by 25 or 30%.
Depth and spacing of holes. Holes in thin-bedded, horizontally stratified rocks are usually drilled 6 in below specified bottom of trench; in thick-bedded, tough limestones, about 12 in below; in tough granites and traps, 18 in below.

For hand drilling in granite, holes are often spaced about 1.5 ft apart. In trenches 2.5 to 3 ft wide, rows, 3 ft apart, of 2 holes each, are common. In a trench 6 ft wide in hard trap 3 holes per row were drilled, the rows being 3 ft apart. In an 8-ft trench in granite, there were 3 holes per row, rows 4 ft apart. In the 6-ft trench named above, about 4.5 ft of hole were drilled per cu yd, the holes going to 1.5 ft below grade. Steam drills made 35 ft of hole per day @ 30¢ per ft. Dynamite, 2 lb of 40% per hole, or 2.6 lb per cu yd of net excavation. Hence, drilling cost $1.35 and blasting 40¢; total, $2.15 per cu yd. The above 8-ft trench was 12 ft deep; holes drilled to 1 ft below grade, making 2.74 ft of hole per cu yd net. Drills averaged 45 ft in 10 hr; cost per ft, 23¢. Dynamite, about 4 lb of 40% per hole, or 1.1 lb per cu yd. Drilling cost 63¢ and blasting 17¢; total, 80¢ per cu yd (pre-war costs).

Cost of trenching in limestone, St Louis, Mo (20), about 1906. Rock was in horiz strata, the upper 4 or 5 ft being seamy and rotten, the rest hard and difficult to break. Rock was excavated 6 in below all pipes of 18-in diam or less, and 9 in below larger pipes. Excavation was paid for to widths 1 ft greater than diam of pipes of less than 18 in, and 15 in greater than the diam of larger pipes. Drill holes were 6 in from side of trench, and staggered 4 ft apart in top rock (Fig 27) and 2.5 ft apart in hard rock. Projections were sledged or shot off. Holes were drilled in 2 lifts, top holes going halfway through the ledge, bottom holes 0.66 to 0.75 the thickness of ledge. Drilling was single-hand, with 1.75-in bits, 10 ft being drilled in 8 hr. Dynamite, about 4 300 lb (2.25 lb per cu yd). Aver rock broken per 8-hr day per quarry man, 0.96 cu yd. Overbreakage, about 20%. Cost of earth excavation, 50¢ per cu yd. The cost of the rock work was as in Table 23.

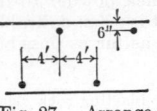

Fig 27. Arrangement of Trench Holes

Table 23. Cost of Trenching in Rock per Cu Yd. St. Louis, 1906

Size of pipe, in	Length of pipe, ft	Aver depth in solid rock, ft	Cu yd excavated	Foreman @ $5, ¢	Quarrymen @ $3	Laborers @ $2, ¢	Total direct labor	Blacksmith, ¢	Dynamite, ¢	Total cost, breaking rock	Cost of removal	Backfilling cost, ¢	Grand total
21	370	14	600	56	$3.50	24	$4.30	20	40	$4.90	$1.40	15	$6.45
18	287	12	317	85	3.24	34	4.43	20	40	5.03	1.40	15	6.58
18	314	13	380	84	2.76	44	4.04	20	40	4.64	1.40	15	6.19
15	222	11	206	87	3.13	39	4.39	20	40	4.99	1.40	15	6.54
15	251	8	180	89	2.15	66	3.70	20	40	4.30	1.40	15	5.85
Aver	.....	11.9	......	74	3.10	36	4.20	20	40	4.80	1.40	15	6.35

Special carriages, for carrying a boiler, and a drill mounted on a bar, were used in sewers at Havana, Cuba. Wt per outfit, 5 000 lb; drills were Sullivan, 3.25-in. Rock varied from very soft to flint-like hardness. Time studies of 4 machines drilling 40 holes: total drilled, 366 ft; aver depth of hole, 9.15 ft; aver drilling time, 26.4 min per hole = 2.9 min per ft; changing steel, 1.4 min per ft; moving drill on bar, 0.6 min per ft; moving machine from hole to hole, 1.0 min per ft; total time, 2 231 min; average per ft, 6.1 min (20).

11. SUBAQUEOUS EXCAVATION

Methods employed are: exploding dynamite on the rock surface, unwatering the rock by cofferdams or caissons, and drilling from platforms or scows. This work is a branch of Civil Engineering, to books on which the reader is referred (12, 20).

BIBLIOGRAPHY

1. A Review of Drilling. G. J. Young. *E & M Jour*, Sep 10, 1921
2. Rock-drill Steel. R. J. Day. *E & M Jour*, Apr 14, 1923
3. Blasting Rock in Mines, Quarries and Tunnels. A. W. and Z. W. Daw, Spon & Chamberlain, N Y, 1898
4. Tests of Drill Bits. C. R. Forbes and J. C. Barton. *Trans Amer Soc C E*, Vol 58, p 3
5. Blasting. Synoptic and critical treatment of the literature of the subject. Dr. H. Brunswig. John Wiley & Sons, Inc, N Y, 1912
6. Reclaiming Short Lengths of Drill Steel by Welding. *Eng & Con*, Vol 56, p 150
7. Deep Drilling with Hammer Drills and Sectional Rods. H. R. Drullard. *E & M Jour*, May 1, 1924
8. Deep-hole Prospecting at Chief Consol Mine. C. A. Dibble, *Trans A I M E*, Vol 72, p 677
9. Commercial Explosives, Selection and Uses. D. P. Allison. *E & M Jour*, Feb 2, 1924, p 197
10. Report by Construction Service Co on Cost of Hauling by Horses and Traction Engines. *Eng & Con*, Dec 8, 1909
11. Rock Drills. E. M. Weston. McGraw-Hill Book Co, N Y, 1910
12. Rock Drilling (especial reference to open-cut excavation and submarine rock removal). R. T. Dana and W. L. Saunders. John Wiley & Sons, Inc, N Y, 1911
13. Handbook of Steam-Shovel Work. Construction Service Co, Pub by Bucyrus Co, So Milwaukee, Wis
14. Effect of Tamping on Efficiency of Explosives. W. O. Snelling and C. Hall. *Tech Paper* 17, U S Bureau of Mines
15. Subways and Tunnels of New York. Gilbert, Wightman and Saunders. John Wiley & Sons, Inc, N Y, 1912

16. Excavation for the Arrowrock Dam, Idaho. C. H. Paul. *Eng News*, July 17, 1913
17. Selection of Explosives Used in Engineering and Mining Operations. C. Hall and A. P. Howell. *Bull* 48, U S Bureau of Mines
18. Excavating Machinery. A. B. McDaniel. McGraw-Hill Book Co, N Y
19. Handbook of Construction Plant; Cost and Efficiency. R. T. Dana. Clark Book Co, N Y, 1914
20. Rock Excavation; Methods and Costs. H. P. Gillette. Clark Book Co, N Y, 1916
21. Handbook of Cost Data. H. P. Gillette. Clark Book Co, N Y
22. Loading Well-drill Holes in Quarry Blasting. J. B. Stoneking. *Bull* du Pont Explosives Service
23. Energy of Explosives and Toughness of Rock in Selecting Explosives. W. O. Snelling. *Eng & Con*, Jan 8, 1913
24. Efficient Blasting in Metal Mines. E. A. Anderson. *E & M Jour*, Nov 29, 1924
25. Blast-hole Drilling with Keystone Cable Drill. Keystone Driller Co
26. Springing Bore Holes. C. S. Hurter. *Bull* du Pont Explosives Service, June, 1924
27. Coyote Hole or Tunnel Blasting. G. E. Willman. *Bull* du Pont Explosives Service, Mch, Apr, 1925; J. C. Cushing, *Eng & Con*, July 18, 1923
28. Effect of Stemming on Effic of Explosives. *Tech Pap* No 7, 17, U S Bur Mines
29. The Do and Don't of Loading Dynamite. *E & M Jour*, Aug 12, 1922
30. Filling Tamping Bags above Ground. G. S. Brown. *Bull* du Pont Explosives Service, Oct, 1925
31. How to Avoid Waste of Explosives. R. N. Van Winkle. *Eng & Con*, Sep 5, 1923
32. Safety in Quarry Blasting. A. La Motte. *Bull* du Pont Explosives Service, Nov, 1925
33. Prevention of Misfires. E. F. Brooks. *Min & Sci Pr*, Dec 16, 1916
34. Blasting Granite with Compressed Air. *Eng & Con*, Sep 15, 1920
35. Underground Quarrying. R. H. Summer. *Bull* du Pont Explosives Service, Aug, 1925
36. Considerations in Changing a Quarry from Hand to Steam Shovel Method. I. Warner. *Eng & Con*, Dec 21, 1921
37. Drilling and Blasting. R. E. Tally. *Jour* Min Cong, Apr, 1924
38. Quarry Blasting Problems and Their Solution. J. Barab. Pub by Hercules Powder Co
39. Secondary Blasting. J. B. Stoneking. *Bull* du Pont Explosives Service, Aug, 1924
40. Steam Shovel Operation. C. M. Haight. *E & M Jour*, Feb 14, 1924
41. Changes in Open-pit Mining. *E & M Jour*, May 24, 1924
42. Underground Deep-hole Prospecting at Eagle-Picher Mines. W. F. Netzeband. *Trans* A I M E, Feb, 1927
43. Recent Changes in Explosives and Their Use. W. Cullen & J. E. Lambert. *Trans* Instn Mining & Met, Vol 45, p 283 (1936)
44. Misfires in Metal Mining. *U S Bur Mines*, Rep Invests No 2156

16. Excavation for the Arrowrock Dam, Idaho. C. H. Paul. Eng News, July 31, 1913
17. Dislocation of Explosives Used in Excavating and Mining Operations. G. Hall and A. F. Howell. Bull 15, U S Bureau of Mines
18. Excavation Machinery. A. B. McDaniel. McGraw-Hill Book Co, N Y
19. Handbook of Construction Plant, Cost and Efficiency. R. T. Dana. Clark Book Co, N Y 1911
20. Rock Excavation, Methods and Cost. H. P. Gillette. Clark Book Co, N Y, 1916
21. Handbook of Cost Data. H. P. Gillette. Clark Book Co, N Y
22. Loading Well-drill Holes in Quarry Blasting. A. B. Stoughton. Bull du Pont Explosive service
23. Theory of Explosives and Toughness of Rock in Secondary Explosives. W. O. Snelling. Eng & Min Jour, Aug 3, 1918
24. Efficient Blasting in Metal Mines. W. M. Anderson. E & M Jour, Nov 29, 1924
25. Blast-hole Drilling with Keystone Cable Drill. Keystone Driller Co
26. Springing Bore Holes. C. S. Hurter. Bull du Pont Explosives service, June 1924
27. Coyote Hole or Tunnel Blasting. G. R. Wilson. Bull du Pont Explosives service, Feb-Apr 1924
28. Effect of Atmosphere on Tiles of Explosives. Tec. Pap No 7, U S Bu Mines
29. The Do and Don't in Loading Dynamite. E & M Jour, Aug 13, 1927
30. Pillar Tamping bags above Ground. G. S. Brown. Bull du Pont Explosives service, Dec 1924
31. How to Avoid Waste of Explosives. R. N. Van Winkle. Rock & Coal, Sep 5, 1923
32. Safety in Quarry Blasting. A. La Motte. Bull du Pont Explosives service, Nov, 1925
33. Prevention of Abuses. F. E. Brooks. Min & Sci Pr, Dec 16, 1916
34. Shearing Granite with Compressed Air. Eng & Con, Sep 15, 1920
35. Underground Quarrying. R. H. Sammer. Bull du Pont Explosives service, Aug, 1925
36. Considerations in Changing a Quarry from Hand to Steam Shovel Method. R & Water & Coal, Dec 21, 1927
37. Drilling and Blasting. R. T. Tully. Peele Min Cong, Apr, 1924
38. Quarry Blasting Problems and Their solution. J. Barab. Bull by Hercules Powder Co
39. Secondary Blasting. J. B. Sanderson. Bull du Pont Explosives service, Aug, 1924
40. Steam Shovel Operation. G. M. Haight. E & M Jour, Feb 14, 1924
41. Change in Open-cut Mining. M & M Jour, May 21, 1921
42. Underground Drop-hole Preparation at Eagle-Picher Mines. N. F. Cleveland. Tec A I M E, Feb, 1927
43. Recent Changes in Explosives and Their Use. W. Cullen & J. E. Lindsey. Trans Instn Mining & Met, Vol 45, p 255 (1935)
44. Misfires in Metal Mining. U S Bur Mines, Rep Invests No 3139

SECTION 6

TUNNELING *

BY

CHARLES F. JACKSON

MINING ENGINEER

Note. Numbers in parentheses in text refer to Bibliography at end of this section.

* This section was prepared for the first and second editions by David W. Brunton and John A. Davis. It has been almost entirely rewritten by Charles F. Jackson.

TUNNELING

Introduction. The following discussion deals with tunnels or adits of small cross-section and larger tunnels in which the entire area is excavated in one operation, in contrast to the tunnels where an advance or pilot heading is driven first and enlarged later to full section. It includes, however, tunnels driven by the heading and bench method, wherein a top heading is carried only a round or two in advance of the bench. For methods of enlarging, timbering and lining railroad tunnels, see the works of Drinker, Prelini (27), Stauffer (28), Lauchli (29), publications of the mining and civil engineering societies and the technical press. "Rock Tunnel Methods" (30) contains summaries of data from "The Explosive Engineer" and illustrations of methods employed in R R tunnels, also data on mine and other tunnels of small cross-sec. Additional data on tunnels and drifts driven in immediate connection with mine development will be found in Sec 10, where full details of procedure and costs are given.

1. REPRESENTATIVE TUNNELS

Tables 1 to 3 contain data on 28 tunnels, from various sources as noted. Tables 1 to 7 present summaries of data on different phases of tunneling operations.

It may be remarked that many of the examples given are of tunnels for purposes other than mining. Within the past decade, comparatively few important mine tunnels have been driven.

2. ORGANIZATION OF WORK

Organization of work in tunnel driving depends chiefly on rate of advance required, size of cross-section, power and equipment available, and magnitude of project; in some cases, especially in the last few years, laws governing hours of work are a factor. For each tunnel job there is an approx rate of advance for max economy, depending on whether there are penalties for finishing after, and bonuses for finishing before, a given date; whether prompt completion will effect savings in total operating costs of the mine or other project to be served; overhead costs; and other similar considerations. Rapid advance requires a high degree of organization; precision in performing the several operations in the work cycle; equipment to provide adequate ventilation for continuous work at the face; and often other special equipment not essential in slower work. A break-down at any point in the work cycle is apt to disorganize the entire job and increase costs. Up to a certain rate, which varies with conditions, rapid driving obviously results in spreading supervision and fixed charges over a greater footage, thus reducing cost per ft; but constant pressure to attain max speed involves sacrifice of numerous small economies otherwise possible, and tends to increase the direct cost per ft.

One shift of drilling and blasting, with mucking and tramming on the opposite shift, constitutes the simplest organization. With the latest drilling equipment and enough machines at the face, almost any round can easily be completed in an 8-hr shift. In a tunnel of large section, a round of deep holes may break more muck than can be hand-shoveled in one shift, whereas modern power loaders will clean up as large a round as can be pulled. Thus the organization of the mucking shift will depend on whether loading is by hand or machine. If by hand, the mucking shift may have to work overtime, or two mucking shifts may be needed, obviously increasing the speed of driving. Some advantages and disadvantages of one-shift operation under ordinary conditions follow. ADVANTAGES: 1. Drilling and mucking are done on separate shifts; the heading is clear when the drill-shift comes on, so that the machines can be set up at once for the next round. Runners and helpers therefore waste no time in mucking, preparatory to mounting the drills; an important point when columns are used, because, for setting up, the debris must be cleared down to the floor. 2. During drilling, runners and helpers are not hampered by the muckers, avoiding the waste of time due to both crews working together. 3. Starting promptly, the round can usually be completed within the allotted time. But, in any case, sufficient extra time is available without delaying the following shift. 4. Drilling and mucking shifts can be arranged to avoid loss of time in waiting for smoke to clear away; a serious consideration where ventilation is poor. DISADVANTAGES: 1. Since daily progress is limited by the advance from a single round the total speed is slower. As most tunnels are useless until completed, if work is not pushed the capital invested in equipment is tied up too long, whence the charge for interest and depreciation is increased. 2. Realization of benefits

Table 1. Tunnel Data

No	Name	Location	Purpose	Date	Bib No	Length, ft	Shape	Rock section Width, ft	Rock section Height, ft	Rock
1	Big Creek No 3	Fresno, Calif.	HE	1921–23	1	8 813	RA	21 and 15	21 and 15	Gr
2	Britannia Ext (a)	British Columbia	De	1932	2	1 497	R	12	10 (b)	Sl and Vol
3	B. C. Nickel	British Columbia	De	1934	3	4 629	R	10	8.5	Grd and Hbl
4	Burleigh	Silver Plume, Colo.		1869		6 600	R	6	7	Gr and Gn
5	Cascade (c)	Washington	Dr and Tr	1926–27	4	41 131	RA	9	8	Gr
6	Chicago Ave	Chicago, Ill.	RRP	1924 et seq	5	43 296	RA	17.5	18.6	LS
7	Chipeta	Ouray, Colo.	WS	1907–08	6	1 835	S	7.5	7.5	Hard
8	Colorado River	Calif.	De	before '36	7	480 980	Hs	17.8	17.8	Gr and Cg
9	Eureka X. C.	Mich.	WS	1927	8	924	R	11	9	Gr, Sl, Qze, ore
10	Florence Lake	Calif.	HE	1920–25	9	67 634	{H: RA, B: R}	15	9	Gr
11	Halkyn	North Wales	Dr	1933 (d)	10	495	R	15	7	LS
12	Hetch-Hetchy, Mtn Div	Calif.	WS	1917–23	11	58 080* / 41 184†	R	13 1/3	14 1/4	Gr and Grd
13	Kerber Creek (Rawley)	Bonanza, Colo.	Dr and De	1911–12	12	6 235	T	7–8	7	An
14	Laramie-Poudre (e)	Larimer Co, Colo.	Irr	1909–11	13	9 123	O	10	8	Gr
15	Mammoth	Calif.	Dr and De	1911–12	14	3 008	R	9.5	9	Porphyry
16	Moffat (f)	Colo.	WS	1923–24	15	32 383	S	8–9	8	Gn and Gr
17	New Haven (g)	Conn.	WS	1927–29	16	20 500	Hs	8	8	SS, Sl, Trap
18	Newhouse	Idaho Springs, Colo.	Dr and Tr	1893–1910	17	22 000	S	8	8	Gn
18a	Newhouse	'' ''	'' ''	'06 (7 mo)	17	1 967	R	6	9.5	
19	Ojuela	Durango, Mex.	Dr	1928	18	5 407	R	8.5	9	LS and Sh
20	Owyhee No 5	Oregon.	Irr	1930–31	19	11 200	Hs	11–12		Basalt
21	Roosevelt	Cripple Crk, Colo.	Dr	1908–12	20	16 857	R	10	6	Gr
22	Sheep Creek	Alaska	De	1912–14	21	8 707	R	10	8	Sl, Grs
23	Snake Creek	Heber, Utah	Dr and De	1910–16	22	14 000	R	9.5	6.5	Diabase
24	Strawberry	Wasatch Co, Utah	Irr	1906–12	23	19 100	A	8	9.5	LS and SS
25	United Verde Ext	Jerome, Ariz.	Tr	1917–18	24	12 384	RA	11	10.5	Cg, D, Qze and Porph
26	Utah Metals	Tooele, Utah	Tr	1906	25	11 780	R	10	8	Qze
27	Waterville	North Carolina	HE	1927–29	26	32 709	Hs	15	16.5	Qze and Ark
28	Claremont	Oakland, Calif.	WS	....	37	18 004	RA	12	12	SS, Sh, Vol and CGr

A, arched roof; An, andesite; Ark, arkose; B, bench; Cg, conglomerate; CGr, cemented gravel; D, diorite; De, mine development; Dr, mine drainage; Gn, gneiss; Gr, granite; Grd, granodiorite; Grs, greenstone; H, heading; Hbl, hornblendite; HE, hydro-elec; Hs, horseshoe section; Irr, irrigation; LS, limestone; O, oval; Porph, porphyry; Qze, quartzite; R, rectangular; RRP, RR pioneer heading; S, square; Sh, shale; Sl, slate; SS, sandstone; T, trapezoid; Tr, mine transport; Vol, volcanics; WS, water supply.   (a) part of driving 10 000-ft extension; (b) with 3 × 3-ft drainage ditch; (c) pioneer heading parallel to main heading; (d) 2 weeks' driving, Jul 1–15; part of 12-mile tunnel; (e) one heading only; (f) water supply (pioneer heading); (g) total of 3 sections.   * Lined.   † Unlined.

Table 2. Tunnel Data—*Continued*

Numbers in left-hand column refer to tunnels so numbered in Table 1

No	Drill round			Drills			Mucking method	Shifts per day	Men per shift			Haulage		Length timbered
	Type	No of holes	Av ft pulled	No	Type	Mounting			Drill	Muck and tram	24-hr total	Type	Car, cu ft	
1	CV / HB	36-42H / 18B	10-8H / 18B	4-5	L	VC and HB	AS	2	11 (h)	6 (i)	....	TL-BL	108	300 ft
2	....	....	6	4	4″ L	Crg	ESc	2	4	4	22 (j)	TL	120	40%
3	Py	29	6.4	3	4″ L	HB	AS	1D, 1M	4	8	39 (j)	BL	25	little
4	....	25-31	....	2*	4″ Bu	VC	hand	2	4	4	7 (j)	horse	54	none
5	Py	....	7-9	6	3 1/2″ L	Crg	ES	2	12	....	....	TL	27	115 ft
6	CV, HB	26-34	8.56	2	3 1/8″ P	VC and Tr	ESc	2	3	5	42 (j)	GL	20	55%
7	Dr	46	5.7	4-6	AFL	HB	hand	3	8-12	8	16 (j)	mule	54-135	none
8	....	15-19	6+ / 6.85	4	4″ L	Carriage	CES	3	8	same 8	54-60 (j)	CTBL	60	....
9	Py / CV	45	9H / 18B	....	L	VC	ESc	3	....	8	32	TL	108	none
10	F	24	....	2	....	HB and VC	AS (k)	2	5 (l)	....	....	CTBL	54-81	....
11	....	46H / 15B	6.7	4	4″ L	HB	Sc	3	4	5-6	53 (j)	BL	16	1 618 ft
12	Py	36	8	2-3	L	HB	MW, HS	2 and 3	5	9	37 (j)	BL	16.5	630 ft
13	CV	42	6.35	3	L	HB	hand	3	5	7	50 (j)	mule	14	....
14	Dr	28 (m)	6.35	4	3″ P	HB	hand	3	5	6	35 (j)	mule	54	....
15	....	23	5	3-4	....	....	hand	3	....	6	....	TL	....	....
16	CV	19	7.5	4	{3 1/2″, 4″ L}	Crg	ES	3	5	9	64 (n)	TL and BL	48	1 000 ft
17	CV	26-30	11.5	3-4	do	VC	CES	1D, 1M	6 or 8	5	25-29	BL	35	....
18	CV	25	4.5-7	2-3	3″ L	HB and VC	hand	3	5	4	32 (j)	TL	40	none
18a	(p)	20-22	....	2	L	HB	AS (q)	2 or 3	3	9	21 (j)	TL and mule	81	804 ft
19	Dr	28	7.8	4	3 1/2″ L	Crg	CES	3	10	7	92 (n)	BL	16	none
20	....	19	8	2-3	3 1/2″ L	HB	hand	3	8	....	27 (j)	GL	30	350 ft
21	CV	30+	5	4	3 1/4″ P	HB	hand	3	5	4	70 (n)	mule	20	2 500 ft
22	....	22	4	2	3 1/4″ L	HB	hand	3	8	....	8 (j)	hand and BL	47	....
23	....	....	....	3-4	4″ L	VC	hand	3	2	....	36 (j)	horse	....	....
24	CV,HB / HB	16H, 2B / 27	4.8 / 5-6 (r)	2	....	VC and HB	hand	2	4	4	36-40 (j)	TL	32	500 ft
25	....	....	10 (s)	....	....	HB and VC	MW	2	4	....	....	mule	....	most
26	CV	39	....	2	3 1/2″ L	HB	CES	3	....	....	....	TL	60	
27	....	....	6-8	....	3 1/2″ L	....	....	....	....	....	....	GL and TL	50	
28	....	18	....	....	....	....	....	....	....	....	....	BL		

AFL, auto-feed Leyner; *AS*, air shovel; *B*, bench; *BL*, battery locomotive; *Bu*, Burleigh piston drill; *CES*, Conway elec shovel; *Crg*, carriage; *CTBL*, combination trolley-battery locomotive; *CV*, center V-cut; *D*, drilling shift; *Dr*, draw-cut; *ES*, elec shovel; *ESc*, elec scraper; *F*, flat shovel; *GL*, gasolene locomotive; *H*, heading; *HB*, horiz bar; *HS*, Hoar shovel; *L*, Leyner-type drill; *M*, mucking shift; *MW*, Myers–Whaley shovel; *P*, piston-type drill; *Pu*, pyramid-cut; *SC*, scraper; *TL*, trolley locomotive; *Tr*, tripod; *VC*, vert column. (h) includes drill boss and 2 nippers; (i) train crews only; (j) underground crews only; (k) steam shovel, air driven; (l) includes 1 nipper; (m) ground variable, 13–61 holes per round; (n) includes shop and other surface labor; (p) double pyramid-cut; (q) Nordberg-Butler loader; (r) station heading; (s) portal heading. * First use of machine drills in a U S mine tunnel.

Table 3. Tunnel Data—*Continued*

Numbers in left-hand column refer to tunnels so numbered in Table 1

No	Explosive		Ventilation		Ft advance per month		Cost of excavation per ft
	Strength, %	Lb per ft	Method	Pipe diam, in	Aver	Max	
1	40 and 60	115–120	Ex–Bl	24	450	......	$190.00 (t)
2	40	....	Ex	22	....	......	25.83 (u)
3	60 and 40	29	Ex–Bl	14	....	630	23.76
4	60	....	fan Ex	10 and 12	100	......	20.00
5	60	31	Ex–Bl	20	620–952	1 157	....
6	60	....	Bl	....	375±	......	....
7	40	14.5	comp air	....	342.5	......	12.02
8	40	....	Ex–Bl	20 and 22	540	1 269	46.00±(v)
9	60 and 80	....	{ fan Ex / comp air }	....	924 (w)	......	....
10	40 and 60	....	{ Root / Ex–Bl }	....	480±	......	....
11	60	20.5	fan Ex	20	495	......	24.01 (x)
12	40 and 60	....	....	....	300–770	......	....
13	40 and 60	12.17	PBl	....	351	555	19.88
14	60	31	PBl–Ex	16	413	......	39.54
15	40 and 60	24	fan Ex	10	301	......	20.77
16	40 and 60	22.7	Bl	12	1 158	......	....
17	40 and 60	17.4	PBl	12	550±	......	....
18	40 and 60	17.3	PBl–Ex	18	244	......	28.80 (y)
18a	40 and 100	....	....	....	281	......	22.44
19	40	22.7	PBl–Ex	16	714	......	21.36
20	40	18.6	PBl–Ex	15	843	......	....
21	60 and 100	25.0	PBl–Ex	16–17	285	......	27.27
22	60	34	fan Ex	15	544	......	31.08
23	40 and 60	16	PBl–Ex	16	250	......	25–30
24	40	....	PBl–Ex	14	300	......	26.70
25	40 and 60	....	PBl	....	524 (z)	......	....
26	40 and 60	....	fan Ex	12	250	......	15.00
27	60	28	PBl	....	520	......	....
28	25 and 30	20	PBl	15	{ 408* / 569† }	......	....

Bl, blowing; *Ex*, exhausting; *Ex-Bl*, exhaust, then blow; *PBl*, pressure blower. (*t*) 21 × 21-ft tunnel; cost includes heavy expense for road construction and other preparatory work; (*u*), includes proportion of construction and equipment costs and other capital charges; (*v*), dry sections, excavation only; (*w*) one month only; (*x*) based on £1 = $4.65; (*y*) cost of 2 759.5 ft for year ended Aug 31, 1900; (*z*) portal heading. * West portal. † East portal.

to be derived from the tunnel is delayed. In case of a drainage adit the extraction of ore below water level is delayed; or, if the adit is intended to lower the cost of underground transport, loss on the added tonnage handled in the old way should be charged against the slower driving of the tunnel. With an irrigation tunnel, an entire season's crops may be lost because of the increased time required by the one-shift system. 3. Overhead charges are operative during full period of construction; these charges per ft of tunnel are smallest when the max number of hours per day are employed in driving. Finally, although one-shift work is cheaper in wages, this may be offset by losses due to delay in completing the tunnel.

Two shifts will obviously make faster progress than one shift, the direct cost per ft being the same or more or less, depending upon organization and equipment. With hand mucking it is usually necessary to work the drilling and mucking crews simultaneously, although there is advantage in having the muckers start an hour or so before the drillers in order to make room for the latter to work over the muck pile. In this system, drills are usually mounted on a horiz bar set over the muck pile, and the top and breast holes are drilled first while the muckers are removing the rock beneath. With vert column mounting, the shift first mucks back from the face to make room for the set-up. A disadvantage of the horiz bar and drilling over the muck pile is the chance of drilling into a missed hole with a vert column set-up; time is lost unless the muckers come on ahead of the drillers; in either case, working the two crews together usually results in congestion at the face and loss of efficiency. With mechanical loading the work is usually planned for a clean set-up of the machines for each round, unless two complete cycles per shift are desired, when it may be necessary to use a horiz bar set-up. The machines may be mounted on horiz bars, vert columns, or drill carriage, and enough machines are employed to drill a deep round and shoot in 4 to 5 hrs or less. Mucking can usually be completed in 2 to 3 hrs, leaving a clean set-up for the next shift.　The mucking time varies but little with size of tunnel section, providing the mucking machine capacity is sufficient.　In some tunnels two complete cycles are completed in a shift using mechanical loaders, horiz-bar drill mountings over the muck pile, or a drill carriage, with adequate ventilation for removing blasting fumes, and facilities for quickly changing cars at the face.　Where two cycles are completed per shift, separate mucking-machine and loading crews are sometimes employed, each of which works two high-pressure periods, with an intervening rest period partly devoted to overhauling gear and equipment, sorting steel, preparing for blasting, etc.　For one complete cycle a single crew will usually suffice, the drillers operating the mucking machine after blasting.

Three shift organization is similar to that for two shifts, except that each crew must usually be composed of men capable of taking up the work at any point in the cycle where the previous crew leaves off.　Unlike 2-shift organization, if delays occur there is no time between shifts to complete unfinished work.

Table 4.　Typical Time Cycles in Representative Tunnels

Numbers in left-hand column refer to tunnels so numbered in Tables 1–3, which show number, type and mounting of drills, and mucking method

No	Name	Bib No	Aver ft of hole per round	Time cycle			
				Drill min (a)	Blast min (b)	Muck min (c)	Total hr : min
2	Britannia...............	2	215±	140	47	150	5 : 37
3	B. C. Nickel...........	3	290±	390	120	210	8 : 00 (d)
5	Cascade Pioneer........	4	234	105	38	130	4 : 33
(e)	Copper Basin..........	7	493±	174	60	288	8 : 42
9	Eureka................	8	202	140	40	105	4 : 45
11	Halkyn................	10	234	138 (f)	....	(g)	
	Halkyn (h)............	10	360±	186	69	80	5 : 35
14	Laramie-Poudre........	13	....	286–403	38–45	(i)	5 : 24–7 : 28
15	Mammoth..............	14	130	540–585	62–95	390	{ 2+ rounds { in 3 shifts
16	Moffat No 5............	15	234	121	59	116	4 : 56
17	New Haven............	16	312	360	(j)	300	(k)
19	Ojuela................	18	208	140	47	150	5 : 37
20	Owyhee No 5..........	19	172	110	40	78	3 : 48
22	Sheep Creek..........	21	140	254	23	245 (i)	4 : 37
(l)	Burra Burra crosscut. . .	34	....	120	60	120	5 : 00
25	United Verde Ext......	24	{ 230± (m) } { 190± (n) }	270–300	(j)	90	8 : 00
(p)	Montreal crosscut......	32	(q)	320	75	223	11 : 15 (r)

(a) includes barring down, setting up, drilling, tearing down;　(b) includes blowing holes, loading, firing, blowing smoke;　(c) includes moving in, mucking, moving out;　(d) mucking during drilling;　(e) 3 shifts, 5 drills jumbo-mounted, elec shovel;　(f) aver with 6.5-ft rounds;　(g) 37 ton per hr;　(h) aver one month when 1 086 ft were driven, pulling 9.3-ft rounds, 3 drills;　(i) during drilling;　(j) included with drilling;　(k) 2 rounds per day;　(l) 2 shifts, 2 drills, vert column mounting, elec scraper;　(m) portal heading;　(n) station heading;　(p) 3 shifts, 6 drills carriage-mounted, scraper;　(q) 32 holes, 6.1-ft round;　(r) track laying, lunch and delays, 57 min.

3.　SURFACE PLANT

Aside from requirements for office, camp buildings, and power plant or transformer stations, which vary widely with size and location of job, and time required for its completion, the usual surface plant comprises: air compressors, bit sharpeners (or detachable-bit grinders), heating furnaces, blacksmithing equipment, explosives magazine, ventilating fans or blowers, and car-dumping facilities.　In some cases, a small machine and electrical shop may also be required for making repairs to cars, track switches, loading and haulage equipment; but where the tunnel is driven at an established mine, most or all of these facilities may be already available.

4.　DRILLING EQUIPMENT

Drills and accessories.　The old piston-drill has been superseded by faster drilling hammer-type machines.　The use of hollow drill steel and wet drilling has become almost universal, and with growing understanding of the danger to health from dusty air, wet drilling is advocated under all conditions.　Mounted drifters with 3, 3 1/2, or 4-in pistons are commonly employed, the size depending to some extent upon hardness of rock and depth of holes. Mounted jackhammers of smaller piston diam are sometimes used in soft, easily drilled ground, and hand-held drills for vert holes in benches, where the heading-and-bench system is employed. Air pressures of 90 to 100 lb. are usual. Recently, standard makes of automatic-feed drills have come on the market and have found favor in numerous large tunnels. They are of two general types, those that feed by vibration of the machine and those with pneumatic feed. Accessories comprise rubber air and water hose, line oilers, manifolds for connecting hose from several drills to the mains, and drill mountings.

Drill Mountings comprise horiz bars and clamps, or vert columns with arms and clamps, or drill carriages. If drilling and mucking are carried on simultaneously, the horiz bar is preferable, since it can be set up over the muck-pile as soon as the back has been trimmed of loose rock and made safe. With vert columns, some muck must be shoveled back from the face before the set-up can be made, involving loss of time and rehandling of part of the muck by hand. Vert set-up behind a muck-pile interferes with efficient drilling; water from the drills dams up behind the muck and the hose must be carried over the pile and down to the drills. Horiz bar is sometimes preferred to carriage mounting, because muckers and drillers can work simultaneously.

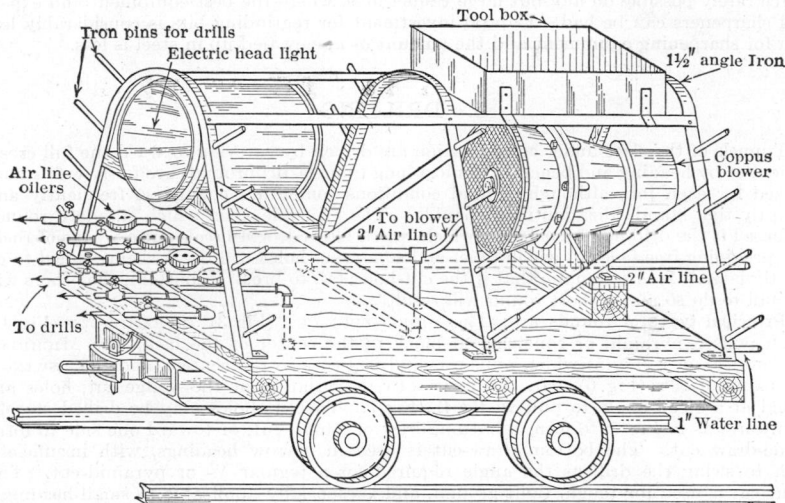

Fig 1.   Drill Carriage, Montreal Mine

Fig 2.   Hezzlewood Drill Tender

In the east portal of the Cascade tunnel, the superintendent was satisfied that he could make better time with a bar than with a carriage (4). 0.5 hr was allowed after blasting to clear the heading, and 20 min were required to bar loose rock, during which time the bar, 4 drills and 160 steels were brought up and some mucking was done where dirt lay against the face. Finally the set-up was made, the entire preparations requiring about 1.5 hr. Drillers stood on the muck pile. Mucking started with the "fly rock" and proceeded to the face. "By the time the shovel loader is close up and ready to dig into the last of the pile, the drillers have finished all but 5 or 7 bottom holes. ... We manage to pick up a round in the course of 48 hr by this work cycle. We count on 3 rounds a day and try to make or save enough time to gain an extra round every 2 days." While it is probable that extra speed can be gained with a bar, it is questionable whether as good direct costs can be secured as with a carriage.

Drill carriage or "Jumbo" has gained favor in recent years, but its use is limited to clean set-ups where it can be run right to the face. It usually runs on the tunnel track, but may be mounted on a caterpillar crawler. It is variously designed and constructed, but consists essentially of the carriage proper upon which are mounted the columns, bars, arms and drills, with individual air and water hoses attached. Manifolds and line oilers may be mounted on the carriage (Fig 1) or carried on a tender (Fig 2). The manifolds are connected to the mains by large hose. Drill steel is carried on the carriage or on a tender as the case may be. The tender in Fig 2 was used in the Ojuela tunnel (19) and in addition to carrying steel, air and water manifolds and a tool box, was equipped with a Coppus blower. Drill carriages permit a quick set-up, as the mounted machines, equipped for drilling, are run to the face with drill steel sorted and conveniently racked. When drilling is finished, the equipment is readily and quickly removed.

Drill steel. In American tunnels, hollow, 1 1/4-in round, lugged-shank steel is commonly employed for 3 1/2 or 4-in drifter drills; 1-in quarter-octagon or 7/8-in octagon steel is often used with lighter machines in easy drilling ground, or for vert down holes in benches. Machines with anvil-block chucks and plain shanks without lugs are seldom used in the U S, but are standard in many Canadian mines. Steels are commonly made up in lengths for 24-in changes; sometimes for 18, 20, 30-in changes, with corresponding gage changes of 1/8, 3/16, or 1/4-in. Here the standard U S practice of using a starter of 2 1/2 or 2 3/4-in or even 3-in gage might be improved, for it has been found in some mines that deep holes can be drilled in hard, abrasive ground, with 1 5/8 or 1 3/4-in starters and 1/16 to 3/32-in gage changes for a 24-in run, by exercising proper care in forming, gaging and heat treatment of the steel. Drilling speed increases rapidly with decrease in size of hole, and with corresponding decreases in steel loss, air consumption and time required to complete the round. A cross bit with full reaming edges (that is, having all 12 points in the same circumference) has been successful; gage loss is usually less, whence gage changes and bit size can be smaller to finish with same diam of hole. Detachable bits have come into favor in recent years. For tunnel work their chief advantages are: perfect forming of each bit, uniformity of gage and uniform results of heat treatment, which are attainable in the factory to a degree rarely possible on any but large tunnel jobs, where the best equipment and expert steel sharpeners can be had. Capital investment for regrinding bits is considerably less than for sharpening equipment and the amount of money tied up in steel is less.

5. DRILLING

Tunnels of the sizes under consideration are driven by carrying forward the full cross-section, or by heading and bench. In most long tunnels, drill rounds are fairly well standardized for each job, although ground conditions sometimes change so frequently and abruptly that standardization is impossible. The principle upon which standard rounds are based is the drilling of cut-holes, which, when blasted, will break out a wedge of rock, thus providing free faces to which relief and square-up holes will break, being timed to go slightly later. It is axiomatic that if the cut-holes fail to break to bottom, the others will also fail to do so and a short round will result.

Principal types of rounds are: The V OR WEDGE-CUT (Fig 3); PYRAMID-CUT (Fig 4), which pulls a pyramid or cone-shaped block in the center of the face; the MICHIGAN OR "BURNT"-CUT (Fig 5) which pulls a cylindrical core in the center; and the "SWING" OR SLABBING-CUT (Fig 6). In the DRAW-CUT, a variation of the wedge cut, holes are drilled at a steep angle to pull wedge W, Fig 7. The cut holes may be drilled steeply downward, as in Fig 7, to form a bottom-draw or "toe"-cut, or toward one side to form a side-draw cut. The bottom draw-cut is used in narrow headings, with insufficient room to swing the drill at the angle required for a regular V- or pyramid-cut. The burnt-cut is used for tough, tight ground, and is especially applicable to small headings, where there is not room to swing the machines for drilling conventional cut holes. The two center holes (marked black in Fig 5) are drilled normal to the face, and are not loaded; they merely form lines of weakness for the surrounding cut holes to break to and some space for the rock to expand into. The slabbing-round (Fig 6), as used in an 8 by 12-ft heading, consists of 28 holes in 4 rows of 7 holes each, one above the other; 3 or 4 holes of each row at the right can be drilled from a single column set-up by using a long arm. The 4 shortest holes (4 1/2 ft) are blasted first, followed in succession by the 5 1/2 and 6 1/2-ft holes, etc, each tier breaking in turn to the free face provided by the breaking of the preceding tier. The pyramid-cut ordinarily comprises from 3 to 6 holes, although 4 holes will break in most ground. Fig 8 shows a double pyramid-cut in the Ojuela tunnel for pulling a long round; 4 short holes, 14–12 and 27–28, are blasted first, pulling a shallow pyramid or cone, followed by the long cuts 15–16 and 19–22, and then for enlarging the opening, the two relief holes 13–11. In the diagram the circled numbers indicate order of firing, and boxed figures the number of cartridges of 40% gelatin dynamite used in average limestone rock. All holes were spaced so that after the cut had been fired no charge carried

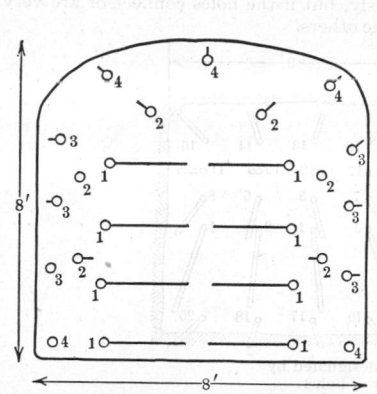

Fig 3. V-cut Round. In trap rock, this round proved effective with 12–14 cartridges of 60% gelatin dynamite in each cut hole. From 10 to 12 cartridges of 60% special dynamite in other holes completes the charge. Advance by each round averaged 11–13 ft, using 13-ft holes. Figures in diagram indicate order of firing electric blasting caps. In easier ground, as sandstone, 2 easers and 2 side holes are not used; the 60% special dynamite also is replaced by 40% special dynamite.

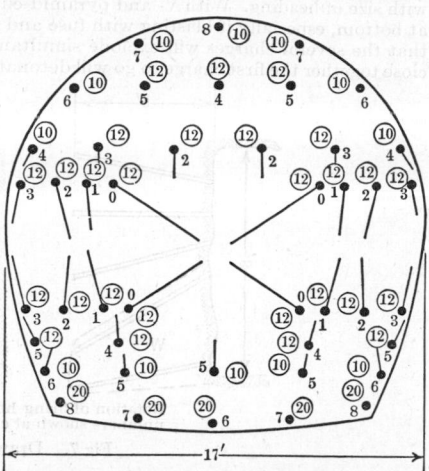

Fig 4. Pyramid-cut Round. Drill round used in Colorado River and in Copper Basin No 1 tunnels was built around a pyramid cut, using 11.5-ft holes. Circled figures indicate cartridges of 1 1/4 by 8-in, 40% or 60% ammonia gelatin, and uncircled figures, the firing order. This typical round could be easily modified to conform to changing conditions.

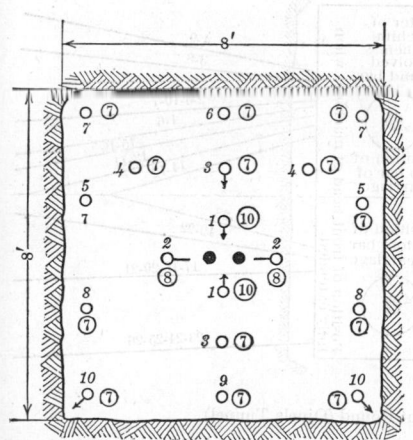

Fig 5. Michigan or "Burnt"-cut Round. (For explanation of numerals at each hole, see note under Fig 4)

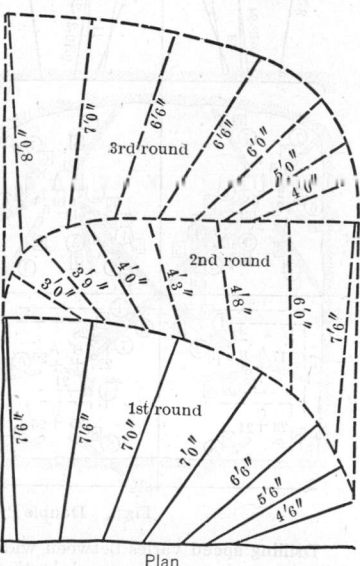

Plan

Fig 6. "Swing" or Slabbing Round

more than 2.5 ft of burden. Each top machine on the carriage drilled 8 holes from two settings; each bottom machine, 6 holes. Fig 9 shows a heading-and-bench round, with a vert V-cut in the heading and flat lifter holes in the bench, while Fig 10 shows one with a

I—7

vert V-cut in the heading and nearly vert "plugger" holes in the bench. The total number of cut, relief and square-up holes required for any type of round obviously varies with toughness of rock, the position, number, and direction of fracture or bedding planes, and with size of heading. With V- and pyramid-cuts, the cut holes should be drilled to connect at bottom, especially if blasting with fuse and cap. It is virtually impossible to cut fuse so that the several charges will explode simultaneously, but if the holes connect or are very close together the first charge to go will detonate the others.

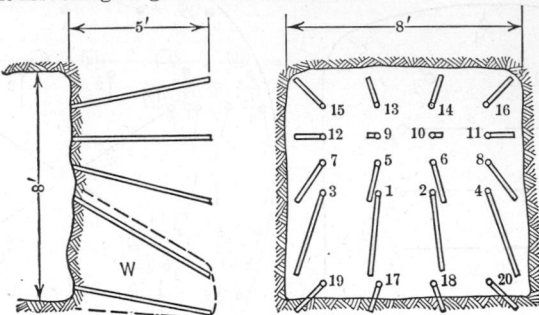

Rotation of firing holes designated by
numbers shown at collar of holes

Fig 7.   Draw-cut Round

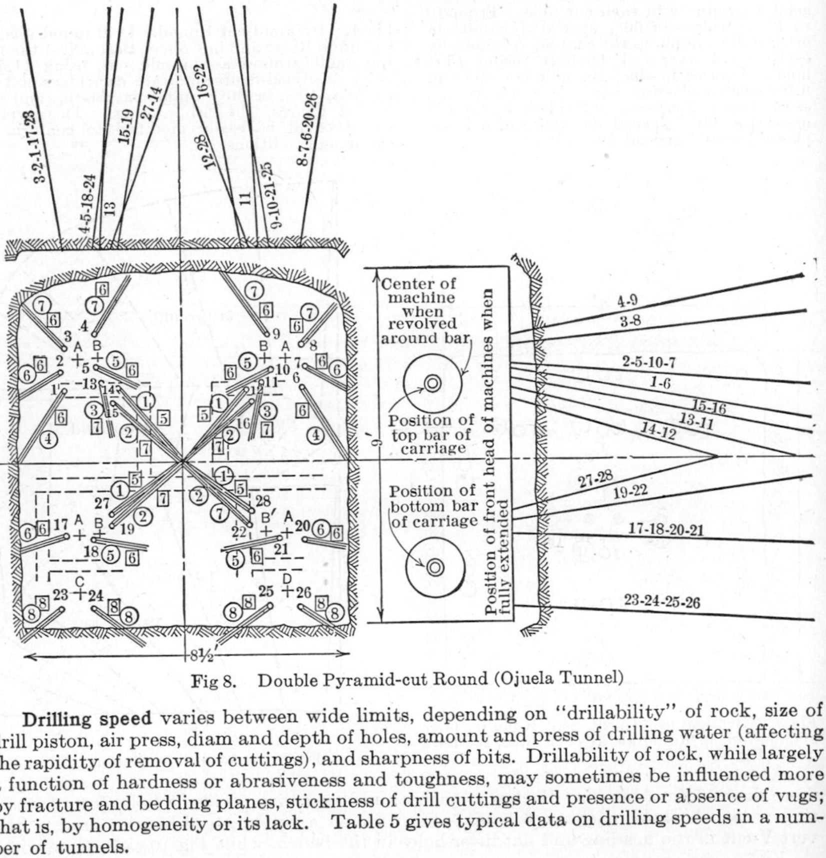

Fig 8.   Double Pyramid-cut Round (Ojuela Tunnel)

Drilling speed varies between wide limits, depending on "drillability" of rock, size of drill piston, air press, diam and depth of holes, amount and press of drilling water (affecting the rapidity of removal of cuttings), and sharpness of bits. Drillability of rock, while largely a function of hardness or abrasiveness and toughness, may sometimes be influenced more by fracture and bedding planes, stickiness of drill cuttings and presence or absence of vugs; that is, by homogeneity or its lack. Table 5 gives typical data on drilling speeds in a number of tunnels.

Table 5. Typical Drilling Speeds in Tunnels

Tunnel	Bib No	Rock	Drill size and type	Steel section	Bit gages, in Start	Bit gages, in Change	Length of run, in	Depth of holes, ft	Drilling rate per machine In per min	Drilling rate per machine Ft per min
Big Creek	1	Gr	4" L	1 1/4" HR	2 3/4	1/8	....	9–11 H, 13–21 B	....	21 H
Britannia	2	Sl, igneous	4" L	1" hexagon	2 1/4	3/32	24–28	7 to 8	....	30 av
Cascade Pioneer	4	Gr	4" L	1 1/4" HR	2 1/2	1/8	30	10–13	....	34
Colorado River	7	SS, Cg, Gn*	3 1/2" AFL	1/4" HR	....	....	....	11.5	....	40±
Copper Basin	7	Gn, Cg	3 1/2" AFL	1 1/4" HR	....	....	....	11.2	....	34±
Eureka	8	{ Gr, Sl, Qze; ore }	4" L	1 1/4" HR	....	....	24	8.4 aver	{ 8.1 Gr; 16 Sl }	20
Halkyn	10	LS fissured	4" L	1 1/4" HR	....	....	....	6.5–7.5 (a)	{ 30 (b); 2.5 }	37.7
Kerber Creek (Rawley)	12	An	L	1 1/8" HR	....	....	....	5.2 aver	....	12.2
Laramie-Poudre	13	breccia, Gr	L	....	....	....	....	7.5 aver	....	7.1
Mammoth	14	porphyry	3" P	....	....	....	....	....	....	11 (c)
Moffat No 5	15	Gn, Gr, Sch	3 1/2, 4" L	1 1/4" HR	2 5/8	....	18, 24	9.0	....	35.8
New Haven	16	SS, Sch, trap	3 1/2, 4" L	1 1/4" HR	....	....	....	13 aver	....	18±
Newhouse	17	Gn, Sch	L	....	....	....	....	....	....	14.5
Ojuela	18	LS, Sch	3 1/2" L	1 1/4" HR	2	....	30	10 and 8	....	28.4
Owyhee No 5	19	basalt	3 1/2" L	1 1/4" HR	....	1/8	24	9 aver	....	32.5
Sheep Creek	21	Sl, Gr, Mg	3 1/4" P	2, 1 3/4, 1 1/2" Cr	2 3/4	1/4, 3/16	20	5.5 to 8	7	8.4
Snake Creek	22	diabase	P	....	....	....	....	....	....	8–12
Srawberry	23		3 1/4" P	....	....	....	....	6.0 aver	....	13 (d)

AFL, auto-feed Leyner; An, andesite; B, bench; Cg, conglomerate; Cr, cruciform; Gn, gneiss; Gr, granite; H, heading; HR, hollow round; L, Leyner type; LS, limestone; Mg, metagabbro; P, piston drill; Qze, quartzite; Sch, schist; Sl, slate; SS, sandstone. (a) changed later to pull 9-ft round (31); (b) under ideal conditions; (c) only 2.5–3.5 ft in silicified porphyry; (d) test run. * Variable.

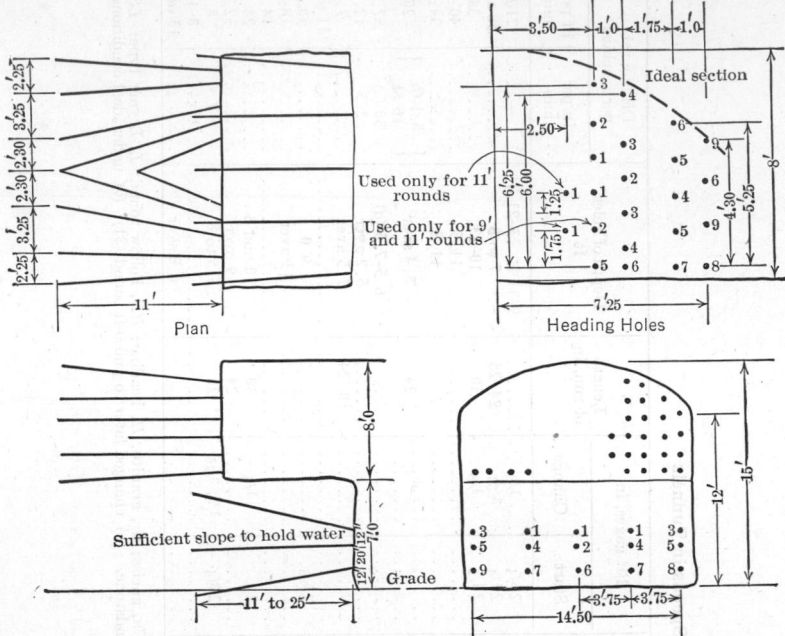

[Fig 9.   Heading-and-bench Round, using Flat Bench Holes.   (Numbers indicate order of firing)

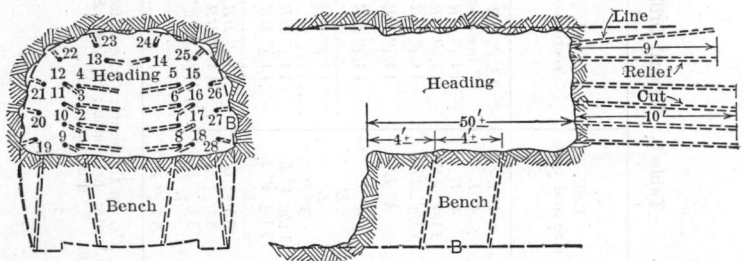

Fig 10.   Heading-and-bench Round, using Down-holes in Bench.   (Numbers indicate order of firing)

6. CHARGING AND BLASTING

Charging.   Rules prescribed for transport, handling, and use of explosives should be observed, and primers prepared as recommended by the explosives manufacturers. The approved methods of inserting the detonator in the cartridge (Sec 4) insure against its being accidentally pulled out when charging and prevent kinking the fuze and consequent breaks in the powder train, or abrasion of the insulation on leg wires. The detonator should lie in the axis of the cartridge and be pointed in the direction of bulk of charge. Before charging, holes are blown clean with compressed air. The cartridges are then pushed in, one at a time, and pressed firmly with a wooden tamping bar. To insure filling the entire area of the hole, the cartridges are often slit, so that the explosive will be pressed out against the walls of the hole. Care should be used to avoid breaking the fuse or damaging leg wires. Explosive manufacturers usually advocate placing the primer last (on top of charge), or next to last in the hole. There is no accepted rule that gives best results under all conditions. Thus in tunnel work, if the primers are near the top, the cut holes, which go first, may cut off the primers in one or more relief or square-up holes, especially in seamy or schistose ground. If the primers are at or near the bottom, a cut-off hole will throw unexploded dynamite into the muck pile. Table 6 gives data from

Table 6. Blasting Data for Tunnels Listed in Tables 1 to 4

No	Bib No	Explosive and strength, %	Size of cartridge, in	Detonators	Primer location	Stemming	Detonated by	Fired by	Method of handling misfires
1	30	40 and 60 GD	1 1/4 × 12	No 8 Ins and 7 delays	(a)	S, B	(h)	foreman	reblast
2	30	40–60 LFD	1 1/4 × 8	No 8 caps	(a)	none	fuse	foreman	(i)
3	30	90 BG	1 1/4 × 8	No 8 caps	(c)	C	fuse	blaster	reblast
4	30	40 and 60 GD	1 1/4 × 8	No 6 caps	...	Sc	fuse	shift boss	......
5	30	40 and 60 GD	1 1/2 × 10	No 8 elec delays	(d)	S and C	(j)	shift boss	reblast
6	30	40 and 60 GD	1 1/2 × 8	No 8 Ins and delays	(d)	none	(j)	shift boss	......
7	30	40 GD	1 1/2 × 8	No 8 elec	(d)	S or Rd	(j)	shift boss	......
8	30	40 GD	1 1/2 × 8	No 8 Ins and delays	(d)	S or Rd	(j)	shift boss	......
9	30	90 BG	1 1/4 × 8	No 8 caps	(d)	C	(j)	blaster	reblast
10	30	80 and 40 GD	1 1/8 × 8	No 8 delay	(d)	M, B	(j)	boss	reblast
12		80 GD / 60 GD	1 1/4 × 8	delay elec	(b)	C	250v (j)	shift boss	......
13	18, 30	40 GD	1 1/4 × 8	No 8 caps	(b)	.....	cap and fuse	shift boss	reblast
14	30	40 GD	1 1/8 × 8	No 6 caps	(e)	.....	cap and fuse	miner	......
15	30	40 and 60 GD	.... × 8	No 6 caps	(e)	none	cap and fuse	miner	......
18	30	60 AG	1 1/2 × 8	No 6 Ins and 6 delays	(f)	none	(j)	boss drill	reblast
19	30	40 or 60	1 1/4 × 8	No 8 Ins and delays	varies	Sg	110v d c or 220 a c (j)	foreman	......
20	30	60 and 40 GD	1 1/4 × 8	Ins and delays	...	S and Sg, B	(j)	foreman	reblast
21	30	60 or 40 GD	1 1/4 × 8	No 8 delays	varies	E	(j)	foreman	reblast by foreman
22	30	40 and 60 GD	1 1/4 × 8	No 8 Ins and delays	...		110v a c (j)	boss	......
23	30	60 gelatin	1 1/4 × 12	No 6 Ins and delays	varies	S	220v (j)	foreman	reblast or blowout
24	30	40 and 60 LFD	3/4 × 12	No 8 Ins and 8 delays	(d)	C and Rd, B	440v (j)	shift boss	reblast
27	30	60 GD	1 1/4 × 8	No 6 caps and 8 delay elec	(c)	S	220v (j)	boss	blowout with comp air, reload
28	19, 30	40 GD	1 1/4 × 10	No 8 Ins and 4 to 6 delays	(d)	S and C	220v (j)	boss	blowout with comp air, reload
X	21	60 LF	7/8 × 8	Nc 8 caps	(d)	paper or S	cap and fuse	foreman	directed by foreman
Y	1	60 and 40 LFD	1 1/4 × 8	No 8 up to 8 delays*	(d)	C	440v (j)	foreman	......

AG, ammonia gelatin dynamite; B, in bags; BG, blasting gelatin; C, clay; E, damp earth; GD, gelatin dynamite; Ins, instantaneous; LF, low-freezing; LFD, low-freezing gelatin dynamite; M, mill tails; Rd, rock dust; S, sand; Sc, sandy clay; Sg, screenings; X, Sheep Creek tunnel; Y, Big Creek tunnel. (a) 2d in. hole; (b) 3d from bottom; (c) top; (d) 2d from bottom; (e) near bottom; (f) next to top; (h) special power line; (i) drill adjacent hole; (j) special firing switch off power line; × Parallel connection.

a number of tunnels and indicates in each case the preference as to the primer position. Fuse or leg-wires are brought out along one side of the hole, pulled straight but not tight, and the rest of the hole filled with stemming (tamping). Though sometimes omitted, stemming is advocated by all makers of explosives; it increases the work done, and by confining the explosive causes more complete detonation and less fume. Paper tamping bags different in color from the explosive cartridges are in general use and are convenient. They are preferably filled with dry sand, fine rock screenings, or clay (see Sec 4).

Order of firing, with fuse blasting, is controlled by cutting fuse in different lengths, and to some extent by the order of "spitting"; with bunch blasting the order of firing is determined by the length of fuse only, since all fuses are spit at almost the same instant. Electric detonators are especially effective for cut holes, by insuring simultaneous detonation of all the charges even though the bottoms of the holes do not connect, a result virtually impossible with fuse. Order of firing is usually: (1) cuts, (2) relievers, (3) breast, side and top square-ups, and (4) lifters. The lifters go last to throw the muck away from the face (Fig 3 to 10).

Fuse vs electric blasting. Elec detonators for tunnel rounds are now generally preferred, and are advocated by the Bur of Mines for safety. With delay detonators, one closing of the firing switch causes the holes to go in proper rotation, and since there are no men at the face when firing, the danger (with fuse) of overstaying the safe time limit is avoided. However, modern fuse is almost uniform in rate of burning, and the use of igniters or "spitter" fuses to give warning has greatly reduced this danger. Some operators consider fuse safer than electric blasting, contending that danger from stray currents is greater than the hazards with fuse. "Bunch blasting" (32), as developed by the Anaconda Copper Mining Co, might be applied to tunnel work with good results as to both timing and safety. In wet tunnels good waterproofing of both fuse (or wires) and caps is essential. Here, electric blasting has a decided advantage, because of the difficulty of keeping fuse ends dry Burning fuse adds to the smoke, which must be cleared before recharging cut holes (if that be necessary), or preparing the remaining holes. Also, if fuse "side-spits," due to imperfections or abrasion of the tape while loading, the charges will explode by ignition instead of by detonation, reducing effectiveness and increasing the quantity of noxious fume (see Sec 4).

Firing. When blasting with fuse, there should be at least two men at the face and precautions taken against leaving them in the dark. After all holes are charged, fuses are cut to the lengths for proper order of firing, and their ends slit to expose a short train of powder for lighting. Carbide lamps are often used for lighting, but may be blown out by the "spit" of a fuse. Igniters, now on the market, or notched "spitter fuses" (Sec 4) are better, and are advantageous in warning the miner when his safe time is up. For successful electric firing care must be taken in connecting leg wires together and to the leads; wires should be twisted together, not merely looped or hooked. Bare connections must be protected against short-circuiting, especially under wet or damp conditions, by being raised off the ground and preferably taped. With a blasting machine, the holes must be connected in series, but either series or parallel connection may be used when firing from a lighting or power circuit. For a blasting machine, leg wires should be connected first, then connections made to the lead wires, and lastly, after everyone has retired from the face, the lead wires are connected to the machine. With power-circuit firing, connections are made in the same order, but a locked safety firing switch should be used, so that the power connection can not be made until the box is unlocked and opened. As an additional precaution, a second switch, kept open until ready to blast, may be placed across the leads between firing switch and face, well back from the latter. The chief precautions in electric firing are to keep the detonators short-circuited until the moment of connecting them to the blasting circuit and to keep the lead wires short-circuited until they are connected to the source of current. In some ground it is necessary to load and blast the cut holes, then return to the face and, if they have not broken to bottom, reload them and other holes, and blast a second time. Although this involves waiting for smoke from the first blast to clear, with loss of time if ventilation is poor, it may save time in the long run when the ground is such that the cuts fail to bottom up.

Misfires result in lost or short rounds, loss of time for refiring, and hazards in drilling and mucking. Unexploded powder in the bottom of a hole may be drilled into or, if in the muck pile, may be struck with a pick and exploded. After every round, missed holes and unexploded powder must be looked for. Various methods are advocated for dealing with missed holes. If elec firing has been used the lead wires should be disconnected from the source of power, short-circuited and wound back out of the way. With fuse, men should not return to the face for at least one half hr, preferably longer. Having uncovered the missed hole, many prefer to remove the stemming (a method condemned by the Bureau of Mines), exposing the top cartridge and then reblast with a fresh primer. If the stemming is picked out, great care is necessary and no metal tools are permissible. It is safer to blow out the stemming with compressed air, or wash it out with water. A still safer, but more time-consuming method, is to drill and blast a parallel hole close enough to detonate the missed hole, taking care not to drill into the latter.

7. MUCKING EQUIPMENT

Hand mucking requires no special comment. Some hand work is necessary even with mechanical loading, for cleaning up, handling fly rock, and, where drilling and mucking go on simultaneously, shoveling back from the set-up. Mechanical loading depends for its success upon continuous operation during the mucking period. Mechanical loaders are of 2 kinds: drag scrapers and shoveling machines. See Sec 27 for details.

Scrapers. Scraping equipment for tunnel headings comprises a double-drum elec or comp-air hoist, mounted on a movable slide; a scraper of the hoe, semi-hoe, or box type; pull and tail ropes; tail sheaves, and a scraper slide, or ramp. The latter is mobile and is usually on trucks running on the mine track, but can be mounted on a caterpillar crawler. Fig 11 shows a common type of slide with hoist mounted on top. For low headings, the slide may be built with the hoist mounted underneath the ramp. The loading boom extends back over the car and has an opening in the bottom through which the rock falls. Fig 12 shows a loading unit used at the Montreal mine, Wis (33). The slide and boom are mounted on 2 large cars, coupled to a locomotive tender on which is mounted the slusher hoist. When the cars are filled, the entire unit moves under its own power to the dump. The use of 2 large cars, together holding 380 cu ft, minimizes loading delays due to waiting for cars. The usual types of scrapers, many of which are suited to tunnel work, are illustrated and described in Sec 27. Their advantages are: flexibility, low first cost, and small power consumption (especially if the hoist is elec driven). Aside from labor, rope renewals are the largest single item of expense. Scrapers usually show no direct cost saving over hand loading in tunnels of less than 7 by 7 or 8 by 8-ft cross-sec.

Shovel loaders in a number of successful types are on the market, ranging from low machines suited to tunnels of moderate height, to converted power-shovels, like those for surface excavation. They are usually mounted on wheeled trucks and run on the tunnel track, but may be mounted on crawlers. Among these, the Conway shovel (Sec 27), which requires little headroom, is especially suited to mine tunnels of large cross-sec. A machine of this type requires tractive effort to force the dipper into the muck pile, and the dipper loads onto a short conveyer extending back over the car. For smaller headings, small shovel-type loaders are popular; that shown in Fig 13 uses traction to force the dipper into the pile; it is close-coupled to a mine car, into which the dipper discharges. For headings larger than about 9 or 10 by 12 ft, the larger loaders compete with scraper and slide.

8. MUCKING OPERATIONS

Hand shoveling. With modern high-speed drills, rounds can be completed in less time than they can be mucked by hand, hence, the depth of round that can be pulled economically is often limited by the rate at which muck can be removed. In 3-shift work, mucking must be finished when the drillers are ready to lower the bar for drilling the lifters, else they may be unable to complete the round by the end of the shift. With 2 shifts, drilling and mucking on both, there is some leeway and the muckers can start an hour or two before the drillers. But, if the rounds are too deep, more than 1 shift may be needed for mucking, involving overtime and increasing cost. With hand-mucking, shallow rounds are often found to give max rate of advance. Thus, at the Kerber Creek (Rawley) Tunnel (12), max progress with two 8-hr shifts, drilling 8-ft rounds, was 414 ft in a month, or 15.5 ft per day. In good drilling ground 2 rounds of 4.5 to 5.5 ft could be made in 1 shift, giving an advance of 18 to 22 ft per day. "Mucking by this method would be much facilitated, because fully 25% more could be landed on the muck-plates, and, if necessary, a third shift of muckers could be used." The number of muckers that can work around a car is limited; if too many, they interfere with one another. Analyses at a number of tunnels show that a shoveler requires a $2\frac{1}{2}$ to 3-ft width of floor space, so that in a 10-ft tunnel there should not be more than 4 shovelers; in a 6-ft tunnel, only 2 shovelers. For speed work, extra muckers may be required to relieve one another. Their time need not be lost, since, when not actually shoveling, they can switch and handle cars, pick down the muck pile, etc, the change in working position affording physical relief.

In the Laramie-Poudre tunnel (13), 6 muckers worked as follows:
When car 1 was filled, 2 shovelers (A and B) took it to the rear, while 2 others (C, D) took empty car 2, previously thrown on its side off the track, set it on the track and pushed it into position for loading. Meantime the remaining men (E, F) stopped picking down the rock pile, took the shovels

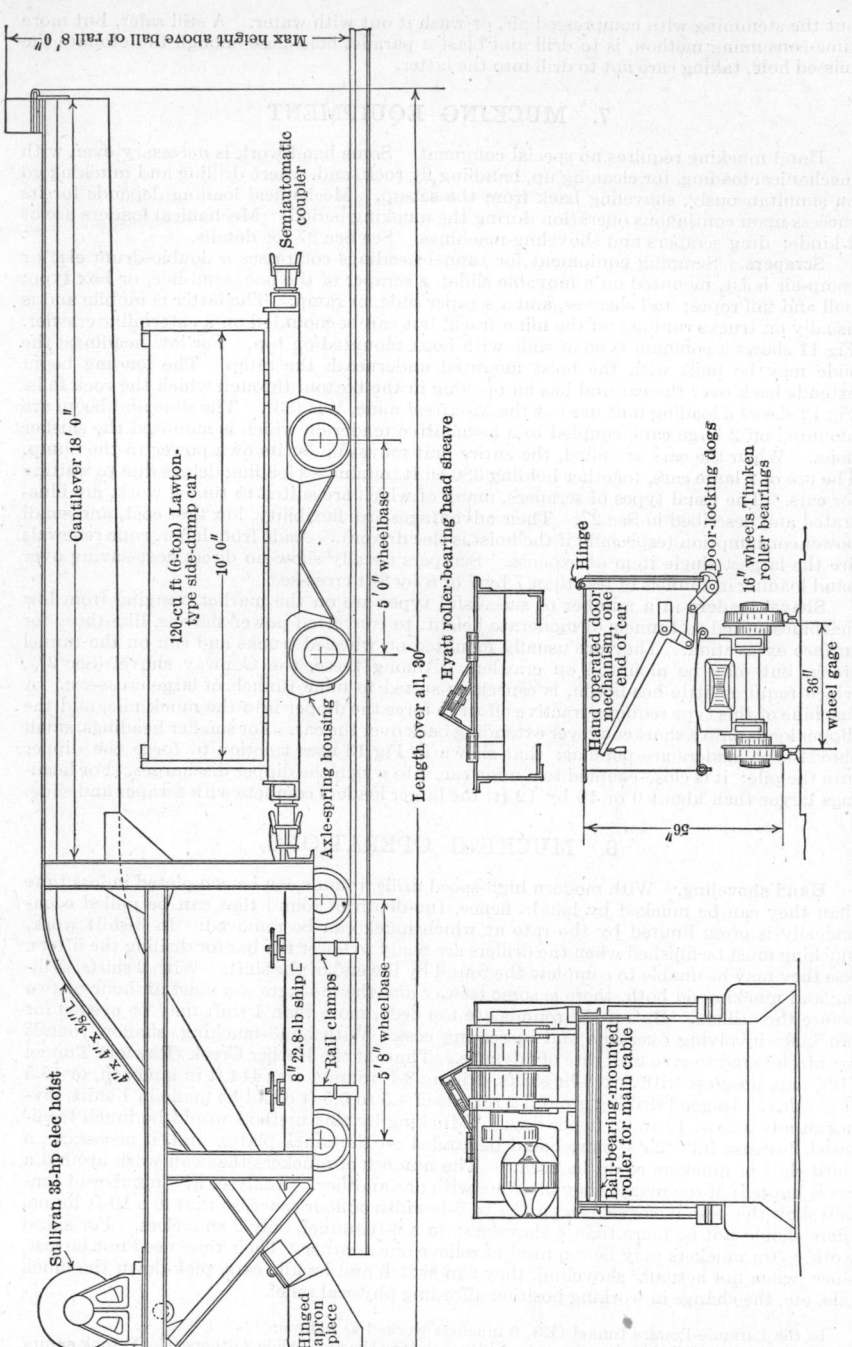

Fig 11.   Scraper-slide Mucking Machine and 120-cu ft (6-ton) Side-dump Mucking Car, Britannia Mine

left by A and B and assisted C and D in filling car 2. Car 3 was then brought up by A and B close to where car 2 was being filled, and was thrown on its side in the position formerly occupied by car 2. A and B then picked for the other 4 men, while car 2 was being loaded. When filled, car 2 was removed by C and D, while E and F set up the third car and loaded it with help of A and B. A fourth empty car was meanwhile brought up by C and D, who then took their turn at picking. The cycle was completed when E and F took the third loaded car to the rear, brought back an empty and resumed their original position on the muck pile. Thus, each man spent two-thirds of the time in tramming or picking muck, either of which is easier than loading, and relieves the monotony of shoveling. In this methodical procedure there is no lost motion. Cars of 16-cu ft capacity were filled in an aver of 3 or 4 min. At the Rawley tunnel (12) where a similar system was used with 4 shovelers, 25 17-cu ft cars were loaded in 2 hr; in another case, 20 cars in 1.75 hr, including all delays in making up trains.

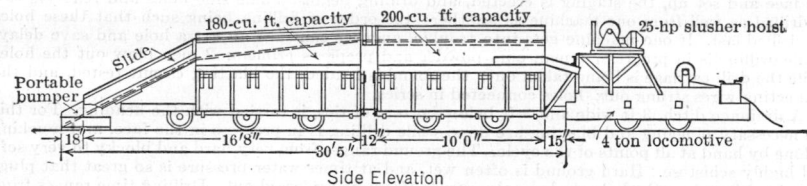

Fig 12. Scraper-loading Unit, Montreal Mine, Wis

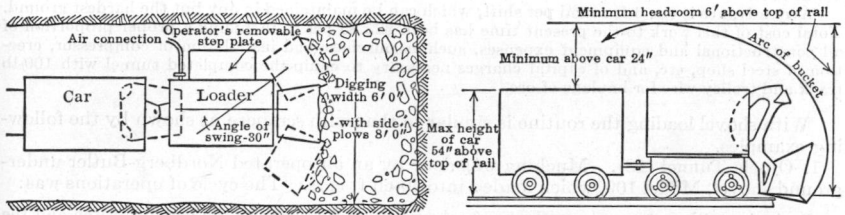

Fig 13. Shovel-type Loader Close-coupled to Mine Car for Small Headings

Mechanical loading is not well adapted for drilling and mucking simultaneously, although with small dipper loaders this may be done as at the B. C. Nickel Co's tunnel (3). The routine for driving the long Eureka crosscut at the Burra-Burra mine, Ducktown, Tenn, is typical. The crosscut is in schist and graywacke, 8 by 8 ft in section. As a speed of 500 ft per month was all that was required to reach the objective on the desired date, only 2 shifts were worked, as follows (34):

A scraper operated by a double-drum, 25-hp elec hoist was mounted on a portable frame of mine-track gage, upon which was supported a steel incline for loading into 4-ton cars, spotted by a cable-reel locomotive. Sidings for empty cars were kept within 700 ft of the face. The few minutes needed for switching cars caused no delay, as this time was employed in preparing the muck pile for easy loading. The drill crew began at 7 a m, and, with a clean set-up, started drilling with two 144-lb drifters mounted on columns. At 9 a m the round was about finished, and was usually shot and smoke blown out by 10 o'clock. As the ground broke well, the entire heading was generally shot in one operation. The mucking crew, coming on at 9, oiled and overhauled the equipment, to be ready by 10 o'clock to begin mucking. While mucking out, the drillers overhauled their equipment, sent out dull steel, brought in and sorted fresh steel, and took a short rest period. Mucking was usually done by noon, and a second round drilled and shot by 3 p m. Two shifts each of drillers and muckers completed 4 rounds, making an aver advance of 18 ft per day of about 20 hrs. Each drill crew consisted of 2 drill runners (one acting as shift leader), 2 drill helpers, and 1 steel nipper. The nipper helped the muckers on his shift, besides keeping the drillers supplied with steel. The mucking crew comprised a hoist man, helper at the face, and motorman who spotted and changed cars, hauling and dumping the loaded cars, while the drillers were at work. A foreman had charge of both shifts. The job was organized on basis of 2 high-pressure work periods for each crew, with an intervening period of rest. For completing two rounds per shift, wages were: shift leaders, $8.16; drillers, $7.16; scraper man, $7.16; drill helpers, $6.16; steel nipper, $5.16; scraper helper, $5.16; motorman, $4.08. Except the motorman's wage, these rates were 40 to 90% above the standard. If the 2 rounds were not completed, the men received only the regular daily rate.

The 4 100-ft haulage tunnel at the Britannia mine (2) is 10 × 12 ft. Low cost was more important than speed, the aim being to attain max effic with small crews. The heading crew per shift comprised 1 shift boss, 4 miners, 2 muckers, 1 motorman and 1 brakeman; also 1 trackman and helper and 1 ditchman on day shift, and 1 steel sharpener and helper. The cycle of operations was as follows:

After blasting, 2 miners bar down, 2 rig equipment for drilling holes for "Lewis wedges," 2 muckers clean out for the scraper slide, and the train crew bring in cars and slide. A hole is drilled in each wall at the face, wedges are driven in, a chain is stretched across, on which the tail sheave is hung; the mucking machine is meanwhile clamped to the rails and connected to the 440-volt 3-phase a c power line, and mucking begins. While a 120-cu ft or 6-ton car is being filled the train crew hang an empty on the car switcher, the full car is pulled back, and the empty dropped on the rails and pushed to the mucker. Filling cars averages 3 to 4 min, and switching 1 to 3 min, according to distance. The car switcher is moved up about every 500 ft. One side of heading is scraped out first; when the tail sheave is switched to the other side, 2 or 3 men clean up along the wall with shovels and hand scrapers. The permanent rail is kept 30 ft from the face, so that the scraper can dig to bottom of the ties over the whole area.

After mucking is completed, a light rail extension is laid, over which the drill carriage is run to the face and set up, the staging is erected, and drilling begins. Some side holes and relievers can be drilled as well from one machine as another; the order of drilling being such that these holes are drilled last. If one machine gets into trouble, another can take an extra hole and save delay. While drilling is in progress, 1 man cuts powder and prepares primers; 2 men blow out the holes while the drill carriage is being taken out; the round is loaded, the blasting circuit tested, and the connecting wires strung out; holes connected in series.

A drainage ditch, 3 ft wide and 3 ft below bottom of ties, is carried with the heading. For this the necessary plugging and blasting are done while drilling is in progress in the face, and mucking is done by hand at all points of the cycle. The ground ranges from very hard and blocky to very soft and highly schistose. Hard ground is often wet, and at times water pressure is so great that plugs must be driven into the holes to keep the powder from being forced out. Drilling time ranges from $1\frac{1}{4}$ to $5\frac{1}{2}$ hr, but 2 to $2\frac{1}{2}$ hr is usually sufficient. Timbering was necessary in one place only for about 40 ft.

Aver advance is one 6-ft round per shift, which can be maintained in any but the hardest ground. Total cost of this work to the present time has been \$25.83 per ft, including a proper proportion of all constructional and equipment expenses, such as purchase and installation of compressor, erection of steel shop, etc, and of capital charges necessary to equip the completed tunnel with 100-lb track and trolley wire for haulage of ore.

With shovel loading the routine is similar to that with scrapers, as shown by the following examples.

1. **Ojuela Tunnel (18).** Mucking was done by an air-operated Nordberg-Butler underground shovel, Model 109, which loaded into 40-cu ft cars. The cycle of operations was:

Beginning with a clean set-up, the power shovel was pulled back to the passing switch and the drill carriage pushed to the face. Each of the 4 machines drilled a prescribed number of holes. During drilling the shovel runner overhauled and oiled the shovel and the track crew cleaned up along the side to prepare for laying track and pipe. When drilling was completed, the motor pulled the drill carriage back to the portable turnout and the round was blasted. After waiting 10 min after the last shot, about 1 000 ft back from the face, the entire crew cleaned up the track to the point at which the muck pile was about 1 ft high. The shovel followed the drive crew and necessary connections were made when the muck pile was reached. Three men pushed one 40-cu ft car from a group of 6 empties from the portable turnout switch to the shovel, after which another empty was placed on the passing switch to be exchanged as soon as the first was filled. Loaded cars were returned to the loaded side of the portable turnout, and the train hauled out. Empties were kept on opposite side of the switch.

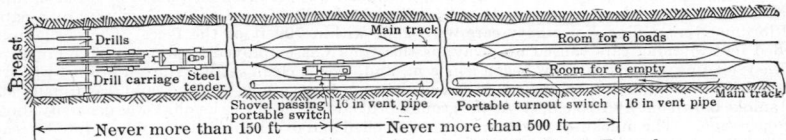

Fig 14. Movable Switches and Passing Track, Ojuela Tunnel

Considerable time was saved by keeping the passing switch (Fig 14) within 150 ft of the face; when the distance between the turnout and passing switches became so great that an empty could not be returned while the mechanical shovel was filling a car, the turnout switch was moved ahead. While loading was in progress, one machine man and the drill-carriage boss inspected the drills, replaced dull with sharp steel, filled the oilers and prepared for drilling the next round. The table shows time consumed in the various operations.

	Hr : min			Hr : min	
	Aver	Best		Aver	Best
Taking drill carriage to face and setting up..............	0 : 30	0 : 15	Cleaning up ahead of shovel.....	0 : 15	0 : 07
Total drilling time............	1 : 50	0 : 55	Loading (aver of 20 cars @ 40 cu ft per round).................	2 : 00	1 : 45
Tearing down, blowing, charging, blasting..............	0 : 35	0 : 25	Interval, end of loading to start of setting up.................	0 : 15	0 : 07
Waiting for smoke...........	0 : 12	0 : 05	Total time................	5 : 37	3 : 39

2. Owyhee Tunnel No 5 (19). General procedure was as follows: the blower exhausted powder smoke from the face for 10 min aver; it was then reversed, blowing in fresh air. A train of 81-cu ft cars, with mucking machine at head end and locomotive at rear, proceeded from nearest passing track to the face; the shovel (Conway, Type 50) started loading on reaching the first fly-dirt and continued until the face was clean. 3 miners and helpers then rigged up 3 machines on a horiz bar, and, working from a staging, put in the upper holes; one miner and helper, drilling from a horiz bar, put in the lifters; the drilling completed, the miners tore down and blew out the holes. The holes were wired by the shift boss or powder man, and fired with delays from a switch, the compressor-house attendant reversing the blower on hearing the shots. Aver time for each operation during 3 good months, 3 283 ft being driven in 212 shifts, 15 shifts of which were devoted to timbering, was: ventilating, 10 min; shoveling, 1 hr 18 min; setting up, 31 min; drilling, 1 hr 19 min; tearing down, blowing holes, loading and blasting, 1/2 hr; total time, complete round, 3 hr 48 min. Per round: ft advance, 7.82; no of holes, 19.2; ft drilled, 172; no of cars, 16.9; lb powder, 146.6 (18.6 per ft advance). Per shift: rounds, 2.12; ft advance, 16.6. Depth of holes, 9 ft.

Table 7. Mucking Rates in Various Tunnels

| Tunnel | Bib No | Mucking equipment | Aver cu ft per round | | Mucking, aver time per round | Car capac, cu ft | Aver loading time per car, min |
			Solid measure	Car measure	Hr : min		
Big Creek No 3..	1	Marion No 20 (c)	140 (a)	....	(b)	108	...
Britannia Ext...	2	scraper (e)	28	....	....	120	3–4
B. C. Nickel....	3	Butler (c)	20	....	3 : 30	25	...
Cascade Pioneer.	4	Myers–Whaley (e)	26	....	2 : 00	54	...
Chicago Ave....	5	scraper (e)	90	220	6 : 00	27	1
Colorado River..	7	Conway (e)	70+	110–120	2 : 30	54 and 135	...
Copper Basin...	7	Conway (e)	100	....	4 : 48	135	...
Eureka.........	8	scraper (e)	18–29	58	1 : 45	60	...
Mammoth......	14	hand	540	....	6 : 30	14	3–3.7 (d)
Moffat No 5....	15	Conway (e)	22	38	1 : 56	54	1.9
New Haven.....	16	Conway (e)	32	70	5 : 00	48	...
Ojuela.........	18	Butler (c)	23	30	2 : 30	40	3–4
Owyhee........	19	Conway (e)	27	51	1 : 18	81	1.5–2
Sheep Creek ...	21	hand	12	....	4 : 05	30	(f)

(a) Two 8-ft heading rounds and one 16-ft bench round. (b) 8–10 hr, including preparation and moving out. (c) Comp-air drive. (d) 3 men shoveling, 1 tramming. (e) Elec drive. (f) 10–12 ton per hr, 4 muckers shoveling, 2 resting.

9. TRAMMING AND HAULAGE

Mucking by hand. Any delay in tramming or prompt replacement of loaded with empty cars affects mucking efficiency and may upset the entire cycle of operations. There are various methods for minimizing the time required to handle the cars. Due to the extra effort for hand shoveling into high cars, or throwing muck to the back of long ones, small light cars are usually preferable, although they involve more shifting per yd handled. Light cars are changed quickly, as empties can simply be tipped off the track, to allow loaded cars to pass, and replaced for pushing them to the face. Another method for light cars is to use a "slick-sheet," beside the track and close to the face, on which an empty is kept always ready. When a car is loaded, it is pushed past the slick-sheet, an empty brought to the face, and another empty placed on the sheet. At the Sheep Creek tunnel (21) the slick-sheet was never more than 50 ft from the face; another sheet, a few hundred ft farther back, held a train of empties. The loaded cars were run back past the empties, made up into a train and hauled out. The empties were then run singly to the sheet at the face. As the sheets were set at same height as top of the rail, cars had only to be lifted the height of the flange.

Mechanical loading has brought about the use of larger cars, which are loaded by machine as quickly as small cars by hand. To reduce switching delays, thus increasing actual loading time, special methods and equipment have been developed. The commonest are movable switches and passing track, and the crane car-lift ("cherry picker"). Fig 14 shows switches and tracks in the Ojuela tunnel (18); for details of car changing routine, see Art 8. Fig 15 shows a form of "cherry picker" employed in the Wachusett-Coldbrook tunnels (35).

It is an air-lift hoist, traveling on a transverse beam or bar near roof of tunnel. An empty car is raised by the hoist, transferred to one side, the loaded car switched back, and the empty then returned to the track ahead of the train and pushed alongside the loader. Thus, for each car switched, the train moves its complete train length, backward and forward; plus any distance greater than normal between the cherry picker and the face; plus the working clearance for car and shovel at the face. Time studies at the Moffat tunnel, where a cherry picker and 50-cu ft cars were used, showed that actual loading consumed 28% of total loading time, and switching 24%. At the Owyhee tunnels (19) with same equipment, except that cars were of 81 cu ft capac, the number of cars to be switched was reduced by 60%, thus saving 13 to 19 minutes per round. When loading by scraper and slide, a large car can be used, although its height must be limited to allow room for the loading boom above it and clearance for the scraper as it passes over the boom. Fig 12 shows the equip-

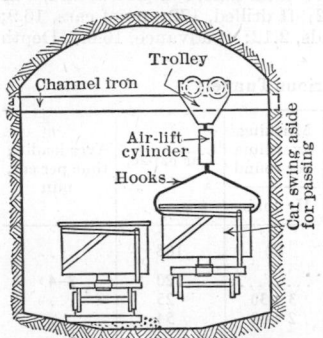

Fig 15. "Cherry Picker"

ment devised at a Wisconsin mine (33), where 2 cars (190 cu ft each) and a locomotive comprise a loading and haulage unit. With this, an aver round of 6.1 ft in a 9 X 14-ft crosscut was mucked out in 3 hr 9 min aver. The entire unit goes out to the dump, 3 or 4 trips being required to clean up a round. Other devices for saving time in switching are the "grasshopper" and the conveyer (Sec 27). The former, applicable only to a high tunnel, consists of a steel frame straddling the tunnel track and traveling on a wide-gage track. A hinged ramp at each end is lowered to permit running a string of empty cars on and off the deck of the frame which is high enough to allow cars to pass through under it. The empties are pulled up the rear ramp by an air hoist, and lowered singly on the front ramp, as required by the loader. The conveyer may be used where headroom is less; it consists of a belt mounted on a framework straddling the tunnel track. The mucking machine loads through a hopper onto the conveyer, which is long enough to cover a string of cars. Table 7 gives data on tramming and haulage time, which are virtually the same as mucking time, the operations being concurrent.

Type of car used will depend largely upon dumping facilities. Solid-body cars may be of large capac, yet low. Their first cost and repair costs are comparatively small, and spillage along the track is a minimum, due to the absence of doors around which leakage may occur. These cars require a rotary dump, and involve rehandling the muck in another car or skip for final disposition; the extra cost of plant may not be warranted. Granby-type cars (Sec 11) have certain advantages, especially for fast dumping, but require a fixed dumping ramp. In most tunnel jobs the muck is spread over a considerable area near the portal, simply by fanning out the pile, and for this side-dump cars are ideal, although they may be too high for easy hand loading, and even for mechanical loading if the tunnel headroom is small. Gable- or rocker-bottom cars are commonly employed in the smaller tunnels. (For different types of cars, see Sec 11.)

Haulage is usually by locomotives, which are also used for switching at the face and for moving drill carriages, mucking plant, timber, and supplies. Storage-battery locomotives are ideal for short hauls, and have the advantage of eliminating trolley wires, especially important at and near the tunnel face. Combination trolley-battery locos, often used in long tunnels, run on the batteries for spotting and switching cars near the face, and operate as trolley locos for the long haul out to the dump. Cable-reel trolley locos are employed similarly. On some jobs a small battery-loco is used at the face for spotting and switching, and a separate trolley-loco for the long hauls.

10. VENTILATION (see Sec 14)

Adequate ventilation is a requisite for rapid and economical tunnel driving and to protect workmen against dust and gas hazards. In tunnel work it usually implies mechanical ventilation, for prompt removal of gases after blasting and supplying fresh air at the face. Good ventilation is required during drilling and mucking, for diluting and sweeping out harmful dusts; under high-temp conditions, for immediate physical relief of the men; and, under explosive-gas conditions, for diluting and removing gas.

During drilling, or the operation of air-driven shovels or scrapers, exhaust air affords some ventilation and cooling effect. Just before firing around, the comp-air line is usually opened to blow against the face, diluting the powder gases and gradually moving them back from the face. At velocities up to about 30 ft per min, the gases move back as a cloud; higher velocities result in churning and dilution, without materially hastening this movement. Removal is therefore very slow unless a blower or fan is installed at the tunnel portal; it is connected to a pipeline which is suspended in an upper corner of the tunnel and extends as close to the face as possible without danger of its being injured by blasting.

Blowing vs exhaust systems. The relative merits of continuous blowing, continuous exhausting, and blowing followed by exhausting, are still debated. Local conditions may influence results obtained by different methods. Data in Table 3 indicate a majority preference for the exhaust system. Arguments for and against may be summarized as follows. With blowing only, the gases are churned about at the face, but are eventually caught in an outgoing current of air through the tunnel. Thus even if they are quickly removed from the face, men returning to work must pass through a gassy zone unless they wait long enough for the gas to discharge at the portal. The ventilating pipe can not be carried close to the face, because of flying rock from the blast; but, when blowing, flexible tubing can be attached to the pipe to carry air to the face, and is quickly rolled back a safe distance before the blast. While with non-collapsible tubing the same practice is possible when exhausting, it is seldom attempted. Blowing at the face causes a rapid cooling effect on the men; whereas, when exhausting, movement of air at the face is hardly felt, although the volume of fresh air may be the same. With straight exhaust, the movement of fresh air from the portal is usually along the floor near the face, thence upward, and out through the ventilating pipe. Due to the necessary distance from end of the pipe to face, the gas may take some time to reach the pull of the exhaust; but, when caught, it is immediately sucked out of the pipe, and the tunnel is clear to the portal, so that men can return to the face in fresh air. During drilling and mucking, blowing dilutes concentrations of dust (or strata gases, like methane), and sweeps them from the face, whereas exhausting often fails to reach the greatest concentrations. When drilling, the drill exhaust aids somewhat in driving the dust back to the ventilating pipe.

In general, it would appear that max results can be obtained under normal temperature conditions by the following sequence: (1) blow from compressed-air line at the face during and immediately after blasting, thus driving the gases back to the end of the exhaust pipe, whence they are drawn out; (2) as soon as gases are removed by the fan or blower at the portal, extend flexible tubing to near the face and reverse the current, blowing fresh air in; (3) continue blowing during mucking and drilling. On some jobs the system is operated *blowing* for 10 or 15 min following the blast, supplementing the effect of the compressed air jet, and is then reversed, operating *exhausting* during the rest of the cycle. Under high-temp or explosive-gas conditions, continuously blowing systems are preferable.

Blowers. The high-pressure mechanical ventilation required for long tunnels may be produced by positive-pressure blowers, low-pressure centrifugal or propeller fans installed in series, or centrifugal compressors (see Sec 14). Tunnel contractors usually prefer positive-pressure blowers, although some centrifugal compressors have been employed in recent years.

11. TUNNEL SUPPORT

Support for the tunnel roof and sides may be required while driving. If it must be kept close to the face, the rate of advance is retarded, and the cycles of operation already outlined may have to be changed to include a timbering period. Placing timbers after blasting each round may require as much or more time than drilling or mucking. Some ground stands well when freshly broken, though after continued exposure it may slack, crack or slab off. In such cases the placing of supports may safely lag some distance behind the face, causing little if any hindrance to driving operations. Temporary timbering is often used during driving and replaced later by permanent supports or lining. Permanent supports are of timber, structural steel, or concrete; brick or masonry was often used in the earlier R R tunnels. Concrete may be poured around forms, where a strong lining is needed to support heavy broken ground; or, where there is no great weight

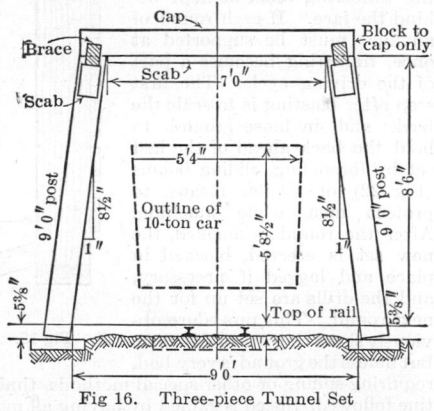

Fig 16.   Three-piece Tunnel Set

and it is only necessary to prevent air-slacking, a thin layer of "gunite" suffices. For permanent support, timber should be well seasoned and treated with preservative. It is easily framed on the job and quickly erected without use of special tools or equipment. For temporary support, in local stretches of bad ground while advancing the heading, timbers are readily cut and framed to suit requirements.

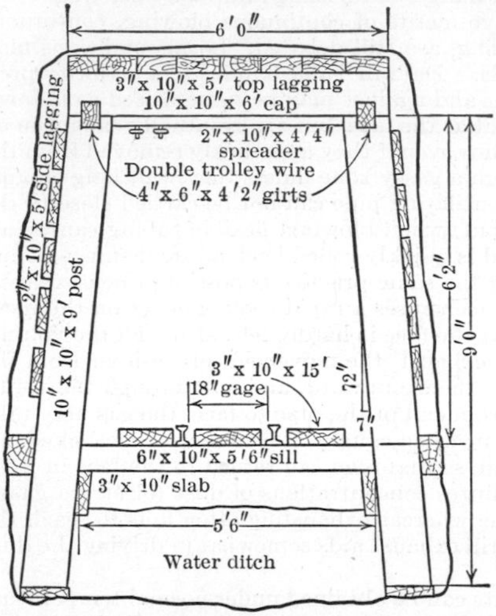

Timber sets comprise several timbers forming a framework across the tunnel section. The commonest form for narrow tunnels is the 3-piece set, consisting of a cap and two posts. Fig 16 shows a typical 3-piece set, with posts battered to resist side pressure. Fig 17 is a set used in the Park-Utah drainage tunnel, where a water ditch of large capacity was required (36). Posts may be dapped into the ends of the cap, or held apart at the top by a "scab" piece spiked to under side of the cap. Collar and toe braces between adjoining sets resist longitudinal movement of the sets. The batter of the posts is 1 to 1.5 in per ft, which is usually sufficient to prevent the bottoms of the posts from pushing inward unless side pressure is excessive and the bottom soft. The set in Fig 18 has "batter blocks" to prevent displacement of the posts by swelling ground. The back of the tunnel often stands better if arched (Fig 3 and 4), especially in wide headings. Similarly, arched sets (Fig 19) are customary in wide tunnels. Where only the back

Fig 17. Drainage Tunnel Set with Ditch under Track

requires support and the walls are strong, posts may be omitted and the arch timbers set in hitches cut at the break-line of the arch (Fig 20). In swelling ground, where the bottom tends to heave, an inverted arch set (Fig 21) may be used. Size of timbers and interval between sets depend upon size of tunnel, and pressures to be withstood. The back

and walls between sets may or may not require support by lagging. Swelling ground should not be close-lagged, but spaces left between adjacent pieces of lagging, through which pressure can be relieved.

Routine and speed of timbering depend largely on how close the timbering must be kept behind the face. If each round of advance must be supported at once, timbering becomes a part of the driving cycle. The first step after blasting is to scale the back; and, in loose ground, to hold the back ahead of the last set by forepoling, sliding booms (Fig 22) or similar means, to protect men while mucking. After the round is mucked, the new set is erected, blocked in place and lagged if necessary, and the drills are set up for the next round. This procedure obviously slows the rate of advance, but unless the ground is very bad,

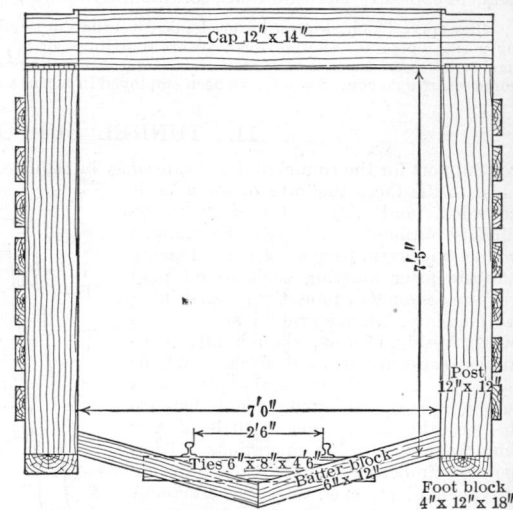

Fig 18. Set with Batter-blocks in Swelling Ground

requiring spiling or other special methods, timbers can be standardized and a regular routine followed. Speed is gained by having all materials and supplies at the face before work begins; timber for a complete set, blocks, wedges, lagging and tools, should be brought in with the crew.   Where the timbering lags a considerable distance behind the face, a special timber crew is usually employed.   With suitable scaffolding, work can proceed without interfering with driving operations.   A movable scaffold, with a working deck several sets long and high enough to allow the tunnel cars to pass under it, may be advantageous.

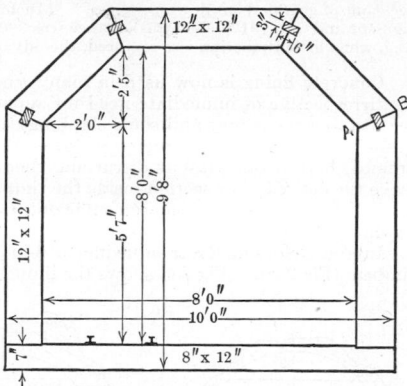

Fig 19.   Arch Tunnel Set

In the Claremont tunnel (37), sequence of operations was; (1) excavation and timbering, interrupted from time to time to construct the concrete invert; (2) placing forms and pouring the concrete arch.   Tunnel sets were 5-piece (arch), with 6-ft posts and were 4, 5 or 6 ft apart, depending on the ground.   Timbers were 8 by 8 in, later changed to 8 by 12 in.   Drilling and blasting averaged 2½ hr; mucking, with a Conway machine, 3 hr.   After blasting, the top lagging boards were driven forward and mucking was started.   After clearing out the face the timber set was erected and blocked in place, side lagging being placed where necessary. Advance per round, 4 to 8 ft and 24 ft total advance was often made in a day.   About 5.5 hr were required for drilling, blasting and mucking, leaving some 2.5 hr for timbering; thus it was possible to complete a round and timber it in an 8-hr shift.   However, timbering close to the face usually precludes completing two rounds per shift, though it may not do so where the ground is not bad and the work is highly systematized.

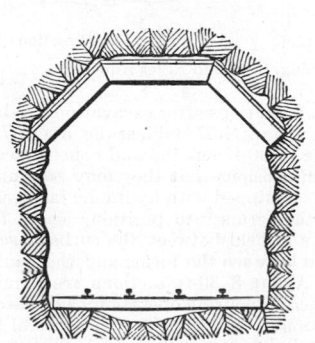

Fig 20.   Arch Set without Posts

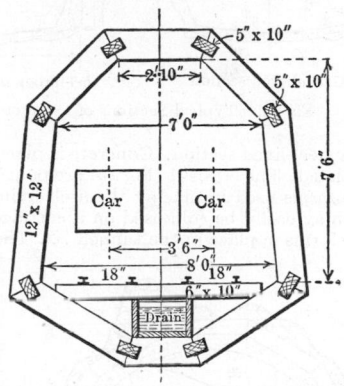

Fig 21.   Inverted Arch Set for Swelling Ground

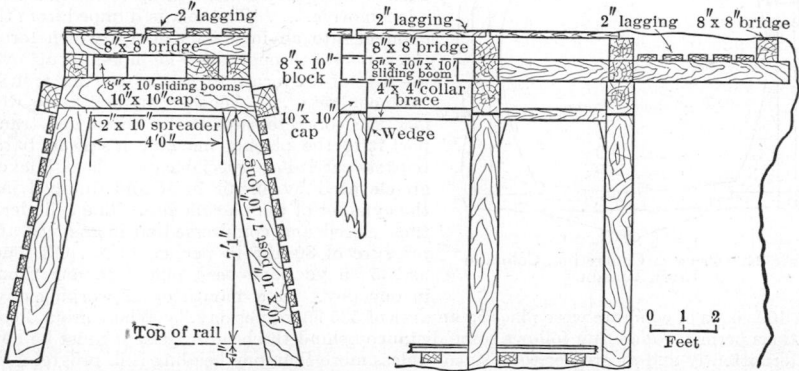

Fig 22.   Sliding Boom for holding the Back ahead of Last Set

In the B. C. Nickel tunnel, where little timbering was required, the timbers were set by the muckers under direction of the shift boss while the machinemen were drilling the lifters. At the Big Creek tunnel (1) it is stated that "bad sections of ground were timbered as broken, which threw the cycle out of gear and cut down progress." Much of the Rawley tunnel (12) had to be timbered during Sept and Oct, 1912, when the advance was 390 and 185.5 ft, respectively; during June, July and Aug, when little timbering was required, the advance was respectively 488, 555 and 421 ft.

Concrete lining is now used in many tunnels, especially aqueducts, designed for long life, irrespective of immediate need for support; in the course of time many rocks disintegrate to some extent and some slabbing occurs if they are not sealed off. In most mine tunnels and some others which have to be timbered during driving, the concrete is poured around the timbers without disturbing them, the tunnel having been driven oversize, to leave the desired clear section inside the timbers. Sometimes 2 or 3 in of concrete over the face of the timbers is considered sufficient, the thickness of course being much greater between the sets.

In the Colorado River aqueduct a 6-in thickness of concrete was maintained inside timbers (Fig 23b). Fig 23a shows the lining in untimbered sections of this tunnel and Fig

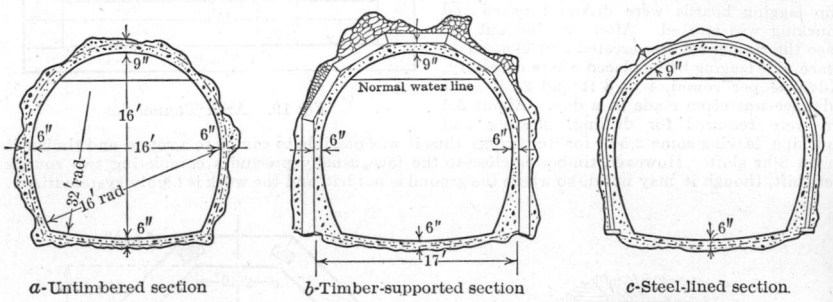

a-Untimbered section   b-Timber-supported section   c-Steel-lined section.

Fig 23. Typical Sections of Concrete Tunnel Lining, Colorado River Aqueduct

23c, a steel-lined section. Concrete is placed in separate sections after excavation has been completed. The curbs A (Fig 24) are poured first, then the arch B and last the invert C (7). "The forms used in placing the arch lining are made in 30-ft lengths and constructed so they may easily be collapsed on a carriage to such dimensions that they may pass under other forms in place in the tunnel. . . . The carriage is equipped with hydraulic jacks, used

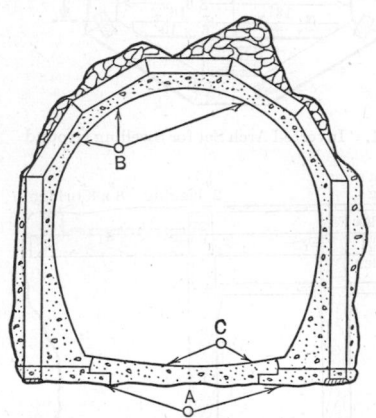

Fig 24. Order of Concreting, Colorado River Aqueduct

to expand the forms into position, where they are braced and held between the curbs by screw jacks placed between the forms and the haulage track. . . . About 8 30-ft sections are required at each concrete pouring operation. The batches are proportioned by weight in quantities of 1 cu yd each, at batching plants outside the tunnel, placed in specially designed batch cars and pushed into the tunnel and up to the mixer by a locomotive. . . . The mix is dumped from the cylinder into an ingenious pump, which forces the concrete through an 8-in pipe-line up over the tops of the forms to the advancing arch of fresh concrete. . . . Another method is to wet-mix the concrete outside the tunnel and transport it to the placing machine inside in batch buckets carried on special cars. These buckets are elevated by an air hoist and dumped into the cylinder of the placing gun. The cylinder is then closed and compressed air introduced at a pressure of 80–125 lb per sq in. . . . As much as 735 cu yd have been placed in one tunnel in one day. In a month of 27 working days, 14 400 cu yd of concrete were placed; an aver of 535 cu yd per day." Where ground conditions permit, concreting follows some distance behind the heading, else it must be done intermittently and at greater cost, since (unless more than one heading is in progress) the concreting crew will be busy only part of the time. Minimum thickness of concrete is generally from 6 in upward, the arch usually thicker than the walls. The forms are of wood, steel, or wood on steel. Concrete is placed by hand, gravity, pump, or pneumatic cylinder. Gravity is common for sides and invert; pneumatic cylinder for the arch, even on same job.

Gunite. Where no great weight is expected, slabbing is often prevented by a $1/4$ to $3/4$-in coating of gunite (mixture of about 2.5 to 3 parts sand to 1 cement), applied to the rock walls with a cement gun. The fresh rock should be coated as soon as broken, all loose rock being first removed and the walls cleaned thoroughly. In the United Verde Ext tunnel gunite was used successfully in a 4 090 ft section, and in 1930 had held for over 10 years (38). The tunnel is 10 by 10 ft; a 3 : 1 sand-cement mix was applied in 2 coats. Total cost of labor, materials, machinery repairs and supplies, was $5,772.23, or $1.40 per lin ft of tunnel treated, or 46c per sq ft.

12. DRIVING THROUGH LOOSE OR RUNNING GROUND

Conditions range from ground which is merely loose and heavy to those where water under pressure may force soft-material into the heading. For the first condition, forepoling

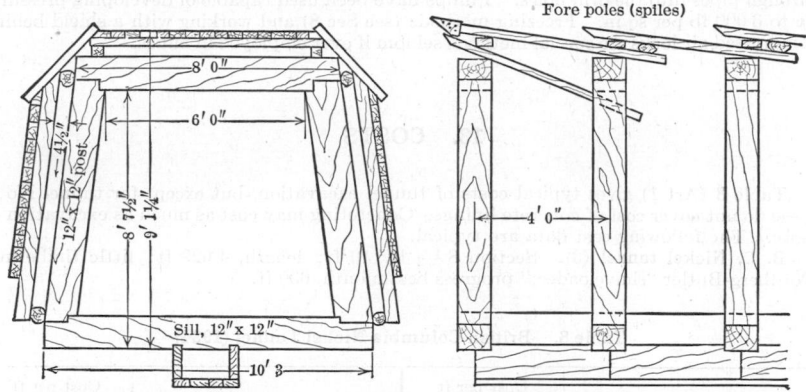

Fig 25. Forepoling with Regular and Bridging Sets

with or without breast boards usually suffices. Methods differ in detail, but in general involve the driving of spiling over the last set of timbers, so that room is left below or (with side spiling) inside, for erecting the next regular set (Fig 25).

Fig 26 shows the swinging false set with a 3-piece arch cap for very heavy ground. It can be applied with even greater facility to the ordinary horiz cap. There are no tail

Fig 26. Swinging False Set

blocks, nor does the spiling have to be driven across 3 sets of timbers, as in Fig 25. The weight on front ends of spiles is carried by the swinging false set, and the spiling can be driven with less hammering than is required with the tail blocks. The posts of the false set rest and rotate on the sill of permanent set, and when first erected occupy the position shown by dotted lines. They carry a cap of heavy steel pipe *b*, which supports front end of spiles *a*. While driving, the only pressure to be sustained is that of the rock above and in front of *a*; whereas, with tail blocks, a few pounds weight on front end of a spile brings 4 or 5 times as much weight on its supports. As the spiling is driven, turnbuckle *c* is slowly unscrewed, allowing the false set to fall forward, until the spiles are nearly horiz. When all spiles have been driven home, and the supporting block *d* placed under them, the turn-buckle is slacked still farther, until the swinging set loosens. Then the hanging rods are unhooked from the eye-bolts and the false set is advanced to its next forward position.

This system requires that the timbers for at least 5 or 6 sets from the face shall be connected by tie rods, as shown. This is an advantage, because, by screwing the timbers up tightly against the braces, they can be more easily blocked in position. Also, the timbers are held in place so rigidly that, if hard ground occurs in any part of face, heavier charges of explosive can safely be used than if timbers were held in place only by blocks and wedges.

Where there is water pressure, special methods sometimes have to be adopted, such as drilling holes ahead of the face and pumping in cement grout to seal off the water (see Sec 8). The liquid cement is drawn from mixing tanks into a pump chamber and discharged through pipes into the drill holes. Pumps have been used capable of developing pressures up to 3 000 lb per sq in. Freezing methods (see Sec 8) and working with a shield behind compressed air locks are special methods seldom if ever employed in mines.

13. COSTS

Table 3 (Art 1) gives typical costs of tunnel excavation, but except for tunnel No 1, these do not cover cost of concrete linings. Concreting may cost as much as excavation or more. The following cost data are typical.

B. C. Nickel tunnel (3). Section 8 1/2 by 10 ft; length, 4 629 ft; little timbering; Nordberg-Butler "shuveloader;" progress best month, 630 ft.

Table 8. British Columbia Nickel Tunnel (1934)

	Cost per ft				Cost per ft	
	505 ft	4 563 ft			505 ft	4 563 ft
Drilling and mucking:				Tramming:		
Wages...................	$ 8.02			Wages...................	$ 1.38	
Machine shop............	.24			Machine shop............	.16	
Drill steel loss............	1.30			Supplies.................	.08	
Machine drill parts........	.97				$ 1.62	$ 1.55
Supplies: tools...........	.84			Air shovel operation:		
oil..............	.03			Wages...................	$ 1.04	
	$11.40	$ 8.89		Shop....................	.29	
Explosives:				Supplies.................	.27	
Powder @ $7.50 per case...	$ 2.93				$ 1.60	2.02
" @ $8.75 " " ...	2.39			Pipe laying (air and water)		
Fuse @ $44 " " ...	.44			Wages and supplies.......	0.26	.44
Caps @ $21.50 per M...	.14			Ventilation pipe line:		
Handling exp and capseal...	.04			Wages, shop and supplies...	0.16	.26
	$ 5.94	5.58		Lighting: wages and supplies..	0.80	.64
Timbering:				Compressor operation.......	0.56	.58
Wages...................	$ 0.18			Steel sharpener operation.....	1.49	1.36
Supplies.................	.09			Engineering................	0.19	.25
	$ 0.27	.19		Office.....................	0.48	.29
Track laying (surface and				Superintendence............	0.61	.43
underground):				Carbide....................	0.05	.06
Wages...................	$ 0.62			W. C. B. assessments........	0.46	.43
Machine shop............	.04			Total...................	$26.62	$23.76
Supplies.................	.07			Portal expense.............		.41
	$ 0.73	.79				$24.17

Halkyn Tunnel, No Wales (10).   Section, 10 by 8 ft; data for 495 ft driven July 1-15, 1933; scraper loader.

Table 9. Halkyn Tunnel, Cost per Ft. British currency converted at £1 = $4.65

	Labor	General supplies	Explo-sives	Shops	Comp air	Power	General exp	Total
Drilling and mucking.........	$ 9.11	$0.50	$5.77	$0.08	$1.34	.....	.....	$16.80
Traffic......................	1.11	.03	.06	.08	.....	.....	.....	1.28
Hoisting....................	.76	.04	.....	.02	.....	$0.17	.....	.99
Mine, general...............	.70	1.16	.....	.04	.....	.....	.....	1.90
Surveying...................	.40	.06	.....	,....	....	....	$0.02	.48
Drill repairs and sharpening...	.13	.12	.....	.11	.20	.....	.....	.56
Overhead...................	.35	.01	.....	.01	.....	.01	.24	.62
Slusher repairs...............	.04	.....	.....	.....	.....	.....	.....	.04
Tunnel support..............	.06	.04	.....	.....	.....	.....	.....	.10
Ventilation.................	.....	.....	.....	.....	.15	.06	.....	.21
	$12.66	$1.96	$5.83	$0.34	$1.69	$0.24	$0.26	$22.98
Superintendence...								1.03
								$24.01

Kerber Creek (Rawley) Tunnel (12). Section 7 to 8 by 7 ft; length, 6 235 ft; 1 618 ft timbered; hand mucking; mule haulage; best month's advance, 555 ft; aver, 351 ft.

Table 10. Kerber Creek Tunnel, Cost per Ft (1912)

Underground	Labor	Suppl and repairs	Total	Surface	Labor	Suppl and repairs	Total
Drilling and blasting Explosives........	$2.82	$0.42⎱ 2.01⎰	$5.25	Power plant Fuel.............	$1.07	$0.18⎱ 1.31⎰	$ 2.56
Mucking..........	2.14	.02	2.16	Blacksmithing......	.60	.13	.73
Tramming.........	1.02	.11	1.13	General surface.....	.67	.16	.83
Track and pipe.....	.44	....	.44	Salaries, office, travel-			
Timbering.........	.87	.31	1.18	ing, etc...........	.....	....	1.98
General...........	1.17	.27	1.44	Permanent plant *...	.....	....	2.13
				Boarding house.....	.....	....	.04
				Grand total.....	.....	....	$19.87

* $3.24 less $1.11 credit.

Mammoth Tunnel (14): Section, 9.5 by 9 ft; length 3 008 ft; mostly untimbered; hand mucking; aver advance, 301 ft per mo.

Table 11. Mammoth Tunnel, Cost per Ft (1912)

Operation	Labor (a)	Material	Air	Power	Total
Drilling.............................	$4.772	$0.131	$1.206	....	$6.109
Mucking.............................	3.474	.390	....	....	3.864
Timbering...........................	.069	.100	....	....	.169
Piping..............................	.271	.834	....	....	1.105
Explosives...........................	4.000	....	....	....	4.000
Making drill tools.....................	.017	.357	....	....	.374
Repairing drills (Burleighs).............	.044	.333	....	....	.377
Sharpening steel......................	.271	....	....	....	.271
Track and wiring.....................	.172	1.266	....	....	1.438
Electric lights........................	.026	.038	....	....	.064
Car and locomotive repair.............	.051	.209	....	....	.260
Electric tramming.....................	.814	.133	....	.052	.999
Foreman.............................	1.165	....	....	....	1.165
Supt, engineering and office...........	.530	....	....	....	.530
Widening tunnel......................	.044	....	....	....	.044
Total actual work................	$15.720	$3.791	$1.206	$0.052	$20.769
Pipeline to portal.....................	....	....	....	....	.118
Extension of tramroad.................	....	....	....	....	.224
Grading for yards.....................	....	....	....	....	.523
Misc preparation.....................	....	....	....	....	.599
Total cost.......................	....	....	....	....	$22.233

(a) Wage rates: foreman, $6; machinemen, $3.50; chuck tenders and pipemen, $3.25; muckers, trammers and motormen, $3.

Newhouse Tunnel (17).   Section, 8 by 8 ft; length, 22 000 ft; 1 000 ft timbered; hand mucking; aver progress, 244 ft per mo; driven in 1902–09.

Table 12.   Newhouse Tunnel, Cost per Ft (1909)

	May	June	July		May	June	July
Advance, ft.........	264	323	305	Fuse and caps......	$ 0.46	$ 0.22	$ 0.49
Labor *............	$7.65	$5.59	$6.06	Drill repairs.......	1.24	1.02	0.93
Transport.........	1.42	1.34	1.34	Use of machines and			
Power.............	2.15	1.79	1.86	drill steel........	.38	.62	.66
Blacksmithing and				Rail, ties, air, etc...	1.59	1.58	1.66
steel sharpening...	2.35	1.18	1.22	Sundries...........	1.69	0.54	0.48
Explosives.........	3.64	3.83	4.02	Total..........	$22.57	$17.71	$18.72

* Wage rates: drill runners, $3.25; helper, $3; trammers, $2.75; miners, $3; muckers, $2.75; timbermen, $3; blacksmith, $4.

Ojuela Tunnel (18).   Section, 8.5 × 9 ft; length, 5 407 ft; no timbering except at portal; Nordberg-Butler "shoveloader"; aver monthly progress, 714 ft; driven in 1930. Cost per ft, including supervision: drilling and blasting, $3.99; loading, $1.55; haulage, $1.44; rock disposal, $0.32; ventilation, $0.36; general, $2.67; air drills, steel, etc, $3.48; power, $0.84; explosives, $3.77; other supplies, $2.94; construction equipment, not included above, $11.92; total, $33.28.

Sheep Creek Tunnel (21).   Section, 10 × 8 ft; length, 8 707 ft; untimbered; hand mucking; aver advance, 596 ft per mo; best month, 661 ft; driven between Dec 1, 1912 and Apl 1, 1914.   Wage rates per hr: machinemen, muckers and carmen, 50¢; shift bosses, 58¢; blacksmith, 60¢; tool sharpeners, 50¢; tool sharpener helpers, 40¢; blacksmith helpers, 35¢; compressor men, 40¢; electricians, 50¢; timekeepers, 45¢; carpenters, 60¢.   Cost per ft: wages, $14.72; bonus, $4.14; lighting, $0.28; explosives, $4.47; tool replacement, $1.35; lumber and misc supplies, $0.75; store expense and transport, $0.38; power and comp air, $2.53; loss on boarding house, $1.17; depreciation, mining tools, $1.29; total, $31.08.

Snake Creek Tunnel, Utah (22).   Oval section, about 13 ft high, 11 ft wide at widest part; lined with 15 in of reinforced concrete. Table 13 shows cost of driving and concreting 305 ft of tunnel through heavy, water-bearing ground in 1910–12.

Table 13.   Snake Creek Tunnel, Cost per Ft

Driving tunnel			Reinforced concrete lining		
Materials and supplies:			Materials and supplies:		
Timber.....................	$5.42		Cement.....................	$8.53	
Powder....................	.32		Steel......................	5.78	
Supplies...................	2.36		Gravel and sand..............	.10	$14.41
Tramming (feed)...........	.74		Labor:		
Power....................	1.78		Placing concrete and reinforce-		
Cement bulkheads..........	.09	$10.71	ment.....................	$5.89	
Labor *:			Gravel, sand and water.......	5.40	
Supervision................	$6.66		Fitting reinforcement.........	.70	
Timbering.................	13.65		Plastering ditch.............	.57	12.56
Mucking..................	9.42		Total concreting..............		$26.97
Tramming.................	3.85		Driving......................		50.66
Compressormen...........	3.31		Grand total cost...........		$77.63
Outside general.............	.85				
Aspen filling...............	.57				
Blacksmith................	1.13		* Wage rates: drill runners, $3.25; helpers, $3;		
Insurance.................	.51	39.95	miners, $3; muckers, $2.75; trammers, $2.75;		
Total driving............		$50.66	timbermen, $3.		

BIBLIOGRAPHY

1. Big Creek Tunnel, Cal. *E & M J*, Dec 6, 1924, p 885
2. Britannia Extension; U S Bureau of Mines, *Inf Circ* 6815
3. Merrett, E. J. Tunneling at B. C. Nickel Mines, *Trans* Can Inst Min & Met, Vol XL, 1937
4. Cascade, Washington, *Comp Air Mag*, March, Apl, May, 1927
5. Chicago Ave Rock Tunnel Methods Hercules Powder Co, reprint from *Explosives Engr*, p 42
6. Bunce, W. H. Tunnel Driving at Low Cost. *Min & Sci Pr*, July 11, 1908, p 60
7. Green, Arthur C. Power Loading on the Colorado River Aqueduct. *Trans* A I M & M E, Vol 126, 1937, p 162, 1936; *Expl Engr*, Nov 1937, p 338
8. Eureka Rock Tunnel Methods. Hercules Powder Co, reprint from *Expl Engr*, p 32

9. Florence Lake. Rock Tunnel Methods. Hercules Powder Co, reprint from *Expl Engr*, p 62
10. Allan, J. C   Twelve-Mile Bore to Drain Halkyn Lead District, North Wales. *E & M J*, June, 1934, p 253; *Comp Air Mag*, Sept 1937, p 5412
11. Hetch Hetchy Tunnel. Rock Tunnel Methods, p 51
12. Russell, W. C.   Driving a Long Adit, Bonanza, Col. *E & M J*, Feb 1, 1913, p 272; Simonds and Burns, *Trans* A I M E, Vol 45, p 147; *Eng & Cont*, Apl 2, 1913, pp 365–367
13. Laramie-Poudre Tunnel, *Eng Rec*, July 2, 1910, p 11; Jan 14, 1911.   Speed of Driving, Comparison of Laramie-Poudre with Recent European Tunnel Records, *Proc* Am Soc Civ Engrs, Vol 38, p 217, 707 (1912).   Brunton, D. W., Laramie Tunnel, *Trans* A I M E, Vol 43, p 99
14. Mammoth Tunnel.   *E & M J*, Dec 21, 1912; *Eng & Cont*, Jan 15, 1913, pp 58–60
15. Moffat Tunnel, Colo, *E & M J*, Nov 15, 1924, p 765.   *Comp Air Mag*, 1925, Feb, p 1133; March, p 1165; Apl, p 1205; May, p 1237; *Min & Met*, Nov 1925, p 554
16. New Haven, Conn.   Rock Tunnel Methods, p 44
17. Bain, H. F.   Driving the Newhouse, Roosevelt and Gunnison Tunnels, *E & M J*, Apl 19, 1902, p 552; *Min & Sci Pr*, Dec 4, 1909, p 743
18. Savage, John P.   Tunnel Driving Methods at the Ojuela Unit of the Compañia Minera de Peñoles, Ojuela, Durango, Mex. Bur of Mines, *Inf Circ* 6480, 1931, 8 pp
19. Hines, Pierre R.   Owyhee Tunnels.   A I M & M E, Contrib Paper No I, 1933
20. Roosevelt Tunnel, Cripple Creek, Colo.   *E & M J*, Nov 27, 1909, p 1061; Oct 2, 1915, p 545; *Eng News*, Jan 4, 1917; *Proc* Inst Civ Engrs (England), Vol 180, p 362
21. Driving Sheep Creek Tunnel.   *E & M J*, Oct 17, 1914, p 693
22. Snake Creek Tunnel, *Min & Sci Pr*, Jan 13, 1912, p 108.   McKay, G. R., Lining Tunnel in Swelling Rock.   *Eng Rec*, May 25, 1912, p 565
23. Lytel, J. L.   Strawberry Tunnel.   *Eng Rec*, Apl 22, 1911.   Zalinski, E. H.   Driving Strawberry Tunnel.   *E & M J*, June 10, 1911, p 1153
24. Rock Tunnel Methods, p 37
25. Palmer, L. A.   Utah Metals Company Tunnel, *E & M J*, Nov 16, 1918, p 857
26. Rock Tunnel Methods, p 69
27. Prelini, Charles.   Tunneling, 1902
28. Stauffer, D. M.   Modern Tunneling Practice.   Pub by *Eng News*, N Y, 1906
29. Lauchli, E.   Tunneling; Short and Long Tunnels of Small and Large Section, Driven Through Hard and Soft Materials.   McGraw-Hill Book Co, N Y 1915.
30. Rock Tunnel Methods; Drilling, Blasting, Excavation, Ventilation and Lining.   Reprinted from *Explosives Engr*, pub by Hercules Powder Co, Wilmington, Del
31. Richardson, J. B.   Driving a Mine Drainage Tunnel in Wales. *Comp Air Mag*, Sep 1937, pp 5412–5414
32. Carrigan, J. J.   Anaconda Method of Bunch Blasting, *Min & Met*, Aug 1936, p 384
33. Schaus, O. M.   Mining Methods and Costs at Montreal Mine, Wis.   Bur of Mines, *Inf Circ* 6369, 1930, 29 pp
34. McNaughton, C. H.   Mining Methods of Tennessee Copper Co, Bur of Mines, *Inf Circ* 6149, 1929, p 5
35. Corner, D. C.   Wachusett-Coldbrook Tunnel, Bur of Mines, *Inf Circ* 6399, 1931, 6 pp
36. Hewitt, E. A.   Mining Methods and Costs at Park-Utah Mine, Park City, Utah, Bur of Mines, *Inf Circ* 6290, 1930, 18 pp
37. Young, George J.   Driving the Claremont Tunnel   *E & M J*, May 25, 1929, p 832
38. D'Arcy, Richard L.   Mining Practice at United Verde Extension Mining Co, Jerome, Ariz   Bur of Mines, *Inf Circ* 6250, 1930, p 6

SECTION 7

SHAFT SINKING IN ROCK

BY

HOMER L. CARR, MINING ENGINEER

REVISED FOR THE SECOND AND THIRD EDITIONS BY

JOHN A. CHURCH, MINING ENGINEER

Note.—Numbers in parentheses in text refer to Bibliography at end of this section.

SHAFT SINKING IN ROCK

1. CROSS-SECTION OF SHAFTS

Rectangular section divides naturally into rectangular compartments, requires least excavation for given hoisting area, is adapted to framed timber or steel support and is most widely used in metal mining for sinking in rock. Inclined shafts are almost always rectangular, though if concrete-lined they may have arched roof. ROUNDED SECTION (circular, elliptical, oval) better resists lateral pressure, involves less air friction per unit

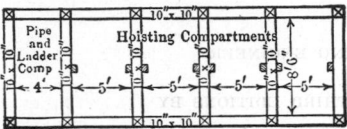

Fig 1.   Rectangular Shaft

of area, requires some form of lining other than framed support, and is adapted to rectangular hoisting compartments by using the surplus segmental areas for ventilating, pipe and ladder spaces. Circular section has max strength and for air shafts requires least excavation for a given air volume. Oval or elliptical section is stronger than rectangular and shares its space economy, but is difficult to keep plumb during sinking. In U S colliery shafts, straight sides and rounded ends (Fig 3) combine convenience of dividing into compartments with efficient air passages.

Compartments of a vert shaft may be side by side (rectangular or oval form), or in pairs across the shaft (all forms). Cage compts are best in line (Fig 1), to simplify trackage at stations, but large modern shafts often combine cage compts of full shaft width with paired skip compts (Fig 2; also applied to rectangular form, Fig 25). Inclined shafts usually have compts side by side, though "double-deck" slopes have been sunk; they are said to be cheaper than shafts of like capac but of 2-compt width.

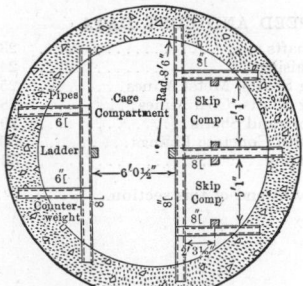

Fig 2.   Circular Shaft

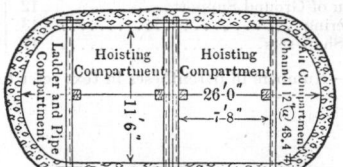

Fig 3.   Modified Elliptical Shaft

In heavy ground the oblong section (Fig 1) can be more effectively supported than the square; the long axes of compts should lie across the shaft, to reduce distance between dividers and give better support to wall plates. Oblong section favors a wide collar between cut holes, with economy of powder (Art 6). In steep strata the short axis of vert shaft should follow the strike, to minimize the unsupported rock span and so guard against movement along the dip during sinking. Forman shaft (Comstock lode) was L-shaped, with 3 compts in line and a service compt offset at one end; it invited unequal ground pressures, was costly to maintain and proved unsatisfactory.

2. SIZE OF SHAFTS

Sectional dimensions depend on: purpose, required capac (in terms of product, mine supplies and men transported, or vol of air passed); amount of water to be raised; hoisting method (cage or skip); character of ground; and unit costs of sinking and operating. Sinking cost per ft of depth is minimum for a section of approx 4 or 5 by 6 ft; smaller sections impose cramped positions on miners and preclude the most effective placing of drill holes; hence cost more.

Prospect shafts are often of minimum size, and may have but 1 compt, for both hoisting and ladderway.

Air shafts may have 1 or 2 compts, the second being a small ladderway with fireproof curtain wall. Single-compt shafts in solid rock are often circular and unlined, though smooth lining reduces air friction. Davis–Daly shaft (Butte) has an octagonal section, circumscribed about a circle of 6.5 ft diam inside a smooth timber lining; its coeff of air friction for 1 800 ft depth was 1.29×10^{-9} at 90 000 cu ft per min, compared to 8.8×10^{-9} for a rectangular unlined shaft of like depth and capac. Boring a shaft full-size by shot drill (Sec 9, Art 23) implies circular section and smooth walls, ideal for passing air; an air shaft of 5 ft diam was bored at Grass Valley, Calif, to 1 125-ft depth. That section is most economical, for which interest on first cost, plus cost of forcing air against the shaft resistance, is minimum.

Working shafts. For general service, design becomes more elaborate with depth and capacity. Shafts used solely for hoisting water often have no ladderway and operate automatically. Two-compartment shaft (one compartment for unbalanced hoisting, with pipe and ladderway) is suited only to shallow mines of small production, where low sinking cost means more than power economy at the hoist. Three-compt shaft, including pipe and ladderway, permits balanced hoisting, but in 24-hr duty 30–50% of the time is spent in handling men and supplies, hence is best suited to moderate production. Time is saved for hoisting ore by adding a service compt, which may be merely part of the man-way reserved for a small cage (to transport mine officials and minor supplies), or a distinct compt with cage, often counterweighted, for entire handling of men, timber and supplies (Fig 4). In wet shafts it is convenient in handling pumps; and in firm ground may be long enough to handle timber laid sidewise on trucks (Fig 25); it may serve also for further sinking. Four-compt shaft usually comprises 1 service and 2 (balanced) hoisting compts, with pipe and ladderway. In a five-compartment shaft, the service compt develops into 2 balanced cage-ways, with 40–60% spare time available for hoisting ore; there are also 2 regular hoisting compts (often skipways), and a pipe and ladderway. Sometimes ladderway and pipeway are separate compts. In this way, or by multiply-

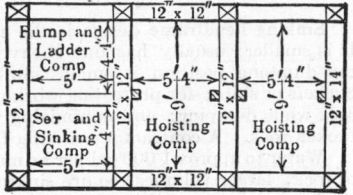

Fig 4. Shaft with Service or Sinking Compartment

ing hoisting compts, six- and seven-compt shafts are developed; on the Rand a 6-compt shaft with 2 main hoists and 1 auxiliary for miscellaneous service has ample capac for the working area conveniently reached from one shaft, but time lost in frequent inspection of a deep single-lift shaft may make a 7th compt advisable. The 6-compt Vlakfontein No 1 shaft is 43×14.5 ft, the 7-compt Wolhuter shaft 46×9 ft rock section.

Size of compartment for hoisting depends upon the horiz area of cage or skip, with clearances (Sec 12). In U S metal mines, for cage carrying 0.75 to 1-ton cars, cageways may be 4 by 5 to 5 by 7 ft inside timbers; in coal mines, with larger cars, 6 by 10 or 7.5 by 12 ft. In a service compt, the cage may be proportioned to size of loaded timber truck, not of ore car.

Rock section for framed steel or timber support is cut to allow 3 or 4 in outside of shaft sets, for blocking and wedging; a greater clearance involves needless expense. For monolithic concrete linings, shaft walls are dressed to allow a minimum thickness of concrete.

3. SINKING PLANT

Temporary sinking plant at a new site comprises: hoisting apparatus (windlass, whim or engine, with rope and buckets, skips or cages); tripod, derrick or headframe; provision for waste disposal; equipment for removing water (bailing tanks or sinking pumps); boiler plant or elec power substation; air compressor; and housing and accessories. At a working mine the existing power supply is available, and (for deepening a shaft in use) hoisting service also. Temporary plant should be designed not to interfere with installation of permanent plant; the sinking hoist is placed away (often on opposite side) from site of permanent engine, unless opposite a service compt for later use as a service hoist; the sinking headframe is designed to permit erection of permanent frame and placing of shaft collar while sinking. Use of permanent hoist when ready promotes sinking effic.

Windlass and whim (Sec 12) are often used in starting a shaft and in sinking through surface soil before the power hoist is installed. Amount of water influences depth to which their use is practicable; for depths over 20 to 30 ft their application is mainly to new work in remote regions, or where mechanical power is not available.

Sinking engines should be strongly built, of duplex type; many lives depend on their reliability. For depths to say 500 ft, and hoisting with ordinary bucket (Sec 12), a friction-gear engine of 12 to 30 rated hp is ample, depending on size of shaft. A single deep-flanged drum of 14-in diam, gear-driven by air or steam cyls 6.5 by 8 or 7 by 9-in, or by 25-hp elec motor, will handle 0.5-ton bucket at 300 ft per min. Greater depth requires a larger hoist, preferably of reversing type. A 5-ft drum geared to a 200-hp a c or 150-hp d c motor will hoist a 2-ton bucket or a cage with 1.5-ton car at 600 ft per min; suitable for a 12 by 16-ft rectangular or. 17-ft circular shaft to 1 000 ft depth. In deep Rand shafts, two drums 8-ft diam, 2-ft face, geared at 3 : 1 to 2 steam engines, cyls 16.5 by 33 in, hoist 2-ton skip or 3-ton bucket at 1 500 ft per min; deep circular shafts have been sunk with two 3-ton buckets in balance (6). For a 2 500-ft shaft at Kirkland Lake, Ont, a 72 by 36-in double-drum hoist was used, with a 150-hp a c motor, overall capac (single line), 7.5 ton at 1 000 ft per min; for cost, see below.

Tripod of timbers bolted together at top, where sheave is suspended, forms a simple sinking headframe. A second sheave may be fastened to bottom of tripod leg nearest the hoist, to lead rope off horizontally.

Stiff-leg derrick is often used for sinking through surface soil; it does not exert pressure on ground immediately surrounding shaft, nor interfere with placing timbering or masonry of permanent shaft collar. Donaldson (1) recommends for colliery shafts a derrick with 40-ft boom and 30-ft mast of 12 by 12-in timber. Where derrick is used for sinking to depths of 100 ft or more, provision should be made to prevent it from swinging when bucket is in the shaft.

Sinking headframe design is the same in principle as for permanent frame (Sec 12). It is smaller; usually has one sheave; and distance between sheave and crosshead in the dumping position is small. Sinking frame should embody features for dumping buckets or skips; for protecting workmen on surface and in the shaft from falling pieces of rock while dumping; and minimizing work of topmen, in dumping buckets and removing broken rock. A contractor's sinking frame is portable, easily erected and dismantled.

Water to approx 1 000 gal per hr may be hoisted, much of it filling voids in bucket-loads of rock; larger volumes require sinking pumps. With increase of water, cost of sinking rises, speed decreases. Ample capac of boiler plant is more important than steam economy, especially if there is danger of sudden inflows of water that may drown the pumps.

Cost of plant. For 500-ft depth, handling 30–40 gal per min, cost in 1910 was given as follows (1); present costs are roughly 50–75% higher:

Hoisting engine	$1 000	2 buckets	$150
Two 80-hp boilers and setting	1 800	Rope	150
Pipe and accessories	500	Buildings	500
150-hp feed-water heater	300	Dump cars and rails	300
14-in compressor	1 750	Electric lighting plant, 10 kw	750
3 drills and steel	1 000	2 sinking pumps	500
Shaft bar and clamps	100	Small tools and sundries	500
Derrick	400		
Headframe	500	Total	$10 200

Cost of erecting and dismantling plant, $1 000 to $2 000.

For 2 500-ft depth at Kirkland Lake, Ont, a shaft 17 by 9 ft rock sec required the following in 1931 (30); costs include installation:

Road to site, 0.5 mile	$ 2 297	Blacksmith shop	$ 3 360
Hoist (see above)	26 823	Office and equipment	1 420
Compressor, 1 000 cu ft per min	8 494	Misc surface plant	3 265
Hoist and compressor house	1 960	Drills and accessories	2 282
Headframe, A-type, wood, 60 ft high	2 938	Drill steel, 4.5 ton	1 095
Cars, 2 of 1.5 ton, and trackage	510	Buckets, 3 of 1.5 ton	300
Elec power substation	7 086	Sinking pumps, motors	3 137
Surface pumps, motors, pipe lines	1 269	Total	$66 236

4. SINKING ORGANIZATION

Two general systems of organizing underground work in sinking: (a) Machine men drill and blast the round, and lower-priced men handle the muck. The two crews may work together or on separate shifts; if together, good management is needed to prevent interference, and if on separate shifts, to maintain a rigid schedule. When well organized, this is usually the cheaper system. (b) Labor is used indiscriminately to drill and muck.

No interference is possible, and no rigid schedule necessary; each shift takes up the work as left by preceding shift. With 3 shifts, this system makes for speed, but at slightly greater cost per ft of shaft, because skilled labor is used for mucking. It is usual with hand drilling and hammer drills, both of which can be adapted to local variations in the rock and therefore tend toward a flexible drilling schedule. Shaft raising, and breaking ground by moiling present special problems.

Examples of system 1: No 5 TAMARACK shaft, Mich (18); 2 drilling and 2 mucking shifts per 24 hr with minimum interference; the former drilled and blasted a center cut and one side; muckers first cleared the remaining bench, and then the side already blasted; second drilling shift, beginning in middle of the mucking shift, then drilled and blasted the remaining bench, ready for second mucking shift. CENTRAL 3-compt shaft, North Star mine, Calif; day shift, 8 drillers, 1 mechanic, 1 tool nipper, 1 hoistman, drilled round of 40 holes for 5-ft advance, removed extension skip guides, and blasted; afternoon shift, 5 muckers, 2 timbermen, 1 hoistman, lowered extension guides to bottom, lowered the sinking bulkhead and placed next set of timbers, wedged guides in place and mucked about 25 skiploads of 2.5 ton per load; night shift, 5 muckers, 1 hoistman, mucked same amount; rock was mucked into loading pans and handled to skip by air hoists; any delay on day shift meant loss of 24 hr. McPHERSON shaft, Ducktown, Tenn, 8.5 by 19 ft; deepened while in regular daytime service, hence the sinking routine: day shift underground, 4 timbermen, 1 hoistman, on surface 1 hoistman, 1 laborer, kept timbering within 20 ft of bottom, took down loose ground and left bottom safe for mucking; afternoon shift underground, 4 muckers, 1 lander, 1 hoistman, loaded 393 cu ft rock with 8-cu ft bucket, hoisted by 25-hp elec hoist; night shift underground, 4 drillers, 1 hoistman, drilled and blasted half-round of 20–24 holes, total 140 ft; other half-round was drilled and blasted next night.

Examples of system 2: PABST H shaft, Ironwood, Mich; sunk with 12 hammer drills in slate and granite; a round of 50–53 holes was fired in 2 relays, as follows: drilling entire round, 6 hr; blasting first relay, 2 hr; blowing out smoke, 1.5 hr; mucking first relay, 8 hr; blasting second relay, 0.5 hr; blowing smoke, 1.5 hr; mucking second relay 6 hr. This cycle, with timbering and bailing, overlapped the shifts, and the shaft crews performed all functions as required. Advance per round 9 ft. COPPER MOUNTAIN, B C; 3-compt shaft; shift comprised 1 boss, 7 miners, 1 hoistman, 1 dumping bucket, 1 trammer; 18 holes per 6-ft round. Cycle as follows: cleaning and barring down, 1.2 hr; mucking, 11.6 hr; picking and cleaning bottom. 1.1 hr; setting up and drilling, 4.9 hr; charging and blasting, 0.5 hr; blowing smoke, 1 hr; placing shaft set, 4 hr; backfill behind sets, lagging and extending pipe lines, 2.5 hr; lost time, 2 hr; total, 28.8 hr. See also Table 1.

Special cases: DAVIS-DALY air shaft, Butte (11) (Art 2), was raised simultaneously from 9 levels; each raise required 2 miners and one man at a small hoist in the level. MIAMI No 5 shaft, Ariz, was chiefly in fissured conglomerate, which retained powder fumes and was therefore MOILED without blasting; 3 men using hammer drills with bull-bits broke enough rock for 4 muckers; monthly advance, 100 ft. VAN DYKE No 1 shaft (same district) traversed 760 ft of conglomerate, MOILED as above with hammer drills and bull-bits; a V-cut 12 in deep was made across the shaft, then enlarged to a depth of 18 in and width sufficient to receive bucket; 1 driller on each bench then loosened rock in "bites" 8 in wide, using the drill to pry toward the cut; 1 mucker followed each drill.

Delays are due to: removing drills, etc from shaft bottom preparatory to blasting; clearing bottom of smoke; clearing shaft walls and timbers of loose pieces of rock and securing bad ground after blasting; lowering timbers, which may be put in place during drilling.

Where pumps are used, the suction is removed from bottom and pump stopped before blasting; in very wet shafts, this may result in several feet of water accumulating at the time of blast, which acts as a cushion to protect timber and pumps, and absorbs much of the powder smoke. This water must be pumped or bailed before miners can go down.

With 2 shifts per day, much of the above work may be done between shifts; there is also time to make up for unusual delays. With 3 shifts, no such opportunity exists; speed is increased, but at slightly greater cost per ft than with 2 shifts.

Bonus system lends itself readily to shaft sinking, and in many cases has increased speed and reduced cost per ft. Bonus is paid (as a percentage of wages or fixed sum) per ft of advance in excess of a given standard; thus, at McPherson shaft (see above), men on drilling and mucking crews received $2 per ft of excess over a monthly aver advance of 2 ft per day.

Safety precautions (3). No other operations should be carried on, nor tools nor material raised or lowered to or from other points in shaft, while men are at work in bottom, unless they are protected from falling material by a well constructed TIMBER PENTICE extending over nearly the entire area of shaft, with closable openings for passage of buckets. In deepening a working shaft, an ample ROCK PENTICE should be left, or timber bulkhead built before sinking begins.

Trap doors, normally in closed position, should be provided at collar to cover shaft opening, with added set of trap doors when dump point is above collar, to prevent possibility of falling rock breaking through the collar doors. At Woodbury shaft every man in the shaft was provided with a felt hat stiffened with resin and shellac; these are hard and will resist severe blows from fragments of falling rock.

Buckets or skips should stop at least 15 ft above bottom, until rung down by one of sinkers. Ladderways should be provided to within such distance from bottom as will prevent injury to them from blasting; from end of these, chain, wire rope or wooden extension ladders, should go to bottom of shaft to assure safety of men against failure of hoisting engine, fire or inrush of water.

When elec hoists are used, elec lights in shaft bottom advise sinkers of interruptions in current In some districts the law provides that all blasting in shaft sinking shall be done by electricity.

Table 1. Month's Labor Record and Time Cycle, Creighton No 3 Shaft

	Max	Min	Aver		Max	Min	Aver
Advance, ft	164	112	136	Drill shifts	308.3	267.8	294.7
per drill shift	0.54	0.39	0.46	Rounds	21	16	18
per round	8.3	7.0	7.5				
Ft drilled	7 671	6 630	6 993	Percent of time			
per drill shift	25.3	21.7	23.7				
Powder, lb	12 800	6 150	9 719	Drilling	34.6	26.8	29.0
per ft advance	114.3	37.4	71.4	Blasting	13.1	5.2	7.1
Tons rock hoisted	6 200	3 565	4 358	Blowing smoke	5.8	2.2	3.1
per ft advance	37.8	28.5	31.9	Shoveling	57.5	45.4	50.7
per shoveler shift	5.7	3.4	4.1	Timbering	3.9	2.2	3.0
				Setting up drills	6.4	4.1	4.8
				Miscel delays	5.1	0.7	2.3
	Man-shifts				Man-shifts per ft		
Drillers	513.6	417.1	475.5		4.2	2.9	3.5
helpers	519.0	416.3	481.2		4.1	3.0	3.5
Shovelers	1080.8	983.5	1053.6		9.3	6.6	7.7
Surface trammers	467.0	338.0	373.0		3.2	2.4	2.7
Shift boses	111.0	95.0	103.7		1.0	0.6	0.8
Nippers	93.0	82.0	86.1		0.7	0.6	0.6
Hoistmen	93.0	79.0	88.5		0.8	0.6	0.6
Timbermen	112.7	76.9	98.1		1.0	0.5	0.7

Creighton No 3 shaft, Canadian Copper Co, 5-compt, rock section 35 by 9 ft, inclined 55°; sunk with 12 3 1/8-in piston drills on 6 columns, 2 men per drill; powder, 40% Forcite, with elec delay-action fuses; little timbering required; crew drilled, mucked and timbered as required.

5. DRILLING

Drills used in shaft sinking are: hand-churn, single or double hammer, and piston or hammer machine drills. HAND-CHURN DRILL in the hands of energetic workmen may be advantageous in soft rock. Hole is usually started with hammer and drill. More care must be taken in shaping the bit than for hammer drilling, and a low temper is desirable. HAND-HAMMER DRILLING is best applicable with low-priced unskilled labor. A large number of shallow holes, approx 3–4 ft, are drilled per round.

Advantages of hand work: (a) Saving in plant, especially in beginning small operations. (b) Flexibility in placing holes to take full advantage of peculiarities in the face, thus saving powder. (c) Use of lighter charges per hole than customary with machine-drilled holes, with less shattering of shaft walls, less injury to timbering and less over-breakage (beyond desired rock section); therefore greater ease in setting timber. (d) Effectiveness when blasting the bottom in benches, for which machine drilling is less advantageous. This system lightens the burden on each hole, thus saving powder, but interferes somewhat with mucking, especially when only one hoist is used. (e) Avoidance of delays incident to setting up drills and removing them before blasting.

Hammer drills (Sec 15), which work best in down holes, are almost always used for shaft sinking. Advantages: (a) flexibility in placing holes, almost equal to that of hand work; (b) effic with high-priced labor; (c) rapidity of set-up and transfer from one set-up to another, as compared with piston drills.

Piston drills (Sec 15) were long used in heavy shaft work, and are best suited to a fixed plan of locating holes, though here as elsewhere they have been largely superseded by the hammer drill.

Mounting. In rectangular shafts drills maybe on SHAFT BARS, placed across the longer axis of shaft. Tripods are sometimes used in U S colliery practice, but are less rigid and more cumbersome than bars, and for rectangular shafts have little to recommend them;

Table 2. Examples of Drills and Bits Used in Sinking

Mine	Type of drill	Bit length (ft) and gage (in)									
		ft	in	ft	in	ft	in	ft	in	ft	in
No 261, Caretta, W Va......	Rotating hand-hammer	....	1 3/8	....	1 1/4	....	1 1/8	....			
Pim shaft, S E Mo.	Jackhammer.	2	1 7/8	4	1 3/4	6	1 5/8	8	1 1/2	......	
Macassa, Ont *....	Water-Leyner	2 1/2	1 7/8	4 1/2	1 3/4	6 1/2	1 5/8	8 1/2	1 1/2	......	
"　　" †....	"　　"	2	1 7/8	3 1/2	1 13/16	5	1 3/4	6 1/2	1 11/16	8 1/2	1 5/8
Matahambre, Cuba	S-49 Ingersoll-Rand......	2	2	4	1 3/4	6	1 5/8	8	1 1/2	......	
Vlakfontein No. 1, Rand.........	Hand drifters.	3	2	5	1 7/8	6 1/2	1 3/4	7 1/2	1 5/8	8 1/2	1 1/2

* Down to 2 000-ft depth.　　† Beyond 2 000 ft, harder rock.

for circular or elliptical shafts they are preferable to bars, which are then harder to set up. In Europe sinking frames have been devised for circular shafts, on which drills are mounted so as to command entire shaft section. The frame with drills attached is raised to the surface before blasting (22).

Machine drill repairs. The practice of overhauling machine drills at the shop after each round has resulted in very low repair costs: at Pyne shaft (Birmingham, Ala, 1918–19), $1.14 per ft of shaft; at Pabst H shaft (Ironwood, Mich, 1917–19), $2.51 per machine-month, or 0.5¢ per ft of hole.

6. LOCATION AND DEPTH OF DRILL HOLES

For max effic of explosive (Sec 4, 5) drill holes are located so that most of them break to 2 free faces. One or more key or cut holes, drilled at an angle to the face, are blasted before the others, which are placed to utilize the additional face thus formed. In general, hand-drilled holes take advantage of rock cleavages, cracks and shape of face, rather than follow a rigid plan; the shaft bottom is then sometimes carried in benches stepped upward on either side of the cut holes. Machine-drilled holes are usually located by a definite plan, which makes for systematic work, though it may sacrifice some economy in powder. If a shaft-bar is used, symmetrical location enables several holes to be drilled from one set-up (Sec 6, Art 4).

"V," center or wedge cut is commonest. In simplest form it consists of pairs of holes inclined so as to bottom close together, and forming 2 rows parallel to shorter axis of shaft.

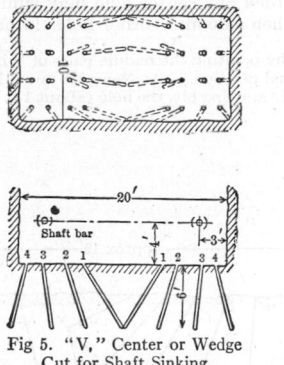

Fig 5. "V," Center or Wedge Cut for Shaft Sinking

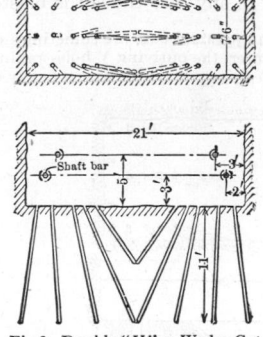

Fig 6. Double "V" or Wedge Cut

In Fig 5, rows 1 are cut holes and are blasted first; rows 2, 3 and 4 are then fired in order. Fig 6 shows a double V-cut for greater depth; in hard ground this may be supplemented by a few shallow vert holes along the center-line of the V; in soft ground one hole of each pair may be drilled only to half depth. The cut is usually midway between shaft ends, though in large shafts some engineers place it near one end and fire the remaining holes in order, retreating toward the other end. This tends to throw the muck toward the cut and facilitates clearing the other end for the drills, which can resume work while the cut end is being mucked. Local conditions, as rock cleavages, reentrant angles, and position of hoisting compartment, sometimes influence position of cut. Dynamite is most effective when pairs of cut holes meet at the bottom and are fired simultaneously. The angle of the V should be as great as good results permit.

Pyramid cut comprises a ring of holes inclined so as to bottom close together and blast out a sump in center of shaft. It is typical of circular shafts (Fig 7), though applied also to rectangular shafts of approx equal axes (Fig 8; numbers show order of firing). Davis-

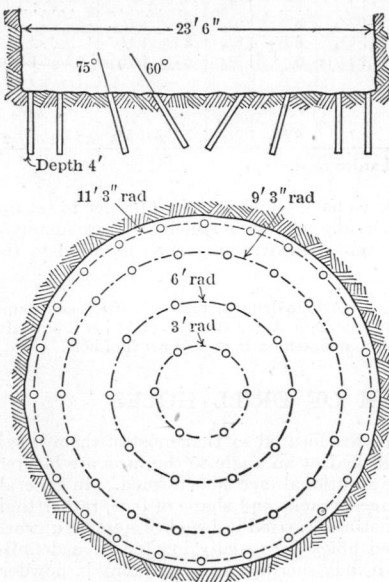

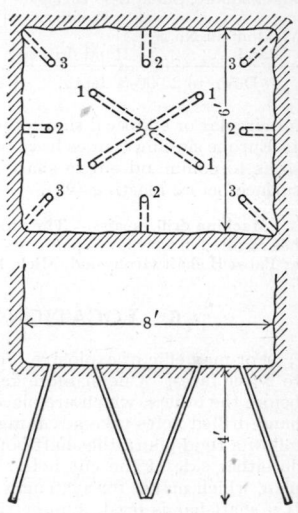

Fig 7.   Pyramid Cut for Circular Shaft
(Randfontein)

Fig 8.   Pyramid Cut for
Rectangular Shaft

Daly octagonal shaft (Art 2) was raised with a 4-hole pyramid cut at center and 8 corner holes per round. In small shafts and favorable rock one center hole may suffice to blast the sump. In any case the cut is blasted first, then side and corner holes in order.

Wedge and pyramid cuts are sometimes combined by pointing the middle pairs of V holes toward a common center, the outlying V holes taking their usual position. At Newport mine, Mich, a 4-in hole was drilled at shaft center with a heavy drill, 4.75-in starting bit, the hole (about 1 ft deeper than

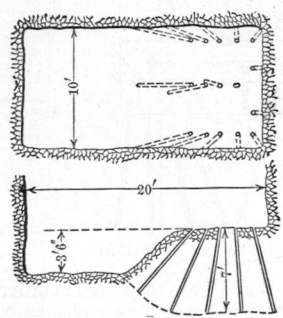

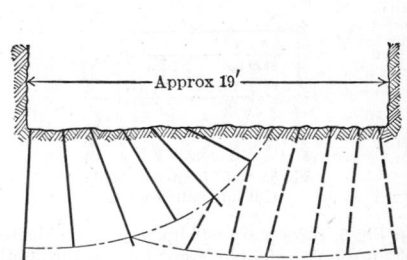

Fig 9.   Bench or Stope Cut

Fig 10.   Bench Cut at McPherson Shaft

the regular round) being left uncharged, to provide a free break for 8 surrounding pyramid-cut holes, 4 on 9-in radius (instantaneous firing) and 4 alternately spaced on 18-in radius (first delay).

Bench or stope cut is sometimes used in tight ground (Fig 9). The cut alternates from side to side of shaft, always leaving 2 more or less free faces and thus saving powder. Broken rock is thrown, not upward as with wedge and pyramid cuts, but toward opposite end of shaft, with less risk of damage to timber and pumps. The bottom is always lower at one end or the other, facilitating mucking and drainage. A modification, in McPherson shaft, Tenn, is shown in Fig 10; the holes in solid lines were drilled and blasted first, then those shown dotted.

Bottom cut, like that for tunnel work (Sec 6, Art 5), is sometimes useful for flat, inclined shafts (Fig 11).

Depth of hole depends on type of drill, character of rock and shape and size of shaft. As holes are deepened, the width of V cut ("collar") is increased, reducing the number of side holes and total footage per round; but to secure sufficient diam at bottom, holes 10 or 12 ft or more in depth require very heavy drill steel, in lengths inconvenient to handle in the bucket. Usual depth of HAND-DRILLED holes is 2–5 ft. With PISTON DRILLS, depth should be the max consistent with powder economy, to reduce percentage of time lost in setting up, and in hoisting and lowering drills between rounds. For each case this max should be determined by test; roughly, depth of hole may be assumed at one-half, in soft rock three-fourths the width of shaft. Practice of drilling deep holes and blasting them 2 or even 3 times is wasteful of powder unless, before charging, they are partly filled with sand or other easily removable material. With HAMMER DRILLS, ease of set-up makes the factor of lost time less important, but the steel is smaller than that of reciprocating drills, and holes

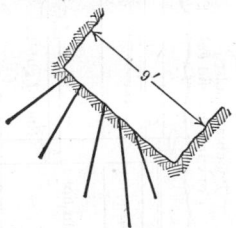

Fig 11. Bottom Cut for Inclined Shaft

more quickly taper to a diam too small to hold enough powder for good results; max depth of hole then depends on ability of steel to keep its gage.

At Woodbury shaft, Mich, 10-ft holes were possible in soft slates, but in granites and quartzites, with 2¼-in starting bit, 8 ft was maximum. In very hard rock at Gordon shaft, Tenn, piston machines drilled 5 to 7-ft holes and made approx 5 ft advance per round; the hammer type drilled 2 to 4-ft holes with approx 2 ft advance per round, but greater sinking speed.

7. EXPLOSIVES AND BLASTING

Explosives (Sec 4). In American practice, 40% gelatin dynamite is generally used for sinking where holes are drilled by hand or reciprocating drills. For shallow rounds in easy ground, 30% may serve; for aver rounds in difficult ground, 50 or 60%; for deep rounds, 60 or 80% in cut holes (used at Morenci to break an 8-ft round in easy ground), in some districts, 2 sticks of 60% are placed on bottom of hole, remainder 40%; sometimes 2 or more sticks of "100% gelatin" are placed at the bottom. On the Rand, 60–74% gelignite has been used in recent sinkings. Proper amount and strength of charge should be found by trial. Where timbering must be carried close to the bottom, the higher strengths may damage timber; a factor in proportioning charge and depth of round.

Table 3. Consumption of Explosive in Shaft Sinking. (Examples from practice)

Rock sec, ft	Dip	Ground	Gelatin		Rock sec, ft	Dip	Ground	Gelatin	
			%	Lb per cu yd*				%	Lb per cu yd*
9 × 7	60°	hard	40	10.0	8 × 21	vert	medium	40	5.3
6 × 12	73°	medium	40	6.2	9 × 17	"	varied	40–60	5.2
9 × 17	70°	soft	40	5.3	8 × 21 2/3	"	medium	50	5.0
10 × 20	25°	hard	40	4.0	7 1/6 × 16	"	hard	40, 60	4.9
13 1/2 × 14	vert	{ hard, } { fract'd }	50	6.9	7 × 17	"	firm, hard	60	4.5
					7 3/4 × 16 1/2	"	hard	40, 60	3.8
7 2/3 × 19 1/3	"	tough	50	6.7	8 1/2 × 19	"	swelling	35	3.5
8 × 17	"	medium	40	5.5	17 × 24	"	.....	40, 50	3.3
7 × 17	"	sheared	40	5.5	8 1/2 × 28	"	slabby	40	2.6
8 × 16 1/2	"	firm	40	5.3					

* Solid measure.

Table 3 indicates that consumption of explosive per cu yd tends to decrease with increasing size of shaft section, but depends chiefly on breaking characteristics of the rock.

Blasting may be done with ordinary cap and fuse, elec fuse igniters or elec caps, preferably of the delay-action type (Sec 4, Art 10). In some districts the law requires elec firing in sinking. Firing a round of holes in proper order lightens the burden on all except the cut holes and lessens danger of injury to timbering. For ORDINARY FUSE, some engineers advise 2 equal lengths of fuse and 2 detonators in each hole. Fuse wound around 2 properly placed nails or hooks and cut at one nail, with caps crimped on the severed ends, will show by the mark of the other nail where it should be cut and spit at blasting time.

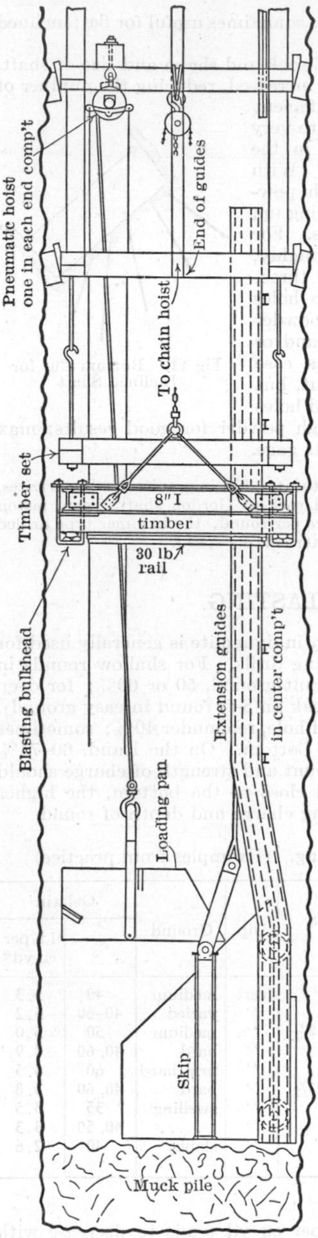

If shot-firers begin spitting (lighting fuse) at ends of the shaft, and work toward the middle, they finish near the bucket and avoid danger of stepping on lighted fuse and putting it out. This method involves cutting fuse to different lengths, because the cut holes are then the last to be spit and should be the first to explode. When spitting begins at the cut, fuses of uniform length insure proper order of firing; and if for any reason the entire round is not spit, at least the cut and neighboring holes will explode. A time-keeper fuse, cut to burn out about 2 min before the first explosion is due, serves as a warning. In wet shafts on the Rand, fuse is spit by torch, or "cheesa stick," made by splitting blasting gelatin, wrapping it around a pine stick 18 in long and covering with clay. The resulting fumes are absorbed by the water without bad effect.

8. MUCKING

Mucking, or loading broken rock into hoisting conveyance, occupies 40–60% of sinking time. Methods: (1) hand shoveling direct into bucket or skip, or (2) into loading pans, dumped into bucket or skip by mechanical means; (3) mechanical loading in large shafts with scraper or (rarely) caterpillar shovel.

Hand shoveling loads 9–13 cu ft per man-hr (measured in place), depending on character of muck, conditions at shaft bottom and promptness of hoisting service. Rock in 20 to 200-lb pieces can be loaded by hand faster than an equal wt of fines can be shoveled. Shoveling in a shaft bottom is difficult, though when the 2 ends are blasted alternately, it is facilitated by laying steel plates to receive the muck in the end not blasted. Empty bucket should always be ready at bottom, to avoid delays. In large shafts, where more shovelers are employed than can crowd around the bucket or skip, 2 compartments may be used for hoisting.

For VERTICAL SHAFTS, a bucket or skip may be suspended from bottom of sinking cage, which has long guide shoes to permit lowering below the last set of timber. In other cases, sinking crossheads (Sec 12) are used to prevent the bucket from swinging. Double cross-head (Marquette Range) comprises (a) upper head clamped to hoisting rope, (b) lower head loose on rope and resting on bucket; the latter is kept from rotating by 2 additional ropes extending from upper head through the lower head to the bail. Blocks at lower end of guides stop the lower head and release the catches that attach it to the bucket, which, with the upper head, then continues down until bucket is on bottom (6). Skips loaded by hand are made low at the back, to reduce lift of shovel. Guide shoes are either long enough to engage lower ends of guides when skip is on bottom, or extension guides are provided, which may reach 45-ft length and are removed when blasting (Fig 12 shows special form at North Star mine, Calif, for offsetting skip to one side of bottom). For INCLINED SHAFTS, buckets sliding on skids, or sus-

Fig 12. Use of Loading Pan for Mucking (AIME, *Tech Pub* No 324)

pended from a carriage running on a cableway, and skips running on regular track, are in general use. Temporary track, capable of being raised on blasting, reaches from end of timbering to shaft bottom.

Loading pans (Fig 12) are shallow and open at one end or side to facilitate filling by shovel. For dumping into skip, they are lifted by 7 to 10-hp air hoist mounted on timbering above or on sinking stage. They are loaded while skip is being hoisted and lowered, and save time; at the Colorada shaft, Cananea, they increased sinking speed 20%.

Scraper (Fig 13) is suited to long, narrow shaft section. At Champion mine, Mich, it first scraped the muck to the end opposite loading end; a slide was then clamped to a horiz bar across the shaft, the hinged apron of slide resting on the bucket; scraper was then reversed for loading, after which the hinged apron was turned back, scraper rope pulled aside and bucket hoisted. Two full

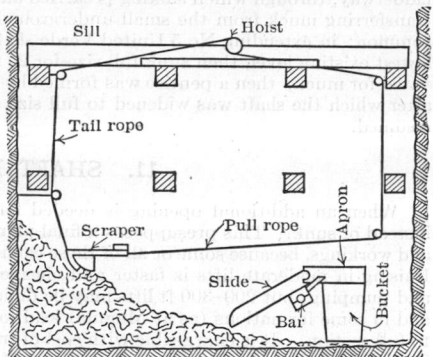

Fig 13.   Scraper in Shaft Bottom, Champion Mine, Mich

scraper loads filled a 0.5-ton bucket in 20 sec; round trip of bucket, 2.5 min.   In one case a small Butler shovel was used to muck the shaft bottom.

9.   VENTILATION (See also Sec 14)

While sinking, enough air must be delivered at shaft bottom to remove powder smoke and rock dust, and enable sinkers to work in reasonably pure atmosphere.

Natural ventilation, set up automatically, may serve to great depths; in some cases, mechanical ventilation must be adopted at the outset.   Some of the factors governing natural ventilation are: character and temp of surface atmos, temp of strata penetrated, and amount of water falling in shaft.   Natural ventilation may be aided in several ways. If a small portion of shaft area is partitioned off by a brattice, and this compartment carried up into the headframe by a chimney, difference of air head will cause circulation. Where steam sinking pumps are used, the warmth usually suffices to establish a rising current; a steam jet directed upward from shaft bottom will accomplish same result.

It often happens that, even with no brattice, the space around the steam pipes is upcast, while the opposite side is downcast.

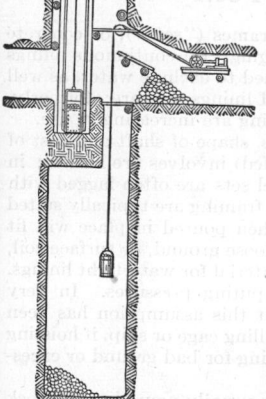

Fan or blower on surface, connected to a wooden or sheet-iron pipe 12–18 in diam, reaching close to shaft bottom, may be used to force down fresh or exhaust foul air.   A fan may be used to exhaust blasting fumes promptly; it is then reversed to supply fresh air.   If the pipe or chimney be of wood, the boards should be matched and painted to reduce leakage.

Where compressed-air drills are used, the exhaust generally removes dust and prevents vitiation of air.   Powder smoke is readily blown out by opening the air valve at the bottom after blasting.   Spraying water down the shaft facilitates clearing powder smoke.

10.   SINKING IN A WORKING SHAFT

Working shafts are frequently deepened while regular mining operations are being carried on above.   Sinkers should be protected from falling objects by a rock pentice (Fig 14); or by a heavy timber bulkhead, sometimes loaded with 10 or 15 ft of waste rock.

Fig 14.   Sinking Under Rock Pentice

There are two general methods;   (a) rock is hoisted direct to surface through special sinking compartment; (b) rock is hoisted to the lowermost working level, by a small elec or compressed-air hoist, whence it is raised to surface by regular hoisting plant.   The pentice may be left across entire shaft area, in which case a short incline must be sunk

I—8

from the level above before the shaft is widened to full section. If the pentice is left across bottom of hoisting compartments only, a small opening may be cut in line with the ladderway, through which sinking is carried on (Fig 14). In large shafts, special means of transferring muck from the small underground sinking hoist to main hoisting system are common: in extending No 5 United Verde shaft, the shaft was first bulkheaded above the lowest existing level, then sunk full size for 20 ft, and 2 skip pockets of 70-ton capac excavated for muck; then a pentice was formed by sinking only the manway for the next 30 ft, after which the shaft was widened to full size, the bulkhead removed and regular sinking resumed.

11. SHAFT RAISING

When an additional opening is needed for existing workings, a shaft may be raised instead of sunk. This presupposes a final plan of underground connections between shaft and workings, because some or all of these connections must be driven before raising begins. Raising in moderate lifts is faster and cheaper than sinking, because it avoids mucking and pumping; but 200–300 ft lifts may be difficult and costly, involve ventilation troubles, and in some formations (as at Magma) lead to serious overbreak when raises are enlarged to full section. It is chargeable with cost of tramming muck to the hoist (unless the muck is used for filling), but profits by lower cost of hoisting with permanent plant instead of a small uneconomical sinking hoist.

Methods. For speed, raising may proceed from several levels simultaneously. The raise may be made of the smallest section consistent with effic, and enlarged to full shaft section after holing through. If raising is done in sections, errors of alinement can be corrected while enlarging. Temporary timbering in the pilot raise may be partly salvaged. Shafts are also raised at full section, especially if made in only one lift.

Shaft No 2, Harold Mine, Minn, was raised 90 ft at full rock section of 18.5 by 8.5 ft, using the shrinkage system (as in stoping) for support, except in 2 cribbed manways at shaft corners. Normal cycle: (a) wedge-cut in center and pyramid-cut over each manway; (b) manways cribbed to within 3 or 4 ft of back and wedge-cut blasted; (c) remainder of 1 end drilled, its manway cribbed close to back and covered with rails and lagging, and the entire end blasted; (e) manway cleared for access and other end drilled and blasted. Only enough muck was removed to provide working space until, when excavation was complete, it was slowly drawn down to keep pace with permanent timbering (17).

For its Pilares shaft, Moctezuma Copper Co drifted to line of shaft at the 1 600, 1 700 and 1 800 levels and drove 4 by 7-ft pilot raises on shaft center-line from the 1 600 and 1 800, the former holing through to the sump on the 1 400, 167 ft above. In each raise, shrinkage stoping to full section was started 20 ft above the bottom and carried up the full lift; the shaft was then timbered downward as in preceding example.

12. DESIGN OF GROUND SUPPORT

Types of support: (a) timber, steel or pre-cast concrete frames ("sets"), or concrete rings poured in place, spaced at intervals with or without lagging; (b) continuous linings of brick, stone, C-I tubbing or concrete poured in place designed to exclude water, as well as to resist ground pressure. In the U S, brick, stone and C-I linings are rare; formerly, timbering was almost universal but concreting and steel framing are increasing in use.

Choice of support depends on ground and water conditions, shape of shaft and cost of materials. Timbering is increasingly costly and (unless proofed) involves fire hazard; in swelling ground it fails slowly and with ample warning. Steel sets are often lagged with wood, thus incurring some fire hazard. Both timber and steel framing are typically suited to rectangular sections. Concrete avoids fire hazard and when poured in place will fit any section; used chiefly in shafts of long, life, except where loose ground, or surface soil, requires close lining in any case. In the U S, it is the usual material for watertight linings.

Design for strength. There are no exact rules for computing pressures. In very wet ground some engineers assume full hydrostatic head, but this assumption has been criticized as too severe. Lining must withstand impact of a falling cage or skip, if hoisting rope breaks; otherwise it is proportioned by experience, allowing for bad ground or excessive water, which may increase the pressure.

Anchorage to shaft walls. Continuous concrete linings are usually poured to the rock at many or all points, keying into the shaft walls. Tubbing, masonry linings, and all framed support require special anchorage, by means of wedging cribs or bearer sets, resting on hitches in the shaft walls at intervals of say 30–100 ft.

Shaft collar is raised far enough above surrounding surface to exclude surface drainage and facilitate disposal of waste rock; on level ground it may be 15–20 ft high, inclosed by waste fill. Incidentally, it often provides foundations for the headframe. When the collar is in solid rock, framed support begins with a COLLAR SET, of heavy members extended on firm ground beyond the excavation; this is virtually the first bearer set, from which regular sets are hung by HANGING BOLTS, until the next bearer is placed below. When the collar is raised above the surface, the collar set may rest at ground level on timbers or concrete piers, and carry the superstructure; or it may be supported on posts and bracing until waste has been dumped beneath it.

In traversing soft overburden the shaft may be cribbed (Art 13), or preferably concrete-lined. Concrete lining should be sealed in bedrock to exclude water, and timbering may be built up inside the lining or connected to guide bolts embedded in the concrete.

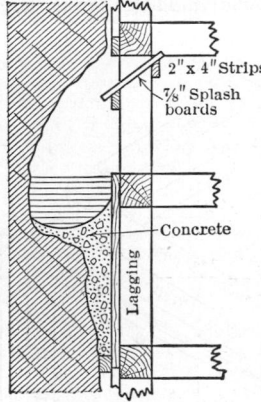

In shallow overburden, a conical pit, dug to bedrock, facilitates building the collar; it is refilled when collar is in place.

Water rings are placed at intervals in vert shafts to intercept falling water, which is then led to a sump and pumped to surface. A groove is cut around the shaft to a depth of 1.5 or 2 ft, on the edge of which a dam is made of timber embedded in clay or concrete, or of clay or concrete alone, to form a channel behind which water is collected and led thence to a sump. In timbered shafts,

Fig 15. Water Ring for Timbered Shaft

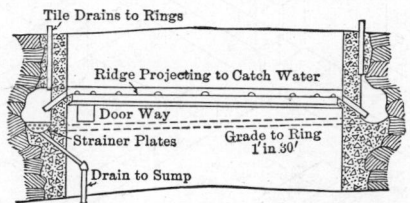

Fig 16. Water Ring for Concrete-lined Shaft
(*Mines & Min*)

water is guided into the ring by short planks placed in an inclined position to intercept its fall (Fig 15). In concrete-lined shafts (Fig 16), the rings are placed behind the lining, water being led to them by lines of tile pipe, placed vertically in or behind the concrete; a small projection on inside of lining serves to catch the water falling in shaft. The ring should have sufficient grade to the outlet pipe.

Grouting behind a continuous lining is often effective in checking inflow of water. For grouting in advance of sinking, see Bib 8.

13. TIMBERING

Cribbing consists of timber, round, hewn on 2 sides or squared, built crib-fashion against the shaft walls. In large shafts it is used chiefly in traversing soft overburden, though in heavy ground it is sometimes carried to depth. Small shafts are often cribbed throughout.

In simplest form cribbing is of undressed timber, cut to length but not framed, held in place skin to skin by vert strips nailed inside the crib corners; or plank is set edge to edge, with ends halved into each other, or cut square and held by nailed strips. In CLOSE CRIBBING, timbers, skin to skin, are framed as in Fig 17, 18, 19, 20, where A = half the thickness of piece; that is, $A = 2B$. In OPEN CRIBBING, A exceeds half the thickness, and some space is left between crib timbers (Fig 19); that is, A is greater than $2B$.

If ground permits, several feet of cribbing are placed at a time, each section being built up from a set wedged in place at bottom; otherwise, sets are placed singly as sinking proceeds.

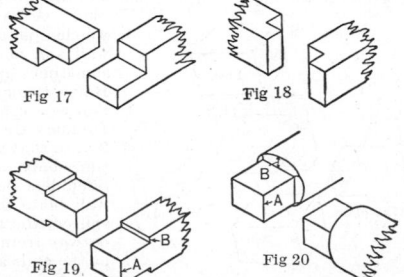

Fig 17, 18, 19, 20. Cribbing Joints

Vertical-shaft sets. Each set (Fig 21) comprises 2 WALL PLATES and 2 END PLATES, respectively on the longer and shorter sides of shaft section, and 4 corner posts or

STUDDLES, to preserve spacing and support the sets. All members are usually of same timber size. Compartments are separated by DIVIDERS (buntons), usually of same depth as plates, but narrower. Posts are also generally placed opposite the ends of each divider, of same size as the divider, or smaller.

Guides are bolted to end plates and dividers, into which guide backing posts are sometimes framed (16) just behind the guides, to stiffen and support them; or guide girts (16) may be framed into studdles between sets, like extra end plates or dividers. Sometimes space is provided for a 2 or 3-in filler between guide and end plate or divider; then, if the set is distorted by ground pressure, alinement of guides can be preserved by varying the thickness of filler.

For shaft sets, sawed timber is preferable to round, in permitting more accurate framing of joints. Timber sizes: 6 by 6-in for small shafts in firm ground; to 14 by 14-in for large

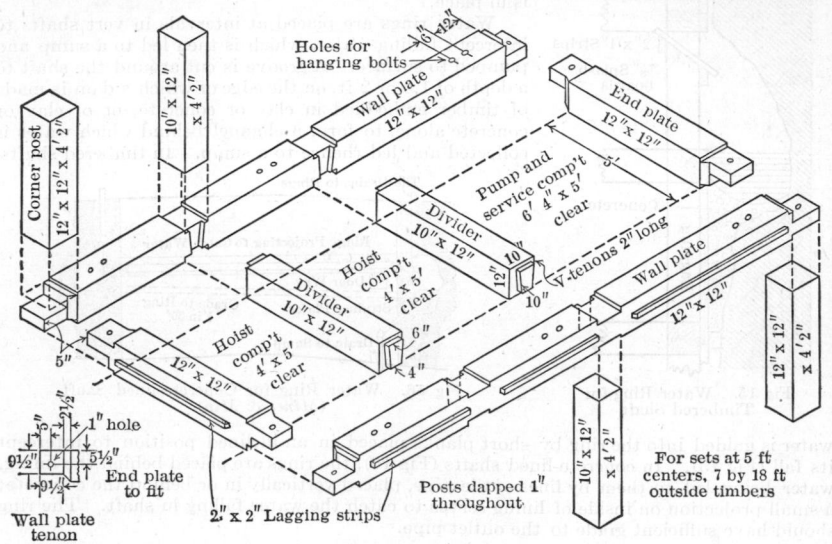

Fig 21. Shaft Set

shafts in heavy ground; under aver conditions, 10 by 10-in plates are common. Vert spacing of sets varies with character of ground, often in the same shaft; 6–7 ft clear is max for solid rock; 4–6 ft is usual; in bad ground, intervals are smaller.

Details. For plates, TENONS (horns) are 0.5 the thickness of piece. Wall plates are always mortised in the upper half, end plates in the lower; whence the former carry the latter when assem-

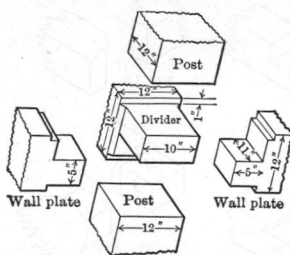

Fig 22. Framing for Spliced Wall Plate (16)

bled. A 1-in hole may be bored in center of tenon, with a wooden pin to hold plates together during assembly. To bring wall and end plates in contact for their full depth, they are sometimes given a 45° bevel at base of each tenon (Fig 21); at Butte, tenons are shortened by 0.25–0.5 in, to assure full contact between beveled surfaces when sets are wedged in place. Dividers are usually framed with a V-tenon at each end (Fig 21), so that the wt of the piece tends to hold it in place. Sometimes only one side of tenon is sloped, the other side being vert. Shoulders on either side of tenon provide bearing against the wall plate for its full depth. If a long wall plate must be spliced, the splice is best made at the divider separating hoisting compartment (Fig 22). Posts are squared at the ends and brought to a true bearing on the plates. Plates and dividers are usually gained to receive ends of posts, which thus resist side press. If gains are omitted, posts are blocked and wedged.

Framing must be accurate, to avoid cutting and trimming underground. Accuracy is secured by using a timber-framing machine or carefully made template; or failing these, by first drawing a center line lengthwise on the best of the 4 faces of a timber and referring all framing measurements to this line as a base. If no face is true, one may be trued for the purpose. The side on which base line is drawn should face inward after assembly.

Hanging bolts (Fig 23) are chiefly to facilitate assembly. A bolt consists of 2 duplicate parts; threaded ends are passed through the respective wall plates and secured by washers and nuts; the other ends are hooked to each other. For adjustment, the bolts are 3–4 in longer than required by the exact spacing of sets when in final position. Diam of bolts varies from 0.75 to 1.25 or 1 3/8 in. Large C-I washers prevent nuts from cutting into timber; 2 or 3 bolts per wall plate are required, depending on length of plate.

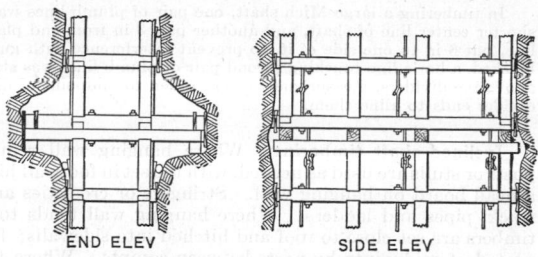

END ELEV   SIDE ELEV

Fig 23. Bearing Timbers (16)

Assembly. Shaft bottom is carried as far as possible in advance of timbering, to minimize injury to timbers by blasting and permit timber and drill crews (if separate) to work simultaneously, under precautions for safety of the men below.

Details. Temporary staging at proper height is placed across shaft section, hung from timbering above, or laid on special stulls; or blasting set (see below), if decked; in large work a sinking stage or platform (with opening for bucket) may hang constantly above the bottom, and serves for placing sets. The right- or left-hand wall plate is lowered into horiz position on the staging, usually by timber clevis or rope sling. Hanging bolts having been put in both the new plate and the corresponding plate in set above, the hooks are engaged. When both wall plates are in position, the end plates are put in, their tenons resting on tenons of wall plates (temporary wooden pins sometimes used). Dividers and posts are then placed, and hanging bolts screwed up until the new set is in accurate position. The set is blocked and wedged against the rock walls until proper alinement is secured. Wedging is done at corners and opposite ends of dividers.

In bad ground timbering is carried close to bottom, timbermen sometimes standing on the muck pile. If there is no room for swinging a long wall plate into horiz position under sets already placed, the plate is spliced, or dividers are temporarily omitted from the last few sets; but since the tenon of a divider extends under the post above, the divider can be placed subsequently only by cutting a recess in the post just above its base. This recess is later filled by a block spiked in place.

Bearing sets, or bearers (Fig 23), placed at intervals of 50–100 ft of depth, furnish anchorage for the entire shaft structure and carry its wt if the blocking and wedging of regular sets become loose. Normally, wedging should hold the regular sets as solid as bearers, but alternate wet and dry periods may loosen them. Bearers may be regular sets, with end plates extended and wedged into hitches in the shaft walls; or (preferably) extra timbers, of same breadth as plates but deeper as desired, hitched into the walls directly beneath certain timbers (usually end plates) of regular sets, which rest on them. In the latter case, plates are framed as usual, but the gain or dap on lower face of wall plate, instead of receiving top of post, now fits a similar gain in the bearer, which is also gained on its lower face to receive top of post. With heavy timbering, or in ground where it is difficult to cut a reliable hitch, extra bearers may be placed under the dividers. Sometimes bearer and end plate or divider are bolted together. Bearers may possibly carry the full wt of timber to the next bearing set above, and if necessary are built 2 and even 3 timbers deep. Instead of individual hitches, a continuous hitch may be cut all along the shaft wall to carry a sill (Fig 23), on which the bearers are seated and wedged.

Lagging is necessary except in solid rock free from tendency to spall off. Materials: round poles placed skin to skin, saw-mill slabs, or ordinary 2-in plank; galvanized corrugated steel and buckled plates have been tried.

Where ground permits, lagging is cut to lengths spanning 2 or more sets, and put behind wall and end plates after several sets have been placed. If each set must be lagged as soon as placed, 2 by 2-in LAGGING STRIPS (Fig 21) are nailed to outer faces of plates, and lagging in single lengths is placed with ends abutting on these strips. Space between lagging and shaft walls is packed with filling to prevents walls from "starting." CLEATS may be spiked to upper and lower faces of plates, and lagging placed behind these cleats, standing between instead of behind the sets. Cleats facilitate renewal of lagging, but are structurally weak and unfit for heavy ground.

Vertical-shaft alinement of timbering. Shaft sets are first alined roughly with a straight-edge placed on inside faces of 2 sets above; final alinement is by at least 2 plumb lines, set by permanent reference points in timbering above. Vert marks are made in selected places on timbers by saw or scratch awl, and, by carpenter's square and wedging, the marks are brought into same vert plane as the plumb line. Blocks are sometimes used as gages where lines are hung near shaft corners.

In timbering a large Mich shaft, one pair of plumb lines was hung 3 in from wall plates on the shorter center line of shaft, and another pair 3 in from end plates on a line parallel to long center line, but 6 in to one side of it, to prevent interference with guides. After the 4 corners had been blocked, a horiz line touching second pair of plumb lines was stretched lengthwise of shaft and just above the dividers, measurements were taken to midpoint of dividers, and wedges driven opposite divider ends to aline them.

Inclined-shaft timbering. Where hanging wall requires no special support, single posts or stulls are used as needed, with toe set in footwall hitch and the head wedged against a head board on hanging wall. Stringers or cross ties are always added to support skip track, pipes and ladders. Where hanging wall tends to spall, but sides are firm, horiz timbers are set close to roof and hitched into sidewalls; for long spans, they may be supported at midpoints by posts between compts. Where both hanging wall and sides are weak, or both require lagging, 3-piece tunnel sets are used (Sec 6). Compartments are formed by placing additional posts as required. Where footwall is bad, the 4-piece tunnel set is sometimes used.

In heavy ground, inclined shafts are timbered like vert shafts, with sets placed approx normal to dip of shaft. If end plates are inclined more steeply than the true normal, move-

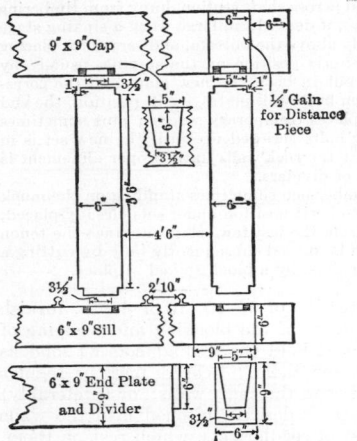

ment of hanging wall along the dip wedges them more tightly in place; in general (9), head of plate may be raised above normal position $1/8-1/4$ in (30°–45° dips), or $1/4-3/8$ in (50°–75° dips), per ft of plate length. For dips greater than 70°–75°, framing differs from that of vert-shaft sets. Cap and sill (corresponding to wall plates) usually extend beyond end plates, which may be framed with V-tenons (Fig 24) or, if studdles are used, with square tenons; end plates are thus held in position during blocking and wedging. For strength, cap is often of deeper section than sill. Cap, sill and end plates may be gained or mortised to receive square ends or tenons of studdles, which in a flat shaft are lightly loaded and small. A collar set and bearers are used, the latter generally spaced at longer intervals than in vert shafts. Hanging bolts are used only for steep dips.

Inclined-shaft alinement of timbering. Azimuth and dip of an existing shaft are found by setting a transit at shaft collar and sighting a target at the bottom (or some intermediate) set, with target and telescope offset at fixed distances

Fig 24. Inclined-shaft Timbering
(after Truscott)

from sill and end plate. New timbering is often alined with spirit level, carpenter's square, plumb line and straight edge, checked every few days by transit.

In each cap and sill, before assembly, a tack is driven at the same relative point; then, tacks on the new sill, the sill last preceding, and a third several sets above, are alined with a stretched string, the new sill being wedged to alinement and leveled with spirit level. For the cap a second string is stretched as before, with plumb line attached at the last preceding set; the cap is wedged until plumb line touches the sill string. Dip is maintained with straight edge, which should span 3 sets and is often triangular, with its top horiz when the bearing edge is at required dip. To aline new timbering with transit, the instrument is set over or under a tack some distance above, back-sighted for azimuth and sighted on new timber, which is shifted by wedging until its tack is cut by the vert cross-hair. Telescope is then set at established dip, its height measured and slant height to plane of sills calculated; target of leveling rod is set at this slant height, the rod grounded on the new sill and rested against new cap (thus lying normal to line of sight), and the set wedged up or down until the horiz cross-hair bisects target. Corners of set are then tested with square, and sill with spirit level, corrected if necessary, and again checked by transit. In deep shafts this method permits slight errors in the compt farthest from transit; hence, a set-up is made and tacks driven in the end hoisting compt, usually 1–2 ft from shoulder of cap or sill, errors being thrown to ladderway. Steep dips require an auxiliary telescope; the tripod is often replaced by a bracket screwed to timbers, or by a stretcher bar (Sec 18, Art 3).

Swelling ground is difficult to hold unless provision is made for cutting away protruding rock and easing the timbering. This is best done, without interrupting hoisting, by making the shaft opening large enough to allow a 2.5 to 3-ft space outside of the shaft sets. Auxiliary or jacket sets (16) are then placed and wedged around the regular sets. Floors may be laid on jacket sets and lagging placed outside of them in the usual way; occasionally, regular sets are also boxed in with plank. In the space thus provided, work of easing timbers proceeds as required.

Cylindrical shafts may be lined during sinking by lagging driven behind wooden or steel rings placed at vert intervals of 4–6 ft (23), which in turn are kept in place by wood or steel distance pieces. Steel plates are also used. Such linings afford temporary support before placing permanent metal or masonry lining.

Timber preservatives are sometimes used to combat decay and fire hazard. Timber for an Alaskan shaft was pressure-treated with zinc chloride against decay; specified retention, 1 lb dry chloride per cu ft of wood. Timber for the Capote shaft, Cananea, was treated against decay and fire hazard with a hot solution of 27% triolith (90% NaF, 6–7% potassium or sodium bichromate, and phenol) and 73% sea salt; max temp in treating tank, 190–200° F; wood preheated for 12 hr, and soaked in solution 24 hr. Timber may be fireproofed by coating with gunite; for details (Tramway shaft), see Art 15.

Protection during blasting is required when timbering must be carried within 20–30 ft of shaft bottom. Logs swung by loops of chain close under timbers of lowest set are often enough. For better protection, a BLASTING SET is hung below the lowest shaft set and lowered as needed, e g by chain blocks; it may be of green timber, sometimes half-round, or (at Macassa mine, Ont) 8-in channels, framed to match the shaft sets in plan. At Copper Mountain, B C, a blasting set of H-beams was used, open in center compt, covered over end compts with 2 thicknesses of ³/₈-in punched plate. For blasting set at North Star mine, Calif, see Fig 12; end compts solidly covered, center compt with iron door.

14. STEEL SHAFT-SETS

Steel sets are of structural shapes, arranged and named like the members of timber sets. Shapes are selected that furnish convenient riveted or bolted connections (Fig 25).

Wall and end plates act as beams under lateral press, and as columns under axial press of ground. Normally, dividers in vert shafts act as columns, but in moving ground, or inclines subject to creep of hanging wall, they may also resist bending, due to rigid connection. Posts act as columns, unless distortion of shaft support produces bending stress. Plates and dividers must therefore have relatively large least radii of gyration (Sec 43, Art 28), and for heavy duty are often H-beams, placed with flanges vert for max resistance to lateral ground press. Angle posts permit easy connection (Fig 25) and eliminate permanent hanging bolts. I-beams are common for bearers. Steel cross ties, and T-rails alone or reinforced by angles, have been used as plates, I-beams, paired channels and Z-bars as buntons, and rails as posts where wt of shaft framing is carried by lower bearers. Composite sections involve a shop cost that single shapes avoid. Guides are often of wood, though

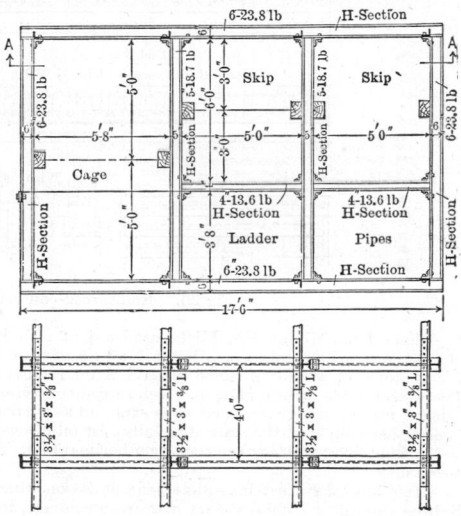

Fig 25. Steel Timbering for 5-compartment Shaft

steel has been used; cast-steel racks, sometimes bolted on steel guides to engage safety dogs, seem of doubtful value, as they must function under heavy impact. If size of compartments and space under the previous set permit, a steel set is framed at surface and lowered intact; otherwise it is shop-riveted in parts and assembled underground, with bolted connections. Chain blocks are used to swing the framing into place.

Preservation. Shaft steel may be painted with a mixture of 8 parts coal tar, 1 kerosene and 1 portland cement, applied hot to cleaned surface. Steel has been coated with gunite (Art 15); first cleaned and covered with chicken wire for reinforcement. Troughed shapes, as H- and I-beams, placed with flanges vert, should be concrete-filled between upper flanges, to prevent collection of water.

15. CONCRETE FRAMING AND LINING

Concrete may be pre-cast above ground in reinforced members like those of a timber set and similarly put in place; or poured underground in a succession of rings around the shaft (with bare rock between) virtually as monolithic sets; or poured in a continuous lining; or used in the form of pre-cast blocks for walling. Linings poured underground or walled are equipped with wood, steel, or pre-cast or monolithic concrete dividers. Gunite, or sand concrete applied by air jet, is used as protective coating on timber and steel (Art 14), and even as shaft lining in firm ground.

Pre-cast shaft sets, with members corresponding to those of timber sets, have been successfully used in both vert and inclined shafts.

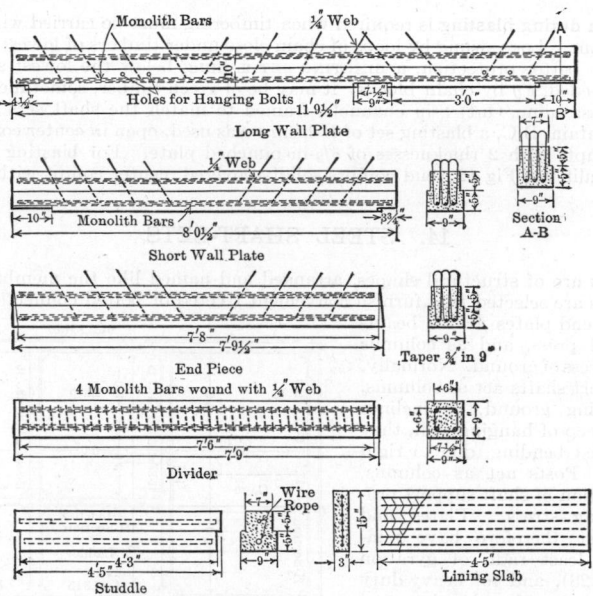

Fig 26. Reinforced-concrete Shaft Sets (34)

Oliver Iron Mining Co, Mich, used a 1 : 2 : 3 mixture, poured wet, in molding sets for vert shafts; Ahmeek Mining Co, Mich, a 1 : 3 : 5 mixture for plates and dividers, and 1 : 2 : 4 mixture for studdles of an 80° inclined shaft. After removing forms, members were allowed to harden for several weeks before placing. Reinforced concrete slabs, of a 1 : 2 : 3 or 1 : 2 : 4 mixture, were molded for lining between successive sets and as partitions between compartments. Where used as lagging between sets, the slabs generally rest on offsets on the plates, space between slabs and rock walls being filled with broken rock or other material. Slabs used as compt partitions may be bolted to dividers.

After blocking a set into alinement, it is sometimes bonded to the rock by placing a wooden bottom and filling around the set with fresh concrete, thus approaching the RING method. Members may be molded with reinforcement protruding from ends or outer faces, to be embedded in the fresh concrete bond; Fig 26 shows stirrups of web reinforcement (Sec 43, Art 14), protruding thus from wall plates. Holes are cored for assembling and hanging bolts. Due to their wt, concrete sets require more labor for assembly than timber sets, and long wall plates may be cast in 2 or more sections.

In a 3-compt shaft of Ahmeek mine (20), concrete sets (Fig 26) replaced 12 by 12-in timbers. Costs (prewar) per set delivered at shaft mouth: timber, $37.60; concrete, $22.50. Unit costs: timber, $28 per M; crushed stone, 35¢ per cu yd; sand, 60¢ per cu yd; cement, $1.15 per bbl; reinforcement, $12 per shaft set. 7 men placed 1 set per 9-hr shift. At American shaft, Zaruma,

Ecuador, with cement at $2.85 per 94-lb sack and reinforcing (0.5-in deformed bars) at 4.5¢ per lb, cost of casting 2-compt set (reported 1925) was $15; 3-compt, $22. Cost per ft of shaft, including removal of old timber: labor, $23.57, supplies, $34.09; members were placed crib-fashion, 6 in apart.

Ring method provides monolithic concrete lining in horiz bands, separated by intervals of bare rock. In the cylindrical City Deep shaft, Rand, rings 18 in high at 10-ft intervals furnish entire support in firm rock and serve as anchorage for continuous brick or concrete lining in heavier ground; each ring is bonded with 20 steel pins sunk in the rock.

A square shaft at Jerome, Ariz, 13 by 13 ft in clear section, was continuously lined for 1 550 ft and ringed for 450 ft below. Rings 30 in high on 6-ft centers were each reinforced with 5 3/4-in horiz and 10 3/8-in vert bars, spot-welded at shop. Bottom form was a wooden sill with projecting pieces of ship-lap shaped to rock profile; forms for inner face were of steel, well braced. Concrete was poured to rock, not less than 8 in thick. I-beam and channel dividers (flanges up) and angle attachments for wooden guides completed the "set." Costs (1925), Table 4.

Table 4.   Cost of Ring Method of Lining

For rings:	Per ft of depth		
	Excavation	Concreting	Total
Labor...........	$52.07	$ 16.60	$ 68.67
Supplies.........	7.68	26.51	34.19
Explosives.......	8.47	......	8.47
Comp air.........	2.08	......	2.08
Shop work......	0.26	5.90	6.16
Repairs.........	6.55	......	6.55
Engineering.....	......	1.05	1.05
Miscellaneous....	......	0.05	0.05
Total........	$77.11	$ 50.11	$127.22
Continuous lining...	68.17	146.84	215.01
Saving by ring method, per ft.........			$ 87.79
Per cu yd of concrete:			
Ring method (mix 1 : 2 : 4).............			$61.30
Continuous lining (mix 1 : 3 : 5)........			58.80

Continuous lining is combined with dividers of various types (5). Partition walls may be cast with the lining; they have openings at intervals to relieve suction of passing cage or skip, are equipped for attachment of guides, and designed for impact due to possible breakage of rope. Walls may be thinner if carried at intervals on steel beams. Dividers of steel, timber or pre-cast concrete are common. If seated with ends embedded in the lining, they are difficult to replace; whence, hitches are often cored for them, or they are supported on short lengths of steel beam embedded in the concrete; in either case they are bolted in place. If used to support guides, pre-cast concrete dividers are reinforced against impact and vibration.

Reinforcement of lining may be of standard structural design (Sec 43), or of old drill steel, rails or hoisting rope. Inward pressure causes compression in a circular lining, but may induce tension at inner face of a rectangular or flat oval lining; where lining of any form is exposed to local thrust, the principal factor is apt to be shear. Steel rope, resistance of which is purely tensile, thus finds its max value as horiz reinforcement near the inner face of a flat wall, but due to stretch, may not take full tension until adjacent concrete has begun to fail. Reinforcing bars are preferable.

In main portion of auxiliary shaft, Gallup American Coal Co, N M, 25 by 10 ft clear, horiz reinforcement comprised 0.75-in round bars, 10.5 and 18.5 ft long (2 ft lap) on sides, spaced on 9-in centers; and 12.5 ft long on ends, spaced 12 in apart. Vert reinforcement, 0.5-in round bars 14 ft long, spaced 24 in apart and lapped 2 ft. Horiz end and vert bars placed alternately near inner and outer faces of wall. In concreted portion of a hoisting shaft of Lake Superior Coal Co, W Va, reinforcement comprised 0.75-in square corrugated bars, spaced 6 in apart when laid horiz and 24 in apart when placed vert.

Anchorage of lining poured to rock depends on skin friction, aided by leaving points of rock projecting into the concrete. This is usual practice, but linings have also been formed in the clear and anchored only at intervals.

In traversing a shear zone, 200 ft of the Barron shaft, Pachuca, Mex, were concrete-lined to elliptical section, with axes 14 and 10 ft inside lining. The lowest 9 ft were poured to rock as a BASE; 106 ft higher a second base was cast, 3 ft high, and 41 ft above this a third, 5 ft high; between these bases, and for 35 ft above the third, lining was formed clear of the rock and intervening space backfilled. The last 35-ft lift joined a rectangular section above. In the rectangular Chief Consolidated shaft, Utah, in heavy ground, a lining 8 in thick was formed in the clear for 1950 ft of depth, with a RING poured to rock every 10 ft and a heavy reinforced bearer-section deeply hitched every 100 ft.

Details. Mixtures range from 1 : 2 : 4 to 1 : 3 : 6. Wall thicknesses are 8–18 in. Before concrete is placed, flows of water should be stopped by grouting or vented through pipes laid in the forms, to prevent separation of cement and aggregates.

Mixing and placing. Concreting is best carried upward from below, although in a deep shaft, it may proceed in several horizons at once, to allow time for setting without delaying the crew.

On small jobs, the mixer may be located in nearest underground level; on large work it is usually at or near the surface, and if located a few feet below level of supply, can receive raw materials by chute, with convenient use of measuring-hoppers. Batches are delivered to the forms by cage or bucket, or by piping. In one case a hopper car was used, discharging through the cage floor into a short telescoping pipe erected at the forms; buckets may deliver to forms direct. In many large shafts concrete has been piped from mixer directly to place. In the 380-ft Songo shaft, Birmingham, Ala, a 4-in pipe without gaskets delivered into a 5-in Y, with bottom plugged and a branch discharging to forms through sectional spouts of 18-gage iron; concrete was thus placed for $3 less per cu yd than in the nearby Pyne shaft, where a bucket was used. The 5-compt Sacramento shaft (36), Bisbee, Ariz, was lined 1645 ft during time spared from hoisting; a mixer in the end service compt discharged into a 4-in column, composed of 10-ft lengths with flanges carefully faced; to reach farthest skip compt, an expanding elbow was inserted at pouring level and connected to a 6-in horiz pipe, which discharged through a 45° malleable elbow into 1 length of 8-in galv-iron pipe leading to the forms. Compressed air was admitted at back of expanding elbow to blow concrete through the horiz pipe. 67 lengths of 4-in column and 6 C-I elbows required renewal during the work.

Cyprus Mines concreted a circular shaft, 14.75-ft inside diam, working downward. A steel bulkhead, of diam 6 in greater, floored with wood and provided with door for bucket, was hung below lining by four 5-ton chain blocks; a 1.75-in angle, rolled to 13.75-ft diam, was bolted through washers to the deck, with 1.5-in clearance between, through which 1-in boards were extended to rock and wedged in place, as a base for concrete, the bulkhead being centered by 3 radial arms sliding in guides. Forms of flanged corrugated steel, 16 in high, in 36-in sections, were bolted in place, after which the bulkhead was pulled up snug; usually 3 tiers of forms were placed and poured at once, with steel shaft dividers placed in the middle tier of every alternate pour; concrete was piped from surface; mucking proceeded during concreting.

Forms are of wood or steel, 2.5–12 ft high; aver about 5 ft. If greased, they are easier to strip, and leave better surface. On large jobs, and where curtain walls are cast with the lining, standardized steel forms save time; they are made in sections, each sometimes comprising several hinged parts, and designed for rapid assembly.

At the Sacramento shaft (36), steel forms 5 ft 9 in high were used for a 5-ft course: bolts were embedded near upper edge of each course to engage holes along lower edges of forms when latter were placed for next course above, thus securing alinement and holding forms against pressure of wet concrete. Steel forms are much used for circular and elliptical linings. If the shaft is timbered for safety while sinking, the lagging may serve as the inside forms.

Gunite (21) is sand concrete applied by a "gun," which pipes the dry materials under air press to a movable nozzle, where water is added and the resulting paste sprayed in place as a thin coating. Uses: to preserve timber and steel (Art 12, 13), to fireproof timber, to prevent air slacking of rock, and as shaft lining in firm ground. Surface to be coated is thoroughly cleaned; to secure bond, timber and steel are covered with wire mesh, and timber may be wet before coating. Mixtures vary from 1 : 2.5 to 1 : 5 at the gun, bur are enriched during placing, due to rebound of the sand; 1 : 3 mixture at the gun becomes 1 : 2.5 in place. One bag of cement yields 32 sq ft of 1 : 4.5, or 22 sq ft of 1 : 3 nominal mixture, 1 in thick in place; 0.6 cu yd of coating requires about 1 cu yd of materials. The 1 : 2.5 nominal mixture is used to waterproof; its ultimate compressive strength is 4 500, that of 1 : 3 mixture is 4 000 lb per sq in. Cement should be screened; sand should be clean, not over 0.25-in size, and not quite dry. Usual sizes of gun require 110–225 cu ft free air per min at 40–75 lb press; the air should be dry.

Tramway shaft, Butte, was fireproofed by coating to 2 000-ft depth; lagging was removed just above and below each level and coating carried to rock, thus sealing the timber in a series of air-tight sections; timber was covered with 27-gage diamond-mesh metal lath and wet just before coating. Mixture 1 : 3, applied in two 0.25-in layers; tests showed that keeping the coat damp for several days prevented shelling off under heat. 4 men with gun coated 100–150 sq ft per hr; 100 sq ft required 3.5 sacks cement, 0.85 ton sand, 94 sq ft lath, 1.5 lb staples and nails, and 23 man-hr in all (3.6 for lathing, 2.7–4 for coating).

In 1918, 900 ft of colliery slope, including timbers, were coated with 0.5 in gunite, at $3.09 per ft; 100 sq ft required 1.67 sacks cement, 5 sacks sand and 2.4 man-hr (shaft and compressor crew only). In Cary A shaft, Wis, steel sets and wood lagging were covered for 263 ft of depth with meshed reinforcement and coated 1.5 in thick, in 1 to 3 layers; total cost, $13.60 per 100 sq ft, requiring 3.8 sacks cement, 0.6 cu yd sand and 1.24 man-days labor; 1 foreman and 6 men coated 14 260 sq ft of wall and 3 750 sq ft of steel in 32 working days. A hoisting shaft of Lake Superior Coal Co, W Va, was lined for 185 ft with reinforced gunite. Gunite RINGS 10 in thick, were made every 10 ft and reinforced with bars 12 in apart grouted into holes in the rock; in shattered ground heavy concrete brackets were substituted for gunite rings. Between rings (or brackets) gunite walls were 3 in thick; mixture, 1 : 3. Gunite also used as facing for 55 ft of ordinary concrete lining.

Concrete-block walling, used chiefly in Europe, is adapted to circular shafts. Except for shallow depths, it is divided into lifts, each built on its own curb ring, best made of concrete poured to rock as in the ring method. Blocks are segmental, from 6 in thick, 9 in high, 12 in long on outer face, of 1 : 2 : 4 mixture (6), to 3.2 in thick, 30 in high and about 36 in long, as in a circular shaft at Charleroi, Belgium. The blocks were dowelled for alinement and reinforced; after placement, rods were passed through ring bolts protruding from the outer face, and bonded in the concrete backing; mixture, 1 : 1 : 2. An interlocking reinforced block in Z-form has been used in Belgium. Walling is built clear of the rock, and space behind filled with concrete.

16. MASONRY LINING

In Europe, circular shafts in dry or moderately wet ground are often lined with hard-burned brick or cut stone, laid in lime mortar or, in wet ground, cement mortar. Brick and stone are preferably shaped to the required curve, though for diams over 12 or 14 ft, ordinary brick may be used. Lining is backfilled with clay, sand, cinder or other fill, rammed in place. Large volumes of water, not too great for pumping, are excluded by COFFERING, which in simplest form consists of brick laid in cement and carefully backfilled, or more elaborately of concentric walls, up to 8 in number, filled between with clay or concrete; both horiz and vert joints are broken. For concrete block lining, see Art 15.

Anchorage is provided at intervals by a C-I WALLING CRIB (Fig 27), which is cast in segments, usually 8 to the circle, wedged or bolted together on a continuous hitch cut in the rock and dressed level. Ring is made watertight by fir sheathing driven into the joints.

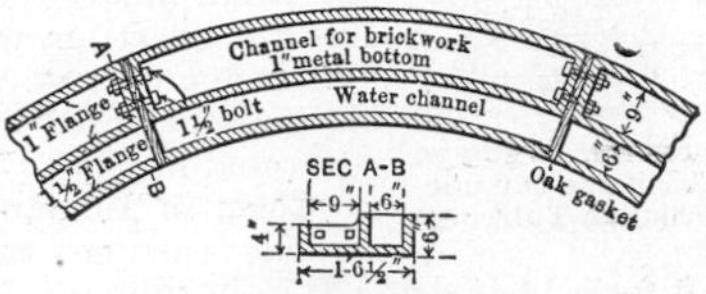

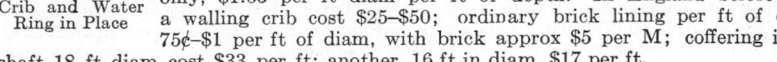

Fig 27. Walling Crib and Water Ring Combined

Placement. Shaft is sunk with temporary wood lining (Art 13) to firm rock, and a walling crib placed, on which the wall is built to surface from a stage hung in the shaft. Correct curvature is maintained by wooden templates, and alinement by plumb lines. On resuming sinking, a shelf of rock is left under the crib until wall has been brought up from next crib below. The shelf is then cut away a little at a time and replaced by walling, using temporary props for crib above. For coffering, wedging cribs like those used in tubbing (Art 17) may be employed. Walling cribs are sometimes of wood, and in firm ground may be omitted, masonry resting directly on rock.

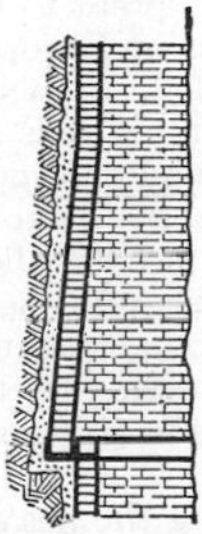

Walls (single) are usually 9–18 in thick; coffering may be designed (23) for hydrostatic head, and is thicker. Water rings (GARLANDS) are of wood or C-I, often cast integrally with walling cribs (Fig 27). At each ring, lining may be gradually offset as in Fig 28, to leave shaft area clear. Weep holes are left in the masonry; in coffering these may be lined with wood or C-I PLUG BOXES, sealed when masonry is completed.

Cost. For diam of 18–21 ft, Redmayne (22) in 1925 estimated cost of sinking and lining, excluding wall material, at $3.25 per ft of diam per ft of depth; for diam less than 18 ft, slightly less; for labor only, $1.65 per ft diam per ft of depth. In England before 1915, a walling crib cost $25–$50; ordinary brick lining per ft of depth, 75¢–$1 per ft of diam, with brick approx $5 per M; coffering in one shaft 18 ft diam cost $33 per ft; another, 16 ft in diam, $17 per ft.

Fig 28. Walling Crib and Water Ring in Place

17. TUBBING

Tubbing is a watertight lining of C-I rings for circular shafts, used in very wet rock formation underlaid by an impervious stratum, to which lining can be sealed above mineral deposit. Vol of water must not be too great to be pumped during sinking.

Rings are cast to shaft radius in flanged segments approx 4.5 ft long. If D = shaft diam (ft), P = hydrostatic head (ft), measured to outcrop of water-bearing strata (which may be above shaft collar), then thickness (in) of web or flange = $\sqrt{P}(0.05D + 0.125) \div 14.14$, minimum 0.5 in; width of flange (in) = $\sqrt[3]{P}(D + 15) \div 35.09$, increased to nearest in or half-in above; minimum up to 10-ft diam = $0.684\sqrt[3]{P}$; after Lupton (25). Acid water calls for extra thickness.

Flanges may project inward or outward; if inward, they are faced by machine and bolted together with lead gaskets (segments 18–36 in high); outside-flange segments (30–60 in high) are rough castings wedged against the rock, with pine or lead gaskets in the joints. Inside-flange tubbing is the stronger and avoids stress due to wedging, but being bolted, may incur abnormal stress in shifting ground due to its rigidity. Space between tubbing and rock is best concreted. A cored hole in each segment aids handling and vents water during placement.

Placement. Anchorage and sealing against water are provided by WEDGING CRIBS (usually ring castings, Fig 29) projecting outside the lining and seated in a continuous groove around the shaft. The seat is dressed level and covered with pine sheathing (0.5–0.75 in thick) and tarred flannel, or with fresh concrete; on this the crib segments are assembled, with pine or tarred flannel gaskets. Between crib and rock, small pieces of

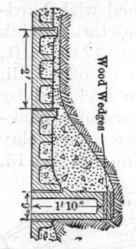

Fig 29. Wedging Crib and Outside-flange Tubbing

oak are placed and packed with dry moss, into which wooden wedges are driven; finally chisels are used to open the way for more wedges until no more can be driven, the crib having been propped down against the wedging until secured by wt of lining. Placing then proceeds upward; except with SUSPENDED TUBBING, hung from crib above, and used where ground requires support close to bottom. Air or gas trapped behind the lining may exert abnormal pressure and is carried past the sealed crib through by-pass pipes; or better, vented through a check valve in the crib itself, finally escaping at top of tubbing. Wedging cribs are usually 30–75 ft apart, or wherever rock affords an effective seal. In sinking by freezing (Sec 8), with no room outside shaft circle for hitches, tubbing has been anchored by a few rings with deeply corrugated outer faces, concreted in place.

Costs in England before 1915 were $40–$100 per ft of depth, installed; castings, $25–$35 per ton; placing, $6–$10 per ton. Costs per ft for a 14-ft shaft: 0.75-in tubbing, $44; placing, $5; gaskets, wedges, etc, $2. Preparing seat and placing wedging crib, $200. Costs are now approx twice the above (22).

18. KIND-CHAUDRON PROCESS (2, 25, 27)

Conditions for use are as for tubbing (Art 17), but with inflow of water too great to be pumped during sinking. Such conditions are rare in the U S, but common in Europe.

Method. The shaft is excavated under water, by massive drop tools, called TREPANS, the method being an extension of the rod system of boring (Sec 9). The water stands at its natural level until the work is finished. A small shaft may be bored first and enlarged to full diam, or the full section bored in one operation. On completing boring, the bottom is cleaned with a special tool, and the lining (inside-flange tubbing, Art 17) is put together at the shaft mouth and lowered as rings are added. The lowest ring is the MOSS-BOX (see below), specially designed to seal the lining to the underlying impervious stratum. When lining is in place, the space between it and the shaft wall is filled with cement grouting, lowered in trip-bottom boxes, and the shaft is pumped out. An effective seal is essential.

Plant required consists of a suitable headframe (with facilities for handling the heavy boring tools), power plant, boring rods, small and large trepans, sludgers and special tools.

Trepans are massive steel frames, to the lower edge of which are attached chilled-steel bits weighing about 100 lb each. Bits are placed unsymmetrically to cover entire area of shaft bottom as trepan rotates; they are also set to slope the shaft bottom towards center, thus facilitating removal of cuttings. Trepans are inspected frequently and dull bits removed. Wt for a small bore, 2–15 ton; for large, 15–30 ton. An enlarging trepan (Fig 31) has a projection extending into advance bore, and a crosshead fitting the shaft, to preserve alinement; the crosshead may carry bits to dress the shaft wall. Strokes per min 8–25; length of stroke, 6 in to 2 ft. Tools are suspended from the walking beam by rods and temper screw (Sec 9), which feeds down as boring progresses.

Boring. Usually the shaft is started by ordinary methods, and a shallow hole, of diam of small trepan (Fig 30), is made at shaft center. In this the trepan is started, and cuts an advance bore of 4 to 10-ft diam, usually kept at least 30 ft ahead of the enlargement, sometimes cut to full depth before enlarging begins. Cuttings from the small trepan are removed by sludger (Sec 9); those from large trepan are caught in a bucket suspended in the advance bore. Where shaft walls cave badly, they may be lined temporarily with sheet-steel casing, hung from the surface or rested on a shoulder of rock left for the purpose. Diam of shaft below must then be reduced.

Permanent lining. MOSS-BOX is a double telescoping ring with outside flanges, between which dry moss is placed and secured while lowering by means of wire netting. When seated, the wt of tubbing telescopes the rings and compresses the moss against the shaft wall, forming a watertight joint. Sometimes concreting alone (without moss-box) is depended on for sealing; special bits on the enlarging trepan then cut a level seat for bottom flange of regular tubbing.

With deep shafts and excessive wt of tubbing, the lining as a whole is made buoyant by placing above the moss-box a false bottom or diaphragm, in which a vert EQUILIBRIUM PIPE is inserted, equipped with valves for admitting water as desired and thus controlling

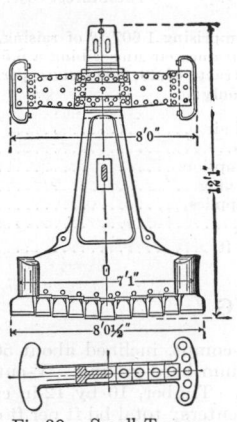

Fig 30. Small Trepan

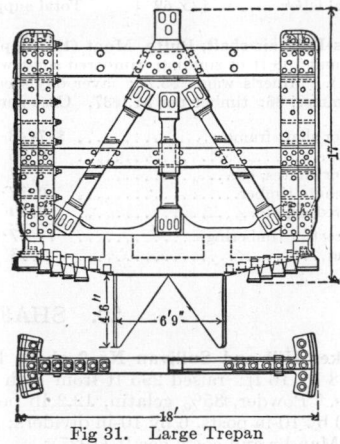

Fig 31. Large Trepan

buoyancy. When lining is finished and sealed, and shaft pumped out, wedging cribs (Art 17) are placed below the moss-box and sinking proceeds by ordinary methods.

Speed and cost. Aver rate of sinking to 600 ft depth in northern France (24), 12–33 ft per month; cost (before 1915) $66–$200 per ft.

Costs of sinking 14.5 ft diam shafts in the Ruhr district, Germany, to mean depth between 164 and 1 148 ft prior to 1915, were (27): plant and equipment, 50% of first cost, $25 000 to $35 000; miscellaneous, $12 500 to $25 000; tubbing per ft, $90 to $195; concrete per ft, $12; power and supplies per ft, $60 to $105; labor per ft, $135 to $210.

Kerr (23) gives cost of sinking only, exclusive of tubbing, at $83 to $250 per ft; ordinary rate of advance, 9–12 in per day. In general, pre-war cost of 12-ft shafts ranged from $100 to $300 per ft; 14 to 16 ft shafts, $250 to $500 per ft.

SPEED AND COST DATA

Of the following cost examples, all but three are dated 1920 or later, and fall within the period of higher wages and prices that followed the World War. Costs prior to 1916 should be increased 50-60% for use as guides to current practice. For cost examples of steel shaft support, see Ross shaft, Art 20, and Matahambre No 2 shaft, Art 21.

19. SMALL SHAFTS

201-ft prospect shaft, southwest U S, 5 by 7.5 ft, no water. Hoist and 6 by 8-in vert compressor powered by tractor engines; 25-ft headframe cost $165. Drilling and blasting 3 hr, mucking 6–7 hr, timbering 6 hr. Round, 8–13 holes, aver of 40 sticks, 1 1/8 by 8 in, 40% dynamite. Sets 5.5-ft centers, 4 by 6-in plates, 4 by 4-in posts and dividers. Sunk in 98 days. Cost (reported 1935):

	Total	Per ft		Total	Per ft
Labor	$2 267.50	$11.28	Lights	$ 6.60	$ 0.03
Insurance	135.00	0.67	Gasolene	35.00	0.17
Explosive	175.00	0.87	Oil, grease, coal *	9.65	0.05
Lumber	381.35	1.90	Pipes, bolts, nails	33.35	0.17
* For blacksmithing.			Total	$3 043.45	$15.14

Alaska-Juneau No 53 prospect shaft (7), 7 by 9-ft rock section, 60° incline, sunk by contract for 300 ft through hard rock. Shaftmen earned aver of $9.28, hoistmen $4.50 per shift. Round, V-cut, 24 holes, 5–6 ft deep. Powder, 40% special gelatin, 23.5 lb per ft. Timber, 8 by 8-in plates, 6 by 8-in dividers, sets 6 ft apart, 37.5 bd ft per ft. Costs per ft (1931):

Labor:		Supplies:		Power:	
Shaftmen	$20.19	Explosive	$4.97	Drilling	$ 0.80
Pumpmen	4.27	Timber	0.98	Hoisting	0.40
Timber framing	0.69	Pipe lines	0.11	Ventilation, lights	0.05
Steel sharpening	0.42	Drill repair	0.25	Total power	$ 1.25
Miscel	0.12	Miscel	1.20	Supervision	$ 1.00
Total labor	$25.69	Total supplies	$7.51	Total direct cost	$35.45

Davis-Daly air-shaft, Butte, Mont (11): depth 1 805 ft, comprising 1 607 ft of raising, 90 ft of stations and 108 ft of sinking; timbered solid with octagonal frames circumscribing a 6.5 ft circle (1920–21). Miner's wage, $5.75; aver day's earning on contract, $6.28; explosives per lb, 20¢; timber framer, $6; timber per M, $37. Cost per ft for raising only:

Timber for shaft frames	$ 7.48	Compressed air	$ 0.86
Framing	0.76	Drill repairs	0.69
Timber for chutes, etc	1.47	Steel consumption	0.39
Cutting chute timber	0.37	Steel sharpening	0.28
Blocks, wedges, etc	0.99	All other supplies	0.33
Total cost of timbering	11.07	Labor	14.76
Explosives	2.33	Total per ft	$30.71

20. SHAFT RAISING

Bunker Hill and Sullivan No 2 shaft, Idaho (7); 3-compt, inclined about 50°, rock section 8 by 16 ft; raised 295 ft from 19th level in medium hard ground. V-cut round, 24 holes. Powder, 35% gelatin, 12.2 lb per ft of shaft. Timber, 10 by 12-in caps and sills; 10 by 10-in posts, 6 by 10-in dividers; sets at 5-ft centers; total bd ft per ft of shaft, 153.3 Man-hr and costs per ft (1927):

Labor:	Man-hr	Cost	Supplies:	Cost
Bosses @ $7.50	0.06	$ 0.47	Explosive	$ 2.05
Timbermen @ $5.50	0.61	3.30	Timber	3.68
Shaftmen @ $5.00	1.08	5.41	Miscel	0.17
Helpers @ $4.50	0.11	0.41	Total	$ 5.90
Timber framing	0.21	0.64	Power:	
Sharpening steel	0.10	0.35	Drilling	$ 1.11
Total labor	2.17	$10.58	Hoisting	0.33
			Total	$ 1.44
			Total direct, per ft	$17.92

Pilares shaft, Sonora, Mex (7). 345 ft of pilot raises, 4 by 7 ft; enlarged to full rock section of 12 by 20 ft; see Art 11. Total completed depth, 379.5 ft. Powder: in pilot raises, 5 lb per ft of raise; total, 10 lb per ft of shaft. Costs (1924–25):

	Per ft of raise	Per ft of full section shaft				
		Raises	Enlarging	Timbering	Miscel	Total
Labor:						
Breaking	$2.45	$2.23	....	....	....	....
Mucking	0.67	0.61	....	....	....	....
Total shaft	$3.12	$2.84	$4.82	$.....	$.....	$ 7.66
Shop labor	....	....	0.08	0.66	0.34	1.08
Framing timber	....	....	....	3.76	....	3.76
Placing timber	....	....	....	8.33	....	8.33
Sundry labor	....	....	....	....	3.18	3.18
Total labor	$3.12	$2.84	$4.90	$12.75	$ 3.52	$24.01
Explosive	1.92	1.74	1.14	....	0.30	3.18
Timber	0.33	0.30	....	29.30	4.24	33.84
Incline charges	....	....	....	0.11	....	0.11
Supplies	0.08	0.08	....	....	2.71	2.79
Drills and tools	2.32	2.11	1.46	....	0.29	3.86
Total	$7.77	$7.07	$7.50	$42.16	$11.06	$67.79

Ross shaft, Homestake Mining Co, So Dak (28); 6-compt, 14 ft by 19 ft 3 in outside steel sets; designed for 5 200-ft depth; sets installed at end of 1934 for 3 242 ft. Sunk from surface, 137 ft; raised full size for 250 ft from 800 level, but wt of broken rock crushed the timbering; shaft was raised elsewhere with 6 by 6-ft pilot raises in center of shaft area, then enlarged to size. Steel sets (6-ft centers): plates and dividers, 6-in 25-lb H-beams; posts, 3.5 by 3 by $^3/_8$-in angles; the 2 skipways laced with 14-gage galvanized corrugated steel; ladders and sollars of steel; all steel specified to contain 0.20–0.25% copper. Upper 308 ft of shaft concreted solidly outside of sets, at cost of $46.27 per ft; total of 150 ft concreted below in sections of 1 to 3 sets; elsewhere the shaft walls were gunited. Costs per ft of 3 241.5 ft of steel-supported shaft (1933–34):

Excavation	Pilot raises	Enlarg- ing	Total	Steel support	Shapes	Corrug lacing	Total
Mining: Labor	$ 9.19	$13.77	$22.96	Invoice cost	$21.13	$6.35	$27.48
Explosives	2.73	3.11	5.84	Unloading, etc	2.08	.....	2.08
Air and drills	3.20	2.54	5.74	Installing:			
Timbering	4.24	0.67	4.91	Labor	6.92	1.06	7.98
Trackage	0.34	0.56	0.90	Hoist labor	2.15	0.11	2.26
Pipe	0.49	0.25	0.74	Power	0.33	.....	0.33
Hoist and hoisting	1.82	1.26	3.08	Air and drills	0.12	.....	0.12
Haulage	0.85	2.87	3.72	Miscel suppl	3.21	0.13	3.34
Elec supplies	.....	0.05	0.05	Clips for fastening	.....	0.39	0.39
Miscel	1.13	1.43	2.56	Total	$35.94	$8.04	$43.98
Surveying	0.12	.....	0.12	Sollars, ladders, railings			2.52
Total	$24.11	$26.51	$50.62	Shaft doors, guides, chairs			3.50
				Surveying			0.32
				Total per ft			$50.32

Total cost:		Stations	$ 5.49
Excavation (above)	$50.62	Piping and wiring	13.82
Steel supports (above)	50.32	General construction	0.66
Concreting and guniting	11.40	Total per ft	$132.31

21. WORKING SHAFTS, METAL MINES

Typical estimate of total cost per ft, including supervision and general maintenance, of sinking a vert 3-compt shaft 8 by 17-ft section to 1 000-ft depth is given by Elsing (29):

Labor:		Explosive	$ 5.50
Shaft	$30.00	Timber	7.50
Blacksmithing	2.00	Power	2.25
Timber framing	2.75	Insurance	2.00
Hoisting	2.75	Miscel supplies	7.00
Total labor	$37.50	General expense	3.25
		Total	$65.00

Moderate flow of water will increase cost 10–15%.

United Verde No 5 shaft, Jerome, Ariz. Rectangular section 7 by 14 ft; sunk in 1925 from 2 400 to 3 150-ft level through medium quartz porphyry:

Drilling speed, in per min	10	Water pumped, gal per hr	5 000
Per round:		Cost per ft:	
Advance, ft	4.5	Labor (drill, muck, timber)	$31.85
No of holes	32 to 35	Explosive (except caps and fuse)	5.20
Sticks of powder	260	Total cost per ft	$52.70

Butte district, Mont (15), operating more than 60 shafts, affords steady employment to specialized sinking crews. Sinking in 1920 cost approx $100 per ft, including equipment. Anselmo mine shaft, 3-compt, 19 by 6.5 ft outside timbers, was then being sunk in altered granite and rhyolite porphyry. Labor, 5 miners per shift, on contract at $40 per ft; also 1 shift boss and 1 topman per shift. Clipper drills (4, in hard rock 5) made round of 30 holes in 4 hr, in 10 rows of 3 across the shaft; V-cut holes 9.5 ft deep, pointed at 45° from 4.5–5 ft collar; side holes 5.5–6 ft deep; after finishing a round, drills were overhauled. Powder, 40% gelatin, 100–125 lb per round. Timber, 12 by 12-in; set placed in 1.5–2 hr.

Water Lily shaft (12) Eureka, Nev, 3-compt, 15.5 by 5.75 ft outside timbers, was sunk 427.5 ft in 31 days (Sept, 1920) through porphyry and 60 ft of limestone; in another month, 416 ft, all in limestone. Rock hoisted through 2 compts, partly lined to prevent buckets from catching on timbers; non-rotation ropes, no crossheads. A bonus was based on monthly advance. 3 shallow drill rounds were more effective than 1 or 2 deeper rounds. Sets of 8 by 8-in timber placed 5-ft centers; lagging, 2 by 12-in. Data for record month: aver advance per day, 13.8 ft; shaft sets placed per day, 2.8; rounds per day, 3; holes per round, 23.9; buckets (17 cu ft) per shift, 72.5; 9 hammer drills on the job; aver number in use at one time, 5; gelatin, 35% in porphyry, some 50% in limestone, lb per ft, 15.25. Regular daily wage: shaftmen, $5.25; hoistmen, $5; topmen, $3.75. Shaftmen per shift, 5.7. Timbermen per day, 4.8. Total delay for month, due to repairs and failure of power, 13 hr

Porphyry shaft, Inspiration Mine, Ariz, rock section 17 2/3 by 13 1/3 ft, timbered. 2–4 unmounted Clipper drills made aver round of 30 holes in 4 hr. Record advance for 7 months, Feb–Aug, 1922, 1 037 ft, in a total of 1 403 ft.

	Ft sunk	Cu yd rock	Man-shifts			Shifts per ft advance			Shifts per cu yd		
			Shaftmen	Topmen	Hoist-men	Shaft	Top	Hoist	Shaft	Top	Hoist
Max month	209	1823	936.6	179.0	93	7.3	1.3	0.8	0.83	0.15	0.08
Min month	128	1116	653.0	164.2	84	3.1	0.8	0.4	0.36	0.09	0.05
Aver month	148	1292	833.4	169.2	90.7	5.6	1.1	0.6	0.64	0.13	0.07

Bisbee Queen shaft, Ariz (29), 8 by 17 ft, 3 compt, no water. Sunk 823 ft from surface; best month's advance, 235 ft. Contract price for labor and explosive, $40 per ft; contractor paid $8 per man-shift ($9 if month's advance reached 200 ft). Insurance, 5.5% of payroll; elec power, aver, 2¢ per kw-hr; powder, 16.5¢ per lb; timber, $30 per M bd ft delivered. Cost per ft (1927):

Labor:
Shaft.............. $30.93
Blacksmiths........ 2.07
Timber framing..... 2.84
Hoistmen........... 2.77
　Total........... $38.61

Power................. $ 2.39
Insurance............ 2.15
Trucking............. 1.31
Office and general..... 2.06
Preliminary exp...... 2.14
　Total............. $10.05

Supplies:
Explosive........... $ 5.49
Timber............. 7.60
Misc supplies...... 7.40
　Total........... $20.49
Grand total.......... $69.15

Wisconsin zinc district (14). In 1920, 2- and 3-compt shafts, traversing 10–40 ft of overburden and varying depths of rock, with not more than 500 gal of water per min, were sunk at usual rates of 65–85 ft per month and cost $20–$50 per ft.

Ajax shaft, Cripple Creek, Colo (10), vert, 3-compt, 15 ft by 6 ft 2 in outside timbers, was deepened 502.5 ft below 1 481 ft in 1915–16. Labor: 2 8-hr shifts, each of 4 shaftmen, 1 hoistman, with topmen and skippers as needed; day shift drilled, blasted and timbered; night shift mucked and sometimes timbered; overtime as needed. 4 hammer drills made 40 holes per round; aver depth, 4 ft. Plates and corner posts, 10 by 10 in; dividers and interior posts, 8 by 10 in. Drill bits per round, aver, 126.5. Total time, 293 days; max monthly advance, 95 ft; aver ft per round, 3.03. Per ft advance, aver: machine-shifts, 1.3; sinking hoist-shifts, 0.86.

	Aver wage	Per ft		Per ft
Drillers......................	$5.25	$ 6.51	40 and 60% powder, 20.7 lb @ 19.42¢....	$ 4.02
Muckers......................	4.50	6.47	Fuse, 143 ft @ 0.6¢....................	0.86
Timbermen....................	5.25	5.11	Caps, $1.75 per 100...................	0.24
Hoistmen.....................	4.13	3.75	Timber, 232 bd ft, $28.33 per M.......	6.57
Shift bosses..................	5.00	1.51	Machine drills.....................	1.79
Machinist, blacksmith..........	4.50	0.49	Pipe.............................	1.53
Topmen, skippers.............	4.00	1.19	Iron and steel.....................	1.01
Pipemen, repairers.............	4.00	0.74	Miscel............................	0.91
Total labor....................		$25.77	Total supplies....................	$16.93

Hoisting waste, @ 60¢ per skip... $5.61
Air for drills, @ $2 per machine shift... 2.65
Air for sinking hoist, @ $2.50 per shift... 2.14
Sharpening steel, @ 10¢ per bit... 4.18　14.58
　Total cost per ft.. $57.28

Macassa mine, Kirkland Lake, Ont (30). Vert 3-compt shaft, 9 by 17 ft rock section. Timbering, 8 by 8-in, sets at 7-ft centers; bd ft per ft of depth, sets 85.0, blocking 17.2, sheathing 5.0, guides 12.5, total 119.7; plus 18 linear ft of 8-in poles for lagging. 38 holes, 300 ft drilled per round by 4 drills. For cost of sinking plant, see Art 3. Wage scale: shaftmen $6 plus bonus, aver about $8.50 total; hoistmen $5.20, deckmen $4.15 per shift, topman $150 per month, all plus bonus; blacksmith $7; surface laborers 40¢ per hr. Man-hr and costs per ft (1931–32):

	Man-hr per ft depth (171 ft)	Cost per ft of depth, Apl, 1932							
		Sinking labor and supervision	Drills, repairs, steel; air and water lines	Power	Explosive	Timber	Concreting collar	Other supplies	Total
Drilling and blasting.	8.52	$10.38	$6.62*	$2.90	$6.37	$....	$....	$0.22	$26.49
Mucking.............	11.53	10.88	....	.....	.....	.....	.....	0.17	11.05
Timbering..........	2.61	3.54	....	.....	.....	6.09	.....	.....	9.63
Hoisting............	4.44	2.99	....	2.97	.....	.....	.....	2.22	8.18
Decking and disposal.	7.90	3.57	....	.....	.....	.....	.....	0.03	3.60
Ventilation.........	.....	.....	1.52	0.05	.....	.....	.....	.....	1.57
Pumping and drainage	0.65	.....	....	0.54	.....	.....	.....	1.70	2.24
Concreting collar....	.....	.....	....	.....	.....	.....	0.22	.....	0.22
Supervision and workmen's compensation	2.80	4.81	....	.....	.....	.....	.....	.....	4.81
Miscellaneous.......	4.21†	.....	....	0.12	.....	.....	.....	0.51	0.63
Total direct.......	42.66	$36.17	$8.14	$6.58	$6.37	$6.09	$0.22	$4.85	$68.42
Proportion of general charges..									2.51
Total cost per ft..									$70.93

* Includes $3.06 labor, $3.56 material. † Includes 3.28 man-hr of blacksmithing, steel sharpening, drill repair and general surface.

Magma No 7 shaft, Ariz (7); 7.5 by 16.5 ft. Costs for 1 465 ft of depth (1931):

Preparation and plant expense	Labor	Supplies	Total
Hoist installation......	$886	$568	$1 454
Headframe.............	976	574	1 550
Collar.................	....	....	1 623
Change room...........	318	440	758
Stations...............	928	211	1 139
Tail drifts.............	913	232	1 145
Total...........................			$7 669
Total per ft of shaft..............			$5.24

Sinking crew (per ft)	
Jiggers............................	$ 4.39
Shaftmen...........................	10.37
Toplanders.........................	2.62
Bonus..............................	22.03
Total..............................	$39.41

Total cost per ft	Labor	Supplies	Power	Total per ft
Preliminary.........................	$ 1.71	$ 1.19	$....	$ 2.90
Sinking crew (above).................	39.41	......	......	39.41
Explosive............................		5.54	......	5.54
Timber..............................	1.42	10.20	......	11.62
Compressed air......................			1.16	1.16
Hoisting.............................	4.84	0.71	0.22	5.77
Pumping.............................	0.08	0.05	......	0.13
Air and water lines..................	0.12	0.64	......	0.76
Power lines.........................	0.03	0.02	......	0.05
Ventilation..........................	0.02	0.34	......	0.36
Dump...............................	0.26	0.05	......	0.31
Miscellaneous.......................	1.12	0.87	......	1.99
Total direct.......................	$49.01	$19.61	$1.38	$70.00
Preparation and plant expense (above)...				5.24
Total cost per ft..				$75.24

Magma No 5 shaft, Ariz (31), vert, 4-comp, 8 by 21-ft rock section, sunk from surface to 2 531-ft depth. 24-hr cycle: setting up 0.5 hr, drilling 5.5 hr, blasting 1.5 hr, mucking 13.5 hr, timbering 3 hr. Timber, 10 by 10-in, sets 4-8 ft apart. Powder per ft, 25 lb 40% gelatin. Costs (1925-28):

Sinking plant expense	Labor	Supplies	Total
" 500 " hoist*.............	....	......	$ 3 242
" 2550 " hoist*........	$ 921	$ 776	1 697
Towers..............	1 201	1 629	2 830
Collars and sheaves....	850	2 463	3 313
Skips and cages.......	2 935	810	3 745
Pumps and motors.....	3 206	8 713	11 919
Change and dry room..	3 171	303	3 474
Total...................			$30 220
Total per ft of shaft..............			$11.94

Sinking crew (per ft)	
Jiggers @ $6.00†......................	$ 3.85
Shaftmen @ $5.50†...................	16.39
Toplanders @ $4.13†..................	2.96
Trammers @ $4.13†..................	0.58
Sinking bonus.......................	29.76
Total...............................	$53.54

* Installation cost. † Base wage.

Total cost per ft	Labor	Supplies	Power	Total per ft
Sinking crew (above)	$53.54	$.....	$....	$ 53.54
Explosive	......	4.12	.....	4.12
Timber	2.08	14.76	.....	16.84
Compressed air	......	......	2.61	2.61
Hoisting	4.84	0.38	1.30	6.52
Pumping	5.96	0.71	1.32	7.99
Air and water lines	0.84	1.72	......	2.56
Power lines	0.58	2.13	......	2.71
Ventilation	0.08	1.38	......	1.46
Dump	1.14	0.53	......	1.67
Miscellaneous	2.20	2.28	......	4.48
Total	$71.26	$28.01	$5.23	$104.50
Sinking plant expense (above)				11.94
Total cost per ft				$116.44

Matahambre shaft No 2, Cuba (32), vert, 8 by 25-ft rock sec, 4-compt, sunk 2 057 ft from surface; water, max 5 gal per min. First 70 ft concrete-lined; supported below with steel sets: plates and dividers, 6-in 25-lb H-beams; posts, 3 by 3 by $^3/_8$-in angles. Below 1 050-ft depth, double end plates used, the outer plates overlapping the ends of wall plates. 12 bearer sets of 12-in 31.8-lb I-beams under wall plates and dividers. Total steel, including pockets and stations, 541.3 lb per ft of shaft. Lagging, 2-in plank. Holes per round, 32–33; ft drilled per ft of shaft, 44.5; advance per round, 4.92 ft. Powder, 30 and 40% gelatin, 28.3 lb per ft. Power, 918 kw-hr per ft. (1929–31).

Cost per ft of preparing site, and sinking equipment

	Labor	Suppl	Total		Labor	Suppl	Total
Eng'g and supervision	$0.51	$0.08	$0.59	Blower	.....	$0.64	$0.64
Preparing site	0.29	0.04	0.33	Bin and dumping gear	$0.24	0.47	0.71
Concrete collar	0.74	1.48	2.22	Buckets	.....	0.24	0.24
Transformers and line	0.43	1.01	1.44	Drills	.....	1.57	1.57
Water and air lines	0.36	1.70	2.06	Drill hose	.....	0.33	0.33
Hoist and headframe	0.61	5.66	6.27	Drill steel	.....	0.83	0.83
Hoist cables	0.01	0.50	0.51				
Hoist house	0.08	0.29	0.37	Total	$3.27	$14.84	$18.11

Man-hours and total cost per ft

	Man-hr per ft			Cost per ft				
	Direct	Indirect	Total	Total labor	Supplies	Power	General expense	Total
Engineering and supervision	9.16	.....	9.16	$ 6.80	$ 0.04	$.....	$.....	6.84
Drilling & blasting	8.55	4.18	12.73	10.42	0.93	3.69	......	15.04
Smoke delay	1.71	.....	1.71	1.40	......	......	......	1.40
Mucking	17.97	3.25	21.22	16.90	1.45	......	......	18.35
Shaft support	7.92	7.15	15.07	12.34	45.05	......	......	57.39
Ladders, guides	2.36	1.22	3.58	2.93	3.74	......	......	6.67
Concreting	1.78	.....	1.78	1.46	.85	......	......	2.31
Hoisting	9.63	3.46	13.09	9.00	4.19	7.17	......	20.36
Dumping and rock disposal	3.19	4.86	8.05	3.02	0.44	......	......	3.46
Ventilation	0.16	0.90	1.06	0.87	3.21	0.70	......	4.78
Water and air lines	1.07	.....	1.07	0.88	0.03	0.10	......	1.01
Explosive	....	......	......	......	6.70	......	......	6.70
Contract bonus and crew exp	....	......	......	......	......	......	16.72	16.72
Shop charges and misc repair	....	......	......	......	......	......	4.50	4.50
	63.50	25.02	88.52	$66.02	$66.63	$11.66	$21.22	$165.53
Preparing site and sinking equipment (above)								18.11
Total cost per ft								$183.64

22. WORKING SHAFTS, COAL MINES

No 261 mine, 2 hoisting shafts, Caretta, W Va (33). Skip shaft, rectangular with oval ends, 12 by 28 ft on axes of rock sec, 563 ft deep. Manway shaft, same shape, about 16 by 29 ft, 572 ft deep. Both sunk from surface through sandstones and shales, water-bearing for first 300 ft; about 200 ft in each shaft were grouted. Concrete-lined, steel buntons; no temporary timbering required except near surface. Concrete, cu yd per ft of shaft: skip shaft, 3.87; manway 4.48. Powder 40% gelatin, lb per ft: skip shaft, 15.3; manway, 19.8. Man-hr and costs (1922–23):

Man-hour per ft	Skip shaft	Manway	Man-hour per ft	Skip shaft	Manway
Drilling, blasting	17.0	22.2	Rock disposal and miscel		
Mucking	32.1	43.8	surface	0.6	3.4
Guides, buntons	5.4	10.2	Miscel, including grouting	9.6	9.8
Concreting	17.4	26.6	Supervision	10.6	15.3
Hoisting	10.6	15.3			
Pumping and piping	2.0	5.3		105.3	151.9

Cost per ft	Skip shaft			Manway shaft		
	Labor	Supplies	Total	Labor	Supplies	Total
Excavation	$ 57.50	$ 50.74	$108.24	$ 74.00	$ 65.90	$139.90
Concrete	25.30	37.00	62.30	27.10	42.88	69.98
Guides	1.34	2.53	3.87	1.93	2.19	4.12
Buntons	3.06	4.61	7.67	4.65	6.95	11.60
Formwork (surface)	0.20	0.13	0.33	0.16	0.11	0.27
Reinforcement		3.58	3.58		3.69	3.69
Grouting	18.80	5.80	24.60	20.29	6.91	27.20
Piping				0.25	0.45	0.70
Miscellaneous				2.17	1.46	3.63
Total	$106.20	$104.39	$210.59	$130.55	$130.54	$261.09

No. 261 mine, air shaft (33), circular, 19 ft rock diam, concrete-lined to 17-ft inside diam, 563 ft deep; sunk from surface near the preceding Grouting for depth of 168 ft. Concrete, cu yd per ft of shaft, 2.62; powder, 40% gelatin, 13.7 lb per ft. Man-hr and costs (1922–23):

Man-hr per ft	
Drilling, blasting	18.4
Mucking	32.5
Guides, buntons	3.4
Concreting	18.3
Hoisting	11.6
Pumping and piping	3.5
Rock disposal and miscel surface	1.9
Miscel, including grouting	4.8
Supervision	11.6
Total	106.0

Costs per ft	Labor	Suppl	Total
Excavation	$51.90	$45.57	$ 97.47
Concrete	16.30	23.70	40.00
Formwork (surface)	0.08	0.06	0.14
Reinforcement		0.15	0.15
Grouting	11.19	1.82	13.01
Piping	1.00	1.80	2.80
Miscellaneous	1.68	1.12	2.80
Total	$82.15	$74.22	$156.37

Sevier Valley shaft, Utah, (7); vert, 3-compt, 17 by 25-ft rock sec, 182 ft deep; concreted. Costs per ft (1924–26):

Sinking labor:		Total sinking:		Concreting:	
Bosses	$ 7.00	Labor	$40.10	Labor	$ 42.00
Shaftmen	18.50	Explosive	3.56	Bonus, eng'g, super-	
Hoistmen	5.00	Miscel	7.94	vision	5.43
Topmen	4.60	Total	$51.60	Supplies	117.50
Other	5.00			Total concrete	$164.93
Total	$40.10			Total sinking	51.60
				Total cost, per ft	$216.53

23. WITWATERSRAND SHAFTS

Shafts of large capacity on the Witwatersrand, So Africa, rectangular and timbered, were estimated (19) in 1920–21 to cost approx £40–£50 per ft, or, at aver sterling exchange of $3.75 then prevailing, $150–$190 per ft.

City Deep, Ltd. Low hoisting capac and cost of sinking and maintenance in heavy ground precluded use of inclines below 5 300-ft depth; hence, for 7 000-ft depth, a vert circular shaft of 20-ft clear diam was designed to hoist 2 000 ton ore daily, handle all men and supplies and pass 300 000 cu ft air per min. Hoisting planned in 2 stages of 2 500 and

4 500 ft, lower stage being the shorter to reduce size and heating effect of underground electric hoist. Shaft comprises 2 cageways, with pipe and cable space (no ladderway); concrete-ring supports (Art 15) carry wooden sills outside cageways, for attachment of pipes, cables and guides, the latter acting only on one side of cage, without central dividers. Sinking plant: 18 by 54-in direct-acting steam hoist, drums 7 by 3 ft; 15 by 30-in geared hoist; 18 by 48 bailing engine; 3-ton buckets; 40-in Sirocco fan. 9 water-fed sinking Leyner drills made 35–40 holes per round; aver advance, 2 ft per 8-hr shift. Water, 30 000 gal per day. First 2 950 ft (in firm rock), sunk in 1920–21, cost £29–6s per ft, or, at aver sterling exchange of $3.75 then prevailing, $110 per ft (19).

Government Gold Mining Areas. Southeast 7-compt shaft was sunk 233 ft from 1 738 to 1 971 ft, during Mch, 1912. Rock: 155 ft quartzite, 78 ft shale. 7-lb hammers used in double-hand drilling (benches drilled single-handed). Ventilation by brattice. Water was hoisted. (An example of sinking with hand drilling, now largely replaced by machine).

Labor per shift:		Depth holes	3.5 to 5 ft
1 White foreman		Aver advance per mo	194.3 ft (b)
1 White assistant foreman		Water, gal per min	21.0
82 Native drillers (a)		Timber, pitch pine:	
4 White timbermen (a)		Wall plates	9 by 9 in
11 Native helpers		End-plates	9 by 9 in
Size, rock sec	45 by 10 ft	Dividers	7 by 9 in
Number holes per round	40 to 45	Guides	4 by 8 in

(a) Timbermen worked 1 shift per day, drillers 3 8-hr shifts. (b) Aver of Jan, Feb, Mch, 1912.

Randfontein ventilation shaft, circular, 23.5 ft rock diam, 22 ft inside lining. Crew, white foreman and 40 natives per shift. Round, 58 holes. Lined with concrete, lowered in self-dumping buckets to sinking platform. Costs per ft (1925–27) are converted at aver sterling exchange then prevailing of $4.85.

Sinking 3 421 ft of shaft	$ 71.78
Concreting 3 071 ft of shaft	37.20
Hoisting	14.93
Shaft equipment	9.98
Surface equipment	24.05
Total cost per ft	$157.94

Simmer & Jack Mines, Ltd; 6-compt. 13.5 by 38-ft rock sec, designed for 6 350-ft depth, started 1934. Water, 400 gal per min, pumped into skips. Sinking crew, 2 whites and 60–66 natives per shift. Drilling aver round of 104 holes, 5 ft deep, with 18 drills, requires about 3.5 hr; mucking, 4.5 hr. More than 5 000 ft of shaft was sunk at aver of 204 ft per month. Timbering, 9 by 9-in pitch pine, 239 linear ft per set; interval of sets, 6 ft. Bearers of steel H-beams every 100 ft.

Vlakfontein No 1 shaft, vert, 6 compts in line; 14.5 by 43-ft rock section. Round of 100 holes: cut holes, 7 ft deep; others, 6 ft; 18–20 hand-held drifter drills; drilling time 2 hr, 46 natives at shaft bottom. Mucking crew, 80 natives; mucking time for 225 tons, usually 4 hr. Period from blast to blast, 7 to 9, usually 8 hr. Advance, 13–14 ft per day; month of Mch, 1936, 422 ft; aver for 8 months, Feb–Sept, 1936, 350 ft. Pitch pine timber: 9 by 9-in plates and dividers; 8 by 8-in corner posts; 4 by 10-in inner posts; sets 6.75 ft c-c. Steel bearers under end plates, and under dividers between compts 2 and 3, 4 and 5, and 5 and 6. Bearers for compts 4, 5 and 6 placed every 100 ft, others every 200 ft. Timbering crew, 2 timbermen and 16 natives, working during drilling period. This is one of the most recent shafts sunk on the Rand.

24. SHAFTS WITH CONCRETE LININGS

Edith shaft, Jerome, Ariz (35), 3-compt, rock sec approx 17 by 8 ft, was concrete-lined in 1921; mixture, 1 : 2 : 5. Upper 575 ft and 2 stations (Section A, see below) lined by contract, company paying actual expenses, contractor receiving bonus of half the saving below successful bid; in lower 630 ft with 5 stations (Section B), labor received bonus based on aver daily progress for entire job. In both cases ground was practically the same, and shaftmen received current shaft wages aside from bonus. See following table for details.

Section A: 575 ft depth; 1231 cu yd concrete; aver advance per working day, 7.2 ft Section B: 630 ft depth; 1174 cu yd concrete; aver advance per working day, 9.1 ft	Labor, including supervision	Cement, sacks @ $1.10	Sand and gravel, cu yd @ $2.50	Power, kw-hr @ 2¢	Reinforcement, lb @ $0.10	Lumber for forms	Bonus	Total cost per ft
Per ft lined:								
Section A: quantity......	....	11.4	2.6	44.1	10	....	......	....
cost...........	$15.35	12.56	6.51	0.88	1.00	1.50	5.35	43.15
Section B: quantity......	....	9.9	2.3	46.5	10	....	......	....
cost...........	$ 8.04	10.92	5.69	0.93	1.00	1.50	3.26	31.34
Total lining: quantity.....	....	10.6	2.4	45.4	10	....	......	....
cost........	$11.53	11.70	6.08	0.90	1.00	1.50	4.26	36.97
Per cu yd concrete:								
Section A: quantity......	....	5.3	1.2	20.6	4.7	......	......	......
cost...........	$ 7.17	5.87	3.04	0.41	0.47	0.70	2.50	20.16
Section B: quantity......	....	5.3	1.2	25.0	5.4	......	......	......
cost...........	$ 4.32	5.86	3.05	0.50	0.54	0.80	1.75	16.82
Total lining: quantity....	....	5.3	1.2	22.7	5.0	......	......	......
cost........	$ 5.78	5.86	3.05	0.45	0.50	0.75	2.13	18.52

Cost of supervision: Section A, $10 per day; Section B, $225 per month.

Sacramento shaft, Bisbee, Ariz (36). Timbering replaced by concrete lining (1915–16) for 1 645 ft of depth. 1 service, 2 skip and 2 cage compartments; concrete walls cast between skipways and between skip and cageways; pre-cast concrete dividers, 10 by 10 in and 6 ft 2 in long, between cageways. Shaft remained in service 14 hr daily, with 10 hr allowed for concreting. Aggregates were stored in special bins on top, trammed through adit to shaft at 71 ft below collar and chuted to mixer located 1 set below.

For delivery to and design of forms, see Art 14. Aver wall thickness, 15 in; thin lining and all partitions reinforced. Concrete poured at 3 different horizons in rotation. Shaft crew: 2 men in each compt, 1 pipeman, 1 foreman, total 12. Mixer crew: 1 man measuring aggregates, 4 tramming, 1 helping to dump cars and measuring cement, 1 tripping to mixer and measuring water, 1 foreman discharging mixer, total 8; when mixer was idle, its crew pre-cast the dividers or handled timber. Aver time per 5-ft course: loading tools and cleaning shaft, 30 min; removing timbers, 98 min; raising and setting forms, 84 min; connecting concrete pipe, 28 min; mixing and pouring, 78 min; unloading cages and cleaning tools, 17 min; miscel, 39 min; total, 6 hr 14 min. At first, 1 course was completed in 8 hr; later 2, and once 3 courses in 10 hr. Aver wages per day: shaftmen, $5.47; pipemen, $6.22; electricians, $5.22; laborers at quarry, $2.40; laborers mixing concrete, $2.

Cost per cu yd of finished concrete (6 270 cu yd)			
Lining and partitions:		**Pre-cast dividers:**	
Quarrying and crushing	$1.13	Aggregates..........	$ 1.69
Transport to bins.....	0.22	Cement..............	4.13
Cost of bins..........	0.34	Labor mixing........	5.02
Cost of aggregate...	$1.69	Reinforcement.......	3.12
Cement..............	3.44	Pipe cores..........	0.80
Mixing..............	0.56	Forms..............	0.39
Cost of piping.......	0.39	Miscel..............	0.58
Cost of forms........	0.75	Total.............	$15.73
Total............	$6.83		
Total expenditure..$42 796.47		....................$3 663.32	
Cost per ft of shaft..... 26.01		.... 2.23	

Cost of concreting per ft of shaft depth (1 645 ft)				
Shaft and surface alterations..............	$0.73	Miscel supplies........		$ 4.98
Alining guides..........	0.34	New guides, ladders:		
Shaft labor:		Labor.........	$0.93	
Removing timber	$3.08	Timber........	0.41	1.34
Setting forms....	3.04	Hoistmen.............		1.13
Pouring concrete.	2.62	Supervision..........		2.05
Pipework.......	1.41	Accident compensation.		0.05
On power cables.	1.00	11.15	Total.............		$50.71
Concrete (as above)....		26.01	Credit timber.........		1.70
Pre-cast dividers (as above)..............		2.23	Net total cost per ft..		$49.01
Reinforcement........		0.70			

Speculator shaft, Butte, Mont. In places, bad ground required use of jacket sets outside regular timbering (Art 13), and kept special crew constantly on shaft repair. 500-ft section of timbering replaced by concrete lining, anchored by bearer rings 6 ft high, hitched deeply into rock walls, with 15-in wall between bearers formed clear of rock and backfilled. Mixture 1 : 2 : 4. Comparative repairs: when timbered, 32 man-shifts per day, $5 833 per month (1920 equivalent); when concreted (aver of 6 months in 1920), 2.4 man-shifts per day, $389.75 per month (34).

Granite Mountain shaft, Butte, Mont (34), caved from 1 700 to 2 800-ft level after a fire in 1917. To reopen in 1918, caved section was concrete-lined for 1 340 ft, of which 813 ft were first steel-framed for immediate support. Steel sets: plates, 7 700 ft of 6-in 12.5-lb I-beams; vert members 8 130 ft of 10-in 25-lb I-beams; connections, $3/8$-in angles and splice bars, with $5/8$-in rivets. Shaft sec, 4-compt, 20 ft 9 in by 7 ft 6 in outside of sets. Concrete lining: anchored with bearers at selected points; wall, 15–20 in thick, formed clear of rock between bearers, and backfilled except for clearances of 4 in or less, where concrete was poured to rock. Solid partitions: 10 in thick between main hoist compts, 9.5 in thick between main hoist and man hoist, 9 in thick between man hoist and pipeway. Mixture 1 : 2 : 4; total cu yd in place, 6 380; cement 38 280 sacks, sand 3 190 cu yd, crushed rock 1 075 cu yd, slag 4 655 cu yd, reinforcement of 376 tons. 7 sections in progress at one time. For costs see following table:

	With steel frame			Without steel frame		
Day's work...............	15			30		
Ft of shaft concreted.......	82.5			75		
Cost per ft	Labor	Material	Total	Labor	Material	Total
Forms...................	$ 9.65	$ 1.34	$10.99	$ 3.40	$ 0.25	$ 3.65
Reinforcing.............	6.55	10.90	17.45	5.20	14.10	19.30
Strip and set forms.......	20.50	....	20.50	16.70	....	16.70
Concreting..............	17.60	....	17.60	7.95	....	7.95
Handling material........	9.15	....	9.15	9.15	....	9.15
Cement.................	....	13.35	13.35	....	11.50	11.50
Sand...................	....	2.26	2.26	....	1.60	1.60
Slag...................	....	4.90	4.90	....	3.45	3.45
Concreting per ft.......	$63.45	$32.75	$96.20	$42.40	$30.90	$73.30
Structural steel............	....	31.40	31.40	....	....	....
Placing steel..............	4.80	....	4.80	....	....	....
Total per ft..........	$68.25	$64.15	$132.40	....	....	....

Denn shaft, Ariz (37), 2 242 ft deep, of which 2 230 ft were concreted to replace old timbering; work done during a shutdown. Shaft has 3 compts to 1 350-ft depth, including 2 hoist and 1 large compt for piping and dinky hoist; below 1 350 ft, 4 full compts. Concrete lining: thickness 10–36 in, depending on the ground, with 8-in curtain walls reinforced in heavy ground with I-beams. Concrete placed, 9 934 cu yd, requiring 10 934 bbl cement, 5 991 ton sand, 9 052 ton crushed rock, 55 750 lb celite, which facilitated removal of forms and kept aggregate in suspension; mixture, 1 : 3 : 5. Batch, $1/3$ cu yd, containing 1.51 cu ft cement, 4.59 cu ft sand, 7.56 cu ft rock; total, 13.66 cu ft of materials for 9 cu ft of mix. Mixed on surface and delivered by 4-in pipe to a sinking bucket with discharge spout, thence by iron launder to the forms. Crew, 7 men and shift boss; 3 men on mixer and charging chutes at surface. Ft of shaft lined in 30 days, 455 max, 115 min (heavy ground), 234 aver. Total cost (reported 1932), $178 972, including about $30 000 due to shut-down, and with no credit for salvage, of which there was some. Following costs for concreting per overall ft of shaft do not reflect change in shaft plan below 1 350 ft; costs per cu yd are absolute.

	Total	Per ft	Per cu yd		Total	Per ft	Per cu yd
Cement.............	$33 569	$15.05	$3.38	Direct labor........	$ 46 159	$20.70	$ 4.65
Sand...............	6 157	2.76	0.62	Eng'g and supervision	4 496	2.02	0.45
Rock...............	11 865	5.32	1.20	Hoisting..........	19 250	8.63	1.94
Celite..............	793	0.36	0.08	Water and light.....	3 373	1.51	0.34
Steel..............	1 807	0.81	0.18	Miscel.............	13 358	5.99	1.34
Timber.............	2 495	1.12	0.25	Total concret'g...	$162 539	$72.89	$16.36
Miscel..............	522	0.23	0.05	Plant (below).....	16 433	7.37	1.66
Total material......	$57 208	$25.65	$5.76	Total.........	$178 972	$80.26	$18.02
Guide pockets........	3 989	1.79	0.40				
Handling materials....	11 337	5.09	1.14	Cost of concreting plant			
Testing materials.....	2 057	0.92	0.21	Mixing plant....................			$ 1 586
Plant maintenance....	1 312	0.59	0.13	Plant for handling materials.......			2 141
				Concrete forms...................			10 824
				4-in pipe column.................			1 882
				Total...................			$16 433
				Total per ft concreted.........			$7.37
				Total per cu yd..............			$1.66

BIBLIOGRAPHY

1. Practical Shaft Sinking. F. Donaldson. McGraw-Hill Book Co, N Y, 1910
2. Shaft Sinking under Difficult Conditions. J. Riemer. Trans by Corning and Peele. John Wiley & Sons, N Y, 1907
3. Rules and Regulations for Metal Mines. *Bull No 75*, U S Bureau of Mines, 1915
4. Safe Mechanical Equipment for Use in Shaft Sinking. R. H. Kudlich. *Tech Paper No 276*, U S Bureau of Mines, 1922
5. Present Practice in the Design and Sinking of Shafts. R. G. Johnson. *Coal Age*, Sept 13, 1923
6. Shaft Sinking Equipment. L. Eaton. *E & M Jour*, Mch and Apl, 1932
7. Shaft-Sinking Practices and Costs. E. D. Gardner and J. F. Johnson. *Bull No 357*, U S Bur of Mines, 1932
8. Recent Developments in Mining Practice on the Witwatersrand. R. S. G. Stokes. *Trans Inst Min & Met*, Vol 45
9. Inclined-Shaft Timbering. A. Neustaedter. *E & M Jour*, Feb 22, 1919
10. Cost of Shaft Sinking at Cripple Creek. *E & M Jour*, Aug 15, 1925
11. Octagonal Ventilation Shaft of Davis-Daly Copper Co. J. L. Bruce. *Trans A I M E*, Vol 66, p 252
12. Breaking the World's Record in Shaft-Sinking. W. Fitch, Jr. *Min & Sci Pr*, Nov 26, 1921
13. Shaft Sinking in Extremely Tough Rocks. W. Y. Westervelt. *Eng & Con*, Mch 10, 1915
14. Development Practice in the Wisconsin Zinc District. E. R. Shorey. *Min & Met*, Aug, 1920
15. Shaft Sinking Methods in the Butte District. H. Drullard. *E & M Jour*, Mch 20, 1920
16. Shaft Sinking Methods at Butte. N. B. Braly. *Trans A I M E*, Vol 46, p 151
17. Shaft Raising at the Harold Mine. C. F. Jackson. *E & M Jour*, Apl 7, 1917
18. Sinking No 5 Shaft at the Tamarack Mine, Michigan. W. E. Parnall, Jr. *Proc Lake Sup Min Inst*, Mch, 1901
19. Scheme for Working the City Deep Mine at Depth of 7 000 Ft. E. H. Clifford. *Trans Inst Min & Met*, Vol 30
20. Concrete Timbering of Mine Shafts. E. R. Jones. *Coal Age*, Oct 26, 1912.
21. Application of Cement Mixtures by Machinery. G. J. Young. *E & M Jour*, Mch 26, 1921
22. Modern Practice in Mining (Vol 2). R. A. S. Redmayne. Longmans, Green & Co, London, 1925
23. Practical Coal Mining. Geo L. Kerr. Griffin & Co, London, 1914
24. Practical Coal Mining (Vol 1 & 2). W. S. Boulton. Gresham Pub Co, London, 1907
25. Cast-iron Tubbing. A. Lupton. *Iron & Coal Tr Rev*, Feb 1, 1895
26. Sinking by Kind-Chaudron Process. *Proc Instn C E*, England, Vol 71, p 178; *Rev Univ des Mines*, Oct, 1902
27. Leistungen und Kösten Schachtabteufen im Ruhrbezirk. L. Hoffmann. *Glückauf*, Vol 37, 1901
28. Construction and Equipment of the Ross Shaft, Homestake Mining Co. Bjorge, Ross, Johnson, Staple and Wiggert. A I M E, *Tech Pub* 621
29. Cost of Shaft Sinking. M. J. Elsing. *E & M Jour*, Oct 26, 1931
30. Shaft Sinking Methods and Costs, and Cost of Plant and Equipment at the Macassa Mine, Kirkland Lake, Ont. G. A. Howes and C. F. Jackson, *Inf Circ* 6674, U S Bur of Mines
31. Mining Methods and Costs at the Magma Mine, Ariz. F. W. Snow, *Inf Circ* 6168, U S Bur of Mines, 1929
32. Sinking and Equipment of the No 2 Shaft at Minas de Matahambre. D. D. Homer and R. H. Cromwell. *Explosives Engineer*, Feb, 1933
33. Shaft Sinking Methods, Practices, and Costs of the Consolidation Coal Co at its No 261 Mine, Caretta, W Va. L. E. Kelley. *Inf Circ* 6602, U S Bur of Mines, 1932
34. Use of Cement and Concrete in the Underground Workings of the North Butte Co. R. Linton. *Proc Eng Soc of Western Pa*, Vol 38
35. Cost of Concreting Mine Shafts. E. E. Campbell. *Eng and Con*, Nov 16, 1921
36. Concreting the Sacramento Shaft at Bisbee. *Min & Sci Pr*, Oct 7, 1916
37. Concreting the Denn Shaft. F. P. Brunel. *E & M Jour*, Dec, 1932

SECTION 8

SHAFT-SINKING IN UNSTABLE AND WATERBEARING GROUND

BY

FRANCIS DONALDSON, M. E.

REVISED FOR THE SECOND EDITION BY

EDWIN S. JARRETT, C. E.

AND LARGELY REWRITTEN FOR THE THIRD EDITION BY

RALPH H. CHAMBERS, D. ENG.

Note.—Numbers in parentheses in text refer to Bibliography at end of this section.

SHAFT-SINKING IN UNSTABLE AND WATERBEARING GROUND

1. DIFFICULTIES AND AVAILABLE EXPEDIENTS

Underground water is the principal cause of difficulties arising in sinking a shaft in unstable ground, as sand, gravel, clay, or silt. Even in dry soils, the removal of lateral support around an excavation may cause a fall, or flow, of the material into the excavated space, and when water is present this tendency is greatly increased. The first requisite of the shaft is, therefore, a lining or wall; but, if water is pumped out the ground-water will flow under the lining into the excavation, carrying with it the finer particles of the soil; or partially liquefied clay or silt may be forced up into the shaft by the superincumbent weight. In such case, continued excavation and pumping may cause a continued flow, with slips and falls of the ground, distortion of shaft lining, subsidence of the surface around the shaft mouth and settlement of the sinking equipment and adjacent buildings. This situation may prevent further progress, except by a change of method. Hence, sinking methods requiring pumping have been largely replaced by those in which pumping is unnecessary.

Boulders in soft ground often cause trouble and expense. They may force the shaft out of plumb, or their removal may require excavation to some depth below the lining, at the risk of flow of the surrounding ground with the consequences noted above. The presence of many boulders may cause large and unforeseen increase in cost, or even jeopardize success.

Seal to rock. The shaft having been sunk to rock, or other stable and impervious stratum, a watertight seal must be made between the shaft lining and the rock, and this, at a depth where the hydrostatic pressure of the ground-water is a maximum, may be difficult.

Lateral pressure against the shaft lining varies in different kinds of ground and increases with the depth. Pressure per sq ft above ground-water level is usually not more than 30 lb per ft of depth below surface; below ground-water level, rarely more than 60 lb per ft of depth below surface, except that in partially liquefied clay or silt it may reach 90 lb.

Borings. The success and cost of shafts are so dependent upon the nature of the ground that careful preliminary study of subsurface conditions must be made. The borings are often too few in number or too inconclusive, and a shaft is sunk under adverse conditions which might have been avoided by locating it elsewhere, or which could have been more easily and cheaply surmounted by adopting some other method. Borings in soft ground are usually of the kind known as "wash borings" (Sec 9), which may be of little value unless properly sampled in their original and undisturbed position in the ground strata.

Methods of sinking in unstable ground are now well standardized. Older methods, such as vertical poling boards (analogous to the method used for tunneling), lining the shaft by horiz timbers suspended from trusses across the shaft mouth, or vertical shields jacked down below the timber lining, have been replaced by cheaper and more reliable methods. Among these are:

(a) Wood or steel sheet-piling, braced by horiz timbers or steel beams; or wood lagging placed horizontally between the flanges of steel beams, which are driven in advance of the excavation. These methods may be used to depths of 50 to 75 ft, or more, in dry ground, or where the water level has been previously lowered by pumping.

(b) Drop-shafts, with walls of reinforced concrete built above the surface, which sink as excavation advances. This is usually the cheapest and most reliable method for depths of 50 to 200 ft, or more.

(c) The pneumatic method, which is generally used in connection with drop-shafts in sinking through quicksand, or strata of boulders below the ground-water level, or when the sealing of the shaft to rock may be difficult. The limit of depth attainable by this method is about 115 ft below the ground-water level.

(d) Forced drop-shafts, for depths not attainable by ordinary drop-shafts.

(e) Freezing method, which is used for very deep shafts also.

(f) Grouting methods.

2. SHEET-PILING

Wood sheet-piling may be used as a temporary lining for small depths above water-level (Fig 1). This consists of planks, 10 to 12 in wide and 3 to 4 in thick, driven vertically around the sides of the excavation and braced by horiz timbers. The edges of the plank are usually tongued and grooved (Fig 2), or splined (Fig 3). The piles are set up in the bottom of a preliminary pit, around two sets of horiz bracing which serve as a guide frame, and are driven by hand, or by steam or air hammers, as excavation advances. Usually the piles are not more than 24 ft long and, if this length is not sufficient, two or more drives of piles are made, successively deeper. As each drive, below the first, must be set to clear the breast timbers above, the necessary excavation is thus increased. If cross-bracing is required it will interfere with the driving of the piles below, and it is therefore desirable, when the horiz dimensions of the shaft permit, to drive the piles around octagonal frames (Fig 4).

Lowering the ground-water level, by use of well-points, is often possible with wood piling. Well-points are perforated pipes, usually 2.6 in outside diam and 3.5 ft long, connected with 1.5 to 2-in pipes and driven 3 to 5 ft apart around the space to be excavated. The tops of the pipes are joined to a header pipe, just above water-level, and a pump is connected with the header. The bottoms of the well-points should not be much more than 25 ft below the pump. Pumping should begin some time in advance of the excavation, depending upon the nature of the ground. Lowering the ground-water level is most successful in medium and coarse sand and gravel. In very fine sand, clay and silt it is rarely feasible. The location of the well-points, when used in connection with wood sheet-piles, is shown in Fig 4, 5.

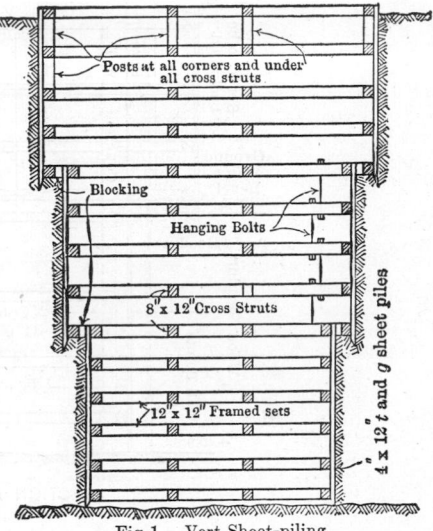

Fig 1.   Vert Sheet-piling

Wood lagging is a method of temporary shaft lining, which has recently come into use (Fig 5). It consists of square-edged wood planks, 10 to 12 in wide and 3 to 5 in thick, placed as the excavation advances behind the flanges of previously driven vert steel H beams. The steel beams are braced by sets of horiz timbers or steel beams. They may be 12 in deep, 53 lb per lineal ft, or larger or smaller, as required; driven to their full length in advance of the excavation, by steam or compressed-air hammers, and may be pulled out and salvaged on completion of the permanent lining. This method is applicable to depths of 50 ft or more, in dry ground, or to about 25 ft below original ground-water level, when this can be previously lowered by well-points, as already described. But the feasibility of the method depends upon whether the steel H-beams can be driven in proper location. With many boulders this may not be possible. The ground-water level can not be lowered below the tops of the well-points, and when these are driven to rock the water level may be 4 or 5 ft above the rock; in which case it may be necessary to use vert sheet-piles, wood or steel, to complete the excavation to rock.

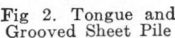
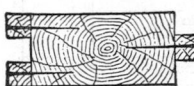

Fig 2. Tongue and Grooved Sheet Pile   Fig 3. Splined Sheet Pile

Steel sheet-piles can be used as a temporary or permanent lining. These are rolled, with edges which interlock with each other (Fig 6), in a great variety of widths and weights, and in flat, U-shaped and Z-shaped sections. Widths are from 8 1/2 to 19 5/8 in, weights per ft, from 21 to 64 lb, and the section moduli from 1.4 to 9.3-in cubed. They are rolled by Carnegie-Illinois Steel Co, Bethlehem Steel Co, Inland Steel Co, and the Jones & Laughlin Co, in the U S, and the Larsen, Kloeckner and Hoesch sections in Germany.

The special advantage of steel sheet-piles is that they are driven in advance of the excavation to their full length, down to rock or other impermeable stratum. There is thus a shield between the surrounding ground and the excavation. Steel sheet-piles are braced by sets of horiz timbers or steel beams, placed as excavation proceeds. In very soft ground the piles when exposed by excavation may be bent inward by ground pressure, to obviate which temporary bracing may be required at short vert intervals. Joints between sheet-piles are not entirely watertight and pumping is often necessary. The piles are threaded into each other and set up in a preliminary pit around two sets of the horiz bracing, used as a guide frame. They are driven by steam or compressed-air hammers, 2 or 3 ft at a time, successively around the frame until all are down to their full length. A permanent concrete lining may be built inside of the sheet-piles, after which the piles may be pulled

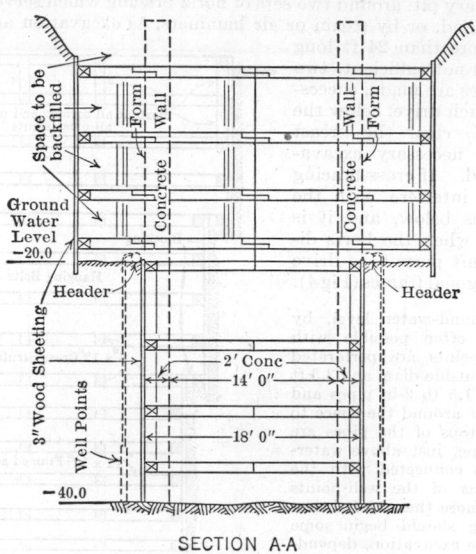

SECTION A-A

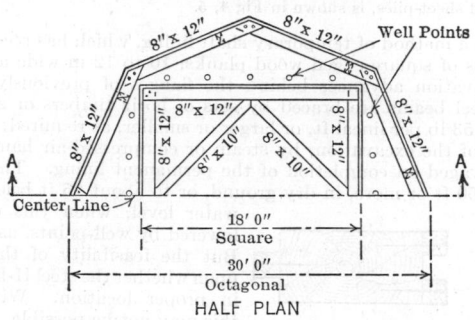

HALF PLAN

Fig 4.   Sheet-piling with Octagonal Frames

and salvaged. Shafts can be sunk to 75 ft depth by using steel piles, except in presence of many boulders.

In general, a combination of methods is used for sinking (Fig 7): wood sheet-piles, or wood lagging between vert steel beams, down to water-level, and steel sheet-piles below. Most of the excavation by any of these methods can be done by clam-shell or orange-peel buckets, operated by a stiff-leg derrick and a three-drum hoisting engine. The boom of the derrick should be at least 60 ft long, so that the mast and hoisting engine may be set far enough from the shaft mouth to be unaffected by the sinking operations.

Cost of sinking is usually least for horiz wood lagging. Steel piling costs more than the other modes of support, but can be used in partially liquefied clay or silt, where other methods are not feasible. At present-day prices and hourly labor rates of 40 cts for com-

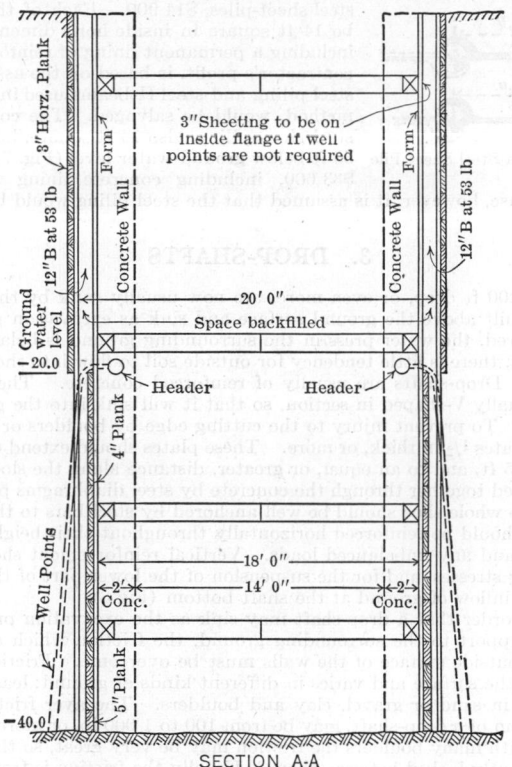

SECTION A-A

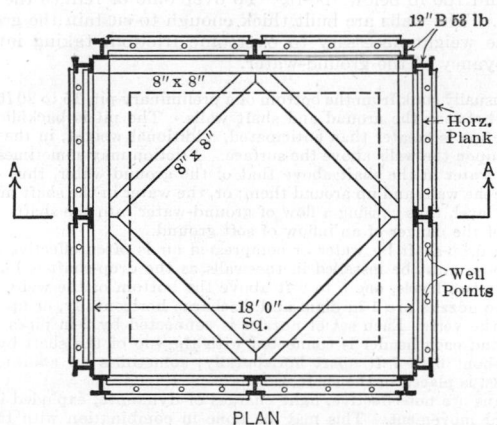

PLAN

Fig 5. Wood Lagging on Sheeting

mon labor, 75 cts for carpenters and $1 for hoisting-engineers, the cost of a 40-ft shaft, sunk by each method, is about as follows: wood sheet-piles, $13 600; wood lagging, $12 100;

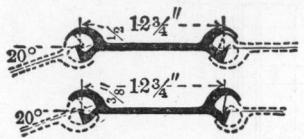

Fig 6.   Lackawanna Steel Sheet Pile

steel sheet-piles, $14 900.   Each of these shafts would be 14 ft square in inside horiz dimensions.   The cost, including a permanent lining of reinforced concrete and contractor's profit, is based on the assumption that the steel piling and steel H-beams used in the wood-lagging method, would be salvaged.   The cost of a shaft with steel sheet-piling, also 14 ft square, but 75 ft deep and 55 ft below ground-water level (Fig. 7), would be about $33 600, including concrete lining and contractor's profit.   In this case, however, it is assumed that the steel piling would be left in place.

3. DROP-SHAFTS

Shafts 50 to 200 ft deep, or even more, are now usually sunk by this method.   The shaft walls are built above the ground surface and sink as excavation proceeds.   As no pumping is required, the water press in the surrounding ground is balanced and, except in soft clay or silt, there is little tendency for outside soil to flow into the excavation.

Reinforcing.   Drop-shafts are usually of reinforced concrete.   The cutting edge at the bottom is usually V-shaped in section, so that it will sink into the ground below the excavation level.   To prevent injury to the cutting edge by boulders or by blasting, it is shod with steel plates $1/2$ in thick, or more.   These plates should extend up on the outside of the walls 3 to 5 ft, and to an equal, or greater, distance along the sloping inside faces. They are connected together through the concrete by steel diaphragms placed at frequent intervals, and the whole shoe should be well anchored by steel bars to the concrete walls. The shaft walls should be reinforced horizontally throughout their height, to sustain the ground pressure and any unbalanced loads.   Vertical reinforcement should also be provided for bending stresses, and for the suspension of the lower part of the shaft from the upper, in case of inflow of ground at the shaft bottom (Fig 8).

Friction.   In order that a drop-shaft may sink as the excavation proceeds, and thus furnish lateral support to the surrounding ground, the friction which develops between the ground and outside surface of the walls must be overcome.   Friction increases with the depth below the surface and varies in different kinds of ground: least in silt and successively greater in sand or gravel, clay and boulders.   The aver friction, between the surface and bottom of a drop-shaft, may be from 100 to 1 000 lb, or more, per sq ft of contact surface.   With many boulders the friction may be very great, so that the drop-shaft becomes permanently locked between them.   Usually the friction is from 350 and to 700 lb per sq ft, and in most cases it is safe to estimate the aver at 500 lb per sq ft for depths of 100 ft or less, and 700 lb below 100-ft.   To overcome or reduce the friction, there are several expedients.   The walls are built thick enough to sustain the ground pressure and also to furnish the weight necessary to overcome friction, taking into account loss of weight due to buoyancy of the ground-water.

Drop-shafts are usually sunk from the bottom of a preliminary pit, 15 to 20 ft deep, thus reducing the area of contact between the ground and shaft walls.   The pit is backfilled after the shaft is finished.   If the friction is greater than anticipated, additional weight, in the form of pig iron, or sand, can be loaded upon the walls above the surface.   Friction may sometimes be reduced by raising the level of the water in the shaft above that of the ground-water, thus causing a back flow under the bottom of the walls and up around them; or, the water in the shaft may be pumped down below ground-water level, thus causing a flow of ground-water into the shaft.   This must be carefully done because of the danger of an inflow of soft ground.

Jetting around a drop-shaft by water or compressed air is often effective in reducing friction. Piping for this purpose must be installed in the walls as the drop-shaft is built.   Jetting nozzles are usually placed at two levels, one 5 to 8 ft above the bottom of the walls, the other 8 to 12 ft above the first.   The nozzles are 1-in diam and discharge horizontally, or upwards at an angle of 22 1/2 degrees from the vert.   Each set of nozzles is connected by 2-in pipes with a horiz header 2 1/2 to 4-in diam, and each header is connected with the top of the shaft by a 4-in riser.   The nozzles should be about 6 to 7 ft apart horizontally; sometimes an additional set, discharging vertically downwards, is placed in the shaft walls.

When other means are not effective, light charges of dynamite, exploded in the shaft bottom, may start downward movement.   This may be done in combination with the other expedients.

Sinking.   Excavation is done by orange-peel or clam-shell buckets, operated by the equipment described in Art 2.   The shaft must be kept vertical and, in uniform ground, this can be done by excavating uniformly around the cutting edge.   Deviation from the vertical may be remedied by excavating on the high side, or placing additional weight

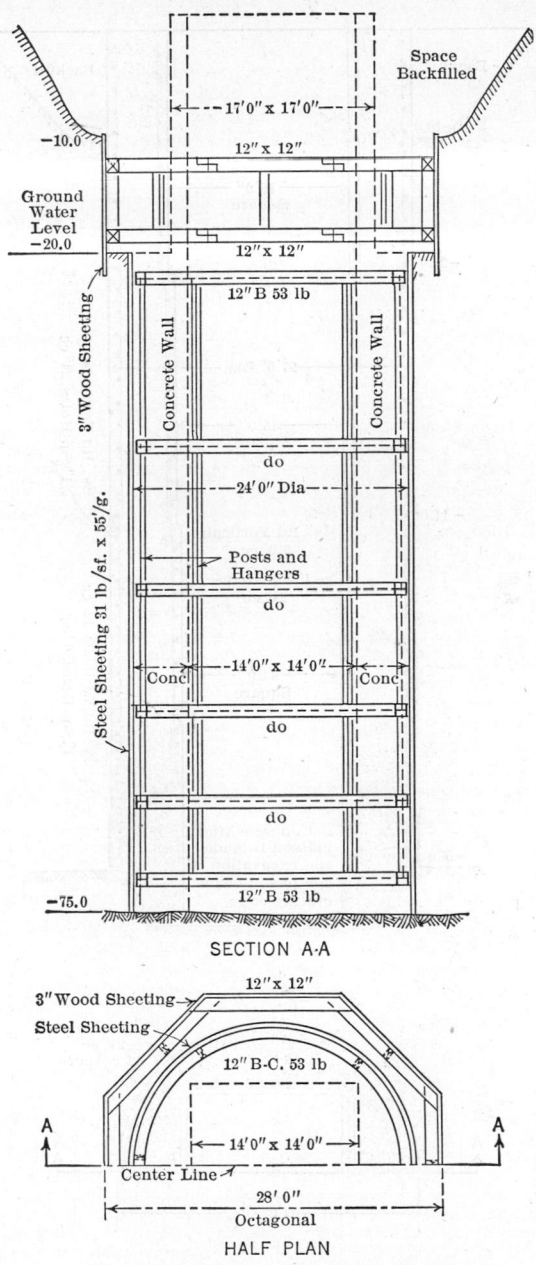

SECTION A·A

HALF PLAN

Fig 7. Combination Method of Sinking

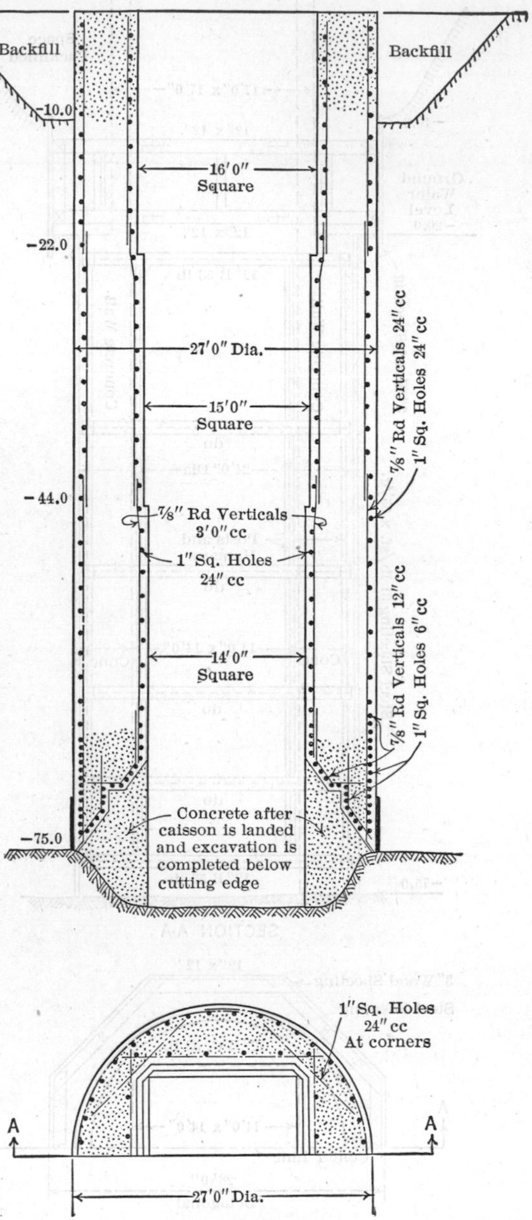

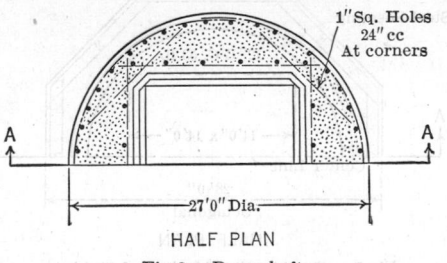

Backfill

Backfill

−10.0

16′ 0″
Square

−22.0

27′ 0″ Dia.

15′ 0″
Square

7/8″ Rd Verticals 24″ cc
1″ Sq. Holes 24″ cc

−44.0

7/8″ Rd Verticals
3′ 0″ cc

1″ Sq. Holes
24″ cc

14′ 0″
Square

7/8″ Rd Verticals 12″ cc
1″ Sq. Holes 6″ cc

Concrete after
caisson is landed
and excavation is
completed below
cutting edge

−75.0

1″ Sq. Holes
24″ cc
At corners

A   A

27′ 0″ Dia.

HALF PLAN

Fig 8.   Drop-shaft

on that side. It is especially important to keep the shaft vertical during the early part of the sinking. It is sometimes desirable to sink a deep shaft in two sections, the lower section from the bottom of the upper section. An example of this is a shaft for the St. Albert Colliery, St. Albert, Canada (Fig 9).

If boulders are encountered, the ground under them may be cut away until they roll into the excavation, but care must be taken to avoid an inrush of ground and displacement of the shaft. Drilling and blasting by divers may be required. It is important to keep the weight of the shaft well in excess of the resistance due to friction, or to make use of the other expedients already mentioned, so that the cutting edge may always be buried in the ground below the bottom of the excavation. This is especially necessary in very soft ground.

Sealing to rock. When the cutting edge has reached rock or other firm stratum, a watertight connection must be made between the shaft bottom and the rock. Just above the rock level there is often a stratum of boulders, gravel and sand, through which the ground-water flows under heavy press. It may then be necessary to use the pneumatic method (Art 4). It is possible, however, to seal the whole bottom of the shaft with concrete and grout with cement around the shaft bottom, through holes drilled through the concrete. The concrete is then removed.

The sealing of the St. Albert shaft is an example. The upper section of shaft was sunk 107 ft through sand and clay, and 13 ft into a 25-ft stratum of clay, the presence of which made it easy to pump out the upper shaft, and start the lower, which was sunk through the clay stratum, and sand and gravel below it, to rock at 200 ft depth. As the rock was soft shale it was excavated by orange-peel bucket until the cutting edge reached a depth of 215 ft. A weighted wooden box of conical shape (Fig 10) was then lowered, and concrete (1–2–4 mixture) placed around and over the box until the whole shaft bottom was sealed. The concrete was placed by covered buckets, lowered through the water and emptied through their tripping bottoms. After allowing the concrete to set the shaft was pumped out and cement grout was forced into the surrounding ground through holes drilled through the concrete. When the grout had set the concrete plug and the wooden box were removed in sections (Fig 10). Only a small infiltration of water occurred, which was soon stopped by fine materials flowing in from the surrounding ground.

Cost. At present day prices and labor rates (Art 2) and including contractor's profit, the cost of a drop-shaft, 14 ft square in inside dimensions, sunk and sealed without unusual difficulty, would be $450 to $500 per vert ft. In Art 2 the cost of a shaft 14 ft square inside and 75 ft deep, sunk with steel sheet-piles, was given as $33 600. A shaft of same size, sunk as a drop-shaft, would cost about $37 200. In the first case the depth is almost the limit to which a shaft can be sunk by piling, while drop-shafts can go to much greater depths at a decreasing cost per linear ft, as depth increases. In presence of boulders, sinking by steel piling would involve difficulties that might prove insurmountable, whereas, with drop-shafts boulders are readily handled unless present in great numbers, and even then they can be removed by using the pneumatic method (Art 4). For very soft ground, however, steel piling has a very definite place.

I—9

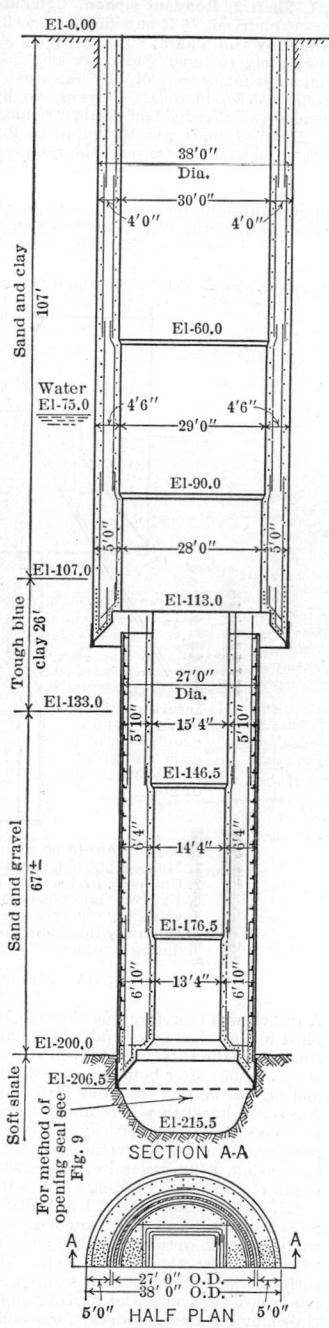

Fig 9. Drop-shaft in Two Sections. St. Albert Colliery, Canada

I. Shaft 2, Rondout siphon, Catskill aqueduct. The caisson for soft-ground portions of shaft was cylindrical, 26 ft outside diam, walls 2 ft 6 in thick. Shoe was built of 0.5 by 20-in steel plates, with 4 by 1-in filler at cutting edge, and was anchored to concrete by 80 3/4 by 30-in rods, attached alternately to inner and outer plates. Concrete consisted of 1 cement, 2 sand, 5 stone. Inner and outer forms were of 2 by 6-in vertical wood lagging, supported by angle-iron rings, tied through walls with 5/8-in rods. Caisson was built in 5- and 10-ft lifts to full depth of 55 ft, lifts being bonded together by 1-in vertical reinforcing rods, 4 ft c-c.

Finished shaft was 10 ft 8 in by 22 ft in clear. Borings showed 60 ft soft ground, the upper 6 ft being sandy loam, and the rest a material resembling blue clay when dry, but was completely saturated in place, flowing "like cold molasses and very sticky." On bed rock, and surrounded by soft soil, were numerous hard boulders of all sizes. The shaft site was leveled, shoe assembled upon short planks laid on ground, and concrete forms started. 5 ft of concrete was placed and allowed to set for a week; 10 ft more was then placed and when sufficiently set, sinking was begun. Mud was loaded into shaft buckets, sometimes with shovels, sometimes with water buckets, by men standing on plank rafts. Concrete was added as caisson sank. At a depth of 45 ft a layer of very soft mud was encountered, which ran in under one side of shoe, throwing caisson 2 ft out of plumb.

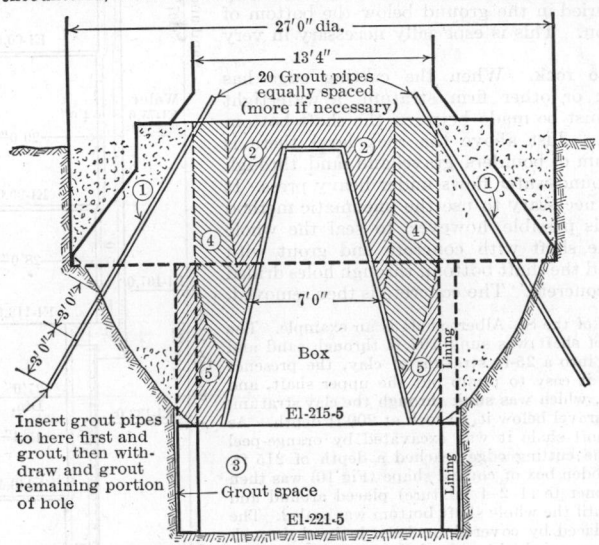

Operations to be followed in numerical order:
1. Make grout holes and grout up as indicated
2. Cut away first section of plug as shown
3. Excavate and place portion of lining before cutting plug to full size
4. Cut away second section of plug as shown
5. Cut away third and last section of plug to full opening and commence lining upwards

Fig 10.   Method of Opening the Seal, St. Albert Shaft

A trench was therefore dug through surface loam on high side of caisson, the material from it was piled against low side, and when sinking was resumed the caisson straightened up. About 6 ft from rock, the shoe was stopped by boulders for long enough time to allow mud to stick to caisson walls, so that after boulders were blasted out it was necessary to load caisson with 200 tons of clay, and also to agitate the mud with compressed air blown through 1.25-in pipes built into the wall. A layer of hardpan was found just over the rock, into which the cutting edge sank deep enough to seal the caisson automatically. Average progress, from building shoe to sealing of caisson was 1.2 ft per day, including concreting and delays. Cost per ft, before 1914: concrete and shoe, $61; labor excavating, $39; general expense, $32; total, $133. Before sinking was stopped by boulders, at depth of 50 ft, skin friction was less than 380 lb per sq ft; afterward, at same depth, over 500 lb.

II. Colliery shaft for D, L & W RR Co, near Wilkes-Barre, Pa (Fig 11). Caisson was of concrete, rectangular section, with rounded corners, and divided into 3 compartments by cross walls. End compartments were arranged to permit further subdivision by timber buntons. Outside dimensions 28 by 59 1/2 ft; total height 90 ft. Thickness of walls at bottom: sides 7 ft; ends, 5 ft 4 in; outer surfaces vertical, inner surfaces stepped, in lifts of 9 ft 8 in; thickness at top, 2 ft 8 in; main walls reinforced vertically and horizontally with 1- and 1.25-in rods. At 7 ft above shoe, caisson was closed by an air-tight deck, for sealing caisson to rock under air pressure (12).

Ground was leveled, shoe assembled, and 20 ft of concrete placed. Sinking was carried on day and night, each shift consisting of a foreman and 16 men in shaft. After shoe reached rock, the soft ground was held back temporarily with timber blocks wedged into place under horizontal

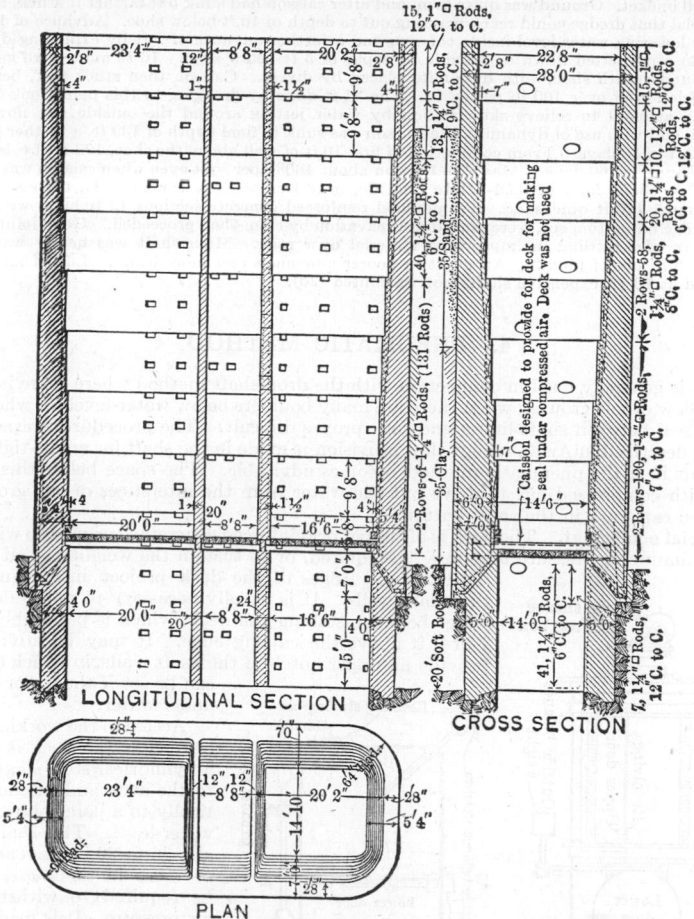

Fig. 11. Del, Lack & Western Colliery Caisson. (*Eng News*)

portion of the shoe. As this stratum was not firm enough to make a permanent seal, the shoe was undercut and shaft excavated 4 to 5 ft larger all around than inside section of caisson at bottom. In blasting, great care was taken not to break the ledge under shoe and blocking. Sound rock was found 15 ft below cutting edge, and a wall was built up to underside of caisson. Drain pipes disposed of water breaking through blocking, and were grouted after wall was finished and concrete had set. During construction of this wall, water was led to the pipes by building a small brick dam upon the ledge. Total depth of soft ground, 70 ft; average progress, including building of caisson and construction of temporary seal, about 7 in per day. Skin friction, somewhat less than 700 lb per sq ft.

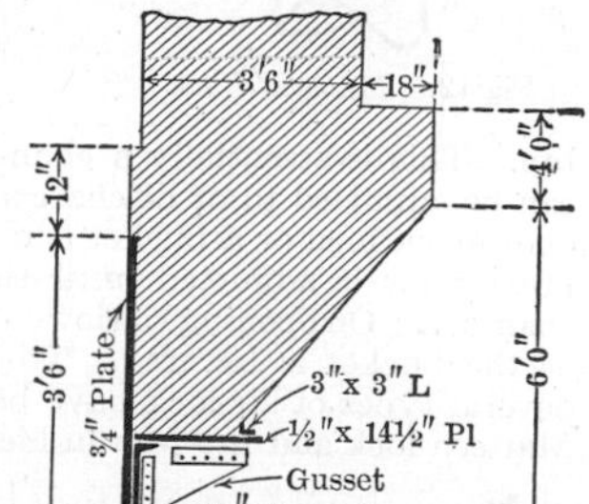

III. Colorado River siphon, Arizona (17). Shaft 30 ft outside diam. Walls 3.5 ft thick, except for 10 ft above cutting edge (Fig 11a). Shoe was assembled on bottom of a pit 10 ft deep, and concrete walls were carried up 10 ft before sinking began. Excavation by hand to depth of 73 ft, making 62 ft sunk and about same height of walls built in 71 days. Pumps were used for lower 45 ft. When inflow amounted to about 1 000 gal per min, inrushes of ground under shoe prevented further progress; the caisson was then flooded and dredged with a 1/2-cu yd

Fig 11a. Cutting Edge of Shoe, Colorado River Caisson (Rivets on outside countersunk)

clam-shell bucket. Ground was quite firm, and after caisson had sunk 5 ft farther it stuck, although all material that dredge could reach was dug out to depth of 10 ft below shoe. Advance of 11 ft was made by lowering water level inside caisson, and a further advance of 2 ft by exploding dynamite charges in pipes jetted down on outside to depth of 5 ft below shoe. 16 ft more were gained by blasting underneath shoe, with dynamite placed by divers. Caisson then stuck fast, being held by skin friction of over 400 lb per sq ft. The 34 ft done by dredging to this point took 50 days. Successful attempt to relieve skin friction by water jetting around the outside was now made; by which, and with use of dynamite, the caisson was sunk to final depth of 139 ft, a further penetration of 32 ft in 38 days. From completion of first 10 ft of wall above the shoe, 128 ft of caisson was built and sunk in 160 days. Max skin friction about 460 lb per sq ft even when caisson was flooded.

IV. Two shafts for Norwood-White Coal Co, near Des Moines, Iowa (1921), both 8 by 12 ft, sunk through 110 ft quicksand. Premoulded reinforced concrete sections 12 ft high, with simple cutting edge on bottom sec, were placed as excavation by clam-shell proceeded. Good joint secured by cutting edge settling in impervious material over rock. Main shaft was nearly water-tight and only 8 in out of plumb. Air shaft in poorer alinement and more leaky. Life of mine being estimated at 10 yr, expensive shafts not warranted (20).

4. PNEUMATIC METHOD

This is generally used in connection with the drop-shaft method where there is danger of an inflow of soft ground; when there are many boulders below water-level; or when making the seal between shaft lining and rock proves difficult. The procedure is exactly the same as described in Art 3, except that provision is made in the shaft for an air-tight deck, to be put in if the pneumatic method becomes advisable. The space below this deck is filled with compressed air, to drive out the water from the interstices of the ground, so that men can work in the shaft bottom.

Special equipment. The deck is of timber or reinforced concrete, designed to withstand the maximum air pressure that may be required, or to sustain the weight placed upon it for sinking. Edges of the deck project into a notch in the shaft walls. It is usually necessary to pump down the water before installing the deck, which is preferably placed 7 or 8 ft above the cutting edge. It may be advisable to provide an upper notch in the shaft walls, in which the deck can be set if the lower notch is under water.

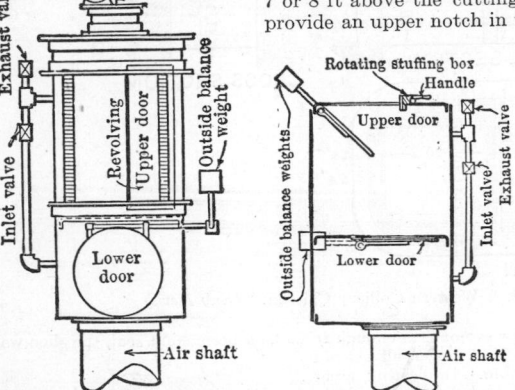

Fig 12. Mattsen Lock   Fig 13. Moran Lock

Access to the working chamber below the deck is through a cylindrical steel shaft, bolted to the deck and extending vertically to a point above ground water-level. This shaft is usually 36 to 60 in diam and $3/8$ in or more in thickness, as may be required to withstand the air pressure. It is made in sections 10 to 15 ft long, bolted together with rubber gaskets at the joints. The shaft is equipped with ladder rungs.

To prevent escape of compressed air through the shaft an air-lock is mounted on the top. This is essentially a chamber with two doors and means whereby compressed air can be admitted to or discharged from it. When the lower door is closed and the upper door open, men or a bucket can enter the lock. The upper door is then closed and compressed air is admitted until the pressure within the lock equals that in the working chamber. On opening the lower door, the men go down the ladder to the working chamber, or the bucket is lowered. To leave the working chamber, the operation is reversed. Several types of air-lock have been devised, but at present those generally used are the Mattsen lock and the Moran lock (Fig 12, 13).

The upper door of the Mattsen lock is in the side, opening and closing by rotating about the axis of the lock. The rope by which the bucket is hoisted runs through a stuffing-box in the top. The bucket can not, therefore, be hoisted through the top, but must be dumped through the side door; or the hoisting rope must be detached and another hooked to the bucket. The upper door of the Moran lock is in the top, and is in two sections which close around the hoisting rope; or, in another form, there is a single door working in a slot closed by a stuffing-box, which is vertically above the center of the lower door. When a bucket is lowered into the lock it is swung over until the hoisting rope enters the stuffing-box, and the door is closed. The air in the lock having been equalized, the lower door is opened and the bucket lowered into the working chamber. Usually, only one shaft and air-lock are required; men, buckets and materials passing through the same lock. Airlocks should be placed above the level of the ground-water, so that in case of a sudden loss of air pressure and the flooding of the working chamber, the workmen can escape into the lock.

Excavated materials are shoveled into buckets and hoisted from the working chamber by a derrick and double-drum hoist at the surface. Buckets are 24 to 33 in diam and 33 to 46 in high, depending on the shaft diam and size of the lock. To facilitate dumping, they have a steel bail at the top and a ring on the bottom.

When the excavated material is granular, or is soft clay, and the air pressure is sufficient, the spoil can be discharged from the working chamber to the surface by a blowpipe. This is a 4-in pipe running vertically from a point above the surface, through the deck and into a water-filled pit in the bottom of the working chamber. A quick-acting valve is placed in the pipe just below the deck. The excavated material is piled around the bottom of the pipe, the valve is opened for a short interval, and the air pressure forces the spoil up and out of the upper end of the pipe. The stream of spoil issuing from the blowpipe is deflected by an elbow, the back of which is of chilled cast-iron to resist wear and is renewable.

Compressed air is supplied to the working chamber by a low-pressure compressor, with a standby in case of breakdown. The piping, 3 to 4-in diam, should be in duplicate. For drilling, a high-pressure compressor may also be necessary. Smaller pipes are provided for electric light wires and a signal whistle. The principal features of a drop-shaft equipped for the pneumatic method are shown in Fig 14.

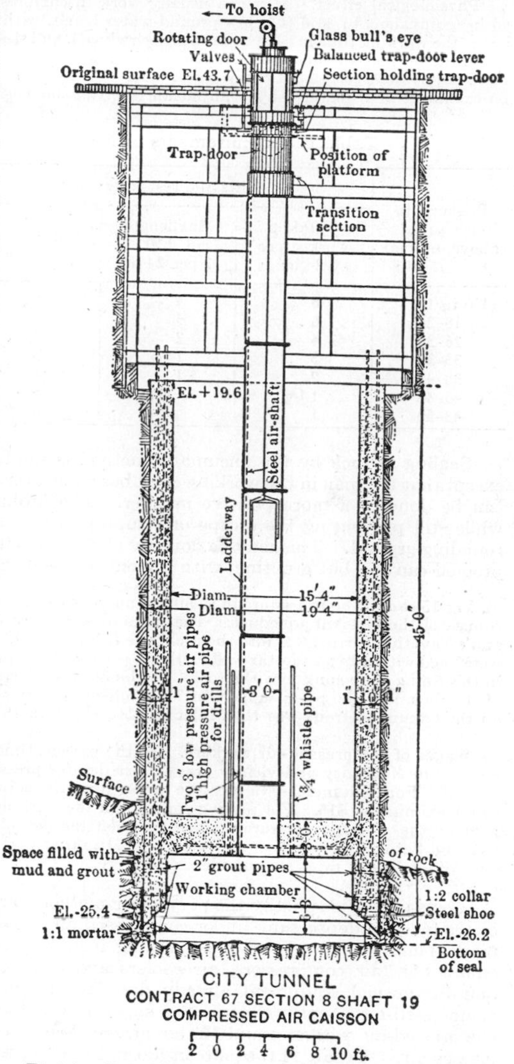

Weighting. To cause the shaft to sink, by overcoming the uplift of the compressed air plus the external friction, the walls must usually be heavier than those of an ordinary drop-shaft; or weight is added on top of the shaft, or on the deck. But, the escape of the compressed air under the cutting edge and up the outside of the shaft may materially reduce the exterior friction. In ground other than soft clay or quicksand, the shaft may sometimes be started by suddenly reducing air pressure in the working chamber (the men having left it).

CITY TUNNEL
CONTRACT 67 SECTION 8 SHAFT 19
COMPRESSED AIR CAISSON

Fig 14. Drop-shaft equipped for Pneumatic Method

Air supply. The air pressure may be greater or less than corresponds to the depth below ground-water level. A thick bed of clay may cut off water and so reduce the pressure; or the water may lie below such a stratum, artesian in character and under heavy pressure. Greater depths than would otherwise be attainable can be reached in gravel, boulders or loose rock, by maintaining a lower pressure than is required and blowing out through blowpipes the water entering the working chamber. Or the water level may be lowered by pumping through holes in the shaft walls above the deck. The supply of air for ventilation (30 cu ft per man per min) is usually less than is necessary to replace air escaping under the cutting edge.

Physiological effect. Men can usually work in compressed air, up to a pressure of 18 lb per sq in (equivalent to 41.6 ft below ground-water level), with little inconvenience. At higher pressures, the working time in each 24 hr must be reduced, and time spent in passing from the compressed air to the normal air must be increased. The maximum pressure in which men can work is about 50 lb (equivalent to 115.5 ft below water level). All men who are to work in compressed air should be examined and qualified by a physician (see Caisson Disease, Sec 15).

Table 1. Requirements of New York Law for Caisson Work

Pressure, lb per sq in above, normal	Shifts and rest intervals			Decompression	
	Total hr worked per 24 hr	Max length of shift; 2 per 24 hr	Min time in open air, hr	Pressure, lb per sq in	Min rate, lb per min
Up to 18	8	4	1/2	Up to 15	3
18–26	6	3	1	15–20	2
26–33	4	2	2	20–30	1 1/2
33–38	3	1 1/2	3	30 and over	1
38–43	2	1	4	....	......
43–48	1 1/2	3/4	5	....	......
48–50	1	1/2	6	....	......

Sealing to rock by the pneumatic method is similar to that for ordinary drop-shafts, except that the men in the working chamber have direct access to the work, which therefore can be done in a more positive manner. The problem is to stop the inflow of water, while still preventing the escape of compressed air below the cutting edge into the surrounding ground. This may be done by plastering with moist clay, or by a strip of waterproofed canvas, but grouting with cement or chemicals is often necessary.

Fig 15 shows the procedure in sealing a number of shafts sunk in connection with the NY City tunnel, of the Catskill aqueduct. The ledge rock was leveled, the shaft walls supported on posts, and excavation carried 3 ft into the rock, one ft larger in diam than the shaft shoe. The rock walls were lined with a 1 to 2 mortar wall, with a 3/4-in clearance outside the shoe. Grout pipes imbedded in this lining were sunk into the rock. A thick layer of oakum was placed under the cutting edge of the shoe, and the posts supporting the drop-shaft were shot out, thus allowing the shoe to drop on the oakum. Grout was then injected into the rock through the pipes imbedded in the shaft walls.

Wages of compressed-air workers. At the present time (1937), union wages of compressed-air workers in N Y City and vicinity are $12 per day for pressures up to 18 lb per square inch above normal. For each increase in pressure (approximately as in Table 1) the rate is increased by 50 cts to a maximum of $15. For placing concrete in the working chamber, 50 cts are added to the rate paid at the working pressure. Gang foremen receive $1 additional. Double time is paid for work on Saturdays, Sundays and holidays. In other parts of the U S, particularly in the South and Middle West, rates are considerably lower.

Costs of shafts sunk by the pneumatic method vary greatly with their diam, character of ground and depth sunk under compressed air. To the ordinary cost of the drop-shaft method must be added cost of assembling, installing, repairing and dismantling the sinking equipment (air compressors, air coolers and receivers, boilers or electrical connections and the special equipment already described); fuel or electric power; maintenance of compressed-air supply; experienced supervision; dressing and bathing facilities for the compressed-air workers; and the greatly increased cost of excavation done under compressed air. A shaft 14 ft square inside and 125 ft or more in depth, sunk in part and sealed by this method, may cost, including contractor's profit, $550 to $600 per vertical ft, or more, depending upon character of the ground.

Advantages. Notwithstanding its higher cost, the pneumatic method, within the limit of depth for which it can be used, is the most reliable. The men have direct access to the work; boulders can be blasted and the excavation made without danger of influx of the surrounding ground, or displacement of the shaft. Even if a drop-shaft becomes locked in the ground by boulders and refuses to sink farther, a new shoe can be assembled below the first one and jacked down, using the weight of the shaft walls as a reaction. Walling can be built on the new shoe as it moves downward. For these reasons all drop-shafts should be provided with notches in the walls, at one or more levels, so that, if necessary, a deck can be put in and the pneumatic method used.

I. Shaft 19, N Y aqueduct (Fig 14). For structural reasons not related to sinking, both vertical and horizontal reinforcement of concrete was made unusually heavy. The wall thickness of 2 ft, for a required inside diam of 15 ft 4 in, was at least 1 ft less than ordinarily required for a caisson of same depth. The deck was a 3-ft slab of reinforced concrete, cast integral with caisson walls, and was cut out after seal was made. Except for the concrete deck, the design was typical: a 36-in circular opening was provided in deck and a vertical line of 36-in flanged steel pipe (air shaft) was led from opening to top of caisson, where air lock was attached. Opening was formed by casting bottom length of air shaft into the deck; (where deck is of wood or iron, the lower flange of air shaft is bolted to it). Air shaft was long enough to keep lock always above ground-water level, so that, in case of accident to lock or to air-compressing plant, the caisson men would not be trapped by rising water. Air shaft had ladder rungs so arranged as not to interfere with operation of bucket.

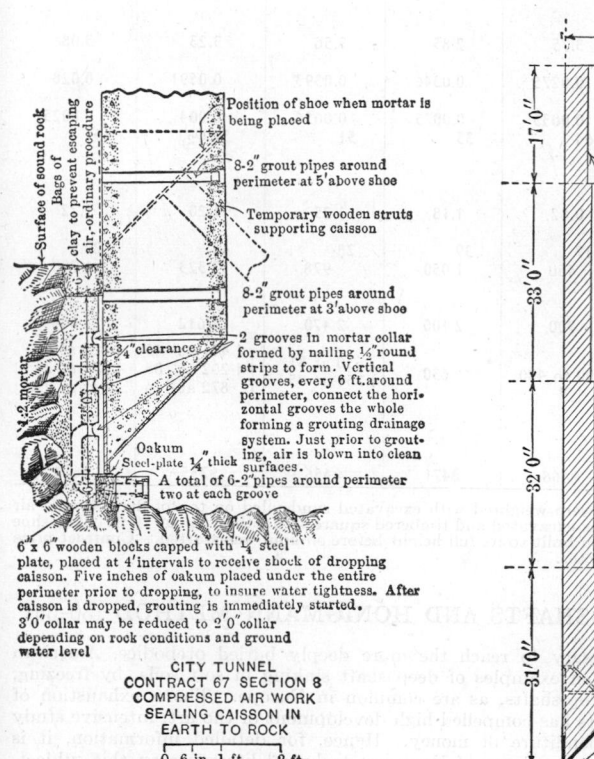

Position of shoe when mortar is being placed

8-2″ grout pipes around perimeter at 5′above shoe

Temporary wooden struts supporting caisson

8-2″ grout pipes around perimeter at 3′above shoe

2 grooves in mortar collar formed by nailing ½″round strips to form. Vertical grooves, every 6 ft around perimeter, connect the horizontal grooves the whole forming a grouting drainage system. Just prior to grouting, air is blown into clean surfaces.

3/4″clearance

Oakum
Steel-plate ¼″ thick

A total of 6-2″pipes around perimeter two at each groove

½″ mortar
Surface of sound rock
Bags of clay to prevent escaping air-ordinary procedure

6″ x 6″ wooden blocks capped with ¼″ steel plate, placed at 4′intervals to receive shock of dropping caisson. Five inches of oakum placed under the entire perimeter prior to dropping, to insure water tightness. **After** caisson is dropped, grouting is immediately started.

3′0″collar may be reduced to 2′0″collar depending on rock conditions and ground water level

CITY TUNNEL
CONTRACT 67 SECTION 8
COMPRESSED AIR WORK
SEALING CAISSON IN
EARTH TO ROCK

0 6 in 1 ft 2 ft

Fig 15. Sealing Details for Drop-shafts

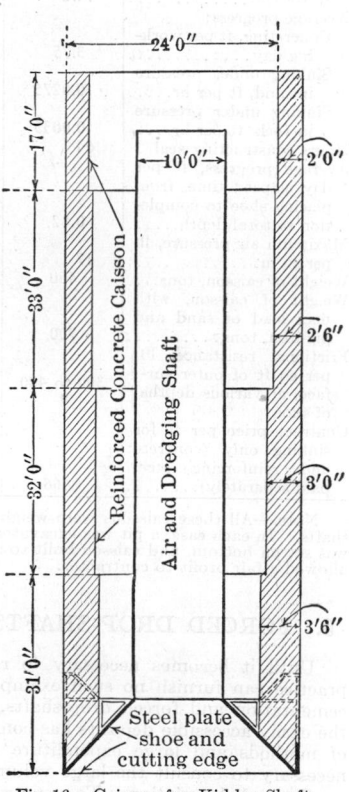

24′0″

17′0″

33′0″

32′0″

31′0″

Reinforced Concrete Caisson

Air and Dredging Shaft

10′0″

2′0″

2′6″

3′0″

3′6″

Steel plate shoe and cutting edge

Fig 16. Caisson for Kidder Shaft, Cleveland-Cliffs Iron Co

Besides the air shaft, one or two 3-in inlet air pipes, fitted at bottom with check valves, a 0.75-in whistle (signal) pipe, a high-pressure air pipe, a conduit for electric wires, and sometimes a 4- or 6-in discharge or "blow" pipe, are led through deck. In deeper caissons, 2 air shafts were provided, fitted respectively with a material lock and a man lock.

II. Kidder shaft, Cleveland-Cliffs Iron Co, Mich. Caisson was 24 ft outside diam (Fig 16). Air shaft, 10 ft diam, was used first as a dredging shaft for a clam-shell bucket, which excavated to a depth of 87 ft. As it then became necessary to use compressed air, a deck and air lock were bolted to the top. Ledge rock was reached at 104 ft. Shoe was sealed to rock at 113 ft. Average progress, 0.72 ft per day elapsed time.

III. Two colliery shafts, near Terre Haute, Ind, 16 and 20 ft inside diam, were sunk in 1923 by pneumatic caissons, through 140 ft of sand and gravel, 111 ft of which were water-bearing. Caissons and working chamber roofs were of concrete. Air press reached 51 lb per sq in. One caisson landed on a coal stratum and then penetrated fireclay before reaching rock. Lubricating pipes were used. Shafts were near Wabash River and water conditions were probably affected by this proximity. Some difficulty in controlling the sinking of the caissons.

Table 2.   Details of Sinking 5 Reinforced Concrete Caissons, Catskill Aqueduct

	Shaft 19	Shaft 20	Shaft 22	Shaft 23	Shaft 24
Outside diameter, ft	19 1/3	19 1/3	19 1/3	24	24
Inside diameter, ft	15 1/3	15 1/3	15 1/3	18	18
Total height, ft	45	105.3	100	123	105.6
Number of locks	1	2	2	2	2
Concrete proportions, cement: sand: stone	1 1/3 : 2 : 4	1 1/3 : 2 : 4	{ 1 1/3 : 2 : 4 to 1 : 2 : 4	1 1/3 : 2 : 4 to 1 : 2 : 4	1 1/3 : 2 : 4 to 1 : 2 : 4
Depth sunk under compressed air:					
In sand, ft	11	77	50.3	105	59.5
In rock, ft	14.2	33.7	13.7	14	10
Average progress:					
Concreting, ft per working day	3.75	2.85	3.56	3.23	3.08
Sinking under pressure in sand, ft per hr	0.0275	0.0346	0.0393	0.0591	0.028
Sinking under pressure in rock, ft per hr	0.0035	0.0075	0.0056	0.004	0.0025
Hours constructing seal	64	35	51	51 1/2	51
Average progress, ft per day elapsed time, from placing shoe to completion to total depth	0.82	1.18	1.25	1.20	1.22
Maximum air pressure, lb per sq in	17	39	28	46	29.5
Weight of caisson, tons	460	1 050	978	2 323	1 780
Weight of caisson, with max load of sand and pig-iron, tons	700	2 100	2 470	4 612	4 046
Frictional resistance, lb per sq ft of outer surface, at various depths of shoe	300 to 400	630	{ 630 at 81 { 751 at 95	{ 1 411 at 45 { 1 202 at 86 { 872 at 116	1 685 at 49 1 101 at 79 945 at 93.5
Contract price per ft for sinking only (concrete and reinforcing steel paid separately)	$466	$471	$456	$735	$614

Note.—All these caissons were weighted with excavated sand piled on top of deck around air shafts.   In each case, a pit was excavated and timbered square to depth of about 20 ft.   The shoe was set on bottom, and caisson built to its full height before sinking was started.   Contract price allowed a fair profit to contractor.

5. FORCED DROP-SHAFTS AND HONIGMANN METHOD (30–35)

Until it becomes necessary to reach the more deeply buried orebodies, American practice can furnish no such examples of deep shaft sinking in soft soils, by freezing, cementation and forced drop-shafts, as are common in Europe. There, exhaustion of the easily accessible deposits has compelled high development of the art, intensive study of methods and large expenditure of money. Hence, for detailed information, it is necessary to consult the large volume of European technical literature on this subject.

General description. To penetrate depths of quicksand and other unstable, water-bearing material, beyond the limit of open or pneumatic caissons, a method has been developed in Germany of jacking down a telescopic series of iron drums, inside of and reacting against a previously installed concrete curbing. The latter is strong and heavy, and built into it, near the top, is an internal cast-iron flange, the REACTION RING. This, anchored by vertical rods extending to the shoe, resists thrust of the jacks, which are attached to and bear against under side of ring. The caisson is sunk by dredging in the open to a depth of 50 or 60 ft; then a concrete floor (SEAL) is placed in the bottom (under water if necessary), and shaft is unwatered. A cast-steel shoe, with an outside diam slightly less than inside diam of curbing, is set on the concrete floor, and a cylindrical drum, of flanged and bolted cast-iron segments (similar to shaft tubbing, Sec 7) is built up from shoe to under side of the jacks. The concrete seal is then broken, thus admitting water to natural level, and the drum is jacked down, the material being excavated under water by grab bucket, "mammoth" pump, or sack borer (described below). Finally, the jacks are removed and more segments of lining added as required. With hydraulic jacks, a drum 20 ft outside diam can usually be forced down 250 to 300 ft before it sticks. If rock lies still deeper, the bottom is again sealed, the shaft is unwatered, a second drum of smaller diam is built inside the first, the jacks are shifted inward to bear upon it, and sinking is resumed. Frequently a second drum has been necessary; less often, a third (3).

Details of construction of curbs, drums and sinking plant are shown in Fig 17 and 18. A head-frame handles the machinery, which includes: trepans, similar to those used in the Kind-Chaudron boring method for rock (See 7), for breaking up the concrete floor and any boulders or partly cemented ground that may be met; the curbing, with reaction ring and hydraulic jacks; and sinking drums. The outer drum (Fig 17) is the patented Pattberg compound, the cast-iron shell of which is lined with 22 in of strong brick or concrete, for additional weight and stiffness; the second is a simple iron-segment drum. The compound drum is made necessary by the great earth press at depths of 300 or 400 ft, a number of shafts having been lost by collapse of unsupported iron drums, notwithstanding use of segments 3.5 in thick. The segments are about 5 ft high, flanged and bolted on both horiz and vert joints, and 8 to 10 of them make up a ring. The shoe must be very strong and heavy, and anchor and reaction rings and all bolts must be designed to carry safely the full thrust of the jacks. For considerable depths, the grab bucket used in ordinary caissons has been superseded by the mammoth pump in firmer, and the sack-borer in softer, soils.

Mammoth pump (Fig 17) is essentially an air-lift pump (Sec 15). Inside the hollow stem of the trepan is a small pipe carrying compressed air to a point near bottom of the cutting tool and releasing it into the stem. The air lightens the column of water in the stem, and discharges it at the surface, carrying with it the material pulverized by the borer.

Sack-borer (Fig 18) is a large auger-like tool, with its stem in center of shaft. The stem is composed of a series of lengths of heavy flanged pipe, terminated at upper end by a splined section, on which is mounted a large horizontal gear-wheel. A wire rope, from hoisting engine drum to swivel link at top of stem, suspends the sack-borer. The stem is rotated through the gear-wheel by another engine, and is lowered gradually by hoisting rope. New sections of borer stem are added as shaft is deepened. Cross arms are attached to the stem at intervals, having rollers at their ends which bear against sides of shaft and keep stem in line. Material cut by the rotating borer is swept into two heavy, open-mouthed canvas sacks, fastened to backs of cutters. From time to time the borer is raised and emptied. In an improved form, the sacks are mounted on a frame sliding on guides attached to cross arms on stem, and are hoisted by an independent engine. The sack-borer is best adapted to clay and sand.

I. Shaft 5, Rheinpreussen colliery, Homburg am Rhein, Germany, was started in 1901 with a brick caisson 29.2 ft inside diam, walls about 3.5 ft thick. This reached a depth of 65 ft. Concrete plug, 9 ft thick, was then placed on the bottom, under water, the shaft was pumped out, the anchor ring, rods and reaction ring (designed for a pressure of 3 000 tons) were erected, and an inner truly vertical, brick lining was built, reducing inside diam to 25.68 ft. A compound sinking drum with outer and inner diam of 25.52 and 21.32 ft respectively was then constructed, and sinking was begun with a percussion borer and mammoth pump. The concrete was bored through in 4 days, and thereafter the average progress was about 5 ft per day. The compound drum stuck at 245 ft, and shaft was filled for 60 ft with sand and gravel (instead of concrete). Shaft was next pumped out and an iron drum, 3.5 in thick and 19.35 ft inside diam, was built up to the jacks. This drum stuck at 315 ft; the shaft was again partly filled and pumped out, and another drum, 17.38 ft inside diam was forced to a depth of 343 ft, where the shoe entered clay firm enough to permit shaft to be pumped out. A fourth drum, 15.3 ft inside diam, was finally forced to the coal measures, at a depth of 508 ft. The sinking took 3 years, the average progress being about 6 in per day (3).

II. Sterkrade shaft, near Holten, Germany, was started with a brick caisson 24.6 ft inside diam, which was sunk to a depth of 59 ft. The excavation was continued by hand to 131 ft, where an iron sinking drum, 22 ft inside diam, was constructed. This drum was forced to 264 ft; a second drum, 19.3 ft diam, to 433 ft; and a third, 16.75 ft diam, to 448 ft. Here the water was found to be successfully shut out, and sinking was continued by hand (3). For cost, see Table 3.

Average cost per ft of sinking-drum method in Germany, at various depths, is given by Henry Louis (1) as follows: 82 to 164 ft $260; 164 to 328 ft $593; 328 to 492 ft $817; 492 to 656 ft $1 040.

Sassenberg process of hydraulic flushing reduces skin friction and adhesion in some soils. Shoe and 4 lining rings above it are about 1.5 in larger outside diam than the rest of the lining, and in the shoulder thus formed are water passages, connected through pipes to a high-press pump. By operating this pump during sinking, the drum is partially surrounded by a film of water.

The forced-drop-shaft has been used in sinking a number of shafts. At present, however, it has been replaced by the Honigmann method, or by freezing, or cementation.

Honigmann method (35). The essential difference between this and a forced drop-shaft is that the lining is installed after the excavation is completed, instead of closely following the cutting tool. The advantage of this is that the cast-iron tubbing can be assembled and bolted together above the surface, before it begins to sink. Access for calking the outside of the joints can therefore be had, and the cost of assembling and placing the lining is reduced.

Honigmann observed that the walls of a boring in sand fell in, even when the hole is filled with water to a level above that of the ground-water, but if the walls were coated with clay they remained

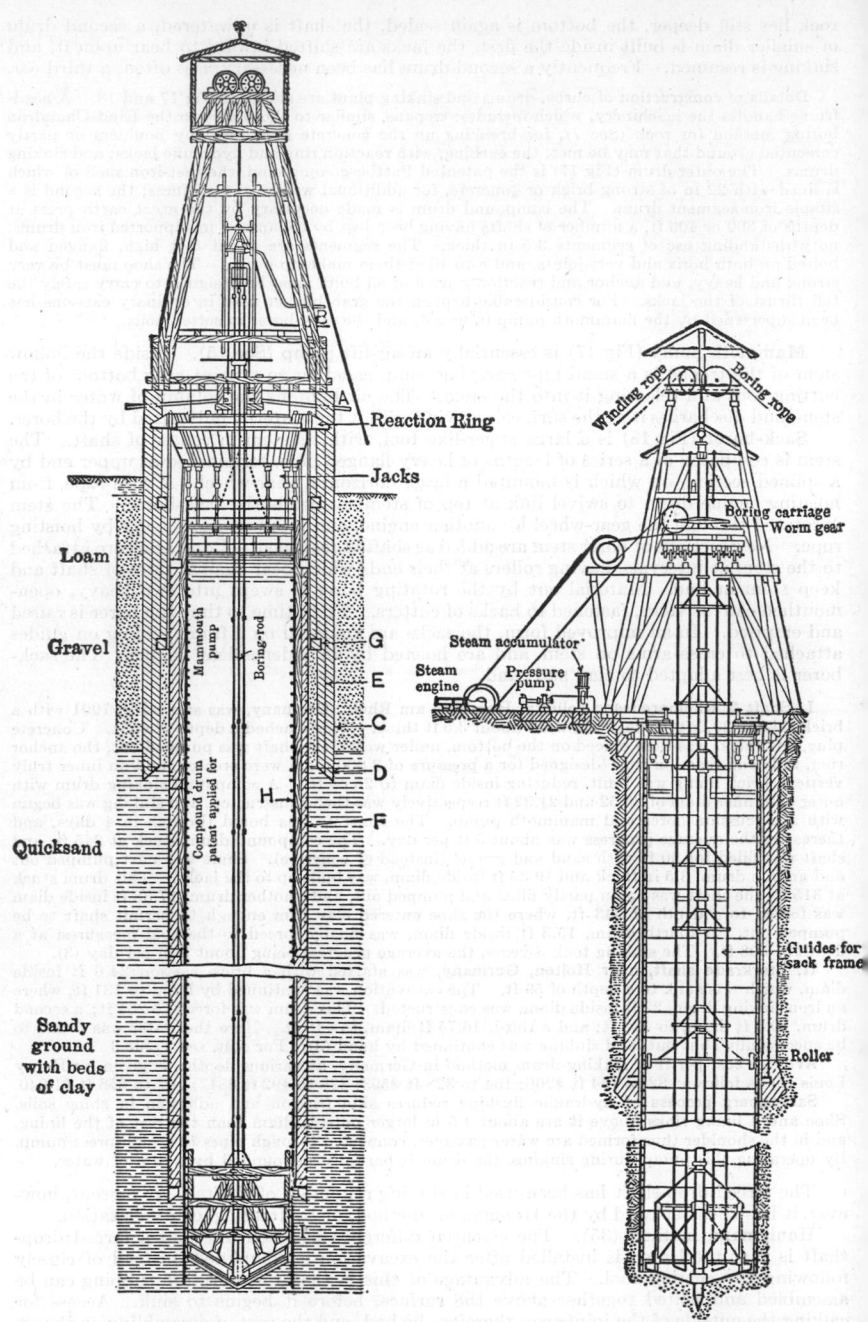

Loam

Gravel

Quicksand

Sandy
ground
with beds
of clay

Reaction Ring

Jacks

Mammouth pump

Boring-rod

Compound drum patent applied for

A

B

G

E

C

D

F

H

Fig 17. Honigmann Method, Mammoth Pump and Borer. Shafts IV and V, Rheinpreussen Colliery, Germany. A, Suction Pipe and Overflow; B, Compressed Air; C, Caisson; D, Shoe; E, Anchor Rods; F, Compound Lining; H, Cast-iron Lining (Riemer)

Winding rope

Boring rope

Boring carriage
Worm gear

Steam accumulator

Steam
engine

Pressure
pump

Guides for
sack frame

Roller

Fig 18. Sack Borer. Adolf Shaft, Eschweiler Mining Co, Germany (Riemer)

Table 3. Cost of Sterkrade Shaft

Brick caisson, 59 ft @ $285..........................	......	$16 800
1st iron drum sunk 133 ft @ $502		
Segments................................	$32 900	....
Labor and supplies.........................	33 900	66 800
2nd iron drum sunk 169 ft @ $715		
Segments................................	75 300	....
Labor and supplies.........................	45 900	121 200
3rd iron drum sunk 15 ft @ $6 060		
Segments................................	71 500	....
Labor and supplies.........................	19 300	90 800
Depreciation of plant and fittings, 50% of new value...........		43 300
Total..		$338 900
Less salvage on tubbing recovered from inner drums...........		35 700
Total cost for 376 ft......................................		$303 200
Cost per ft..		807

standing. The theory is that the increased head of water in the boring, over that in the ground, causes a pressure against each grain of sand in the walls. As the water flows between and around the grains, the pressure is equalized, with no force to resist the force of gravity which caused the sand to fall. But, if the walls of the hole are coated with clay, no water can enter between and behind the sand grains in the walls, and there is therefore a pressure against the inside face of each grain to keep it in place. This idea he applied to large borings like shafts.

The boring tool of the Honigmann method (Fig 17) is an inverted cone, with the apex at the center of the excavation, provided with steel knives which cut the ground as the tool is rotated. The hollow stem is extended through the tool to the bottom of the conical pit thus made. Compressed air is carried down through a small pipe in the stem and discharged just above the bottom. The stem thus becomes a mammoth pump (Fig 17), which discharges at the surface the material loosened by the borer. The shaft is filled with an emulsion of clay to a level considerably above that of the ground-water, to provide support for the excavation walls. At the surface the spoil deposits from the discharged water by sedimentation, the water being returned to the shaft with an additional admixture of clay if necessary. To coat the sides of the shaft properly, the percentage of clay in the water varies with the character of the ground. In clayey soil, 15% is considered sufficient; in sand, 20% and in gravel, 35%.

The shaft excavation is never made to its full diam in the first cut. It is begun with a diameter of 6.5 to 8 ft and completed to the bottom. The diam is then increased by one or more successive cuts, with larger tools mounted on the stem. Between the tools, the stem carries a cylindrical guide fitting closely to the walls of the first cut, which must be true and plumb; otherwise, the installation of the sinking lining would be difficult.

The first ring of the tubbing or lining, which has a cutting edge on the bottom, is assembled over the mouth of the shaft. It is laid out in a true circle, leveled with its axis coinciding with the shaft axis, and hung by threaded rods to the tower over the shaft. This ring is bolted up with lead gaskets in the vertical joints. The second ring is assembled and similarly bolted to the first. The gaskets are then calked from the outside and a false bottom of concrete is placed in the bottom of the assembled rings. By means of the threaded rods the two rings are lowered in the shaft and additional rings are added and calked. Because of the false bottom, the assembled rings will eventually float in the water, and, to continue sinking, water must be run into the cylinder. When the lower edge of the tubbing reaches a point about 3 ft above the shaft bottom, the space under the false bottom and around the outside of the lower rings is filled by a tremie with cement grout between the lining and shaft-walls. The lining is then lowered into the grout, and when it has set, the grouting behind the lining is continued to the top of the shaft. The false bottom is then cut out by jackhammers, after borings through it have tested the watertightness of the grouting.

This method is simple and ingenious in all its details. It requires little material and equipment and few men, and is much less costly than the freezing method hereinafter described. It is best suited to soft ground, but strata of cemented sand and gravel, sandstone or limestone can be passed if not too thick. A great advantage is the security afforded the workmen, in not being exposed to accident during sinking and lining the shaft. The method can not be used, however, if a subterranean water course or absorbent stratum is encountered, which might carry away the water in the shaft. This situation developed while a shaft, 17 ft net diam, was being sunk for the Dutch Govt; after reaching a great depth, the work had to be abandoned. Another disadvantage is that the excavation may get out of line, if inclined hard strata are encountered. Trouble may also arise because of the swelling of the walls of the excavation and sticking of the lining during its descent. To obviate this the bottom of the lining is furnished with a conical piece which is removed after the false bottom is cut out.

The Honigmann method has been used successfully for a shaft 19.7 ft net diam, excavated to a diam of 24 ft and sunk to a depth of 1 385 ft. The Dutch company (La Societé Mijnbouw) holding the rights states the cost and rate of progress as follows (39):

Depths, meters	Cost per meter	Monthly progress
to 100	15 000–25 000 francs	15–20 meters
100–200	25 000–37 000 "	10–12 "
200–350	37 000–52 000 "	9–11 "
350–500	52 000–75 000 "	8–10 "

The above costs apply to 1933, or early 1934, when the franc was worth 6 1/4 to 6 1/2 cents, U S currency. Furthermore, these costs are much lower than would be possible in the U S.

6. FREEZING METHOD (3, 6, 7, 8, 14, 18, 22, 24)

General principles. This method was invented by F. H. Poetsch in 1883 and introduced into this country by Charles Soöysmith. Its essential feature is the solidifying, by freezing, of water-bearing ground in which the shaft is sunk. The freezing is sometimes continued into water-bearing rock. The method has been much used in recent years in England and on the Continent, for shafts 200 to more than 2 000 ft deep. Vertical holes,

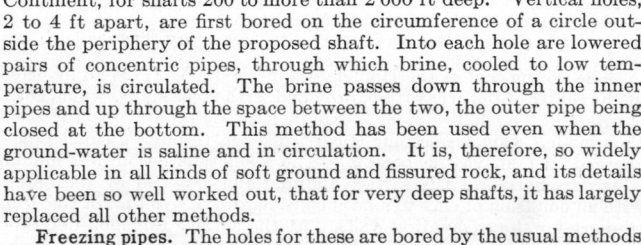

2 to 4 ft apart, are first bored on the circumference of a circle outside the periphery of the proposed shaft. Into each hole are lowered pairs of concentric pipes, through which brine, cooled to low temperature, is circulated. The brine passes down through the inner pipes and up through the space between the two, the outer pipe being closed at the bottom. This method has been used even when the ground-water is saline and in circulation. It is, therefore, so widely applicable in all kinds of soft ground and fissured rock, and its details have been so well worked out, that for very deep shafts, it has largely replaced all other methods.

Freezing pipes. The holes for these are bored by the usual methods and, in soft ground, are cased (Sec 9). They must be vertical, or nearly so; otherwise the distances between them, at the bottom, may be too great to permit the formation of a complete ice wall. In very deep shafts, due to the difficulty of keeping the borings vertical and properly spaced, the freezing is sometimes done in stages, each 200 to 300 ft deep. Each section of shaft is then excavated and lined before freezing the succeeding section. In this case, the holes for the freezing pipes are driven outward, at a slight vertical angle, from the bottom of the preceding section. In the most recent practice, however, the holes are bored continuously from the surface to the bottom of the proposed shaft; their direction being checked at frequent intervals and, in case of deviation, is corrected, or in case of great deviation, additional borings are made. The usual form of freezing pipes is shown in Fig 19. The outside pipe, 4 to 6 in diam, closed at the bottom, is lowered into the casing and tested hydraulically. The casing is then withdrawn so that the ground may close around the freezing pipe. The inner pipe, one in or more in diam, is lowered into the outer pipe. Both pipes are connected at the top to header pipes, to and from which the brine is pumped from the central freezing plant.

Ring pipes connected with freezing plant

Additional borings should be made, one at center of the proposed shaft and others inside and outside of the circle of the freezing pipes. These are used to take the ground temperatures at different levels, for checking the formation and maintenance of the ice wall. As saline solutions freeze at lower temperatures than pure water a leak in the piping may cause a weak spot, or a hole, in the ice wall,

Fig 19. Freezing Pipes, Dawdon Colliery, England

making necessary a longer period of freezing.

Ice wall, in its several phases of formation, is shown by Fig 20. It must be thick enough to withstand the pressure to which it will be subjected, and the freezing pipes are located accordingly. Frozen sand is stronger than clear ice. Abby's experiments show that frozen saturated sand crushes at about 2 500 lb per sq in at a temperature of −25° C, and at about 1 700 lb at −12° C. It should therefore carry safely 300 lb per sq in and, assuming full hydrostatic pressure on the outside of the ice cylinder, the thickness of the wall, for a shaft 300 ft deep and 20 ft diam should be about 7.5 ft.

Freezing plant. Ammonia, compressed and expanded, is generally used as the refrigerating medium. Carbonic acid is occasionally used because lower temperatures are obtainable. The brine, chilled by expansion of the ammonia and circulated through the freezing pipes, is commonly $CaCl_2$, but $MgCl_2$ is recommended, as it has less tendency to precipitate at low temperatures and clog the piping. The capacity of the freezing plant depends upon the diam and depth of shaft, thickness of the required ice wall, and the time allotted to the freezing of the ground.

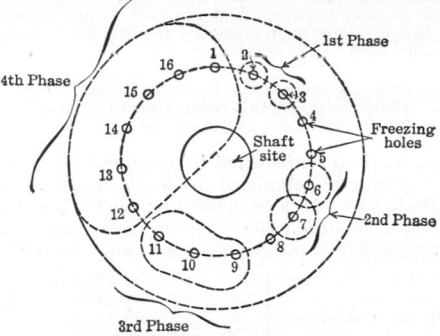

Fig 20. Formation of Ice Wall

Sinking, after the ground is frozen, is done by drilling and blasting with light charges, but, to avoid cracking the ice wall, pneumatic hammers are often preferable.

Lining. Shafts of 200–300 ft, or even more, may be lined with concrete, but care must be exercised because of the effect of the frozen ground upon the concrete. Shafts of great depth are usually lined with cast-iron rings (tubbing), bolted with lead gaskets and backed with concrete.

Thawing. After completing sinking and lining, the ground is thawed by filling the shaft with water, or by gradually raising the temperature of the circulating brine and continuing circulation for a long period, or by the aeration of the shaft. During this time, in deep shafts, the lining requires continual tightening and calking.

Average speed of sinking, considering the process as a whole, depends largely upon the boring, and is quite variable. If holes prove to be nearly plumb, both boring and freezing are expedited; but, if some of the holes deflect badly near the bottom, new holes must be bored, and the irregular spacing of the pipes makes necessary a longer freezing period.

Table 4. Speed of Sinking by Freezing

Shaft	Location	Depth sunk by freezing, ft	Time, months			Average progress, ft per month
			Boring	Freezing only	Sinking and lining	
Anhalt government salt mine, No 6.	Germany	310	17	5.5	7	10.5
Marie mine..........................	"	180	6.5	5.5	4.5	10.9
Consolidated Sophie lignite mine...	"	262	6	2.5	6	18.1
Castlereagh shaft..................	England	259	10.5	6	12	9.1
Theresa shaft.....................	"	113	10	13	6	3.9

I. Shaft 6, Anhalt government salt mine, Leopoldshall, Stassfurt, Germany. Twenty-six 5-in holes were bored in a circle, 26.25 ft diam and cased to depth of 325 ft. The boring was difficult, and, as shown in Table 4, consumed 17 months. Freezing was continued for 3 months before sinking was begun. After only 30 ft had been sunk, a small leak broke through in shaft bottom, and flooded shaft. Sinking was stopped and freezing continued for 2.5 months more, after which a progress of over 60 ft per month was maintained to a depth of 202 ft. The shaft was lined with iron tubbing (Sec 7), the space behind being filled with concrete mixed with water containing calcined soda. Sinking and lining were prosecuted alternately until the tubbing was sealed to rock at 325 ft. Aside from difficulty of boring the holes, this sinking was entirely successful (3).

II. Theresa and Castlereagh shafts, Dawdon, County Durham, England, were first sunk (with pumping) through very wet rock to depths of 350 and 204 ft respectively. It was then decided to continue them by freezing through underlying sand to the coal measures at a depth of 463 ft. Thirty-eight holes were bored around each shaft, including two extras at each, on 30-ft circles, 7 well drills being used. The holes were 8 and 10 in diam, lined with 6.25-in casings. The freezing plant comprised two 135-h p steam engines, driving 4 ammonia compressors. As shown by Table 4, the freezing of Theresa shaft was especially slow, 13 months elapsing before sinking could be begun. Both shafts were successfully sealed to rock in 2.5 years (19).

III. Chapin shaft, Iron Mountain, Mich (7) was sunk in 1888–9, through 95 ft sand, gravel and boulders, with water level 10 ft below surface. Twenty-six 10-in casing pipes were put down in a 29-ft circle; inside of these were 8-in freezing pipes, inclosing 1.5-in circulating tubes. Casings were then withdrawn. Ice machine was a Linde (ammonia type) of 50 tons daily refrigerating capacity (1 ton equals cooling effect of 1 ton melting ice). Freezing fluid was saturated solution of commercial CaCl$_2$; velocity of flow in the 1.5-in pipes, 2 ft per sec. In about 21 days after starting ice machine, the frozen ring was complete and excavation was begun. Rock was reached in 135 days (including a 30-day stoppage, when shaft was allowed to fill with water). There was some trouble and delay from leakages through ice wall, the elapsed time being about 200 days.

   IV. In Campine district, North Belgium, so great an advance has been made in developing the freezing process for shafts 1 500 to 2 000 ft deep to the recently discovered coal measures, that previous applications of the process do not maintain their former importance as examples to be studied. Sinking in stages by freezing has in some of these shafts alternated with cementation. Some of the most notable work is the sinking of 2 shafts for the Helchteren and Zolder project, where 2 034 ft of ground were frozen by a single current of refrigerating fluid in 7 months' time. Sinking and lining took 21.5 months; cost, aside from fuel and tubbing, $1 177 per ft (22).

   H. Muller gives (1917) estimates of cost, under two different assumptions, for a shaft sunk 300 ft by freezing in stages, at $1 100 and $1 600 per ft, respectively (29).

   V. Two shafts, sunk by freezing for the Houthaelen Coal Mines (42) in the Campine district were completed in 1932 and 1934. Cementation was first tried and abandoned. Shaft I was sunk to 2 106.3 ft; shaft II, about 230 ft from shaft I, to 2 139.1 ft. Both passed through 1 968.4 ft of water-bearing ground to a much fissured stratum of sandstone about 33 ft thick, overlying the coal. The soft ground above the sandstone was as follows:

Tertiary deposits		Secondary deposits	
sand	426.5 ft	tufa	203.4 ft
clay	232.9 "	chalk	147.6 "
sand	183.7 "	marl	380.6 "
clay and marl	298.6 "	sand	78.7 "
sand	16.4 "		810.3 ft
	1 158.1 ft		

In each case a preliminary pit was sunk, 42.7 ft diam and 15.6 ft deep.

   The borings for the freezing pipes, begun Sep 5, 1927, for shaft I and Nov 20, 1927, for shaft II, were spaced about 3.5 ft c–c, on the circumference of a circle 36.1 ft diam. The borings were 2 066.9 ft deep for shaft I and 2 093.2 ft for shaft II, continuous from surface to full depth. The plumbness of the borings was checked by the Denis-Foraky teleclinograph and in case of deviation the direction was corrected (Sec 9). The theoretical number of freezing pipes for each shaft was 32, but 5 additional borings were required for shaft I and 4 for shaft II. The borings were cased to 1 148 ft, below which no casing was installed. The freezing pipes were lowered into the borings and their headers, in the bottom of the preliminary pits, were connected with the freezing plant.

   Net diam of each shaft was 16.4 ft. The cast-iron tubbing lining was 19.4 ft outside diam; behind it was placed 1.3 ft of concrete, so that the diam of the excavation was 22 ft. At center of each shaft an additional boring was made, in which were placed concentric pipes for drawing off water at 4 levels, viz: at bottom of the preliminary pit, at bottom of the clay (656 ft below surface), at top of the tufa (1 158 ft depth), and in the marl at 1 739 ft. These pipes were to draw off excess water after the closing of the ice-wall. The amount of the water was 24 525 gal in shaft I and 41 889 gal in shaft II. For test purposes additional borings were made from the bottom of the preliminary pits. These were on the circumference of circles, around the center of each shaft, with diameters of 21.3, 32.8, 36.1 and 41 ft. The total length of casing for borings was 132 961 ft; of outer freezing pipes, 152 334 ft; and of inside freezing pipes, 147 711 ft.

   The freezing plant was in six units (total, 2 891 h p), each unit of a capacity equivalent to 100 tons of ice per day, melted from and at 32° F. The elec power for the sinking operations was 1 285 h p, supplied from an outside source. A standby Diesel unit of 800 h p was installed. Ammonia was used at a pressure of 15.4–26. 4 lb, reduced to 1.1–2.2 lb at the condensers. Chloride of calcium, at 27°–15° Baumé, with point of freezing at about − 16.6° F, was used as the circulating brine.

   The ground was frozen to 2 050.5 ft for shaft I and 2 091.5 ft for shaft II. Freezing for shaft I began June 13, 1930 and to Dec 6, 1930, when excavation was begun, 19 842 500 000 btu had been used for refrigeration; equivalent to 68 898 tons of ice melted from and at 32° F. At a depth of 2 106.3 ft (Dec 15, 1932), 45 637 750 000 btu had been used, equivalent to 158 464 tons of ice melted from and to 32° F. For shaft II freezing began Jan 29, 1931, and when excavation was begun (July 6, 1931) 17 858 250 000 btu had been used, equivalent to 62 008 tons of ice melted. At depth of 2 139-ft (Jan 9, 1934) 67 464 500 000 btu had been used, equivalent to 234 252 tons of ice melted. The flow of brine through each freezing pipe was 282.4 cu ft per hr, at velocity of 3.67 ft per sec in the descent and 0.98 ft per sec in the riser pipe.

   The performance of the freezing plant and the formation and maintenance of the ice-wall was, at all times, under strict surveillance. Temperatures of the ammonia throughout its circuit were taken every 3 hr; also the temperatures at the start and return of the brine, and the pressure and discharge of the pumps. A weekly check of the discharge from each freezing pipe was made.

Meters installed at the central station measured the general discharge of the brine and electric indicators warned of any considerable loss. The closing and progress of formation of the ice-wall was checked: (a) by temperatures taken at every 328 ft down to the 1 640-ft level, at the center boring of the shaft and in each of the other 4 series of borings made for this purpose; (b) by amount of water pumped from each of the 4 levels in the center boring.

Excavation and lining of shaft I begun Dec 6, 1930; completed Dec 15, 1932; aver progress per working day, 3.33 ft. Shaft II, begun July 6, 1931, reached 1 177.8 ft June 3, 1932, when a rupture of the ice-wall occurred, due to breakage of one of the freezing pipes. After repairs, excavation was resumed Jan 12, 1933 and completed Aug 1, 1934. Average progress per working day, 3.6 ft. Nearly all excavation was done by jackhammer; only in sandy tufa and chalk were the ordinary mining methods used. At the bottom of the preliminary pit the non-frozen core was about 20 ft diam; at 328 ft, this core was only 3–7 ft diam and thence to 1 148 ft the ground was frozen to the center, or nearly so. At top of the tufa was found a non-frozen core containing water under pressure. Below, the ground was completely frozen.

These shafts were lined with cast-iron tubbing, the possible pressures upon which were computed as the hydrostatic pressure multiplied by the following coefficients: 1.8 for sand; 1.5 for mixed sand, clay and marl; 1.25 for marl; 1.0 for tufa and chalk. The ultimate compressive strength of cast-iron was taken at 85 000 lb per sq in, for thicknesses of 2 3/8 in or more, and 71 000 lb per sq in for thicknesses of 3 15/16 in, or more. Safety factor of 6.3 was used in soft ground and 5.3 in firm ground, the thickness being determined by the cylinder formula. These computations gave thicknesses of 1 3/16 to 6 11/16 in. The rings were about 5 ft high; bolted with lead gaskets. In upper part of shafts the excavation was made to some depth before starting lining, which was then built up from the bottom. Below this, lining kept pace with excavation. The lining segments were provided with holes for grouting.

On completing excavation and lining, and before thawing was begun, all bolts in the lining were tightened, lead joints were calked and cement grout injected at a pressure equal to half the pressure which each ring might be called upon to support. Thawing was done by progressively warming the brine in the freezing circuit, and by aeration of the shaft interior. Other shafts sunk by this method in the Campine district have been thawed by inundating the shafts, with the idea of keeping the tubbing in balance and avoiding a sudden thaw, but this method stops all work below and prevents observation of the behavior of the lining. As tubbing adjusts itself for some time after it is placed, joints which open must be cared for. After thawing was ended, another calking and tightening of bolts was necessary. Before this, leakage through joints was about 600 gal per hr per 328 ft of depth, but after recalking and tightening the joints, leakage was only about 6.5 gal per hr per 328 ft; practically watertight. Thawing of shaft I was begun Nov 22, 1933 and completed Oct 6, 1934, 7 2/3 years after beginning work. The time for thawing shaft II was not reported. The freezing pipes were removed down to the 1 148-ft level. The holes which were occupied by them were filled with cement grout.

7. CEMENTATION AND GROUTING METHODS (25–28, 43)

The idea of filling fissures and voids, in the ground, with cement is old. By injecting cement in a boring in the Lens mines, M. Reumaux succeeded in 1882 in closing a large flow of water. From 1900 the method has been much used for shaft sinking. In 1904–7, La Compagnie des Mines de Béthune sank 4 shafts by cementation, and later several others at Lens and Liévin were successfully completed. Thereafter, the method spread over France and other countries (39). It is most successful in fissured rock; in quicksand, it is entirely unsuccessful, because the bore-holes can not be kept open except by casing, or by clay coating (Honigmann method, Art 5), both of which prevent cementation. Also in spongy ground such as tufa the cement coats the surface but does not penetrate the pores. Fissured chalk and limestones lend themselves best to this method. In the first applications, 6 to 8 borings, 5.5–6 in diam, were made to full depth around the site of proposed shaft. A mammoth (air-lift) pump was lowered gradually into each bore hole, so that the induced flow of ground-water would wash out the mud from fissures and voids. Then water under pressure was pumped into the holes, to force any remaining mud back into the ground, and cement grout was injected under pressure. In the Saclier method the grout is injected into all holes simultaneously; in the later Portier method injection is made into each boring singly, one at each end of a shaft diameter, then at each end of a diameter perpendicular to the first, and finally at ends of other diameters. Pressure is maintained until the grout has set, otherwise it might be washed out by the flow of ground water.

François method employs 20–24 borings, 1.5–2 in diam, in two concentric circles around the site of the shaft. They are not immediately bored to full depth, but deepened after each injection of cement. The pressure on the grout is 1 500 to 3 000 lb per sq in or even 4 500 lb. The grout is injected into each hole separately. After injection, boring is resumed when the grout has taken its initial set, but is not yet hard. In certain clayey ground chemicals are first injected, to coat the ground particles and facilitate flow of the grout. The theory of the François method is that more bore holes of the larger number used are likely to reach fissured ground, and small diameter holes cost less than larger ones.

Also, injection of grout in a part of the bore hole, instead of its whole length at one time, is more likely to fill the smaller fissures, and great pressures still further increase the chances of success. The chemicals used before grouting are silicate of sodium and sulphate of aluminum, injected separately; the combination of the two forming silicate of aluminum, a white colloidal precipitate. This, under pressure is dehydrated, leaving a solid filling in the capillary fissures which the grout could not enter and covering the clayey walls of larger fissures, thus facilitating entrance of the grout.

Only the Portier and François methods are now used. Both are cheaper than freezing, or the Honigmann method, but are applicable only to cementable ground. Shafts sunk by cementation are lined with reinforced concrete, or with cast-iron tubbing.

Injection of other materials has also been used to shut off water, but only in shallow shafts.

Joosten method uses sodium silicate, injected under pressure and followed by an injection of calcium chloride. These form an insoluble calcium silicate, which sets so quickly that the casing pipes must be pulled as the calcium chloride is injected, to prevent their being immovably set in place. The chemicals penetrate to a distance of about 3 ft around the end of the casing pipes, which are spaced accordingly. This method is especially useful to consolidate the ground around the bottom of a shaft, at its junction with the rock, but has recently been used successfully for shaft sinking itself.

Asphalt grouting has been used considerably in the U S, and is better than cement grouting for fissured rock where there is a large flow of water. The asphalt is pumped into the ground as a hot fluid, which solidifies in the water. Its injection is facilitated by steam, or by a method patented by G. W. Christians, consisting of an electrical resistance wire in each casing which keeps the asphalt hot. The asphalt is injected at a pressure of 50 lb, or more, and can be forced for a long distance into open fissures.

Clay grouting (43). In case of large cavities, as frequently found in limestone, thoroughly mixed clay and water, pumped in under a pressure of 100 lb per sq in, or more, has been successfully used. At the Madden Dam, Panama Canal Zone, as much as 70 000 cu yd of clay grout were used to fill cavities around the rim of the reservoir, at a cost, exclusive of drilling, of $5.35 per cu yd. Clay grouting is not efficient in seams containing running water, as it is easily eroded.

Choice of method for sinking in soft, water-bearing formations is often a matter of great difficulty, and the reconnaissance borings, upon the results of which the decision rests, should be in sufficient number and so carefully made that a thorough knowledge of the ground is obtained. The cementation method is probably the cheapest when the ground can be cemented, but it can not be used in quicksand or clay. Honigmann method is almost as cheap, in some cases cheaper, when the ground is soft, and diam and depth of shaft are not too great. The freezing method has the widest application, but is too costly for ordinary depths where another method could be used. It can however compete with the Honigmann method in harder ground for shafts of large diam and great depth.

BIBLIOGRAPHY

1. Practical Coal Mining, Ed by W. S. Boulton. Gresham Pub Co, London. Section IV, by Henry Louis. Vol I, p 131, to Vol II, p 230. Special methods of shaft-sinking, as drop-shaft, Pattberg, freezing, given in detail, with costs
2. Practical Shaft Sinking. F. Donaldson. McGraw-Hill Book Co. Methods of sinking through hard and soft ground
3. Shaft Sinking under Difficult Conditions. J. Reimer. Transl by Corning and Peele. John Wiley and Sons
4. Rogers Concrete Drop-shaft, Iron River, Mich. P. B. McDonald. *Min & Sci Pr*, Dec 30, 1911
5. Cement Grout and Compressed Air in Shaft Sinking. R. G. Johnson. *Coal Age*, Feb 24, 1912
6. Process and Cost of Shaft Sinking by the Freezing Method. Prof Stegemann. *Glückauf*, Mar 16, 1912
7. Shaft Sinking by Poetsch Method. *Mines & Min*, Nov, 1911
8. Shaft Sinking by the Freezing Process. S. F. Walker. *Mines & Min*, Aug, 1909
9. Sinking in Wet Rock by Injecting Concrete. J. Lombois. *E & Min Jour*, Mar 27, 1909. For records of other European undertakings of same nature, see *Ann des Mines*, Nov, 1907 (abs in *E & M Jour*, Aug 1, 1908); *Ann des Mines*, April, 1908; *Bull Soc de l'Ind Min*, Apr 21, 1906 (abs in *E & M Jour*, July 28, 1906)
10. Sinking through Sand at Newbiggin Colliery. F. M. Bainbridge and W. M. Redfearn. Drop-shaft method. *Iron & Coal Trades Rev*, Sept 17, 1909
11. Concrete Shafts through Quicksand. Fred. W. Adgate. *Mines & Min*, Dec, 1909
12. Sinking the Woodward No 3 Shaft. R. V. Norris. *E & M Jour*, June 4, 1910
13. Sinking of Astley Green Shafts, England, by Drop Shaft and Underhanging Tubbing. Pilkington and Wood. *Iron & Coal Trades Rev*, June 17, 1910
14. Study of Freezing Process. W. Walbrecker, *Glückauf*, serial, beginning Oct 22, 1910
15. Shaft Sinking against Water in Fissured Ground by Cement Injection. A. L. Shrager. *Trans Inst of Mining and Met*, London, Vol 20, p 454
16. Sinking for Pier Foundation, Tunkhannock Viaduct. *Eng Rec*, May 3, 1913
17. Sinking Caisson of Colorado River Siphon, Ariz. *Eng News*, Aug 23, 1912
18. L'emploi de la Congelation. F. Schmidt. *Bull Soc de l'Ind Min*, Vol IX
19. Sinking Theresa and Castlereagh Shafts. *Trans* Instn Min Eng (Great Britain), Vol 32, **p 551**
20. Sinking Two Drop Shafts for Norwood-White Coal Co, Iowa. *Coal Age*, Feb 3, 1921

21. Sinking Two Shafts near Terre Haute, Ind, by Pneumatic Caisson Method. *E & M Jour,* Sept 29, 1923
22. Freezing Method in Shaft Sinking to Coal Beds in North Belgium. *Coal Age,* June 5, 1924
23. Discovery and Development of Coal Deposits of Campine, Belgium. *Min & Met,* Aug, 1922
24. Sinking through Wet Strata at Great Depths. Discussion of Hand Sinking, Cementation, Shaft Boring and Freezing. H. Huller. *Col Guard,* Sept 14, 28, 1917
25. François Cementation Process in So Africa. *Trans Chem, Met, and Min Soc, So Africa,* Vol 18 (1918); Vol 24, p 186 (1924)
26. Cementation Process (François System) Applied to Mining. *Col Guard,* Mch 9, 1917
27. Cementation at Lay Hall Colliery Shafts, England. *Col Guard,* Mch 2, 1917
28. Jed Shafts, near Welch, W Va. Lining with Concrete and Sealing by Cementation. *Coal Age,* Jan 2, 1915
29. Earth Pressure and Thawing of Frozen Shafts. *Bergbau,* June 13, 1929, p 333
30. Die neure Entwickelung des Honigmannschen Schachtbohrverfahrens. H. Bochum. *Bergbau,* Nov 27, 1930, p 705
31. Deutsche Abteufarbeiten in Russland. K. Demel. *Glückauf,* Dec 24, 1932, p 1193-8
32. Untersuchungen über die Abbindetemperaturen von Beton und ihre Nutzanwendung beim Ausbau eines Gefrierschachtes. R. Gruen and H. Beekman. *Zement,* Jan 31, 1932, p 36
33. Das Chemische Verfestigungsverfahren nach Dr. Joosten, etc. A. Kleinlogel. *Int Bergwirtschaft und Bergtechnik,* Mch 15, 1932, p 29
34. Schachtabteufen nach dem verbeserten Honigmann-Verfahren. G. Duyfjes. *Glückauf,* Nov 15, 1932, p 1032
35. Honigmann Shaft-boring Process for Sinking through Soft Waterbearing Strata. G. Knox. *Proc So Wales Inst Engrs,* July 15, 1932, p 263-80
36. Shaft Sinking by Freezing. W. L. Lowe-Brown. *Engineer,* May 26, 1933, p 516 and 526
37. Das Tiefkälteverfahren beim Schachtabteufen. H. Joosten. *Montanistische Rundschau,* Mch 16, 1933, p 1-4; Apl 1, p 1-6, Apl 16, p 4-8
38. Untersuchungen über Guss und Stampfbeton für Gefrierschächte. E. Gabor und H. Hoeffgem. *Glückauf,* Apl 8, 1933, p 305
39. Le Fonçage de Puits de Mine en Terrains Aquifères. M. Biquet. *Les Principaux Procédés Spéciaux.* Paris, Dunod, 1934
40. Water Hazards. G. D. Breffit. *Junior Instn of Engineers,* London, Journal and Record of Trans, 1835, p 440
41. Der Neubau des Eingestürzten Schachtes Augusta Victoria 3. G. Schmidt. *Glückauf,* Nov 9, 1935, p 1069
42. Creusement de Deux Puits par le procédé de la Congélation. A. Ampe. *Revue de l'Industrie Minérale,* Dec 15, 1935, p 603
43. *Construction Methods & Equipment,* June, 1937, p 66 (McGraw-Hill Book Co)

SECTION 9

BORING

BY

ARTHUR F. TAGGART

SCHOOL OF MINES, COLUMBIA UNIVERSITY

LARGELY REWRITTEN FOR THE THIRD EDITION BY

ROBERT S. LEWIS

PROFESSOR OF MINING, UNIVERSITY OF UTAH

Note.—Numbers in parentheses in text refer to Bibliography at end of this section.

BORING

1. WASH-BORING RIGS (DRIVEPIPES)

These rigs are for sampling soft strata overlying solid rock, to ascertain depth of bedrock below surface, and to sink standpipe for diamond drills. Rarely used for depths exceeding 100 ft. For testing superficial deposits much time is spent in moving from point to point; hence a light, portable outfit is necessary, as follows: 1 derrick, with 20-ft legs of 4 by 4-in timber, complete with windlass and sheave for 1.25-in rope (Fig 1). Truck wheels should be heavy, about 40-in diam, one tight and one loose on axle. 50 ft of 1 1/8-in hoisting rope. Flush-joint casing, 2.5-in, 5-ft lengths, for the probable maximum depth of hole; also a few lengths, each 1, 2, 3 and 4 ft. (Sleeve couplings can be used, but are troublesome in sinking and pulling.) 1 casing driveshoe; 1 casing drivehead; 1 casing tee. Flush-joint, 1 1/8-in drill rods, in 10-ft lengths, with couplings, totaling 10 ft longer than casing. Add two 5-ft lengths. (0.75-in gas pipe can be used in light sandy material.) 1 hoisting water swivel and coupling; 1 hoisting swivel; 3 cross chopping bits; 1 chisel bit; 1 bushing, water swivel to casing; 1 shoe for taking dry samples; 1 worm auger; 1 hand forcepump, 4-in cyl by 4.5-in stroke; 15 ft, 1.5-in suction hose, with coupling and strainer; 50 ft, 0.75-in 4-ply rubber pressure hose, with couplings for pump and water swivel; 1 axe; 2 5-ft crowbars; 15 ft of 3/8-in chain, with hook and ring; 1 coldchisel; 2 hose couplings; 1 150-lb drive-block; 2 three-cornered 6-in files; 2 10-in flat files; 1 machinist's hammer; 1 oiler; 1 pick; 1 galvanized pail; 1 saw; 1 screwdriver; 1 shovel; 1 tape line; 2 36-in pipe tongs; 1 tool box; 2 hose unions; 3 Stillson wrenches, 10, 14 and 24-in; 2 monkey wrenches, 6 and 15-in; sample boxes and 4-oz wide mouth bottles; 1 firing battery; dynamite, electric detonators and 400 ft insulated copper wire; 1 pair sister hooks for 1.25-in rope; 1 shovel; 1 pair combined nippers and pliers; 1 brace with bits 0.25 to 1 in; 4 pairs Brown's patent pipe tongs, 2 No 3 and 2 No 4; 1 pair pipe clamps for 2.5-in casing; 2 10-ton jack screws; extra valves, liners and packing for pump; 4 balls candle-wick; 1 hank sash cord; 1 1-gal oil can and lubricating oil; 1 wagon. This outfit, for 50-ft holes, costs $350 to $400, and will last several years.

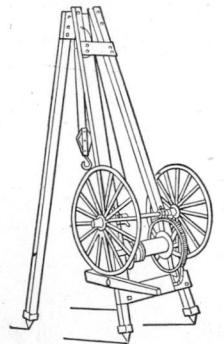

Fig 1. Derrick for Wash Boring

Operation (1). A pipe of the required diam is sunk, the core is broken up by a jet of water, or, if necessary, by a chisel bit, and the disintegrated material is brought to surface by the current of water. For penetrating SOFT GROUND, a smaller pipe carrying water under pressure is worked ahead inside the drivepipe as fast as the loosened stuff is carried to surface. In such material the drivepipe sinks of its own weight, or can be made to do so by rotating it by cross-bars (brace head), weighted by old carwheels, if necessary. In HARDER MATERIAL, a chisel bit is attached to lower end of wash pipe, and churned up and down to cut a hole below the drivepipe. Cuttings are washed to surface by a stream of water issuing from holes in the sides of bit. In this case the rig shown in Fig 2 is used, ropes A and B passing through a double block in the derrick. In GRAVELS the fine material is washed out, leaving coarser pebbles in the hole. If small enough, these are bailed out with a sand pump. If too large, they are broken with a cross chopping bit before pumping. BOULDERS are drilled through ahead of the casing, then broken with dynamite. The charge, made up for electric firing, is lowered to the proper depth by the leading wires. Before shooting, the casing is raised several feet to prevent injury. After shooting, casing can usually be driven through the broken rock. For testing overburden 2.5-in drivepipe and 0.5 or 0.75-in water pipe for drill rods are common sizes.

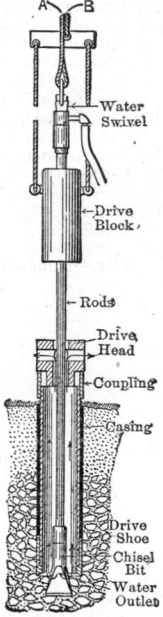

Fig 2. Chopping Bit in Combination with Drive Pipe

For deep holes or holes in bad ground, several strings of pipe may have to be sunk, before reaching bedrock. OBLIQUE HOLES can be sunk by wash boring, but cost increases rapidly with degree of deviation from the vertical. In SOFT SOILS, and when samples are not required, pipe can be flushed down rapidly by attaching a water swivel and drivehead to the pipe itself; then driving and twisting the pipe ahead, while pumping down water. The water washes the core from under the shoe and rises outside of the pipe. Crew for a wash-boring rig consists of a foreman, 3 or 4 laborers, and a team.

Pulling casing. Drivepipe is pulled from test holes after they have served their purpose. If possible, this is done by attaching windlass rope to the pipe by a swivel head; then pulling while the pipe is twisted with tongs. If necessary, clamps are put on the pipe and it is raised by jacks or levers; a bight of chain around the pipe will sometimes take place of a clamp. By proper arrangement of clamps, the drivehead may be caused to give an upward blow on the pipe. Pulling pipe is often more difficult than placing it, especially in clay.

Speed. In soft soils, 12–18 ft per hr may be made to depths of 50 ft. In stiff clays, 5–6 ft per hr is good work. In holes over 100 ft deep, in sand, 12–15 ft per day is aver progress.

Cost of wash boring depends on the speed of advance, size of crew, wages paid, distance apart of holes, character of country, water supply, and climate.

In exploring a route for the N Y State Barge Canal, 666 holes were sunk by wash boring in alluvial soil, clay, sand, gravel, and hardpan. Aver depth of holes drilled in any month, 14 to 47 ft. Lowest monthly aver cost per ft was $0.18, in Sept, 1906, when 49 holes averaging 40.5 ft deep were sunk in easy soil. Highest monthly cost, $2.70 per ft, in July, 1905, when 3 holes averaging 47 ft were sunk in clay, sand, and hardpan. Aver for 666 holes, totaling 18 130 ft, was $0.35 per ft. Crew: 1 foreman, 3 laborers, a double team and driver. Charge for labor and team ranged from 87 to 98% of total cost (1). In making the Bahio dam borings for the Panama Canal, aver cost of 115-ft holes, in material ranging from quicksand to coarse gravel, was $0.83 per ft, including $0.14 for freight and traveling expense, and $0.15 for plant.

2. AUGER AND HAND CHURN DRILLING (2)

Augers are used for wells and for prospecting in soft ground. Fig 3 shows typical outfit for wells in middle west and south, consisting of derrick, windlass, auger, rods, and handles for rotating the rods. Rotating may be done by a horse, and in some more elaborate rigs horse power drives both rods and hoist. Fig 4 shows typical augers for well work, varying in diam from 6 to 24 in. Form A is used for clays, B when considerable sand is present, C in sand, and D in clayey ground containing boulders.

Fig 3. Well Borer Operated by 3 Men

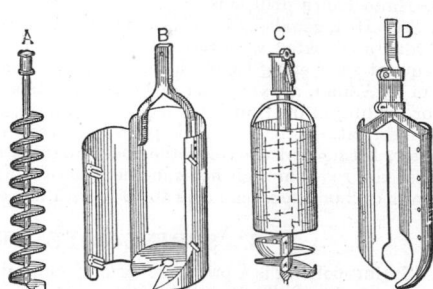

Fig 4. Four Types of Earth Augers

Holes to 700 ft deep have been bored with this type of rig. On Long Island, wells 250 ft deep are bored with the auger rig more cheaply than with power machines. SMALL AUGERS, 1.5 in upward, with post-hole diggers and chisel drills as accessories, have been largely used for prospecting and geological work.

C. Catlett lists following outfit as used by him in prospecting soft, superficial iron-ore deposits: (a) 2-in auger bit of steel or Swedish iron with steel point, twisted into a spiral, thickness of blade not less than 0.25 in, length 13 in, pitch of spiral 4.25 in. This was welded to one end of an 18-in length of 1-in iron pipe which was threaded at other end. (b) 2-in chisel bit, made of 1 ft of 1⅜-in octagon steel, welded, like the auger, to an 18-in length of 1-in pipe threaded for connection. (c) 10 ft of 1.25-in iron rod, threaded both ends for connection with 1-in pipe.   (*d*) Lengths of 1-in pipe with couplings.   (*e*) Iron handle, length 2 ft, with central eye and set screw.   (*f*) Sand pump or sludger, 1 in diam, 2 ft long, with a leather flap valve.   (*g*) 2 pipe tongs.   (*h*) Oil can, 25-ft tape, flat file, spring balance, water bucket.   The auger was turned by 2 men, standing on opposite sides of hole. Enough water was added to soften the material.   Hard ground was penetrated with the chisel bit. Two men operated to depth of 25 ft; 3 men, 25 to 35 ft, a rough frame 15 to 20 ft high being built for the third man.   Table 1 records the work done by one of these outfits in favorable circumstances. A similar outfit was used in prospecting residual iron deposits at Moa and Mayarí, Cuba.   B. Halberstadt lists a similar outfit for coal prospecting, costing about $25.

Table 1.   Prospecting with 2-in Auger and Chisel Bits

Hole	Material	Depth, ft	No men	Time, hr	Hole	Material	Depth, ft	No men	Time, hr
1	Sand, gravel, clay, ore.	16	2	10	6	Sand, ore, clay, sandstone...............	19	2	8.5
2	Surface ore, clay......	40	{ 2	11	7	Sand, sandstone, clay,	52	{ 2	15
			{ 3	4		flint.................		{ 3	4
3	Clay, sandstone, flint..	18	2	5	8	Sand, sandstone, clay,	63	{ 2	5
4	Mostly clay..........	29	2	5		ore, flint...........		{ 3	25
5	Clay and ore.........	26	2	6					

At Toronto, Can, in similar work, the cost of 30 to 70-ft holes with labor at $2 per shift was 29 to 55¢ per ft, respectively in clay and made ground.   Supplies and blacksmith repairs comprised 15% of total cost per ft.

E. Low states (2) that boring 450 6-in holes, averaging 13.26 ft deep, with pod auger, in earth, clay, sand, and gravel, 3 men to a crew, the aver progress was 40 ft per day; length of moves 200 ft; cost about 18¢ per ft.

R. V. Thompson, Ophir Hill Consol Mining Co, Utah, used a 2-man sand auger for sampling piles of mill tailing varying from coarse dry sand to wet clayey slime with 35% moisture; all –200 mesh.   Holes averaged 50 ft.   Core-barrel, just above cutter, was a section of 6.5-in pipe, 9.5 in long, with a wood fiber cover wired in place.   Two cutter blades, 6⅚₆-in diam by ⅛-in thick, were brazed on a 0.75-in pipe.   A short tripod and chain blocks were used to pull auger when core-barrel was full.   Aver speed, 10 ft per day; aver cost, 85¢ per ft.   Casing was used in sampling a dry sand with no clay binder.

Post-hole diggers are used alone or in connection with earth augers.

New Market Zinc Co, Tenn, used an ordinary post-hole digger for prospecting a deposit of zinc carbonate and silicate, in tough, residual dolomite clay, 10 to 75 ft thick.   The strap by which the handle was attached to the cutting blade was reinforced.   Upper end of handle was threaded and attached to a 10 or 12-ft piece of 1-in gas pipe, making a 15-ft handle.   From a ring at upper end of gas pipe a rope passed over the pulley in an ordinary 3-leg derrick, by means of which the digger was churned.   In ordinary soil half-a-dozen drops filled the tool, which will extract 3 or 4-in lumps of ore.   Boulders were broken by dynamite and churned up.   Two men made 20–40 ft per day.

Hand churn drill is used for shallow holes, where conditions do not warrant machine drills.   Hexagonal ⅞-in steel 8 ft long is common, with chisel point, which for extra hardness is coated with Stoodite by an acetylene torch, and then ground; thus avoiding frequent sharpening by blacksmith.   In soft rock, holes 5.5–6 ft deep are drilled in 30–35 min by 1 man, at labor cost of 18–20¢ per hole; in harder rock, 3 or 4 times these figures. For drilling in overburden of coal-strip mines, a string of hollow rods may be used, with a chisel bit.   A ball valve is placed between rods and bit.   As the hole is kept full of water, lifting and dropping the rods produces a pumping effect, causing the cuttings to enter the rods through holes in the side of the bit and then rise to discharge at surface. Crews of 2 or 3 men can drill to 70 ft with fair effic (4).

3. SPRING-POLE DRILLING RIG (3)

Spring-pole rig is a primitive form of churn drill, useful where fuel and water are scarce, transportation difficult, labor cheap, and where few holes are to be drilled.   For such work, due to low first cost, maintenance, and operating cost, it rivals the power churn drill in cost per ft of hole.   Fig 5 shows usual outfit: spring-pole, 20–30 ft long, with ratio of lengths on the two sides of fulcrum of 1 to 3 or 5.   Anchorage may be a pile of rocks, or a wooden frame.   Fig 6 is a special form.   Drilling is done by a chisel bit on a string of iron rods, suspended by rope and swivel from the spring-pole.   The rods are churned up and down with aid of the pole by 1 or 2 men, and turned in a direction that will tend to tighten the screw joints.   Water is poured into hole to keep cuttings in suspension, and pumped out, as necessary, with a sand pump.   Holes 75–200 ft deep can be drilled.

Equipment: round spring-pole, 6 in small end by 10 in butt; derrick and windlass with platform for foot wrench; 50 ft, 1-in Manila rope, to attach rods to spring-pole; 50 ft, 1-in rope for lifting rods with windlass; 250 ft, 0.5-in rope for sand pump; splicing iron, 10 in long; iron-bound oak pipe-driver, 4 ft long, 12 by 18 in; 3-in earth auger; 5 pieces 2-in drivepipe, 1, 2, 3, 4 and 5 ft long; 33 pieces 2-in drivepipe, 6 ft long; drivehead and driveshoe; pipe lift; chain wrench for pipe 5 in outside diam; alligator wrench for pipe 5 in outside diam; 2 screw-jacks for loosening casing; 2 clamps for holding and raising pipe with jacks; 1 rod 1 ft 8 in, 1 rod 3 ft 8 in and 1 rod

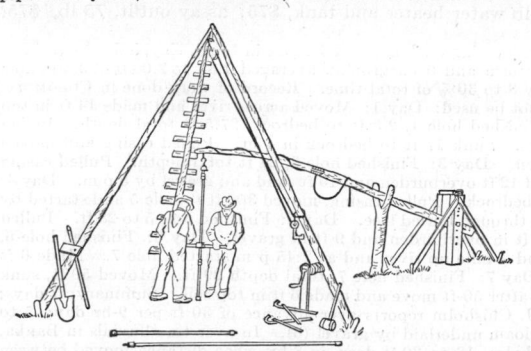

Fig 5.   Spring-pole Drill

Fig 6.   Spring-pole Rig Operated in Pit

5 ft 8 in between shoulders; 16 rods 11 ft 8 in between shoulders (all rods 1.25 or 1.5-in round iron, with 1.25-in square section near joints).   6 3-in drills, of 2-in octagon steel; 2 swivels, for windlass and spring-pole ropes; brace head; reamer; foot wrench; hand or disconnecting wrench; sand pump for light drillings and 1 for coarse or pasty drillings; grab for drills and rods; grab for pump; 2 water barrels; black oil for rod and pipe joints; blacksmith's and pipe fitting and threading tools; carpenter's tools.   Fig 7 shows several of the tools used.   Cost of a rig for 250 ft will not exceed $400 (3).

Speed of drilling.   In shales and soft sandstones, 1.5 and 2-in holes, 8–10 ft per shift for first 100 ft, and 4–8 ft for second hundred, are fair averages.   In the same rocks 3-in holes will advance 7–8 ft per shift for first 100 ft and 4–5 ft for second hundred.

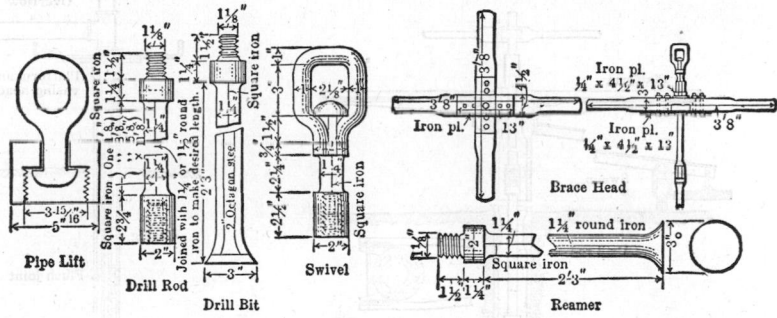

Fig 7.   Parts of Spring-pole Drill

4.   EMPIRE DRILL

This drill is well adapted to testing placer deposits where depth is not over 100–125 ft, and, due to its light wt, is useful in remote regions where transport is difficult and labor cheap.   It is generally worked by hand.   A power drive can be used, but decreases accuracy of sampling for Au, Pt or Sn.   Costs: $1 per ft for shallow, easy drilling, to say $3.50 for deeper holes.   Outfit (Fig 8) consists of a string of seamless high-carbon, flush-joint pipe, with a toothed bit.   Near upper end of pipe, above the surface, is a circular steel platform, on which stand 4 men.   By a sweep, platform and pipe are rotated by man or horse power.   In loose ground, the pipe sinks due to turning and wt of platform and men; or, a 200-lb driving ram is operated by the men while the pipe is rotated.   Core is brought to surface by a drilling "pump," on a string of rods within the pipe; 8 or 10 strokes being required to fill the pump with the sample, which is then withdrawn for examination, and drilling is resumed.   In running ground, the pipe is driven to a firm stratum, before pumping out the core.   Generally, 3–4 in of core are left in bottom of pipe as a plug to prevent entrance of unwanted material.   For depths over 30 ft, a spring counterbalance minimizes wt of the rods.   Equipment for a 50-ft, 4-in hole, including pipe, weighs about 2 200 lb; cost, approx $1 000 at N Y; for a 6-in hole, wt is 3 200 lb; cost, $1 500.   All can be sectionalized into 1-man packs of 75 lb.   One 30-ft hole per day can be made in aver placer ground (see below), by 6 to 8 men.   Additional equipment: 180-lb sample rocker, $65; 120-lb steel dump box, $55; 150-lb water heater and tank, $75; assay outfit, 75 lb, $75.

Examples.   Cost and speed.   Prospecting on ISLAND OF BANKA in tough clay, holes 11 to 32 ft deep, with raw crew, 4 men on platform and 6 on ground, averaged 1.33 to 2.06 ft of 3.5-in hole per hr.   Actual boring occupied only 8 to 30% of total time.   Record of work done in COLOMBIA, in a jungle where steam drill could not be used: Day 1: Moved across river and made 14 ft in top soil and 11 ft in gravel.   Day 2: Finished hole 1, 2.5 ft to bedrock, 27.5 ft total depth.   Pulled casing and moved 100 ft before noon.   Sunk 17 ft to bedrock in 4 hr.   Pulled casing and moved to hole 3 and made 9 ft in overburden.   Day 3: Finished hole 3, 24 ft total depth.   Pulled casing and started hole 4 by 2 p m.   Drilled 12 ft overburden and 10 ft sand and gravel by 5 p m.   Day 4: Finished hole 4, total depth 28 ft to bedrock.   Pulled casing, moved 300 ft to hole 5 and started by noon.   Made 22 ft by 5 p m, passing through buried tree.   Day 5: Finished hole 5 to 28 ft.   Pulled casing and began hole 6.   Made 14 ft in overburden and 9 ft in gravel.   Day 6: Finished hole 6, to depth of 32 ft.   Moved across and 1 mile up river and at 2:45 p m started hole 7.   Made 6 ft in overburden and 9 ft in gravel.   Day 7: Finished hole 7, total depth 29 ft.   Moved 50 ft, sunk hole 8, 22 ft to rock.   Started hole 9 after 50-ft move and made 6 ft in top soil.   Summary: 7 days; 213.5 ft drilled; 30.5 ft per day.   J. Chisholm reports aver advance of 30 ft per 9-hr day; 5 to 30-ft holes; 6-in drill; 9 to 10 ft of loam underlaid by gravel (6).   In aver tin alluvials in Banka, native crews of 8 men make 4 to 8 holes, 18 to 30 ft deep, in 8 hr, when distance moved between the holes does not exceed 60 ft.   One blacksmith can do repairs and sharpening for 8 outfits (7).   Following are figures on work with two 4-in Empire drills in Siberia, when the thermometer read from 0° to −45° F (7).   Total depth, 6 696 ft; time, 193.5 days.   Percent total time in field, 81, as follows: drilling, 63.7; putting on pipe, 2.9; pulling pipe, 5.0; clearing surface, 1.8; moving from hole to hole, 2.8 (aver time, 17 min); moving from line to line of holes, distance 6 083 ft (aver time per move, 2 hr 5 min), 3.1; lost time while drilling, 1.8.   Percent total time lost, 18.9, as follows: moving camp (twice), 1.8; storms, 8.8; holidays, 5.2; resting screws, 3.1.   Crew of 7 men on each drill.   Aver time per day, 8 hr 20 min.   Aver advance per hr of total time per drill, 2.1 ft.   E. F. Wilson prospected some 250 acres at Quebradas, Guatemala, drilling 83 holes, aggregating 3 147 ft, in hard ground with many large boulders.   Total actual drilling time, 1 060 hr; aver, 2.97 ft per hr; cost for labor, 97¢ per ft.

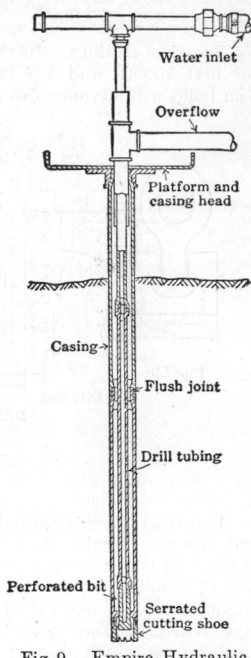

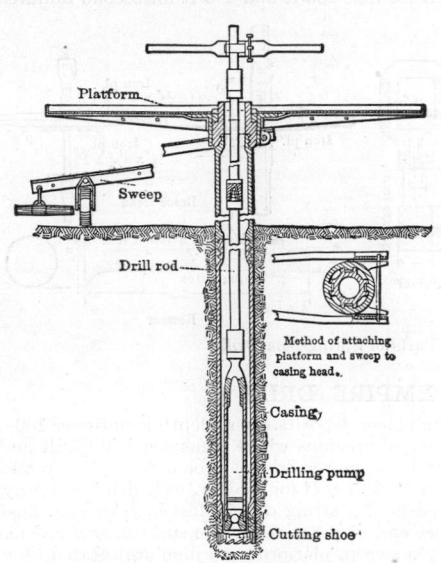

Fig 8.   Empire Drill in Operation   Fig 9.   Empire Hydraulic Jetting Drill

Empire hydraulic testing drill comprises a gasolene-driven force pump, casing, cutting shoe, drill tubing, jetting bit and platform (Fig 9).   Casing, 2 5/8-in, with flush joints.   Drill tubing, 1 1/8-in, with its bit is connected to the pump.   Perforations in the bit let water escape just above edge of bit.   It is sometimes possible to wash down some distance without casing.   When casing is needed, men stand on platform and churn the string of tools, the material being washed out of hole. Casing can be driven by striking on a drive head with a wooden maul. On reaching bedrock, the casing is pulled by chain tongs and light jack, or by a heavy casing jack. A light core-drilling rig can be used for coring to small depths in bedrock. Drill is driven by a water motor, operated by the pump. Wt of complete outfit for depth of 50 ft, 800 lb; cost, approx $1 030.

Empire drill (Ward type), with light derrick, is also used for prospecting to depths of about 100 ft. For driving the pipe or for drilling, a bar or 2-in pipe is put through a loop on the spudding arm, which is worked by 2 men for raising and dropping the drill stem. The pipe is 4 ⁵⁄₈ in outside diam, and ⁹⁄₁₆ in thick. Complete outfit for 50-ft poles weighs about 2 600 lb; approx cost, $800. Speed of drilling depends on accuracy of test desired, as well as kind of ground; a 50-ft hole in aver placer gravel takes 2 days; a 30-ft hole is often made in a day.

5. MISCELLANEOUS RIGS FOR SHALLOW BORING

Mackintosh outfit is used in soft material, to reach bedrock or ground-water level; not suitable for hard rock or very stony soil. Depth of holes, rarely over 50 ft; has been used for locating placer gravels below overburden, and sampling subsurface water.

A series of 4-ft by 0.5-in rods are coupled by 1-in nipples, and have a nickel-steel, 1 1/16-in driving point. One man operates the tool by a lifting and driving device of two 15-in hinged steel

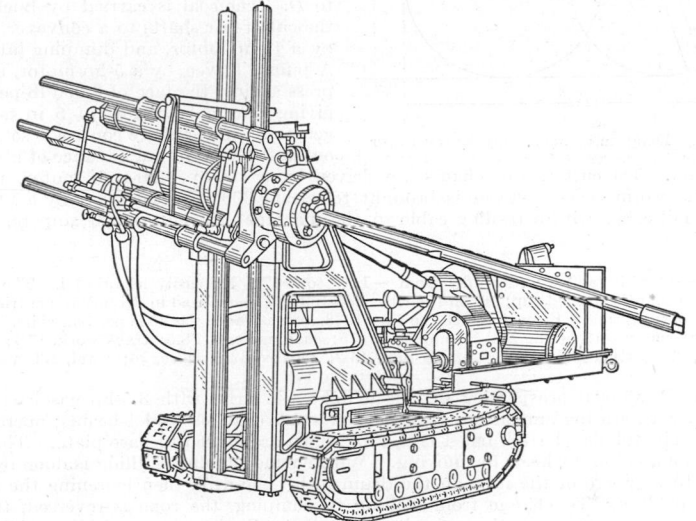

Fig 10. Stripborer Drill

arms. When the arms are folded, they will pass over the rods; but, when brought into alinement, the jaws grip the rods. By bearing down and turning on the arms, the rods are forced down. On reversing the position of arms, and pulling and twisting, the rods are withdrawn. The outfit can also be used for horiz or upward boring underground, requiring only 4 ft width of operating space. In tough ground on surface an anvil ring is attached to the top rod. Striking on it is an annular hammer, which is dropped and raised (as in Fig 2).

The borer can make 20 holes 20–30 ft deep in a day. Outfit for 50 ft: 12 rods, 1/2 in by 4 ft, with nipples; 1 driving point, 9 in long by 1.25 in diam, and another, 18 in long by 1.25 in; driving head; core tube, 24 in by 3/8 in; lifting and driving head; total wt, 50 lb. Extras: additional rods, auger tool, pulley block, 30 ft of 5/8-in wire rope and swivel hook for lifting rods.

Core samples are taken by replacing the driving point by a core-barrel, 24 in long and 3/8-in bore, the rods being hammered and rotated to cut the core. Two ports in top of core-barrel allow escape of solids picked up as core enters the tube. To take SAMPLES OF WATER, a driving point with 1 aperture is used, sliding in a sleeve also having an aperture. When lowered, the sleeve is kept in its top position by friction on the sides of the hole. On reaching water, the rods are raised a few inches in the sleeve, to bring the 2 apertures together. Water enters and is retained by giving the rods a half turn.

Stripborer drill is self contained, caterpillar or skid mounted, for horiz holes 2–6-in diam, to 100-ft depth, in easily drilled material, without use of water (Fig 10). Operated by 30-hp Diesel engine or elec motor. Rods are in 10-ft lengths. The 3-wing, toothed bit is faced with tungsten-carbide. The twin-cylinder oil feed has a travel of 30 in, and can exert a 5-ton press. Two vert hydraulic cylinders adjust position of the drilling head. Total wt, 10 000–10 500 lb; cost, $9 400. At one coal mine, 1886 6-in holes were drilled in shale to aver depth of 48.4 ft, at 46.5 ft per hr.

Concore core-drill is a small, light machine, for 1.5–16-in holes, chiefly used for cutting test specimens, as from dams and walls. Holes can be drilled in any direction, as the base-plate is bolted against the face of the material to be drilled. Usual diam of core is 4 in, in lengths of 12–15 in; length of feed, 2–5 ft. The toothed bit, of mild steel, is faced with tungsten carbide. Wt of drill, with 4-hp gasolene or 3-hp elec motor, 240 lb; with 4-hp air-motor, 190 lb. Rate of drilling 4, 6 or 8-in cores is 30–45 min per ft.

McKinlay entry borer. Two of these, installed in New Orient coal mine, Nov, 1927, have been developed efficiently (5). Cutter bars E and F (Fig 11), each 7 ft 2 in long, have 6 rows of teeth, with an axial bit at center. The bars, 5 ft apart, make overlapping

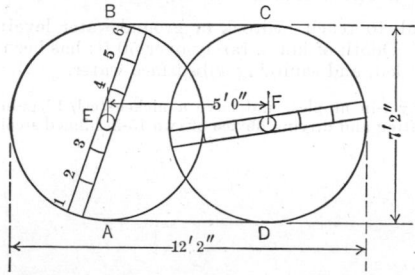

circular grooves AB and CD, by means of teeth 1 and 6; teeth 2, 3, 4 and 5 cut concentric grooves around the bit. Coal between the grooves is broken out by bevel rollers. Back of the cutter bars are toothed chains, supplementing the cutters' work by removing the coal from B to C and A to D. The coal is carried by buckets on the cutter-bar shafts to a conveyer, driven by a 15-hp motor, and dumping into a car. A pump, driven by a 5-hp motor, exerts a press against the face of 3 000 lb per sq in, giving a normal advance of 5 in per min; generally, the pressure control is set to kick out at 2 400 lb, for an advance of about 3.5 in per min. The cutters and chains are driven by a 100-hp, 460-rpm motor, through bevel and worm gears. Power is brought to within 300 ft of the borer by a 1 000 000 circular mil cable, with a trailing cable to the machine; current is 200 ampere, at 240 volts.

Fig 11. Diagram of McKinlay Entry Borer

Curves of 80-ft radius, and grades from −11% to +17% are easily negotiated. The smooth surface left and the arched support on the ribs, no explosive being used in driving the entries, minimize cost of timbering. From Apl, 1934 to Jan, 1938, aver advance was 45 ft per 7-hr shift. Typical time study (minutes): boring and loading coal, 175; changing cars, 78.5; track work, 17.1; waiting for locos, 27; setting jacks, 17.8; setting bits, 46.2; repairs, 32.4; misc, 26; total, 420 min.

P. A. P. alluvial prospecting drill is a light 4-in drill, with 3.5-hp gasolene engine mounted with gearing and drum, on a base of small channels and I-beams; operated by 2 men. The tubular derrick has 4 legs, 2 of which are hinged to base plate. The outfit can be mounted on 2 wheels for moving. With engine running, drilling is done by tightening a turn or two of the rope on the drum to lift the drill, then loosening the rope to allow it to drop. To change from drilling to pumping, the rope is reversed, the drill being attached to one end, the pump to the other. Equipment for drilling 50-ft holes: drill with engine, gears, drum and derrick; 125 ft of 1-in rope; bit; jarring clamps; 50 ft 4-in casing; drive head; cutting shoe; pipe clamps; sand pump; pipe wrenches; Barrett jacks; net wt, about 2 450 lb.

Buda-Hubron drill is for shallow boring, for soil testing, etc. An attachment for drilling small holes in soft rock can be furnished. Standard rig makes holes to 30-in diam and 24 ft deep; 42-in holes can be drilled to 10 ft; 50-ft depths are possible. The helix cutter resembles a post-hole digger, but has lips and teeth for boring in frozen ground and shale. Engine rotates a square shaft carrying cutter, the weight of which forces it down until 15–18 in of dirt is built up on the cutter. Rotation is then stopped, lifting clutch engaged and 2 roller chains bring dirt to surface, where the drill is automatically stopped and locked; then, a moment's rotation throws dirt off by centrifugal force. In hard soils, press is brought on the drill spindle by a feed lever, pumped up and down by hand, as in working a jack. The helices are in sizes from 13 to 42 in. In aver soil, 2 men can drill about 1 ft per min; in shale, 18-in holes, 20 ft deep, in 40 min. In soft soils, a twin cyl, 12-hp gasolene engine is used; cost with special base for mounting on a 1.5-ton truck, $1 935. For harder soils a 25-hp, 4-cyl engine is used. Cost of truck-mounted outfit, $2 346; wt, 2 700 lb. With caterpillar treads, winch and derrick, cost is $5 250.

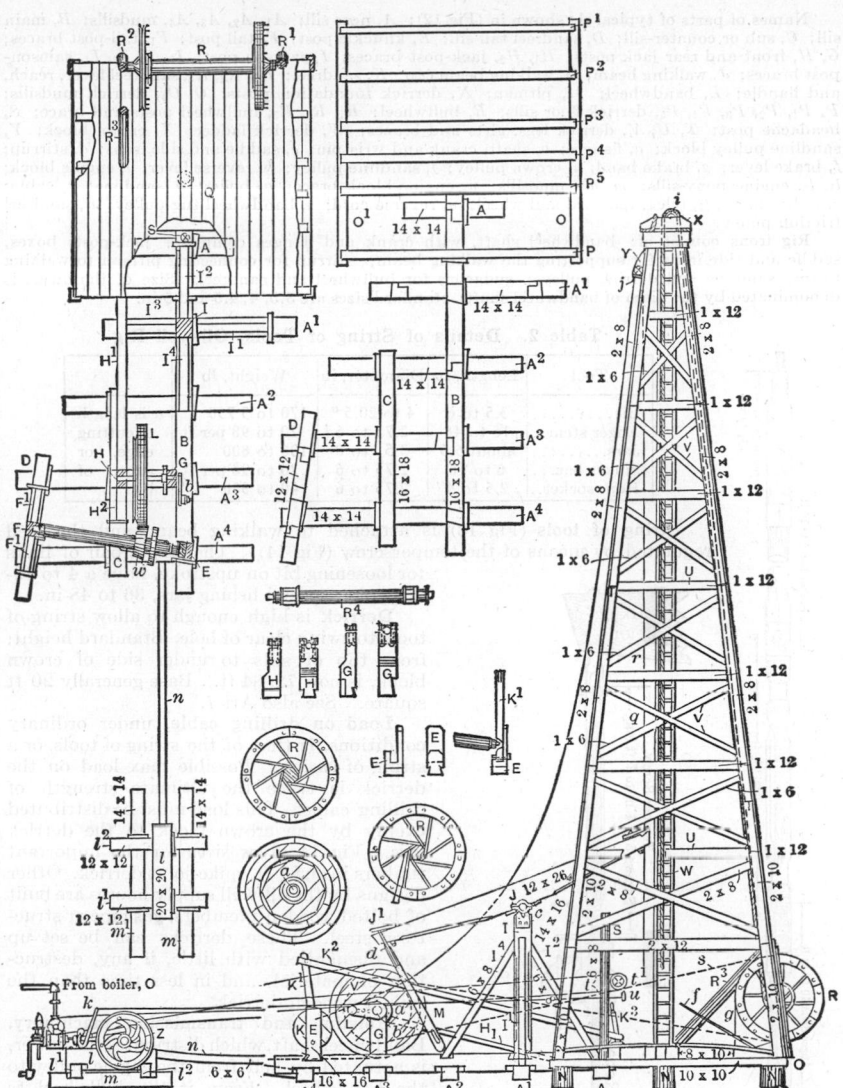

Fig 12.   Standard Oil-well Rig

6. CABLE-TOOL DRILLING FOR OIL

This old method, for oil, gas, sulphur or water, is also called churn drilling. In 1859, the first oil well in the U S was drilled near Titusville, Pa, using a steam rig; depth, only 69.5 ft. The rotary method of drilling (Art 7) is now exclusively used for deep wells, say over 6 000 ft, but statistics show that about 45% of the oilwells in the U S are still drilled by cable tools.

There are 2 general classes: the standard rig, with stationary derrick (Fig 12), and the portable rig; both consist essentially of a band-wheel, bull-wheel, walking-beam, samson post, pitman, crank and wrist pin, sand reel for bailer, and may also include a calf-wheel (Fig 19).

Standard rig developed in Pennsylvania, is commonly used in the eastern fields for oil and gas wells.

Names of parts of typical rig shown in (Fig 12): A, nose sill; A_1, A_2, A_3, A_4, mudsills; B, main sill; C, sub or counter-sill; D, sandreel tail-sill; E, knuckle post; F, tail post; F_1, tail-post braces; G, H, front and rear jack posts; H_1, H_2, jack-post braces; I, samson post; I_1, I_2, I_3, I_4, samson-post braces; J, walking beam; J_1, walking beam cap; K, sandreel; K_1, K_2, K_3, sandreel lever, reach, and handle; L, bandwheel; M, pitman; N, derrick foundation posts; O, O_1, derrick mudsills; P, P_1, P_2, P_3, P_4, P_5, derrick floor sills; R, bullwheel; R_1, R_2, R_3, bullwheel posts and brace; S, headache post; T, U, V, derrick legs, girts and braces; W, derrick ladder; X, crown block; Y, sandline pulley block; a, flanges; b, shaft, crank and wristpin; c, saddle and side irons; d, stirrup; f, brake lever; g, brake band; i, crown pulley; j, sandline pulley; k, reverse lever; l, engine block; l_1, l_2, engine pony-sills; m, m_1, mudsills; n, engine-block brace; o, boiler; q, sandline; r, cable; s, bull rope; t, t_1, telegraph cord and wheel; u, reverse cord; v, bandwheel tug pulley; w, sandreel friction pulley.

Rig irons consist of: bandwheel shaft, with crank and flanges complete; jack-posts boxes, saddle and side irons for supporting the walking beam; stirrup for connecting pitman to walking beam; sandline and derrick pulleys; gudgeons for bullwheel and sandreel. Size of the outfit is denominated by the diam of bandwheel shaft; standard sizes are 3.5, 4, 4.5 and 5-in.

Table 2. Details of String of Tools, Oil-well Rig

Tool	Length, ft	Diameter, in	Weight, lb	
Bit.........	3.5 to 6	4 to 20.5 ^{a}	170 to 3 750	a is length
Auger stem..	16 to 48	2.75 to 6	20 to 98 per ft	of cutting
Jars.........	about 5.5	3.5 to 8	100 to 800	edge, or
Sinker bar...	6 to 16	2.75 to 6	20 to 98 per ft	gage, of
Rope socket..	2.5 to 4	2.75 to 6	40 to 350	bit.

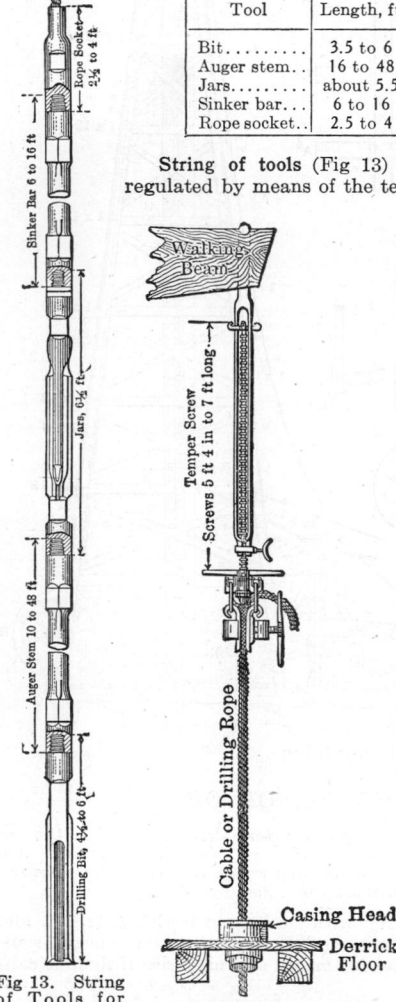

Fig 13. String of Tools for Standard Oil-well Rig

Fig 14. Method of Suspending Drilling Rope

String of tools (Fig 13) is attached to walking beam, and the feed regulated by means of the temperscrew (Fig 14). The jars, a pair of links for loosening bit on upstroke, have a 4 to 12-in stroke; special fishing jars, 36 to 48-in.

Derrick is high enough to allow string of tools to swing clear of hole. Standard height, from top of sills to under side of crown block, is now 72–84 ft. Base generally 20 ft square. See also Art 7.

Load on drilling cable, under ordinary conditions, is that of the string of tools, or a string of casing. Possible max load on the derrick is twice the ultimate strength of drilling cable. This load must be distributed evenly by the crown block to the derrick legs. Fig 14 gives sizes for the important timbers in an 84-ft, spike-joint derrick. Other designs by the oil-well supply houses are built of bolted wooden members, gas pipe or structural steel. These derricks can be set up and dismantled with little, if any, destruction of material, and in less time than the spiked wooden derrick.

Hoisting and transmission machinery. Bandwheel shaft, which distributes the power, is actuated by belt from the engine pulley to the bandwheel. From it the bullwheel is driven by a crossed rope running in grooved pulleys, the sandreel is driven by friction from the bandwheel, and the walking beam is actuated through crank, wristpin and pitman. Bullwheel carries drilling cable and casing line. It is thrown out by throwing off its crossed driving rope. When not connected with the engine it is controlled by a band brake. Sandreel is used to run the bailer in and out of the hole. When the sandreel lever is pulled forward, the friction pulley engages the bandwheel and bailer is hoisted. Speed of lowering is controlled by throwing the friction pulley against a friction post (not shown).

Cants, arms, handles, and shafts for bullwheel, bandwheel and sandreel can be purchased from well-supply houses. Engine throttle is controlled by the telegraph cord running from the telegraph wheel on the headache post. Reversing lever is controlled by a rod running to the headache post.

Ropes. Hawser-laid Manila cable, or wire rope, is used for drilling. Wire rope, though causing more wear on casing, is best in holes filled with water, where the buoyancy and stretch of hemp rope may interfere seriously with action of the string of tools. The usual WIRE ROPE is 6-strand and 19-wire extra strong cast-steel hoisting rope. For sand-lines, 6-strand 7-wire cast-steel rope is the rule. For data on ropes see Sec 12.

Power. For steam the engine is single-cyl, 12 by 12-in, with a 40-hp boiler; for deep drilling, a 14 by 14-in engine and 75-hp boiler. Boiler press, 100–150 lb; hp, 80–150, at 100–300 rpm of engine. With elec power, the motors are 25–65 hp; 2 motors being coupled to a common countershaft for deep drilling. When Diesel or gasolene engines are used, they are usually 50–75 hp, up to 150 hp for deep drilling. More attention is being paid to fuel economy than formerly.

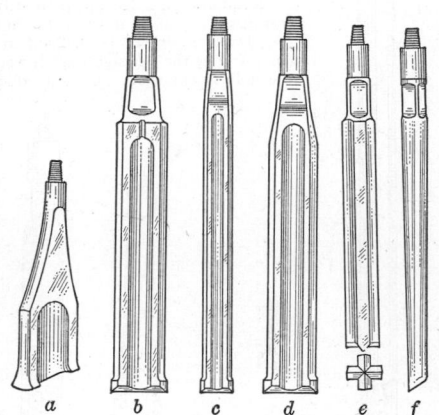

Bits (Fig 15): spudding bit (*a*), for sand, gravel or clay, is thinner than the rock bit, as its action is merely to stir and mix the material with water; "Mother Hubbard" bit (*b*), for hard rock, completely fills the hole, and keeps it straight; *c* is the regular bit for water-well drilling; *d* is California pattern of Mother Hubbard bit; star bit (*e*) is for hard, creviced rock, its 4 wings tending to keep the hole straight; placer bit (*f*) is made thin to stir up rather than crush the gravel, as in placer drilling (Art 14).

Spudding, employed for the first 150 to 200 ft of hole, consists in churning the tools up and down on a short length of

Fig 15.   Churn Drill Bits (Star Drilling Mach Co)

cable. Two methods of actuating the cable are employed: (*a*) one or two turns are taken around the bullwheel shaft, the operator grasping free end of cable. By alternately tightening and loosening the cable on the revolving shaft, the tools are raised and dropped; (*b*) end of drilling cable is attached to the bullwheel and a "jerkline" passed from bandwheel crank to a SPUDDING SHOE (Fig 16) placed on the drilling cable, a few feet above bullwheel. The weight of the tools is held by bullwheel band brake and churning motion is obtained by the jerk on drilling cable.

A special form of BIT (Fig 15a) is used for spudding through surface soil. While spudding, water is poured into the hole to make a mud which will hold cuttings in suspension.

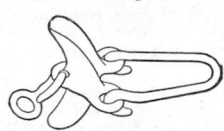

When sludge becomes so thick that fall of the bit is impeded, tools are withdrawn, and hole cleaned out with BAILER (Fig 17). String of tools for this work usually omits sinker bar and jars. If surface soil will stand without support until bedrock is reached, the hole is drilled "open." When rock is reached, the tools are withdrawn and conductor pipe is lowered into hole and seated firmly in rock to prevent entry of surface soil. If soil caves, drive pipe must be driven ahead of bit.

Fig 16.   Spudding Shoe

Driving pipe. A shallow hole is dug and in it is placed the first length of drivepipe with shoe and drivehead. The pipe is plumbed and earth filled in around it. Driving is done by a block running in guides in the derrick or by drive clamps bolted to a square on the stem. Weight is raised and dropped by either of the methods described under Spudding. When the pipe has been driven to refusal, the core is churned up and hole bailed. Lengths are added to the pipe as necessary (Art 8).

Drilling. After the hole has been spudded to such depth that there is about 100 ft of cable in the hole, the walking beam is brought into play. The drilling cable is wound onto the bullwheel, pitman connected with one of the inner holes on crankshaft, temperscrew hung on forward end of walking beam, the tools rested on bottom of hole, and the cable let out until there is about 4 in slack in the jars. The cable is wound with marline at the point where the temperscrew clamps grip it, temperscrew is clamped on, and the bullwheel slacked off, thus transferring the weight to the walking beam. About 25 ft of cable is run off the bullwheel and thrown on the floor to prevent lashing. On starting engine, the tools are picked up with a shock as the links of the jars come together, thus preventing the bit from sticking in the hole. Downward stroke of the string of tools is quicker than the movement of the end of the walking beam, because of the spring in the cable, action of the tools being that of a weight suspended by an elastic cord. As hole deepens, the bit is fed down by temperscrew (Fig 14). For the first 200 ft or so the cable is twisted to keep the hole round. Beyond this depth, the twist in the cable itself is sufficient to bring the bit to a new seat at each stroke. When temperscrew has run out, it will usually be advisable to pump out the cuttings. Slack of the drilling cable is taken up on bullwheel, temperscrew clamps loosened, temperscrew run back, pitman thrown off the wristpin, and rear end of walking beam lowered. Tools are hoisted, swung to one side, and the bailer run in. After hole is pumped out, the tools are again lowered, attached to walking beam, and drilling is resumed.

Reamers (Fig 18) are primarily for enlarging a hole already drilled (below casing that is to be lowered farther), or for dressing a rifled hole. Under-reamers (*A*, Swan, *B*, Ideal) have 2 cutting wings, which are forced outward by springs. On pushing the reamer past lower end of casing, and churning it up and down, the hole is enlarged. *C* is a solid eccentric under-reamer; *D*, a round reamer

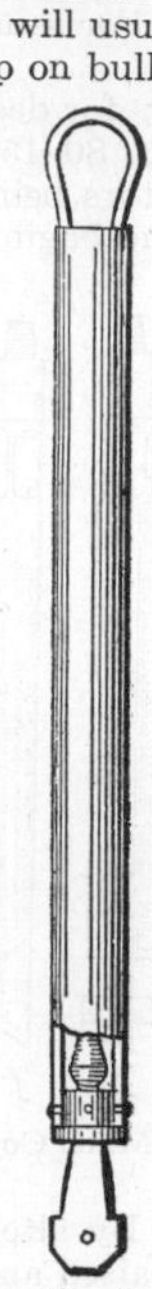

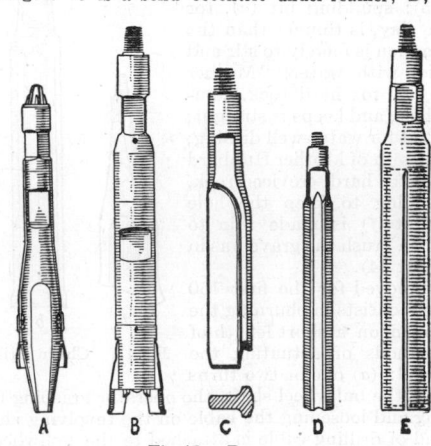

Fig 17. Dart
Bailer

Fig 18.   Reamers

for straightening or dressing a hole; *E*, hollow reamer for removing cuttings from around the top of an object in the hole that is to be fished out.

Fishing tools are for recovering lost or broken tools from the hole. The commonest ACCIDENTS in drilling are: (*a*) sticking of the tools, due to wedging of the bit or caving of the walls; (*b*) breakage of some member of the string of tools; (*c*) unscrewing of a joint in the string of tools, resulting in loss of the lower portion; (*d*) breakage of drilling cable; (*e*) breakage of the sandline; (*f*) sticking of the bailer; (*g*) "freezing" or sticking of the casing; (*h*) loss of a part of the string of casing; (*i*) loss of some small article by dropping into the hole.

Catalogs of Oil Well Supply Co (Pittsburgh) and other makers contain cuts and descriptions of the tools for dealing with different accidents, and expert drillers sometimes devise special appliances. Fishing tools are too numerous to be detailed here; following are a few brief notes. STUCK DRILLING TOOLS. If continued jarring with the drilling jars fails to loosen tools, a SPEAR may be run into the hole on a separate line, and churned around the string. Failing this, the rope is cut off close to rope socket by a ROPE KNIFE; after which an attempt is made by a SLIP-or HORN-SOCKET, attached to long fishing jars, to grip the tools. BROKEN ROPE may be picked up by a serrated ROPE SPEAR. If part of string of tools becomes unscrewed in the hole, it can often be recovered by lowering a sinker bar on a string of tubing and screwing it onto the lost tools; or the horn-socket may be used. If a broken string is battered or forced into the walls of the hole, a SPUD is used to drill around the lost part, which may then be gripped by a horn-socket. Many other cases arise.

If fishing fails to recover the lost article it may often be broken up by drilling, or blown into the side of the hole with dynamite; or the hole may be diverted at some point above. This latter operation is accomplished by obstructing the hole at the desired point with some material more resistant than the rock being drilled (flint, steel or even old cordage will serve) and then drilling with a string of tools of smaller diam than the standard size for the hole, the bit being sharpened to a chisel edge. A hole is rarely abandoned because of an accident.

Combination rig (Fig 19) is designed for both cable-tool and rotary drilling. Formerly, it was considered best to drill to oil sands with rotary tools, and then bring in the well with cable tools, since rotary tools might pass through oil sands where the formation

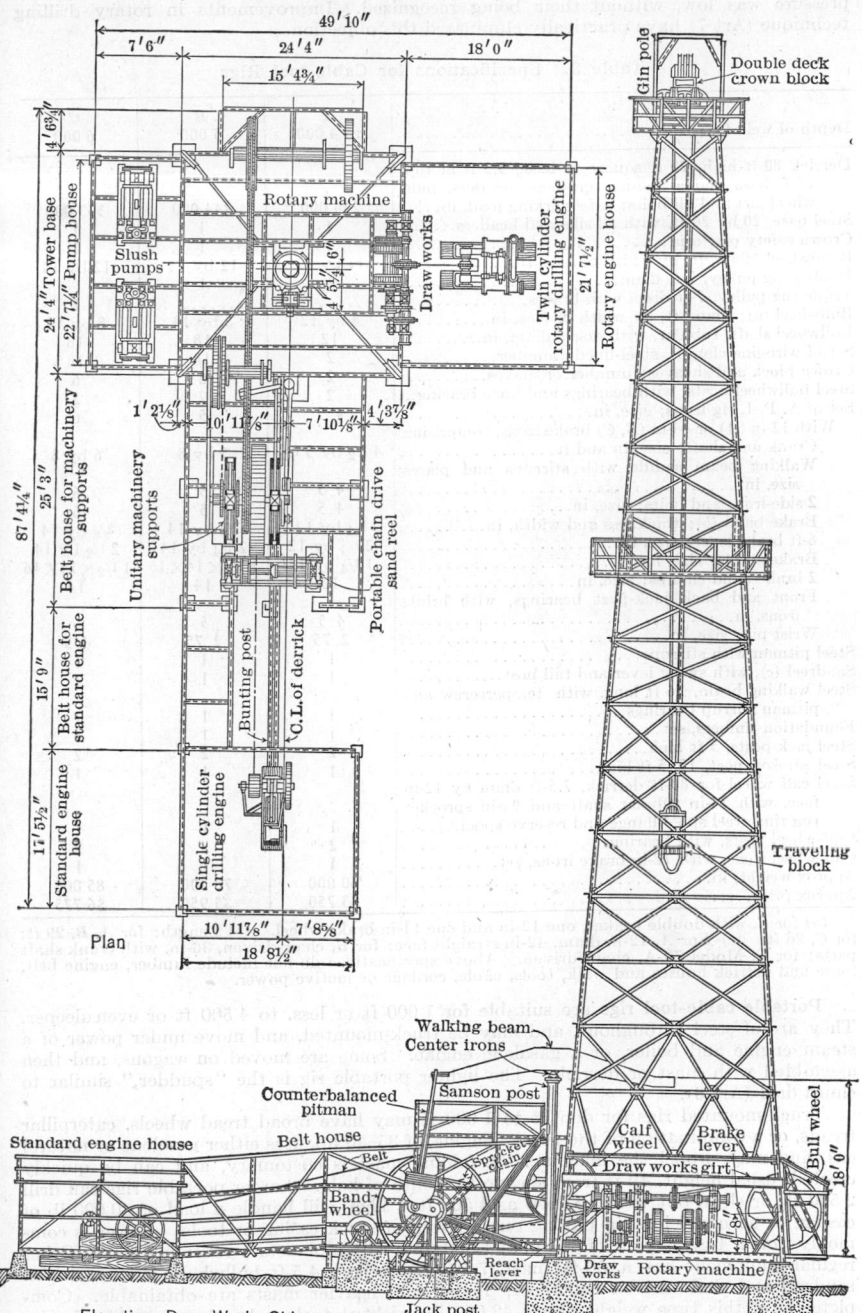

Fig 19. Combination Rig (Cable-tool and Rotary). (Emsco Derrick and Equipment Co)

pressure was low, without their being recognized. Improvements in rotary drilling technique (Art 7) have practically eliminated this objection.

Table 3.   Specifications for Cable-tool Rigs

Depth of well, ft	A to 4 000	B 5 000	C 6 000
Derrick 80 ft high, 20 ft square at base, 5.5 ft at top, with base plates, ladder, gin-pole, headers, bullwheel girt and all bolts; safe working load, lb	244 000	244 000	333 000
Steel base, 20 by 20 ft, with all sills and headers	1	1	1
Crown safety platform	1	1	1
Bandwheel, diam, ft, by width of face, in	11 by 12	12 by 14	12 by 14
Double-tug pulley, 7-ft diam	1	1	
Triple-tug pulley, 7-ft diam with braces			1
Bullwheel (a); diam, ft, by width of face, in	8 by 12	8 by 14	8 by 14
Bullwheel shaft, tubular, with dogs; diam, in	12	18	18
Set of wire-line clamps, steel-lined; number	2	18	18
Crown block and sheaves; number of shaves	2	6	6
Steel bullwheel posts, with bearings and knee bracing	2	6	6
Set of A. P. I. rig irons; size, in	4.5	5	6
With 12-in (A) or 14-in (B, C) brake irons, comprising:			
Crank and shaft; size, in and ft	4 1/2 by 5 1/2	5 by 8	6 by 8
Walking beam saddle with stirrups and plates; size, in	4.5	5	6
2 side-irons and bolts; size, in	4.5	5	6
Brake band (b); thickness and width, in	1/4 by 12	1/4 by 14	3/8 by 14
6-ft brake lever; size, in	2 1/4 by 12	2 1/4 by 14	2 1/2 by 14
Brake staple; size, in	1 1/4 by 12	1 1/4×14×16	1 1/2×14×16
2 brake-band clamps; size, in	12	14	14
Front and back jack-post bearings, with bridle irons, in	4.5	5	6
Wrist pin; size, in	2.75	2.75	3.5
Steel pitman with stirrups	1	1	1
Sandreel (c), with swing lever and tail post	1	1	1
Steel walking beam, 26 ft long, with temperscrew and pitman stirrup bearings	1	1	1
Foundation timbers, set	1	1	1
Steel jack-posts, 5 ft high	2	2	2
Steel samson post, 15. 5 ft high	1	1	1
Steel calf wheel for 80-ft derrick, 7.5-ft diam by 12-in face, with 24-in tubular shaft and 90-in sprocket tug rim, steel spool flange and reserve spool	1	1	1
Calf-wheel posts, with bearings	2	2	2
Calf-wheel irons, with 12-in brake irons, set	1	1	1
Approx weight, lb	60 000	78 500	85 000
Approx price	$3 750	$5 950	$6 775

(a) for C, with double brakes, one 12-in and one 14-in brake wheel.   (b) Length: for A, B, 29 ft; for C, 26 ft.   (c) For A, 12-in diam, 42-in straight face; for B, chair-driven, 36-in, with crank shaft parts; for C, Model 70-A, chain driven.   Above specifications do not include lumber, engine belt, forge and derrick houses and walk, tools, cable, cordage or motive power.

Portable cable-tool rigs are suitable for 1 000 ft or less, to 4 500 ft or even deeper. They are of steel throughout, and may be truck-mounted, and move under power of a steam engine and boiler, or a gasolene engine. Some are moved on wagons, and then assembled with mast or derrick. The lighter portable rig is the "spudder," similar to churn drill (Art 3).

Truck-mounted rigs for depths to 1 000 ft may have broad tread wheels, caterpillar treads, or a combination of the two. Engine, of 35–40 hp, uses either gasolene or natural gas, and may propel the machine. A folding mast is customary, and can be quickly erected; usual height, 40 ft from sheave to mouth of hole. Larger portable rigs can drill 2 500 ft, or clean out wells as deep as 4 500 ft. They will handle a load of 40 000 lb of casing, or an equal load in pulling out a string of stuck casing or tools. Power is commonly from a 4-cyl engine, of 90 hp, at 1 000 rpm, with a planetary reversing gear. Other regular equipment has a 56-ft mast, 7.5-ft bandwheel, 4.5-ft bullwheel, friction driven sandreel and chain-driven calfwheel; higher and heavier masts are obtainable. Complete rig of this type weighs about 42 000 lb, without tools. Another portable rig, for which the individual parts are assembled where required, can drill to 3 000–4 500 ft. Masts are 60–65 ft high, of 50 000 lb capac, and can handle 2 lengths of casing at one time, with a 100-hp engine. Total wt, 25 400–35 500 lb. Tractor rigs are often used with a standard derrick, and are important in drilling exploration holes, to secure samples of strata within relatively shallow depths.

Examples. Fort Worth Spudder, Model C, drills to 1 500 ft. Drum holds 2 500 ft of 5/8-in cable. Mast, 38 ft; bandwheel, 60 in; hp, 20–30; wt of machine, less power plant and tools, 13 600 lb; cost $1 550. Main sills on back end can be extended for mounting engine; or, engine may be placed 40–60 ft away, with belt drive, to avoid danger of igniting well oil. Model Jumbo J, for 5 000 ft, has a 52-ft mast; drum for 9 100 ft of 1-in cable; engine, 100–150 hp. Weight, without engine or tools, 39 800 lb; cost, $5 700. Local conditions determine details of outfit. Thus, the Jumbo J complete with tools, for east Texas field costs $8 000–$9 000, but in Montana about $15 000. Fig 20 shows No 3 National belt-driven rig for 4 000 ft, with 65-ft steel mast that will handle 50 000 lb of casing, or 100 000 lb with aid of shear poles. Lighter rigs are made for 2 500–3 500 ft, with 65-ft mast, 3-sheave shear poles, hoisting blocks, 300 ft of 5/8-in cable, 65-hp Ajax engine, boiler, and gas burners; wt, 70 000 lb; cost, $9 500. A smaller outfit with Diesel engine, weighs complete 8 000 lb; cost, $6 500. Accessories: 100 ft 12-in belt; belt clamps; 4.25, 5 and 5.5-in by 34-ft drill stems; two sockets; 5.5-in drilling jars, 4-in stroke; 5 sets of bits, 65/8, 8.25,

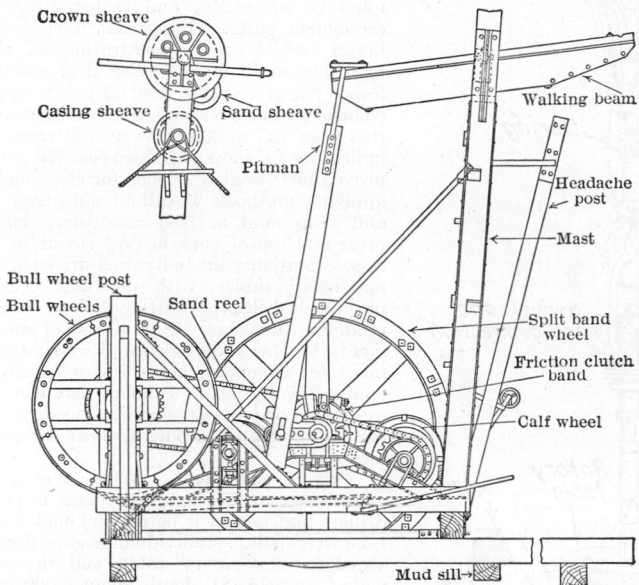

Fig 20.   No 3 National Portable Drilling Rig

10, 12.5 and 15.5-in by 7 ft; set of bit gages; 5 bailers, 14-in by 16 ft, 10.75-in by 20 ft, 9-in by 25 ft, 7-in by 30-ft and 5.5-in by 30 ft; 2-in bailer dump; 4 500 ft 7/8-in cable; two 4 500-ft sand lines, 5/8 and 9/16-in; 2.75-in by 6-ft temperscrew; set 14-in cable clamps; 60 ft of 3/8-in wire line for raising temperscrew; No 2 tool jack; BJ tool brace; 1.5-ton derrick crane, with trolley; 2-ton ball-bearing chain-hoist; swivel wrench; bit pulley, with 5/8-in by 8-ft endless chain; six 5-in Hay Fork pulleys; 500 ft 1-in casing line; set (2 each) extra heavy center-latch elevators for bits, with 72-in links; two sets 15.5-in casing tongs with bushings; 8-ft casing pole; 37 by 20-in casing block; 37 by 20-in triple-sheave block; No 3 slack tub; No 3 derrick forge; 400-lb anvil; set 450-lb tool wrenches with liners; rear casing wagon; 3 KW steam-turbine rig lighters; tool box; No 743 pipe vise; No 1 and 00 stocks and dies, complete; hand tools, pipe cutter, fittings and about 200 ft each of 2-in and 1-in black pipe. Approx total wt, 20 000 lb; cost, $10 300. Costs as of 1938.

7. ROTARY DRILLING FOR OIL (see also Sec 44)

This important method had its inception in 1882, when the Baker brothers, drilling contractors, of Yankton, Dak, tried a crude bit on a rotating string of pipe, pumping water down the pipe to raise the cuttings in the annular space between pipe and walls of hole. About 1895, they interested 3 Texas water-well drillers, Johnston, Aikin, and Rittersbacker, formed the American Well and Prospecting Co, and built the first rotary outfit in Spindletop oil field, Texas, in 1901. The method has since been highly developed.

In rotary drilling, the bit, of various designs (Fig 24) depending upon the material drilled, is screwed to a string of heavy drill pipe (20–30 ft lengths), at upper end of which is a rod of square section, 30–60 ft long ("grief stem" or "Kelly"). This passes through a square hole in a horiz "rotary table," driven by engine or motor (Fig 21). During rotation, the Kelly and attached drill pipe, suspended by a swivel from a hook and multiple hoisting block, are free to move up and down. The cable is reeved under the hoisting block and over sheaves in the crown block at top of derrick down to the hoisting drum, which, driven through chains and sprockets with clutches, has 3 or 4 speeds. This apparatus is called the "drawworks." A "slush pump" forces muddy water through the swivel, down the drill pipe, thence through holes in the bit, and back outside the pipe to surface, bringing with it the cuttings. The discharge goes to the mud pit, where it is screened and settled for reuse.

Since about 1933, the technique has greatly improved. Drilling to 15 000 ft requires heavy, rugged equipment. Effects of temp of 200°–300° F must be controlled, and faster drilling done to economize costs. Important factors leading to better results are: concentrating wt close to bit by using more and heavier drill collars; hence, fewer failures at the neutral point, where tension changes to compression; increasing speed of rotation from 125 to 300 or even 400 rpm; use of wt indicators to show the load carried on bits; improved bits; shaker screens for cleaning mud fluid; applying methods of colloid chemistry to control and keep mud in best condition; higher steam press and use of superheated steam to lessen line losses; unitizing the individual drives of drawworks and rotary tables, with resultant better control; improved drill-pipe and tool-joint connections to minimize breakage; general use of survey instruments to check divergence of wells; better equipment for deflecting holes where required; use of equipment for shallow holes that can be quickly assembled or moved; skidding casing racks, pumping and drilling equipment, even derricks, to next location.

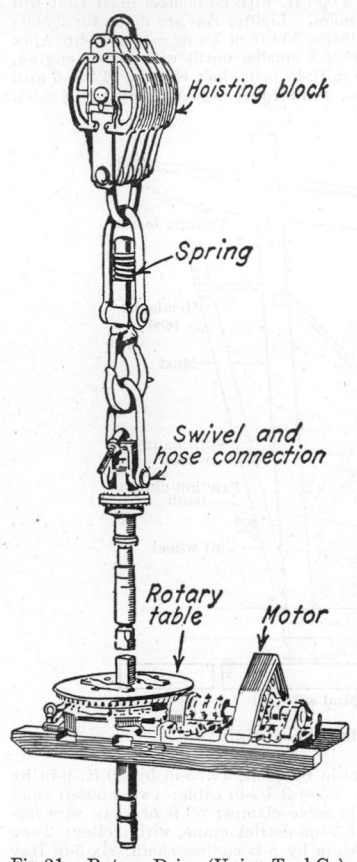

Fig 21. Rotary Drive (Union Tool Co)

Driving equipment. Where fuel is cheap and good water available, steam plant is preferred, as drillers understand it better and engine can readily take overloads. Individual engine drives are favored for the rotary table and drawworks. In Okla City field (8), depth about 6 000 ft, 2 125-hp to 4 100-hp boilers are used; steam press, 250–350 lb. Water for steam rigs, 1 800–3 000 bbl per day, plus 400 bbl for slush pumps. For deep drilling in Calif (13 000–15 000 ft), plants range from 6 125-hp boilers at 250 lb press to 5 135-hp at 350 lb, steam superheated to 650° F. Sometimes a central boiler plant serves several wells. In Louisiana, for 10 000-ft wells, usual plant is 3 125-hp boilers, at 350 lb press, and 14 by 14-in twin engine. An effic steam plant, near Bird Island, Gulf of Mexico, comprises: 2 125-hp, 350-hp boilers, with feedwater heater and superheater, mounted on a barge; 136-ft derrick and substructure on piling; twin vert 12 by 12-in engine for drawworks; twin vert 7.75 by 7-in engine for rotary table; 14 by 7.25 by 18-in duplex pump; 7.25 by 18-in power pump, driven by twin vert 7.75 by 7-in engine with V-belt. Drilling below 7 100 ft, possibly to 12 000 ft, insulated steam lines and condenser reduced back press on engines and returned heated, clean water to boilers; approx 47 bbl of fuel oil and 300 bbl of water consumed daily for all purposes, the rig taking 200 bbl (18). If natural water is hard, a lime, soda-ash or alum chemical treatment is used. In Okla City field (9), such a plant treated 260 000 bbl water per day, at aver cost of 1 to 3¢ per bbl.

Diesel power is common where gas is corrosive because of sulphur content, and water too hard for boilers. As gas engines are limited-torque machines, a friction clutch is required to pick up load. The heavy loads in deep drilling impose severe strains on clutch and transmission parts. But, gas engines are economical; under aver conditions, 2 350-hp Diesels consume 7.5–10 bbl fuel oil, and 3–5 gal lubricating oil per day. With enclosed cooling system, water lost through evaporation averages 50 bbl per day. In KMA field, Tex, trend is toward two 225–250 hp Diesels for depths to 4 000 ft; fuel and lubricating oil cost 39¢ per ft on 11 000-ft wells, to 26¢ on 6 400-ft wildcat wells. In proved fields, costs are 19¢ per ft on 6 700-ft wells to 14¢ for 4 000-ft, where drilling conditions are average and fuel-oil is $1.70 per bbl. Total water for Diesel rig is about $1/20$ of that for steam. In an Eastern field, drilling to 6 000 or 8 000 ft, 2 200-hp 6-cyl gas engines used 40 000–50 000 cu ft of gas per day, and 100 bbl water. A steam rig in same region used 15–20 ton coal per day.

Electric power is flexible, easy to control and has high effic. First cost of a Diesel-electric rig is relatively high; operating and maintenance costs, low. Twin-motor drive is used on deep wells. Motors must be explosion proof, if well is gassy. Diesel-elec plant, with dc motors and Ward–Leonard control, is a very flexible unit. For medium duty, 2 260-hp Diesels drive 2 125-kw, 1 200-rpm dc generators, with two 150-hp, 200-volt, 900-rpm shunt motors, or one 150–300-hp, 220–400 volt, 450–900 rpm motor. Wash-down and fresh-water pumps use 2 5-hp 115-volt motors. Separate generators drive drilling and pump motors. For hoisting, 400-volt generators are in series. A drilling motor develops half full load at 220 volts and 450 rpm; hoisting motor, full load at 400 volts and 900 rpm. Two drilling motors are sometimes used.

Table 4. First Cost and Annual Charges of Prime Movers (10)

Type	First cost	Per-cent	Annual fixed and operating charges	Per-cent
Steam...............................	$18 700	100	$37 800	100
Alternating current...................	31 160	166	24 500	65
Variable voltage, ac or dc............	32 650	175	27 500	73
Gasolene engine, direct drive..........	41 090	220	40 500	107
Variable voltage (gasolene) dc.........	39 580	211	37 000	98
Diesel engines, direct drive...........	42 500	227	26 600	70
Variable voltage dc, Diesel drive......	45 540	244	24 800	66

In Okla City field, to 1932, some 25 wells were drilled by elec power. Equipment ranged from two 65-hp motors to one 250-hp motor for drilling; slush pump motors, 150–250 hp. An aver for 21 wells, aver depth 6 484 ft, was 54.35 kw-hr per ft drilled. Delays in 7 wells caused abnormal consumption of current (8).

Special drilling outfits include: Oilwell-Hild or Ideal Halliburton differential drive, and Hydril rotary outfit; first two give close control over wt on bit; the last has a vert engine (geared to the rotary table), which lifts and lowers the drill stem by hydraulic jacks, and thus exerts a downward press on drill pipe, if drilling must be done under press, as when "heaving" formations are encountered (8). Hydraulic feeds are also obtainable. In general, use of weight indicators, improved bits, long lengths of heavy drill collars, and frequent surveys, have tended to faster drilling and closer control over the deflection of holes.

Derricks. Before standardization of equipment was begun by American Petroleum Inst, each manufacturer used his own specifications. As most makers have adopted API standards, much equipment is now interchangeable. There are 9 regular sizes of steel derricks (Table 5) and 8 of wood.

Sizes of wood derricks are same as in Table 5, except that No 10 has a 22-ft base. Columns 5, 6 and 7 give approx data for aver designs. Heights are measured vert from floor joists to bottom of water-table beams in top of derrick. API capac of steel derricks, stamped on name plates, is 4 times the static load capac of a single leg, based on safety factor of 2 at the yield point, or factor of 3.5–4 on ult strength of steel, omitting wt of derrick and vibration of live

Table 5. American Petroleum Institute's Steel Derricks

No	Height, ft	Base, ft	Water table opening, ft	Capacity, lb	Weight, lb	Approx price, 1938
8	66	20	4 1/3	159 000	9 730	$ 800
9	73	20	4 1/3	159 000	10 560	825
10	80	20	5 1/2	244 000	13 350	1 000
11A	87	20	5 1/2	244 000	14 080	1 050
11	87	24	5 1/2	333 000	16 560	1 200
12	94	24	5 1/2	333 000	18 530	1 300
16	122	24	5 1/2	537 000	30 120	2 300
18	136	26	5 1/2	645 000	37 980	2 660
18A	136	30	5 1/2	800 000	47 090	3 400

loads. It is good practice to assume the max crown-block load plus wt of derrick to be equal to the API safe working load. To this add wt of substructure and machinery supported by foundation piers, and distribute the total to determine max load on piers. Assume 1 1/8-in plow-steel cable, of 94 000 lb ult strength; if reeved 10 times through crown and traveling blocks, effective load on crown block is 94 000 × 10 − [(10 × 3.4%) × 940 000] = 620 400 lb; 3.4% being the loss per reeve. Due to eccentric loading of crown block and angular pull of drawworks and dead-end lines, a horiz component of the load is applied to top of derrick, reducing its capac. API specifications state: approx 20% reduction, if dead-end line is anchored to corner of derrick opposite drawworks side; approx 7% reduction if dead-end line is anchored to calf-wheel opposite drawworks; if the dead-end line is anchored to derrick on same side of drawworks, the derrick capac is reduced about 40%. Derricks are designed for wind load of 70 miles per hr. Derricks like Emsco or Ideco are built in 6–12 subsizes for each standard API height; main leg angles ranging from 5 by 5 by 3/8-in to 8 by 8 by 5/8-in. Special reinforcing members may be used, at added cost of $600–$850; that is, a No 18 derrick may be had in capacities of 243 000– 1 132 300 lb. After completing the well, the reinforcement may be transferred to another derrick, the stripped derrick handling the pumping equipment. In general, a well should flow for at least 2.5 years to warrant replacing original derrick by a light one when pumping begins. Since wells are now being drilled to 10 000 or even 15 000 ft, derricks of 136, 175 and 185 ft are coming into use; one company proposes 250 ft. A new design in the Wasco field, is 178 by 26 ft, but instead of the usual uniform taper it is tapered slightly at first, to 18 ft square at 125 ft (the "fourble" board), giving more space for stacking drill pipe in stands of 4 lengths or "fourbles," within the derrick.

Tall Calif wood derricks have legs of five 2 by 12 and one 2 by 10-in plank, to form continuous laminated angles. Inside girts, 1.5 by 12 in, 16 ft apart; outer girts, two 2 by 12 in, spaced 8 ft, with 2 by 8 bracing. A combination wood derrick, 122 by 24 ft, requires approx: 40 500 bd ft Oregon fir and 11 540 bd ft redwood; wt, with wood parts of operating mechanism, about 146 750 lb; corrugated iron siding, roofing and nails, 2 960 lb. Wood derricks are now little used, except for shallow wells to keep cost low; local ordinances may prohibit them within 500 ft of a building. A small red-wood derrick in one field cost, with casing racks and mud ditch, about $1 900.

Erecting derricks is done at fixed charge by skilled crews specializing in such work, or by oil company's men. Extras include: cellar, at top of hole, 6 to 20 ft deep and walled with concrete; derrick foundations; woodwork and corrugated iron for roof and wind break around bottom of derrick. Derricks may be set on a steel substructure, 7–8 ft high, that carries rotary table, drawworks and engine; or on concrete pillars, or steel extension legs may be used. A 122 by 24-ft derrick, API capac 465 000 lb, with concrete cellar and all woodwork, costs about $4 500. Approx cost of 136 by 26-ft derrick, API capac 935 000 lb: steel, $9 500; erection, $1 000; woodwork, $1 500; concrete, 100 cu yd, $1 800; total, $13 800. Concrete may amount to 70, 80, or 100 cu yd, at $12–$19 per yd. For a 150-ft derrick, Macco Construction Co gives aver labor cost of $1 500, equally divided between steel, concrete, and woodwork. To this add: say 70 cu yd concrete, 18 000 bd ft of lumber at $35 per M, and about $150 for corrugated iron. In Wyoming, erecting foreman is paid $14 per day; rest of crew, $11.50; labor on concrete, 80¢ per hr; 9 skilled men can erect an aver derrick in one day, all foundations being in place, and gin pole and hoist ready. An oil company gives following generalized costs:

94-ft derrick, steel cost, $1 600, cost erected, $3 000
122-ft   "   "   "   2 300, "   "   4 000
136-ft   "   "   "   2 800, "   "   5 000
178-ft   "   "   "   6 000, "   "   10 000

To reduce cost one company is trying out a portable derrick of 3 28-ft sections; total height, 84 ft; capac 323 000 lb; derrick will hold 2-joint stands of pipe (about 30 ft per joint), or say 6 000 ft of 3-in pipe, or 4 000 ft of 4-in. It is for drilling only; can be erected in 5.5 hr and dismantled in less time. Salvaging a 136-ft steel derrick costs about $250 for dismantling; loss in bolts, etc, $100–$150; total loss, $400. Local laws may require breaking out concrete and restoring ground to original condition. Salvage of woodwork, about 60%; large timbers can be reused; also form lumber and casing racks.

Skidding derricks from one location to another is increasing (11). Four skid plates, 10 by 10 ft on top and 7 by 7 ft at bottom, are connected to derrick legs by ball-and-socket joints. Another type is a heavy timber sled runner of two 8 by 10-in timbers, with tapered steel-shod shoes on each end, so that the derrick can be moved in either direction. One caterpillar tractor may do the hauling; 2 are better; 3 may be required. Dry ground resists skidding. Time to prepare derrick for moving is 14 to 16 hr; actual moving time, 40 min to 3 hr, at 1 mile an hr under good conditions; a 175-ft wood derrick was moved 3/4 mile for $1 000; distances of 3 miles have been reached.

Mud fluid (Sec 44). Functions are: to raise cuttings from the well; to cool and lubricate bit and drill pipe; to hold solids in suspension when drilling is stopped; to seal off minor oil, gas and water-bearing strata, by building up an impervious coating on walls of hole; to exert through its wt a press exceeding that of surrounding strata, thus preventing blow-outs of gas or oil (see Table 6).

Successful drilling to 12 000-15 000 ft, where the temp may be 260°-300° F, demands definite control over the mud fluid by applying principles of colloid chemistry. As clay contains only about 5% colloidal matter, more must be added to make suitable drilling mud. Good muds having marked fluidity when in motion are plastic when at rest, due to colloidal "gel-forming" (12, 13, 14). "Aquagel" (largely Bentonite) is a gel-forming substance; used alone with water, it gives a mud of 64 lb per cu ft, or 2-5% of it (by wt) is added to ordinary mud. "Gel strength" cannot be measured directly, but by noting the viscosity at outflow, and again after the mud has stood for 5 min; the difference indicates the "gelling" rate. This is important in very deep holes, where changing bits may take 8-10 hr. If gel strength is too low, cuttings will settle and cause bit or drill pipe to stick in the hole; if too high, it is difficult to start circulation on resuming drilling. Wt for wt, viscosity of colloids is 10 times that of solids; hence, percent of solids must be kept as low as consistent with necessary wt of fluid. Also, the higher the percentage of solids, the longer it takes to form the impervious coating on the hole walls. To remove solids at outflow, vibrating screens are best; mesh, 20 to even 60 in presence of much fine sand; 30 mesh is common for deep holes, where outflow may not exceed 200 gal per min; 20 mesh has been used for 750-gal flow.

To determine viscosity, the Marsh viscosimeter is standard; a funnel 6-in diam at top and 12 in long, with a $3/16$-in tube at bottom. It is filled with 1 500 cc of mud, and 1 000 cc is run into a measuring flask, the time required being noted with a stop watch. In laboratories, the Stormer viscosimeter is widely used. Wt of muds is found by the Braun Mud-rate hydrometer.

Formation pressures. Normal press is the hydrostatic head equal to depth of hole; but, due to geologic changes, press may vary from normal. In Calif, formation press rarely exceeds the hydrostatic; Table 6 shows the relation in Gulf Coast fields. When press is hydrostatic or less, a mud of 9.5 lb per gal (sp gr 1.4) is satisfactory if it contains proper amount of colloids (Fig 22). Viscosity should be between 25 and 30 seconds by test, to prevent entrainment of gas in the mud that might cause a blow-out. Assume 0.5 cu ft sand per ft of hole, containing 0.2 cu ft gas at 1 500 lb press; drilling speed 0.5 ft per min, releasing 0.1 cu ft gas at hole press or 10 cu ft at surface; 200 gal (27 cu ft) mud or

Table 6. Formation Pressures in Some Gulf Coast Oil Fields (16)

Name of field	Depth of observation, ft	Observed press, lb	Equivalent hydrostatic press, lb	Press of column of mud, at 10 lb per gal
Anahuac............	7 045	3 190	3 057	3 663
Conroe............	5 103	2 228	2 215	2 653
Corpus Christi......	4 020	1 528	1 744	2 090
Dickinson..........	8 010	3 775	3 476	4 165
"	9 100	4 231	3 949	4 732
Flour Bluff.........	6 624	3 026	2 874	3 444
Hastings (83 wells)..	6 035	2 731	2 619	3 138
Saxet..............	5 700	2 537	2 473	2 964
South Houston......	4 705	2 172	2 041	2 447
Sugar Island........	3 725	1 665	1 617	1 937
Thompsons.........	5 225	2 197	2 268	2 717

1 900 lb circulated per min at 9.5 lb per gal or 71.1 lb per cu ft. At surface the mud-gas mixture occupies 27 plus 10 or 37 cu ft, weighing 1 900.5 lb, or 51.36 lb per cu ft. As the aver wt of mud in the hole is $1/2(51.36 + 71.1)$ or 61.2 lb per cu ft, the mud would be blown out. At a 15 000-ft well in the Wasco field, the mud was degassed in a steel cylinder, fitted with baffles, where it was subjected to a vacuum of 12-14 in, increasing its wt 10 lb per cu ft. Vol of gas from wells varies greatly in different fields; from 10 to 40 cu ft per bbl of oil, to as high as 100 000 cu ft. In some wells the mud is so badly "gas cut" that it must frequently be replaced by new mud.

When gas press is high, the mud may be weighted with a heavy material, as Baroid (mainly barytes), or Calox (Fe_2O_3), both of about 4.2 sp gr. As wt material adds little to viscosity, using too much causes some to settle out. The mud should be thinned, so that the clay just stays in suspension. Tested by diluting a sample in a beaker until free water shows on top after standing; then mix in the heavy material, until desired wt is reached (Fig 22). Gel strength may be increased by adding alkaline or soluble salts; decreased by sodium tannate or sodium gallate (15). Viscosity of an aver mud increases when temp exceeds about 185° F. As max dispersion of colloids occurs when the mud is slightly alkaline, the effect of chemical treatment should always be determined (17). Fig 23 shows a device for testing behavior of a mud; filter paper is placed over the screen F and cylinder C filled with 600 cc of mud; C, with its top closed by cap A, is set on support K. Air, or nitrogen, in the cylinder should be sufficient to maintain press at 100 lb for 3 hr; amount of water present being noted at intervals. Finally, pour out mud and remove filter cake; remove the soft layer by a gentle stream of water, measure thickness of cake and note its compactness; thickness and water loss are influenced by sand and salt content, gel-strength, viscosity, wt and percentage of solids; hence the test shows the

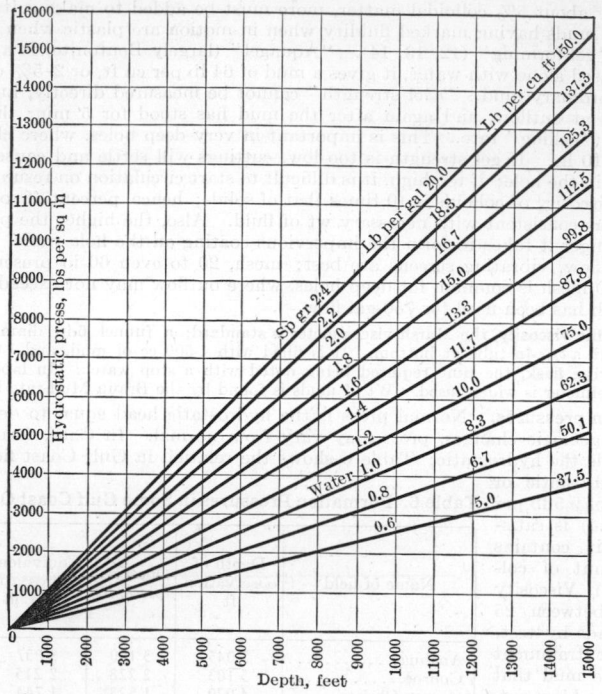

Fig 22.   Pressures of Mud Fluids

over-all behavior of the mud and whether colloidal content is sufficient; a thick cake and high water loss are undesirable. Use of molten sulphur instead of mud is being investigated, for penetrating loose formations and consolidating them. On freezing, it makes an impervious supporting wall, nearly as strong as concrete.

Rotary bits and speed of drilling. Heat-treated alloy steels are used for bit heads; blades are drop forged from chrome-nickel steel and hard surfaced with Stellite or tungsten carbide; roller teeth wear longer, and cones have ball-bearings to insure free operation. Bits are designed in groups for service in: hard formations (chert, dolomite, basalt and quartzite); medium hard formations (limestone, hard shale and anhydrite); softer material (shales, salt, gypsum and chalk). Roller bits are customary for hard rock; fishtail (drag) bits for softer strata.

In Fig 24, A is Reed roller bit for hard ground; B, Hughes bit for medium ground and C for medium ground; D is 4-blade scraper or drag bit; E the Reed replaceable fishtail bit; F, Hughes roller

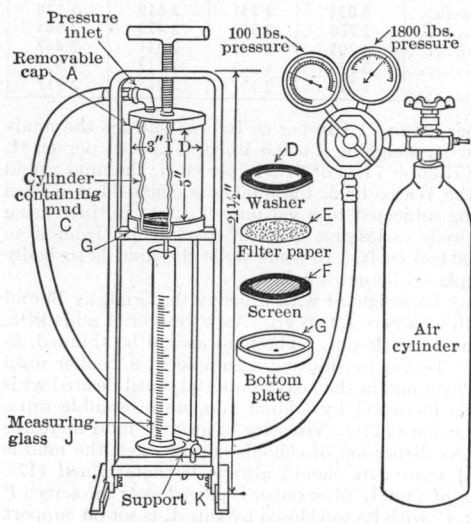

Fig 23.   Baroid 100-lb Tester

bit for softer material. Many special bits are used instead of fishtail bits for soft top formations (19). In deep holes, requiring 5–10 hr to run drill pipe out and back for changing bits, any increase in footage per bit has a marked effect on total drilling time. Roller bits can not be dressed, and are scrapped. Fishtail bits can be sharpened, or new blades put on. Assume cost of $10 per hr to operate a rig. Fishtail bit costs $150, drills 32 ft in 8 hr, and 3 hr are required for round trip from bottom of well; then, $5 for dressing plus $110 for 11-hr operation makes $115 total. Actual drilling rate may be 4 ft per hr, but including round trip only 2.91 ft per hr, at $3.595 per ft. If roller bit drills 200 ft in 50 hr, with 3 hr for round trip; then $150 for bit, plus $530 for 53-hr operation, make $680 total. At drilling rate of 4 ft per hr, over-all aver is 3.77 ft, at $3.40 per ft. This comparison shows 29.55% increase in speed and 5.4% decrease in cost (20). Roller bits are generally rented from makers, not sold outright; rental, from $62, for 3.75 to 4.25-in

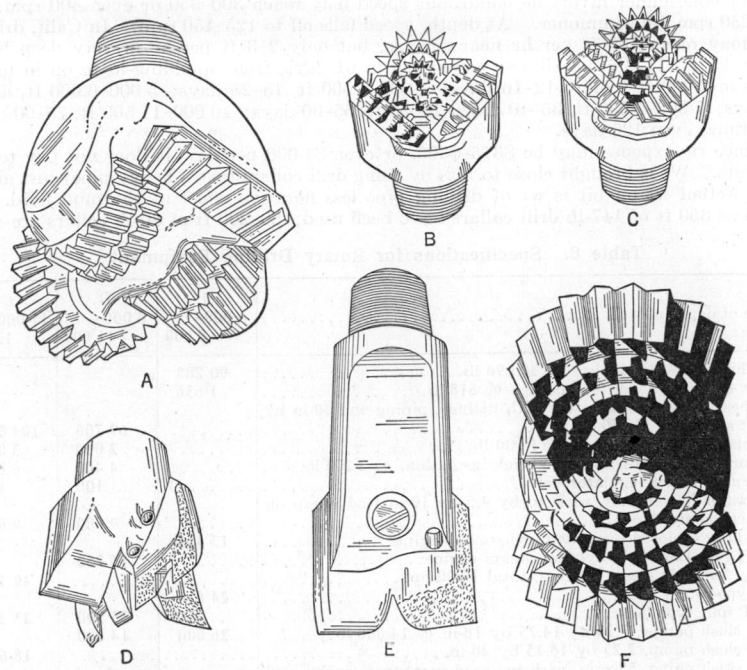

Fig 24. Rotary Bits

size, to $700 for 25 1/8 to 26-in size. REPLACEABLE-BLADE FISHTAIL BITS cost $30 for 4.25 to 5.5-in head, to $150 for 15 to 25-in head. Blades cost $2.75 per in, that is, a 10-in blade, $27.50; 4-blade drag bits, with blades welded in, from $60 for 6 to 7-in bit, to $199 for 20 1/8 to 23-in. For bits with 2 or 3 blades, deduct $10–$30 for each blade less than 4. In Rio Bravo field, Calif, one company used roller bits in drilling to 11 200 or 11 600 ft; three 17.5-in bits to 2 500 ft; then 12.25-in bits to 10 000 ft and 11-in below, totaling 75 to 85 bits per hole.

Table 7. Performance of Bits in a 15 004-ft Well, Wasco Field, Calif

	Type	Size, in	No	Footage	Hours	Ft per hr	Ft per bit
	1	20 1/2	1	497	10	49.7	497
	2	14 3/4	1	221	4	55.3	221
	1	14 3/4	10	4 787	200	29.3	378.7
	1	9 5/8	1	29	4	7.3	29
	3	9 5/8	4	1 375	100	13.73	343.3
	4	9 5/8	6	1 061	202	5.3	176.9
	5	9 5/8	29	2 771	904	3.1	95.6
	8	6	4	16	16	1	4
	5	6	59	2 514	684	3.7	42.5
core bits	9	6	35	544	....	....	15.5
	10	6	4	44	....	....	11.0
	9	5 7/8	17	232	64	3.6	13.7
	10	5 7/8	2	26	7	3.7	13.0
	11	5 7/8	3	46	12	3.8	15.2

In Appalachian area, hard coarse-grained sandstone was drilled at rate of 1 ft in 15 min.   Thin-bedded sandstone, 3 400–7 443 ft deep, required 50 8.75-in bits; time, 3–48 min per ft.   In a chert, six 8.75-in bits were used in first 20 ft; drilling rate, 25–200 min per ft (21).   In drilling 1 468 ft, largely anhydrite, in La, 15 hard-faced 12.5-in bits were used; time, 339 hr; aver per bit, 98 ft; aver hr run, 22.6; aver speed, 4.3 ft per hr; cost, at \$148 each, \$2 220; aver bit cost per ft, \$2 (22).   In a Texas field, 9-in holes from surface to 1 400 or 1 800 ft required 3 or 4 fishtail bits; below, through sharp sands, broken limestones and shales to 3 650 ft, 8–13 roller bits were used.   Weight on bits, about 1 000 lb per in of bit diam (23).

Proper rotative speed and close control over wt on bits are essential (24).   In upper part of hole, under favorable conditions speed may reach 300–350 or even 400 rpm, but 150–250 rpm are commoner.   At depth, speed falls off to 125–150 rpm.   In Calif, drilling rate may reach 160 ft per hr near surface, but only 2–3 ft per hr in very deep holes.   Recently, an 11 500-ft well was completed in 61 days, from spudding-in to oil in tanks.   Wells of 2 000 ft require 12–16 days; 4 000–4 500 ft, 18–25 days; 5 000–6 000 ft, about 30 days; 7 000–7 500 ft, 35–40 days; 8 000 ft, 55–60 days; 10 000–11 500 ft, 75–90 days, sometimes even 120-days.

Since rig expense may be \$375–\$500, or even \$1 000 per day, it does not pay to use dull bits.   Wt is brought close to bits by using drill collars (extra heavy pipe) just above bit.   Actual wt on bit is wt of drilling pipe less flotative effect of the mud fluid.   As much as 350 ft of 147-lb drill collars have been used; 80–200 ft of 80-lb collars are com-

Table 8.   Specifications for Rotary Drilling Equipment

Range of depth of well, ft	A 6 000– 8 000	B 8 000– 11 000	C 11 000– 15 000
3 125-hp locomotive boilers @ 30 096 lb	90 288		
2 6 by 4 by 6-in boiler feed pumps @ 818 lb	1 636		
Superheated steam generators with fittings, piping and 30-in by 42-ft stack, @ 34 850 lb		69 700	104 550
Steel-clad boiler insulations @ 1 000 lb		2 000	3 000
Gas burners in steel frame, fire brick insulation, @ 2 200 lb		4 400	6 600
3-in type G boiler regulator valve		100	100
Feed water heater unit, with 10 by 4.5 by 10-in feed pump on structural steel base		9 600	9 600
12 by 12-in enclosed horiz twin-cyl steam engine	13 455		
12 by 12 by 12-in twin-cyl vert steam engine		16 750	
2 10 by 9-in vert steam engines, total 1 300 hp			42 300
Unit type rotary hoist	24 810		
No 9-P unit type hoist		33 300	33 300
Steam slush pumps, 7.25 by 14.75 by 18-in @ 14 000 lb	28 000	14 000	
Steam slush pump, 7.25 by 16.25 by 20-in			18 600
Power slush pump, 55 rpm, with twin-cyl vert steam engine and V-belt drive (a)		38 860	60 955
Parkersburg Hydromatic brake, type R		5 500	5 500
2-speed rotary drilling unit, with 7.75 by 7-in vert engine and 27.5-in Model 35 rotary, on skids		23 400	
No 7272 rotary drilling outfit			23 400
27.5-in Model 35 oilbath rotary table with drill-stem bushings	9 875		
Vibrating mud screens @ 1 600 lb	1 600	3 200	3 200
Set of rotary slips (b)	166	174	174
Square Kelly, Cr-Ni steel with upset ends (c)	3 105	5 330	5 330
6-in by 60-ft Cr-Ni steel drill collar with 6-in bore down, 5-in box up		8 537	8 537
1 500 ft 1-in 6 by 19 A P I right or Lang lay plow-steel casing line	2 600		
2 500 ft 1 1/8-in 6 by 19 A P I right or Lang lay plow-steel casing line		5 075	5 075
Extra heavy side door elevator (d)	270	314	314
Set of 2.75 by 84-in weldless elevator links	476	270	270
Casing hook (e) with safety latch	1 665	3 000	5 025
Center-pin crown block (f)	5 000	8 350	8 350
Set of 2 6 5/8-in extra heavy BJ rotary tongs	714	714	714
6-in oilbath swivel (g)	2 350	3 400	3 400
Streamline roller bearing traveling block	5 600	10 050	10 050
Rotary hose with Hartman couplings (h)	750	900	900
Total weight, lb	192 560	266 924	359 244
Approx cost f o b Los Angeles	\$40 000	\$74 000	\$88 000

(a) B, pump 7.25 by 18-in, engine 7.75 by 7-in; C, pump, 7.75 by 20-in, engine 10 by 9-in.   (b) A, 5 9/16-in; B and C, 6 5/8-in.   (c) A, 5.25 by 40-in; B and C, 6 by 51-in;   (d) A, 6-in; B and C, 6 5/8-in.   (e) A, 8-in Wigle hook; B, No 150 Triplex; C, No 300 Triplex.   (f) B and C, California heavy-duty type.   (g) B and C, type Imperial 150-B.   (h) A, 2.5-in by 45 ft; B and C, 3-in by 45 ft.

moner. Wt on bits is generally shown by wt indicators, like the Martin Decker. In principle, a slight offset is made in the dead-end line. As the press making this offset is balanced by a small quantity of fluid back of a flexible diaphragm, it is a measure of the load on the line. Pressures are recorded either in lb, or "points" which must be converted into lb. The fluid press causes a hollow shaft, with smaller shaft inside, to move the recording pointer and vernier hand on the dial; a continuous record is kept on the other dial. In the "Quintuplex" form, the instrument records: steam press in engine as a measure of the torque required in drilling, rpm of rotary table, mud press in pumps, wt of drill pipe and of mud.

Examples of rotary-drill outfits. It is estimated that in U S 29 014 wells were drilled in 1937, of which 20 091 were oil wells, 2 531 gas wells and 6 392 dry holes (25). Aver depth, 3 230 ft. About 55% were rotary drilled. Rotary outfits are costly compared to the cable-tool, but are best for depths over 6 000–8 000 ft. Recently a deep well was completed in hard formation, after cable-tools failed to make further progress. Drilling equipment is subjected to hard usage, and its life is short. One operator states 1 095 actual operating days, or approx 4.5 years of elapsed time, as the serviceable life of a rotary outfit (25). Roughly, a light outfit costs $50 000, medium outfit $70 000, and a heavy outfit $98 000 (26).

A steam-driven rotary, for 2 000–3 000 ft, is as follows: two 100-hp locomotive type boilers, complete, each 27 090 lb; two 6 by 4 by 6-in boiler feed pumps, for 250 lb steam, with water end for 500 lb, each 818 lb; one 11 by 11 semi-enclosed twin-cyl horiz steam engine, 7 635 lb; two 12 by 6 by 16-in slush pumps, each 8 300 lb; one 17-in oilbath rotary table, complete, 5 985 lb; 1 set 4.5-in rotary slips, 152 lb; 1 chrome nickel-steel square Kelly, 4.25-in by 40-ft long, 2 060 lb; 1 unit type rotary hoist, 13 500 lb; 1 500 ft of 1-in 6 by 19 API or Lang-lay plow-steel casing line, 2 600 lb; one 7-in Wigle casing hook, with safety latch, 1 196 lb; one 2.5-in by 45-ft Thermoid No 325 rotary hose, with couplings, 620 lb; 4.5-in double side-door elevator, 150 lb; set 2.25-in by 72-in weldless elevator links, 304 lb; set 4.5-in extra heavy BJ rotary tongs, 674 lb; center-pin crown block, 2 770 lb; 4-sheave roller-bearing traveling block, 3 775 lb; 6-in oilbath swivel, 2 350 lb; total wt, 116 047 lb; approx cost, fob Los Angeles, $24 000 in 1938. The above specification does not include derrick, drill p.pe, bits, steam lines, and misc tools.

Steam rotary equipment for depths to 5 000 ft (L. G. E. Bignell): 15-in sheave crown block; 66-in 4-sheave traveling block; 150-ton hook; 100-ton swivel; 27.5-in rotary table; hoist; double drive of two 7.75-in by 7-in vert steam engines, on skid base, with pillow blocks, clutches and sprockets; 7.25-in by 14-in slush pump; superheat steam generator; feedwater unit, consisting of 5- and 10-in by 6-in by 12-in heater pump, 10-in by 4.5-in by 10-in boiler feed pump, oil separator, 5-kw generator and steam turbine, skids, piping and valves; total approx wt, 140 000 lb; approx cost, $36 000. Additional items include: derrick, 4.5-in drill pipe, steam lines, wire line, and misc rig tools.

"**Slim-hole**" **exploratory drilling** refers to holes of small diam, bored by portable outfits. The first of these were diamond drills (Art 17), long used in oil fields, and recently built heavy enough for depths of 4 000 ft. Such a drill, mounted on a truck, has a folding mast or tripod. The automobile engine supplies power, with a special engine for the slush pumps. A similar truck-mounted outfit for driving a rotary drill has been developed especially for slim-hole work. It has a 60-ft folding derrick, and hydraulic feed for the drill pipe. A 6.25-in hole can be bored to 4 000 ft. Wt is about 64 000 lb, not including drill pipe; price, $35 000. Machines for 7-in holes to 6 000 ft weigh 75 000–80 000 lb; cost up to $45 000. For elec or Diesel engine drive, cost is $4 000–$10 000 more. Another slim-hole portable unit is mounted on skids. Gas engines are used; derrick of standard type. Diesel units cost about $40 000 each, as against $51 000 for a steam rig. Diesel unit in Table 9 drilled 6.25-in holes in west Texas for about $3 a ft. It is predicted they will be so improved that a skilled crew can drill holes for $2.50 a ft, everything included. One company found that holes in same formations and to same depth could be completed in 200 hr less time by 5 9/16-in drill pipe and 9 7/8-in bits, instead of 3.5-in stem and 6.75-in bits (reasons not explained, Apl, 1938).

Table 9. Comparative "Slim-hole" Drilling Costs
(L. G. E. Bignell)

	Light steam rig, 9 7/8-in hole, per ft	Diesel unit, 6 3/4-in hole, per ft
Rig labor....................	1.30	$1.42
Transport....................	.28	.14
Bit cost.....................	.36	.522
Fuel........................	.375	.088
Supervision.................	.092	.092
Supplies and repairs........	.395	.325
Indirect costs (wire lines, deprec, misc charges).................	.645	.83
Totals....................	$3.45	$3.43

Use of seismograph (Sec 10A) for oil prospecting has created demand for light, mobile, fast-drilling rig for shallow holes of small diam for blasting. Cores may be taken, if desired. As many as 240 shot-holes, averaging 100 ft, have been drilled by one machine in 30 days, 16 hr per day. One type is mounted on a steel frame for placing on a truck, barge, trailer or skids; powered by two 4-cyl gasolene engines, for pump and drilling. Pump,

Table 10. Report on 60 Oil Wells in Nowata County, Okla, in Aug, 1936
(8 Star " K " Spudding Machines)

24 Drillers, 31 days at $6	$4 464	
24 Tool dressers, 31 days at $5	3 720	
1 Tool pusher, monthly wages	400	
1/2 General supt's salary	250	
1 Sample man, $150, and 1 office man, $125	275	These 60 wells were 445 to 460
1 Man on engines	150	ft deep; total, 27 120 ft. Time
Labor total	$9 259	includes moving, drilling, clean-ing out, and setting casing.
Labor insurance, $11 per $100	$1 018.49	1 000 ft of 0.75–in pipe line
Interest on investment of $40 000 at 6%	200.00	(not included in above cost)
Deprec and up-keep, 5-year basis	666.66	drilled 30 wells (13 650 ft of hole), averaging over 10 ft of
Expense of 3 cars, for supt, tool pusher, and sampler	350.00	hole per ft of pipe. Cost 1.5¢
Insurance and taxes	200.00	per ft. Total cost, $0.5008 per
Gasolene, 2 gal per machine, 11¢ per gal	1 298.44	ft.
Engine oil, 2 qts per engine per 24 hr, 75¢ per gal	93.00	
Total expense	$13 085.59	
Cost per ft of hole, $0.4825		

4 by 5-in, or 4 by 6-in duplex. Derrick is of tubular design, 24 ft high; capac, 12 ton. Bore is 3.25-in, to pass 2 $^3/_8$-in pipe and tool joints. For drilling to 500 ft, with 2 $^3/_8$-in pipe, machine weighs 12 000 lb; cost, about $10 000. Accessories: drill pipe and collars, 4 wing drag-bits, rotary hose, suction hose, slips for setting casing and tools.

Comparison of cable-tool and rotary drilling. The CABLE-TOOL driller can stop the hole in the most productive formation, with little danger of mudding off a producing stratum. If bottom water is drilled into, the actual depth of well is known and shutting off water is thus easier. Costs of equipment and operation are lower than for rotary drilling, but drilling speed is less, and it is difficult to complete a well where oil or gas pressures are high; tools may be blown out. The well can be filled with water or mud, but drilling is then very slow. More strings of casing are required, with much under-reaming. Cable-tools use less water, and wt of equipment transported is less. ROTARY METHOD, though drilling about 10% faster than cable-tools, is used almost exclusively in soft formations and for holes deeper than 4 500–5 000 ft. As mud fluid controls high formation press, holes can be kept open for greater depths, and fewer strings of casing are necessary. Improved methods of drilling and surveying make it possible to keep hole practically vert, or to deflect it in any desired direction. Better coring equipment enables operator to determine nature of strata, and avoids danger of drilling through productive sands. Rotary bits can drill hard rock in which cable-tool bits make little progress.

8. CASING BOREHOLES AND OIL WELLS (27)

Casing is used: to prevent walls of hole from caving; to shut off water from running into oil formations; to close off oil or gas-bearing strata, in order to drill deeper, or prevent migration of oil and gas to surface or into porous strata above the producing horizon. In hard rock there is a little danger of caving, but holes in shales, sands and clays must be cased. If water is struck, it is shut off by a "water string" of casing, "landed" in some suitable stratum below the water and above the oil horizon, and the space outside is sealed with cement. If caving or water-bearing strata prevent carrying a single string of casing to bottom, several telescoping casings are used, from the surface down. Through the final "oil-string" the oil flows to surface. To admit oil or gas, the oil string is perforated, or a length of screened casing set at the producing stratum. A "liner" is a casing extend-ing from bottom of hole up to and past the lower end of nearest water-string, or the last cemented casing. It saves running a full oil-string to the bottom; the latter is preferable, but more expensive. For rotary drilling fewer casing strings are required than for cable-tool, because the mud fluid plasters and shuts off water-bearing or weak strata. When the position and thickness of the formations are known in advance, the casing program can be pre-determined. If possible, the oil-string should be not less than 5.75 or 6 $^5/_8$-in diam, to insure sufficient space for the pump (Sec 44).

Kinds of casing pipe. Conductor or surface pipe is the lining through surface soil. It may be about 25 ft of riveted No 8 gage, or ordinary stove pipe. Seamless slip-joint cas-ing (Table 11) has one end of each length belled out, to receive 5.5 to 6.75 in of straight casing to make the joint.

Inserted-joint threaded casing is used for light press; for drive-pipe (Table 12), the threads are cut so the ends meet in middle of coupling, to take the driving blow. Flush-

Table 11. Seamless Slip-joint Casing (weights and dimensions are nominal)

Size O D, in	Wt per ft, lb plain ends	Casing Thickness, in	Casing Internal diam, in	Joint Bell-end Wall thickness, in	Joint Bell-end Internal diam, in	Length of male end insert, in	Test press, lb per sq in	Price per ft, del'd near Los Angeles
11 3/8	52.56	0.435	10.880	0.400	11.875	5 1/2	1 400	$3.30
13 3/8	45.97	0.330	12.715	0.310	13.500	5 1/2	950	3.36
14 1/2	49.70	0.325	13.850	0.306	14.625	5 1/2	850	....
16*	63.50	0.375	15.250	0.355	16.125	5 1/2	900	5.22
16	73.72	0.4375	15.125	0.410	16.125	5 1/2	1 000	5.91
18 5/8	73.09	0.375	17.875	0.356	18.750	6	750	6.72
18 5/8 *	84.50	0.435	17.755	0.413	18.750	6	900	7.53
20*	104.00	0.500	19.000	0.473	20.125	6 3/8	950	10.08
22	101.00	0.4375	21.125	0.417	22.125	6 3/4	750	....
22	115.00	0.500	21.000	0.474	22.125	6 3/4	850	11.18

  * Tentative API standards. On special order, casing has holes for tack-welding drilled in the bell. Permissible variation in wt is 10% above and 5% below; minimum tensile strength, 80 000 lb per sq in; in random lengths of 35–40 ft, unless otherwise ordered.

joint pipe serves for driving in sand or gravel. Casing is for lining to any depth, when hard driving is not required. A casing string of 250–500 ft is often set and cemented to form the surface string; advisable in deep wells to prevent blow-outs. Anchors ("blow-out preventers") are placed at top of casing, to hold the well under control if necessary. To lessen the number of casing sizes on the market, API Pipe Specifications list standard sizes (Table 13). Plain-end casing costs about 15% less than threaded; welded joints eliminate possible leakage, and effic is higher; as welded joints need less clearance, inner strings may be larger. By welding 2 40-ft joints outside, and then joining them at the hole, cost is reduced 5–12% below that of coupled casing (28).

  Examples of casing programs. (a) for depth of 3 150 ft: set 15.5-in to 600 ft; 12.5-in to 1 200 ft; 10-in to 1 800 ft; 8.25-in to 2 400 ft; 6 5/8-in to 3 000 ft; 5 3/16-in to 3 150 ft. (b) depth, 8 500 ft: 50 ft of 24-in, 600 ft of 16-in, 7 540 ft of 9 5/8-in, 8 000 ft of 7-in, 500 ft of 5.75-in. (c) depth, 13 333 ft: 60 ft of 26-in, 310 ft of 18 5/8-in, 3 250 ft of 13 3/8-in, 6 640 ft of 7-in, 13 333 ft of 5-in liner. (d) depth, 10 960 ft: 99 ft of 20-in, 1 494 ft of 13 3/8-in, 10 950 ft of 5-in.

Table 12. Drive Pipe, Lap-weld and Seamless (weights and dimensions nominal)

Size, in	Wt per ft, lb Threaded, and with couplings	Wt per ft, lb Plain ends	Thickness, in	Pipe diam, in External	Pipe diam, in Internal	Couplings Length, in	Couplings External diam, in	Test press, lb per sq in Lap-weld	Test press, lb per sq in Seamless
2	3.75	3.65	0.154	2.375	2.067	3 5/8	2.841	1 900	2 500
2 1/2	5.90	5.79	0.203	2.875	2.469	4 1/8	3.389	2 100	2 500
3	7.70	7.57	0.216	3.500	3.068	4 1/8	4.014	1 900	2 300
3 1/2	9.25	9.10	0.226	4.000	3.548	4 5/8	4.628	1 700	2 100
4	11.00	10.79	0.237	4.500	4.026	4 5/8	5.233	1 600	2 000
5	15.00	14.61	0.258	5.563	5.047	5 1/8	6.420	1 400	1 800
6	19.45	18.97	0.280	6.625	6.065	5 1/8	7.482	1 300	1 600
8	25.55	24.69	0.277	8.625	8.071	6 1/8	9.596	950	1 200
8	29.35	28.55	0.322	8.625	7.981	6 1/8	9.596	1 100	1 400
8	32.40	31.27	0.354	8.625	7.917	6 1/8	9.596	1 200	1 600
10	32.75	31.20	0.279	10.750	10.192	6 5/8	11.958	800	1 000
10	35.75	34.24	0.307	10.750	10.136	6 5/8	11.958	850	1 100
10	41.85	40.48	0.365	10.750	10.020	6 5/8	11.958	1 000	1 300
12	45.45	43.77	0.330	12.750	12.090	6 5/8	13.958	800	1 000
12	51.15	49.56	0.375	12.750	12.000	6 5/8	13.958	900	1 100
14 O D	57.00	54.56	0.375	14.000	13.250	7 1/8	15.446	800	1 000
15 O D	61.15	58.57	0.375	15.000	14.250	7 1/8	16.446	750	950
16 O D	65.30	62.57	0.375	16.000	15.250	7 1/8	17.446	700	900
18 O D	81.20	76.84	0.409	18.000	17.182	7 1/8	19.921	700	850
20 O D	90.00	85.57	0.409	20.000	19.182	7 5/8	21.706	600	800

  Permissible variation in wt is 6.5% above and 3.5% below; made with threads and couplings, and random lengths unless otherwise ordered; wt per ft, including couplings, based on length of 20 ft; all sizes have 8 threads per in, except 2-in which has 11.5.

Table 13. API Casing Sizes (Short Coupling Lap-welded and Grade C and D Seamless and Electric Welded) (a)

Size, O D, in	Wt per ft — Threads and couplings	Wt per ft — Plain ends	Casing internal diam, in	Couplings — Threads per in	Couplings — Length, in	Couplings — External diam, in	Test press — Lap-weld	Test press — Grade C	Test press — Grade D	Length — Lap-weld Collapse *	Length — Lap-weld Tension ‡	Length — Grade C Collapse *	Length — Grade C Tension ‡	Length — Grade D Collapse *	Length — Grade D Tension ‡	Ultimate burst — Lap-weld	Ultimate burst — Grade C	Ultimate burst — Grade D
4 3/4	16.00	15.75	4.082	10	6 5/8	5.364	21	25	28	47	39	65	62	82	76	70	105	133
4 3/4†	16.25	15.75	4.082	10	7	5.650	21	25	28	47	59	65	93	82	120	70	105	133
5	13.00	12.82	4.494	10	6 5/8	5.491	15	19	25	30	38	41	61	52	75	50	76	96
5	15.00	14.87	4.408	10	6 5/8	5.491	18	23	28	37	39	51	61	65	76	59	89	112
5	18.00	17.93	4.276	10	6 5/8	5.491	22	25	28	49	39	67	61	85	76	72	108	137
5	21.00	20.67	4.154	10	7 1/8	5.800	25	25	28	59	38	82	61	103	75	84	127	160
5 1/2	17.00	16.87	4.892	10	7 1/8	6.050	17	21	28	34	38	47	60	59	75	55	83	105
5 1/2	20.00	19.81	4.778	10	7 1/8	6.050	20	25	28	43	38	59	60	75	74	65	98	124
5 3/4	14.00	13.55	5.290	10	7 1/2	6 9/16	12	15	20	21	36	28	58	36	72	40	60	76
5 3/4	17.00	16.35	5.190	10	7 1/2	6 9/16	15	19	24	28	36	39	57	49	71	48	73	92
5 3/4	19.50	19.10	5.090	10	7 1/2	6 9/16	17	22	28	36	37	49	58	62	72	57	86	109
5 3/4†	20.00	19.10	5.090	10	8 1/2	6 3/4	17	22	28	36	58	49	92	62	118	57	86	109
5 3/4	22.50	21.79	4.990	10	7 1/2	6 9/16	20	25	28	43	36	60	58	75	72	66	99	125
5 3/4†	23.00	21.79	4.990	10	8 1/2	6 3/4	20	25	28	43	58	60	91	75	117	66	99	125
6	20.00	19.64	5.352	10	7 1/8	6.765	16	21	27	33	37	45	58	57	73	54	81	102
6 5/8	20.00	19.49	6.049	10	7 5/8	7.390	13	17	22	24	37	33	56	41	70	43	65	82
6 5/8	22.00	21.42	5.989	10	7 5/8	7.390	14	18	24	27	37	38	56	48	70	48	72	91
6 5/8	24.00	23.58	5.921	10	7 5/8	7.390	16	20	27	32	37	44	57	56	70	53	79	101
6 5/8	26.00	25.65	5.855	10	7 5/8	7.390	17	22	28	36	37	50	57	63	70	58	87	110
6 5/8	28.00	27.64	5.791	10	7 5/8	7.390	19	24	28	40	37	56	57	71	70	63	94	119
7	20.00	19.54	6.456	10	7 5/8	7.656	12	15	19	20	36	27	55	34	69	39	58	74
7	22.00	21.53	6.398	10	7 5/8	7.656	13	16	22	23	36	32	55	41	69	43	64	81
7	24.00	23.64	6.336	10	7 5/8	7.656	14	18	24	27	36	37	56	47	69	47	71	90
7	26.00	25.66	6.276	10	7 5/8	7.656	16	20	26	31	37	42	56	54	69	51	77	98
7	28.00	27.73	6.214	10	7 5/8	7.656	17	21	28	35	37	48	56	60	69	56	84	106
7	30.00	29.71	6.154	10	7 5/8	7.656	18	23	28	38	37	53	56	67	69	60	90	115
7	40.00	39.89	5.836	10	7 5/8	7.656	25	25	28	58	37	80	57	101	70	83	124	158
7 5/8	26.40	25.56	6.969	8	8 1/8	8 1/2	13	16	22	23	35	32	54	41	67	43	64	81
7 5/8	29.70	29.03	6.875	8	8 1/8	8 1/2	15	19	25	28	36	39	54	50	67	49	73	93
7 5/8	33.70	33.04	6.765	8	8 1/8	8 1/2	17	21	28	35	36	48	55	61	68	56	84	107
8	26.00	25.22	7.386	10	8 1/8	8.888	12	15	19	19	35	26	53	34	66	38	57	73
8 1/8	28.00	26.67	7.485	10	8 1/2	9 3/32	12	15	20	20	34	28	52	35	64	39	59	75
8 1/8	32.00	30.64	7.385	10	8 1/2	9 3/32	14	17	23	25	34	35	52	44	65	45	68	86
8 1/8	35.50	34.56	7.285	10	8 1/2	9 3/32	16	20	26	31	34	42	53	54	66	51	77	98
8 1/8	39.50	38.42	7.185	10	8 1/2	9 3/32	17	22	28	36	34	50	53	63	66	58	86	110
8 1/8	40.00	38.42	7.185	10	8 1/2	9.300	17	22	28	36	59	50	92	63	118	58	86	110
8 5/8	28.00	27.01	8.017	8	8 1/8	9.593	11	13	18	16	33	23	51	29	64	35	53	67
8 5/8	32.00	31.10	7.921	8	8 1/8	9.593	12	16	20	21	34	29	51	37	65	41	61	77
8 5/8	36.00	35.13	7.825	8	8 1/8	9.593	14	18	23	26	34	36	52	46	65	46	69	88
8 5/8	38.00	37.22	7.775	8	8 1/8	9.593	15	19	25	29	34	40	52	50	65	49	74	93
8 5/8	43.00	42.32	7.651	8	8 1/8	9.593	17	21	28	35	34	48	52	61	65	56	84	107
9	34.00	32.77	8.290	8	8 1/8	10.010	12	15	20	20	33	28	50	35	63	39	59	75
9	38.00	36.91	8.196	8	8 1/8	10.010	13	17	22	25	33	34	50	43	63	44	67	85
9	40.00	38.92	8.150	8	8 1/8	10.010	14	18	24	27	33	37	50	47	63	47	71	89
9	45.00	44.02	8.032	8	8 1/8	10.010	16	20	27	32	33	45	51	57	64	53	80	102
9 5/8	36.00	34.86	8.921	8	8 1/8	10 5/8	11	14	18	18	32	24	49	31	62	36	55	69
9 5/8	40.00	38.93	8.835	8	8 1/8	10 5/8	12	16	21	21	32	30	50	38	62	41	61	78
9 5/8	43.50	42.69	8.755	8	8 1/8	10 5/8	14	17	23	25	32	35	50	44	63	45	68	86
10	33.00	31.88	9.384	8	8 1/8	11.002	9	12	15	13	31	17	48	22	61	31	46	58
10 3/4	40.50	38.87	10.050	8	8 1/2	11 3/4	10	12	16	14	30	20	46	25	58	32	49	62
10 3/4	45.50	44.21	9.950	8	8 1/2	11 3/4	11	14	19	18	31	25	47	32	59	37	56	70
10 3/4	51.00	49.50	9.850	8	8 1/2	11 3/4	13	16	21	22	31	31	47	39	58	42	63	79
10 3/4	55.50	54.21	9.760	8	8 1/2	11 3/4	14	18	23	26	31	36	47	45	59	46	69	87

Table 13. API Casing Sizes (Short Coupling Lap-welded and Grade C and D Seamless and Electric Welded) (a)—Continued

Size, O D, in	Wt per ft — Threads and couplings	Wt per ft — Plain ends	Casing internal diam, in	Couplings — Threads per in	Couplings — Length, in	Couplings — External diam, in	Test press, 100 lb per sq in — Lap-weld	Test press — Grade C	Test press — Grade D	Collapse* (Lap-weld)	Tension‡ (Lap-weld)	Collapse* (Grade C)	Tension‡ (Grade C)	Collapse* (Grade D)	Tension‡ (Grade D)	Ultimate bursting press — Lap-weld	Ultimate bursting press — Grade C	Ultimate bursting press — Grade D
11 3/4	47.00	45.55	11.000	8	8 1/8	12.866	9 1/2	12	16	14	29	19	45	24	56	32	48	60
11 3/4	54.00	52.56	10.880	8	8 1/8	12.866	11	14	19	18	29	25	45	32	56	37	55	70
11 3/4	60.00	58.81	10.772	8	8 1/8	12.866	12	16	21	22	29	30	45	38	57	41	62	79
12	40.00	38.46	11.384	8	8 1/8	13.116	7 1/2	10	13	8	28	11	43	14	54	25	38	48
13	40.00	38.17	12.438	8	8 1/8	14.116	6 1/2	8	11	5	27	7	41	9	52	21	32	41
13	45.00	43.33	12.360	8	8 1/8	14.116	7 1/2	9 1/2	12	7	27	10	42	13	52	24	37	46
13	50.00	48.46	12.282	8	8 1/8	14.116	8 1/2	10	14	10	27	14	42	17	52	27	41	52
13	54.00	52.52	12.220	8	8 1/8	14.116	9	11	15	12	27	16	42	21	53	30	45	57
13 3/8	48.00	45.97	12.715	8	9	14 3/8	7 1/2	9 1/2	12	7	26	10	40	13	51	24	37	47
13 3/8	54.50	52.73	12.615	8	9	14 3/8	8 1/2	11	14	10	26	15	41	19	51	28	42	54
13 3/8	61.00	59.44	12.515	8	9	14 3/8	9 1/2	12	16	14	27	19	41	24	51	32	48	61
13 3/8	68.00	66.10	12.415	8	9	14 3/8	11	14	18	17	26	24	41	30	51	36	54	68
14	50.00	47.89	13.344	8	9 1/8	15.151	7	9	12	6	25	9	39	11	51	23	35	44
16	55.00	52.35	15.375	8	9	17	6	7 1/2	10	3	24	5	37	6	48	19	29	37
16	65.00	62.57	15.250	8	9	17	7	9	12	6	24	9	38	11	48	23	35	44
16	75.00	72.71	15.125	8	9	17	8	10	14	10	24	13	38	17	49	27	41	52
16	84.00	81.96	15.010	8	9	17	9	12	15	13	24	18	38	22	49	31	46	49
18 5/8	78.00	75.00	17.855	8	9	19 3/4	6	8	10	4	23	6	37	7	47	20	31	39
18 5/8	87.50	84.50	17.755	8	9	19 3/4	7	9	12	6	23	9	37	11	47	23	35	44
18 5/8	96.50	93.96	17.655	8	9	19 3/4	8	10	13	8	24	12	37	15	48	26	39	49
20	90.00	84.75	19.190	8	10 1/8	21 9/16	6	7 1/2	10	4	22	5	35	7	45	20	30	38
21 1/2	92.50	89.03	20.710	8	9	22 5/8	5 1/2	7	9	3	23	4	36	5	46	18	27	35
21 1/2	103.00	100.06	20.610	8	9	22 5/8	6	8	10	4	23	6	36	7	47	20	31	39
21 1/2	114.00	111.04	20.510	8	9	22 5/8	7	9	12	6	23	8	36	10	47	23	34	43
24 1/2	100.50	96.62	23.750	8	9	25 5/8	4 1/2	6	7 1/2	2	21	2	34	3	44	15	23	29
24 1/2	113.00	109.27	23.650	8	9	25 5/8	5	6 1/2	8 1/2	2	22	3	34	4	44	17	26	33

(a) All weights and dimensions nominal. Permissible variation in wt for any length of casing, 6.5% above, 3.5% below; carload wt not more than 1.75% below nominal. † API External upset casing; external diam and length (in) of upset are: for 4 3/4-in casing, 5 and 4 5/8 respectively; for 5 3/4-in casing, 6 and 5 3/8; for 8 1/8-in casing, 8 3/8 and 5 3/8. *As salt water is almost always encountered, length of string is based upon 2 ft of water column per lb of collapsing press; for length of string for fresh water, multiply by 1.155; safety factor in Table, 2. ‡ Safety factor, 2.5. Note: wt per ft with threads and couplings is based on 20-ft length, including coupling. Taper of threads: on 10-thread pipe, 3/8-in diam per ft of length; 8-thread pipe, 0.75-in.

Drill pipe (Table 14), smaller and heavier than casing, must be strong enough to transmit engine torque from surface to the bit.

Table 14. API Special Alloy Seamless Upset Drill Pipe, Grade D
(min tensile strength, 95 000 lb)

Size, O D, in	Wt per ft, lb	Price per 100 ft* — With threads and couplings	Price per 100 ft* — With threads only	Size, O D, in	Wt per ft, lb	Price per 100 ft* — With threads and couplings	Price per 100 ft* — With threads only
2 3/8	4.80	$ 35.68	$34.94	4 1/2	16.60	$123.38	$120.82
2 3/8	6.65	50.88	49.81	5 9/16	19.00	141.49	138.55
2 7/8	6.45	49.32	48.29	5 9/16	22.20	167.26	163.78
2 7/8	8.35	62.18	60.88	5 9/16	25.25	188.78	184.86
2 7/8	10.40	77.83	76.21	6 5/8	22.20	167.26	163.78
3 1/2	8.50	64.96	63.60	6 5/8	25.20	188.77	184.85
3 1/2	11.20	85.76	83.97	6 5/8	31.90	237.82	232.88
3 1/2	13.30	99.67	97.60	7 5/8	29.25	227.69	222.92
4 1/2	12.75	94.53	92.56	8 5/8	40.00	328.66	321.71
4 1/2	13.75	102.03	99.91	8 5/8	46.50	381.36	373.30

* Fob Calif R R terminals; min carload, 60 000 lb.

Results in the 15 004-ft Continental Oil Co's well indicate that, in drilling to great depths, even slight deviation would cause failure of the pipe from friction against the walls; "protection" casing eliminates friction. Special alloy steel pipe (yield point, 100 000–120 000 lb per sq in) is stronger than API Grade D, and would therefore extend drilling limit.

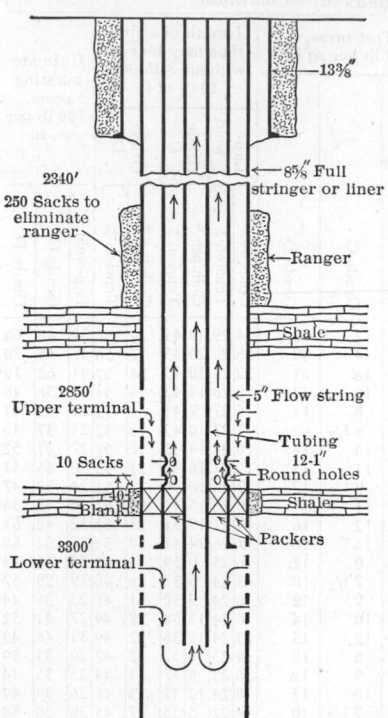

2340'
250 Sacks to eliminate ranger

13⅜″

8⅝″ Full stringer or liner

Ranger

Shale

2850'
Upper terminal

5″ Flow string

Tubing 12-1″
Round holes

10 Sacks

30⅝
Blank

Shale

Packers

3300'
Lower terminal

Fig 25. Multiple Zone Production (*Oil Weekly*)

Tubing, 1.5–4 in diam, is hung in well at completion for the flowing oil (Sec 44). It prolongs the flowing life of a well by creating back press from friction; frequently reduces the gas-oil ratio; and is ready when pumping begins. By control valves (flow "beams") at the surface, oil is flowed through tubing, or through both tubing and space between it and casing. Fig 25 shows how one well can be made to produce from 3 different zones; lower terminal zone, through tubing; upper terminal, through space between tubing and 5-in flow string; "ranger" zone is cemented off, but would produce through space between 5-in and 8⅝-in strings on sealing this space below the ranger and perforating the 8⅝-in line at that zone. Mechanical perforators can be used, or the recent "gun-perforator" (29). The latter is a steel cylinder, containing 10–12 short 45-caliber gun barrels; it is lowered inside the casing, and shots fired by elec control; by reloading, 180 holes have been made at 3 200 ft depth in 7 hr, and 1 431 holes at aver depth of 8 000 ft in 73 hr; holes can be placed 6 in apart in a spiral.

Handling casing. Each string has a steel shoe (Fig 26), of slightly larger diam than the casing. Shoe may be serrated, for cutting through small obstructions, but this is not desirable where casing is to seat tightly on solid formation, for shutting off water. To drive casing, clamps are bolted on the squared end of drill stem, and by operating the drilling tools as in spudding (Art 6), the clamps

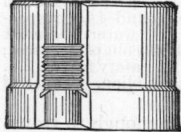

Fig 26. Driving Shoe

Fig 27. Driving Heads

Fig 28. Casing-pipe Ring

strike the casing drive-head (Fig 27). Hard driving may deform or telescope casing; it is safer to drive by a rod or casing spear, set inside near the bottom, and striking this with the jars.

Table 15. Commercial Lengths (ft) of Casing, Drill-pipe and Tubing

Casing (a)			Drill-pipe (b)			Tubing (b, c)		
Aver	Range	Not over 5% of carload	Aver	Range	Not over 5% of carload	Aver	Range	Not over 5% of carload
20	18–22	18–20	20	18–22	18–20	21	20–24	18–20
30	25–32	.....	28½	27–30	26–27	30	28–32	.....
34	over 32	.....	.....	.....	.....	.....	.....	.....

(a) Jointers not over 5% of carload. (b) No jointers shipped. (c) Max variation in any carload, 2 ft.

For lifting casing a clamp and elevator are used.   Fig 29 shows a heavy clamp, with slips for gripping flush-joint casing.   Two steel links pass through the elevator eyes and hang from the hook under the traveling block.   On lowering into the hole, casing is held, while elevator is being released, by slips dropped into the pipe ring (Fig 28), resting on

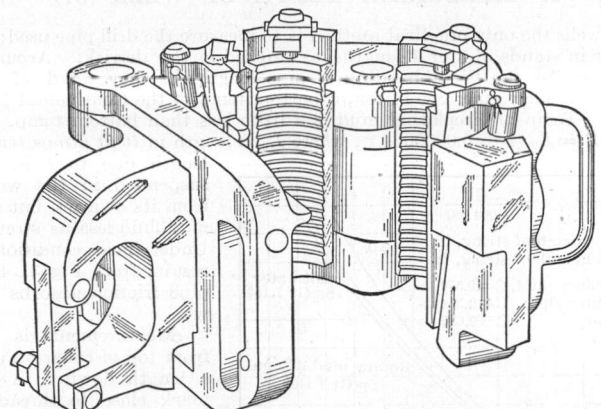

Fig 29.   Ideal Door Grip Tubing Elevator

top of conductor pipe.   When wt of a long casing string becomes great, the pull on the derrick can be lessened by "floating" the casing.   A plug, screwed on lower end, buoys the string in the mud fluid.   Fig 30 shows a plug that serves to guide the casing, and aids in floating it by a ball valve excluding outside fluid, and through which cement can later be pumped down for cementing casing in place.

Casing troubles include collapsing, telescoping, freezing, parting and splitting (30).   If casing pipe is dented or partly collapsed, swages are driven by the jars down and back past the injured place.   This may so weaken the pipe that an inner string of casing is necessary.   If casing parts, it may be recovered, by a bulldog spear, trip spear, bell socket, or an overshot; for details of these and other casing fishing tools see makers' catalogs.

If casing is so damaged that it cannot be recovered, it may be drilled past (sidetracked), if ground is soft and caving; sidetracking in hard ground is difficult.   Drilling on the damaged casing, with the regular string of tools, is continued until it is sufficiently displaced to insert a new string, which must usually make a slight bend to get by.   "Frozen" casing, or if collar-bound by loose material, can generally be freed by raising and lowering it 15–20 ft a few times; or, bailing out may cause enough hydrostatic pressure outside the casing to clear away obstructing material.   If hole is too small, casing should be pulled above the tight place and the hole reamed.   Heavy pulling on frozen casing may wreck the derrick; jarring may be more effective.   A strong pull can be exerted by screw or hydraulic jacks on the surface, while the casing is vibrated by a spear and fishing jars.   A casing cutter or splitter can be used to cut off casing at a desired point, or to split frozen casing for pulling it more easily.   In rotary drilling, rotary jars give the same effect as jarring with cable-tools.

Strength of casing.   Resistance of lap-welded pipe is given by Stewart's formulas (National Tube Co): $P = 50\,210\,000\,(t \div d)^3$, and $P = 86\,670\,(t \div d) - 1\,386$, where P = collapsing press, lb per sq in; d = outer diam, in; t = thickness, in.   First formula is for values of P less than 580 lb, or $t \div d$ less than 0.023; second formula, for greater values.   Allowable hydrostatic press on casing $P = 2St/d$, where P is in lb per sq in, t is thickness of pipe wall, in; d is outside diam, in; and S, allowable fiber stress (14 000–16 000 lb per sq in for lap-welded steel, Grade A seamless; 18 000–20 000 lb for Grades B and C; 24 000–26 000 lb for Grade D; 12 500–14 000 lb for iron).   Bursting press is computed by same formula, replacing S by tensile

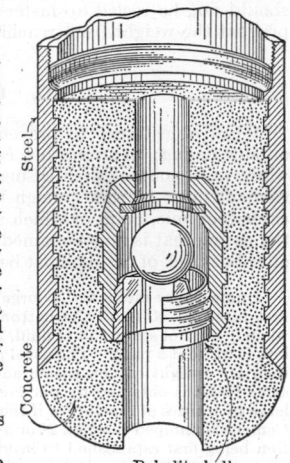

Bakelite ball valve and seat

Fig 30.   Baker Cement Float Shoe

strength: 48 000 lb per sq in for Grade A, 70 000 for Grade B, 75 000 for Grade C, 95 000 for Grade D, 42 000 for WI.

9. MEASURING DEPTH OF WELL (31)

For deep wells the only practical method is to measure the drill pipe used; each length separately, or in stands of 3 or 4 lengths, as stacked in the derrick. Accuracy requires corrections: (a) for the slight bending of pipe lengths as they stand off the vertical; (b) for expansion due to increase in temp (bottom temp of the Continental 15 004-ft well was 300° F). Temp of circulating mud is a little less than bottom temp. Amount of expansion is $L = L_0 (1 + 0.0000069\ t)$, where L_0 is length in ft at atmos temp, and L is length due to $t°$ F. Drill pipe suspended in the well stretches from its own wt, but salt water or mud fluid lessens stretch (Fig 31). Under field conditions, multiply results from Fig 31 by 0.666, as pipe friction absorbs about $1/3$ of wt.

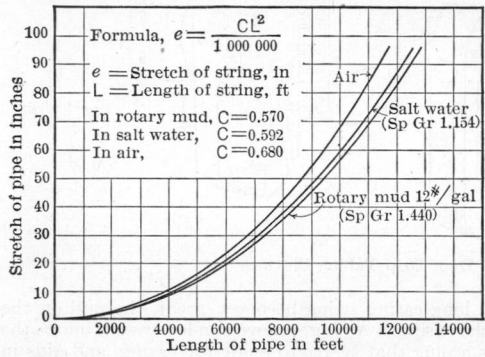

Fig 31. Stretch of Casing, Tubing, or Drill Pipe in Uniform Strings, freely Suspended in Various Flotants, without Float Plug (*Oil Weekly*)

Measurement is best made from top of collar on upper end of a length down to a centerpunch mark close to threads on lower end. After screwing on a length, the distance from the mark to top of collar below is added to previous measurement. For cable-tools, measurement may be made by a weighted mine rope, but the method is subject to errors, due to stretch and slippage on the reel. By using a counting mechanism as a rough check, and placing on the rope calibrated marks at 100-ft intervals, it is possible to reach an accuracy of 1 in 5 000, provided the rope is periodically recalibrated; it should not be reeled up faster than 1 ft per second; cuttings or caved material may prevent the weight from reaching bottom (31).

10. CEMENTING CASING (33)

Chief objectives: to prevent oil or gas from passing up and water from going down outside casing; to strengthen casing against collapse by outside press; to exclude corrosive water from contact with casing; to reduce gas-oil ratio; and to strengthen leaky casing. Cement must be thin enough to be readily pumped. To provide space for cement in a cable-tool hole, diam of which is a little greater than the casing couplings, the hole above the casing seat is under-reamed. Rotary holes are usually enough larger than casing, but all solids back of casing must be removed, as a thin skin of cement may be cracked (33–35).

Dump-bailer method. A large special bailer lowers the cement into the hole, the casing being first lifted 20–40 ft off the bottom, and kept above the level of the cement. For a dry hole, or when it will not stand full of fluid, 20–40 sacks of cement may be placed first, and the casing lowered into it without a plug. The usual practice is to place the cement, and fill casing and hole with water; then put a tight cap on casing and lower it, thus forcing the cement up behind the casing. The same result is obtained by putting a cement plug in the casing shoe, but this is unsatisfactory for large quantities of cement, or if there is a high-pressure flow of gas, oil, or water. TUBING METHOD. Cement is pumped through 2- or 3-in tubing, reaching to within a few ft of bottom of hole; circulation being first established to insure that the cement will rise freely outside the casing. It is prevented from rising inside by packing or a plug, closing the space between bottom of tubing and casing; or, without a plug, the casing is tightly capped and filled with water. After placing the cement, the tubing is flushed out by pumping down water, which returns inside of casing. Water should be kept in the casing until the cement has set. This method requires considerable time for handling the tubing; but, any desired amount of cement can be left in the casing, there is less danger of caving in cable-tool holes due to the smaller volume of wash water, and cement can be placed under a high pressure. CASING METHODS. Cement is pumped through the casing, with or without plugs between the cement and the fluid above and below. Without plugs, the water pumped on top of the cement must be measured, so that the exact position of the cement left inside the casing will be known. The TWO-PLUG or PERKINS METHOD is usual. One plug is long enough to reach up into the casing from bottom of hole, but is tapering at the top, so cement can pass between it and the casing. The other plug, set with a tight gasket on top of the cement, is then forced down by pumping until it strikes a spacer, a stick of soft wood 5–25 ft long, standing on lower plug; amount of cement left inside the casing is thus adjusted. Position of top plug can be checked at any time by the amount of water pumped in. This method is simple, effective, and adapted to both cable-tool and rotary holes. One plug only, placed above the cement, may be used. A shoe guide stops it at the lower end of casing; or the plug is long enough to touch bottom, while its upper end is still inside the casing. Another device is the BAKER FLOAT COLLAR, placed between two casing lengths; if placed on top of the last length, a ball closing against a seat shuts out mud, and so floats the casing into place. As cement is pumped down, the ball drops, letting the cement pass. Cement and collar are drilled out after cement has set. MULTIPLE-STAGE CEMENTING (Halliburton Oil-well Cementing Co) is another method for large-scale work.

Formation-testing permits testing for production without the expense and work of setting casing, or testing cementing for leakage. Fig 32 shows the Johnston tester. Body of tester is above the packer, and the "anchor," a short length of perforated pipe, extends below. Main hole is topped above the formation to be tested, and a smaller hole with a reamed tapered shoulder is drilled with a core-drill. The well is filled with mud fluid and tester is run in on an empty drill pipe. When the packer is seated, it seals the hole below. The fluid below runs through a valve into tester and up into the drill pipe. The formation is thus relieved of wt of the mud column and is practically under atmos press, whence gas or oil will flow into anchor under its own press. After about $1/2$ hr a valve is closed to retain sample in tester and latter is withdrawn after release by equalizing the press above and below.

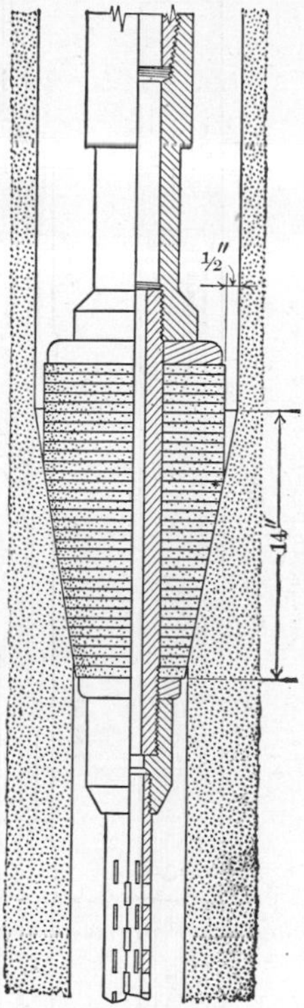

11. SAMPLING BOREHOLES (see also Sec 10)

In **cable-tool holes,** sampling is done with the bailer, which brings up a sludge containing some unpulverized material. The sample is stirred and washed for settling the coarser particles, from which the nature of the strata is determined.

In **rotary drilling** sampling is more difficult. The circulating mud brings up the cuttings, which, if coarse, are generally caught by vibrating screen or improvised baffles or riffles in the ditch or launder through which the mud flows.

Fig 32. Johnston Formation Tester

A fairly accurate sample is obtainable by stopping drilling, leaving the bit on bottom and pumping mud through drill pipe to clean out cuttings. The first cuttings showing in the mud come from last stratum drilled. As this procedure requires several hours in deep holes, it is not often used. Time required for cuttings to be brought to surface by the circulating mud may be computed (37) by the formula: $N = \dfrac{D(R^2 - r^2)}{x^2 yzE}$, where:

N = minutes for cuttings to rise from bottom to surface; D = depth of hole, in; R = radius of hole, in; r = outer radius of drill pipe, in; x = radius of pump cyl, in; y = stroke of pump, in; z = number of strokes per min; E = effic of pump, usually 60%. Also, paint or dyes may be placed in the mud and time noted for reappearance at the surface.

Accuracy of samples. As drilling crews, whether cable or rotary, generally try to make speed, samples may be far from accurate. At best, pulverized material is hard to identify, and is frequently contaminated by particles from upper part of hole. As the plastering of a rotary hole with mud tends to seal up the oil sands, productive sands have been drilled through unrecognized. Cable-drilled holes also have passed through an unrecognized oil sand. The need for more accurate samples has caused rapid improvement in core sampling.

Core samples are usually taken of each stratum drilled to determine porosity, permeability, and water-oil ratio. In rotary coring, the bit is attached to the drill pipe; for cable-tools, the core bit and barrel replace the regular bit, and are operated similarly. The holes are 3.75 to 9.75-in; cores, 1.25 to 3-in. Rotary core drills comprise those with the usual inner and outer tubes, and the retractable type. In the first, the inner barrel rotates with the drill pipe, or may be non-rotating. The latter gives a higher core recovery,

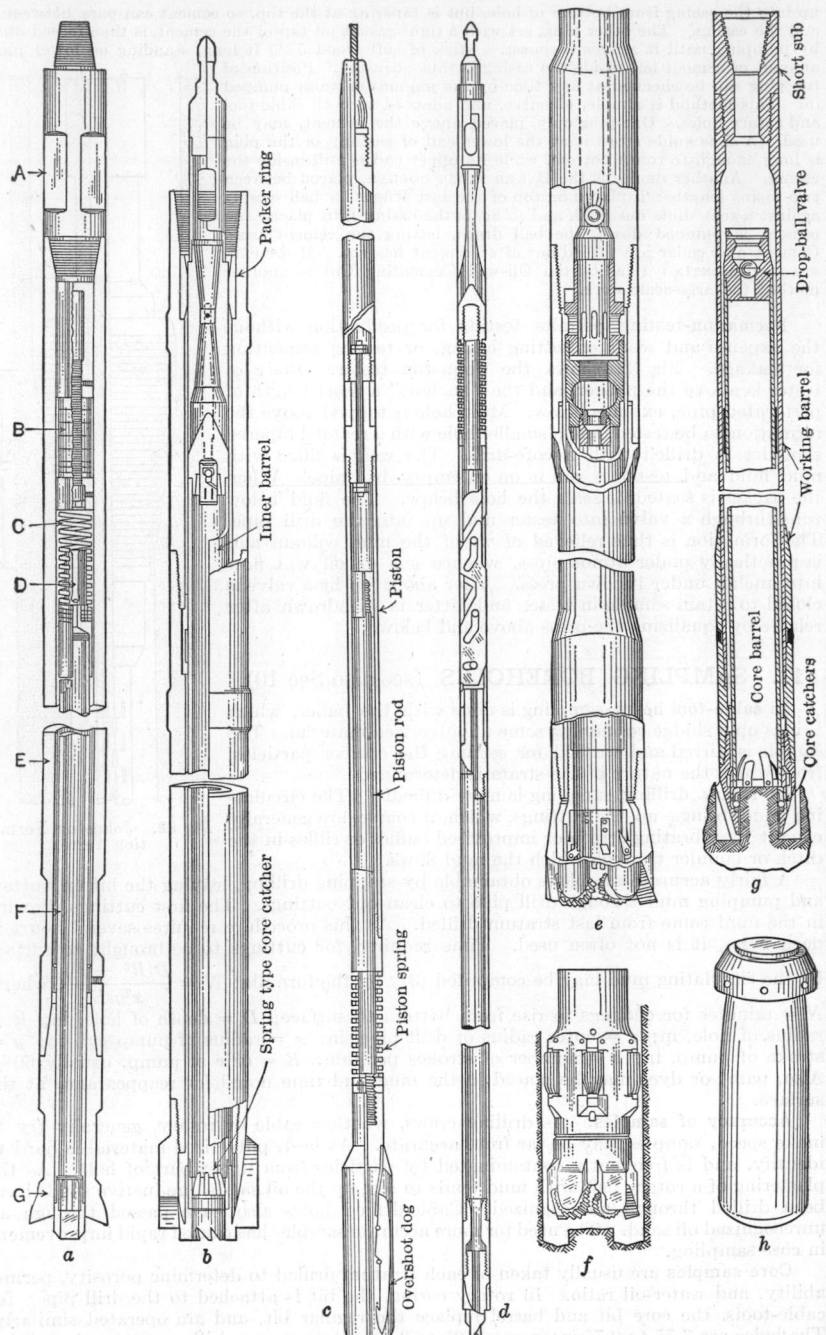

Fig 33.   Core Drills for Oil Wells

especially in softer formations, cutting cores up to 5.5-in or larger. The retractable type cuts cores of 1.25-2.5 in. The outer barrel carries a bit cutting a full-sized hole, but has a central opening into which the cutting head can project for taking core. For coring, the barrel is dropped into the drill pipe from the surface, and automatically locks itself on the bit. When core has been cut, an "overshot" (Fig 33c) is lowered on a wire line to retrieve the core drill, thus saving the time of making a round trip with drill pipe. About 1 min per 500–1 000 ft is allowed for the barrel to drop through the drilling mud; retrieving speed, 300 ft per min. In soft formations, a main bit may drill several hundred ft, and the retractable core drill be used for all or any part of the distance, without raising the drill pipe. This corer has saved 35 round trips of the drill pipe, in coring 750 ft. Coring speeds are usually 50–75 rpm, ranging from 25 to 110. Fig 33(a) shows Elliott cable-tool core drill, in which A is upper sub, B adjustable weight, C spring, D valve, E and F outer and inner barrels, and G bit. Fig 33(b) is Elliott wire-line retractable rotary core drill, and (c) is overshot assembly for retrieving the inner assembly after core has been taken. Drilling assembly (d) is to replace inner barrel in (b) when no cores are taken. (e) is Reed core drill with hard-rock bit; (f) same bit with reamer; (g) Hughes' core bit for soft rock. (h) is core-barrel plug, fastened in lower end of core barrel with light rivets, which shear off when plug strikes bottom of well, the plug rising to top of core barrel and making way for incoming core.

In general, the smaller the core diam, the poorer the recovery, but small diam is necessary at great depths. Most difficult to core are conglomerates and shales, as they break up and wedge in the barrel. In Okla City field, about 50% of length cored is recovered, when larger than 2-in diam. Length of core has only slight effect on percentage recovery (38). Under favorable conditions, nearly 100% core recovery is possible. Recoveries in deep Calif well were: 428.5 ft of core represented by 78.7% recovery; 30 ft of core, 68.1%; 137 ft, 59.1%; 6 ft, 23.1%; 40.5 ft, 88.1%. For costs of coring, see Table 16, 17.

Table 16. Cost of Cable-tool, Coring, Bradford-Allegheny Field (L. G. E. Bignell)

Name of oil sand	Ft cored	Time, days	Recon-ditioning bits and shoes	Rent of core-barrel, and labor	Cost per ft of core
Bradford....	38	3	$ 84	$130	$5.63
Chipmonk...	35	3	72	130	5.77
Bradford....	90	4	130	160	3.22
Richburg....	17	1	54	110	9.64
Trenton.....	34	5	95	150	7.20
Kane........	54	3	75	155	4.26
Clarendon...	28	3	90	130	7.86
Haskell......	45	4	110	140	5.55
	341			Average	$5.32

Table 17. Cost of Rotary-drill Coring, Northern Louisiana (22)

Performance:	
Drilling depth, ft....4 560–6 087	
Number of cores..........	35
Total ft of core...........	316
Total ft recovered........	234
Aver percent recovery.....	74
Aver length of core, ft.....	7
Costs:	
31 cores at $17.50......	$542.50
33 cutter heads at $5...	165.00
3 core catchers at $3...	9.00
Total..............	$716.50
Aver cost per core.....	20.47
Aver cost per ft.......	2.26

12. CONTROLLED DIRECTIONAL DRILLING

A hole may be drilled vertically, or deflected as desired. Wells are deflected if an oil deposit is under a navigable stream, valuable building site, a restricted area, or where topography is precipitous; or a well may be on the downthrow of a fault, making it desirable to direct the hole across the fault into the oil sand, on the upthrow side. The rig is then set in a convenient location, and the hole deflected as desired.

Directional drilling is done by tools that will produce a curved hole, the position of the bottom being checked at intervals by surveys (Art 24). The tools most used are the following. EASTMAN "REMOVABLE WHIPSTOCK" (Fig 34) is a chrome-steel casting, 5.5–13.5 in diam and 9.5–12 ft long, with a wedge-like point to prevent turning after being set in place, and a tapered deflecting groove along one side. A collar at top, loose around the drill pipe but too small to pass the bit, permits retraction when the bit is withdrawn. If, after the whipstock has been removed, the deflection cannot be increased by controlling weight and using special bits, additional whipstocks are set, say 50–80 ft apart. LANE WELLS "KNUCKLE JOINT" (Fig 35) is attached to lower end of drill pipe. By a universal joint, spring-actuated cam and a square shoulder, a diamond-pointed bit is held at an angle (about 5°) to axis of hole. The bit is spudded at first, the universal joint permitting the knuckle joint to take the new direction. After drilling say 20 ft, the knuckle joint is replaced by a regular bit, and the flexible drill pipe readily takes the bend. Finally the hole is reamed to full size. KINSBACH "CASING WHIPSTOCK" (Fig 36), containing deflecting wedge and locking device, is bolted to drill stem, lowered to desired depth, and oriented. By raising slowly, the locking device is tripped; and by applying weight, bolt is sheared, releasing drill stem. A milling tool is then attached, for cutting a hole through the casing, thus deflecting the well. For an uncased well, EASTMAN HYDRAULIC BRIDGER (Fig 37) is attached to drill pipe with arms folded, and lowered to depth, then maneuvered until arms spread outward into sides of hole, locking the device in place. A wedge or whipstock is then set on the bridger to cause deflection.

Hall-Rowe method of deflecting boreholes (59), as applied to diamond drilling (Fig 38). A dry wooden plug A, grooved to admit water, is pushed down the hole with the rods to the desired point of deflection, and is allowed to swell. Clinometer B, with drive wedge C attached by copper rivets as shown, is scribed with a reference line in known relation to position of wedge, and contains a glass tube partly filled with dilute HFl, snugly fitted inside. The assembly is lowered to within a few inches of plug A and then dropped freely, thus shearing the rivets and driving wedge C into the plug. The clinometer is allowed to set for $1/2$ hr, then pulled up, leaving the drive wedge behind. Etched portion of glass tube (see Art 24) shows position of liquid surface of HFl when in hole, and this, in relation to reference line, shows orientation of drive wedge C after placement, also showing dip of hole. "Deflecting wedge" D has a groove of EX diamond bit size (Table 32), cut at a slight angle to axis of wedge and scribed along its center line for orienting. A "pilot wedge" E is screwed to lower end of D and set so that its flat side will fit that of the drive wedge C when D is properly oriented. For attachment to drill rod, a special coupling F is fixed by copper rivet to the ring at top of deflecting wedge D, which is thus lowered into the hole until pilot wedge E rests on drive wedge C. On being rotated until their flat faces coincide, the pilot wedge drops 2 in into place, orienting D. Shearing the copper rivet in coupling F drops the rods 1.5 in farther, but stretch in the rods must be taken into account, amounting at 1 500 ft depth to about 2.5 in. Rods are now withdrawn, the ring at top of D is reamed off with a rose bit, and a deflected hole drilled along the groove with EX bit and core barrel to a point 3 or 4 ft below D. The hole and the wedge D itself are then reamed out with an AX pilot diamond reaming bit, and regular drilling resumed. It requires about 5 shifts to complete one wedging operation properly; aver correction per wedge, about 1.5°.

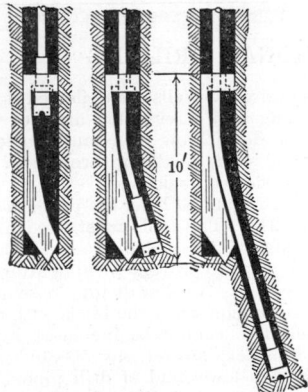

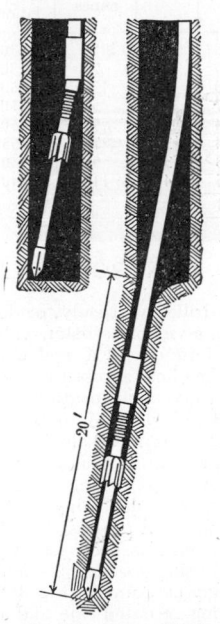

Fig 34.   Eastman Removable Whipstock

Fig 35.   Lane Wells Knuckle Joint

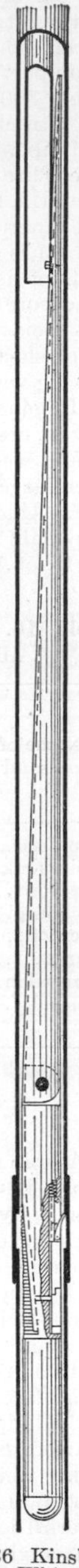

Fig. 36 Kinsbach Casing Whipstock

By using stiff or flexible drill-pipe collars, special bits (Fig 39), or reamers, different speeds of rotation, and varying wt on bit, the degree of deflection can be controlled. A vert hole is difficult to control, as it tends to corkscrew. A drift (deflection) angle of about 6° is most desirable, though it may be as much as 15°. Total deflection may be 50–60° from the vert. Hardness and dip of strata have an important effect on deflection (38, 39). Cost of directional tools and supervision have averaged about $1 000 per well. Assuming $1 200 for extra rig time, the total cost would be say $2 200 for deflecting a 3 600-ft hole. In one case, a 3 600-ft hole was deflected nearly 700 ft

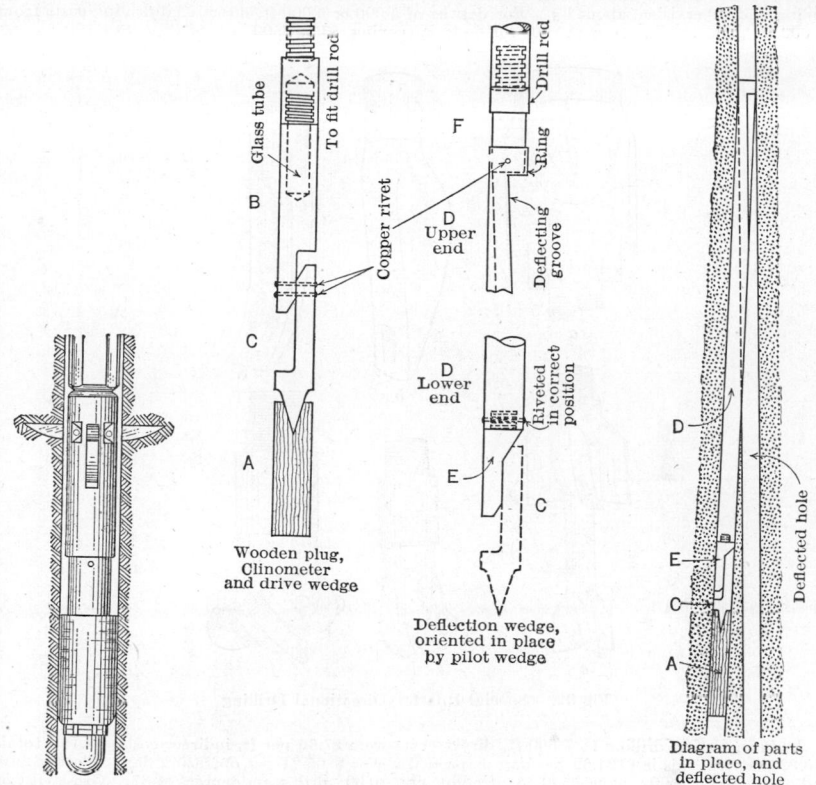

Fig 37. Eastman Hydraulic Bridger

Fig 38. Hall-Rowe Wedging Device (Canadian Inst Min & Metallurgy)

horizontally, missing its objective by only 8 ft. A high degree of accuracy is attainable by drilling slowly and making frequent surveys. Most directional drilling and surveying equipment is owned by firms specializing in the work; or equipment may be rented by oil companies. There is a saving in both time and cost by starting directional drilling at the proper point, rather than attempting to drill a perfectly directed hole from top to bottom.

13. COST OF OIL-WELL DRILLING

As no standardized form of accounting is followed, data on costs may be confusing. Actual drilling time varies greatly in different fields, depending upon local conditions and previous experience of the operator. Hence, aver figures should be used only as a general guide. Costs may be segregated as follows: 1, rig and equipment; 2, pipe and fittings; 3, casing and "cellar" connections; 4, production equipment; 5, construction labor; 6, drilling labor; 7, contract labor; 8, water, supplies and rig repairs; 9, fuel and power; 10, circulating fluids; 11, trucking; 12, outside and company rentals; 13, repairs; 14, indirect charges; 15, supervision.

Examples. In KMA field, Tex, where the sands are productive from 400 to 1 700 ft, a well can be drilled and "put on pump" for $2 000. Recent deep drilling disclosed new oil sands at about 3 700 ft; wells drilled with rotary to 3 650 ft, and completed with cable tools; time, 30 days per well, which may be lessened as drillers become familiar with field.   Flowing wells reach stage of delivering to tanks for about $25 000, of which $12 000 is for contractors, and $13 000 is for piping, separators and tanks.

In Calif the following figures are for aver conditions: wells of 4 000–4 500 ft, completed in 18–25 days, cost, $35 000; 5 000–6 000, 30 days, $45 000; 7 000–7 500, 35–40 days, $60 000–$65 000; 8 000, 55–60 days, $75 000–$90 000; 10 000–11 500, 75–90 days, $150 000–$170 000.   A rig costing about $100 000 should drill 5 wells.   Cost of rig and casing, about 1/3 of total; drilling tools, 1/3; drilling and supervision, about 1/3.   For depths of 5 000 or 6 000 ft, directional drilling costs from $2 000 for good conditions to $10 000 for bad; surveying, $350–$500.

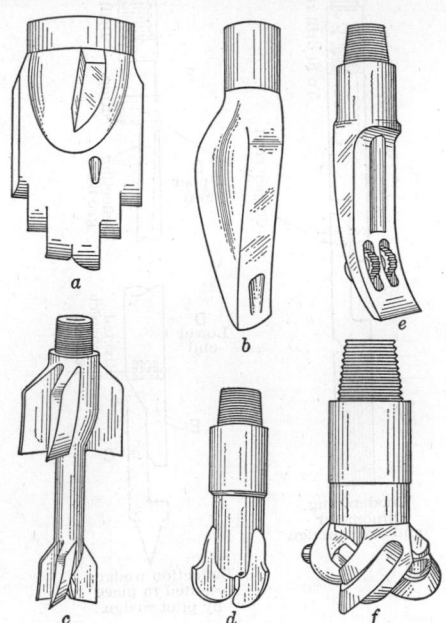

Fig 39.   Special Bits for Directional Drilling

In Penn, rotary drilling to 7 500 ft, direct costs were $7.66 per ft, indirect costs, $3.16; total, $10.82 per ft.   This is $724.62 per day elapsed time, or $805.21 per operating day.   Cost of bits and parts, $2.32 per ft; payroll, $1.81; freight, etc, $0.62; drill stem deprec, $1.37.   Gross cost of other wells, drilled 1937–38: cable-tool well, 7 050 ft, in Washington Co, $149 000, or $21.13 per ft; rotary well, 7 502 ft, in Westmoreland Co, $94 371, or $12.58 per ft; rotary well, 6 454 ft, Potter Co, $7.78 for drilling and $1.53 for casing; total, $9.31 per ft.

Table 18.   Approx Costs of California Oil Wells

Field	Av depth, ft	Av cost per ft	Field	Av depth, ft	Av cost per ft
Huntington Beach.......	4 350	$13	Kern River............	2 800	$13
Kettleman..............	8 800	22	Lost Hills.............	1 500	12
Stockton...............	5 300	13	Mountain View........	5 300	15
Greeley................	7 800	13	Semi-Tropic and Trico..	2 400	16
Torrance Refinery......	7 200	12			

Cost of "bare" well, excluding production facilities, is about 95% of above figures.

Most wells in Table 23 were drilled in 1938, and represent latest practice.   Higher cost of the deeper wells due to more complicated casing problems and harder formations.   Wide variation in cost of rigs or derricks; on deeper wells, derricks were moved to new locations, and depreciated approx 10% per move.   Now, the derrick is considered part of drilling equipment, and daily rental is charged, based on 1 000 days' life; thus, a $6 000 derrick

Table 19. Segregated Costs in California (1937) and Wyoming Oil Fields
(numbers in col 1 refer to notes at end of table)

	Ventura District				Midway Dist
	5 400 ft	2 280 ft	9 380 ft*	1 550 ft	4 500 ft
1	$ 4 494.72	$ 2 675.68	$ 3 549.58	$1 921.78	$ 646.16
2	23 463.77	10 682.18	9 114.37	2 633.39	12 289.41
3	1 042.75	28.05	66.25	72.31	14.92
4	66 166.99	33 222.64	105 406.50	8 546 43	21 930.48
5	861.10	219.69	....	290.78	980.28
	$96 029.33	$46 828.24	$118 136.70	$13 464.69	$35 861.25

	Los Angeles District				Midway Dist
	3 620 ft	3 460 ft	5 440 ft	3 900 ft	3 120 ft
1	$ 3 965.25	$ 2 901.58	$ 4 411.40	$ 4 105.24	$ 2 823.63
2	23 021.13	23 079.73	22 983.38	22 957.78	6 369.81
3	17.09	7.09	34.38	28.75	53.96
4	25 531.05	25 520.89	28 494.76	19 022.70	14 877.82
5	607.36	615.86	644.03	645.95	710.91
6	1 302.00	1 434.00	1 318.20	1 577.40	....
	$54 443.88	$53 559.15	$57 886.15	$48 337.82	$24 836.13

	Los Angeles District				Midway Dist
	3 780 ft	490-3 875 ft	3 625-6 810 ft	3 650 ft	1 270 ft
1	$ 3 191.81	$ 1 355.45	$ 3 937.17	$ 4 101.07	$ 458.74
2	11 705.38	13 056.57	17 596.51	21 234.43	2 605.92
3	679.33	801.50	512.23	80.35	....
4	26 878.58	84 491.32	97 909.60	23 390.60	13 542.44
5	156.63	643.86	2 958.49	1 297.38	124.84
6	....	....	....	1 252.80	....
	$42 611.73	$100 348.70	$122 914.00	$51 356.63	$16 731.94

	Kern District				
	7 200-7 460 ft	1 990 ft	4 760 ft	1 720 ft	4 850 ft
1	$ 2 428.67	$ 917.21	$ 1 436.99	$2 016.19	$ 2 549.49
2	23 388.44	7 627.53	15 574.14	3 408.89	11 556.68
3	1 615.86	104.55	290.80	85.82	274.75
4	106 401.48	10 456.30	18 173.99	7 372.22	23 328.33
5	1 298.23	4 578.58	413.45	514.23	312.69
	$135 132.68	$23 684.17	$35 889.37	$13 397.35	$38 021.94

	So Wyoming †	No Wyoming
	5 560 ft	6 070 ft
1	$ 2 233.07	$ 2 109.73
2	59.82	20 933.19
3	2 200.66	125.02
4	146 328.32	187 677.65
5	31 772.29	499.53
	$182 594.16	$211 345.12
6	credit 5 786.78	
	$176 807.38	

1. Drilling rig, derrick, crown block, permanent parts, foundations, timber.
2. Casing, tubing and control head.
3. Rigging materials that remain (except derrick), as water connections and drilling lines.
4. Labor and expense: (a) drilling labor, pipe lines, electric work; (b) drilling materials: mud, reagents, cement, rope; (c) expense of outside drilling contractors, building rig, surveys of well, formation testing, cementing, coring, fuel for power, special drilling tools; (d) company transport of materials, roads, etc; (e) drilling-tool rental, core bits, drill pipe, draw-works, rotary equipment, power plant, water piping during drilling (special rental costs, depending on field, $65-$150 per day).
5. Bringing in, sucker rods, Christmas tree assembly, actual flow lines.
6. Piling, contract job.

* Redrilled from 1 980 ft. † Wildcat well, abandoned.

Table 20. Cost of Completed Wells in Los Angeles Basin, 1937-38

Depth, ft	Cost, $	Depth, ft	Cost, $	Depth, ft	Cost, $
3 630	59 986.03	3 900	53 650.60	3 890	54 888.25
3 600-3 651	62 890.83	4 130	64 706.60	4 075	59 682.25
3 600	65 621.30	3 310	39 805.01	3 000	33 179.65
3 590	50 610.55	4 000	59 585.41	3 900	55 107.17
5 650*	98 487.10	2 950	33 564.38	3 920	59 858.64
3 590	52 092.90	3 000	38 022.79	.....	....

* Exploratory well.

Table 21. Drilling Costs, California

| | San Joaquin Valley | | Coastal Ventura | Los Angeles Basin (d) | Inland Ventura |
	(a)	(b)	(c)		(e)
Depth, ft...........................	8 500	15 000	6 900	6 500	8 000
Equipment: Casing....................	$23 506	$ 51 420	$26 200	$28 065	......
Derrick and rig...................	16 964	18 900	16 960	16 615	......
Other, prorated....................	.....	18 490	2 720	1 820	......
Cement, drilling mud, chemicals.........	.....	42 495	3 700	1 815	......
Labor.................................	14 384	54 720	14 105	11 725	$ 41 832
Power or fuel (gas, elec)..............	.....	6 825	2 200	1 625	......
Special services (as coring, surveying).....	.....	10 460	6 175	500	2 804
Unusual expense due to local conditions...	.....	(f)	3 000	500	......
Other operating costs, prorated.........	37 184	104 845	41 490	26 210	150 204
Total drilling cost.................	$92 038	$308 155	$116 550	$89 275	$194 840
Average cost per foot...............	$10.83	$20.60	$16.90	$13.72	$24.30

(a) Routine development drilling in fairly easy formation, with moderate dips.
(b) Wildcat (exploratory) well, deepest ever drilled; cost very moderate for such wells. Production or development wells may be drilled here for $15–$17 per ft. Most of strata in the area are easily drilled; dips flat or slight.
(c) Routine drilling of development well in hard, steeply-dipping beds.
(d) Routine drilling of development well in medium hard sediments; dips moderate.
(e) Very difficult area of moderate dips; extremely hard formations for coring. Many fishing jobs caused by drill-pipe twist-offs.   (f) See casing item.

Table 22. Drilling Costs, California Oil Fields

Field	Dominguez	Montebello	Playa del Rey	Richfield	Rosecrans	Sta Maria Valley	Rio Bravo
Aver depth, ft........	7 500	6 400	6 300	4 600	7 800	4 500	11 500
Time, days..........	45	45	35	30	40	25	80
Surface equip't........	$ 7 000	$ 7 000	$ 7 500	$6 000	$ 7 000	$ 4 000	$10 000
Casing, etc..........	22 000	16 000	12 000	8 000	20 000	15 000	30 000
Labor (a)............	15 000	12 000	10 000	10 000	14 000	10 000	20 000
Power or fuel........	4 500	4 500	4 000	3 000	4 500	3 500	10 000
Other costs..........	36 500	30 500	21 500	18 000	34 500	17 500	90 000
Total.............	$85 000	$70 000	$55 000	$45 000	$80 000	$50 000	$160 000

(a) Construction and drilling.

Table 23. Cost of Oil Wells, California

Area	Depth, ft	Days time	Rig, complete	Road and grading	Drilling	Casing and cement	Production equip't	Total	Per ft
San Joaquin.....	1 815	16	$2 660	$ 854	$ 6 226	$ 5 118	$ 3 873	$ 18 731	$10.32
" "	1 687	11	3 170	685	4 028	3 943	4 604	16 430	9.74
" "	8 350	40	8 400	700	31 000	22 600	12 100	74 800	8.96
" "	8 200	48	8 400	800	36 400	20 000	15 100	80 700	9.84
" "	1 714	20	3 000	140	6 220	3 040	2 680	15 080	8.79
Los Angeles basin	6 650	54	4 605	215	32 990	34 260	7 125	79 195	11.91
Coastal.........	5 766	58	6 620	670	34 000	18 200	4 400	63 890	11.08
"	7 450	77	8 307	1 330	60 709	27 738	8 602	106 686	14.32
"	1 500	15	110	110	7 820	3 200	900	12 140	8.09
"	1 675	20	100	720	8 813	4 180	1 612	15 425	9.21

cost $6 per day; shallow wells have been drilled with portable masts, no derrick cost charged. Wildcat wells vary greatly in cost, of fuel, water, mud and kind of formation; 2 recent wildcats, to 10 000 ft in San Joaquin valley, cost $26 and $8 per ft respectively; in the first large quantities of weight material were used to hold back caving shale, and finally a protective casing-string was set; in the other well, no casing or weight material were necessary. Cost of daily operation for light gas-engine equipment, for drilling to 5 000 ft, averages about $400 per day. Heavy steam drilling equipment, for 10 000 ft costs $600–$750 per day, depending on cost of fuel and water. Extra heavy steam equipment for 15 000-ft wells costs from $750–$1 000 per day.

Table 24. Drilling Costs (L. G. E. Bignell)

	Depth, ft	Aver costs		Depth, ft	Aver costs
Oklahoma City, Okla....	6 500	$100 000	Kettleman Hills, Calif...	7 200	$150 000
East Texas Field, Texas..	3 650	12 500	Perry, Noble Co, Okla..	5 200	40 000
Sulphur Bluff, Texas....	4 500	21 500	Victoria, Texas.........	4 300	27 500
Conroe, Texas..........	5 200	27 500	Tioga, Penn *..........	4 012	17 000
Pettus, Texas..........	4 000	25 000	McPherson Co, Kan *...	3 350	35 000
Government Wells, Texas	2 400	18 500	Mt Pleasant, Mich *....	3 800	18 000
Western Kan...........	3 400	32 500	Panhandle, Texas *.....	3 000	17 500
Cunningham, Kan.......	3 050	25 000	Bay City, Texas........	7 500	45 000

* Type of equipment, cable-tool; all others, rotary.

Table 25. Costs of California Wells (J. E. Brantly)

	Kettleman Hills		Los Angeles Basin		
	(a)	(b)	(c)	(d)	(e)
Depth, ft...........................	8 600	8 400	3 904	3 850	7 405
Overall time, days..................	120	160	42	46	82
Labor..............................	$23 130.67	$31 024	$6 375	$7 125	$16 883
Earthwork.........................					870
Pits and ditches.....................	1 255.00	1 374	610	641	
Miscellaneous expense...............	10 659.50	12 852	3 980	4 880	4 300
Rigging up.........................			820	830	1 205
Bits and coring tools................	7 945.51	14 170	2 420	3 020	4 950
Mud fluid..........................	1 860.00	2 560			
Transport..........................	2 011.67	3 012	810	860	1 360
Fuel *.............................	4 800.00	9 600	2 580	2 760	8 200
Water @ 1.5¢ per bbl...............	1 800.00	2 400	380	404	1 230
Tool rental, deprec and capital repairs..	20 860.00	26 750	3 522	4 830	9 685
Indirect operating exp...............		3 705	1 260	1 485	3 920
Overhead...........................	5 480.00		1 680	1 800	2 860
Total intangible costs..............	$79 802.35	$115 197	$24 437	$28 635	$55 463
Roads and earthwork.................	$ 2 500.00	$ 3 260	$ 1 800	$ 2 200	
Derrick erected.....................	7 450.00	8 500	11 600	12 400	$ 7 460
Permanent well equipment...........	44 750.00	42 800	28 800	27 650	28 640
Total capital items.................	$54 700.00	$ 54 560	$42 200	$42 250	$36 100
Total cost........................	134 502.35	169 757	66 637	70 885	91 563

(a) Flat-dip area. 2 drag bits, 22-in; 20 drag bits, 14.75-in; 15 rock bits, 12.25-in; 40 rock bits, 83/8-in. 16-in surface casing, 95/8-in water-string, 65/8-in oil-string or liner, 3-in tubing. (b) Steep dip area. 2 drag bits, 22-in; 32 drag bits, 14.75-in; 26 rock bits, 12.25-in; 48 rock bits, 83/8-in; reamers, guides, core-heads. 16-in surface casing, 95/8-in water-string, 65/8-in oil-string or liner, 3-in tubing. (c) Straight hole, soft formation. 185/8-in, 11.75-in and 85/8-in casing and liner, 3-in tubing. (d) Directionally drilled, soft formations. 185/8-in, 11.75-in and 65/8-in casing and liner, 3-in tubing. (e) Soft formations. Producer. 133/8-in surface pipe, 9-in water-string, 65/8-in liner, 2.5-in tubing. * Gas @ 10¢ per M (a, b) and 20¢ (c, d, e).

Table 26. Cost of Well in Texas Panhandle, 1937 (J. E. Brantly)

Depth, 3 200 ft; cable tools; pumping well; 40 days drilling; 15 days shooting and cleaning out

Company labor..........	$ 1 015	Drilling labor...........	$ 2 429
Payroll tax............	36	Payroll tax............	72
Compensation ins.......	166	Compensation ins.......	396
Pump test.............	25	R. S. & E.............	480
Water and gas lines.....	39	Bits..................	646
Pits..................	150	Mud fluid.............	81
Water................	653	Transport.............	482
Fuel.................	156	Equip't...............	167
Transport.............	173	Wire lines............	350
Derrick erection........	512	Overhead..............	917
Lumber...............	120		
Fishing...............	15	Total..............	$ 6 020
Supplies..............	46	Company exp, contra.....	11 149
Cementing............	616		
Shooting..............	596	Total..............	$17 169
Miscellaneous..........	75	Tool rental and capital re-	
Well equip't (a)........	6 756	pairs.............	3 927
Total..............	$11 149	Total..............	$21 096

(a) 10.75-in, 7-in, 2-in.

Table 27. Cost of Oil-well Drilling in Kansas, Oklahoma, Texas and Gulf Coast

State and County	Depth, ft	Cost, dollars						
		Drilling rig	Derrick and rig equip't	Casing and tubing	Misc supplies and equip't (a)	Well head and pumping equip't	Total cost	Aver per ft
Kansas (b)								
Barton	3 356	13 885	2 997	5 560	4 360	2 356	29 158	8.69
Reno	4 057	16 093	3 326	6 661	3 927	5 262	35 269	8.69
Reno	3 383	13 911	3 044	7 327	4 963	3 807	33 052	9.77
Rice	3 331	14 124	3 339	4 480	3 344	6 285	31 572	9.48
Rice	3 258	13 531	3 213	4 371	2 808	6 100	30 023	9.22
Russell (c)	3 072	11 283	1 857	4 711	2 979	1 906	22 736	7.40
Stafford	3 561	6 130	3 240	6 172	4 010	7 047	26 599	7.47
Stafford	3 546	13 995	3 335	6 471	5 079	5 704	34 584	9.75
Stafford	3 550	11 880	3 285	5 757	3 137	7 145	31 204	8.79
Stafford	3 625	10 604	3 257	5 864	4 247	6 910	30 882	8.52
Oklahoma (b)								
Hughes	4 153	18 879	1 080	6 537	4 456	2 208	33 160	7.98
Hughes	4 215	19 494	1 236	6 472	3 586	1 484	32 272	7.66
Lincoln	4 245	20 479	960	7 348	3 097	1 076	32 960	7.76
Lincoln	5 002	23 421	1 128	8 670	5 413	1 024	39 656	7.93
Noble	4 871	22 089	881	8 142	3 757	2 235	37 104	7.62
Noble	5 098	22 941	1 364	7 170	7 635	1 347	40 457	7.94
Oklahoma	6 693	38 008	1 275	10 474	8 433	3 677	61 867	9.24
Payne	4 302	22 030	1 202	7 705	4 094	1 329	36 360	8.45
Payne	4 501	20 522	997	7 610	2 854	1 915	33 898	7.53
Pottawatomie	4 449	20 404	1 778	7 475	4 009	1 192	34 858	7.84
Pottawatomie	4 415	21 134	1 553	7 546	4 308	935	35 476	8.04
Seminole	4 628	25 855	3 278	8 325	7 025	5 284	49 767	10.75
Seminole	4 434	23 841	3 690	9 338	6 506	4 684	48 059	10.84
Seminole	3 942	21 796	4 434	6 711	1 590	1 206	35 737	9.07
Logan	5 080	25 563	1 073	8 134	3 461	2 384	40 615	8.00
Logan	5 070	22 963	861	8 048	4 077	2 304	38 253	7.54
North Texas (d)								
Gray	3 343	11 375	1 974	1 724	4 098	525	19 696	5.89
Gray	3 290	10 920	......	3 060	4 380	818	19 178	5.83
Carson	3 295	12 235	......	9 997	5 853	2 573	30 658	9.30
Hutchinson	3 040	8 549	......	1 560	5 720	2 959	18 788	6.18
Hutchinson	3 095	10 045	......	4 569	3 710	2 384	20 708	6.69
Hutchinson	3 073	11 330	......	1 469	4 355	1 977	19 131	6.23
Hutchinson	3 100	11 188	......	2 034	5 802	2 107	21 131	6.82
West Texas (e)								
Ector	4 135	22 432	924	6 657	4 799	373	35 185	8.51
Ector	4 206	23 174	......	6 907	4 915	3 476	38 472	9.15
Pecos (c)	491	1 515	......	480	696	938	3 629	7.39
Pecos (c)	444	1 300	......	491	837	884	3 512	7.91
Pecos	1 416	5 109	......	3 491	941	812	10 353	7.31
Pecos	1 408	5 123	......	3 014	1 027	586	9 750	6.92
Ward (c)	2 503	7 842	......	4 742	2 236	635	15 455	6.17
Ward	2 518	11 677	......	4 574	2 270	855	19 376	7.69
Ward	2 524	10 703	......	4 841	1 873	1 036	18 453	7.34
Texas Gulf Coast (f)								
Brazoria	6 080	22 039	......	14 723	5 777	1 336	43 875	7.22
Brazoria	5 994	18 761	......	14 902	6 935	1 425	42 023	7.01
Brazoria	5 991	22 356	......	16 712	4 970	1 190	45 228	7.55
Chambers	6 616	26 115	1 315	14 142	7 512	2 715	51 799	7.83
Galveston	5 198	23 878	5 853	11 617	10 388	1 145	52 881	10.17
Galveston	6 346	17 117	......	14 601	11 687	413	43 818	6.90
Galveston	6 272	15 977	1 607	15 283	11 152	1 123	45 142	7.20
Galveston	6 065	18 930	......	13 898	7 716	1 843	42 387	6.99
Galveston	8 000	40 092	......	23 364	13 725	3 068	80 249	10.03
Harris	4 832	13 913	4 740	11 765	5 965	1 489	37 872	7.84
Harris	4 800	14 153	......	11 528	7 942	1 396	35 019	7.30
Louisiana Gulf Coast (f)								
Acadia	7 222	37 100	2 617	28 379	18 729	2 333	89 158	12.35
Acadia	7 250	45 000	2 545	17 864	17 165	2 621	85 195	11.75
Cameron	3 199	8 079	744	3 542	5 147	1 208	18 720	5.85
Cameron	5 887	11 740	......	12 944	6 193	2 290	33 167	5.63
Cameron	5 930	14 678	......	8 708	5 353	1 193	29 932	5.05

(a) Misc labor, tools and supplies; freight, hauling, drilling mud, fuel, water, acidizing, shooting, cementing. (b) Chiefly alternating limestone and shale beds, relatively hard. (c) Drilled with cable tools; all other holes drilled chiefly or entirely with rotary. (d) Medium hard sand and shale, very hard dolomitic limestone. (e) Medium hard sands, shales and anhydrite; medium to very hard limestone. (f) Soft sands and shales; heaving shale, salt-water flows and steep dips often cause high costs.

14. PORTABLE CHURN DRILLS FOR PROSPECTING

For placer drilling, light power drills are largely used for depths of 15–30 ft. As shallow deposits become scarcer, deeper, sometimes buried, channels are prospected to 300–400 ft. Lead and zinc deposits are sampled by churn drills to 400–600 ft, as in Tri-State district. For porphyry copper deposits, churn drills may reach 1 000–1 500 ft. Water wells and blast holes are usually within 200–300 ft. Large blast-hole drills grade into "spudders" for oil wells of 4 000–5 000 ft depth.

Setting up. Level rear wheels by blocking, taking wt off front axle by jacks. Caterpillar treads should have ground leveled for them. For the deeper holes a platform in front of drill supports tools and extra bits. Derrick is raised by the aid of engine, and guy wires, if used, are anchored.

Drilling is almost always by spudding with wire lines. Tools are dropped about 60 times per min for placer drilling; quick stroke keeps the gravel in suspension after loosening and avoids pulverizing. In copper and lead-zinc deposits, speed of stroke is 38–50 per min for heavy tools. Some prospecting requires cased holes; blast holes are rarely cased, except at top; tools lighter than for standard rig. For holes deeper than 100–150 ft, jars are desirable. At Miami, Ariz, prospecting holes averaged 600 ft; casing generally needed below 400 ft; bits, 10, 7 5/8 and 6.25-in; 1 000–1 500 ft holes in porphyry may be started with 23–26-in stove-pipe casing; bottom diam of hole, 4 in.

In Tri-State district, for 400–600 ft, standard bit is 6.25-in, with 26-ft stem and jars; wt, about 2 000 lb (42). When drilling fractured ground, where several strings of casing are needed to obtain accurate samples, holes are started with 8 to 10-in bits and finished with 4 7/8-in, though the latter lack wt, are slower in drilling, and, if ground is bad, the hole may have to be abandoned to avoid losing tools due to caving (43). In Tri-State mines, underground churn drilling is sometimes done by special compressed-air drills, for prospecting where surface is covered by tailings or buildings; they require only 18-ft headroom for 60-ft holes. In some copper mines, churn drills are set on floor of drift, and need only 12–14 ft headroom, a 50 to 60-ft vert raise being driven for taking the crown sheave. For prospecting copper deposits in difficult rhyolite, a churn drill, starting with 14-in bit, was replaced at 800 ft by a small rotary outfit, making a 9.5-in hole; holes drilled to 1 295 ft, 5-in cores sometimes taken. Material caught on a 60-mesh screen permits identification of rock, and shows whether sulphides are present. A max speed of 82 ft per 8-hr shift has been attained; aver on several holes over 1 000 ft deep, about 30 ft per shift.

Moving. For small drills roads should be about 9 ft wide. Large caterpillar drills, max width 9.75 ft, can climb a 30% grade; speed on level ground, nearly 1 mile per hr; small machines can make 4–5 miles per hr in high gear; 2 miles in low. Non-traction drills are moved by caterpillar tractors, or mounted on auto-trucks; sometimes by the engine winding in a cable attached to a tree. A 6-horse team can pull a 12 000-lb drill on good roads; a 10-horse team, an 18 000-lb drill.

Hollow-rod rig. For shallow boring, holes should be smaller than 4.25-in (the economical limit with cable tools). Hollow rods are then used, instead of rope, for 2 to 4-in holes (45). In the hydraulic method, by means of valves in the rods, cuttings are forced to surface by self-pumping action; in the jetting method (more effective in soft ground) water is pumped down the rods to bring up the cuttings between rods and wall of hole or casing. These rigs drill to 1 000 ft and more.

Bits. To loosen the gravel in placer prospecting, bits are long and thin, compared to blunt, heavy rock bits, which exert a crushing action (see Fig 15). A detachable bit is finding favor; its cutting edge is bolted to body of bit, reducing the wt carried back and forth to blacksmith shop (see Sec 5).

15. DATA AND COSTS FOR PROSPECTING DRILLING

Placer drills. The light Hillman Airplane drill (Fig 40) will drill and handle casing to 75 ft or even more, at rate of about 20 ft per day. Two 20-ft holes per day are often made in shallow testing; at 85¢ per ft in Calif, to $2 per ft in Alaska. Specifications:

Wt of drilling tools, lb	400	Overall length of frame, ft	6
Strokes per min (30–60) aver	50	Overall width of frame, in	37
Length of stroke, in	15–30	Diam drive casing, in	4 or 5
Heaviest piece (drill-stem) lb	150	Diam drive shoe, in	5.5 or 6.5
3-hp gasolene engine, lb	260	Cu in of core sample per ft of	
Longest piece of derrick, ft	6.5	hole	260 or 390
Height of derrick from ground, ft	17		

Drill can be mounted on sled runners, or a two-wheel trailer; dismantled, it can be transported on muleback or in an airplane. Wt without tools, about 1 600 lb; aver cost, with 100 ft of casing and tools, $1 300 fob Seattle.

A larger machine will drill and pull casing to 300 ft, at about 30 ft per day; 26-hp gasolene engine; 28-ft derrick; drive shoe, 7.5 or 9.5 in; wt without tools, for sled or truck mounting, 5 850 lb; with caterpillar mounting, 11 200 lb; wt of tools, 1 000–2 500 lb; cost, with tools and 100 ft of 5 or 6-in casing, $4 500. Keystone No 71 placer drill is an all steel crawler, with 3 speeds. Bit, 5 5/8 in; wt of string of tools, about 1 200 lb; 25-hp gasolene engine; height of mast, 34 ft. Cost, fully equipped, $5 000–$5 500; wt, not including tools, about 14 000 lb. String of tools: bit, 4 ft 10 in long, 250 lb; drill stem, 4.25 in by 20 ft, 690 lb; jars, 250 lb; wt, complete, 1 350 lb.

In testing a placer deposit, actual drilling time may be a relatively small part of total elapsed time. The systematic boring of the Mammoth area, New Zealand (41) was done by 2 petrol drills, powered with 20-hp automobile engines; casing, 6-in, with 7.5-in driving shoe. Holes, 10–20 ft deep; 118 holes drilled in about 4 months; cost, $3.75–$4 per ft; 3 men on each drill. Wages: driller, $4 per day, panner, $3.75, man on gravel pump, $3.25. On a British Col placer (1934), drilling was done with 3 Keystone drills, 1 having capac of 1 500 ft, the others, 300 ft; 1 628 ft of hole cost $2.60 per ft. In 1935, 4 782 ft were drilled, with 6-in casing; cost, $3.42 per ft (including road building). In 1937 drilling cost $2 per ft. Most holes, 200 ft; none deeper than 300 ft.

Base-metal prospecting. In Tri-State district drills are all gasolene, mounted, 5.5–6.25-in spudders, for 400–600 ft holes in shale, limestone and chert; work by contract at $1 per ft aver. The chert wears bits rapidly. Aver speed, 25 ft per day. Costs: wages 55¢; power 6¢; repairs 4.5¢; supplies 18¢; insurance 2¢; taxes 3¢; deprec 2.5¢; total 91¢

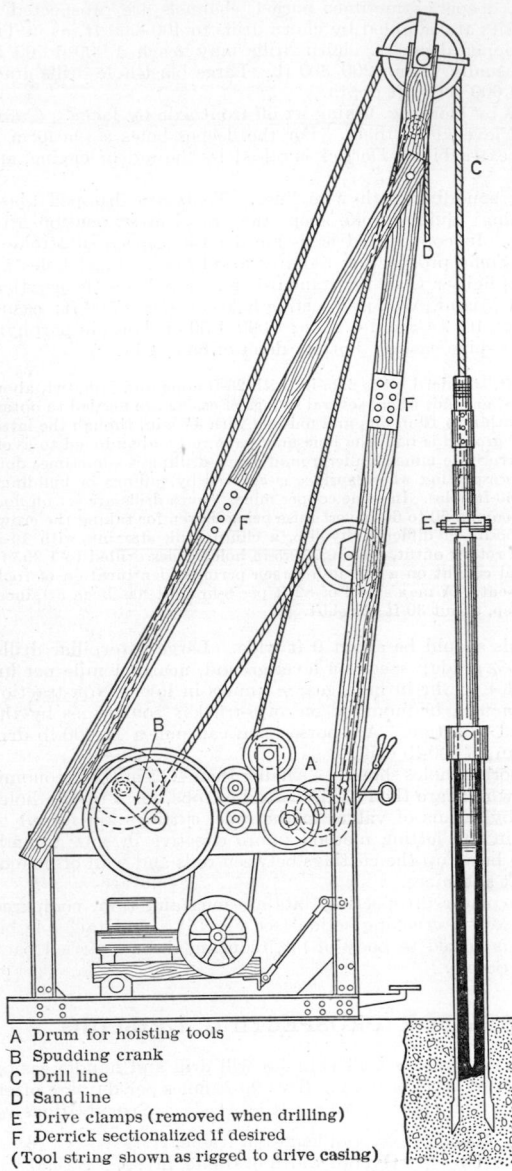

A Drum for hoisting tools
B Spudding crank
C Drill line
D Sand line
E Drive clamps (removed when drilling)
F Derrick sectionalized if desired
(Tool string shown as rigged to drive casing)

Fig 40. Light Placer Drill (C. K. Hillman Co)

(42–44). Underground churn-drilling costs $2–2.50 per ft for 60-ft holes. Solid sulphide ore, drilled with 6-in holes by Armstrong elec drill: depth, 33 ft; speed, 12–18 in per hr; cost per ft, labor $1.08, supplies 5¢, sharpening bits 76¢, misc 9¢; total $1.98. Churn-drill prospecting at Chino mines, Nev Consol Copper Co, N M, in 1930, with

Table 28. Drill Pipe, Drive Shoes and Stems (C. Kirk Hillman Co)

	Drill pipe				Drive shoes		
Outside diam, in	Inside diam, in	Cross-sec area, sq in	Vol per ft depth, cu in	Cutting edge diam, in	Cross-sec area, sq in	Vol per ft depth, cu in	Ft driven to cut 1 cu yd
4	3.826	11.4969	137.9628	5.25	21.6475	259.77	179.6
5	4.813	18.1938	218.3255	6.5	33.1832	398.1978	117.1
6	5.761	26.0666	312.7997	7.5	44.1788	530.1150	88.0
8	7.625	45.6636	547.9632	9.75	74.6621	895.9450	52.08

Drive-pipe, in	Wt per ft, lb	Round drill stems, in	Wt per ft, lb	Round drill stems, in	Wt per ft, lb	Core rise: in 4-in pipe, with 5.25-in shoe, per ft depth, 22.6 in; in 5-in pipe, with 6.5-in shoe, per ft depth, 21.9 in; in 6-in pipe, with 7.5-in shoe, per ft depth, 20.3 in; in 8-in pipe, with 9.75-in shoe, per ft depth, 19.6 in
4	14.983	3 1/8	26.08	4.25	48.23	
5	20.778	3.25	28.21	4.5	54.07	
6	28.573	3.5	32.71	4.75	60.25	
8	43.388	4	42.73	5	66.76	

Sanderson rigs, in fractured, silicified porphyry. Holes started at 13 in, followed by 10, 8, 6, 4.5 and 3-in bits, according to ground and depth. Crew: driller 72¢ per hr; tool dresser 53¢; sampler 52¢. Aver depth: special gasolene rigs, 749 ft, aver cost, $4.15; steam Cyclone drill, 775 ft, aver cost, $4.66; gasolene No 14 traction rig, 363 ft, aver cost, $2.97 per ft. Deep churn-drilling, Star elec rig, with standard 85-ft steel derrick for holes averaging 1 000 ft deep in monzonite porphyry. Holes spudded with 26-in cross bit and jars. Stove-pipe casing, 26, 23 and 20-in, placed as needed, followed by regular casing, 15.5, 12.5, 10 and 8-in. Samples taken every 5 ft. Max speed, 5 ft per hr; aver, 1 ft; total cost per ft; $11.41, of which labor was $6.69 and supplies, $4.72. Iron ore sampling, Mich and Minn. Glacial drift covering varies from a few ft to 300 ft or more; many large boulders. Orebodies often contain layers of taconite, requiring alternate steam churn and diamond drilling. As ore is soft, hard taconite layers are blasted or reamed, to keep casing close to bottom for reliable samples. Light diamond drill is direct connected, or belted churn drill. Menominee and Cuyuna ranges. Ore is overlain by greenstone, diorite, diabase and slate. Costs, $1.75 to max of $3.50 per ft when in manganiferous iron ore. On Vermillion and Marquette ranges, costs are $4–$4.50 per ft; Mesabi range, $2.50–$3.50 for churn drilling; diamond drilling, $3.50–$4.50 per ft. Rate of drilling, 10–20 ft per shift.

16. BLAST-HOLE DRILLING (see also Sec 5)

Holes are shallow, moves short, and no casing is used. Holes, 9 and 10-in at wide spacing, but 6-in holes often used for quarry and open-pit blasting. Speeds of 9 and 6 in drills are about the same, because the 9-in has heavier tools, stem about 2 700 lb as against 1 500 lb for the 6-in. A steel-frame type (Loomis Machine Co) has capac of 600 ft; safe working load for 31-ft mast, 9 ton; stroke, 13–37 in, is adjusted by a sliding pitman connection to spudding beam; power, gasolene engine, 20 hp at 1 200 rpm. Wt, truck mounting, 8 200 lb; cost $1 945; wheel mounting, 8 800 lb, $2 170; with solid rubber-tire wheels, 8 700 lb, $2 331; with pneumatic tires, 8 500 lb, $2 331; with crawler, 13 000 lb, $3 360; 6-in tool outfit weighs 2 790 lb; 8-in, 3 540 lb. Traveling speeds; 0.5, 7/8, 1.5 and 2.5 miles per hr.

Table 29. Bucyrus-Armstrong Churn Drills

	27-T drill				42-T drill		
Diam of hole, in........	6	6	6 5/8	6 5/8	9	10	12
Height of derrick, ft....	33	40	33	40	47.5	47.5	47.5
Drilling string, lb.......	1 401	1 833	1 582	2 064	4 300	5 100	5 100
Drill stem, in by ft.....	4.5 by 10	4.5 by 14	4.75 by 10	4.75 by 14	6.5 by 16	7 by 16	7 by 16
Wt of bit, lb..........	250	250	250	250	500	600	600
Length of stroke, in.....	27, 33, and 40				24, 30, 38 and 48		
Frame, width by length.	6 ft 6 in by 10 ft 9 in long				9 ft 9 in by 22 ft 7 in		
Caterpillar treads.......	9 ft 5 in wide by 11 ft 9 in long				11 ft 3 in wide by 13 ft 9 in		
Power.................	36-hp gasolene eng; 15-hp motor or Diesel engine				80-hp Diesel engine		
Wt without tools and cable...............	18 265 lb with gasolene eng; 18 160 lb with motor				49 000 lb for Diesel; 45 300 lb with motor		

Drill stem as above is in 2 pieces. Advantages: stems can be reversed when lower box-joint is worn; lighter pieces easily handled; only one spare needed; no welds, hence less breakage. Bucyrus-Armstrong drill 29-T is an intermediate size, for holes 6–12 in diam; wt, 22 870 lb, without tools.

(Table 30. Cost of Drilling **51 300 ft** of 9-in Hole, Aver Depth, **60 ft** (in porphyry, with Armstrong 29-T drills; speed, 0.264 ft per min)

	Cost per ft
Operating labor...........	$0.224
Labor sharpening bits......	0.021
Supplies: Power..........	0.011
Comp air...............	0.009
Casing.................	0.053
Sharpening.............	0.018
Tools and misc..........	0.045
Repair labor..............	0.018
Supplies................	0.016
Total per ft...........	$0.415

50 ft deep, in back line (5 ft behind) 45 ft deep (see also Sec 5).

Fig 41 shows tools for drilling and fishing; for bits, see Fig 17; Z bit often used in fissured ground.

Blast-hole drilling, Chino mines, N M, is done with 12 elec drills, caterpillar mounted, 6-in holes. Crew, driller and helper. Collars of holes are cased in shattered overburden; holes usually spaced 20–30 ft, 6 ft from edge of bank; in hard ground, 18 ft apart. When bank is steep and height less than 50 ft, holes may be drilled to 5 ft below grade, to break bottom. In banks exceeding 60 ft, "slope holes" are drilled, in conjunction with toe holes by machine drills. In hard ground and high banks, holes are sometimes staggered, 30 ft apart in each line; holes in front line

Table 31. Drilling in Porphyry, Garnetized Limestone and Rhyolite
(Bucyrus-Armstrong elec tractor drill)

	1936			1937		
	Per 8 hr	Per ton	Per ft	Per 8 hr	Per ton	Per ft
Operating labor.................	12.19	0.0033	0.16	14.57	0.0043	0.19
Supplies and repairs..............	7.31	0.0020	0.10	9.73	0.0029	0.13
Power.........................	.62	0.0002	0.01	.66	0.0002	0.01
Power lines.....................	1.25	0.0003	0.02	2.69	0.0008	0.04
Water service..................	3.00	0.0008	0.04	4.31	0.0013	0.05
Steel sharpening................	2.51	0.0007	0.03	2.78	0.0008	0.04
Other expense..................	5.74	0.0016	0.08	2.65	0.0007	0.03
Total.........................	32.62	0.0089	0.44	37.39	0.0110	0.49

Drilling speeds in quarries with Bucyrus-Armstrong drills. In traprock, drill 29-T averaged 3.34 ft per hr total time; 4.87 ft per hr actual drilling time, 8-in holes. In hard limestone, with 24-T drill, 5.2 and 6.6 ft, respectively, in 9-in holes. In a hard limestone quarry, Ill, Loomis No 44 and No 2 Clipper drills made in 1937 over 100 000 ft of 6-in holes, averaging 55 ft, at 6 ft per hr actual drilling time. Costs: drilling labor, 16.17¢; incidental labor, 3.33¢; supplies, 2¢; elec power, 3¢; total, 24.5¢ per ft.
Drilling hard siliceous hematite (1937) with 20-T Bucyrus-Armstrong machines, 9-in bits, for hardest ore; smaller type, 6-in bits, for soft. Costs: 9-in holes, $1.89–2.01 per ft, and $0.089 per ton ore; 6-in holes, $1.69–2.28 per ft, and $0.147 per ton ore. Drilling speed, about 2 ft per hr.

·17. DIAMOND DRILL

Construction. The boring column (Fig 42) consists of: bit X, set with diamonds; core shell V, containing lifter W; core-barrel U; hollow rods P, rotating within casing strings M and N. The drill rod is driven by gasolene engine, mounted on a steel frame; through a swivel, water is pumped into rods, a hose connecting pump and swivel; rods are raised and lowered by a drum and wire rope, the latter passing over a block at top of derrick.
Casing is in 4 standard sizes, EX, AX, BX, and NX, for rods and couplings E, A, B, and N (Table 32). Other slightly different sizes are obtainable. Casing flush on outside when coupled is "flush-coupled casing"; when without couplings, "flush-joint casing."

Table 32. Nominal Dimensions of Rods, Casing and Cores

Size		Casing and casing coupling, outside diam, in	Casing coupling, inside diam, in	Casing bit, outside diam, in	Core-barrel bit, outside diam, in	Drill rod, outside diam, in	Diam of hole by core-barrel bit, in *	Approx diam of core, in
Casing, coupling and casing bits	Rod and rod coupling							
EX	E	1 13/16	1 1/2	1 27/32	1 7/16	1 5/16	1 15/32	7/8
AX	A	2 1/4	1 29/32	2 5/16	1 27/32	1 5/8	1 7/8	1 1/8
BX	B	2 7/8	2 3/8	2 15/16	2 5/16	1 29/32	2 11/32	1 5/8
NX	N	3 1/2	3	3 9/16	2 15/16	2 3/8	2 31/32	2 1/8

* Assuming hole 1/32 in larger than bit.

Core-barrels are: single-tube, rigid double-tube, and swivel double-tube. SINGLE-TUBE barrel requires less time to remove core and reconnect the barrel, and in many kinds of rock makes faster progress than double-tube barrels. DOUBLE-TUBE BARREL has an

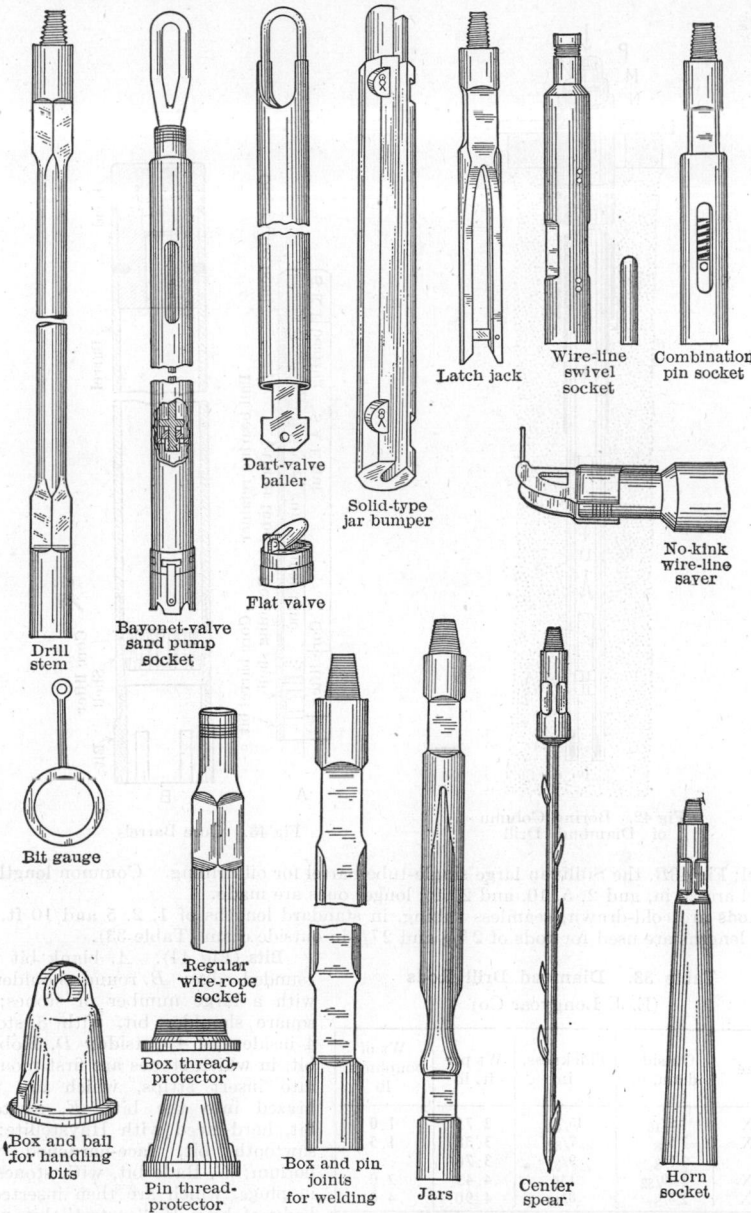

Fig 41. Drilling and Fishing Tools for Churn Drilling (Bucyrus-Armstrong)

inner tube revolving with outer tube, and the circulating water is carried to bit without coming in contact with the core, to prevent washing of soft core, and reduce grinding between separate pieces of core in the barrel. In the SWIVEL-BARREL, the inner tube is mounted on ball-bearings, and as it does not revolve, is desirable for friable rock. Cores larger than standard are obtained with special fittings. For fragile rock, large diam cores are better than small. Fig 43A shows the Sprague and Henwood double-tube, ball-bearing

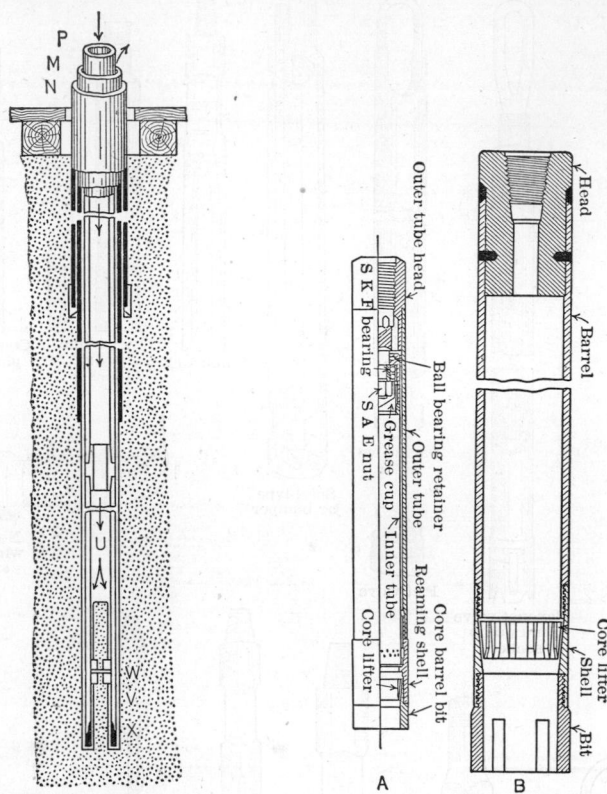

Fig 42. Boring Column
of Diamond Drill

Fig 43. Core Barrels

barrel; Fig 43B, the Sullivan large single-tube barrel for oil drilling. Common lengths of barrel are 20 in, and 2, 5, 10, and 20 ft; longer ones are made.

Rods are cold-drawn, seamless tubing, in standard lengths of 1, 2, 5 and 10 ft, but 20-ft lengths are used for rods of 2 3/8 and 2 7/8-in outside diam (Table 33).

Table 33. Diamond Drill Rods

(E. J. Longyear Co)

Size	Outside diam, in	Thickness, in	Wt per ft, lb	Wt of couplings, lb
EX	1 5/16	15/64	2.75	1.0
AX	1 5/8	7/32	3.38	1.5
A	1 5/8	9/32	3.76	...
BX	1 29/32	1/4	4.43	2.0
NX	2 3/8	3/16	4.90	4.0

Bits (Fig 44). A, blank bit with rounded edge; B, round shoulder bit with a large number of stones; C, square shoulder bit, with 8 stones, 4 inside and 4 outside; D, Kobelite bit, in which stones are first moulded into insert strips, which are then brazed into the bit; E, sawtooth bit, hard-faced with Haystellite; F, sawtooth bit, face-hardened with borium; G, Bade bit, with stones set in plugs, which are then inserted in body of bit; H, "castset" bit, made by setting stones in a mould and pouring in molten metal; I, sawtooth bit, in which plugs of hard metal are set. Sawtooth and hard-faced fishtail bits may be used in the softer rocks. A solid bit, making no core, may be used for boring in barren strata above ore horizon; its face is slightly recessed;

rim diamonds are set with usual clearance, and holes through bit admit water to face. In soft ore, cores have been taken with a square-shouldered blank bit, with water courses cut in it (Art 18). Diamonds are always set to "cover" one another as bit rotates.

Types of drills range from portable, hand-operated machines for depths of 300–400 ft, to the heavy, engine-driven type for great depths.   A recent diamond-drill hole in So Africa is 10 718 ft deep; 2 others, 7 408 and 7 770.   Compact drills are made for underground service, and truck-mounted or motorized forms for surface work. With improved bits rotative speeds have been increased from 300 or 400 to 1 000 or even 1 200 rpm, increasing drilling rate by 50% or more.   High speed requires changes in design: working parts are enclosed and run in oil; chucks have countersunk bolts; ball-bearings used throughout,

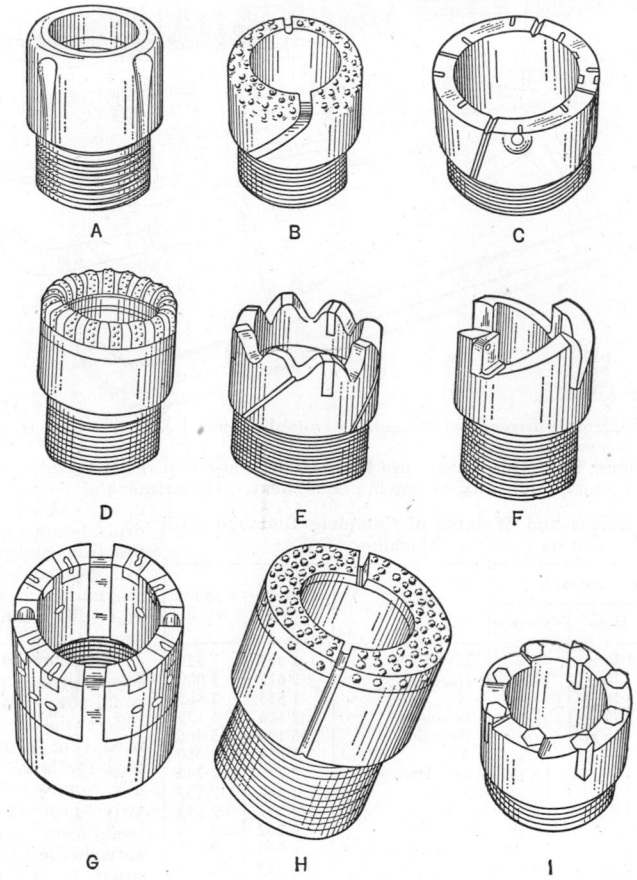

Fig 44.   Diamond-drill Bits

and provision made for pressure greasing. The No 22 Sullivan drill has a capac of 1 150 ft with EX fittings (Table 32), or less depth with larger fittings; driven by compressed air, steam, elec, or gasolene engine, these drives being interchangeable.   Wt of air- or steam-driven drill, without pump, is 1 390 lb.   Fig 45 shows a Longyear UG straight-line gasolene drill, capac 1 500 ft of E hole; wt complete, 1 959 lb; gasolene motor, 20 hp, consumes 8–12 gal per shift; can be moved by fastening the steel cable to a tree and winding it in.   Sullivan No 40 drill has a 42-hp Buda engine; capac, 1 500 ft of 3-in core, or 2 200 ft of 2-in core (greater depth for smaller core); hydraulic feed swivel-head has piston travel of 18 in.   This drill can be equipped with a 12 or 22-ft Kelly bar for oil-well drilling (Sec 44); mounted on an I-beam frame, which is slid out over the hole while drilling, but is retracted 18 in by a rope and cathead when hoisting or lowering rods; wt complete,

8 316 lb. About 70% of diamond drills are driven by gasolene engines; 20% by elec motors; 10% by steam, or, for underground drills, by elec or compressed air. Steam power is familiar to most drillers, easy to handle, and by throttling permits close control

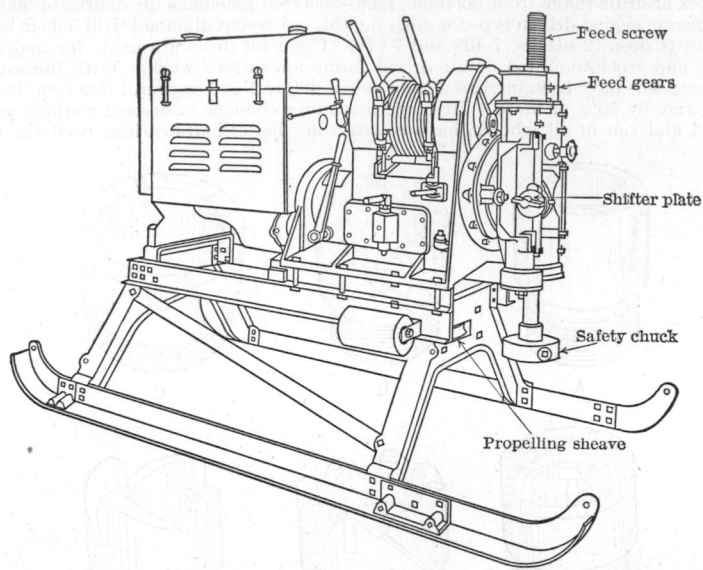

Fig 45. Gasolene-driven, Swivel-head, Screw-feed Diamond Drill (E. J. Longyear Co)

over operations; its disadvantages are higher initial cost and boiler upkeep (state boiler codes must be met), difficulty of moving equipment. Department of Forestry, Canada, insists on use of gasolene drills, because of danger of fire from steam rigs (46). For gasolene rigs, cost of fuel and transport are low and drilling can be started promptly.

Table 34. Prices and Weights of Complete Diamond Drill Outfits (Sullivan Machinery Co)

Capac, ft	Diam, in		Power	Approx price	Approx wt, lb
	Hole	Core			
350–400	1 15/32	7/8	Hand	$ 1 689	1 325
500	1 15/32	7/8	Gasolene	2 017	3 000
500	1 15/32	7/8	Air	1 833	2 865
750	1 15/32	7/8	Gasolene	2 566	5 175
750	1 15/32	7/8	Electric	3 195	5 485
750	1 15/32	7/8	Air	3 651	6 250
1 250	1 7/8	1 3/16	Gasolene	3 777	7 780
900	1 7/8	1 3/16	Air	3 887	7 107
1 250	1 7/8	1 3/16	Electric	4 557	7 555
2 200	1 7/8	1 3/16	Steam	4 762	8 730
1 400	2 23/64	1 41/64	Steam	4 948	9 940
1 350	2 63/64	2 9/64	Steam	6 098	16 104
1 500	2 63/64	2 9/64	Gas portable	8 596	20 390
1 500	2 63/64	2 9/64	Diesel portable	11 496	24 090
4 000	2 63/64	2 9/64	Gasolene	15 000	36 474
4 200	2 63/64	2 9/64	Diesel	17 000	38 688
5 500	2 63/64	2 9/64	Steam	20 000	40 574
800	2 63/64	2 9/64	Gas motorized	7 150	9 800
1 200	2 63/64	2 9/64	Gas motorized	9 500	13 000
1 800	3 1/2	2 9/16	Gas motorized	11 050	15 000
2 300	3 1/2	2 9/16	Gas motorized	16 500	21 000
2 300	3 1/2	2 9/16	Diesel motorized	17 750	21 750
1 800	7 3/8	......	Gas motorized	50 000	37 500

Feed mechanisms. On hand drills and many small power rigs a positive differential screw-feed is used (Fig 46); hydraulic feed for large drills (Fig 47). SCREW-FEED. In the swivel-head (Fig 46), the feed-screw spindle A is threaded left-handed; rotated by spline-quill B, having 3 locked-in splines; spindle rotates with B, but is free to move up or down, and is driven by bevel gear C, being keyed to B and meshing with the drive gear. All rotating parts have ball-bearings. On the lower end of B is gear D, which drives countershaft E by meshing with gear F, keyed and locked onto the countershaft. At top of countershaft are 3 feed gears G, meshing with corresponding gears H, keyed to feed nut I, which is threaded to take the feed-screw spindle. The feed gears have different ratios;

sliding key J, on shaft K, which operates within countershaft E, is moved into engagement with any one of the 3 gears by handwheel L.   When the feed shifter L is in its lowest notch it gives the fastest feed; second notch is neutral position; third, intermediate feed; fourth, another neutral; fifth is the slow feed.   The rate of feed is varied at will by slowing down, and operating the shifter handwheel.   Gears give speeds of 200, 400 and 600 rev of the spindle per in of feed; other gears of 50–1300 rev are obtainable.

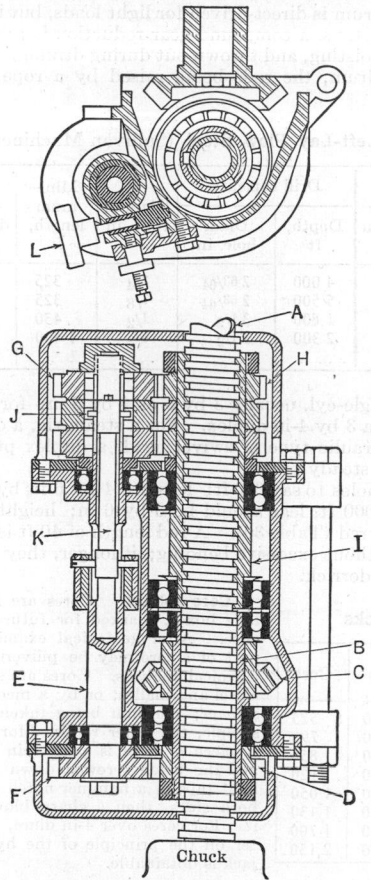

Fig 46.   Differential-gear Screw Feed
(Sullivan Machy Co)

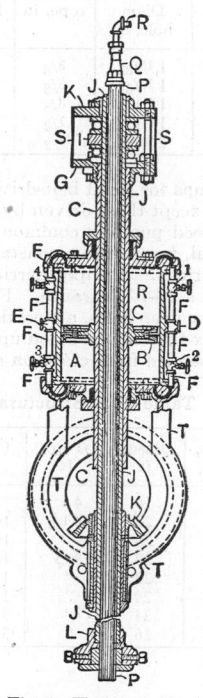

Fig 47. Hydraulic Feed

HYDRAULIC FEED is used almost universally on large drills.   In Fig 47, A is the hydraulic cylinder, B the piston, C a hollow piston rod, D pressure-water inlet, E discharge-water outlet, 1 and 2 inlet valves, 3 and 4 outlet valves.   By opening diagonally opposite valves the piston rod is raised or lowered.   This motion is transmitted through roller friction head S to collar I, which is rigidly fastened to hollow drive rod J. J is rotated by bevel gear K, driven from the bevel pinion T on crankshaft.   The drill rods P, passing through J, are gripped by chuck L, being thus rotated and fed forward.   A pressure-gage measures the thrust on the rods.   Hydraulic feeds are made also with 2 cylinders, the piston rods being yoked together and the drive rod carried in the yoke.   Usual advance per run with single-cylinder feed is 1 ft; with double-cylinder feed, 2 ft.   Both screw and hydraulic feeds are mounted on a swivel head, which admits boring in any angular direction.

Differential vs hydraulic feed.   Considerable difference of opinion exists as to their relative merits.   For any given setup, screw feed gives a constant advance and records the varying pressure on the bit, thus apprising the runner of slight differences in hardness of rock, and of presence of thin seams and small crevices.   This information is often invaluable when the core is much broken and its record consequently incomplete.   But, in strata of frequently varying hardness, it is necessary to run through soft strata at reduced speed, so that the bit may not be damaged on meeting a hard stratum. With hydraulic feed the pressure is constant, and rate of advance varies more or less automatically as hardness of the rock varies. Thus, danger to the bit in passing from soft to hard rock is lessened. The runner of the hydraulic-feed drill can instantly take advantage of changes in the formation, varying the rate of advance, within the limits imposed by the rock, merely by turning a valve. Three different speeds are the limit with screw feed, unless gears are changed.

Hoisting drum. For small drills the drum is driven by gearing from the crankshaft; in some machines, 2 or more drum speeds are available by use of shifting gears, which form integral parts of engine. For large drills, drum is direct-driven for light loads, but in deep holes, when wt of drill rods may be several tons, a compound gear-reduction is provided, the gears being thrown in by a lever when hoisting, and thrown out during drilling. Small belt-driven drills rarely have a hoisting drum, the rods being raised by a rope coiled around a niggerhead.

Table 35. Wire Hoisting Ropes, 6×37 Left-Lay Plow Steel (Sullivan Machinery Co)

Drill capacity		Diam of rope, in	Minimum length, ft	Min sheave diam, in	Drill capacity		Diam of rope, in	Minimum length, ft	Min sheave diam, in
Depth, ft	Diam hole, in				Depth, ft	Diam hole, in			
400	1 15/32	3/8	100	10	4 000	2 63/64	3/4	325	28
750	1 15/32	3/8	250	12	5 500	2 63/64	7/8	325	30
1 250	1 7/8	3/8	260	12	1 800	3 1/2	1/2	430	22
2 200	1 7/8	1/2	150	16	2 300	3 1/2	3/8	1 400	14
1 400	2 23/64	1/2	150	20	....	......	....	....	....

Pumps for small belt-driven rigs are single-cyl, usually 3 by 5 or 4 by 5 in; for larger drills, except those driven by steam or air, a 3 by 4-in duplex. For a steam rig, a duplex, boiler-feed pump is common; for the hydraulic type of swivel head, a duplex pump is essential, to provide a constant flow under steady press.

Derricks. A tripod derrick serves for holes to say 600 ft; legs are 4 by 6 in by 22 ft, to give a 20-ft clearance. For holes to 1 000 ft, legs should be 6 by 6 in; height 30 ft. For very deep holes, a steel derrick is preferred (Table 36). A rod length of 40 ft is about the max that can be stood up in derrick without excessive bending; if longer, they should be suspended from crabs on a track in the derrick.

Table 36. Structural Steel Derricks

Height, ft	Base, ft	Top, ft	Capac, lb	Wt, lb	Cost
45	16	4 .	35 000	4 000	$ 525
66	20	4 1/3	168 000	10 000	790
73	20	"	168 000	10 700	850
80	20	5.5	168 000	12 930	920
87	20	"	168 000	14 200	1 050
94	24	"	168 000	16 100	1 130
122	24	"	367 000	26 300	1 700
136	26	"	367 000	118 000	2 150

Core splitter. Cores are kept in long boxes, marked for future reference. After geological examination, part of a core may be pulverized for chemical analysis. Cores are split by chisel and mallet, or by a mechanical splitter; one half being taken as the sample, the other retained for record. A piece of core is placed in splitter and the blade screwed down tightly; light taps of a hammer notch core on both sides, then a sharp blow splits it. For cores over 4-in diam, a splitter on the principle of the hydraulic jack is obtainable.

18. DIAMOND DRILLING OPERATIONS

Setting up. An area 20–25 ft sq is graded, and drill and pump set on a plank floor. For deep holes or light machines, derrick legs rest on the floor, to counteract upward pressure when drilling. For shelter: in summer, a canvas fly; in winter, a shanty of wood or galvanized iron, which may be sectionalized for moving. To erect a steam rig, with 3-leg derrick and wooden shanty, easy grading, takes say 100 man-hr; to dismantle, say 25 man-hr. UNDERGROUND SETUPS of a small drill can be made in mine drifts, which should be widened to about 7 ft at the drilling place. Rods 1 ft long can be used, but 5–10-ft lengths save time.

Drilling under water. Drill is mounted on a scow, anchored to bottom, or supported on spuds. If current is too rapid to permit stable setting, a platform is built on piles, or a heavy standpipe is driven from the scow, securely guyed, and the drill set on a platform clamped to top of pipe. Portable drills are set up by blocking the front wheels, securing front of drill with guys, and centering derrick over the drive rod. Two men can make such a setup in 2 to 4 hr, and dismantle in about half that time.

Sinking standpipe is generally done by wash boring (Art 1). On reaching rock the standpipe is chopped or bored in a few inches, to make a tight joint, prevent influx of surface material, and insure return of drilling water to the surface. Sinking standpipe is an uncertain operation. In soft and medium clays and fine gravels, 10-12 ft per hr is not unusual. In bouldery gravel or hardpan, aver speed may be less than 1 in per hr. In rock, speed of sinking standpipe may not exceed drilling rate; in bouldery ground, considerably less.

Drilling. Following is the normal sequence of operations: Slide or swing feed mechanism away from hole. Set safety clamp in position over standpipe. Connect up bit, core shell (with core lifter), core barrel, and 1 length of rod, and lower through the safety clamp until only a few inches project; then grip by the clamps. Screw hoisting swivel into upper end of a section of rods, swing rods into place with the hoist and screw them into the rod joint projecting from the hole. Loosen the clamp and lower the string on the hoist brake until only a few inches project from hole. Tighten the safety clamp, and unscrew the hoisting swivel. Repeat these operations until within a rod length of bottom. Bring feed mechanism back into place. Attach water swivel and lifting bail to the last length; lower it through the drive rod, and screw it into place. Run the feed to highest position, and tighten the chuck. Loosen safety clamp. Connect water swivel to pump and start the pump. Start drill and run downward until pressure shows that bit is against rock. While drilling, adjust feed as necessary. When measurement of rod indicates that core barrel is full, or laboring of pump and engine suggest that it is blocked by broken pieces of core, stop the drill. Keep pump running until water issuing from hole shows that sludge has been well removed. Hoist rods by reversing the operations of lowering. Extract core, and place it in core boxes. Change bit often enough to prevent diam of hole from falling below gage, and to guard against loss of diamonds from wear of the metal surrounding them.

Casing or cement grout is used to support the walls of a drill hole when they cave so as to prevent progress or vitiate samples. Casing is flush-joint tubing large enough to allow the bit to pass. Table 37 gives usual sizes. If hole is continued of same diam below the caving ground, it is reamed before casing is put in. As diamond drill holes are never straight, casing is a difficult operation. Casing is usually twisted and driven down. Sometimes a "casing bit," set with a few diamong chips, is placed on lower end of the

Table 37. Flush-coupled Casing

Size	Outside diam, in	Inside diam, in		Wt, lb per ft with coupling
		Casing	Coupling	
EX	1 13/16	1 5/8	1 1/2	1.81
AX	2 1/4	2	1 19/32	2.91
BX	2 7/8	2 15/32	2 3/8	5.74
NX	3 1/2	3 1/16	3	7.8

tubing, which is then operated as in regular drilling. CEMENT GROUT is more and more used instead of casing. In badly caving ground the drill is driven as far as is safe, and the core and sludge saved. Then the grout is pumped down the rods or lowered in a bailer. After it has set, the resulting "plug" is drilled through, and a deeper section of hole is sampled and grouted. Quick setting cements are used. Adding 25% of luminite cement to ordinary cement shortens setting time to about 2 hr.

Cementing is usually cheaper than casing, and allows the hole to be started at a given diam without considering possible future support. In shattered ground rods may have to be pulled frequently, due to blocking of core barrel. In soft ground, also, if core is desired, frequent withdrawal is necessary or a double core barrel used. In fissured ground, part or all of the water will be lost. If there is standing water in fissured strata, the sludge will deposit in crevices close to the drill, and re-enter the hole when water current stops. Hence, water must be pumped through the rods during hoisting, and the rods flushed down in lowering. Bran, sawdust, manure, or cement, are pumped down the hole in an attempt to stop the crevices.

Accidents and fishing. Commonest accident is LOSS or breakage OF A DIAMOND. Usual mode of recovery is to send down an old bit, the end of which is filled with wax. The diamond imbeds itself in this and is brought to surface. When the hole can not be cleaned to bottom, for using the waxed bit, a lost diamond may sometimes be recovered by the bailer. The following device has been used. A screen was placed in top of core barrel and a screen clack valve set in an old bit, which was screwed to bottom of barrel. The rods were lowered through a stuffing box and water current reversed. Sludge containing the lost diamond was washed into the core barrel and held between the two screens. In Fig 48, *A* is a casing tap for screwing on casing or rods; *B* and *E*, male and female taper taps for recovering rods; *C* and *D*, for rod couplings; *F*, *G*, combination spear to recover rods or couplings.

Parting of rods in a hole, may be due to fracture, stripping of threads, or unscrewing. If they become unscrewed, it is usually a simple matter to screw them together again. When threads strip or rods break, a recovery tap (threaded inside or outside according to nature of the break) is lowered on a line of rods and manipulated until it engages the broken part. Casing breaks are similarly treated. JAMMING OF RODS may be due to caving, to a mud rush, to working with worn bit, or to too little clearance between rods and casing. A caving hole usually gives some warning, but casing or grouting is often neglected in the haste for progress. Jamming from a sudden cave can sometimes be averted by reversing and running back the feed without stopping the engine, meantime pumping more water. A mud rush will not often occur while pump is running. If the pump is started before lowering the rods to the bottom, and kept running while hoisting until the rods are above danger zone, jamming will not occur. Pulling jammed rods, when powerful jacks are necessary, elongates the rods, with consequent weakening, and the threads may be stripped.

Loss of bit, due to breakage below core barrel, is a baffling and serious accident. If possible, the bit is picked up by a recovery tap. Difficulty in using a tap is that the bit may lie on its side; furthermore, it offers little resistance to turning, and may turn with

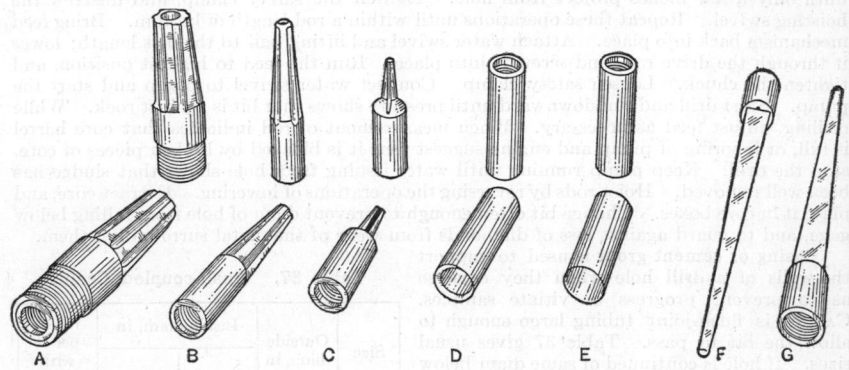

A   B   C   D   E   F   G

Fig 48. Diamond-drill Fishing Tools (Sullivan Machy Co)

the tap. Bits have been recovered by reaming the hole to a size allowing use of a bit large enough to make a core containing the lost bit. If the bit cannot be recovered, the hole is diverted at some distance above it and continued (Art 12). Loss of time due to accidents is often a serious factor in drilling.

Operating crew of a diamond drill consists of a runner and one or more helpers. The runner should be a good mechanic and repair man, besides being experienced in drilling. By observing behavior of engine, pump, and rods, a good runner can learn much about character of the ground being drilled. This knowledge is valuable as added to the testimony of core and sludge, and furnishing a warning of possible trouble in the hole. Many operators will not entrust the running of an hydraulic-feed machine to a runner who has not had 2 or 3 years' experience as helper on a similar drill, nor give a man work on a deep hole unless he has had experience with shallow ones. In general, less experience is required of runners for screw-feed machines. The helper is fireman and assists the runner in handling rods. A skilled bit setter is usually required, who may act as foreman for as many drills as he can set bits for.

A group of drills will require a general foreman. Team and driver are needed for part or all the time, to haul fuel, attend to water supply, and help in moving. Wages for a runner are usually slightly higher than miners' wages in a given district. Helper is paid usual helper's wages of the district. Bit setter is paid the same or a little more than the runner, minimum wages being $200 to $250 per month. Diamond drill manufacturers have lists of experienced runners and bit setters available for work. These men are paid traveling and living expenses besides regular wages.

Quantity of water per day depends upon: size of drill; boiler consumption; diam and depth of hole; sp gr of sludge; whether rock is hard or soft; whether hole leaks or is tight; and water is saved and reused. Loss of water varies greatly in shattered formations. If no water channels are cut in bit and core barrel, the max size of particle that can pass upward has a diam equal to clearance of the outside diamonds; with water channels, size of particle is determined by clearance between rods and walls of hole. A rising current of 12–18 in per sec is usually sufficient, except for very heavy material, as magnetite or galena. Quantity of water to produce desired veloc varies with diam of hole and rods (Table 38). With this rising current, the veloc in the small space around the core is much higher, sometimes causing so great a loss of core in soft rocks that veloc must be reduced. In general, much water means rapid drilling and low core recovery; little water increases core recovery at expense of progress, and too little may result in a burned bit. If the hole is tight and nearly all the water pumped down returns to surface, the overflow from sludge box can be reused; loss of water is then about 25%; reused water must be freed from oil. Measurements at 3 drill holes, where all return water was saved, show that 76–80 gal per hr were used; holes, 1.5 in, cores $7/8$ in. Drilling a 3-in hole and recovering 2-in core in broken formation when prospecting for coal, required 305 gal of water per hr; in fairly deep drilling, 105–123 gal per hr may be used.

Table 38. Vol of Water Required to Produce a Veloc of 1.5 ft per sec
(E. J. Longyear Co)

Size rod	Size hole or casing	Gal per hr
E	EX hole	120
E	AX "	390
A	AX "	192
A	BX "	660
A	NX "	1 400
B	BX "	432
B	NX "	1 182
N	NX "	732
E	EX casing	204
A	AX "	300
B	BX "	540
N	NX "	822

19. TIME DISTRIBUTION IN DIAMOND DRILLING

Table 39. Approx Time for Hoisting and Lowering Rods (E. J. Longyear Co.)

Depth of hole, ft	Time for pulling rods, removing core and lowering
500	40 min
1 000	90 "
1 500	2 hr
2 000	2.5 "
2 500	3.25 "
3 000	4 "
4 000	5– 6 "
5 000	6– 7 "
6 000	9–10 "

Time effic, the percentage of total working time spent in actual drilling, rarely exceeds 60%, and depends on depth and character of overburden, time for hoisting and lowering rods, and delays (Table 39). Time for handling rods depends on depth of hole, and length of rod sections between breaks. Number of lifts depends on nature of ground, kind of bit, and kind and length of core barrel. Uniform rock sometimes cores the full length of barrel; in broken ground, cores break up and tend to jam in the barrel or be lost. Double core barrels (Art 17) tend to overcome this difficulty. A solid bit needs to be raised only to change it. Table 40 shows distribution of delays in 1 200 shifts at United Verde mine (50). Due to 8-hr law, 1 hr aver was taken for traveling to working place and return; adding 0.5 hr for lunch left 6.5 hr. Actual drilling time, 68.88% of total time.

Table 40. Delays in Diamond Drilling (50)

Cause of delay	Percent of total working time
Moving	17.02
Cementing	3.55
Reaming	0.56
Casing ground	0.73
Fishing, rods or bits	0.94
Repairs	1.54
Bits	1.25
Air and water	1.73
Supplies	0.89
Surveying holes	0.36
Mine department	1.46
Drill and equipment	1.09
Total	31.12

Table 41. Time Distribution in Diamond Drilling (51)

Operation	Hours	Percent
Churn drilling near surface	110.0	2.5
Drilling, AX casing bits	150.5	3.2
Drilling, EX bits	3 444.7	74.2
Drilling, AX bits	14.0	0.3
Total actual drilling	3 719.2	80.2
Moving and setting up	279.5	6.0
Repairing machinery	114.5	2.4
Delay, lack of water	27.5	0.6
Cementing	225.0	4.8
Inclination tests	137.5	2.9
Fishing for lost bits	9.0	0.2
Reaming undersized hole	9.0	0.2
Changing water pump	12.0	0.3
Fishing for lost core	17.0	0.4
Installed lighting plant	4.0	0.1
Reaming EX casing	67.0	1.4
Threading pipe	4.5	0.1
Laying water line	4.0	0.1
General	14.5	0.3
Total	4 644.2	100.0

In drilling 10 192 ft (17 angle holes) in about 12 months (Lupa gold field), most of the work was in sheared rocks (Table 41). Cores were EX ($7/8$ in). Time for lowering and raising rods, removing cores and incidental work is included with EX drilling time. Progress was considerably delayed by frequent pulling of the rods, due to core-blocked bits and barrels (51).

In 3 deep holes in So Africa, ratio of actual drilling days to total elapsed time was: 7 408-ft hole, 60%; 7 770-ft, 43.6%; 10 718-ft, 70.7%. Cores: 1 $^3/_8$, 2 $^1/_2$ and 1 $^3/_8$ in respectively.

Table 42. Underground Diamond Drilling, El Potosí Mine (H. A. Walker)

Type of drill	Drilling time, min per ft	Percent of total time				
		Actual drilling	Placing rods	Handling core	Coming, going and lunch	Delays
Small electric...............	7.3	42.4	10.0	18.8	18.8	10
Small air....................	7.3	36.0	8.0	27.2	18.8	10
All small drills.............	7.3	40.8	9.5	20.9	18.8	10.
Large 11 SE elec............	7.8	46.4	8.1	16.7	18.8	10
Large 6 UGE elec...........	7.6	50.1	8.0	13.1	18.8	10
Large air...................	7.2	49.3	8.0	13.9	18.8	10
All large drills.............	7.5	48.6	8.0	14.6	18.8	10

Table 42 shows results at El Potosí mine, Mex, from Oct 18, 1934, to Mch 16, 1935, with 4 small machines, capac 250 ft, and 3 larger drills of 700 ft capac. The expected performance, ft per shift, is higher than any past averages; but in drilling limestone, under proper power supply conditions, these figures are attainable. Number of ft drilled each time the rods were lowered is assumed as 8 for the small machines and 14 for the large. Using 5- and 10-ft rods should give 62% theoretical core recovery for the small drills and 71% for the large.

20. DIAMONDS, BIT-SETTING, AND LOSS OF CARBONS

Diamonds are of 3 classes: white or slightly tinted crystalline brilliant; less pure crystalline form, known in trade as "bort" or "bortz"; and the opaque, somewhat porous "carbonado" or black diamond, composed of very small diamond crystals in amorphous carbon or graphite, known as "carbon." The white diamond, and similar but imperfect bort, have cleavages along which they can be split, and when cut they refract light brilliantly. Carbon is black, grayish black, or tinged green or brownish. A fresh fracture resembles broken steel. C. E. Wooddell gives a modified Mohs' scale of hardness (Table 43).

Table 43. Modified Mohs' Scale for Different Substances (47)

South American brown bort...............	10.00	South American carbon..	9.82	Fused alumina (3.14% TiO$_2$)..............	9.06
South American ballas..	9.99	Boron carbide.........	9.32	African crystallized corundum............	9.00
Belgian Congo, yellow..	9.96	Silicon carbide, black....	9.15		
Belgian Congo, white..	9.95	Silicon carbide, green....	9.13	Quartz...............	8.94
Belgian Congo, gray opal	9.89	Tungsten carbide (13% C).................	9.09		

Table 44. Prices per Carat of Carbon and Bort (Diamond Drill Carbon Co)

Year	Best quality carbons, 2 carats and over	Best quality small bort, of 0.05–0.20 carat	Fair quality bort
1932	$130–120	$6.50–7.50	From $3 to $7 per carat, depending on quality
1933	115– 70	6.50–7.50	
1934	115– 90	7.50–8.50	
1935	110	7.50–8.50	
1936	70– 65	7.50	
1937	70– 65	7.50	

The scale shows carbons to be below diamonds in hardness, but hardness should not be confused with toughness. White diamond or bort is commonly a single crystal, except "ballas," in which crystallization starts from a central point, making the stone practically impossible to cut; fit for drill bits, but very scarce. Bort splits readily along 3 planes, and is more brittle than carbon. Carbon has no cleavage, hence is less liable to break in hard rock. Selection of good stones requires experience, lacking which, an engineer should buy through a reliable dealer or diamond-drill manufacturer.

Bit-setting is a delicate and important operation. Diamonds must have such clearance that the metal of the bit will not come in contact with the rock, and must "cover" one another, so that no part of the area to be cut will fail to be touched by a diamond at each rev of bit. It was formerly common practice to use a few carbons of large size.

For softer rocks, a square shoulder bit (see Fig 44C) might contain: 8 stones, totaling 12–16 carats, and 4 1-carat stones; in the iron regions, 6 or 7 stones aggregating 14 carats, to 16 stones totaling 18–30 carats. Later, the round shoulder bit was developed (Fig 44A, B), with more and smaller stones, equalizing wear and increasing drilling speed (48). As large carbons are now more costly, the use of smaller sizes, 5–20 per carat, and also of scrap carbon, is increasing. In one type of bit, the number of stones recommended is: EX bit, 50; AX, 60; BX, 80; NX bit, 100. Stones, when set, should project about $1/64$ in beyond the metal of the bit. Soft rocks require larger clearance for good core recovery and to prevent "plugging" or sticking. Cavities cut in the bit are shaped for the individual stones, which are seated with a backing of Babbitt metal or copper, carefully tamped around the stone with hammer and punch. Stones are so set that their cutting surfaces slope away from the direction of rotation. Setting a large number of stones involves so much labor that various mechanically-made bits have been developed. In the "Castset" bit (Fig 44H) the stones are placed in a mould and molten bit-metal is poured around them. In the Kobelite bit (Fig 44D) the stones are set in a metal powder, pressed or sintered into disks or strips, brazed onto the bit (49); 200 or more stones may be set in this recommended bit. In the "S. A. Produits Boart," 30–40 carats of bort are crushed to a powder and mixed with a metal powder, as iron, formed into a ring and sintered, the ring being soldered to face of bit. The abrasive ring is about $3/8$ in thick, and the bit can be used until most of the ring is worn away.

Tests have shown: that drilling effic increases with rotative speed, but diamond wear reaches a max at about 1 000 rpm; that costs for bits change little between 450 and 1 500 rpm, but are considerably higher above and below these limits; that bits with 40 stones give minimum cost at about 740 rpm, and those with 70 stones at 1 000 rpm; that a bit with 100 stones cuts 50% faster, and has 57% greater durability than a 40-stone bit. Thus, most effic drilling is with bits set with many small stones and run at high speed (49).

Diamond wear depends on hardness of rock, cleavage of minerals composing the rock, shape and quality of diamonds, mode of setting and size of bit, and skill and care of runner. Hard, broken and faulted rock is difficult to drill and diamond loss is high. Runner's lack of skill and care increases breakage and loss of diamonds, rather than wear. In starting a new bit, it should begin rotation a few feet above bottom of hole, and then be fed slowly down to contact with the rock, to seat itself properly, without causing side pressure on outer diamonds. Inferior carbons and bort will serve for soft rock and cost less; but if used in hard rock, rotative speed must be slow to avoid undue breakage (53). Drilling in ground varying from soft schist to massive sulphide, with EX and AX bits, containing 120–150 bort stones of about 20 per carat, loss was .02–.10 carat per ft of hole. In South Africa goldfields, in shear zones of fractured rock containing bodies of quartz and intrusive dikes, the size of bort varied from 6 to 15 stones per carat for face of bit; total number, 45–60 per bit; aver loss .048 carat per ft, in drilling 10 000 ft of hole. Table 45 shows loss of diamonds in different rocks, with bits having 10 carbons totalling 15–20 carats, to 60 stones totalling 12 carats. Bort bits usually had 25 stones of 0.25–0.5 carat each, for outter or gage stones, and about 75 stones, of 0.066 to 0.1 carat, for face ("track") stones (50).

At Bunker Hill and Sullivan mine, Idaho, a light Mitchell drill for 1 3/8-in hole and 7/8-in core is used both on surface and underground (52). Aver depth of 35 holes, 195 ft. Ground is tilted quartzite beds, but drills fairly well unless sheared and faulted. Bits contain about 40 stones, totalling 6.4–8.75 carats (Table 46).

Table 45. **Wear on Bits in Various Rocks (50)**

Kind of rock	Loss per ft, carats
Black schist	0.002607
Massive sulphide	.004320
Hard massive sulphide	.010244
Quartz porphyry	.004009
Hard quartz porphyry	.009928
Bedded sediments	.001167
Diorite	.003505
Hard diorite	.014781
Greenstone	.002497
Hard greenstone	.005757
Quartz	.032585

Table 46. Carbon Consumption, Bunker Hill and Sullivan Mine (52)

No of bits	Aver ft per bit	Carats per bit		Total carats	Loss, carats		Percent loss	Carbon cost per ft
		Range	Aver		Total	Per ft		
10	14.6	6 –6.4	6.233	62.33	18.6107	0.1275	29.85	$0.9562
9	15.0	6.61–6.8	6.665	59.99	20.9207	0.155	34.87	1.1625
22	19.45	6.81–7.0	6.904	151.89	34.6724	0.08101	22.83	0.6076
11	21.27	7.21–7.4	7.289	80.18	13.9540	0.05963	17.40	0.4472
14	21.43	7.41–7.6	7.480	104.74	19.4623	0.06487	18.58	0.4865
16	20.69	7.81–8	7.872	125.95	21.102	0.06375	16.75	0.4781

21. RECOVERY OF CORE

Core recovery may reach 100% in hard uniform rocks. It is lowest in loose, soft, cleavable and broken rocks, where, unless the drill is run almost dry, and rods are raised every few inches, recovery may not be more than 10%. Vibration of rods causes low recovery. For good recovery in hard rock the drill should be run with low speed and heavy press; in soft rock, the reverse. Recovery is invariably less in upper than in lower portion of holes, due to decomposed rock near surface.

Table 47.   Core Recoveries (E. J. Longyear Co)

Location	Kind of rock	Core recovered, %
Arizona...............	Monzonite..........	33.5
	Quartz porphyry....	48.4
	Breccia and andesite..............	54.1
Alabama..............	Coal..............	94.8
Michigan..............	Trap, conglomerate and amygdaloid...	66.4
	Sandstone..........	18.8
Menominee Range ⎫ Mich...	Slate..............	36.0
Gogebic Range ⎭	Iron formation......	16.1
Mesabi Range ⎫ Minn...	" "	28.6
Cuyuna Range ⎭	" "	42.9
	" "	19.9
Wisconsin.............	Granite............	83.5
New York.............	Shaly limestone.....	69.1
Kentucky.............	Limestone..........	60.5
Cuba................	Schist.............	23.7
Cuba................	Pyrite.............	80.3

Table 48. Core Recovery at United Verde Mine (50)

Kind of rock	Percent recovery
Black schist.............	85.5
Quartz porphyry.........	88.8
Hard quartz porphyry....	94.0
Diorite.................	87.8
Greenstone.............	79.2
Hard greenstone.........	87.1
Massive sulphide........	93.6
Hard massive sulphide....	95.3
Quartz.................	88.3

Size of hole is determined by the depth to be bored, and purpose of hole. To obtain a core in soft, friable minerals, as coal and salt, the inside diam of bit should not be less than 2 in. For hard rock or ore, a $13/16$-in to $1 1/8$-in core is large enough. If the stratum or orebody to be sampled lies deeply, the hole must be begun larger than this for larger and stronger rods, and to give room for casing without excessive reaming, should casing be necessary. At United Verde mine, Ariz (Table 48), holes were 25–2 200 ft deep: 79% from 5° below horiz to 12° above; 84%, from E to AX size; 14%, AX to N; and 2%, N size or larger (50). In the Lupa goldfield, So Africa, (Table 41), core recovery for 9 762 ft of EX hole, including 50 ft of surface weathered rock, was 92.5%; excluding weathered rock, 95%. In deep holes on the Witwatersrand (7 400–10 718 ft), core recoveries were 92 and 97.3% for $1 1/8$-in core, 96.4% for $2 1/8$-in core.

22. SPEED AND COST OF DIAMOND DRILLING

Speed is affected by: kind of rock and surface covering; depth, direction, and situation of hole; quantity of water in hole; kind of drill, fittings, and accessory outfit; core requirements; labor, climate, and continuity of work; percentage of delays. Rate of advance is higher in uniform rock than in alternating hard and soft strata; low, in shattered and fissured rocks. Hard uniform rocks that core well drill faster than soft rocks which grind up in the core barrel. Caving decreases speed. With proportionate increase in weathered surface covering, there is usually a fairly consistent decrease in speed and increase in delays; bouldery formations also decrease speed. Since many factors affect drilling rate, a complete record of each case is needed fully to interpret results; there is great difference between actual and overall drilling rate.

Table 49. Progress in Diamond Drilling from Surface (E. J. Longyear Co)

No of holes	Depth of holes, ft	Progress per shift, ft While drilling	Overall
6 in limestone............	200–1 000	28.6	17.2
4 " shale.............	1 000	33.1	21.1
6 " iron formation.......	1 200	10.1	7.2
3 " gypsum.............	1 000	22.6	13.3
4 " clay..............	300	23.0	16.1
5 " traprock............	1 200	12.2	9.3
4 " norite.............	1 000	18.4	12.6
2 " serpentine...........	300	21.4	14.3
5 " basalt and granite....	1 000	9.1	6.2
6 " porphyry...........	600–2 000	9.0	6.2

Table 49 includes contracts on which steam drills were used; more modern gasolene, air or elec drills give higher speeds; 40–70 ft per 8-hr shift underground is not uncommon. Gasolene surface drills, with their high rotative speed and freedom from delays, make old drilling rates practically obsolete.

Table 50. Typical Diamond Drill Costs per Ft

Material	Clay	Gypsum	Limestone	Limestone	Limestone	Limestone	Shale	Norite (nickel)	Porphyry (copper)	Porphyry	Iron formation
Core diam, in	3	2	7/8	7/8	7/8	7/8	1 1/8	1 1/8	7/8	1 1/8	1 1/8
Aver depth, ft	250	225	....	....	....	....	....	1 450	1 000	....	....
Total footage	54 000	4 300	4 800	3 000	11 000	95 000	2 895	....	....	7 200	2 200
Labor	$0.45	$0.72	$0.86	$0.64	$0.40	$0.30	$0.82	$0.90	$0.97	$1.64	$1.30
Supplies	0.22	0.37	0.24	0.15	0.14	0.03	0.24	0.04	0.18	0.38	0.50
Power	0.08	0.00	0.05	0.04	0.03	0.06	0.07	0.22	0.02	0.00	0.10
Freight, etc	0.08	0.07	0.10	0.36	0.02	0.06	0.21	0.00	0.00	0.16	0.08
Miscellaneous	0.18	0.20	0.13	0.06	0.01	0.04	0.10	0.25	0.17	0.12	0.13
Insurance	0.07	0.03	0.18	0.01	0.01	0.00	0.01	0.00	0.05	0.11	0.18
Diamonds	0.03	0.20	0.16	0.05	0.18	0.17	0.10	0.12	0.40	1.07	0.60
Total	$1.11	$1.59	$1.72	$1.31	$0.79	$0.66	$1.55	$1.53	$1.79	$3.48	$2.89

Material	Limestone (silver)	Limestone (silver)	Sediments (gold)	Shale	Schist	Schist (gold)	Gold, Alaska	Shale	Gypsum	Gypsum	Asbestos
Core diam, in	7/8	7/8	7/8	1 1/8	7/8	7/8	....	2	2	3	1 1/8
Aver depth, ft	700	....	800	2 300	....	....	....	....	625	1 100	....
Total footage	80 000	45 100	28 000	2 300	2 000	....	3 050	2 950	4 350	....	6 550
Labor	$0.16	$0.22	$0.54	$0.64	$0.70	$0.75	$0.80	$0.71	$0.57	$1.28	$0.98
Supplies	0.04	0.06	0.13	0.16	0.17	0.12	0.08	0.13	0.39	0.48	0.18
Power	0.02	0.06	0.08	0.04	0.03	0.06	0.21	....	0.05	....	....
Freight, etc	0.00	0.00	0.00	0.36	0.11	0.02	0.00	0.39	0.13	0.15	0.22
Miscellaneous	0.06	0.05	0.00	0.03	0.08	0.10	0.01	0.04	0.07	0.03	0.03
Insurance	0.00	0.00	0.03	0.01	0.08	0.06	0.00	0.03	0.03	0.07	0.03
Diamonds	0.14	0.11	0.26	0.05	0.48	0.19	0.64	0.06	0.33	0.47	0.39
Total	$0.42	$0.50	$1.04	$1.29	$1.65	$1.30	$1.74	$1.36	$1.57	$2.48	$1.83

Between the horiz and vert, the inclination of the hole has little effect on speed. In the same formation, holes pointing upward drill slower than those pointing downward, because of the awkwardness of arrangements at mouth of hole. Occurrence of much water in such a hole adds to inconvenience in drilling, and tends to retard progress.

Whether the drill is working underground or on surface makes no appreciable difference in speed, once the drill is set up. Moving is usually more difficult underground, but the moves are likely to be shorter and several holes are often drilled from one setup. Holes drilled from scows into subaqueous strata always advance more slowly than those in similar formations where the drill can be set up firmly. Rate of advance per drilling hr increases with size of drill. But, rate per working hr may be greater with a light than a heavy drill, when holes are shallow and moves frequent.

In rock which cores well, the longer the core barrel used the faster the advance. In soft friable rocks, if high core recovery is essential, use of double core barrel will increase speed. Taking cores 2 in and smaller, size of core has no appreciable effect on speed, provided drill is not working beyond its rated capacity. Larger holes will drill more slowly. Holes drilled with a solid bit advance faster than those with an annular bit, unless the hole is of large diam. Best quality of carbons, well set, gives fastest progress.

Holes drilled by contract usually show higher speeds than those on company account, unless great difficulties are met and contractor can not finance added expense. Bonus system is sometimes successful. The danger in contract and bonus systems is that unless a minimum percentage of core recovery is stipulated increased speed may be gained at expense of core recovery. Unfavorable climate, cold or tropical, retards drilling. Drilling 24 hr per day usually gives a greater speed per working hr than one-shift work. In the latter, time is wasted in starting up, and usually also at end of shift, due to fact that it is unsafe to leave the drill with the rods in the ground (see also, Prospecting, Sec 10).

Drilling at Phelps Dodge United Verde Mine. Most diamond drilling is "short-hole" work, 100–500 ft deep, for delimiting known ore areas, prospecting stope walls, determining structure or geological formation, and to aid locating development headings. Occasional long holes, 1 000–2 200 ft, are drilled for prospecting outlying ore areas. Ground drilled varies from soft chlorite schist and metamorphosed quartz porphyry to hard rhyolite-porphyry, diorite and massive pyrite carrying quartz and jasper; highest speeds are in massive sulphide ores. A Boyle BBU drill is used for short holes, with E bits; Longyear UG drill, in harder ground, for depths of 200–1 000 ft; Sullivan C hydraulic drill, for deeper holes. The ES $9/16$-in bit is used where depth requires surveying, and 1 $7/8$-in bit for holes that may require grouting or casing. A Wright bore-hole surveying instrument is used for holes over 500 ft deep, to check deviation in bearing and inclination. Core boxes with corrugated removable metal trays carry core to the diamond drill shop. Representative sections of core from holes of particular interest are kept as a permanent record; otherwise, the entire core is sent to assay office; part of the pulp is saved for future analysis.

Max footage at United Verde (1930) was 33 376 ft, by 5 to 6 drill crews, 1 foreman and 2 bit setters. Present work is done by 1 crew, with foreman who sets bits and supervises other work. In holes averaging 250 ft, footage is 40 ft per shift in aver schist or porphyry, and 25 ft in hard sulphide. For 1 500-ft holes, with setups permitting 20-ft changes of rods, footage is 10 ft per shift. Bort is generally used in all kinds of ground; carbons sometimes for outer ("gage") stones in broken quartz or siliceous sulphide. Bort loss, 0.02–0.1 carat per ft. Cutting edges of bits are rounded and set with bort averaging 20 stones per carat. The E bit (1 $7/16$ in) averages 120 stones and requires 7 hr for setting; the ES (1 $9/16$ in) bit usually has 100 stones, 6 hr for setting; the A (1 $7/8$ in) bit takes 150 stones and 9 hr aver for setting. Recovery of stones from used bits, aver 50%. Costs in Table 51 are direct only, not including cost of cutting stations or overhead. Wages: runner $6.95, helper $5.67 per shift. About 60% of foreman's time was charged to drilling.

Table 51. Cost of Drilling 6 922 Ft of Hole in 1937, United Verde Mine

Labor......................	$0.82
Carbon....................	0.31
Supplies..................	0.02
Compressed air and water.....	0.02
Miscellaneous..............	0.02
Total....................	$1.19
Number of holes...........	58
Aver depth, ft.............	119
Max depth, ft.............	507
Ground classification:	
Hard siliceous sulphide.......	6.3%
Aver sulphide..............	31.9
Schist....................	27.5
Porphyry and diorite........	34.3

NOTE.—Total carbon loss for above holes, .031 carat per ft; max in any month, .098 carat.

Drilling in Lupa Goldfield, Tanganyika, Africa. About 10 000 ft of hole were bored in 1 year. As water was unfit for boilers, Longyear UG-A screw-feed drill with Ford motor was used; rated capac, 1 100 ft of EX hole. Water pumped, 3 000 gal per hr. Total equipment cost, including rods, casing, bits, core barrels and fishing tools, was about $12 500, fob North Bay, Canada. Wages: bit setter, $275 per month, and drill runner, $200, both plus expenses; native helpers, $2.50–$4.50 per month, plus food; 2 8-hr shifts, 6 days per week, with 1 driller and 3 helpers. In 1 year (1934–35), 17 angle holes totaling 10 192 ft were bored by contract, on a cost-plus-15% basis, the company furnishing equipment. Rocks drilled: weathered, 4.4%; diorite, 55.2%; sheared rocks, 30.5%; aplite and diabase dikes, 7.1%; granite, 1.9%; quartz veins, 0.9%. For core recovery, see Art 20. Holes were 120–1 325 ft deep. Drilling was delayed considerably by core-blocked bits and barrels, due to: fractured rock, small angle of intersection of holes with joint or bedding planes, fragments of rock falling to bottom of hole, and crooked core barrel. Bits had 12–16 bort outside, and 10–14 inside, 6–8 stones per carat; face of bit, 22–30 stones, 10–15 per carat. Reaming shells had 3 rows of 12 stones each, increasing slightly in clearance in each row, and averaging 3 or 4 per carat. EX bits averaged 54.8 ft of hole per bit; AX casing bits, 6.6 ft; AX steel-set casing bits (hard cutting teeth), 6.3 ft; EX reaming shells, 600 ft per shell. Aver diamond loss, 0.048 carat per ft, cost $0.335. Holes surveyed by hydrofluoric acid method (Art 24) every 50 ft; aver deflection in 600-ft holes, 1° per 100 ft. Costs, including wages and living expense of drillers, diamond loss, gasolene, oil, native wages and food, general supplies, and office expenses, were $1.837 per ft; to which add $1.938 to cover 50% of plant, traveling expense of crew from Canada and return, transport of machinery, insurance, housing, machine shop and a 15% local operating fee; total cost per ft, $3.775 (51).

Drilling at Noranda Mines, Canada. E rods are used for holes to 1 000 ft, with space for 5-ft pulls to 200 ft, 10-ft up 600 ft, and 20-ft pulls for greater depths. Drill is a Longyear UG; rods, 5 and 10 ft long; reamer, 2.5 in long, outside diam $5/16$ in; double-tube core barrels, 5, 7 and 10 ft long; diam of core, $15/16$ in; core recovery, 97%. As drilling was not on contract, more stress was laid on core recovery than speed. Four machines drilling in massive sulphide, rhyolite and diabase during 1937, averaged 21 ft per 8-hr shift, including time for moving and setting up; aver depth of holes, 250 ft; max speed, 60 ft in an 8-hr shift. Wages: runners, 73¢ per hr; helpers, 56¢. Estimated cost per ft during one year: material (mostly parts), 18¢; labor, including setting bits, 80¢; bort and carbons,

23¢; overhead, including compressed air, 31¢; total, $1.52. Bits set with bort, 12–15 stones per carat; reamers, with carbons of 0.25–0.5 carat each. For special work a Long-year Prospector Drill was used, with 5-ft rods, 1 1/16 in outside diam; reamers, 1 1/8 in long, outside diam, 15/64 in; bit 7/8 in long, 5/8-in inside diam; core barrel, 5 ft; diam of core, 5/8-in; core recovery, 97%. Drilling speeds for 4 000 ft averaged 25 ft per 8-hr shift; max footage, 40 ft. Costs not available.

Witwatersrand, So Africa. Table 52 gives details of the deepest holes yet bored by diamond drill (contract costs from Sullivan Mach'y Co, So Af). In other deep holes, in the Far East Rand Areas, the formations comprised about 700 ft of dolerite, sandstones and shales, followed by dolomite, amygdaloidal diabase, quartzites, volcanic breccia and hard slates, each sometimes of great thickness but flat dip. Sullivan N and P drills were used, with 60-ft derricks; 3 8-hr shifts, 6 days a week. Holes were started vertically with 3-in bits; casing, 2 7/16 inside diam; then 2.25-in to 2 000–3 000 ft and 1 7/8 in to 5 000 ft. Speeds varied greatly: in dolerite, max for 24 hr, 149–186 ft; max for 1 month, in dolerite, quartzite, shale and breccia, 1 295–1 357 ft; for 1 year, with 4 machines, 4 925 ft, 1.5-in holes (54).

Table 52. Costs of 3 Deep Diamond Drill Holes, Witwatersrand, So Africa
(J. A. Woodburn)

	Nigel Reef	Doornkop No 46	Gerhard-minne-bron		Nigel Reef	Doornkop No 46	Gerhard-minne-bron
Type of drill..........	(a)	(a)	(b)	Setting up equipment....	$ 0.35	$ 0.50	$ 0.31
Geologic section, ft (c):				Fuel..................	1.25	1.83	1.25
Dolomite............	300	....	4 188	Transport..............	0.54	0.50	0.31
Quartzite............	....	5 600	5 712	Water supply...........	0.44	0.48	0.42
Diabase.............	900	....	....	Labor.................	4.81	5.31	4.95
Witwatersrand series..	6 208	2 170	818	Carbon and bort........	1.87	2.21	1.73
Total depth, ft.....	7 408	7 770	10 718	Bits, core-barrels, shells ..	0.88	0.83	0.60
				Oils and supplies........	0.38	0.58	0.31
Time analysis, days:				Repairs, general.........	0.48	1.96	0.21
Setting up..........	17	29	41	Renewals...............	0.46	0.44	0.17
Cementing..........	23	67	14	Machine shop...........	0.17	0.10	0.17
Surveying..........	7	10	20	Casing.................	0.60	1.27	0.46
Deflecting hole......	22	41	......	Travelling..............	0.21	0.17	0.21
Breakdowns.........	21	17	5	Supervision.............	0.73	0.58	0.73
Fishing jobs........	90	63	6	Housing................	0.31	0.33	0.31
Sundays, holidays....	65	96	113	Overhead...............	0.31	0.44	0.31
				Insurance..............	0.17	0.21	0.17
Total non-drilling...	245	323	199	Depreciation...........	1.35	1.21	1.42
Actual drilling.....	235	250	482				
Elapsed time.....	480	573	681	Total cost per ft (e)..	$15.31	$18.95	$14.04
Aver ft per day (d).....	31.5	31	22				
Core recovery, %.......	92	96.4	97.3				
Diam of hole, in........	2 1/16	2 15/16	2 1/16				
Diam of core, in........	1 3/8	2 1/8	1 3/8				

(a) Sullivan P-2.   (b) Sullivan No 50.   (c) In descending order from surface.   (d) Of actual drilling time.   (e) Converted from British to U S currency at 1 sh = 25¢.

Bunker Hill and Sullivan mine, Idaho. A light Mitchell drill makes a 1 3/8-in hole, 7/8-in core; bits of about 40 stones, totaling 6.4–8.75 carats; cost, $7.50 per carat, plus $7.90 for setting; shells, $7.50 per carat, plus $4 for setting; salvage stones bring $7.50 per carat, scrap stones 80¢ per carat. Table 53 shows costs in ground of aver hardness (A), and in fault zone (B); also for 4 088 ft of one hole (52).

Table 53. Cost as Effected by Kind of Rock, Bunker Hill and Sullivan Mine

Rock	Footage	Labor	Bits	Shells	Comp air	Oil and misc	Total cost	Per ft
A	227	$96.00	$89.28	$5.39	$24.33	$13.44	$228.44	$1.0064
B	24	37.50	129.65	2.77	8.28	2.75	180.95	7.5395
Cost per ft for 4 088 ft }		$0.464	0.925	0.095	0.096	0.090	....	$1.670

U S Bureau of Reclamation. Diamond drilling for possible dam sites, Texas, with Longyear, Sullivan, and Knight and Stone machines. In easy limestone, 4 700 ft were bored at aver of 21 ft per 8 hr; aver depth, 150 ft. Time includes water testing every 10 ft, and driving casing through as much as 50 ft of overburden, and moving from hole to hole. For holes 40–100 ft deep, in fractured gneiss, core recovery was 65–100%, cost over $3 per ft. Nine holes, in limestone, aver 100–150 ft deep cost about $1 per ft; others, up to $1.87 per ft. At Marshall Ford dam, a Sullivan air drill bored 27 000 ft, at a cost (to contractor) of $0.35 per ft; other shallow holes, $0.68 per ft. At Grand Coulee dam, diamond drilling was contracted at $2.95 per ft for 84 vert holes, and $3.50 for 15 angle holes, all in hard granite.

Climax Molybdenum Co (1937–38) drilled 12 467 ft of 1.5 to 2 3/8-in exploratory holes (Table 54) in granite and schist; range of depth, 200–1 540 ft, aver 600; aver speed, 14.81 ft per 8-hr; core recovery 50%.

Table 54. Cost of Diamond Drilling, Climax Molybdenum Co

	Cost per ft		Cost per ft
Preparing station..	$0.222	Power........	$0.087
Drilling..........	2.732	Surveying....	0.004
Reaming........	0.057	Assaying.....	0.085
Cementing........	0.216	Core storage..	0.032
Casing...........	0.021		
Carbon loss......	0.042	Total......	$3.498

Salt beds of western Texas and New Mex. Diamond drilling was done by contract (1927–29) to depths of 1 000–2 750 ft, to test potash content of beds; cores, 2.5-in. As KCl is soluble, a saturated solution of common salt plus MgCl was used instead of water. Total footage, 20 400 ft; core recovery, 98%.

Kennecott Copper Corp, Alaska, has done much exploratory diamond drilling by contract, mostly in dolomite, all underground work. Nearly all holes are at angles of 5–10° to horiz. For 60 800 ft of 1.5-in hole (7/8-in core), aver cost from 1920 to 1931 was $2.15 per ft. Later costs (1937) are about the same.

Sullivan mine, Kimberley, B C. Underground diamond drilling by contract in chert, quartzite and massive sulphide ore (pyrrhotite, galena and sphalerite). Cores, 3/4 in for holes less than 200 ft. Costs, $2–$2.12 per ft.

Homestake mine, So Dak. The orebody, a steep-dipping replacement in schists, slates and quartzites, is best prospected by horiz holes across the strike. All drilling is now done underground; parallel holes, 100 ft apart, and 50–450 ft deep (Table 55).

Table 55. Underground Diamond-drilling Costs, Homestake Mine, S D

Year	No of holes (a)	Total footage	Aver per 8-hr (b)	Aver depth, ft	Core recovery, %	Labor (c)	Carbon loss	Bort loss	Repair parts (d)	Shop	Misc (e)	Power (f)	Total
1932	85	9 334	15.8	110	79	$.80	$.41	(h)	$.04	$.07	$.08	$.03	$1.43
1933	96	10 004	......	104	......	.92	.14	$.17	.05	.04	.04	.02	1.38
1934	84(g)	9 703	......	115	......	1.00	.20	.11	.03	.03	.05	.02	1.44
1935	113	12 004	......	106	......	.96	.29	.06	.06	.03	.03	.02	1.45
1936	84	10 215	......	121	......	1.13	.31	.09	.08	.03	.06	.02	1.72
1937	134	19 417	16.4	145	......	.89	.26	.12	.17	.03	.02	.02	1.51
1938, 4 mos	75	10 417	20.0	138	91	.72	.09	.11(i)	.02	.04	.02	.02	1.02

(a) Nearly all horiz holes, from 7 by 7-ft drifts; (b) including all delays for moving; (c) includes bonus; (d) includes charging off new equipment; (e) oil and supplies; (f) compressed air; (g) includes an inclined hole from surface, 1 018 ft deep; (h) carbon bits only; (i) cast bort bits, except in broken ground.

El Potosí mine, Mex. In 1934, 58 726 ft of holes were drilled with electric machines, which saved 8¢ per ft over air-driven drills. Table 56 gives costs.

Matanuska coal basin, Alaska. Core drilling in sandstone, and clayey shale that clogged bits and required frequent pulling of rods. Speeds: shale, 2.5–6 ft per hr; sandstone, 10 ft; aver, including pulling of rods, 1.3 ft per hr; 8 holes, 676–1 820 ft; contract price, $4.25, plus $3 per ft of core recovered (58).

Star mine, Rhodesia. Zinc silicate orebody, in limestone and schists (60). Drilling bad in schist; good in limestone; 10 700 ft of hole; aver depth, 275 ft; aver per shift, 11.76 ft; core recovered, 74%. Table 57 gives costs.

Table 56. El Potosí Mining Co, Mex (H. A. Walker)

	Cost per ft (1938)	Cost per ft (1934)
Labor.............	$0.2187	$0.1658
Carbon and bort....	0.1140	0.1417 (c)
Power, air and elec..	0.0643	0.0224
New rods...........	0.0125	0.0087
Misc..............	0.0490	0.0570
Supplies...........	0.0479	0.0264
	$0.5064	$0.4220
Total footage.......	45 129 (a)	80 128 (b)

(a) Includes 9 275 ft elec drilling; (b) 58 726 ft elec drilling; (c) lost bit increased cost 7.4¢ per ft.

Phelps Dodge Corp, Morenci branch, Ariz (Apl, 1938). Data on 11 holes of 750 ft aver depth: total aver working hr, 574; contract price, $3.50–$3.69; total aver cost, including eng'g, sampling and general expense, $6.03. Casing, 25% of all holes. Drilling was in shattered ground, largely monzonite granite.

Purchase vs rental of prospecting drills is a question usually decided by local conditions. If only a few holes are necessary, renting or contract work often preferable; for a large amount of drilling, purchase of equipment may be cheaper (57).

Table 57. Diamond Drilling Costs at Star Mine, Rhodesia (60)

Direst costs, per ft	
Setters, runners and helpers	$1.135
Carbon loss	0.352
Materials	0.248
Power	0.223
Moving drills	0.005
	$1.963
Indirect costs: general expense, surveying, amortization, etc	2.284
Total	$4.247

23. SHOT-BORING WITH CALYX DRILL; SHAFT BORING

Construction. Like the diamond drill, the bit is rotated by hollow rods, driven by an engine and gearing on the surface. Chilled-steel shot, $1/16$ and under, to $1/8$-in, are the abrasive medium. Fig 49 shows bit for small holes. The shot, fed into the rods with the wash water, pass to the inner periphery of core barrel and bit; thence under the bit, some being crushed, others remaining unbroken and are rolled around under its edge. Diagonal slots in the bit allow passage of wash water to the annular space outside, without displacing and lifting the shot. The sludge collects in a hollow cylinder ("calyx"), above the core barrel and open at the top. As the rods are of smaller diam than the calyx, the veloc of the rising water is decreased, permitting deposition of the coarser sludge in the calyx (Fig 50); to carry this material to the surface would require a large quantity of water under high press. In large machines, the wt of rods gives sufficient press on the bit; in smaller sizes, added press is applied by a rack feed and hand wheel. Speed of rotation, 50–100 rpm. Instead of using a mechanical core lifter, as in the diamond drill, the drill core is gripped by wedging it in the barrel with angular pieces of quartz, dropped through the rotating rods. Inclined holes can not be more than about 35° off the vert, as the shot tends to run to lower side of bit. A complete Calyx-drill outfit, delivered in the West, costs $8 000–$10 000.

The Calyx drill can bore holes from a few inches diam to 6 ft or more. An important application is the boring of mine ventilating shafts and chutes for ore and waste (for the latter, see Sec 10, Art 23). A bored shaft will often stand without support, where shattering of walls by explosives in usual shaft-sinking methods would require timbering;

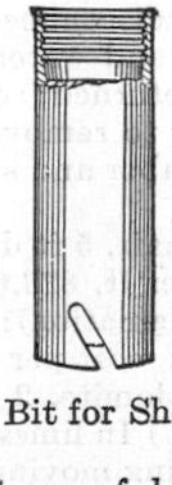

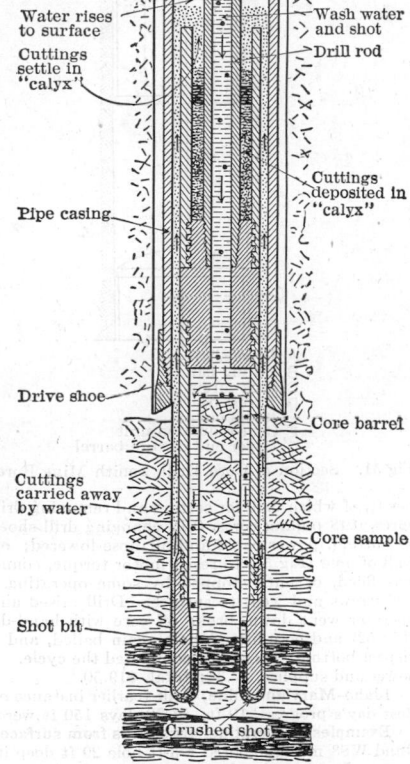

Water rises to surface — Wash water and shot
Cuttings settle in "calyx" — Drill rod
Pipe casing
Cuttings deposited in "calyx"
Drive shoe — Core barrel
Cuttings carried away by water — Core sample
Shot bit
Crushed shot

Fig 49. Bit for Shot Boring

Fig 50. Calyx Drill

hence the advantage of boring a ventilating shaft, leaving smooth walls, without fire hazard. Early methods for holes of large diam involved actuating the drill from surface;

but a recent drill designed by Newsom (64, 81) has driving mechanism and operator in a cage just above core barrel at bottom of hole (Fig 51).

Zenith mine, Minn (65, 81). Vert ventilating shaft, 5.5 ft diam, through 15 ft of alluvium by hand, 1 193 ft bored in rock; total depth, 1 208 ft; elapsed time, 7 mos. Formations: greenstone, some quartzites, chert and diorite. Surface plant: stiff-leg derrick, 60-ft boom, working load 30 ton, impact load 95 ton; main hoist, 200 hp, normal line pull 13 200 lb, rope speed 450 ft per min; man hoist, 25 hp; power-cable reel with 25-hp motor; air-hose reel with 11-hp motor; air compressor at 40 cu ft per min for ventilation. Drill (Fig 51): 100-hp motor; speed of core barrel, 52 rpm; wt on cutting shoe, about 6 ton; length inside core barrel with new shoe, 15 ft 2 in. Core puller, inside length 8 ft; bailer; man cage (for 2 men); muck bucket. Aver drilling rate, 5.8 ft per day; best week, 77 ft; aver per drilling cycle, 8.46 ft. Shot consumption for 714 ft of hole, 32 lb per ft. Total man-hr, 15 320; direct crew man-hr, 11 044; crew-hr, 4 933 total, 4.13 aver

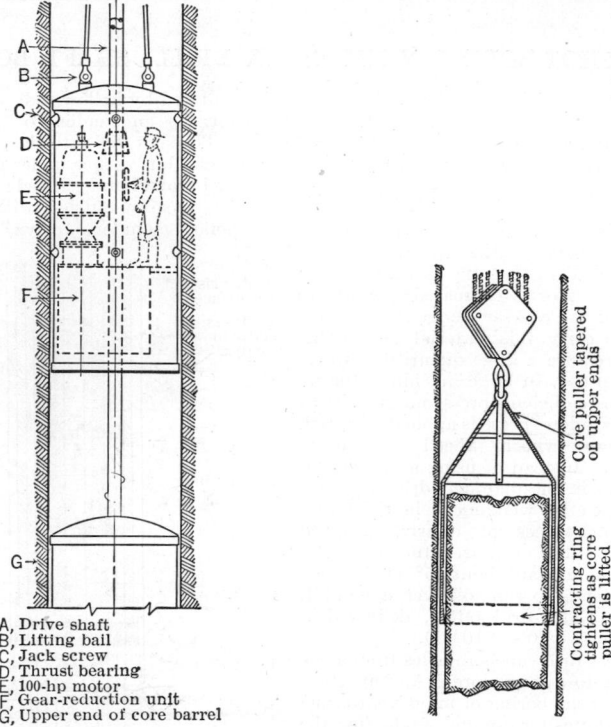

A, Drive shaft
B, Lifting bail
C, Jack screw
D, Thrust bearing
E, 100-hp motor
F, Gear-reduction unit
G, Upper end of core barrel

Core puller tapered on upper ends

Contracting ring tightens as core puller is lifted

Fig 51. Section of Core Drill, Zenith Mine Borehole   Fig 52. Core Lifter, Zenith Mine Borehole

per ft, of which 0.39 for setting and removing drill, 0.96 drilling, 1.05 bailing, 0.53 mucking broken cores, 0.48 pulling cores, 0.12 changing drill shoes, 0.60 lost time. Operating cycle: drill lowered to bottom, power cable and air hose lowered; operator went down, tightened jackscrews against wall of hole (Fig 51) to resist motor torque, connected cable and hose, and drilled until core barrel was filled, or until stopped by some operating condition; he then disconnected cable, released jackscrews and went to surface. Drill raised and inspected; sludge and water bailed from hole; operator went down, broke off core with hand-driven wedges, and returned; core puller lowered (Fig 52) and core lifted; hole again bailed, and operator went down to remove broken rock and inspect bottom; his return completed the cycle. Direct cost per ft: labor and supervision, $12.16; power and supplies, $7.34; total, $19.50.

Idaho-Maryland mine, Calif (earlier instance of same method). Shaft, 5 ft diam, 1 125 ft deep. Best day's progress, 10 ft; in 30 days 150 ft were bored; aver cost per ft, $23.67.

Examples of operating large drills from surface (U S Bureau of Reclamation): (*A*) An Ingersoll-Rand WS3 machine bored a 3-ft hole 29 ft deep in gneiss, in 27 shifts; cost per ft, $24.19. Badly fractured rock and a flow of water made drilling difficult. (*B*) In dolomite, 2 holes 46 and 56 ft deep were drilled by same machine in 36 shifts; cost per ft, $23.60. (*C*) In limestone, an Ingersoll-Rand W-3 machine drilled 993 ft of hole (2 of them 92 ft deep), including moving, laying pipe lines and setting up, at aver of over 3 ft per shift; cost per ft, $12.56. Of this total, 211 ft cost $8.12 per ft. (*D*) Grand Coulee Dam: 8 holes, 3-ft core, 386 ft aggregate depth, were bored at an aver speed of 0.33 ft per hr actual drilling time; cost per ft, $31.40; shot used, 9 130 lb. (*E*) Kennett Dam: 2 36-in holes, total depth 187 ft, cost $26.63 per ft; shot used, 4 650 lb.

24. DEVIATION AND SURVEYING OF BOREHOLES

Deviation or drift. Few diamond or rotary drill holes exceeding 100 ft deep are straight; deviation is least in cable-tool holes. In general, deviation increases with depth; also, holes bored at only a slight angle to dip of strata tend to parallel the bedding planes. Surveys to 3 000 ft of 8 deep holes on the Rand showed that: at 1 000 ft, all holes were nearly plumb; at 3 000 ft, 2 were over 25° off plumb (54). At the Britannia mine, B C, horiz holes drilled toward an underlay footwall curved downward, those toward the hanging wall curved upward; holes drilled obliquely to hanging wall curved downward; thus, holes tend to become normal to dip and strike (Fig 53). Holes have been started as much as 25° off true direction in order to reach given objectives (67). Deflection generally seems to vary inversely as length of core barrel (68); worn or short core barrels, or light rods, or excessive press on bit, aggravates tendency to deflect. Drift of oil wells has caused so much trouble that holes are regularly surveyed to keep deflection under control, and successful directional drilling depends on accurate survey methods to determine both drift angle (deviation from vertical) and bearing. Methods and instruments commonly used for oil-well surveys may be classified as follows:

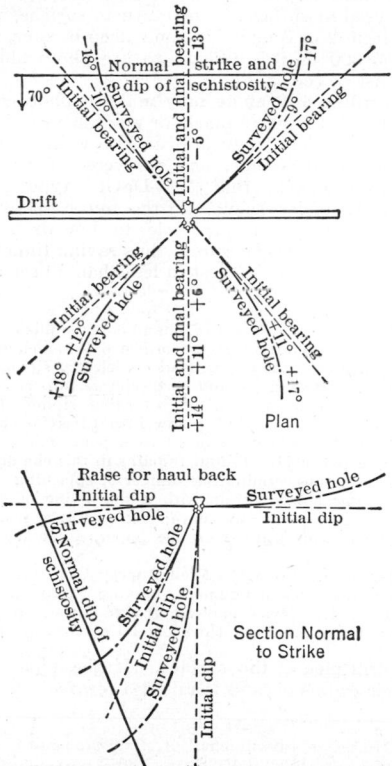

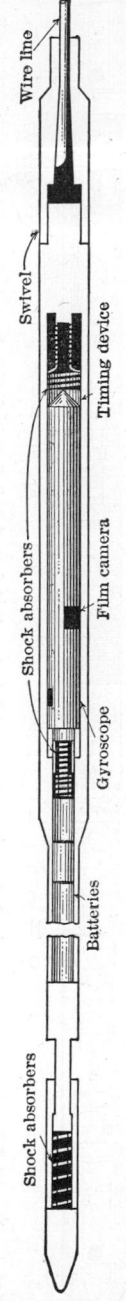

Fig 53. Deflection of Horizontal Diamond-drill Holes in Shear Zone
(*E & M Jour*)

Fig 54. Surwel Gyroscopic Clinograph

Surwel Gyroscopic Clinograph (Fig 54) is used in either an open hole or casing. Readings of drift angle and bearing are taken at any desired interval, going down or coming up, thus giving check readings. The instrument, electrically operated, maintains a fixed bearing, set beforehand, as desired; it carries a non-magnetic watch, compass dial and thermometer. An elec film camera, operated at will, with double lenses and timing contact, records time in seconds, temp, and inclination from the vert; capac, 50 ft of 16-mm film, 1 000 records. Instrument weighs 45 lb, its protective steel case, 1 300 lb. It is lowered on a $9/16$-in wire line, or on the drill rods. The error of closure between two check surveys, in and out, should not exceed 1% of well depth. Time for a round trip in a 9 500-ft well is about 3.5 hr on wire line, or 7.5 hr on drill rods.

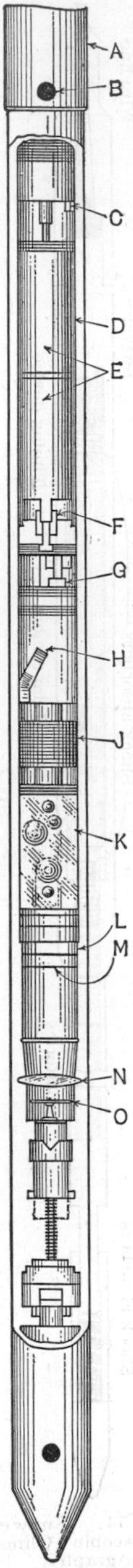

Photo-magnetic instruments record on sensitized paper disks the drift angle (indicated by a delicate plumb bob), and the compass bearing. They do not give reliable compass readings inside casing, but, if lowered 8–10 ft beyond casing, are practically free from magnetic interference. There are 2 forms: MULTISHOT INSTRUMENT (Fig 55) has recording film for a number of observations; SINGLE-SHOT INSTRUMENT makes one record only (Fig 56), disk a reading to 5° within 5 min, disk b reading to 24° drift, within 20 min. Position of plumb bob image, the x mark on concentric circles, shows drift angle. Bearing is read by drawing a straight line from center of disk through x, or intersection of plumb bob cross hairs, to rim of disk on which bearings are printed. Disks are available for drift angles up to 70°, but accuracy decreases somewhat as drift angle increases. A single-shot instrument is loaded in daylight from a clip of sensitized disks. Time of lowering is set beforehand on the instrument watch, which closes an elec contact when taking record, a synchronized watch being used at surface. On return to surface, the developed disk is available within 2 or 3 min. In some deep borings, where bottom temp may reach 250–300° F, it is difficult to use photo films. At about 240° the camera must be cooled.

Instruments recording drift angle only make a photo record, or mechanical record in form of a punch mark, or graphic record in form of a curved stain on a paper scale. They are run into well like the preceding, or dropped through the drill pipe, and recovered by raising the pipe. When dropped into the well, this "Go-Devil" type has protective spring guides on outside of its casing. TOTCO DRIFT RECORDER makes a punch mark on a disk with concentric circles to show drift angle. It can be raised from the well at 3 000 ft per min, thus saving time in deep holes. The recording mechanism comes to rest in less than 10 sec after reaching its position in the well.

Syfo Clinograph (Fig 57). The orifice chamber 4 is filled with a definite amount of fluid, which passes slowly through orifice 6 into delivery chamber 7, filling this chamber slowly until the upper bend of delivery siphon 8 is reached. The siphon action causes part of the liquid to discharge into recording chamber 12, and to rise quickly into upper bend of recording siphon 13, discharging thence into receiving chamber 16. The inflow into 12 is faster than the discharge, causing liquid to rise above bend in 13 to a point midway between top and bottom of recording paper 11. Liquid remains in this chamber less than 30 sec, and then drains out, thus eliminating danger of splashing the chart when raising instrument. Liquid leaves a stain with a sharp line of demarcation on recording paper, in form of a sinuous curve; vert distance from high to low point, as measured by the scale printed on the paper, gives angle of deviation from the vert.

Oriented core barrel (Eastman Oil Well Survey Co) takes a core, while simultaneously, with a single-shot instrument, making a photographic record of drift angle and bearing. The device makes a groove in the core, in line with a marker which shows in the photograph, thus correlating core with survey data.

Orientation of drill pipe at the surface. If the pipe is allowed to turn freely while being lowered, and is raised a few feet on touching bot-

---

Fig 55. Eastman Multishot Instrument. *A*, Drill-pipe sub. *B*, Orientation hole. *C*, Locking pins. *D*, Inner barrel. *E*, Batteries. *F*, Shock absorber. *G*, Start and stop switch. *H*, Contact-actuating clock. *J*, Electric motor. *K*, Film box. *L*, Lighting unit. *M*, Camera. *N*, Condensing lens. *O*, Compass on gimbals

tom and then lowered again, the orientation at the bottom is fairly close to the measured orientation at the surface (69). Rotation at surface is measured by sighting a distant point, and then measuring the turn of each section of pipe as lowered. In one hole having a drift angle of about 24° (at which friction of drill pipe in hole would have great effect) the survey at a depth of about 4 050 ft gave a bearing of N 36° 15′ W, as against a magnetic bearing N 35° 45′ W. Although this method is quite satisfactory, the magnetic method is usually preferred (70).

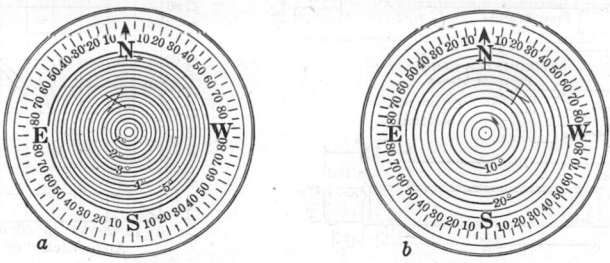

Fig 56.   Photo Records (Lane Wells Co)

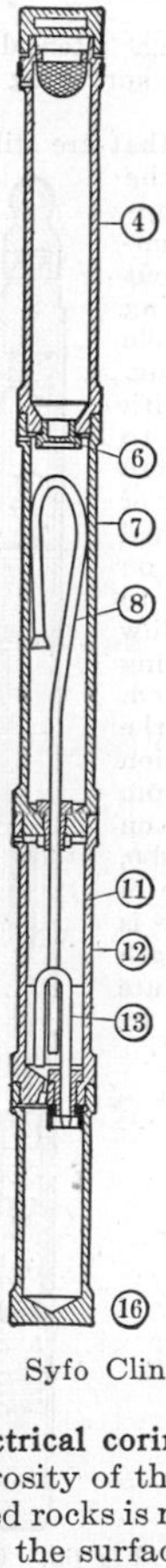

Fig. 57. Syfo Clinograph 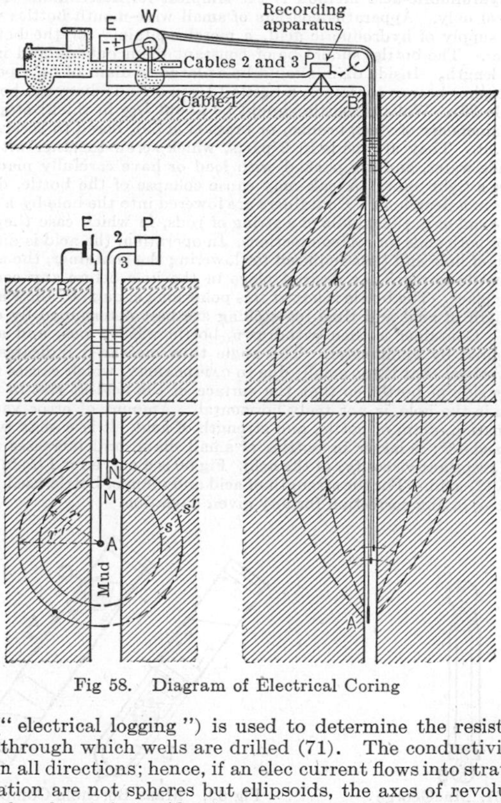   Fig 58.   Diagram of Electrical Coring

Electrical coring (Fig 58) (" electrical logging ") is used to determine the resistivity and porosity of the formations through which wells are drilled (71). The conductivity of stratified rocks is not the same in all directions; hence, if an elec current flows into stratified ground, the surfaces of propagation are not spheres but ellipsoids, the axes of revolution of which are perpendicular to the plane of stratification, whence the direction of dip of the formations can be determined. The principles of electrical and magnetic geophysical prospecting have also been applied with some success to the survey of boreholes (for details, see Bib 71, 72 and Sec 10A).

Borehole surveying is largely done by surveying concerns on basis of rental charges for equipment or service fees. Among them are: E. J. Longyear Co, Eastman Oil Well Survey Co, and Lane-

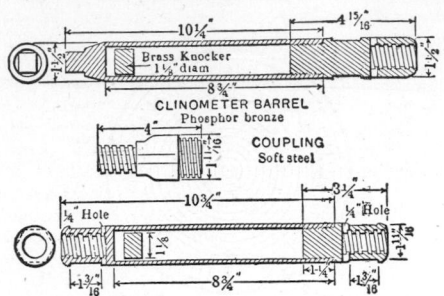

Fig 59.   Two Types of Hydrofluoric-acid-bottle
Container

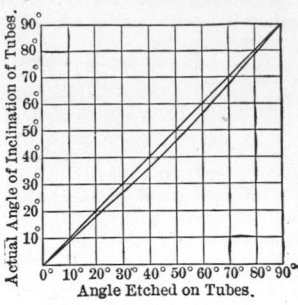

Fig 60.   Curve of Capillarity
Correction

Wells Co; some of them combine surveying with controlled directional drilling. Rental charges range from $4.50 or $5 per day to $150 per year, with a certain minimum fee; surveying charges, $16–$20 per hr of actual work, plus a standby charge and transport costs.

Following are descriptions of several older methods of borehole surveying that are still useful.

Hydrofluoric-acid method is the simplest for determining deviation from the vertical only. Apparatus consists of small wide-mouth bottles with rubber stoppers, supply of hydrofluoric acid, a metal container for the bottles, and a goniometer. The bottles should be of constant diam outside and inside, throughout their length. Inside diam should be as large as diam of hole permits. By using a phosphor-bronze container, a bottle $1\frac{1}{8}$ in outside diam can be used in an E hole (Table 32). Walls of bottle should be about $1/32$ in thick; stopper, tight fitting. Containers are of steel, bronze, or brass (Fig 59), bored to receive the bottle with snug fit. They are made in 2 parts, which screw together with fine threads, to exclude water, and are packed with lead or have carefully machined surfaces to insure a tight joint. A leak may cause collapse of the bottle, due to pressure of water in a deep hole. Containers are lowered into the hole by a wire; or attached to the end or in the middle of a string of rods, in which case they are threaded on one or both ends for rod connections. In operation, the acid is diluted according to depth of hole and time required for lowering the container, the aim being to allow the bottle to reach the desired place in the hole before any considerable etching takes place. The bottle is left at this point long enough to allow a line to be etched. Strength of acid and time for etching are best determined by experiment on the spot. Container is then withdrawn, bottle washed out, and angle of deviation measured by goniometer. The angle thus measured indicates a deviation from the vertical that is too small; due to CAPILLARITY, which causes the acid to rise on upper side of bottle, so that the surface of the acid at rest in the inclined tube, when in the hole, is not truly horizontal. Amount of error varies with angle of inclination, diam of bottle, and strength of acid. It is a max when the bottle is inclined 45°; is larger in bottles of small diam, and increases with the strength (and resultant viscosity) of the acid. Fig 60 is a curve for $1\frac{1}{8}$-in bottles and dilute (1 to 12) acid. For the strength of acid and diam of bottle used a curve should be plotted, giving correction for any given deviation.

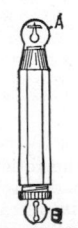

Fig 61. MacGeorge
Gelatine Tube

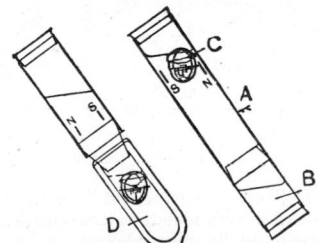

Fig 62.   Maas Borehole Compass

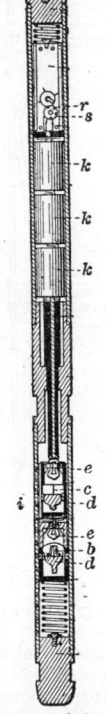

Fig 63.   Oehman's
Apparatus

Gelatine method (MacGeorge's). Apparatus consists of a container as above, and a tube to fit it. The tube (Fig 61) contains in the upper bulb A a small compass and in the lower bulb B a glass plummet, both floating in gelatine. The gelatine is heated in the bottle until it is liquid, then placed in the container, lowered to the proper point in the hole and allowed to set. When the tube is withdrawn it is placed in a goniometer with vert and horiz circles, the compass needle is brought into the meridian, the plummet made vert, and the amount of vert and horiz deviation read.

Maas borehole compass employs a combination of the above methods. It consists of a 1 1/8 by 6-in tube A (Fig 62), in one end of which is placed dilute hydrofluoric acid; in the other a gelatine solution and a small compass C. For holes so deep that the gelatine would set before the compass is in position, a small thermos bottle D contains the gelatine and compass, and a 3-in tube is used for the acid.

Photographic methods. OEHMAN'S APPARATUS (Fig 63) (73). Plumb bob c and magnetic needle b, have an electric light e above each, and photographic paper disks below on gimbals d, d. Clockwork r, s completes the circuit with battery k at a set time, at which the shadows of plumb bob and needle are photographed in the positions they take according to the deflection of the borehole. J. S. OWENS (74) has devised an instrument that gives a series of clinometer and compass readings recorded on sensitized paper by electric lights, the recording mechanism being controlled by clockwork. One insertion gives simultaneous records of essential data for each point in hole surveyed. F. Humphreys (75) describes a photographic instrument which records position of a plumb bob clinometer in relation to the quadrants of a compass. A line through the centers of plumb bob shadow and image of compass dial gives direction of drift, the distance between these centers showing drift angle on the graduated circles. The instrument is not designed for deviations greater than 35°. The Wright surveying instrument uses radio-active matter to affect a photo film (for details, see Bib 76).

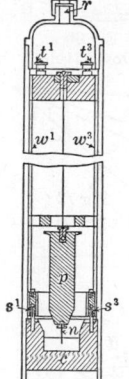

Fig 64. Transmitter of Briggs' Clinophone (after Redmayne)

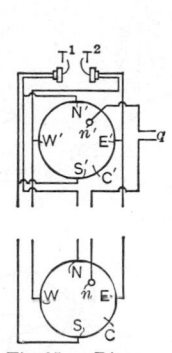

Fig 65. Diagram of Electrodes in Surface Receiver of Briggs' Clinophone

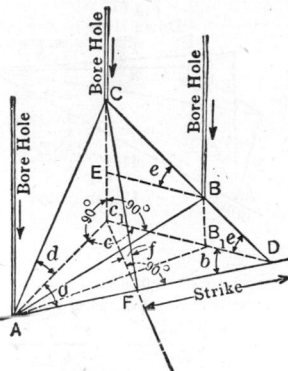

Fig 66. Computation of Borehole Data

Briggs' clinophone was designed for very accurate surveys of boreholes for the freezing and cementation methods of shaft sinking (Sec 8). Tests show that errors in readings seldom exceed 1 min. The transmitter (Fig 64) comprises: plumb bob p, with a needle n at the end dipping into vulcanite cup c, in which are 4 electrodes N, S, E, W of platinum foil. Each electrode connects at upper end to a plug and socket s' and s^3, and these in turn to upper terminals t', t^3, etc. A central terminal is electrically connected to needle n. A 5-strand cable passes through gland r to a receiver at the surface, which has 4 similar electrodes N', S', E', W', in a cup c' which, with cup c, contains weak salt solution (Fig 65). Needle n' is fixed in a metal holder. Alternating current is supplied through wires q. Telephone transmitters T', T^3 on surface are connected separately to N–S and E–W directions.

On lowering instrument into the hole, after plumb bob p and needle n are at rest the operator moves needle n' until the sound in both telephones is the same. Needle n is then in same position in cup c as needle n' in the hole in cup c'. The position of n' is recorded by a scale on bottom of c'. The instrument is oriented by the rods used to lower it, which have scarfed joints, thus making practically a solid rod, and any rotational movement of the transmitter in the hole is indicated at the surface. As a check, the rods can be turned through 180° and readings taken also on return trip. Readings are taken rapidly, the only time lost being that for the plumb bob to come to rest. The instrument is very accurate for small deflections; for greater deflections, the plumb bob is shortened.

Kiruna method (77) uses the electric deposition of copper from solution to make a mark within a cylinder, instead of etching by HFl. Used successfully in Sweden.

Use of survey results: (a) determination of dip and strike of a stratum or orebody cut at 3 places; (b) determination of dip from the core, the strike of the stratum or orebody being known; (c) determination from drill core of the true thickness of stratum.

Strike and dip. Theodore Simons (78) gives a convenient method of calculating strike and dip from 3 holes. In Fig 66, A = lowest point at which vein is cut; B = point of intermediate elevation; C = point of highest elevation; B_1 and C_1 = projections of B and C on horiz plane through A; d = angle of inclination of line connecting A and C; e = angle of inclination of line connecting B and C; c = horiz angle between above lines; b = angle between line of strike and extension of horiz projection of line connecting C and B; f = angle of dip; $m = \tan d \div \tan e$; $n = 180° - c$. Then $\tan b = \sin n \div (m + \cos n)$, from which the strike is obtained, and $\tan f = \tan e \div \sin b$.

Dip of a bed. E. E. White (79) gives a method for determining the dip of a bed from a hole not at right angles to the strike of the bedding, knowing this strike and the direction

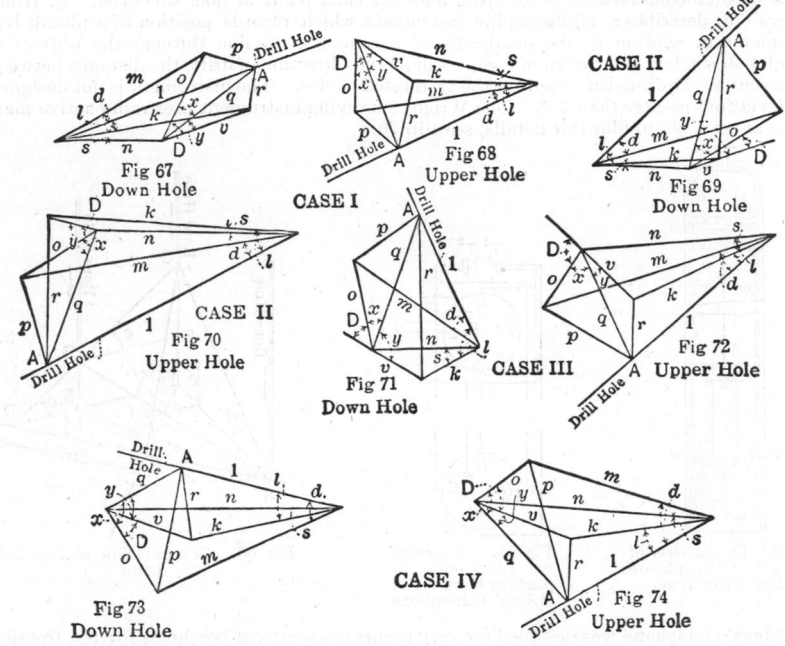

Fig 67. Down Hole — Fig 68. Upper Hole — CASE I — CASE II Fig 69. Down Hole — CASE II Fig 70. Upper Hole — Fig 71. Down Hole — CASE III Fig 72. Upper Hole — Fig 73. Down Hole — CASE IV Fig 74. Upper Hole

Fig 67–74. Various Combinations of Drill Hole and Bed (*E & M Jour*)

of the hole. In Fig 67, 1 = inclination of hole from horiz; d = angle between bedding and axis of hole, as obtained from core; S = difference in strike between bedding and hole; D = true dip of strata; p = length of a perpendicular from any point A on the hole to the bedding plane; r = length of perpendicular from A to the horiz plane through the intersection of the hole with the bedding plane; mon represents a bedding plane; kvn is a horiz plane through the intersection of the hole with the bedding plane; qop and qvr are planes through A perpendicular to n. If length of hole from A to point of intersection with the bedding plane is taken as unity, $\cos I = K$; $\cos d = m$; $\cos S = n \div K$; $\sin I = r$; $\sin d = p$; $n = \cos I \cos S$; $o = \sqrt{m^2 - n^2} = \sqrt{\cos^2 d - \cos^2 I \cos^2 S}$; $q = \sqrt{o^2 + p^2} = \sqrt{\cos^2 d - \cos^2 I \cos^2 S + \sin^2 d} = \sqrt{1 - \cos^2 I \cos^2 S}$; $x = \sin^{-1}\dfrac{p}{q} = \sin^{-1}\dfrac{\sin d}{\sqrt{1 - \cos^2 I \cos^2 S}}$; $y = \sin^{-1}\dfrac{r}{q} = \sin^{-1}\dfrac{\sin I}{\sqrt{1 - \cos^2 I \cos^2 S}}$.

Four cases arise: $D = x + y$, when beds dip in same direction as the hole, but more steeply (Fig 67, 68). $D = y - x$, when beds dip in same direction as the hole, but less steeply (Fig 69, 70). $D = 180 - y - x$, when beds dip in opposite direction to the hole, and more steeply than a plane perpendicular to the plane through the hole and the strike line of the beds (Fig 71, 72). $D = x - y$; when beds dip in opposite direction to the hole, and less steeply than a plane perpendicular to the plane through the hole and the strike line of the beds (Fig 73, 74).

J. N. Justice (40) gives a method for determining true thickness of a bed, knowing its dip, the direction of the hole as surveyed, and distance penetrated by the hole through the bed. In Fig 75, AB = plan of portion of hole in the bed; CAD = line of strike; EB = projection of strike line through B; AE is perpendicular to CAD; d = angle of dip; F = angle between direction of dip and direction of hole; P = apparent angle of dip; T = true thickness; $A''B$ is known in length and direction from the core and survey. The derived formulas are: $\tan P = (AE \tan d) \div AB = \cos F \tan d$; $T = A'A'' \cos d = A''B \,(\sin a \cos d - \cos a \cos F \sin d)$; $AA'' - AA' = A''B \sin a - AB \cos F \tan d$.

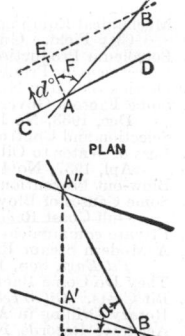

PLAN

VERTICAL SECTION ON A-B
Fig 75. To determine Thickness of Bed

25. CHOICE OF BORING METHODS

Chief factors: (a) depth of hole; (b) speed and information desired; (c) first cost of outfit; (d) operating cost; (e) character of materials penetrated; (f) transport facilities.

For shallow work in earth or soft rock, a hand rig is preferable; for holes over 50 ft deep, or in hard rock, a power rig should be used, unless first cost, including transport, outweighs the saving. Speed generally increases with size and wt of rig, except that in shallow holes and frequent moves the time for dismantling, moving and setting-up may offset speed. The question of operating cost is so closely related to purpose of the work, character of strata penetrated and labor available, that each case must be considered separately. In hard, shattered rock, churn drills are preferable to diamond drills. Small rotary drills will bore ground that can not be satisfactorily penetrated by churn drills, but the question of sampling by rotary coring is not yet fully worked out. Large rotary outfits can go to greater depth than cable-tools. Diamond drills have been successful in sampling ore where no core could be made, the sludge being saved and assayed. To secure information as to physical character of ore or rock, a core drill is necessary.

Table 58. Drill Manufacturing and Supply Companies (incomplete list)

* Cable-tool and rotary drills	Wash-boring	Oil-well rigs *	Portable churn drills	Diamond drills	Shot drills	Mackintosh Boring & Prospecting Tool, and P.A.P. alluvial drill
Allsteel Products Mfg Co, Wichita, Kan.		✕				
Boyle Bros Drill'g Co, Salt Lake City, Utah.				✕		
Bucyrus-Erie Co, So Milwaukee, Wis.			✕			
Chicago Pneumatic Tool Co, N Y.				✕		
Climax Rock Drill & Eng Wks Ltd, London.						✕
Cyclone Drill Co, Orrville, Ohio.	✕		✕			
Ingersoll-Rand Co, N Y.				✕	✕	
Keystone Driller Co, Beaver Falls, Pa	✕	✕	✕			
E. J. Longyear Co, Minneapolis, Minn				✕		
Loomis Machine Co, Tiffin, Ohio.	✕		✕			
National Supply Co, Pittsburgh, Pa.		✕				
N Y Engineering Co, New York.	✕					
Oil Well Supply Co, Pittsburgh, Pa.		✕				
Republic Supply Co, Los Angeles, Calif.		✕				
Sprague & Henwood, Scranton, Pa.				✕		
Star Drilling Mach Co, Akron, Ohio.		✕	✕			
Sullivan Mach'y Co, Chicago, Ill.	✕	✕		✕		
Well Mach'y & Supply Co, Fort Worth, Texas.		✕				

BIBLIOGRAPHY

1. Wash-drill Borings in N Y State Barge Canal. E. Low. *Eng News*, Jan 17, 1907
2. Earth-Auger Borings on N Y State Barge Canal. E. Low. *Eng News*, Mch 21, 1907
3. Spring-pole Drilling. E. G. Tuttle. *Sch Mines Quart*, Vol 16
4. Prospecting for Coal in the Mid-West. H. P. Nicholson, *Min & Met*, Dec, 1937
5. McKinlay Entry Driving Machines at New Orient Mine. F. E. Snarr. *Min Cong Jour*, Oct, 1938
6. The ABC of Empire Drilling. J. P. Hutchins and N. C. Stines. *Min & Sci Pr*, Jan 7, 28, 1911
7. Drilling Alluvium in Siberia. R. E. Smith and H. G. Hann. *Min Mag*, July, 1913
8. Mechanical Equipment Used in Drilling and Production of Oil and Gas Wells in the Oklahoma City Field. Gustave Wade. U S Bur Mines, *Tech Pap* 561 (1934)
9. Petroleum Production. W. F. Cloud. *Univ of Oklahoma Press*, 1937
10. Investment in Prime Movers. A. H. Albrecht. Prod Bull 207, *Am Pet Inst*, June, 1931
11. Derrick Skidding Now Highly Skilled Art. Brad Mills, *Oil Weekly*, Aug 22, 1938
12. Some Factors Governing Use of Weight-Material in Drilling Wells. *Drilling Mud*, Nov and Dec, 1933, No 10, 11
13. Selection and Control of Drilling Mud in Deep Wells. *Drilling Mud*, Mch, Apl, 1935
14. Loss of Water to Oil Bearing Formations as a Basic Cause of Low Production. *Drilling Mud*, Apl, 1937, No 4
15. Blow-out Prevention and Control. W. Y. Viette and A. G. Levy, *Oil & Gas Jour*, June 6, 1936
16. Some Causes of Blow-outs During Drilling and Means of Prevention, with Special Reference to Gulf Coast Region. C. B. Carpenter. U S Bur Mines, *Inf Cir* 6938, Mch, 1937
17. Private communication from W. L. Heater, Mgr Bariod Sales Co
18. A Modern Steam Rig That Approaches Stationary Power Plant Efficiency. M. L. Cashion, *Pet Engr*, Sep, 1937
19. They Do Come Back. G. Triplet. *Oil Weekly*, Jan 17, 1938
20. Bit Costs. *Oil Weekly*, May 23, 1938
21. Rotary Drilling in Appalachian Area. J. F. Robinson. *Oil & Gas Jour*, Aug 11, 1938
22. Accurate Records Kept in North Louisiana Wildcat Drilling. G. Weber. *Oil & Gas Jour*, May 26, 1938
23. Drilling Practice in K M A Field. *Oil & Gas Jour*, Jan 20, 1938
24. Rotary Drilling Handbook. J. E. Brantly. Pub, Russel Palmer, N Y, 1936
25. More Footage. L. J. Logan. *Oil Weekly*, Jan 31, 1938
26. Expenditures. B. Mills. *Oil Weekly*, Jan 31, 1938
27. Deep Well Drilling. W. H. Jeffery, 3rd Ed. Gulf Publishing Co, Houston, Texas
28. Welding Oil-Well Casing. L. H. Hodell. *Min & Met*, Aug, 1937
29. Casing Perforation by Gunfire and Its Application to Oil Production. E. R. Smith. *Min & Met*, May, 1936
30. Casing Troubles and Fishing Methods. T. Curtin. U S Bur Mines, *Bull* No 182
31. Well-depth Measurements. C. E. Reistle and S. T. Sikes. *Oil Weekly*, June 13, 20 and 27, 1938
32. Designing Data for Oil Well Casing and Tubing. Jones & Laughlin Steel Corp *Handbook*, No O C-3
33. Cementing Oil Wells. H. Pennington. *Oil Weekly*, Oct 19, 1928
34. Proper Practice for Handling Cementing Jobs. Rakestraw and Parsons. *Oil Weekly*, Feb 13, 1931
35. Oil Well Cementing in Gulf Coast Area. W. T. Doherty. Bull 212, *Am Pet Inst*, N Y, 1933
36. Preservation of Hole Size in Cable-tool Drilling. M. Tucker. *Oil & Gas Jour*, May 5, 1938
37. Taking Samples With Rotary. J. R. Suman. *Oil Weekly*, July 3, 1920
38. Crooked Hole Problems on Gulf Coast. P. C. Murphy and S. A. Judson. *Oil & Gas Jour*, Mch 27, 1930
39. Wilmington Drilling and Production. C. J. Dean. *Calif Oil World & Pet Ind*, May 5, 1938
40. Controlled Directional Drilling High Point in Petroleum Engineering, Calif. *Oil World & Pet Industry*, July 20, 1938
41. Alluvial Boring in New Zealand. L. A. Crozier. *Chem Eng'g & Min Rev*, May 8, 1936
42. Miami-Picher Zinc-Lead District. S. Weidman. *Univ of Oklahoma Press*, 1932
43. Churn Drilling Practice in Tri-State Zinc-Lead District. W. E. Netzeband. *Min Cong Jour*, Jan, 1935
44. Private communication from Evan Just, Mch, 1938
45. Structure Drilling as Applied in Western Mesaba Mining Practice. H. C. Bolthouse. *Min Cong Jour*, Nov, 1936
46. Gas Core Drills Replace Steam Equipment. *E & M Jour*, Jan, 1935
47. Comparing Hardness of Electric Furnace Products and Natural Abrasives. *Trans Electrochem Soc*, 1936
48. Diamond-Drill Bits and Carbon. E. R. Storms. *E & M Jour*, Mch, 1933
49. Recent Developments in Diamond Drilling Practice. K. Sundberg and O. Lindquist. *Bull Inst Min & Met*, London, No 402, Mch, 1938
50. Diamond Drilling at United Verde Mine. M. G. Hansen. U S Bur Mines, *Inf Cir* 6708, Apl, 1933
51. Diamond Drilling in Lupa Goldfield, Tanganyika, Africa. J. Q. St. Clair. *Jour Chem, Met & Min Soc of S Africa*, Jan, 1937
52. Diamond Drill Practice at Bunker Hill & Sullivan Mining & Conc Co. J. E. Brown. *Min Cong Jour*, Jan, 1935
53. Diamond Drilling With Special Reference to Oil-Field Prospecting. F. A. Edson. U S Bur Mines, *Bull* 243
54. Diamond Drilling in Lupa Goldfield, Tanganyika, Africa. J. Q. St Clair. *Jour Chem, Met & Min Soc of S Africa*, Feb, 1937
55. Special Features of Core Drilling in Salt Beds of Western Tex and New Mex. J. S. Wroth. U S Bur Mines, *Inf Cir* 6156, Aug 1929
56. Mining Methods and Costs at El Potosí Mine. H. A. Walker. U S Bur Mines, *Inf Cir* 6804, Nov, 1934
57. When Planning to Diamond Drill. W. Sack. *E & M Jour*, June, 1938
58. Core-drilling for Coal in Alaska. G. A. Waring. *Min & Met*, Apl, 1934
59. Diamond Drilling Practice. C. H. Hitchcock. *Trans Can Inst of Min and Met*, Apl, 1933

60. Diamond Drilling Costs and Practice. G. C. Master. *Min Mag*, July, 1932
61. Gold Mining at the Haile Mine in South Carolina. H. A. Bradt and E. Newton. *Min Cong Jour*, Oct, 1938
62. Large-diameter Core Drills for Geologic Exploration. B. C. Moneymaker and P. P. Fox. *Mining Tech*, A I M M E, Nov, 1938
63. Calyx Core Drill. M. P. Tierney. *Min Cong Jour*, Nov, 1938
64. Shaft Boring Found Inexpensive and Safe. J. B. Newsom. *E & M Jour*, Sep, 1936
65. Sinking a Ventilation Bore Hole in Minnesota. B. S. Richards. *Min Cong Jour*, Oct, 1938
66. Boring at the State Coal Mine, Wonthaggi, Australia. V. J. McLeish. *Proc* Australian Inst Min & Met, No 103, 1936
67. Diamond-drill Practice at the Britannia Mines. F. Ebbutt. *E. & M. Jour*, Sep 22, 1928
68. Deviation of Diamond Boreholes. A. F. Skerl. *Tran* Inst Min and Met, Vol 43, Dec 21, 1033
69. Bore-hole Surveying by Orientation. R. P. McLaughlin. *Oil & Gas Jour*, Mch 27, 1930
70. Improved Device for Orienting Drill Pipe. J. B. Murdoch. *Pet Engr*, Jan, 1938
71. Electrical Coring, a Method of Determining Bottom-hole Data by Electrical Measurements. C. M. Schlumberger and E. G. Leonardon. *Trans* A I M M E, Vol 110, 1932
72. Laboratory Orientation of Well Cores by Their Magnetic Polarity. E. D. Lynton. *Am Assoc Pet Geologists*, Vol 21, No 5, May, 1937
73. Diamond Drilling and Borehole Surveying. J. I. Hoffman. *Trans* Inst Min & Met, Jan, 1926
74. New Instrument for Surveying Boreholes. J. S. Owens. *Bull* Inst Min & Met, Jan, 1926
75. Photometric Survey of Boreholes. F. Humphreys. *Jour* Chem, Met & Min Soc of S Africa, May, 1934
76. Surveying Diamond Drill-holes. W. R. Storms. *E & M Jour*, Apl, 1933
77. Borehole Surveying by Kiruna Method. S. Lundberg. *E & M Jour*, Apl 26, 1924
78. Calculations of Strike and Dip. T. Simons. *E & M Jour*, Apl 11, 1914
79. Dip of Bed from Drill Cores. E. E. White. *E & M Jour*, Sep 19, 1914
80. Diamond Drilling in West Africa. J. N. Justice. *Trans* Inst Min & Met, Vol 12

SECTION 10

PROSPECTING, DEVELOPMENT AND EXPLOITATION OF MINERAL DEPOSITS

BY

JAMES F. McCLELLAND, E.M.

VICE PRESIDENT, PHELPS DODGE CORPORATION

ASSISTED BY

W. W. LYNCH, E.M. AND EDWARD K. JUDD, E.M.

Acknowledgment is also due to the authors of individual articles as listed below, and particularly to O. B. Perry, E.M., for supervising revision of the articles on Placer Mining; also to many engineers and company officials who have generously contributed other data.

This revision of Section 10 for the Third Edition, made in 1938 and 1939, is based on the revision made by the author in 1926, with the aid of R. K. Warner, J. L. Fozard and H. DeWitt Smith.

NOTE.—Numbers in parentheses in text refer to Bibliography at end of this Section.

PROSPECTING, DEVELOPMENT AND EXPLOITA-
TION OF MINERAL DEPOSITS

1. DEFINITIONS

Mining includes surface operations, as quarrying in open cuts and the working of placers, as well as underground work. In a given mineral deposit, mining operations may be divided into 4 stages:

Prospecting, or the search for minerals.

Exploration, or the work of exploring a mineral deposit when found. It is undertaken to gain knowledge of the size, shape, position, characteristics, and value of the deposit.

Development, or the driving of openings to and in a proved deposit, for mining and handling the product economically.

Exploitation (mining), or the work of extracting the mineral.

These terms are used loosely. It is often difficult to distinguish between prospecting and exploration, or between exploration and development, as the different kinds of work insensibly shade into one another; an arbitrary differentiation between them is usually established at a given property. Confusion also arises when the terms are extended to describe operations on a property containing several orebodies. In such cases, prospecting for new orebodies is a part of exploration. In certain mineral deposits, prospecting and exploration are done in one operation by boring; as in the disseminated lead ores of S E Mo, and in those Mesabi iron ores and gold placers that are mined by open-cut methods.

Prospect is a mineral property before exploration has proved it to be worthy of development.

Since methods of prospecting and exploring a mineral deposit are based largely on its geological characteristics, a genetic classification of mineral deposits is invaluable (Art 3; Sec 2, Art 17). Methods of development and mining are determined largely by the shape and position of a mineral deposit. From this standpoint ore deposits are classified as:

Veins. Tabular-shaped deposits of non-sedimentary origin, usually dipping at high angles.

Beds. (1) Tabular deposits, lying conformable to the stratification of inclosing rocks; (2) detrital or sedimentary superficial deposits.

Masses. Large orebodies of irregular shape standing at any angle. Fig 4 shows outline of a massive orebody.

The following terms are commonly used in metal mining (letters refer to Fig 1–5). For coal mining terms, see Art 102 *et seq.*

Hanging wall or " hanging." Ore limit or wall-rock on the upper side of a dipping orebody (h); called " roof " in bedded deposits.

Footwall or " foot." Ore limit or wall rock on the lower side of a dipping orebody (f); called " floor " in bedded deposits.

Shaft. A vert or inclined opening, giving access to and serving the various levels of a mine (d, e); an " inside " shaft is one which does not open to the surface; a flat or low dipping inclined shaft is called " slope " in coal mines.

Crosscut. A horiz opening, like a tunnel, and running through country rock or ore at a considerable angle to the strike of formation or orebody (g).

Drift. A horiz opening, lying in or near the orebody, parallel or nearly parallel to its strike (k).

Level. The horizon at which an orebody is opened up, and from which mining proceeds. The term is often used in the same sense as " drift," or to cover all horiz workings on one horizon. Thus, the drifts and crosscuts in Fig 2 would be called the 1st level, or the workings on 1st level.

Winze. An opening (m) like a small shaft, sunk from an interior point in the mine.

Raise (Cornish, " rise "). A shaft or winze excavated upward (l) as for connecting adjacent levels. Terms winze and raise are used interchangeably to describe a completed opening as at (n), Fig 1.

Tunnel. Technically defined as a nearly horiz underground passage, coming to surface at both ends. In mining, the term is used also for such a passage open to daylight at only one end. Tunnels may be crosscut tunnels (p), Fig 5, or drift tunnels (r), Fig 1; the term " adit " is also used to describe any tunnel with one end open to the surface, although formerly limited to tunnels driven primarily for drainage purposes.

Stope. An underground excavation (*s*, Fig 1) resulting from actual mining of ore, as distinguished from other excavations in ore, as drifts, crosscuts, raises, winzes. The verb "to stope" is used loosely, but usually to denote the general plan and work of breaking ground in stopes.

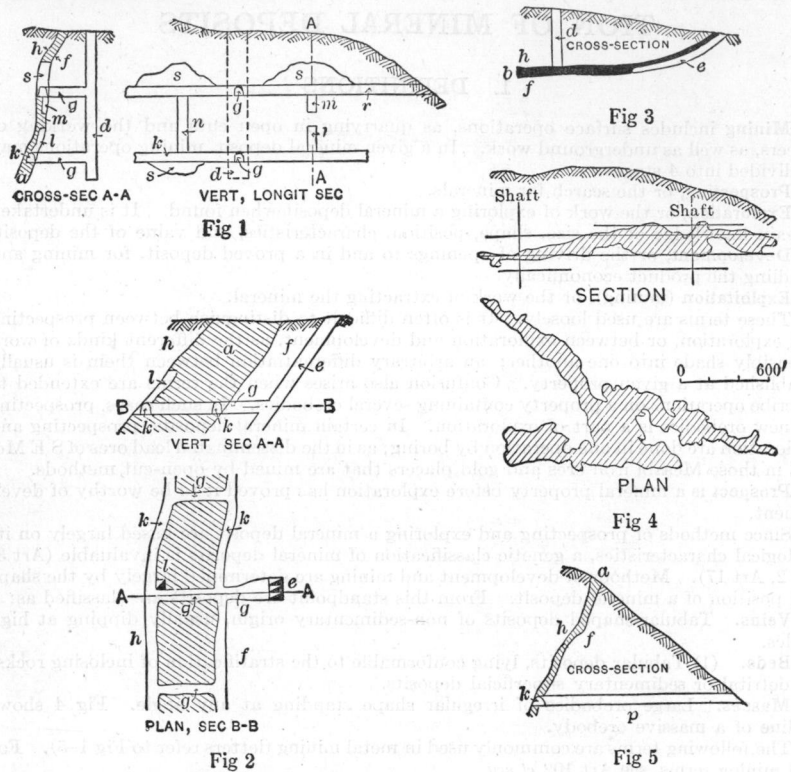

Fig 1

Fig 2

Fig 3

Fig 4

Fig 5

Back. The ore between a level and the surface, or between 2 levels; also designates the roof of a drift, crosscut, or stope.

For comprehensive glossaries of mining terms, see Bib (1).

PROSPECTING AND EXPLORATION

2. CONDITIONS WARRANTING PROSPECTING

Search for mineral is largely guided by knowledge of the geological associations and peculiarities of known orebodies. It is done chiefly by miners who have absorbed the details of ore occurrence in mines where they have worked. However, they are keen observers, and have been responsible for most ore discoveries. Some deposits have also been found by inexperienced men, and some famous orebodies have been found accidentally. Crane (2) lists 130 gold and silver mines in the U S, of which 11 were discovered by chance. See also Bib (479).

Theoretically, the trained economic geologist should make the best prospector, but the chance of finding commercial orebodies is so small that such men can not afford to prospect unless employed by mining corporations. Engineers generally direct the work of exploration, and scientific prospecting is commoner than formerly. Economic geology aids by indicating favorable localities and eliminating unlikely ones. Most plans for exploration are based (often unconsciously) on theories of origin of the orebody concerned (Art 3).

Cost of prospecting and exploration should be kept low on account of the high risk involved. Simple methods should be employed and unnecessary expenditure for equipment avoided. It is impossible to estimate the cost of strictly prospecting work; while fairly accurate unit costs for trenches and test pits can be obtained, the required amount of such work can not be determined in advance. Closer estimates are possible for systematic exploration. Examination of a mineral property generally gives an idea of the amount and kind of work required to prove its value. The estimated cost of this work, compared with geological possibilities, furnishes a measure of the risk involved (Sec 25).

Presence of outcrops warrants prospecting, to determine whether shoots of commercial ore exist at any points along them. Since exposed outcrops of well known types of orebody have now been fairly thoroughly prospected in all but the most inaccessible regions, the field for prospecting at present lies in search for new or rare types, or for those orebodies the outcrops of which are covered. However, air transport has expanded the fields open to prospecting of the older sort, besides making it possible to develop and exploit outlying discoveries, as in northwestern Canada, New Guinea and central Africa (646).

In arid regions, surface exposures of rocks are often covered with a black or brown stain (MnO_2), known as "desert varnish." In such cases, if an orebody and the adjacent rocks are equally resistant to erosion, outcrops can not be distinguished unless pieces are broken off. There are undoubtedly exposed outcrops of this kind which have not been found. Their discovery is fortuitous, or results from patient detailed tracing of float (Art 4) (502).

Presence of float, as pieces of ore, or specks of metal or ore minerals, justifies prospecting. Such discoveries must be considered in connection with local geology. Thus, it is useless to seek the source of quartz float in a schist or slate area where individual quartz stringers are too small to be of economic value.

Favorable geological conditions. Many data have been collected about geological associations and characteristics of different types of orebody. Recognition of these characteristics in a new district warrants prospecting. Conversely, geological conditions may prohibit prospecting; thus, search for coal is useless in igneous formations. Common associations and characteristics of orebodies are given in Art 3. It is important to note that geological conditions at one place may be superficially similar to those at another and yet not be accompanied by workable ore deposits. Many geological conditions affecting occurrence of oil and other mineral deposits are recognizable from the air, with or without photography, but interpretations are more trustworthy if based on previous acquaintance with the ground. Features most clearly recognized: contacts between different formations and general character of each; faults; folded structures; quartz and other outcrops; oxidized cappings. For cost of aerial exploration, see W. E. D. Stokes, Jr, Bib (103).

Ancient workings and dumps of ore, waste, or slag exist in different parts of the world, and lead to prospecting in their vicinity. Much historical information about old EUROPEAN and SPANISH-AMERICAN mines is available. Occasionally, an old book or record has afforded a clue to the location of an ancient source of mineral. Reasons advanced for the abandonment of ancient mines are: (a) wars or attacks by savages, (b) pinching out or faulting of orebody, (c) occurrence of water, (d) lack of technical knowledge on the part of the ancients. a, b, and c may be valid reasons; water in particular prevented mining much below groundwater level. Most old workings show evidence of skilful mining (3); the ancients did not work orebodies the metallurgy of which was unknown. No development was done in advance of mining; frequently, the cost of acquiring property was merely the cost of prospecting. The slave labor used was the only capital invested, and did not disappear when the mine was abandoned or exhausted. The purchasing power of metals was higher than at present. In such circumstances the ancients could work small, irregular, and low-grade orebodies. The existence of old workings is not conclusive evidence of the existence of ore workable under present economic conditions.

G. R. Carey (4) in 1901 investigated ancient workings in RHODESIA, where there are numerous outcrop workings on auriferous quartz veins of which there is no written history. Aver depth of workings, 30 to 60 ft, occasionally 100 ft; in most cases mining had been confined to narrow pay streaks; aver stope width, about 2 ft. Indications were that the ore had been crushed, sorted, and washed. The following conclusions from this work are suggestive: (a) Length of old workings = length of pay shoots at the surface. (b) Strike of vein is shown by course of the workings. (c) Dip of vein is toward the steeper bank of the old excavations (since hanging wall over an open cut breaks down under long weathering), and may be determined from dip of the footwall bank of the excavation. (d) Width of vein can not be determined from, but is usually less than, the width of the old workings. Very narrow veins are indicated by narrow workings, with small dumps containing much waste. (e) Grade of pay shoots, vague, but above aver grade of dumps, if high values be rejected. (f) Large and numerous dumps in comparison with size of workings, especially dumps containing large pieces, indicate low-grade ores. Small, sparse dumps along strong workings indicate that whole vein was worked as payable, and that its grade was probably good. Roughly, the value of a vein is proportional to the ratio between extent of old workings and extent of the dumps. (g) No light is thrown by old workings on permanence of the vein or on its gold values in depth.

3. GEOLOGICAL DATA FOR PROSPECTING AND EXPLORATION

By Alan M. Bateman, Professor of Economic Geology, Yale University

a. Introductory

Most mine exploration rests upon geological theory or knowledge as to probable position, form, size, extension, mineral character, or value of an ore mass. Correct geological knowledge frequently enables one or more of the above features to be determined in advance of exploration, often with considerable accuracy. In some cases geology furnishes no clue, and exploration is necessarily blind. Following are some common conditions under which geology may aid in exploratory work, with methods by which results may be secured (see also Sec 2).

Sources of information: (a) PROCESSES OF ORIGIN OF A DEPOSIT determine its form, size, and geological position, the mineralogy and value of its primary ore, the probability of its occurrence in undeveloped districts, and success or failure of exploration for more ore in a partly developed district. Production of ore masses is only one of many effects of ore-building processes. Other effects, if recognized, may assist in discovering ores. Favorable indications do not insure ore occurrence, but, if they are entirely lacking, ores of the type not indicated will almost certainly not be found. (b) PROCESSES OF SUPERFICIAL ALTERATION acting on an orebody after its formation. These yield inferences from nature of outcrop as to what lies beneath a barren gossan, the value of undeveloped orebodies, depth to which developed ores may be expected to go, and often the presence or absence of any orebody at all. (c) TIME OF FORMATION OF A DEPOSIT, relative to other geologic events, determines the time relation between undeveloped ore masses and faults, intrusive rocks, metamorphism, sediments, and all geologic events that have occurred in a given district, and promises to yield valuable data. (d) KNOWLEDGE OF DISTURBANCES THAT HAVE AFFECTED AN OREBODY subsequent to its formation is useful when a deposit has been faulted, drag-folded, or affected by regional metamorphism. Faulted portions of ore-bodies may often be located. If effects of metamorphism are not too profound, the origin of the deposit may still be determined and used as under (a). In extreme cases of metamorphism, geology furnishes little aid.

Materials of mineral deposits and their formation. Mineral deposits are localized concentrations of special substances of the earth's crust; some are of common rock-making minerals. Of the 1 400 mineral species, about 30 are common rock-forming minerals and 200 occur in mineral deposits.

Metalliferous deposits consist of: (1) ORE MINERALS, containing one or more metals; they are mostly metallic; one or more metals may be obtained from a single mineral, or the same metal from several minerals; they are PRIMARY or HYPOGENE, and SECONDARY or SUPERGENE. (2) GANGUE minerals, usually discarded; mostly non-metallic minerals or rock; some are utilized, as rock gangue for road metal, fluorspar for flux, quartz for abrasive, calcite for soil dressing. (3) ORE, a mixture of ore minerals and gangue, from which metals may be extracted at a profit. Whether material is ore or worthless depends upon value of product and cost of extracting and marketing it; also upon content of byproducts or gangue minerals that can be utilized. Quantity of metal varies from 0.00016%, in case of some gold ores, to 60% for iron ores. Some ores have common metal associations, as Ag and Au, Ag and Pb, Ag and Co, Zn and Pb, Cu and Ni, Fe and Mn, Sn and Wo.

Non-metallic deposits consist of solids, liquids, or gases, and are mostly used in their natural state. They are mainly common substances, as fuels, rocks, sands, salts, and various non-metallic minerals. The deposits, gem stones excepted, consist mainly of the desired materials, which must usually be "processed" for market.

The materials of mineral deposits are formed by: (1) CRYSTALLIZATION FROM MELTS, as magnetite; (2) SUBLIMATION, as sulphur; (3) DISTILLATION, as petroleum; (4) SUPERSATURATION, as nitrates; (5) REACTION OF GASES WITH OTHER GASES, LIQUIDS, OR SOLIDS, as cassiterite, sulphur, magnetite; (6) REACTION OF SOLUTIONS WITH OTHER SOLUTIONS, GASES, OR SOLIDS, the commonest process, giving rise to most ore minerals by direct deposition, replacement, oxidation, reduction, adsorption or catalytic action; (7) PRECIPITATIONS BY BACTERIA, as iron and manganese oxides; (8) UNMIXING OF SOLID SOLUTIONS, upon cooling, as ilmenite from magnetite; (9) COLLOIDAL DEPOSITION, as manganese; (10) WEATHERING PROCESSES, placers, clays, bauxite.

In formation of most ore minerals, water has played the dominant part. Their deposition is greatly influenced by temp and press; a drop in temp or press commonly causes deposition of minerals in solution.

Stability of minerals. Most minerals change state in response to environment, and thus are indicators of geological conditions. High-temp minerals perish at the surface and take forms stable under the new conditions, like pyrrhotite to limonite; surface minerals change to stable forms at depth, as clay to mica or garnet; some are persistent, as gold or diamond. Other minerals change molecularly; chalcocite formed above 91° C is isometric, but on cooling changes to orthorhombic; below 91° C it forms directly as orthorhombic; isometric chalcocite, therefore, indicates primary origin.

Geologic thermometers. The above conditions yield geologic "thermometers," which indicate conditions of formation of ores and help diagnose ore deposits. They are established as follows: (1) DIRECT MEASUREMENTS, as of fumaroles; (2) MELTING POINTS, as stibnite at 546° C or bismuth at 271° C, which means that the Cobalt, Ont, ores containing Bi must have been formed below that temp; (3) DISSOCIATION, as calcite at 900° C or pyrite at 610° C; (4) INVERSION POINTS, as "high" quartz (a high-temp variety formed above 573° C) changes below 573° C to "low" quartz; isometric chalcocite changes to orthorhombic below 91° C, and argentite changes to the lower-temp form of acanthite at 179° C; (5) EXSOLUTION (separation from solution with lowering temp); cubanite and chalcopyrite exsolve at 450° C, bornite and chalcopyrite at 475° C, and covellite and chalcocite at 75° C; (6) RECRYSTALLIZATION, as native copper at 450° C and silver at 200° C; (7) LIQUID INCLUSIONS, as Tri-State sphalerite, formed between 115° C and 135° C, thus indicating a hypogene origin; (8) CHANGES IN PHYSICAL PROPERTIES; fluorite loses color at 175° C.

Magmas, rocks, and ores.   Most metalliferous and many non-metallic deposits result from igneous activity: (1) some igneous rocks are themselves ores, as corundum syenite, and magnetite porphyry; (2) certain ores are closely related to igneous rocks, as nickel to nörite; (3) some igneous intrusions are bordered by contact metamorphic ore deposits; (4) mineral deposits are also formed from volcanic emanations, fumaroles and hot springs; (5) veins are clustered in zonal arrangement outward from igneous intrusions.

When a magma begins to crystallize it undergoes differentiation, yielding basic, intermediate, and silicic fractions. Normally, basic minerals crystallize first and sink in the melt to form basic fractions. Magnetite, chromite, platinum and nickel generally accumulate with such basic fractions and may form ore deposits within the intrusive. As the basic minerals are subtracted, the residual "rest-magma" becomes progressively more silicic, and granitic magmas eventually become rich in silica, alkalies, and water; some may be squeezed into fissures to form pegmatites, containing many valuable minerals. With progressive crystallization the final aqueous extracts gather the metals and rare elements. These mother liquors constitute the magmatic solutions that give rise to most of the valuable mineral deposits.

The result of differentiation is to yield: (1) IMMISCIBLE SULPHIDE LIQUIDS, which settle and form magmatic sulphide deposits; (2) CRYSTALS of silicates and oxides, forming igneous rocks or ore deposits; (3) GASEOUS EMANATIONS, which escape and carry out valuable substances; (4) RESIDUAL LIQUIDS, containing metals. Gaseous emanations may react upon invaded rocks to produce contact metamorphic deposits, or may escape outward with their load of metals, later to condense and mingle with meteoric waters to form mineralizing solutions. Residual liquids may leave the magma as liquids and also constitute metallizing solutions. Thus, the magma may yield mineral deposits within itself and supply gases and hot liquid solutions to form the multitude of contact metamorphic and hydrothermal deposits that are the offspring of magmas.

Classification of mineral-forming processes.   Recognition of mineral-forming processes and the resulting deposits is the basis upon which prospecting, exploration, and to some extent, development, depend. It is only when these processes are understood that assumptions and predictions as to geologic position, form, size, continuity, character of ore beneath croppings, and often their value, are reliable. Following table classifies mineral-forming processes rather than ore deposits, and is not opposed to the classification in Sec 2, Art 17. It is the basis of the practical considerations that follow.

Classification of Mineral-forming Processes

Process of formation	Resulting mineral deposit
Magmatic concentration	Syngenetic magmatic deposits (early and late)
Sublimation	Sublimate deposits
Contact metamorphism	Contact-metamorphic deposits
Replacement	Massive, lode, and disseminated replacement deposits
Filling of cavities	Fissure veins, and other cavity fillings
Sedimentation	Sedimentary iron, manganese, phosphate, coal
Evaporation	Saline deposits
Residual concentration	Residual deposits; oxides of aluminum, manganese, iron
Mechanical concentration	Placers
Oxidation and supergene enrichment	Oxidized and secondary enriched deposits
Metamorphism	Metamorphic deposits, asbestos, talc

b. Magmatic Concentrations

Origin is due to magmatic processes during consolidation; some, like nickel and diamond, are large and rich. Some ores, like magnetite, may form also by processes other than magmatic, but others, like Cr and Pt are formed only by magmatic processes. The orebody may constitute the whole of an igneous intrusion, as in the magnetite bodies at Kirunavaara, Sweden; more commonly, the useful mineral constitutes a relatively small part of the igneous mass, and occurs in disconnected, isolated masses near its borders or center. They originate by differentiation; some represent segregations of early formed crystals; others, injections of concentrated melts; others injections of residual liquid melts; and others injections of accumulations of segregated immiscible liquids.

Type	Process	Example
I. Early Magmatic:		
A. Disseminated crystallization	Crystallization in situ	Diamond pipes
B. Segregation	Fractional crystallization	Chromite deposits
C. Injection	Concentration and injection	Kirunavaara, Sweden
II. Late Magmatic:		
A. Residual liquid segregation	Fractional crystallization residue	Taberg; Iron Mt, Wyo
B. Residual liquid injection	Filter pressing	Adirondack magnetites
C. Immiscible liquid segregation	Concentration of immiscible liquid	Insinzwa, Africa
D. Immiscible liquid injection	Same, with injection	Sudbury offset deposits?

Recognition. Magmatic deposits are composed only of magmatic minerals; labradorite and olivine are formed in no others. Typical hydrothermal minerals, as rhodochrosite, barite, sericite, chlorite, are absent. They are associated with an igneous rock of which they are a part or the whole, are never surrounded by a halo of typical hydrothermal wall-rock alteration, and constitute a small group of ores, each associated with its own rock type. They are distinguished from contact metamorphic deposits by absence of contact metamorphic minerals, and from replacement deposits by absence of hydrothermal minerals and alteration.

Occurrence. Magmatic concentrations occur as irregular marginal segregations, rarely as central segregations, also as dikes and irregular intrusive masses. Some are stratiform with enclosing igneous bodies, as the platinum and chromite deposits of the Bushveld, So Africa. They occur only in association with the mother igneous rock.

Valuable products. Some of the valuable magmatic mineral products are:

Deposit	Minerals	Parent Rock
Native Metals		
Pt	Pt, and with chromite or Ni-Cu-Co sulphides	Peridotite family
Pt metals	Osmium, iridium, palladium, etc	"
Au, Ag	By-product metals	"
Oxides		
Fe	Magnetite, some hematite	Syenites, anorthosites
Fe-Ti	Titaniferous magnetite	Gabbro family
Ti	Ilmenite	"
Cr	Chromite	Peridotite, serpentine
Al	Corundum	Nepheline syenite
Sulphides		
Ni-Cu	Chalcopyrite, pentlandite, polydimite, sperrylite with pyrrhotite, some pyrite	Norite
Ni	"	"
Cu	Bornite and chalcopyrite	Silicic rocks
Precious Stones		
Diamond	Diamond, garnet	Kimberlite
Garnet	Pyrope, almandine	Ultra-basics
Peridot	Peridot (olivine)	Peridotite

Practical applications. Segregations are marginal in position and irregular in form. Only those of large horiz dimensions are likely to extend far below the surface. New ore can be expected only in or adjacent to parent rocks, and marginal positions afford greatest possibility for exploration.

Extensions in depth are generally unlikely to exceed surface dimensions in case of segregations; tonnage possibilities can not safely be predicted on surface showings. Stratiform layers may have great extension along strike and in depth, as the Bushveld deposits; dikes and large injections may reach considerable depth. The walls are not generally abrupt, but merge into parent rock; hence exploratory workings in transitional portions are unpromising. Underground exploration for new ore masses not revealed in outcrops is hazardous; surface exposures are apt to equal or exceed the size and number of masses found in depth. In all igneous deposits, the primary minerals near surface generally persist to max depth of deposit; changes in tenor with depth are accidental rather than zonal.

Search for orebodies in undeveloped districts. Igneous deposits are not accompanied by an obvious aureole of rock alteration; the only indications available to the prospector are actual ore, and the kind of igneous rock with which such ores are generally associated. These are valuable guides; their absence throws suspicion on any reputed occurrence; search for diamonds in Arkansas was initiated by discovery of the correct type of rock. Common associations are given in the preceding paragraphs. The correct rock mass being discovered, search should be made particularly about its margins. Peripheral igneous bodies bear a definite relation in size to the parent igneous rock, since large orebodies can not be concentrated from small rock masses. If size of the igneous mass can be determined it affords a clue to size of possible ore masses. Some sulphide bodies lie in embayments of igneous bodies, hence such places should be prospected.

Magmatic orebodies occurring as dikes differ from ordinary dikes only in their mineral content; their expectation in a district can not be predicted by geologic features; they are "where you find them." Dikes of ore, though rare, are particularly reliable bodies upon which to count for persistence in depth. They can be recognized by: (a) igneous minerals, (b) lack of accompanying rock alteration; (c) included irregular fragments of country rock, not crusted by ore minerals, as in cavity-filled deposits.

c. Sublimation

This very minor process accounts for certain deposits associated with volcanoes and fumaroles; they have been directly volatilized by heat and subsequently redeposited in the same form at lower temp and press. Sublimates deposited around volcanoes are rarely present in commercial quantities. Sulphur of this origin has been mined in Japan, Italy and Mexico.

d. Contact Metamorphism

Contact metamorphism or pyrometasomatism (648) gives rise to distinctive ore deposits, where certain igneous rocks invade carbonate rocks. The deposits are characterized by an assemblage of diagnostic high-temp minerals resulting from reaction of the magmatic vapors on the host rocks. The characteristic features of such deposits are: (a) proximity to intrusive, (b) calcareous host rock, (c) distinctive mineral association, (d) intimate associations of ore and gangue minerals. The new minerals result from recombinations of former minerals, accessions from the magma, and combinations of both. The accession minerals (including ore minerals) are deposited by metasomatic replacement.

Minerals of contact metamorphic deposits (common minerals marked with asterisk).

Minerals partly of recrystallization and partly accessions

*Grossularite garnet	*Diopside	Gahnite	Staurolite	Paigite
*Andradite garnet	Augite	Andularia	Quartz	Topaz
Axinite	Forsterite	Albite	Siderite	Apatite
Tourmaline	*Tremolite	Biotite	*Ilvaite	"Skarn"
*Wollastonite	*Actinolite	*Calcite	Graphite	Pyroxene
*Scapolite	Hornblende	Fluorite	Ludwigite	Garnet
*Epidote	*Vesuvianite	Zoisite	Hulsite	*Epidote
*Hedenbergite	*Spinel	Andalusite		

Mineral accessions from intrusive rock

*Specularite	Bornite	Molybdenite	Cassiterite	Tetradymite
*Magnetite	*Sphalerite	Arsenopyrite	Willemite	Altaite
*Chalcopyrite	Pyrrhotite	Galena	Pyrite	Scheelite

Original rock minerals

Clay	Quartz	Calcite	Dolomite

The most diagnostic minerals are lime silicates, magnetite, and specularite with sulphides, in intimate relationships. Common types of deposits and mineral associations are:

Metal	Chief metallic minerals	Examples
Iron	Magnetite, hematite	Cornwall, Pa
Copper	Chalcopyrite, bornite, pyrite, pyrrhotite, magnetite	Morenci, Ariz
		Cananea, Mex
Zinc	Sphalerite, magnetite, pyrite, pyrrhotite, galena	Hanover, N M
Lead	Galena, sphalerite, magnetite, chalcopyrite, pyrite, pyrrhotite	Inyo Co, Cal
Tin	Cassiterite, wolframite, magnetite, pyrrhotite	Saxony
Tungsten	Scheelite or wolframite, molybdenite	Mill City, Nev
Molybdenum	Molybdenite	Yetholin, Australia
Gold	Arsenopyrite, native gold	Hedley, B C

Practical considerations. Contact metamorphic deposits are mainly confined to certain rock types. They are not associated with extrusive rocks, such as rhyolite and

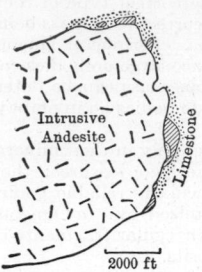

andesite, but only with granular, deep-seated intrusives; they are rare with extremely silicic or basic rocks and are most common with intermediate types, as monzonite, granodiorite and diorite. Position of deposits is influenced by faults and by dip of host rocks; such channelways conduct vapors outward from intrusive. They are usually confined to within 100 ft of intrusive contact (Fig 6); hence search should be directed to marginal areas, or where channelways extend outward, as at Rochester, Nev; large roof pendants included in intrusive are particularly favorable sites for ore, as at Mackay, Idaho. Inferences from outcrops as to form and size are unreliable, because orebodies are so irregular in form. Orebodies are irregularly distributed in contact aureole and generally unconnected; hence much exploration is required and predictions of extensions far beyond exposed places are unsafe. Irregularities in tenor are common, and aver grade is low.

Fig 6. Contact Metamorphic Deposits of Magnetite in Limestone, surrounding Intrusive Mass of Andesite, Iron Springs, Utah. (Shading = Ore; Stipling = Contact Minerals.) After Leith

e. Replacement

This is the dominating process of mineral deposition in epigenetic deposits. It is a gradual process of simultaneous solution of minerals and rocks, and of deposition in the same space, volume for volume. Thus, a cubic meter of limestone may be replaced by a cubic meter of sulphides, which often retain the limestone structure. The interchange is not molecular, but is of molecular proportions. Replacement is accomplished by liquid or gaseous solutions and almost any rock may be replaced by ore, although carbonate rocks are most susceptible; it is helped by fractures or schistose structures in the host rocks; takes place at normal temperatures (supergene enrichment) and at low, intermediate, and high temperatures. Replacement bodies are commonly surrounded by a halo of rock alteration, particularly those in igneous rocks. Replacement bodies may be massive, lode-fissure, or disseminated.

Criteria of replacement: (a) structure of original rock preserved in ore; (b) unsupported nuclei of original rock surrounded by ore (such as could not have remained suspended in an open cavity); (c) doubly terminated crystals that have grown freely on all sides; (d) crystals and ore faces intersecting original rock structures. DISTINCTIONS: from magmatic deposits by above criteria and hydrothermal mineralogy; from contact metamorphic deposits (emplaced by replacement) by lack of contact metamorphic mineral assemblages and presence of hydrothermal minerals (these two types grade into each other); from cavity fillings by above criteria and lack of crustification and vugs.

Features affecting search for and exploration of replacement bodies. The form and size, often not predictable, are controlled by: (a) homogeneity of rock; (b) form and

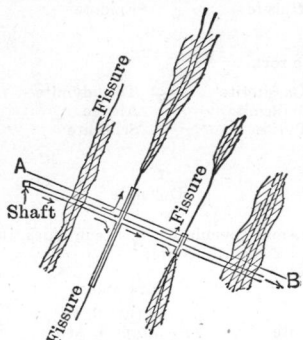

structure of host rock; (c) number and distribution of channels of access; (d) mode of replacement. Since replacement can not occur without entry of solutions, channels of access are important guides to ore sites; an orebody may occur where a fissure intersects a congenial bed of limestone; thus more ore may be expected where similar fissures intersect the same bed. Form of replacement masses in homogeneous rocks like limestone is generally determined by arrangement and distribution of minute fissures. In non-homogeneous rocks, like alternating beds of lime and shale, flat

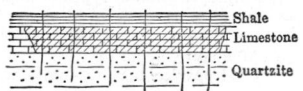

Fig 7. Plan of Flat Shoots in Thin Sedimentary Layers. (Arrows show Direction for Crosscuts and Drifts)

Fig 8. Narrow Bed between Unfavorable Formations (Replaced along Fissure Zone so as to give Deposit a Bedded Form). Cross-sec

shoots develop in the limestone where it is intersected by fissures (Fig 7); closely spaced fissures result in wide bedded shoots (Fig 8). Replacement may begin in disconnected centers, causing disseminated deposits; if continued, the centers coalesce to form a large solid orebody. Such ore boundaries are generally sharp (Fig 9–12). For full discussion, see Bib (649).

Search in sedimentary rocks. Most replacement deposits in sediments are localized by fissures that cross favorable beds; the ore spreads out within beds on either side of fissure, giving rise to tabular-shaped bodies (Fig 12). Undersides of impervious beds are particularly favorable. Search should be made by following fractures toward a favorable bed, and crosscutting in that bed normal to trend of fissure system (Fig 7, 12). SEARCH IN IGNEOUS ROCKS should be conducted along fracture zones, or within areas of intense hydrothermal alteration.

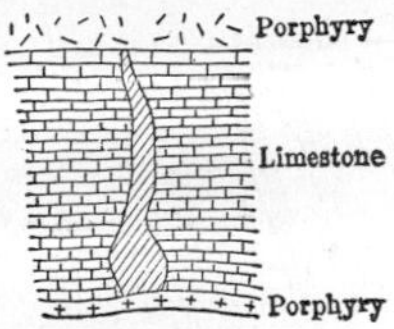

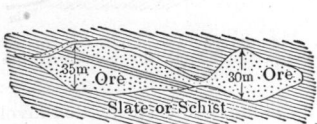

Fig 9. Oreshoot in Limestone, Leadville, Colo. (Greatest Extension across Bed, because of Dominant Control of Fissured Area). Cross-sec. After A. A. Blow

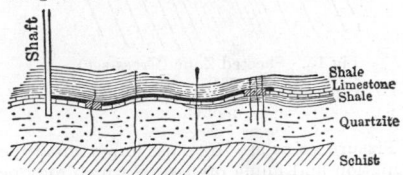

Fig 10. Irregular Replacement Orebody in Limestone (Showing Tendency toward Greatest Extent Parallel to Bedding Planes). Longit sec. After A. A. Blow

Fig 11. Massive Replacement of Shattered Clay-slate and Graywacke, Rio Tinto, Spain. (Form determined by Extent of Zone of Shattering). Plan

Fig 12. Section on *AB* (Fig 7), showing Position of Favorable Bed, and Occurrence of Ore in it along Fissures; also Position of Drift beneath Cap Rock

Outcrops of replacement bodies. Replacement veins are irregular in outline; outcrops may not be commensurate in size with underlying orebodies. Disseminated replacements in igneous rocks are confined to, limited in size by, and have extent of, the fractured area in which they are localized. Replacements in sedimentary rocks generally have greatest extension parallel to bedding planes; hence, in flat rocks, outcrops are large in proportion to volume of ore. Inclined beds, as at Leadville, Colo, outcrop only where the edges of including limestone are eroded; slight outcrops then often represent large deposits and justify search in depth. Mineralized fractures should be followed downward to favorable beds where lateral exploration can be carried on. In vert beds, replacement bodies often have an adequate outcrop, which represents expectations below.

Examples of some replacement deposits. In the following are given, first the ore, second the type, and third the location. IRON: magnetite, Dover, N J, Lyon Mt, N Y; hematite, Iron Mt, Mo. COPPER: disseminated, porphyry coppers, Utah Copper; lode, Kennecott, Alaska, Magma, Ariz; massive, Bisbee, Ariz, Noranda, Que, Boliden, Sweden. LEAD: massive, Leadville, Sullivan, B C; lode, Coeur d'Alene, Idaho, Tintic, Utah; disseminated, S E Mo. ZINC: massive, Flin Flon, Manitoba, Silesia; lode, Franklin Furnace, N J. GOLD: lode, Homestake, S D, Kirkland Lake and Porcupine, Ont. SILVER: lode, Cerro de Pasco, Peru, Park City, Utah. TIN: pipes, Transvaal. MERCURY: lode, Almaden, Spain. MOLYBDENUM: disseminated, Climax, Colo, Utah Copper, Utah.

f. Cavity Filling

This consists of deposition from solutions of ore minerals in pre-existing openings in rocks. The kinds of cavities that are filled and the resulting mineral deposits are:

Cavity	Deposits	Cavity	Deposits
Fissures	Fissure veins	Irregular caves	Cave deposits
Shear zones	Shear zone deposits	Channels	Cave deposits
Joints	Ladder veins	Gashes	Gash veins
Tension cracks	Stockworks	Breccias	
Saddles	Pitches and flats	Volcanic	Pipes
	Saddle reefs	Collapse	Breccia fillings
		Tectonic	"
		Pores	Disseminated
		Vesicules	Vesicular fillings

Cavity-filling deposits generally display comb structure or crustification, consisting of layers of different minerals on or about country rock (Fig 13), with crystals projecting toward former opening; vugs are common. Minerals are typically hydrothermal, ranging from normal- to high-temp minerals; commonly, intermediate to low. Cavity-filling deposits grade into replacements, usually accompanied by some replacement of walls or included country rock (Fig 14). The replacement part may constitute the bulk of a deposit; hence, prompt recognition of this feature is desirable.

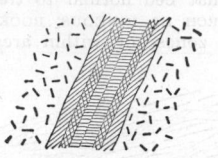

Fig 13. Single Filled Fissure

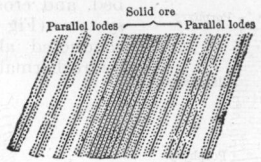

Fig 14. Replaced Sheeted Zone

Fig 15. Sheeted Zone (Cross-sec), showing Largest Number of Cracks at Seat of Heaviest Movement

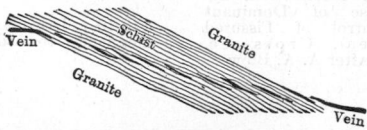

Fig 16. Vein dividing into Lenses *en echelon* on passing at Small Angle through Cleavable Formation

Fissure veins are the most important type of cavity filling. Their formation involves formation and filling of fissure, which may occur simultaneously or be separated by long time intervals. VARIETIES: (*a*) simple filled cracks; (*b*) sheeted zones (Fig 15), consisting of closely spaced parallel cracks filled with ore; (*c*) single, fat lenses, commonly in schists (Fig 16); (*d*) composite, wide zones of nearly parallel fissures connected by diagonals (Fig 14).

Physical details. Most fissure veins are narrow and inclined. When exposed at surface, the outcrop is straight or curved, depending upon dip of fissure and surface relief.

Veins are seldom planes; usually of complex curvature, and characterized by pinches and swells (Fig 17), branches, horses or included masses of country rock, anastomosing (Fig 29), and brecciation. Walls are frozen or free, and may be marked by selvage or gouge, or they may be commercial, that is, ore grades into country rock with no definite wall.

Practical considerations. Prospecting, exploration and development are often based upon assumption that fissures continue considerable distances along the strike observed at one point. This leads to errors in locating shafts, adits, or crosscuts to intersect vein, and in locating claims with respect to vein apex.

Knowing the aver strike reduces risk in predicting extensions from a single exposure; trenching, and observation of aver strike should precede selection of sites for openings. Aver trend of other fissures in district is suggestive. If bedrock is covered, surface exploration for continuation of a fissure may be guided by projecting its apex on to a topographic map (see Art 5). DIP of fissures has little relation to their size or continuity. Most fissures have high dip (50°–90°); the North Star vein (dip about 20°), Grass Valley, Cal, is an exception. It is not true that veins of low dip are never wide. Dip may vary greatly; projections of dips observed at only one point are unsafe unless attested by geologic habit of other fissures of district. Fissure veins generally have small displacement; large faults in a district are not often mineralized; much exploration has been wasted on them.

Fissure systems. Except in case of a few large veins, like Comstock Lode, fissure veins seldom occur alone. The strains that produce fissures of small displacement generally find relief in many cracks. Fissures of approx same trend form a SYSTEM. There may be several systems in a district; intersecting systems may be of different age and displace each other, as at Butte (Fig 18), or may be COGNATE, formed contemporaneously due to same cause (Fig 19, 20). Varieties of cognate systems: (a) parallel, (b) intersecting, like cleavage in augite (Fig 20), (c) fan-shaped, (d) radial, as at Cripple Creek, Colo.

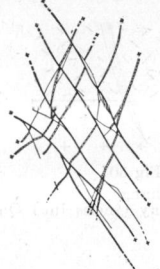

Practical considerations. It is often erroneously assumed that the wall of a vein means the limit of metallization. Since parallel fissures are common (Fig 21, 22) crosscutting is advisable, especially in early stages of development, and has yielded fruitful results, as at Camp Bird, Colo, and Kennecott, Alaska.

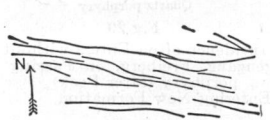

Fig 18. Superposed Vein Systems of Different Ages, Butte

Fig 19. Vein System; Fissures All Cognate. (Part of a System in Harz Mts)

Fig 20. Two Intersecting and Mutually Alternating Systems, Forming a Cognate Group

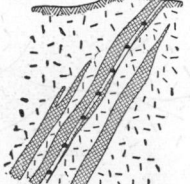

Fig 21. Large Filled Fissure with Parallel Lodes

Fig 22. Two Parallel Lodes overlooked through Insufficiency of Lateral Exploration

Fissures of same system are generally of same age and mineralization; those of cognate groups are mineralized alike. Fissures of different systems usually have different minerals, ores, and values (Freiberg, Saxony); veins of different ages may also have different ownership rights. Younger fissures pass through and fault earlier ones, and such intersections do not carry same apex rights as junctions of cognate fissures. An intersecting cognate system (Fig 20) will be mineralized alike; two different intersecting systems will be mineralized unlike. Relative ages may be determined by: (a) relation to rocks of known age, one cutting a porphyry and the other cut by it; (b) if of different ages, one generally faults the other in same direction; ore of older is crushed and dragged, and ore banding of younger passes through older (Fig 23). Termination of one vein against another does not imply faulting, since the two may be cognate (Fig 20); (c) in contemporaneous cognate fissures the ore bands will not be broken, but

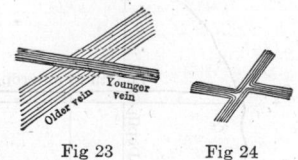

Fig 23   Fig 24

turn from one into the other (Fig 24). These may suffer post-mineral movement simulating different ages.

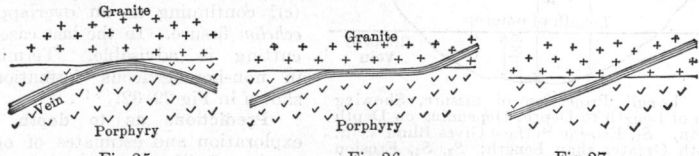

Fig 25. Fissure Deflected by New Formation, due to Small Angle of Incidence
Fig 26. Fissure, first Deflected, then Entering New Formation
Fig 27. Fissure at Small Angle of Incidence may enter thus without Change

Effects on fissures of change in formation. Since rocks fracture differently, fissures generally change in passing from one formation into another (Fig 25–32). This change is often for the worse, since initial exploitation usually starts on widest and richest portions. A fissure meeting a new formation at a low angle of incidence may be deflected (Fig 25) or refracted (Fig 26); rarely, there is no change (Fig 27). The higher the angle of inci-

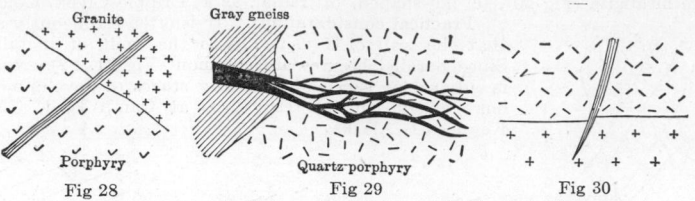

Fig 28   Fig 29   Fig 30

Fig 28.   Fissure at High Angle of Incidence often Enters without much Change
Fig 29.   Change in Gottlob Morgengang, Freiberg, on Passing from Gray Gneiss into Quartz-porphyry (after Beck)
Fig 30.   Fissure Pinching Out on Entering New Formation

dence, the less the probable change (Fig 28). Passage into a more brittle rock causes spraying (Fig 29); into less rigid rocks, pinching (Fig 30-31); into tough rocks (shales), dying out (Fig 32); and angling into a fissile rock causes an *en echelon* dispersion into lenses (Fig 16).

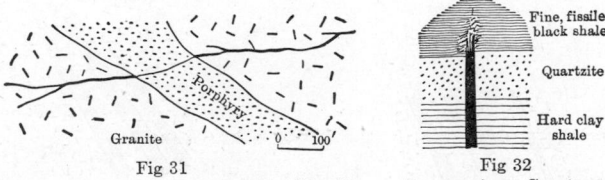

Fig 31   Fig 32

Fig 31.   Seven-thirty Vein, Georgetown, Colo, Pinching on Passing from Granite into Porphyry (Bull 260, USGS)
Fig 32.   Large Fissure Ending Abruptly on Passing into Easily Distorted Shale, Ouray, Colo (Bull 260, USGS)

Practical considerations. A geologic map, showing formations in path of fissure vein along strike and dip, permits predictions as to expected behavior. Any change in formation may produce a physical or mineral change in a fissure vein. Outcrops of veins restricted to one of several equally exposed formations indicates the latter are unfavorable. Most favorable are homogeneous formations, as monzonite. A fissure vein can not enter a rock later in age than itself, for example, an intrusive andesite.

Fissure veins terminate within a homogeneous formation by: (1) abutting a fissure or fault (Fig 18); (2) splitting into diverging stringers (Fig 29); (3) pinching to a mere crack (Fig 30). The possibilities of pinching are (Fig 17): (*a*) a pinch intervening between two swells, (*b*) a final termination, (*c*), continuing as an overlapping *en echelon* fissure. In the last case, crosscutting is advisable. Terminations in non-homogeneous formations are shown in Fig 29-32.

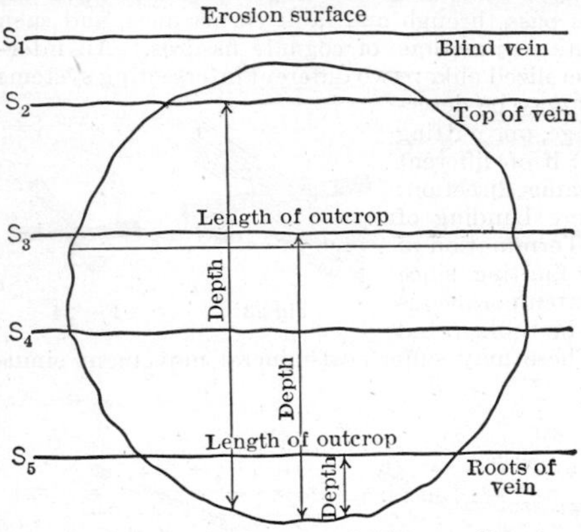

Predictions as to depth. Deep exploration and estimates of ore tonnage and life of mine depend upon predictions as to expected depth. If no change of formation is indicated,

Fig 33.   Longit Projection of Fissure, Showing Relation of Length to Depth, Depending on Depth of Erosion. S_1, Erosion Surface Gives Blind Vein; S_2, Depth Greater than Length; S_3, S_4, Erosion Revealing Medial Sections, with Depth Approx Half the Length; S_5, Roots of Vein, Length Greatly Exceeding Depth

low-temp and press minerals often mean shallow depth, while medium- to high-mean greater depth. Strong fault fissures commonly extend to depth, weak ones are apt to be shallow. As a rough rule, the depth will equal about half the length, depending upon the depth of erosion. Shallow erosion may fail to expose a " blind " vein; progressively deeper erosion may reveal the top, medial portion, or roots of a vein. If the top is exposed, the depth may equal the length; if the medial portion, half the length; if the roots, less than half the length. This is based on assumption that fissure veins originally are roughly circular, lens-shaped bodies (Fig 33). With erosion surface at S_2, the depth is practically a diam; at S_3 or S_4, the outcrop is a diam and the depth a radius; at S_5, the outcrop is a chord and the depth only part of a radius. Depth of erosion may be estimated by: (a) top of vein is indicated if enclosing formation has not suffered much erosion, as in Boulder batholith, Mont; (b) rarely, fault scarps may indicate recency and lack of erosion; (c) extent of associated placers may roughly measure the amount of erosion; (d) contrast between zone of secondary enrichment (see later) and primary ore permits an estimate of amount of erosion; a thick zone of rich secondary sulphides overlying low-grade primary ore means

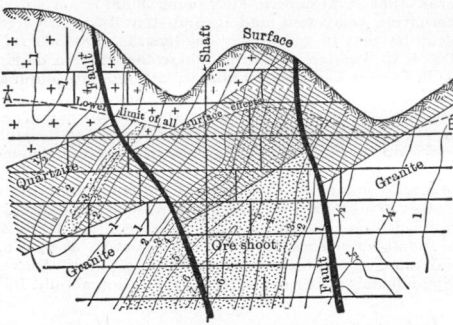

Fig 34.   Assay Sec on Plane of Vein, Showing Lines of Equal Widths of Vein Filling. High Values (Shaded Areas) Correspond to Relatively Great Widths, and Show that the Two are in Some Way Related

extensive erosion of upper part of vein; (e) district habit of veins may afford a clue; all veins of Cobalt, Ont, are shallow.

Ore shoots. Commercial minerals of most veins are concentrated in ore shoots of various shapes and sizes. Common types: 1, open space, due to available open space, or "swells"; 2, intersection, due to vein intersections; 3, impounded, due to damming of solutions by impervious barriers; 4, wall-controlled, due to effect of wall rock upon precipitation; 5, structure-controlled, due to decrease of temp and press; 6, recurrent, due to successive periods of metallization; 7, unsolved, includes many. RECOGNITION by mineralogy, assays, and plotting of distribution.

Geological assay maps help determine localization and expectation of shoots and aid exploration. Plot a longit sec of vein, showing rocks, fissures, oxidized, enriched, and primary zones, vein widths by contours, and outlines of ore shoots (restricted to primary ores, Fig 34-36). The superposition may show a definite relation between ore shoots and influence of wall rock, as within diabase dikes

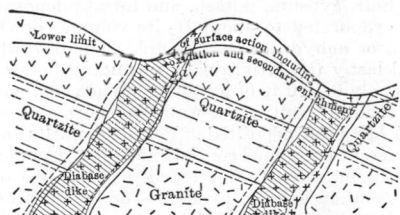

Fig 35.   Sec of Veins Showing Geology Platted on Walls (Solid Lines = Far Wall; Dotted = Near Wall. Shading Shows how Ore Shoots Occur only between Diabase Walls)

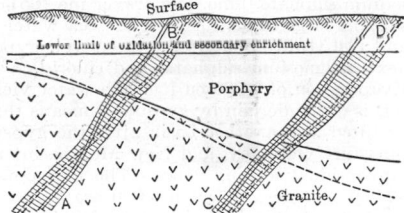

Fig 36.   Sec Along Vein (Solid Lines = Geol on Far Wall; Dotted, on Near Wall. Shading Indicates High Value, or Commercial Ore. Ore Shoots Due to Presence of Older Intersecting Vein)

(Fig 35) (hence other dikes suggest places for exploration); or to intersecting fissures (Fig 36), showing that other fissures of same system may also localize shoots; or to widths of fissure (Fig 34). If vein occupies a fault fissure, the geology of both walls may be plotted on separate tracings, which can then be shifted over each other until the geology coincides, thus giving the fault displacement (both walls are on same drawing in Fig 34-36). Shoots may be independent of above causes; then the only guiding rule for search is that they are apt to recur at fairly regular intervals.

Examples of fissure veins. GOLD: Cripple Creek, Colo; Mother Lode, Cal; El Oro, Mex; Kalgoorlie, Aust. SILVER: Pachuca, Mex; Potosí, Bolivia; Cobalt, Ont; Tintic, Utah. SILVER-LEAD: San Juan, Colo; Przibram, Bohemia; Freiberg, Saxony. COPPER: Butte, Mont; Cerro de Pasco, Peru. LEAD: Clausthal, Prussia; Linares, Spain. TIN: Llallagua and Huanuni, Bolivia; Cornwall, Eng. ANTIMONY: Hunan, China. MERCURY: New Idria, Cal. TUNGSTEN: Kiangsi, China.

Other important cavity filling deposits. SHEAR ZONES are wide zones of fracturing impregnated by ore minerals. They constitute large and important deposits of Cu, Au, Zn and other metals. Mostly, replacement deposits. LADDER VEINS are short, transverse, cooling-joint cracks in dikes.

Transverse lengths are no greater than width of enclosing dike, but longit lengths may be great. Where closely spaced, the dike as a whole may be worked, as at Morning Star, Victoria. STOCK-WORKS are masses of rock traversed by a network of small veinlets, so closely spaced that the whole mass may be mined. Their typical habitat is in upper part of a stock. Stockworks make large deposits of Sn, Au, Cu, Pb, Zn and other metals. Most of the world's lode tin comes from stock-works, that at Altenberg, Ger, being 3 000 ft across. SADDLE REEFS are openings occurring when alternating competent and incompetent beds are folded into close anticlines. A vert cross-sec resembles that of a saddle. Leg-lengths, 100–300 ft; a single axis was horizontally followed for 3 000 ft in Bendigo, Australia, where 300 million dollars in gold were produced from such deposits. Saddles occur one below another; at Bendigo, mining has reached 4 600-ft depth. PITCHES AND FLATS are tension cracks accompanying gentle warping in sediments. Wisconsin lead and zinc ores are examples. SOLUTION CAVITIES in the form of caves, galleries, and gash veins are a source of Pb, Zn, Cu, Hg and many other ores. They occur only in soluble rocks, generally resting upon an insoluble rock. BRECCIA FILLINGS are spaces in breccias occupied by ores: (a) volcanic breccia pipes (Bassick mine, Colo); (b) collapse breccia deposits, due to collapse of rock overlying a large solution cavity; these are common in Utah, Ariz, Colo, and Mex, and contain large deposits of Cu, Zn and Ag-Pb ores; at Bisbee, Ariz, they form a crackled surface area, 1 000 ft above the ore; (c) tectonic breccias, resulting from tectonic stresses; these contain large Zn deposits in Tenn. PORE SPACE FILLINGS are found where rock pores are impregnated, as by Cu, vanadium and radium minerals, and oil in sandstone. VESICULAR FILLINGS are the filling of lava vesicles or blow holes, as in Lake Superior amygdaloidal copper deposits. Exploration should follow the tops of lava flows.

g. Sedimentation

Sedimentary processes (650) give rise to commercially valuable deposits, as Fe, Mn, Cu, uranium, phosphates, sulphur, magnesite, bentonite, building stones, cement rocks, commercial clays, and coal. The world's largest reserves of Fe, phosphates, and clay are of sedimentary origin. The deposits are relatively thin, but widely distributed; those of Fe, as the Clinton ores of the U S, and the " minette " ores of Central Europe, occur over hundreds of square miles.

Practical considerations. Such deposits vary little in thickness or grade over short distances; hence relatively few openings are necessary to delimit ore and estimate values. A single ore bed may be repeated in outcrop by folding or faulting. Exploration is guided by fixing the position of beds in the geologic column and by revealing the structure from surface mapping.

h. Evaporation

Evaporation of bodies of marine, lake, and subsurface waters yields commercial deposits of salt, gypsum and anhydrite, potash, nitrates, borates, sodium carbonate, sodium sulphate, lime, and travertine (651). Salt, gypsum, potash, and nitrate deposits support large industries. When sea water is evaporated to about $1/2$ its volume, Fe_2O_3 and $CaCO_3$ are deposited; to $1/5$ vol, gypsum or anhydrite; to $1/10$ vol, common salt; next, magnesium sulphates and chloride; and lastly the bittern salts, including potash. Evaporation of 1 000 cu ft of sea water yields only 0.7 cu ft of gypsum. When common salt is not underlain by gypsum it means that a cut-off body of sea water has been shifted or tilted into another basin after the gypsum has been deposited. Potash deposits (as Stassfurt, Germany, and New Mex basin) represent enormous concentration by draining into residual settling pools. The U S potash basin, recently developed, has an area of 40 000 sq miles, of which 3 000 are known to contain sylvite, carnallite, or langbeinite; present potash mining is centered in 33 sq miles near Carlsbad, N Mex.

Practical considerations. Statements given for " sedimentation " above apply also to marine products of evaporation. Salt and gypsum alternate in layers; they also alter-nate with potash beds. Beds are generally horiz, and search is made by vert drilling.

i. Residual Concentration Deposits

These result from removal of undesired materials and accumulation of an insoluble residue of desired substances by weathering. Requirements: (a) rocks containing valu-able minerals that are insoluble; (b) climatic conditions favoring chemical decay; (c) gentle topography, on which residue can be retained (erosional plateaus are especially favorable); (d) long-continued crustal stability, to allow quantity accumulation. In one case, the residue is an accumulation of a pre-existing mineral that has suffered no change (iron oxide in limestone, liberated by solution of limestone and accumulated as a residual deposit of iron ore). In another case the residual mineral is caused by weathering, as the feldspar of a syenite decomposes to form bauxite, which accumulates to form a deposit. Source materials: (a) pre-existing deposits, as siderite that yields iron oxide ore; (b) disseminated minerals in rocks, as iron or manganese oxides in limestone or chert; (c) rock minerals that weather to new constituents, as clays, bauxite.

Residual iron ores result from solution of enclosing limestone or chert, and accumulation as hematite or limonite; as at Lake Superior and Mayari, Cuba; also Appalachian brown ores.

Residual manganese deposits are the source of most manganese. They are the accumulation of: (a) manganese oxides disseminated in limestone or dolomite (southern U S); (b) of manganese silicates in crystalline schists (India, Gold Coast, Brazil); (c) of former manganiferous deposits (Butte, Mont).

Bauxite deposits result from special conditions of tropical weathering of aluminous rocks, free from quartz, upon old erosion surfaces. Such weathering is lacking in the soils of temperate regions. Aluminum silicates break down, forming the bauxite, gibbsite, boehmite and diaspore; silica and iron are removed in solution and bauxite accumulates. Deposits of Arkansas come from nepheline syenite; those of France and Southern Europe are beds and pockets from limestone impurities; those of Guiana and Gold Coast are blankets from crystalline schists; those of Russia are transported bedded deposits.

Residual clays result from weathering of aluminous rocks. They consist of kaolinite, halloysite, and impurities. Orthoclase breaks down to form aluminum silicate, and soluble potassium carbonate and silica. The kaolins or china clays come from pegmatite dikes; other industrial clays, from other rocks.

Other residual products include zinc, tin and nickel ores, kyanite, barite, phosphates, tripoli, and ochers.

Practical considerations. Search for these deposits must be confined to present or ancient erosion surfaces. As they are mostly flat blankets they can be explored by vert drilling or test pits. They usually contain impurities, which affect their value.

j. Mechanical Concentrations (Placers)

Placers result from weathering of enclosing rocks or gangue, releasing valuable substances which are then concentrated by water or air. Stream, beach, eluvial, and eolian placers are thus formed. For concentration, the ore minerals must be of high sp gr, chemically resistant and durable. The common placer substances are Au, Pt, cassiterite, magnetite, chromite, ilmenite, native Cu, precious and semi-precious stones, zircon, monazite, and phosphate. The materials are derived from: (a) commercial lodes (Mother Lode) Cal; (b) non-commercial lodes (veinlets of cassiterite); (c) sparsely disseminated minerals (Pt grains); (d) rock-forming minerals (magnetite, zircon); (e) former placers. The most favorable sites for placers are where weathering is deep and topographic relief exists. Stream placers form pay streaks on stream bottoms where swift water slackens, as below rapids, canyons, and inside of meandering curves. Pay-streaks may become buried by stream meandering. Former stream placers may be left as BENCH gravels or HIGH-LEVEL gravels, that have been covered by lavas, and later exposed by stream canyons with different courses.

Eluvial placers are those formed in regions of deep decay, just below the outcrop of the source lodes, where streams have not worked them (gold and cassiterite). BEACH GRAVELS form on sea beaches (gold at Nome, Alaska, and zircon, monazite, and ilmenite in India). EOLIAN placers have been concentrated by the wind in Australia.

k. Oxidation and Supergene Sulphide Enrichment

When ore deposits are weathered, surface waters oxidize many minerals and yield solvents that dissolve other minerals. Thus, the upper part of a deposit becomes oxidized and leached down to the water table, forming the OXIDIZED ZONE. The metallic content of the down-trickling solutions may be precipitated beneath as sulphides, to form the SUPERGENE SULPHIDE ZONE. The unaltered lower part is the PRIMARY ZONE. The upper parts are thus impoverished and the lower enriched. Outcrops must be interpreted in the light of these changes; if the ore is in shallow surface workings is primary, no abrupt change may be expected below; if secondary, lower-grade ore may be expected beneath it. Supergene enriched ore may give way beneath to rich primary ore, as at Bisbee, Ariz, or to valueless protore, as at Ray, Ariz. A knowledge of superficial changes and ability to recognize secondary ores, and the characteristics of orebodies beneath superfiical zones, are invaluable aids in prospecting, exploration and development.

Oxidation and solution in oxidized zone (652). On weathering, most metallic minerals are leached or altered to new compounds which require metallurgical treatment different from the original materials. Deposits containing sulphides and arsenides are most susceptible. Water and oxygen act on pyrite to form H_2SO_4 and $Fe_2(SO_4)_3$; the latter attacks pyrite to form more ferric sulphate, which dissolves Cu, Zn, and Ag, forming soluble sulphates of these metals. In the presence of MnO and NaCl it also dissolves Au. The oxidized zone thus becomes impoverished in these metals. Some of the iron sulphate hydrolyses to limonite, which remains behind and forms a rusty gossan or capping. **Gossans and cappings** are indicators of what lies beneath. Other stains than limonite may persist and signify their source minerals. Discovery of gossan warrants exploration. Gossans result from massive deposits; cappings from disseminated or porphyry deposits; both are called croppings. In croppings, the iron of sulphide derivation may become fixed at the site of the original sulphides, forming INDIGENOUS limonite, or be dissolved and removed, forming TRANSPORTED limonite. The former indicates the previous presence of Cu; the latter, the lack of it, pyrite predominating. The explanation is that Cu accelerates formation of the insoluble ferric iron, while free acid, yielded by pyrite oxidation, tends to keep the Fe in soluble ferrous state, so that it can be transported. Recognition of the two types of limonite provides inferences as to character of underlying ore. Indigenous limonite occupies the voids vacated by sulphides; it is never outside of the voids; its structure indicates the kind of predecessor sulphide. It is compact, hard, and has subdued colors. Transported limonite has moved outside of the voids; in presence of reacting gangue it is precipitated as a halo around the void and floods the rock; in inert gangues it may move far, forming paints and crusts in cracks. FALSE GOSSANS are formed by transported limonite which, distant from its source, has met precipitating agencies such as carbonates. They lack indigenous limonite and do not overlie ore. Copper likewise may migrate from its original site and be precipitated by limestone as copper carbonates. Such stains are deceptive because they do not overlie ore; they show no voids, no indigenous limonite, and no indigenous copper carbonate.

Inferences as to hidden deposits (653). FORM AND SIZE of gossan are generally the same as those of underlying deposit; a fissure-vein gossan is of obvious shape; irregular replacement or contact deposits also give irregularly shaped gossans; sheeted lodes may be indicated by sheeting in the gossan. The outline of "porphyry" deposits can be determined by mapping features characteristic of copper in capping. The gossan may be much larger than original deposit, due to "mushrooming" or spilling over of Fe_2O_3 from original sulphide site. CROPPING MINERALS, if present, give positive clues as to mineral content. Their absence does not indicate lack of ore beneath. Specks of relict sulphides often persist in quartz. Stains of Cu, Mn, Co, Ni and Mo may indicate corresponding minerals. VOIDS, if lacking, indicate absence of underlying ore; if present, their abundance indicates former sulphide abundance, and shape may indicate minerals, as pyrite and galena cubes, or arsenopyrite spears. LIMONITE COLORS are indicative: seal brown, maroon, and orange colors indicate Cu; yellows and brick reds, pyrite; deep browns and yellowish browns, chalcopyrite; orange to chocolate, chalcocite or galena; tan to brown, sphalerite. LIMONITE STRUCTURES (653) are quite diagnostic. Indigenous limonite assumes various boxwork structures, as "coarse cellular" indicating chalcopyrite; "fine cellular," chalcopyrite; "cellular sponge," sphalerite; "relief limonite," chalcocite. (For fuller description, see Bateman: Economic Mineral Deposits, Chap 5). ROCK ALTERATION distinguishes primary and supergene metallization. Much sericite indicates much primary metallization; if this is highly kaolinized it indicates extensive supergene alteration with expectation of sulphide enrichment.

Factors controlling and limiting oxidation. Lack of oxygen generally occurs at the water table, but oxidation may extend lower, along fractures in regions of relief; or a rising water table, caused by valley fillings, faulting, or change to humid climate, may drown an oxidized zone. Change to arid climate inhibits oxidation. If erosion is too rapid, oxidation cannot keep pace; if time is too short, oxidation will be limited; cold climate is unfavorable. Permeable rocks aid it; dense rocks retard it. Faults deflect, impound, or cause deep oxidation. Oxidation ceases by refrigeration, burial, and depletion of oxygen by abundant sulphides. Oxidized zones may become stranded above water level, as at Bingham, Utah, or drowned beneath it, as at Miami, Ariz, or in Rhodesia. DEPTH OF OXIDATION may reach 3 000 ft (Lonely mine). In humid regions of low relief it is generally shallow; with high relief, shallow to medium depth. In glaciated regions, post-glacial oxidation is negligible, but in areas protected from deep glacial erosion it may be deep, as at Kennecott, Alaska (2 800 ft). In arid regions it may be very deep under old or mature topography, and shallow under youthful topography.

Ore deposition in oxidized zone. Metallic solutions generated by oxidation may, in passing downward, undergo precipitation in the zone of oxidation, and oxidized compounds of the metals may thus be deposited toward bottom of the zone. These include carbonates, silicates, oxides, or native metals of Cu, Zn, Pb, Ag and others. For example, $CuSO_4$ meeting $CaCO_3$ yields $CuCO_3$ and $CaSO_4$. Modes of precipitation: (a) EVAPORATION AND SATURATION, yielding efflorescences; at Chuquicamata, Chile (654), large copper deposits consist of antlerite, brochantite, chalcanthite and krohnkite; (b) OXIDATION AND HYDRATION, yielding goethite and $PbSO_4$; (c) REACTIONS BETWEEN SOLUTIONS such as NaCl and Ag_2SO_4, yielding silver chloride; carbonated solutions, by which $PbSO_4$ is changed to $PbCO_3$, and carbonates of Cu and Zn are formed; also Cu_2O, CuO, Cu and Ag; Au in $Fe_2(SO_4)_3$ solution is deposited by reduction to $FeSO_4$; (d) REACTION WITH GANGUE OR WALL ROCKS: Cu solutions with $CaCO_3$ yield Cu carbonates; with colloidal silica, chrysocolla; zinc sulphate similarly yields smithsonite and calamine.

Generalizations. Common ore minerals diagnostic of oxidized ores are carbonates, silicates and sulphates of Au, Zn and Fe; oxides of Cu, Co, Mo; chlorides, iodides, and bromides of Ag; and $PbSO_4$, $PbCO_3$, MnO_2 and boxwork limonite. Native Au, Ag, and Cu may be of oxidation or of hypogene origin. If given ores are oxidized, it follows that: (a) such ores will change in character in depth; (b) tenor will change in depth; (c) oxidized ores will be superficial; (d) metallurgy devised for oxidized ores will not apply to underlying ores; (e) extraction plans should be deferred until volume of ore is delimited; (f) future life of a mine generally depends upon what lies beneath the oxidized ores.

Supergene sulphide enrichment.

Metals in solution that escape capture in the oxidized zone trickle down to where there is no available oxygen (generally the water table), and there undergo deposition as supergene sulphides, forming the zone of secondary enrichment. Progressive erosion allows deeper oxidation, releasing more metals to be added below. Rich primary ores are made richer, valueless protore is made commercial. Primary ore may be enriched to 10 times its original metal content. The process applies chiefly to copper and silver ores.

Requirements for supergene sulphide enrichment: (a) preceding favorable oxidation; (b) downward moving erosion surface and water table; (c) sufficient time; (d) primary minerals that, upon oxidation, yield enough $Fe_2(SO_4)_3$ and H_2SO_4, as pyrite will, but chalcopyrite will not; (e) primary minerals susceptible of undergoing supergene sulphide enrichment, as Cu and Ag will, but Pb and Zn will not; (f) permeability of deposit or host rock; (g) absence of precipitants in oxidized zone (in limestone, Cu is fixed as carbonate and no supergene sulphides can form); (h) zone of no available oxygen; (i) underlying precipitants in form of sulphides, etc, because supergene sulphides are deposited only by reaction with them, and not on quartz, etc. If underlying precipitants are lacking, no supergene enrichment occurs.

Mode of precipitation. A metal in sulphate solution is precipitated by one of lower solubility than itself. The relative solubilities of common sulphides, the least soluble first, are: Hg, Ag, Cu, Bi, Pb, Sb, Zn, Ni, Co, Fe, Mn. Thus, Cu will be precipitated by any below it, but by none above; Mn is not precipitated by any of the group. This explains the commonness of supergene sulphide zones of Cu and Ag and lack of Mn; Zn should form such zones but does not; Ni may do so, but most deposits are in glaciated regions. Deposition is by replacement of the primary sulphides. Some reactions are: $CuSO_4 + ZnS = CuS + ZnSO_4$; $14\ CuSO_4 + 5\ FeS_2 + 12\ H_2O = 7\ Cu_2S + 5\ FeSO_4 + 12\ H_2SO_4$; $CuSO_4 + CuFeS_2 = 2\ CuS + FeSO_4$; $Ag_2SO_4 + ZnS = Ag_2S + ZnSO_4$. Thus, a gossan containing evidences of Cu should, under favorable erosional and climatic conditions, have an underlying enriched zone.

Degree of enrichment. INCIPIENT enrichment, characterized by thin coatings or microscopic veinlets of supergene sulphides, indicates weak enrichment or the bottom of the enriched zone. PARTIAL enrichment is where about half the primary minerals are replaced. COMPLETE enrichment (rare) is where primary minerals are largely replaced. Residual nuclei, however, indicate character of primary ores. SELECTIVE enrichment, where only certain selected minerals or grains are replaced, indicates weakness or bottom of zone. PERVASIVE enrichment is where all primary sulphides, grains and veinlets are replaced, indicating vigorous enrichment.

Factors influencing enrichment: (a) WATER LEVEL generally controls the top of enrichment, which in turn conforms to topography at time of enrichment (650). Enrichment rarely occurs above the water table but extends hundreds of feet below it. A sinking water table favors completeness; a rising one stops it. (b) HOST ROCKS must not be reactive; carbonate rocks inhibit enrichment; fractured, friable, permeable ones favor it. (c) FAULTS, if enclosed and impervious, protect underlying ores from enrichment; they also conduct enriching solutions deep into primary zone. (d) TOPOGRAPHY. Tops of enriched zones controlled by water level conform to the then existing topography. Most zones are out of adjustment with present topography. At Morenci, Ariz, enriched zone is related to earlier mature topography, but recent uplift caused canyon-cutting too fast for enrichment to keep apace. Enriched zone may be related to older topography buried beneath lavas and favorable for exploration. (e) RATE OF EROSION. Most favorable conditions for rich, thick, enriched zones are equal rate of oxidation and lowering by erosion, the two continually progressing downward. Too rapid erosion cuts through the enriched zone; if slow, the zone is thin. (f) TIME OF EXPOSURE TO WEATHERING must be great enough to provide thick zones; post-glacial time is too short. (g) PRESENCE OF MINERALS YIELDING SOLVENTS is essential, as iron sulphides; lacking these, solvents for metals are not generated.

Cessation of enrichment is caused by: (a) burial beneath thick sediments or lavas, as United Verde Ext, Ariz; (b) submergence beneath water level; (c) change of climate from (1) humid to rainless, (2) semi-arid to humid, thus raising water table near surface; (3) temperate to cold, causing refrigeration of water level, as Alaska, Siberia; (d) bottoming of ore; (e) complete enrichment, by which practically all acid-yielding yellow sulphides (pyrite, pyrrhotite, chalcopyrite) have been converted to supergene sulphides; further oxidation then only converts secondary chalcocite into copper carbonate, as in part of Inspiration deposit, Ariz. THICKNESS OF ENRICHED ZONES attains hundreds of feet; 3-8 ft at Ducktown, Tenn, 150-400 ft at Ray, Ariz, 450 ft at Magma, Ariz, 1 400 ft at Bingham, Utah. At United Verde Ext mine, Jerome, Ariz, is a fossil-enriched zone 400 ft thick overlain by 450 ft of oxidized zone, the latter buried under 750 ft of sedimentaries and lavas.

Recognition of supergene enriched deposits is essential to intelligent exploration and development, to determine what part of enriched zone is revealed, expectable ore above or below, and tenor and character of primary ore in depth. Criteria are: ZONING. The 3 zones, oxide, supergene sulphide, and primary, are characteristic. Supergene zones must be distinguished from primary enriched zones; former show abrupt mineralogic changes and are generally related to a recent topography, but latter could have a topographic relation to surface existing at time of first metallization. GOSSANS. Enriched ores generally leave some evidence in the gossan, such as rock alteration, stains, and character of limonite boxwork previously discussed. EROSION must have been sufficient to release enough metal to produce enrichment. DISTRICT HABIT is also helpful. MINERALOGY. Sooty chalcocite is the only diagnostic mineral. Other minerals, as chalcocite, covellite, or argentite, are common but also occur under primary conditions; however, if associated with kaolin or other supergene products they become diagnostic. In general, chalcocite,

Common Indicative Ore Minerals

Metal	Minerals generally of primary origin	Minerals usually of secondary (sulphide) enrichment origin	Minerals usually originating in oxidized zone
Copper	Chalcopyrite Bornite *Enargite *Tetrahedrite *Tennantite	Chalcocite Covellite *Sooty chalcocite	Native copper *Malachite *Azurite *Brochantite Antlerite *Atacamite *Chrysocolla *Cuprite *Tenorite
Silver	*Tetrahedrite *Tennantite	Native silver Argentite Pyrargyrite Proustite Stephanite Polybasite Pearceite	*Cerargyrite *Embolite *Bromyrite
Gold	Native gold Gold tellurides	Native gold	Native gold
Zinc	*Sphalerite Willemite	Wurtzite	*Smithsonite *Calamine *Hydrozincite
Lead	Galena		*Cerussite *Anglesite *Pyromorphite Leadhillite
Iron	Pyrite Marcasite *Pyrrhotite *Arsenopyrite Magnetite Hematite *Specularite Siderite	Marcasite	*Goethite *Iron sulphates Hematite

* Invariably primary, secondary, or oxidized, according to column in which name of mineral appears.

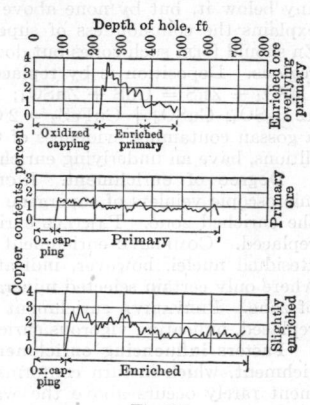

Fig 37

covellite, or argentite in abundance in upper part of sulphide zone, but diminishing with depth, is a safe indication. For other minerals see adjoining Table. CURVES. Curves of copper assays against depth from drill holes (Fig 37) are characteristic. If curves of Fe or S content are superimposed, these cross the Cu curve at top and bottom of enriched zone. MICROSCOPIC CRITERIA are generally conclusive. Texture of supergene sulphides is characteristic. Also, the microscope will reveal if supergene sulphides have replaced only FeS_2, indicating lean pyrite protore beneath; if they replace abundant galena, bornite, and chalcopyrite, commercial primary ores may be expected.

1. Metamorphism

Effect of metamorphism is two-fold; it produces commercial deposits and profoundly alters earlier ones. Those produced are non-metallics, formed by recombinations or recrystallization of rock minerals, and include asbestos, graphite, talc and soapstone, sillimanite and kyanite, emery and garnet. Metamorphism of earlier deposits produces physical rather than compositional changes; ores are made gneissic, particularly those containing galena, which flows readily under pressure; texture becomes streaked, banded, indiscriminate, and mineral content may be obscured.

Asbestos results from hydrothermal metamorphism of various rocks. The high-grade chrysotile varieties are the fibrous form of serpentine, altered from peridotite, serpentine (Quebec) or highly magnesian limestones (Sierra Ancha, Ariz). The commercial amphibole varieties, crocidolite and amosite, occur in banded ironstones in Africa; anthophyllite is mined in N America; asbestos occurs as cross, slip, and mass fiber, in narrow veinlets, separated from the rock mass after mining.

Graphite occurs disseminated in marbles, schists, gneisses, quartzites, and metamorphosed coal beds (a non-metamorphic occurrence is in pegmatite dikes). It is carbonaceous matter, formerly present, which has been recrystallized and segregated into pure carbon flakes. The rock mass is mined as a whole and the graphite extracted.

Talc and soapstone of commerce occur as masses associated with ultra-basic igneous rocks (peridotite, dunite), or as lenses in carbonate rocks. It is derived by hydrothermal alteration of highly magnesian rocks. Talc lenses are mined separately; soapstone masses, quarried, and commercial slabs sawn from large blocks.

Emery is a mixture of magnetite and corundum, with some hematite or spinel; occurs in pod-like lenses in schists or marbles, and results from metamorphism or contact-metamorphism.

Garnets for abrasives (chiefly almandite) occur disseminated in metamorphic rocks and result from metamorphism of aluminum silicates containing Fe, Ca, Mg, Mn, or Cu. Garnet rocks also yield placers of garnet. Adirondack deposits in gneiss contain 7-8% garnet.

Andalusite, sillimanite, kyanite, and dumortierite, used as refractories, also result from metamorphism of rocks.

4. PROSPECTING METHODS

Surface methods: tracing float, tracing by panning, trenching and test-pitting. Search for mineral that does not outcrop and lies at considerable depth is done by geophysical methods (Sec 10A), boring (Art 7), or shaft-sinking (Art. 12; also Sec 7, 8, 9). Methods are varied and combined to suit local conditions or fancy of the prospector.

Tracing float (Cornish, " shoading "). Pieces of ore (float) are broken from outcrops by processes of erosion, and gradually work their way downhill into streams, where they may be carried long distances. The prospector finding float on a hillside, or in a gulch or stream, tries to follow it back to its source. A rough idea of the distance which float has traveled is gained from the size and abundance of pieces, and their roughness or water-worn condition.

Many outcrops which are the source of float are concealed by a covering of soil. In such cases, at some point below the outcrop the float disappears, or " goes down." Trenches or test pits are used to follow float farther. The distance between soil-covered outcrops and the point at which float goes down varies with depth of cover, topography, and climate. On flat slopes (6%) in desert regions of southwest U S, float has been found on the surface within a few feet of outcrops covered with 1 to 2 ft of soil. Two deposits of chromite in Md, in flat, unglaciated country, were found directly under strong surface showings of float. In Marysville district, Mont, at one point float went down on a hillside and was followed by pits for 500 ft before finding the outcrop; bedrock was 10 ft to 12 ft below surface. In the far north, where freezing and thawing have gone on a long time, the " creep " on the hillsides is great, and float may be found far from the outcrop. Practically no importance attaches to the sporadic occurrence of valuable mineral in glacial drift.

In general, tracing float is applicable only in searching for ores tough enough to escape disintegration by erosion. Gold-quartz, or pyritic ores with siliceous gangue, in particular, yield float which is resistant and easily recognized. The value of, and results from, the method depend largely on the personal equation of the prospector. Knowledge of ore, keen observation, physical strength, and unending patience are essentials. Most prospectors use the pan or horn spoon to estimate the content and value of float, largely because of expense and inconvenience of obtaining assays. The U S Geol Survey, the Bur of Mines, and mining bureaus of most western States will identify specimens by visual inspection free of charge. Some State bureaus make assays at reduced prices; free in Alaska, and to licensed prospectors in some Canadian Provinces. Oregon allows 2 free assays per mo to its own residents, but requires full disclosure (with privilege of publishing) as to source of each sample.

Tracing by panning (also called " tracing " in western U S, and " loaming " in Australia). This, like tracing float, is based on recognition of the results of erosion. Weathering releases small pieces of metal and minerals from outcrops, and these migrate downhill as do larger pieces of float.

Fig 38 shows an orebody outcropping under a soil cover, and the usual position of float metal or sulphides derived from it by erosion. In a new district, the prospector works along the bottom of hillsides at an elevation (A) sufficient to avoid the debris brought into the gulch from upstream points. Samples of the top 2 or 3 in of soil are panned. If specks of metal or sulphides are found, panning is continued uphill until the trace goes down at B; then trenches or test pits are dug. The placer miner's pan, or a frying pan 4 to 6 in diam, is used for panning. In practiced hands the latter gives accurate results, and is better where water is scanty. Float found in connection with this work should be crushed and panned as an aid in determining the source of " traces." This method was

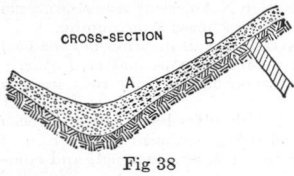

CROSS-SECTION

Fig 38

developed by "pocket hunters," and has been used chiefly in prospecting for gold, which is unaltered by weathering and easily recognized in the pan, even when present in minute particles ("colors"). It was used in Nevada, 1909, to find a concealed outcrop of a very soft vein of cinnabar, first trace found about 700 ft from outcrop. At Pamlico mine, near Hawthorne, Nev (485), gold colors were traced by panning at points along 10- or 20-ft contours. Limits of traces on each contour were marked with stakes. Resultant lines of stakes converged sharply to pockets; more gradually to ends of oreshoots. As in tracing float, correct interpretation of results requires geological knowledge. (See Art 5.)

Trenches (Cornish, " costeaning " ditches), for prospecting and exploration, are confined to shallow soil; economic limit of depth, 6–7 ft, or about as far as a man can cast from a trench with a shovel. Best applied in drift or alluvium, not over 3–4 ft deep. Trenches are usually run at right angles to the formation or the supposed strike of orebody. Prospectors use trenches to follow float or traces under cover. Useless to carry trenches to bedrock, so long as float is found.

The results of tracing close to an orebody are often indefinite, giving no indications of the strike of the outcrop sought. In such cases, several trenches at right-angles to one another are better than a single trench or a series of parallel ones, which may parallel the outcrop and not uncover it. Surface prospecting on property adjacent to developed orebodies is done by a series of parallel trenches at right angles to the strike of the known deposits. This work will uncover outcrops of parallel orebodies if they exist (Art 4, 5, 6). In districts where orebodies have no general trend, such prospecting should be done with 2 sets of parallel trenches at right-angles to each other; their distance apart is from 50 ft to 500 ft, depending on size of known orebodies in the vicinity.

Cross-section of trenches should be as small as possible; it depends on their depth and purpose. In soil 1 to 1.5 ft deep, trenches can be 12 to 14 in wide at bottom and 18 to 21 in wide at top; for depths of 2 to 2.5 ft, the minimum bottom width is about 15 in, width at top about 20 in, varying with character of the soil. These dimensions are satisfactory in following float, but are too small if detailed examination of bedrock is necessary, or if any of the bedrock is to be shot out. In such cases, minimum bottom width is between 2 and 3 ft for trenches 3 ft deep, increasing with depth of soil. In trenches on SLOPING GROUND, work should begin at their lowest point and run uphill, so that they will be self-draining. This is important in frozen ground and tundra of the far north, where there is constant seepage into excavations, due to thawing on exposure to the air. (See Sec 3.) For systematic surface trenching and examples of cost, see Art 6.

Cost per cu yd for NARROW TRENCHES less than 6 ft deep is determined more by character of the soil than by any other factor. Duty of men picking and shoveling in trenching varies from 3 to 10 cu yd per 10-hr man-day; aver, 4 to 5 cu yd. The rate is lower in prospecting work, where much time is spent in examining float and bedrock. Where weathering has been intense, trenches often extend 2 or 3 ft into the decomposed surface rocks. As relative amounts of picking and blasting ground are very variable, no accurate estimates of speed and cost are possible. Wet ground retards progress and makes examination of bedrock difficult.

Test pits (small shafts) are used in alluvium too deep for trenches. Their field is in material free from large boulders and water, and requiring little or no timbering. They are applicable for depths to 100 ft; for over 30 to 50 ft, and, in general, in water-bearing ground, they may be less suitable than boring methods (Art 7; also Sec 9). In deep soil, a test pit is sunk above the point at which float or traces go down (B, Fig 38). If float is found, or if panning shows mineral, the outcrop lies higher; the pit is abandoned and a new one started above. This process is repeated until outcrops are found or the prospector is discouraged.

If character of soil permits, small drifts can be driven from the bottom of a test pit, and float be followed on bedrock. This cheapens the last stages of such work, especially in deep ground. Test pits are not so satisfactory as trenches; they expose only a small area of bedrock and may miss outcrops of narrow and irregular veins. This objection does not hold for large, flat orebodies; in prospecting for these, test pits are located with reference to known ore on adjacent property, or systematically, or at random. (For principles, see Locating drill holes, Art 7.)

Cross-section of test pits may be circular, elliptical, or rectangular. Diam of circular pits is 30 to 36 in; elliptical pits are 36 to 42 in long by about 28 in wide; rectangular pits are rarely smaller than 4 by 4 ft or 4 by 5 ft. In point of cost and speed, small circular pits are preferable to rectangular; the amount of material to be excavated and hoisted from a 36-in circular pit is about 0.35 of that from a 4 by 5-ft rectangular pit. Circular or elliptical pits are excavated with a short-handled pick and shovel; the workman straddles the handle. A windlass is used for hoisting. Galvanized-iron water pails make good buckets for small pits; ordinary windlass buckets are better for larger rectangular pits, 2 buckets or pails being provided for each windlass. A 0.25-in wire rope should be used instead of a hemp rope in small pits over 30 ft deep; at greater depths, the travel of a hemp rope across the windlass barrel is apt to throw the bucket against the walls and dislodge loose material. Objections to circular or elliptical pits, which frequently preclude their use: (a) require labor trained and willing to work in an awkward position; (b) no room for drilling and blasting, if boulders are met; (c) practically impossible to timber them, whereas in rectangular pits a soft stratum can be close cribbed cheaply with plank. Crew on either kind of pit consists of 2 men, one digging, the other on the windlass.

Examples of test-pitting. For brown hematite in GEORGIA and ALABAMA; round test pits, 30 to 36-in diam; depth, to 50 ft; in ordinary unconsolidated material, 2 men sank 10 ft per day (5). In LEHIGH VALLEY, Penn, 2 men sank 30 to 36-in pits to depths of 50 ft at 20 to 30 ft per day (8). In NEVADA, the author sank 40 by 29-in elliptical pits, with Chinese labor, in easy gravel, at 20 ft per 12-hr day for first 40 ft. Below 40 ft, gravel was hard and clayey. Aver speed for depth of 100 ft was about 5 ft per 12-hr shift (contract work). Under same conditions, white labor on day's pay averaged 2 to 3 ft per 12-hr shift in test pits of 4 by 5 ft cross-sec. In another locality, the author sank 11 rectangular test pits; aver cross-sec, 4.1 by 4.7 ft; aver depth, 7.5 ft; material, very hard clayey gravel overlain by 6 in loam; deepest pit, 10 ft; no windlasses used; labor, 161 man-hr; aver speed, 0.51 ft per hr.

E. D. Gardner and C. H. Johnson (18) quote following examples of test pitting in ALLUVIAL GRAVELS: Near Skull Valley, Ariz, in 1932, Mexican laborers at $3 per day sank 5 pits per man-shift, averaging 2 ft wide, 3 or 4 ft long, 3.5 ft deep, in fairly fine, loose gravel; cost about 65¢ per cu yd. On Bear Gulch, Mont, 3 men at $3.50, in 1932, averaged 6 ft per day of 4 by 6-ft shaft, cribbed solid with 6-in round timber, through fine, loose gravel free from water; cost, $3 per ft to 32-ft depth. On Sauerkraut Creek, Lincoln dist, Mont, one man sank a 4 by 5-ft, solidly cribbed shaft 30 ft through dry, loose, hillside wash and moderately firm gravel in 10 days. In Pioneer dist, Mont, in 1932, four men contracted to sink 1 000 ft of shafts, averaging 35 ft deep (range, 10–65 ft) for $1 per ft. Gravel, moderately fine and free from boulders, stood unsupported except for a few ft through surface layer of hydraulic tailings, which was cribbed 4 by 4 ft; below this, shafts were circular, 4.5-ft diam. Working in pairs, and long shifts, men averaged $3.50 per day. Under favorable conditions, 2 men could sink 10 ft per day. Groove sampling was done later. Shafts were spaced 400 ft, or one to 3.6 acres; cost per acre, about $10 for sinking and $4 for sampling. On Gold Gulch, near Bowie, Ariz, about 200 pits were sunk in 1932–33 through 3-30 ft of dry placer ground, consisting of surface layer up to 3 ft of clay soil, 1–6 ft of lime-cemented gravel, with bottom bed of tight, angular gravel, containing large percentage of coarse rock and boulders up to 3 ft diam. Surface pits, 4 or 5 ft wide and about 5 ft deep, were dug by gasolene shovel at 26.5¢ per vert ft. In bottom of each, a pit 2.5 by 4.5 ft was sunk by hand to bedrock at contract price of 75¢ per ft, to 9 ft below bottom of shovel cut, and $1.50 per ft thereafter. No timbering, little blasting, no water. Some contractors earned $6 per 8-hr shift. Groove sampling was done later. On Quartz Creek, near Rivulet, Mont, in 1932, two men sank 5 by 7-ft shaft, closely cribbed, through 12 ft of fine gravel with few boulders too large to handle, in 6 days. Strong flow of water at that depth was pumped by primitive means, and remaining 6 ft to bedrock required 9 days longer; total, 30 8-hr man-shifts to sink 18 ft. Subsequent 5 by 5-ft cribbed shafts were sunk under same conditions by same men to 18 ft at 2 ft per day.

For other details see Art 6; also Sec 3. For use of test pits in systematic surface exploration, see Art 5.

Hydraulic prospecting. Water, where available, is a great aid in stripping off soil for close prospecting of bedrock. Sometimes a small stream can be led by a ditch onto a hillside above the area to be prospected. By breaking into the ditch, water can be made to flow over any desired section of ground, and cuts a trench to bedrock. A series of trenches can thus be excavated.

Booming or hushing. Where water is scanty, small reservoirs are dug on a hillside. When reservoir is full, the water is released, and rushing down the hillside strips off surface soil. Process is repeated, if necessary, until bedrock is clean. Reservoirs may be provided with automatic gates. In other places, a small quantity of water is kept running down a hillside; the soil, loosened by picks, is washed away. Large duties per man-day are thus obtained.

Shallow surface cover is sometimes completely stripped from large areas by hydraulicking with a nozzle (Art 6). M. Sheppard in 1938 gives details of hydraulic stripping of a quarry site, where deeply channelled top of limestone was covered by tough clay to (max 10 ft) aver depth of 3 ft (9). Water was pumped by 4-stage centrifugal pump from a river 300 ft below, and discharged through 1-in and 3/4-in nozzles. In 2 465 hr during 4 winter months, 8 300 cu yd was removed at $1.16 per yd (excluding supt and general), of which: power, 39¢; labor (17 240 man-hr) 64¢; supplies, repairs, 13¢.

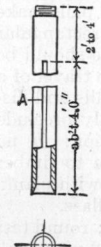

Drivepipes have a limited use in soft soil free from stones (Sec 9). Pipes are 1 to 2 in diam. Fig 39 shows bottom length of pipe. The end is filed to a cutting edge, and has a slot *A*, about 0.25 in wide, in one side; this aids in gripping the soil and facilitates cleaning the pipe. Depending on depth and character of soil, the pipe may be churned down by hand, or driven with a maul, or a weight and tackle from a tripod. Upper end of pipe is protected by a cap while driving; a shoe is used on lower end in stony soil; short lengths of pipe are screwed on as the hole deepens. The pipe is pulled every 1 to 2 ft and contents examined. The method is cheap and gives a sample section of the ground passed through. If soil is underlain by soft or distinctively colored mineral, drivepipes can be used to outline its area. For small diam pipes, limit of depth is usually 15 to 20 ft.

Piercing (or probing). Pointed steel rods are used in search for minerals lying at shallow depths in or under soil. The mineral sought is either much harder or softer than surrounding material, or possesses a characteristic color. Pointed bars are also used, as in Nor Quebec, merely to ascertain depth to bedrock, preparatory to trenching.

Fig 39. Lower End of Drivepipe

In southeastern Alaska, rods have been used to locate quartz veins covered by 2 or 3 ft of moss and humus. First quartz was found in the roots of an overturned tree. The "feel" and sharp clink of the rod against quartz distinguished it from the softer country rock. In Butler and Crenshaw counties, Ala, scattered lumps of brown iron ore, imbedded 3 or 4 ft deep in sandy soil, are located in same manner (15). Foster (10) gives following instances of the use of piercing: in France for buhrstones lying at depths of 10 to 18 ft in soft sand and clay; on the Isle of Man for shallow pockets of soft umber easily penetrated by the rod; in the Furness district, England, for hematite, under 6 to 8 ft of soil (detected by color); in South Carolina, for phosphate nodules, to depths of 15 ft in sand and clay. In Burma, bamboo rods are similarly used to ascertain the depth through clay to underlying gem-bearing gravels.

Sounding is the name given to a unique method of prospecting for phosphates on the Coosau River, S C. Phosphate rock occurs in irregular patches in the river bed, and is mined by dredging. Sounding is done from a boat by dragging a bottle filled with water along the bottom. A string is tied around the neck of the bottle, and a cardboard diaphragm attached to the free end is held against the ear, or the sounder holds the end of the string in his ear with his finger. On finding a deposit, floats are set to show its outline and guide the dredge (11).

Vegetation sometimes grows thickly along outcrops of one geological formation and sparsely on another, thus aiding in working out geological structure, or in limiting areas favorable or unfavorable to ore occurrence. At Cripple Creek, quaking aspens favor areas of tuff and breccia; fir trees grow on granite. In the Leucite Hills, Wyo, along outcrops of potash-bearing dikes, there is a noticeably rank growth of sage brush. In places in the southern Appalachians, the vegetation corresponds to underlying strata (12, 502). Recognition of geological structure from the air, even to very small details, is facilitated by habits of vegetation, particularly in semi-arid regions (647). See 17, Art 26.

Burrowing animals, as woodchucks, prairie dogs, gophers, badgers, also ants, sometimes aid the prospector by the debris they throw out when digging holes. Such material is examined for float, or panned for gold colors or specks of ore minerals (479).

Divining rod is still believed by credulous persons to be efficacious for finding water and mineral (13, 14).

Electroscope. Radio-active minerals have the power of discharging an electroscope; under suitable conditions the rate of discharge is proportional to amount of radio-active substance in the mineral. Electroscope is used by engineers and prospectors to detect radio-activity, and for quantitative tests. Radium is obtained solely from uranium ores, the amount of radium bearing a constant relation to amount of uranium present; normally

1 unit of uranium is accompanied by 3.3×10^{-7} units of radium. Thorium compounds and minerals also discharge an electroscope.

Fig 40 shows a simple electroscope suggested by B. B. Boltwood, which can be made in the field. It consists of a 5-cent piece, a quarter dollar, or an iron washer A; a drop of sealing wax or candle grease C; an upright B made from a piece of tin 0.2 in wide (or a 6d or 8d wire nail flattened at E); and the leaf D. The latter may be a piece of aluminum leaf, about 0.1 in wide, obtainable from any dealer in painter's supplies, or thin tissue paper, both sides of which have been coated with graphite by rubbing with a soft pencil. Leaf is attached to upright with mucilage or flour paste. Bottom of upright B must be insulated from base A by a layer of sealing wax; the wax must not be touched with the fingers after it is in place. A cover protects the apparatus from air currents; for the dimensions shown in Fig 40 an ordinary glass tumbler placed bottom upward will serve. Electroscope is charged by touching the upright with a piece of hard rubber (a fountain pen), or sealing wax, which has been electrified by rubbing on one's hair or sleeve. A protractor drawn on cardboard, so that its center point is at same height above base A as the point E, is placed behind the tumbler and the angle read between leaf and upright. Readings are repeated at regular intervals to determine rate at which electroscope will discharge itself by leakage. The mineral to be tested is placed inside the tumbler; radio-activity is proved by a rate of discharge faster than that due to natural loss of charge.

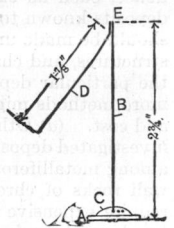

Fig 40. Electroscope

This crude electroscope gives surprisingly accurate quantitative results if handled carefully. Table 1 shows results of tests by H. G. Mead under author's direction, on a series of samples prepared by mixing pitchblende (35.7% U) with inert material in proper proportions to give samples containing 2, 5, 10, 15, and 25% U. Samples were crushed through 20 mesh and placed next to base of electroscope in a small pill box. Same size of box was used for all samples, each being filled level full, and placed in same position with respect to electroscope. Rate of discharge was determined as above, corrected for natural leakage, and net rate of discharge computed in degrees per min per % U. Max errors for paper and aluminum leaves were 0.7% and 1.9% U respectively. Aluminum leaf is much more sensitive than paper, and requires greater skill and patience in manipulation. Scrupulous care is necessary to avoid salting the containers used. For quantitative work a small sample of known uranium content is required to standardize the electroscope; unknown samples may then be tested.

Table 1. Tests for Radio-activity by Electroscope

Per cent U in sample	Paper leaf				Aluminum leaf			
	Rate of discharge				Rate of discharge			
	Deg per min	Leakage, deg per min	Net rate, deg per min	Deg per min per % U	Deg per min	Leakage, deg per min	Net rate, deg per min	Deg per min per % U
2	0.162	0.0105	0.151	0.0755	0.46	0.007	0.45	0.23
5	0.338	0.0105	0.327	0.0654	1.04	0.007	1.03	0.21
10	0.623	0.0105	0.612	0.0612	2.61	0.007	2.60	0.24
15	0.965	0.0105	0.954	0.0636	3.00	0.007	2.99	0.20
25	1.710	0.0105	1.699	0.0680	5.00	0.007	4.99	0.20
Aver....				0.0667				0.216

An outfit for testing ores for radio-activity is made by the Denver Fire Clay Co, Denver, Colo; price, in 1938, about $110.

Fluorescence. A few minerals, notably willemite, scheelite and fluorspar, become fluorescent when subjected to ultra-violet light, as is emitted by an arc of either high or low intensity between iron electrodes, or by mercury-vapor lamp; less vigorously by an argon lamp. Principle has been satisfactorily applied in exploration and development of scheelite mines in Nev and Calif, using portable apparatus which usually requires 110-v alternating current. Such equipment is supplied by: H. T. Strong, Chatham, N J ("Fluorospark" lamp, with quartz lenses for focusing the beam, $100); R & M Mfg Co, Pasadena, Calif (mercury-vapor lamp, adaptable to dry cells, $32.50); Stroblite Co, 35 W 52d St, N Y (a "black-bulb" lamp, illuminating a circle 6 ft diam at 3 ft distance, $15). Prices are as of 1938. Since each mineral responds most actively to wave lengths within a certain range, character of the light is more important than its intensity. For scientific principles and some practical applications, see Bib (88).

Geophysical prospecting methods include gravimetric, magnetic, electrical, seismic, temperature, radio-active, and micro-gas surveys. See Sec 10A for underlying principles, applicabilities and limitations, and interpretation of observations.

Methods have developed rapidly in recent years, and are used with success in many localities. They are not universally applicable or successful, and in considering their use the following observations should be borne in mind: (a) Methods (with possible exception of simple dip-needle survey) are too expensive to apply to "wildcatting"; better devoted to exploration for deposits whose presence has been indicated by other prospecting methods, or whose existence and probable form are reasonably suspected from geological evidence, such as extensions of known deposits, parallel orebodies in same formation, or deposits known to occur only in certain geological relations. (b) Any geophysical survey should be made under direction or cooperation of a geologist acquainted with formations, structures, and character of deposits in the locality. (c) Method must be appropriate to the particular deposit; no single method is applicable to all conditions, and where 2 or more methods might be applied to a given deposit, they may differ in reliability, speed, and cost. (d) Other conditions causing physical effects similar to those expected from the investigated deposit must be absent. Examples: graphitic zones or water-bearing selvages among metalliferous bodies explored by earth-resistance; disseminations of magnetite in wall rocks of chrome-ore lenses surveyed magnetically. (e) Most geophysical methods require expensive and delicate equipment, operated by trained personnel. Much work has been done for mining companies by contracting firms specializing in this business. Magnetic surveys, however, even with most refined instruments, can be conducted satisfactorily by usual mine engineering staff. (f) No method can do more than indicate existence of a deposit capable of affording the observed effects. Such a deposit may or may not contain profitable amounts of metal. Examples: copper or nickel in pyrite or pyrrhotite; gold with magnetite in a buried river channel. (g) Where 2 methods are applicable, both should be employed, since each may best disclose certain features. A magnetic survey for precise work should explore both vert and horiz components of the field. (h) Some deposits, as sphalerite and fluorite, not readily responsive to any geophysical method, have been found by tracing faults or porous areas of rock with which such deposits were known to be associated, such geological features being fairly easily indicated by appropriate electrical methods (334). For details see Sec 10A.

5. SYSTEMATIC SURFACE EXPLORATION

Value of thorough surface exploration is apt to be underestimated. It furnishes information which may either discourage further effort, or permit intelligent planning of subsequent work. Where feasible, it is an essential preliminary to underground exploration. It prevents overlooking important exposures, and secures a large amount of information with a smaller total footage of openings than haphazard work.

Factors involved are as follows (see also Art 12): Surface work can be done at much less COST and greater SPEED than underground work; from this standpoint its feasibility should always be considered because of the high RISK of opening unproved orebodies. TYPE OF OREBODY and DEPTH OF SURFACE SOIL are related factors. Cost of surface work increases rapidly with depth of cover. Trenching at close intervals, or complete stripping, is necessary to find and follow short, narrow, irregular veins on the surface. In general, these operations are not feasible where average depth of soil exceeds 2 to 3 ft (see Art 4 and Cobalt, Art 6). Outcrops of wide veins, beds, and masses are cheaply explored by trenching, where soil is not over 6 to 7 ft deep. Necessity for continuous openings, as trenches, decreases as the size and uniformity of the orebody increases; test pits give adequate data respecting size, shape, and value of large uniform orebodies, and in dry surface drift are feasible to depths of 30 to 50 ft or more. Deep wet alluvium precludes surface openings; when present, exploration must be by boring or underground work (Art 7). AMOUNT OF WEATHERING. Value of results from surface exploration depends on amount and reliability of information afforded by outcrops. Where rocks are fresh, or erosion has kept pace with weathering, an outcrop is a reliable section of an orebody; in such case, if surface results are negative, it is unwise to attempt underground exploration. Values have often been entirely or partly removed by leaching from the upper parts of an orebody (Art 3). Surface exploration may still determine its size, shape, irregularities, and location and size of shoots. These factors alone may decide whether further work is justified, and if so the best location for it. Leached outcrops generally indicate the character of mineralization in depth. Weathering in some cases has been so intense that it is practically impossible to trace outcrops on the surface, or to get any definite information from them; underground work is then the only alternative.

Methods vary with type of orebody; judgment determines extent and detail of the work. First essential is a map showing property lines, topography, geology, outcrops, dips and strikes, pits, trenches, underground work, assays, location of float or traces, and all obtainable details. MAP should be on a scale of not less than 100 ft to 1 in; for small areas, 40 or 50 ft to 1 in is better. Compass and hand level, plane table or transit are used in mapping, depending on accuracy desired; a small plane table is convenient and rapid. Numbered stakes may be set on corners of 100 or 200-ft squares, for locating subsequent work. If veins are exposed, their probable extensions are plotted on the map and staked on the ground (see Migration of outcrops). Probable course of faults, contacts, and sedimentary beds are similarly indicated. Such a map shows the relation between different outcrops, and between outcrops, geology, and topography; outlines drift-covered areas; shows where information is needed; aids in eliminating unfavorable areas and in planning exploration.

Geophysical methods (Sec 10A) exemplify systematic exploration preceding the details discussed here. Air-plane surveys (101, 102, 103, 505, and Sec 17, Art 28), with or without photography, are also used for preliminary systematic reconnaissance of large areas.

Tracing float. All pieces of float are labeled and their position noted on map (portions of each piece may be assayed or panned). By showing location of float with respect to topography, geology, and probable outcrop extensions, the amount of excavation necessary to uncover outcrops is often reduced.

Tracing by panning (Sec 31) may be used in a similar way. A level panful of dirt should be taken each time, so that results will be roughly quantitative. The mineral obtained is weighed and kept in numbered bottles, the number and wt of each trace being entered on the map. Blanks should be recorded as carefully as good showings. Having no exposures to guide the work, panning can be done systematically at corners of squares. Panning along exposed outcrops, or below probable location of drift-covered outcrops, is the cheapest way of finding oreshoots and determining their length.

Trenching. For a single orebody a series of trenches is usually dug at regular intervals, at right-angles to course of outcrop. Probable extension of outcrop should be staked on the ground as a preliminary. Distance between trenches is determined by type of orebody and depth of soil; they should be close enough to determine aver width and value of outcrops and to avoid missing oreshoots. Trenches over the latter are closer together than on barren areas.

The first trenches should be as far apart as possible; this generally reduces number, length, and cost of intermediate trenches. It is more satisfactory to follow narrow outcrops by trenching along them. In shallow soil not more than 2 men, in deep soil not more than 4 men, can be employed to advantage in trenching both ways from a single exposure (19). Fig 41 shows general arrangement of trenches on outcrops of large uniform orebodies, planned to avoid high cost of complete stripping. Where large drift-covered areas are explored for suspected mineral, trenches are usually dug along the sides of squares, 50 to 200 ft apart. First work consists of 1 or 2 long trenches, which give information as to geology, depth of soil, etc; this generally divides area into favorable and unfavorable sections. Good showings are explored first. If there are no surface

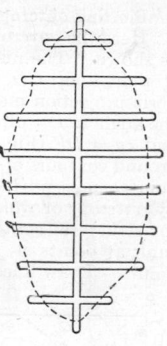

Fig 41

indications, systematic work is started where the soil is shallowest; deep trenching is usually done last (see Cobalt, Art 6).

Test pits for systematic surface exploration are spaced on corners of squares. Principles involved in their location are same as for boreholes (Art 7).

Summary of results. All exposures in exploratory openings are measured and sampled; widths, assays, and any further geological data obtained should be entered on the map, and geological cross-sections made where necessary to interpret structure. Results of shallow exploration may often be summarized by computing from area of orebody exposed the tons of ore per ft of depth. Depth to which the known orebodies must continue to repay estimated cost of development and equipment and yield a profit can then be calculated. This figure, compared with local geology and type of orebody, furnishes a measure of the risk involved (20).

Migration of outcrops. With unwarped veins, beds, faults, and contacts, dipping 90°, the outcrop is in a straight line (the strike), regardless of topography (Fig 42, *A*). Outcrop of such a deposit on flat topography is also a straight line, regardless of its dip (Fig 42, *B*). On rough topography, the outcrop of a vein dipping less than 90° is curved or crooked; its deviation from the strike line increases as its dip decreases (Fig 42, *C*). Width of outcrop of veins of uniform thickness also varies on rough topography.

Many errors in planning mining work are made by assuming that geological surfaces are planes; they are always warped and twisted. Nevertheless, this assumption is useful in exploration work; by means of it an approx location of outcrop between or beyond known exposures can be laid out on the ground or on a contour map. Such approx locations vary in accuracy with depth of soil as well as with bends in the deposit itself; but they help to correlate observed data and reduce the excavation necessary to uncover outcrops. The following graphical methods are sufficiently accurate for this work, and apply to all the geological surfaces mentioned above.

Approx dip and strike of a vein can be measured with a compass at some point, or determined from 3 exposed points (Fig 43). Plot the 3 points A, B and C in plan in their correct relative positions, and note their elevations. Connect high and low points by line BC. Take point D on BC so that $CD : CB =$ (elev A — elev C) : (elev B — elev C). AD is the strike line of plane ABC, and its bearing is measured with protractor from known bearing AC. Draw BE perpendicular to AD. Lay off EF to scale and equal to elev B — elev A. Angle FBE is dip of plane ABC. For accurate solution, see Sec 9.

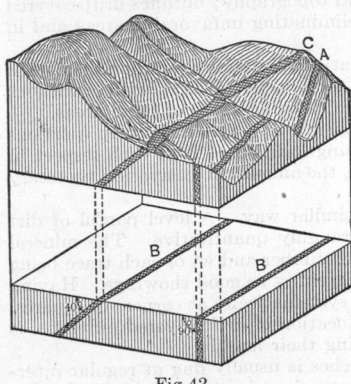

Fig 42

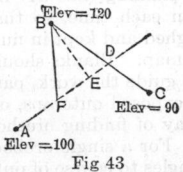

Fig 43

Plotting outcrop on a contour map from a single exposure (Fig 44).

Here the outcrop of a vein or bed is exposed at point A; its strike is line AB; dip 30°, as shown. The underground contours of the vein (considered as a plane) are a series of straight lines, CD, EF, etc, parallel to strike AB. The distance apart of these lines in horiz projection may be found by means of a right-angled triangle xyz (Fig 45), in which the angle $zxy =$ dip of vein, $yz =$ contour interval (the same as that for surface contours), and $xy = DF$ (Fig 44) = required distance. Points of intersection of surface and underground contours of equal elevation mark points on the outcrop, and a line connecting such points represents its probable location. Same methods serve where a vein or bed is exposed by outcrops or work at several points. Fig 46 shows in horiz projection an underground (or structure) contour map of a vein, aver dip 45°, on which 4 shallow shafts have been sunk at points A, B, C, D. Assume that dip and strike are different at each of these points. Draw lines AA', BB', CC', DD', perpendicular to observed strike at A, B, C, and D and on them, by means of dip triangles (Fig 45), mark points at which they would be intersected by successive structure contours. Then draw these contours as shown.

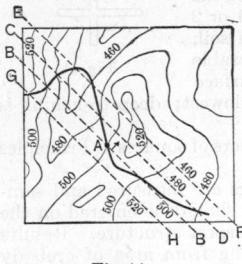

Fig 44   Fig 45   Fig 46

Beds and veins in general change their dip and strike gradually; hence, structure contours should show only gentle curves. If abrupt changes in direction are necessary to connect points of equal elevation, look for faults or other disturbances. Such contour maps are invaluable in planning underground exploration; when superposed on surface topography, they give close indications of the location of outcrops. For further detail of graphic methods, see Bib (21, 22).

Staking probable location of outcrop on the ground is done in different ways: (a) Plot probable outcrop on a contour map, and lay out this line on ground by ordinary surveying methods. (b)

Set up a transit over a known point on outcrop, and place stakes at regular intervals on strike line. Set transit on each stake, and cross-section to find outcrop, as for grade stakes in railroad work. This method involves much calculation, which can be reduced by using slope-stake diagrams. (c) Use transit with Shattuck solar attachment (23); set the attachment so that when it is revolved the deflected line of collimation will generate a plane at right angles to the telescope. Transit is set up over a point on outcrop, main telescope oriented in a line perpendicular to strike and the telescope turned down until line of sight is perpendicular to the dip (vert angle = complement of dip angle). Deflected line of collimation then revolves in a plane parallel to and slightly to one side of plane of vein. If the ground is sighted, each stake will be slightly off the correct line. Error is slight if the outcrop is traced from ono oct up; where many stations are used, the error is cumulative. (d) Transit and top telescope. Loosen capstan screw, so that the top telescope will revolve in a plane parallel to main telescope. Set transit over point on outcrop, orient main telescope in a line at right angles to strike, and turn main telescope down until its line of sight is parallel to the dip (vert angle = dip angle). The top telescope then revolves in a plane parallel to plane of vein. A rod will give true points on outcrop, if sighted on at an elevation = height of instrument + (c ÷ cos dip angle of vein); c, a constant for any instrument = distance between center lines of top and main telescopes. (e) Brunton compass, if set on a light tripod with a ball-and-socket mounting, is accurate enough for tracing outcrops short distances. The spindle of the instrument is tilted to a position at right angles to dip; then sights will rotate in plane of vein. See also "Geophysical Prospecting Methods," Sec 10A.

6. SURFACE PROSPECTING AND EXPLORATION EXAMPLES OF PRACTICE

Nova Scotia (24). Systematic prospecting is done here for gold-quartz veins in regions covered by deep glacial drift. Prospecting is confined to relatively small areas, in which rich float occurs. Surface is fairly level and ordinary conditions causing float to move downhill are absent. The general direction of glacial movement was a little east of south. Following methods apply generally to areas of glacial drift.

Prospecting methods are based on recognition of fact that while glacial drift contains rocks brought from a distance and entirely different from the underlying bedrock, it may be composed largely of material of local origin. Sequence of operations is as follows: Mapping. A contour map is made of the area on a scale of at least 40 ft to 1 in. On this are recorded details of geological structure, drainage lines, course of glacial transportation, distribution of gold-bearing float, position and depth of existing pits. A compass survey is usually sufficient. Panning. About 200 pans are taken from old dumps, surface soil, beds of brooks and sides of old trenches or pits. An exact record is kept, showing location of samples, number of pans taken, character and composition of drift (which may give clue to its source), and number and size of colors in each pan. Results are recorded on the map and summarized by drawing two lines, one enclosing the area in which float gold of any size occurs, and the other limiting the area containing shotty gold and large colors. This inner line incloses the center of gold distribution; within it and near its northern extremity most of the prospecting work will be done. Panning lessens the amount of heavy preliminary work. It usually confirms inferences drawn from the distribution of float and prevents work in barren areas. Two men, panner and helper, usually do this work in 4 or 5 days. Test pits are then sunk. A notebook is kept showing each pit in cross-sec on a large scale. Following details are noted: (a) depth, thickness, slope, mode of formation and composition of each layer in the drift. Each layer is given a number for future reference; (b) results from panning each layer; (c) absence or presence of float, quantity and estimated value per ton, number of pieces, size, degree of wear, and character of each variety and its associated minerals, as an aid to identification; (d) details of bedrock, dip, strike, cleavage, results and direction of glaciation; (e) depth and amount of water encountered; (f) size of pit and number of buckets hoisted; (g) labor, time, and material for sinking and timbering. Items e, f, g are useful for estimating future work. All pieces of gold quartz are kept for comparison with float from other shafts; they are numbered and put in boxes. Cross-sections show no orderly arrangement of strata; more beds occur in one pit than in another; 2 different layers may contain float from same lode. These irregularities are due to different periods of erosion; often transportation takes place in somewhat different directions at different times. But such correlation of various layers as is possible, and a comparison of their contents, give much information about origin and distribution of float gold. Location of pits. A test pit should always be sunk to bedrock near northern limit of area of richest pannings or float. Pits are put down in rows across direction of float movement. If all the gold is in upper layers of drift, its source is probably remote and pits can be placed at some distance apart; if all gold is confined to lower layers of deep drift, the vein is probably not far away. If gold shows only in upper layers, time and money can be saved by sinking only a few pits below the auriferous horizon. If pits on the right end of a row show no gold, the next row is shifted to the left and vice versa. Float gold is distributed from an oreshoot in a more or less fan-shaped form; hence the area to be prospected decreases as the source of the gold is approached. Often, post-glacial drainage has rearranged drift, rendering above methods fruitless unless old drainage and erosion processes can be interpreted.

Cobalt, Ontario. Narrow veins of native Ag, associated with Co and Ni arsenides. Veins occur in diabase, conglomerate, and greenstone; some profitable deposits are 1 in or less in thickness. First discoveries were made by examination of rock outcrops; Co minerals oxidize to pink erythrite or " cobalt bloom." The pink color disappears under weathering, but is a good indicator when the rocks in the vicinity of a vein are freshly broken. All small crevices are examined; if ore is present, the crevice yields a soft black mud, CoO, containing nuggets of native Ag, or arsenates of Co and Ni are found a few inches below surface. Calcite veins are also considered favorable indications.

A large part of the district is covered by shallow glacial drift, in which prospecting is done by trenching. Rectangular coordinate lines are laid out on the surface at intervals of 50 to 100 ft and trenches are dug along these; in deep soil, trenches may be farther apart because of their higher cost. A few preliminary trenches are dug before thorough prospecting is attempted. On a contour map are recorded geology, rock outcrops, known veins, swamps, property lines, areas of deep drift, etc. Trenches are just wide enough for men to work to advantage; to allow cleaning the bedrock, they must be 2 to 3 ft wide at bottom; width at the top depends on depth and character of soil. When depth exceeds 6 ft, trenches are timbered by an occasional stull with uprights or head boards (19). In dry soil, bedrock in trenches is carefully cleaned with brushes; in clayey soil, by washing. Use of water is avoided where possible, as it conceals crevices by filling them with mud. Veins are difficult to recognize, especially in diabase; every likely place is blasted out. Each vein found is stripped as far as it can be followed, and shot out at close intervals.

R. B. Watson, Gen Mgr, Nipissing Mining Co, Cobalt, Ont, furnished following data on systematic prospecting by that company. In 1912 an HYDRAULIC PLANT was installed, to wash all the soil off the surface, for complete inspection of the rock. Water was pumped from Cobalt Lake. Details of installation: one-stage centrifugal pump, capacity 4 800 gal per min against 415 ft head; guaranteed effic, 78%; 650-hp motor, 2 200 volts, 1 180 r p m; spiral-riveted, 16-in pipe line, No 10 gage, with bolted joints to allow adjacent lengths of pipe to be turned through angles of 10° to 15°, without leakage. Some lengths of pipe had flanges on one end and bolted joints on other, giving a little stiffer pipe line. Size of nozzle was from 3 to 4 in, depending on whether a very strong stream was desired, or less force with larger volume. For good results, pressure at nozzle of at least 100 lb per sq in was necessary. When all ground within reach of the nozzle was washed off, usually taking about a day, the pipe line was extended to the next set-up, which had been prepared in advance. After an area had been cleaned, it was examined, surveyed, and then served as a dump for spoil from adjacent areas. Dynamite was used to break rock and scatter heavy boulders. In 1914, the plant ran 79.08% of the time; 153 set-ups were made; aver time lost in setting up, 1 hr 32 min. Aver press at nozzle, 138 lb per sq in. 68 309 ft of pipe were shifted and 18 730 ft of roads were built. 95.55 acres were washed; aver depth of soil, 3.4 ft; 529 415 cu yd were moved.

Table 2. Trenching at Nipissing Mine

Year	No men	Miles of trench	Aver depth, ft
1909	87	33.1	3.4
1910	61	31.7	2.7
1911	25	13.7	2.7

In 1914, on La Rose property, the soil was shoveled off an area of several acres, in strips 20 ft wide; distance between strips was made as small as possible, determined by the height to which men could throw the dirt. Aver depth of soil was 1.9 ft.

Quebec copper-gold belt (Rouyn District); data from K. W. Fritsche and A. B. Parsons (504). Steep-dipping lenses of sulphides containing copper and gold occur usually in rhyolite and andesite, often associated with syenite-porphyry dikes.

Systematic prospecting is done over large areas, much of which is heavily wooded, making traveling without axemen difficult. Typical sequence of operations on a group of 40 claims (8 000 acres): (a) Parallel base lines at half-mile intervals are laid out by transit. (b) " Picket " lines, 200 ft apart, are run at right angles to base lines. (c) An experienced geologist makes observations along the picket lines and directs pick and shovel work or drilling and blasting on likely outcrops. (d) Dip-needle observations are made by young engineers every 50 ft along picket lines, to indicate presence of magnetite and pyrrhotite. Results plotted and maps studied by geologist, together with his own notes. Large areas can now generally be neglected as valueless. (e) On several groups of claims encouraging areas have been studied by electrical prospecting (Sec 10A). (f) If (e) is not done, favorable areas are studied in more detail. Dip needle may be replaced by a magnetometer (Sec 10A), and observations made at 10- or 25-ft intervals on lines 100 ft apart. (g) Promising areas are cleared of timber and brush and trenching begins; first trenches 50-200 ft apart, depending on depth of cover. Table 3 shows how duty of labor in trenching varies with depth, number of roots, amount of water and regularity of bedrock. Oxidized or enriched parts of outcrops (seldom over 2 ft deep) are blasted out before samples are taken. One man channel-samples 40-80 ft of trench per day in 5-ft sections. (h) Outcrops considered good enough are explored by diamond drill. (i) Shafts, crosscuts and drifts are made, and deposits explored further by underground diamond drilling.

Table 3. Duty of Labor in Trenching, Quebec Gold Belt (504), about **1924**

Example No	Dimensions of trenches				Labor, man-days	Cu yd per man-day	Conditions
	Length, ft	Width, ft	Depth, ft	Cu yd			
1	16	3	4				Roots and gravel. No water. Bedrock smooth.
2	30	3	4.5				
3	13	2	2.5	31.9	6	5.31	
4	16	2.5	3				
5	20	2	2				
6	10	6	10	22.2	7	3.17	Gravel, large boulders and water.
7	54	3	3	18.0	7	2.57	Many roots. Bedrock rough.
8	20	3.5	5	12.9	5.5	2.34	Roots, gravel and some water.
9	10	4	7	10.4	5	2.08	
10	10	4	5	7.4	4.5	1.64	Sticky clay, much water.
11	40	3	4	17.8	12	1.98	(a)
12	30	2.5	2.5	6.9	6	1.15	(b)
13	65	....	....	....	3	....	
14	110	....	....	....	4.5	....	(c)
15	75	....	....	....	3	....	
16	72	....	....	....	3.5	....	

(a) 2 ft gravel underlain by 2 ft partly decomposed schist. (b) Partly decomposed schist, hand drilled and blasted; cost of powder not included. (c) Stripping moss, roots and some gravel; aver width of these openings, 2 ft; max depth, 2 ft.

Quebec gold vein. J. Y. Murdoch, in 1938, contributes following data on surface exploration of a group of 5 claims, 125 miles from RR in northern Quebec, performed during 4 summer months by 4 men with foreman and cook; wages $4.50, less $1.25 for board. Men and supplies transported by hydroplane. Previous work had exposed 120 ft length of vein, 6 ft wide. Area heavily wooded, but outcrops numerous; overburden, where trenched, 1-5 ft deep. Trenches perpendicular to outcrop, spaced 10-30 ft apart, were 5 ft wide; where rock blasting at bottom was desired, 6-ft width was better. In clay or sand, 1 man in 1 day dug about 10 ft of trench 5 ft wide and 4-5 ft deep (7-8 cu yd). Total trenching during 4 mos included 400 ft on the known vein, and 1 200 ft in search of parallel veins; rock blasting at bottom of trenches, for sampling below weathered zone, amounted to 200 ft. Double-hand drilling with $7/8$-in hex steel and 6 or 7-lb hammers made 12 ft of hole in 8 hr; holes 2-4 ft deep, loaded with 40% Forcite, 3 sticks for a 3-ft hole, and fired by fuse with No 6 or 8 caps. Channel samples were 1-1.5 in deep and 2-3 in wide; where mineralization was irregular, and free gold appeared, larger samples were taken. Two 10 by 12-ft tents and a 12 by 14-ft cook tent for 6 men. Floors of split poles; tents carefully screened. Staple food supply for the party for 4 mos weighed about 3 000 lb. Essential equipment of tools is listed in Art 13.

Witwatersrand, South Africa. Silicified conglomerates carry Au, and occur as members of a series of sedimentary rocks. The auriferous " banket " reefs dip at 16 to 90°. Faults complicate the work of locating outcrop extensions in places. " The surface is first examined to locate one or more beds of sandstone, with which the reefs are conformable " (25). Topography is closely related to the geology; hard beds form ridges and, in some cases, streams follow fault lines. In shallow soil, indications of the character of underlying rocks are obtained from ant hills; over banket these have generally a yellowish gray color, over basalt dikes they consist of red loam.

Trenches are dug at right angles to the strike of the formation at regular intervals. One trench near middle of property is continuous; the others are made only where the central trench shows that a reef is likely to cross. At each point where reef is found, a small shaft is sunk deep enough to provide samples from points unaffected by surface alteration. In deep soil a small shaft is sunk into solid formation, and a crosscut driven to give a section of the rocks; or 2 or 3 shafts are sunk and connected by crosscuts. Values are remarkably persistent and fairly uniform over large areas of reef; hence, surface exploration gives reliable indications of conditions at depth.

Suan Concession, Korea (480). An area of 15.5 by 10.5 miles was prospected and about 59 000 acres systematically explored in 1905–1916. Orebodies, generally lenticular, to 125 ft wide by 400 ft long, are contact metamorphic deposits around a granitic batholith 6 by 5 miles in area. Some deposits are distant from the contact. Valuable metals: Au, Ag, some Bi and W.

Some of the deposits were exploited by ancients; intensive study of old workings led to discovery of one important orebody and indicated marked surface impoverishment of ore which might have caused ancients seeking high-grade ore to overlook valuable deposits. Known gold placers in streams flowing from high ground at center of batholith furnished another aid to prospecting for ore in place.

A topographic and general geologic survey was made; all known data and all results of prospecting were mapped; maps were made for each square mile on scale of 1 in = 150 ft. Each square mile area was first explored by sinking test pits to bedrock at intervals of 300 ft along creeks and valleys. Systematic samples from each pit were panned and depth of pit, nature of bedrock and results of panning were recorded on map. On finding colors or favorable indications, intermediate pits were sunk 100 ft apart. Detailed study of surface conditions and local geology was made in vicinity of favorable showings. Such areas were then prospected intensively to locate source of mineral; traces were followed by test pits about 100 ft apart until approx line of mineralization was located, then a series of trenches at right angles to this line uncovered outcrops. Many outcrops were discovered, several containing profitable ore. Samples from test pits for panning were taken in 2-ft sections; composite samples, comprising the last 0.5 oz of concentrate in each pan from a given favorable area, were completely analyzed to determine the minerals present. The concentrates were also examined systematically with a microscope, which led to the discovery that small amounts of W were widely distributed around the contact. Native labor, in charge of a foreign miner or prospector, who had underground experience on the property, was used for prospecting; separate crews were employed for preliminary and intensive work. Native wages: 25¢ per 8-hr day for miners and 20¢ per 10-hr day for coolies. On intensive work a crew averaged about 4 square miles in 6 months; cost, about $2 000. Aver cost of test pits, about 5¢ per ft; cost of trenches varied widely, averaging about 7¢ per cu yd.

West Australia (506). Gold-bearing veins occur near porphyry dikes and jasper "bars," often in vicinity of contacts between granite and greenstone; such localities are sought as favorable for detailed prospecting.

Tracing float and "loaming" (tracing by panning, Art 4) are the principal prospecting methods. In arid areas, a "loam bag" of cotton cloth, 6 in diam by 6 ft long, with tapes sewed to it at 9-in intervals, is used for collecting and carrying samples to water for panning. The prospector having found float, colors, or favorable geology, digs parallel rows of holes, 4–6 in deep; holes in a row are about 12 ft apart; rows are about 30 ft apart and lie approx on contours. A sample from each hole is put in the loam bag; samples kept separate by tying the tapes between them. Holes showing colors are marked with stakes; stakes in lower rows indicate trend of traces to one side or other, and guide the prospector in locating the next higher row of holes. Work continues until colors cut out of surface soil, when values are followed in deeper ground by trenching. At times, samples are tested by "dry blowing," a winnowing process wherein the sample is repeatedly poured from a dish or pan (about 15 in diam), held at level of operator's head, into a similar dish on the ground. The wind blows fines aside, leaving coarser material and gold behind. Bib (506) describes dry-blowing machine for testing larger samples.

West Uganda, Africa. N. W. Wilson in 1938 described an exhaustive survey of a 155-sq mile area on SE flank of Ruwenzori Mt, E Africa (96). Region is a few miles N of Equator, at altitudes of 3 500–13 500 ft; lower elevations are generally open, bushy, or grassy; higher ones, densely wooded, cold and wet. Nearest RR at Kampola, 170 miles by air-line. Mapping and detailed prospecting were done concurrently. Three parallel main base-lines were laid out, one near N boundary, one on S boundary, and one midway. These were connected at right angles by grid of parallel traverse lines, 1 200 ft apart in open country, 2 400 ft apart in forest. On traverse lines, vegetation was cleared to width of 5–6 ft, and stakes set every 300 ft. It was considered that any orebody large enough to be valuable, if not actually intersected by a traverse, would be disclosed by neighboring float. Pits were sunk to bedrock at every second stake; also at every crossing of a gulch. Stream beds wider than 6 ft were traversed their full length; narrower ones by cuttings for 300 ft each side of intersection with a traverse line. Stream beds about 1/2 mile wide were not pitted, because numerous large boulders prevented alluvial working. Black-sand residues from panning of pit material were collected into composite samples, representing 5 000 ft of traverse and critically examined at headquarters, together with specimens of outcrop and float. Observations were mapped on scale of 1 : 10 000. Each prospecting party was under 2 Europeans; one with about 70 natives for clearing the lines; other with 10 natives for geological work. Alternate "strips," 6 lines wide, were worked by 2 parties. For close examination of likely spots, subsidiary lines 300–600 ft apart were cleared to width of 20 ft for inspection by engineer in charge.

Clinton hematites occur as stratified beds in the Clinton formation (Silurian age), all along the Appalachian Range, and also in New York, Kentucky, and Wisconsin. The beds vary in thickness from a few inches to 10 or 12 ft; they are subject to all the irregularities of sedimentary rock beds (Art 3; also Sec 2). Prospecting may start from discovery of float or outcrops, or by recognition of some member of the Clinton series with which these ores are associated. Above or below the ore bed there is usually some characteristic stratum which outcrops; measurements from this give an approx location of the ore-bed outcrop at different points along its strike. The outcrop is then uncovered by trenches or test pits. In the south, weathering extends to considerable depths, but on hillsides erosion has kept pace with it and unaltered ore is often within 5 ft of outcrop (5).

To determine thickness and grade of ore, dip, strike, etc, exploratory openings (inclined shafts or drifts) should be driven at regular intervals into unaltered ore. Since these orebodies are of sedimentary origin, they are apt to be uniform in size and tenor over large areas. Exploratory openings may be placed far apart and still give good basis for tonnage estimates (7). Geological structure should be carefully worked out. Diamond drills are used for deep exploration to check outcrop evidence, locate faults, etc (Art 7).

Brown iron ores (limonite) in the Appalachian valley. The two important types are residual deposits and replacement deposits.

Residual deposits consist of masses and boulders of limonite, embedded in clay and lying on an uneven surface of limestone or dolomite. Orebodies are very irregular and are covered by sand and soil. Discontinuous outcrops occur, especially in gullies, or limonite gravel is found (5). Mining is carried on in open cuts, and exploration must show area, aver depth, tonnage, and quality of ore, and depth and character of overburden. Usually a few test pits are put down to determine whether surface indications are connected with orebodies of any size; data on concentration and quality of ore are obtained by washing and analyzing the samples. Different methods are used for exploration if preliminary results are favorable. ALABAMA BROWN IRON ORES are often prospected by pits; first at corners of 200-ft squares, and then at closer intervals for more accurate delineation of boundaries (6). Pits, preferably circular and of 30- to 34-in diam, are sunk by hand, using short-handled (12–18 in) picks and shovels, hoisting by windlass and bucket. In soft material, sides can be supported by hoops of 1/2 by 2-in iron, with 24-in corrugated roofing in 5-ft lengths for lagging, recovered when finished. Unless water interferes, 2 men can sink a pit to 50 ft or more, at contract price (1937) of 25–50¢ per ft. Values may be estimated: (a) all material taken from ore bed, volume of which is calculated from thickness of bed and diam of hole, is quartered down, after breaking lumps, washed to remove sand, weighed, and sampled for analysis; (b) a vert groove, 2–3 in deep and wide, is cut down one side of finished pit, vol of sample measured, and ore contents weighed after washing; method (b) is faster and cheaper. Aver recovery of washed ore, 1 ton from 2.5–3 cu yd, exclusive of overburden. Elsewhere, augers or churn drills are used (26). Similar methods are used in prospecting for, and exploration of, Tenn and Texas brown ores.

Replacement deposits are from replacement of a particular bed (Art 3). They vary widely with dip and nature of rock replaced; methods of prospecting depend upon topography and geol (7).

Brown phosphate rock in Tenn (338). A few pits are sunk at selected points, to check results previously obtained by auger holes (Art 10-a). T V A (in 1936–1938) let contracts for this work, including digging, sampling, and refilling, at 60¢ for first ft, plus 50¢ per ft down to 10 ft; sliding scale for deeper pits made a 20-ft pit cost $16.35; still deeper, $16.35 plus $1.60 per ft. Contractors supplied all tools, and transported samples 40–50 miles to laboratory. Usual sampling practice was to cut a channel, 1 ft square, down one side of pit, recovering phosphate contents by washing. Dry wt of phosphate divided by depth of bed gave recoverable contents per cu ft.

Alluvial gravel. Initial prospecting is often done with test pits, especially in shallow ground free from water; (churn drills for deep or water-bearing gravel). First pits or holes may be located at random; later ones, on regular system or according to information gained. D. L. Sawyer contributes data in Table 4, on test pitting in exceptionally coarse gravel. Pits were 3.5 by 3.5 ft cross-sec; no water encountered; most pits were cribbed with 2 by 12-in planks on edge, notched at both ends; some were sunk on company account and some by contract; crew of 3 men at each pit under either arrangement; High cost of certain pits due to large boulders and fine, running sand.

Table 4. **Labor Costs for Test Pitting in Coarse Gravel, Yavapai Co, Ariz**

Pit depths, ft	Company account			Contract arrangement		
	Aver advance per shift, ft	Labor cost per ft	Earnings per man-shift	Aver advance per shift, ft	Price per ft	Earnings per man-shift
5	4.80	$2.50	$4.00	9.80	$1.75	$5.70
5–10	3.00	4.00	4.00	7.65	2.00	5.10
10–15	2.20	5.50	4.00	4.20	3.00	4.20

7. PROSPECTING AND EXPLORATION BY BORING (See also Sec 9)

Applications of boring in connection with prospecting and exploration are: location of minerals covered by soil, rock, swamp, or water; search for extensions on strike or dip of known orebodies; search for parallel orebodies; location of faults, faulted segments of orebodies, and water-bearing strata; detailed exploration of orebodies for estimating tonnage and value. LIMITATIONS. BOREHOLES vs OTHER OPENINGS. Boring is not always the cheapest method of prospecting or exploration, and may not furnish all the desired information. In such cases, use test pits, shafts, or drifts.

Choice of method in any particular case is based on consideration of following factors. **Type of orebody.** Boring is not best adapted to exploring narrow, steeply dipping veins, small and irregular orebodies or high-grade, spotty deposits, although much of the diamond drilling actively and satisfactorily conducted in Canada is in such deposits. Boreholes, because of their small diam, may miss such orebodies entirely, or pierce them in pinches, swells, barren, or rich spots. Thus, diamond drilling cut a vein at a barren spot on City of Cobalt property, Canada, and failed to discover a rich vein system subsequently found by underground work (508). Boring from the surface is best suited to large deposits of fairly uniform grade, as masses or beds dipping less than 50°. Examples: Lake Superior iron ores, disseminated lead and zinc ores of Missouri, " porphyry copper " deposits, Clinton iron ores, and coal seams.

Cost. In surface drift, boring is done by augers, churn drills, or wash-boring; test pits are sometimes cheaper. Within its limited field an earth auger (Sec 9) will usually put down a 2-in hole for less than 0.2 of the cost of a test pit to same depth. To depths of 20 to 30 ft in surface drift, free from water and requiring no timbering, small test pits usually cost less per ft than churn-drill holes. Pits are better under such conditions for both prospecting and exploration, because of the more accurate information they afford. In soft rock, small shafts often cost less than either churn-drill or core-drill holes to shallow depths (20 to 50 ft). This is true only where no timbering is required and water is absent. In soft porphyry at Ajo, Ariz, 4 by 6-ft prospect shafts, 50 ft deep, cost less than diamond-drill holes to same depth (27). The cost of moving and setting up drills is largely responsible for the high cost per ft of shallow boreholes. For hard rock, and for greater depths in soft rock or alluvium, the cost of boring per ft is 0.2 to 0.5 that of small shafts.

Speed. Boring has little advantage over test pits for shallow work (20 to 30 ft) in dry surface drift requiring no timbering. In rock, and for greater depths in alluvium, speed of boring may be 3 to 10 times that of shafts or other underground openings. Presence of WATER increases cost and decreases speed of underground openings, but does not interfere with boring. Boring is therefore peculiarly applicable to prospecting and exploration in water-bearing formations.

Purpose of work. Many boreholes are made merely to locate strata or orebodies preliminary to sinking or driving to or through them. Thus, in the Clinton iron ores of Alabama, diamond-drill holes are bored at distances of 1 000 to 3 000 ft from the outcrops, to locate the ore bed and anticipate the effect of faults on location of shafts and workings. Similar cases occur in coal mines. On the Rand, also, the reefs under deep-level properties are located by diamond-drill holes before working shafts are begun.

Boring has a special field in prospecting for oil, gas, salines, and sulphur, where the borehole is used subsequently to conduct the mineral to the surface. For work under swamps, lakes, rivers, or deposits of quicksand, boreholes are most useful both for initial prospecting and for exploration based on indications given by geophysical methods (Sec 10A). Inclined holes are sunk from solid ground, or vertical holes from boats or through the ice in winter.

Speed vs cost. Where geological data are of chief interest, speed and cost are paramount factors, samples of the orebody are secondary objects, and boring has an advantage over shaft sinking which increases with depth of the deposit. At the other extreme is the work of detailed exploration to determine tonnage and aver values, in which cost and speed are subordinated to necessity for accurate samples; type of orebody then determines the choice.

Underground openings always give more accurate information and samples, but advantage can be taken of the speed and cheapness of boring in orebodies like the Mesabi iron ores and the " porphyry coppers," where values are uniform over large areas, or vary gradually from point to point. So much work has been done in some districts, as S E Missouri and in certain placer deposits, that empirical factors have been determined, to correct inaccuracies due to boring practice and to irregularities of the orebodies (Art 6).

Transport. In remote districts, cost of transporting boring apparatus may be prohibitive, except for shallow prospecting where hand drills can be used, although airplane transport of heavy and bulky equipment is overcoming this difficulty (646). It should be noted that borehole results are susceptible of more accurate interpretation in districts where the details of geology and ore occurrence are well understood; shafts or other openings are therefore sometimes preferable for preliminary work in new districts. Steep or rough topography increases cost of boring, owing to expense of moving drills, and may compel the use of underground methods.

Boring from underground points by diamond drills, and occasionally by hammer drills, is done in many mines, in searching for orebodies, to locate the limits of wide orebodies, or to obtain geological information. Footage may often be saved over holes started from surface. Steep-dipping veins may be cut by holes nearly normal to their plane. Fig 47 shows a hypothetical case, where a crosscut on bottom level failed to cut a vein known on levels above; projection indicated that the vein would be cut at point *A*. Diamond-drill hole No 1 also failed to find the vein. Hole No 2 cut the vein as indicated; a raise was then started at *B* to reach bottom of ore.

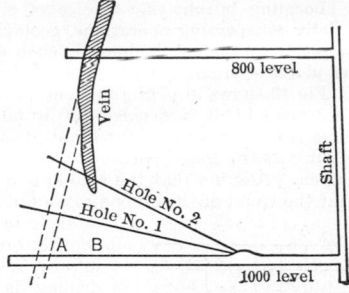

Fig 47. Locating Downward Extension of Vein

At Alaska Treadwell mine in 1913, 4 318 ft of holes were thus drilled to outline portions of the deposit (28). Rocks are hard diorite, quartz, and greenstone, and soft slate containing quartz stringers. A high core recovery was obtained; 90% in one horiz hole, 1 000 ft long. The information was therefore accurate. Drifting and tunneling would have taken 4 times as long, at a cost of $8 to $12 per ft. Cost of drilling was $1.62 to $1.74 per ft. Miami Copper Co did 2 714 ft of vertical diamond drilling from under-

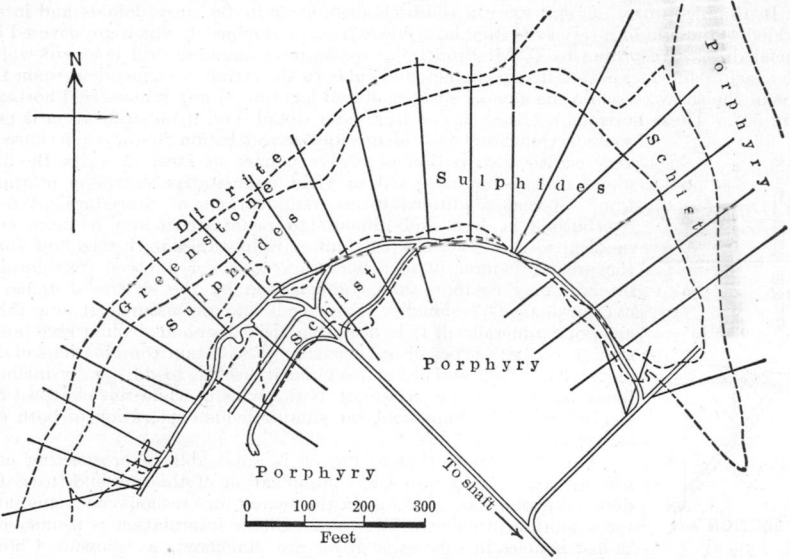

Fig 48. Diamond Drilling on One Level of United Verde Mine, Jerome, Ariz (97)

ground set-ups in 1912 and 1913 (29). Rock was silicified schist, broken into small pieces by fissures, the individual pieces being very hard. The holes caved frequently and were difficult to drill and sample; less than 10% of the core was recovered. Cost, $5.44 per ft; speed, about 5.5 ft per 8-hr shift. These examples show that the advantages of boring are lessened in very difficult formations. Fig 48, from M. G. Hansen (97) in 1933, shows diamond drilling on a level of United Verde mine, Ariz. Orebody is a pipe-like mass of sulphides, dipping about 60°; work was done to ascertain geology and locate walls and commercially mineralized areas. Most holes were nearly horiz, lying at angles between

+12° and −5°, and 150–650 ft deep; deepest, 2 200 ft; several exceed 1 000 ft. For further details, see Art 10-c.

Choice of boring apparatus, from standpoint of depth of holes, speed of boring, first cost, operating cost, convenience of transport and character of formation: for these points, see Sec 9, also Art 10.

Locating boreholes. Choice of sites depends on nature of work to be done. In strictly prospecting operations, geological indications, or the position of ore on adjacent property are the only guides; in such work initial drilling is often done at random. Holes are placed systematically for detailed exploratory work.

Fig 49 shows in plan a mode of prospecting for FLAT MASSIVE OREBODIES. Coordinate lines are laid at intervals of 50 to 60 ft, depending on the type of orebody sought. If there is no adjacent work to indicate the probable location or course of ore, the first hole is sunk at the most convenient point, say at A. In the illustration, this hole would be barren. Assume that the second and third holes are drilled at B and C. They indicate that the trend of the orebody is not along either AB or BC, and subsequent drilling would be done in the directions EF or GH. Instead of drilling hole C, after ore is found at B, holes 3 to 10 might be drilled. An infinite number of variations occur; as a rule, before close drilling is attempted, it is cheaper to establish the general trend of an orebody.

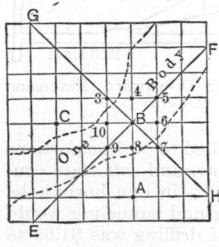

Fig 49

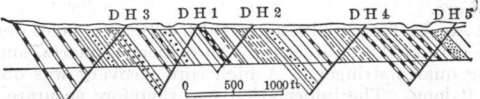

DH3   DH1   DH2   DH4   DH5

0   500   1000 ft

Fig 50. Diamond-drill Holes at Victoria Mine, Mich
(after A. H. Meuche, *Ann Rep* 1909, Mich Geol Surv)

In the MICHIGAN COPPER REGION the orebodies occur in the amygdaloids and inter-bedded sediments of a series of tilted lava flows, truncated edges of which are covered by glacial drift. According to T. M. Broderick, overlapping diamond-drill holes, of which the spacing and inclination in a plane perpendicular to the strike are dependent upon the dips of the series, disclose the general succession and location of any mineralized horizons (Fig 50). These horizons are then drilled in greater detail, and if mineralization is persistent, trenching or underground investigation follows. Because of very erratic distribution of native copper in most deposits, the diamond drill is not expected to yield quantitative sampling information. Special conditions cause modifications of procedure. Where overburden is deep and difficult to penetrate, it may be more economical to drill holes steeper than at right-angles to the bedding, since the greater footage in rock necessary to cover a given stratigraphic interval may be more than compensated by the shorter distance in overburden. Occasionally, where beds and the fissures crossing them are both mineralized, it is desirable that diamond drilling give information on both types of ore occurrence. Certain combinations of dip and strike of beds and of fissures make it possible to do this by inclined holes oblique to the strike of both, which, while not cheapest for either, are most economical for simultaneous exploration of both ore structures.

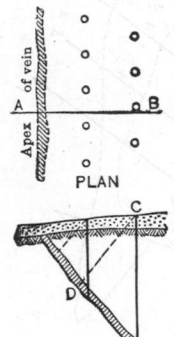

SECTION AB
Fig 51

A plan similar to that in Fig 50 is applicable in prospecting coal formations. Fig 51 shows an amplification of this method, used for detailed exploration of veins, in the search for oreshoots in veins, and for exploring pitching coal seams. Closer information is usually obtained if holes in successive rows are staggered, as shown. Choice between vert and inclined holes (CD, Fig 51) depends on local conditions. Vert holes are cheaper where depth of surface drift is great. They are used in initial drilling where nothing is known of the dip of rocks or orebody, and in general where dip of formation is less than 20° to 30°. Inclined holes are preferred for steeper dips; they are shorter, there is less danger of misinterpreting the thickness of formations penetrated, and they generally cut the short dimensions of vugs and soft layers, which give trouble in both drilling and sampling.

For detailed exploration of flat massive deposits, drill holes are usually located on corners of squares. Some systematic arrangement is desirable to secure impartial samples at regular intervals and simplify subsequent calculations of tonnages and aver values.

Interval between holes is a matter of judgment based on type of orebody. Questions of cost urge that holes be spaced far apart, but accuracy demands that the interval be limited to a distance over which it is safe to expect the orebody to continue without marked irregularities in form or tenor. (See Art 10 for spacing used in different localities.)

Fig 52, from R. V. Norris, shows one method of locating diamond-drill holes used in the PENN ANTHRACITE FIELDS, for determining position and thickness of folded coal seams. Order in which holes were drilled is shown by their numbers. Hole 14 was required to interpret data from 12 and 13. Surface geology and outcrops are valuable aids in constructing such sections. In the Wyoming and Lackawanna valleys, Penn, coal seams often outcrop under present or old river valleys, filled with wash to depths of 50 to 175 ft. Wash borings are made on corners of squares to determine thickness of rock

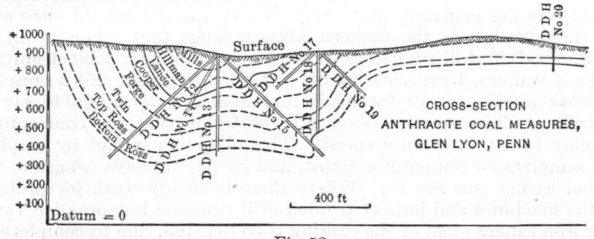

CROSS-SECTION
ANTHRACITE COAL MEASURES,
GLEN LYON, PENN

Fig 52

cover; size of squares varies from 100 to 500 ft, depending on this thickness and on irregularity of bedrock surface.

Prospecting for oil. Data on geology of oil deposits and location of boreholes are given in Sec 44; methods of boring, in Sec 9.

Drill roads are a serious item of expense in swampy districts, and where the topography is steep or rough. Standard rigs and diamond drills (except Missouri type) are moved on wagons requiring roads about 7 ft wide. For traction churn drills (Keystone No 5 and Star No 23), used in porphyry copper districts, hillside roads are made 9 ft wide in the solid. The fill is relied on only in case the machine skids. Max grade advisable is 15%, which is also about the limit for teams hauling fuel and water. Traction drills can climb 28% grades for short distances. Switch-backs are used when necessary; drills can not take so steep a grade while backing as when going ahead. In the Miami district, Ariz, with drill holes spaced 200 ft apart, a minimum of 300 ft of road was required per hole (33). At Miami, about 1 cu yd of material was moved per linear ft of road (34).

Organization of boring work. Good management is especially necessary where many drills are employed. Given suitable drills, economy in large-scale work may be secured by minimizing delays and labor required, and using common labor for roustabout work so that high-priced drillers spend maximum time in actual drilling. Scale of operations limits extent to which these economies are profitable. A map is essential to proper organization, and the points at which holes are to be drilled must be marked on the ground in advance.

Many DELAYS can be prevented by keeping at hand extra bits and small repair parts. Where tubs or barrels are used for samples, enough should be provided at each machine so that drilling can proceed while samples are settling or drying. Supply service for fuel and water should be carefully planned. Roads, if required, should be constructed before drill is ready to move; gasolene-driven diamond drills, mounted on skids and dragged by their own power, minimize expense for roads. FUEL. With coal, boxes or plats at the drill are necessary to prevent waste and give clean fires. Where wood is burned it should be cut to proper length before delivery; similar foresight is used in planning storage and delivery of liquid fuels, building power lines and handling cable for electric-driven drills.

Churn-drill work. The crew comprises a driller, helper, sampler, and sometimes a fireman (helper generally fires when coal fuel is used or when wood is delivered in proper lengths). If two drills are kept near each other, one sampler can look after both; hence, where several drills are in operation, they should be worked in pairs. Under favorable conditions one team can serve 3 or 4 drills within a radius of 0.5 or 0.75 mile. Keeping drills close together also allows easy supervision and use of fishing or other tools in common. A foreman for 3 or more drills will save his wages. Some engineers employ an extra driller or helper for every 2 or 3 drills, claiming that the saving in cost of moving, casing, and upkeep more than offsets the increased labor cost. For moving, setting up, casing, and pulling casing, 4 men (usually the crew of 2 shifts) are employed. For this reason, and in general, 2-shift work (either 8, 10 or 12 hr) is more economical than 3 8-hr shifts (34).

Diamond-drill work. The practice of keeping a number of drills near together has same advantages as for churn drills. Smallest possible crew for 1 drill consists of a drill runner and fireman for steam-driven drills (or a driller and helper for motor-driven drills), on day and night shifts, and a foreman on day shift. Foreman sets bits for both shifts and tends to sampling on day shift; drill runner does sampling on night shift. Except in remote places, it is now common practice to return worn bits for resetting at factory, maintaining a sufficient supply of fresh bits to permit uninterrupted operation. In some localities a drill runner and 2 helpers are used on each shift. In hard rocks giving good cores, where the sludge frequently is not saved, no special samplers are required; the foreman or drill runner can attend to the cores. Where accurate samples depend on saving the sludge, samplers are generally necessary. C. E. van Barneveld cites an illustration of large-scale organization on the western Mesabi range (35). For 30 drills working 1 shift, crew comprised 30 drill runners, 60 helpers, 5 pumpmen, 1 blacksmith, 3 diamond setters, 2 cooks, 4 waiters, 1 superintendent, 1 clerk, 2 foremen, and 3 samplers.

Contract work avoids outlay for drills and makes a considerable saving on small amounts of drilling. The practice is open to objection that the contractor may slight work of sampling to attain drilling speed. This objection is met by employing experienced men as samplers on company account, and by paying days' wages to the drill crew for reaming and casing (see Sec 9). Where there is steady work for drills, it generally pays to buy the machines and import trained drill runners, but practice varies. On the Lake Superior iron ranges most of the drilling is contracted, due to complete organization and equipment of local contracting firms and their reputation for careful work.

E. J. Longyear Co gives following data (1938) on 5 recent diamond-drilling contracts: (*A*) Iron exploration, Mich, 1930–31. Drilling from surface; overburden 50–150 ft deep, or approx 30% of total depth drilled. Carbon bits used exclusively. 4 drills worked two 8-hr shifts per day. Each crew included 1 runner and 2 helpers, while stand-piping through overburden; 1 runner and 1 helper for drilling rock. Aver crew for the job: 1 foreman, occasionally assisting with diamond setting; 1 diamond setter; 8 drill runners; 12 helpers; 2 pump-station men; 1 team and teamster; intermittent truck service as required. (*B*) Test borings at a dam site, Tenn, 1934; about 60% of total boring in overburden. Carbon and bortz bits (set on the job) were used. 4 drills worked 3 8-hr shifts per day, with a crew of: 1 drill supt; 1 diamond setter; 1 asst foreman and setter; 1 clerk; 12 runners; 12 helpers; 3 laborers to prepare locations in advance and assist with moving; 2 pump-station operators; 1 pick-up truck (intermittent truck service as required). (*C*) Iron exploration, Mich, 1937. Drilling from surface, about 2% in overburden. Mechanically set bortz bits used almost exclusively. Of 2 drills, 1 worked 2 shifts, other 3 shifts, employing: 1 foreman and diamond setter; 5 drill runners; 5 helpers; 1 pump-station operator; part-time truck service. (*D*) Iron exploration, Mich. All underground core drilling, with 1 drill working 1, 2, or 3 shifts; carbon bits set on the job. Crew: 1 foreman and diamond setter; 1, 2, or 3 drill runners; 1, 2, or 3 helpers. (*E*) Gold exploration, So Dak. All underground core drilling with 1 drill; mechanically set bortz bits used. Crew: 1 head driller for day shift; 1 driller for afternoon shift; 2 helpers.

Cost of diamond-drill exploration, per ton of ore proved, may range from less than 1¢ in large, uniform orebodies, to over 10¢ in small, erratic deposits. C. K. Hitchcock reported in 1933 that Creighton mine proved 9 225 000 tons of ore with 28 803 ft of drilling at 1.4¢ per ton; Murray mine, 8 560 000 tons with 35 792 ft of hole, at 1.7¢ per ton; Beattie Gold mine, 5 330 050 tons with 8 822 ft, at cost of 0.9¢ per ton proved.

Borehole results are often misinterpreted. Fig 53 shows a case where 2 holes on the flanks of a folded coal seam indicate a thicker horiz seam *A B*. Careless use of data from the hole in Fig 54 would indicate 2 seams instead of the true conditions. Results should be interpreted in the light of collateral geological evidence.

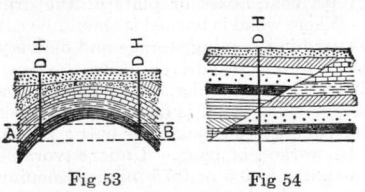

Fig 53   Fig 54

Single holes, while valuable for determining position of an orebody, give no information as to dip or strike, and often furnish erroneous values for thickness. The use of deflecting wedges (Sec 9) in deep diamond-drill holes, for getting a second section of the formation from the same hole, is a cheap means of securing additional data. For survey of deflected diamond-drill holes see Sec 9. A case of error from single holes has occurred in districts such as the Missouri and Wisconsin zinc fields, where churn-drill holes following rich vertical stringers were taken to prove the existence of thick, flat orebodies.

8. SAMPLING BOREHOLES (See also Sec 9)

Accuracy of sampling depends largely upon the character of the material drilled. Diamond drills give accurate samples in hard rocks where core recovery is complete. Accurate samples are also obtainable by churn drills in fine-grained, unconsolidated material, where casing pipe can be driven ahead of the drill bit or sand pump.

Soft, broken formations which cave in the hole are most difficult to sample. In these the efficiency of the diamond drill decreases both for drilling and sampling, and churn drills are commonly used. Vugs, crevices, and brittle sulphides make sampling difficult. Cores are more satisfactory than churn-drill sludge for determining geological details, but careful panning of churn-drill cuttings generally makes it possible to locate changes in formation or mineralization within 2 or 3 ft. A method of " structure " drilling employed on western Mesabi Range (Art 10-b) yields cuttings in coarse fragments, permitting better visual inspection. In coal, cores are necessary to get accurate widths, to locate partings and to secure correct analyses.

Length of samples taken from boreholes varies from 6 in to 10 ft; usual length, 5 ft. In soft, caving ground, or where mineralization is irregular, short lengths are advisable

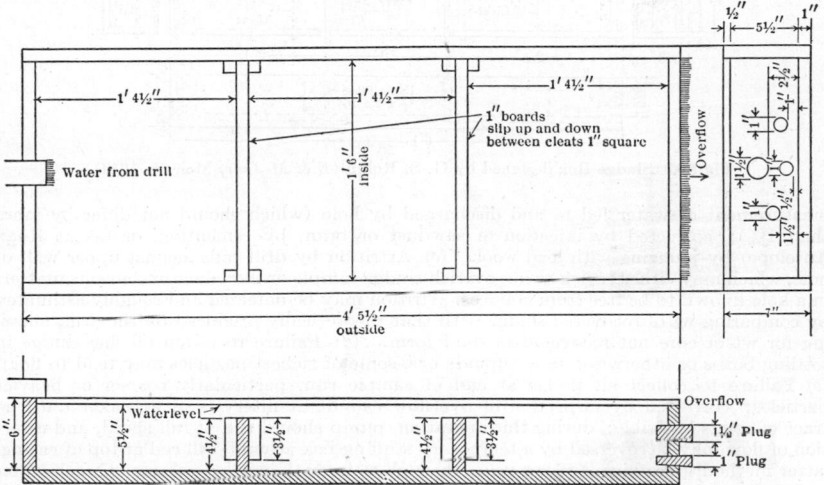

Fig 55. Wooden Sludge Box, Cleveland Cliffs Iron Co

for accurate work. In firmer ground with uniform values, the longer lengths give adequate information and save expense for sampling and assaying. Calculations incident to large-scale boring are simplified by taking samples in 5- or 10-ft lengths and recording measurements in feet and tenths.

Diamond-drill samples consist of core, or sludge, or both. Where complete cores are obtained they are assayed, or the values estimated. In soft, broken rock, where core recovery is low, the sludge must be saved and its assay combined with that of the core. Fine sludge is often difficult to catch, but all must be saved when drilling in ore which is near the merchantable limit of value.

Barrels or specially designed tanks are used for settling sludge in some districts (Art 10) and give accurate results provided enough of them are used, filled and emptied in rotation, to allow entire flow from the hole during a sample run to settle clear. SLUDGE BOXES are sometimes made on the ground. Fig 55 shows a type used many years by Cleveland Cliffs Iron Co; 2 such boxes are commonly connected in series, though frequently the second box collects but little sludge. Fig 56 shows another design (37); in this, the casing pipe projects through the bottom of the box, which allows it to be placed inside the drill shanty. Box is lined with No 26 galvanized iron. The baffles are of 0.25-in iron, hinged at top to $3/8$-in rods. Fig 57 shows a reinforced wooden box, with sheet-iron baffles, widely used on Mesabi Range. With all types of settling device, the sample is collected and transferred to drying pans after the clear water has been siphoned off, or drawn through plug holes. Lime or alum will accelerate settling. Care is necessary to avoid loss of fines; to prevent salting of succeeding samples, the box and drying pans must be thoroughly cleaned. Sludge containing sulphides must be dried cautiously to avoid oxidation and consequent errors in assays.

At Miami, sludge boxes were found inadequate to settle chalcocite slime, and samples were collected in heavy jute bags, which allowed the water to filter through. COMPRESSED AIR was also used there at times, to force cuttings out of the hole and so avoid caves caused by flushing of water. Fig 58 shows method then used for catching samples. Air and cuttings were ejected through one branch of a cross placed in top of casing pipe, a small stream of water being forced into opposite branch. The sack used for collecting sludge allowed no dust or slime to pass, and indicated the air pressure in the hole (29).

Causes of errors in diamond-drill samples: (a) Caving ground (indicated by behavior of drill); corrected by casing or cementing. (b) Loss of sludge in crevices; detected by

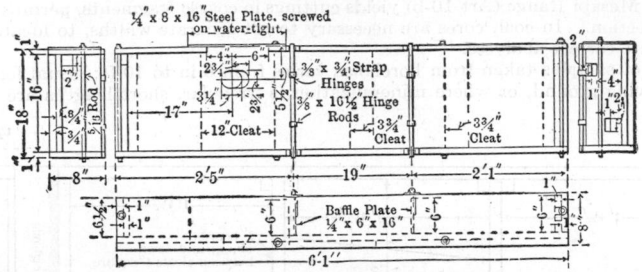

Fig 56. Sludge Box designed by G. S. Rollin (*E & M Jour*, Mch 28, 1914)

measurement of water fed to and discharged by hole (which should not differ by more than 1%); corrected by injection of sawdust or bran, by cementing, or (as at Roan Antelope) by plugging with lead wool. (c) Attrition by drill rods against upper wall of hole, which may either enrich or impoverish sludge sample or introduce extraneous matter; in a hole known to be free from crevices, attrition may be detected and roughly estimated by comparing wt of recovered sludge with that theoretically produced by the drill, allowing for wt of core not recovered in solid form. (d) Failure to retain all fine sludge in settling boxes or otherwise; in a sulphide ore, some of richest particles may tend to float. (e) Failure to collect all sludge at end of sample run, particularly coarser or heavier particles; corrected by inspection of overflow caught at intervals in a beaker until no trace of solids is visible; during this operation, pump should run at full speed, and direction of flow may be reversed by a temporary stuffing box around drill rod at top of casing; latter method gives higher rising veloc through rods, with smaller volume of wash water to be collected, but may not be feasible while drill is running. (f) Adhesion of sulphide mineral particles to greasy drill rods; in sulphide ores, oily rod-dopes should be replaced by soap if lubrication is needed.

H. L. Botsford describes a case of attrition (38) as follows: A hole at a Lake Superior iron mine passed through following strata: soft slate and pyrite, 145 to 215 ft; banded ore and chert, 215 to 470 ft; soft iron ore, 470 to 545 ft; black slate, 545 to 602 ft. Cores from soft ore assayed 5 to 8% more in iron than corresponding sludge, and showed a trace of sulphur; the sludge ran 0.36% S. Cores from slate below 545 ft ran 5.1% Fe; sludge, 40 to 50% Fe. By suspending rods in the hole, and rotating them at normal speed for time necessary to drill 5 ft, nearly as much sludge was produced as when drilling ahead. This test shows that, even in ground not caving so badly as to interfere with drilling, the rods may dislodge enough material from walls of hole to salt the sludge.

G. W. Thomson (39), in drilling 4 holes in Porcupine district, Ontario, found the drag of values shown in Table 5. Orebody consisted of auriferous quartz stringers and lenses in schist, the latter carrying no values. Often the only core recovered from a 5-ft run consisted of short pieces of quartz of a combined length of not over 8 in. Values in the sludge did not correspond with the richer sections of the core, but appeared 5 to 10 ft below. Drag of values was roughly proportionate to depth at which ore was cut; little trouble was experienced from caving. Water supply was small, veloc of rising current being 6–8 in per sec. Theoretically, it takes about 75 min for a current of 8 in per sec to raise a quartz grain 0.08 in diam from a depth of 700 ft. These conditions would cause the larger and heavier particles of sludge to hang back and appear later than the corresponding core. Information as to amount of caving, contamination of sludge from walls, and loss of sludge in crevices can be obtained

Table 5

Hole	Depth, ft	Drag, ft	Angle of hole
1	320	15	76°
2	705	25	76°
3	655	15	90°
4	1 155	35	90°

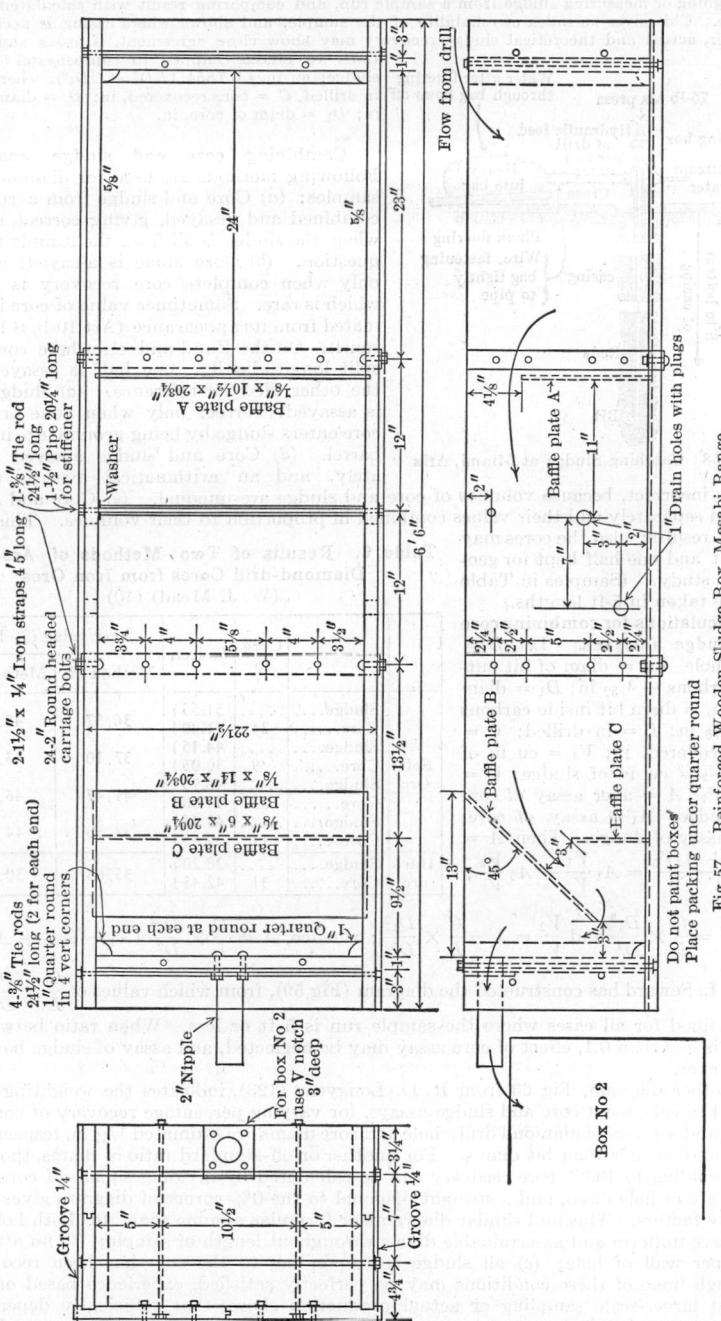

Fig 57. Reinforced Wooden Sludge Box, Mesabi Range

by weighing or measuring sludge from a sample run, and comparing result with calculated wt or volume. This gives an index of reliability of the sample, and shows where casing is necessary; however, actual and theoretical sludge recovery may show close agreement, if losses and additions to sludge happen to compensate. Vol of sludge: cu in $= 0.7854 \, (LD^2 - CD_1^2)$, where $L =$ in drilled, $C =$ core recovered, in; $D =$ diam hole, in; $D_1 =$ diam of core, in.

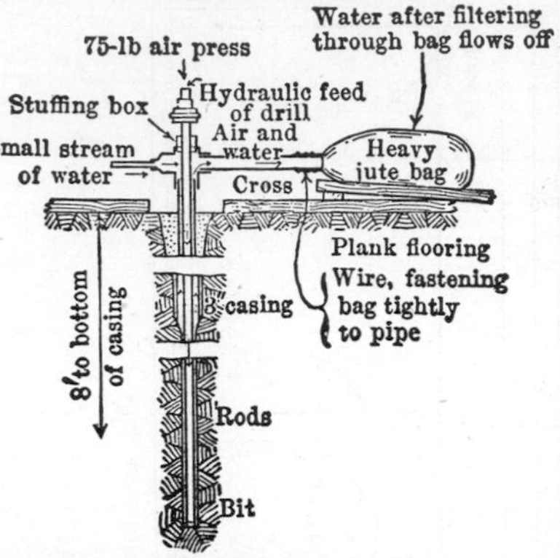

Fig 58 Catching Sludge at Miami, Ariz

Combining core and sludge analyses. Following methods are used for diamond-drill samples: (a) Core and sludge from a run are combined and assayed, giving correct results when the sludge is all from the sample run in question. (b) Core alone is assayed; correct only when complete core recovery is made, which is rare. Sometimes value of core is estimated from its appearance (Art 10-b, S E Missouri). On the Rand and elsewhere cores are split longitudinally; one half is assayed and the other filed for reference. (c) Sludge only is assayed; correct only when none or all of core enters sludge by being ground up in core barrel. (d) Core and sludge assayed separately, and an arithmetical aver is taken. This is incorrect, because volumes of core and sludge are unequal. (e) Core and sludge assayed separately and their values combined in proportion to their volumes. This gives correct results; also the cores may be split and one half kept for geological study. (Samples in Table 6, were taken in 5-ft lengths.)

Calculations for combining core and sludge analyses. Let $D =$ diam hole, in, = diam of bit outside carbons $+ \, 1/32$ in; $D_1 =$ diam core, in, = diam bit inside carbons less $1/16$ in; $L =$ in drilled; $C =$ core recovered, in; $V_1 =$ cu in of core; $V_2 =$ cu in of sludge; $V = V_1 + V_2$; $A =$ aver assay of core and sludge; $A_1 =$ assay of core; $A_2 =$ assay of sludge. Then, $A =$

$$\frac{A_1 V_1 + A_2 V_2}{V} = A_1 \frac{V_1}{V} + A_2 \frac{V_2}{V} \, ;$$

Table 6. Results of Two Methods of Assaying Diamond-drill Cores from Iron Ores
(W. J. Mead) (40)

		Core, in	% iron	Aver value (% Fe)	
				Method (d)	Method (e)
Soft Ore	Sludge....	....	51.55 ⎱	36.37	48.23
	Core......	24	21.20 ⎰		
	Sludge....	....	44.15 ⎱	37.10	43.48
	Core......	9	30.05 ⎰		
	Sludge....	....	48.95 ⎱	41.47	46.35
	Core......	37	34.00 ⎰		
	Sludge....	....	45.45 ⎱	37.55	44.68
	Core......	11	29.65 ⎰		
Hard ore	Sludge....	....	28.20 ⎱	35.63	30.74
	Core......	31	42.45 ⎰		

$$\frac{V_1}{V} = \frac{C}{L} \times \frac{D_1^2}{D^2} \text{ and } \frac{V_2}{V} = 1 - \frac{C}{L} \times \frac{D_1^2}{D^2} \, ; \text{ whence, } A = \frac{C}{L} \times \frac{D_1^2}{D^2} \, (A_1 - A_2) + A_2.$$

H. L. Seward has constructed the diagram (Fig 59), from which values of $\frac{C}{L} \times \frac{D_1^2}{D^2}$ can be obtained for all cases where the sample run is 5 ft or less. When ratio between C and L is less than 0.1, effect of core assay may be neglected, and assay of sludge be taken as the aver.

Another diagram, Fig 60 from R. D. Longyear (123), indicates the weighting to be applied to coincident core and sludge assays, for varying percentage recovery of core and for 4 standard sizes of diamond drill; hole and core diams are estimated $1/32$ in, respectively, larger and smaller than bit diams. For another or off-standard ratio of diams, the point corresponding to 100% core recovery can be calculated by dividing square of core diam by square of hole diam, and a straight diagonal to the 0% corner of diagram gives intermediate factors. This and similar diagrams or formulas assume that: (a) both hole and core have uniform and ascertainable diams throughout length of sample; (b) no attrition on upper wall of hole; (c) all sludge corresponding to the core has been recovered. Although none of these conditions may be perfectly satisfied, experience based on subsequent larger-scale sampling or actual production shows that sufficiently dependable results are attainable by careful attention to drilling and sampling technique. Where particular obstacles to accuracy are anticipated, the methods of calculation employed at Roan Antelope and described in Bib (124, 125) may become necessary, entailing determi-

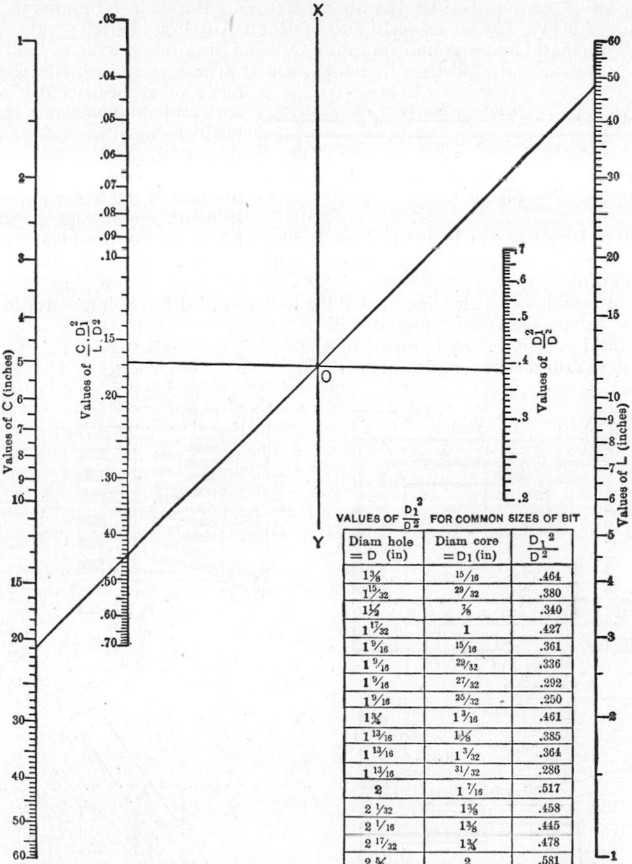

VALUES OF $\frac{D_1^2}{D^2}$ FOR COMMON SIZES OF BIT

Diam hole = D (in)	Diam core = D_1 (in)	$\frac{D_1^2}{D^2}$
1⅜	15/16	.464
1 15/32	29/32	.380
1½	⅞	.340
1 17/32	1	.427
1 9/16	15/16	.361
1 9/16	29/32	.336
1 9/16	27/32	.292
1 9/16	25/32	.250
1¾	1 3/16	.461
1 13/16	1⅛	.385
1 13/16	1 3/32	.364
1 13/16	31/32	.286
2	1 7/16	.517
2 1/32	1⅜	.458
2 1/16	1⅜	.445
2 17/32	1¾	.478
2⅝	2	.581
2 13/16	2	.506
3 1/32	2¼	.551

A straight-edge from *C* to *L* intersects line *XY* at same point as a straight-edge from $D_1^2 \div D^2$ to $CD_1^2 \div LD^2$. Example: 21 in of core (*C*) were recovered in drilling 48 in (*L*) with a bit where $D_1^2 \div D^2 = 0.385$. With straight-edge, connect 21 on scale *C* with 48 on scale *L*; mark intersection *O* on *XY*. Hold straight-edge on *O* and 0.385 (scale $D_1^2 \div D^2$), and read 0.168 on scale for $CD_1^2 \div LD^2$. For solving this problem the 2 positions of the straight-edge are shown by lines passing through *O*.

Fig 59. Diagram for Combining Core and Sludge Assays

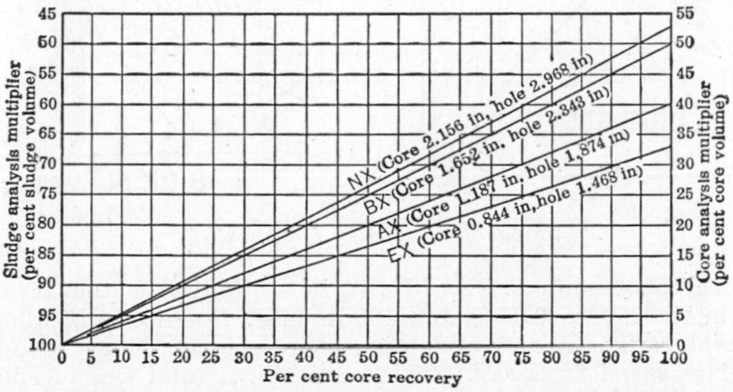

Fig 60. Weighting Factors for Calculating Average Assay of Core and Sludge

nations of sp gr of samples besides the above factors. Borehole estimates in 1930 gave an aver value of 3.44% Cu for easterly end of Roan Antelope deposit; subsequent production and systematic underground sampling in same area raised aver to 3.52%.

At Ajo, Morenci, and elsewhere in Southwest U S, assays are usually combined on basis of respective dry weights of core and sludge from a sample run, both being directly ascertainable (99, 100).

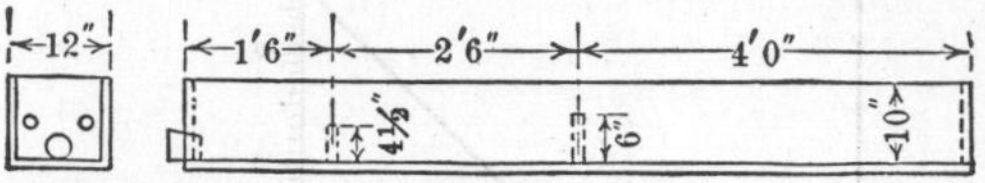

Fig 61

J. M. Weller describes (128) a method of calculation applied under difficult conditions at Round Mt, Nev; it involved length of run, length of core, dry wt of both core and sludge, and theoretical wt of core and sludge corresponding to 100% recovery of each, latter requiring determination of density.

Churn-drill samples (see also Sec 9). With hollow-rod drills, using water for flushing, samples are caught as for diamond-drill sludge. A sand pump is used with rope drills. The 6 to 10-in bits employed with

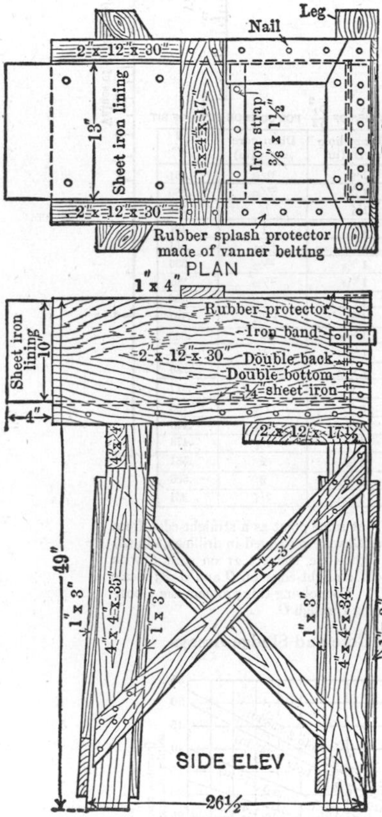

Fig 62

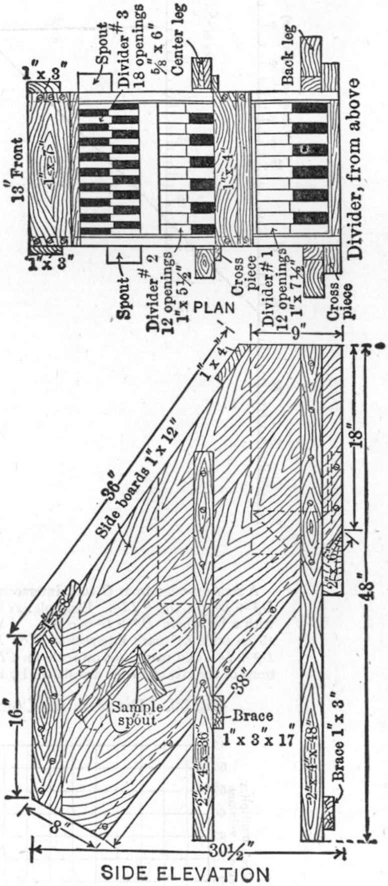

Fig 63

Sludge Splitter, Ray Consol Co

these drills produce bulky samples. At MIAMI, in a 5-ft run, a 10-in bit cut about 450 lb of rock; 7.625-in bit, 260 lb; 6.25-in bit, 180 lb (41). Practice in handling these large amounts of material varies. Water and thin sludge are sometimes wasted, and larger and heavier cuttings saved for assay. This results in a total loss of slime and serious errors in assay, especially when drilling in brittle sulphides.

The sand pump may be discharged into a sluice box (Fig 61) built of 1-in surfaced lumber and set on low horses in front of drill.   The partitions are set loosely between strips nailed to sides of box, for removal when cleaning up.   Sludge is dumped into the 4-ft compt. After settling, water is drained off through plug holes in far end of box.   Remaining sludge and water are swept out through large plug hole into a tub or pails, and dried for assay. Good sampling practice for churn-drill work has been developed in the porphyry copper districts, where the numerous samples taken and necessity for saving chalcocite slime make this work difficult.

At Nevada Consol mine, all sludge and water were poured directly into galvanized-iron wash tubs, and dried over a slow fire to avoid roasting the sulphides.   A 5-ft sample required 4 tubs.   In other districts, the sand pump is dumped into a launder containing split dividers, built like the Jones riffle sampler (Sec 30).

L. S. Cates furnishes drawings of a splitter used by Ray Consol Co.   It consists of a launder (Fig 62), into which the pump is dumped and which in turn spills into the splitter (Fig 63).   Fig 64, 65 are drawings of the riffles.   At Ray, the last split (about 40 lb) was dried for assay.   Five tubs were provided for each drill.   Samples were taken in 5-ft sections.   Sampler kept a record and panned sludge from upper portions of hole.   When specks of mineral appeared, the 4 previous samples were dried, so that assays of ground 20 ft above first visible mineral were obtained and useless assaying and drying avoided (42).   Similar devices are used in other districts, giving a final sample containing 0.25 to 0.0625 of the total cuttings in a sample run, depending on number of splitters used.

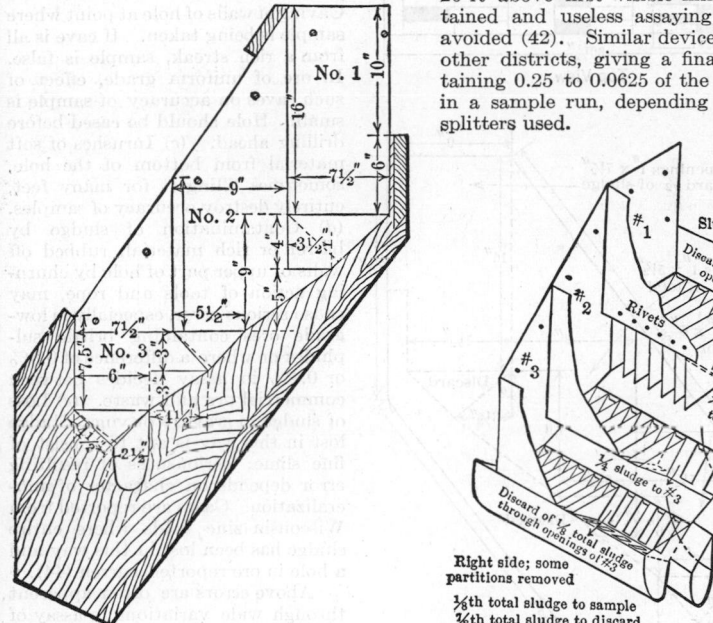

Fig 64   Fig 65.   Riffles of Ray Consol Sludge Splitter

At the Utah Copper mine, churn-drill holes down to 1 500 ft are started as large as 26 in. in diam.   Sampling is in charge of geological dept, one sampler per shift for each rig. Samples cover 5 ft of hole; suction bailer is preferred, and up to 12 bailings have been necessary to recover all sludge.   Sludge from bailer goes into a launder, 2 ft sq cross-sec, usually 30–50 ft long and set on 6% grade, which leads to the split divider (Fig 66); this stands on the bench where the drill is working.   The sludge is cut down to one-eighth of its original vol.   Two samples are taken; one dried at the rig before going to mine assay office, where it is divided, and one portion sent to the mills for analysis, the other analyzed at the mine; the other sample is further cut at the rig for a 50-ft composite wet sample to be used in flotation tests.   Wt of samples can be regulated by opening or closing the cutter openings.   This system has proved satisfactory and is cheaper for installation than a type previously in use; it is also accurate for sampling low-grade copper ores.

Savannah Copper Co, Burro Mtn district, N M, dried samples in an assay office at a distance from drills.   If sludge showed visible mineral, it was reduced in splitter to about

4 gal; if not, it was cut to 1 gal. Final samples were put into 1-gal milk cans, with tight-fitting covers, in which they could be transported in wagons without loss (43). One sampler did sampling for 2 drills, kept notes and checked drillers' measurements of depth.

At MASCOT, Tenn, when churn-drilling in limestone carrying zinc blende, all bailings from each 3-ft advance are sampled and assayed; specimens of cuttings and their acid-insol residues are mounted on cards for compiling records. At CHINO, N M, churn-drilling in disseminated copper ore, a similar permanent record is made by gluing specimens of cuttings to a strip of board, graduated to scale. Bottled specimens are also preserved.

In all sampling work, sluice boxes, splitters, and tubs must be scrupulously cleaned after each sample run, to avoid salting succeeding samples.

Errors in churn-drill samples, besides those due to careless handling of sludge on surface, may occur as follows: (*a*) Caving of walls of hole at some point above sample. This results in high or low assays, depending on whether cave takes place in rich or barren material. (*b*) Caving of walls of hole at point where sample is being taken. If cave is all from a rich streak, sample is false. In ore of uniform grade, effect of such caves on accuracy of sample is small. Hole should be cased before drilling ahead. (*c*) Inrushes of soft material from bottom of the hole, sometimes filling it for many feet, entirely destroy accuracy of samples. (*d*) Contamination of sludge by barren or rich material, rubbed off walls of upper part of hole by churning action of tools and rope, may cause serious error, especially in low-grade ores containing brittle sulphides or where a difference of 0.3% or 0.4% in assay decides between commercial ore and waste. (*e*) Loss of sludge in crevices or vugs. Sludge lost in this way is apt to consist of fine slime; seriousness of resulting error depends on character of mineralization. Cases are reported from Wisconsin zinc fields where entire sludge has been lost in this way and a hole in ore reported barren (44).

Above errors are often apparent through wide variations in assay of adjacent samples, and discrepancies between actual and calculated wts of sludge. Bad caving is, of course, indicated by drill itself. Remedy lies in proper use and handling of casing. In soft material, casing can be kept close to bottom of hole and sometimes be driven ahead of bit (Sec 9). In such holes a safe rule is to drive casing deeper before pumping. In harder rock, practically all sources of error would be eliminated if the drill hole were reamed

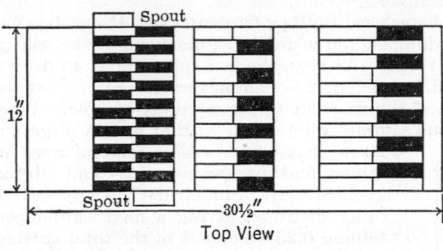

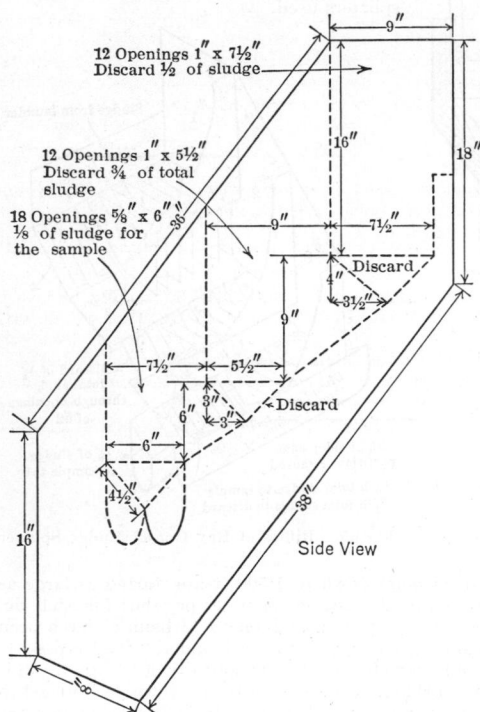

Fig 66.   Splitting Device for Churn-drill Samples, Utah Copper Co

after each sample run, and casing driven to bottom of hole before drilling ahead for next sample. This procedure is costly and offsets advantage of churn drill in both cheapness and speed. Also, for reaming and handling casing in deep holes, a calf wheel is required, which is not usually placed on portable churn drills. An approximation to above procedure is obtained more cheaply by starting hole with a large bit, casing as soon as sludge shows mineral, and continuing hole with a smaller bit. When caving is serious, another casing pipe is inserted inside the first and drilling is resumed with still smaller tools (Art 10-b, Porphyry coppers). In any given district, practice generally represents a compromise between cost and absolute accuracy. Pains are taken to get samples accurate enough for the purpose; beyond that, cost of reaming and casing is avoided.

Another error in churn-drill sampling occurs through failure of sludger to pick up all cuttings. Experiments have been made to determine loss from this source in placer testing. A piston (vacuum) pump in good order should be used. I. J. Stauber, while drilling in Burro Mtn district, N M, made it a rule to bail not less than 15 times after each sample run (43). Fixed rules based on experiment should prevent error from this source. Churning action of tools may produce a concentration of values in sludge in hole. At Ely, Nev, it was found that the first bailerful after drilling ahead assayed higher than succeeding ones (45). This causes no error if all bailings for any advance of hole are put into same sample. In churn-drill holes, values sometimes drag or appear in sludge obtained from points below ore horizon; caused by dislodgment of mineral from walls of uncased holes; or it may be due to incomplete recovery of sludge by pump. In latter case, serious errors may result in interpretation of both thickness and aver value of orebody.

Borehole results should be checked by shafts or raises, especially in new districts and where they are to be used as a basis for calculating tonnage and aver value (see Ajo, Art 10-b).

9. BORING RECORDS

Forms are needed for keeping drilling records and costs, and collating sampling and geological data for preparing estimates of tonnages and grades. The most suitable forms and amount of detail included depend upon the conditions of each case; following examples offer suggestions. Form in Fig 67 is a diamond-drill time record for one shift; that in Fig 68 covers 24 hr of drilling, with attention to details needed (jointly with assays) for compiling a record like that in Fig 73; the data on water recovery in Fig 68 are important as indicating degree of reliability of the sludge samples. Form in Fig 69, from Lake Superior iron district, facilitates calculation of aver grade from assays of core and sludge, combined in proportion to their wt. Form in Fig 70 applies only to churn drilling; that in Fig 71 applies to any kind of drilling. Fig 72 is a combined form for underground diamond drilling; entire form is filed at office, and each drill foreman receives duplicate of left-hand portion. Records in Fig 74, 74a are for exploratory hammer drilling (509).

Printed forms are preferable to notebooks, as they insure uniform data. In small-scale churn-drilling, the sampler's field notes are often recorded in an ordinary surveyor's transit book. The hole is drawn to scale on one page, and rock formation, changes in ground, depths, water-level, character of mineralization, and sample numbers are entered in proper position as they are obtained; the following page is used for explanations and other detail. These notes are transcribed into a similar loose-leaf book for office use, in which assays are also recorded. Complete detail is essential in interpreting results. Besides the above, records should include: date of starting and finishing hole; total depth; location of hole; elevation of collar; time for casing; names of drillers, samplers, and helpers (see also Sec 9).

Platting boreholes. Drawings of drill holes, showing formations and position and assay of ore, are often necessary for intelligent computation of aver values.

DIAMOND DRILL TIME REPORT, Phelps Dodge Corp, New Cornelia Branch

Hole No.............Date....................................Shift.....................

Depth of hole this shift: From...............To..............Advance..................

Time Distribution

| From | To | Time in minutes | | | | Remarks |
		Drilling	Pulling and lowering rods	Cementing	Delays	
(13 lines)						
Totals						

Sampler

Fig 67. Diamond-drill Time Report (original size, 8.5 by 11 in)

DAILY DIAMOND DRILL REPORT, Phelps Dodge Corp, New Cornelia Branch

Hole No........................Co-Ordinates.............................Date............
Drill No........................Size of Core..............
Day Shift, Feet.....Afternoon Shift, Feet.....Graveyard Shift, Feet.....Total 24 Hours, Feet...
Depth of Hole Beginning....................Depth of Hole 24 Hours Later...............

From	To	Length Core		Weight of core	Kind of rock	Ore minerals visible	Hardness of rock	Number of run
		Measured	Computed					
(12 lines)								

General Remarks

Water Recovery	
Run	% Recovery
(4 lines)	

Head Sampler

Fig 68.   Daily Diamond-drill Report (original size, 8.5 by 11 in)

DRILL HOLE NO...............

Location....................................Sec..........T.........R.........State.......
Elevation...................Angle of hole...............Direction of hole.............
Hole started.................Hole completed........................Casing { Pulled......
                                                                           { Left........
Scale—1 inch = 50 feet

Hole drilled by...........................   Material classified by......................

Material	Depth	Angle of hole	Angle of strata	Inches of core	Wt, lb	Sludge					Wt, lb	Core					Wt, lb	Combined Analysis					
						Percentage						Percentage						Percentage					
						Fe	Phos	Mn	SiO$_2$	Al$_2$O$_3$		Fe	Phos	Mn	SiO$_2$	Al$_2$O$_3$		Fe	Phos	Mn	SiO$_2$	Al$_2$O$_3$	S

Fig 69.   Office Record, Diamond-drilling, Lake Superior Iron District

MINING DEPARTMENT, NEVADA CONSOLIDATED COPPER COMPANY
PROSPECT DRILL REPORT   No.........
Hole No...........................   Drill No................
Shift..............................   Date................

HOURS

Drilling	Bailing out	Casing	Pulling casing	Fishing	Moving	Repairs	Miscel
(1 line)							

Depth hole, beginning shift...............ft   Size of casing.........................in
Depth hole, end shift.....................ft   Length of casing.......................ft
Depth drilled............................ft   Size bit used..........................in

Sample No	Depth	Rock sample	Sludge color	Hardness	Caving	No bailers	Is sample reliable
(8 lines)							

REMARKS
Describe condition of hole, supplies needed, etc
(3 lines)

Depth of water level...Driller
Samples sacked..Helper
Samples drying..Sampler

Fig 70.   Daily Churn-drill Report (original size, 4.5 by 7 in)

| HOLE No ____ | DAILY DRILL REPORT | CO-ORD | N____ |

Date_____ Shift_____ Rotary No_____ Churn No.____

NAME ____ ____	Cut Ground			Casing			Repair					Miscellaneous									Delays Due To							
	Drill	Clean out	Ream	U Ream	Out and in	Casing	Dr. Cas.	Pull Cas	Eng & Boil	Rg	Tools	Pump & P	Fish	Move	Ch Line	Splice M	Splice W	Mk Stand	Ch Collar	Sample	Crders	Water	Fuel	Mud	Tools	Casing	Supp	Total Hours	Rate
(7 Lines)																												
Total____																												

	Drill	Ream	U Ream	Core	Kind of Bit		
Diameter of Hole					Standard	Core Barrel	
Depth at End of Shift					Fish Tail	Shoe	
Depth at Begin of Shift					S-H		
Progress during Shift					Drag		

Casing	16 in.	12½ in	10 in.	8¼ in.	6¼ in.	4½ in.	3 in	2 in	Depth	
In at Begin of Shift									Free	
Put in									Sticking	
Pulled out									Parted	
In at End of Shift									Collapsed	

Water Ground Tools

Struck at ____ ft Raising____ Lowering____ Level____ Cased off____
Hard____ Med____ Soft____ Standing____ Caving____ Run in____ Back up____
Working, Free____ Sticking____ Lost____ Recovered____ Depth to top____ Bot____
In fishing, write in details below and on back of this sheet

Sampling, Geology and Remarks

Sample				Formation						COLOR OF SLUDGE	Minerals											Sample					
Sludge	Bit	Core	Depth	Cong	Clay	Schist	S Schist	Granite	Dacite		Blk Iron Ox	Red Iron Ox	Chrysocolla	Malachite	Azurite	Cuprite	Native	Chalcocite	Chalcopyrite	Pyrite	Reliable	Not Rel	Cut to	Sent Office	Sacked Rig	Drying	In Tub
(12 Lines)																											

O. K._____ Foreman   O. K._____ Sampler

Fig 71.   Report Applicable to Boring in General (size 8.5 by 11 in.)

DAILY REPORT, DIAMOND DRILL

Location...Level........................Mine
Prospect No..19....

	Carbons on Hand		Carbons in Bits		Carbons Received		Fragments on Hand	Loss in Drilling
Depth from breast, beginning of shift Feet								
Depth from breast, end of shift......Feet								
Distance drilled..................Feet	Number	Carat	Number	Carat	Number	Carat	Carat	Carat
Distance reamed.................Feet								
......inch casing put in..........Feet								
......inch standpipe put in........Feet								

FROM	TO	FEET	MATERIAL	ASSAYS			
				Cu	Ag	Au	Fe
(3 lines)							

Report cause of delay, accidents, loss or breaking of carbons, etc.   Head Driller.

Fig 72.   Report on Underground Diamond Drilling, Butte, Mont.

Athona Mines (688) employed diamond drill at Lake Athabaska, Canada, in 1935, for systematic exploration of narrow quartz veins in sheared zones carrying erratic free gold; core recovery usually nearly complete. Vert trace of each hole was platted, at 1 in = 50 ft, on separate 11 by 16-in sheet of pure white, muslin-backed paper, using Japanese transparent water colors for tinting. Standardized system of over 200 symbols was adopted for these and related drawings. Plat included contacts, faults, intersections of dikes, interpretation of structures, and assays of core and sludge; also a legend stating: bearing, length, and dip of hole, coordinates and elev of its collar, and length of casing.

PHELPS DODGE CORP, NEW CORNELIA
(Coordinates: N 6084.87, E 3964.93. Elev

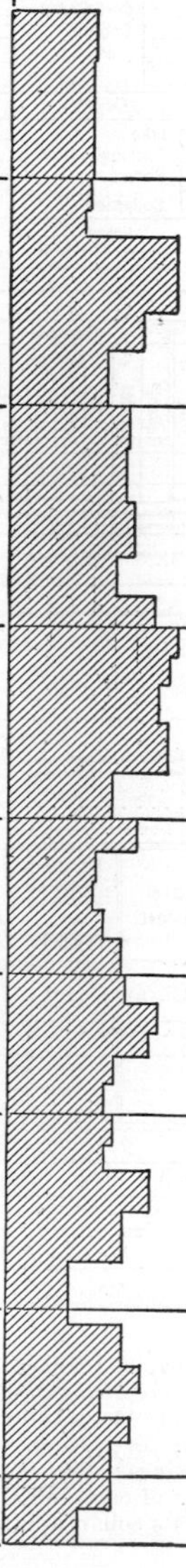

Depth of hole	Total copper, %	Assays calculated to five-foot intervals Total Cu%	Oxide Cu%	Summary of ores cut	Drilling interval From (Ft In)	To (Ft In)	Accepted assay Total Cu%	Oxide Cu%	Sludge sample Total Cu%	Oxide Cu%	Core sample Total Cu%	Oxide Cu%
		....	....	....	0 0	9 3	....	....	....	....	....	....
		....	....		9 3	12 0	0.42	....	0.41	0.03	0.44	Tr
		0.40	....									
		0.39	....		12 0	17 2	0.39	....	0.38	0.05	0.40	Tr
		0.39	....	25′ @ 0.38	17 2	23 2	0.39	....	....	....	0.39	Tr
25		0.39	....									
		0.38	....		23 2	29 11	0.38	....	....	....	0.38	Tr
		0.34			29 11	34 6	0.31				0.31	....
		0.78			34 6	37 2	0.58		....	....	0.58	....
		0.78			37 2	40 3	0.93	....	1.04	0.41	0.25	
		0.62			40 3	45 0	0.60	....	0.68	0.17	0.44	
		0.46			45 0	48 2	0.44	....	0.48	0.08	0.30	....
50												
		0.56	....		48 2	53 0	0.50		0.50	0.04	0.49	
		....			53 0	56 0	0.65		0.67	0.07	0.33	....
		0.55										
		....			56 0	61 0	0.53		0.54	0.05	0.41	
		0.59										
		....			61 0	66 0	0.60		0.61	0.05	0.25	
		0.50			66 0	70 0	0.48		0.50	0.07	0.41	
75		0.68			70 0	75 0	0.68		0.72	0.04	0.38	
		0.79	....	70′ @ 0.61	75 0	80 0	0.79		0.82	0.06	0.50	
		0.75			80 0	85 0	0.75		0.79	0.06	0.60	
		0.60			85 0	88 0	0.59		0.58	0.09	0.62	
		....			88 0	91 0	0.62		0.62	0.06	0.57	
		0.62										
		....			91 0	96 0	0.62		0.65	0.05	0.54	
100		0.49			96 0	100 0	0.46		0.46	0.05	0.46	
		0.60			100 0	105 0	0.60		0.62	0.06	0.50	
		0.41			105 0	110 0	0.41		0.42	0.05	0.38	
		0.40		15′ @ 0.42	110 0	114 10	0.40		0.41	0.04	0.24	
		0.44			114 10	120 0	0.44		0.45	0.03	0.36	
125		0.52			120 0	125 0	0.52		0.54	0.03	0.45	
		0.54			125 0	130 0	0.54		0.56	0.03	0.46	
		0.70			130 0	135 0	0.70		0.74	0.03	0.58	
		0.66			135 0	140 0	0.66		0.66	0.04	0.66	
		0.50			140 0	144 0	0.51		0.52	0.02	0.46	
150		0.46			144 0	149 0	0.44		0.44	....	0.46	....
		0.50			149 0	154 0	0.52		0.51		0.59	....
		0.46			154 0	159 0	0.40		0.40		0.37	....
		0.68	....	85′ @ 0.53	159 0	163 0	0.71		0.77		0.39	....
		....			163 0	165 8	0.64		0.62		0.67	
		0.54										
175		....			165 8	171 0	0.52		0.53		0.46	
		0.30										
		....			171 0	176 0	0.25		0.28		0.14	
		0.54			176 0	179 0	0.59		0.59		0.58	
		0.62			179 0	184 0	0.67		0.62		0.83	
		0.45			184 0	189 0	0.41		0.41		0.39	
		0.59			189 0	194 0	0.61		0.62		0.49	
200		0.50			194 0	199 0	0.49		0.52		0.35	
		0.50	....		199 0	204 0	0.56	....	0.57	....	0.52	....
		0.33	....	....	204 0	208 1	0.25	....	0.25	....	0.27	....

Fig 73.   Upper Part of Consolidated Record of Diamond-drill

BRANCH, Diamond Drill Hole No 191
at collar, 1794.04; at bottom, 1374.04)

Ag Oz/T	Au Oz/T	% SiO₂	% Fe	% Al₂O₃	% CaO	% S	% Water recovery	Inches Run	Inches Core	% Recovery	Description of Rock	Date	Remarks
													Hard ground Air drill and cemented
								33	24	72.7	Mon- Chalco- Bor- zonite pyrite nite	10-12-36	
								62	38	61.3	" " "	10-13-36	Cemented
								72	18	25.0	" " "	10-14-36	
								81	39	48.2	" " "		Cemented
								55	24	43.6	" " "	10-15-36	
								32	27	84.4	" " "		
								37	15	40.5	" " "		Hole cased 38'
								57	20	35.0	" " "		
0.055	0.0075	64.8	3.4	16.0	3.3	0.30		38	23	60.5	" " "		Cemented 38'-48'-2"
								58	39	67.2	" " "	10-16-36	
							97	36	7	19.4	" " "		
								60	18	30.0	" " "		
								60	6	10.0	" " "		
							97	48	25	52.1	" " "	10-17-36	
								60	20	33.3	" " "		
								60	20	33.3	" " "		
								60	40	66.7	" " "		
								36	14	38.9	" " "		
								36	11	30.6	" " "		
							99	60	50	83.3	" " "	10-18-36	
0.063	0.015	64.3	3.4	15.2	3.1	0.41		48	18	37.5	" " "		
								60	26	43.3	" " "		
								60	33	55.0	" " "		
								58	7	12.1	" " "		
							98	70	18	25.7	" " "	10-19-36	
								60	35	58.3	" " "		
								60	43	71.7	" " "		
								60	51	85.0	" " "		
								60	28	46.7	" " "		
							98	48	34	70.8	" " "	10-20-36	
0.080	0.015	63.6	3.6	15.6	3.0	0.38		60	39	65.0	" " "		
								60	32	53.3	" " "		
								60	30	50.0	" " "		
								48	24	50.0	" " "		
							99	32	32	100.0	" " "		
								64	19	29.6	" " "		
								60	37	61.7	" Andesite "		
								36	6	16.7	" " "		
							99	60	40	66.7	" " "	10-21-36	
								60	25	41.7	" " "		
								60	10	16.7	" " "		
0.030	0.005	60.4	3.7	15.0	3.0	0.50		60	28	46.7	" " "		
								60	42	70.0	" " "		
							97	49	28	57.1	" " "		

Hole in Porphyry Copper Deposit; total depth, 420 ft

Hole No....................	ENGINEERING DATA					....................Mine

PROSPECT DRILL HOLE RECORD

Location ....

Level:.........; Block:..........; ....Ft........of Sta Post No......... Elev of Collar........

Course:..............; Pitch:..............; Depth:....................................

Sample No	Oz Au	Oz Ag	% Pb	% Cu	% Zn	% Insol		Formation, etc
(6 lines)								

Remarks:..

Showing followed...Result..........................

Hole suggested...............19....By..................

Fig 74.   Form Used at Chief Consol Mine

This and Fig 74a are printed on opposite sides of a 5 by 8-in card (509)

Hole No....................	OPERATING DATA	..............Mine

PROSPECT DRILL HOLE RECORD

Date Started:...............   Date Finished:.................; Driller:..................

Helper:................

Total Depth:.........Ft. Values?.........   Followed Up?..........First Shipment........

No Machine Shifts:.........   No Man Shifts:.............   Total Labor Cost $........

Adv per Mach Shift:.........   Adv per Man Shift:..........   Labor Cost per Ft $........

Average Cost per Man Shift: $...............

Remarks: (10 lines) ....

Record Complete:............................19....By..................

Fig 74a.   Form Used at Chief Consol Mine (see note under title of Fig 74)

Cleveland-Cliffs Iron Co plats all boreholes on a loose-leaf form of tracing cloth, size 14 by 14 in, on a scale of 1 in = 50 ft (36).   Fig 75 shows a scale plat of part of a diamond-drill hole near Scranton, Penn; col 1 is a classification of strata drilled; col 2 gives continuous measurements from the

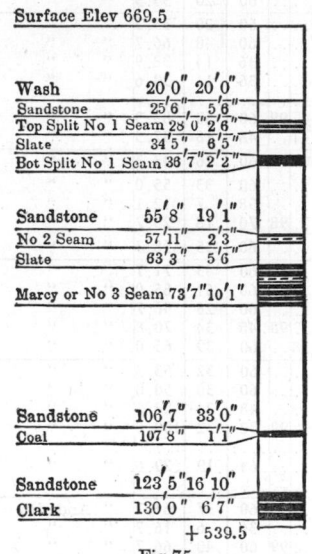

Fig 75

surface; col 3 shows thickness of each stratum.   These drawings are generally made to scale of 1 in = 20 ft; smaller scales will not show details of coal seams (47).   Fig 76 is a form used at Utah Copper mine, Bingham (119) for collating the geologic, mineralogic, and assay data secured at each hole, also indicating the lengths and positions of segments of casing not withdrawn.   If boreholes are surveyed (Sec 9) deviations are shown on plats.

"Core boxes for preserving diamond-drill cores are usually open trays, 5 to 6 ft long, 2 to 4 in deep, and wide enough to take 5 or 6 rows of core; longitudinal partitions divide the box into grooves 1/16 or 1/8 in wider than diam of core. Boxes have 1-in sides and bottom, with 0.5-in slats for partitions. A tray when filled should not be too heavy for

CHURN DRILL HOLE No. 134

Casing Left in Hole	Casing Record	Adopted Assays CU	Character of Material	General Remarks and Minerals
23" Casing 70' with shoe	23" casing	Elev 6698	Silic Porph	8-14-28: Spudded in 23" bit. Pyrite chalcopyrite, chalcocite, covellite, bornite, molybdenite
20" " 100' " "			Silic Porph	Chalcopyrite, pyrite, chalcocite, covellite, bornite, molybdenite
15½" " 323' " "	20" casing	0.88%		
12½" " 130' " "				
200			Silic Porph	Chalcopyrite, pyrite, bornite, chalcocite
				covellite, molybdenite
		Elev 6393		
400	15¾" casing		Silic Porph	Chalcopyrite, pyrite, chalcocite, bornite, covellite, molybdenite
600		1.16%	Silic Porph	Chalcopyrite, pyrite, chalcocite, molybdenite bornite, covellite,
800			Gray Porph	Chalcopyrite, chalcocite, pyrite, covellite, bornite, molybdenite
1000	12½" casing	Elev 5833	Dark Porph	Chalcopyrite, chalcocite, pyrite, covellite, bornite, molybdenite
		0.81%	Limestone	Altered, chalcocite, chalcopyrite, pyrite, covellite, bornite, molybdenite
1200	10" casing	Elev 5573, 0.52% Elev 5543	Dark Porph	Chalcopyrite, chalcocite, pyrite, covellite, bornite, molybdenite
		0.78% Elev 5468, 0.54% Elev 5428	Limestone	Black, large amounts of chalcocite in limestone; in porphyry primary minerals only, chiefly chalcopyrite, bornite, pyrite, unusual amount of bornite
1400	6½" casing	0.80%	Mixed zone of limestone and porphyry, Dark Porph	In limestone; chalcopyrite, chalcocite, covellite
		Elev 5233	with limestone inclusions	In porphyry; chalcopyrite, bornite, pyrite, molybdenite. 2-10-29-Hole completed-Depth 1475'

Fig 76. Condensed Churn-drill Log

one man to handle. Box shown in Fig 77, as used by E. J. Longyear Co, is made of 28-gage galv iron and holds 20 ft of EX (7/8-in) core; a sliding cover (not shown) permits box to be shipped without disarranging its contents.

If much drilling is to be done, cases should be built into which core boxes slide like drawers. Fig 78 shows wooden core box for this purpose; corners are mortised, slats and bottom are nailed in place. It is advisable to mark by an arrow the direction in which core is laid in box; also depths at end of each row. Lost core may be represented by pieces of wood, on which length and character of missing material can be noted (36).

Fig 77.   Galvanized-iron Core Box

For storing large amounts of core so that they will be easily accessible for observation, narrow shelves or trays may be supported at intervals of 1.5 in on the sides of A-shaped frames (48). A piece of corrugated sheet iron makes an excellent table on which to lay

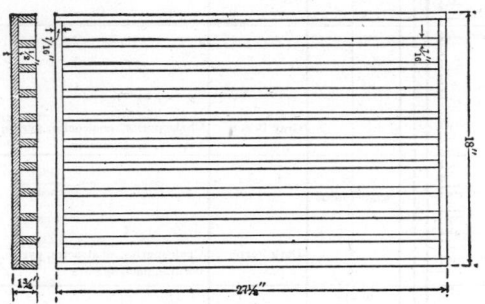

Fig 78.   Wooden Core Box

out core for inspection. A common form of core splitter, obtainable from diamond-drill makers, is shown in Fig 79.

10.   EXAMPLES OF BORING AND SAMPLING PRACTICE

a. Shallow Work with Auger or Drivepipe

Mayarí and Moa districts, Cuba, contain residual brown iron ores, up to 80 ft thick; average 18 to 20 ft. The orebodies have enormous lateral area; in Moa, they are nearly continuous for more than 70 sq miles. There is no overburden, but surface is covered with a heavy growth of timber and underbrush. Ore is clayey and stands a long time in boreholes without caving. S. J. Cox (53) and D. E. Woodbridge (54) gave following data in 1911. Earth augers, used for exploration, were made from ordinary 2-in carpenter's augers with jointed rods (Sec 9). At Mayarí, first borings were on corners of 100-ft squares. Ore is remarkably homogeneous, and interval between holes was successively increased to 300, 500, and finally 1 000 ft. " Results were checked by borings 25 and 50 ft apart on 4 limited areas, widely separated and each representing several million tons."

Subsequent mining has confirmed the values calculated from boreholes. In the Moa district, 1 000 ft was the usual distance between holes, though some drilling was done at greater and smaller intervals. About 900 holes were drilled in an area of 8 100 hectares (1 hole per 22 acres) by the Spanish American Iron Co, 1906. Work was checked and confirmed in 1910 with a new set of borings made by an independent engineer. Two men on an auger put down 10 to 13 holes per day; aver depth, 20 ft. Drillers were paid 1.5 to 2¢ per ft of hole for the first 10 ft. A water boy and sampler were provided for each crew. Occasional test pits were made to allow close study of the ore. Where holes were sampled

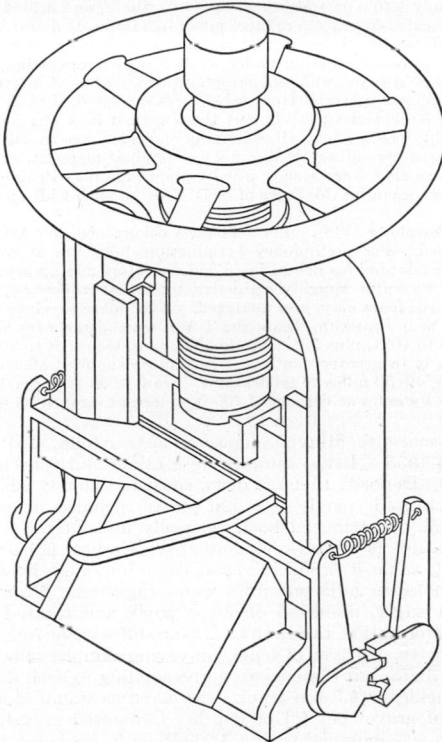

Fig 79. Core Splitter

in sections, cuttings from a 5- or 6-ft length were saved as a sample. Where sectional samples were not taken, auger cuttings were piled on a cloth, coned and quartered down.

Tennessee zinc and barite. Residual deposits of barite and calamine are overlain by clay and soil from a few feet to 100 ft deep (58).

In 1909, Newmarket Zinc Co explored a tract of about 11 acres containing a deposit of zinc carbonate and silicate in tough residual clay, 10 to 75 ft deep. Ore occurs near bed rock. Post-hole diggers (Sec 9) were used for holes at intervals of 50 to 100 ft. Dirt was washed and saved. Two men bored 20–40 ft per day. This simple method gives accurate samples in dry clay, which will stick on the digger and stand in hole without caving (59).

Yellow Aster mine, Randsburg, Cal, in 1934 sampled 2 300 000 tons impounded amalgamation-mill tailings, to ascertain suitability for cyanidation (31). Holes were at corners of 200-ft squares. Post-hole augers proved unsatisfactory. Drilling done by hand with 2-in ship augers, using 3/4-in pipe in 5-, 20-, and 30-ft sections, for turning and lifting with aid of light tripod and tackle. Only casing used comprised short pieces at collars of holes, to support rod clamps while lifting and lowering. Total depth for 97 holes, 2 950 ft; aver, 30 ft; some, over 100 ft. Two crews, of 2 or 3 men each, took 45 days for the work. Each hole was sampled and assayed in 5-ft sections; composite sample representing each hole was required to check calculated aver to within 8¢ per ton.

Florida pebble phosphate fields. Phosphatic concretions rarely exceeding 0.5-in diam occur in sandy clay in horiz beds to 24 ft thick, overlain by 3.5–100 ft of barren sand and clay mixtures, with some thin seams of hardpan; muck and quicksand also occur. COMMERCIAL PRACTICE, described by C. A. Fulton (148) in 1935, usually calls for 16 holes on a 40-acre tract. Vert 4.5-in holes are sunk with hand augers to bottom of matrix bed, at about 5 ft per hr; cost, 30¢ per ft. All cuttings in matrix are recovered, weighed, and sampled. Complete record of each hole includes: (a) depth of overburden; (b) depth of matrix; (c) tonnage (long tons per acre, dry basis) of pebble coarser than 14-mesh; (d) corresponding tonnage of phosphate finer than 14-mesh (not considered in former years, but now recovered by flotation); (e) assay of each size of product for $Ca_3(PO_4)_2$, $Fe_2O_3 + Al_2O_3$, and insolubles. From above data, calculation gives cu yd of overburden and of matrix per ton of recoverable phosphate, and total tonnages, by grades, of phosphate in the tract. Work by U S Geol Surv in 1936, for purpose of CLASSIFICATION only, demanded fewer holes than commercial valuation, only 1 to 3 or 4 per 40 acres (149); these were drilled by hand with 4-in earth auger, inside a casing of extra-heavy 4.5-in steel pipe (4.25 in inside diam), with screwed joints flush outside. Bottom end of casing was notched, points of teeth being spread to excavate a section of 5-in diam. Casing was sunk by twisting under wt of 2 drillers operating auger from platform at top; bottom of casing was always (while in phosphate bed) ahead of auger. Depth of 110 ft was thus reached. All phosphatic material from a hole was collected, drained of its loose water, and weighed, still averaging 33% moisture. It was then washed in a box having a bottom of sheet steel punched with 0.5 by $1/32$-in slots; all remaining on screen was called "pebble," weighed after drying, and calculated as a percentage of damp wt of original material, or "crude." Aver wt per cu ft of undried crude was also ascertained; usually about 125 lb. Pebble contents, long tons per acre, was computed from measured thickness of bed. Cost of such wide-spaced sampling estimated at $8–$10 per acre.

Tennessee brown phosphate (338). For geological occurrence, see Art 97. Earth augers and post-hole diggers are used. For preliminary examination, holes are at corners of 500-ft squares, but 50-ft spacing may be adopted for delimiting a deposit before mining begins. Phosphatic matrix can be recognized, and its value roughly estimated by visual inspection, but samples are taken systematically, washed free from clay, and analyzed. Aver matrix weighs 90 lb per cu ft in place. For prospecting a tract near Franklin, Tenn, the T V A let contracts for auger holes at base price of $1.15 each, for depths to 10 ft, plus 20¢ per ft to 20 ft, plus 35¢ per ft to 30 ft (30-ft hole thus costing $6.65), plus 50¢ per ft to greater depths. Contractors supplied all equipment except augers, and transported samples 40–50 miles to laboratory. From 1936 through 1938, cost to T V A for this prospecting, mainly by holes at corners of 200-ft squares, averaged $5 per acre.

Atolia-Rand gold-scheelite alluvial deposits, near Atolia, Cal, were systematically explored by boring in 1935. Large samples were taken and concentrated in a pilot mill on the property (32). Deposit, 15–65 ft deep, consisted almost wholly of angular gravel to 2-in diam, in which gold (partly free and partly included in quartz fragments) and scheelite were erratically distributed both vertically and laterally; present topography gave almost no indication as to bed-rock contours. Earliest holes were spaced 275 ft in rows 400 ft apart, but, as most promising areas came into view, holes were spaced 50 ft in rows 150 ft apart; holes in adjacent rows were staggered. Two " California cesspool diggers," a large pod auger, mounted on 3-ton truck and rotated by the truck motor, were employed, for latter half of the time on 2 8-hr shifts each, requiring per drill-shift: 1 driller, 1 helper, 1 laborer, 1 driver of truck conveying sample. No casing was necessary. Holes averaged 28-in diam, but dimensions corresponding to each sample were accurately measured; a level truckload (1.5-ton truck) was taken as standard sample, corresponding to about 0.5 cu yd of gravel per yd of depth. Cemented gravel, which could not be handled by the auger, was loosened with a 3 000-lb 24-in chopping bit, or a 2-in hole was drilled 2 ft deep at center of pit and fired with a light dynamite charge. Plow-steel cutting edges of auger were removable for sharpening; 2 sets usually needed per drill-shift. Performance over the whole period (1 drill 1 shift from June 14, 1 drill 2 shifts in July and Aug; 2 drills 2 shifts from Aug 28 to Nov 9) was as follows: total holes, 1 239; total depth, 16 705 ft; total samples, 2 495; total (place) vol of samples, 2 640 cu yd; payment to boring contractor, $0.986 per ft, not including surveying or testing samples. Aver performance during 2 mos, when both drills worked 2 shifts every day (61 days) was: holes per drill-shift, 1.95; depth of hole, ft, 19.4; depth per drill-shift, 37.95 ft; samples per drill-shift, 5.3; vol of sample, cu yd, 1.12; cu yd per drill-shift, 5.9; depth per sample, ft, 7.1; depth per cu yd, ft, 6.4; deepest hole, ft, 67. For details of concentrating samples, see Bib (32).

"Con-Tractor" drill, described by W. A. Van der Hoff (46), has been satisfactory in Sumatra for testing wet alluvials containing numerous 6–8-in pebbles, to depths of 28–30 ft. Drill comprises 24-in pipe or casing, turned by a clamped spur-ring actuated by worm at end of a universal-jointed shaft driven from a Fordson tractor, on which entire equipment is mounted. A toothed cutting shoe aids in displacing large pebbles. Total wt of outfit, about 6 tons; it consumes about 2 gal of kerosene per hr. Water remains in the hole. Gravel is excavated by 2 modified orange-peel buckets, one for coarse pebbles and bits of timber, and one for finer gravel; a third type is used for scraping bed-rock; all operated by winch and cable running over a pulley at top of a gin pole. Tests showed very high recovery of theoretical core.

Chip samples of buried outcrop suspected under as much as 100 ft of overburden have been obtained by a method described by J. Belknap (117). A 3-in pipe in 5-ft lengths was first sunk to bedrock by combined pile-driving and wash-boring, and seated firmly, using plaster paris for sealing, if necessary. Sampling bit (Fig 80) was a hollow cylinder e, 4.5 in long, 1 in outside diam, with 4 triangular teeth at bottom, diverging slightly, and surrounding a central hole f tapering upward, which acted as a trap to hold chips. Upper end of bit was screwed to bottom of a string of 3/8-in pipe c, by which it was raised and lowered, and supplied with a gentle stream of water from hand pump. Impact was applied through another string of 1-in pipe b outside of the 3/8-in, churned by hand from surface, and striking on washers d protecting top of bit; latter could be turned, but was not lifted off bottom until choked with sample.

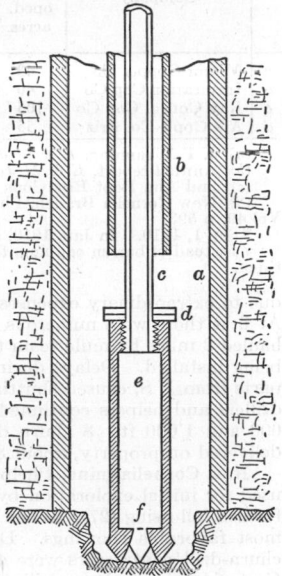

Drive pipes, without boring or pumping, were used for testing a 14-mile stretch of alluvium, averaging 200 ft wide, along Rock Creek, Atlantic City, Wyo, in 1932 (118). Gravel, under 3 ft of barren loam, was 9–12 ft (aver 10 ft) deep; it contained relatively few boulders, none over 18-in diam; of gravel later dug and washed, 65% was finer than 0.75-in. Decomposed bed rock was 2–5 ft deep and most of the gold (small and rounded) was within lower 6 in of gravel. First line of holes, spaced 150–300 ft, followed center line of channel. On other rows across channel, 0.5 mile apart, spacing was 20–60 ft, depending on surface indications. Holes averaged 14 ft deep and were driven through the decomposed bed rock. Pipe or casing, 4-in diam, with cutting shoe of slightly less inside diam to aid in holding core, was driven to refusal by 275-lb hammer operated by a winch driven by a Chevrolet engine on skids and dragged by its own power. Outfit cost $300. Casing was pulled by tripod and tackle (4- and 5-sheave pulleys), assisted by jacks when necessary. Sample was removed (by special spoon) and panned in 6-in sections. Crew of 3 men sunk 140 holes in 2.5 mos at cost of $2 000, or $1.12 per ft; 4 holes were stopped by boulders, but were successfully redriven alongside. At 46 aver holes, 4 by 6-ft shafts were sunk, washing all the gravel in sluice-boxes (@ $20.67 gold); 19¢ from holes; 21.8¢ from shafts; 25¢ from subsequent treatment of 740 000 cu yd along 2 miles of channel. When pipe-sampling, colors worth more than 1¢ each were not included in valuation.

a, 3" casing pipe.
b, 1" hammer pipe.
c, ⅜" stem pipe.
d, 2 washers.
e, sampling bit.

Fig 80.   Chip-sampling Bit

b. Deep Boring in Rock

Porphyry coppers. These orebodies are large, low-grade deposits of copper minerals (usually chalcocite), disseminated in altered and shattered monzonite porphyry, granite, or schist. They have large horiz dimensions and are overlain by leached zones (capping) varying in thickness from 0 to 600 or 700 ft. Attention was first drawn to some of these deposits by favorable surface indications; others were discovered while working higher-grade deposits in their vicinity. Ores range from 0.6% to 3% Cu; lower limit is now a commercial one. BORING PRACTICE in different districts varies only in minor details. Holes are frequently bored on corners of 100 to 400-ft squares; most often, 200 ft; some work has been done with holes placed at corners of equal equilateral triangles; see Utah Copper mine, below. Drill-hole results are checked at intervals by test pits, raises or winzes, and by drifts run on coordinate lines to show variation in copper content between holes. Table 7 shows work done by some of the porphyry copper mines during early stages of their development, and the relative amounts of boring and underground work done before actual production began. An indeterminate part of the footages given for underground work at Miami, Ray, and Inspiration represents development work preparatory to mining; figures for Ajo cover exploration work alone. For details of churn-drilling practice on the porphyry coppers, see Sec 9. For churn-drill sampling practice, see Art 8.

Chile Exploration Co, Chuquicamata, Chile. P. Yeatman and E. S. Berry furnish following data on drilling from beginning of work, April, 1912, to Oct, 1914: High cost was

Table 7. Porphyry Copper Mines, Early Development and Boring

	Company	Area developed, acres	Underground work, ft	Aver thickness of capping, ft	Aver thickness of ore, ft	Tons ore per acre	Total ft of drilling	Depth of drill holes, ft	Date
a	Miami Copper Co	43	73 388	200	....	418 600	19 200	600 aver	1911
b	Inspiration Cop Co	40	27 526	368	167	543 000	45 433	....	1911
c	Ray Consol Cop Co	105	44 753*	242	113.5	395 200	90 000	200-970	1910
d	Ajo Cop'r Co, Ariz	55	5 610	†	50-600	727 000	23 097	275 aver	1913

(a) J. P. Channing, *E & M Jour*, May 27, 1911, and "Copper Handbook," 1910-11.
(b) Annual report, *E & M Jour*, Apr 1, 1911.
(c) 2nd Ann Rept Ray Cons Co, and Edwin Higgins, *E & M Jour*, Apr 23, 1910.
(d) New Cornelia Branch, Phelps Dodge Corp. Data from Ira B. Joralemon, *Trans* A I M E, Vol 49, p 593.
* Sep 1, 1910. In Jan, 1910, about 700 ft of raising had been done alongside of drill holes (62).
† Instead of barren capping, this deposit was overlain by low-grade carbonate ores, 20 to 150 ft thick.

due to extraordinary expenses and troubles incident to starting work in a remote region. At first there were numerous small difficulties in getting fuel to drills; water had to be hauled 2 miles by mule team to an elevation of 1 000 ft, while pumps and pipe lines were being installed. Delays during first 6 months' operation, due to late delivery of repair parts from U S, caused shutting down of some drills for weeks at a time, while wages of drillers and helpers continued. 11 holes were over 1 000 ft deep; many were between 600 and 1 000 ft. 8 churn drills were purchased, costing, with necessary repair parts, delivered on property, about $67 000, or $1.47 per ft of hole drilled.

New Cornelia mine, Phelps Dodge Corp, Ajo, Ariz. Diamond drills exclusively were used for initial exploration by Ajo Copper Co in 1911-1913. Greenway and Joralemon furnish following (27): When work was started, it was decided to drill 1 500 ft of hole on most favorable showings. Diamond drilling could be contracted at $4.75 per ft; no churn-drill contractors were available. The limited time required operation of 2 drills. Cost of buying 2 churn drills was $8 000; cost of churn drilling was estimated as $3 per ft. Assuming sampling costs equal for both drills, and allowing nothing for 2 churn-drill outfits at expiration of work, diamond drilling would save $5 375 on 1 500 ft of hole. These factors led to choice of diamond drills. They gave accurate samples, and the results warranted further exploration. To secure uniform sampling data, work was continued with diamond drills at contract price of $6 per ft. Extremely rough topography and consequent difficult construction of drill roads, also influenced choice of drills.

Holes were drilled on corners of 200-ft squares; company men did the sampling. A low percentage of core was recovered, because of fractured nature of rock. Drill holes were sampled in 5-ft sections. All sludge was caught in barrels (4 or 5 at each hole) and settled, water decanted, and sludge dried and quartered to 3 or 4 lb. Small samples of core and sludge from each 5-ft section were kept for reference. Sludge and core assays were combined on basis of respective dry wts of material recovered. Shafts, 4 by 6 ft, aver depth 50 ft, were sunk to check drill-hole results. Sinking was done by hand drilling, hoisting by windlass, with Mex and Indian labor, usually under contract; to 50-ft depth, a shaft could be sunk more cheaply than a diamond-drill hole. Muck was sampled as shafts were sunk; later, groove samples were cut on all 4 sides of each shaft. A little drifting was done on coordinate lines, to show variation in copper content between adjacent holes, and some raises were put up on drill holes from drifts. Two years were spent in doing the following work: 84 diamond-drill holes, 200 to 1 000 ft deep, total, 23 176.6 ft; 1 059 ft of shafts for checking drill holes in carbonate ore; 175 ft shafts for checking drill holes in sulphide ores; 2 721 ft shafts in advance of drilling; 1 513 ft drifting in sulphide ores; 142 ft raises. Calculations based on this work showed about 40 000 000 tons ore. Shaft samples in carbonate ore averaged 0.005% lower than corresponding drill-hole samples; shaft and raise samples in sulphide ore averaged 0.05% lower than drill-hole samples, and drifts in sulphide gave values higher than values indicated by drill holes at corners of blocks. Table 8 gives cost of drilling, based on 17 310 ft of hole, and cost of sinking 4 000 ft of shaft; superintendence, office and engineering expense are not included. For further details of diamond drilling prior to 1932, see Bib (100).

Recent work at Ajo has not varied greatly from that in the early development. No diamond drilling has been done since Sep, 1937, to which time 270 holes totalling 141 300 ft had been drilled. Aver depth, 523 ft; deepest, 2 200 ft. Aver core recovery from 231 holes was 49.8%; max from any hole, 78.4%; min, 8.3%. In 1937, cost of 10 562 ft of drilling was: contract price, $3.42; supplies, $0.07; sampling and eng'g, $0.80; total,

Table 8. Cost of Early Work at Ajo Copper Mine, Ariz
(Now the New Cornelia Mine, Phelps Dodge Corp)

Diamond drilling	Cost per ft	Shaft sinking	Cost per ft
Contract price..................	$6.00	Labor........................	$ 4.9653
Supplies.......	0.0174	Supplies.....................	1.1877
Miscellaneous.................	0.0379	Blacksmith and carpenter shops.	0.4042
Sampling.....................	0.3422	Miscellaneous................	0.0797
Assaying.....................	0.1370	Sampling.....................	1.1930
Total	$6.5345	Channel sampling.............	2.2860
		Total....................	$10.1159*

* Aver depth, 50; max, 125 ft. Last few ft of shafts, 125 ft deep, cost over $30 per ft.

$4.29 per ft. Recently a few holes were drilled with one of the CHURN DRILLS regularly used for blast-hole drilling, but equipped to handle 1 200 ft of cable. These drills are electric powered, mounted on caterpillars, and self-propelled. Total wt of tools, including 500-lb bit, 2 535 lb. Bits are 9-in diam, drilling a 10-in hole. Holes are cased only at the collar, with one 24-ft length of 10-in casing. In 5 holes averaging 649 ft in depth (max, 775 ft), an aver of 21.6 ft was drilled per 8 hr, or 5.6 ft for each bit change. Excluding supervision and overhead, cost of churn drilling has averaged $1.33 per ft as follows: operating labor (a) $0.46; bits (b) $0.43; power, water, casing, $0.21; transportation (c) $0.04; maintenance, $0.10; sampling, $0.09. Total, $1.33. (a) Driller and 1 helper. (b) Bits sharpened mechanically; aver cost per sharpening, $2.41, incl steel loss. (c) Drill serviced once each shift by a truck having power hoist for handling bits, with driver and 2 helpers.

Chino mines, Santa Rita, N M. Data from H. A. Thorne (63) in 1931. Orebody is roughly elliptical, about 13 500 ft in perimeter and at least 600 ft deep at center. A core of porphyry is surrounded by sedimentaries, both greatly altered and containing disseminated sulphide and oxidized copper minerals; aver grade of open-cut orebody was estimated in 1930 at 1.27% Cu. Leached capping varies from nothing to 150 ft thick. Earliest holes were bored with steam-driven churn drills, at corners of 100-ft squares, later increased to 200 ft; subsequent holes, averaging 900 ft deep, by gasolene-powered drills, starting usually at 13 in; casing used whenever caving occurs, but always upon entering or leaving an ore zone; bits sometimes as small as 3-in. Sludge is bailed at 5-ft intervals and split on riffles into 4 samples for mine, mill, engineers, and reserve. Table 9 gives records of 2 holes, one drilled by steam and one by gasolene power; for each, total labor cost about $23 per shift.

Table 9. Churn Drilling at Chino Mines

	Steam	Gasolene
Depth, ft....................	945	965
Shifts moving and setting up..	7	3.66
" drilling..............	102.08	76.42
" casing..............	2.92	2.92
" total.................	112	83
Aver ft per shift, total time...	8.44	11.62
" " " drilling......	9.25	12.62
Cost per ft:		
Labor moving and setting up	$0.168	$0.088
" drilling.............	2.463	1.828
" casing.............	0.070	0.070
Fuel......................	0.446	0.229
Supplies..................	0.071	0.044
Sampling and assaying.....	0.503	0.487
	$3.721	$2.746

Utah Copper mine, Bingham, Utah. For geological data, see Art 96. Prior to acquisition of the property by Utah Copper Co and its exploitation by open-cut methods, the margins and upper parts of orebody had been explored by many miles of underground work (Fig 81) (119). The Co continued exploration by boring, mainly with churn drills. A few diamond-drill holes were found unsatisfactory, due to wide discrepancies between core and sludge assays in this ground. Earlier churn-drilling to over 2 000-ft depth was done with oil-well rigs with 75- to 80-ft frame derrick. For recent work, a modified Star rig with 80-ft steel derrick is used, operated electrically. Most holes are drilled from benches in the open cut, starting in ground loosened by blasting. Because of this and the depth, holes are begun at 26 in, with stove-pipe casing to 80 or 100 ft; 23-in casing follows, with smaller sizes, even down to 4-in, as required. A max of 50 ft of uncased hole is allowed. Holes are roughly at corners of equilateral triangles, and spaced at about 400 ft, except on nearing limits of orebody, where spacing is 200 ft. For sampling, in charge of a sampler at each rig, see Art 8. Cost of earlier holes was about $20 per ft. Recent (1938) work is done on contract at 50¢ per ft, the company furnishing all equipment and casing. Aver cost of five 1 000-ft holes, $12.43 per ft, incl sampling. Early drilling rate, 4 ft per day; present rate, 12.7 ft from spudding-in to completion.

Northern Rhodesia. Data from Matson and Wallis (125). The bedded, disseminated copper sulphide ores were first explored by churn drilling, which failed to give

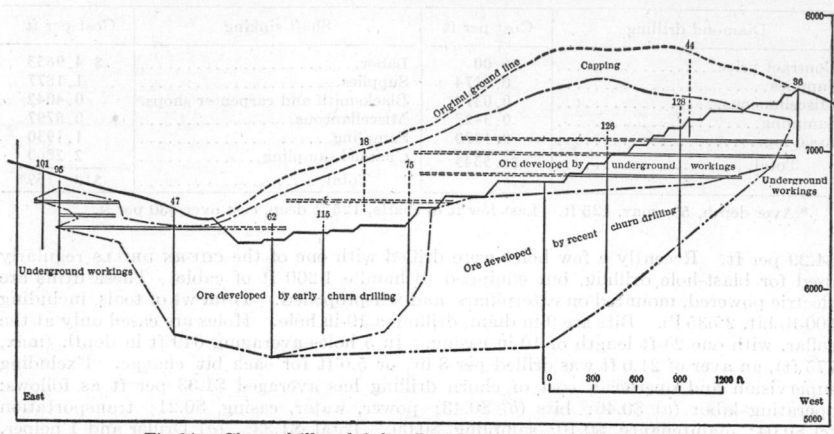

Fig 81. Churn-drill and Other Development, Utah Copper Mine

adequate information as to geological structure and was replaced by core drilling (diamond and shot). Spacings up to 1 000 or even 2 000 ft were considered satisfactory in the early work, due to persistence of the ore strata. Close attention was given to insuring complete return of water, as this was believed to determine reliability of sludge assays better than calculations of theoretical volume of sludge recoverable; if measured flows of descending and rising water failed to agree within 1%, the hole was cased or cemented before proceeding. At end of a run, not exceeding 4 ft, drill was stopped, pump run at full speed, and washing continued (sometimes 45 min or more) until overflow carried no sediment; flow was sometimes reversed for quicker return of sludge. Entire overflow was led by 20-ft swinging launder consecutively to one of 10 or more semi-cylindrical, galvanized-iron tubs, 9 ft long by 3 ft wide, each supported in a wooden frame, and standing in a semi-circular row (Fig 82). Tanks had inside rocker pipes (Fig 83) for decanting water after sludge had

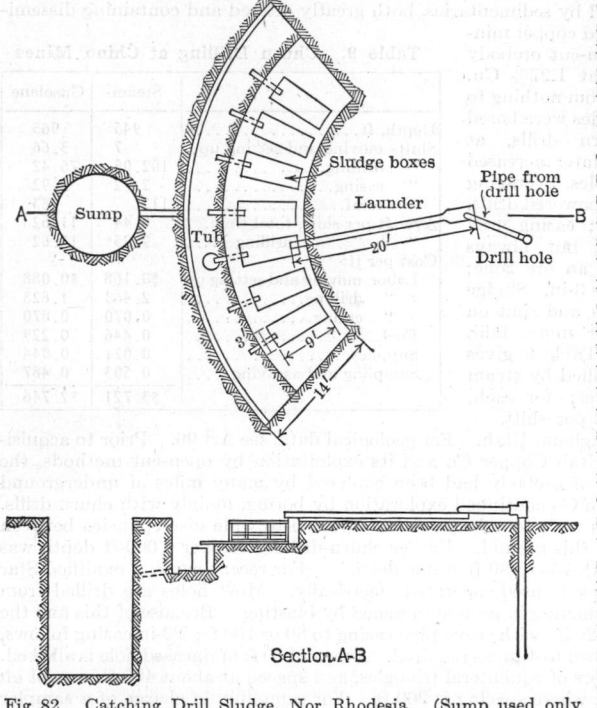

Fig 82. Catching Drill Sludge, Nor Rhodesia. (Sump used only when insufficient fall for natural drainage)

settled; sludge was discharged into a smaller tub by unscrewing the pipe inside, dried, weighed, crushed through 30-mesh, and quartered to two 4-lb samples. Shot-drill sludge, including that from the calyx, was crushed until nearly all material except iron would pass 60-mesh; coarse iron was extracted by magnet, and weighed; that in the fines was determined by analysis, and deducted by calculation. Core was weighed dry and in water, for its sp gr; also measured as to length and diam for calculating sludge recovery; finally split, and one half crushed for sample. For detailed method of calculating aver value for a hole and for orebody, see Bib (125); in discussion, the method was criticized as unduly elaborate.

Lake Superior iron ranges. Ores are masses of soft or hard hematite, in metamorphic rocks. Orebodies were formed by leaching and concentration in troughs caused by folds, faults, and intersections with dikes. Mesabi ores lie horiz and present ideal conditions for exploration by boring. Elsewhere, the iron formation dips steeply, and orebodies, where exposed, show their edges only. Region is drift-covered, but, in Marquette, Eastern

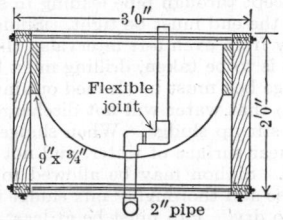

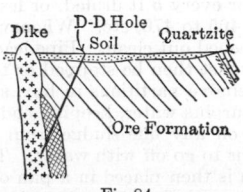

Fig 83.   End Elevation of Sludge Box   Fig 84

Menominee, Gogebic, and parts of Vermilion ranges, there are numerous hard-rock outcrops, to which early exploration was confined.

Surface showings have been taken up and exploration is now limited to diamond drilling for orebodies at depth. Much successful drilling has been done at random, but geological conditions are now so well known that the usual hazard of exploratory work is reduced. C. K. Leith states that with intelligent supervision 2–8% of exploratory drilling should be in ore, depending on the district (50). Maps, published by state and national geol surveys, show location of areas covered by iron formation (51). Within these areas, outcrops, petrology, stratigraphy, and geol structure are studied in detail and magnetic surveys made before drilling is begun. This information tends to eliminate worthless

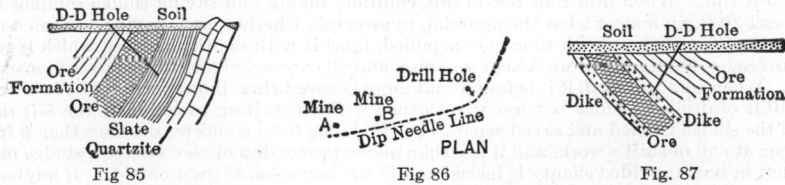

Fig 85   Fig 86   Fig. 87

areas. Highly silicated and strongly magnetic areas, and those in which the rocks of the iron formation are " lean and tight," are nearly barren of commercial orebodies. Prospecting is probably most difficult on Menominee and Gogebic ranges, because of their complicated structure. Usually holes are drilled perpendicular to dip of iron formation. Following examples from P. B. MacDonald (52) are typical.

Fig 84, Marquette range.   Diamond-drill hole, 600 ft deep, located between 2 outcrops, a diorite dike and a low hill of Goodrich quartzite known to overlie iron formation in this district. Hanging wall of dike offered a favorable place for concentration. Fig 85, Marquette range. "Only outcrop is a ridge of Ajibik quartzite, a rock known to underlie Siamo slate usually forming the footwall of ore formation." Dip of formation was determined from the quartzite, and hole started far enough back to allow for thickness of Siamo slate. Fig 86, Amasa district. Good orebodies were known in mines at A and B. No outcrops; surface drift, 100 ft deep. Magnetic survey showed a line of max dip, which indicated a bend in formation about a mile away. Since such angles are favorable places for ore concentrations, a diamond-drill hole was put down at about same distance from max dip line as mines A and B. Fig 87, Crystal Falls district, shows a diamond-drill hole which was abandoned in a fine-grained gray dike thought to be footwall slate. Later microscopic examination revealed its true character and drilling through the dike disclosed 100 ft of ore. For details of practice and costs of diamond drilling in Lake Superior iron districts, see Sec 9. SAMPLING PRACTICE is illustrated by following rules of procedure

(1938) by the Cleveland Cliffs Iron Co, according to E. L. Derby, geologist for the Co. Set SLUDGE BOX (Fig 55) just below floor of drill shanty, in such position that there is room to siphon off water and take out sample without moving box. (Frequently 2 boxes are used in tandem, sludge water flowing from box to box, to insure an accurate sample.) Connect a tee to top of standpipe or casing, and lead a pipe from it to nearer end of sludge box, at such height that it will be level or slant towards sludge box and just rest upon its top, and of such length that it will not project more than 1 in beyond edge of box. The pipe must not exceed 2 ft long; if longer than 1 ft, it must be split on top for 1 ft nearest sludge box, so that sludge collecting in pipe may be seen. Set box level, so that water will overflow evenly across whole width at far end, and wedge partitions firmly in close contact with bottom of box. Top of partitions should be 1 in below water level. Box is now ready to receive sample. While drilling, care must be taken that no water from drill hole escapes around or over the tee, except through pipe leading to sludge box. There must be no leak from box and the plug at the end must be tight. Sludge samples are taken for every 5 ft drilled, or less, preferably from even 5-ft intervals; that is, from 460 to 465, 465 to 470, etc. Whenever a sample is to be taken, drilling must be stopped and hole washed out clean. Pipe leading to sludge box must be cleaned out into the box, and pump must then be stopped or tee turned so that water will not discharge into box. Carefully remove partitions in box, so as not to stir up sludge. When sludge is settled, siphon off surplus water, keeping end of siphon near surface of water, and not disturbing or drawing off any fine sludge from the bottom. Siphon may be allowed to flow until sludge begins to go off with water. Take out hose and thoroughly mix sludge in box to a mud, which is then placed in a pan on a boiler to dry. Pan must be at least 8 by 12 in by 1 in deep, with flat bottom, and is thoroughly cleaned each time before a sample is put into it. If enough water cannot be drawn off, without disturbing sludge, so that sample can be contained in this pan, use a larger pan. When sludge has been cleaned out, remove plug at end of box, wash out with a pail or two of water, then replace plug and partitions, and drilling may be started again. Sludge must be labeled, giving depths between which the sample was taken, and must all be saved and turned over to inspector when drilling in iron formation, or in other ferruginous or red material. While drilling in material from which a sample should be taken, if water is lost, or if sludge does not come up with water, or if it is contaminated with material caving from upper part of hole, drilling must be stopped until hole is put in such condition that good sludge can again be obtained, or until inspector permits drilling to proceed. Whenever drill runs into or out of ore, 1 ft or more thick, drilling must be stopped, and sludge box cleaned out, without waiting to complete the 5-ft run. When drill runs out of ore, continue taking and saving sludge samples for at least 20 ft, no matter what the material, to ascertain whether ore is caving. Keep CORE separate from sludge; each time core is pulled, label it with depths between which it was recovered. Each run of core is kept separate, and all core saved and turned over to inspector. When core is pulled, if it is found that more is saved than in proportion of 1 ft of core to 10 ft of drilling, sludge box must be cleaned out without waiting to complete the 5-ft run, and the sludge labeled and saved separately. If sludge from a shorter distance than 5 ft is in box at end of shift's work, and if less than above proportion of core is saved, sludge may be left in box, provided shanty is locked and box is inaccessible from outside. If anybody can get at the box, and if there is no watchman, sludge must be removed from box, dried, labeled, and placed with other samples.

Mesabi Range, Minn. Ores are massive, flat deposits of hematite, of great horiz extent as compared with their depth. Orebodies are generally less than 200 ft thick, and may extend laterally for a mile or more. They are overlain by soil and glacial drift averaging 65 ft deep. Fig 97 (Art 11) shows a typical section. There are few surface indications of ore. Early practice was to sink test pits through the drift, and as far into ore as permitted by facilities and cost for handling water, hoisting, and ventilation. Exploration was continued from bottom of these pits by boring. At present, both prospecting and exploration are done entirely by boring from surface, which is cheaper, quicker, and avoids dangers from numerous open test pits. Following data on BORING PRACTICE were contributed by J. V. Claypool, Oliver Iron Mining Co, in 1938. Churn drills, with both straight chopping bit and perforated bit and hollow rods, and diamond drills are used, with water under press for flushing cuttings to the surface. Cyclone and Keystone drills are also used in drilling from surface and in open-pit areas; samples recovered with a sludge bucket. Holes are churn-drilled through surface drift to ore or hard rock and cased with heavy 3-in pipe. If iron ore is found, drilling is continued with 2-in casing through the ore to hard rock; diamond drilling then starts, whether the rock had appeared directly under the surface drift or under an orebody. Should the diamond drilling go through the taconite and into more than 5 ft of ore, the hole through the taconite is enlarged by blasting and the 2-in casing is churned down through the blasted rock and the underlying orebody to rock, keeping the casing close to bottom of hole to insure accurate samples. Diamond drilling then continues to a certain depth into taconite, depending on engineer's judgment. One hole in each 40-acre tract may be drilled into quartzite, underlying all iron formation in district.

Land is held in 40-acre tracts, and for preliminary prospecting, 5 holes are put down on each tract. Spacing of the holes varies; common arrangement is to put 1 hole in center and others 250 ft from each corner towards the center. Many companies space their holes about 500 ft apart. Fig 88A shows a spacing used when adjacent tracts are being drilled for same parties. If ore is not found by these 5 holes, tract is temporarily abandoned, although 5 holes are not final proof; should a more thorough examination be desired, other holes (usually) are drilled, the 9 holes being spaced as in Fig 88B. If ore is found, a topographic map is made, coordinate lines are laid out at 100-ft intervals, and detailed exploration is done by drilling holes 100, 200 or 300 ft apart, usually 200 ft. Drilling is done largely by contract; local contractors have established reputation for care and integrity. Crew of 1 drill runner and 2 helpers on each outfit (combined diamond and churn drill).

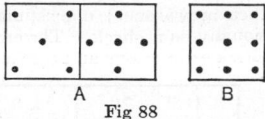

Fig 88

Sampling. C. E. van Barneveld gives following data in 1912 (35). Surface soil is not sampled. Cuttings from both churn and diamond drills are discharged with flushing water through a T in top of casing, and settled in barrels, tubs or a series of settling tanks. Drilling practice favors accurate sampling; churn drill, used in all soft formations, allows casing to be kept close to bottom of hole. In passing from sandy drift into ore, casing is driven into ore ahead of drill bit. Some difficult ground is drilled "dry"; pump is stopped, hole drilled 5 ft with just enough water to form a sludge, casing is driven to bottom, and sludge re-drilled if necessary, and flushed out. Drill holes are sampled in 3, 5, or 10-ft sections, usually 5-ft. Each drill is supplied with 4 to 7 barrels. A hole bored in the side of barrel, 8 in from bottom and fitted with a wooden plug, allows most of the water to be drawn off when sludge has settled; remainder stands 2 or 3 hr and is decanted. Sludge is dried, mixed, and cut into samples for analysis. Core samples are taken in hard formations; 2 to 3 ft of core is recovered per 5 ft drilled in hard ore, slate, and quartzite. Some companies do not sample diamond-drill sludge, if core recovery is more than 30%. Others combine core and sludge analyses. With care, very good samples are obtained; in a clean orebody, drill samples and subsequent mine samples check surprisingly closely. Streaky ores, having alternate layers of hard material and small streaks of soft ore, show much variation; sometimes 6 or 8 points. Very soft fine ore often stays in suspension, and the water comes up muddy.

Structure drilling. For testing the "wash" ores on the western Mesabi Range, consisting of narrow alternate layers of Fe_2O_3 and waste (largely sand) which must be separated to yield marketable ore, a method devised by J. S. Schultz (130) is widely employed. Churn drilling is done with a hollow cylindrical chopping bit, 2 3/8 in outside, 1.5 in inside diam, with 6 chisel-edged notches on its end. Bit is attached by screw joint to 2-in rods; a 3-in casing is used, down which water is pumped and rises inside the rod. This is called "structure" churn drilling; it delivers cuttings in larger fragments than is possible with standard tools, and hence is more informative as to physical character.

Magnetic iron ore, Mineville, N Y. Orebodies are large pitching lenses in gneissic rocks. Diamond drill exclusively is used to explore lenses indicated by outcrops, to determine extent of partly developed orebodies, and to explore in advance of proposed shafts. Orebodies are fairly regular and conform to gneissic structure of the rocks. Formal spacing of holes is of secondary importance; dip, strike and pitch of lens are controlling factors in locating holes. Importance of core recovery is stressed even in rock; complete recoveries are usual in the ore horizon. Cores in ore are classified by eye, into rich, lean, and very lean; each section is split and per cent Fe and P determined. To provide against possible loss of core, sludge samples are taken; experience shows that sludge assays about 5 units Fe in excess of core. All core, including split halves in ore, is stored in racks in a core house. Method of estimating tonnage from drilling is simple. For example, the horiz working face on one lens, at right angles to axis, is 1 850 ft. Three holes were drilled an aver of 738 ft in advance of working faces. Aver thickness of ore at working face and in drill holes was taken as the aver thickness of deposit and multiplied by horiz area to give cu ft of ore. Dip is disregarded purposely, to give conservative estimates. Tonnage is computed by applying weight factors (which vary with Fe content) to total cu ft. Data from E. C. Henry (518).

Southeastern Missouri. The disseminated lead ore occurs in flat masses in dolomite, at depths of 200 to 600 ft. Thickness of orebodies, up to 70 ft; they cover considerable lateral area. Overlying rocks are limestone and shale conglomerates, and dolomite, free from chert. There are no outcrops; prospecting and exploration are done by diamond-drilling from surface. Churn drills are used as auxiliaries to put holes down to bed rock through deep surface soil. Geologic features indicate probable orebearing areas in a broad way. H. A. Guess, V-pres Am Sm & Ref Co, furnished following data in 1915

(Fig 89) (see also Bib 55). "In extending the limits of known orebodies, the only way to do is to feel along with the diamond drill until the full limits of orebody are defined. For this work, holes are close-spaced, usually 200 ft, sometimes 100 ft. For general prospecting for new orebodies, holes are spaced 400 or 600 ft or even farther, either in checkerboard fashion or in lines transverse with supposed strike of ore run. When ore is cut, detailed drilling is begun with spacing of 200 ft or less." Procedure varies with different companies. A solid bit is used until near expected ore horizon; then a core bit with a 5 or 10-ft core barrel, until the hole bottoms in sandstone known to underlie the orebodies. About 25% of total footage is cored. Lead content of cores is estimated from their appearance; one estimator is employed for 10 or 12 drills. Cores are assayed occasionally as a check. Throughout the mineral zone, all sludge is caught and assayed, to check estimations and core assays. Sludge serves as a further record when a considerable

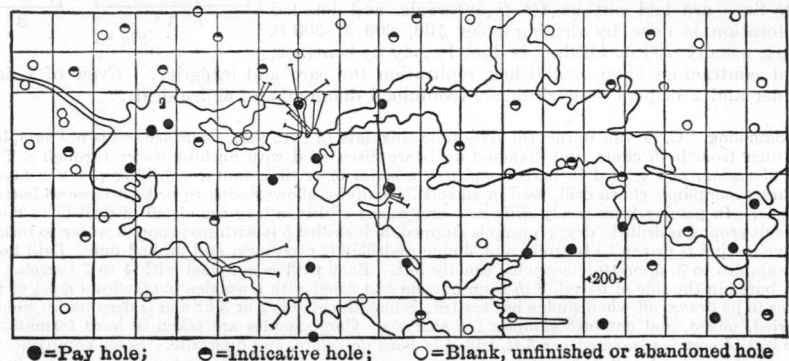

●=Pay hole;   ◒=Indicative hole;   ○=Blank, unfinished or abandoned hole

Fig 89. Boring near Flat River, Mo (H. A. Guess)

part of a soft lead layer is ground up in trying to core it. Combined solid and core-bit drilling has been done by Federal Lead Co. Aver speed of drilling per 10-hr shift: for solid bit, 60 ft; for core bit, 30 ft. Fig 89 shows outline of workings on one orebody, and location of holes for preliminary and final exploration. Short horiz holes are also drilled from different headings, to supplement indications given by holes from surface. Drilling results are used for laying out work and estimating tonnage and value (Art 11). C. F. Jackson (155) states that minimum limits of orebodies considered workable are 7 ft thick, with 15 ft-% lead. Where thickness exceeds 7 ft, if entire section averages less than 2% lead, the workable thickness and its grade are calculated by trial.

Tri-State District. Irregular orebodies of sphalerite and galena in breccia of chert and limestone lie at depths of 75 to 300 ft. Ore occurs in large or small pockets, long narrow stringers, or in horiz sheets 10 to 20 ft thick, of considerable area. Portable churn drills exclusively are used for prospecting; preferred to diamond drills because of fissured ground and brecciated chert. Drilling is mostly contracted; usual prices, 90¢ to $1.25 per ft. In many parts of district, upper extensions of orebodies often occur directly under and 40–50 ft below basins in upper surface of chert formation, which is overlain normally by 30–40 ft of shale, offering no topographical indications. In such areas, "shale" holes are first drilled, at 40–60¢ per ft, until shale of abnormal depth, 90–100 ft, is discovered; deeper drilling is then confined to that portion of the area (156).

Table 10. Exploratory Churn Drilling, Tri-State District

Acres	Holes drilled	Holes in ore	Aver depth, ft	Total cost	Cost per ft
80	129	35	250	$35 000	$1.08
104	129	52	279	53 980	1.50
320	162	49	326	66 015	1.25
105	120	43	305	37 482	1.02
160	219	84	330	79 497	1.10
60	90	......	300	27 256	1.01
80	138	55	235	40 839	1.26
40	78	47	300	26 450	1.13

J. R. Reigart (161) supplies the data in Table 10 on 8 properties in Tri-State district, covering exploratory drilling before active development. Records of several companies in Cherokee Co, Kan, during 12 yr prior to 1932, show that $4 473 300 was spent in drilling 16 281 holes ($274.75 per hole) of which 9 591 holes were on properties which later became producers. C. W. Nicolson (191) in 1938 states that practice favors Keystone No 5 drill, mounted on truck which supplies power; it has a 6.25-in bit and 7/8-in steel rope instead of the 2 1/8-in manila cable formerly used. Steel rope requires springs under sheaves. Drilling speed, 4 ft per hr; cost about $1 per ft. Cuttings bailed every 5 ft in overlying rocks, and every 2.5 ft in ore horizons. Holes are usually at 200–400-ft intervals until ore is found; thereafter at 50-ft or more. W. F. Netzeband (192) states that bore-hole samples are usually high in zinc and low in lead, as compared with ultimate mill recovery.

Southwestern Wisconsin. Following information was contributed in 1938 by J. G. Trewartha, Gen Supt, Vinegar Hill Zinc Co. Very irregular bodies of blende and galena occur at depths of 20–270 ft in limestones and dolomites. They are usually found over basins of broken, oily shale, which apparently permitted a slumping of the limestone, resulting in " pitches," " flats," crevices, and vugs. Ore-bearing solutions have followed these openings, depositing the minerals therein. Churn drills are used to locate and outline the orebodies. CHURN-DRILL PROSPECTING is done in areas where galena was formerly mined to shallow depths, on lands adjacent to and along the trend of known orebodies. The possibility of an orebody is also sometimes suggested by discovery of traces of ore by farmers drilling wells, or by finding crevices on the surface. If ore is struck in churn-drilling, several holes are drilled around the discovery hole and 20–25 ft from it, to determine trend of orebody. Holes are then drilled along this trend with larger spacing; usually started at $6\frac{1}{2}$-in diam; if a hole drills well it may be finished at this diam. In bad ground, casing is set and the hole finished with smaller tools. If casing is used, and the company decides it may later need the hole for mine ventilation, the casing is left in the hole. Blank holes are usually plugged; driller pulls casing, sets a large boulder about 6 ft below collar of hole, which is filled to the surface. Drilling is usually by contract; prices 60¢ to $1 per ft. CUTTINGS are removed from hole at 5-ft intervals, until ore horizon is reached. Thereafter hole is carefully cleaned out every 2 ft. Cuttings are caught in a tub, and an analysis is made for each 2-ft run, if sample carries enough mineral to warrant it. In doubtful cases, the engineer pans a small part of the sample for examination under a microscope; an experienced engineer can thus estimate closely the value in the cuttings. A record is kept of each hole, including: depth where water was first struck, depth at which water stands after hole is completed; and occurrence of open ground. Experience has shown that ore estimates based on drilling records are satisfactory.

Witwatersrand. Data from R. S. G. Stokes (195). In 2 yr ending 1935, about 200 000 ft of prospect boring (chiefly by diamond drill) was done, of which about half was to prove western extensions of the Rand. Steam rigs were most common, but oil or gasolene engines were cheaper to operate, more portable, and required less water. Derricks for deep holes, 60–67 ft high. Direct or reduction-gear drives and hydraulic feed were usual. In uniform ground, So African bortz could replace imported carbons. Final core size was usually $1\frac{3}{8}$ in; occasionally $\frac{7}{8}$ in. Chief difficulties in West Rand were: chert boulders in subsoil, alternating strata of chert and dolomite, and fissures in the latter. Aver advances of 500–600 ft per month were frequent in good ground, with continuous drilling; in 1 case, 982 ft per mo at 2 000 ft depth. Aver cost for deep holes in good ground, 30–40s per ft, including administration and deprec; in bad dolomite, cost might be doubled. Under favorable conditions of Far East Rand, 5 holes totaling 10 382 ft cost £16 000 ($7.50 per ft). Most drilling was on straight contract; when especial trouble was foreseen, on basis of rental, and cost plus 10%.

N E Washington. Walter Sack, in 1938, gives estimated and actual costs for diamond-drilling of closely-spaced holes to 800-ft max, totaling 50 000 ft, for exploring a large, much faulted lead-zinc deposit (206). Lowest contract bid, $3 per ft, plus drilling expenses for Co account, brought estimated cost to $3.85, besides cost of clearing heavily timbered sites and providing drill water. On rental basis for 2 rigs, each averaging 875 ft per mo of 75 shifts, estimated cost per ft was: rental, $0.39; upkeep, $0.06; diamonds, $0.50; operation, $1.10; total, $2.05. Company then purchased 2 complete rigs for $12 000, charging entire price against 50 000 ft of hole, or $0.24 per ft; other items, same as above, gave total cost of $1.90.

c. Diamond Drilling Underground

Josie mine, B. C. Roughly parallel veins of pyrrhotite, carrying chalcopyrite accompanied by Au and some Ag, occur in hard augite porphyrite and diorite. Veins dip 50–80°; oreshoots are related to contacts and intersections of veins with a complex system of steep-dipping dikes. Some dikes are parallel to, others cut veins with or without faulting. When a drift on a vein cuts a dike and ore is not found beyond, a diamond drill may be used to seek faulted segment of vein; or, if there is no fault, to seek ore in a parallel vein. On finding such ore, drifting is transferred to the parallel vein and, later, holes are drilled back to explore extension of first vein. This plan minimizes length of nonproductive drifts and speeds exploration work. Approx limits of shoots are found by " fanning " holes vert and horiz from one set-up, but about 96% of holes are flat. Country rock gives good cores; dikes are broken and boring in them is avoided where possible.

All drills had double-tube (" Stone ") core barrels. Sullivan " E " drill was used for flat holes; outside diam bit, $1\,7/16$ in; core, $7/8$ in. This drill has a rated capac of 450 ft, but was used for holes 600–1 000 ft deep. Down holes were drilled of the same diam with Sullivan " S " drills. Chip bits often used, especially in short holes, but were unsuitable in broken ground. Normally, 2 ft of drilling per ft of development (510).

El Potosí mine, Santa Eulalia, Mex. Data from H. A. Walker (503) in 1922 and 1934. Silver-lead ores occur as irregular replacements in limestone; frequently in form of chimneys 60–300 ft diam, related to a system of vert fissures; also in horiz "mantos" (see Art 37). Diamond drill is used extensively to explore new ground, secure geol data, and determine limits of orebodies; also occasionally to bore holes for drainage or elec conduits. Work done by especial foreman and crew. LOCATION OF HOLES. If stopes or other convenient openings are not available for setting up drill, special drill bases are excavated about 15 ft wide by 25 ft long by 9 ft high, so located as to avoid known bad drilling ground or interference with mining and tramming, to allow thorough exploration, and to cover max possible area from one set-up. Usually a series of horiz holes, 15° apart in azimuth, and a corresponding series of holes pointing downward 15°, are drilled from each set-up. The general direction of the "fan" of holes so drilled in new ground is usually at right angles to the strike of a known fissure system, but the fan frequently extends through 180°. As close drilling is required to avoid missing orebodies, sets of holes are drilled into the same areas from different levels. Holes from different set-ups are then staggered to reduce unexplored distance between adjacent holes to 100 ft max; this requires careful pointing of holes in each set. A transit is used to point the first hole; the others are pointed by means of wooden templates held against rods projecting from the first hole. A spirit level on the feed screw is used to start horiz holes, the rods being carefully centered in the chuck. Location and elevation of the collar of each hole are determined by survey; its direction is computed from the location of two points, as far apart as possible, on the drill rods projecting from the hole. Dips are measured with a Brunton compass. The holes themselves need not be surveyed, as they are comparatively shallow and show only slight deflection from their course. When completed, each hole is plugged and marked with a numbered copper tag for future identification. If ore is found, further drilling to determine size of the orebody, etc, is guided by local conditions. For example: the horiz and dipping holes in one set found an orebody and determined its horiz section. A 30° down hole drilled from same set-up was barren; a 20° down hole was then drilled and located the bottom of the deposit. Development openings were next driven to, and in the ore, and raises put up to determine its upper limits. Ventilation became difficult in the raises, and top of the deposit was located by drilling from a higher level. As these orebodies are mined by underhand stoping, the top of the ore must be found before stopes can be planned. EQUIPMENT in 1934 included following types of drill: (a) EX, air-driven, 2-man, for 700-ft max, 500-ft aver, holes; 10-ft rods, single or double core barrels, $7/8$-in core, bit set with black diamonds, $3/4$-2 carats per stone; costs in col I, Table 11. Same machines with 5-ft rods may be run by 1 man to max 350 ft, sometimes substituting borts or small natural carbons; costs in col II, Table 11. (b) EX, electric-driven by 7.5-hp, 440-volt, a-c motor, with gear transmission and clutch for speed control; pump is direct-connected to 5-hp motor; costs in col III, Table 11. (c) Same type of 2-man drill, but driven by 5-hp, adjustable-speed, induction motor; pump has 3-hp motor. This and preceding type both use 10-ft rods, and bits set with borts, scrap, or small carbons. (d) Air-driven, hydraulic-feed C drill with A rods. 3-man crew, for geol work to 2 500 ft max depth. (e) Light-weight, air-driven, 1-man, for 200 ft max, 150-ft aver, depth; 5-ft rods, double-tube core barrels, giving 0.75-in core; bits set with small carbons; costs in col IV, Table 11. (f) Prospector EX, for max 250 ft, 1-man, elec, with 3-hp motor and multi-speed drive; pump, duplex, double-acting, with 1.5-hp motor. This drill is expected to displace (e) type. For all of 2-man types, except (d), max effic drilling depth is 400–450 ft. The 1-man drills with 5-ft rods require less excavation for sites. Type (c) is more effic than (b); and both (b) and (c) are more economical of power than air-driven drill (a). At this mine, drilling largely in fissured limestone, small natural carbons have proved cheaper than borts or scrap, except as the latter may be salvaged from work requiring large stones.

Aver carbonate ore is soft and gives little core; rods are pulled every 2 or 3 ft and the sludge used for assay. Core recovery in sulphide ore reaches 95% and rods are pulled every 5 or 10 ft. Manganese stains and broken ground in limestone often indicate proximity of ore and aid the driller. Drilling speed in usual limestone is 50–100 ft per 8-hr shift. Diamond loss in 1922 was 5.91 carats in drilling 12 480 ft in limestone and 170 ft in hard galena ore; loss greatest in hard sulphide ores.

Table 11. Cost of Underground Diamond Drilling, El Potosí Mine, Mex (1932)
See accompanying text

U S Dollars per ft for:	I	II	III	IV
Drilling labor (a).......	$0.092	$0.076	$0.090	$0.094
Carbon and borts.......	.166	.119	.053	.095
Power.................	.080	.088	.009	.078
Carbide & lubricants....	.006	.006	.006	.007
Setting bits............	.035	.029	.028	.049
Repairs to drills & pumps	.036	.031	.054	.047
New rods..............	.050	.049	.041	.051
Supervision............	.084	.086	.073	.085
Total direct..........	$0.549	$0.484	$0.354	$0.506
Tools and core boxes....	.008	.008	.008	.009
Moving drills..........	.007	.005	.002	.007
Cutting stations........	.017	.002	.003	.002
New pumps............	.004	.007	.003	.006
Total cost...........	$0.585	$0.506	$0.370	$0.530
Footage during 1932....	15 222	9 275	10 749	9 923

(a) At approx aver 28¢ (U S) per man-hr.

United Verde mine, Jerome, Ariz, employed underground diamond drilling extensively (25 000–30 000 ft per year, 33 376 ft in 1930) for preliminary exploration of its irregular, lenticular, steeply dipping, sulphide replacement orebodies lying within a zone averaging 300 ft wide (97, 227); see also Fig 48, Art 7. Cores were $7/8$–2 in diam, the latter in special cases for taking a large sample. Some holes, to 3 in, have been bored for drainage, conduits, ventilation, or running slime into fire areas. Of all holes to 1933, 64% were between 200 and 600 ft (7% over 1 000 ft), and 79% inclined between $+12°$ and $-5°$. Core recovery in all rock averaged 91.3%, from 79.2% in greenstone to 95.3% in massive sulphide. Cementing was almost invariably used in dealing with caving, broken, or sandy ground. Core pulled every 5 ft, except when a sharp contact was encountered at a shorter interval; all core was crushed for sample, retaining a few pieces for record. Sludge was collected and sampled only while boring in mineral, and its assay combined with that of core on theoretical vol basis depending on core recovery and size of bit.

Following data on PRESENT PRACTICE were contributed in 1939 by C. E. Mills, Chief Engr. Most diamond drilling is now short-hole work, 100–500 ft, to delimit known ore areas, prospect stope walls, determine structure or general geol formation, and to aid locating development headings. Occasional long holes, 1 000–2 200 ft, are drilled to prospect outlying areas. The ground drilled varies from comparatively soft chlorite schist and metamorphosed quartz porphyry to relatively hard rhyolite porphyry, diorite, and hard, massive pyrite carrying quartz and jasper. Most footage is within massive sulphide areas. Representative sections of core from long holes or holes of especial interest are kept for record; otherwise, entire core is sent to the assay office. Part of the pulps is saved for composites and future analysis. EQUIPMENT. A Boyle B B U drill with M-size bits is used for short-hole work; Longyear U G drill is used in harder ground for 200–1'000-ft holes, and Sullivan C hydraulic drill for deep holes. The E bit, giving a $1 9/16$-in hole is used where depth requires surveying, and an AX bit ($1 27/32$-in) for long holes that may need grouting or casing. A Wright bore-hole surveying instrument is used for depths over 500 ft, to observe deviation. BITS. Bortz is used almost exclusively in all ground; carbon occasionally, for gage stones in broken quartz or siliceous sulphide. Bortz loss is 0.02–0.1 carat per ft, depending on kind of ground. Cutting edges of bits are rounded and set with bortz averaging 20 stones per carat. M bit, a special size for short-hole drilling, has 100 stones and requires about 6 hr for setting; its outside diam is EX or $1 7/16$ in, and inside diam of $15/16$ in gives the largest core possible with this size of bit. The $1 17/32$-in E bit averages about 120 stones and requires 7 hr for setting; the $1 27/32$-in AX requires approx 150 stones and 9 hr for setting. Recovery of stones from used bits averages 50%. All-metal CORE BOXES, with corrugated removable trays, are used to handle core from working place to diamond-drill shop. SPEED AND COST OF DRILLING. In short-hole drilling (aver 250 ft), footage per shift is from 40 ft in aver schist or porphyry to 25 ft in hard sulphide. For long holes, set-ups are provided to permit 20-ft changes of rods, and footage per shift is from 30 ft for short holes to 10 ft for 1 500-ft holes. Direct cost per ft during 1937 and 1938 is shown in Table 12. Carbon loss averaged 0.031 carat per ft of hole in 1937, 0.030 carat in 1938; max loss in one month was 0.098 carat per ft. In 1938, footage per drill-shift averaged 25.3 ft; footage per bit, 60.3 ft; loss of carbon per bit, 1.81 carats.   Besides the footage drilled on Co acct, 2 059 ft were drilled by 1 crew on outside contract.

Edwards zinc mine, N Y.   Underground diamond drilling has been found well adapted to discovery and exploration; orebodies are lenticular, roughly parallel, sulphide replacements in limestone, dipping about 40° (253).   Drill stations are cut by company, but drilling is on contract, power and water supplied.   Small, air-driven drills take 7/8-in core. Lateral holes are pointed within 5° above or below horiz; down holes usually at about 45°, to cut ore at right angles.   Core recovery is high; no sludge saved, core assayed only when expert visual inspection is in doubt.   During 1930, 10 holes totaling 3 386 ft cost $2.05 per ft.

Table 12.   Cost of Underground Diamond Drilling at the United Verde Mine

	1937	1938
Labor (a)	$0.82	$0.76
Carbon	0.31	0.16
Operating supplies	0.02	0.10
Comp air and water	0.02	....
Miscellaneous	0.02	....
Total	$1.19	$1.02
Number of holes	58	34
Total footage	6 922	4 585
Aver length of hole, ft	119	134
Max depth of hole	507	526
Percentage of holes in:		
Hard siliceous sulphide	6.3	....
Aver sulphide	31.9	....
Schist	27.5	....
Porphyry & diorite	34.3	....

(a) Aver wages: drill runner, $6.88 in 1937, $6.40 in 1938; helper, $5.60 in 1937, $5.16 in 1938.

Cold Springs ferberite mine, Nederland, Colo. Narrow, steeply dipping oreshoots in granite.   Conventional boring methods are used for exploration, but instead of a diamond bit, "firthite" (tungsten carbide in cobalt matrix) is brazed, with Tobin bronze and oxy-acetylene flame, directly on lower edge of core barrel.   This increases diam of core obtainable with drill employed from 15/16 (with diamond bit) to 1 5/16 in; loss of bit in fissured rock at this mine is also avoided.   Complete firthite crown costs about $75, and the cutting material can be used repeatedly, with care to avoid excessive brazing temp. Max depth drilled in this hard rock during 1931 was 18 ft for 1 setting of firthite.   Total drilled in 1931, 1 932 ft; aver depth, 75 ft; aver cost, $2.16 per ft; aver core recovery, 80% (290).

Hollinger mine, Ont, has used underground diamond drilling extensively (309.2 miles of hole to end of 1934) for exploring intricate and frequently discontinuous quartz veins, dipping about 75°, in a wide shear zone in or adjacent to porphyry.   In 1935, equipment included 8 drills using E S rods (7/8-in core) and 6 E P rods (5/8-in core), all operated by air.   Most core barrels are double-tube; bits set mainly with bortz, usually 9 or 10 per carat, 45–60 stones per bit.   Drilling (2-man crew) is on morning shift only.   E S drills average 45.8 ft per shift.   All drilling is contracted at rate per ft which, with E S machines, is based mainly on percentage of core recovery, 87¢ for 90%, 72¢ for 55% or less; for E P holes, price is 75¢ flat.   Recovery is lower in porphyry than in other rocks.   Contractor pays wages plus a bonus for footage, per 8 hr, above 32 ft with E S, or 35 ft with E P machines.   Most holes are horiz or slightly inclined, aiming to cut vein system normal to strike.   Owing to numerous parallel drifts, where drills can be set up, it is seldom necessary to bore a hole more than 200 ft to gain all information expected at that point (306).

Other examples of cost.   Walter Sack, in 1938, gives estimated costs for underground diamond drilling at 2 places (206).   (A) To prove tonnage and value of known, large, low-grade body of gold ore in WESTERN MONT, already considerably developed.   Total necessary footage not predictable, but estimates were based on four 500-ft holes.   Lowest contract bid ($2.60) plus freight both ways, compressed-air power (from rented compressor), and installing air and water lines, all for Co account, raised estimate to $3.96.   Drill rental for 3 mo ($675), and operating by Co, was estimated to cost per ft (on 2 000 ft): rental and upkeep, $0.36; freight, $0.13; compressor (rent, hauling, and piping), $0.16; fuel and maintenance, $1.03; drilling labor, $1.21; diamonds, $0.30; total, $3.19. Actually, 9 000 ft were drilled in 9 mo, at $2.43 per ft; machine-set bits used.   (B) To cut and sample a vein at 250 and 500 ft below present sump of a silver-lead mine in COEUR D'ALENE DISTRICT, Idaho.   Length of 2 short and 2 longer holes totalled 1 700 ft; diamond drilling not regularly required at this mine; drilling possible on only 1 shift.   Rental for 5 mos ($1 250), $0.74 per ft; frt and upkeep, $0.13; labor (125 shifts), $0.89; comp air (from mine), $0.02; diamonds, $0.50; estimated total, $2.28.   This job was contracted at $2.25 per ft, including everything but comp air.

d. Exploratory Hammer Drilling

Exploration and sampling by SHORT HOLES, drilled with ordinary steel and equipment, as drifters, stopers, or mounted jackhammers, and to max depth of 22 ft, has long been routine practice at many mines for following purposes: (a) Sampling at face of heading or stope; in a massive and fairly uniform ore (as at Miami), drill cuttings may be as accurate as a channel sample, but in a vein with banded structure a drilled sample is likely to be salted with softer (and often richer) vein material, to about same degree as a channel sample; sample holes in such a deposit are obviously unreliable unless drilled to cut the laminations at 45° or over. (b) Exploring from walls of a drift to be advanced in some fixed relative position with respect to walls of orebody; also to ascertain width of latter. (c) Exploring for nearly parallel or branching veins, or offsets behind waste inclusions. (d) Check sampling of a block of ore exposed when square-setting; also, in other stoping methods, to determine grade and location of ore to be broken. Shallow holes for above purpose are usually drilled horiz or slightly upward, and without water. If dependable assay is required, cuttings may be caught in a sack held closely around drill hole, the steel passing through a hole near bottom of sack; if visual inspection suffices, cuttings can be caught in pan or powder box.

Hammer drilling of DEEPER HOLES, often to 150 ft, occasionally to 250 ft (one of 272 ft is on record), is a fairly recent practice made possible by design of a satisfactory coupling for sectionalized drill steel and mechanism for the positive rotation of a long and heavy rod. Within this range of depth and in rock not too hard, hammer drilling compares favorably with diamond drilling as to speed and cost, especially in ground tending to cause loss of diamonds or bits. Chief drawbacks of deep hammer drilling for exploration (its principal use) are: (a) results depend wholly upon return of sludge, loss of which, in fissured ground, is less easily prevented than in diamond drilling; (b) where rock carries narrow stringers of soft ore minerals outside of the main orebody sought, contamination of cuttings by abrasion from wall of hole is more serious than in diamond drilling; in such circumstances, data from a hammer-drill hole may have negative value only. Principal factor limiting depth of a hammer-drill hole is hardness of rock, causing rapid loss of gage; corrected by reaming with sharp bit of same gage before changing to next smaller size, or by applying Stellite to wings of bit. Any positively rotated standard drill can be used, but extra-heavy drifter machines, specially designed for deep drilling, are available; preferred mounting is on a cross-arm supported by 2 columns for extra rigidity. Commonest inclinations lie between 5° and 30° above horiz, insuring rapid return of sludge (assuming ample water supply) without throwing excessive wt on drill; with up-holes of 45° or more, a counterweight must usually be arranged to carry wt of drill steel, commonly 1.25-in hollow round. Down-holes can be drilled, but with more difficulty in recovering sludge; a water swivel to admit compressed air at short, regular intervals aids in lifting sludge. Collection of sludge, when required for assay, is somewhat inconvenient; a good method for up-holes involves drilling a short hole, collaring just below and pointing upward to intersect the deep hole about 1 ft inside of its collar; a short piece of pipe is then wedged into the lower hole, delivering sludge to tubs or settlers (468).

Table 13. Data on Deep-hole Hammer Drilling

Mine and Bib reference	Year	Nature of orebody	Inclination of holes	Depth of holes, ft A = aver M = max	Size at start, in	Advance, ft per drill-shift	Cost per ft L = labor T = total
Chief Consol (509)...	1925	(B)	....	A 80.5	3 1/8	23.5	L $0.60
				M 272	.....	.....	T 1.00
Eagle Picher (569)...	1926	(B)	+10° to 30°	M 148	3 1/4	25	T 1.69
Empire Zinc (319)...	May, '31	(C)	....	M 228	3 1/8	33.1	L 0.40
							T 0.51
New Idria (320).....	1927	(D)	+8° to 50°	A 99.3	3 1/4	30	T 0.75
				M 228			
Burra Burra (180)...	1928	(E)	+15°	M 150	3 3/4	25	T 0.80
Ray (294, 335)......	1928	(F)	+45° to 55°	M 90	3 1/2	23	
Cananea (344)......	1929	(G)	Flat	A 85	3	18.5	
				M 125			
Morning (343)......	1929	(H)	....	A 46	3 1/4	12	L 0.92
				M 129	.....	.....	T 1.10
Edwards (253)......	1930	(B)	±20°	M 50	.....	.....	T 0.99
				A 43			
Roseberry (321).....	1930	(I)	+15°	A 60	3 1/4	10.7	
				M 138			

(B) Irregular beds and chimneys of sulphides in limestone. (C) Thick beds of sulphides in limestone, assoc with quartzite and shale, often fractured and unconsolidated. (D) Narrow, ramifying stringers of cinnabar in medium-hard sandstone and shale. (E) Large lenticular masses of Fe-Cu sulphides, between schist and graywacke walls. (F) Fine stringers and disseminations of sulphide in quartz-sericite schist. (G) Sulphides with quartz gangue in hard limestone and brecciated porphyry. (H) Pb-Zn sulphide and quartz vein in sheared or sheeted quartzite. (I) Massive sulphides in quartz-sericite schist, with quartzite layers.

Chief Consol mines, Tintic, Utah. Silver-lead ore occurs as lenses on bedding planes in limestone and in connecting pipes. Occurrence is irregular. Regular systems of exploratory workings will not find all orebodies, hence proportion of non-productive exploratory and development work is high. Exploration costs have been reduced by boring from underground points. Diamond drills were discarded after 6–8 months' trial, because of high costs due largely to diamond loss. A small churn drill also proved inapplicable. Hammer drills of independently rotated type proved successful. A heavy tunnel machine with 1.25-in steel was used for contract drilling of holes 100–200 ft or more in depth. A lighter, mounted sinker with 1-in steel was used by leasers for holes to 150 ft deep. Double-column mounting was required to preserve alinement of deep holes; a single-column and arm could be used for shallow holes.

Fig 90 shows joint between drill rods and water swivel. Usual water inlet through shank is plugged, and water under good press, supplied by small pump if necessary, is admitted through a forged-steel swivel between shank and bit. For down-holes, swivel can be arranged to take air at $1/4$ or $1/6$ of a revolution; resulting air lift aids in recovering cuttings. McClellan cross bit was used; starting bit, 2.5-in for 1-in steel, 3.125-in for 1.25-in steel. These sizes permit 8 gage drops of $1/8$ in each before hole becomes too small for the joint. If loss of gage is

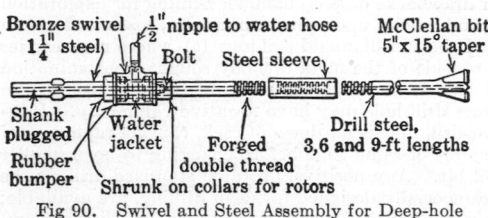

Fig 90.   Swivel and Steel Assembly for Deep-hole Hammer Drilling

too rapid, hole is reamed with a new bit of same gage as the previous one. In some cases 6–8 reaming bits are used before putting in next size. Sludge for each 3 ft of hole is collected in a powder box placed at mouth of hole, and sacked for assay and physical examination. Methods described in Art 8 for careful collection of diamond- and churn-drill samples were considered too complicated for ordinary miners. It was recognized that the sampling practice was liable to error, but character of ore occurrence was such that subsequent channel samples checked hammer-drill samples.

During 19 mo (Oct, 1923, to Apl, 1925) holes totalling 36 232 ft and averaging 80.5 ft deep were drilled in 1 538 drill-shifts (2 men per drill), or 23.5 ft per drill-shift. Deepest hole, 272 ft; 150 ft and over was frequently attained. Labor cost ($5.25 and $4.75 per shift) averaged 60¢ per ft; total cost about $1, compared with $4.94 for diamond drilling under same conditions (509). Fig 74, 74a (Art 9), show record forms used.

Empire Zinc Co, Gilman, Colo. Deep-hole drilling is used for prospecting and planning development. Orebodies are thick, gently dipping, sulphide replacements in limestone, quartzite and shale. In some places, ore and adjacent rocks occur in fractured zones of loose, uncemented, large and small fragments (319). Ore is such that accurate sampling of cuttings is unnecessary. Drills are Gardner-Denver No 34 Turbo drifters, mounted on 2 columns. The 1.25-in drill steel is upset to 1.5 in at both ends, and is oil-tempered after each 600 ft of drilling. Bits: (a) crossbit with center hole for hard or coarse-breaking rock, (b) crossbit with forward-pointing side hole for soft ground, (c) Carr bit for loose and caving ground, in which crossbits are harder to pull. Outer faces of all bits are stellited to retard loss of gage; cutting distance per bit is thereby increased 6–8 times over plain steel; a 125-ft hole can often be bottomed with the starting bit. A bit can be made and stellited in 40 min, at cost of 28.5¢ (1 lb Stellite for 14 bits) and can be used about 12 times before reshaping. Standard sizes: 3 1/8, 3, 2 3/4 in; the former 8 sizes of all-steel bits are not now required. One 228-ft hole, starting at +45°, was drilled by 2 men without aid of counterweight. Hole surveys show no fixed rule as to

Table 14.   Deep-hole Hammer Drilling at Gilman, Colo

(Year ending May 31, 1931)

Total footage................	15,187
Aver ft per drill-shift.........	17.5
Percent time drilling.........	78.2%
" " moving.........	8.3
" " in trouble (a)...	13.5
Cost per ft:	
All underground labor (b)...	$0.608
Maintenance labor (c)......	.193
Supplies (d)...............	.164
Total (e)............	$0.965

(a) Fishing, stuck rods, repairs, air, and water lines. (b) Drilling, timbering, preparing drill stations, pipe work, and clean-up. (c) Outside labor on maintenance and repairs of machines, stelliting, fabricating new equipment. (d) Supplies and new equipment for deepdrill maintenance. (e) Not including 5.2¢ for assaying; 2.4¢ office exp; 9.3¢ for engineers and geologists.

vert deviation, but in hard ground a hole will usually start dropping at start, and fall 12–15 ft in 150 ft; in soft ground, hole usually climbs during first 50 ft, is about on grade at 150 ft, and then drops rapidly. Table 14 gives data on continuous operation of 3 drills during 1 yr ending May, 1931; most of the time was occupied with experimentation; satisfactory operation not attained until last 2 mo, when cost per ft declined quickly to 50.5¢, or about half of what it was 4 mo previously, with corresponding doubling of footage per shift to 33.1 ft.

New Idria quicksilver mine. Seamy and minutely fractured sandstone, erratically impregnated with cinnabar, was prospected by deep-hole drilling at large saving over other methods (320). Accurate sampling not attempted; cuttings from each 3-ft advance were panned. Heavy drifter was mounted usually on cross-arm between 2 columns; in tight places, on horiz bar only. Most holes were 8°–50° above horiz; one, of 147 ft, was 78° below horiz. Aver depth of 87 holes, 99.3 ft; deepest, 228 ft. Starting bit, 3.25-in, reducing by 1/8 in to smallest at 1.75-in. Water at 100-lb press obtained by tapping the pump column. Aver advance per 2-man drill-shift, 30 ft in medium shale and sandstone. Total cost (1931), 75¢ per ft, including purchase of one complete outfit for $1 800.

Tri-State district has used deep-hole drilling, usually to advantage, in proving or disproving occurrences of ore in suspected areas without expensive drifting; cuttings seldom assayed (569). In low headings, drill is mounted on 2 columns; in high headings, on heavy tripods. Holes are usually pointed upward at 10° or over; several were drilled 50 ft at 60° above, and a few to 100 ft or more at 5° below horiz; latter were cleaned by injecting water and air through pipes. To April, 1930, deepest hammer-drill holes were about 150 ft (probably not the limiting depth). A few cost data follow: Federal Mining & Smelting, 2 675 ft, at $1.75 plus estimated 15¢ for deprec. Canam Metals Corp, over 1 000 ft, at $1.70, excluding deprec. Mo-Kas Zinc Corp, several thousand ft, mainly in solid limestone, at 60–70¢, including deprec. Eagle Picher Lead Co, 3 477 ft, at $1.69, including deprec; at same Co's Lucky Jew mine, 1 072 ft largely in solid limestone, at $1.14. Costs usually averaged about $1.70 per ft to 1930, but reductions were expected with added experience.

Roseberry mine, Tasmania. Pb-Zn-Fe sulphide orebody, surrounded by fine-textured quartz-sericite schist with bands of quartzite and quartz veins (321). Exploration is done with Gardner-Denver, 225-lb hammer drills. Holes start at 15° above horiz; deepest, 138 ft. Air consumption (85-lb press), 110 cu ft per min for first 50 ft, to 225 cu ft at 100 ft. Water, 70-lb press, 4 gal per min. To mid-1930, 15 holes totaling 893 ft were drilled in 83 2-man drilling shifts, plus 12 shifts moving and setting up; aver, 10.7 ft per drill-shift, or 9.4 ft per elapsed shift. Max for 1 shift, 30 ft. Diamond drilling (1-in core) in same ground averaged 9 ft per shift. While drilling, changes from rock to sulphides are recognized by color of cuttings; assays showed enrichment of Zn and Pb in slimes from a massive pyrite ore, demanding care in recovery of sludge.

11. ESTIMATES, FROM BOREHOLES, OF ORE TONNAGE AND VALUE

(For survey of boreholes, see Sec 9; for platting boreholes, see Art 9)

Average value of ore in one hole. Let $V_1, V_2, \ldots V_n$ = assays of successive samples; $L_1, L_2, \cdots L_n$ = their respective lengths; V = aver assay of ore. Then

$$V = \frac{V_1 L_1 + V_2 L_2 + \cdots + V_n L_n}{L_1 + L_2 + \cdots + L_n} \qquad (1)$$

If sample lengths are equal, aver assay is arithmetical aver of assays of samples. For methods of averaging assays of diamond-drill core and sludge, see Art 8 and Bib (123, 124, 125, 128).

Average value and tonnage of an orebody are calculated from borehole averages in different ways, depending on ore occurrence and information desired.

Examples. Iron-ore deposits at Moa and Mayarí, Cuba, and placer dredging properties, are examples of surface orebodies with no overburden, and fairly regular bedrock. For such orebodies, estimates may be made thus: Let $V_1, V_2, \cdots V_n$ = aver value or assay of drill holes 1, 2, 3, $\cdots n$; $A_1, A_2 \cdots A_n$ = respective areas of influence of these holes, sq ft; $D_1, D_2, \cdots D_n$ = respective depths of holes, ft; A = total area of deposit; V = aver value of deposit; D = aver depth; T = total tonnage; C = cu ft per ton in place; n = number of holes. Then,

For holes spaced irregularly:

$$V = \frac{A_1 V_1 D_1 + A_2 V_2 D_2 + \cdots + A_n V_n D_n}{A_1 D_1 + A_2 D_2 + \cdots A_n D_n} \quad (2)$$

$$D = \frac{A_1 D_1 + A_2 D_2 + \cdots + A_n D_n}{A} \quad (3)$$

$$T = \frac{(A_1 + A_2 + \cdots + A_n)D}{C} \quad (4)$$

For holes spaced at regular intervals:

$$V = \frac{V_1 D_1 + V_2 D_2 + \cdots V_n D_n}{nD}$$

$$D = \frac{D_1 + D_2 + \cdots + D_n}{n}$$

$$T = \frac{AD}{C}$$

Where ore is overlain by barren material, or occurs in bodies overlying each other and separated by barren or low-grade material, the same methods apply, but only the V, D, and C relating to workable areas penetrated by each hole are considered.

Area of influence of a borehole is the area within which the values shown by that hole are assumed to persist. Theory of averaging samples in general is based on assumption that values vary at a uniform rate between sample points. This assumption is met by so taking the area of influence of a hole that every point within it is nearer to that hole than to any other.

Fig 91 shows general case for holes spaced irregularly. Area of influence for hole No 1 is found by drawing lines 1–2, 1–3, etc, connecting hole No 1 with all those around it. Lines ab, bc, cd, de, and ea are perpendicular bisectors of lines 1–5, 1–4, 1–3, 1–2, and 1–6, respectively. They enclose polygon $abcde$, which is area of influence of hole No 1, which area may be measured with planimeter, or calculated from scaled bases and altitudes of its component right triangles. A different method for defining areas of influence of

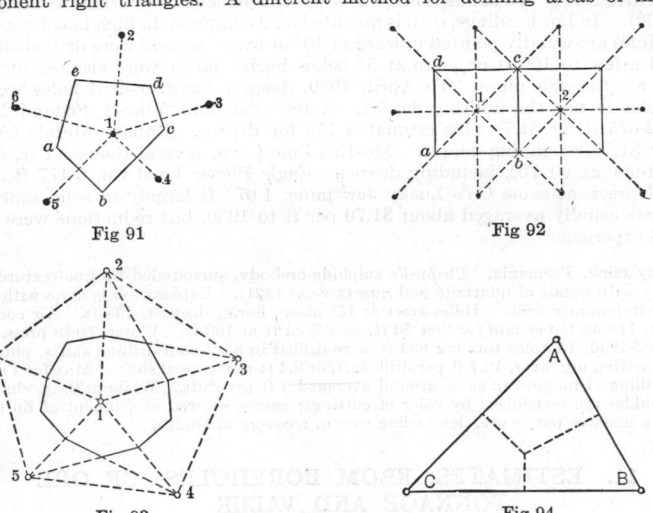

Fig 91   Fig 92

Fig 93   Fig 94

irregularly spaced holes has been used in S E Mo (322). Triangles are first constructed by joining each hole with those nearest to it (Fig 93). Lines are then drawn from each apex to center of opposite side (intersecting at center of gravity of triangle); polygon thus constructed around hole No 1 of Fig 93 has twice as many sides as that of Fig 91. Fig 92 shows construction applied to holes spaced on corners of squares. In this case, area of influence of each hole is a square ($abcd$ for hole No 1), the side of which is the distance between holes. For discussion of these principles, and application to prisms of varying scalenity and to cases where check holes have been drilled in centers of regular blocks, see Bib (512). Another common method for irregularly spaced holes, for which aver values were computed by formula 1, at beginning of Art, is to consider 3 holes in closest proximity as edges of a triangular prism, the depth and value of which are averaged from those of the 3 bounding holes. In Tri-State field, the unweighted, arithmetical aver is employed for depth of prism, and values are weighted only in proportion to depths of ore in the 3 holes (323). This method is less accurate than that by formulas 2 and 3, wherein data of an individual hole are additionally weighted in proportion to the portion of the triangle nearest that hole; that is, to the area of the quadrilateral bounded by 2 sides of triangle and their perpendicular bisectors (Fig 94). To avoid necessity for measuring or computing these quadrilaterals, C. E. Temperley (324) gives a diagram (Fig 95) for thus weighting each of 3 holes involved, requiring only a protractor measurement of angles. (Areas, however, must be ascertained for calculation of tonnage). Having measured the angles of the triangle, to find wt applicable to, say, A, enter bottom of diagram at point corresponding to larger of the 2 other angles, say, B; follow vertically to intersection with curve corresponding to smaller angle, C, and thence horizontally to read wt on A in percentage.

Specific gravity of ore, or cu ft per ton in place, must be accurately determined, since any error will affect computed tonnage. This can be done by: (a) A single, good-sized chunk, suspended by fine wire from a spring balance, may be weighed, first in air, and then submerged in water; wt, lb per cu ft, is then 62.5 × wt in air ÷ (wt in air − wt in water). (b) Apparatus simulating picnometer flask of the physicist can be improvised with water pail and platform scale, and by using a 20–50 lb wt of coarse ore, representing aver grade, results are likely to be more accurate than those obtained on much smaller fragments (see Sec 1); wt in lb per cu ft = 62.5 × dry wt of ore ÷ wt of water displaced;

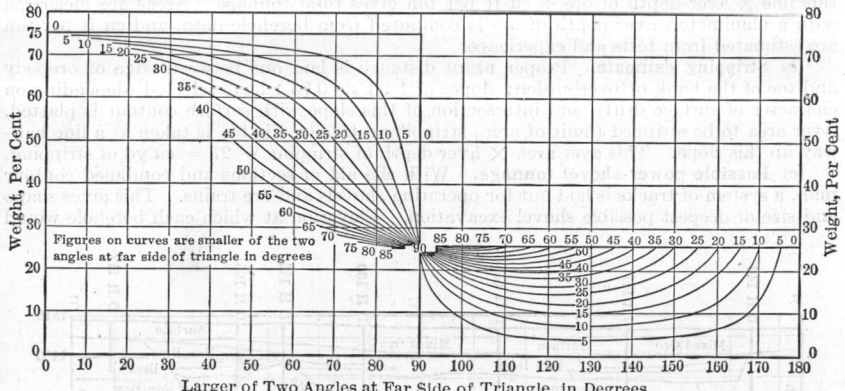

Fig 95. Weighting Factor for Any One of Three Adjacent Boreholes

Larger of Two Angles at Far Side of Triangle, in Degrees

Figures on curves are smaller of the two angles at far side of triangle in degrees

latter obtained by direct measurement or by difference. (c) Using a 500- or 1 000-cc graduated glass cylinder, a known dry wt of fragments to 1-in diam is dropped into a previously noted vol of water in the cylinder, and expansion of vol is observed; wt in lb per cu ft is then 62.5 × wt of ore in gm ÷ expansion of vol in cc. (See 1.)

Mesabi estimates. (Data and drawings from J. F. Wolff, *Mines & Min*, Feb, 1909.) Boreholes, topography, property lines, etc, are first located with respect to a system of

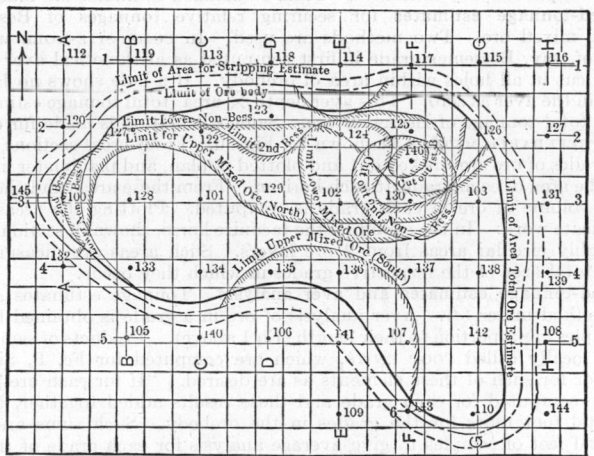

Fig 96. Typical Mesabi Orebody

coordinate lines at 100-ft intervals. From boring data 2 sets of vertical cross-sections, at right angles to each other, are constructed on a scale of 40 ft to 1 in. Analyses of samples placed on sections alongside holes make it possible to outline the layers of different grades of ore. Fig 96 shows in plan a typical orebody, on which 5 E-W sections and 7 N-S sections are laid out. Fig 97 shows section *FF* of this orebody (sample analyses are omitted). From sections, a plan is made, showing superposed contours of surface and top and bottom of orebody. Usually, extension of ore beyond last hole in any section is arbitrarily set at a distance equal to depth of ore in that hole, and bottom of ore is assumed to be a line joining this point with bottom of hole. The 2 sets of sections are checked against each other, and from them, limits of orebody are outlined in plan (Fig 96). Three preliminary estimates are then made as follows:

(a) **Total tonnage** is computed from area of orebody and its aver depth. To allow for wedge shape of edges of orebody, the line marked " limit of area for total ore estimate " (Fig 96) is drawn half-way up the slopes on margins of the orebody. Area enclosed by this line × aver depth of ore ÷ cu ft per ton gives total tonnage. Areas are measured with a planimeter, aver depth of ore is computed from borehole data, and cu ft per ton are estimated from tests and experience.

(b) **Stripping estimate.** Proper BERM distance is laid out between edge of orebody and toe of the bank of overburden; slopes of 1 : 1 or 0.75 : 1 are selected (depending on character of surface drift), and intersection of this slope with surface contour is platted. Aver area to be stripped (limit of area, stripping estimate, Fig 96) is taken as a line half-way up this slope. This aver area × aver depth of stripping ÷ 27 = cu yd of stripping.

(c) **Possible power-shovel tonnage.** With the aid of sections and combined contour map, a system of tracks is laid out for operating shovels and ore trains. This gives shape and size of deepest possible shovel excavation. Elevation at which each borehole would

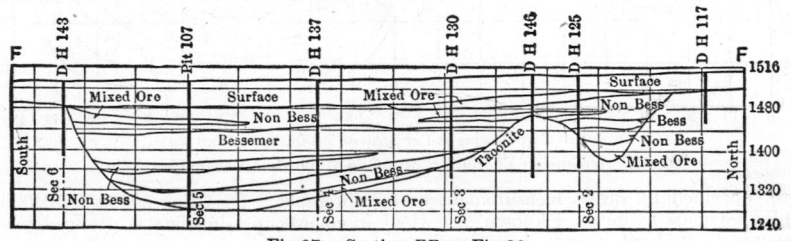

Fig 97.   Section *FF* on Fig 96

be cut by this excavation is noted, and aver depth of ore taken out thus determined. This aver depth × area previously determined (total tonnage estimate) ÷ vol per ton gives the tonnage used for preliminary estimates. Final or detailed estimates are made as follows:

(d) **Graded-tonnage estimates** for securing relative tonnages of Bessemer, non-Bessemer and mixed ore. Two methods are used. In COMPOSITE-HOLE METHOD, aver depth of ore of, say, Bessemer grade is first computed as arithmetical aver of depths of Bessemer ore cut in all holes within area of orebody. If a hole shows no Bessemer ore, it is included in the aver as zero. This aver depth × area (total tonnage estimate) ÷ cu ft per ton gives total tonnage of Bessemer ore. Same calculation is made for other grades. Second and PREFERABLE METHOD is shown by Fig 96. From cross-sections, the outlines of different grades of ore are worked out and plotted in plan, and planimeter measurements are made of the area of each grade at each horizon. From these areas and their respective aver depths, volume of ore in each grade is computed. Plotting the areas of different grades is intricate work. In the example, the taconite horse, shown in section *FF* (Fig 97), cuts out roughly circular areas from 2 ore layers. Such areas are measured and sub-tracted from total area of the respective grades in which they occur.

(e) **Graded-tonnage estimates and aver analysis.** Tonnage estimates are made by the second method under (d). Aver analysis of ore in a grade is obtained by averaging drill-hole samples in proportion to their length (Eq 1 above). Products of sample length × per cent are locally called FOOT UNITS, which are computed for Fe, P, SiO_2, Al, Mn, CaO, and S, or for such of these elements as are desired. "If for each ore-bearing hole, foot units are computed for each grade and these results added together, the sums are respective total foot units for the grades in the orebody. Such sums are divided by respective total feet of samples to give average analysis for each grade of the orebody." TON UNITS is the name given to the products obtained by multiplying tons of any grade by its aver analysis (in Fe, P, etc). Aver analysis of all grades in the deposit is the sum of ton units for each grade ÷ total tonnage of deposit (Eq 2 above). Complete summary (514).

Porphyry coppers. Holes commonly spaced on corners of 200-ft squares. From borehole data, two sets of vert cross-sections are constructed at right angles to each other, and orebody is outlined on each. Usually there is some underground work to aid in this. A. J. Sale (60) recommends that sections be passed through diagonals of squares (*AG*, *BF*, *DJ*, *EI*, etc, Fig 98), instead of on the sides (*AJ*, *BI* ... *AD*, *LE*, etc), thereby increasing distance apart of holes in any section, but bringing sections closer together. Diagonal sections are adjusted to agree at their points of intersection *P*. This method would tend to greater accuracy in orebodies with irregular outlines.   In any case, some cross-sections made through orebody at an angle to regular section lines are desirable, to detect errors and secure correct interpretation of borehole data.   Where underground mining is to be done, sections do not show all irregularities, but are adjusted to outline an orebody of mineable shape.   For orebodies of simple shape, estimates of aver value and tonnage can then be made by Eq 1, 2, 4, above, taking depths D_1, D_2 . . ., etc, as depths of ore in holes.   It is usually better to make planimeter measurements of area of ore in each cross-sec, and use the prismoidal formula (Sec 36, Art 11) for calculating tonnage, taking alternate sections as middle areas.   Aver value of deposit is found as follows: Aver value of ore in each hole is first found by Eq 1 (see beginning Art 11). Where holes are equidistant, the aver value of ore in a section is obtained by combining aver values of holes in proportion to their depths.   Where holes are spaced unevenly, their aver values should be combined in proportion to area of influence of each hole in plane of the section.   For equidistant sections, Σ (section areas $\times$ their respective aver values) $\div \Sigma$ (section areas) $=$ aver value of whole deposit.   Where sections are spaced at unequal distances, they

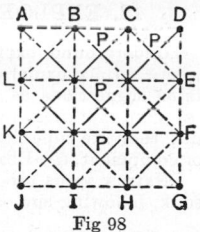

Fig 98

should be combined in proportion to their vol of influence.   Estimates made for both sets of sections should check each other closely.   Usually no allowance is made in estimates for extension of ore beyond last hole in any section.

At RAY CONSOL COPPER Co's property, holes were on corners of 200-ft squares.   Tonnage and aver value of each 200-ft block were calculated separately, using data from 4 corner holes.   L. A. Blackner (61) gives following example of calculation for a block having holes 251, 249, 267, 263 at the 4 corners, the area of rectangle formed by these holes being 84 404 sq ft: Sum of tons in each block gave total tonnage, which was checked by prismoidal calculations from cross-sections.   Aver assay of entire tonnage was obtained by combining aver block assays in proportion to their tonnage (see Table).   In disseminated copper deposits, values usually grade out gradually into rock on sides and bottom of orebody.   In such cases, outlines shown by cross-sections merely represent limits of profitable ore;

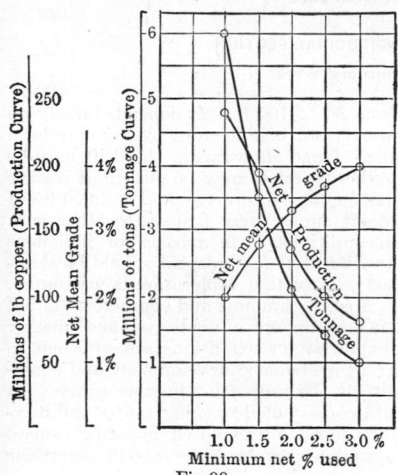

1.0   1.5   2.0   2.5   3.0 %
Minimum net % used
Fig 99

Block Calculation, Ray Cons Mine

Hole No	Thickness of ore, ft	Aver % Cu assay	Ft $\times$ %
251	90	1.77	159.30
249	345	1.86	641.70
267	100	2.65	265.00
263	80	2.62	209.60
Total and aver 615		2.07	1 275.60

Av thickness ore in block = $615 \div 4 = 153.75$ ft.
$84\ 404 \times 153.75 \div 12.5$ (cu ft per ton) = $1\ 038\ 169$ tons.   Av value = $1\ 275.6 \div 615 = 2.07\%$ Cu.

minimum assay varies with copper prices and with methods of mining and milling.   Total tonnage in orebody increases as lower-grade ore is included in it.   A. J. Sale (60) gives a convenient method of analyzing these variables.   Before averages are made, assays of drill samples are corrected for mill recovery, corrected values being called NET PER CENTS. Sets of sections are then constructed to include on margins of orebody ore having minimum net assays of, say, 1, 1.5, 2, 2.5, and 3% Cu. (This range of minima is for illustration only; min marginal grades of less than 1% are included in estimates at several porphyry coppers.) Estimates of tonnage and aver value (net mean grade) are made for each minimum net % used, and results plotted as shown in Fig 99.   Curve of net production, in lb of copper, is computed from known points on curves of tonnage and net mean grade.   Interpolations made on these curves show at once the effect of including ore of any minimum net grade between 1 and 3%.   This device is of course limited to the special conditions outlined above.   See also Bib (513).

In recent work at UTAH COPPER MINE (Art 10-b) holes were drilled as nearly as practicable at corners of equilateral triangles with 400-ft sides; near margins of orebody, 200-ft spacing.   Whole area was divided into 100-ft squares and each block, corresponding in depth to proposed height of bench on that level, was estimated. Where a 100-ft block contained a drill hole, its aver value was taken as that of the hole between elevations of top and bottom of bench; value of a block containing no drill hole was averaged on basis of its distance from nearest adjacent holes. For modes of ascertaining boundaries of profitable ore, especially as to depth of capping, see Bib (119).

12. EXPLORATION BY SHAFTS, TUNNELS, AND DRIFTS

Underground exploration is undertaken where conditions prevent surface work, or where surface exploration gives no information as to underlying orebodies. Art 3 contains suggestions as to location of openings with respect to geology. General rules: (a) keep workings in the orebody; (b) do first work on best showings, to see whether or not they are superficial; (c) cost must be low, due to high risk involved. For selection of equipment, see Bib (515) and Art 13.

Narrow veins are explored as in Fig 100. On each oreshoot, a small shaft has been sunk, following sinuosities of vein (see cross-sec *AB*), and drifts are run on each shoot.

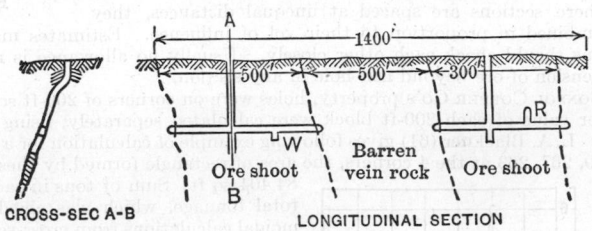

Fig 100.   Typical Exploratory Work

Depth at which drifting starts in such work is from 50 to 100 ft. It depends largely on depth of surface alteration and level of ground water, but is influenced by so many local factors that only general statements can be made. Good showings in the drift may be explored with raises *R* or winzes *W*. In long oreshoots, raises may be put up at regular intervals. Workings are sampled and estimates made of tonnage and value of ore exposed (Sec 25) as work progresses. At different times these figures, together with geol conditions, form a basis for judgment as to whether: (a) prospect should be abandoned; (b) further exploration is warranted, and, if so, its amount and character; (c) net value and amount of ore proved and whether probabilities for extensions are sufficient to warrant systematic development and equipment for the property. Further exploration would consist of deepening shafts and driving other drifts at intervals of 60 to 100 ft. WIDE VEINS are explored by same general methods, but crosscuts are driven from wall to wall at regular intervals to determine width, character, and value of ore.

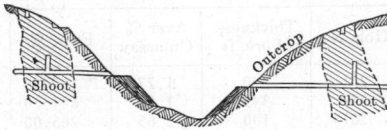

Fig 101.   Longit Sec in Plane of Vein

Veins outcropping across a ravine may be explored with drift tunnels and raises (Fig 101). Tunneling in general is cheaper than shaft sinking; the workings drain themselves, and hoisting is avoided. With STEEP TOPOGRAPHY there is great temptation to drive crosscut tunnels to intersect an orebody in depth (Fig 5, Art 1), lateral exploration being done by drifts, raises, and winzes as before. This involves a higher risk than where workings follow the orebody; the latter may be cut in a pinch and not be recognized; faults, and changes in dip or strike may cause the tunnel to miss the orebody. Large amounts of water occurring near surface may justify use of crosscut tunnels for early exploration. Difficulties of such work should be recognized; tunnels should not be far apart and there should be money enough to continue work, if orebody is not cut at point calculated from its surface dip.

Beds which outcrop are explored by drift tunnels, slopes, or crosscuts. Vert shafts are sunk to reach beds, flat deposits, and masses which do not outcrop. Where overburden is alluvium, test pits are located on corners of squares (Art 4, 5, 6). If such orebodies lie under a rock cover, exploration usually consists of one or more vert shafts, from which a series of drifts and crosscuts are driven to outline the orebody at different levels; raises extending to the capping above determine vert extent of ore.

Exploration *vs* systematic development. There is no sharp separation between the two activities. Drifts and other openings for exploratory work are of small cross-section. Drilling is usually done by hand, and windlass or whim is used for hoisting. Power hoists improvised from automobile engines are economical when shafts go deeper than 50–75 ft. Portable gasolene-powered compressors are useful. Expenditure for more elaborate plant is not made until justified by results of work. For cost and speed of driving small drifts, tunnels, and raises, see Art 20, 21; for cost of shafts, see Sec 7. Factors governing choice of different openings are as given in Art 15, 16. It is desirable to plan and locate exploratory openings with reference to possible future development, but this should be subordinated to the primary object of exploration, as defined in Art 1.

Résumé. (*a*) Main objects of exploration are to reduce mining risk, lessen cost of development, and increase profits of mining by obtaining information upon which intelligent plans of work may be based. (*b*) Cheapest and quickest methods of obtaining this information are by surface exploration and by boreholes. But, in many cases, underground exploration is necessary and cannot be neglected. (*c*) Underground work at first should be so conducted as to obtain information even at expense of making special excavations of no value for mining purposes. Underground exploration should extend far enough in depth to prove character of the unaltered deposit below the zone of surface action, or to prove existence of a sufficiently large body of altered mineral for mining operations. (*d*) Exploration, surface and underground, should be pushed far enough to determine the character and extent of irregularities in thickness and in richness, and to obtain some idea of location and distribution of workable areas and their relations to areas of barren and unworkable ground. (*e*) Number of openings made in the deposit, as shafts and drifts, will depend on local conditions. In deposits of irregular and uncertain character, openings should not be so far apart as to permit large areas of barren or unworkable ground to escape detection. (*f*) If necessary, crosscuts or boreholes should be driven at intervals, to search for and prove parallel beds or fissures, or to prove the deposit itself if wide or thick. (*g*) Assays should be made from time to time on carefully taken aver samples, and these, if required, may be supplemented by working tests on lots of representative ore. (*h*) Exploration and development should be pushed far enough to make sure that there is sufficient mineral to warrant erection of a permanent plant, and far enough to determine all questions affecting profitableness of the enterprise. On the other hand, unnecessary exploration or over-development must be avoided. H. S. Munroe (64).

13. EQUIPMENT AND FOOD SUPPLY FOR PROSPECTING AND EXPLORATION

Surface work. Following is a list of tools and supplies for 4 men doing surface exploration in Nova Scotia (Art 6) (24):

12 picks	1 cold chisel	2 gold pans
6 long-handled, round-point	1 pr tongs	1 tub
shovels [shovels	1–1½-in auger	1 pocket lens
2 short-handled, round-point	1 brace	1 compass (surveyor's or geologist's)
1 stone hammer	1 framing chisel	100 lb mixed 5½-in and 7-in nails
1 striking hammer	1 water barrel	25 lb 3½-in nails
1 blacksmith's hammer	1 portable forge	1 claw hammer
1 crowbar	5 short drill steels	50 ft 1-in hemp rope
1 prospecting pick	1 single jack (hammer)	1 hoisting bucket
1 handsaw	1 cleaning spoon	1 windlass
1 blacksmith's file	2 axes	1 diaphragm pump, 2½-in suction
2 saw files	3 pails	1 combined anvil and vise

In addition: repair parts for pump, 1-in lumber for general purposes; 1½-in lumber for cribbing test pits; enough dynamite, fuse and caps for, say, 20 shots; ⅜-in round iron; hoop iron; camping and cooking outfit for 4 men; 1 month's provisions.

Prospecting, Quebec gold belt. Following supplies were suggested by Frische in 1925 (504), for each man prospecting in Quebec gold belt: *Clothing*—1 complete outfit, including topboots, waterproof pants and coat, 1 suit underwear, 1 duck shirt, 3 pr heavy woolen socks, 1 pr duck pants, 1 roll-neck sweater, 1 towel, 1 pr light canvas shoes, 1 rubber sheet, 2 pr 8-lb blankets, 1 mosquito bar. *Tools*—1 pick, 1 shovel, 1 Hudson Bay axe, 1 geologist's pick, 1 long-handled striking hammer, 1 blacksmith hammer, 1 gold pan, 1 mortar and pestle, 3 drills, ¾-in steel of different lengths, dynamite, fuse and detonators. *Miscellaneous*—Tent, canoe, packsack, map, compass, linen tape (66 ft), magnifying glass, blowpipe, watch, jack-knife, fish-hooks and line, toilet kit, first-aid kit, candles, matches, soap. *Cooking Utensils*—1 frying pan, 1 coffee pot, 1 plate, 1 tin cup, 1 knife, 1 fork, 1 spoon, 3 tin pots with cover and bail, 1 large tin pail, 1 can opener, 2 bread pans, 1 large mixing spoon.

10–78   PROSPECTING AND EXPLORATION

Frische also compiled following from aver of several parties in Quebec gold belt, figures being on a man-day basis (504).

Flour	0.75 lb
Bacon	0.50 "
Beans	0.25 "
Sugar	0.40 "
Rice and barley	0.15 "
Desiccated eggs	0.15 "
Macaroni	0.10 "
Oatmeal	0.10 "
Cornmeal	0.12 "
Dried fruit	0.25 "
Butter	0.08 "
Lard	0.03 "
Cheese	0.05 "
Tea	0.025 "
Coffee	0.01 "
Cocoa	0.01 "
Raisins	0.04 "
Jam and marmalade	0.03 "
Syrup	0.03 "
Salt	0.033 "
Pepper	....
Baking powder	0.01 "
Per man-day	3.048 lb

Milk	0.25 qt per man-day
Oxo	0.10 cube " " "
Yeast cakes	3 pkg per summer
Soda	2 " " "
Powdered jelly	12 " " "
Mustard	1 " " "

Total cost per man-day in 1925............ $0.57

J. Y. Murdoch, in 1938, gives following list of tools provided for 4-months' work by 5 men described in Table 3 and text, Art 7: 1 prospecting pick, 3 rock picks, 3 grub-hoes, 2 round-point shovels, long handle, 2 same, short handle, 2 striking hammers (7-lb), 1 hand saw, 1 cross-cut saw, 1 buck-saw with extra blade, 4 axes (2.5-lb), 6 saw files, 6 flat files (10-in), 1 Buffalo blower, 1 anvil (20-lb), 1 pr tongs, 30 ft 7/8-in hex drill steel, 12 moils, 1 cleaning spoon, 1 pail for tempering, 1 pointed steel, 6-ft, for testing depth of overburden, 1 grindstone, 2 bags blacksmith coal.

Balanced diet for prospectors. Following list is recommended to last 1 man a week (16):

Evaporated milk	3 1-lb cans
Potatoes	2 lb
Other fresh vegetables	4 "
Citrus fruits (3 lb) or apples (or equivalent dried fruits)	6 "
Dry beans	3 "
Cereals (or whole-wheat flour)	6–8 "
Smoked meat	2.5 "
Sugar	3 "
Coffee	1 "
Salt	1/4 "
Butter	1/2 "
Baking powder	....

If water must be carried, 10 gal will suffice 1 man for drinking and cooking for 3 days in hot weather, or about a week in cooler weather.

Northern Ontario. A J. Keast and C. F. Jackson (325) give detailed costs of erecting and equipping a camp for 60 men on preliminary development of Central Patricia, 100 miles N of Savant Lake (Can Nat Ry) Ontario, in 1930. Lumber was sawn on property; sand and gravel were available for concrete. All other materials hauled 120 miles by tractor and sleds at 71¢ per ton-mile.

	Building		Equipment		Building		Equipment
	Size, Ft	Cost	Cost		Size, Ft	Cost	Cost
Bunkhouse 1	18 × 20	$218	$246	Storehouse	24 × 28	$1 060	$498
Bunkhouse 2	20 × 30	875	1 155	Powder magazine	18 × 30	633	......
Bunkhouse 3	16 × 18	155	76	Thaw house	8 × 10	196	......
Bunkhouse 4	32 × 20	316	258	Cap and fuse house	8 × 10	157	......
Cook house	50 × 24	1 694	513	Pump house	8 × 10	133	944
Office and residence	24 × 24	766	39	Water tank, 10 000			
Two small root houses		854	......	gal		541	......
Meat house	24 × 30	613	......	Stable	10 × 10	176	441
Ice house	12 × 14	115	......	Tractor garage	10 × 16	285	......
Blacksmith shop	20 × 28	673	2 986 (a)	Drafting office	6 × 18	220	......
Power house and hoist				Headframe, 40 ft			
room	80 × 28	2 115	36 960 (b)	high		1 411	272
Dry-house	18 × 28	854	157	Sawmill			2 228
Assay office	16 × 28	630	1 641	Electric-light plant			1 083

(a) Including steel sharpener, $2 553. (b) Hoist, compressor, and two 110-hp boilers with feed-water heaters and pumps; cost installed given.

Development from Mch 5 to Sep 20, 1930, included: 500 ft of 6.5 by 16-ft shaft, with 4 shaft stations and sump: 1 776 ft drifting; 1 019 ft crosscutting. Roadmaking, surface exploration, and some diamond drilling were done the previous year. Total cost of buildings, surface and underground equipment, including some items not listed above, $89 854.

Underground exploration, Montana. R. H. Sales furnished following list of supplies and equipment for a crew of foreman, 4 miners and cook working in Flathead Co, Mont, from Dec 1, 1913, to May 15, 1914. They drove 555 ft of tunnels and crosscuts, and sank a 4 by 6-ft shaft 32 ft, using a windlass. Rock, soft porphyry; no water; no timbering required. Wages: foreman, $5; miners on tunnels, $3.50; on shaft, $4. Two frame shacks were built, each requiring 1 000 bd ft of lumber. Total cost, labor, supplies, and equipment, about $5 500. The list was made by a man of wide experience in this sort of work in the NW and includes no unnecessary items (see also Bib 326).

Mining tools and supplies
1 prospecting hammer
2 4-lb striking hammers
1 7-lb   "   hammer
1 8-lb   "   "
3 18-in hammer handles
6 36-in   "   "
3 long-handled round-point shovels
3 5-lb drift picks
4 4l/2-lb "   "
12 pick handles
1 all-steel wheelbarrow
200 lb 7/8-in drill steel
5 lb 3/8-in mild steel
19 lb 5/8-in round iron
600 lb 40% gelatine dynamite
200 lb 60%   "   "
4 200 ft fuse
1 100 6 X caps
3 boxes candles
50 ft 5/8-in manila rope
1 5-lb wedge
1 7-lb   "
Mine car and rails

Small supplies
1 keg 10d nails
2 lb 3d   "
10 lb 8d   "
5 lb 20d   "
30 lb 40d   "
2 pair 4 by 4 steel butts
2 door locks
4 1/4 by 1 1/4-in carriage bolts
15 gal kerosene
1 qt Boston coach oil

Miscellaneous
1 whiskey barrel
4 dinner buckets
1 lantern
1 No 8 Admiral stove
1 No 1 c Columbia heater
1 No 2 c Columbia heater
14 joints 6-in stove pipe
2 joints 6-in stove pipe, with check draft and dampers

Miscellaneous (Con't)
1 tent 12 by 14 ft, 12 oz
1 No 1 galvanized-iron tub
1 zinc washboard
1 Keystone clothesline
2 6-in tent flanges
3 pkg 6/8 brass shoe nails
4 " 4/8 C H Hung nails
1 cobbler set
3 pair half soles
3 "heel lifts
1 wash bowl
1 8 by 10-in mirror   .
1 8-in scrub brush
1 yd 48-in canvas
1 sq 2-ply Ruberoid roofing
1 1/3-pitch tin roof jack
2 yd 36-in oilcloth
25 bars common soap
10 bars hand soap
Medicine chest
Blankets

Blacksmith's tools and supplies
1 pair No 1 blacksmith tongs
1 pair G & D tongs
1 cold cutter
1 40-lb blacksmith vise
1 No 2 blacksmith hammer
1 70-lb anvil
1 No 400 blower
1 hardy
1 hot cutter
600 lb blacksmith coal
1 bottom swage
1 10-in flat file
3 6-in taper files
3 8-in M B files
2 10-in M B files
1 metal worker's crayon
1 10-in wrench

Carpenter's tools
1 No 3 hand axe
2 Jennings bits, 1/2 and 1-in
1 saw set, No 12
1 10-in wood rasp
1 4-ft, 1-man Simonds saw

Carpenter's tools (Con't)
1 6-ft crosscut saw and extra handles
1 4l/2-D B axe
1 33/4-S B axe
1 1.5-in framing chisel
1 level, No 50
1 steel square, No 14
1 10-in brace
1 26-in hand saw
1 clawhammer
1 iron jack plane, No 5
1 22-lb grindstone and hangers
1 adze and handle
1 No 60 axe stone
1 No 11 mason's line
4 pieces blue chalk

Cooking utensils, tableware
4 frypans, Nos 2, 4, 6, and 7
2 dish pans, 14 and 21 qt
2 8-qt milk pans
3 drip pans, 15, 20, and 21 in
1 1-qt pudding pan
6 2-qt pudding pans
4 4-qt pudding pans
3 preserve kettles and covers
2 large saucepans and covers
1 coffee pot
1 tea pot
1 tea kettle
1 pitcher
1 dipper
1 20-in butcher saw
1 10-in butcher knife
1 12-in butcher steel
1 kitchen knife
1 cake turner
1 cast griddle
1 can opener
1 coffee grinder
1 12-qt galvanized iron pail
2 14-qt   "   "   "   "
12 10-in tin pie plates
12 each, plates, cups, saucers, soup bowls, teaspoons, tablespoons
24 knives and forks
1 1-pt syrup pitcher

Provisions (65). Weight of rations, calculated to have sufficient food value to allow men to work and keep healthy, varies from 3.3 to 4.4 lb per man per day; actual consumption in mining camps is often 6 to 7 lb per man-day, difference being largely due to waste. D. E. Woodbridge has found by experience that supplies in the following list are suitable for REMOTE REGIONS and properly proportioned to come out even. Figures are in lb per man per month; wt, 3.3 lb per man-day. Where game is plentiful, cut down on ham and bacon, double the quantity of salt, and add onions and evaporated vegetables.

	Lb		Lb
Flour, cornmeal, hardtack, rice, grits, oatmeal, or similar foods, at least two-thirds of which should be flour prepared for self-raising	42	Butter	3
		Canned milk	2
		Cheese	2
Clear mess pork, bacon, and ham, say one-half pork	27	Tea, coffee, and chocolate	2
Beans and split peas, two-thirds beans	7	Salt, pepper, celery salt, mustard, two-thirds salt	3
Sugar	5	Baking powder, if self-raising flour is not used	1
Evaporated fruits, mostly apple	4	Bottle of lime juice	

Other BALANCED RATIONS for prospectors in the West and SW are given in Bib (327); cost averaged about 50¢ per man-day, which is about a minimum for healthful subsistence.

The old U S ARMY RATION per man-day was: Bacon or pork, 12 oz (or fresh beef, 22 oz); soft bread or flour, 18 oz (or hard bread, 16 oz, or cornmeal, 20 oz). Following were also issued per day to 30 men: Beans or peas, 5 lb (or rice, 10 lb); sugar, 5 lb; vinegar, 1 qt; soap, 1 lb; salt, 1.5 lb; pepper, 1.25 oz. U S FOREST SERVICE recommends following list to serve 1 man 30 days; fresh meat, additional, to be purchased locally:

Bacon, salt	2 lb	Oatmeal	6 lb	Sauerkraut	3 cans
Bacon, smoked	10 "	Onions	5 "	Spinach	3 "
Baking powder	1 "	Pepper	1/4 "	Tomatoes	6 "
Baking soda	1/2 "	Potatoes	15 "	Green Chili	3 "
Beans	5 "	Raisins	2 "	Chili powder	1 small bottle
Butter	2 "	Rice	3 "	Jam	1 jar
Cheese	1 1/2 "	Salt	1 "	Syrup	1 gal
Coffee	4 "	Sugar	12 "	Candles	6
Dried fruit	9 "	Corn	6 cans	Matches	2 large boxes
Flour	24 "	Evap milk (tall)	10 "	Soap, laundry	1 cake
Shortening fat	4 "	Peas	6 "	Soap, hand	1 "

D. J. Williams (328) gives following list of provisions consumed in 30 days by crew of 25 men working for the Hirst-Chichagof Co, at Juneau, Alaska, in 1930. The more important staples are:

Apples and apricots, evap	18.7 lb	Rolled oats	18.8 lb	Beef	632.0 lb
Prunes and figs, evap	37.5 "	Salt	48.0 "	Pork	159.6 "
Baking powder and soda	5.0 "	Shortening fats	60.0 "	Bacon	85.1 "
		Macaroni, spaghetti	17.6 "	Ham	134.8 "
Beans, dry	43.8 "	Sugar	416.3 "	Canned fruits (10's)	89 tins
Peas, dry	11.5 "	Tea	2.0 "	Canned vegets (10's)	72 "
Butter	105.0 "	Yeast	4.0 "	Cond milk (tall)	400 "
Cheese	20.0 "	Cabbage	104.0 "	Sardines (16's)	29 "
Coffee	70.1 "	Carrots	79.0 "	Soap, white	71 bars
Flour, white	475.0 "	Onions	100.0 "	Crackers	10 lb
Flour, graham	16.7 "	Parsnips	30.0 "	Cereals, dry	40 "
Raisins & currants	15.0 "	Potatoes	558.3 "	Vinegar	4 1/2 qt
Rice	12.5 "	Turnips	50.0 "	Salad oil	1.7 "
		Eggs	130 doz		

Principal additions to above: spices, condiments, and flavoring extracts. Gross wt averaged 7 lb per man-day. Bib (328) also gives size and wt of standard packages.

At Iron Mt, Idaho, 20 men, including cooks, consumed following supplies during 4 winter months. Fresh vegetables gave out and canned goods were used. Double the amount of cabbage, turnips, parsnips, and one-half more onions and carrots should have been provided.

Fresh beef	2383 lb	Salt	105 lb	Molasses	2 gal
Fresh pork	581 "	Dried peaches	30 "	Jelly	3 buckets
Fresh mutton	167 "	Dried apples	65 "	Vinegar	6 gal
Fresh fish	100 "	Dried apricots	50 "	Baking powder	8 lg cans
Fresh chickens	112 "	Dried prunes	100 "	Pickles	1 keg
Fresh eggs	69 doz	Raisins	150 "	Lard	25 lb
Case eggs	6 cases	Condensed milk	23 cases	Catsup	1 gal
Ham	472 lb	Canned corn	3 "	Tea	30 lb
Bacon	258 "	Canned tomatoes	5 "	Chocolate	5 "
Butter	330 "	Canned peas	5 "	Cocoanut	6 "
Flour	29 sacks	Canned peaches	1 case	Soda	2 "
Graham flour	50 lb	Canned pears	1 "	Yeast foam	10 pkg
Corn meal	2 1/2 sacks	Canned pumpkin	1 "	Cornstarch	6 "
Coffee	322 lb	Canned oysters	1 "	Chowchow	8 qt
Potatoes	40 sacks	Maple syrup	3 cases	Pepper sauce	2 bot
Carrots	200 lb	Crackers	4 "	Currants	9 pkg
Turnips	100 "	Macaroni	3 "	Hominy	20 lb
Cabbage	200 "	Cheese	77 lb	Matches	1/2 case
Onions	248 "	Sugar	9 sacks	G S soap	1 "
Parsnips	100 "	Oatmeal	3 "	Tar soap	1 "
Apples	600 "	Beans	1 1/2 sacks	Ivory soap	1 "

H. L. Carr, in prospecting placer gravel in Guatemala (work very heavy, negro labor, isolated camp), found weekly food consumption per man as follows:

Black beans	1.4 lb	Lard	0.5 lb	Coffee	0.3 lb
Plantain	3.0 "	Flour	5.0 "	Salt	1.0 "
Ground provisions (sweet potato, cassava, etc)	3.0 "	Rice	2.1 "	Baking powder	0.17 "
		Sugar	1.3 "	Beef, live wt	10 to 15 "

Menu was designed to attract and keep labor; beef, salted and dried immediately after killing. Work done between April and July. (See also *Trans* A I M E, Vol 29, p 157.)

DEVELOPMENT

14. GENERAL

Systematic development. Purposes: (*a*) to provide openings for stoping and transporting mineral; (*b*) to obtain further and more detailed information as to character and size of orebody. Relative importance of these functions depends on type and size of orebody; the second is more important in orebodies of irregular shape and tenor, and in

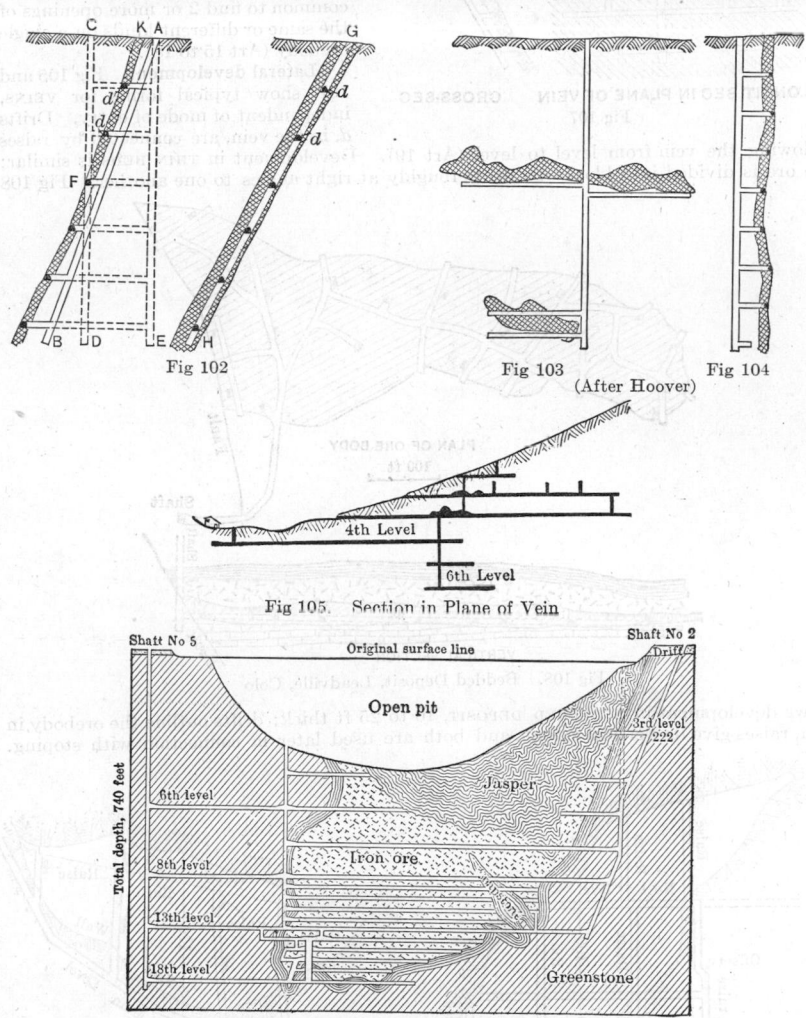

Fig 102

Fig 103
(After Hoover)

Fig 104

Fig 105. Section in Plane of Vein

Fig 106. Chandler Mine, Mich (after Leith)

general during early stages of development. Two problems are presented: MODE OF ENTRY, which involves a decision between vert or inclined shafts, drift or crosscut tunnels, or a combination of these, for reaching the orebody from surface, and LATERAL OR SUBSIDIARY DEVELOPMENT, which deals chiefly with workings within the orebody.

Modes of entry for PITCHING VEINS are (Fig 102): a vert shaft *CD* started in hanging wall; a footwall vert shaft *AE*; a footwall inclined shaft *AB*; or an inclined shaft *GH*, in the vein. Except in the last case, crosscuts are necessary at intervals to reach the vein (Art 19). A vert shaft is the correct mode of entry for FLAT OR VERT DEPOSITS, lying under flat topography (Fig 103, 104).

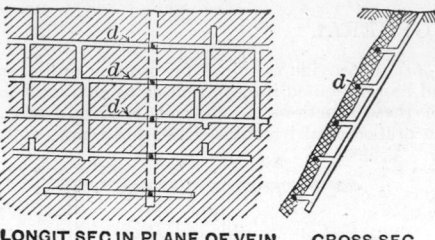

In MOUNTAINOUS REGIONS, entry to veins or other deposits may sometimes be made by crosscut tunnels (p, Fig 5) or drift tunnels (Fig 105). Fig 106 shows entry to a massive orebody, by both vert and inclined shafts. It is common to find 2 or more openings of the same or different kinds on a single orebody (Art 15 to 18).

LONGIT SEC IN PLANE OF VEIN   **CROSS-SEC**
Fig 107

Lateral development. Fig 105 and 107 show typical forms for VEINS, independent of mode of entry. Drifts d, in the vein, are connected by raises following the vein from level to level (Art 19). Development in THIN BEDS is similar; the ore is divided into blocks by drifts roughly at right angles to one another. Fig 108

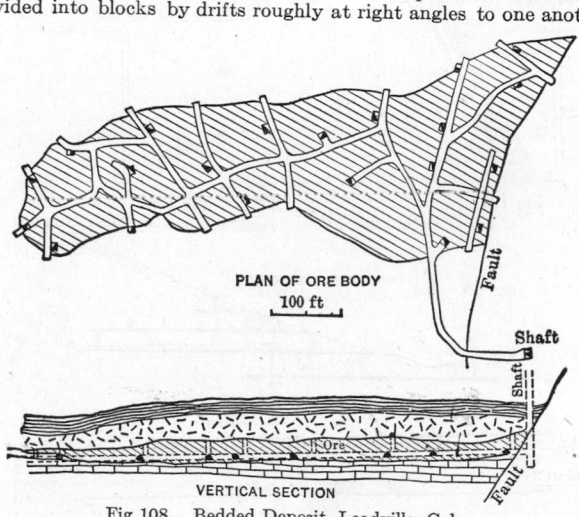

PLAN OF ORE BODY
100 ft

Fig 108. Bedded Deposit, Leadville, Colo

shows development in a BEDDED DEPOSIT, 10 to 25 ft thick; drifts outline the orebody in plan, raises give its vertical extent, and both are used later in connection with stoping.

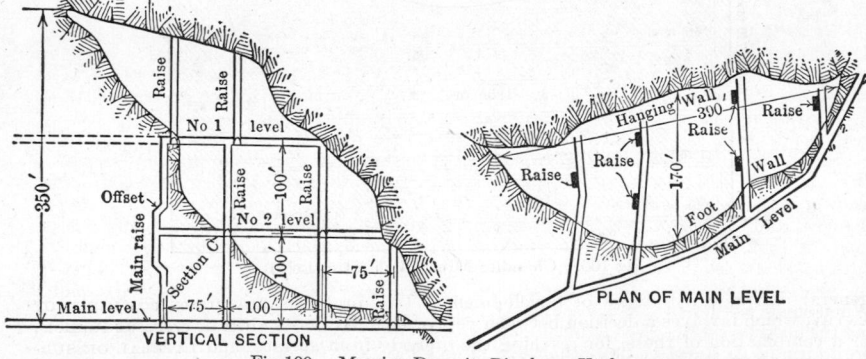

Fig 109. Massive Deposit, Bingham, Utah

Fig 109 shows somewhat similar development of an irregular massive deposit (66). Methods of mining exert a dominant influence on mode of lateral development, especially in large orebodies (see Art 19 to 23). In general, lateral development divides an orebody into blocks, the edges or corners of which afford numerous points of attack and the tonnage and value of which may be computed; the openings also outline payable areas and aid ventilation and drainage.

15. CHOICE OF MODE OF ENTRY

Openings in orebody *vs* those in country rock. (*a*) Ores are often softer than adjacent country rock; if so, it is cheaper and quicker to make openings in them, but cost of maintenance in soft ground may outweigh this advantage, (*b*) Openings in the deposit have an exploratory value; chance of losing orebody is reduced. (*c*) Mineral extracted may pay part of cost of work. These advantages are greater when funds are limited and preliminary exploration has not been thorough. Crosscut tunnels and vertical shafts are in country rock; drift tunnels follow orebody and allow stoping to start at any point.

Inclined shaft in orebody *vs* inclined shaft in footwall. Inclined shafts for large tonnages must be straight. Gradual changes in dip are allowable, but if numerous or sudden they increase hoisting cost and decrease shaft capacity by limiting hoisting speed. A straight incline can not be sunk in a deposit of irregular dip; at some point it must extend into country rock. Hence, in such orebodies the footwall location (*AB*, Fig 102) is generally preferable for large shaft capacity. For small output, a straight shaft is less important, and the exploratory value of a shaft in the deposit often recommends its use. In fairly regular deposits, large outputs can be handled through shafts in either location; choice is then based on other factors (see below).

Michigan copper mine practice (67, 68, 486, 487, 488, 489). The native copper occurs in conglomerate and amygdaloid beds; dip in northern part of district is 37° to 42°. Operators differ as to which shaft location is better. ADVANTAGES OF FOOTWALL SHAFT: (*a*) Bins for loading skips can be placed directly over the shaft, and for the most part are cut in ore; this advantage disappears if skips are loaded direct from cars, as is done in many mines. (*b*) Less timber is required in upper part of a footwall shaft than for a shaft in the vein; hence, there is less danger from fire. Fire is prevented by substitution of concrete and steel supports for timber. (*c*) Footwall location obviates necessity for shaft pillars, which must be left on each side of a shaft sunk in ore, and which tie up large amounts of ore during life of shaft. Mining operations may throw great pressures onto shaft pillars, and, if a "creep" starts, it may destroy the shaft. DISADVANTAGES OF FOOTWALL SHAFT: (*a*) it costs more to sink; (*b*) it requires crosscuts and stations cut in rock; (*c*) it produces no ore while sinking and gives no information as to character of the deposit. Some footwall shafts cost more to maintain than those in the vein and *vice versa*, depending on local characteristics of rock and ore; most shafts have been sunk in the lode. It is an open question whether in new mines a small shaft should not be sunk in the vein, and lateral work carried on from it far enough to prove the orebody. The working shaft could then be raised simultaneously from several levels, and placed in vein or footwall in the light of information obtained.

Tunnels *vs* shafts. Drift and crosscut tunnels can be driven faster and cheaper than shafts. Wet ground increases this advantage, as a tunnel drains the overlying ore and eliminates pumping. Hoisting plant also is not required until operations extend below the tunnel level.

Crosscut tunnels prospect the country rock and may disclose parallel deposits (Art 3). Drift tunnel is usually preferable, if a choice exists. Risk involved in driving crosscut tunnels is higher than for other methods of entry; it increases with length of tunnel and its depth below known ore. It is unwise to begin development with a long crosscut before exploration has shown an adequate tonnage of ore, and either proved or given strong geological evidence of its extension to the tunnel level.

Several long and deep crosscut tunnels have been driven, to provide drainage and economical transportation for groups of mines. They are justified when the saving on known orebodies will amortize cost of tunnel at a profit during life of properties affected.

Drift and crosscut tunnels serve mainly for extraction of ore lying above them; shafts must be sunk from tunnel level or from surface to develop deeper portions of a deposit. Internal shafts require large excavations for hoisting plant, and the latter must be operated by elec or compressed air; underground hoists, however, are increasingly common. When steam hoists are used and power is generated at the mine, saving is effected by placing the hoist on surface close to boiler plant. Combined cost of tramming and transferring ore to tunnel cars is often more than cost of hoisting the extra distance to surface. Questions of convenience in handling ore on surface may modify choice of method. Hoisting plant on surface, but delivering loads to a tunnel at some distance below, is a frequent arrangement in rugged country. Tunnels preserve their drainage function after mining above them has ceased; surface water may be intercepted at the tunnel level, and the head on pumps at lower levels is reduced by difference in elevation between collar of shaft and tunnel level. Saving in pumping may warrant the cost of a new and deeper adit, or the driving of a tunnel to tap workings already opened by a shaft, even though the tunnel is used for drainage purposes only. Length of such a tunnel which it will pay to drive = present value of total saving in pumping cost during probable life of mine ÷ cost per ft of tunnel; for example, with power @ $60 per hp-yr, cost of tunneling @ $20 per ft, and a 10-yr life, it will pay to drive 600 ft of tunnel per 100 000 gal water per day per 100 ft head saved. For recent examples of long drainage tunnels, see Ojuela, Trepca, and Halkyn, Art 20 and Bib (483, 484, 498).

Vertical *vs* inclined shaft. A typical example requiring a decision between the two kinds of shaft arises in case of a pitching vein, as in Fig 102. An inclined shaft is generally sunk in footwall (AB). Vert shaft may be at CD or AE; either location requires more crosscutting than the inclined shaft, and from this standpoint the inclined shaft has an advantage which varies with dip of vein and with depth; this advantage is partly offset by the greater length of incline required to reach a given level. Shaft AE always requires more crosscutting than CD; for CD, the total length of crosscuts is a minimum when $CF = FD$. Depth CD must be assumed in comparing merits of alternative locations. Factors to be considered are:

(*a*) **First cost.** Vert shafts cost more or less per ft than inclined shafts, according to local conditions and the way in which ground breaks. Sometimes drill holes in one or the other can be placed to take advantage of planes of weakness, thereby increasing speed and decreasing cost. Sinking very flat inclines resembles drifting; they usually cost less per ft than a vert shaft of same cross-sec (see Sec 7). Cost per ft of crosscutting (Art 20) is same for either mode of entry. A comparison of total costs is made by applying unit costs to total footage of the different openings involved. For given depth and unit costs of sinking and crosscutting, an angle of dip will be found at which the cost of hanging-wall shaft CD (Fig 102) with its crosscuts is same as that of footwall shaft AB with its crosscuts; on flatter dips, an inclined shaft entry is cheaper, and *vice versa*. Critical angle in most cases is about 70°. For all dips permitting a choice, a footwall vert shaft AE and its crosscuts cost most.

(*b*) **Cost of equipment.** To reach a given level, vert shaft requires less hoisting rope, piping, wiring and timber, than an incline. Cost of surface plant is related to type of shaft in a very general way only; it should be determined for each alternative.

(*c*) **Cost of operation.** Hoisting in vert shafts is usually cheaper than in inclined shafts, because hoisting distance from a given level is less; hoisting ropes last longer; there are no rollers to wear out and replace; rails, and skip wheels, axles and boxes are troublesome; expense of axle lubrication is avoided. As against this, aver length of tram to vertical shaft is greater; extra cost of tramming may more than compensate extra distance to be hoisted in the inclined shaft. Comparisons of operating cost can be made in a manner similar to those of first cost as outlined above.

(*d*) **Relative capacity.** Danger of derailing the skip limits rope speed in inclined shafts to max of 3 000–3 500 ft per min, which is possible only with straight shafts, good rolling stock and well built track. Rope speed in well constructed vertical shafts has reached 6 000 ft per min; hence, they have a larger potential capacity for a given cross-sec. Large skips can be used in inclined shafts without material increase in cross-sec of shaft, and large outputs obtained in spite of lower hoisting speed. Since the track supports a portion of the load, the power for hoisting a given output may not be greater than in a vertical shaft handling same output in smaller loads at higher speed.

(*e*) **Maintenance.** Hanging-wall shaft CD (Fig 102) requires pillars of ore for support between points F and K. In weak ground or over thick orebodies, even if pillars are left, cost of its maintenance may eliminate it from consideration and limit choice to shafts AE or AB, which are unaffected by mining operations. Usually vertical shafts cost less for maintenance than inclines; in the latter, also, it is more difficult to set timber and keep it in alinement. Soft or running ground prohibits the use of inclined shafts.

(*f*) **Depth** modifies the relative importance of the foregoing factors (Art 16). Deep vertical shafts, sunk in the early history of a mine, have same disadvantages as long crosscut tunnels.

(*g*) **Time.** Extra crosscutting required by a vertical shaft may increase the time to reach an orebody at a given level. This is important in planning development in small orebodies to keep ahead of mining; also in deep-level projects (Art 16).

16. FACTORS INFLUENCING METHODS OF DEVELOPMENT

This article deals with the conditions commonly affecting both mode of entry and lateral development. It should be noted that development methods are a compromise between many conflicting factors; local conditions often predominate in final choice.

Topography. It is only in mountainous regions that a tunnel entry secures sufficient backs of ore to warrant its cost. Few important producers have been able thus far to avoid hoisting entirely. Fig 110 illustrates the futility of positive statements. While orebodies dipping less than 15° are best entered by a vert shaft, with topography as indicated by dotted line, an incline might well be justified (Art 18).

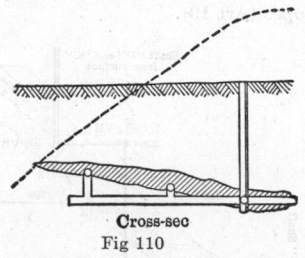

Cross-sec
Fig 110

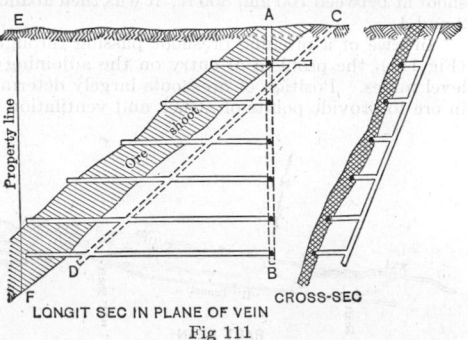

LONGIT SEC IN PLANE OF VEIN
Fig 111

Local geology has a marked influence in determining the position of development openings where their exploratory function predominates (Art 3). Also, location of openings and mode of entry should be planned to avoid danger and expense of passing through faulted zones, water-bearing strata, or bodies of quicksand, which would increase maintenance cost. Many large mines maintain a geological staff; by cooperating with the mining department they can direct exploratory drilling, reduce total footage of develop-

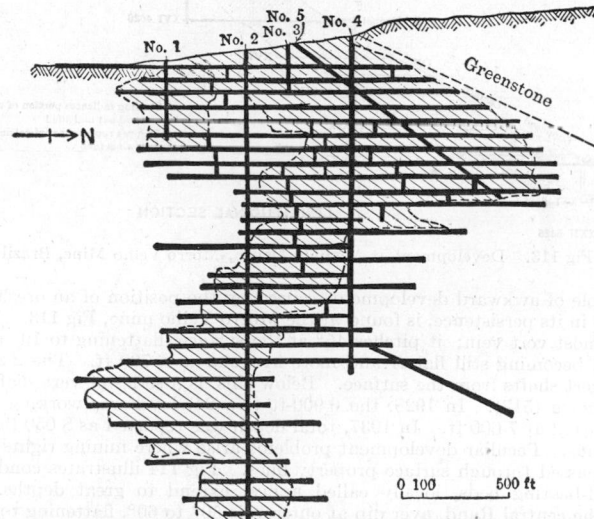

Fig 112. Central Copper Mine (Longit Sec in Plane of Vein)

ment work required, and place the openings where they will have highest exploratory value and avoid bad ground.

Location of oreshoots. Fig 111 shows a single large oreshoot having a flat pitch in plane of vein. With shaft in position AB, length of drifts through barren ground increases rapidly with depth. Inclined shaft CD, if sunk in or under the orebody at an angle to the dip, will reduce amount of dead work; but, results of this plan are often disappointing, because of the usual irregularities of oreshoots. From other standpoints, a choice of the two methods is similar to that between vert and inclined shafts (Art 15).

Fig 112 is an example of such work. The oreshoot lay in a narrow vert fissure, pitching N across a series of conglomerate and amygdaloid beds, and passing into greenstone to the north. During first 6 years after discovery, 4 vert shafts were successively sunk to the 120-ft level. Inclined shaft No 5 was sunk in the vein to shorten lateral haulage to shaft No 4, and to avoid sinking another vert shaft through greenstone where fissure was barren and maintenance cost high; it also reduced surface tramming distance. The incline, which was begun when shafts 2 and 4 were about 500 ft deep, bottomed the shoot at between 700 and 800 ft; it was then abandoned and the shoot followed with shafts 2 and 4.

In case of a pitching oreshoot passing through the end line of a property, as at *EF* (Fig 111), the problem of entry on the adjoining ground is like that presented by deep-level mines. Position of oreshoots largely determines position of raises, as they are kept in ore to provide points of attack and ventilation for stopes (Art 19).

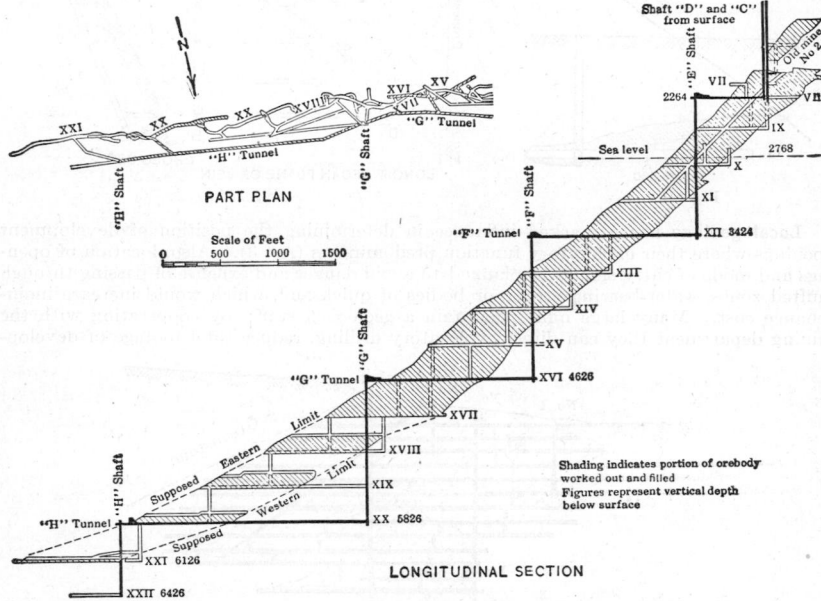

Fig 113. Development at Medium Depth, Morro Velho Mine, Brazil

An example of awkward development, caused by the position of an oreshoot and lack of confidence in its persistence, is found at the Morro Velho mine, Fig 113. The oreshoot lies in an almost vert vein; it pitches 45° at the surface, flattening to 19° at a depth of 6 100 ft, and becoming still flatter and more irregular at 6 700 ft. The 2 264-ft level is reached by vert shafts from the surface. Below this, is a series of vert shafts sunk from tunnels as shown (517). In 1928, the 6 900-ft (No 24) level was working and development had started at 7 000 ft. In 1937, total depth was reported as 8 050 ft.

Deep mines. Peculiar development problems arise where mining rights terminate at vert planes passed through surface property lines. Fig 114 illustrates conditions on the Rand. Gold-bearing beds, locally called REEFS, extend to great depths. Dips vary greatly; in the central Rand, aver dip at outcrop is 50° to 60°, flattening to about 30° in depth. Properties worked from the outcrop are called OUTCROP MINES; those covering adjacent extensions on the dip are known as first row, second row, etc, of DEEP-LEVEL MINES. There are 3 modes of opening a deep-level property underlain by an inclined deposit: (*a*) A vert shaft is sunk to the reef near the rise boundary, and continued as an incline in the footwall, the 2 parts of the shaft being joined by a carefully designed curve; called TURNED-VERTICAL or compound shaft (*XYZ*, Fig 114). (*b*) A CENTRAL VERTICAL SHAFT *AB* is sunk, and the reef reached by crosscuts. (*c*) An arrangement similar to (*a*) except that the vert and inclined parts of shaft are not directly connected. Inclined shaft, operated by an independent underground hoist, delivers ore to pockets which feed skips in the vert shaft. This is STAGE HOISTING (Sec 12). Fig 115 shows arrangement at Crown Mines, Ltd, Witwatersrand (71).

On the Rand the turned-vert shaft has been common for first and second rows of deep-level mines, largely because it brings the mine to the producing stage quicker than a central vert shaft, thus saving interest charges on the large capital necessary to open and equip a deep-level property. Other advantages as compared with central vert shaft, are: saving in crosscuts and raises, and ultimate utility of shaft to any depth. Disadvantages: cost of extra length of inclined section; slower hoisting, due to necessity for slowing down at curve; greater wear and tear on incline and on ropes, especially around the turn. From standpoint of first cost, choice is based on comparison of inclined shaft *YZ* (Fig 114) and vert shaft *CB*; result is governed by dip (Art 15); the flat dips of the Rand obviously favor inclined shafts (20). Some engineers favor the central vert shaft for all cases (for further detail and different points of

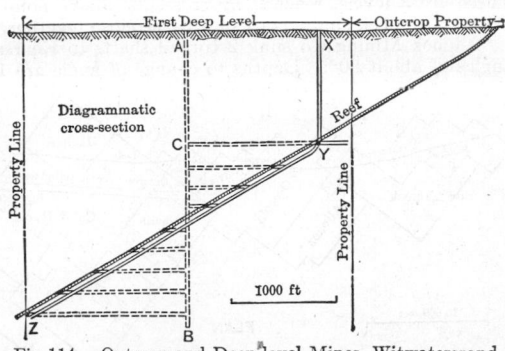

Fig 114.   Outcrop and Deep-level Mines, Witwatersrand

view, see Bib 30, 70, 72, 73). In 1937, several new vert shafts were in progress, expecting to cut the reef at 6 000 ft or more. In 1934, Robinson Deep was stoping at 7 500 ft and developing at 8 500 ft, vert depth, the deepest mine in the world. At 7 large Rand mines, aver depth advanced per year, 1917 to 1935, was 160 ft (195).

Factors of reduced speed and increased wear on hoisting rope, etc, become serious as depth increases, and, combined with mechanical difficulties in deep hoisting, have led Rand engineers to favor stage hoisting for depths over 3 000 ft. If proper storage or rapid transfer is provided at transfer point, stage hoisting greatly increases the capacity of a shaft, since both parts of it can be hoisting simultaneously. Comparative costs of hoisting reported for turned-vert and stage hoisting are in favor of the former; this is to be expected unless depth is great and excess capac of the stage system fully utilized. A turned-vert shaft can be converted to stage hoisting, as in case shown by Fig 115. For stage hoisting designed for 7 000 ft depth, see Bib (516). See also Sec 12.

Michigan copper region. Fig 116 shows approx property lines of a group of mines covering outcrops of Calumet conglomerate and Osceola and Kearsarge amygdaloid beds. Dip of beds, 37° to 38°.

Tamarack Co worked the underlay of the Calumet conglomerate through 5 vert shafts, ranging in depth from 3 409 to 5 308 ft. No 5, the deepest, cut the vein at 4 062 ft; bottom of shaft was over 1 600 ft horizontally from the vein. From the bottom crosscut of

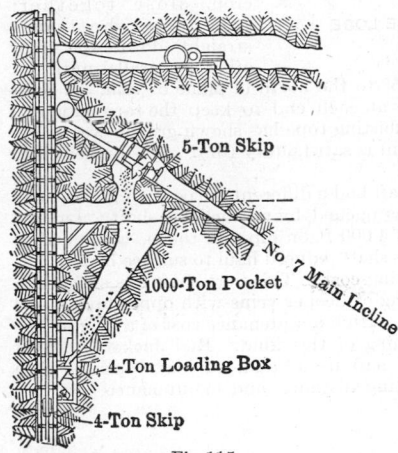

Fig 115

No 3 shaft (depth 5 253 ft) an incline in the vein was operated by a compressed-air hoist. This was to save deepening the shaft and driving long crosscuts, which had high maintenance cost. Calumet & Hecla Co worked this conglomerate bed for length of 2 miles through 10 inclined shafts in the vein, deepest being 9 300 ft on dip (1937). There is also a vertical shaft, the Red Jacket, 4 920 ft deep, cutting lode at 3 287 ft, which handled copper rock from all northern shafts below 56th level; it had crosscuts to lode on every third level from 36th to 81st. Tract lying between Tamarack Jr and Tamarack (Fig 116), about 1 300 ft wide and 6 600 ft long was opened by an inclined shaft, 25 ft in footwall and sunk from 57th level. This shaft dips only 22°, due to position of property lines which forced the shaft to take a direction at an angle to dip of vein. Mine cars were hoisted in this shaft and transported mechanically 1 500 ft on 57th level to Red Jacket shaft. This plan saved a very deep and costly vert shaft.

Lower half of Fig 116 is a projection of property lines on plane of Kearsarge lode, which outcrops as shown and dips 34° to 42°. Ahmeek Co opened its property with 4 shafts, 2 of which were sunk in the lode from outcrop. To develop northern part of property, where outcrop is owned by Mohawk Co, 2 shafts were sunk, starting on angle of 80°; at 980 ft, they curve on a 400-ft radius and enter the Kearsarge lode at 1 275 ft, on angle of 34°. There are 3 levels, reached by crosscuts, above point of intersection of shaft and lode. These 2 Ahmeek shafts start on surface close together, but diverge to N and W.

Allouez Mining Co sunk 2 turned shafts to Kearsarge lode, starting from surface at angles of about 80°. Depths to change of angle are 1 435 ft and 2 307 ft; total depths 3 544 and 3 407 ft (1915).

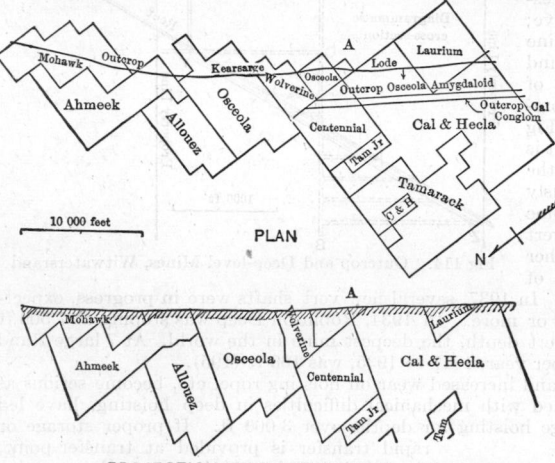

10 000 feet

PLAN

N

PROJECTION ON PLANE OF KEARSARGE LODE

Fig 116

Tamarack, Ahmeek, and Allouez mines are controlled by Calumet & Hecla Co. The turned shafts were sunk in the light of experience gained from the deep Tamarack and Red Jacket vert shafts and their long crosscuts.

Centennial mine has a small tract *A* (Fig 116), covering outcrop of Kearsarge lode, and a right of way 100 ft wide connecting it with the large underlay property shown. Due to these conditions a novel mode of entry was adopted. Two inclined shafts were started in the outcrop, close together; southerly shaft runs straight down the dip; other is parallel until the underlay property is reached, where it curves 15° to the north in plane of vein. A compound curve, 300 ft long, has a slight reverse at each end to keep the rope on idlers, and skip slows down in passing the turn. The hoisting rope has shown greater wear than on the straight incline; otherwise the arrangement is satisfactory (67). For further data, see Bib (486, 487, 488, 489).

North Star mine, Cal. Here a turned-vert shaft had a different purpose. A gold-quartz vein dipping irregularly, but at aver of 26°, was opened by an inclined shaft. Later a 1 592-ft vert shaft was sunk to intersect vein at 4 000 ft on dip and thence continued as an incline to 6 300 ft, or 2 412 ft vertically. This shaft reduced haul to surface by 2 370 ft, and its first cost was justified by saving in hoisting cost. This vert shaft has since been deepened to just below 3 495-ft level for working of deeper veins with opposite dip, and turned-vert hoisting is no longer employed (481). High maintenance cost of a long incline through old workings may also justify an opening of this kind. Red Jacket shaft, of Calumet & Hecla Co, is an example of a vert shaft used as an auxiliary opening with similar purpose. It saved about 2 100 ft hoisting distance, and maintenance cost of a 5 400-ft inclined shaft.

Reopening an abandoned mine on an inclined deposit, the upper parts of which are worked out, presents a similar problem. Choice is between vert, turned-vert, and inclined shaft, and is guided primarily by depth to virgin ground and dip of deposit. Mt Lyon mine, N Y, is an example showing the numerous factors to be considered. Orebody is a mineralized zone 100 to 200 ft thick, containing a concentration of magnetite at or near upper border; workable width 24 to 40 ft; aver dip, 60° to 65°; country rock, very hard gneiss. Mine was worked out to depth of 700 to 900 ft vert. In 1914, it was decided to reopen with an inclined footwall shaft (dip 63°), 25 to 50 ft below deposit. Proposed depth of shaft, 1 200 ft; to be extended ultimately to 1 800 or 2 400 ft. Reasons for choice were: high cost of crosscuts and ore pockets for a vert shaft, because of the very tough rock; cheaper and faster sinking in the lean mineralized footwall zone; freedom of footwall location from subsidence due to mining operations; a vert shaft to develop territory below the old mine would be 100 ft lower than, and 1 000 ft distant from, present concentrating mill, while inclined shaft would deliver ore direct to mill (74).

Handling ore underground. To secure economical handling, haulage drifts and cross-cuts should be straight or change direction by easy curves, and should be driven on regular grade. Importance of these points varies with size and output of mine and method of haulage. Following are extreme cases:

(*a*) In mining narrow veins, as those in Gilpin Co, Colo, the tonnage per shift from any level is small; tramming is done by hand, and drifts properly follow the ore with little regard to straightness. (*b*) At Crown Mines, Ltd, Rand, a main haulage level, 14.5 ft wide and extending full length of property (about 3 miles), connects 2 shafts at a vert depth of 2 200 ft. This drift is straight and lies in footwall. It was designed for elec haulage to handle 9 000–10 000 tons per day. Other main haulageways are to be driven as required at vert intervals of 600 ft. There are also the regular drifts in the reef.

Haulage problems, especially in flat orebodies, influence location of openings. If the shaft or other opening enters orebody at its lowest point, all grades in the haulageways will be in favor of loaded cars. A location favorable for lateral haulage is also favorable for drainage, and *vice versa.* Methods of handling in stopes, dip of orebody, and plans of development are also interrelated (Art 19).

Drainage. In some cases, development work can be planned to reduce pumping costs (see Tunnel entry, Art 14, 15). Drainage also makes it desirable to locate shaft or other openings to tap the lowest point of flat-dipping or basin-shaped orebodies; lateral workings then drain toward shaft and auxiliary sumps and pumps are unnecessary. One function of lateral development is to drain overlying ore. In soft, wet orebodies, like some Michigan iron deposits, this influences amount of development done in advance of mining. New levels are opened in time to let the ore drain before extraction begins. This also tends to regulate flow of water and make pumping operations fairly uniform (76).

Ventilation may require that all development openings be run in duplicate. This is done in collieries, and allows complete control of ventilating currents (Sec 14). In metal mines using little timber, or in very wet mines, proper ventilation may mean a mere supply of fresh air to remove foul air and powder fumes. Then ventilation is often obtained by arranging openings to cause natural draft. In relatively dry mines using much timber, the danger of mine fires demands close control of air currents; usually secured by fan installation, systematic layout of openings, and proper placing of doors. Development headings are often ventilated by auxiliary fans, with metal or canvas tubing carried to the working face (Sec 14).

17. NUMBER OF OPENINGS

Determining factors. VENTILATION AND SAFETY demand at least 2 openings to surface; they are required by law in many districts. In metal mines, stopes reaching the outcrop often afford an adequate second opening; in collieries, rigid ventilation requirements compel at least 2 openings. Other conditions to be considered: (*a*) Required OUTPUT may be in excess of capacity of a single shaft; this is unusual at ordinary depths, as a shaft can be designed to handle large tonnages. In deep shafts, the time required to get men on and off shift through a single shaft is serious; this, together with time for handling timber and supplies, greatly reduces ore-handling capacity. (*b*) SEPARATE OREBODIES may require separate shafts; depending on their size, distance apart, depth below surface, and surface conditions. Separate shafts are sunk to effect a saving over cost of entry from, and handling through, another shaft farther away. This is a matter of estimate in each case; size of orebody concerned must be sufficient to return excess cost of separate shaft out of the saving effected. Cost of shaft sinking increases with depth, that of drifts and crosscuts does not; hence, increasing depth should reduce the number of shafts and increase the area served by each. Topographic or other conditions affecting surface transport may prohibit separate openings; conversely, they may show a saving in surface over underground transport which alone will justify a separate shaft. Above statements apply also to veins in which several oreshoots occur, separated by wide barren or low-grade areas. At a large group of lead mines in S E Mo, formerly producing through 21 shafts, workings have been connected underground and entire output is now hoisted in 1 shaft near mill (155). H. C. Hoover points out that if cost per ft of shaft sinking is 4 times that of drifting, 4 levels through 1 000 ft of barren vein cost no more than 1 shaft 1 000 ft deep (20). (*c*) METHOD OF UNDERGROUND HAULAGE. Fig 117 is a diagrammatic section in plane of an inclined vein in a property of considerable length. If ore occurs scattered throughout whole vein, question arises whether it is better to sink 1 central shaft *A*, or 2 shafts *B* and *C*, placed at quarter points, or several shafts. This is

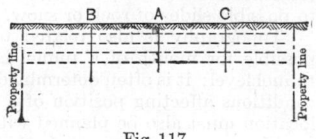

Fig 117

determined largely by method of haulage on levels. Cost of hand tramming per ton increases rapidly with distance; there is a limiting length of tram beyond which a new shaft will save its cost; economic limits for animal and mechanical haulage are higher. Tonnage produced per shift on 1 level affects method of haulage (Sec 11). Where small, it may be possible to install mechanical haulage on every second or third level, ore from levels above being transferred to the haulage level through winzes at distances apart which are within the economic limit of hand tramming.

Michigan copper mines are illustrations of properties covering long distances along the strike of persistent lodes (Fig 116). Hand tramming was formerly universal, and a shaft was sunk about every 1 000 ft along strike. There are instances of 2 shafts 600 ft apart reaching depths of over 3 000 ft. Later shafts were farther apart; aver distance for the district in 1912, 1 600 ft. At Quincy mine, with elec haulage, aver tram is 1 800 ft.

Outcrop mines on the Rand. Where length of property along strike was less than 1 500 or 2 000 ft, only 1 main working shaft was sunk; on longer properties 2 shafts were deemed necessary to facilitate development and for ventilation (25). Transvaal law requires 2 exits. Shafts in first row of deep-level properties are as close as 1 000 ft, but usually 2 000 ft apart. Nearly all tramming is by hand, but labor is cheap. Many deep-level properties have been consolidated and cover large areas (400 to 900 claims of 1.4 acres each); where possible, in such cases, distance between shafts is 3 000 to 4 000 ft (78). Occasionally, where connection could be made with adjoining property, large areas were opened by 1 deep shaft. Mechanical haulage concentrated on a few levels has been introduced as area controlled by one shaft is increased (Art 16). Brakpan mine, East Rand, illustrates the application of the same principles to a flat orebody of large area; property is 6 000 by 14 000 ft; reef dips only 7°. Two shafts were sunk 4 400 ft apart in direction of dip; No 1 cuts reef at 3 098 ft; No 2, at 3 707 ft. They are connected at bottom by an incline 4 500 ft long on dip of reef, from which levels are opened (79).

From standpoint of UNDERGROUND HAULAGE, ideal location for a single shaft is one giving minimum aver tramming distance. It is obviously impossible to determine exactly such location in advance. In massive orebodies like porphyry coppers, the tonnage and shape of which are determined by boring in advance of development, gathering points on each haulage level can be found to which ore can be brought with minimum aver tram, taking into account the required lateral development; the nearest feasible location of shaft to these points gives shortest aver tram.

18. LOCATION OF OPENINGS

Underground conditions affecting location of openings with respect to dip and strike of deposit, and from standpoints of geology, maintenance, haulage, drainage, and ventilation, are discussed in Art 15–17, 19. Shafts for massive deposits, especially those mined by caving methods (Art 70–88), should be located beyond the possible limit of ground movement around the orebody.

Surface conditions. TOPOGRAPHY affects location of openings. Sites for necessary buildings must be available; shaft and tunnel locations are often planned with reference to a mill; permanent mine openings should avoid gulches or places where flooding would result from cloud-bursts; in mountain regions, the location must be planned with reference to possible slides of rock or snow.

Topography is also related to questions of SURFACE TRANSPORT. Lowest location possible for mouth of a tunnel is desirable, as it gives the highest backs of ore above tunnel level; it is often determined by position of a R R for shipping ore, or by topographic conditions affecting position of a spur track to be built from an existing road. A shaft location must also be planned with reference to existing or proposed R Rs, wagon roads, or other means of transport; this concerns handling supplies to the mine as well as ore from it. PROPERTY LINES and their relation to outcrops may affect location of entry (Art 16, Deep mines). In combination with topography, they may limit dump room below a proposed opening and modify its location.

In general, ore and waste should be delivered from a mine opening at a point high enough above the surface to allow gravity transfer to surface transport. Such elevation may be obtained artificially, or position of entry planned to secure it in connection with topography. Ideal location is not possible; a compromise is always necessary.

19. LATERAL DEVELOPMENT

Interval between levels in inclined orebodies varies from 50 to 300 ft; commonest interval, largely the result of custom, is 100–150 ft, but practice tends towards greater distances where feasible.

Factors limiting distance between levels: COST. Drifting is NARROW WORK, costing more per cu ft than stoping; each drift requires timbering, track, pipe, and ditches, which must be maintained during life of stopes above. Cost of shaft stations, and plats or bins, can be reduced by concentrating haulage on alternate or third levels. Possibility of using electric-driven primary breakers underground, together with improvements in mechanical haulage, has increased tendency to concentrate haulage on one or a few levels, especially where large blocks can be broken and handled from stopes. From standpoint of first cost, a long interval between levels is desirable. TYPE OF OREBODY. Highgrade, spotted or pockety mines require levels to be close together to avoid missing orebodies; a wide interval in such cases also adds to cost of reaching and extracting scattered pockets. SUPPORT OF HANGING WALL. Levels sometimes form one side of pillars left to support roof; allowable area of unsupported hanging wall then limits level interval, unless some form of filled stoping is practicable. SPEED OF STOPING and character of ground are related factors; level interval should be such that stopes are completed and abandoned within the time that they can be kept open without undue maintenance cost. Thus, at Leonard mine, Butte, Mont, a 200-ft interval in vert, filled, square-set stopes increased cost and decreased speed of mining in the upper 100-ft lift to an extent which warranted driving intermediate levels at 100-ft intervals (80). METHOD OF MINING. A retreating system, where stopes are started at property lines and abandoned as they are carried back toward entry, may allow a larger level interval than an advancing system. Cost of maintenance of levels themselves generally increases with the time they are kept open. This is again related to speed of stoping and method of mining, and may determine the max interval. In small-scale work, on a short, high-grade oreshoot, the time required to stope one lift determines time available for sinking and drifting through the shoot on next level, and consequently determines level interval; such conditions arise in leasing. DIP OF OREBODY, if over 40° to 45°, allows broken ore to fall by gravity to level below; if less than 10°, cars can generally be run to working faces. In these two cases, the dip does not limit max level interval. On intermediate dips, if ore is shoveled to drift, the level interval should be small; for economic limits of distance with other handling devices in flat stopes, see Art 91 and Sec 27. REGULARITY OF DEPOSIT influences handling methods and therefore the level interval; an irregular footwall increases the limiting angle on which ore slides and always requires some shoveling. Badly faulted deposits require levels placed to reach displaced blocks regardless of other factors; such conditions at Golden Messenger mine, York, Mont, were overcome by numerous, short sub-levels connected by raises to main levels 250 ft apart, on dip (69).

Economic level interval in any mine is a matter of experiment. The deeper levels are usually spaced farther apart than the upper, because early work determines the mining factors, and reduces the exploratory function of these openings. On the RAND, the level interval in some properties has been increased to a startling extent. At Modderfontein B mine, ore is developed in blocks 800 by 1 000 ft; at New Modderfontein, level interval is 500 to 600 ft, with footwall main haulage drifts 1 700 to 2 000 ft apart; at Brakpan mine, level interval varies from 300 to 1 200 ft. This practice, due to an attempt to cut down development cost, has not been uniformly successful. It is made possible in these mines by: (a) very flat dips (7° to 10°), allowing cars to run to stope faces; (b) regularity of vein; (c) knowledge of reef characteristics, resulting in confidence in the continuance of value and size over large areas (75, 79, 81, 82). At MAGMA, Ariz, a nearly vert vein was developed at 100-ft intervals to 2 000 ft; next 2 intervals were 250 and 300 ft. On failure to realize expected economies, due to difficulties with ventilation, handling timber, and maintaining chutes, subsequent intervals were 200 ft, and the larger intervals were each subdivided by an intermediate drift (77).

Raises and winzes. For following indications or exposures of ore up or down from a level, the location of raises and winzes depends entirely on ore occurrence. To determine outline and value of shoots, raises are often made at fairly regular intervals. For this purpose the interval should not exceed that over which ore may be expected to persist without material change in thickness, character, and tenor.

Closer spacing than the level interval is not justified; max distance, 100 to 500 ft or more (see Modderfontein B mine, above), depends on experience with a given orebody. In connection with method of mining, raises and winzes provide entrance to stopes; serve for handling ore, waste for filling, and supplies; stoping usually starts from them. For these purposes, their location varies greatly (see individual mining methods). In veins where ore occurrence is regular, the output required, combined with distance to which development has been carried in advance of stoping, may determine the raise interval. Each stope has a limited tonnage possibility; number of stopes that can be opened simultaneously depends on available points of attack and extent of development. Regarding WEST AUSTRALIA PRACTICE, E. D. Cleland states that, when development is considerably in advance of ore requirements, the winzes (or raises) in lowest level may be 300 to 500 ft apart, and are sunk merely as a guide to future stoping. In upper levels where stoping is in progress, or about to begin, the raise or winze interval must be 125 to 150 ft. This holds for veins having fairly regular ore occurrence; where ore is irregular, no figures can be given (83). S. J. Truscott (30) states that in deep-level RAND mines, where development is kept well ahead of stoping, winzes are 400 to 500 ft apart; throughout the district, the interval is from 200 to 500 ft. Up to the limit fixed by loss of interest on money spent in advance development, the smaller the number of winzes (that is, the greater the interval between them), the less the cost of development.

Ventilation. Connections between levels are essential where natural ventilation (Sec 14) is relied upon. Raises for stoping usually suffice for ventilation; ventilation requirements may control their location. For example, delays while waiting for smoke to clear after blasting limit speed and increase cost of drifting; with natural ventilation, delays increase with length of drift beyond a raise holed to level above. On important work, blowers are used, and make the raise interval independent of ventilation; but, with natural ventilation, there is an economic limit beyond which either increased cost or slowness of drifting makes a new raise advisable. This limit, controlled largely by local factors and policy, is 250 to 500 ft or more. Mechanical ventilation in metal mines is increasing, especially in large or deep mines. Experience proves that its expense is justified by increased effic of labor and operations (Sec 14).

20. DRIFTING AND CROSSCUTTING

Sec 6 gives data on choice of drills, mountings, and explosives; comparison of 1-, 2-, and 3-shift work; methods of charging and firing; mucking; driving through soft ground.

Mine drifts and crosscuts differ from tunnels as follows: (a) usually of smaller cross-sec; (b) less emphasis laid on precise alinement and shape of sec; (c) in breaking ground, advantage may be taken of relative softness of orebodies and adjacent rocks, of planes of weakness due to banding, slips, or well marked walls; (d) tunnels are usually more permanent than drifts and crosscuts, and hence may require more elaborate timbering; (e) some tunnels bear entire cost of installing and operating the plant for drilling, ventilation and transport; for drifts and crosscuts, such overhead is usually distributed over many openings.

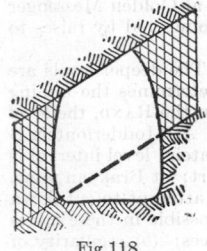

Fig 118

Shape of cross-section of CROSSCUTS is same as that of tunnels (Sec 6). UNTIMBERED DRIFTS and crosscuts should have an arched back, which tends toward self-support and reduces subsequent spalling. Importance of arched shape is less in strong rock and narrow openings; in flat-dipping or bedded deposits the hanging wall often forms the back of drift and gives no trouble if not broken into (Fig 118). Shape of TIMBERED DRIFTS varies with irregularities of ore occurrence and method of mining (Fig 141–147; see also Art 30–42).

Size of cross-section for typical drift sand crosscuts is given in Table 18. It depends on following factors: (a) In EXPLORATION (Art 12), cross-sec is made small; this lessens cost, largely by reducing amount of muck to be handled. Smallest section advisable is 6 to 6.5 ft high by 3.5 to 4 ft wide. Smaller openings rarely effect a saving, because cramped space reduces efficiency of labor. (b) SIZE OF CAR determines minimum width of development drifts and crosscuts (see Sec 11, Art 3, 4, 6); small cars for hand tramming, 24 to 28 in wide and holding 1 600 to 2 000 lb, require a minimum clear width of 4 to 4.5 ft for single track, and 7.75 ft for double. For larger cars, cross-sec of opening is designed to fit. Clearance between sides of car and posts of drift sets is usually 12 in minimum; this gives 18 to 24 in between car and lagging, or room enough for a man to stand without being caught. For safety in untimbered openings, at least 24 in should be left between car and wall on one side of drift; clearance on other side may be only 4 to 6 in. Minimum clearance between cars on double-track is 6 to 8 in. Larger clearances are always desirable, especially for high speed and heavy cars. (c) METHOD OF LOADING. Shovelers need a total width of about 7 ft to work on both sides of a small car at face of a drift. Some mechanical loaders (Sec 27) will work in an opening 6 by 4.5 ft in clear; many require more room. (d) DRAINAGE DITCHES for handling large amounts of water may increase width of drift or crosscut beyond that required by car. (e) Requirements for VENTILATION (Sec 14) may determine minimum size of opening. (f) In veins to 8 or 10 ft wide, drifts in oreshoots are often carried full width of vein, thus reducing cost per ton of ore obtained.

(g) HEIGHT OF DRIFTS and crosscuts is a matter of headroom; 6.5 ft clear is the minimum. Height of trolley wire above rail in haulageways is fixed by statute in some states.

Drifting and crosscutting by hand drilling is done in connection with exploratory work (Art 12) in small mines, where expense for plant is not justified, and in districts where skilled labor is not available for running machine drills. Drill holes are not spaced systematically, but placed to take advantage of all irregularities in the face. Drilling is done double-hand in hard ground and single-hand in aver ground; hand auger is cheapest and best for soft ground containing few hard streaks, and in coal.

In small drifts, 7 to 12 holes, 2 to 2.5 ft deep, are necessary to advance face 1.5 to 2 ft. These figures vary widely with hardness and toughness of rock; in aver ground an advance of 0.7 to 1 ft per shift in a 1-man drift or crosscut is good work.

Examples. At BODIE, Cal, 1 miner drilling single-hand in 5 by 7-ft drifts and crosscuts, width of veins 3 to 30 in, vein rock varying from hard banded to soft granular quartz, country rock firm, fairly hard andesite, advanced 1.304 ft in drifts and 1.187 ft in crosscuts per 8-hr shift (84). At RHYOLITE, Nev, 1 miner drilling single-hand in drifts 4.5 by 6.5 or 7 ft, in fairly soft mineralized porphyry, made 0.5 to 3 ft per 8-hr shift, aver 1 ft (tracklaying, mucking, and tramming was done by other men). Following data apply to a tunnel driven by hand in ARIZ (1913): cross-sec, 5 by 7 ft; length, 374.5 ft; aver tram to dump, 875 ft; rock, fairly soft porphyry; no timber required; 3-shift contract work by Mexican labor, 1 miner and 1 helper on each shift doing drilling, blasting, mucking, and tramming. Tunnel was completed in 500 man-shifts in 91 days. Aver advance per man-shift, 0.75 ft, varying from 0.359 to 0.852 ft; aver progress per day, 4.12 ft; explosives consumption, 2.32 lb of 40% dynamite per ft of advance.

Table 15 gives data for Mexican labor (1910). Daily advance (3 shifts) was fair, but progress per man-shift low. Ventilation was poor in timbered drifts No 3 and 4. Dynamite consumption was low, due to character of rock and size of cross-sec.

Table 15. Drifting and Crosscutting, Esperanza Mine, El Oro, Mex, 1910 (85)

		Width, ft	Height, ft	Kind of ground	Distance driven, ft	Aver daily advance, ft	Lb 60% dynamite		Labor per ft		Aver advance	
							Per lin ft	Per cu ft	Miner shifts	Peon shifts	Per man-shift, lin ft	Per man-hr, cu ft
1	Crosscut..	5	7	(a)	496	2.51	1.34	0.038	3.2	0.14	0.3	1.31
2	Crosscut..	5	7	(b)	829	2.47	2.07	0.059	3.3	0.567	0.26	1.14
3	Drift.....	7	8	(c)	66	2.18	1.09	0.019				
4	Drift.....	5	7	(d)	635	2.21	3.08	0.088	3.35	0.62	0.25	1.09
5	Drift.....	5	7	(e)	793	2.22	3.35	0.096				
6	Drift.....	5	7	(b)	143	2.58	0.43	0.012				

(a) Fairly hard andesite. (b) Friable quartz. (c) Soft swelling andesite. (d) Moderately hard shale. (e) Hard, tight andesite.

A. L. Oke gives following data on hand work by native labor at mines in Mexico and Argentine (86): MEXICAN MINE; double-hand drilling; 7/8 and 3/4-in steel; long handled, 8-lb hammers; Mexican dynamite, 40% and 60%, depending on ground; dry, hot, poorly ventilated mine; aver ground tough, rather than hard; fairly clean hanging wall to break to; 8-hr shifts. Aver progress per man-shift in softer drifts, 0.76 to 0.91 ft; in hard ground, 0.31 ft. Max advance in drifting in a week of 11 shifts, 3 men on day and 2 men on night shift, 32 ft. Men drilled about 9 ft of holes per shift in soft ground; 3 to 3.5 ft in hard ground. ARGENTINE MINE; single-hand drilling; 7/8-in steel; short-handle hammers, 6 to 8 lb; English gelignite and gelatin; dry, cool mine, poor ventilation, rock andesite and granite; shifts 8–10 hr. Aver progress per man-shift in drifts and crosscuts in soft ground, 0.91–1.22 ft; in hard ground, 0.37 to 0.55 ft. Usual advance in drifts, 2 shifts, 1 man on each, excluding Sundays, was 50–60 ft per month in softer ground; 20–30 ft in hard ground. Men drilled about 10 ft of hole per shift in soft ground; 5–6.75 in hard ground.

G. L. Schmutz in 1920 (523) compares powder consumption at a Mexican mine, in hand and machine drilled drifts, as follows (figures in lb per ft advance). Hand: min 3.0, aver 4.5, max 7.0. Machine: min 5.0, aver 8.0, max 14.0. By more careful control of powder, aver was cut to 3.61 and 7.39 respectively.

Table 16 shows how hand work economizes powder by skilful but unsystematic placing of holes, an advantage offset, however, by slower speed per man-shift (492). Machine drilling was by light, mounted drifters; hand drilling all 1-man work, in slightly softer ground. Machine drifts, 4.5 by 6.5 ft, 10% timbered; machine raises, 5 by 5, or 5 by 10 ft. Hand drifts, 4 by 6 ft; raises, 5 by 5 ft. Two expert hand-drillers on opposite shifts in a drift averaged 1.2 ft advance per shift each, tramming 600 ft.

R. B. Dickson records (56) hand driving of 60 ft of 3.5 by 6.5-ft drift in a fairly soft vein at high elev in San Juan district, Colo. Round of 10 15.8-in holes was drilled at 83 in per shift; aver advance, 0.682 ft per man-shift (about 20% of time being otherwise occupied); explosive (40% gelatin), 4.21 lb per ft advance.

C. L. Larson gives data (in 1914) from Chiksan mines, KOREA (87); Drifts 5 by 7 ft, in quartz veins; 3 shifts, 4 men (Koreans) per shift, double-hand drilling. From 4 to 7 ft of hole is drilled per man-shift. Two 10-hr shifts give cheaper work, but less speed. Monthly advance, from 30 ft in hard to 70 ft in good ground. Dynamite consumption (gelignite, 60%), 2 to 2.5 lb per linear ft. Cost per ft, excluding hoisting, about $3.40, of which $0.16 is for timbering. Cross-cuts, 4 by 6 ft, are untimbered; 2-shift work of 2 men each; in soft schist, dynamite consumption was about 2.2 lb per linear ft; in hard schist and granite, about 4.8 lb; cost per linear ft in soft ground, $2.67; in hard ground, $4.14. Wages: hand drillers, $0.25; muckers and trammers, $0.20 per shift.

Table 16. **Hand *vs* Machine Development, Questa, NM**

Period of 6 mo in 1930	Machine work	Hand work
Footage of drifts...............	2 602	959
" " raises...............	475	477
Cost per ft:		
Drilling, labor only............	$1.00	$3.20
Mucking and tramming........	1.75	1.60
Timbering, labor and material..	.30	.30
Explosives (40% gelatin)......	1.25	0.70
Track......................	.30	.15
Steel sharpening.............	.33	.23
Pipe, drill repair, hose, oil......	.63	....
Comp air, labor and material..	.97	....
Supervision.................	.28	.28
Total direct cost............	$6.81	$6.46
Interest and deprec on compressor and drills...............	.60	....
	$7.41	$6.46

Practice in drifting in MESABI IRON MINES, Minn, illustrates speed obtainable with HAND AUGER DRILL in soft hematite. C. E. van Barneveld (35) gives following data (in 1912). Work was on contract; two 10-hr shifts; 2 men on each shift. Men did their own timbering, track-laying, and local tramming to distances of 300 ft. Drilling was done with hand augers, 3.5, 4, 6, and 8 ft long; hard streaks were broken up by 3 and 6-ft gads, of 1.25-in drill steel. Main drifts were 9 ft wide by 8 ft, inside timbers of unframed 3-piece sets. A round consisted of 5 to 7 6-ft holes. A 6-ft hole was drilled in 10 to 30 min; back holes were loaded with 7 to 10 sticks 40% dynamite, lifters with 6 sticks. Upper holes were fired and mucked first. This reduced powder cost, but entailed delays, twice a round, for smoke to clear; where ventilation was poor, entire round was fired at once. Aver monthly progress, 100 to 125 ft. Rate of advance in smaller drifts was from 200 to 225 ft per month on a 4-man contract. Progress in hand-driven rock drifts, 25 to 40 ft per month.

Machine drills. In this and other articles, terms are used as follows: DRIFTERS, hammer drills attached to cradle, mounted on bar or column, usually run wet; rotation, automatic; feed, either automatic or by hand. PISTON-DRILLS are now virtually obsolete. JACKHAMMERS, light, hand-held hammer-drills, but often mounted for drifts or crosscuts in soft to medium ground. STOPERS are of hammer type, with an air-operated feed leg; some types automatically rotated; others, hand-rotated; usually unmounted; occasionally mounted by attaching air-feed cylinder to column or bar (Sec 15).

Machine-drill rounds. The term ROUND means location, direction, depth, and number of holes for breaking a given face of ore or rock. Rounds for development openings are classified according to type of "cut." Term CUT refers to location and direction of holes blasted first to provide a free face (Art 26) to which other holes may break. Drift and crosscut rounds are DRAW-CUT, INVERTED OR TOP DRAW-CUT, VERT V-CUT, HORIZ V-CUT, PYRAMID-CUT, and BURNED CUT, with various combinations and variations.

Data in Table 18, generously contributed by managements and engineering depts of mines listed, show the effect of character of ground and size of cross-sec on number and arrangement of holes, type of drill, powder consumption, and duty of labor. They cover present practice (1938) in important districts of U S, Canada, and Cuba, and include examples in Mexico. Of the 79 examples, 13 are draw-cut rounds, 2 inverted draw-cuts, 11 vert V-cuts, 7 horiz V-cuts, 20 pyramid cuts, 11 burned cuts, 5 of which combine a burned cut with a very acute pyramid, 1 uses no cut, 1 has no system, and 1 uses both draw and burned cuts. Hardness of rock does not seem a controlling factor in choice of cut, since all types are found in hard, medium, and soft rocks. Theoretically, the angle of wedge or pyramid should increase in proportion to toughness of rock; but it has been found that a burned cut is better adapted than any form of angled cut to certain tough rocks. No definite rules can be laid down as to type of round, number of holes and depth of round; choice is determined by experience (also see Table 17).

Fig 120–137 show some rounds to which Table 18 refers. Numbers at holes indicate firing sequence.

Pointing holes is of prime importance. Successful breaking requires locating charges at most efficient points in face. Much experimental work has been done at individual mines to determine best practice under varying conditions (89, 519, 520, 531, 536). Table 17 gives data for spacing and pointing holes.

Note.—Use of table. Ex 1. Round 7 ft deep, distance between collars of 2 cut holes 48 in; in table on 7-ft line find 24 in (0.5 spacing) in 16° column, indicating that 2 holes will intersect if drilled toward each other at this angle; table also shows that holes will each be 7 ft 3 in deep at point of intersection.   **Ex 2.**   It is desired to bottom a 6-ft lifter 4 in below bottom of drift, collar of hole being 6 in above bottom: opposite 6 ft in table find 10 inches under 8°, which is the required angle for lifter.

Table 17.   Displacement and Length of Drill Holes.   After C. H. Waters (519)

Depth of round, ft.	Angle between axis of hole and normal to face														
	2°	4°	6°	8°	10°	12°	14°	16°	18°	20°	22°	24°	26°	28°	30°
	Inches between collar of hole and projection of its bottom on the face (a)														
3	1	2	4	5	6	8 **1**	9 **1**	10 **1**	12 **2**	13 **2**	14 **3**	16 **4**	18 **4**	19 **5**	21 **6**
4	2	3	5	7	9	10 **1**	12 **1**	14 **2**	16 **2**	18 **3**	20 **4**	22 **5**	24 **6**	25 **6**	28 **8**
5	2	4	6	9	11 **1**	13 **1**	15 **2**	17 **2**	20 **3**	22 **4**	24 **5**	27 **6**	29 **7**	32 **8**	35 **10**
6	3	5	8	10	13 **1**	15 **2**	18 **2**	21 **3**	23 **3**	26 **5**	29 **6**	32 **7**	35 **8**	38 **10**	42 **11**
7	3	6	9	12	15 **1**	18 **2**	21 **2**	24 **3**	27 **4**	31 **5**	34 **7**	37 **8**	41 **10**	45 **11**	48 **13**
8	4	7	10	13	17 **1**	21 **2**	24 **3**	27 **4**	31 **5**	35 **6**	39 **8**	43 **9**	47 **11**	51 **13**	55 **15**
9	4	8	11	15	19 **2**	23 **2**	27 **3**	31 **4**	35 **5**	39 **7**	44 **9**	48 **10**	53 **12**	57 **14**	62 **17**
10	4	9	12	17 **1**	21 **2**	25 **2**	30 **4**	34 **5**	39 **6**	44 **8**	48 **9**	54 **11**	59 **14**	64 **16**	69 **19**
11	5	10	14	19 **1**	24 **2**	28 **3**	33 **5**	38 **6**	43 **7**	48 **8**	53 **10**	59 **12**	64 **15**	70 **17**	76 **20**
12	5	11	15	20 **1**	26 **2**	31 **4**	36 **5**	41 **6**	47 **7**	52 **9**	58 **11**	64 **14**	71 **16**	77 **19**	82 **23**

(a) Numbers in bold-face type indicate distance in inches which, when added to depth of round, gives length of hole required to reach that depth.

Hole directors, as used in 7 by 8-ft drift headings by Crown Mines, Witwatersrand, have improved speed and effic, and reduced cost; during a test period of 20 mo, with 6-ft holes in headings of same size, aver advance in 403 " directed " rounds was 4 ft–11.5 in,

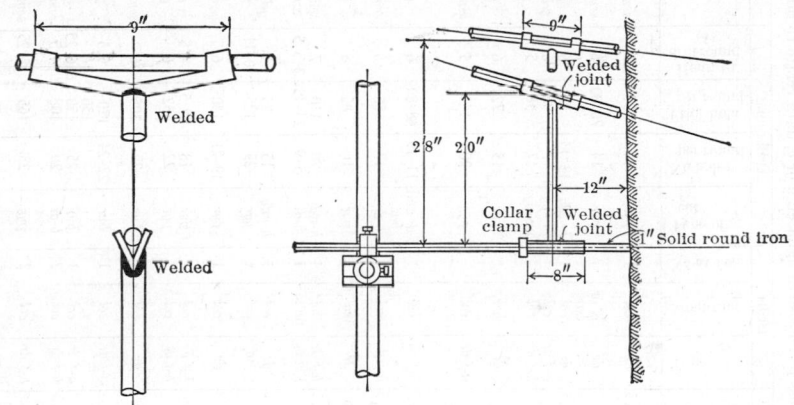

Fig 119.   Hole "Directors" for Headings

against 3.5 ft per round in undirected headings (89).   Customary pyramid-cut round of 20–24 holes requires a set of 3 directors (of which 2 are shown in Fig 119), with radial lengths of 24, 32, 44 in.   Supporting ends of the Y-s form open saddles, the axes of which are permanently fixed (by welding) at such angles with horiz axis of drift as experiment shows most effective.   The 50-lb mounted jackhammer is alined in a saddle by aid of a short piece of drill steel, or the starting bit.   After clamping the drill, the " director " is swung aside, revolving on the 1-in axial bar previously secured by arm and clamps on the vert column and a shallow hole at center of face.

Drill mountings.   Table 18 contains 57 examples of drifts or crosscuts drilled from a vert column, as against 7 cross-bars, 2 tripods, 5 drill carriages, and 8 unmounted drills. With a COLUMN, work is almost always arranged so that drillers have a clean face for starting.   The examples of CROSS-BARS, except one, are where speed is sought through simultaneous drilling and mechanical loading.   Uppers are drilled from a bar set above muck pile, while the loader cleans bottom of face.   On completing mucking, bar is re-set for the lower holes.   By this procedure, Lloyd mine, Ishpeming, Mich, advances a 10 by 10-ft drift with a pyramid cut through cherty slate at 375 ft per month, working 3 shifts 5 days per week.   CARRIAGES, mounting 4–6 drifters (generally automatically fed) and

Table 18. Data on Drifting and Crosscutting Practice, as of 1938

(Unless otherwise designated *d* or *c*, data relate to both drifts and crosscuts)

Example No	Mine and location	Type of ground	Section Height, ft	Section Width, ft	Drills Type	Drills Mounting	No at face	Type of cut	No holes per round	Ft of hole per round	Hours to drill round (a)	Explosive Type	% Ngl	Lb per ft advance	Mucking	Timbering	Advance per round, ft	Advance per month, ft	Man-shift Drill and blast	Man-shift Mucking	Man-shift Timbering	Man-shift Total
	AREA 35 SQ FT OR LESS																					
1	Hiawatha No 2, Stambaugh, Mich. (c)	h hematite	6.5	3.5	dr	col	1	pyr	14	56	7	semi-gel	60 (b)	10	scraper	none	3.5	var	0.23	0.29		0.52
2	Climax, Climax, Colo	h to m-h frac granite	6.5	5	dr	col or bar	1	pyr	14	70-80	8	semi-gel	45 (b)	10	hand and m-shov	oc'l set	4-5	var	0.2	0.4	var	0.6+
3	Humboldt, Mill City, Nev	h hornfels	7	4.5	h-f dr	col	1	h-wdg	13-15	88	6	gel	35	10.5	hand	none	4.5	122	0.222	0.388		0.610
4	Flin Flon, Flin Flon, Man.	s sch and diss ore	7	5	h-f dr	col	1	bur-pyr	17	98	6	gel dyn	60	16.6	hand	none	4.24	var	0.50	0.25		0.75
5	Flin Flon, Flin Flon, Man.	s sch and diss ore	7	5	h-f dr	col	1	bur-pyr	17	98	5	gel	40 and 60	11.86	hand	none	5.02	var	0.432	0.216		0.648
6	Bluff, Britannia Beach, B C (c)	h silic ore	7	5	dr	bar	1	pyr	15	72	6	gel	40	18.7	hand and m-shov	none	3.9	300	0.258	0.516		0.774
7	Matahambre, Prov Pinar del Rio, Cuba (d)	h silic breccia	7	5	a-f dr	col	1	pyr	20	140	5.5	semi-gel	45 and 60 (b)	8.42	m-shov	none	6.08	146	0.328	0.328		0.656
	AREA 35-64 SQ FT	sh and quartzite																				
8	Empire Star Group, Grass Valley, Cal	diab and diorite	7	5.5	h-f dr	col	1	b-dr and b dr	11-19	48-80	6	gel	40 (d) 60 (c)	11-13	hand	oc'l sets or stulls	3.75	90	0.32	0.48		0.80
9	Idaho Maryland, Grass Valley, Cal	tough por	7	5.5	a-f dr	col	1	bur, b dr	17	80	6	semi-gel	48 (b)	11.2	hand	none	4	100	0.25	0.25		0.50
10	Victoria, Britannia Beach, B C (c)	tough sul	7.5	5-6	dr	col	1	h-wdg, b-dr	16	85	6	gel	40 and 60	24.4	hand or m-shov	none	4	120	0.25	0.50		0.75
11	Presidio, Shafter, Tex.	h silic ls	7.5	5.5	h-f dr	col	1	h-wdg	20	110	7	semi-gel, am-gel	40	7.38	m-shov	none	5	110				0.677
12	Inspiration, Inspiration, Ariz.	m-s sch	8	5	j'ham	none	1	b-dr	5-9	25-45	3-5.5	gel dyn, gel	30	2-4	m-shov	string and sets	5	var	0.15	0.10	0.15	0.40
13	Murchie, Nevada City, Cal (d)	h diorite	7.5	5.5	dr	col	1	pyr	15	75	5	semi-gel	40	15	hand	oc'l set	3-3.5	70-80	0.33	0.67		1.0
14	Frisco, S.F. del Oro, Chih, Mex	silic sh and h sul	7	5.5	a-f dr	col	1	pyr	25	125	10-11	gel	60	14	hand	none	4	90	0.94	0.72		1.66
15	Wright-Hargreaves, Kirkland Lake, Ont	h por	7.5	6	dr	col	1	bur	19-21	140	6	semi-gel	70	9.25	hand	none	6	156	0.33	0.33		0.66
16	La Colorada, Cananea, Mex.	brec por	8	6	h-f dr	col	1	pyr	18	89.5	4.5	gel	40	9	m-shov	none	5	120	0.62			0.62
17	Homestake, Lead, S D.	h sch	7	7	h-f dr	col	2	pyr	22	132	6	gel	40	12	hand and m-shov	none	6	160	0.3	0.3		0.6
18	Franklin, Franklin, N J	ls, peg, gn	7+	7-	dr	col	1	bur	25	205	6	semi-gel	45 (b)	12	hand and m-shov, scraper	oc'l set	7.5	var	0.266	0.266		0.532
19	Junction, Bisbee, Ariz.	ls and chert	8.5	6	a-f dr	col	1	bur	22-24	120-130	5.5	gel	40	12-16	m-shov	oc'l set	5.5-6	110	0.18	0.10		0.28
20	Junction, Bisbee, Ariz.	mass ls	8.5	6	a-f dr	col	2	bur	25	150	6-6.25	gel	40	16-18	m-shov	oc'l set	5.5-6	110	0.18	0.10		0.28
21	Crescent, Kellogg, Id.	h quartzite	8	6.5	h-f dr	col		b-dr	20	108	4.5	semi-gel dyn	45 (b)	20	m-shov	none	5	235	0.4	0.2		0.6
22	Lake Shore, Kirkland Lake, Ont	h por	7.5	7	h-f dr	col	2	pyr	23	165	5.25	semi-gel	70	10.28	hand	oc'l stull	6.25	165	0.32	0.32		0.64

No.	Location	Rock																				
23	Hollinger Cons, Timmins, Ont	grnstn and por	9.0	6–7	h-f dr	col	1	pyr	21	147	6.5	gel	40 55	12.4	hand	none	hand	156	0.33	0.33	0.33		0.66
24	United Verde, Jerome, Ariz.	h sul or por	8.5	6.5	a-f dr	col	2	pyr	28–30	165	5.5	am dyn	55	17	m-shov	oc'l	m-shov	135	0.40	0.40	0.25	0.18	0.83
25	C & H Conglom, Calumet, Mich	felsitic conglom	7	8	dr	col	2	pyr	18–22	120	6	gel	60	10.75	scraper	none	scraper	100–120	0.45	0.45	0.20		0.65
26	Scott, Hockerville, Okla.	h l.s and flint	7	8	h-f dr	col	1	bur	18–23	117–150	8–9	gel dyn	30 35	18	hand	none	hand	140	0.26	0.26	0.27		0.53
27	Mullen, Shulsburg, Wis.	m-s dol	7	8	j'ham	col	2	pyr	8–18	52–117	4–6	am dyn	35	9.69	hand	none	hand	360	0.35		C.67		0.67
28	Bunker Hill, Kellogg, Id.	h to m-h quartzite	8	7	h-f dr	col	2	pyr	17	102	3–4	semi-gel	60 (b)	10–12	m-shov	none	m-shov	250	0.35	0.35	0.25		0.60
29	McIntyre, Schumacher, Ont.	h sch and quartz	7.5	7.5	h-f dr	col	2	bur-pyr	24	190	6	semi-gel	45 (b)	12	hand	none	hand	179	0.29	0.29	0.29		0.58
30	Horne, Noranda, Que.	rhyo and mass sul	8	7	dr	col	2	bur	28	181	6	gel	40	15	hand	none	hand	145	0.345	0.3	0.338		0.683
31	Steward, Butte, Mont (c)	m-h granite	9	7	a-f dr	col	2	bur	23	167.7	8.5	semi-gel	40	12.6	m-shov	none	m-shov	160	0.3	0.3	0.3		0.6
32	Tintic Standard, Dividend, Utah	h quartzite	9	7	a-f dr	col	2	b-dr	12	66	3.5	semi-gel	40	9.5	m-shov	oc'l sets	m-shov	200	0.360	0.360	0.295		0.675
33	Magma, Superior, Ariz (d)	h diabase	8	8	h-f dr	bar	1	b-dr	23	133	5.5	gel dyn	40	18	m-shov	none	m-shov	250	0.4	0.4	0.6		1.0
34	Balmat, Balmat, N.Y.	meta l.s	8	8	j'ham	col	2	bur	29	190	5.5	semi-gel	40	12.5	m-shov	none	m-shov	156	0.35	0.35	0.07		0.40
35	Burra Burra, Ducktown, Tenn	m-h sch and gruske	8	8	h-f dr	col	2	pyr	23	150	5.5	am dyn	40	15	scraper	none	scraper	90	0.35	0.35	0.17		0.52
36	Pecos, Terrero, N M	h diabase	8	8	a-f dr	col	1	b-dr	18	98	8–9	gel dyn	40	15	hand	sets	hand	60	0.8	0.8	0.81	0.375	1.995
37	Area Over 64 Sq Ft Mt Hope, Mt Hope, N J (f)(d)	gn	8	9	h-f dr	none	2	pyr	22	136	4	gel	40	13.8	hand	oc'l sets	hand	133	0.5	0.5	0.5	0.146	1.0
38	Geneva, Ironwood, Mich	m-s hematite	8	9	j'ham	none	1	t-dr	11	47	2.1	semi-gel	45 (b)	5.2	scraper	sets	scraper	160	0.177	0.177	0.177	0.125	0.50
39	Spruce, Eveleth, Minn.	compact hematite	8.5	8.5	j'ham	none	2	2-hole	12–15	72–90	2–3	dyn	60	6.2	scraper	sets	scraper	175	0.125	0.125	0.125	0.125	0.375
40	Dome, So Porcupine, Ont.	h basalt	8	10	dr	col	2	pyr bur-pyr	29	240	6	gel dyn	40	16	scraper	none	scraper	(e)	0.375	0.375	0.25		0.625
41	Geneva, Ironwood, Mich.	granite	8	10	dr	car'ge	4	v-v	32	228	4.1	gel dyn	60 & 80	30.6	scraper	none	scraper	524	0.635	0.635	0.325		1.01
42	Zeibright, Nevada City, Cal(d)	tough dike	9	9	h-f dr	col	3	bur	42	336	8	gel	45 (b)	25.6	m-shov	none	m-shov	175	0.6	0.6	0.4		1.33
43	Sullivan, Kimberley, B C	chert	9	9	h-f dr	bar	3	b-dr	16	52	8	gel	60	20	m-shov	none	m-shov	75	0.83	0.83	0.50		1.33
44	Sullivan, Kimberley, B C	quartzite	9	9	h-f dr	bar	1	b-dr	16	88	6	semi-gel	60	15.4	m-shov	none	m-shov	100	0.50	0.50	0.50		1.0
45	Ray, Ray, Ariz (d)	s sch	9	9	h-wdg	col	2	h-wdg	20	110	6	am gel	60	7	scraper	sets	scraper	100	0.4	0.4	0.2	0.4	
46	Pioneer, Ely, Minn.	grnstn	9	9	dr	col	2	pyr	20	122	7	am dyn	45	14.5	scraper	none	scraper	130	0.32	0.32	0.41		0.73
47	Soudan, Soudan, Minn.	grnstn	9	9	a-f dr	col	2	pyr	15	90	5	am dyn	50	14.5	scraper	none	scraper	140	0.75	0.75	0.58		1.33
48	Soudan, Soudan, Minn.	jasper	9	9	a-f dr	col	2	pyr	16	84	32	am dyn	50	21.5	scraper	none	scraper	55	2.9	2.9	0.5		3.4
49	Spruce, Eveleth, Minn.	cherty form	9	9	a-f dr	col	2	v-v	15–21	105–147	8	gel dyn	60	12	scraper	none	scraper	132	0.42	0.42	0.19		0.61
50	Page, Page, Id (d)	h quartzite	8.5	8.5	h-f dr	col	2	h-wdg	16–32	96–92	4.5	gel dyn	40	12–20	m-shov	sets	m-shov	260	0.300	0.300	0.225	0.075	0.6
51	La Colorada, Cananea, Mex.	brec por	9.5	8.5	pyr	col	2	pyr	21	201	6.25	gel	40	12	m-shov	none	m-shov	180	0.66		0.16		0.66
52	Bonne Terre, Bonne Terre, Mo	dol	8.5–9	10	j'ham	col	2	v-v	28–32	240–276		gel	60	11.3	m-shov & scraper	none	m-shov	var	0.52	0.52			0.48
53	Creighton, Creighton Mine, Ont	diorite	10	9	h-f dr	col	3	bur-pyr	34	289	7.1	am dyn	55 40	23	m-shov	steel beams	m-shov	224	0.531	0.531	0.344	0.080	0.955
54	Montreal, Montreal, Wis. (d)	q'tz slate	9	10	a-f dr	col	2	v-v	23	125	3.5	gel	60	23	scraper	sets	scraper	200	0.33	0.33	0.33		0.67
55	Montreal, Montreal, Wis.	hematite	10	10	j'ham	none	2	v-v	16	96	2.5	gel	40	7.25	scraper	none	scraper	250	0.25	0.25	0.125	0.125	0.375
56	Zenith, Ely, Minn.	h grnstn	9	10	a-f dr	col	2	pyr	20	200	7	gel	40	26	none	sets	scraper	182	0.29	0.29	0.29		0.58
57	Newport, Ironwood, Mich (c)	granite	9	10	a-f dr	car'ge	5	bur	31	279	7.5	semi-gel	60 (b)	21.9	none	none	scraper	255	0.664	0.664	0.516		1.18
58	Newport, Ironwood, Mich (c)	q'tz slate	9	10	a-f dr	car'ge	5	bur	23	241	7.5	gel	35 & 80	13.8	scraper	none	scraper	325	0.297	0.297	0.250	0.093	0.64
59	Miami, Miami, Ariz (d)	s to m-h sch	10	9	a-f dr	col	2	h-wdg	17	113.5	5	gel dyn	40	8	scraper	sets	scraper	160	0.48	0.48	0.32	0.48	1.28

Table 18. Data on Drifting and Crosscutting Practice, as of 1938—(Continued)

(Unless otherwise designated d or c, data relate to both drifts and crosscuts)

Example No	Mine and location	Type of ground	Section, ft Height	Section, ft Width	Drills Type	Drills Mounting	No at face	Type of cut	No holes per round	Ft of hole per round	Hours to drill round (a)	Explosive Type	% N gl	Lb per ft advance	Mucking	Timbering	Advance, ft Per round	Advance, ft Per month	Drill and blast	Mucking	Timbering	Total
60	Mountain Cons, Butte, Mont. (d)	m-h sul quartzite	10	9.5	h-f dr	col	1	t-dr	18	109.5	8	semi-gel	40	9.25	hand	sets	5.75	92.7	0.346	0.346	0.172	0.864
61	Sunday Lake, Wakefield, Mich. (d)		9	11	dr	car'ge	5	bur	26	195	4	gel	60 & 80	29.9	scraper	none	7	501	0.75	0.25	...	1.00
62	Lloyd, Ishpeming, Mich. (d)	silic sl	10	10	dr	bar	2	pyr	21	126	5	semi-gel	60	19	m-shov	none	6	375	0.50	0.17	...	0.67
63	Bates, Iron River, Mich. (d)	h hematite	10	10	dr	col	2	pyr	26	156	5	am-gel	45 (b)	11	scraper	none	5.5	var	0.35	0.35	...	0.70
64	Inspiration, Inspiration, Ariz.	m-s sh	10	10	j'ham	none	1	b-dr	12–23	63–121	6.5	gel dyn	30	7	m-shov	sets	5.5	var	0.2	0.3	0.2	0.7
65	Godfrey, Hibbing, Minn. (d)	s hematite	8–12	10	j'ham	col	2	none(g)	12	72	3–6	am gd	60	6.5	scraper	sets	6.3	200	0.13	0.16	0.13	0.42
66	Pioneer, Ely, Minn.	m-h h'matite	10.5	10.5	a-f dr	col	2	pyr	23	130	4.5	am-gd	45	9	scraper	sets	5.5	100	0.30	0.35	0.15	0.80
67	Champion, Painesdale, Mich.	basalt	10.5	10.5	a-f dr	col	4	v-v	23	204	2.7	gel	40	17.5	scraper	sets and stulls	5.5	500	0.6	0.37	0.37	1.34
68	Champion, Painesdale, Mich.	basalt	10.5	10.5	a-f dr	col	2	v-v	34	204	5	gel	40	17.5	scraper	sets and stulls	5.5	250	0.6	0.37	0.37	1.34
69	Zenith, Ely, Minn.	h hematite	10	11	h-f dr	col	2	v-v	28–32	182	8	semi-gel	60 (b)	16.7	scraper	sets	6	156	0.33	0.16	0.17	0.66
70	Ruth, Ruth, Nev.	por	11	11	h-f dr	col	1	b-dr	20–24	120–144	4–5	gel	40	8	hand to belt	sets	5	100	...	0.37	...	0.9
71	Ruth, Ruth, Nev.	ls	11	11		none	1	b-dr	8–15	48–90	1.5–3.0	gel	30	5	hand to belt	sets	5	80–100	...	...	...	1.0
72	Ruth, Ruth, Nev.	s por, sh and ls	11	11	h-f dr	col	1	b-dr	5–7	30–42	2	gel	30	var	hand to belt	sets	5	100	...	...	...	1.2
73	Ruth, Ruth, Nev.	s por, sh and ls	11	11	j'ham	none	1	b-dr	2–7	12–42	0.5–1.0	gel	30	var	hand to belt	sets	5	100	...	...	...	1.2
74	Morning, Mullan, Id (d)	sheared quartzite	13	9–15	h-f dr	col	2	h-wdg	22–30	132–180	6	gel dyn	40	15–20	m-shov	sets	5	65	0.8	1.6	0.8	3.2
75	Ahmeek, Ahmeek, Mich (d)	amygdaloid	9	14	dr	col	2	irreg	32	200	20	am dyn, gel	66 }, 40 }	13.5	hand	none	5	100	0.5	0.8	...	1.3
76	Muscoda No 6, Bessemer, Ala (d)	h hematite	10	14	h-f dr	tripod	1	v-v	14	110–120	6	am dyn	40	14	scraper	steel	5	200	0.4	0.6	0.35	1.35
77	Climax, Climax, Colo.	h to m-h frac granite	11	13	dr	bar	2	pyr	24–36	250–350	16	semi-gel	45 (b)	15–20	scraper	oc'l set	10	60	0.4	0.375	var	0.775+
78	Montreal, Montreal, Wis (c)	grnstn	9	16	a-f dr	ear'ge	6	v-v	38	315	4	gel	60	32	scraper	(gunite)	6.5	300	1.0	0.67	0.04	1.71
79	Limestone No 5, Bessemer, Ala	ls	14	20	h-f dr	tripod	2	v-v	15	143	6	am dyn	60	23	scraper	none	6.5	70	0.54	0.54	...	1.08

(a) Incl time for setting-up and dismantling drills. (b) Bulk strength. (c) Crosscuts only. (d) Drifts only. (e) 423 ft working 2 shifts and Sundays; 173 ft working 1 shift weekdays only. (f) Inclined at 15°–20° downward. (g) Lower center breast hole points up slightly. h = hard. m-h = medium hard. s = soft. m-s = medium soft. sh = shale. sch = schist. dol = dolomite. por = porphyry. sul = sulphide. grnstn = greenstone. peg = pegmatite. gn = gneiss. dr = drifter. h-f dr = hand-fed drifter. a-f = automatic-fed drifter. j'ham = jackhammer. col = column and arm. bar = bar. pyr = pyramid cut. bur = burned cut. b-dr = bottom-draw cut. t-dr = top-draw cut. v-v = vert or center V-cut. h-wdg = hor V-cut. gel = gelatin. semi-gel = semi-gelatin dynamite. am-dyn = ammonia dynamite. m-shov = mechanical shovel. oc'l = occasional. var = too variable to permit averaging.

used in conjunction with scraper loading, tend to rapid work in large headings in Lake Superior iron district; one mine advances a 9 by 11-ft drift 500 ft per month through quartzite, completing a 7-ft round per shift on a 7-day week, 3-shift basis.   At 2 mines near Birmingham, Ala, in drifts 14 and 20 ft wide and 10 and 14 ft high, respectively, drills are mounted on TRIPODS on top of muck pile, working at one side while scraper cleans the other. Unmounted JACKHAMMERS are employed in both large and small headings in medium-soft schist at Inspiration, Ariz; occasionally in the softer ground at Ruth, Nev, using bottom-draw cuts in both; also in sub-levels through medium-tight hematite at Montreal mine, Wis, with V-cuts.   Oliver Iron Mining Co uses un-

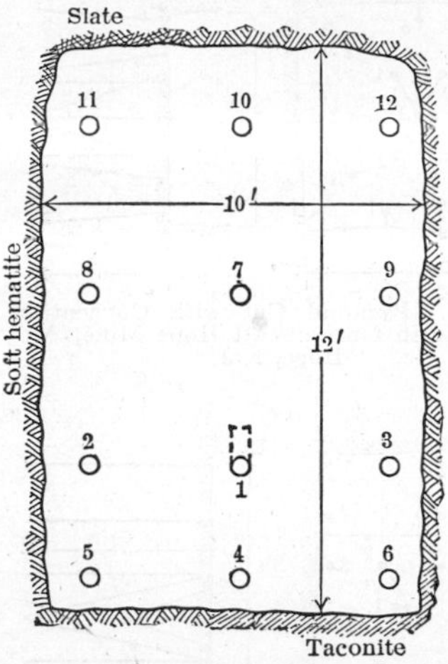

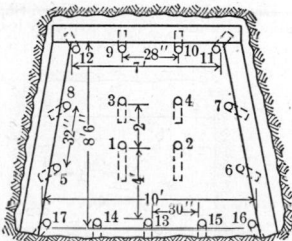

Fig 120. Jackhammer Round in Soft Iron Ore, Godfrey Mine, Hibbing, Minn; holes 6 ft deep, and all (ex No 1) drilled straight into face

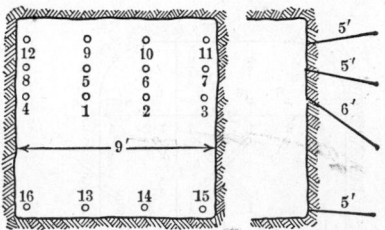

Fig 121.   Bottom-draw Cut in Quartzite, Sullivan Mine, Kimberley, B C

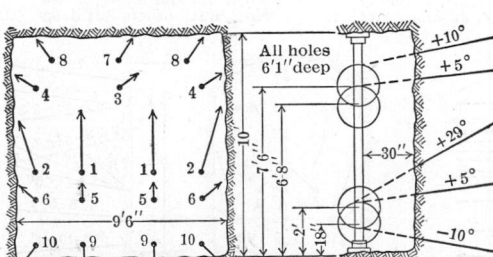

Fig 122.   Bottom-draw, Jackhammer Cut in Schist, Inspiration Mine, Inspiration, Ariz

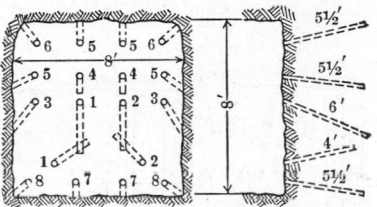

Fig 123.   Wedged Draw Cut in Hard Diabase, Pecos Mine, N Mex

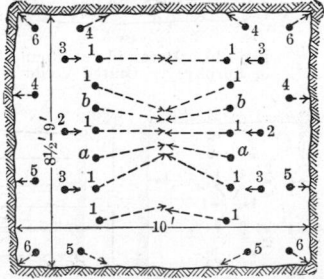

Fig 124.   Top-draw Cut in Blocky Sulphide Ore, Mountain Con Mine, Butte, Mont

Fig 125.   Vert V-cut in Dolomite, Bonne Terre Mine, Bonne Terre, Mo. Holes a, a and b, b, sometimes omitted; 8 side holes are 7.5 ft deep; all others, 9 ft

mounted jackhammers in headings at 3 of its soft-ore mines (Table 18); at Godfrey mine, Hibbing, a 10 by 10-ft drift is advanced 6.3 ft per round without use of angled cut holes.

An unusual mounting sometimes used in 7 by 6-ft headings at Vipond mine, Ontario, when speed requires 2 rounds per day, consists of a horiz bar set 3 ft below roof of drift (or just above muck pile), with a short vert column supported by clamp at middle of bar and braced against roof; drill is carried by cross-arm on the column. Upper holes can

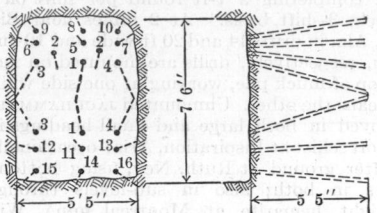

Fig 126. Horiz V-cut in Hard Limestone, Presidio Mine, Shafter, Tex

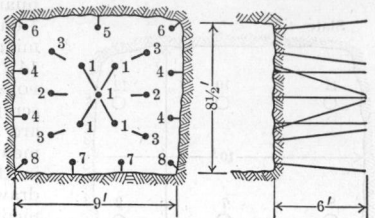

Fig 127. Pyramid Cut with Concentric Relievers, in Gneiss. Mt Hope Mine, Mt Hope, N J

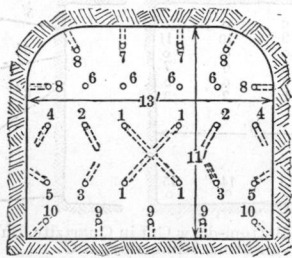

Fig 128. Pyramid Combined with Wedge Cut, in Fractured, Silicified Granite. Climax Mine, Climax, Colo

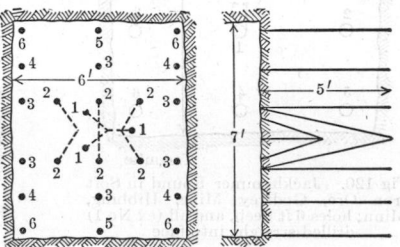

Fig 129. Double Pyramid Cut in Hard Shale and Massive Sulphide. Frisco Mine, S F del Oro, Chih, Mex

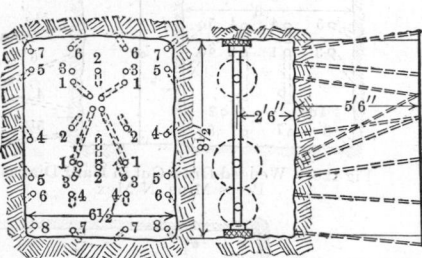

Fig 130. Pyramid-cut Round in Hard Sulphide or Porphyry. United Verde Mine, Jerome, Ariz

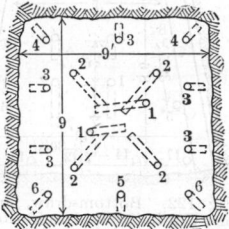

Fig 131. Reinforced Pyramid Cut in Jasper, Soudan Mine, Soudan, Minn. Holes No 1, 4.5 and 5.5 ft; holes No 2, 6 ft; others 5 ft deep

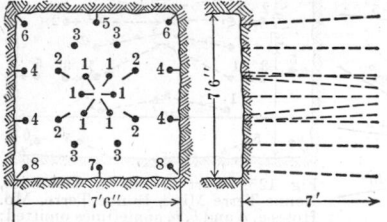

Fig 132. Deep Pyramid Cut in Hard Schist and Quartz. McIntyre Mine, Schumacher, Ont

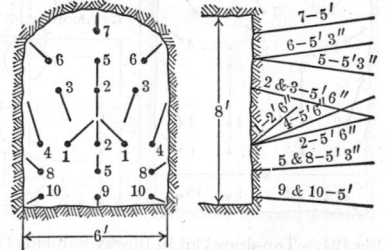

Fig 133. Pyramid Cut in Brecciated Porphyry. La Colorada Mine, Cananea, Mex

thus be drilled during mucking, on completing which, the vert column is swung down and braced against floor for drilling lower holes. Runner, helper, and 2 muckers advance 5 ft per shift with a 20-hole round, pyramid-cut (493).

Choice of drills for drifting and crosscutting. DRIFTERS are customary for hard ground. Practice favors the lighter, 1-man drills when ground can be drilled efficiently by them. As JACKHAMMERS are lighter, cheaper, and consume less compressed air, they are favored in soft ground, either mounted or hand-held; for a round of very few holes in soft ground, time for set-up may not justify use of mounting. STOPERS, though not designed for drifting or crosscutting, are occasionally useful for this work. Fig 138 shows an inverted draw-cut drilled with stopers at Cripple Creek, Colo (92); except the lifters, all holes point upwards. In using stopers for drifting, it is necessary to support tail piece of drill; Fig 138 shows a simple device, consisting of a sprag, wedged across drift, 4–6 ft from face and 3 ft from floor, a loose piece of 2 by 10-in plank furnishing a base for drill.

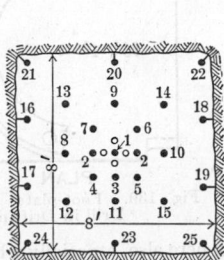

Fig 134. Burned Cut in Tough Limestone, Balmat Mine, Balmat, N Y. Holes average 6.5 ft deep

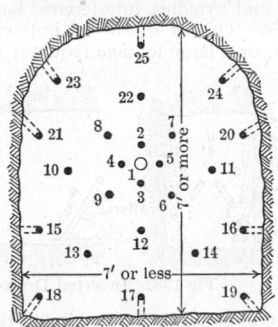

Fig 135. Burned Cut, Franklin Mine, Franklin, N J. Central holes, 8.5 ft deep; others, 8 ft. Center hole, unloaded, has 3-in diam. Holes fired in sequence, as numbered, using fuses all of same length. Loaded and fired in 4 rounds: Nos 2–5, Nos 6–9, Nos 10–14, Nos 15–25

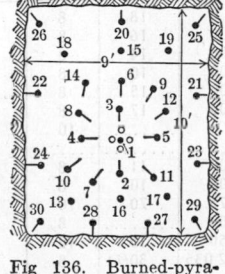

Fig 136. Burned-pyramid Cut, Creighton Mine, Ont

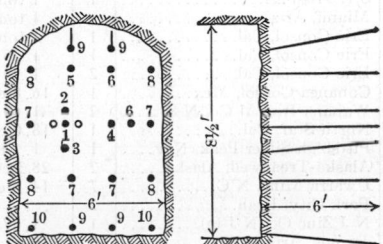

Fig 137. Burned Cut in Cherty Limestone. Junction Mine, Bisbee, Ariz

An A-frame of 2 by 10-in plank (indicated by dotted lines) forms a better support. Fig 139 shows an inexpensive foot-plate, for setting a stoper at any angle from horiz to vert; it is of $^3/_8$-in plate, with ears turned down at corners to hold plate to a plank; to the plate is riveted an angle iron bent to U-shape (94). At Butte, Mont, drifting with JACKHAMMERS, leasers rested the drill in a wooden trough 6 ft long, laid against face in line with hole to be drilled. Drill was held to its work by a short steel lever fitting into holes in bottom of trough (126). Similar device for drilling low, flat holes in S E Mo is like a narrow ladder, with sides at such distance apart that drill can slide on their inner edges (see Art 31); cross pieces on under side, 2 in wide and 2 in apart, offer leverage for end of a pinch bar holding jackhammer to its work. In this easy-drilling limestone, 80–100 ft of hole (starting at 1.75 in) is aver per machine-shift. The jackhammer, when used for higher holes, can be carried by an S-hook of heavy wire hanging from the lugs on end of a piece of drill steel of suitable length standing with its bit on the floor.

Of the 68 DRIFTERS listed in Table 18, 33 are hand-fed and 21 automatically fed (others not specified). The data are not definitely comparable, but it is noteworthy that automatic feed has become widespread. Drifters of medium wt are most numerous; 50 are between 150 and 185 lb, as against 10 lighter and 8 heavier. The heaviest drills in the list, 250 lb, are mounted on a carriage and drill a V-cut round in a 9 by 16-ft heading in greenstone at Montreal mine, Wis; also used with column mounting in a 9 by 10-ft drift at same mine. Of 11 jackhammers, 3 are mounted, 8 unmounted.

Hand mucking and tramming. Speed of drifting and crosscutting is often more dependent on time required for mucking than for drilling and blasting. It is usually cheaper to alternate drilling and mucking crews at any one face, thus giving drillers a clean drift in which to set up, and avoiding interference between drillers and muckers. This is especially important if drilling is difficult, or a large footage required per round.

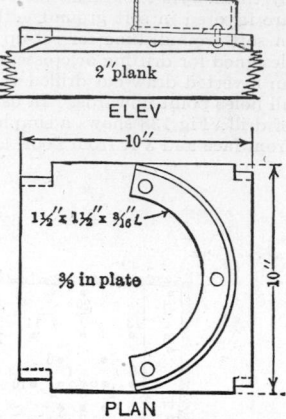

Fig 139. Foot-plate for Stope
Drill in Drifting

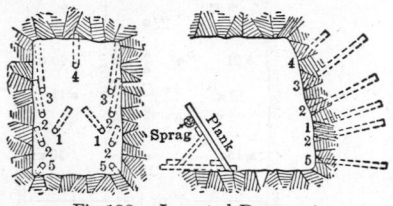

Fig 138. Inverted Draw-cut

General points as to mucking in tunnels (Sec 6) apply here also, especially where speed is desired. Table 19 gives mucking and tramming duty. A plat of sheet iron or plank,

Table 19. Data on Mucking and Tramming by Hand (55, 67, 106–111, 122, 522, 532)

	Location	No of men	Size of car	Distance trammed, ft	Cars per shift	Length of shift, hr	Tons per man-hr
Shoveling from a rock floor	S E Missouri................	1	1 ton	0	18	8	2.25
	Miami, Ariz.................	1	1 ton	2 400	16	8	2.00
	Erie Consol, Cal............	1	1 ton	100	14	8	1.75
	Erie Consol, Cal............	1	1.25 ton	1 000	10	8	1.57
	Erie Consol, Cal............	2	1.25 ton	1 000	15	8	1.17(d)
	Cananea Consol, Mex........	1	16.8 cu ft	300	17	8	1.79(c)
	Wabana Iron M Co, N S.....	2	1.65 ton	0	....	10	1.60
	North Star, Cal............	1	18.0 cu ft	0	....	.....	2.00
	Pittsb'gh-Silver Peak, Nev...	1	1.1 ton	700	11	8	1.52
	Alaska-Treadwell, Alaska.....	2	28.3 cu ft	600	10	8	0.88(c)
	Uwarra Mine, N C..........	7	14.4 cu ft	275	70	10	0.72(e)(c)
	Park City, Utah............	2		1 000	....	8	0.60
	N J Zinc Co, N J (g)........	1	1.07 ton	250	15	10	1.60
	Jerome, Ariz...............	2	19 cu ft(c)	1 500–2 035	30(h)	8	1.78(c)
	Mineville, N Y.............	3	1.5 ton	....	13(c)	8	0.80(c)
Shoveling from a plat	Tonopah, Nev..............	1			....	4.5–5	2.0–3.3
	Liberty Bell, Colo...........	1	33 cu ft	200	15(f)	8	3.09
	North Star, Cal............	1	18 cu ft	0	....	.....	3.00
	Joplin, Mo.................	1	(a)	0	....	8	2.46
	Cananea Consol, Mex........	1	16.8 cu ft	300	20	8	2.11(c)
	Ohio Copper Co, Utah.......	1	20.6 cu ft	100	16	8	2.05(c)
	Pittsb'gh-Silver Peak, Nev...	1	2.1 ton	1 000	6	8	1.58
	Alaska-Treadwell, Alaska.....	2	28.3 cu ft	600	11	8	0.98(c)
	Mich amygdaloid mine........	1		600	....	9	1.56–1.72
L'd'g from chute	Ohio Copper Co, Utah.......	1	20.6 cu ft	150	80	8	10.32(c)
	Br Columbia Cop Co, B C...	1	2.15 ton	450	31.5	8	8.46
	Pittsb'gh-Silver Peak, Nev...	1	1.1 ton	700	45	8	6.19
	Cananea Consol, Mex........	1	16.8 cu ft	300	40	8	4.22(c)
	Alaska-Treadwell, Alaska.....	1	21.7 cu ft	400	30	8	4.06(c)
	Erie Consol, Cal............	1	1.25 ton	1 500	20	8	3.12
	Utah Copper Co, Utah.......	2	1 ton	90	65	8	4.04

(a) Bucket, capac 800 lb. (c) On basis of 20 cu ft = 1 ton. (d) Lower duty, probably because of insufficient work to keep 2 men fully occupied. (e) Negro labor. (f) Bonus work, record for 2 months. (g) Aver for year 1916. (h) Aver range, 24–42. Bonus for speed of advance.

laid on floor close to face before blasting, increases output per mucker-hr. Data on loading and tramming from chutes are included for comparison and for use in estimating on raises (Art 21 and Sec 11). Rate of mucking is also affected by size of pieces; observations by author in Colo gave following data:

Car, 28 by 28 by 54 in; capacity, 2 500 lb; 1 man mucking small material on rough floor filled car at rate of 3 tons per hr; with good floor, 5–6 tons. In loading muck containing many big pieces, which had to be lifted into the car, 1 man loaded 4 tons per hr; 2 men loading mixed material from rough floor and taking their time handled 2.0 tons per man-hr. 2 men, 1 picking and 1 shoveling, made following rates per man-hr: in large and small material mixed, 2.9 tons; all big pieces, 3.2 tons; all fine muck, 3.5 tons.

A detailed study of underground shoveling, made by Phelps Dodge Co, was described by G. T. Harley in 1919 (539). Shovel found best adapted to mining work is shown in Fig 140, the blade holding an aver of 21 lb broken ore, and having a plain welded back. Harley concludes that to obtain highest shoveling effic underground, every shoveler should be placed in a particular stope or working place, directly in charge of a shoveling boss. This boss should have had large experience in shoveling, have learned correct shoveling methods, and should be able to instruct men and gain their confidence. Each man should be taught: (a) necessity of using correct type of shovel for given work; (b) proper way to handle a shovel; (c) range of usefulness of wheelbarrow and car; (d) advantage of using a platform to shovel from; when shoveling has progressed beyond the platform, time should be taken to shift it and scrape the broken ore forward on to it; (e) the broken ore should be thoroughly loosened with a pick; effort is wasted in trying to shovel packed material; (f) shoveling should be done at a good steady pace, speed depending on length of job; it is waste of time and energy to try to rush through the work; (g) besides the amount of rest inherent in the work itself (rest gained while picking down, tramming, etc), definite rest periods should be maintained. When each

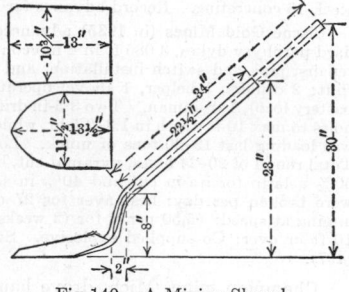

Fig 140. A Mining Shovel

man has been thoroughly instructed in the methods of shoveling, he should be placed in general run-of-mine work among the more experienced shovelers, so that another new man may take his place for instruction. For further details, see Sec 3.

Mechanical loading in drifts and crosscuts.

For current practice in design and operation of loaders, see Sec 27. The following examples illustrate their applications in metal mining.

Scrub Oak magnetite mine, N J, has used a Nordberg-Butler shovel in its tramming drifts, 8.5 ft high by 11 ft wide; in 1 shift, shovel loaded about 57 tons from each of 2 headings at opposite ends of same drift. Advance, 6.5 ft per shift by each drilling crew. Ore averaged 16 cu ft per long ton. Loading equipment included shovel, storage-battery locomotive, and 5-ton Granby car; all operated by 2 men, who also extended track in 5-ft sections; shovel and car were both transferred from heading to heading by locomotive. Previously, loading crew had been 4 muckers and 1 locomotive engineer per shift per heading; shovel thus saved 8 man-shifts (costing $3.16 per ft of drift) at an expense of 60¢ per ft for deprec, interest, power, repairs, and supplies; net saving, $2.56 per ft (494).

Ojuela, Mex. A 9 by 8.5-ft drainage tunnel was advanced 714 ft per mo (during 7 mo) in limestone, shale, and several diorite dikes 10–80 ft thick (484). Speed was gained by continuous 3-shift work, carriage mounting of drills, and mucking by Nordberg-Butler (No 109) air-operated shovel, loading 34 tons per hr into 40-cu ft dump cars; height of car above rail, 4 ft–7 in. Haulage by 2.5-ton Mancha storage-battery locomotive. Aver round of 8 ft required 5 hr–37 min, of which: drilling, 1 hr–50 min; loading 20 cars, 2 hr.

Mineville, N Y, magnetite mines have advanced footwall haulage drifts 10 ft high by 15 ft wide at aver of 5 ft (max 7 ft) per 8 hr, with 4 men. Two drillers complete a wedge-cut round of 28 holes, 7–7.5 ft deep, and blast, in 5.5 hr; operators of air-driven shovel and elec loco (both meanwhile employed elsewhere) then load about 50 tons in 3 hr, to pocket at incline. Explosive, 125 lb 40% gelatin per round (495).

Humboldt mine, Morenci, Ariz, using a Conweigh shovel, advanced a 9.5 by 10.5-ft heading on 14th level 2 343 ft through porphyry in 8 mo of 1928, or at aver of 11.3 ft per day, compared with previous hand-mucking rate of 7.3 ft. Water collecting in the downgrade heading hindered mucking. With 2 drills on vert columns, a horiz V-cut round of 21 holes, 8–9 ft deep, plus 1 short bottom hole for ditch, was finished and fired in 5.25 hr; usual break, 7.5–8 ft, or 9 tons per ft. After 45 min for smoke to clear, shovel crew of

3 men loaded 70 tons in 6 hr; hence, 2 complete rounds per day. Double track, with transferable cross-over switch, expedited handling cars (99).

Magma mine, Ariz, drives haulage levels in diabase wall rock, 8 by 8 ft where untimbered. Two drifters, on horiz bar, drill upper half of a 13-hole pyramid-cut, while air-driven shovel is mucking. Depth of holes, 7 ft, is adjusted to break about 38 tons, which can be mucked by comp-air shovel into 2-ton cars while holes are being drilled, requiring about 5 hr, including first set-up; shoveling takes 4 hr. Bar is then moved down, and lower holes are drilled in 1 hr. Charging and blasting, 1 hr, lunch and lost time, 1 hr, makes 8 hr for a 5.5-ft advance. Crew of 2 drillers, 2 helpers, 1 loader operator does whole job, including laying track and pipe lines. One helper operates storage-battery loco (77).

Trepca Mines drove a development and drainage tunnel 8 776 ft (all but 945 ft in weak schist requiring steel support clear to the face) between Oct 19, 1929, and May 12, 1931 (496). Arched heading, 9.8 ft high at center by 12.8 ft wide, usually required a horiz V-cut of 22–26 holes, 7.9 ft deep, drilled in 1.5–2 hr by 4 drifters on a carriage. Aver advance, 6.6–7.5 ft per round; explosive (65% ammonia dynamite) 16.8–20.2 lb per ft. Nordberg-Butler shovel, air-operated, loaded 60 met tons from an aver round into 41 cars (25–30 cu ft) at 3.5 min per car, or 2.25–2.75 hr per round. Entire cycle, during 4 mo free from unusual delays, averaged 6.5 hr. Ditching done independently by hand work. Of total crew of 132 men underground, in 3 shifts, 51 worked at face, 21 erecting steel, 15 concreting. Record advance for 1 month, 879 ft; aver for 8 mo in 1930, 778 ft per mo.

Siscoe Gold Mines (in 1935) advanced an 8 by 8-ft crosscut, in medium schist intersected by hard porphyry dykes, 3 086 ft in 4 mo continuous 3-shift work except Sundays, which were used for repairs, pipe and switch installation, and misc work. Little timbering was necessary. Crew per shift: 2 drillers, 1 helper, 1 shovel operator (Eimco Finlay), 1 switchman, 1 motorman (storage-battery loco), 1 trainman. Two 3.5-in drifters, mounted on horiz bar above muck pile, drilled 12–14 holes to max 10-ft depth in 1.3–2.5 hr, while shovel was at work; drills then idle for 1 hr, while shovel was loading last 12–20 tons of muck. Lower holes were then drilled from new set-up in 1–1.5 hr. Total round of 20–24 holes, pyramid-cut, broke from 7.5 ft, in hardest, to 10 ft in softest rock, using 60% gelatin forcite in cut and 40% in square-up holes. Never less than 3, and often 4 rounds were broken per day; best aver for 27 days, 27.7 ft. Labor was contracted on bonus system, aiming at speed: $5.50 per ft for (2 weeks' aver) advance under 6 ft per round, to $7.50 per ft for 10 ft or over; Co supplied explosive. Switches for the 20-cu ft cars were installed every 200 ft (497).

Champion mine, Mich, drove haulage levels 8 ft high, 9 ft wide in barren rock and 13–14 ft wide in ore; little timbering needed (488). In 14-ft drift, a wedge-cut of 34 or 35 holes, breaking about 5.5 ft, was drilled from 2 vert columns. Two horiz holes near upper corners were the deepest, to leave stubs to receive split pins for attaching tail-rope block of scraper. "Osana" scraper slide was 6 ft wide at bottom and 4.5 ft over car; incline, 30°. Hoe scraper, 43 in wide. Motor, d-c, 15 hp. Two drillers and helper on each of 2 shifts performed whole operation, including tramming and dumping into skip. Aver 2 hr to muck a round (about 50 tons). Aver advance, 0.56 ft per 8-hr man-shift; explosive, 17 lb per ft.

Britannia mine, B C, driving a main haulage tunnel 10 ft high by 12 ft, with a 3 by 3-ft ditch, used 4 drills on carriage for a pyramid-cut of 29–33 holes, 7–8 ft deep, in 2–2.5 hr (498). Crew on each of 2 shifts: 1 boss, 4 drillers, 2 muckers, 1 motorman, 1 brakeman; additional crew, on day shift only, 2 trackmen, 2 steel sharpeners, 1 ditcher; total 23 men in 24 hr. In all but hardest ground, advance was 6 ft per shift. "Osana" slide loaded a 6-ton (120-cu ft) car in 3–4 min; switching car, 1–3 min. Hoe scraper, 42 in wide, was operated by tail-rope block hung from chain stretched between Lewis wedges in 2 upper corner holes, after firing. Permanent rail was kept 30 ft back from face to permit clean scraping; temporary rail for drill carriage was laid in advance. Ditcher, in rear, drilled and fired at will.

Eureka-Asteroid mine, Gogebic Range, Mich, used scraper slides in headings: main levels, 9 ft high, 11 ft wide; untimbered haulageway, 8 by 10 ft; sublevels, 8 by 9 ft (delivering to chutes). Slides have displaced power shovels, proving cheaper in first cost, operation, and maintenance, and simpler to handle. With them, untimbered rock 9 by 11-ft crosscuts have been advanced 800–900 ft in a month (499); one made 924 ft through hard rock in 31 days of 3 shifts, 32 man-shifts per day. Four drills, on 2 columns, could be set up, drill 24 wedge-cut holes, and torn down in 2.3 hr. After 40 min for charging, firing, and smoke to clear, scraper loaded 26 cars (of 60 cu ft) in 1.75 hr; total round, 4.75 hr.

Mt Isa, Queensland, uses scraper loading in haulage crosscuts (9 ft high by 10 ft wide, with side ditch) and stope sub-levels (10 ft high by 12 ft wide). Former is advanced with center-wedge cut of 27 holes, 7.5 ft deep, breaking 7 ft with 110 lb 60% gelignite; latter with a pyramid-cut of 32 holes, 9 ft deep, breaking 8–9 ft with 70 lb of 60% and 70 lb of 40% gelignite. Working alternately in 2 headings, 4 drillers and 2 muckers make 1 round per shift. Hoe scraper, 34 in wide, is reinforced and weighted with 2 sections of 42-lb rail. Motor, 15 hp, a-c, 440 volt; rope, 0.5 in; cars, 75-cu ft capac (500).

Roan Antelope mine, Rhodesia, introduced in 1930 its own design of portable slide scraper operated by native labor, with great advantage over hand loading (501). One 10 by 12-ft main drift in ore advanced 277 ft in 25 days, drilling and loading alternately on two 8-hr shifts. Crew of 7 natives with European boss ran 2 heavy drifters with 13-ft steel; loading crew, 7 natives, one running the scraper, and 1 European. Haulage, by battery loco and Granby cars.

Muscoda No 6 mine, Bessemer, Ala, uses scraper slides, made in company's shop, for dragging Clinton hematite ore from gently pitching rooms to the rise, and advancing haulage levels (507). Latter are 20 ft wide by 10.5 ft high. Round of 13 holes, 6.5–9.4 ft (total 112.4 ft), arranged for vert-wedge cut, is drilled from a tripod over one side of muck pile, while scraper is clearing other side. Charge of 59 lb of 45% dynamite breaks 7.5 ft, or 1.494 ton per lb. Slide, only semi-portable, must be dismantled for moving; bottom is of 15-in channels, 18 ft long, flat side up, and bolted together, with upper ends resting on 12 by 12-in timber across props. It is set near one wall, leaving space on other side for movable hoist, which has 2 loose drums driven by clutches from 50-hp, d-c, reversing motor. Hoe scraper weighs 2 700 lb and drags about 2 tons.

Halkyn lead district, No Wales. A drainage tunnel, 10 ft wide by 8 ft high, with ditch 4.5 ft wide by 2.5 ft deep, was driven through tight limestone, requiring support only at long intervals (483). During a normal 4 weeks free from unusual delays, 101 rounds advanced 653 ft, aver 163.25 ft per week of 138 hr, with a crew of 53 men per day, 12 per shift being at the face. Rock was hoisted, and delays from inrushes of water and mud from fissures were frequent. Two drifters on horiz bar drilled 36 holes, 8 center-cut 7.5 ft deep, the rest 6.5 ft, in about 2.25 hr. Usually 5 other 5-ft holes. for the ditch, were drilled by jackhammer, and fired with the round. Aver break of 6.33 ft required 140 lb of 60% gelignite, including 9.5–13 lb for ditch. Box-type scraper, 38 in wide, proved better than hoe type for this finely broken rock. Two scraper loads filled a 1 600-lb (capac) car, 1 car per min. Aver cycle: removing scraper and setting up drills, 31 min; drilling 36 face and 5 ditch holes, charging and firing, 2.75 hr; waiting for smoke, clearing track, setting up scraper and slide, 48 min; loading 54 cars (43 tons), 79 min; total, 5 hr–26 min.

Miami Copper Co has considerably modified its mechanical mucking practice in drifts. As originally installed (see 1927 edn, p 521) a train of 8 cars was loaded without uncoupling, by scraper and a bridge sheet between every 2 cars. As described by A. J. McDermid (511) in 1930, cars are loaded singly, and switched by storage-battery loco from a distance up to 50 ft from face. "Osana" scraper slide, built in Co shop, has a 25-hp d-c motor, for a 2-drum hoist carrying 100 ft of 0.75-in rope for load and 125 ft of same size for tail rope; pulley for latter is held at face by 2 eyebolts set in plugger holes as soon as booms and caps have been advanced. Hoe scraper is 48 in wide, with Stellited cutting edge. Muck from an aver 6.25-ft advance fills 15 75-cu ft cars; with high pile, 4 scraper loads fill a car in 3 min; about the same time for switching. Scraper cleans up enough for laying track and timbering to face, but sides behind toe of slide are shoveled by hand. According to information from Miami in 1938, 2 automatic-fed drifters put in a wedge-cut of 17 holes (aver 6.7 ft) in 5 hr; this breaks 10 ft high by 9 ft wide with 50 lb of 40% gelatin; 3-piece drift sets of 10 by 10-in timber are spaced at 6.25-ft c-c. One advance is made in 2 shifts, as follows: setting up, drilling, blasting, 5.5 hr; clearing smoke, 0.5 hr; timbering (advancing booms and caps), 2.0 hr; mucking, 4.0 hr; timbering (posts), 4.0 hr; total, 16.0 hr. Working 2 shifts per day, aver monthly advance is 160 ft.

N'Kana mine, N Rhodesia, drives main haulageways in shales and sandstones, 12 by 12 ft with ditch, on 0.4% grade, drilling and scraper-mucking on alternate shifts (528). With 3 drifters on columns, 1 miner and 11 natives drill 30 holes, with 12–13.5-ft steel; firing with 60% gelignite breaks about 11 ft. Ditch drilled by jackhammer. Scraper crew, of 1 operator and 12 natives loads muck in 4 hr; rest of shift on misc work. Hoe scraper is 45 in wide, weighs 1 000 lb, and is dragged by 35-hp motor hoist with 5/8-in wire rope. Track is kept within 30 ft of face; with 30-ft turnouts every 300 ft. A 6-ton storage-battery loco handles 180-cu ft Granby cars. Best monthly advance, 303 ft in 26 days (2 shifts) in an up-grade, and 265 ft in 25 days in down-grade heading (retarded by water). Costs per ft during 6 months: Breaking, $11.67; mucking, $6.67; timbering, $0.30; track laying, $3.79; elec equipment, $1.87; total, $24.30 (at $1 = 4.11 sh).

Butte, Mont. Data from H. M. Courtney (615) in 1938. Mechanical shovels have practically displaced scrapers, as drifts tend to be narrow and crooked. Anaconda Co (end of 1938) had 75 shovels, of several makes; in first half 1938, 54 shovels loaded 270 545 tons, including ore from half of all silling operations. Untimbered drifts are 8–9 ft high and 6–7 ft wide; timbered drifts, 10–11.5 ft high and 8–9 ft wide, outside of timbers. In wide ore, drifts sometimes advance at full width of ore, 16-22 ft. All drifting is contracted, usually 2, sometimes 3 men (2 drillers, 1 shoveller) on a shift; wherever possible, 2 or 3 headings are worked by same gang, usually on 2 (sometimes 3) shifts. Working practice varies considerably, depending mainly on width of face; for details, see Bib (615). Cars are of 3 sizes. Aver loading times: 14–16 cu ft (0.75-ton), 1 min; 30 cu ft (2-ton),

2.5 min; 52 cu ft (4-ton), 4 min. In one case, 2 adjoining headings, 9 by 7.5 and 9 by 7 ft, were driven by 3 men on a shift, 3 shifts per day, making "burned cuts" with 2 drills on a carriage; in 1 week of 18 shifts, 458 holes totalling 2 960 ft were drilled for an advance (both headings) of 100 ft (aver 5.5 ft per round); week's work included tramming 811 cars to station, and cutting drainage ditch.

Routine of work in drifting and crosscutting. Effic is increased by systematizing operations. This presupposes reasonably uniform ground conditions, proper equipment, experienced men, and competent supervision. On completing a round the following is the cycle of operations: examining the face for missed holes, new set-up, drilling, tearing-down, charging, blasting, clearing smoke, and mucking. Inclusion of timbering depends on strength of ground. Track-laying and extension of air and water lines must be fitted into the routine in a way to avoid delay and interference. Number of drills used depends on size of opening, hardness of ground, and the limitations as to hour of blasting and time for clearing smoke; in some places, blasting may be done only at end of shift. Effic of mechanical mucking depends on keeping the loader supplied with empty cars. Procedure may be governed more by speed requirements than by consideration of cost; thus, 3-shift work is usually more costly, but may be desirable for speed. Routine may best be maintained if there be 2 or more headings in which individual crews may alternate their work. Following examples (numbers refer to Table 18) illustrate general principles.

Ex 22, Lake Shore mine, Kirkland Lake, Ont. Ground, hard porphyry; drift, 7.5 ft high, 7 ft wide; 2 drills at face; mounting, column; holes per round, 23; advance per round, 6.25 ft; hand mucking; advance per mo, 165 ft. ROUTINE: 7 am to 2:45 pm, setting up, drilling and blasting; 2:45 to 7 pm, heading idle, clearing smoke; 7 pm to 3 am, mucking and laying track.

Ex 62, Lloyd mine, Ishpeming, Mich. Ground, cherty slate; drift, 10 by 10 ft; 2 drills at face, on cross-bar; holes per round, 21; advance per round, 6 ft; mucking by power shovel; advance per mo, 375 ft. ROUTINE: 8 to 8:30 am, trimming sides and back; 8:30 to 9 am, setting up; 9 am to 1 pm, drilling upper half of round and mucking; 1 to 2:30 pm, drilling lower half; 2:30 to 3:10 pm, tearing down; 3:10 to 3:40 pm, charging and blasting; 3:40 to 4:00 pm, clearing powder smoke by blowing with 5-hp fan through water spray; same procedure on afternoon and night shifts.

Ex 41, Geneva mine, Ironwood, Mich. Ground, granite; drift, 8 ft high, 10 ft wide; 4 drills at face, on drill carriage; holes per round, 32; advance per round, 6.95 ft; mucking by scraper, slide, and 340-cu ft car; advance per mo, 524 ft (3 shifts per day, 26 days per mo). ROUTINE: 7 to 8 am, setting up; 8 to 11:05 am, drilling; 11:05 to 11:55 am, charging and blasting; 11:55 am to 12:25 pm, blowing smoke; 12:25 to 3 pm, mucking; 3 to 4 pm, setting up; and so on through 3 shifts.

Ex 53, Creighton mine, Ont. Ground, quartz diorite; drift, 10 ft high, 9 ft wide; 3 drills at face; mounting, vert column and arms; holes per round, 34; advance per round, 8.3 ft; mucking by power shovel; advance per mo, 224 ft. ROUTINE: 8 am to 4 pm, mucking previous round, drilling, and tearing down; 5 to 10:30 pm, blasting and clearing smoke; 10:30 pm to 1 am, timbering; 1 to 8 am, idle.

Ex 33, Magma mine, Superior, Ariz. Ground, hard diabase; drift, 8 by 8 ft; 1 drill at face on cross-bar; holes per round, 23; advance per round, 5 ft; mucking by comp-air shovel; advance per mo, 250 ft. ROUTINE: Work is on 2 shifts, drilling and mucking simultaneously. Drilling schedule: 8 to 8:30 am, traveling to working place; 8:30 am to 12:00 m, setting up and drilling; 12 to 12:30 pm, lunch; 12:30 to 2:30 pm, drilling; 2:30 to 3 pm, charging and blasting; 3 to 3:30 pm, counting explosions in round and replacing ventilation tubing into face; 3:30 to 4 pm, traveling to shaft collar. Mucking schedule: 8 to 8:30 am, traveling to working place; 8:30 am to 12:30 pm, mucking; 12:30 pm to 3:30 pm, laying track, cleaning ditch, making up primers, taking down ventilation tubing; 3:30 to 4 pm, traveling to shaft collar. Night shift repeats cycle.

Hand mucking *vs* mechanical loading. In about 76% of 79 headings listed in Table 18, some form of mechanical loading is used. A similar table of 105 headings, in 2nd edn (1927) of this book, showed 13% mechanical loading. Small mines are probably not adequately represented in either table to make these percentages truly representative, but the data suffice to indicate a marked increase of mechanical loading in recent years. This does not necessarily signify that mucking costs are always reduced by adopting mechanical loading, but saving has often been effected, especially in headings of large cross-sec (see Sec 27). Loaders may be used where speed is essential, even though hand mucking might be cheaper. Sacrifice of cost to speed is often justified where labor is cheap but inefficient. Table 18 shows that mechanical loading is much commoner in large headings than in small. In 59 headings larger than 6 by 8 ft, loaders are used exclusively in 46 cases; in 4, the muck is hand-shoveled to a conveyer belt; in 20, having a sec 6 by 8 ft or less, loaders are used exclusively in only 4 cases; occasionally, in 4 others.

Scrapers *vs* **power shovels.** Table 18 indicates that both scrapers and power shovels are used widely in development headings. Scrapers find greater favor than shovels in the soft-ore iron mines of Lake Superior region, while the power shovel seems more popular in the " hard rock " mines. Data available are not conclusive; continued improvements in design are being made in both.

Timbering in crosscuts is similar to that for tunnels (Sec 6), but is generally lighter on account of smaller cross-sec and shorter life of these openings. This may be true also of drifts, but timbering in the latter is often designed to support filling or ore in the stope (Art 38–39). Usual forms of drift timbering: (*a*) HALF SET (Fig 141), cap resting in a hitch at one end and on a post at the other; used where back and one side of drift require support; (*b*) THREE-QUARTER SET (Fig 145, *A*) cap and 2 posts, used where back and both

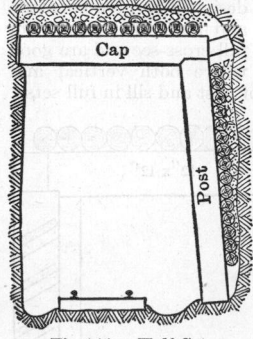

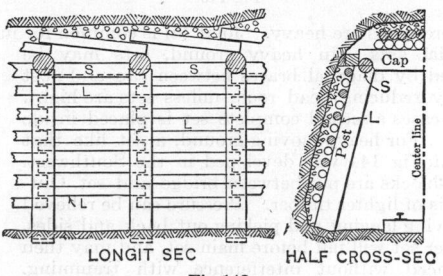

LONGIT SEC   HALF CROSS-SEC

Fig 141. Half Set   Fig 142

sides require support; is the commonest set; (*c*) FULL SET (4-piece), made by adding a sill to the three-quarter set, is used where the floor is soft (Sec 6). Longit mud sills, sometimes found in large tunnels, are seldom used in mines, due to difficulty of replacement. In important haulageways and drainage tunnels, lower side walls may be concreted, forming ledges on which to stand the posts. Posts of sets usually have a batter of 1.5 to 2.5 in per ft of vert height; increased where lateral pressure is heavy and sets must be maintained for a considerable time (Fig 142). Round or sawed timber is used for drift sets (for comparison, see Art 49; also Sec 6). SIZE OF TIMBERS. Round timber is usually 6 to 12 in diam; for heavy ground and large openings, up to 24 in diam or more.

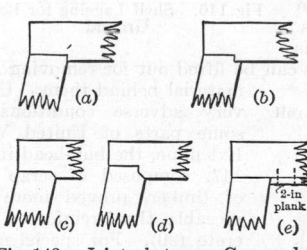

Fig 143. Joints between Cap and Post

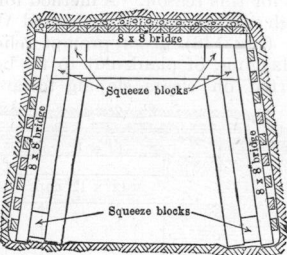

Fig 144. Timber Set for Heavy Ground

Ordinarily, lightest sawed timber used is 6 by 6 in; sizes to 12 by 12 in are common. SPACING OF SETS depends on size of timbers, weight of ground, and length to which available lagging will cut without waste; usual interval is 4 to 6 ft; in heavier ground, 2 to 3 ft; in extreme cases, sets are placed skin to skin. LAGGING (*L*, Fig 142), used to prevent falls of ground between sets, is of round 4 to 6-in poles, half-round mill slabs, or 2 to 4-in plank. Plank is used where tight joints are necessary, and in districts where all timber is imported and plank is as cheap as other forms. Length of lagging usually = distance *c* to *c* of sets; it may cover only back of sets, or back and one or both sides; in rare cases sills are lagged also. Lagging on back is usually placed skin to skin; on sides, open lagging (Fig 142) is generally sufficient. Space between lagging and walls is best packed with broken rock. SPRAGS (stretchers) (Fig 142, *S*) are distance pieces to brace the sets longitudinally; they are heavy lagging poles, or 4 by 6 or 6 by 6-in timber, cut to fit between sets at joint between cap and post, and spiked in place; in shifting ground, feet of posts are braced also. Sets are firmly wedged to wall; blocking and lagging often form adequate lateral bracing. JOINTS. Simple forms are desirable; object is to get full strength of

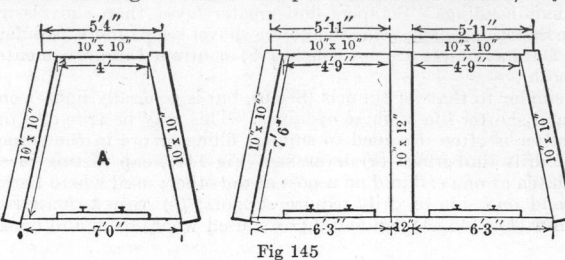

Fig 145

timbers with as little framing as possible. Fig 143 shows typical joints: (*a*) is cheapest to frame, but cap may split under vertical pressure; (*b*) avoids this danger; (*c*) is as good as (*b*) and cheaper to frame; (*d*) and (*e*) are designed to give both cap and post the strength of full cross-sec and are good where both vertical and lateral pressures are heavy. Joint (*a*) is common for junction of post and sill in full sets.

Special sets. In heavy ground, sets may be reinforced by diagonal braces between cap and post (seriously reducing head room unless sets are high). In some cases a second complete set is placed inside the first. For heavy moving ground, a set like that shown in Fig 144 was developed in the Southwest. Squeeze-blocks are put between bridge and set. Outside set is of lighter timber. Pressure can be relieved by removing lagging and picking out back and sides. The outer set will fail before main set, and may then be replaced without interference with tramming. Under a stope, to give height for placing chutes, the bridge in Fig 144 may be supported on short posts instead of blocks (318). In wide openings, various forms of RAFTER SETS (Sec 6) are sometimes used, or center posts placed (Fig 145). At switches and turnouts special sets are required (Sec 11). In soft, swelling ground, press on sets can be relieved by letting loose material squeeze through spaces between lagging; at United Verde Ext mine, vert lagging of 16-lb rail spaced at 6 in was used in some places for this reason. A method for timbering drifts through swelling ground in United Verde and Braden mines (Fig 146) gives prompt relief of local press. Wall lagging, of plank cut to fit between posts, is supported on cleats sloping toward walls; planks can

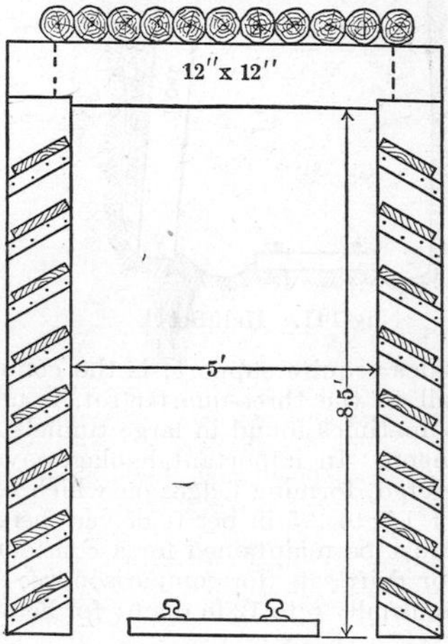

Fig 146.   Shelf Lagging for Loose Ground

be lifted out for removing loose material behind them. Under very adverse conditions, in some parts of United Verde Ext mine, the bulkhead in Fig 147, composed of scrap ends of timber, proved more serviceable than reinforced concrete (90). For special methods of advancing headings in soft, heavy ground, where timber is required at the face, see Sec 6. In rock which disintegrates on exposure to air and moisture, guniting with 2 coats of cement mortar may often save expense of replacing timbers; but it

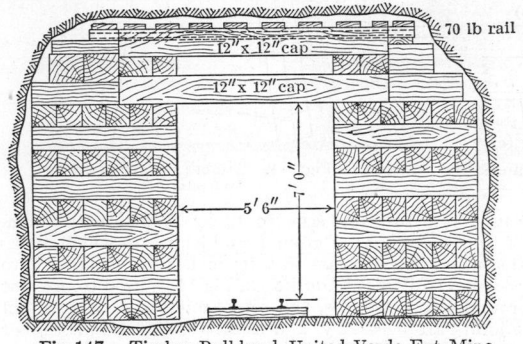

Fig 147.   Timber Bulkhead, United Verde Ext Mine

is useless if ground is subject to even slight movement.

Steel sets are less common in metal than in coal mines (Art 111). Frood mine (93) places 7-in Ni-steel I-beams, on 11.5-ft centers, across tops of its footwall haulage drifts 9 ft wide by 10.5 ft high. Ends of beams are cemented in hitches or rested on concrete pilasters. Lagging is of 4-in Ni-steel I-beams (usually 4, spaced across width of drift) with blocks and wedges supporting the back. Many mines utilize second-hand steel for support of shaft stations or other wide openings.

21. RAISES

General. Raises are preferable to winzes wherever feasible, as they can be driven faster and cheaper. When steeper than about 40°, there is practically no mucking cost, because broken material falls or slides to level below and is loaded into cars through a chute; on flatter slopes, mucking is necessary, but often done cheaply by scraper. In strong ground, little or no timbering is necessary where pitch is less than about 45°; in steeper raises timber is needed to support men when drilling. Raises at about 45° are usually cheaper per ft than those flatter or steeper, but advantage of lower cost over steeper raises may be offset by their greater length. Some mines find a pitch of about 60° most economical from all standpoints. Vert or very steep raises usually have 2 compartments, manway and chute, and are carried up like a shrinkage stope (Art 67), only the necessary amount of broken rock from each round being drawn to give working space at

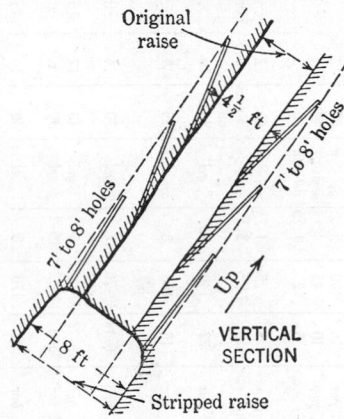

Fig 148. Enlarging a Raise by Stripping from Bottom

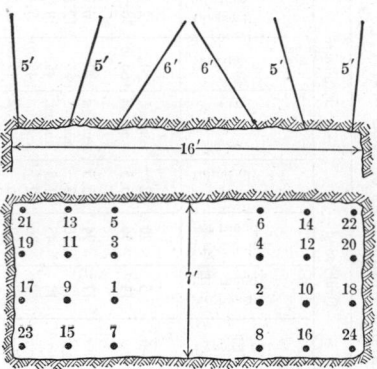

Fig 149. Simple V-cut, Sullivan Mine, Kimberley, B C

the face. Manway may be separated from chute side by lined stulls, or built of cribbing or lagged sets. "Pilot" raises are common as first step in sinking large shafts, where access is possible from one or more levels; raises are then enlarged, beginning at top, by methods resembling underhand stoping (Art 35) with great economy in labor of mucking. At Braden mine, pilot raises for a large vert shaft were zig-zagged at 50°. Fig 148 shows a method of stripping a pilot raise to full sec, starting at bottom (522).

In certain foreign countries, native labor is more adept at sinking winzes than driving raises. In such cases winzes are often sunk to meet raises from below, thereby increasing development speed without increasing cost of work.

Data on raises in Table 20, generously contributed by the managements and engineering departments of the mines listed, show present practice (1938) in raising in the U S, and give information on cross-sec, drill rounds, explosives, speed of advance, etc.

Cross-section of raises is usually square or rectangular. Width in narrow veins is often full width of vein; minimum possible width is about 2.5 ft; 3.5 ft is better; must be increased on dips less than 45°.

Cross-sec should be long enough to provide room for 2 compartments and the necessary timbering, also to allow cut holes to be placed efficiently; 5 to 7 ft is usual practice in small openings. Prospecting or exploratory raises, and those driven solely for ventilation in connection with mining, are kept small to reduce cost. Cross-sec of raises for handling ore or waste is adapted to amount of material passing and size of pieces. In connection with square-set stopes, dimensions of raises are often determined by size of sets (Art 48); if raise is for inside hoisting, cross-sec is computed as for shafts.

Drills and mounting. Unmounted stopers are used for raising unless the pitch is very flat, in which case bar-mounted drifters may be better. These are sometimes used in very hard ground, even in steep raises. Among the examples in Table 20, stopers with automatic rotation greatly outnumber hand-rotated stopers.

Arrangement of holes. In raising, all types of round are used, as in drifts; similarity between raising and drifting increases as the dip flattens. Table 20 indicates in general the rounds required for different rocks and cross-sec of raise. Fig 149–158 show some of

Table 20. Data on Raising Practice, as of 1938

Example No	Mine and location	Type of ground	Inclination, °	Section Length, ft	Section Width, ft	Drills Type	Drills Mounting	Drills No at face	Type of cut	No holes per round	Ft of hole per round	Hours to drill round (a)	Explosive Type	% N.G.[1]	Lb per ft	Type of timbering	Advance Per round	Advance Per month	Man-shifts Drill and blast	Man-shifts Mucking	Man-shifts Timbering	Man-shifts Total
	AREA 30 SQ FT OR LESS																					
1	Inspiration, Inspiration, Ariz.	m-s sch	45-90	3.5	3.5	h-r stop		1	t-dr	5	20	2	am-gel	30	2.1	stulls	4	var	0.125	0.062	0.063	0.25
2	Hiawatha No 2, Stambaugh, Mich	h hematite	90	3.5	3.5	a-r stop		1	pyr	14	56	5.5	semi-gel	60 (b)	10		3.5	var	0.15	0.08		0.23
3	Balmat, Balmat, N Y	ls	45-90	4	4	a-r stop		1	bur	17	94	5.5	semi-gel	40	6.75	crib	5	130	0.20			0.20
4	Pioneer, Ely, Minn	s grnstn	55-90	4	4	h-r stop		1	mod V	12	56	5	am-gel	45	12.5	crib	4	120	0.25	0.13	0.25	0.63
5	Pioneer, Ely, Minn	s hematite	55-90	4	4	a-r stop		1	pyr	10	45	3	am-gel	45	10	crib	4	140	0.125	0.125	0.25	0.50
6	Bates, Iron River, Mich	h hematite	90	5	circ	a-r stop		1	bur	9	36	1.5	semi-gel	45 (b)	5.4	oc'l stull	3.5	var	0.143			0.143
7	Franklin, Franklin, N J	ls, peg and gn	50 and 90 (c)	4.5	4.5	a-r stop		1	pyr	17	150	2	semi-gel	45 (b)	6.25	stull	8	var	0.25			0.25
8	Soudan, Soudan, Minn	grnstn	65-90	4.5	4.5	a-r stop		1	pyr	12	48	6	am-dyn	50	10	stulls	3.5	50	0.57	0.07	0.50	1.14
9	Inspiration, Inspiration, Ariz	m-s sch	50-60	5	5	h-r stop		1	t-dr	5-7	25-35	3	am-gel	30	2.5	crib	5	180	0.10	0.025	0.225	0.35
10	Miami, Miami, Ariz	m-h to s sch	55	5	5	h-r stop		2	t-dr	9	50	2	gel dyn	40	5	crib	6	60	0.33		0.33	0.66
11	Burra Burra, Ducktown, Tenn	sch and sul	45-90	5	5	a-r stop		2	pyr	17	110	5	am-dyn	40	7.5		5.75	var	0.53			0.53
12	Flin Flon, Flin Flon, Man	h sul	65	5	5	a-r stop		2	pyr	16	88	6	gel dyn	60	14.11		4.71	var	0.48			0.48
13	Flin Flon, Flin Flon, Man	s sch	65	5	5	a-r stop		2	pyr	16	100	5	gel dyn	60	12.84		5.02	100	0.395			0.395
14	Ray, Ray, Ariz	s sch	60-90	5	5	j'ham or a-r stop		1	pyr	10	45	4	semi-gel	40	4	crib	4	315	0.125	0.125		0.25
15	Godfrey, Hibbing, Minn	slate	90	5	5	a-r stop		1	none	5	25	1.75	gel-dyn	60	2.5		5		0.10	0.05	0.05	0.20
16	Godfrey, Hibbing, Minn	s hematite	90	5	5	j'ham		1	none	5	25	1.75	gel dyn	60	2	crib	4.13	194	0.10	0.05	0.05	0.20
17	Matahambre, Prov Pinar del Rio, Cuba	mass sul	42-50	7	4	a-r stop		1	mod pyr	16	74.5	3.5	semi-gel	45 and 60 (b)	6.3	stulls	5.5	135				0.484
18	Mt Hope, Mt Hope, N J	mass magnetite	35-90	5	6	a-r stop		1	bur	22	140	var.	gel	40	10		5	130	0.4			0.4
19	Hollinger, Timmins, Ont	grnstn and por	40-50	6	5	a-r stop		1	bur	18	108	8	am dyn	55	9.1	crib	5	150		0.40		0.4
	AREA 30-60 SQ FT																					
20	Ruth, Ruth, Nev	m-h por and ls	50-65	7	4.5	h-r stop		1	pyr	6-14	30-70	1-2.5	gel	30	4		5		0.20	0.15		0.4
21	Junction, Bisbee, Ariz	ls and sul	50-90	8	4	h-r stop		1	pyr	18-24	90-120	5	gel	40	12	stulls	4.5	40-45	0.20	0.15	0.31	0.66
22	Ruth, Ruth, Nev	s por and ls	50-65	7.5	4.5	h-r stop		1	var	3-8	12-32	0.5-2	gel	30	var	crib	2-4	60-120		0.05		0.25
23	Homestake, Lead S D	h sch	80-90	7	5	a-r stop		2	bur	23	170	8	gel	40	14	stulls	7.3	70	0.70	0.05	0.05	0.80

No.	Mine and location	Rock				Method			Round				Explosive			Timbering						
24	Presidio, Shafter, Tex	h ls	90	7	5	h-r stop			V	18	72	7	semi-gel	40	7.38	stulls	3.5	45				0.677
25	Champion, Painesdale, Mich	basalt	70	9	4	a-r stop		2	bur	27	162	6	gel dyn	40	16	stulls	6	80	0.4	0.35	0.4	0.8
26	Spruce, Eveleth, Minn	cherty form	90	6	6	a-r stop		1	pyr	9–15	54–90	4–6	gel dyn	60	8.5	oc'l crib	5	160	0.35	0.025	0.025	0.375
27	Spruce, Eveleth, Minn	compact hematite	90	6	6	j'ham		1,2	2-hole	10	60	2–3	gel dyn	60	6.2	crib	5	160	0.175	0.025	0.225	0.425
28	Zeibright, Nevada City, Cal	tough dike	80	6	6	a-r stop		2	pyr	26	208	10	gel dyn	45 (d)	13.2	sprags	7.5	50 (d)	1.1			1.1
29	Bunker Hill, Kellogg, Id	quartzite	45	7	5.4	a-r stop		1	2-hole	12	72	5	semi-gel	45 (b)	10	stulls	5	150	0.2			0.2
30	Humboldt, Mill City, Nev	h hornfels	70	8	5	h-r stop		1	cent V	14–16	68	6.5	gel	35	12	stulls	3	70	0.33	0.16	0.75	1.24
31	La Colorada, Cananea, Mex	bree por	90	8	5	h-r stop		1	cent V	18	99	4.5	gel	40	8	stulls	5	80	0.30	0.20		1.0
32	Empire Star Group, Grass Valley, Cal	diabase and diorite	30–35	8	5	h-f dr or j'ham	col	1	t-dr	14	70	6	gel	40	7–10	stulls	4	104	0.30	0.20	0.05	0.55
33	Horne, Noranda, Que	h rhyolite	45	7	6.5	a-r stop		2	bur	23	160	10	gel	40	14		5.23	146	0.765			0.765
34	McIntyre, Schumacher, Ont	h sch and qtz	45–50	7	6	a-r stop		2	bur-pyr	26	180	3.5	gel dyn	40	11		5.7	var	0.4			0.4
35	Dome, So Porcupine, Ont	h basalt	50	9	5	a-r stop		2	cent V	24	130	4	dyn	40	20	stulls	5	154	0.40	0.10	0.25	0.75
36	Magma, Superior, Ariz	diabase	80	8	6	h-r stop		2	cent V	20	108	6	gel dyn	40	19	crib	4	100	0.5	0.25	0.25	1.0
37	Morning, Mullan, Id	h quartzite	51	10	5	a-r stop		2	cent V	19–26	114–156	5	gel	40	15	stulls	5	50	0.75	0.45	0.40	1.60
38	Montreal, Montreal, Wis	s hematite	65	10	5	j'ham	feed, leg	1	pyr	10	50	2	gel	40	4.5	crib	4.5	200	0.125	0.125	0.25	0.50
39	Junction, Bisbee Ariz	ls	50–90	10	5	h-r stop		1	bur	18–26	90–130	3–6	gel	40	7–12	crib	4.5	30–40	0.20	0.15	0.33	0.68
40	Murchie, Nevada City, Cal	h diorite	60–70	10	5	a-r stop		1	pyr	14–18	80	5	gel dyn	40	10–12	stulls	4	100	0.25	0.25	0.25	0.75
41	Bluff, Britannia Beach, B C	m-h breccia	57+	9	5	a-r stop		2	cent V	18–24	96–130	14	gel	60	25	stulls	3.35	126	0.50		0.25	0.75
42	Frisco, S F del Oro, Chih, Mex	h mass sul	65–90	11	6	a-r stop	col	2	end V	28	140	6	gel	60	17.7	stulls	4.1	35	1.7	1.7	1.7	3.4
43	C & H Conglom, Calumet, Mich	felsit conglom	38	8	5	h-f dr	col	2	pyr	18–20	120	8–9	gel and dyn	30–35	10.75		4.5	120	0.45	0.2		0.65
44	Scott, Hockersville, Okla	flint and h ls	50–60	8	7	h-f dr		1	bur	18–23	117–150		gel and h ls	45 and 60 (b)	18		6–7	140	0.26	0.27		0.53
45	Geneva, Ironwood, Mich	h jasper	60–90	10	7	a-r stop		1	V	21	80	13.75	semi-gel	45 (b)	10	crib	3–3.5	60	1.14	0.25	0.32	1.71
46	Geneva, Ironwood, Mich	m-h hematite	60–90	10	6	j'hcm auger		1	cent V	12	60	10.15	semi-gel		6	crib	4–4.5	90–95	0.70	0.20	0.22	1.12
47	Lake Shore, Kirkland Lake, Ont	h por	50–90	10	6	a-r stop		2	pyr	23	142	5.5	gel	40	14.32	stulls	5.82	154	0.343	0.343	0.343	0.687
48	Wright-Hargreaves, Kirkland Lake, Ont	h por	75	12	5	a-r stop		2	end V	28	154	5	semi-gel	70	19	stulls	4	130	1.02	0.51		1.53
	Area 60 Sq Ft or More																					
49	Bonne Terre, Bonne Terre, Mo	dol	40±	9	7	j'ham	feed, leg, feed	2	cent V	26–28	192–208	6.25	gel	60	12.6		4.5	var	0.44	0.09		0.53
50	Lloyd, Ishpeming, Mich	m-s hematite	65–75	11	6	j'ham		2	cent V	20	100	3.5	gel or semi-gel	40	6	crib	5	80–100	0.8		0.8	1.6
51	Crescent, Kellogg, Id	quartzite	70–80	11	6	a-r stop		2	cent V	28	152	6	semi-gel	45 (b)	20	sets	5	150	0.40	0.15	0.35	0.90
52	United Verde, Jerome, Ariz	por or h sul	90	11	6	a-r stop		2	end V	32	180	5	semi-gel	50	20	stulls or crib	4.75	50–60	0.5	0.1	0.5	1.1
53	Newport, Ironwood, Mich	s hematite	63–70	11	6	a-r stop		2	none	12	66	1	gel	35	6	crib	5	81	0.20	0.175	0.175	0.55

Table 20. Data on Raising Practice, as of 1938—(Continued)

Example No	Mine and location	Type of ground	Inclination, °	Section, ft Length	Section, ft Width	Drills Type	Drills Mounting	Drills No at face	Drill round Type of cut	Drill round No holes per round	Drill round Ft of hole per round	Drill round Hours to drill (a)	Explosive Type	Explosive % N gl	Explosive Lb per ft advance	Type of timbering	Advance, ft Per round	Advance, ft Per month	Man-shifts per ft advance Drill and blast	Man-shifts per ft advance Mucking	Man-shifts per ft advance Timbering	Man-shifts per ft advance Total
54	Newport, Ironwood, Mich.	q'tz slate	70	11	6	a-r stop	....	2	bur	17	93.5	3.5	gel	35&80	10.2	crib	5	112	0.325	0.150	0.175	0.65
55	Page, Page, Id.	h quartzite	45	10.5	6.4	a-r stop	....	2	cent V	16-25	80-125	4	gel	40	15	sets	5	65	0.4	0.1	0.3	0.8
56	Pecos, Terrero, N M.	mass sul	90	12	6	h-r stop	....	1	end dr	24	144	11	gel dyn	55	10	sets	5	60	0.65	0.15	1.20	2.00
57	Creighton, Creighton Mine, Ont	mass and diss sul	65-90	11	7	a-r stop	....	2	end bur	32	248	11	am dyn / gel dyn	40	25.7	crib	7	97	0.775	....	0.340	1.115
58	Climax, Climax, Colo.	m-h frac granite	45-60	12	7	a-r stop	....	1-2	pyr cent V	18	108	2 drill shifts	semi-gel	45 (b)	10-15	stulls	5	var	0.4	....	0.3	0.7
59	Idaho-Maryland, Grass Valley, Cal	tough por	40-90	18	5	a-r stop	....	2	cent V	24	135	8	semi-gel	45 (b)	12	sets	5	125	0.4	....	0.4	0.8
60	Tintic Standard, Dividend, Utah	h quartzite	90	13	7	a-r stop	....	1	pyr	26	143	16	semi-gel	40	10	sq-sets	5	45	0.40	2.663		3.063
61	Sullivan, Kimberley, B C	chert	60	16	7	h-f dr	col	2	cent V	18	54	14	gel	60	25	stulls	3	48	1.5	....	0.5	2.0
62	Sullivan, Kimberley, B C	mass sul	40	16	7	a-r stop	....	2	cent V	24	120	6	gel	60	22	....	4	100	0.5	....	....	0.5
63	Steward, Butte, Mont.	h sul	50-90	18	8	a-r stop	....	2	cent V	44	250	16	semi-gel	45 (b)	18.8	sets	5.75	31.4	0.765	0.509	0.255	1.53
64	Lake Shore, Kirkland Lake, Ont	h por	70-90	18	10	a-r stop	....	2	cent V	36	236	11	gel	40	20.57	sets	6.1	125	0.737	0.061	0.677	1.475
65	Ahmeek, Ahmeek, Mich.	amygd	34	30-40	7-7.5	h-f dr	col	2	cent V	30-35	210-245	14	am dyn	66		....	4.5-5.5	100	1.0	1.6	....	2.6
66	Victoria, Britannia Beach, B C.	tough sul	70-80	14	vein	a-r stop	....	2	cent V	28+	232	6	gel	40	30	sets	6.5	40-50	0.3-0.6	....	0.3-0.6	0.6-1.2

(a) Including time for setting-up and dismantling drills. (b) Bulk strength. (c) 80% are vert; 20% at 50°. (d) Same crew also does other work. h = hard. m-h = medium hard. s = soft. m-s = medium soft. ls = limestone. dol = dolomite. gn = gneiss. grn = greenstone. sul = sulphide. a-r stop = automatically rotated stoper drill. sch = schist. grnstn = greenstone. por = porphyry. peg = pegmatite. h-r stop = hand-rotated stoper. h-f dr = hand-fed drifter. j'ham = jackhammer. t-dr = top-draw. pyr = pyramid. bur = burned. cent V = central V-cut. mod pyr = modified type between pyramid and V-cut. gel = gelatin. semi-gel = semi-gelatin dynamite. am = ammonia gelatin or dynamite. oc'l = occasional. var = too variable to allow averaging; in case of monthly advance, variations occur with distance above level, but are due principally to irregular number of days devoted to raising.

the raise rounds named in the table; numbers at holes indicate order of firing. Where timbering is used, round should be planned to minimize injury to timbers; in 2-comp raises, cut holes are usually over the chute compartment rather than the manway (Fig 162).

Number of holes per round for raises is shown in Table 20. Distance between holes

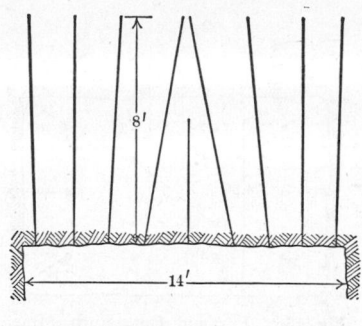

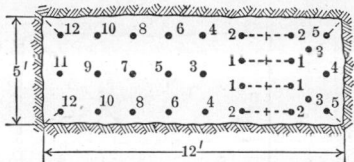

Fig 151.   End V-cut, Wright-Hargreaves Mine, Kirkland Lake, Ont. Holes average 4.5 ft deep

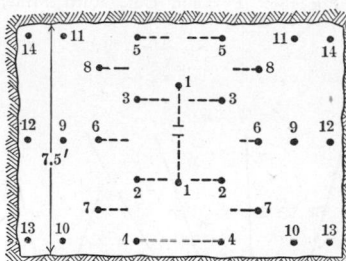

Fig 150.   Reinforced Center V-cut in Tough Sulphides. Victoria Mine, Britannia Beach, B C

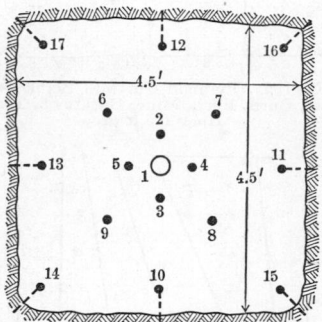

Fig 152.   Burned Cut, Franklin Mine, Franklin, N J. Holes 8.5 ft deep. Center hole not loaded; others fired in sequence, as numbered, using fuses all of same length. Two rounds loaded and fired separately: Nos 2–9, Nos 10–17

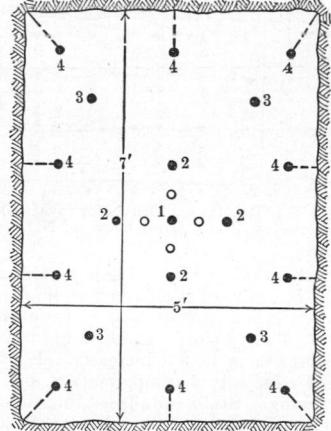

Fig 153.   Burned Cut, Homestake Mine, Lead, S D. Holes 7 ft–4 in deep

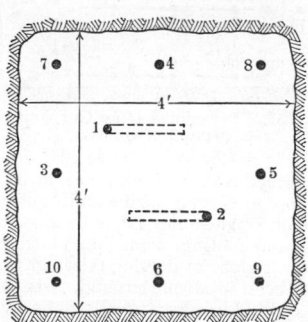

Fig 154.   X-cut in Soft Hematite, Pioneer Mine, Ely, Minn. Holes 4.5 ft deep

increases with size of cross-sec; larger space allows cut holes to be placed to better advantage with a drill of a given length, and deeper rounds can be pulled.

Loading and tramming from raise chutes (see Table 19 for data).

Timbering and general procedure. Fig 159 shows mode of driving a small inclined raise (113). Up to dip of 40° no timber is required to support men; above 30°, it is best to place small horiz stulls 4 or 5 ft apart and 6–10 in above footwall. Muck collects behind these, forming steps which aid in climbing raise and supporting drills; the steps also catch steel and tools, dropped accidentally. Support for tail-piece of stope drill may

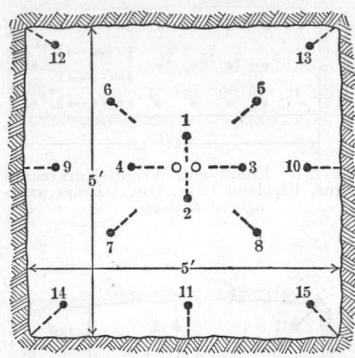

Fig 155. Pyramid Cut with Blank Center, Burra Burra Mine, Ducktown, Tenn. Holes 6.5 ft deep

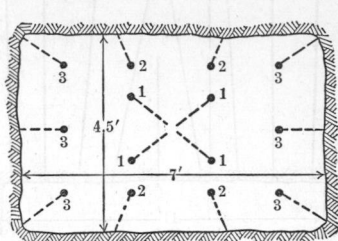

Fig 156. Pyramid Cut, Ruth Mine, Ruth, Nev. Holes average 6 ft deep

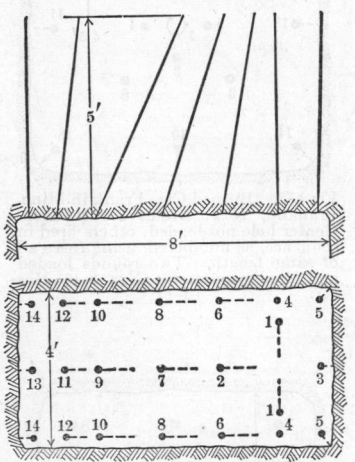

Fig 157. Pyramided Draw Cut, Junction Mine, Bisbee, Ariz

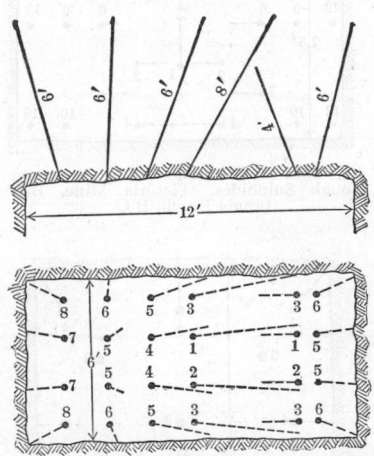

Fig 158. Reinforced Draw Cut in Massive Sulphides, Pecos Mine, Terrero, N Mex

be obtained from a plank brace, as in Fig 159. In steep raises, timbering is usually necessary to support platforms and ladders, even when the ground itself requires no support. In small, single-compartment raises, simplest timbering is a row of stulls across each end, to serve as footing for drilling platforms (Fig 160). The platform is moved up, round by round. Safety of driving raises in this manner decreases as height increases. For larger raises, even in strong ground, it is better to divide raise into 2 compartments, one for a pipe and ladderway; usually done by stulls or cribbing. Stulls are placed in pairs 4–5 ft or more apart along pitch of raise, one at one end of the raise and the other 2–4 ft toward the middle (Fig 161). Inside row is lagged to form a partition between manway and chute. Platforms may be left as desired in manway compartment and ladders staggered for safety. If manway is small, pockets (P, Fig 161) may be cut at intervals of 30–40 ft for storing drill and tools. Muck may be drawn completely after each round, but it is usually best to draw only enough to give working room at top. Fig 162 shows 2-compartment raise in strong ground, with cribbed manway. In weak ground, square-sets (Art 47) or "double" cribbing are often used. Fig 163 shows a double-cribbed raise at Magma

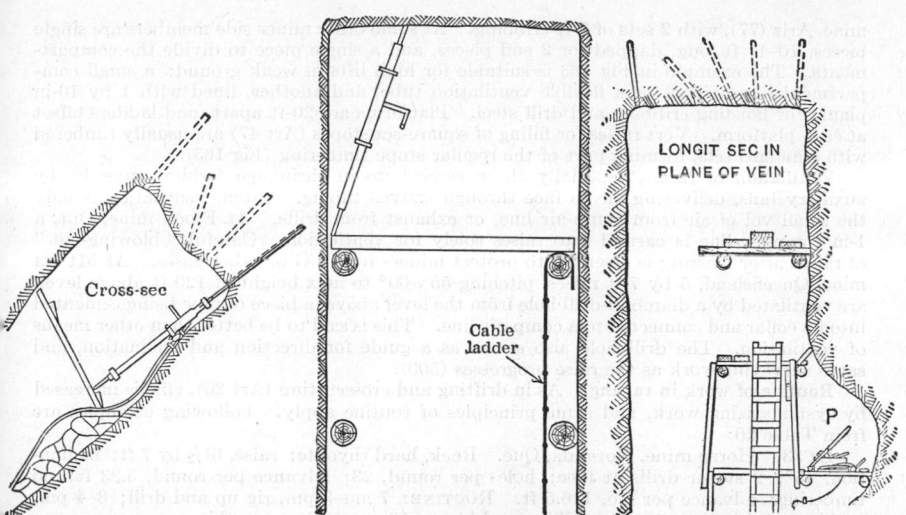

Fig 159.   Draw-cut for Small
Inclined Raise

Fig 160.   Use of Stulls in Single-
compt Raise

Fig 161.   Draw-cut for Small
Vert Raise

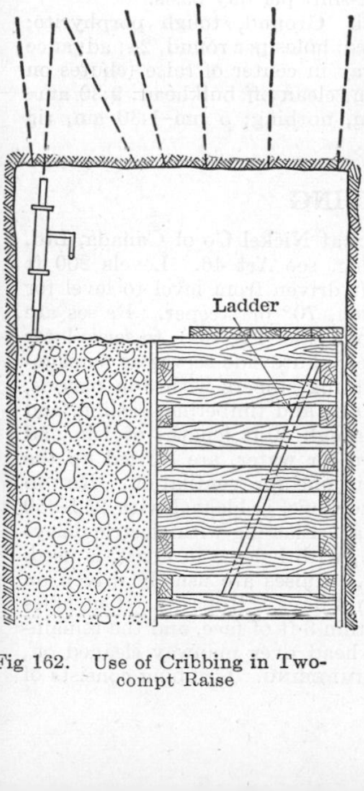

Elev and Sec

Fig 162.   Use of Cribbing in Two-
compt Raise

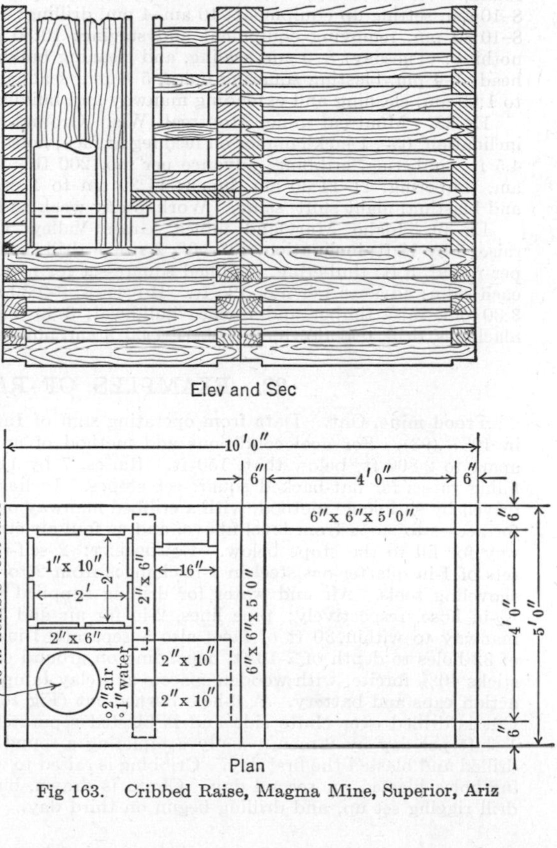

Fig 163.   Cribbed Raise, Magma Mine, Superior, Ariz

mine, Ariz (77), with 2 sets of 5-ft cribbing. At some other mines side members are single pieces, 10–11 ft long, dapped for 2 end pieces, and a single piece to divide the compartments. The example in Fig 163 is suitable for high lifts in weak ground; a small compartment is provided for a flexible ventilation tube, and another, lined with 1 by 10-in plank, for hoisting cribbing and drill steel. Platforms are 20-ft apart, and ladders offset at each platform. Vert raises for filling of square-set stopes (Art 47) are usually timbered with standard sets, forming part of the regular stope timbering (Fig 165).

Ventilation of raises, especially those carried up in shrinkage fashion, may be by auxiliary fans, delivering air to face through canvas tubing. Often, ventilation is only the small vol of air from comp-air line, or exhaust from drills. At Frood mine, Ont, a 1-in comp-air line is carried into raises solely for ventilation. Careful "blowing-out" of raises after blasting is essential to protect miners from CO or other gases. At Mt Isa mine, Queensland, 5 by 7-ft raises, pitching 55°–60° to max height of 120 ft above level, are ventilated by a diamond-drill hole from the level above, a piece of pipe being cemented into its collar and connected to a comp-air line. This is said to be better than other means of ventilation. The drill hole also serves as a guide for direction and inclination, and saves surveying work as the raise progresses (500).

Routine of work in raising. As in drifting and crosscutting (Art 20), effic is increased by systematizing work, and same principles of routine apply. Following examples are from Table 20:

Ex 33. Horne mine, Noranda, Que. Rock, hard rhyolite; raise, 6 1/2 by 7 ft; inclination, 45°; 2 stoper drills at face; holes per round, 23; advance per round, 5.23 ft; no timbering; advance per mo, 146.5 ft. ROUTINE: 7 am–3 pm, rig up and drill; 3–4 pm, nothing; 4–12 pm, complete drilling and blast; 12 pm to 7 am, nothing.

Ex 57. Creighton mine, Ont. Ground, disseminated to massive sulphide; raise, 7 by 11 ft; inclination, 65°–90°; 2 stoper drills at face; holes per round, 32; advance per round, 7 ft; timbering, cribbed manway; advance per mo, 97 ft. ROUTINE: (Monday) 8–10 am, setting up equipment; 10 am–4 pm, drilling; 4–5 pm, nothing; 5–8 pm, drilling; 8–10:30 pm, removing equipment and staging; 10:30 pm–1 am, blasting cut; 1–8 am, nothing; (Tuesday) 8–9 am, scaling, and cleaning bulkhead; 9 am to 1 pm, raising bulkhead; 1–4 pm, blasting squaring holes; 5–8 pm, scaling, and cleaning bulkhead; 8:00 pm to 1:00 am, cleaning and extending manway and building staging.

Ex 38. Montreal mine, Montreal, Wis. Ground, soft hematite; raise, 5 by 10 ft; inclination, 65°; 1 jackhammer on feed leg at face; holes per round, 10; advance per round, 4.5 ft; timbering, cribbing; advance per mo, 200 ft. ROUTINE: 7–8 am, mucking; 8–11 am, timbering; 11–11:30 am, lunch; 11:30 am to 1 pm, timbering; 1–3:30 pm, drilling and blasting; night shift, same. Work, 5-day week and 2-shift per day basis.

Ex 59. Idaho Maryland mines, Grass Valley, Cal. Ground, tough porphyrite; raise, 5 by 18 ft; inclination, 40°–90°; 2 stoper drills at face; holes per round, 24; advance per round, 5 ft; timbering, modified square-set for manway in center of raise (chutes on each side); advance per mo, 125 ft. ROUTINE: 8-9:30 am, clean off bulkhead; 9:30 am–3:30 pm, raise timber and replace bulkhead; 3:30–5 pm, nothing; 5 pm–1:30 am, rig machines, drill, tear down, and blast; 1:30–8 am, nothing.

22. EXAMPLES OF RAISING

Frood mine, Ont. Data from operating staff of Internat Nickel Co of Canada, Ltd, in 1937 (93). For geol conditions and method of mining, see Art 46. Levels 200 ft apart to 2 800 ft; below that, 150 ft. Raises, 7 by 11 ft driven from level to level for filling raises for flat-backed square-set stopes. Inclination, 70° or steeper. Raises are driven by shrinkage method, with a cribbed manway on one side (Fig 164), to serve later for access to stope from level above, and as foul-air outlet; chute side serves as passageway for fill to the stope below. EQUIPMENT: 2 self-rotating stopers with 3-in pistons, sets of 1-in quarter-oct steel in 1-ft changes from 2 to 10 ft, and timbering, scaling, and shoveling tools. Air and water for drilling supplied through 50-ft lengths of 1-in and 1/2-in hose, respectively; pipe lines, 2-in for air and 1-in for water, are carried up the manway to within 30 ft of face; also a separate 1-in air line for ventilation. ROUND of 32 holes to depth of 7-10 ft, depending on ground conditions, is blasted with 250–350 sticks 40% forcite, with wooden spacers and clay tamping. Blasting with electric delay-action caps and battery. A 6-hole burned-cut (Fig 164), with holes 2 in apart, is used. Cut is drilled over chute side and is blasted separately. Raises are usually driven on 1 shift per day by 2 men, usually completing a round in 3 days. ROUTINE. Cut holes drilled and blasted the first day. Cribbing is raised to within 3 ft of face, and the remaining holes blasted on second day. Chute is drawn, bulkhead over manway cleaned off, drill rigging set up, and drilling begun on third day. TIMBERING. Cribbing consists of

5-in squared jackpine, dapped back 6 in from each end. Two pieces of 7-ft cribbing are placed from foot to hanging wall about 8 ft apart, as bearers to hold cribbing in place during later stoping. Chute side of cribbing is lined with 4 by 8-in by 7-ft plank. A 20 by 24-in plank-lined compartment is carried along the footwall side, in corner of manway for hoisting materials during raising. Platforms built every 15 ft, with staggered ladder along the footwall. A control chute (Fig 164) is constructed about half way between levels, so that the raisemen can more effectively control drawing off broken rock. Chute at foot of raise is drawn periodically by the motor-haulage crew.

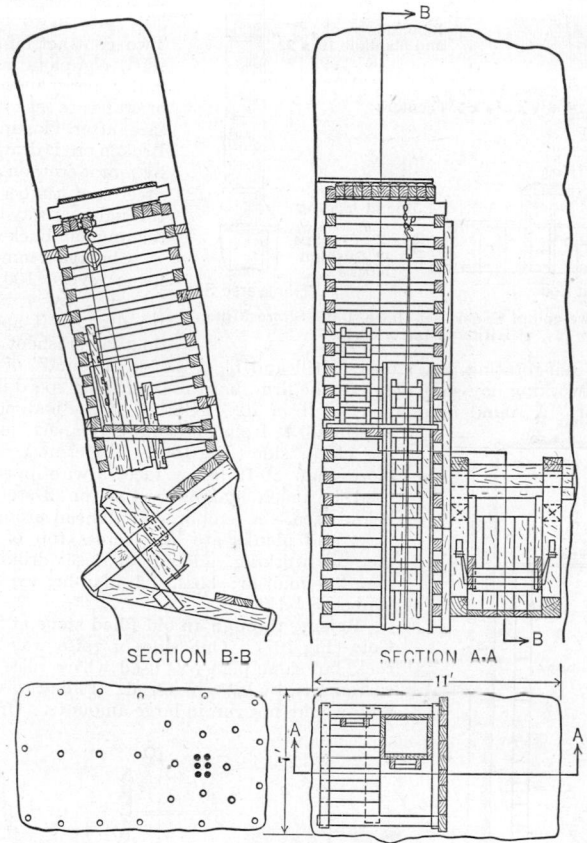

SECTION B-B   SECTION A-A

Fig 164. Plan and Sec of Fill Raise, Frood Mine, Ont

Lake Shore mine, Ont. Data from L. S. Weldon in 1936 (95). For geol conditions and method of mining, see Art 46. Square-sets are used in driving vert raises for delivering waste fill to square-set stopes. Raises are both 2- and 3-compt, with manway for access from level above. In 3-compt raise, manway is in center set; chutes on both sides permit simultaneous filling of both sections of a double-rill stope. Fig 165 shows 2-compt raise. Sets are 8 ft high, with posts on 5-ft 4-in centers; caps and girts, 8 by 8-in; posts of light, round timber; chute lining, 3 by 8-in. Round is of 22–28 holes, double-pyramid cut over the chute end of raise being commonest. Two drillers and a helper drill the round and blast cut holes in one shift. Aver advance, 5.8 ft per round, but skilled miners can break 6.25 ft per round. Two timbermen, on next shift, draw the chute, raise and block the sets, blast the remaining holes, and prepare for next round. A novel feature in square-set raises is a 16 by 22-in opening ("pigeon hole"), cut in chute lining below the bulkhead; it serves as a vent to release the force of blasting concussion, as an exit after placing the bulkhead, and to aid the clearing of blasting fumes by blowing compressed air.

United Verde mine, Ariz. Levels, 150 ft apart, are connected by vert or steeply dipping, 6 by 11-ft raises. In soft ground, manway at one end is cribbed, 56 in sq in clear, with 5 by 8-in pine, set on edge and notched at corners; lined stulls suffice in harder ground. Round for hard ground, usually of 32 5–6-ft holes, end-draw cut, drilled with stopers, takes 95 lb of 50% gelatin to break 4.75 ft. Two contract miners, in 1 8-hr shift, complete raise at rate of 0.91 ft per man-day. Cribbing or stulls are set to within 7 ft of face after blasting 2 rounds. Broken ore is drawn from chute by motor crew on another shift. Steel and timber are hoisted through manway by tugger and rectangular bucket.

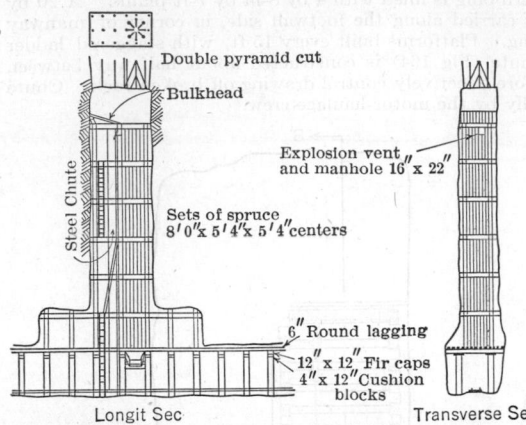

Double pyramid cut
Bulkhead
Explosion vent and manhole 16″ x 22″
Sets of spruce 8′0″x 5′4″x 5′4″centers
Steel Chute
6″ Round lagging
12″ x 12″ Fir caps
4″x 12″Cushion blocks
Longit Sec
Transverse Sec

Fig 165. Two-compt Square-set Raise, Lake Shore Mine, Kirkland Lake, Ont

miners, with self-rotating wet stopers, drill and blast a "burnt-round" of 26 6-ft holes in 2.5 shifts, working day-shift only; in the firm, hard rock, drilling speed in 1.5-in holes is 3.9 ft per hr. A round takes about 84 lb of 40% gelatin. Raise is divided by a row

Champion mine, Mich, connects levels, 100 ft apart on 70° dip, by 4 by 8-ft raises usually 200 ft apart in a productive oreshoot (488). Two of stulls 3 ft from one end, 3 ft apart, and lagged on the chute side (Fig 166). Uppermost stull is never more than 30 ft below face, a wire-rope ladder being used to reach staging resting on 2 stulls about 7 ft below face. A temporary bulkhead protects the manway, and planks are laid across top of chute while men are working. Per ft of raise: drilling and blasting, 6.6 man-hr; boss, 1.1 man-hr; explosives, 14 lb; timber, 8 bd ft.

Raising through an old filled stope at Silver Plume, Colo (Fig 167). One side of raise was next to solid rock, but same plan was used where raise was entirely surrounded by loose material. Filling was well packed, and would not run in large amounts. Original vein, 2

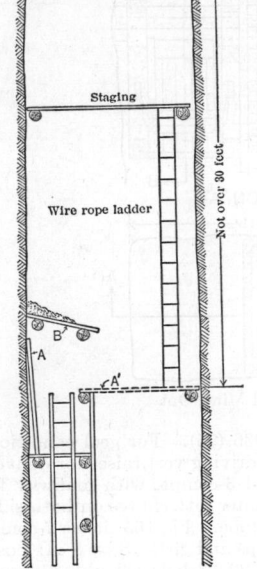

Staging
Wire rope ladder
Not over 30 feet
B
A
A′

Fig 166. Top of 4 by 8-ft Raise, Champion Mine, Painesdale, Mich. (Planks A are laid across at A′ when men ascend to start a new round. Sollar B is to protect main ladderway)

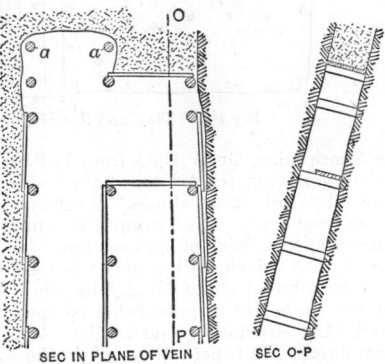

a
a′
O
P
SEC IN PLANE OF VEIN   SEC O-P

Fig 167. Raising at Silver Plume, Colo

to 4 ft wide; walls, fairly strong. Timbering consisted of 3 rows of short stulls about 4 ft apart, set in hitches, and dividing raise into a manway and chute. 2-in plank was spiked to middle row of stulls, to form a tight partition between compartments. Plank was also used for lagging the outside spreaders. Only half the face of the raise was advanced at one time, topmost stulls on other side being covered with planks to form a roof for protection of miner when at work. Excavation was done with a bar, loose material falling into chute below. When face had been advanced about 2 ft, temporary stulls *a* were put in and covered with plank. Miner stood under these and barred down face on other side of raise. Permanent stulls were put in when raise had advanced far enough, the lagging and partition being kept as near as possible to face. Ore in chute was kept as low as possible, so that a sudden cave would not fill up chute and imprison men.

Data on hand drilling in raises and winzes, given in Table 21, are for work done at Esperanza mine, Mex, in 1901 (85); Mexican labor, 3 8-hr shifts. Figures show clearly that the duty of this labor, in cu ft excavated per man-hr, is higher in raising than sinking; they also indicate a slightly higher aver duty in raising than in drifting and crosscutting (Table 15). Raise No 4 (Table 21), driven by machine drill, shows higher powder consumption per cu ft than others; this is generally true of machine-driven as compared with hand-driven openings.

Table 21. Raises and Winzes (Hand-drilling)

No		Width, ft	Height, ft	Kind of ground	Total length raised or sunk, ft	Aver daily advance, ft	Lb dynamite, 60% Ngl		Labor per ft		Aver advance	
							per lin ft	per cu ft	Miner-shifts	Peon-shifts	Per man-shift, lin ft	per man-hr, cu ft
1	Raise....	11	6	(c)	285	1.04	2.78	0.042	4.81	0.93	0.17	1.43
2	Raise....	11	6	(b)	476	1.31	1.75	0.027	6.69	0.82	0.13	1.10
3	Raise....	10	5.5	(c)	22	1.57	3.36	0.061	....	....	....	....
4	Raise *..	11	6.0	(d)	629	1.04	5.56	0.086	5.27	0.79	0.16	1.36
5	Winze...	10	5	(a)	96	1.33	1.95	0.039	7.30	0.48	0.13	0.80
6	Winze...	11	6	(e)	58	0.74	3.30	0.050	7.17	1.13	0.12	0.99
7	Winze...	11	6	(f)	40	0.94	1.20	0.018	10.71	1.66	0.08	0.67
8	Winze...	11	6	(d)	421	0.76	4.46	0.068	5.23	1.21	0.16	1.21

* Driven by machine; all others, hand-drilling. (a) Friable quartz. (b) Fairly hard quartz. (c) Fairly hard andesite. (d) Hard quartz. (e) Moderately hard shale. (f) Hard andesite. Ventilation poor in No 1, 3, 7; fair in No 4 and 8; good in other openings.

G. L. Schmutz in 1920 (523) gives comparative data in Table 22 for powder consumption in hand- and machine-drilled raises and winzes at a Mexican mine.

More careful control cut the aver powder consumption per ft in hand-driven winzes to 2.92 lb, in hand raises to 3.02 lb, and in machine-driven raises to 5.08 lb.

Table 22. Lb Powder per Ft Advance in a Mexican Mine

	Raises		Winzes	
	Hand	Machine	Hand	Machine
Minimum	3.0	3.0	3.0	3.0
Average	4.5	5.5	4.5	5.5
Maximum	7.0	9.0	7.0	8.0

23. WINZES

General. Work is same as for sinking small shafts (Sec 7). Hoisting is done by windlass, to small depths. Below 30–50 ft, 2 men are required, and small air or elec hoist is best (Sec 12, 15, 16); in some regions this may entail hiring of certificated engineman. In U S, winzes are less common than raises and are seldom for other than exploratory purposes, as they incur expense for hoisting and possible pumping, and can be advanced less rapidly. In So Africa, Mex, and wherever native labor is familiar with underhand working, winzes are commoner. They are sometimes drilled by hand, but usually with jackhammers, making an end or center-wedge cut like those in shafts. Examples follow.

Edwards zinc mine, N Y, sunk a 10 by 7-ft winze, inclined 42°, 300 ft through silicified dolomite footwall (253). Round of 33 holes, of which 8 formed a center-wedge cut about 6 ft deep, was drilled by 3 men, 1 with a mounted jackhammer and 2 with unmounted sinkers, on day shift. Same crew laid track of 30-lb rail on steel ties fastened to footwall by 1.5-in pins; permanent track ended 20–40 ft from bottom, slide rails spanning the interval; protective bulkheads were built 60 ft apart. No timbering required, but hoist compt was separated from ladderway by stulls and plank. Round charged with 100 lb of gelex, fired electrically with instantaneous caps and 6 delays, usually broke 4.5 ft. Mucking done on night shift by 3 men, 2 shoveling into 1-ton skip, while 1 operated 50-hp elec hoist and trammed to shaft.

Elkoro mines, Jarbidge, Nev. Entry is through adits. Winzes up to 150 ft deep have been much used for both exploration and production; vein averages about 6 ft wide and dips 70° (112). Winzes have 2 timbered compartments, 4 by 4 ft clear, hoisting with single 24-cu ft skip which dumps into 100-ton pocket above tramming level. While sinking, a bucket, of 1 200-lb capac and sliding on round poles, is used. Table 23 gives costs per ft (1930) for sinking 646 ft of 7 by 11-ft winzes at 0.36 ft per man-shift in fairly hard ground, moving 2 665 tons of rock and ore. Wages, $5.25–5.50 per 8 hr.

Table 23.   Cost per ft of Winze Sinking, Elkoro Mines, Nev

Labor	$15.146	Man-hours:	
Supervision	.293	Drilling and blasting	5.350
Compressed air	.936	Timbering	3.443
Steel sharpening	.315	Shoveling	5.696
Power	.434	Hoisting and tramming	7.443
Explosives (@23¢ lb)	2.106	Supervision	0.310
Timber	2.762	Total labor	22.242
Other supplies	.799	Explosives (40%) lb	9.177
Outside, incl assaying	.463	Timber lin ft	3.065
General exp	.565	Lumber bd ft	19.576
	$23.819	Labor was 69.71% of total cost	

Mt Hope magnetite mine, N J. Ore below the 1 000-ft level is developed by inclined winzes, 8 ft high by 9–10 ft wide, pitching at 14°; rock, hard granitoid gneiss (529). Two 150-lb drifters mounted on columns make a 22-hole round, including a 5-hole pyramid-cut about 5 ft deep, which is then blasted with 100 lb of 40% dynamite. Mucking usually starts in same 8-hr shift and is finished, together with rail laying, in next shift. Crew of 2 drillers, 1 helper, 3–4 muckers, aver 4.8 ft advance in 2 shifts. Contract price, $11.75–$12.50 per ft, Co supplying all but explosives. Cost of 809 ft sunk 1930, $19.72 per ft.

Tezuitlan mine, Puebla, Mex, uses winzes sparingly to explore massive sulphide deposits (533); sunk 5 by 8 ft with jackhammers, hoisting in 250-lb buckets with air tuggers. Hoist compt, 5 by 5 ft, is separated from ladder-way by planked stulls. Cost per ft of 46 ft sunk in 1930–31, at rate of 0.59 ft per 8 hr, is compared in Table 24 with cost per ft of 862 ft of raises, of same dimensions and timbering, advanced at 0.921 ft per 8 hr.

Table 24.   Winzes *vs* Raises, at Tezuitlan, Mex

	Winzes, per ft		Raises, per ft	
Drilling and blasting	8.101 man-hr	U S $ 2.540	10.880 man-hr	U S $ 2.245
Timbering	1.514 "	.472	1.399 "	.260
Shoveling	15.482 "	4.852	7.172 "	1.341
Hoisting and tramming	12.757 "	3.996	13.470 "	2.708
Supervision	1.873 "	.551	1.873 "	.551
Surface		1.235		1.235
Total labor	39.727 man-hr	$13.646	34.794 man-hr	$ 8.340
Explosives (40% gel)	10.978 lb	2.503	5.484 lb	1.250
Timber	27.304 bd ft	.758	26.212 bd ft	.728
Power (mainly air-comp)	251.43 kw-hr	.769	188.58 kw-hr	.577
Other supplies		4.870		2.960
Total direct cost		$22.546		$13.855

For other comparisons between winzes and raises in Mexican mines, see Tables 21, 22, Art 22.

Mexican Corp. Winzes proved more satisfactory and but slightly more expensive than raises for developing steeply pitching sulphide veins in graywacke and shales, at Fresnillo, Mex (535); this result is due partly to familiarity with jackhammers and scarcity of good timbermen. Winzes are 5 by 7 ft, and divided by stulls and planking into a 4 by 5-ft hoisting and a 3 by 5-ft ladder compt. Buckets, of 5.5–9-cu ft capac, sliding on 4 by 6-in skids, are hoisted with 7.5-hp elec, single-drum hoists. Contract prices (1935) were $5–$7 (U S) per ft, to depth of 150 ft.

Mt Isa mine, Queensland, sinks 5 by 7-ft untimbered winzes, usually to connect with raises from below, and seldom more than 75 ft deep; inclination, 58°–60°. Ore is shale, carrying sulphides. Jackhammer round, of 6 pyramid-cut and 10 wall and corner holes,

5 ft deep, breaks 4–5 ft with 30 lb of 60% and 20 lb of 40% gelignite. Windlass used for hoisting, as Gov't regulations require certificated engr for power hoists, and he does nothing else. Of 3-man crew, 2 are at bottom while drilling, and at top while mucking (500). **Alaska Juneau.** Data from L. H. Metzgar in 1932. To develop the north orebody down to 1 000 ft below haulage level, 2 winzes at 60° inclination were sunk through slates, gabbro, and quartz stringers (564). One, 7 by 11 ft, had two 4 by 4.5-ft compartments, the other, 7 by 13 ft, 2 hoisting compartments and a manway. V-cut rounds were drilled with wet jackhammers; 8 cut holes were fired first with 40% gelatin and their muck hoisted before drilling rest of round. In smaller winze 3 men, in larger, 4 men drilled and blasted on one shift, and a like crew mucked into 0.75-ton buckets on next shift; another man ran air hoist. There were 3 shifts per day. Same crews placed 8 by 8-in timber sets at 6-ft centers. Small flow of water was bailed by hand; 10-in exhaust fans provided ventilation. For other data see Table 25.

Table 25. Winze Sinking at Alaska Juneau

	No 53 (7×11 ft)	No 91 (7×13 ft)		No 53 (7×11 ft)	No 91 (7×13 ft)
Total depth sunk..........	1 100 ft	488 ft	Costs per ft:		
Men per shift.............	4	5	Direct labor.............	$25.98	$29.94
Av wages, contractors......	$9.88	$10.43	Indirect labor and super...	2.22	2.55
" " others in shaft...	5.50	5.50	Timber and hanger bolts .	2.21	2.89
" " hoistmen........	4.50	4.50	Explosives (22 lb in No 53)	4.15	5.66
Holes per round...........	28	34	Other supplies...........	1.01	1.01
Advance per 8 hr, ft........	0.89	1.10	Power..................	1.58	1.25
" " mach-shift, ft..	0.95	0.68			
Advance per round, ft......	4.74	4.10	Total cost..........	$37.15	$43.30

Winzes sunk with Calyx drill, United Verde mine, Ariz. Data furnished 1939 by C. E. Mills, Chief Engr. Calyx drilling at this mine has been for: (a) sinking vert waste chutes for filling stopes (Art 62); (b) ventilation openings, where vol of air passed does not exceed 60 000 cu ft per min; (c) exploratory shafts. The Calyx is not intended to displace usual drilling in raises, and is not applicable to following of irregular orebodies; it is limited also to nearly vert holes. A drill making a 4-ft hole began in Oct, 1937, and to end of 1938 made 863.5 ft, mainly on 1-shift (2 or 3-man) work; one hole, 241 ft, was for shaft development; another, 281.5 ft, for ventilation; and 4 holes were for passing fill.

Calyx drilling of large holes is described in Sec 7, 9. Fig 168 shows arrangement in United Verde mine. Usual design of drilling barrel was improved by making it of 2 concentric 0.5-in shells spaced ³/₈-in apart by a filler plate slotted so as to deliver water and shot directly under cutting edge. Total equipment, incl rods, weighed 14 tons; cost, $12 800. For a 10-ft drill spindle, station excavation is about 22 ft high, 4 by 6 ft at top, and 8 by 16 ft on floor. SPEED AND COST. Footage per drill-shift depends on hardness of ground, its condition as to fracturing, cementing required, and vol of water raised. Badly fractured ground, which can not be cored or pulled, incurs delay for hand mucking. Best month's progress at United Verde, 133.5 ft in 51 shifts. Table 26 gives effic data and direct operat-

Table 26. Data on Calyx Drilling of Winzes, United Verde Mine

	Aver ground	Hard silic sulphide	Aver
Depth of holes, ft.............	281.5 max	56.5 min	144
Footage per drill-shift..........	2.76	0.79	
Speed, in per hr..............	14.1	1.57	
Drilling time, % of total.......	20.4	72.2	
Shot, lb per ft of hole..........	22.8	103.5	40.7
Bit wear, in per 100 ft of hole...	6.6	42.9	14.9
Direct operating costs, per ft:			
Labor (a)...................	$6.62	$19.00	$10.77
Shot......................	2.92	7.16	3.18
Other supplies..............	1.13	0.07	0.67
Timber and explosives.......	.18	.05	.10
Electric power..............	.25	.89	.55
Total....................	$11.10	$27.17	$15.27

Typical time distribution, aver ground: Drilling, 39.1%; Pulling rods, 10.9%; Pulling core, 10.1%; Mucking core, 14.6%; Pumping or bailing, 6.9%; Repairs, 0.4%; Miscellaneous, 4.8%; Delays, 0.6%; Lunch and changing shifts, 12.6%; Total, 100%.

(Note a). Usually 3 men @ aver $6 per shift; reduced to 2 men when drilling alone occupies a whole shift or more.

Aver cost of cutting stations................................ $345
Aver cost of moving and setting up drill.................... 285

ing costs. CHIEF ADVANTAGES of calyx drilling (where applicable) compared with raising are: (a) relative safety; (b) avoidance of dust and difficult ventilation; (c) in case of waste passes, no interference with stoping. Chief drawbacks are cost of cutting drill stations, moving and setting up equipment, and relatively high price of drill.

Winzes sunk with Calyx drill, Butte, Mont. Data in 1939 from J. A. O'Neill, Eng Research Dept, and J. J. Carrigan, Gen Supt, Anaconda Copper Mining Co. At Butte, Calyx holes are used for ventilation during development of lower levels. On starting a new level from a shaft, a hole is drilled from the next higher level at a point 100 ft or more from shaft, and used to exhaust air from lower level; this leaves the whole shaft area free to furnish fresh air, and eliminates partitioning it for up-cast and down-cast. A second hole, 1 000–2 000 ft farther from shaft, or near the main orebody, serves same purpose when development has proceeded that far. The first hole, near the shaft, may then be used for pipes or other service. Holes are 100–150 ft deep, and can pass 20 000 cu ft of air per min by using a high-speed fan.

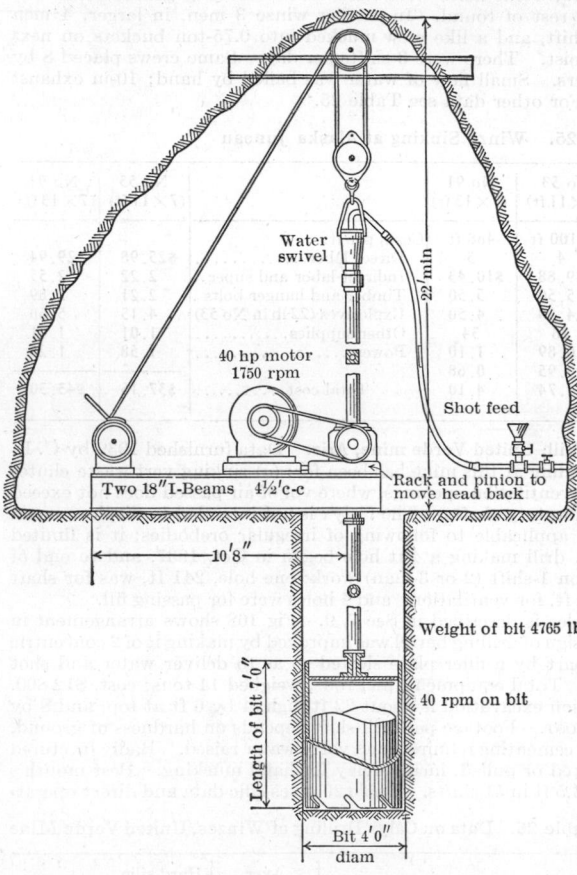

The drill bit used at Butte is 36 in diam, overall length, 6 ft; rotated at 100 r p m by a 30-hp elec motor. Equipment includes a single-drum air hoist for handling pumps, mucking bucket and cementing ring. Two sizes of shot used: $1/16$-$1/8$-in in soft ground, and $1/16$-in or finer in hard ground. The bit developed at Butte consists of a cast-steel cutting shoe with 1.25-in wall, having shot tubes extending from tops of slots in the cutting shoe to top of core barrel; this avoids introduction of shot between inside of bit and the

Fig 168. Set-up of Calyx Drill, United Verde Mine, Jerome, Ariz

core. A special hoisting bail, for pulling bit out of the hole, has an air connection which admits air under press and assists in raising the bit to the water level in the hole. Water is pumped from the hole by a high-head, single-stage centrifugal air-driven pump, using 3-in fire hose for discharge, and 1-in air hose for power. Mucking of broken cores is done with short-handled tools and a special bucket. Solid cores are handled as usual, with a core puller when necessary. In weak ground, walls of holes are cemented with quick-setting cement, using a collapsible steel-ring form 4 ft high, thus avoiding re-drilling of cemented sections. Drilling station is usually a crosscut from main drift; floor area, about 13 by 14 ft. To pull and store 20-ft rod sections, an excavation 20–25 ft high and 7 by 7 ft horiz sec is necessary over the hole to be drilled. OPERATING CYCLE: (1) drilling; (2) pumping; (3) pulling core or mucking; (4) cementing if required. Drilling (incl pulling bit) takes about 40%, pulling core and mucking about 30%, pumping 10%, cementing 10%, and misc work (delays and repairs) about 10% of total operating time after drilling begins; these figures vary considerably from hole to hole, depending upon the kind of ground, amount of cementing required, and water encountered. In hard ground, drilling speeds of 10–12 in per hr have been made. Shot required, 11–25 lb per ft. Between 1.5 and 3 ft of hole is finished per shift. Cost per ft of hole, $15 to $25, incl cost of machine, installation, and operation.

EXPLOITATION

24. GENERAL CLASSIFICATION OF MINING METHODS

Fundamental differences between underground methods of mining metals and coal, and between placer and other forms of surface mining, suggest the following general classification:

    I. Underground Metal-mining Methods......... (Art 25 to 93)
   II. Open-cut Methods......................... (Art 94 to 101)
 III. Coal-mining Methods..................... (Art 102 to 111)
 IV. Placer-mining Methods.. .... (Art 117 to 131)

25. CLASSIFICATION OF UNDERGROUND METAL-MINING METHODS

General. These methods are based largely on the means of supporting the COUNTRY ROCK, and the ore itself, during stoping. Timber is generally required for auxiliary or temporary support. In some cases, timber is used only locally, to support men or slabs of rock or ore; in others, large amounts are employed, as an integral part of the method.

General plans underlying most of these mining methods are: (a) Surface and overlying rocks are supported by permanent PILLARS left in the orebody; chambers or STOPES are excavated between pillars, the removal of the ore being incomplete. (b) Chambers are excavated in the orebody, with or without use of timber, and filled either contemporaneously or subsequently with waste (as broken rock, sand or gravel). Under the support afforded by FILLING, the pillars are mined; filling, if contemporaneous, serves also to support men and stope walls during mining. (c) A small section of the orebody is mined and overlying material allowed or forced to cave, the process being repeated in adjacent sections. Or, successive portions of the deposit are undermined and then broken down by weight of the overlying rocks, sometimes assisted by their own weight. CAVING METHODS make no attempt to support the surface above the deposit.

These general plans are combined and varied in many ways. In veins or masses, the blocks of ore between LEVELS are usually mined in descending order; to facilitate supervision, stoping is concentrated on as few levels as possible; number of levels (lifts) worked simultaneously depends on the size of deposit, distribution of "pay" ore, and output required. In large, uniform deposits, the ideal procedure is to develop one lift while that above is being mined, and at same time to sink the shaft to the level below. Relative times required for these 3 operations, together with the nature of orebody, determine sequence and extent of development work in advance of mining. Development on a level is often not completed before stoping has been started on that level. In flat beds, mining and development may proceed almost simultaneously, the workings being extended outward in all directions from point of entry; such methods are called ADVANCING SYSTEMS of mining. In RETREATING SYSTEMS, development openings are first driven to the property boundaries, where mining begins, the working faces being carried back toward point of entry. These terms apply also to work in veins and masses.

Factors determining applicability of underground metal-mining methods: shape, size, regularity, and dip of orebody; mineralogical character and value of ore; distribution of pay ore; strength and physical character of ore and of wall rock or overlying material; relation of deposit to surface and to other orebodies and to existing shafts on same property; class of labor; availability, character, and cost of timber and material for filling.

These factors are interdependent and of varying importance. The method chosen must be safe and should give maximum profit and extraction. Last 2 factors are closely related, since a method which sacrifices part of the orebody often yields maximum total profit. High-grade orebodies usually call for some form of a selective and relatively high-cost method of mining that results in max extraction. Low-grade orebodies usually call for low-cost methods, which may yield a relatively low extraction. If possible, such methods should be so planned that low-grade ore and pillars, left on first working, may be recovered in the future if desired. Improvements in mining and metallurgical processes constantly tend to lower the tenor of profitable ores. Moreover, extended periods of high prices of metals may permit profitable mining of ore left standing in times of lower prices.

Classification of underground metal-mining methods. A logical classification, based on the factors outlined above, is impossible, because of their complex relations. TYPE OF STOPE is used here as a basis of classification; the stopes themselves are grouped, according to modes of supporting walls and men, as follows:

I. Open Stopes.........	(Art 29 to 44)	IV. Shrinkage Stopes.....	(Art 67 to 69)
II. Timbered Stopes.....	(Art 45 to 57)	V. Caving Methods.....	(Art 70 to 82)
III. Filled Stopes........	(Art 59 to 66)	VI. Combined Methods...	(Art 83 to 88)

This arbitrary classification is adopted for presenting the details with a minimum of duplication. For more detailed classification of metal-mining methods from standpoint of their applicability to different types of orebody, under different conditions as to character of ore and wall rocks, see Art 93.

26. BREAKING GROUND IN STOPES

Breaking ground covers the work of blasting, including locating, drilling, charging, tamping and firing drill holes. For charging and firing, and choice of explosive for different kinds of work, see Sec 4 and 5.

Fig 169 shows a drill hole AB in vertical section; top A and bottom B of a hole are called its COLLAR and TOE. Holes pointing downward are DOWN HOLES or WATER HOLES, water being usually kept in them while drilling; horiz holes, or those at a slight angle above or below, are FLAT HOLES (FT, Fig 173); holes drilled steeply upward are UPPERS (UP, Fig 173); flat holes which will not hold water, and uppers, generally were called DRY HOLES prior to development and general use of "wet" stoper and hammer drills (see Sec 15). In Fig 169, the rock surfaces CD and DG are FREE FACES, and EF is the LINE OF LEAST RESISTANCE of hole AB. Length of line BG, at right angles to AB, is the BURDEN on the toe of the hole. (For further data on blasting, and remarks on Theory of blasting, see Sec 5). In practice, the arrangement of holes and weight of charge are matters of judgment, based on experience under similar conditions and modified by experiment with the rock or ore to be broken. Methodical placing of holes, guided by a mechanical device (Art 33), improved stoping effic in certain So African gold mines; adjustment of the device is based upon experiment.

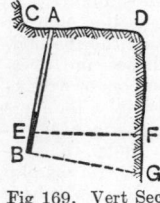

Fig 169. Vert Sec

Breast stoping. Ore is broken by flat or slightly inclined holes, drilled in a vertical face (or breast) of considerable lateral area, which is being advanced in a horiz or nearly horiz direction; work resembles that of advancing the face of a very wide drift. This method is used in flat, thin beds; also in parts of masses or wide veins, to provide openings for other methods of attack (Art 30).

Slabbing is a term often used to designate breaking ground by taking a slab off a free face as at A, Fig 170. It is also called SLASHING or SIDESWIPING.

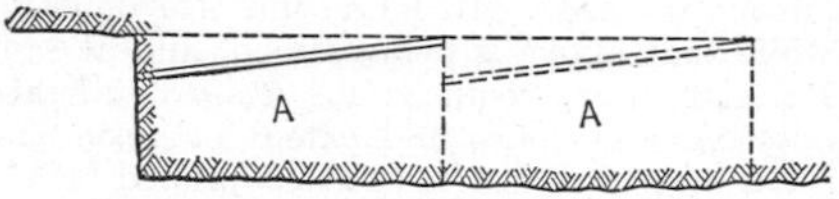

Underhand stoping. Ore is broken in horiz slices, in descending order; miners stand on ore and drill holes downward; for different forms of stope which result, see Fig 205 to 211, Art 35. Certain applications of underhand stoping are called BENCHING. See Fig 182, 183, 188, and accompanying text.

Horiz sec

Fig 170. Slabbing

Overhand stoping. Ore is broken in horiz or inclined slices, in ascending order; miners work beneath and close to back of stope; holes may be flat, uppers, or down holes. For different forms of overhand stope, see Art 38, 39.

Underhand and overhand methods are employed under widely different conditions as to size and nature of orebody; in both, the stope faces are usually maintained in steps or benches (Fig 205, 222, 224). Ore is blasted in blocks from free ends of benches; in nearly all cases there at least 2 free faces, to which a hole can break.

Caving (Art 70–82). A portion of the orebody is undercut and allowed to fall and crush under its own weight.

Objects sought in breaking ground are: (a) to break ore from stope face; (b) to break ore into pieces of a size suitable for handling.

Very large pieces of ore clog chutes and mill-holes and can not be handled in cars; they must often be broken in stopes by sledging or BLOCKHOLING (Sec 5), thus requiring additional labor and explosive. On the other hand, while shallow holes, close spacing of holes, and high grades of dynamite, all produce fine breaking, they do so at greater cost. These factors are usually easily adjusted in narrow stopes; in wide deposits and in large-scale operations, tendency is to increase depth and spacing of holes and to blockhole large lumps (extreme case, Fig 174). Use of large loading chutes and gates (Art 90), large mechanically hauled and dumped cars, and primary crushers underground, permits coarser primary breaking and reduces amount of blockholing. Ideal practice is that in which cost of breaking from face plus cost of blockholing to a size that can be efficiently handled is a minimum; plans adopted depend on costs of labor, explosive and power; the jackhammer drill has greatly cheapened blockholing. In general, breaking of ore in stopes to a smaller size than necessary for handling should be minimized.

27. BREAKING GROUND IN STOPES BY HAND DRILLING

General. Conditions for hand drilling: (a) in narrow veins, for breaking ore with minimum admixture of waste; often, narrower stopes can be carried by hand than by machine; stope-drills compete with hand drilling in this respect; (b) in mines of small output, usually of high-grade ore, where tonnage does not justify cost of compressor and machine drills; (c) where power is costly and labor is cheap and unskilled; such conditions led to former extensive use of hand drilling in the Rand mines (Art 33) now almost completely replaced by jackhammers; (d) in very soft ores, where hand auger drills may be preferred to power augers or pluggers with auger bits; (e) in the early life of mines, where stoping is started to provide funds before exploration has proceeded far enough to warrant large investment for plant: (f) for various local reasons, as:

At a mine in Park City, Utah, ore was sorted in large stopes into smelting and milling grades; drilling was easy and hand work favored because it allowed careful breaking, which aided sorting. At another mine, orebody was so flat and thin that machine drills could not be used and most drilling was done single-hand. At the old and extensive mines of Potosí, Bolivia, newer workings have modern equipment. Amounts of ore left in old levels do not justify cost of installing air lines, hence, such ore is still mined by hand drilling. Before introducing wet stopers at Tintic, Utah, hand drilling was used to reduce dust in mining soft galena ores, which entailed danger of "leading" the miners.

Single-hand drilling is done in medium hard ore, a miner drilling 4 to 7 ft of hole per shift; speed of drilling varies widely with character of rock; in many districts, men on day's-pay drill a certain number of holes or footage and no more, regardless of kind of ground. Fastest drilling is usually done in vert water-holes, speed decreasing as inclination of hole flattens and is least for horiz holes or flat uppers. Speed increases in steep uppers, provided: (a) ground is dry, so that cuttings run out freely; (b) skilled hammermen are available; (c) there is room for miner to get a full arm swing. These relationships vary with the rock, and should be considered in planning stoping operations. Speed of drilling decreases with depth of hole. Economic limit for single-hand holes is about 3 ft; usual depth in stopes, 2 to 3 ft; 3.5 to 4.5-lb hammers are used; drill steels, $3/4$ in to $7/8$ in (Sec 5).

Double-hand drilling is done in hard ground; increase in speed is not proportional to increase in labor. It is best applied to nearly vert down holes, as in underhand stopes; rarely used for systematic stoping work in U S. Drill steel, $7/8$ to $1 1/8$ in; hammers, 6 to 8-lb; ordinary depth of holes, 4 to 6 ft.

In very soft ores, churn drills (jumpers) or hand-augers are more effic than single-hand work (Sec 5). Churn drills are best in down holes, and under suitable conditions will do faster work than any other hand drill; they have a very limited application in stoping. Augers are used for breast and down holes; both auger and churn drills require soft ore, free from hard streaks or nodules. Where the latter are present, or where the ground "ravels," bits with pyramidal points ("bull points") struck with a single or double-hand hammer are sometimes used to break up such obstructions. Layout of hand-drilled holes is similar to machine drilling (Fig 171-175); stope faces are carried in benches 2-3 ft high; holes are roughly parallel to free faces, but work is not systematic, since a hand miner utilizes slips and irregularities of face to aid in breaking ground; hence, consumption of explosive per ton broken is usually less than with machines.

Minimum width of stope that can be carried by hand drilling is usually 2.5 ft; narrower stopes may be possible in thin, steeply dipping veins, with well marked slips on vein walls, but men work at a disadvantage in them; min limit of width is increased by flat dips.

Data on stoping by hand drilling. Following data, though old, still illustrate duty of labor in such work; the number of skilled hammermen in the U S has decreased greatly in the past 20 years.

STANDARD CONSOLIDATED MINE, Bodie, Cal. C. E. Grunsky gives following data for 1912 (84). Narrow auriferous veins occur in firm, fairly hard andesite. As dips were steep, there was no handling in stopes except for shoveling to chutes. Vein matter was hard banded to soft, porous, granular quartz; sometimes a soft clay, containing quartz stringers. Drilling was single-hand. Stopes were back-filled with waste, excess waste being hoisted to surface. Stopes were kept as narrow as possible; minimum width, 1.5 to 2 ft. Table 27 shows effect of width of vein on output per man stoping; it is based on tons ore, not on tons of vein and wall-rock broken. Aver powder consumption was about 2.4 lb per ton broken, and in veins with hard ore and walls it exceeded 3 lb per ton. A SMALL MEXICAN MINE. Data from R. H. Allen (129). Vein, 10 to 80 ft wide; footwall, strong rhyolite breccia; hanging wall, badly broken andesite; as ore was soft or cut by clay seams, it required but little explosive. Overhand stopes were supported by square-sets (Art 45), filled with waste to within 1 floor of the back; vein was mined in 15 to 24-ft sections, along strike. All labor was Mexican; single-hand drilling; 9-hr shifts. Figures cover 7 months of 1912, during which time 17 253 tons of ore were mined. Table 28 gives details. BERLIN, NEV. Very hard quartz vein, carrying gold and silver; aver width, 2.4 ft; dip, 22° to 43°; wall rocks,

Table 27. Overhand Stoping by Hand. Narrow Veins

Width of vein, in			Vein filling	Dip of vein	Tons ore broken per man-shift
Aver	Variation				
	From	To			
3	.....	.....	Hard	Steep	0.38
5	4	6	Hard	Steep	0.42
5	4	6	Soft	Steep	1.21
8	3	17	Medium hard	Flat	0.91
9	6	13		Flat	0.99
12	8	18		Steep	1.46
18	14	20	Hard	Steep	1.44
28.5	9	42	Soft	Flat	1.91

strong andesite; vein mined by overhand stoping in open stopes; very little wall rock was broken; drilling was single-hand, holes flat or pointing slightly down. A miner averaged 3 20-in holes per 8-hr shift; 33.6 pieces of drill steel dulled per miner-shift. In Apr, 1905, 948 tons of ore were broken in 809.25 miner-shifts = 1.16 ton per shift. DALY JUDGE MINE, Park City, Utah. In 1907, single-hand miners averaged 12 ft of hole per shift in soft ore and 6 ft in quartzite. TINTIC, UTAH. L. A. Palmer gives data on work in 1912 (135). At Sioux Consol mine, much ground was so soft that holes for blasting were made by a pointed steel ("bull-prick"); 1 man broke 25 tons per shift. At Iron Blossom mine, in overhand square-set stopes, medium hard ore, 1 single-hand miner broke 7 to 10 tons per shift. FRANKLIN FURNACE, N J. Before machine drills were introduced, 2 men, drilling double-hand in 3 holes totalling 8 ft per 10-hr shift, breaking about 8 tons, or 4 tons per miner-shift (98). NEGAUNEE, MICH. In 1904, speed of drilling 5-ft water holes, double-hand, in soft hematite, was about 4 ft per hr; grade of jasper in the ore reduced speed greatly (136). CAVOUR MINE, Virginia, Minn (in 1914). Ore was soft hematite, somewhat harder than usual Mesabi ground. 2 miners with hand augers made 5 6-ft holes in about 2 hr. Air-driven augers averaged 1 ft per min (137). BRITISH COLUMBIA. Double-hand drilling of 6-ft water holes in firm augite porphyry; starting bit, 1.75-in; finishing bit, 1.25-in; 7/8-in steel. 2 men averaged 14.8 ft of hole per 10 hr (133). BRADEN COPPER Co, Rancagua, Chile. In 1909 native miners averaged 13.5 ft of holes per 9 hr, single-hand; ore is fractured and brecciated andesite and tuff, moderately hard (138). EL TIGRE MINE, Sonora, Mex. In vert quartz veins about 4 ft wide, Mexican contract labor, drilling single-hand in overhand stopes, put in about 10 ft of hole per shift. So AFRICA. Before introducing jackhammers in Rand gold mines (about 1920), most drilling in reefs less than 5 ft wide was done single-hand, in down holes, with 7/8-in steel. In hard, unoxidized ore (Art 33) a Kaffir "boy" made 1 3-ft hole per shift, breaking about 0.6 ton of ore; in stopes less than 3 ft wide, holes were usually 2 ft deep; in soft oxidized ore, drilling rate was doubled. RHODESIA. Quartz veins dip 65°. Native single-hand drillers make about 2 ft of hole per shift in hard quartz. Stoping is generally underhand; holes, 2 to 3 ft deep; a 2-ft hole in a stope 4 ft wide breaks about 0.6 ton of ore, if stope face is well

Table 28. Overhand Stoping by Hand; Mexican Labor

	Total shifts	Shifts per ton	Tons per man-shift
Shift bosses (a).....	236.85	0.0138	72.80
Miners.............	3 488.33	0.2021	4.94
Shovelers (b).......	1 382.40	0.0802	12.48
Powder boys.......	311.25	0.0180	55.40
Blacksmiths.......	163.50	0.0095	105.50
Total.........	5 582.33	0.3236	3.09

	Quantity		Tons per unit
	Total	Per ton	
Dynamite, 40%....	1 194.3 lb	0.0692	14.49
Fuse..............	7 826.0 ft	0.454	2.20
Caps, 5 X........	4 162.0	0.241	4.15
Candles, No 15 L...	28 800.0	1.67	0.60
Carbide..........	98.0 lb	0.0057	176.0
Drill steel........	110.0 lb	0.0064	155.3
Pick steel........	3.6 lb	0.0002	
Hammers.........	4.0		
Shovels, No 2 D....	34.0	0.002	507.0
Picks.............	6.0	0.0004	
Handles...........			
Blacksmith coal....	4 090 lb	0.237	4.22

(a) Proportionate part of bosses' time. (b) Shovelers in stopes.

benched (139). RUSSIA. Eiderlinsky gold mines (1915). Quartz veins 2 to 7 ft wide, dipping 28° to 71°, occur in granodiorite. In hand-mined stopes, 2 native miners, working double-hand on a bonus system, drilled up to 10 ft of hole per 8 hr. Min task per shift was 4.42 ft of horiz hole in overhand stopes, or 5.83 ft of water hole in underhand stopes. 7/8-in steel was used, with cutting edge from 1 to 1.5 in (140). CHIKSAN MINES, Korea (in 1914). Gold ore occurs in shoots in 4 to 8-ft quartz veins, dipping 65° or over; country rocks, schist and granite. Korean contract miners, working overhand in shrinkage stopes, drilled 4 ft of hole per shift, breaking 0.5 to 0.57 ton per man-shift; consumption of 60% gelignite was about 0.4 lb per ton (87).

28. BREAKING GROUND IN STOPES WITH MACHINE DRILLS

(For definition of names of machine drills as used here, see Art 20)

Breast stoping. See Art 30.

Underhand stoping (see also Art 35, 36). Fig 171 shows 1 bench of an underhand stope. All holes are down holes, usually in rows across the stope. Jackhammers are commonly used for this work, but occasionally mounted hammer drills are preferable; the latter are mounted on tripods in wide stopes or on bar mounting in stopes up to 8 or 10 ft wide. Height of benches depends on width of stope, nature of ground and size desired for broken ore; depth and spacing of holes vary widely, depending largely on

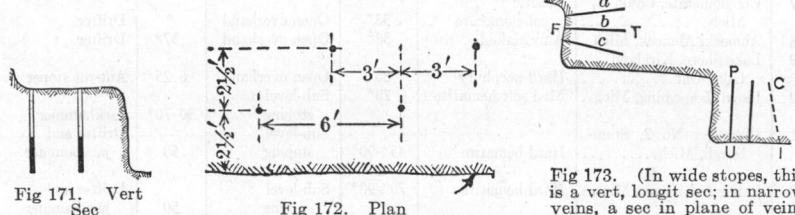

Fig 171. Vert Sec   Fig 172. Plan   Fig 173. (In wide stopes, this is a vert, longit sec; in narrow veins, a sec in plane of vein)

last two factors. High benches can not be broken efficiently in narrow stopes; usual height in stopes up to 10 or 15 ft wide is 5–8 ft.

Usual limit of depth of hole by either heavy mounted hammer drills or jackhammers, 16–20 ft. Deep holes make for cheap breaking; objections to them: (a) long steels are awkward to handle; (b) ore may break in large pieces difficult to handle along stope face. Objection (a) has been overcome in some mines by jointed drill steel. Objection (b) may not be serious; deep holes usually make steep stope faces, where large pieces come to rest at foot of bench convenient for blockholing. Usual depth of holes in wide underhand stopes is less than 12 ft. Burden broken with holes as in Fig 171 depends on local conditions and must be determined by trial. In easy ground, max distance between holes and between rows of holes is 0.75 to 1 × depth of hole (Art 26). In tight ground, as at Alaska-Treadwell, 12-ft holes were 6 ft apart in rows 2.5 ft apart, and staggered as in Fig 172 (133). For further detail, see Breast stoping, Art 30.

Overhand stoping comprises STEPPED-FACE and FLAT-BACK STOPES (Art 38). Fig 173 shows a stope face. Benches are broken by flat (breast) holes, running across stope, as *FT*, or by uppers, *UP*. Uppers pointed as at *IC* cause cuttings to fall clear of drill. In narrow veins, uppers are parallel to dip to avoid breaking into walls. For safety and economy, stope face should be kept normal to dip.

Uppers *vs* breast holes. In general, uppers are more apt to make a ragged stope back than breast holes. With breast holes, miner is less exposed to danger of ground falling from jar of machine. Hence, for safety, breast holes are preferable in wide stopes. In schistose ground, choice may depend on direction of schistosity, because in some mines holes parallel to it are difficult to drill and break badly. Improvement of stopers in recent years, including automatic rotation, makes uppers preferable where ground conditions allow their use. Stoper drills avoid the loss of time in setting up and "tearing down" mounted drills. Less skill is required to operate stopers than mounted drills.

Uppers are common in overhand narrow stopes on steep dips; breast holes are used in such stopes on low dips. This is true of both hand and machine drilling; type of drill used also affects choice (see below under Choice of drills for stoping). Uppers may be drilled with either mounted hammer or stope-drills, usually the latter; breast holes, with hammer drills, which, in stopes up to 8 or 10 ft wide, are mounted on bars; in wider stopes, usual mounting is a column braced between back of stope and filling or timber.

Height of bench in machine-driven, overhand stopes depends on same factors as for underhand work. In narrow stopes, benches are 3–6 ft high; in wide stopes, breast-hole

Table 29. Breaking Ground in

Example	Mine and location	Type of ore	Dip	Stoping method	Width of stope, ft	Drills Type
1	Scott, Hockerville, Okla..	Mainly hard flint	Hor	Breast and bench	8–120	Drifter
2	Mullen, Shullsburg, Wis..	Soft to med dolomite	Hor	Breast and bench	8–100	Jackhammer
3	Bonne Terre, Bonne Terre, Mo...........	Dolomite	Hor	Breast and bench	15–300	Jackhammer
4	Muscoda No 6, Bessemer, Ala...........	Hard oolitic hematite	15°	Room and pillar*	110	Drifter
5	Limestone No 5, Bessemer, Ala...........	Hard limestone	17°	Room and pillar*	30	Drifter
6	Empire Star Group, Grass Valley, Cal.....	Quartz veins in diorite	15°–35°	Open overhand*	4–5	Stoper and jackhammer
7	Conglomerate, Calumet, Mich..............	Felsitic conglomerate	38°	Open overhand	*	Drifter
8	Ahmeek, Ahmeek, Mich..	Amygdaloid	38°	Open overhand	37*	Drifter
9	Lake Shore, Kirkland Lake, Ont...........	Hard porphyry	80°	Open overhand	6.25	Aut-rot stoper
10	Lloyd Ishpeming, Mich..	Med soft hematite	70°	Sub-level stoping	30–70*	Jackhammer
11	Hiawatha No 2, Stambaugh, Mich.........	Hard hematite	45°–90°	Sub-level stoping	50	Drifter and jackhammer
12	Bates, Iron River, Mich..	Hard hematite	70°–90°	Sub-level stoping	50	Drifter and jackhammer
13	Balmat, Balmat, N. Y...	Mass sulphides and altered limestone	30°–90°	Sub-level stoping*	30–100	Jackhammer
14	Horne, Noranda, Que....	Massive sulphide	90°	Sub-level stoping*	60	Drifter
15	Horne, Noranda, Que....	Hard rhyolite	90°	Sub-level stoping*	105	Diamond drill†
16	Burra Burra, Ducktown, Tenn...............	Hard massive sulphide	50°	Sub-level stoping	10–40	Drifter and* jackhammer
17a	Flin Flon, Flin Flon, Man	Massive sulphide	65°	Sub-level stoping*	30	Drifter
17b	Flin Flon, Flin Flon, Man	Massive sulphide	65°	Sub-level stoping*	30	Drifter
18	Sullivan, Kimberley, B C	Massive sulphide	23°	Spiral bench glory-hole	60	Drifter
19	Idaho Maryland, Grass Valley, Cal.........:..	Medium hard quartz	50°–80°	Shrinkage	3–6	Aut-rot stoper
20	Dome, So Porcupine, Ont	Hard quartz-ankerite dike.....	65°	Shrinkage	5	Aut-rot stoper
21	Nevada-Mass, Mill City, Nev................	Massive garnet, scheelite, etc	70°	Shrinkage	5–6	Drifter
22	Frisco, Chihuahua, Mex	Hard massive sulphide	60°–70°	Shrinkage	10	Drifter
23	Zeibright, Nevada City, Cal.................	Tough, siliceous dike	80°	Shrinkage	10*	Aut-rot stoper
24	Mt Hope, Mt Hope, N J..	Massive magnetite	70°	Shrinkage	15	Jackhammer
25	Dome, So Porcupine, Ont	Hard quartz and greenstone	90°	Shrinkage	25–100	Drifter
26	Homestake, Lead, So Dak................	Hard schist	60°	Shrinkage	60	Drifter
27	Crescent, Kellogg, Idaho.	Hard siderite and quartzite	65°–80°	Hor cut-and-fill	4	Aut-rot stoper
28	Matahambre, Pinar del Rio, Cuba...........	Massive sulphide	45°	Hor cut-and-fill	8–10	Jackhammer
29	McIntyre, Schumacher, Ont.................	Hard quartz	Steep	Hor cut-and-fill	12	Drifter
30	Hollinger, Timmins, Ont..	Schist and quartz	70°–80°	Hor cut-and-fill	12.5*	Drifter

Stopes by Machine Drilling

Drills — Mounting	Depth of hole, ft	Ft hole per drill-shift	Tons broken per drill-shift	Explosive — Type	% Ngl	Lb per ton	Notes
Col or tripod	6 & 14*	40 80	54	Am or gel	35–30	1.17	* 6 ft in headings; 14 ft in benches; bench holes horiz, frequently chambered. (Art 31)
Improvised board	6 & 14*	60–140	40–45	Bulk powder and gel	35	0.89	* Same as preceding
Col in breast, none on bench	9–10*	95	75	Gel	60	0.37	* Breast and bottom bench holes horiz; upper bench holes vert. (Art 31)
Tripod	8.5	100	75	Am	40	0.75	* Rooms mined by breast and bench. (Art 40)
Tripod	8.5	100	70	Am	60	0.58	* Rooms mined by breast and bench. (Art 34)
Col	5	35–50	14	Gel	35 & 40	2.6	* Stopes back-filled. (Art 39)
Col	8–9	50–60	30	Gel	40	0.9	* Lode 12 ft thick (Art 39)
Col	7	60	22	Am	66	0.90	* Lode 7 ft thick. (Art 41)
None	7*	51.3	12.24	Semi-gel	70	1.16	* Holes vertical or nearly so.
None	6–14	50	35	Dynamite	40–60	0.45	* Sub-level interval, 20 ft
Col for drifter	8 & 10*	48	35	Semi-gel	60†	0.75	* 8 ft in slice; 10 ft on u-h bench; 8 ft on o-h bench. † Bulk strength
Col for drifter	6, 8, & 10*	90	150	Semi-gel	45†	0.45	* 8 ft in slice; 10 ft on u-h bench; 6 ft on o-h bench. † Bulk strength
None	10	60	38	Semi-gel	40	0.51	* With underhand benching
Col	20†	50	190	Gel	40	0.20	* With ring drilling. † With sectional steel. (Art 43)
Col	40–66	25	100	Gel	40	0.20	* With ring drilling. † "Prospector" type. (Art 43)
Col for drifter	8–10	64	75	Am	40	0.33	* Slabbing with drifter; benching with jackhammer. (Art 43)
Col	7.5†	70.5	66.2	Gel	50	0.59	* Data apply to slashing. † Av; max, 10 ft. (Art 43)
Col	22 & 26†	43	225.1	Gel	60	0.31	* Data apply to benching. (Art 43). † All holes chambered
Tripod	10*	100	85	Gel	60	0.25	* Holes are lifters inclined at +40°
None	6†	72	14	Semi-gel	45*	1.9	* Bulk strength. † Holes are vertical
None	8–10	120–150	45–50	Dynamite	40	1.3	
Col	7	65	14	Gel	35	1.8	(Art 68)
Col	7	54	19	Gel	40	1.4	
None	8	80	35	Gel	45	1.15	* Varies 4–20 ft
Air-fed leg	11.6*	36.6	82.4	Gel	40	0.36	* Av; some, 14 ft. (Art 68)
Col	10	80–100	60	Gel and am	40	0.7	
Col	10*	25	25	Gel	40	1.25	* Flat holes with burden of 3½ ft. (Art 68)
None	4	80	8	Semi-gel	45*	2.0	* Bulk strength
None	4.8	52	40.3	Semi-gel	45 & 60*	0.37	* Bulk strength. (Art 62)
Col	11	87	52	Am and gel	55 & 40	0.51	(Art 60)
Col	7.5	85	37	Am	55	0.85	* Av; varies 5–50 ft. (Art 62)

Table 29.　Breaking Ground in Stopes

Example	Mine and location	Type of ore	Dip	Stoping method	Width of stope, ft	Drills Type
31	La Colorada, Cananea, Mex	Brecciated porphyry	90°	Hor cut-and-fill	30	Drifter
32	Soudan, Soudan, Minn	Hard hematite	70°–85°	Hor cut-and-fill	15–60	Drifter
33	Murchie, Nevada City, Cal	Hard granodiorite	60°–70°	Incl cut-and-fill	4	Drifter and aut-rot stoper
34	Wright-Hargreaves, Kirkland Lake, Ont	Hard quartz and porphyry	75°	Incl cut-and-fill	6	Drifter
35	Champion, Painesdale, Mich	Basalt	70°	Incl cut-and-fill*	12–30	Drifter
36	Campbell, Bisbee, Ariz	Siliceous sulphides	70°–90°	Incl cut-and-fill	30–48	Drifter
37	United Verde, Jerome, Ariz	Hard sulphide or porphyry	65°	Incl cut-and-fill	30–50	Drifter
38	Lake Shore, Kirkland Lake, Ont	Hard porphyry	80°	Flat-back square-set	10	Drifter
39	Page, Page, Idaho	Sheared quartzite	30°–60°	Flat-back square-set	5–50	Drifter
40	Pecos, Tererro, N M	Hard massive sulphide	70°	Flat-back square-set	5–50	Jackhammer
41	Victoria, Britannia Beach, B C	Massive sulphide	70°–80°	Flat-back square-set	6–36	Drifter
42	Creighton, Creighton Mine, Ont	Massive and dissem sulphides	55°	Flat-back square-set	60	Drifter
43	Badger, Butte, Mont	Med to hard sulphides	65°	Rilled square-set	7	Aut-rot stoper
44	Lake Shore, Kirkland Lake, Ont	Hard porphyry	80°	Rilled square-set	7.75	Drifter
45	Lake Shore, Kirkland Lake, Ont	Shattered porphyry	80°	Rilled square-set	10	Drifter
46	Magma, Superior, Ariz	Altered diabase	80°	Rilled square-set	15	Hand-rot stoper
47	Morning, Mullen, Idaho	Sheared quartzite	90°	Modified square-set*	5–20	Drifter
48	Bunker Hill, Kellogg, Idaho	Sulphide and quartz	40°–45°	Vertical-face square-set	5–100	Drifter and aut-rot stoper
49	Tintic Standard, Dividend, Utah	Galena in limestone	Massive	Vertical-face square-set	Irregular	Hand-rot stoper and jackhammer
50	Campbell, Bisbee, Ariz	Soft sulphide and oxide	60°–90°	Mitchell slicing	12–15	Jackhammer*
51	La Colorada, Cananea, Mex	Brecciated porphyry	90°	Top-slicing*	40	Jackhammer
52	Pioneer, Ely, Minn	Soft hematite	45°–75°	Top-slicing	11*	Jackhammer
53	Godfrey, Hibbing, Minn	Soft hematite	7°–10°	Top-slicing	11*	Jackhammer
54	Spruce, Eveleth, Minn	Compact hematite	Flat	Top-slicing	9*	Jackhammer
55	Montreal, Montreal, Wis	Soft hematite	62°	Sub-level caving	50	Jackhammer
56	Geneva, Ironwood, Mich	Soft hematite	65°	Sub-level caving	22	Auger
57	Zenith, Ely, Minn	Hard hematite	90°	Sub-level caving	20	Drifter
58a	Newport, Ironwood, Mich	Soft hematite	65°–70°	Sub-level caving*	10†	Auger
58b	Newport, Ironwood, Mich	Soft hematite	65°–70°	Sub-level caving*	20	Auger

benches are 6–12 ft high, broken by 2–3 rows of 6–12 or 14-ft holes (a, b, c, Fig 173). Benches broken by uppers are usually 5–8 ft high and holes have corresponding depths. Table 29 shows practice as to depth of hole. In square-set stopes (Art 46), depth of either breast or upper holes is determined by dimensions of sets.

Character of ore may influence depth of hole, and therefore height of bench; comparatively shallow holes may be used in very soft ore, because blasting merely chambers the bottoms of deeper holes, failing to break. In cut-and-fill stopes, height of bench is usually limited to 7–8 ft, because of chute-timbering details (Art 47). Also, smaller height of bench lessens danger to shovelers working under high backs. In shrinkage stopes, height of bench depends largely on blockiness of ground, and means provided for secondary breaking. If blasting chambers are provided under stope and no block-holing is required in the stope, benches may be as high as 12 ft. If ground is blocky and there are no blasting chambers, height of bench may be limited to 3–4 ft (Art 67–69).

by Machine Drilling—(*Continued*)

Drills Mounting	Depth of hole, ft	Ft hole per drill-shift	Tons broken per drill-shift	Explosive Type	% Ngl	Lb per ton	Notes
Col	10	100	190	Gel	40	0.32	
Tripod	8	24 max	13.8	Am	50	1.19	
Bar or col	5–7	60–70	11–12	Gel	40	2.0	
Col	5.5	66	20	Semi gel	50	1.44	(Art 65) * With sub-levels. (Art 63).
Col	12	24†	15	Am	66	0.30	† Drilling 1/3 shift
Col	6–7	90–120	50	Gel	30 & 40	0.75	(Art 65)
Col	6–8	90	25	Gel	50	0.80	(Art 65)
Col	6	76.5	27.3	Semi-gel	70	0.54	
Col	5–6	104	20	Dynamite	45	0.80	
None	5.5	49.5	25	Gel	40	0.675	
Col	7	70–100	30–45	Am	30	1.5–2.0	
Col	6	82	27	Am	55	0.73	(Art 62) * Av; range 2.75–5.5 ft.
None	4.5*	30.3	27.2	Semi-gel	45†	0.38	† Bulk strength
Col	6	76	20.1	Semi-gel	70	0.725	(Art 46)
Col	6	65	35	Semi-gel	70	0.324	
None	3–6	....	......	Gel	35	1.6	
Col	5–6	80	25–50	Semi-gel	45	0.75	* Combining stulls and posts
Col for drifter	6	125–150	40–50	Semi-gel	45*	0.41	* Bulk strength. (Art 46)
None	3.5–4	60 max	12	Semi-gel	40	1.0	* Occasional column-mounted drifter (Art 55)
None	5–7	50–90	50	Gel	30 & 40	0.75	
None	8	72	56	Gel	40	0.25	* Pillar mining
None	4.5–5	65	19.7	Am-gel	45	0.77	* Width of slice
None	6	200	......	Gel	60	0.45	* Width of slice
None	6	120	......	Gel	60	1.0	* Width of slice
None	8	48	90	Gel	40	0.50	(Art 76)
None	5–6	65	50	Semi-gel	45*	0.50	* Bulk strength
Col	8–10	100	125	Semi-gel	60*	0.27	* Bulk strength * Advancing slice. †-Width of slice
None	6	102	55	Gel	35	0.93	
None	6.5	125	125	Gel	35	0.49	* Caving slice

Fig 174 shows a cheap method of breaking ground, combining caving with ordinary overhand work, which has been used in large flat-back shrinkage stopes (Art 67), in several porphyry copper mines and with modifications at Homestake, S Dak. At Ray Consol mine, Ariz, vert shrinkage stopes are 10–15 ft wide in soft ore, and 15–20 ft wide in harder ground. Pairs of 6-ft holes, drilled along each side of stope (Fig 174), break shaded areas; this robs central portion A of its support and causes it to fall by gravity (61). This principle was also used in wide stopes at Alaska Gastineau (530) (Art 87). A similar method has been used at Braden mine, Chile.

Rill stopes (see Art 38). Fig 175 shows sections through stope faces (133) using the original "rill cut" which was designed for wet down holes to avoid dust and favor hand drilling. Holes are drilled in rows across stope. With introduction of "wet" stopers, this type of cut is largely outmoded. For more recent form of benches in rill stopes, see Art 65.

Ring drilling. Holes are drilled radially from within a raise or drift large enough to accommodate drilling.　Holes break to free face generally parallel with plane of drilling. Fig 176 shows application to sub-level stoping (Art 43).　For an example of ring drilling from raises, see Beatson mine, Art 68.

Choice of drills.　Stope-drills are not used ordinarily for breast stoping, as they are awkward for flat holes.　For this work, the choice depends on hardness of ore; in very hard ores, heavy mounted hammer-drills are required; under aver conditions these or lighter mounted drills are used; in very soft ores light jackhammers or air-driven augers are the logical choice.

Many of the remarks on choice of drills for drifting (Art 20) apply here.　For down holes in underhand stoping, jackhammers are effic.　In steep-dipping overhand stopes, where the holes are uppers, stope-drills are best under aver conditions.　They are light and

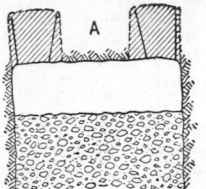
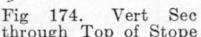
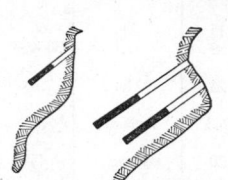
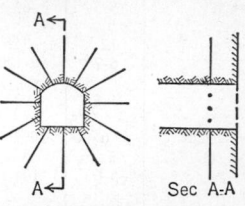

Fig 174.　Vert Sec through Top of Stope

Fig 175.　Rill Cut (after H. M. Thomas)

Fig 176.　Breaking Ground by Ring Drilling

allow holes to be pointed as desired; delay in setting up, incident to mounted-drill work, is avoided and that due to changing steel is reduced.　Question of safety of stope backs may dictate use of flat holes drilled by mounted hammer drills, instead of uppers drilled by stopers.

Breaking ground in overhand stopes on flat dips (20° to 30°) resembles breast stoping. In general, mounted drills are used: (a) in ground that is very hard or that fitchers badly, even if soft; (b) in large-scale blasting with deep holes in large stopes.　MINIMUM WIDTH OF STOPE in which heavy or light mounted drills operate efficiently is about 4.5 ft; this width is apt to be exceeded, especially for large drills.　Stope and plugger-drills can be used in stopes about 3 ft wide on steep dips, but constant supervision is required to maintain this minimum.　Min stope widths on flat dips are ordinarily greater than above; determining factor is headroom in which men are willing or able to work efficiently.　In narrow orebodies, where clean mining is desired, these factors influence choice of drill and also choice between hand and machine drilling (Art 27).

Underhand _vs_ overhand breaking.　(See Art 44).

Data on breaking ground by machine drilling in stopes.　Table 29 presents data generously supplied in 1938 by managements and engineering departments of the mines listed.　It applies only to stoping methods in which all or most of the ore is broken by direct drilling and blasting, as distinguished from those caving methods in which only a small part of the ore is thus broken.　Differences in character of orebodies, mining methods, and local conditions cause wide variations in duty of labor, drills, and explosives. The table is valuable as showing present practice and results under widely differing conditions.　For further information, see descriptions of individual mining methods.

OPEN STOPES

An open stope, strictly speaking, is a stope in which no timber or filling is used to support walls or men; a finished stope is an open cavity.　Various authorities consider unfilled timbered stopes (Art 45–57), shrinkage stopes (Art 67), and some other forms as open stopes; as used here, the term comprises stopes in which walls are supported by pillars of ore, or by stulls and other simple forms of timbering.

29.　GOPHERING

"Gophering" is a name applied to mining in irregular drifts or other openings, which "follow or seek ore without regard to maintenance of a regular grade or section" (1); the method is also called "coyoting" in western U S; in general, the term designates any small-size, irregular, unsystematic workings.

Gophering is a poor man's method, used in small excavations where walls require little or no support; obviously it may be employed in portions of veins, beds or masses, but has no place in systematic mining. If used to mine rich seams in a large orebody, gophering often results in temporary profit but eventual loss, as the irregular openings increase cost of, or prohibit, mining the remaining low-grade portions. On the other hand, gophering has a place in mining small irregular portions or isolated parts of an orebody, where cost of systematic development is not justified by probable tonnage to be won. This is especially true of small, high-grade, spotted deposits, and where Mexican or other native labor, skilled in this work, is available. Such work, done by "leasers," may be an important adjunct to regular mining.

Native miners in Mexico, South America, India, and elsewhere, are adepts at gophering; no stope development is done in advance; ore is followed up, down, or laterally, as values vary, and workings soon become intricate. Miners sometimes carry ore to surface in baskets or sacks, holding 75 to 150 lb; inclined winzes or ladders connect workings at different elevations; Mexicans use "chicken ladders," logs 10 to 15 ft long, 8 to 10 in diam, set on end, and with notches cut on one side. Breaking ground in gophering is generally done underhand; openings are rarely timbered or filled.

30. BREAST STOPING

General. The term "breast stoping" denotes primarily a method of breaking ground in any stoping system by advancing nearly horizontally a vert face or "breast" of ore, usually 10–12 ft or less in height, which has not previously been cut off at top or bottom (Art 26). It logically becomes the name of the mining method used in horiz or flat-dipping orebodies up to 15–18 ft thick, when mined by open stoping. It is not applied to the method of mining such orebodies when caving, filling, or square-setting is involved, even though the ore is broken by "breasting." It does refer, however, to a method applied to thicker flat-lying deposits, in which the upper 6–8 ft is broken by true breast stoping, the lower portion by benching (Fig 182); in this case, the term "breast and bench" is more descriptive and is often used. Roof support in breast stoping is usually by permanent or semi-permanent pillars of ore.

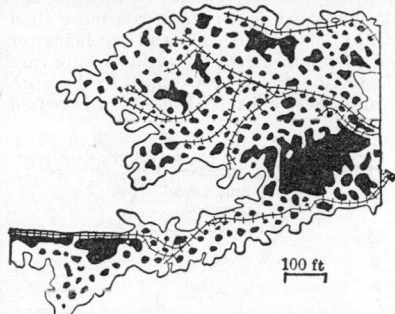

Fig 177. Plan of Part of a Mine in S E Missouri, worked by Breast Stoping

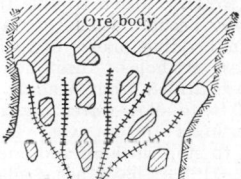

Fig 178. Plan of Breast Stope

Applicability. Breast stoping is usually applied to relatively thin, flat or low-dipping bedded deposits or veins where both ore and roof are strong. It is rarely used for thicknesses over 100 ft, though some older workings of S E Mo, where the method is common, are over 200 ft high. In this district, a stoping height of 40 ft is now rarely exceeded. It is a low-cost method, which usually sacrifices some ore in permanent pillars; hence, especially suited to low-grade ores where high extraction is not of first importance. As the method is moderately selective, in that areas of uneconomic grade can be left unmined, uniformity in distribution of values is not a requisite to its use.

Development. In flat-lying bedded deposits, a vert shaft is sunk to bottom of orebody; practically no lateral development precedes mining, although orebody may have been outlined by borings; stopes follow the ore outward from shaft (Fig 177). Where the method is applied to deposits of moderate dip, development usually depends on local conditions; for example, breast stoping may be used only as a supplement to another method in mining flat-dipping portions of a vein of variable dip.

General plan of work. In flat deposits less than 12–15 ft thick, the method resembles the driving of wide drifts, intervening ore being cut through at intervals to form pillars. Fig 178 shows different stages of work; obviously, the face can be advanced in any direction. Same general principle applies in flat orebodies of greater thickness; Fig 177 is a plan of a mine in S E Mo, showing application of method over a large area. In deposits with moderate dips, face of stope may be carried parallel to either dip or strike. As dip increases, the work of breaking ground may be the same as that of open stoping in narrow veins, either underhand (Art 35) or overhand (Art 38). Where the face advances downward, the openings are sometimes called DIP WORKINGS.

Breaking ground. Methods vary locally and with thickness of orebody; see examples of practice, Art 31, 32, 33.

Support of roof in breast stoping is by pillars; in low-grade uniform deposits (as beds of calcareous shale used for making cement or in beds of rock salt), systematic arrangement and uniform size of pillars are feasible and desirable (Art 34).

Pillars may be of any shape and size (Fig 177), but in metal mines are roughly circular in horiz sec. They are splayed out at top and bottom to increase area of support and bearing on roof and floor. Fig 179 shows a means of dealing with a shelly roof, or one which scales on exposure to air; it is feasible only for light pressures and in strong, low-grade ore. Where roof is fissured with parallel joints or cracks, stoping may unkey large slabs; this danger is partially averted by a systematic staggered arrangement of pillars.

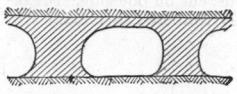

Fig 179.   Vert Sec

In some S E Mo mines, ore occurs in overlapping beds separated by barren limestone. These are worked from separate levels, care being taken that the pillars in upper and lower beds shall be directly over each other.

In the TRI-STATE and S E Mo DISTRICTS, pillars are larger and spaced closer in weak ground and left where possible in low-grade or thin parts of orebody. They are placed with regard to haulage tracks to avoid awkward curves, and are 10 to 60 ft diam, with intervening roof spans of 18–80 ft. Slabs of rock scaling from roof between pillars cause serious danger and trouble in breast stoping; in thin portions of deposit, slabs are supported by vert props; in thick orebodies, all shelly ground is removed from heading roof before bench is advanced. Even with this precaution, roof-men are constantly employed in Mo lead mines to bar down slabs in worked-out areas near stope faces or over traveling ways; where possible, slabs are taken down with bars and gads; this costs more than blasting but is safer; black powder used for blasting; holes drilled by hand or plugger or stope drill. Fig 180 shows details of staging used to support men and drills taking care of high backs at Bonne Terre mine of St Joseph Lead Co; 3 men accustomed to the work can put up 3 or 4 sections, or take down 6 to 8, in an 8-hr shift. All material is reused except eye-bolts, which are left wedged into roof (163, 521). Much trouble from slabs is caused by accumulations of water under pressure in bedding planes of roof rock; at some mines vert holes ("drain holes"), 8–10 ft deep, are drilled from heading into roof every 8–10 ft, to allow water to escape (164). REINFORCEMENT OF PILLARS: Gunite has been used to stop slacking and crumbling of old pillars. Pillars have been enlarged and strengthened by building forms around them and filling with concrete. Old pillars have been reinforced with tie rods, or by placing vert steel rods against face of pillar and wrapping with old cable (155).

Handling ore. Tracks are laid on floor of deposit, from point of entry to the stope faces (Fig 177, 178). In thin deposits, tracks run into headings; in thick, they extend to foot of benches. Where more than 1 bench is worked, the heading ore is shoveled to foot of lowest bench; general slope of benches is kept steep to minimize handling. Broken ore is shoveled into cars by hand or machine, and trammed to shaft by hand, or by animal or mechanical haulage, depending on distance and output; in some mines, buckets ("cans") are mounted on light trucks, reducing cost of haulage and hoisting equipment.

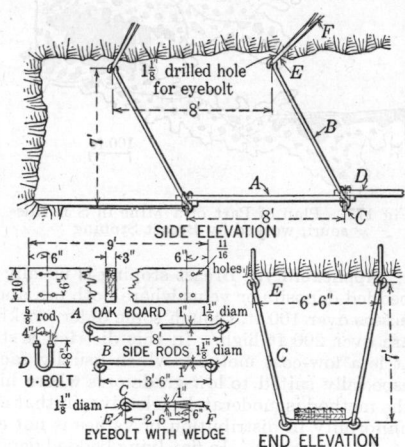

Fig 180.   Hanging Scaffold or Staging

In some TRI-STATE MINES, shoveling plats of 2-in oak plank are laid at foot of stope bench. Work is usually done on contract. At Hartley mine, Kan, C. M. Anderson, Supt, states in 1932 that, in low ground, all loading is done by hand into cans holding 1 400 lb. In high ground, both hand and power-shovel loading are used. Aver rate of loading of shoveler is 35 tons per 8-hr shift (323). At Picher, Okla, a shoveler on contract loads into cars 30–40 tons per shift (115).

Machine loading, S E Mo. Conditions are favorable for mechanical loading. St Joseph Lead Co used the St Joe shovel (see Sec 27) for nearly all mucking in its Mo properties until 1936 (116), when scrapers were first tried and proved effic in robbing pillars, recovering ore left in floors, and in general supplementing power-shovel work. In 1937, standard scraper equipment comprised 35-hp double-drum hoists and 54-in scrapers. Ore is either scraped up a ramp to a loading platform over the cars, or pulled into chutes (127). Power-shovel operators work under a bonus system; a task is set at regular daily wage, with bonus for excess tonnage. Usual task is 42 2.5-ton cars, varying with conditions from 32 to 48 cars (155). In TRI-STATE DISTRICT, hand shoveling is common in small mines; mechanical loaders used in some large mines (see Table 30). At Barr mine, Kan, using 25-hp elec shovel, 10-cu ft dipper and 1.5-ton cars, usual performance in 1929 was about 100 cars per shovel-shift; occasional max of 116 cars in 4 hr (143). Scrapers have also been used to advantage in some Tri-State mines. See Art 31, 32.

Table 30. Comparison of Cost of Loading with Power Shovel and by Hand at Hartley Mine, Kan, in 1932 (323)

Power shovel	¢ per ton	Hand shovelers	¢ per ton
Connected energy charge	0.382	Contract price	21.202
Power consumed	0.946	Shovels and picks	0.167
Depreciation and repairs	3.070	Total	21.369
Interest charge	0.776		
Labor (one operator with helper and extra trammer)	7.830		
Total	13.004		

Note. Small revolving shovel driven by 15-hp elec motor; can operate in a 9-ft room, loading into cans holding 1 400 lb. Data for power shovel cover 127 working days, in which 16 565 tons were loaded.

Percentage of ore left in pillars depends on: (a) CHARACTER OF ROOF, which determines max allowable width of heading that will stand unsupported, and therefore the distance between pillars; (b) CHARACTER OF FLOOR. A soft floor requires pillars of large area, or closely spaced, so that their bearing power will not be exceeded; (c) STRENGTH OF ORE determines minimum section of pillars to withstand pressure of overlying rock; (d) DEPTH OF DEPOSIT determines total wt to be carried on pillars, where deposit has such lateral extent that overlying rocks do not arch, and become self-supporting (see Subsidence, Art 114). These factors are interrelated; their effect can not be definitely determined in advance in new districts; the percentage of ore left in pillars may be fairly constant in a given mine, but varies widely in different localities. For example: H. A. Guess in 1914 estimated, for S E Mo district, that 15% of area mined was left in pillars (55). C. F. Jackson, 1929, estimates 10% left in pillars at largest property in the district (155). At Hartley Grantham mine, in Kan, where ore occurred in brecciated, loose formation, O. W. Keener in 1930 stated that approx 40% of the area of developed orebody was left as pillars on first mining, but that a high total extraction is expected when pillars are pulled or robbed (157). At Barr mine, Kan, in 1929, 15–18% of area mined was left in pillars; it is planned eventually to mine pillars in good ore, but leave permanently those in lean ore (143).

Recovery of ore from pillars. A mining-method like breast stoping is justified by its simplicity and cheapness and because, where properly applied, it yields a max profit in spite of sacrifice of pillar ore. Use of method is usually confined to low-grade deposits, where value of ore in pillars does not repay cost of replacing them by artificial supports. Some recovery of ore in pillars is often possible (see St Joseph Lead mine, below). Also, conditions may re-

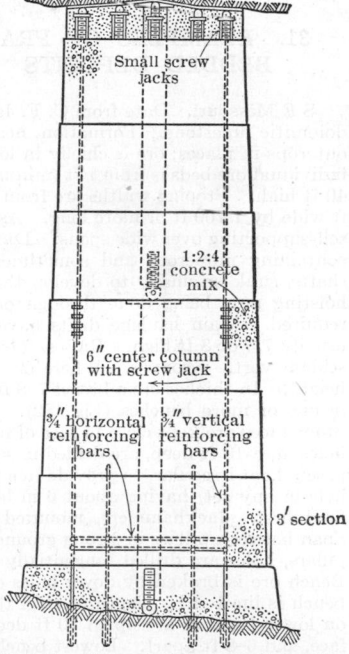

Fig 181. Concrete Column replacing Ore Pillar, S E Mo

quire leaving in pillars on first mining a relatively large percent of the ore; then pillar robbing or recovery becomes important. Recovery of ore from pillars is costly and requires extreme safety precautions.

In S E Mo, some pillars left years ago have proved unnecessarily large and considerable ore has been recovered by reducing their size. In 1937 the St Joseph Lead Co started to remove many high-grade ore pillars under the protection of concrete pillars (Fig 181) built and located with care near the pillars to be removed. Bottom of concrete pillar has a diam that permits tapering to a min of 8 ft. Base of pillar is doweled to floor by drilling 16 2-ft holes, in which are grouted vert reinforcing rods 9–12 ft high; these support circular forms 3 ft high, of 10-gage iron. Concrete is blown into the forms through a 4-in pipe by comp air. When the pillar is within 1 ft of the back, numerous 3-in screw jacks are placed on its top, with 2-in iron plates on top of the jacks, which are then tightened, and space around them is filled to the back with concrete. Such pillars have been built to height of 47 ft (127).

According to information from C. W. Nicolson in 1938, efforts to recover pillars in the Tri-State district have been confined mainly to "gouging" by leasers. In recent years, some companies of the Okla-Kan section have trimmed and removed pillars quite extensively where ore reserves were exhausted. Many orebodies in this region are long and narrow, and the amount of ore originally left as pillars does not aver more than 10% of total (0–15%). Many original pillars were either unnecessary or too large; by removing or trimming them, the ore recovered, in individual mines, is probably 1/3 of the original pillar tonnage. These ore pillars have not been replaced by other support, due to the high cost. Pillars 100 ft high have been successfully removed. When companies complete their own efforts, certain portions of the mine are usually turned over to leasers, who trim and remove pillars while retreating, recovering about 50% of the remaining pillar tonnage. Nicolson estimates that the combined work of company and leasers gives an ultimate recovery of about 2/3 of the original pillar tonnage in leased areas, or about 1/2 for the entire mine. Some falls of ground occur, but surface is unaffected, as deposits are overlain by strong beds of flint and limestone.

31. EXAMPLES OF PRACTICE, BREAST STOPING IN FLAT BEDDED DEPOSITS (S E Mo, Tri-State District, and Wis)

S E Missouri. Data from C. F. Jackson (155) in 1929. Disseminated galena occurs in dolomitic limestone. Formation, nearly horiz, has normal thickness of about 365 ft and outcrops in places; ore is chiefly in lower 100 ft. In the property described, thickness of individual ore beds is from 7 ft (min mining height) to over 200 ft, but stopes rarely exceed 40 ft high. Stoping widths are from a few to several hundred ft; some orebodies are 800 ft wide by 1 200 ft or more long. As a whole, the ore is in flat beds and the formation is self-supporting over wide spans. DEVELOPMENT. Property described covers a large area, containing numerous and sometimes widely separated orebodies. A number of vert shafts, sunk originally to develop the separate areas, were later connected by crosscuts, hoisting now being done through one vert shaft, with drifts, crosscuts, and raises as required. Main haulage drifts have min of 8 by 12-ft cross-sec. Other openings are usually 7.5 or 8 ft high. Raises, 6 by 9 ft, are commonly driven at an inclination of 45°, seldom vert. STOPING. Where ore is not over 9–10 ft thick it is breasted out to full height. In thicker ore a breast 7–8 ft high is driven at top of the ore; lower part is mined in one or more benches (Fig 182). Pillars of ore are left for roof support as required. Stope faces are kept close to face of heading. In breasting thin ore and driving headings, holes, *a*, 8-10 ft deep, are drilled in sets of 3, one above the other. Face of breast is purposely kept irregular, to provide free faces to break to. Burden on holes is 3–4 ft; middle hole in any set, having about 6 in less burden than others, is loaded more heavily, and fired first. Jackhammers, mounted on columns and with pneumatic feed, are used. Span between pillars in strong ground is 30 ft, decreasing to 16 ft in weaker. In turning pillars, holes are drilled tangentially to face of pillar (*b*, Fig 182) to avoid shattering it. Bench ore is broken by down holes drilled with hand-held jackhammers. Depth of top bench is limited by length of steel that can be handled in heading, usually 6 ft. Holes on lower benches are up to 10 ft deep. Bench or stope holes are drilled 3–4 ft back of face, and 6–8 ft apart. Lowest bench is mined with down holes if the ground breaks to a bedding plane with a resultant smooth bottom; otherwise, this bench is broken with "lifters" and "splitters," *c* and *d*, Fig 182. For lifters, drill rests on 2 parallel strips of wood laid on floor and connected on their underside by 2-in cross slats, with 2-in spaces. Driller uses a pinch bar, with a slat as a fulcrum to exert press on back end of drill; this device allows miner to stand while drilling. Several headings and stopes may be worked together in a given area. One man does the drilling for a heading and the stope behind it. The rock drills easily and 80–100 ft of hole is aver per shift. In a heading or in breasting thin ore, a miner breaks about 30 tons per shift; in bench or stope, 90–120 tons per machine-shift is common. Powder consumption varies: an aver of 0.459 lb of 40% ammonia gelatin per ton was used in mining 49 700 tons at this property in one month in 1929. Miners work on contract, based on ore broken; prices vary with height of stope and nature of ground. For data on breaking ground at Bonne Terre mine, S E Mo, see Ex 3, Table 29.

Tri-State District (S W Mo, S E Kan, and N E Okla). Breast stoping is used exclusively for flat bedded deposits of sphalerite and galena in flint and chert. Overlying rock is usually strong flint, standing well; sometimes, heavily fractured flint or limestone requiring close spacing of pillars. Main types of deposits: SHEET GROUND averages 7 ft thick, and is low-grade, crude ore assaying about 3.5% Zn and 0.5% Pb. It was mined extensively in S W Mo before 1918, at an aver depth of 150 ft, and since then locally, in Kan and Okla, at depth of about 350 ft. BRECCIATED GROUND occurs in beds, 6–30 ft thick, the most prolific being 20 ft thick; occasionally, in strong shear zones, mineralization extends through several beds, forming deposits 180 ft thick; aver grade of crude ore, 7.5% Zn and 1.0% Pb. This type of deposit has been mined largely in Kan and Okla from 1915 to 1938, at aver depth of 250 ft, and to some extent in Mo at shallow depths. For methods of exploring these deposits, see Art 10-b. DEVELOPMENT. Entry is by single-compt vert shafts, usually 6 by 6 ft inside timber, and sunk to lowest ore horizon. Most mines are opened on only 1 level. If shaft cuts ore, no lateral development is necessary in immediate ore area, but various "pull drifts" may be driven to isolated orebodies. Such drifts, rarely timbered, are 7 by 7 ft to 8 by 10 ft. STOPING. Breast stopes are carried with a single vert face in thinner deposits (6–12 ft), sometimes to 18 ft. In thicker deposits, a heading 7–8 ft high is driven at top of orebody; its face is kept 15–20 ft ahead of bench. Sometimes several benches 10–15 ft high are carried, making total height of excavation as much as 100 ft. Benches are broken with flat holes drilled from tripod or "stope boards" (Fig 185). According to C. W. Nicolson (191), hand loading into cans 32 in diam and 32 in deep, holding 1 400 lb, continues to be generally used. A aver shoveler loads about 25 tons per shift; under favorable conditions some men can load 50 tons per shift. Experiments with power shovels have not been

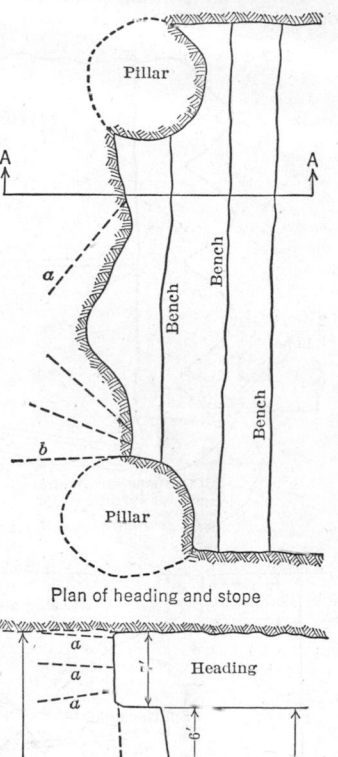

Plan of heading and stope

Fig 182. Breaking Ground by Breast Stoping, S E Mo

Vert Sec A-A

generally successful. Recently, several of the larger companies have installed scrapers, with good results (see below for scraping at D. C. & E. mine). For further data on scraping practice in Tri-State district see Art 91 and Sec 27. Operating and cost data at 2 representative mines of Picher district are shown in Table 32.

No 1 mine, Picher, Okla. Data from W. F. Netzeband (115) in 1929. Fig 183 shows stoping in ore 25–40 ft thick; for faces about 40 ft high, a round of 6 splitters and 3 stope holes are used. Slope of bench is kept at about 45°. Holes are drilled with 20-ft steels; splitters, with a rise of 1 in per ft; stope holes downward, 1 in per ft. Bench holes were formerly squibbed, or chambered, before final charge was loaded, but this practice has been abandoned in recent years. Aver stope or splitter hole breaks about 250 tons; powder consumption, 0.75 lb per ton. Ordinarily, 30% ammonia dynamite is used, but for wet work or poor ventilation, gelatin powder of same strength is substituted. In headings, about 40 tons per machine-shift are broken; in benching, 60–75 tons. Pillars are 20–60 ft diam, depending on ground, and height of roof; aver pillar diam, about 30 ft. Spacing varies, 40–100 ft c-c, aver 80 ft. Pillars represent about 15% of total area mined, but many are recoverable.

Hartley mine, Kan. Data from C. N. Anderson (323) in 1932. Sphalerite and galena occur in flat beds of chert about 300 ft below surface; sometimes in irregular masses.

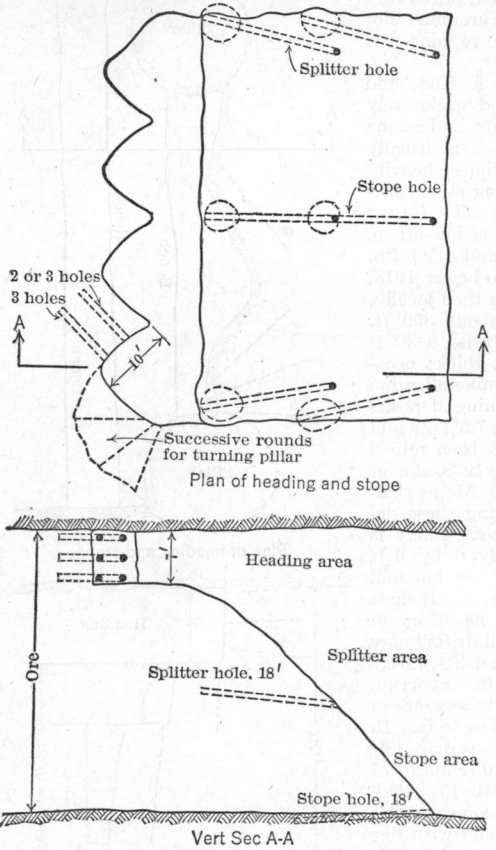

2 or 3 holes
3 holes
A
Successive rounds
for turning pillar
Plan of heading and stope

Heading area
Splitter hole, 18′
Splitter area
Stope area
Stope hole, 18′
Ore
Vert Sec A-A

Fig 183.　Stope and Heading Rounds, Breast Stoping,
Tri-State Distr

Mineable ore is 8–25 ft thick. Fig 184 shows methods of breaking ground. Pillars are 20–30 ft diam and spaced an aver of 40 ft edge to edge. Care is taken not to break a flint stratum overlying the ore, as roof may become slabby and dangerous. In low ground, mining is done by breast stopes with a single vert face; detail of work is similar to that for headings. Thicker ore is mined with headings and benches. Heading is 7 ft high; between pillars the face is in zig-zag form; drill round comprises 6–8 holes, 8–10 ft deep, by column-mounted drills. Midway between heading and floor, "splitters" are drilled 8–10 ft apart to depth of 12–14 ft, from tripod mountings. Floor or stope holes point slightly downward; they are 16–18 ft deep, drilled within a foot or two of mine floor; drills for these holes are mounted on either a tripod or "stope-board" (Fig 185). Aver tons broken per machine-shift in low ground, 71; in high ground, 72.5. In low headings with poorer ventilation, 35% gelatin is used; in high ground, 40% permissible explosive. Chambering of splitter and stope holes is rarely necessary. Over a 6-mo period, 180 212 tons were mined with powder consumption of 1.12 lb per ton.

D. C. & E. mine, Oronogo, Mo. Data from C. W. Nicolson (173) in 1938. Orebodies lie in sheet-ground horizon, about 150 ft below surface. Deposits are of considerable extent laterally, but have an aver vert thickness of only 7 ft. Sphalerite and galena occur in horiz bands, or in vugs in a flint gangue; aver assay of crude ore, 3.5% Zn and 0.4% Pb. From 1920 to 1937, this district was idle, due to low metal prices. D. C. & E. mine was reopened to determine whether mechanization would make mining profitable. Scrapers used for loading, and belt conveyers for transport to shaft. Results were successful. DETAILS. Mine is served by vert shaft (1) (Fig 186), formerly equipped with cage but refitted with 2-ton skips, loaded from a 50-ton storage hopper (2) at the shaft. Conveyer belt (3), 24-in wide, speed 350 ft per min, delivers to this hopper. Scraper (4) loads through a grizzly with 9-in openings to a reciprocating feeder and thence to belt (3). Other scrapers (8) load through grizzlies to cross-conveyers (7), which deliver at speed of 30 ft per min to belt (6) and thence to belt (3). Three-drum scraper hoists are driven by 25-hp motors. Scrapers are 48 in wide and hold 1 500 lb of ore; they have manganese-steel shoes 10 in wide, which handle about 11 000 tons and are then discarded. Pull-in cables are 0.5 in; pull-back cables, 3/8 in. In a test run, one scraper delivered 160 tons 100 ft to the belt in 2 hr. Economical limit of scraping distance, 150 ft, scrapers at points

(8) thus handle all ore in a semi-circle of 150-ft radius. Drilling is by 3.5-in automatic-feed drifters, with long guide shells permitting steel changes of 36 in; mounted on hydraulic columns. Each machine ordinarily drills 12 10-ft holes per shift. Detachable bits are used, 2.5-in on hollow steel; aver life, 14 ft of hole. Costs. Experimental work in mechanization showed a production rate of 19.4 tons per man-shift underground, as against 12 tons for other sheet-ground mines, and 7.65 tons for Tri-State district as a whole; also a cost reduction per ton from $1.23 for entire Tri-State district, or $1.08 for other sheet-ground mines, to $0.61 (see Table 31).

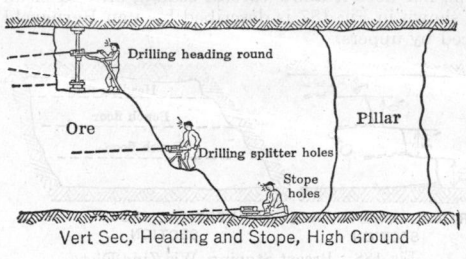

Fig 184.   Breast Stoping, Hartley Mine, Kan

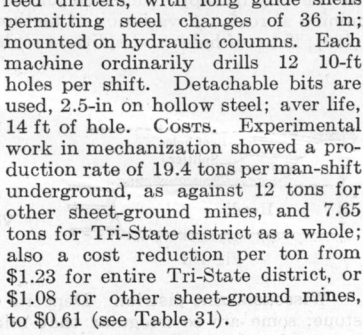

Fig 185.   Drill Mounted on Stope Board

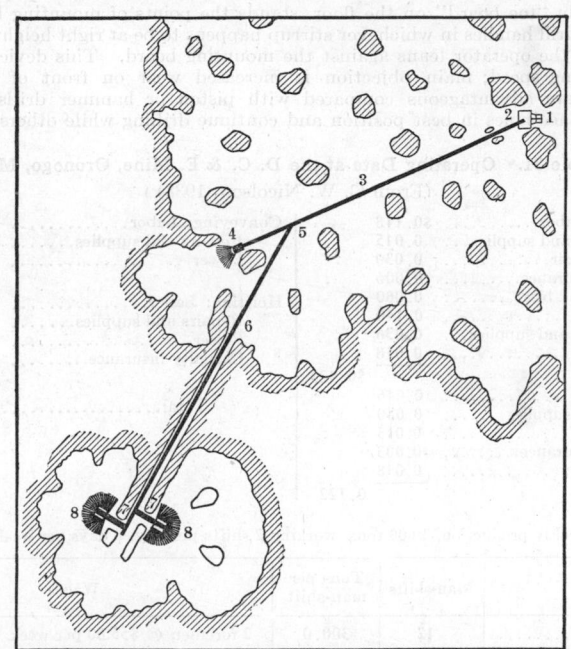

Fig 186.   Part of D. C. & E. Mine, Oronogo, Mo, showing conveyer system and location of scrapers

Fig 187 shows a different method of breaking used at one mine in Joplin district (158); upper 12 ft of deposit was very tough, lower 12 ft broke easily. Heading was driven in softer ground on bottom of orebody by methods described above; drill holes, 12 ft deep. Upper stratum was broken with 12–14-ft holes, placed as shown; splitter holes were squibbed, roof holes being left as drilled, as squibbing would tend to loosen roof and make it dangerous; heading was carried 50–100 ft ahead of stope. This method proved cheaper in this mine than the usual plan. 5 drills broke an aver of 325 tons per 8 hr.

This plan resembles overhand stoping in wide veins; is not applicable to thick beds, due to difficulty of supporting men and drills; nor does it allow careful scaling of, and clean mining at roof. A variation of method shown in Fig 187 is described by Van Barneveld (482); flat roof holes and splitters replaced by uppers.

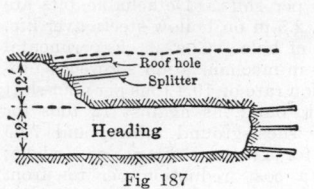

Fig 187

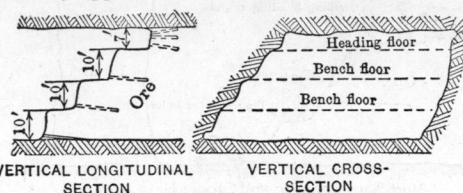

Fig 188. Breast Stoping, Wis Zinc Dist

Wisconsin zinc district. Deposits of ZnS and PbS occur in pitches and flats in limestone; some are so irregular that mining is practically gophering; larger deposits are commonly mined by breast stoping. Orebodies are from 5 to 70 ft high, 20 to 300 ft wide; and 500 to 7 000 ft long; roof is generally solid, thick-bedded limestone; deposits lie at depths of 75 to 200 ft. J. G. Trewartha, Gen Supt, Vinegar Hill Zinc Co, contributes following data on this district in 1938: Orebodies mined by breast stoping (Fig 188). Face of heading is kept not more than 8–10 ft ahead of stope. Wet jackhammers, weighing 45 lb and using 0.75-in hex steel, are used for all holes in heading and stope. A home-made mounting is used: a 2 by 6-in board with 2 steel points set in one end and a series of steel stirrups bolted at 8-in intervals to one face of board. Operator lays a 2 by 10 or 12-in "toe board" on the floor, stands the points of mounting board on this and hangs the drill handles in whichever stirrup happens to be at right height for the hole. While drilling, the operator leans against the mounting board. This device has greatly increased drilling speed; main objection is increased wear on front of the machine. Jackhammers are advantageous compared with piston or hammer drills on column; operator can place holes in best position and continue drilling while others are mucking

Table 31. Operating Data at the D. C. & E. Mine, Oronogo, Mo

(From C. W. Nicolson, 1938)

Breaking: Drill labor	$0.118		Conveying: Labor	$0.014
Drill repairs and supplies	0.015		Repairs and supplies	0.008
Compressed air	0.030		Power	0.003
Casualty insurance	0.006			$0.025
Drill steel and bits	0.060		Hoisting: Labor	0.015
Explosives	0.140		Repairs and supplies	0.013
Misc repairs and supplies	0.036		Power	0.014
Supervision	0.018		Casualty insurance	0.001
		$0.423		0.043
Scraping: Labor	0.046		Total	$0.613
Repairs and supplies	0.040			
Power	0.015			
Casualty insurance	0.003			
Supervision	0.018			
		0.122		

Weekly production, 3 600 tons, working 2 shifts per day, 6 days per week

	Man-shifts	Tons per man-shift	Wages	
Supervision	12	300.0	2 foremen @ $55.00 per week	
Drilling and breaking	90	40.0	10 drill runners	@ $4.94
			5 drill helpers	@ 4.31
			(Base rates $4.05 and $3.55)	
Scraping	44	82.4	4 scraper operators	@ 4.94
			3 scraper helpers	@ 4.31
Conveying	15	248.0	2 conveyer men	@ 3.80
Hoisting	12	300.0	2 hoistmen who also run compressors @	4.50
Miscellaneous	12	300.0	2 men, 1 on surface, 1 underground, @	3.80
Total	185	19.4		

down the stope. There is no fixed round of holes. An aver of 45–50 tons is broken per drill-shift. Water-resisting gelatin dynamites are used, aver about 35%; aver consumption, 0.8–0.9 lb per ton broken; see Ex 2, Table 29.

Table 32. Operating Data, Typical of Picher Dist, Kan and Okla (C. W. Nicolson, 1938)

	Sheet ground	Brecciated ground
Thickness of ore, ft { Min.	7	8
Max.	9	35
Aver.	8.5	21
Spacing of pillars, ft, aver.	50	70
Diam of pillars, ft, aver.	20	30
Tons per man-shift, total.	10.3	10.8
Tons per machine-shift, breaking.	57.9	66.2
Footage drilled per machine-shift.	81.2	66.0
Tons per man-shift, hand loading.	......	24.2
Tons per man-shift, scraper loading.	76.0	61.8
Lb explosive per ton, ore breaking.	1.15	0.80
Aver depth of holes, ft.	8.72	10.3
Aver footage drilled per bit forged (or purchased).	2.05	10.51
Breaking cost:		
Labor.	$0.168	$0.120
Drill repairs and supplies.	0.014	0.026
Compressed air.	0.043	0.039
Other repairs and supplies.	0.019	0.014
Drill steel, bits and shop expense.	0.105	0.032
Explosives.	0.160	0.115
Total breaking.	$0.509	$0.346
Shoveling cost per ton, hand loading.	(0.246)	0.208
Shoveling cost per ton, scraper loading.	0.132	0.139
Total cost (breaking, loading, tramming, pumping, hoisting, ventilation and maintenance) per ton.	1.04	0.760

Note. These figures are from two typical mines under good management. SHEET-GROUND MINE: Gangue, hard and abrasive chert containing many vugs which force steel off line, breaking or binding steel. Explosive often breaks back into vugs, causing hole to fail. Bits forged on 1.25-in hollow round steel, lugs on shanks. Drifters, 4 in diam, hand-cranked, mounted on column. Explosive, 40% ammonia or gelatin. All loading by 3-drum scraper hoists on steel slides mounted on caterpillar treads. Tramming to shaft by rope haulage. Hand-loading cost given is cost prior to installing scrapers. BRECCIATED-GROUND MINE: Gangue, brecciated flint, better drilling than sheet ground. Mined heading and bench. 2.5-in detachable bits on 1.25-in hollow round lugged steel. Drifters 3 and 3.5-in. Explosives, 30% ammonia or gelatin. Loading, 80% by hand into cans, 20% by scraping into hoppers. Scraping cost includes drawing ore from hopper into cans and spotting on lay-bye. Tramming to shaft by rope haulage; some mules for gathering service.

32. BREAST STOPING IN DIPPING DEPOSITS (see also Art 33)

Park City, Utah. Fig 189 shows old workings of Silver King Coalition Co. J. Humes gives following data in 1915 (134): silver-lead orebodies occur largely as replacements in limestone; thickness, 1.5 to 25 ft; dip, 10° to 30°; oreshoots are irregular in outline and make off from fissures which gave access to mineralizing solutions.

For mining THIN BEDS, exploratory drifts, in the ore bed, follow the fissures; when a drift cuts ore, stopes are started to the dip and carried as far as broken rock can be shoveled out. If ore continues, a small hoist is installed, track laid on floor and mine cars run to stope face. If deposit is

Fig 189. Part of Silver King Mine, Park City, Utah. (Aver dip, 18°; aver thickness of ore, 2.5 ft)

thin, enough footwall is shot out to admit car. If the temporary inclines strike barren rock, tracks are turned and follow the ore. In orebodies of large lateral extent, small drifts (sub-levels) are run to right and left from main incline. Stoping proceeds up and down dip from sub-levels, in which run small cars dumping into cars on the incline. Many deposits are so flat and thin that machine drills can not be used with advantage. This method permits mining orebodies without excessive preliminary development, and is well adapted to handling broken ore on flat dips. More recent practice is described by M. J. Dailey in 1930 (159). Method is termed "overhand," as faces are advanced up the dip. In thicker portions, modified square-sets are used, with caps extending across 3 posts. Stopes are often back-filled as stoping advances, timber being recovered when possible. Weaker parts of deposit are mined in sections 50 ft wide. Around edges of orebodies, where ore is thin and less support required, 8 to 10-in round stulls, with headboards, are used.

Barton Hill mine, Mineville, N Y. Orebody is a bed of strong magnetite; thickness, 0 to 20 ft or more; aver dip, between 15° and 25°, rising to 35° or 40° in places. Hanging

Fig 190. Part of Barton Hill Mine, Mineville, N Y

and footwalls are very strong tough gneiss, the former fairly smooth, the latter warped by 2 series of ridges, the axes of which are parallel and normal to strike; this complicates ore handling. MINING METHOD. Deposit was first attacked at several points along outcrop by breast stoping to the dip. Mine cars were hoisted to surface on inclined tracks on footwall; Fig 190 shows 2 inclines, also pillars for roof support (note that inclines were swung

to right or left as needed to follow ore); temporary horiz tracks were also laid to reach remote portions of stope faces, or for stoping along strike at points above bottom of inclines; these are typical dip workings. More recent practice, described by A. M. Cummings (495) in 1928, is shown in Fig 191. Deposit is opened by parallel shafts, 400–600 ft apart, following dip of orebody along footwall. At intervals of 1 000–1 500 ft on dip are haulage levels for transferring ore from auxiliary shafts to main hoisting shafts. Intermediate stoping levels extend from shafts on footwall at intervals of 30–100 ft, depending on width, dip, and faulted or folded conditions of orebody. Leaving 20-ft shaft pillars on each

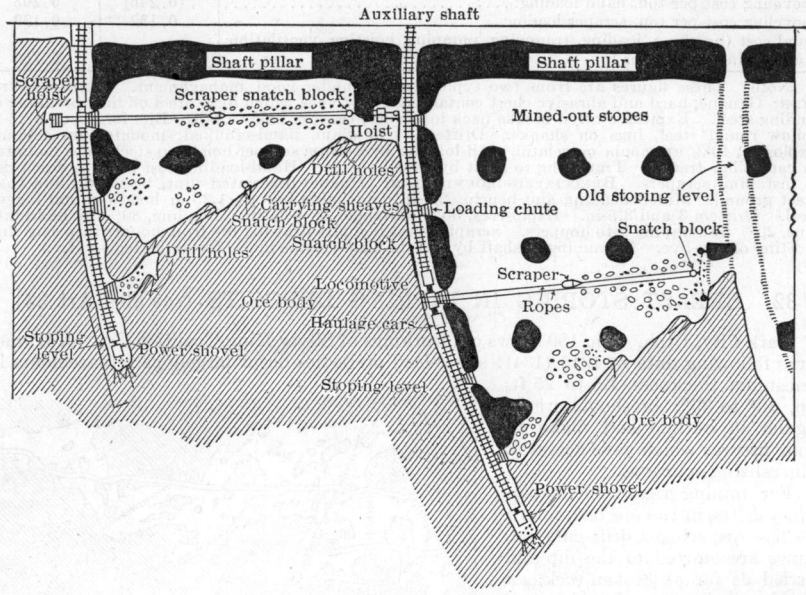

Fig 191. Breast Stoping, Mineville, N Y

side of shaft, mining starts by cutting loading chutes on upper side of stoping levels every 50 ft. Ore is then breasted out as in Fig 191. Pillars, roughly circular and 20–60 ft diam, depending on height and character of roof, are spaced about 50 ft c–c. Where ore is more than 15 ft thick, a 7-ft heading is carried at top of ore; bottom ore broken by underhand benching. Ore is scraped to loading chutes, which deliver to cars (Fig 192). Pillars represent about 25% of total ore. Plans call for eventual recovery of much pillar ore by a retreating method.

Sherritt Gordon mine, Manitoba. Data from E. L. Brown, Gen Supt, in 1933 (162). Ore is coarse-grained mixture of pyrite, chalcopyrite, and sphalerite, with rock inclusions.

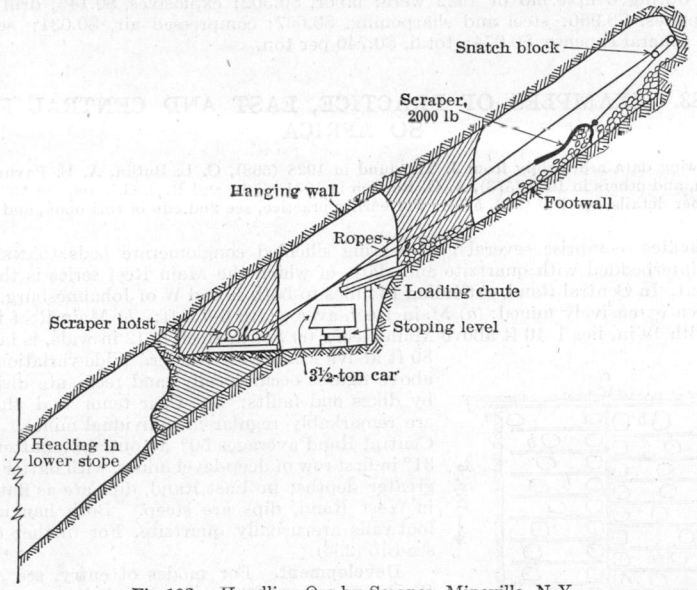

Fig 192. Handling Ore by Scraper, Mineville, N Y

Two lenses occur in shear zones along contact between massive gneiss on hanging wall and

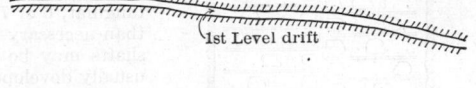

conglomerate and quartzite on footwall. Dips, 30° to vert. Aver width of ore 15.5 ft; sometimes exceeds 50 ft. Walls sharply defined. DEVELOPMENT (Fig 193). Main shaft is in footwall, inclined at 51°. Main haulage level, at depth of 500 ft on the incline, is along footwall contact, about 1/3 of face being kept in ore; it is double-track, 7 ft high by 15 ft wide in central part of orebody, 7 by 8 ft toward ends. Above, at intervals of 150 ft, are two sublevels, 4 by 6.5 ft, in footwall, 10–15 ft from the ore. Raises, 5 by 5 ft, 120 ft apart along strike, extend from haulage level to bottom of pillar left to protect surface. STOPING. For method where dip exceeds 45°, see Art 36. In flatter dips breast stoping is used. Stope sections extend 50 ft each way from raises, making stopes 100 ft long, with 20-ft pillars between. Ore is breasted upward along dip to full thickness of lode unless thickness exceeds 8 ft, in which case a heading-cut, 6.5 ft high, is carried along hanging wall, and the bottom removed by underhand stoping with jackhammers. Ore is handled by scrapers. Raise to level above

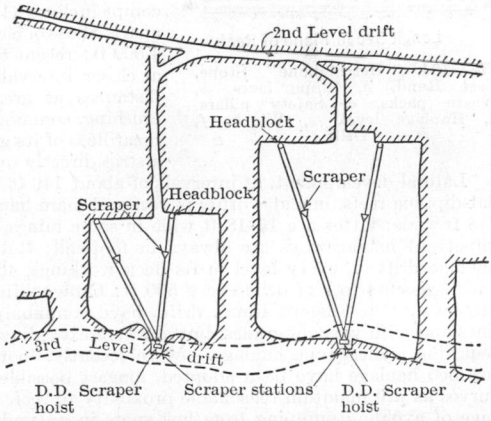

Fig 193. Breast Stoping in Flat-lying Section of Orebody, Sheritt Gordon Mine, Manitoba

serves as manway, and for air and water lines. Ore is handled on haulage level in 80-cu ft Granby cars, by storage-battery locos. STOPING COSTS, with above-described method during 6 first mo of 1932 were: labor, $0.302; explosives, $0.146; drill repairs and supplies, $0.066; steel and sharpening, $0.067; compressed air, $0.031; scraping, $0.054; general expense, $0.074; total, $0.740 per ton.

ART 33. EXAMPLES OF PRACTICE, EAST AND CENTRAL RAND, SO AFRICA

Following data are mainly from J. Thorlund in 1928 (568), C. L. Butlin, A. E. Payne, C. B. Brodigan, and others in 1930 (573), A. G. Boyden in 1931 (576), and R. S. G. Stokes in 1936 (195). For further details, see Bib (538, 556). For earlier practice, see 2nd edn of this book, and its Bib.

Orebodies comprise several gold-bearing silicified conglomerate beds (BANKETS or REEFS) interbedded with quartzite and slate, of which the Main Reef series is the most important. In Central Rand, extending 14 miles to both E and W of Johannesburg, 3 beds have been extensively mined: (a) Main Reef, aver width 6–7.5 ft; (b) Main Reef Leader, aver width 18 in, lies 1–10 ft above Main Reef; (c) South Reef, 8–12 in wide, is in places 80 ft above Main Reef Leader. Wide variations from above figures occur locally, and reefs are dislocated by dikes and faults; but their tenor and thickness are remarkably regular in individual mines. Dip in Central Rand averages 50° at outcrop, flattening to 31° in first row of deep-level mines, with flatter dips at greater depths; in East Rand, dips are as flat as 6°; in West Rand, dips are steep. Both hanging and footwalls are usually quartzite. For further details, see Bib (254).

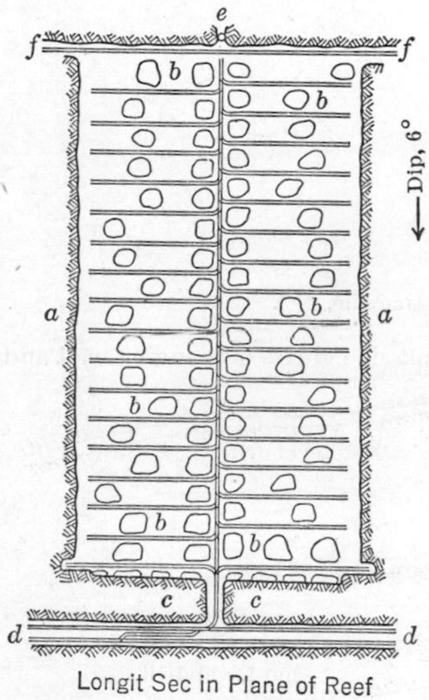

Fig 194. "Herringbone" Stope, East Rand. a, Stope faces. b, Waste packs. c, Safety pillars. d, Haulage level. e, Winch. f, Drift

Longit Sec in Plane of Reef

Development. For modes of entry, see Art 15. Workings tributary to inclined shafts from surface are nearly exhausted. Several vert hanging-wall shafts for hoisting from 5 000–6 300 ft in a single lift have recently been completed. Most of them are rectangular, 6 or 7 compartments, and are made larger than necessary for hoisting to aid ventilation. Such shafts may be 2 miles apart. Intervening areas are usually developed by "sub-inclines," delivering ore to haulage levels connecting with vert (or turned-vert) shafts. These inclines, of which 30–40 are constantly advancing on the Rand, are usually in footwall; some, designed to reach 8 000 ft (vert), are concreted. Three-compt inclines (17.5–22.5 ft wide) are 2 000–3 000 ft apart; those of 5 compts (35 ft wide) are spaced 3 000– 4 000 ft; recent trend is towards the smaller inclines at closer intervals, to reduce hauling and ventilating distances at great depths. As precaution against crushing, common practice is to stope at least 1 reef, regardless of its gold value, as early as possible from a strip directly over an incline.

Lateral development, at intervals of about 140 ft vert, or as much as 1 000 ft horiz in flat-dipping reefs, includes drifts in reef and main haulage drifts in footwall. Former are 7–8 ft wide; latter are 15–18 ft wide in some mines, usually narrower. On deep levels, important haulageways are always in footwall; Robinson Deep (Central Rand) has a haulage drift on every level in its deep workings, 40–50 ft (normal to dip) in footwall, with crosscuts to reef drift every 500 ft; Crown Mines has footwall drift only at every 5th level. On Eastern Rand, drifts have commonly been driven in reefs, on straight lines and with varying grades, but nowhere exceeding 15%, to follow undulations of reef, requiring endless-rope haulage. More recently, footwall drifts on uniform 0.6% grade for loco haulage have been adopted, longest possible tangents being connected by such curves as will maintain reasonable proximity to reef. This system has incidental advantage of avoiding pumping from low spots in an undulating drift. With any system of footwall development, stoping areas are approached by crosscuts, raises, and ore-passes.

Stoping methods may be classed generally as breast stoping, but the nature of the reefs and problems arising from mining at great depth have resulted in unique practice. Press from hanging wall, with danger of rock bursts, demands special means of roof support, described hereafter. Experience with rock bursts has led to reversal of former practice respecting use of ore pillars for support; leaving of pillars is now generally avoided as a rock-burst menace. Present modes of support are based on principle that settlement is inevitable, subject only to control, not to avoidance. Backfilling, usually with sorted waste, is common method of control. Fig 194 shows the "HERRINGBONE SYSTEM" of breast stoping on the East Rand. Level interval is about 600 ft, along the dip. A raise, or winze, or a combination of the two, is driven between levels near middle of a stoping area, with a track connected with the tracks on each haulage level. A winch, with compressed air or elec drive, is installed at upper end, as at e. Stoping starts by widening the raise laterally on each side, by slabbing rounds drilled with jackhammers. Horiz and parallel branch tracks are then started at 30-ft intervals and advanced to keep within reach of the stoping face. Cars (1-ton) are loaded and trammed by hand to the incline, where they are hoisted or lowered to the haulage level above or below. In stopes 600 ft or more in dip length, a second winch may be installed at a mid-point for delivery of cars to the lower drift,

while the winch at top hoists to the upper drift from upper half of stope. Roof support is by "waste packs" (backfilled).

Fig 195 shows the "CROSSCUT AND BOXHOLE" method; it has been used on flat dips in E Rand, but has more recently given way to scraper methods. It is adaptable to widths of ore too small to permit use of main-haulage cars in stopes; in very narrow reefs, cars may have only 5-cu ft capac. Crosscut x is driven under a centrally located raise or winze, driven in reef between levels. Steeply inclined raises (" boxholes "), g, with chute pockets at bottom, are then driven 90 ft apart.

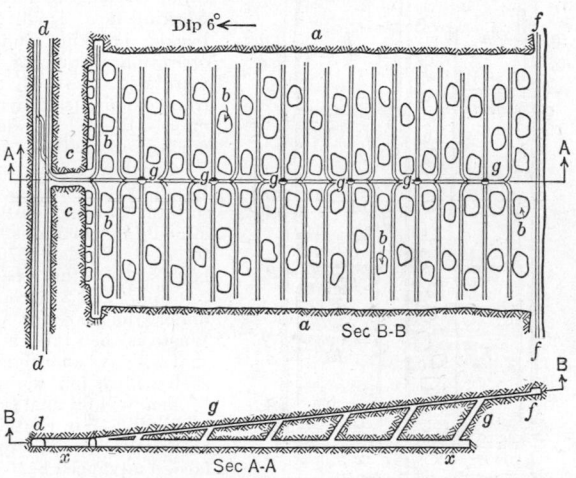

Fig 195. "Crosscut and Boxhole" Stope, East Rand. a, Stope faces. b, Waste packs. c, Safety pillars. d, Haulage level. f, Drift. g, Raises or "boxholes"

Stope faces are advanced both ways from raise, in direction of the strike. Three parallel and nearly horiz tracks, about 30 ft apart, extend in both directions from top of each boxhole. Track is usually 20-lb rail, laid on 3 by 4-in hardwood ties; gage, 18–30 in. Ore is hand-trammed to boxholes, whence it is drawn into cars on main level. Waste packs are the roof support.

Fig 196 shows "SCATTER PILE" ("skeleton shrinkage") method, developed at Modder B mine, but also used elsewhere on E Rand and on steeper dips of Central Rand. According to C. L. Butlin (573), area between 2 main levels is divided by horiz openings, o, to form stoping blocks not longer than 200 ft on dip, extending both ways from a centrally located raise (or winze), r. A central, inclined track through raise r connects with haulage tracks on main levels, over which cars are hoisted or lowered by winch, e. Horiz branch tracks in openings o are depressed in footwall to allow scrapers to discharge into cars through loading chutes l. Stoping starts by breasting both ways from raise r. Broken ore is shoveled back 12–18 ft from face into a pile paralleling the face; it reaches the roof but gives no support to it, this being supplied by temporary timber packs, metal props, or other means described below. Purpose of pile is to prevent scattering of ore on blasting; hence the name "scatter pile." Ore from blasts is thrown back into the pile until the working space is too small for the drillers; scraper then removes enough to restore ample working space; ore thus removed from pile toward face is about 40% of total broken. At rear of pile, waste is sorted out for building waste packs. Sorted ore is scraped to cars on next lower horiz tracks; floors are then swept to recover fines. Scraper hoists, with air or elec (15–35 hp) motors, are moved from block to block. Stokes estimates (195) that scrapers, where suitable, save 6 pence per ton in cost of handling, as against hand loading. Saving in stope trackage, usually requiring footwall excavation, is also an important economy in favor of scrapers, which are being widely used throughout the Rand for sundry mining methods. On Central Rand (dip 30°–50°), the "scatter pile" principle is widened, in that ore behind the advancing face, aided by timber support, maintains a safe working place. In such case the method is locally called "SHRINKAGE," since, as in "scatter pile" mining, about 40% of the broken ore must be removed continually from the side of pile toward the face to maintain working space for drilling; but stope faces advance laterally by breast stoping and miners stand on footwall rather than on broken ore; hence, the method is not "shrinkage" by usual definition (see Art 67). In Rand practice, sorting at rear of advancing pile precedes removal of ore from stope by means best suited to conditions, and waste is packed so as to allow roof to settle with minimum disturbance. A pile 10 ft wide usually suffices for roof support near face; unless ore is reclaimed from pile within 60 ft of face, crushing and compacting by roof press make sorting of ore difficult and inefficient. Cited advantages of so-called "shrinkage" system are: rapid advance of face; good roof support near working face; small loss of fines. Cited drawbacks: breaking and reclamation are separate operations, requiring divided attention of miner; ventilation less easily controlled; heat is generated from oxidation of pyrite in broken ore; ore pile may be diluted by waste from hanging or footwall during reclamation.

For thin reefs under heavy press, as in Central Rand, RESUING has shown its advantages, provided suitable partings exist; to 1936, City Deep had mined 4 000 000 tons by this method. According to A. G. Boyden (576) in 1931, advance of face begins by erecting a barricade of lagged 7-in stulls, 7 ft apart and 2 ft from face, leaving enough space under the roof for waste to be thrown over. Waste is then broken above the reef to a height that will give an ultimate width of about 42 in. At such width, for example, 25 in of waste, when broken, will fill final excavation completely; if the remaining 17 in contains sortable waste, it must be hoisted, or used for filling elsewhere. Waste face is advanced 8–10 ft, or until the pile reaches the barricade, the roof being supported on short props. Ore is then broken away from footwall, with light shots or air-driven gads, and discharged through chutes or moved by scrapers to the haulage level. As short props drop out, they are replaced by longer ones, keeping roof safe until next row of lagged stulls is set. The retreating edge of reef stops 1–2 ft from the waste face; after cleaning the floor, a new barricade is erected and operation repeated. At an individual face, waste stoping may take 12–16 days, extraction of reef, 6–8 days, extra shovelers working during latter period.

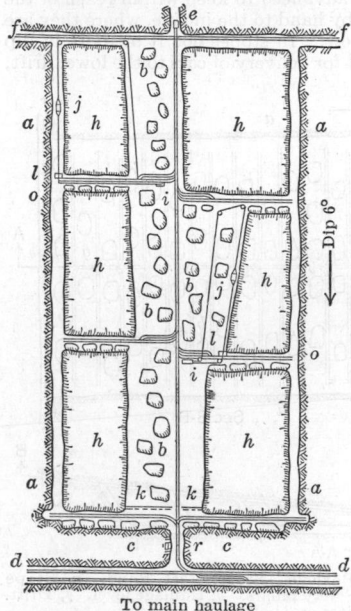

Fig 196. "Scatter-pile" Stope, Modder B Mine. *a*, Stope faces. *b*, Waste packs. *c*, Safety pillars. *d*, Haulage level. *e*, Winch. *f*, Drift. *h*, Piles of broken ore. *i*, Transportable scraper hoists. *j*, Scrapers. *k*, Brattice. *l*, Loading chutes. *r*, Raise entry to stope

In all the above-described methods, stoping faces are maintained on nearly straight lines, usually parallel with dip, unless the prevailing direction of fractures makes it easier to control roof settlement behind a face advancing at some other angle. Faces are 200–400 ft long, on dips over 30°; 400–1 000 ft on flatter dips. When opening a stope from a drift, the tendency to abrupt falls of ground ("rock bursts") can be counteracted by stoping to a width of 8–10 ft on the dip side of drift, in advance of similar stoping to the rise, and packing the spaces with artificial support rigid enough to keep the drift open, but permitting enough settlement to relieve concentrated stresses in hanging wall. Control of roof settlement and avoiding of bursts are helped by rapid advance at face; for this reason (and also to provide more favorable conditions for use of scrapers, where applicable) drilling in some deep mines is concentrated at certain places almost to point of congestion, and at expense of drilling efficiency.

Breaking ground in stoping. Fig 197 shows the general shape of stope face, maintained to provide free faces, and the manner of placing holes. Usually, one hole will break or loosen whole width of reef. According to H. Simon (89), in a 40-in stope, a 42-in hole with about same burden, and loaded with 2.7 lb of 50% dynamite, will break about 7 sq ft of stope area, or 2 tons. Fig 197 also shows a "hole director," which, in various forms, is used widely on the Rand. The one shown (89) is of $3/4$ or $7/8$-in steel tubing, with welded joints, and weighs about 5 lb; it is made in different sizes for varying character and thickness of reef, on basis of records by efficiency engineers. With the instrument held in plane of reef, the inner end of arm A is placed at the point of the face where the hole is to be collared, and end of arm B is moved against the face. Arm A then indicates proper direction of the hole to give the burden for which the "director" is designed. Miner or foreman marks with chalk on the face and roof the direction which the hole is to take and its depth. Simon states that, in general, max effic is secured when area of rock in plane of "director" is 63% of area of rectangle indicated.

Until about 1920, drilling in thin or steep reefs was done by hand (p 582, 2nd edn), one 3-ft hole, breaking 0.5 ton, being a day's work for a native driller. In wider reefs, mounted drifters were used, drilling 4 holes per shift and breaking about 6 tons in a 4-ft stope. Nearly all drilling is now done with unmounted, 50-lb, wet jackhammers. These have been effective in reducing the minimum necessary stoping width, and the amount of waste broken and sorted in working a thin reef, and allowing !production from reefs previously unprofitably narrow or low-grade. Table 33, from A. E. Payne (573), shows results in one mine before and after introducing jackhammers.

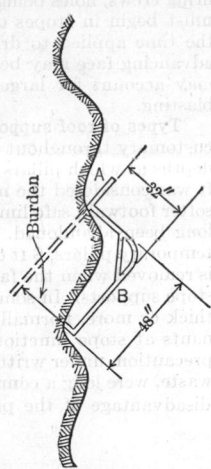

Fig 197. Hole Director

Table 33. Reef and Stoping Widths, Van Ryn Deep

Year	Fathoms stoped (a)	Reef width, in	Stope width, in	Waste width, in	Method
1919	8 771	36	66	30	By hand in Main Reef Leader
"	24 693	48	74	26	Mounted drill in same
1928	42 547	39	51	12	Jackhammer in same
"	26 402	20	37	17	Jackhammer in small leaders
"	68 949	32	46	14	Jackhammer in all reefs worked

(a) "Fathom" = 36 sq ft

Another advantage of the jackhammer as compared with reciprocating drill is that the smaller holes and lighter charges are less destructive to the brittle and fissured hanging wall. A third and most prominent effect has been a great increase in rate of drilling and breaking. In favorable ground, a jackhammer can drill 80 3-ft holes in a shift; aver over whole Rand, 75 ft of hole per drill-shift. Table 34, from A. E. Payne (573) shows stoping performance with jackhammers in 1928, in 6 mines under same management.

Table 34. Jackhammer Stoping in a Group of Rand Mines, 1928

Mine	Fathoms broken	Stoping width, in	Fathoms per drill-shift	Tons per drill-shift
A	140 284	66	3.64	60.14
B	52 087	39	1.83	17.60
C	89 228	45	3.05	33.97
D	126 156	45	1.47	16.60
E	69 026	46	1.85	21.20
F	32 569	51	1.78	22.81

Table 35. Aver Stoping Effic in a Group of Rand Mines

	1931	1935
Stoping width, in..................	44.2	46.9
Fathoms broken per drill-shift.......	2.43	2.60
Tons " " "	26.73*	30.42*
Ft of hole per drill-shift............	85	90
Ft of hole per ton broken...........	3.18*	2.96*
Number of holes per fathom........	9.5	9.5
Aver depth of hole, ft..............	3.7*	3.6*
Ngl cont of explosive, lb per fathom ..	5.0	5.0
Cost of breaking, per fathom	29s 9d	27s 8d
" " " " ton...........	2s 8.3d	2s 4.2d

* Calculated and interpolated by author

Stokes (195, p 216) gives the data in Table 35, on a representative group of mines, but states that variable conditions (such as the possible incomplete recovery of fine ore) render it difficult to compare stoping efficiencies.

Other factors contributing to improved effic of breaking in stopes: (a) increasing use of "hole directors"; (b) employment, in some mines, of a "cleaning shift," preceding drill shift by about 1 hr and making faces ready for drillers; (c) increasing employment of shot-firing crews, holes being loaded by miners at end of their shift, as heretofore; since blasting must begin in stopes on the return air course, delayed firing may considerably increase the time applied to drilling in these stopes; (d) in deep mines, where roof press on an advancing face may be controlled as in longwall coal mining, the natural crushing of reef may account for larger tonnage, recovered by hand pick or air-driven gads, than the blasting.

Types of roof support. ORE PILLARS, aided locally by stulls or other supports, were customary throughout the Rand to a vert depth of 1 000 ft. Local conditions govern as to depths at which pillars may be left without danger of rock bursts. In Central Rand, 2 000 ft was considered the max permissible depth for pillars in stopes; on Eastern Rand, with softer footwall, safe limit is considered to be 4 000 ft. As a rule, pillars at great depth have long been abandoned. Stokes (195) states an exception at Modderfontein East, where temporary pillars, 8 ft diam, are cut systematically to support the face. Each line of pillars is removed when the face has advanced enough to cut a new line and build the permanent stope supports. In some deep mines with wide reefs and large stopes, intrusive dikes, 50 ft thick or more, normally left standing as pillars, have caused trouble by bursting. Remnants at stope junctions present same objection as pillars; they are mined with special precaution, under written instructions to all concerned. PIGSTYES, or cribs filled with ore or waste, were long a common form of support, but have largely given way to other types. A disadvantage of the pigsty was its fire hazard and tendency to fail through rotting of

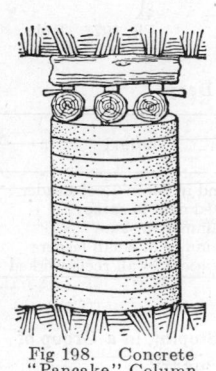

Fig 198. Concrete "Pancake" Column

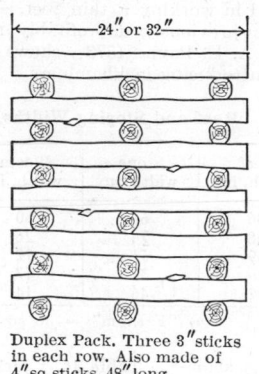

Duplex Pack. Three 3″sticks in each row. Also made of 4″ sq sticks, 48″long

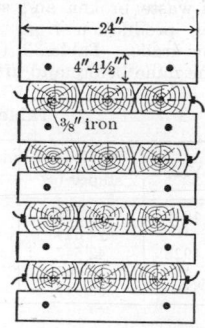

Chock Mats, Also made of 4 pcs 48″long

Fig 199. Two Types of All-timber Support, Rand

timber (later reduced by use of timber preservative). CONCRETE "PANCAKE" COLUMNS (Fig 198) were introduced at Van Ryn Deep and soon nearly displaced pigstyes in that and some other mines of East Rand. A pancake is a circular reinforced-concrete disk, 30 in diam, 4 in or more thick, with a 4-in hole at center for handling. A level footing is concreted and allowed 1 day to set. Disks are then piled one on another, with a little sand between to cushion irregularities, to within 1 or 2 ft of roof, which space is packed with wooden blocks and wedges, providing some compressibility. A. E. Payne (573) shows that during one month in 1930, an East Rand mine used 2 409 columns (18 473 disks) in stoping 282 168 sq ft of area, stoping width averaging 52.5 in; area served by each column was thus 117 sq ft. Pancake columns are not effic on dips over 30°. At increasing depths their use has declined in favor of all-wood or waste packs, which permit better control of roof settlement. MONOLITHIC CONCRETE COLUMNS have been used in some mines of E Rand, but at increasing depths they are being displaced by more compressible supports. According to J. Richardson in 1926 (571), a steel-plate sectionalized form, 33-in diam, is filled with concrete to within 18 in of roof; reinforcement, wire-rope rings 30-in diam, 1 ring per in of height. One man can build a column 42 in high (for a 5-ft stope) in 3–5 hr. When concrete has set, space at top is packed with wood blocks and wedges. Where used, such columns serve mainly for protecting track-ways, reinforcing edges of pillars, and as corners for waste packs. RAIL PROPS, pieces of steel rail, each standing on a sole-plate in a sand box, are used for temporary support in "scatter pile" stoping (see above) in Crown deep-level mines of Central Rand. A single stope may require 400 such props, in 8 rows: 2 in working space at advancing face, 4 buried in broken ore, 2 holding open space for sorting. Last row is recovered and moved to front when replaced by packed waste. SAND FILLING (Art 92), according to Stokes (195), is no longer used on Central Rand, but is still common in

E Rand to support worked-out areas before extracting hanging-wall bands of ore. TIMBER PACKS and CHOCK MATS are favored for face support, having advantage of ready compressibility (after serving initial purpose) when weight comes on waste packing behind and around them, thus aiding control of roof settlement. "Duplex pack mat" (Fig 199) is of 3-in round or square pieces, 24–32 in long, piled 3 pcs on 3; or of 4-in squared pieces 48 in long. "Chock mats" (Fig 199) are of 6-in timbers, slabbed on 2 sides to give depth of 4–4.5 in; 3 pcs 21 in long, or 4 pcs 48 in long, are threaded on 2 3/8-in bolts and drawn together tightly. A chock of any height can thus be built. WASTE PACKS consist of back filling with waste, usually from sorting. One type, WIRE PACK, is made by enclosing an area, commonly a 6-ft circle, with woven fencing of 6-gage wire and 6 by 18-in rectangular mesh, attached to light wood props, and filling the enclosure with coarse waste or ore packed solidly to the roof. A 6-ft diam pack 4 ft high requires 9.3 sq yd of fencing. Ends of wire being joined, failure of props has no adverse effect. Such packs are used on dips to 50°. They are fire- and rot-proof.

Rand mine costs. According to Stokes (195) aver costs in 1935, excluding some old mines with diminishing development and capital charges, were roughly as in Table 36.

Table 36. Average Rand Costs Per Ton Milled, 1935

	s.	d.		s.	d.
Development......	3	0	European wages...	5	1
Mining..........	12	2	Native wages.....	4	0
Milling..........	2	9	Supplies..........	7	4
General operating..	1	9	All other costs....	3	7
Office and misc....	0	4		20	0
	20	0			

34. SYSTEMATIC ROOM AND PILLAR METHODS IN BEDS

Term "room and pillar" covers many different methods of cutting up a deposit by excavating rooms, in which sense it includes breast stoping (Art 30, 31). Methods described below differ from breast stoping mainly in being more systematic; rooms and pillars are generally rectangular and laid out with almost mathematical regularity; the pillars may be left for permanent support, or recovered by robbing operations. These are colliery methods applied to mining salt, iron ores, etc, but may generally be simplified in these deposits because of less rigid ventilation requirements. For details of coal-mining methods, see Art 102 *et seq*.

Suitable deposits for exploitation by room and pillar are flat or slightly dipping beds of uniform tenor and character, and of large area. Cheap, abundant, strong mineral, and a strong roof and floor are necessary if permanent pillars are left; where ore in pillars is recovered by robbing, a very strong roof may "hang" over large areas and cause trouble by dropping suddenly (Art 103).

Detroit Rock Salt Co, Mich. Data from H. D. Keiser (526) in 1930. Room and pillar mining (Fig 200) is applied to a horiz bed of rock salt 30 ft thick, 1 100 ft below surface. Overlying rocks, chiefly limestones, dolomites, sandstones and shales. Formation immediately above salt bed is of limestone, gypsum and salt; that beneath, shale and limestone. Entry is by 2 vert shafts. Haulageways are driven 40 ft wide and 300 ft apart. Bed is mined by rooms, 40 ft wide, 25.5 ft high, running parallel with and at right-angles to haulageways on 80-ft centers, leaving permanent pillars 40 ft square; extraction, about 75%. Bottom heading, 11 ft high and width of room, is advanced 20 ft in 3 to 3.5-ft rounds, of 32–36 holes arranged alternately as (*a*) 3 wedge cuts and (*b*) a wedge cut with 2 slabbing cuts (Fig 201 *A*). Upper bench is then broken to full height in 5 stages (Fig 201 *B*) by 14

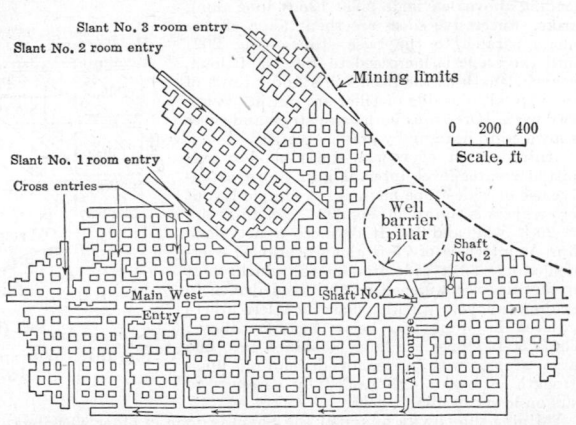

Fig 200. Plan of Workings, Detroit Rock Salt Co, Detroit, Mich

holes in stages 2, 4, 5, and 24 holes in stages 3, 6. A 9-ft hole, 1.5 in diam, is bored by elec auger in about 1.5 min. Explosive, 60% ammonia dynamite. When 1 000 to 1 500 tons are broken in a room, salt is loaded into 3-ton cars by elec shovel with 0.75-yd dipper, at about 600 tons per 9 hr. Large lumps broken by blockholing with augers or pneumatic picks, with air from a portable compressor.

Clinton iron ores, Birmingham, Ala. Orebodies are beds of hematite, interbedded in sandstones and shales. They extend many miles along the strike and have been opened over 2 000 ft on dip. Leaching has removed lime from upper parts, producing enriched soft ore for depths down to 400 ft on dip; below this, ore is hard. W. R. Crane (542) gives following data in 1924. Two seams have

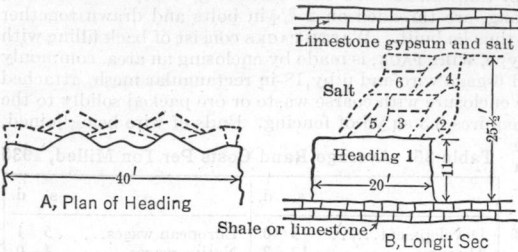

A, Plan of Heading
Shale or limestone   B, Longit Sec

Fig 201.   Breaking Ground in Detroit Rock Salt Mine

been mined, Big Seam and Irondale. Former is more important source of ore. It is 15–22 ft thick, divided by a slate band, from a knife edge to 30 in thick, in 2 parts: "upper bench," 10 ft aver thickness, "lower bench," aver 8 ft. Irondale seam is 3–8 ft thick, aver 6 ft. Due to folding, local dips are from 8°–50°, usually 16°–30°; hanging wall largely sandstone; footwall shale. METHODS OF MINING. Entry is by inclined shafts, 14–16 ft wide, in the deposit. Aver distance between slopes in various groups of mines, 1 333–2 475 ft. Level interval, 65–200 ft, present tendency being toward the higher figure. Manway raises, 12–15 ft wide, are driven 75 ft on each side of and parallel to the slope, leaving a shaft pillar. Headings 15 ft wide on each level are driven to manway raises. Beyond the raise the heading is widened to 20–45 ft, aver 35 ft, by breast stoping. In older workings, with smaller level

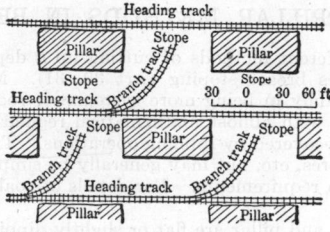

Fig 202.   Branch Tracks for Working Wide Stopes

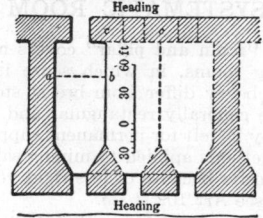

Fig 203.   Stope Layout for Scraper Loading

interval, driving the headings with connecting raises at 100-ft intervals constituted the first mining. Pillars were then robbed, retreating from points midway between slopes, with estimated extraction of 80–90%. Present practice in mining upper bench of Big Seam is to use a "wide-stope" method, as follows. At intervals of 150–200 ft along the headings, preliminary raise stopes 25–30 ft wide are carried by overhand stoping to the heading above, leaving a pillar 125 ft long along strike. Successive slices are then taken off the pillars parallel to the raise stopes (Fig 202) until the stope is increased to 130–150 ft long, or such length as the back will stand. Rows of props paralleling side of pillar are put in to support back. Ore from both raise stope and slices is lowered to heading by gravity planes.

Introduction of POWER SCRAPERS has permitted greater level interval and more extensive use of wide-stope method. A simple layout for scrapers is shown in Fig 203. Headings are 18–20 ft wide and 150 ft or more apart along dip. At intervals of 75 ft along headings, overhand stopes 20 ft wide are started, which, 20 ft up the dip, are widened to 50 ft and driven to heading above. Small pillars are left where required in stope and below heading above. These 50-ft stopes are later combined into one large stope, with a length depending upon strength of back. Ore hauled by scrapers to cars on lower heading tracks.

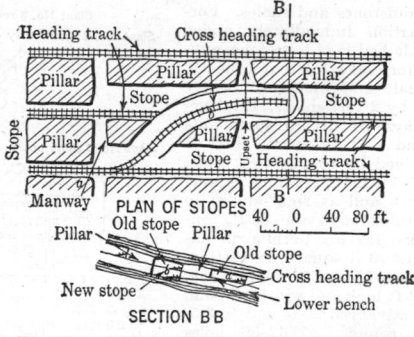

Fig 204.   Working Lower Bench of Big Seam by Cross-heading

Mining the LOWER BENCH of Big Seam is done in older workings where conditions are favorable. It involves taking up the floors of the old pillar-supported stopes. Stopes 30–35 ft wide and several hundred ft long are mined. A branch track is turned off heading track, and extended diagonally across the stope through the cross-heading in the arch pillar to the middle or bottom of next stope above, thence parallel to main heading track (Fig 204). Stope is then extended by underhand method full length of old heading. Pillar robbing, the final operation, is started in workings farthest away after stoping is completed, and carried back toward slope. Pillars are mined by slicing parallel to the heading, and breaking through pillars up the dip until all possible ore is recovered.

Tennessee Coal, Iron & R R Co, Muscoda, Ala. Data from C. E. Abbott (167) in 1936. Company mines a high-grade limestone for its steel works from a bed 40–50 ft thick, dipping 17°, and lying 330 ft above and parallel with a bed of Clinton iron ore, also mined at same place. Limestone bed was entered from beneath by a rock slope from haulage drift of the iron mine, 2 500 ft inside of outcrop to avoid decomposed rock and watery strata; then opened by a slope with 12 by 20-ft entries on both sides, 200 ft apart. Rooms, turned up-dip at 70-ft centers, are 12 by 12 ft in sec for first 20 ft; then widened to 30 ft, and again narrowed to 8 ft when within 15 ft of next entry above, to which they break through near top of bed, for ventilation. Remaining 25–30 ft of good stone in roof is broken down in slices 8 ft thick, starting at lower end, with upper holes drilled normal to dip by 4-in wet hammer drills on tripods standing on broken rock; until room is finished, only enough rock is drawn, by scrapers discharging into cars in entries, to make room for drillers. Explosive is 42%, water-resistant ammonia dynamite. Practically no timber is required. Resemblance to coal mining is emphasized by occurrence of CH_4, probably from an overlying bed of bituminous shale, requiring circulation of 25 000 cu ft air per min, and the precautions observed in gaseous coal mines.

Blue Diamond mine, Arden, Nev. Data from W. G. Bradley (193) in 1932. A gypsum deposit is worked as a side-hill quarry until capping becomes excessive; then by room and pillar underground. Bed is 12–20 ft thick, nearly horiz; capping rarely exceeds 100 ft of soft sedimentaries; roof is a firm, 2-ft bed of clay and gypsum. Headings 10–25 ft wide enter from wall of quarry at intervals of about 25 ft. Crosscuts of same width, 20 ft apart, form pillars about 20 by 25 ft, containing 25% of original volume. Pillars are robbed by slabbing, until only 8% of original volume remains. Caving of ground above mined-out area is then induced, as a safety precaution, by blasting out the pillar remnants; gypsum thus broken is not recovered. Jackhammers drill 50 ft of 1.25-in hole per hr. In a 14 by 25-ft heading a round requires 17 10–13-ft holes, arranged for center draw-cut, loaded with Hercomite No 6 powder (25% strength) and 1 stick of 30% gelatin in middle of each hole; little secondary blasting is needed to reduce to size for hand loading. Aver advance, 8.5 ft per round, breaking 1.14 ton per ft of hole, with 0.5 lb powder per ton broken.

35. OPEN UNDERHAND STOPES, NARROW VEINS

Applicability is to narrow veins at any dip, but best suited to steep dips. Strong walls are desirable for any dip, and are usually essential in steep veins from standpoints of safety and ore dilution. In steep veins, the method is usually limited to orebodies requiring no

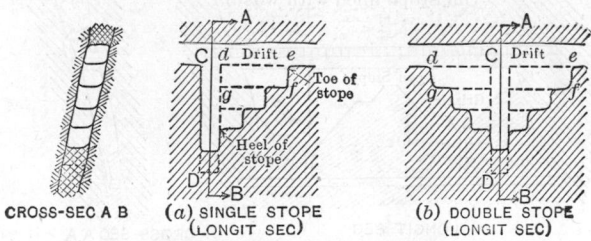

CROSS-SEC A B   (*a*) SINGLE STOPE   (*b*) DOUBLE STOPE
                (LONGIT SEC)   (LONGIT SEC)

Fig 205. Simple Underhand Stopes

sorting (see "Handling waste," below). Strength of ore is rarely a determining factor in applicability of method to narrow veins.

General plans of mining by underhand stoping are shown in Fig 205, 206.

Details vary with modes of breaking ground and handling ore and waste. In simplest case, (*a*) and (*b*) Fig 205, floor of level is broken into with a winze as at *C*, from which a horiz slice *defg* is excavated from wall to wall; as face *ef* advances, the winze is deepened and another slice started. Process is repeated by advancing successive slices, forming step-like faces, converging toward bottom of stope, as is characteristic of underhand work. Stopes like (*a*) Fig 205 are SINGLE STOPES; those like (*b*), DOUBLE STOPES. Terms TOE and HEEL sometimes designate top and bottom of stope. Fig 206 shows a better plan, known as the

CORNISH METHOD. Stope is worked around a raise or winze between 2 levels. Where work is carried on as in Fig 205, all ore except that from first slice is shoveled into buckets and hoisted out to the level above. In Cornish method, broken ore falls through raise to level below, and is loaded by a chute into cars; such stopes are self draining. This method is used instead of that in Fig 205 wherever possible.

Underhand stoping as in Fig 205 is convenient for mining ore below a level without preliminary development, but its use increases cost of mining by the cost of hoisting ore out of the stope. Though such stoping is not used for systematic mining on a large scale,

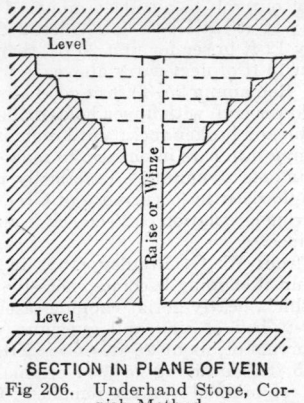

SECTION IN PLANE OF VEIN
Fig 206.   Underhand Stope, Cornish Method

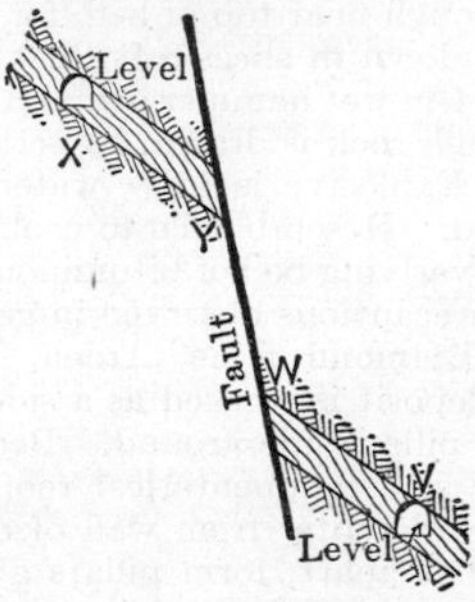

Fig 207.   Cross-sec

it is useful: (a) for mining small, irregular oreshoots with spotted values; often such deposits can be explored only by stoping them; this work approaches gophering (Art 29); (b) for mining isolated or faulted portions of orebodies, as XY, Fig 207, where development openings required to get underneath them would be too costly or difficult to maintain; (c) for small-scale work, lacking funds for preliminary development.

Fig 208, P. B. Scotland (178), shows underhand stoping in a narrow vein with firm walls by Arizona Copper Co. Stoping began near top of untimbered raises, put up in the oreshoot 25 to 50 ft apart. An arch pillar was left; working floor was kept cone-shaped to

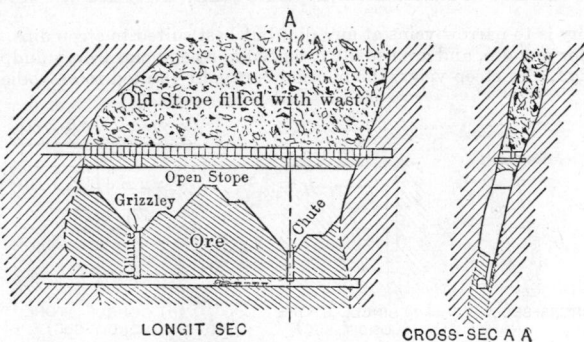

LONGIT SEC   CROSS-SEC A A
Fig 208.   Underhand Stoping, Morenci, Ariz

reduce shoveling; a grizzly of logs, over top of chute, prevented large pieces of ore from entering and clogging it.

Development. Drifts are usually driven in veins. On steep dips, level interval may be limited by safety factor (Art 14–19).

Breaking ground (see Art 26 to 28).

Support of levels. Underhand stoping, carried on as in Fig 205, 206, destroys the drift floor over a stope. Communication with parts of level beyond stope can be maintained by: (a) A row of stulls placed as at S (Fig 209) and lagged, and tracks laid on them; with this plan there is always a break ef at end of the stope, which is bridged temporarily with timber. Where vein is much flatter than in Fig 209, stulls are set nearly normal to hanging wall; waste may be placed on the lagging to support car tracks. (*b*) A LEVEL-PILLAR (or ARCH PILLAR), left over back of stope, as at *P*, Fig 209; it is formed by driving a drift *G* from the raise and stoping below it. Opening *G* is a STOPE-DRIFT (Cornish, STOPE-DRIVE) or SUB-DRIFT. Choice between (*a*) and (*b*) depends largely on grade of ore. A level-pillar may also be required to support stope walls, in which case, depth of pillar depends on degree of support deemed necessary.

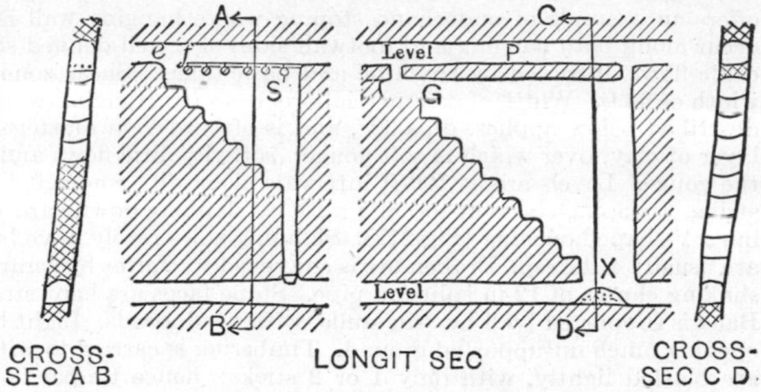

Handling ore. All broken ore must be moved along face to heel of stope; amount of shoveling required depends on: (*a*) general slope of stope face, which may be varied by changing the proportionate length and height of the benches; (*b*) dip of vein, which, together with

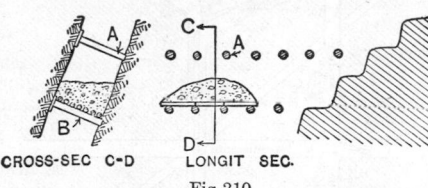

Fig 209.   Simple Underhand Stopes

slope of stope face, determines the pitch of the footwall corner of the stope, and amount of broken ore which will "hang" and require shoveling. These factors are less important where conditions allow use of scrapers (Sec 27).

For economical handling, benches should be high and close together; higher benches are possible in wide than in narrow veins (Fig 214 shows extreme case). Very high benches reduce number of points of attack in a stope, which, for a given tonnage in a narrow orebody, requires more stopes kept open simultaneously. Heel of an underhand stope eventually reaches the level below. If ore in the back of the level is mined as at *x*, Fig 209, the advantage of loading from a chute is lost, unless back of drift is replaced by lagged stulls, as is often done. Sometimes pillars of ore are left over the level.

CROSS-SEC C-D   LONGIT SEC.

Fig 210

Handling waste. In steep veins, sorting of waste is rarely practicable in underhand stoping, and all the vein matter is usually sent to level below. In narrow veins, where general slope of stope face is kept sufficiently flat, waste may be sorted and stored on stulls (Fig 210). On flat dips, regardless of vein width, waste may be stored on footwall.

Support of walls. In a steep vein the area of unsupported and inaccessible walls overhanging a stope constantly increases. This makes an open underhand stope dangerous in weak ground, and is a serious disadvantage. Both foot and hanging walls must be carefully examined, and all loose stuff barred down before the stope faces leave them. In narrow veins, slabs may be supported by STULLS (*A*, Fig 210); larger areas of walls, by ARTIFICIAL PILLARS of waste piled on rows of stulls (*B*, Fig 210). Stulls are placed roughly opposite benches; their diam varies, with width of vein and local conditions, from 8 to 14 in or more; distance between

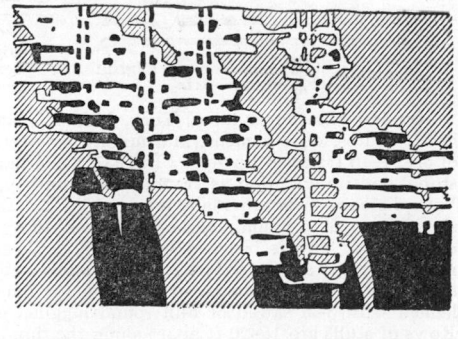

▮ Ore   ▨ Low-grade or waste

Fig 211.   Underhand Stoping (Sec in plane of vein)

stulls, 3 to 6 ft; round 4 to 6-in poles make good lagging. For details of hitches, blocking and placing stulls, see Art 38. PILLARS OF ORE may be left where desired. As a whole, working by underhand stoping depends on pillars of ore for supporting walls.

Fig 211 shows actual underhand stopes covering a large area of vein. Mine was opened by inclined shafts in the vein (note SHAFT PILLARS on each side of shafts). As in other methods involving pillar support, an attempt is made to reduce loss of ore in pillars by leaving them, where possible, in low-grade or narrow parts of vein.

Pilgrim mine, Chloride, Ariz. Data from E. F. Hastings (540) in 1937. This mine offers an example of underhand stoping where hanging wall is weak. Gold-bearing veins occur along both hanging and footwall sides of a well defined shear zone in a series of volcanic flows, intruded by rhyolitic and basic dikes. Shear zone dips about 30°, with aver width of 60 ft. Width of commercial ore, 3–18 ft. Hanging-wall vein, to which the method described below applies, dips 32°, and is of hard vein matter or a breccia. Above it is a layer of clay, over which is soft gouge; soft rhyolitic flows and latite predominate behind the gouge. Levels are at 100-ft intervals along dip, connected by raises 60 ft apart along strike. Stoping starts at top of a raise by slabbing downward with jackhammers, producing a V-shaped opening (Fig 212). Slabbing holes rarely have burden greater than 2 ft and are usually 4 ft deep. Broken ore is conveyed by scrapers, or loaded by hand into shaking chutes of 12-in split fan pipe. Stope faces are kept straight to facilitate scraping. Back is supported by 8 by 8-in stulls, with headboards. Light burden on drill holes avoids opening much unsupported ground. Timbering is carried to within 4 ft of face. Drill holes are blasted lightly, with only 1 or 2 sticks; hence timber is rarely broken by blasting. After ground has remained open for a few weeks, back begins to weather and slough, and starts to cave. Thus, filling the mined-out area with caved material follows advancement of stope faces. Under the protection of the stulls, the ground near the face remains open long enough to complete the stoping. In effect, the method is one of retreat.

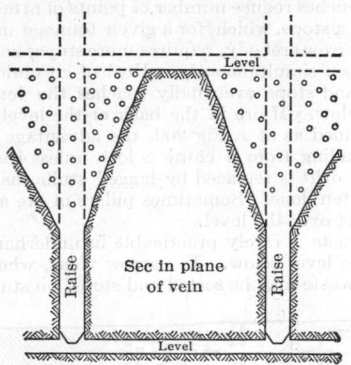

Fig. 212. Underhand Stoping, Pilgrim Mine, Chloride, Ariz

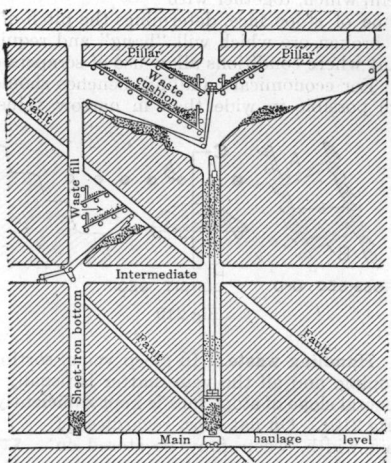

Fig 213. Underhand Stoping, Golden Messenger Mine, York, Mont. (Longit sec in plane of vein)

Golden Messenger mine, York, Mont. Data from S. H. Lorain (69) in 1937. For geol features, development, and mining by overhand stoping, see Art 40. Usual width of ore, 4–10 ft; aver dip, 40°. In 1937, underhand stoping seemed to be successful in one stope, and its adoption as standard was anticipated. Fig 213 shows general procedure. Vert distance between main levels, 150 ft. Intermediate level shown has no special significance as to mining method. Raises, 10 by 5 or 6 ft in sec, are spaced irregularly as convenient. Ore is benched downward in slices, and delivered to and down a central raise by scrapers. Stope face is kept at a low inclination to afford secure footing for miners, drilling with jackhammers. Protection for miners is by rows of 8-in stulls 7 ft apart, lagged with 3-in sawed or 5-in round lagging, and covered with a thin layer of waste. Rows of stulls are 15–20 ft apart along the dip, depending on the ground.

36. OPEN UNDERHAND STOPES, WIDE VEINS

General. Narrow-vein methods (Art 35) can sometimes be extended for use in wide deposits. In veins over 15 to 18 ft wide, the usual economic limit for stulls (Art 38), pillars of ore must be left to support walls and slabs. These methods are therefore limited to orebodies with strong walls and strong ore where dip is steep, or with at least a strong hanging wall where dip is flat.

Candelaria Mining Co, Chihuahua, Mex, has mined a vert oreshoot (length over 100 ft, aver thickness, 33 ft, crumbly porphyry footwall) by underhand stoping. Horiz timber trusses placed across stope supported the walls at intervals of 4 to 6 ft vertically and 5 to 8 ft horizontally. This was tried because ground was very wet, and the water level was lowered so slowly that it was inadvisable to delay production until the orebody could be attacked from below (179). Some stopes were timbered with square-sets (see Art 45), but elaborate timbering in wide underhand stopes is not generally feasible.

Heading method has a limited application to wide, steep-dipping veins or lenses. Fig 214 shows its simplest form. A shaft is sunk in orebody, and levels started at 50 to 100-ft intervals along dip. Drifts are run out 15 to 50 ft; then a vertical or inclined raise is put up to within 20 or 30 ft of level above. From top of raise a drift, or HEADING, is started and widened to walls of deposit. Ore below the floor of heading is broken down into the raise. When stope is well opened it has appearance shown in Fig 214; heading is kept only a short distance in advance of bench; auxiliary raises R may be made for access to stope; pillars of ore may be left irregularly as required. (Note similarity between shape of

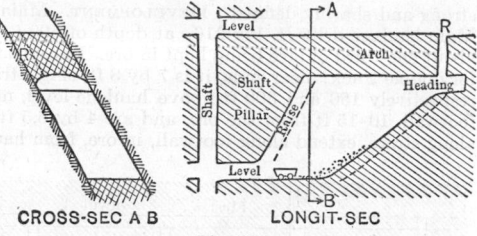

CROSS-SEC A B   LONGIT-SEC

Fig 214

stope face and method of breaking ground here and in breast stoping, Fig 183, 184.) Bench may be broken in vertical steps, or in slices parallel to the face, as shown by dotted line (Fig 214); deep holes and heavy charges may be used for blasting.

Above method is simple and requires little dead work; it leaves a high inaccessible back over stope, and over floor on which trammers work; breaking ground is cheap, but all broken ore must be handled by hand shoveling or mechanical loaders (Sec 27) and much blockholing and sledging may be necessary. From 20% to 50% of the ore is left in pillars, some of which may be recovered at considerable expense by first filling stopes with waste rock. It is sometimes possible to break the arch pillars into the open stope below, beginning at boundary and retreating toward shaft; in old workings this is apt to be dangerous.

Fierro, N M. Data from L. M. Kniffin (168) in 1930. Irregular, lenticular replacement bodies of hard magnetite, aver 40 ft thick (200 ft max), dip 50°–60°; ore and walls

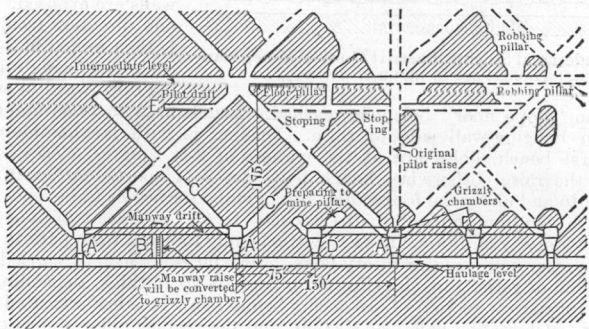

Fig 215. Underhand Stoping, Fierro, N M (168). (Longit sec in plane of orebody)

strong, though fractured by minor faults with small displacement. Developed by adit and haulage drift along footwall, 350 ft below outcrop, with chute raises A 150 ft apart and manway raises B midway between them (Fig 215). At 25 ft above level, each chute raise is enlarged to a grizzly chamber (bars with 16-in openings), above which 2 diverging 7 by 10-ft inclined raises C with min slope of 38° are driven to intersect similar raises from adjoining chutes. Raises are connected by an intermediate level 175 ft above haulage drift, and by a subdrift E 25 ft below the intermediate, leaving a 15-ft floor pillar. Underhand stoping begins from this subdrift, and proceeds downward by benching with jackhammers until the triangular block between 2 raises is reduced to a small protective pillar above the grizzly chamber. Manways between main chutes are then converted to chutes, as at D, with grizzly chambers for mining, in similar manner, the triangular blocks above them. Low-grade patches usually afford the necessary pillars; where good ore must be thus sacrificed, most of it is recovered later, with estimated loss of 10% of marketable ore. No timber is required in stopes except for temporary bulkheads and manways; most of it is used repeatedly. Output averaged 10.1 long tons per man-shift underground in 1929. Explosive (50% gelatin) per long ton, 0.355 lb for stoping, 0.096 lb for secondary breaking, and 0.580 lb for all purposes, including drifting and raising.

Sherritt Gordon mine, Manitoba. Data from E. L. Brown (162) in 1933. Two lenses of ore, 4 200 and 5 800 ft long, occur in shear zones along contact between gneiss band on hanging wall and highly squeezed conglomerate and quartzite on footwall. Ore is a coarse-grained mixture of pyrite, chalcopyrite, and sphalerite, with rock inclusions. Width of ore, from few inches to over 50 ft; aver, 15.5 ft; dips, 30° to vert. Walls are strong and sharply defined. DEVELOPMENT. Main shaft is in footwall, on incline of 51°. Main haulage drift H, Fig 216, at depth of 500 ft on incline, was driven along footwall, about one-third of face being kept in ore. In central portion of orebody, drift is 7 by 15 ft, for double track; near ends, it is 7 by 8 ft, single track. "Second" and "first" level drifts, respectively 150 and 300 ft above haulage level, measured on inclination of shaft, are in footwall, 10–15 ft from the ore, and are 4 by 6.5 ft in sec. Raises, 5 by 5 ft, 120 ft apart along strike, extend along footwall, in ore, from haulage level to surface, or to uppermost mining limit. Crosscuts connect raises with drifts on the 2 upper levels. STOPING. For method used in flat dips, see Art 34; underhand mining is used where dip exceeds 45°. Along footwall side of haulage drift, at 30-ft intervals, " boxholes " (chute raises) are driven. A "stope floor" (Fig 216) is first cut out above haulage level by slabbing around tops of boxholes, until both walls are exposed, and by funnelling the boxholes until they connect with each other. At elev of "second" level, a breast-stope cut (Art 30) is started by slabbing around a raise until both walls are exposed. Retreating in one direction from the raise, is then mined in 8-ft vert slices, each slice being mined by benching downward in successive 10-ft

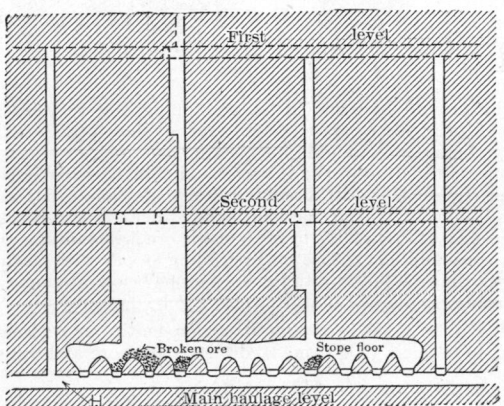

Fig 216. Underhand Stoping, Sherritt Gordon Mine, Manitoba. (Longit sec in plane of orebody)

cuts until the "stope floor" below is reached. Bench next to raise includes whatever ore exists on hanging-wall side of raise. Drilling is with jackhammers, holes 10 ft deep. On first bench, holes are at the corners of 2-ft squares, close-spaced to avoid hang-ups in the raise; otherwise, bench holes are 3 ft apart. A "goat path," 3–4 ft wide, is cut into and along the footwall at top of stope for access to benches. Crosscuts to this path are driven from footwall drift ("second" level) to reduce traveling distance along the path. Ladderway and pipe lines are carried along footwall from path to bench. While working on benches, miners wear safety belts. Stope faces are usually carried back 50–55 ft from center line of raise, thus leaving rib pillars 10–20 ft thick, depending on width of ore. If a lean or narrow section of ore occurs before stope face has retreated to the regular pillar location, such section is left as a pillar, and the regular pillar stoped out. After the benches of first lift above haulage level have retreated 30–40 ft back from center-line of raise, a similar stope is started at the elev of the "first" level. Later, a third series of benches is started from a sub-level above the "first" level. Broken ore falls through the open stope to the boxholes below, and is drawn off at the haulage level. All stoping is done on contract; rates in 1932, covering labor and explosives, were 30¢ per ton on widths over 15 ft, to 50¢ per ton on widths less than 6 ft. In 1931 and first half of 1932, STOPING COSTS per ton were: labor, $0.298; explosives, $0.21; drill repairs and supplies, $0.055; steel and sharpening, $0.067; comp air, $0.028; misc and general, $0.089; total, $0.747. Underground base-wage scale, per shift: motormen, $4.25; machine-men, pipe fitters, trackmen, cagers, $4; helpers, loaders, muckers, nippers, $3.50. Powder cost, $9.05 per case 40% gelatin dynamite.

Above method might be classed as sub-level stoping (Art 43), but underhand mining is the dominant feature. Differences from ordinary sub-level stoping are that sub-levels are much farther apart, and sub-level drifts are not driven in the ore.

37. UNDERGROUND GLORY-HOLE METHOD

This method, also known as UNDERGROUND MILLING, is an adaptation of opencut methods of same name. The top of a raise is widened in all directions, making a funnel opening (GLORY, or MILL HOLE), widened and deepened by underhand stoping. Face of hole usually carried in benches, forming in plan rough concentric circles or ellipses around the raise (Fig 218). Slope of face must be steep enough for broken ore to slide to the raise.

Often, before underground milling begins, sub-levels are run through the orebody to connect raises at vert intervals of 25–50 ft. Sperr states that, for economical work, raise interval on each sub-level should not exceed 25 ft. This condition can be met by inclined raises branching from main vert raises. Economic interval between raises and sub-levels depends also on hardness of ore. (Full discussion of branched-raise method in Bib 182.)

Applicability. Method is limited to large orebodies, as masses or wide veins, with strong walls and ore. Glory-hole walls become inaccessible as stoping progresses, with great danger from falling slabs in any but strong ground. Application of method to narrow inclined deposits is limited to those having dips steep enough for the footwall to clear itself by gravity. Ore breaking and handling are cheap, high benches being carried with deep holes. Since no sorting is possible in stopes, orebodies must be uniform.

Fayal mine, Minn (183). Hematite, underlying a cover of 65–90 ft glacial drift, was formerly mined by underground milling in rooms 24 ft wide, 60 ft high, and up to 100 ft long. A drift was run under center of proposed room, with raises to top of ore about 50 ft apart. A wide drift was then run over top of room and timbered with saddle-back stulls (Art 38) and heavy lagging, under which ore was milled into raises. Pillar widths, 23 ft. When a room was mined out it was filled, intervening pillars being mined by top slicing (Art 70). Timbering backs of glory holes is rarely feasible.

Section 21 mine, Marquette Range, Mich (153, 184). Fig 217, 218, show method of mining a steep-dipping lens of medium hard hematite; footwall, diorite, hanging,

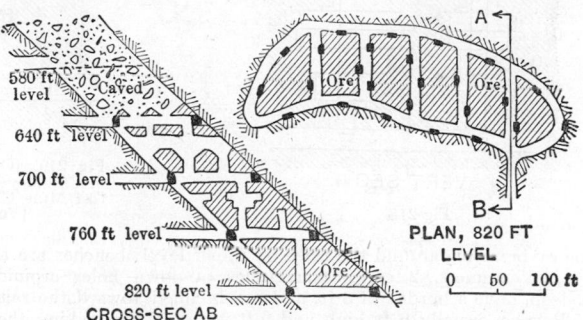

Fig 217. Glory-hole Mining, Marquette Range, Mich

jaspilite. Shaft was in footwall. To open a level a crosscut was driven from foot to hanging; walls were then followed until drifts connected (see plan, Fig 217); crosscuts were driven between foot and hanging-wall drifts at intervals of 50 to 60 ft. Footwall raises were put up to level above for ventilation, when development had advanced far enough for a chute to be operated without interfering with other work on level; other raises were as shown, all vert or nearly so, excepting a few next to hanging. Ideal cross-sec (Fig 217) shows stages of work; on 820-ft level, development is partly completed; milling has started in raises above 760-ft level; between 700 and 640 ft, a more advanced stage is shown; work on 640-ft level has reached final stage of removing pillars. To explain the method 4 operating levels are shown; in practice, all stages of work occur simultaneously in different parts of a lift. Fig 218 shows detail of milling. Breast stopes S are started near top of each raise, leaving a 6 to 10-ft chain pillar under level above, which supports the level until ore above has been removed. Ore below breast stope is milled into raise, and milling continues downward to lines *abcef*, where ore will no longer slide on face of stope. Robbing the V-shaped pillars over level above then begins from raises r, the pillars being thinned down until they will just support caved material above. Ore is dumped into open stopes below. Holes are then drilled in remaining pillars and in level-pillars L, all being fired together in sections, beginning at boundary and retreating. Broken ore from pillars is drawn through chutes b and e; some ore is lost by mixing with waste, which falls when pillars are broken. At this mine a rigid geometrical plan could not be followed, because of numerous intersecting dikes. An attempt was made to locate development raises to reach thickest portion of pillars on level above. This method proved economical and safe; no timber was required except for chutes, and ventilation was good. It is stated that the percentage loss of ore through contamination with waste was low.

El Potosí mine, Chihuahua, Mex. Data from H. A. Walker (174) in 1934. Highly irregular lead-zinc-iron sulphide replacements in limestone have been worked to depths of 2 800 ft. Orebodies are in 2 typical forms: chimneys, of which a large one may have a horiz area of 10 000 sq ft and depth of 1 000 ft or more; and "mantos," long, ramifying, nearly horiz channels, 30–150 ft wide, 8 or 10–20 ft (rarely 60 ft) high. There are 3 vert shafts, one for ventilation only. Level interval, 165 ft. Fig 219 shows method of mining chimneys. A 5 by 7-ft raise, centrally located, is driven from one level to next above, and near the bottom has a bulldozing chamber.

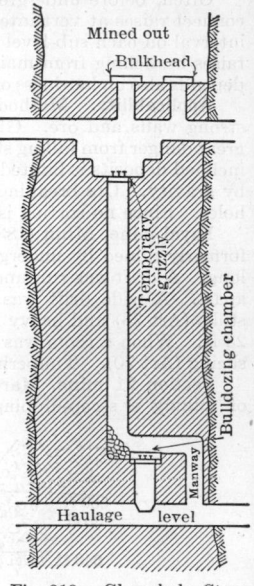

Fig 219. Glory-hole Stope in Chimney Deposit, El Potosí Mine Chihuahua, Mex. (Vert sec)

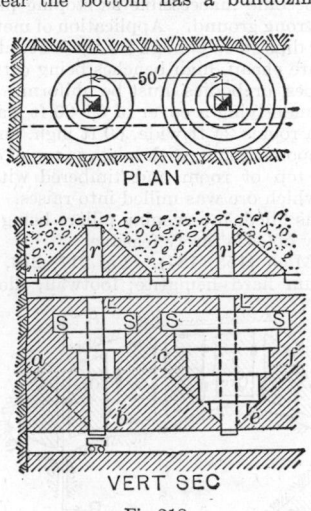

Fig 218

Mining begins by breasting around the raise on upper level; benches are then started by drilling, with jackhammers, 2 concentric circles of down holes around top of raise. Holes, 6–8 ft deep, have a burden of 3 ft, and are inclined toward the raise. Explosive, 30% gelatin. Benches usually 6 ft high and 6 ft wide. After making the initial bench, a grizzly, with 10–12-in openings, built across the raise, prevents boulders from entering and blocking the raise, and is a safety measure. The grizzly is moved downward for successive benches. It is of old rails supported by wooden stringers. Grizzly in bulldozing chamber below is of crossed rails, with 10-in square openings. Access to benches is from level above by wire-rope ladders. Pathways along benches have cable handholds. Men are guarded from slipping down glory hole by ropes around their waists. In an unusually wide chimney an intermediate level is driven about half way between main levels, and the block between main levels is mined in 2 stages. A 10–15-ft shell of ore is always left directly above a level, whether main or intermediate, as a protection until stope below is finished.

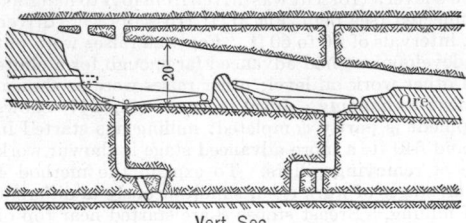

Vert Sec

Fig 220. Glory-hole Stoping in a Thick Manto, El Potosí Mine, Chihuahua, Mex

Wide mantos are mined as shown in Fig 220. From a haulage level beneath the manto, raises, 150–200 ft apart, are driven to level above, or to top of the manto. Mining procedure is same as in chimneys until ore will no longer run into raises by gravity; then scrapers are used, with triple-drum hoists and 15-hp elec motors (Art 91 and Sec 27).

Mascot mine, Mascot, Tenn. Data from H. A. Coy (175) in 1930. Veinlets and seams of sphalerite occur in dolomitic limestone beds dipping 18°–22°. Thickness of ore varies to max of about 100 ft. The strong dolomite hanging wall will stand indefinitely over unsupported widths of 100 ft; mineralized dolomite does not stand well without support.

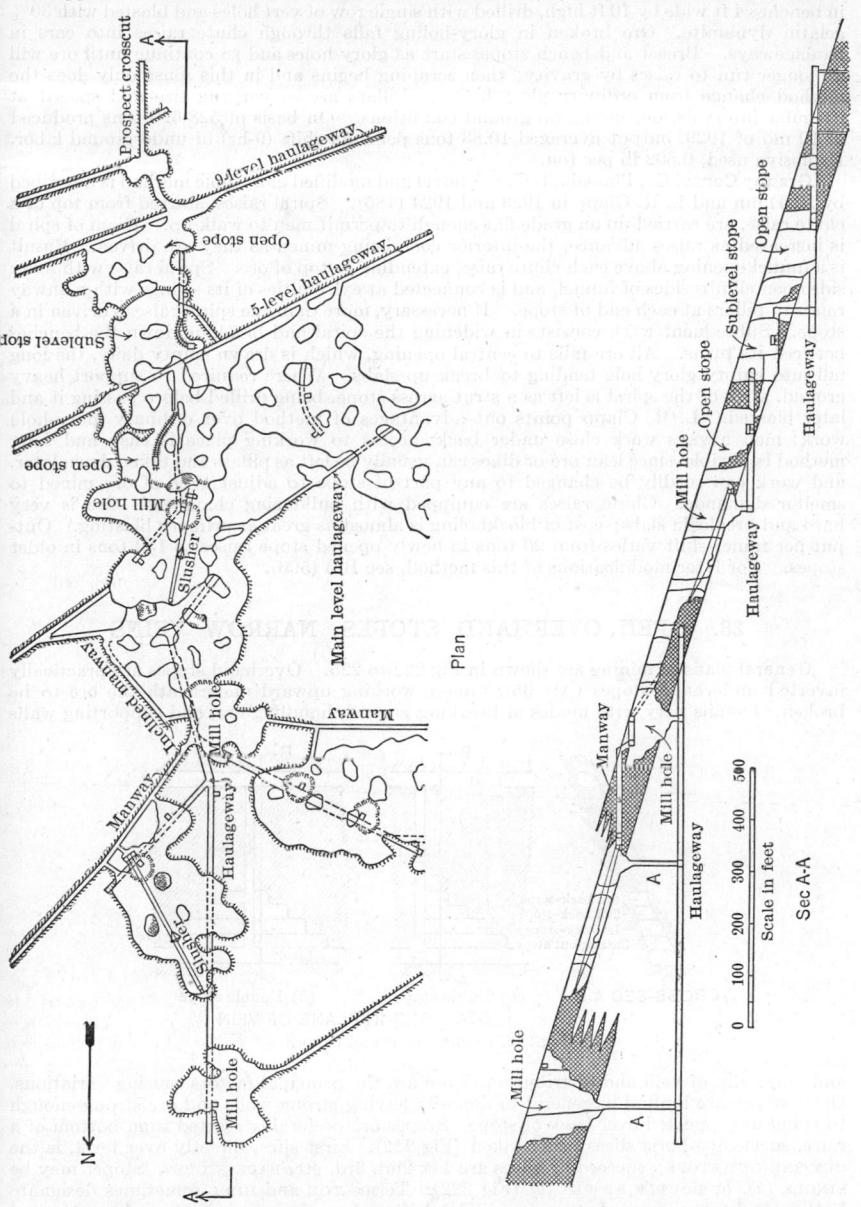

Fig 221. Part of Mascot Mine, Mascot, Tenn (175)

A vert shaft is started in hanging wall. From a main haulage level, at depth of 520 ft, 2 inclines extend up and down the dip, and from these, working levels are driven in ore at varying intervals (Fig 221). From some of the levels, crosscuts into the footwall allow the mineralized beds to be attacked from below through 5 by 5-ft vert chute raises A, which are later reamed to 10 by 10 ft. In such case, mining is by glory-holing; where development within the footwall is not warranted, ore is mined by breast and bench (Art 31), shoveling or scraping of ore being necessary. In either case, a raise is driven to top of ore and a heading, about 8 ft high, is advanced under the roof. Ore below is mined in benches 4 ft wide by 10 ft high, drilled with single row of vert holes and blasted with 30% gelatin dynamite. Ore broken in glory-holing falls through chute raises into cars in haulageways. Breast and bench stopes start as glory holes and so continue until ore will no longer run to raises by gravity; then scraping begins and in this sense only does the method change from ordinary glory-holing. Pillars are of varying size and spaced at irregular intervals, depending on ground conditions. On basis of 528 626 tons produced in 10 mo of 1929, output averaged 10.83 tons per man-shift (9-hr) of underground labor. Explosive used, 0.502 lb per ton.

Granby Consol Co, Phoenix, B C. A novel and modified glory-hole method is described by R. Dunn and L. R. Clapp in 1923 and 1924 (185). Spiral raises, started from top of a chute raise, are carried up on grade flat enough to permit men to walk up. Diam of spiral is increased as raises advance, the interior cone being mined as they are driven. Result is a funnel opening above each chute raise, extending to top of ore. Spiral raise with inner side open climbs sides of funnel, and is connected at extremities of its swings with manway raises in pillars at each end of stope. If necessary, more than one spiral raise is driven in a stope. Subsequent work consists in widening the spiral and breaking down the benches between its turns. All ore falls to central opening, which is drawn empty daily, the long fall into empty glory hole tending to break up slabs. Where required to support heavy ground, a rib of the spiral is left as a strut across stope, being drilled before passing it and later blasted. L. R. Clapp points out advantages of method over ordinary glory-hole work: men always work close under back; access to working place is easy and safe; method is flexible, since lean ore or dikes can usually be left as pillars and taken down later, and work can readily be changed to any part of stope to adjust type of ore mined to smelter demands. Chute raises are equipped with bulldozing chambers. Ore is very hard and breaks in slabs; cost of blockholing is almost as great as primary blasting. Output per miner-shift varies from 20 tons in newly opened stope raises to 150 tons in older stopes. For later modifications of this method, see Bib (596).

38. OPEN OVERHAND STOPES, NARROW VEINS

General plans of mining are shown in Fig 222 to 225. Overhand stopes are practically inverted underhand stopes (Art 35), miners working upward underneath the ore to be broken. Details vary with modes of breaking ground, handling ore, and supporting walls

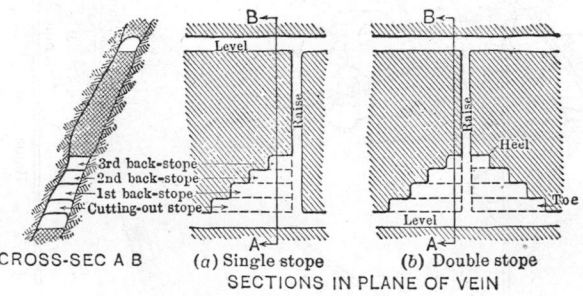

CROSS-SEC A B   (*a*) Single stope   (*b*) Double stope
SECTIONS IN PLANE OF VEIN
Fig 222. Open Overhand Stopes

and men; dip of vein and distribution of ore are the principal factors causing variations. Open stopes are limited in general to deposits having strong walls and ore strong enough to stand unsupported over back of stope. Stopes are preferably started from bottom of a raise, successive horiz slices being taken (Fig 222). First slice, directly over level, is the CUTTING-OUT STOPE; succeeding slices are 1st, 2nd, 3rd, etc, BACK-STOPES. Stopes may be SINGLE (*a*), or DOUBLE STOPES (*b*) (Fig 222). Terms TOE and HEEL sometimes designate bottom and top corners of stope face. The drift and cutting-out stope may be excavated together making a DRIFT STOPE (Art 41). RILL STOPES have a longit sec like an inverted V (*b*, Fig 222); inclined faces may be produced by keeping the faces of successive back-stopes close together, or by using inclined slices (Fig 223). Stoping with inclined slices is more useful in filled than in open stopes. In FLAT-BACK STOPES (horiz or longwall stopes), the face is advanced in a general line parallel to the level, by keeping faces of successive back-stopes far apart (Fig 224). Many combinations between rill and flat-back stopes are found. The number of back-stopes advanced simultaneously determines number of points of attack, and this, in combination with width of vein, determines daily output obtainable from a stope. If back-stopes are too close together, miners working on adjacent faces interfere with each other. General term STEPPED-FACE OVERHAND STOPE denotes stopes like Fig 222, or intermediate forms between this and Fig 224. All these terms describe overhand stopes of same form in wide orebodies.

Local conditions may require stopes to be opened in the back of a drift without first driving a raise, as in mining portion WV of vein in Fig 207, or in case of small irregular oreshoots with problematical

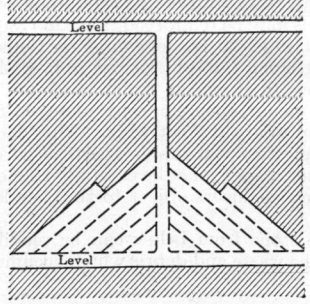

Fig 223.   Inclined Slice (Sec in
plane of vein)

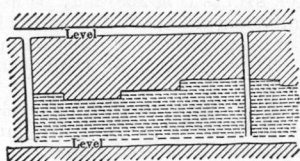

Fig 224.   Flat-back Stope
(Sec in plane of vein)

extent above the level.   Raises insure natural ventilation, furnish points of attack for starting stopes, and provide entry and facilities for lowering timber, etc, into the stope.

Development.   Fig 107 shows typical development in a vein, providing requisite openings for overhand stoping.

Breaking ground (see Art 26 to 28).

Support and protection of levels.   Broken ore from an open overhand stope slides or falls to level below; hence a barrier is necessary between level and stope to protect men and keep broken ore off haulage tracks.   Protecting the back of level also allows broken ore to be loaded through chutes (Art 90) and avoids shoveling.   Practice varies with dip

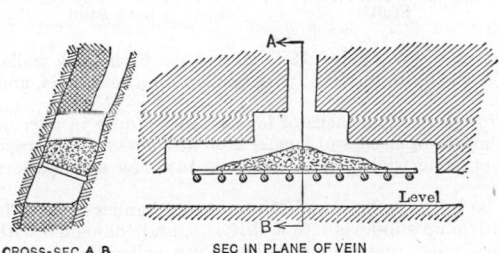

CROSS-SEC **A B**   SEC IN PLANE OF VEIN
Fig 225.   Overhand Stope, Stull Timbering

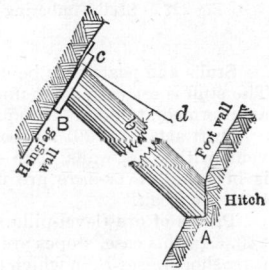

Fig 226.   Stull Timbering

and width of deposit, character of walls, and local custom.   STULLS usually protect back of level in narrow veins having walls strong enough to support them; Fig 225 shows common arrangement; a cutting-out stope is taken before the stulls are placed; distance between stulls and back of cutting-out stope, 7 to 10 ft.

Stulls are of round timbers, diam, 8 to 24 in or more; usual spacing, 3 to 5 ft, rarely exceeding 6 ft; occasionally, they are close together (Quincy mine, Art 41).   LAGGING poles, 4 to 6-in diam, or slabs or planks (see Timbering drifts, Art 21) are laid on the stulls. In open stopes, a 3 to 4-ft layer of broken ore is left on lagging to protect it from blasts and falling ore; this is removed when stope is finished.   A pocket called a HITCH is cut in footwall with a moil or plugger-drill to receive foot of stull, which is flattened as at A, Fig 226, to prevent it from rolling.   Hitch may be only 1 or 2 in deep in strong rock; a weak footwall may require hitches 6 or 8 in deep or more; loose ground must be removed before cutting hitch.   Head of stull is square and to distribute pressure rests against HEADBOARD B (sometimes called a cap) of 2 to 4-in plank; where necessary, wedges are used between headboard and hanging.   Headboards and blocking are compressed by initial creep of ground and protect stull from splitting.   Stulls are set at a steeper angle than the normal to the hanging wall.   In Fig 226, line cd is normal to hanging wall; angle *dcb* is ANGLE OF UNDERLIE. Setting of stulls varies. W. E. Sanders states angle of underlie should be about 0.25 × angle of dip of vein (186); T. Johnson favors a max underlie of 10° for dips of 60° or over, and a ratio of about 1/8 between angle of underlie and angle of dip on flatter dips (187); usual practice in U S is between these limits. Object of setting stulls with an underlie is to prevent their falling under weight of ore or waste, and to cause them to tighten under small settlement of hanging wall. Foregoing detail applies to placing stulls in both overhand and underhand stopes, as well as to stulls over levels. If footwall is weak a FALSE STULL may be set underneath main stull (Fig 227). In steep-dipping or vertical veins with poor walls, stulls over levels may be reinforced, Fig 228 (186).

Max economic length of stulls, placed as in Fig 226, is 12–20 ft, depending on timber supply, facilities and room for handling timber underground, lateral pressure from walls, and relative cost of alternative methods. Usual max width of vein in which single stulls are used to protect levels (also for supporting slabs and men in open stopes) is about 15 ft. SADDLE-BACK STULLS (Fig 229) may be used in veins up to about 25 ft wide. They lack lateral rigidity, and are apt to fail by buckling sidewise; they will support vertical wt of broken ore or waste, but do not resist wall pressure; joint at apex must be carefully framed and fitted. They have a limited application, and many engineers object to them under any conditions.

Advantage of stull timbering for levels is that the stope from below can be readily broken through to level above, and without disturbing the waste and debris which accumulate on stulls under exhausted stopes.

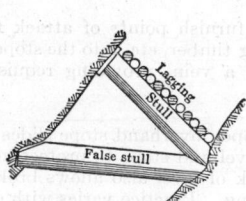

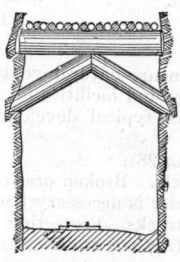

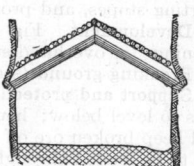

Fig 227. Stull Timbering   Fig 228. Reinforced   Fig 229. Saddle-
                                        Stull   back Stull

Stulls and posts may be used in steep-dipping veins, 12 to 20 ft wide, with weak walls. The stull is set with a flat underlie (generally in hitches), with posts under both ends, and at intermediate points if required.

Drift sets (Art 20) are common for protecting backs of levels under stopes in narrow veins with weak walls; like stulls, they are placed and lagged after the cutting-out stope is broken. HALF-SETS are used where one wall is weak; THREE-QUARTER SETS, where both are weak.

Pillars of ore (level-pillars) may be left over level at bottom of overhand stopes; Fig 230. In this case, stopes are opened from a sub-level (stope-drift) *A*, and connected with it by short raises *B*, in which chutes are built; wedge-shaped piles of ore, collecting between chutes on top of level pillars, are cleaned off by shoveling when stope is finished. Pillars may sometimes be recovered prior to abandonment of level. In open stopes, choice usually depends on comparative cost of timbering, extra cost of the sub-level, and net value of ore left in pillars (20).

Packwalls may be built above level on flat dips and holes left in them at intervals for chutes (for detail, see below under Support of walls). Need for protecting the level diminishes as dip of vein decreases; no protection is necessary where dip is less than 20°; for varying practice on dips of 30° to 40°, see Art 39 to 41.

Support of level above stope. Pillars of ore are left where it is necessary to keep the upper level open (Fig 252). Such pillars may be also required to support walls. See below and also Mohawk mine, Art 41.

Support of men. On dips less than about 40°, men can stand on and work from footwall, no provision for their support being necessary; on steeper dips, timber staging is required. Stulls in rows 6 to 12 ft apart vertically are used in veins where width does not exceed max economic stull length; interval between stulls is 4 to 6 ft (Fig 231); men stand on temporary platforms of plank, slabs or lagging laid on stulls; temporary stulls may be put wherever required to keep miners up to the face. Stopes thus timbered are STULLED STOPES (for examples, see Art 39). Square-sets and other timbering are used in open stopes in steep-dipping veins, too wide for stulls (Art 45 to 54).

Support of walls in individual stopes, in veins worked by open overhand stope methods, is limited by definition of open stope to timbering, pillars of ore or waste, and artificial pillars. Stulls are commonest timber support in narrow veins (see above, under Protection of levels, for economic limits of length). When placed as in Fig 231, they support loose slabs. Stulls do not adequately support very shelly walls, or those which slough off on exposure to air; for such cases square-sets or other timber (Art 45 *et seq*), with lagging along walls, may be employed. Open stopes are not adapted to veins with weak walls; filling systems (Art 59 to 66) usually preferable. Timbering in general is to support slabs or to hold walls temporarily until the stope can be abandoned and allowed to cave; it will not permanently support the weight of rock overlying a deposit. For examples of stulled stopes, see Art 39.

Artificial pillars. Usually, in narrow veins, waste is piled on stulls (Fig 210). Fig 232 shows an overhand stope thus supported. H. C. Hoover states (20): "This system

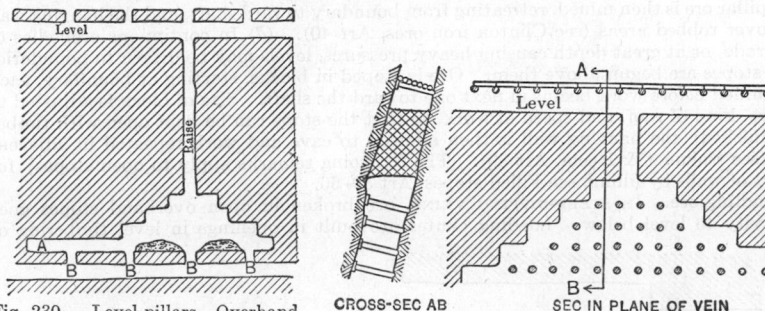

Fig 230. Level-pillars, Overhand Stope (Sec in plane of vein)

CROSS-SEC AB

SEC IN PLANE OF VEIN

Fig 231. Stulled Stope

implies a strong roof which does not demand continuous support; it effects economy in stulls by using waste which accumulates underground; artificial pillars also apply to cases where stulls alone are not sufficient support, and yet where complete filling or square-setting is unnecessary; under propitious conditions they have the comparative advantage over timber systems of saving timber and over filling systems of saving imported filling." Inverted V shape of pillars (Fig 232) allows broken ore to slide to the level without especially built passes; when this system is employed, more special staging must be provided for miners than in square-set or filling systems.

Cribs or cogs are used for roof support in flat deposits; examples, Art 33. They are adapted to temporary support, prior to abandoning a stope or filling it with waste. For similar use of CONCRETE PILLARS, see Fig 181, 198, and text.

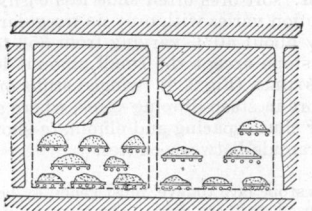

Fig 232. Artificial Pillars (After Hoover)

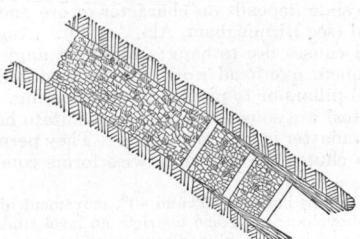

Fig 233. Packwall (After Johnson)

Packwalls (Fig 233) are sometimes built on the upper side of levels in veins dipping 30° or less, to protect them and to support the hanging wall when ore is completely removed; they may also be employed as artificial pillars in stopes. T. Johnson (187) comments on Rand practice as follows: packwalls should be built nearly at right angles to plane of deposit, and not with vertical end walls, which may fail by slumping "upbrow" (up the dip); in long packs, middle portions of walls bulge and eventually fail. Stulls are placed as in Fig 233, with or without lagging to steady the walling until weight comes on; small timbers serve this purpose. Small waste should be thrown in while walls are being built, to form bedding for large boulders and give solidity. It is advisable to bind walls to inside of pack with pieces of old pipe, rails, rope or boards, particularly at corners. For wire-bound packs on Rand, see Art 33.

Pillars of ore may be left in an overhand stope, where the hanging wall will stand unsupported between them, and where net value of ore in pillars will not pay for alternative modes of support.

Low-grade or waste portions of an ore-shoot are usually left as pillars; temporary pillars of ore (as level-pillars) are common; use of pillars for permanent support is confined to low-grade orebodies, usually to extensive deposits lying on flat dips. For examples see Art 40, 41.

Control of hanging wall over entire mine, in veins worked by open overhand stoping: (a) In veins where ore is in shoots, the barren areas often serve as pillars; support in individual stopes is obtainable by one of the above methods, depending on size of stope and character of walls, and stopes will remain open indefinitely or cave after they have been abandoned. For permanent support to protect shafts, surface buildings, etc, exhausted stopes may be filled. (b) Where ore is continuous over long distances, the hanging wall may be supported on permanent pillars of ore. Flat-dipping, low-grade amygdaloid copper deposits (Mich) furnish an example of this practice (Art 41). (c) In continuous orebodies, stoping on each level may be carried to property line or to limit of ore, leaving temporary pillars, often of large size, to support roof. As much as possible of the pillar ore is then mined, retreating from boundary toward shaft, and the hanging wall caves over robbed areas (see Clinton iron ores, Art 40). (d) In continuous orebodies of good grade, or at great depth causing heavy pressures, levels may be driven to boundaries before stopes are begun above them. Ore is stoped in blocks, starting at boundary, each being mined before work begins in next one toward the shaft. Size of block is adjusted to pressure, kind of roof, and speed of work, so that the stope can be kept open with timber until finished; the hanging wall is then allowed to cave and work repeated in adjacent block (see Calumet & Hecla, Art 39). The foregoing remarks apply to open stopes; for support of walls by filling, see Filled stopes, Art 59–66.

Handling ore. In STEEP-DIPPING VEINS, ore broken in open overhand stopes goes by gravity to level below. Loading chutes are built in openings in level timbering or

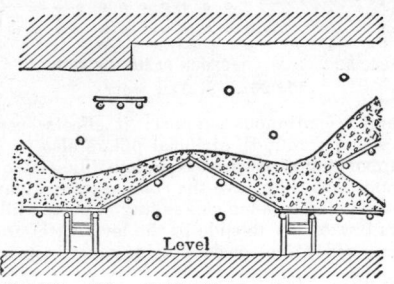

Fig 234. Wing Stulls (Sec in plane of vein)

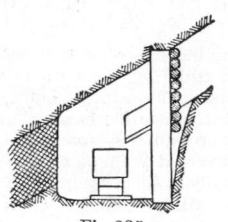

Fig 235

pillars at intervals of 15 to 30 ft (for details, see Art 90). Minimum angle on which ore will slide depends on character of ore and footwall; soft ores often slide less easily than hard (see Birmingham, Ala, Art 40). Angle of friction varies with ore; an irregular foot-wall causes ore to hang; minimum angle, usually about 40°; varying from 35° to 45°. In open, overhand work, no ore is stored in the stope except the small amount left on level-pillars or to protect level timbering. WING STULLS (Fig 234) (winged stulls or wing chutes) are sometimes used to facilitate handling ore in steep-dipping veins, where all the vein matter is sent to surface. They permit wider chute spacing and eliminate shoveling into chutes ore that otherwise forms cones or pyramids between chutes.

On dips between 35° and 40°, movement of ore from stope face to level must generally be aided by shoveling. In some districts no level timbering is used on these dips. The ore runs into the level and is shoveled into cars, or slides onto platforms at foot of stope, high enough for ore to be shoved off into cars or shoveled with a low lift (see Mich copper mines, Art 39 and 41). In West Australia, levels are timbered on flat dips, as in Fig 235, drifts being far enough in the footwall to give room for cars below lip of chute; this kind of timbering is used in filled stopes also (83). In flat deposits (less than 35°), scrapers and other mechanical devices are used to reduce shoveling and cheapen stope transport (see Art 91; also Sec 27).

Handling waste. Sole means of storing waste sorted from ore in open overhand stopes on steep dips is by piling it on stulls (Fig 232). Since this provides limited storage, these stopes are not suited to ores containing much waste which it is desired to sort out underground. In flat stopes, some waste may be utilized for packwalls or filling cribs, or it may be left on floor in middle of stope, but the cost of shoveling much waste to this point is usually prohibitive, and if it is left promiscuously on stope floor it interferes with transport to the level and is mixed again with ore.

39. EXAMPLES OF PRACTICE, OPEN OVERHAND STOPES (Stulled)

Cripple Creek, Colo. During days of great activity in this district, open overhand stoping with stulls was widely practiced. Veins mined with stulled stopes were narrow and nearly vertical, with sound walls of andesite, tuff, breccia, etc, and strong, often high-grade ore, in irregular shoots. Wolcott gave following data in 1908 (142). Fig 236 shows method of stoping and timbering in veins up to 8 or 10 ft wide, where back-stopes were broken with uppers. A flat-back stope was carried, with stulls 5 to 7 ft below back, and enough lagging on top row for a working platform.

Formerly (1906) 2.25-in piston-drills were used and height of slice taken in one back-stope was 4 ft. Permanent stulls were say 7 to 8 ft apart vert and 5 to 7 ft horiz; 2 slices were taken across a stope before setting second row of stulls. Part of the broken ore was left on lagging, or temporary stulls (sprags) were put in to keep men up to the back while mining the second slice. In later practice, stope-drills were used, making deeper holes, and 6 to 8-ft slices were broken in one operation. Manways *M* were often formed at ends of stope by lagging a vert row of stulls.

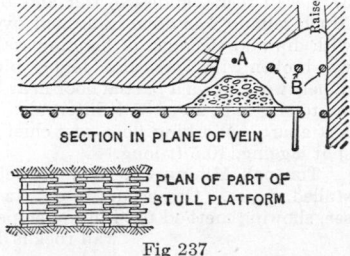

SECTION IN PLANE OF VEIN

PLAN OF PART OF STULL PLATFORM

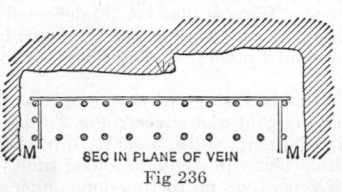

SEC IN PLANE OF VEIN

Fig 236

Fig 237

Portland mine (in 1907). Some stopes were carried, as in Fig 237, with stulls 4 or 5 ft below back of stope. Small piston-drills were mounted on a bar at *A*, in stopes less than 8 ft wide, or in wider stopes on a column set between the back and a muck pile on lagging. Stulls were spaced 5 ft horiz and 7 or 8 ft vert, with lagging poles, 6.3 ft long, as shown. The lagging supported broken ore, provided a place for machine men to stand without staging, and prevented large pieces from falling and injuring stulls below. A flat-back stope was carried in 8-ft slices. As face advanced, lagging at the rear was removed and muck dropped down, large boulders being broken before they were allowed to fall. Lagging was reused on higher rows of stulls (*B*, Fig 237).

Wright-Hargreaves mine, Ontario. Data from L. B. Smith (176) in 1934. Gold ore occurs in fissure veins in porphyry. Metallic minerals are chiefly pyrite, tellurides, chalcopyrite, free gold, and molybdenite. Veins range in width to 15–18 ft, but are usually narrower. Three main veins: (*a*) " North " vein is a well defined fracture, bordered by brecciated porphyry which is penetrated by quartz veinlets; walls are indefinite and determined by values, close sampling being necessary; dip, nearly vert; (*b*) " South " vein is of crushed and silicified porphyry, penetrated by stringers and bunches of quartz; usually there are 2 smooth, well defined walls which are weak and shatter easily; dip, nearly vert; (*c*) " Inclined " vein is a narrow quartz band accompanying a calcite-filled

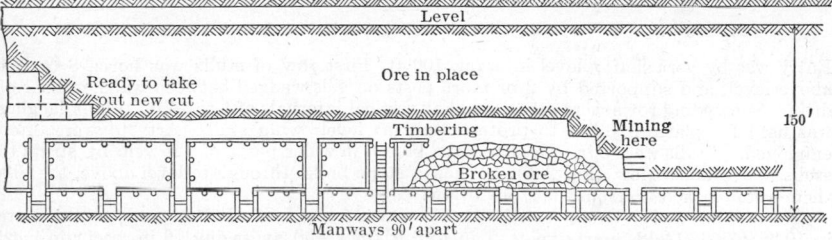

Fig 238. Open Overhand Stope, Wright-Hargreaves Mine, Ont. (Longit sec in plane of vein)

fracture; walls, highly altered porphyry and hanging wall is very weak. DEVELOPMENT. Level interval, 150 ft, with drifts in ore. STOPING METHODS. Shrinkage stoping (Art 68) is used in some cases where ore is over 6 ft wide and walls are good. Filled rill stopes (Art 65) are used in some parts. Open stoping with square-sets (Art 46) is used where ore is over 10 ft wide and walls are bad. Open stoping with stulls is commonest method and is suitable for widths to 10 ft, where walls are too weak for shrinkage stoping, but not weak enough to warrant square-setting; advantages, flexibility, continuity of operation, and safety to men. OPEN STOPING WITH STULLS (Fig 238). Back of drift is first raised to height of 15–16 ft above rail. Stulls are then placed over the drift at 6-ft centers except for chute sets, which are at 5-ft centers. Stulled manways are carried up 90–100 ft apart. Stope breasts are 8 ft high; usually 3 are advanced simultaneously in a given section, and lagged-stull floors are placed under each 24-ft cut. Chutes are raised by carrying two lines of stulls 8 ft apart vert, lined with 8-ft half-round timber. Mat of broken ore on floors prevents timber breakage and affords footing for miners. As the cuts advance, ore is drawn through chutes as in shrinkage mining. As rock is drawn, loose walls are stulled. Stoping routine eventually consists of advancing mining, followed by drawing of ore and mucking; muckers are followed by timbermen, who set stulls, raise, chutes, and place floor stulls and lagging. Flooring is of 6 to 8-in round timber, split down center and laid alternately round and flat side up. When stopes reach height of 40 ft, tugger hoists are used to hoist timber up manways.

Liberty Bell mine, Telluride, Colo (131). Quartz vein, aver width, 4.3 ft; aver dip, 57°; wall rocks, andesite, tuff and breccia; pay ore occurred in shoots of variable size. Much mining was done in stulled overhand stopes, stoping practice and details varying with dip and strength of hanging wall. C. A. Chase gave following data in 1911. Ore was broken with vertical or highly pitched holes, drilled with stope-drills or hand augers, miners working on a partial floor near back of stope. Wing stulls (Art 36) deflected broken ore to chutes at 25 to 35-ft intervals. Stulls, 8-in diam up, were placed 5 ft apart in floors 7 ft apart. Working floor was chiefly of 6-in round timber; stoping floors, of round or split lagging, 10.5 ft long.

Tonopah Mining Co, Nev. Much mining in early history of the camp was done in stulled stopes. Ore occurs in quartz veins carrying gold and silver. Fig 239 is a cross-sec, showing method used in upper part of Mizpah vein; width, 5–30 ft; dip, about 70°; wall rock is dry andesite, which will stand for a long time. Ore is broken averaged $15–$25 per ton; no sorting done under ground.

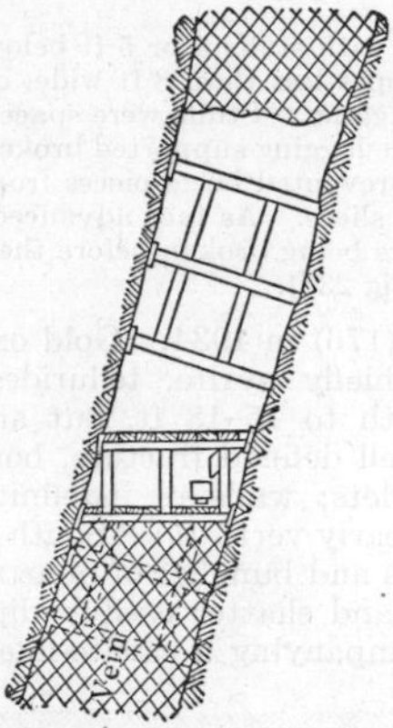

Fig 239 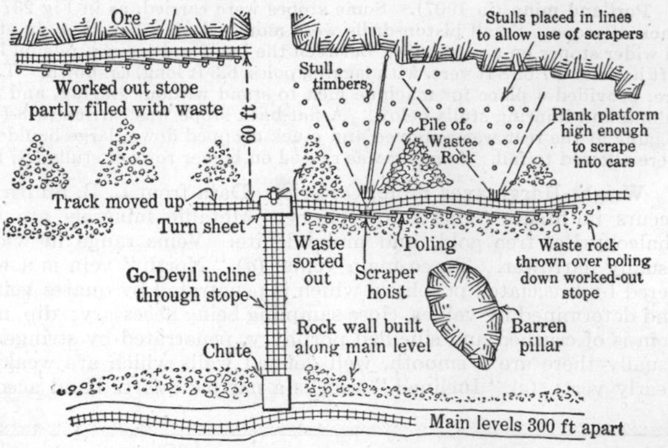   Fig 240. Handling Ore in North Star Mine, Calif (578)

Entry was by vert shaft; level interval, 100 ft. First row of stulls was horiz, 8 or 9 ft above level, and supported by 2 or more posts on sills wedged between walls on floor of drift. Succeeding rows were set as usual at vertical intervals of 6 to 15 ft. Plank lagging was used for platforms and to protect stulls at level; wing stulls (Art 36) were often employed. Stulls were 8 in or less in diam, braced in wider parts of the vein by struts to stulls above and below (Fig 239). When a stope broke through to level above, the sills there were blocked up from the stulls below.

North Star mine, Grass Valley, Calif. Data from J. A. Fulton and A. B. Foote in 1926 (578). Gold quartz veins, 1 in to 6 ft thick and averaging 16 in, occur in hard granodiorite. Portions of vein as narrow as 4 in are sometimes mined; aver stoping width, 42 in. Dip is flat, averaging 26°.

Main levels, 5 by 7 ft, are run on vein at 300-ft intervals. Stopes are carried up overhand, with stull support as shown in Fig 240. Sub-level tracks are laid at 60-ft intervals for scraping and 30-ft for shoveling, being moved up as stope face recedes. Broken ore is shoveled or scraped into cars of 1 500-lb capac on the sub-levels, and handled to main level by a go-devil plane (Art 91). About half the waste broken is sorted out in stopes. Stulls are used for temporary support and to keep blasted ore from being blown down stope. Production is 0.95 ton per miner-hr and 0.9 ton per shoveler-hr, which includes stowing waste, or 0.47 ton per man-hr in stope; ore recovery, probably over 90%. Footwall is swept with brooms before stope is abandoned.

Calumet & Hecla mine, Mich (67, 482, 489). Following paragraphs describe practice on the CALUMET CONGLOMERATE LODE, which has been worked about 2 miles along strike and to depth of over 8 000 ft down dip. Recent annual reports indicate that work in deeper parts of mine has been stopped and recent work confined to extraction of pillars, retreating toward the surface. For practice in amygdaloid lodes, see Art 41.

Physical characteristics of ore and wall rocks. Calumet conglomerate lode is 12–20 ft thick and dips 36°–38°. Lode consists of pebbles of felsite and quartz porphyry, cemented by a mixture of rock and native copper. Tenor of ore mined is about 2% copper. Ore is tough and abrasive. Hanging wall is shelly diabase. Footwall is a fragmental amygdaloidal layer of diabase, relatively weak and with tendency to burst upward into openings when subjected to concentrated pressure, as from caving hanging wall. This condition was an important factor in selecting a retreating system of mining.

General plan of mining in the conglomerate bed differs from amygdaloid practice (Art 41), because of the weak hanging wall and great depth of mine; a retreating system is required by these conditions and also by high temperatures at depth, which necessitate good ventilation at working face; in advancing systems, much of the air current is apt to short-circuit through old stopes close to shaft. Stoping is begun either at the boundary or midway between adjacent shafts, retreating toward shaft; small blocks are stoped rapidly, held open temporarily by stulls and then allowed to cave; the only pillars left are the

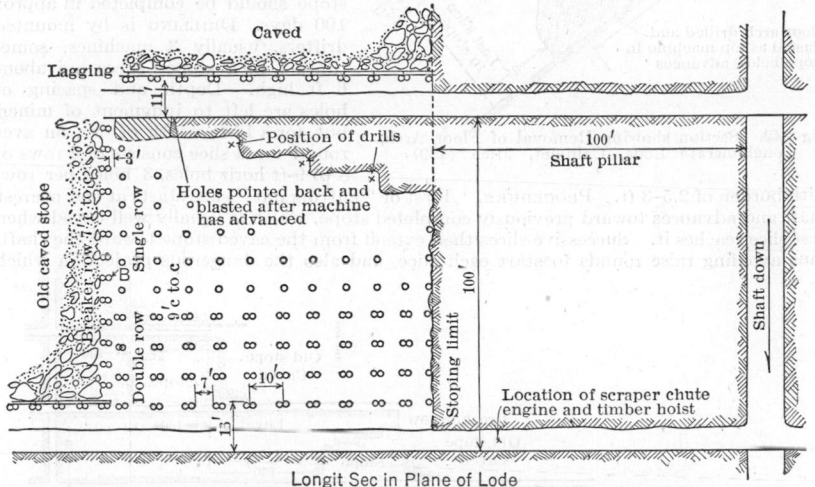

Fig 241. Open Stope, Conglomerate Lode, Calumet, Mich (489)

shaft pillars, extending 100 ft along strike on each side of shaft; these are robbed after hanging wall has settled around them, beginning at bottom and retreating up the dip.

Development. There are numerous inclined shafts in the lode and several vert shafts which cut through lode at depth. Level interval is about 100 ft; higher stopes can not be worked out quickly enough to allow control of hanging wall in lower portions of stopes. Drifts are 8 by 8 ft, and follow the footwall to take advantage of better ground and a well marked slip; double-track drifts in Red Jacket workings are 7 by 11 ft; drift-stopes (Art 41), where tried, have proved difficult and costly to maintain. A 7 by 7-ft raise is put up between levels at boundary or in the end stope on the level, for ventilation and to furnish points of attack for stoping; as stoping progresses there is enough open space between solid and caved ground for these purposes.

Stoping. Data from Henry Vivian, Ch Engineer (489) in 1931. Successive overhand back-stopes are about 6 ft high. Hanging wall supported by stulls during active life of stope, but caves later. Length of stope standardized at 100 ft; height limited to 100 ft. These dimensions permit mining entire stope before caving starts. An advancing system was used to depth of 6 000 ft, leaving floor pillars 8–15 ft thick under each level; these were later crushed by the caving of mined-out areas above and below, but were recovered profitably. Since 1909, and below 6 000 ft, a retreating system has been used exclusively; no floor pillars are left, so that all the lode material is mined.

Details. Length of block stoped in one operation depends on speed of work and length of time that hanging wall can be held with timber; therefore on thickness of ore and character of roof. LENGTH OF STOPES has been consistently shortened as depth increased. At first, stulls were used entirely for timbering stopes; later, due to increase in lode thickness, square-set timbering (Art 46) was standard and stopes were 200 ft long. Below 5 500 ft on dip, the lode was generally less than 20 ft thick and stulls were again used, length of stope then being reduced to 100 ft. SPACING OF STULLS in lower part of stope has become standardized, but spacing in upper part depends on foreman's judgment.

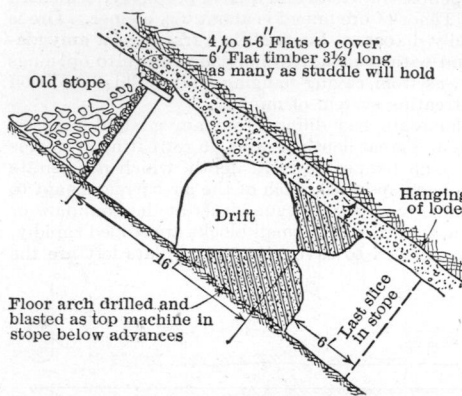

Fig 242. Section showing Removal of Floor Arch, Conglomerate Lode, Calumet, Mich (489)

Present practice (1931) calls for 4 rows of 18–24-in stulls, set in pairs with about 7-ft clear space between timbers in horiz rows and about 9 ft c-c between rows measured down dip (Fig 241). These double stulls (" batteries ") cover about 40% of height of entire stope. Above this height, stulls are placed singly, with a variable increase in spacing, depending on appearance and behavior of hanging wall; the top 20–25 ft of the stope may need no timber. Experience shows that a stope should be completed in approx 100 days. DRILLING is by mounted drifters, usually 3 machines, sometimes 4, in a stope; slices are about 6 ft high. Depth and spacing of holes are left to judgment of miner, but, for a 12-ft width of ore, an aver round for a slice consists of 4 rows of 8 to 9-ft horiz holes, 3 holes per row,

with burden of 2.5–3 ft. PROCEDURE. First or " cutting out " slice starts at end nearest shaft and advances toward previously completed stope, which is usually well caved when first slice reaches it. Successive slices then extend from the caved stope toward the shaft, thus avoiding raise rounds to start each slice, and also the dangerous projection which

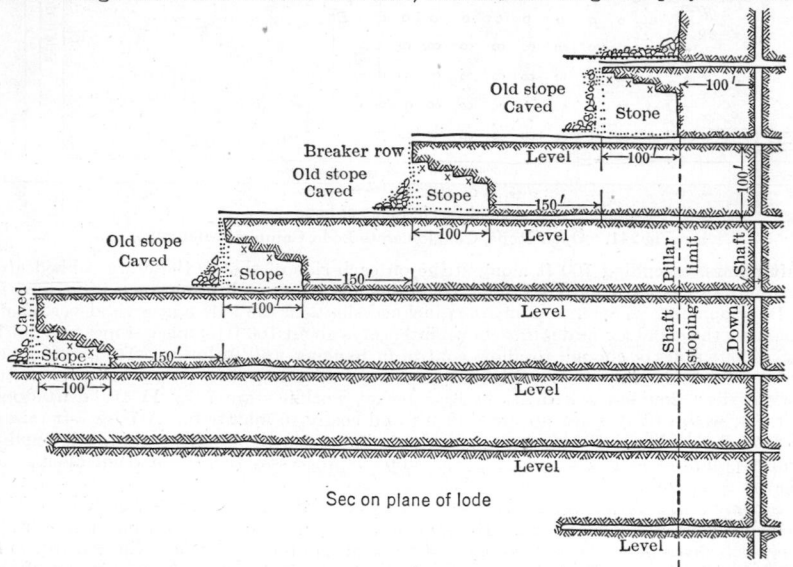

Fig 243. Retreating Stoping System, Conglomerate Lode, Calumet, Mich. (x indicates position of drills)

would exist at the caved end if a slice were approaching it. Just before completing a stope to the level above, a row of doubled 2-ft or larger stulls (" breaker row " B, Fig 241) is placed 3 ft back from the face of solid ore in the block next to be stoped; pairs of stulls are spaced 3 ft apart on the dip. This maintains a safe space from which the successive back-stopes can be started. As the top slice of each stope is cut, the floor arch of level above is drilled, but actual breaking of the arch is deferred until slice has advanced enough to leave a short length of protecting arch above the driller (Fig 241, 242). Last timbering in stope is to place heavy lagging along upper side of the lowest row of stulls; this facilitates recovery of floor arch from below. A complete mining operation on either side of a shaft is a series of 4 retreating stopes on 4 successive levels, the top stope leading the next below by approx 150 ft, and so on down (Fig 243). No attempt is made to hasten caving of hanging wall in stopes by removing timbers. Regulation of time of caving, if necessary, is by increasing or decreasing number of stulls placed during active stoping. Handling stoped ore. Tendency is for ore to break into slabs, so that, in spite of the relatively flat dip, most of the broken ore runs to drift below. For retreating stopes, chutes are rarely built, tho ore being scraped from the floor up a portable scraper incline high enough for cars to run underneath. About 15% of the ore from upper faces is scraped down to level by same scraper used to fill cars. Mine cars are of 3.75-ton capac and are end-dump; gage, 4 ft. Haulage is by storage-battery loco. Duty of labor. In 1930, production by above method was 6.33 tons per man-shift charged to stoping; for all underground labor, 3.06 tons per man-shift.

40. EXAMPLES OF PRACTICE, OPEN OVERHAND STOPES
(Support by Pillars of Ore)

Edwards mine, St Lawrence County, N Y. Data from J. B. Knaebel (253) in 1932. Lenticular masses of zinc ore (pyrite and marmatite), aver about 17% Zn, occur as replacements in silicified dolomite. Lenses are 5–25 ft thick, 100–200 ft long on the strike, and may extend down dip to vert depth of 1 700 ft. Aver dip, 40°–45°, with local variations from 0 to 90° Ore drills easily, but is

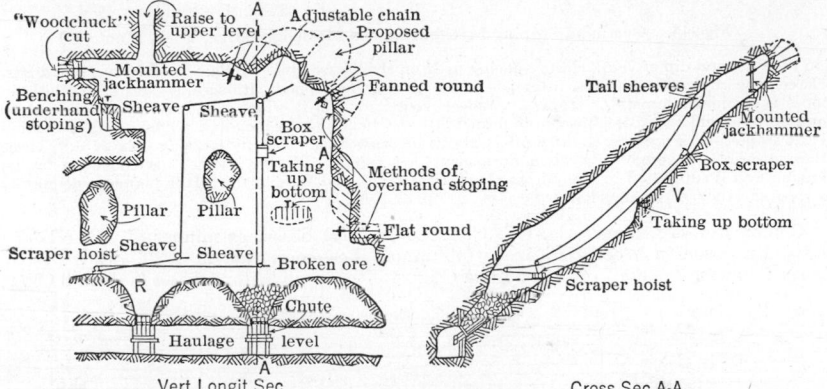

Fig 244. Breaking and Handling Ore in Open Stopes, Edwards Mine, St Lawrence Co, N Y (253)

tough and difficult to break. Both walls generally strong, but sometimes slab badly. Large horses of waste are infrequent; sorting in stopes has not been feasible. Development. Main shaft is vert; in hanging wall to 1 100 ft; thereafter in footwall. Level interval was at first 100 ft; now (1932), 200 ft. Lateral development is by drifts, crosscuts, and raises, irregularly spaced according to requirements of stoping and ventilation. Stoping. Formerly some shrinkage stoping was done, but with flattening of dip in depth, reworking of old stopes, and for flexibility, open stopes with pillars superseded old methods. Stoping is overhand or underhand, or a combination. Overhand stoping. Chute raises R (Fig 244) are driven up dip on footwall, 30–40 ft apart, to height of 15–30 ft above drift; raises are connected at top and then belled to funnel shape. Fig 244 shows methods of advancing faces and of placing holes. Thicker parts of deposit are mined in 2 parts: first an overhand stope at least 6 ft high is driven under the hanging wall; later the bottom is taken out in benches; this work resembles breast and bench stoping (Art 30). Drilling is chiefly by mounted wet jackhammers, occasionally with stopers for cutting around pillars on steep dips. Rounds in overhand stoping, as at A (Fig 244), are of 9 8-ft holes. Pillars are left in lean or barren material where possible, their size and spacing depending chiefly on extent to which hanging is fissured or seamed; usually spans of 40 ft or more will stand during life of stope. Pillars are oval in outline, not more than 25 ft long; long dimension parallel to dip. Vert holes take up the bottom. Handling broken ore. Where dips exceed 42°, ore runs to chutes with a little hand-shoveling. In stopes flatter than 42°, mechanical scrapers have lowered costs. Duty of labor. During 1930, output per man-shift of all underground labor and surface labor chargeable to underground operations was 5.06 tons.

Golden Messenger mine, York, Mont. Data from S. H. Lorain (69) in 1937. Gold-bearing veins are quartz and sulphide replacements along fractures in diorite; the gold associated chiefly with pyrite, sometimes galena and sphalerite. Values are generally uniform, with some enriched pockets. Usual width of workable lode, 4–10 ft. Dips vary from 30° to 60°; usually about 40°. Veins are cut by numerous post-mineral faults, mostly of small displacement. Ground drills and breaks easily. Hanging wall is blocky, requiring occasional support. DEVELOPMENT is by 2 tunnels (haulage levels), 150 ft apart vert, from which the orebodies are reached by raises and sublevels. Extraction drifts are driven in the veins. STOPING. Main output has come from overhand stoping; a novel underhand method has also been used (Art 35). For overhand stoping, chutes (*C*, Fig 245) are installed along the drift under the stope, 15–30 ft apart, depending on loca-

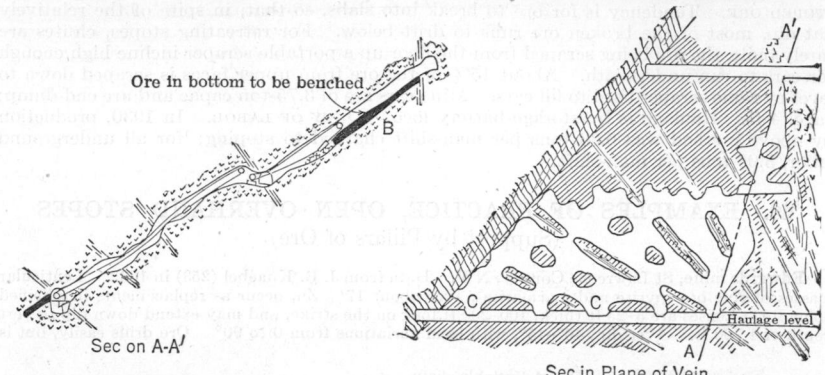

Fig 245. Overhand Stoping Method, Golden Messenger Mine, York, Mont (69)

tion of faults and dip of vein; closer spacing used on the flatter dips. Pillars are left over the drifts, between the chutes. Chutes at intervals of 60–75 ft are equipped with scraper hoists. Drilling in stopes is by jackhammers or stopers. Where vein is over 6 ft wide, a cut is first taken next to hanging wall, and ore in the bottom is mined later by bench *B*. Elongated pillars along fault lines divide stopes into segments, slightly offset above or below each other by faulting (Fig 245). These pillars are holed through only when necessary for scraping. Within the sections between faults, hanging wall is supported by ore pillars about 10 ft diam, and 15 ft apart. It is planned ultimately to recover much of these pillars.

Clinton iron-ore mines, Ala. T. C. DeSollar (177) describes mining of upper bench of the Big Seam in Woodward Iron Co's mines, Bessemer, Ala, in 1933. Entry is by slopes, following the ore. At No 3 mine (Fig 246) the "top" slope met a fault at 3 636 ft

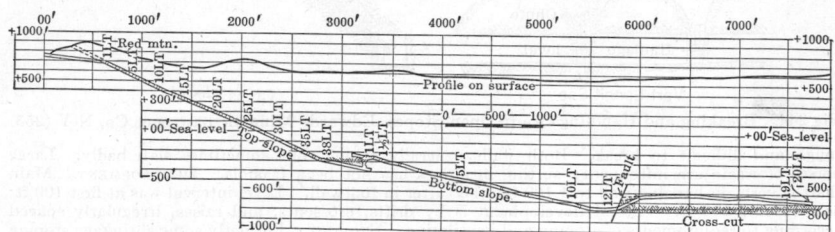

Fig 246. Sec through Slope of No 3 Mine, Woodward Iron Co, Bessemer, Ala

along the incline, requiring a second or "bottom" slope, the two being connected by a 2 300-ton storage pocket. "Top" slope has 20 by 10-ft cross-sec, and hoisting is done in balance with 2 10-ton self-dumping skips. Ore is handled on "bottom" slope in 2.25-ton wooden or 5-ton steel cars, hauled by elec hoist; a rotary car dump is installed above the storage pocket. Drifts from slopes are 9 ft wide, if broken ore is loaded by hand, or 12 ft wide, if mechanical (ramp and scraper) loading is employed; they are driven rapidly to property lines, and opening of rooms, starting 25 ft inside of line, retreats towards main slope. Room necks, 12 ft wide and 75 ft apart, are driven 25 ft up the dip, and an all-steel ramp, mainly of 16-ft lengths of 12-in, 25-lb channel-iron, is installed at each one (see Sec 27). A double-drum, 55-hp hoist, mounted on a self-propelling truck on track parallel with haulage track, and operating a 3 100-lb box-type scraper, serves 3–5 stopes on a level. Inside the neck, a room is widened to 30 ft and carried up to next level, usually

220 ft, occasionally 300 ft. A slab 10 ft wide is then taken from each side, making rooms 50 ft and pillars 25 ft wide. When a group of stopes is finished, a slab is taken from side of drift, from which track and pipes are removed. Recovery from first mining is about 65%; further recovery of 10% is expected from splitting of pillars. Ore drills and breaks easily. With drill on tripod, 2 men make 14–18 holes, finishing at 2-in diam and 8 ft deep, per shift; a blast breaks 100–125 tons. Two or 3 drills work at once in a stope, accumulating broken ore in 2 stopes while a third one is being scraped and 2 others started. This permits the hoist to work for several days from same position; scraper is not removed from stope until completed. Full stope crew includes 4–6 drill men, 1 hoist engr, 1 motorman, 3 muckers. Drill steel is 1.25-in hollow round, with star bits. Explosive, low-density ammonia dynamite in 5.75 by 1.5-in cartridges, received daily from manufacturer and immediately transferred to underground magazine; detonated with No 6 tetryl caps. Aver daily output (2 8-hr shifts) at this mine is 3 000–3 300 long tons.

Tennessee Coal, Iron & R R Co mines the Big Seam at Muscoda, Ala, under conditions similar to those at the Woodward mine (above). As described by E. M. Ball and A. W. Beck (507) in 1937, the main slope had reached bottom of the basin at 6 260 ft from outcrop and under 1 600 ft of cover. From this slope or its branches, haulage levels 20 ft wide, 10.5 ft high, are turned at right angles at 230-ft intervals, and laid with standard-gage double track; grade not to exceed 8%. Each room, up the dip, is entered by 2 or 3 necks 20 ft long; in former case, room is 110 ft wide and yields 16 000

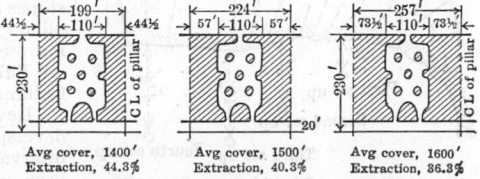

Fig 247. Pillar Spacing, Muscoda, Ala

tons of ore (210 lb per cu ft solid) in its length of 190 ft; a 3-neck room is 160 ft wide and yields 24 000 tons. Small (20-ft) circular pillars are staggered over stope areas, usually 5 in a 110-ft stope; 8-in posts used as required. Width of pillar between adjoining rooms is adjusted to depth of cover, as shown in Fig 247. It is planned to extract pillars on retreat. Two drifters on tripods are used in each stope, making V-cuts and slabbing rounds; no secondary blasting required. Explosive is ammonia dynamite, equivalent to 45% gelatin. Ore is scraped from rooms and haulage headings by 50-hp, double-drum hoist, mounted on self-propelling truck on a parallel track, scraper discharging its 2-ton load over a steel ramp into 5-ton cars. Data on first 6 months of 1937: tons per man-shift in actual production, 16.5; per man-shift underground, 7.11; tons per lb explosive, 1.5; bd ft timber per ton, 0.873; kw-hr per ton for scraping, 1; for air compression, 4.65.

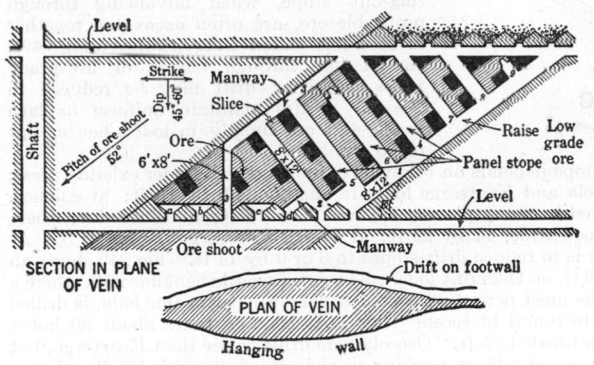

Fig 248. Panel System of the Herman Mine

Herman mine, Placer Co, Calif. Quartz vein, 8–12 ft thick, dipping 45°–60°, occurs in schist. Country rock is blocky, with cross fractures; on the hanging wall is a layer of soft slate. Ore is in shoots, about 200 ft long, pitching about 52°. Level interval, 150 ft. Underhand square-setting was tried and abandoned, due to its danger and expense. Open stoping with pillar support (Fig 248) was used. Stope was opened by driving raises 1 along the bottom of oreshoot and on the footwall; also the manway 3 and the chute raises *a* to *d*. Panel stopes, 2 to 9, were then carried up. Chute *E* was cut when necessary. Pole bulkheads were constructed between pillars if required to divert ore. When the panel stopes were fully opened, the pillars on both sides were sliced and finally cut through, leaving small pillars shown in solid black. All these stope pillars were then drilled and blasted. Finally, the pillars under the level above were blasted, allowing caved material from the stope above to follow down until it rested on the pillars above the lower level. Data from S. H. Brockunier in 1919 (570).

41. EXAMPLES OF PRACTICE, MICH AMYGDALOID MINES
(Support by Pillars of Ore) (67, 153, 170, 486)

Michigan amygdaloid copper deposits, Keweenaw Peninsula, carry native copper in volcanic flows of vesicular basalt (amygdaloid), interbedded with flows of compact diabase, the whole series tilted on dips from 35° at the north to 73° at south end of Range. All beds tend to flatten slightly at depth, which has reached over 9 000 ft (on incline) in some workings. Profitable beds occur at 5 out of 17 recognized copper-bearing amygdaloidal horizons. Distribution of copper is irregular; average tenor of all ore, less than 1%. Hanging wall is diabase, usually strong, but often rough and irregular. Footwalls of some lodes may contain offshoot orebodies, and copper-bearing cross-fractures are fairly common throughout the Range.

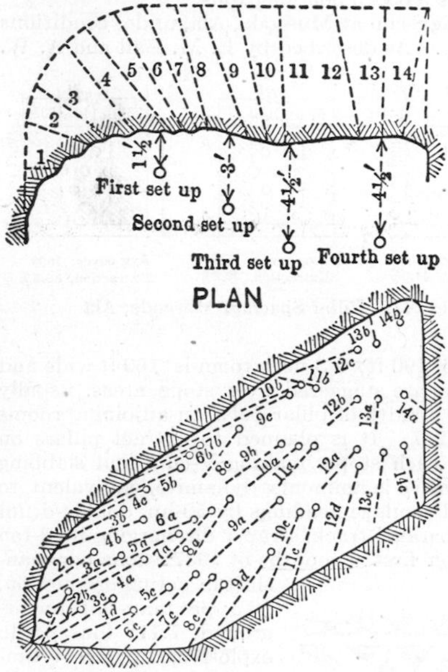

PLAN

VERT SEC

Fig 249. Drift-stope

General plan of mining. Open overhand stopes are used for beds on dips of 35° to 45°, pillars being left for roof support. For mining steep-dipping beds with weaker walls, see Baltic mine, Art 63. For practice in the Calumet conglomerate, see Art 39.

Development. For modes of entry and development, see Art 15 to 17. Early level intervals of 100 ft or less (on dip) have now been enlarged to 160 ft in some mines; aver about 125 ft, though 150 ft is common. In irregular Osceola lode, 120 ft proved better than larger or smaller interval. Inclined-shaft pillars, formerly 50 ft wide, are now 200 ft on each side of shaft, to insure support at 5 000 ft vert depth. Crosscuts, when required, are 7 ft high, 8–12 ft wide.

Drifts. Strong hanging wall permits lateral development openings of large cross-sec without excessive cost for maintenance. Hence, the development drift and the cutting-out stope, when advancing through profitable ore, are often excavated together in openings called DRIFT-STOPES (Fig 249). In passing through barren or low-grade zones, width of drift may be reduced to 7–8 ft. Drifts maintain uniform haulage grade and are mostly in lode; hence, apt to be crooked.

Details. Size of drift-stope depends on behavior of hanging wall under existing press; at medium depths in Osceola and Kearsarge lodes it was about 9 by 19 ft; at Allouez, where hanging was shattered in many places, size was 9 by 18 ft; at Wolverine, where hanging was strong and lode wide, 11 by 25 ft; at North Kearsarge, 10 by 16 ft. At increasing depths, tendency is to reduce drift-stopes to 8 or 9 by 14 ft. Fig 249 shows an earlier typical stope, 9 by 19 ft, on OSCEOLA lode. The cut, towards hanging wall, where a well defined slip and also the most persistent copper usually appear in this lode, is drilled and blasted first. Complete round in recent 8 by 14-ft heading takes about 30 holes, loaded with 40% gelatin, to break 4.75 ft. Osceola lode drills easier than Kearsarge, but is harder to break. Two contract miners, working on opposite shifts with 108-lb column-mounted jackhammers, advance a round per day, mucking being done by others. In deeper levels of KEARSARGE, former practice of pointing cut towards hanging wall (where good parting occurred) has been abandoned, due to falls induced by breaking of roof rock. The cut in 9 by 14-ft stope-drift is now taken 5 ft into footwall (Fig 250), leaving lode matter across whole width of roof. Two contract miners on opposite shifts drill 35 holes to break 5.5–6 ft per day, using mainly semi-bulk powder with 2–3 sticks of 50% gelatin at bottom of each hole. Other men muck by hand. At AHMEEK mine, in Kearsarge lode, a 9 by 14-ft drift-stope is advanced 5 ft per day of 2 shifts (aver 100 ft per mo), drills and supplies being brought down between shifts, and hand mucking proceeding while 1 man drills with 154-lb, hand-fed, column-mounted drifter. A round requires 32 holes averaging 6.25 ft deep, each loaded with 2.1 lb of 66% low-density ammonia dynamite and 2 sticks of 40% gelatin at bottom. There is no standard round; holes left to judgment of miner.

Stoping (67). Stope widths between walls vary from 8 to 20 ft. GENERAL PLANS of work: (*a*) A stope of profitable width, usually 8 to 12 ft, is first opened along hanging wall; later, any ore occurring below the arbitrary footwall of first stope is broken in benches; this method is followed in Osceola workings of C & H Co, Fig 251 (486). (*b*) Stope follows footwall. Ore less than 12 ft thick is broken in one operation; where thicker, a stope 10 to 12 ft high is advanced a short distance on footwall, then ore on back is blasted down. Opinions differ as to better method: under plan (*b*) it is difficult to reach and trim the hanging wall in stopes 16 to 18 ft wide; under plan (*a*) the mining of footwall ore starts at top of stope, for breaking ore onto the fairly smooth floor of first stope; this leaves less ore to be shoveled out when stope is finished than when floor is mined up the dip.

Drilling and blasting. Presence of coarse copper reduces drilling speed and may cause abandonment of holes. Drills are mounted on columns, which in places must be 10–13 ft long. With 1-man machines it is usual to work 2 drills close together for mutual aid in setting-up. Contract drilling, with bonus, is the rule in amygdaloid stopes; in Osceola lode, bonus base is 50 ft of hole per drill-shift; in Kearsarge lode, 40 ft; holes are inspected and measured by shift-boss, and an improperly placed hole is not counted towards bonus. At AHMEEK mine, on Kearsarge lode, advancing a stope face 37 ft wide by 7 ft high, up a 38° slope, 30 7-ft holes in 3 horiz rows are drilled by 154-lb, column-mounted, hand-fed drifters, at 60 ft per drill-shift. The 2 vert rows at center make a V-cut. Explosive (66% low-density ammonia dynamite), 0.9 lb per ton broken; output, about 22 tons per drill-shift. In OSCEOLA lode, aver output is 25 tons, with explosive of same grade.

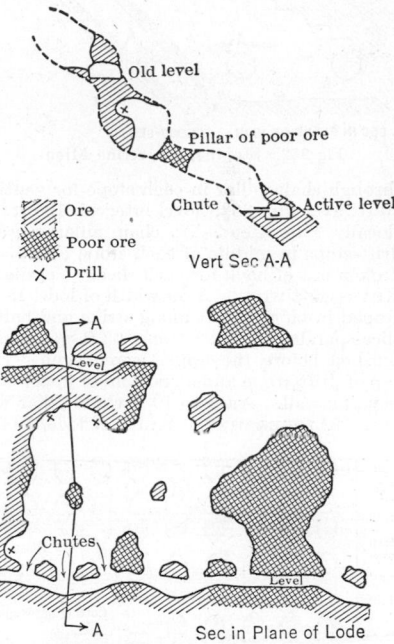

Vert Sec A-A

Sec in Plane of Lode

Fig 251. Open Stope, Osceola Lode

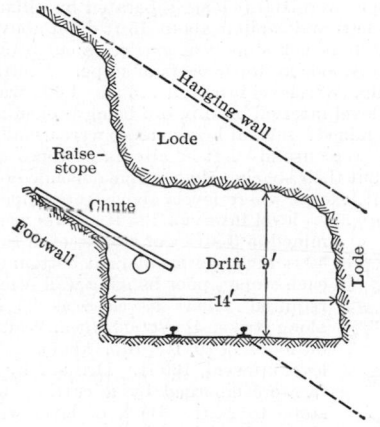

Fig 250. Section at Bottom of Stope, Kearsarge Lode

Pillars of ore support hanging wall in stopes; their size and spacing depend on same factors as in breast-stoping (Art 30). Wherever possible, areas of low-grade ore have been utilized for pillars, leading to irregularity. Recent practice on deeper levels aims at more systematic use of relatively small pillars for temporary support; roof ultimately allowed to cave. Aver spacing has been about 40 ft along strike, less along dip; interval ranges in different mines from 25–60 ft. Axis of pillars is at right-angles to dip. Pillars flare slightly at top and bottom, with upper sides shaped to shed broken ore [falling from above; diam varies from 8–15 ft or more. Little timber is used in stopes; a stull or two may be put under a slab, or to hold up broken ore for supporting men and drills.

Handling ore in stopes. Dip of amygdaloid lodes is great enough (generally 38°–54°) for most of the ore to fall to level below; fine ore clings to footwall and irregularities in the latter make some shoveling or scraping necessary.

Formerly all ore slid from stope onto a plank platform (SOLLAR), alongside track in the level, and was shoveled thence into cars. Since chutes were not used, fine breaking in stopes was unnecessary; about 60% was over 4-in size; large pieces lifted into cars by hand; trammers used short D-handled shovels. Later practice generally adopts scrapers, discharging through hardwood plank chutes, which are dismounted and used repeatedly. Footwall at Quincy mine is so rough that practically all ore must be shoveled to drift (see Fig 254 and text). STOPE FLOORS ARE CLEANED before stope is abandoned, sometimes by scraper. At Mohawk mine, ore remaining on stope floors has been shoveled into semicircular steel chutes, 32-in radius, laid on the broken ore, and supported on wooden horses at the level for dumping into cars; they were moved along the stope floor as it was cleaned up; 4 shovelers and 2 trammers handled 42 tons per shift.

Stoping generally begins at a RAISE-STOPE, say 24 ft on strike by full width of lode, put up between levels as far as possible from the shaft.

Examples of stoping. WOLVERINE MINE is on an amygdaloid lode with strong hanging wall; dip, 41°; aver width, 14 ft; Fig 252 shows stoping method; level interval, 100 ft; levels were opened as drift-stopes. Gound was mined in blocks 75 ft long, running from level to level; 2 pillars *A*, say 15 ft diam, were left at top of drift-stope in each 75-ft block, with an 8 to 10-ft chain pillar along the back to support level above. A raise *R* was put

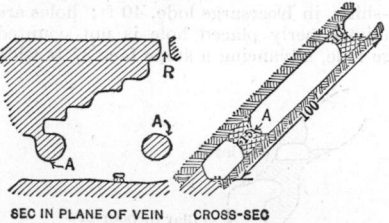

SEC IN PLANE OF VEIN   CROSS-SEC
Fig 252. Stoping, Wolverine Mine

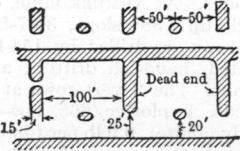

Fig 253. Stoping, Mohawk Mine (Sec in plane of lode)

through chain pillar in each stope for ventilation. MOHAWK MINE. Aver width of lode, 20 ft; aver dip, 38°; level interval, 100 ft. Stopes were 100 ft long, separated by pillars (locally, "dead ends"); chain pillars were also left, and a pillar about 13 ft diam above drift-stope in middle of each stope (Fig 253). A flat-back stope was carried, a cut being broken out of back for each slice. Ventilation was poor in upper parts of stope. NORTH KEARSARGE MINE. Aver width of lode, 18 ft; dip, 38°; level interval, 125 ft. Lode was stoped in blocks 20 ft along strike and half the level interval on dip, ore being broken in slices parallel to dip. Upper 62 ft was similarly mined; several lower stopes were usually finished before the upper were begun. Pillars were usually left in alternate stopes at top of drift-stope and at bottom of upper stope, but their spacing along strike depended on hanging wall. An 8 to 10-ft chain pillar was left, except where levels above were stoped out. ALLOUEZ MINE. Width of lode, 16 ft; dip, 38°; level interval, 125 ft. Lifts were

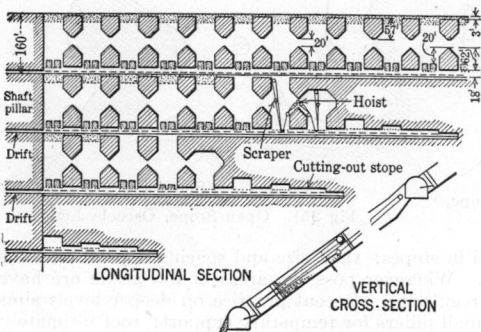

LONGITUDINAL SECTION

VERTICAL CROSS-SECTION

Fig 254. Stoping Method, Quincy Mine, Showing Use of Light Scraper and Portable Hoist

mined in 3 series of stopes, each say 40 ft high, with pillars at bottom of each stope; poor hanging wall often required pillars as close as 25 ft along strike. HANCOCK MINE. Width of lode, 8–10 ft; dip, about 45°; level interval, 100 ft. Drifts, 6 by 7 ft, were enlarged by a cutting-out stope to 24 ft. Back of level was timbered with stulls 4–6 ft apart, lagged with 4–6-in poles. A 2 by 4-ft hole was left in lagging at 25-ft intervals, with a sollar under it about 4 ft above track. Some broken ore remained in stope to protect lagging and aid in setting up drills; the rest was drawn onto sollars, sorted and loaded. Ground was good, requiring no stope timber.

Pillars were left where ore was poor, also a chain pillar, 6–10 ft thick. QUINCY MINE. A lode about 10 ft thick, dipping 38° to 54°, has been worked at great depth (9 150 ft on dip). Stopes at Quincy were at first 100 ft wide, alternating with pillars of same width. As depth increased, these dimensions had to be changed to 50-ft rooms and 50-ft pillars; this made workings safer, percentage of extraction greater, and tenor of copper rock stamped increased. Fig 254 (482) shows layout for use of light reversible hoe scraper.

Osceola lode is erratic as to shape and mineralization of oreshoots (486); aver dip 37°; no systematic arrangement of pillars is feasible. Occasional·rich pockets in footwall are discovered by minute examination of floor as stoping proceeds; if isolated by more than 4–5 ft of barren footwall, such pockets may be mined by special stopes from crosscuts; if within that distance, they are mined by underhand jackhammer work from main stope. Levels at 120-ft (slope) intervals are opened as drift-stopes (see above); in workable ore, chute raises, 9 ft wide by 5 ft high, are opened on 25-ft centers (Fig 251); latter equipped with nearly level chutes of hardwood plank and old rails, delivering about 4 ft above track. Scraper, when required, is 4 ft wide and operated by double-drum air or elec hoist with 0.5-in rope.

Retreating systems are attempted in most amygdaloid mines, especially as depth and pressure increase. Hence, drifts or drift-stopes must reach the boundary before stoping begins above them. This reduces cost of drift maintenance and avoids the following disadvantages of the advancing system: (a) blasting in stopes injures tracks on level; (b) mucking in stope and in drift or drift-stope interfere; (c) small pieces of ore rolling from stope onto rails often derail cars; (d) danger from slabs falling from stope into drift; (e) sometimes a stope caves, and ore from points beyond must then be run to level below; this is troublesome and costly, especially on flat dips.

Kearsarge lode has been mined for a strike distance of 6 miles within C & H ground, and to depths of 4 000–5 000 ft (on 38° dip). To 3 000 ft, usual method was open stopes with pillars of barren rock or poor ore. Later modifications adapted to heavier press, described by O. Potter in 1931 (486), include stoping on retreat and use of " rib pillars," latter to control roof settlement without attempting to prevent it. Levels at 150-ft (slope) intervals are advanced as 9 by 14-ft stope-drifts to boundary. Starting there, chute raises (R, Fig 255) 5 ft high and 21 ft c-c are driven about 10 ft up the footwall and enlarged at upper ends to full profitable width of lode, leaving a brow over the chute (Fig 250). From top of last raise on drift, a "cutting-over" drift (D, Fig 255) starts back towards the shaft, breaking into tops of successive raises and funneling them. When 4 such chutes have been completed, a stope 37 ft wide and full height of lode is started over chutes No 2, 3, leaving No 1, 4 open for ventilation. As the "cutting-over" drift advances, more 37-ft stopes are started, each centered over 2 chutes, leaving a 5-ft "rib pillar" between every 2 stopes; this pillar is holed through, at about 25-ft intervals, for access and ventilation (Fig 255). Width of pillar is varied according to experience; no timber is required except an occasional prop under a slab that can not be barred down.

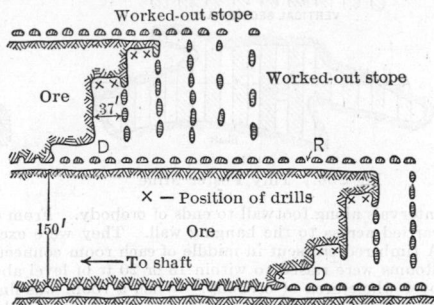

Fig 255. Open Overhand Stopes with Rib Pillars, Kearsarge Lode (Projection on plane of lode dipping 38°)

Four 1-man drills in 2 adjoining stopes can about keep pace with 1 drill in "cutting-over" drift, combined output of the 5 drills being 220–250 tons per 2-shift day. When a stope is finished and all ore withdrawn, pillars of better-grade ore are blasted down; under strong roof, a whole row can sometimes be recovered; those that remain are expected to crush so as to allow gradual subsidence; total recovery from stoping area, 95% of pay ore. About 85% of broken ore can be loaded (into 5- and 8-ton cars) by gravity, with a little help from trammers. For the rest, and always when extracting pillars or working under bad roof, 4-ft scrapers operated by 2-drum air hoists with 0.5-in rope are used. Storage-battery, 7-ton loco hauls 2 to 4 8-ton cars; 3-ton loco for 5-ton cars; max haul, 5 000 ft; usually not over 2 500 ft. Advantages of this system: (a) all holes are drilled upward and parallel to dip; hence more easily directed to avoid breaking either wall. (b) When roof falls in old stopes, caving stops at first solid line of pillars. (c) Small expense for timbering. Chief drawback is that all mining is substantially the advancement of a heading, with adverse effect on powder consumption and output per shift.

42. PILLAR AND CHAMBER WORKINGS

The term denotes methods of mining in which large chambers are excavated, leaving pillars of ore for permanent support. Chambers may be mined as underhand stopes, glory holes, or overhand stopes. Support for men in overhand stopes is afforded by accumulation of broken ore (Shrinkage stopes, Art 67), or by square-sets (Art 45 et seq); chambers are rarely filled with waste to support men (see Rimogne quarry, below).

The method is a development of room and pillar work in beds (Art 32), for mining masses or wide veins. In typical cases, workings are a series of large open stopes, separated by a network of vertical and horiz pillars of ore. Synonymous terms are CHAMBER WORK-

INGS, PILLAR WORKINGS, ROOM AND PILLAR, PILLAR AND STALL, ROOMING (see index for other use of same terms; also Art 104–6).

Chamber workings are a very old form of mining, obsolete for metalliferous deposits, except in rare cases; they are useful for exploiting cheap and abundant minerals, as salt or slate, where much of the deposit (40% to 70%) can be sacrificed in pillars for securing cheap support and low mining cost. Recovery of pillars is generally costly, often impossible, and workings are left in such shape that a change to other methods is difficult.

Requirements of method: (a) large deposits, as masses, wide veins or thick beds; (b) deposits of strong mineral or rock, with strong walls, which will stand unsupported over back and on walls of chambers; (c) cheap minerals, which will not pay cost of installing other methods; (d) deposits of uniform value, as no sorting is done in chambers.

Examples of practice which follow, while old, well illustrate principles, variations and applications of the method.

Tilly Foster mine, N Y. Orebody was a steep, lenticular mass of strong magnetite, embedded in gneiss; in horiz sec, it was about 200 ft wide by 300 ft long; dip, about 60°. Fig 256 shows method of mining part of the deposit. An inclined shaft was sunk in footwall, with wide drifts at 100-ft

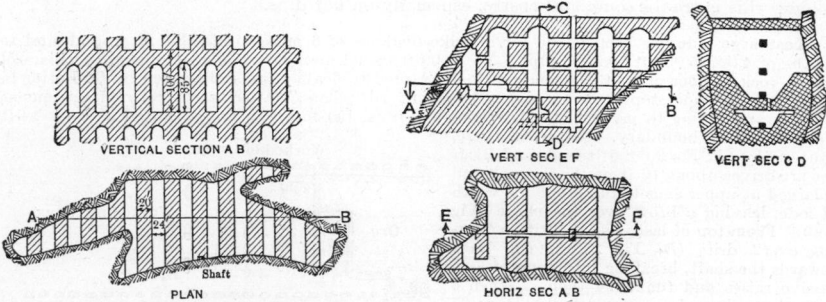

Fig 256. Tilly Foster Mine   Fig 257. Republic Iron Mine

intervals along footwall to ends of orebody. From drifts, rooms 24 ft wide, with 20-ft pillars, were carried across to the hanging wall. They were excavated overhand as shrinkage stopes (Art 67). A timbered crosscut in middle of each room connected with footwall drift for access and transport. Rooms were raised to within 15 or 20 ft of level above, leaving a floor of that thickness extending over whole area of orebody. When a room was finished, all broken ore was drawn, and the room abandoned. More than half of the orebody was left in pillars. Attempts to fill old rooms with concrete and to mine pillars under this support failed; many pillars were eventually recovered by open-cut (200, 201).

Republic mine, Marquette Range, Mich. Fig 257 shows former method for mining wide portions of a hard hematite deposit, having in places a horiz sec exceeding 150 by 400 ft (202). A vert shaft was sunk in the deposit, with a 70-ft pillar to protect it; drifts were driven at intervals of 30 to 50 ft and connected by winzes about 60 ft apart; from winzes, chambers 30 ft wide were opened from wall to wall, leaving 30-ft pillars. Top of chamber was a breast stope, with arched back, ore being mined underhand, starting at top of a winze. At places, the glory-hole method (Art 37) was used. Where a level-pillar was left, the heading method (Art 36) was employed (Fig 257, vert sec CD), the chambers being 50 to 150 ft high. At other places, 2 series of 30-ft rooms were driven at right-angles to each other, leaving 30-ft square pillars. About half of orebody was left in pillars; some of this ore has since been recovered after filling old stopes with waste. For hard ore, shrinkage stopes are now used, with subsequent filling (Art 68).

Rio Tinto mine, Spain. Orebodies are lenses of pyrite, with enough chalcopyrite to carry an aver of about 3% Cu. Length of deposits, 1 200–6 500 ft; width, generally proportional to length, max 250 ft; depth, 500–1 800 ft. Deposits usually occur along contacts between porphyries and clay slates, or along other lines of weakness in either rock. Nearly all have at some period been exploited by pillar and chamber (locally, pillar and stall). J. Allan gives following details (203). Lode was divided into horiz slices, alternate slices being worked by series of galleries at right-angles to each other; between every 2 networks of galleries was left a solid floor of ore of varying thickness, depending on strength of ground. Ordinarily, galleries were 13 by 13 ft; 16.5 by 20-ft and 20 by 20-ft sections were also tried, but proved unsafe in weaker parts of deposit; smaller openings were preferable, which could be made larger on entering good ground and smaller in weak ground. Face of galleries was attacked by a small top heading, leaving a bench about 8 ft high (compare Heading method, Art 36). Fig 258, from Foster (10), shows work in one deposit; entry was by vert shaft in footwall, with levels 41 ft apart, connected by vert raises. Alternate levels were used as main haulageways. Drifts and crosscuts, 10 to 11.5 ft square, were driven at right-angles on each level, at 33-ft centers, with pillars 21 to 23 ft square, the pillars being superposed in successive lifts. Chambers were then made by heightening and widening spaces between pillars. In firm ore, pillars were about 10 ft square and chambers 30 to 33 ft high; under aver conditions, pillars were 15 to 20 ft square, chambers 20 to 25 ft high. Vert sec (Fig 258) would be the same, whether taken parallel or at right-angles to strike; it shows successive stages of work in different levels. At many mines in the district, only 33% of the total ore was won by this method; in case shown, extraction averaged 50%; in firm ore, it might reach 73%. Chamber workings were adopted because they offered a cheap and ready method of obtaining large tonnages; ore was so plentiful that recovery of pillars was neglected. Many mines have stripped the overburden and mined old pillars by open-cut. Orebodies once worked in this manner have been reworked by a modified crosscut method (Art 64). Virgin ground at Rio Tinto is now worked by filled, flat-back stopes (Art 60) (549).

Underground slate quarries are typical of correct use of chamber workings. Following examples illustrate methods; further detail in Bib (10, 169, 204, 205).

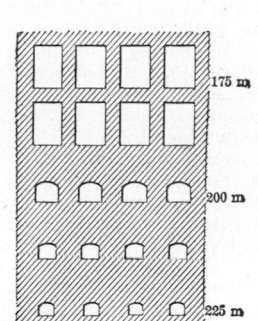

Fig 258. Rio Tinto Copper
Mine, Spain. (Vert sec)

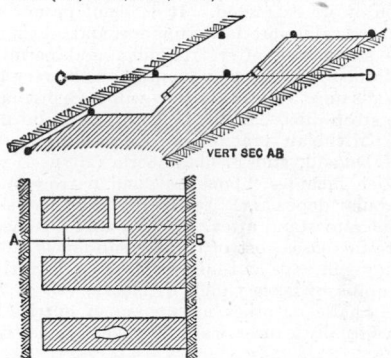

Fig 259. Underground Slate Quarry, Wales

Festiniog District, N Wales. Slate beds, 30–120 ft thick, dipping 20° to 35°, are opened by inclined shafts or by adits; levels are about 50 ft apart. Transverse chambers are opened 30 to 50 ft wide along strike (Fig 259), with pillars of about same size. With hand drilling, sides of pillars follow planes of weakness at right-angles to cleavage; these are askew to dip and deviate a little from perpendicular. Where channelers are used, pillars are vert and normal to dip. A chamber is started by a 4 by 4 or 4 by 6-ft raise along hanging wall at center or corner of proposed chamber; the raise is then widened to full width of chamber, widening and raising usually proceeding simultaneously. Floor of widened raise is carried back toward hanging wall by cutting off slices parallel to cleavage. A bottom cut is first made across width of chamber by a bar channeler drilling close-set 2-in holes; ribs between holes are broken with a chisel bit. Other cuts are made higher up and also along chamber walls, and blocks blasted down with small charges. Chambers and pillars on successive levels are under and connect with each other. Vert distance between floor of chamber and hanging wall may reach 120 ft. Main drifts are destroyed by work in the lift below, communication being maintained by run-around drifts in hanging, or by bridges; intermediate drifts are also run. Slate from development is all lost, and about half of the total is left in pillars. Further loss in splitting reduces net yield to about 13% of the deposit. L. Mayer states that in 1908 the Oakley quarry, with 1 500 men, produced 6 000 tons of slate per mo (169). One chamber may provide work for a small crew for 10 or 15 years. Elsewhere in the district, conditions allow chambers to be 100–150 ft and pillars 24–50 ft wide. No means have been devised for mining pillars. Men work under high unsupported roofs, but, though pillars often collapse, fatal accidents are rare. Backs are examined and trimmed from ladders erected in 30-ft sections, and held by guy ropes; 3–6 men take 1 week to build up a 100-ft ladder. In 1922 a hand-held hammer drill and a hydraulic rotating drill were being introduced (550).

Rimogne quarry, French Ardennes. Principal slate bed dips 22° to 45°; thickness, 0–200 ft. Long chambers (30–50 ft wide) are excavated along the strike, instead of across it, as at Festiniog. They reach from foot to hanging, with pillars about 13 ft wide along dip, sides of pillars being normal to dip. Chambers are mined as overhand filled stopes (Art 60); much of the waste is used as filling (205).

Anjou, France. Slate beds 130–500 ft thick stand almost vert. Outcrops are generally covered by a considerable thickness of worthless slate. They were formerly worked in large isolated chambers, each with its own entry from surface. A vert shaft was sunk to good slate, and an arched room excavated over top of proposed chamber by breast stoping. Floor was mined underhand in 10–13-ft benches. Slate blocks were handled in a stone skip attached to a trolley on a cable brought down the shaft and fastened to an eye-bolt in floor of chamber. Horiz sec of chamber was a circle or a rectangle, with maximum area of 21 500 to 27 000 sq ft; some chambers were 360 ft deep. Similar methods have been used for mining rock salt at Marmoras, Hungary (205).

Avery Island salt mine, La. Deposit is a dome-shaped mass, in places over 2 000 ft thick, overlain by 16–25 ft of soil, and has been worked on 2 levels at 90 and 160 ft depth. A. G. Wolf (551) describes methods in 1921. Deposit is opened by a 500-ft shaft. Parallel 7 by 7-ft drifts, put in on 120-ft centers, are widened by breast stoping till they form rooms 60 ft wide, leaving 60-ft pillars. Pillars are broken through in both directions, so that a series of regularly spaced pillars 60 ft square is left. Rooms and breakthroughs are then mined overhand by men working on ladders or on broken salt. Rooms are carried to a height of 60 ft at center. Drilling is done with air-driven augers, sometimes making 100 ft of hole per hr. All shoveling done by hand on contract.

43. SUB-LEVEL STOPING

This method, also known as sub-stoping, was developed in Michigan iron mines about 1902. It is an open-stope method and distinct from sub-level caving (Art 75, 76).

Applicability. Sub-level stoping is a relatively low-cost method, in terms of cost per ton of ore extracted. It does not permit very effective sorting, and is therefore applied where values are fairly uniform and sorting is not essential. Ore should be strong enough to stand well after trimming, and permit benches to stand under their own weight. Method may not be advantageous in very hard ore, due to high cost of driving sub-levels. Walls must be firm, or they will cave prematurely and dilute ore. Method is best adapted to steep dips, but has been successful on flat dips at Roan Antelope mine (see below).

Michigan practice. Following data and drawings are from F. W. Sperr, P. B. McDonald, and F. C. Roberts (208). Type of deposit mined by sub-level stoping in Mich includes " pockets " and narrow ends of large lenses; in general, steep-dipping, tabular deposits, 12 to 100 ft wide. Ore should be free from slips, and strong enough for backs to stand after trimming and benches to stand under their own weight (very hard ore increases cost of driving sub-levels and is a disadvantage). Walls must be firm, or they will cave and mix with ore, and overlying capping should be strong, so as to permit stoping of large panels or blocks.

Shafts or other **development** entries should be outside of the orebody, as mining eventually causes walls to cave. Level interval, 100 to 150 ft vert, each level having

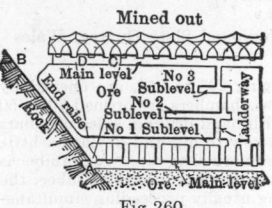

Fig 260

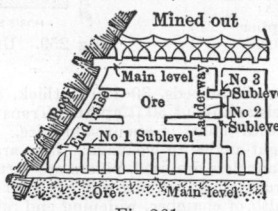

Fig 261

a main haulage-drift from which crosscuts are run to the walls to outline the deposit. Chute-raises are put up from drift and crosscuts to about 25 ft above level floor. Drift and crosscuts are planned so that centers of raises are 15 to 30 ft apart; in 25 to 40-ft orebodies

raises alternate on opposite sides of haulage drift; some wider bodies have 2 parallel haulage drifts, connected at intervals by crosscuts, to facilitate motor haulage. At end of deposit (or at end of panel to be stoped) a raise is put through to level above. Fig 260 shows procedure when end of orebody slopes forward. The triangular block *ABC* is broken by underhand stoping and handled to the level through the end raise; and ladderway and sub-levels 1, 2, and 3 are driven. If end of deposit slopes backward or is vert, sub-levels are started from end raise as well as from ladderways (Fig 261). Lowest sub-level (No 1) is at top of chute-raises; vert interval between sub-levels, 20 to 25 ft; they are closer in soft than in hard ore. Stoping. A sub-level usually consists of a single drift in middle of the deposit. Where ore is less than 40 ft wide, sub-level No 1 (Fig 261) is first widened to the deposit walls; a breast stope about 12 ft wide and of same height as sub-level is then carried across end of deposit, and worked back toward ladderway. Down holes are drilled around tops of chute-raises, and uppers in back of breast stope, the former being blasted first, to give a funnel shape to tops of raises (Fig 262). One round of back holes breaks a block 8 or 10 ft high across width of deposit and about 12 ft along strike, broken ore falling into finished raises and to chute gates in main level. After this work has proceeded 20 or 30 ft toward ladderway, sub-level No 2 is similarly opened. Holes are drilled in floor and back of breast stope and fired together, breaking off the bench of ore over sub-level No 1, and an 8 or 10-ft slice off back over No 2, broken ore falling into the open stope below. This procedure is repeated on each sub-level. Fig 262 shows appearance of work after stope is well opened; faces of SUB-STOPES retreat uniformly, being kept 20 to 30 ft apart. Each main level in turn forms the top sub-level of the series. When the ladderway is reached, a new ladderway and set of sub-levels will have been opened to the rear. Thus, men on each sub-level work under solid ore, and far enough back from open stope to be safe from falling slabs. Fig 263, 264 show application to orebodies 50 to 100 ft wide. A stope about 1/3 the width of the ore is first carried back through middle of deposit, leaving a pillar on each side. After central stope has advanced 60 to 100 ft, crosscuts K and drifts M (Fig 263) are driven on each sub-level; drifts M are extended and form benches along face of pillars (Fig 264) and benches B (Fig 263) are carried across ends of pillars to walls. Pillars are then mined by holes drilled from benches B, as in the central stope; each bench is kept a safe distance in advance of the one above. A vert sec through DJ or $D''J''$ (Fig 263) would be like Fig 262; vert sec through $D'J'$ would show the central stope worked back to a vert face.

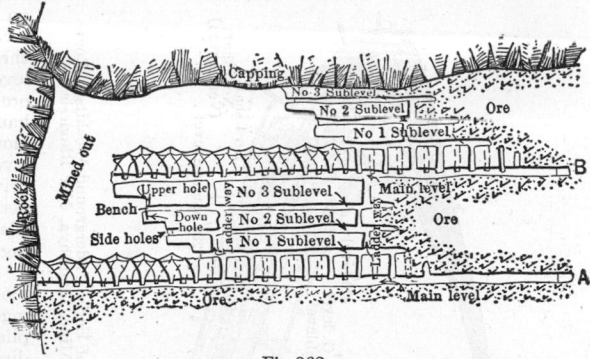

Fig 262

In long orebodies, stopes in Mich are about 250 ft long, separated by pillars containing ladderways. Length of stope is adjusted to prevent premature caving of walls; horiz pillars can also be left underneath main levels. Ore in pillars may be mined later by tip-slicing (Art 70), or by sub-level caving (Art 75, 76), if stopes are first filled. Filling for stopes between 2 levels may be drawn down and reused in lift below, allowing walls above to cave. Bib (545) gives examples of sub-level stoping, but no costs. ADVANTAGES of method are its safety and small timber consumption in suitable orebodies. Due to numerous points of attack, large tonnage can be broken in a small stope, most of it being

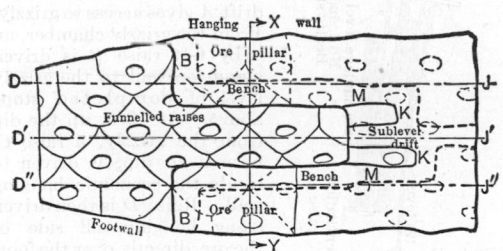

Fig 263. Plan of Sub-level Stope in Wide Orebody

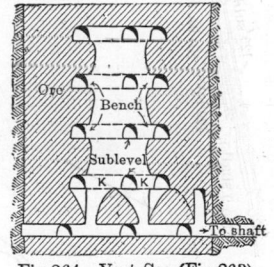

Fig 264. Vert Sec (Fig 263)

immediately available for loading (132). Small charges break large tonnages from benches and backs (breaking in breast stopes is more costly); aver powder consumption moderate. CHIEF DISADVANTAGE is large amount of narrow work in preliminary development, cost of which increases with hardness of ore. This cost is obviously greatest in narrow orebodies. Large pieces may require blockholing in chutes.

Roan Antelope mine, Luanshya, Nor Rhodesia. Data from material generously furnished in 1938 by W. J. MacKenzie, Mine Supt, through courtesy of Frank Ayer, Gen Mgr. Fig 266, 267, 268, and 269 were prepared by Mr. Bert Cole of the Co's staff. Sub-level stoping, introduced by R. M. Peterson, has proved highly satisfactory.

Geological features. Disseminated copper sulphides occur throughout a 10 to 45-ft band of well bedded argillaceous sandstone and shale; aver, 3.44% Cu. The mineralized beds forming the orebody are in an asymmetrical plunging syncline; hence the outcrop is hair-pin shaped; dips vary from flat to 90°. Plan of early underground workings, Fig 265 (501), indicates general shape of orebody. Hanging wall shades into lean and barren shales, quartzites, sandstones, and dolomites. A band of calcareous biotite schist on footwall, about 3 ft thick, sometimes has high copper content. Below the schists are feldspathic quartzites and conglomerates, or, in some parts, shales.

Development is by several inclined shafts in ore and a main vert shaft starting 180 ft back of footwall of one limb of orebody (Fig 265). In the steeper portions of orebody, haulage drifts above 420-level were at 100-ft vert intervals; below, 200 ft apart. In the flat section at the "nose" of orebody, intermediate haulageways were driven in footwall

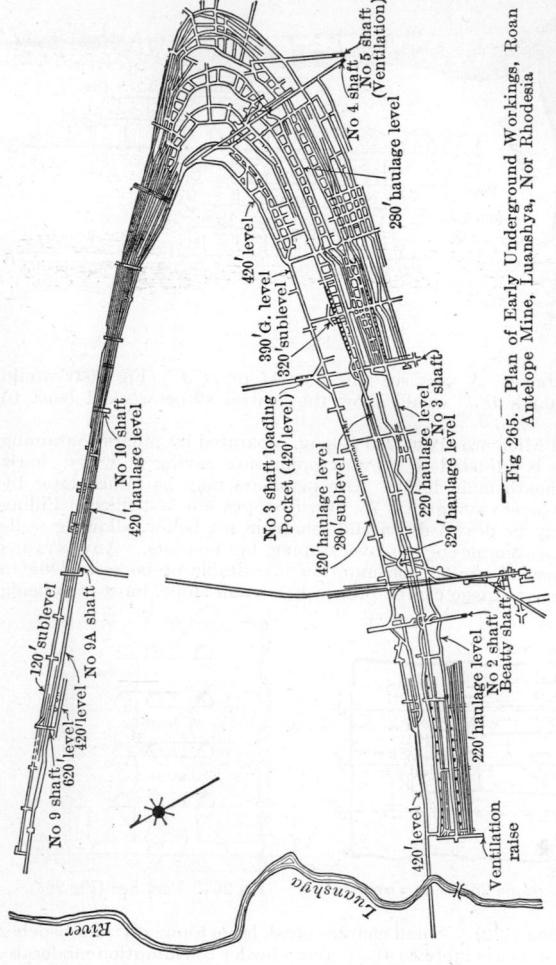

Fig 265. Plan of Early Underground Workings, Roan Antelope Mine, Luanshya, Nor Rhodesia

on the 220-, 280-, and 350-levels, ore from which dropped through ore passes to the 420-level. In steeper parts of orebody above the 820-level, haulage drifts were in ore along footwall. Below 820-level, haulageways will be driven in footwall rock as permanent openings for ventilation and service for stoping.

Stoping. There are 3 modes of procedure, depending on the dip. Fig 266 applies to "FLAT ORE," or to dips of 12°–30°. Haulage drifts K, 9 by 12-ft section, are driven in footwall, usually at 75-ft vert intervals. For each stope, an inclined chute raise R (min dip 55°) is driven from haulage drift to orebody. A grizzly is placed over the raise at the elev of the economic footwall. Grizzlies are 10 by 7.5 ft, with 16-in openings, and made of 6-in I beams covered with mild-steel wearing plates. A sub-level drift A gives access to grizzly. From the grizzly chamber, an 8 by 6-ft raise B is driven along footwall to the grizzly level of completed stope above. At 10 ft up the dip from the grizzly, a raise C, normal to dip, is driven to locate the economic hanging wall. Raise D is then driven along hanging-wall side of the ore, directly over the foot-wall raise. Two sets of sub-level drifts are driven 50 ft apart; one set, E, 2 ft below the hanging wall; the other,

F, 4 ft above the footwall. Stoping up the dip is done in "sections," each extending from one pair of sub-drifts (hanging-wall drift and footwall drift beneath it) to the next above. Starting at raise C, the first operation is the cutting of a "slice" G (Sec BB) between the foot- and hanging-wall raises, advancing up the dip to the first pair of sub-drifts. This is done by drilling uppers in the back of footwall raise and down holes in the floor of hanging-wall raise. Cutting the slice is followed by "trailing." A hanging-wall "trail," H, is a slot, 6–10 ft wide and 6–8 ft high, cut out at top of stope face and extending up the dip. Similarly, a footwall trail, I, is cut. When a section of stope has been "sliced" and "trailed," the resulting bench is drilled and blasted. Broken ore is scraped to the grizzly with a 48-in hoe-type scraper, operated by a 30-hp elec, double-drum hoist. "Trailing" and breaking of benches proceeds laterally to stope widths averaging 40–50 ft. These operations, always preceded by "slicing," continue up the dip to the level above. If the stope above has caved, the lateral pillar or sill *S* is left; otherwise the sill is mined. Rib pillars separating the stopes strikewise are 10–15 ft thick. For stoping, drills are 3-in stopers and $2\,5/8$-in jackhammers. Production rate of such a stope is 250–300 tons per day with 8-hr mining shift and approx 16 hr of scraping.

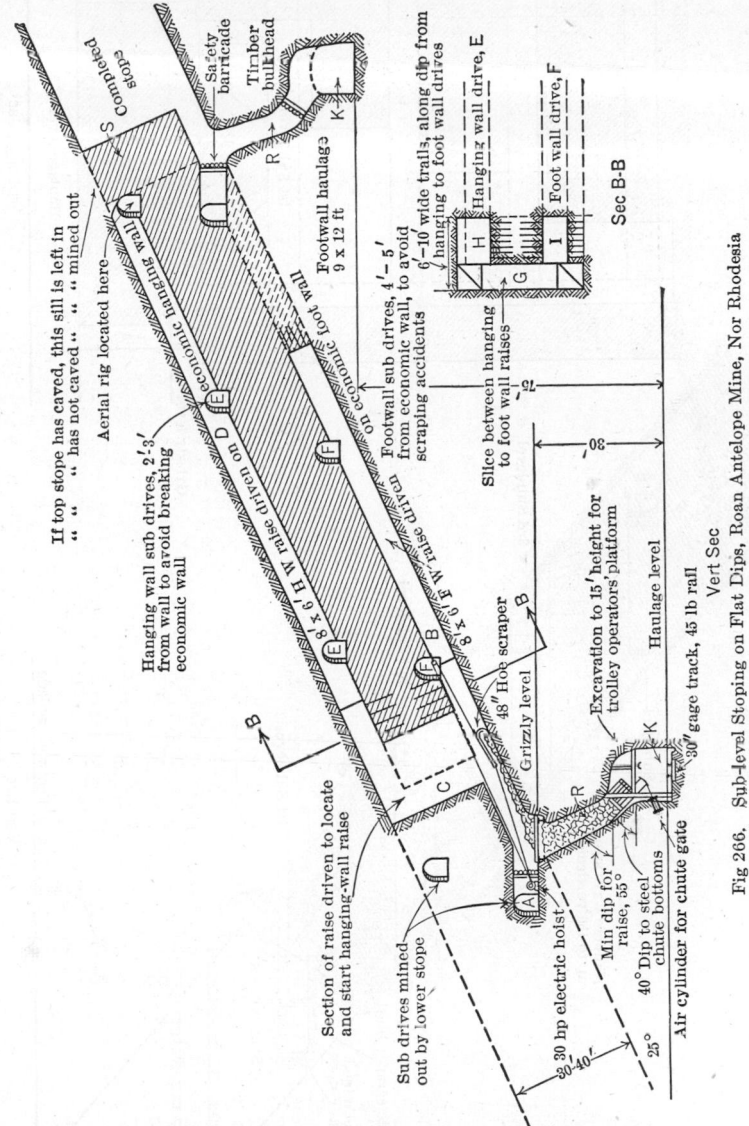

Fig 266. Sub-level Stoping on Flat Dips, Roan Antelope Mine, Nor Rhodesia

Fig 267 shows method used in "SEMI-STEEP" ore, on dips of 30°–45°. Haulage drifts, 9 by 12 ft, are driven in footwall at vert intervals up to 150 ft. Sub-level drifts are along both foot and hanging wall, 25 ft apart vertically. A stoping "block" comprises 4–6 stopes, 40–60 ft wide (strikewise), the stopes being separated by rib pillars 12–15 ft thick. Chute raises, *A*, are driven from a haulage drift to the ore, on center lines of the rib pillars, so that each may serve 2 stopes. A few feet below the economic footwall, a

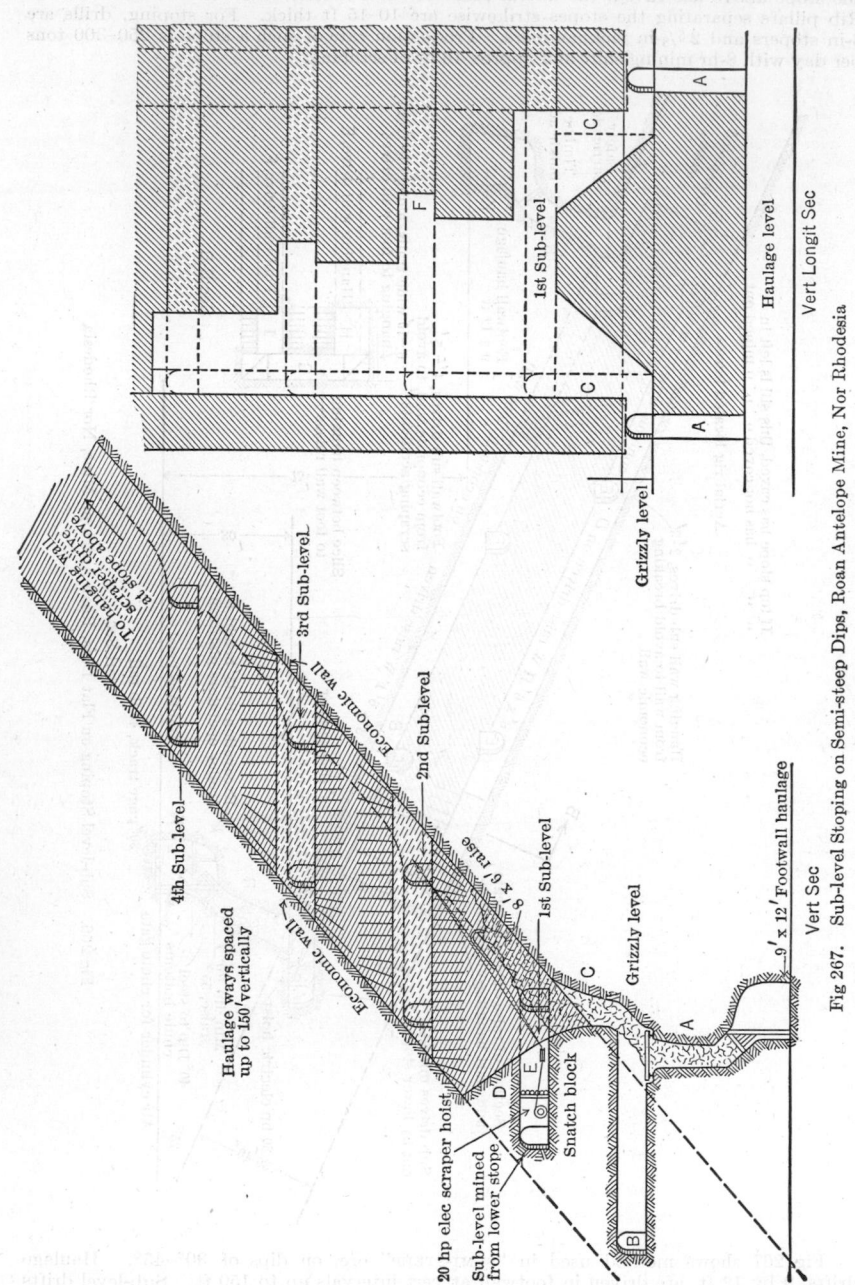

Fig 267. Sub-level Stoping on Semi-steep Dips, Roan Antelope Mine, Nor Rhodesia

grizzly is placed over each chute raise; height of grizzly above haulage level, about 30 ft. A sub-level drift *B*, at the same elev, with crosscuts to the grizzlies, serves as a travelway. A short drift runs from each grizzly to edge of the stope, from which point a raise *C* is driven along the pillar line to a footwall sub-drift (1st sub-level), about 50 ft above the haulage level. From there an 8 by 6-ft "mining" raise is driven on footwall and along the pillar line to the grizzly level of the completed stope above the next higher main level. When this raise reaches the 2nd sub-level, raises *C* are belled out and the back of the mining raise mined out to the point where a protective brow *D* is left over that portion of crosscut *E* which houses a scraper hoist. When the mining raise reaches the third sub-level, an opening on the second, 12 ft wide and 7 ft high, is cut from foot to hanging wall, connecting with the hanging-wall drift. The back and floor of this opening are drilled and blasted, breaking out the slice between first and second sub-levels. As the mining raise advances, successive slices along the pillar line and between sub-levels are similarly removed. On completing a slice below a given sub-level, a horiz "trail" *F*, or notch, is cut from foot to hanging wall, connecting the open ends of the sub-drifts at this elev. Benches thus formed are drilled and blasted into the open stope below. Movement of broken ore to "mill hole" *C* is aided by a scraper and 20-hp elec hoist; an "aerial rig" (Fig 268) permits

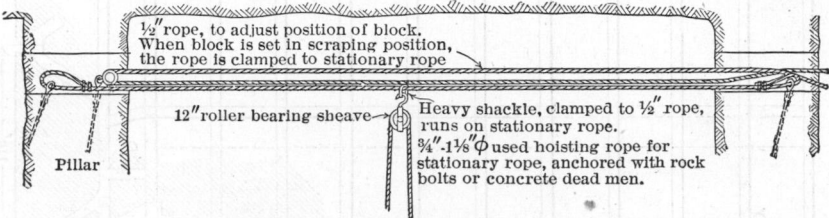

½" rope, to adjust position of block. When block is set in scraping position, the rope is clamped to stationary rope

12" roller bearing sheave

Heavy shackle, clamped to ½" rope, runs on stationary rope.
¾".1⅛" Φ used hoisting rope for stationary rope, anchored with rock bolts or concrete dead men.

Pillar

Fig 268.   "Aerial Rig" for Scraper Sheave, Roan Antelope Mine, Nor Rhodesia

easy movement of the headblock to any desired point across width of stope. Production from this type of stope is 300–400 tons per day, with 8 hr mining and 16 hr scraping.

Fig 269 and 269*a* show method in "STEEP ORE," on dips of 45°–90°. A haulage drift is driven in footwall. As it advances, chute raises *A* are driven 110 ft apart, to cut the ore-body just below the grizzly level, 55 ft above haulage level. Chute raises are branched strikewise to give a c-c spacing between grizzlies of 55 ft. From each grizzly, a crosscut *B* is driven to connect with a hanging-wall sub-drift *C*, which serves as a travelway between grizzlies. Haulage- and grizzly-level development are carried on concurrently, so that the grizzly level may serve as a return air course in driving the haulage drift. From each grizzly, drifts are driven about 10 ft in both directions along footwall and from their ends, raises *D* are driven to first sub-level, 25 ft above grizzly level. These raises are later funnelled both strikewise and toward the hanging wall, and are known as "mill holes." Sub-level drifts are centrally located in the orebody, at 30 to 35-ft vert intervals. Standard length of stope is 70 ft. Rib pillars between stopes vary in width from 10 to 20 ft, depending on strength of ground. Height of stopes is 420–660 ft vert, or as much as 750 ft along the dip. "Block pillars" *E* are often required to support the 70-ft span of hanging wall between main rib pillars. Position of block pillars is determined by inspection and records of previous stopes in the block.

A stoping " block " is 800–1 000 ft in length along the strike, forming 8 or 12 stoping panels respectively. The block is developed by a central service raise *F*, 8 by 6 ft, and a muck raise, spaced either 86 ft or 45 ft apart. With the former spacing, the muck raise *G* is later used for opening the last stope of the block; with the latter spacing, about 40% of length of raise serves for establishing the "block pillars" within this stope. The service raise is advanced by a "bulkhead pent-house" (transfer chute) system, whereby muck from raise is hand-trammed on the sub-levels into the muck raise, which is driven ahead of the service raise. Ladders, comp-air line, water line, tugger hoist, track, and ventilation line are kept within 50 ft of the service-raise face. As each sub-level elev is reached, crosscuts, driven off the service and muck raises, are connected by a sub-level drift. As each sub-level is established, the drift is driven to the extremities of the block. When the first level above the grizzly level reaches the block extremity, the first mining raise *H* is started from the grizzly excavation and driven, on the economic footwall, up the side of the main rib pillar. This raise is extended as each sub-level drift above reaches the pillar. When the raise reaches the second sub-level, the stope floor is cut on first level and the raises from the grizzly properly belled. As cutting of floor and belling of mill holes is completed, stoper holes in the back of the first level are blasted. When this work has retreated 25 ft from the mining raise, floor cutting is begun on the second level, the first opening being 10 ft along the strike and from foot to hanging wall. Holes in the back and floor are drilled and blasted, making a slot between first and second levels. This operation is repeated on each upper level, but only after the level below has retreated at least 10 ft. It may be necessary to make 2 cuts in the slot with down holes, in which case the blasting of up holes on a level lags behind blasting the down holes. When the

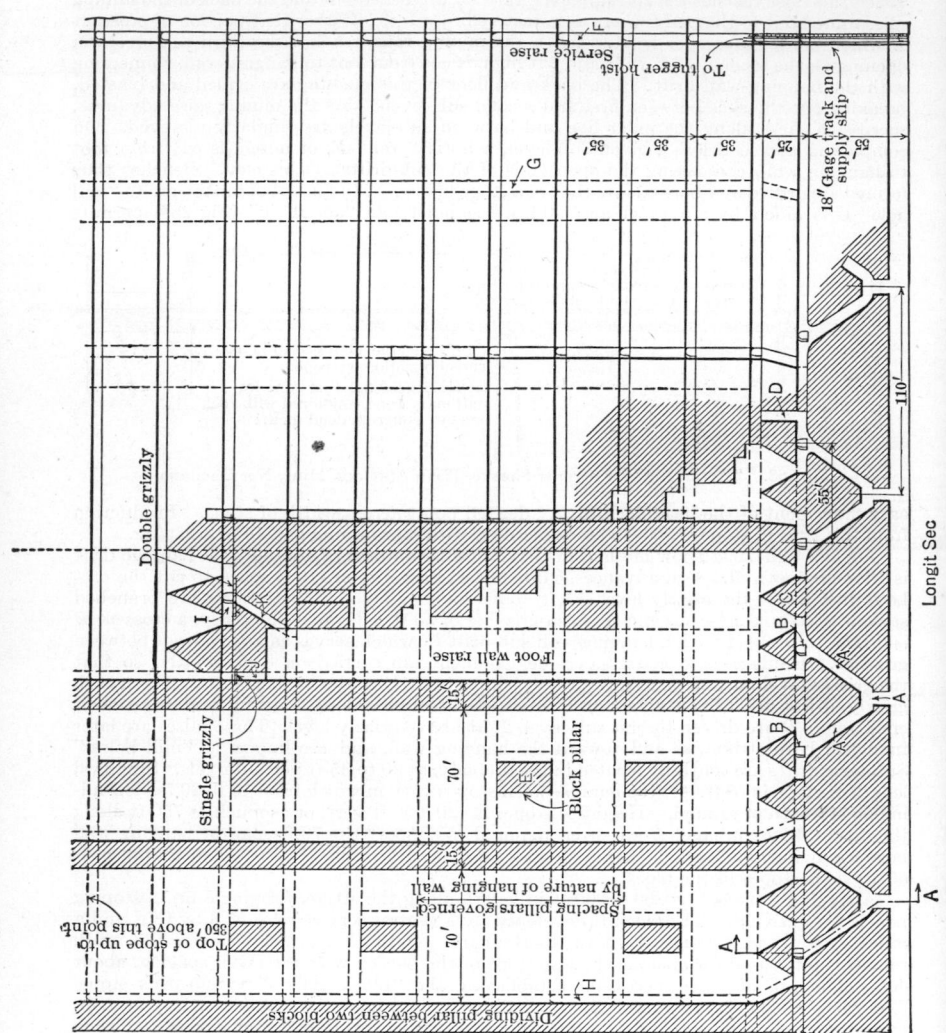

slot has been cut, regular benching begins. This consists of cutting a trail 8–10 ft wide from foot to hanging wall, drilling the back and floor, and blasting the bench into the stope.

In some parts of the mine the hanging wall will not stand up for completion of stopes 600–700 ft high. A RELAY SYSTEM is therefore used, whereby an intermediate grizzly level *I* is opened approx midway up the panel. The regular mining raise is driven from the lower grizzly level (so located with respect to the footwall and rib pillar as to allow for wear by scouring) to the intermediate grizzly level. If the nature of ore permits, this raise is enlarged from 6 by 8-ft size to an opening 30 ft along the strike by the distance from foot to hanging wall. This opening is carried up to the sub-level immediately below the intermediate grizzly level; from there a 6 by 6-ft raise J is driven to the grizzly level. Branch raise K is also driven from this level to hole into the grizzly level about 50 ft from the mining raise. Grizzlies are placed on these openings and mill-hole raises are driven to the sub-level above the grizzly. Normal stoping follows. Ore from upper part of stope passes through the grizzly into the enlarged mining raise below, lower part of which provides good "ore-pass" storage. When the upper half of stope is completed, the intermediate grizzlies are removed and the mill holes bulkheaded. The lower half is then completed and if little sloughing of waste rock has occurred above, the sill at the intermediate grizzly level is blasted out and recovered. Production in these stopes is 6 000–20 000 tons per mo, depending on width of ore, which is 9–35 ft. Break per machine-shift is 50–130 tons.

R. M. Peterson in 1932 (501) cites following factors favoring use of sub-level stoping at Roan Antelope: (1) a working place can always be barred and made safe, and sub-level exit is always at hand; (2) working and drilling conditions in stopes are always the same; native labor does best in repetition tasks; (3) pillar spacing can be varied as conditions demand; (4) stoping can be shut down or opened up to full capac at short notice, without affecting ore grade or causing wastage of reserves.

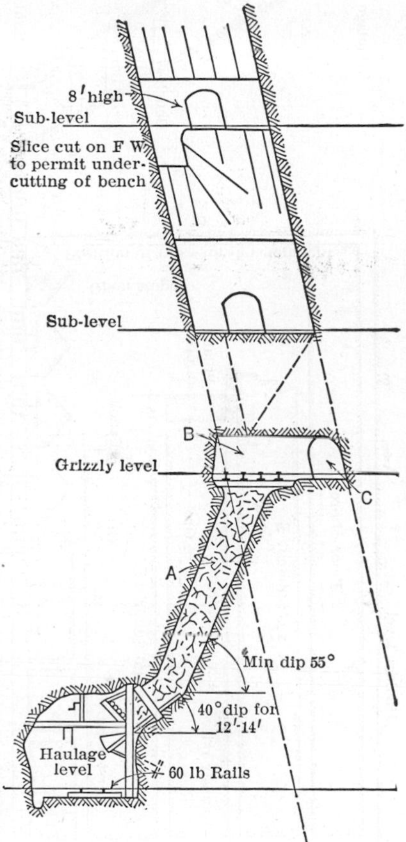

Burra Burra mine, Ducktown, Tenn. Data from C. H. McNaughton (180) in 1929. Orebody is an irregular lenticular mass of iron sulphides, carrying 1.6% Cu in chalcopyrite. Walls are highly metamorphosed schists and graywackes, usually standing unsupported over 100-ft spans; walls are firmer than ore, which tends to break into coarse blocks, but does not readily break free from walls. Orebody, nearly 0.5 mile long, ranges from a few feet to max of 180 ft wide, and varies in dip from 75° at surface to 50° at 1 600 ft, with local dips as low as 35°. DEVELOPMENT. Entry is by an inclined shaft in footwall and a vert shaft in hanging. Crosscuts to orebody and haulage drifts are driven at 196-ft vert intervals. STOPING. Sub-level stoping, first adopted in 1925, has largely replaced former shrinkage and glory-hole mining. Fig 270 shows method for widths less than 40 ft. Haulage levels, H, are driven on footwall; raises, R, are put up in ore along footwall at some convenient distance apart, 340 ft in Fig 270. At vert intervals of 40 ft, sub-drifts, S, 4 by 6 ft, are driven between raises in ore near footwall. At 40-ft intervals along the haulage

Fig 269a. Typical Sec through Chute Raise A—A of Fig 269

drift, 4 by 5-ft raises, P ("pull holes"), are put up on footwall to first sub-drift. These are widened at top to expose walls and are funneled. Grizzlies with 20-in spaces are placed at bottom of "pull holes," directly over haulage level. Stoping begins on second sub-drift at a raise, by cutting out the raise to full width of orebody between the first and second sub-drifts. Then, a crosscut ("notch"), 5 ft wide by 6 ft high, is driven to hanging wall from second sub-drift; the floor of the notch provides a "bench" from which down holes are drilled to form a second bench 6 ft below. These operations are repeated until the stope faces reach the shape shown in Fig 270. Benches below the first are 10 ft deep. Stoping is done as on the sub-drifts above; the work on a lower sub-drift is kept far enough ahead of that on the sub-drift above to assure that the men are always working under the protection of solid ground. Mounted hammer drills are used for horiz holes in cutting notches (slabbing), and jackhammers for vert holes on benches. Slabbing rounds are drilled with 3 flat holes in a vert row and 10 ft deep, with 2–2.5-ft burden; bench holes are 4–5 ft apart along stope face, with burden of 2.5 ft. Blasting is done at night with a bulky 35% powder and elec detonator. In 1929, an aver of 48 tons of ore per machine-shift was broken; powder consumption, 0.33 lb per ton; bulldozing on grizzlies required an added 0.167 lb powder per ton. In a block 320 ft long, stope development, comprising 2 raises between levels, 4 sub-drifts, and 8 "pull holes," amounts to 2 210 ft and develops 93 tons of ore per ft. WORKING IN WIDE ORE. Where the orebody exceeds 40-ft width, sub-level stopes 40 ft wide are carried across the orebody, with 40-ft pillars between them, as in Fig 271. From a main-level drift D in footwall, 20–30 ft from the ore, crosscuts C are driven under center lines of stopes. Manway raises R are driven from footwall drift to main level above, paralleling the footwall and along center lines of alternate pillars. At 40-ft vert intervals, sublevel drifts S are driven from a manway raise to center lines of adjacent stopes, along which 4 by 6-ft sublevel crosscuts L are driven to hanging wall. At 40-ft intervals along main-level crosscuts, "pull hole" raises P are driven to first sublevel crosscut. From the last "pull hole" in a crosscut, an inclined raise H is driven to hanging wall and thence along the wall to the main level above. Stoping starts by breasting out the ore to the pillar lines on first sub-level and funneling the "pull-hole" raises, as in Fig 271, beginning at hanging wall and working toward the foot. Starting at second sub-level, hanging-wall raise H is widened to full width of stope between first and second sub-levels, benches are developed, and mining proceeds as described above for the longit stopes. In 1929, no pillars between sub-level stopes had been extracted, but pillar recovery by undercutting and breaking with long holes (up to 120 ft, with sectional steel) was anticipated. Advantages of sub-level stoping over previous shrinkage methods are reflected in the accompanying costs per ton for stope labor for year 1928.

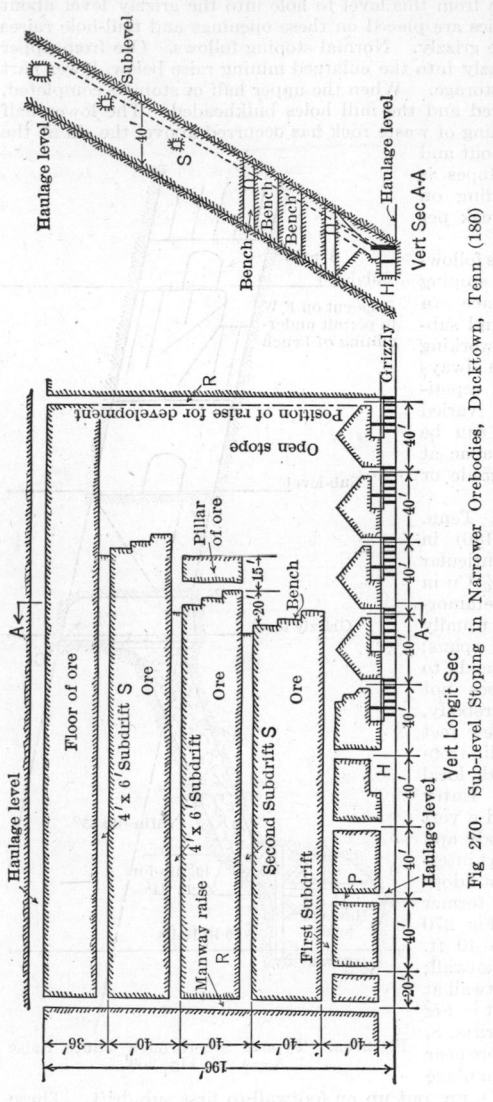

Fig 270. Sub-level Stoping in Narrower Orebodies, Ducktown, Tenn (180)

Horne mine, Noranda, Quebec. Data from H. M. Butterfield and E. Henderson (120) in 1934, and from O. Hall in 1937 (121). Supplementary information was generously

Cost of Stoping Labor, Burra Burra Mine

	Drilling in stopes	Blockholing and loading	Total
Sub-level stopes . . .	$0.094	$0.079	$0.173
Shrinkage stopes . . .	0.128	0.144	0.272

contributed by the management in 1938. Sub-level stoping is applied to principal, or "H," orebody, a large, irregular, generally vert body of massive sulphide carrying values chiefly in copper and gold, occurring as a replacement of brecciated rhyolite. From depth of 500 to 1 200 ft, and from 1 500–3 000-ft level, orebody averages about 1 000 000 tons per 100 ft of depth. It narrows like an hour-glass near the 1 250-level and widens again at 1 500-level. Portion above 1 250-level is called "Upper H"; that below, "Lower H." These main portions aver about 600 ft long, varying in width from 40–540 ft. Ore is unusually strong. GENERAL DEVELOPMENT. Mine is served by 3 vert shafts; one, near the center of "H" orebody, is used as a service shaft; other two, in country rock, are for ore-hoisting. Level interval is 125 ft below depth of 600 ft. Main-level drifts are 7.5 by 8 ft. STOPING.

A modified form of sub-level stoping was used in mining "Upper H" orebody. Main difference from usual procedure is that raises, on 40° incline, take the place of sub-level drifts or crosscuts. Method was originally developed by E. Hibbert and employed at the Mother Lode mine, Greenwood, B C, Bib (207) and p 586, 2nd edn of this book. Fig 272 shows general plan of work. Orebody was divided into vert stoping panels 46 ft wide, separated by 35-ft pillars. From a haulage drift, usually within the orebody, inclined chute raises were driven on center lines of both stopes and pillars, and grizzlies installed, as at G. From each grizzly, a raise R was driven at an inclination of 40° to a height set as a limit of the particular block for which it was to serve, about 190 ft in Fig 272. From the back of this raise, at 26-ft centers, 6.5 by 7-ft raises S were driven on 40° incline to intersect raise T from a level above, parallel to raise R and marking another limit of the stoping block; in Fig 272, raise T is about 150 ft from R. Purpose of raises S corresponds with that of sub-level drifts in the usual sub-level stoping. Other stoping blocks above, separated from each other by inclined pillars, were similarly developed, Fig 273. About 30 miles of raises were driven in developing "Upper H" orebody. Raises R and S in the stoping panels were later widened by slabbing rounds to full stope width of 46 ft. Assay sections, from sampling raises during driving, afforded an accurate outline of the orebody and full knowledge of the ore grades. These data, together with the great number of working faces, permitted close control of grade during the widening of raises and also in subsequent bench mining. The numerous working faces also afforded easy control of tonnage.

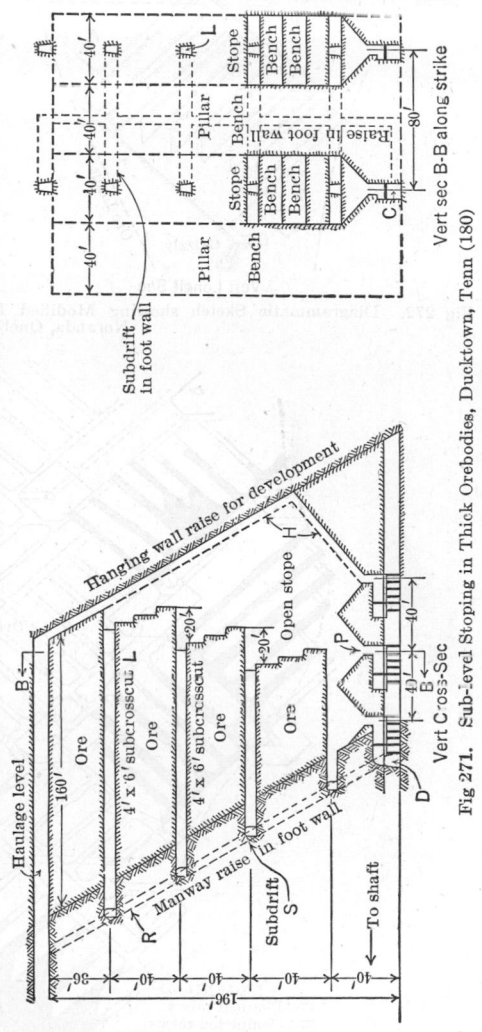

Fig 271. Sub-level Stoping in Thick Orebodies, Ducktown, Tenn (180)

This mode of stope development was followed by underhand mining of the blocks of ore B (Fig 272) between the widened raises of the stope panels. General stope face was carried in inverted steps, benching on the face of each block being done in advance of that on face of next block above. At first each face was mined in 2 cuts, as at C, by down holes with jackhammers, the miners having to wear safety belts. Later practice was to break the faces with a single cut, by drilling long holes from beneath, using jointed drill steel. (This method would seem to require carrying general stope face parallel with raise R, rather than as shown in Fig 272. Author.)

In general, mining of pillars follows filling of completed stopes, but, if permitted by wall conditions, pillars are blasted out before the adjacent stopes are filled. Where this is done, pillars are drilled from the central raises concurrently with stope drilling. Much exper-

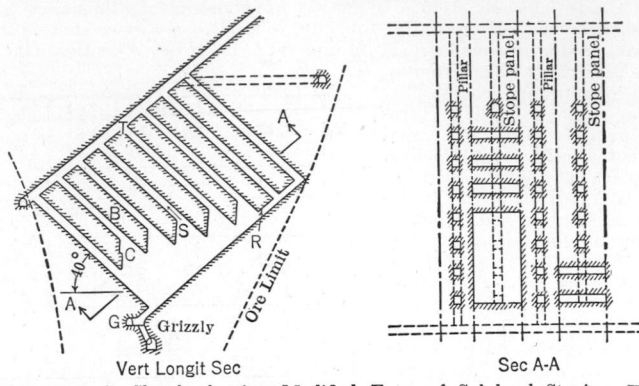

Fig 272. Diagrammatic Sketch showing Modified Form of Sub-level Stoping, Horne Mine, Noranda, Quebec

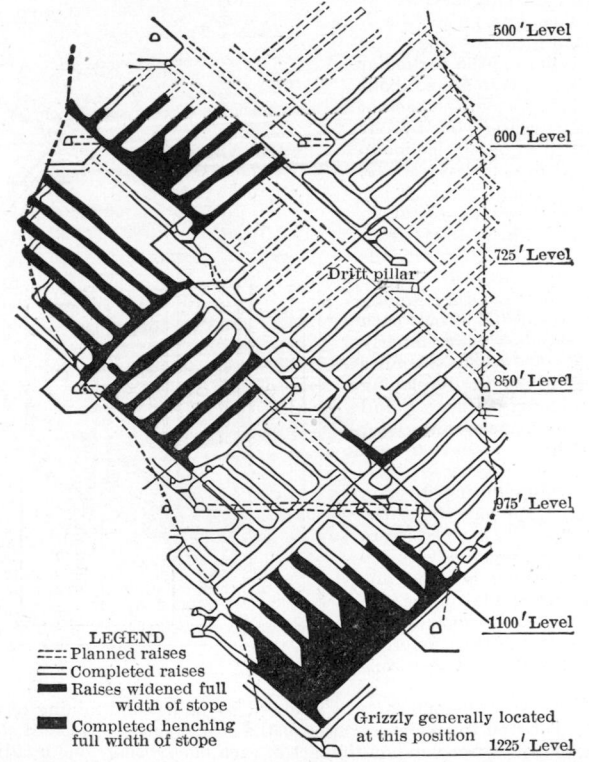

Fig 273. Longit Sec through a Stope Panel, "Upper H" Orebody, Horne Mine, Noranda, Quebec

imenting has been carried on to find a filling material which will cement itself; best mixture is 50% granulated slag, 38% crushed slag, and 12% mill tailings (rich in pyrrhotite). After several months of oxidation and consolidation, drifting through this type of fill is like drifting in rock. For mining strong, low-grade pillars next to, well compacted fill, a method resembling sub-level caving (Art 75) has been devised: blocks are mined from top downward, removing about 30% of the interior of a block; upon simultaneous blasting

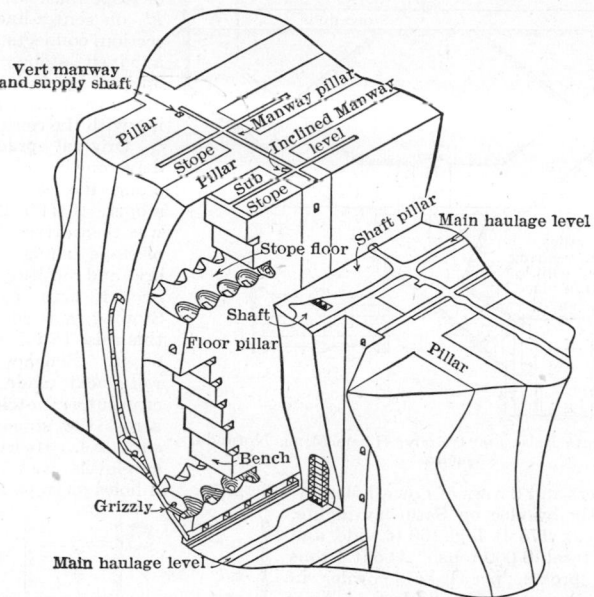

Fig 274. Sub-level Stoping, "Lower H" Orebody, Horne Mine, Noranda, Quebec

of the rest, the fill caves in on top of the broken ore as it is drawn out. When removal of one block is completed, the next block below will be attacked. In higher-grade ore and under less ideal conditions, filling methods (Art 59), square-sets (Art 45), or top-slicing (Art 70) may be employed.

The more usual form of sub-level stoping is employed in "LOWER H" OREBODY, with lifts of 250 ft. This orebody is divided by 1 longit pillar and 4 transverse pillars into 10 stoping segments, generally 60 ft wide (Fig 274). All pillars except 2 are 40 ft wide; shaft pillar and 1 other, 60 ft. Level pillars extend 50 ft above and 25 ft below levels, giving stope height of 175 ft (Fig 275). Main-level drifts are parallel with and near a pillar line of a stope section. Chute raises (Fig 276) are 30 ft apart. About 25 ft above the haulage level, grizzlies, 16 ft long with 20-in openings, are set crosswise of stope section; inclined raises are driven from each end of grizzly to reach the stope floor at the pillar lines. At stope-floor elevation, a drift A (Fig 276) is driven along a pillar line, breaking into the grizzly raises on this side. From this drift, beginning at the contact end

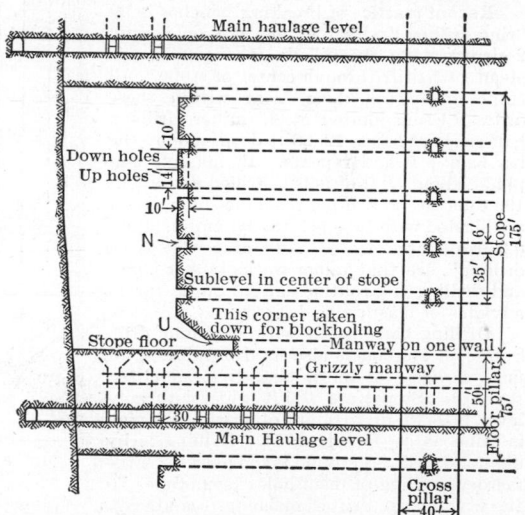

Fig 275. Side Elev, Horiz Sub-level Stope, "Lower H" Orebody, Horne Mine, Noranda, Quebec

of the stope, the stope floor is breasted out across to the other pillar; the grizzly raises are coned out as they are exposed. During mining, the stope-floor undercut U is maintained one drawhole in advance of stope face. A manway drift M, on center-line of the stope section, connects all grizzlies of a given stope. Stopes are opened by 5 sub-levels, 35 ft apart vertically, each connecting with the central main shaft.

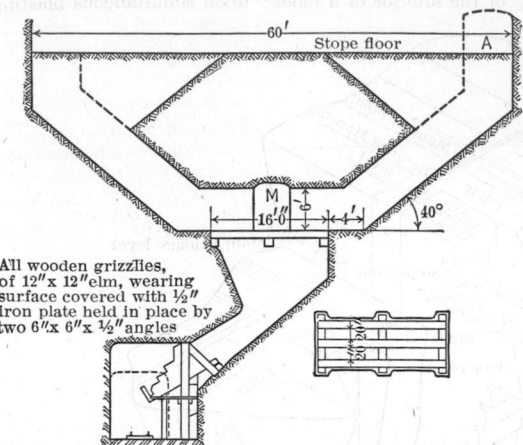

A'll wooden grizzlies, of 12″ x 12″ elm, wearing surface covered with ½″ iron plate held in place by two 6″ x 6″ x ½″ angles

Fig 276. Chute Raise and Grizzly, Horne Mine, Noranda, Quebec

Original practice was to drive one line of sub-level drifts along the center line of the stopes, A (Fig 277). A raise was then driven the full height of stope, along the contact of ore and wall-rock, and connected with each sub-level. Stoping started by widening this raise to full stope width of 60 ft. Benches, 10 ft wide, were next made by driving a crosscut or notch N (Fig 275) across the stope face at each sub-level. Benches between sub-levels were broken by 2 rows of uppers and 2 rows of down holes, A (Fig 277). All holes in stope face were fired simultaneously by elec on Saturday nights, making a break 175 ft high, 60 ft wide, and 10 ft thick; total, 8 000 tons. About 4 tons of ore were broken per lb of powder in primary blasting. Some secondary blasting was done on stope floor before the ore entered the raises to grizzlies; in blockholing, miners worked under protection of brow of lowest bench.

Recent practice of breaking benches is by "ring drilling." Each sub-level is opened by 2 drifts along the pillars, B (Fig 277), instead of 1 drift through center of stope. All stope drilling is done from within these drifts. Using jointed steel, miner drills a half circle of holes, 12–20 ft deep, moves the bar back 6 ft and repeats. In massive sulphide, about 50 ft of hole is drilled and about 190 tons are broken per machine-shift. Holes are blasted with 40% gelatin dynamite, about 0.2 lb per ton of ore. Advantages of "ring drilling" are that miner works in safe place, and drilling is a routine carried on as far in advance of blasting as desired.

Drilling blast holes with diamond drill. Sub-level stoping is also used in mining, for flux, a body of hard, slightly mineralized rhyolite. Stopes are 105 ft wide, with sub-level interval up to 60 ft; otherwise, the plan is same as at B (Fig 277). Drilling is by diamond drill, as ground is too hard for satisfactory drilling of deep holes (sometimes 60 ft) with usual drifter machine (see above). Light, "prospector" diamond-drill machine is used. About 30 ft of hole is drilled, breaking 150 tons, per drill-shift. Powder con-

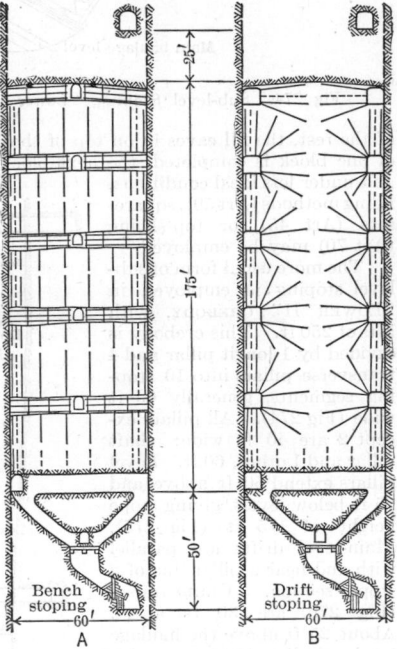

Bench stoping
A

Drift stoping
B

Vert Cross-Secs

Fig 277. Methods of Breaking Ground, Horne Mine, Noranda, Quebec. Dotted lines represent "helper" holes drilled between the main rows to insure a clean break on the walls

sumption per ton is about same as in sulphide stopes, namely 0.2 lb of 40% gelatin per ton. For additional details of diamond drilling, see Bib (121, 616).

Costs. Mr. O. Hall (121) states (1937) that cost of exploration and development is about 30¢ per ton. Cost of mining, exclusive of development, averages about 90¢ per ton, as follows: stoping, 30¢; grizzly blasting, 10¢; mucking and tramming, 14¢; hoisting, 8¢; steel and tools, 7¢; rock drills, 5¢; power and misc, 16¢; total, 90¢.

Flin Flon mine, Manitoba. Data from M. A. Roche (565) in 1931, from Roche and J. P. Caulfield (566) in 1935, and W. J. Marshall (567) in 1936. Main orebody, of massive sulphide, contains Au, Ag, Cu, and Zn. Hanging wall is hard, fine-grained greenstone, free from faults and schistose areas. Footwall varies from quartz porphyry to soft talc schist, and is somewhat flatter than hanging wall. General dip, about 70° Width of ore, from 450 ft (including waste horses) at the surface to about 40 ft on 900-ft level. Ore is very heavy and hard. A sub-level mining method is employed, with heavy equipment for scraping ore to loading chutes, and cages in service raises. DEVELOPMENT. Main hoisting shaft is vert, sunk in hanging wall about 500 ft from outcrop and centrally located in respect to orebody. Vert interval between main haulage levels, formerly 260 ft, is now 520 ft. Fig 278 shows general layout. Haulage drifts, 10 by 10 ft, are driven in footwall, parallel to orebody. Crosscuts, 10 by 10 ft, are generally 250 ft apart and driven far enough into hanging wall to allow room for ore trains. Crosscuts are usually on center-lines of 40-ft pillars between stopes. Service raises, driven 20–30 ft in footwall, are on center-lines of pillars; they may be vert or inclined to conform with dip of orebody, and are equipped with cages. From each crosscut, a raise is driven at a point near center (crosswise) of orebody to 12 ft above the roof of crosscut. At about 6 ft above the roof, a 36-in manganese-steel grizzly is built across the raise. Drifts S (Fig 278) called "scram drifts," 10 by 10 ft, connect the raises; they are at a 5% up-grade to a point midway between raises. At intervals of 40 ft along the "scram drift," 7 by 7-ft draw raises are driven to bottom of the first sub-level which is about 46 ft above the back of the haulage level. Stoped ore drops through the draw raises to "scram drift," in which a scraper drags the ore to the grizzlies for loading into cars beneath. The draw raises start from backs of single-round crosscuts, thus providing a brow to limit the height to which the broken ore can pile up in the scram drift, so the scraper can always pass over the ore pile and get behind it to move the ore. A raise at the longit center of stope is driven from the first to the highest sub-level of the block to be mined in one "lift." Original lifts of 260 ft have been increased to 520 ft. Stopes are developed by sub-level drifts, 5 by 7 ft, near center of orebody and at 40-ft vert intervals. They are driven from the service raises in the pillars. STOPING. When the draw raises are completed to first sub-level, they are coned out to connect with each other (Fig 278). Actual stoping starts on second sub-level, at the center raise. The ground around the raise is drilled and blasted through to the cones below, and the raise is widened laterally until both walls are exposed. While this is being done at the second sub-level, a 10-ft bench, from foot to hanging wall, is made on each side of the raise. These benches are then drilled with 2 rows of 6–8-ft vert down holes, 5 ft apart along the bench and 18 in to 2 ft apart across it. Two successive cuts, each of 12-ft holes, complete the vert slice to the undercut stope below. Working at the open ends of the second sub-level drift, the miners then drill horizontally to establish another 10-ft bench from foot to hanging wall. When 2 benches have been completed on any sub-level, benching starts on the next sub-level above. This gives a sequence in which the benching from one sub-level is not more than 2 benches ahead of that from the sub-level above; hence, miners are protected from mining operations above them, and, at the same time, enough support is left for the overhanging ore, so that the men above can work in safety. Fig 279 shows a typical scram drift in plan and section. Double-drum scraper hoists with 150-hp motors are used. Scrapers are 84 in wide, arc type, made of manganese steel, and weigh 3 600 lb. Lead rope is 1.25-in, 6 by 7, plow-steel; tail rope, 1.25-in, 6 by 19, plow-steel. Rope speed, 300 ft per min; aver load, 2.4 tons, per trip, or a capac of 307 tons, per hr for continuous scraping. Crew consists of 1 operator and 1 bulldozer; latter blasts down hung-up raises and assists operator. Scraper loads into 10-ton cars, spotted beneath grizzly. LONG-HOLE DRILLING IN STOPES. W. J. Marshall (567) describes in 1936 an apparently successful experiment, in which the bench between 2 sub-levels is broken in a single cut by drilling holes about 24 ft deep, tapering from 3 in at collar to 1⁵/₈ in at bottom. Drilling is by drifter on a cross-arm between 2 vert columns. Holes usually dip about 70°; their spacing lengthwise of bench is 5–8 ft; rows about 4 ft apart. Holes are sometimes sprung before loading. Number of sticks of powder per hole is from 85 for an unsprung hole to 160 for one sprung 3 times. An aver of about 40 ft is drilled per machine-shift. In breaking 21 500 tons, an aver of 6.02 tons was broken per ft drilled. Cited advantages of long-hole drilling: (a) Elimination of mucking on benches. (b) Greater safety. In ordinary benching, second and third benches are sometimes dangerous for the men, due to narrowness of ledge. (c) No difference in break, compared with 3-bench method, has been noticed. (d) Lower mining cost per ton.

McIntyre mine, Schumacher, Ont (171). Waste rock is mined by sub-level stoping to provide fill for horiz cut-and-fill stopes described in Art 60. Block of rock opened for

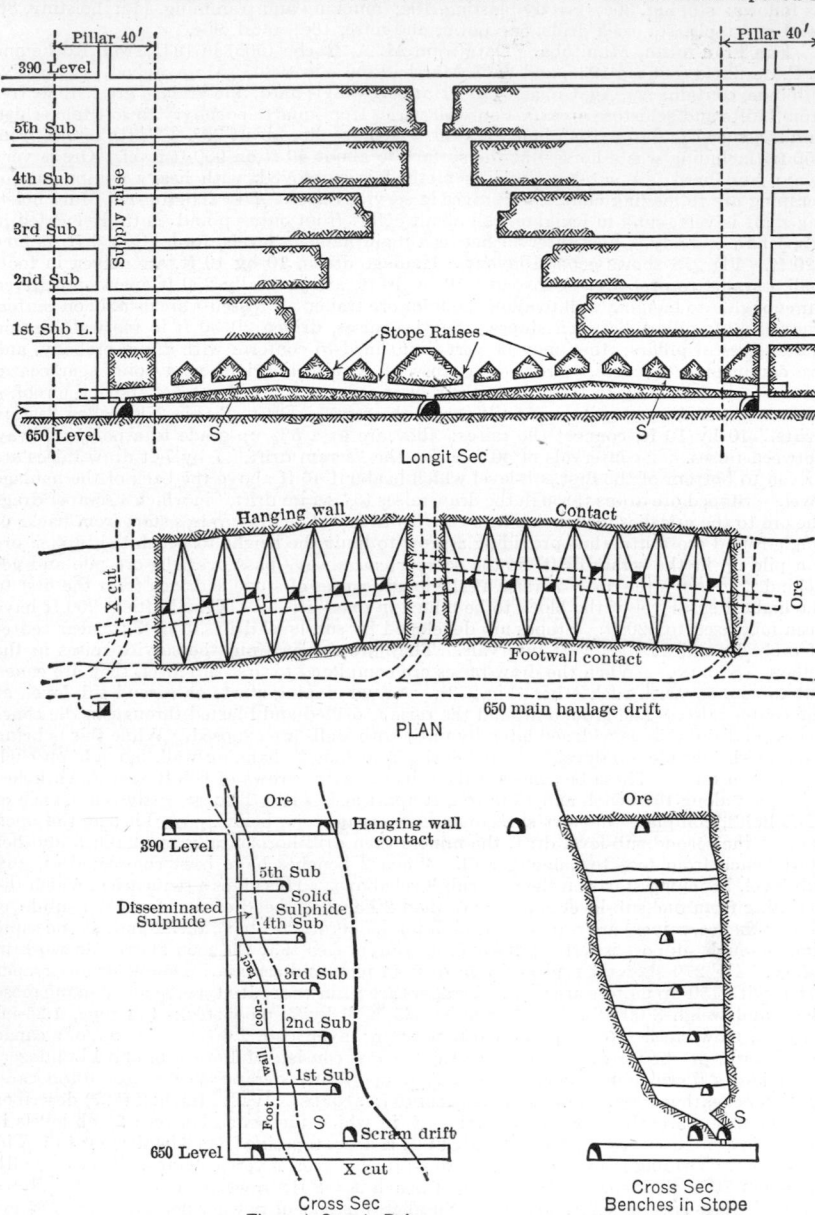

Fig 278.   Typical Sub-level Stope, Flin Flon Mine, Manitoba

sub-level stoping is 270 ft long, 110 ft wide, and 175 ft high (Fig 280). A 9 by 9-ft drift is driven under center of block and a grizzly level driven 29 ft above rail. Sub-levels, 6.5 by 5 ft, are 25 ft apart vert. End of block is opened first by a 24-ft shrinkage stope,

carried full width and height of block; thereafter rock is broken by vert holes drilled up and down from crosscuts or notches driven across the block from the sub-levels.
Mount Isa Mines, Ltd, Mount Isa, Queensland.   Data from J. Kruttschnitt and V. I. Mann (500) in 1937.   Ore deposits are replacements in zones of shearing and folding in a thick series of shales dipping 55–60°.   Strike and dip of orebodies conform in general

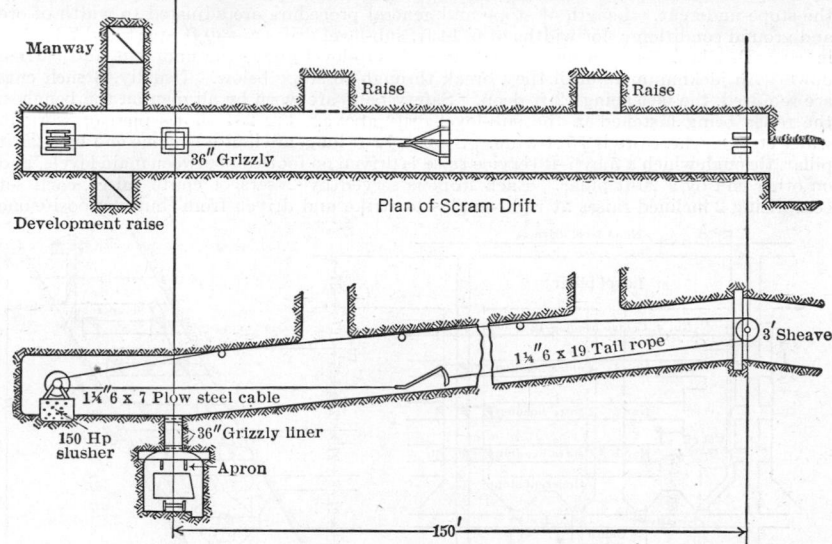

Fig 279.   Layout of Scram Drift, Flin Flon Mine, Manitoba

with those of shale beds.   Below oxidized zone, ore comprises Ag-Pb-Zn sulphides, usually interbanded with pyrite and pyrrhotite.   Aver metal content of ore is about 4.8 oz Ag per ton, 8.2% Pb, and 8.1% Zn.   Principal orebody, as known, has max length of 2 000 ft and proved depth of 1 200 ft.   Mineralization occurs over a stratigraphic

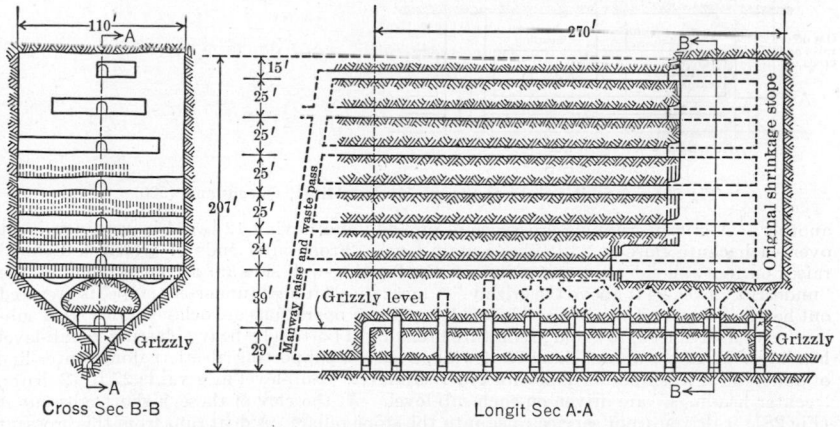

Fig 280.   Mining Waste Rock for Filling, McIntyre Mine, Schumacher, Ont.

thickness of 160 ft, permitting, in part, stoping across full width; usually, stoping is confined to a 32-ft band of ore along hanging wall and a 40–70-ft band along footwall.   Upper part of orebody, largely oxidized, was mined by surface glory-hole (Art 99); sub-level method was used in sulphide ores below.   GENERAL DEVELOPMENT.   Mine is served by 2 main vert shafts and 2 auxiliary vert shafts.   Main shafts are in footwall; one for service, the other for hoisting ore. Level interval in original sub-level stoping was 200 ft vert. For new work, levels are 175 ft apart. Haulage drifts and crosscuts are 10 ft wide and 9 ft high. Main-level development depends on stope lay-out; where width of ore exceeds 75 ft, stopes run across the lode and are developed by crosscuts; for widths less than 75 ft, stopes are longit and served by drifts.

Longitudinal stopes. Haulage drift is located centrally respecting the orebody at the stope-undercut. Length of stope and general procedure are adjusted to width of ore and ground conditions; for widths of 6–14 ft, sub-level drifts are 30 ft apart and 7 by 5 ft in sec. Benches, 6–8 ft wide, are cut at each sub-level above the undercut and carried down with jackhammers until they break through to stope below. Usually, 3 such cuts are required, the last being 12 ft deep. Safety belts are worn by all men on the benches, the ropes being fastened in the sub-level drift above. Fig 281 shows plan of work in wider stopes, where ore is 75 ft wide. Stopes, 72 ft long, are limited on one end by a 25-ft pillar, through which a 5 by 7-ft service raise is driven on footwall between main levels, and on other end by a 20-ft pillar. Each stope is served by 2 sets of chute raises, each set comprising 2 inclined raises at right-angles to strike and driven from chutes opposite one

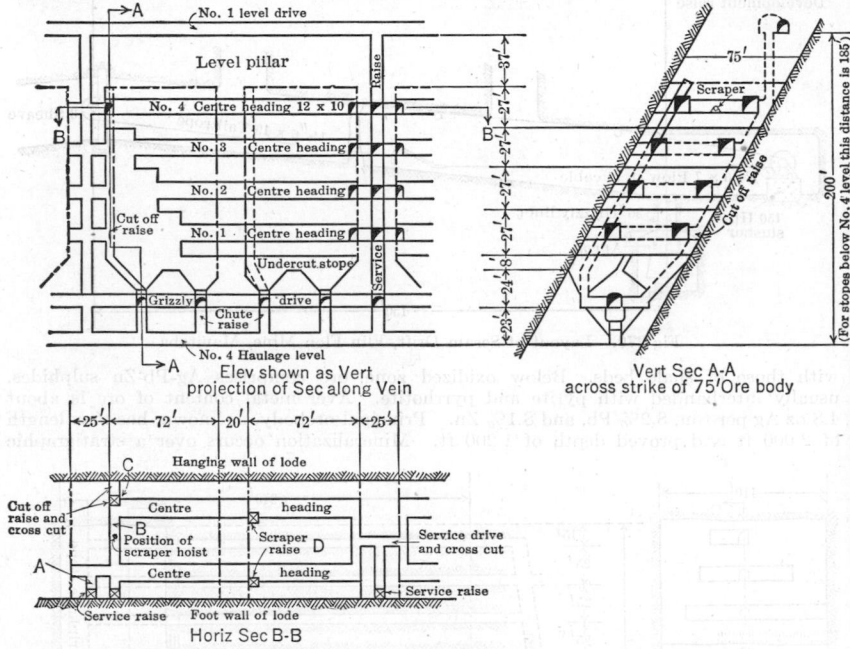

Fig 281. Longit Sub-level Stope, Mt Isa Mines, Queensland (500)

another. A grizzly, running crosswise of orebody and having 12 by 24-in openings, is set over each chute raise at 23 ft above main level. From outer ends of grizzlies, inclined raises on footwall side and vert raises on the hanging-wall side are driven to floor of the "undercut" level, 24 ft above the grizzly. A horiz slice 8 ft high (under-cut stope) is breasted out here, and tops of raises are "belled," but these operations are delayed until No 1 sublevel is well advanced, to avoid premature breaking of bottom by heavy blasting in sub-level headings. In stopes approaching 75 ft wide, a narrow supporting rib is left along center-line of undercut as a temporary pillar for No 1 sub-level. Sub-level interval is 27 ft; 2 drifts, "center headings," are driven on each sub-level. At the elev of these, a short crosscut *A* (Fig 281) is driven from service raise into the stope pillar. A drift runs from this crosscut to the pillar edges, and along each side thereof crosscuts *B* are driven to the ore limits. "Center headings" are 12 ft wide by 10 ft high. Crosscuts *B* later serve as points of attack in mining out a vert slice, or "cut-off stope," at the end of sub-level stope. Broken ore from center headings is scraped to cut-off raise *C* until headings advance to "scraper raises" *D*, which then become the mucking transfer. "Cutting-off" operations at end of the stope at which mining will start are carried on concurrently with sub-level development, but timed to avoid interference with driving sub-level headings. Breaking ground

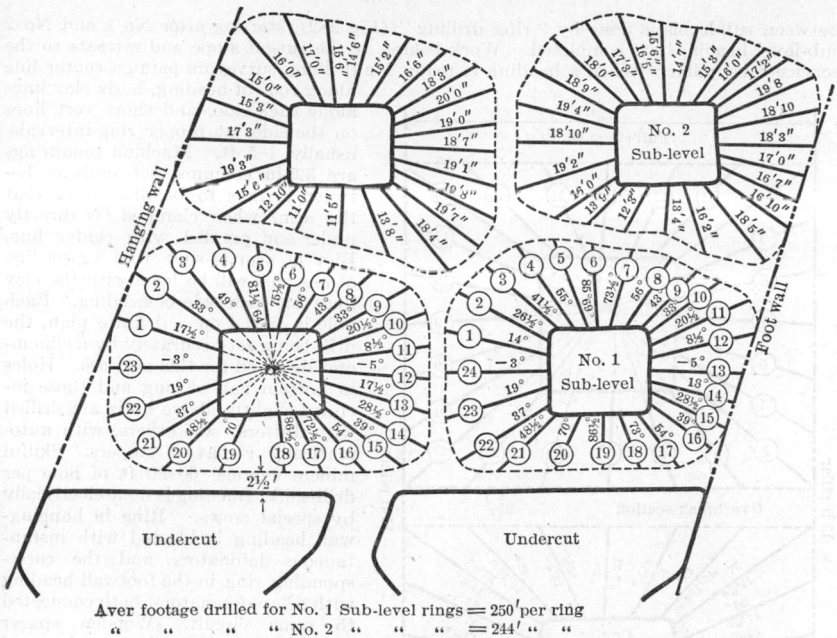

Aver footage drilled for No. 1 Sub-level rings = 250' per ring
"   "   "   " No. 2 "   "   = 244' " "
"   " tonnage broken per ring for No. 1 Sub-level = 372 tons
"   "   "   "   " " " No. 2 " "   = 380 "

Fig 282.   Ring-drilling Diagram for Longit Sub-level Stope, Mt Isa Mines, Queensland

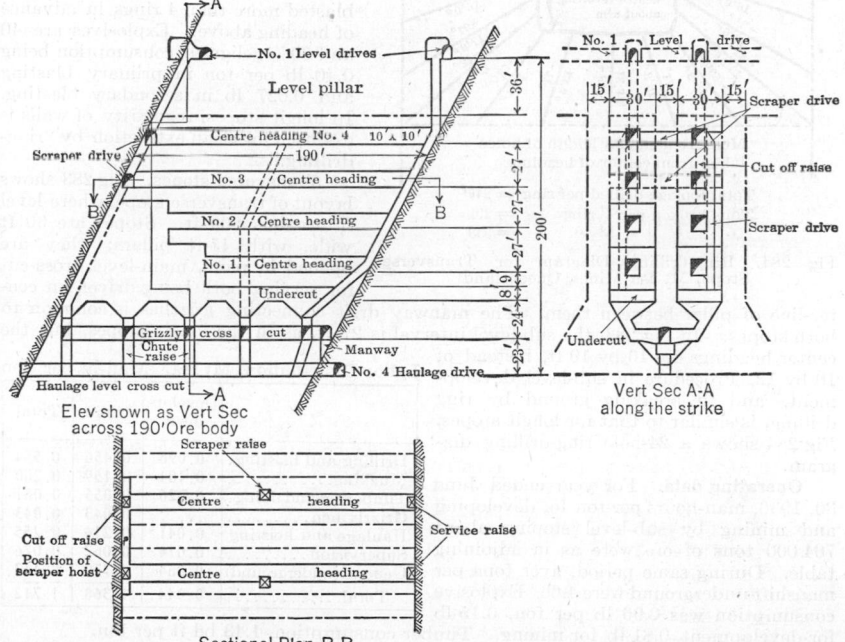

Fig 283.   Transverse Sub-level Stope, Mt Isa Mines, Queensland (500)

between sub-levels is done by "ring drilling" (Fig 282), starting after No 1 and No 2 sub-level headings are completed. Work begins at the cut-off stope and retreats to the service-raise pillar. When a heading is ready for drilling, surveyors paint a center line along roof of heading, horiz elev lines along each side, and short vert lines on the sides at proper ring intervals. usually 4–5 ft. Machine mountings are 3.5-in columns, set midway between 2 rings to be drilled, so that the arm, when clamped, is directly under and parallel with center line. Elev of arm is such that center-line of machine will be level with the elev lines on each side of heading. Each hole is drilled on a definite plan, the drill being set accurately by a clinometer designed for this purpose. Holes in bottom half of ring and those inclined slightly above horiz are drilled with drifters; the others, with automatically rotated stopers. Skilful miners average 60–90 ft of hole per drill-shift. Blasting is done electrically by special crews. Ring in hangingwall heading is blasted with instantaneous detonators, and the corresponding ring in the footwall heading with delay detonators, both connected to same circuit. Wooden spacer plugs, 1.25 in by 8 in, are inserted between sticks of powder for wider distribution. Blasting on sub-levels is kept in step, so that no heading is blasted more than 4 rings in advance of heading above. Explosives are 40 and 60% gelignite, consumption being 0.40 lb per ton in primary blasting and 0.027 lb in secondary blasting. In longit stopes, regularity of walls is essential for clean extraction by "ring-drilling."

Transverse stopes. Fig 283 shows layout of transverse stope, where level interval is 200 ft. Stopes are 30 ft wide, with 15-ft pillars; they are opened in pairs, main-level cross-cut for serving both being driven on center-line of pillar between them. The manway drift connecting grizzlies is common to both stopes. In Fig 283, the sub-level interval is 27 ft, as in the longit stopes, but the center headings are 10 by 10 ft, instead of 10 by 12. Procedure in sub-level development, and in breaking ground by ring drilling, is similar to that for longit stopes. Fig 284 shows a 24-hole ring-drilling diagram.

Operating data. For year ended June 30, 1936, man-hours per ton for developing and mining by sub-level stoping about 704 000 tons of ore were as in adjoining table. During same period, aver tons per manshift underground were 4.66. Explosive consumption was 0.96 lb per ton, 0.15 lb for development, 0.81 lb for mining. Timber consumption, 1.43 bd ft per ton.

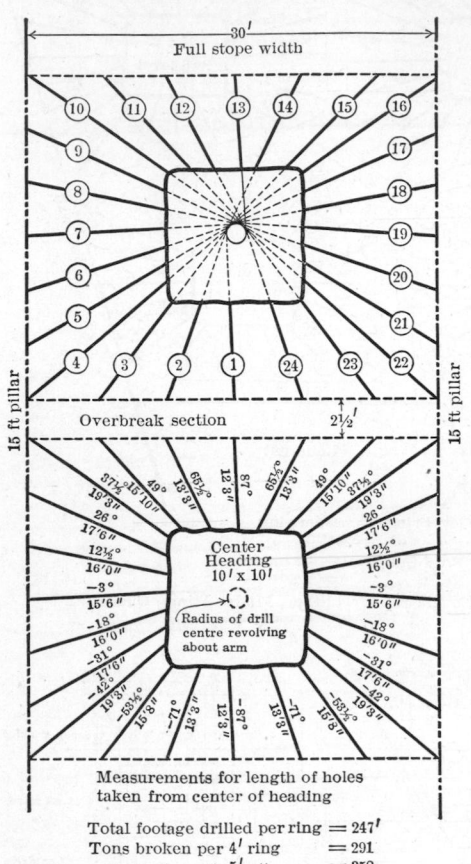

Total footage drilled per ring = 247′
Tons broken per 4′ ring = 291
"   "   " 5′ " = 358

Fig 284. Ring-drilling Diagram for Transverse Stope, Mt Isa Mines, Queensland

Labor Distribution, Mt Isa. Man-hr per Ton

	Development	Mining	Total
Drilling and blasting.	0.098	0.456	0.554
Mucking.............	0.101	0.159	0.260
Timbering and filling.	0.026	0.055	0.081
Grizzlymen.........		0.043	0.043
Haulage and hoisting	0.041	0.214	0.255
Supervision.........	0.014	0.062	0.076
General (underground)	0.064	0.379	0.443
Total.............	0.344	1.368	1.712

Summary. Following factors led to choice of sub-level stoping at Mount Isa: (a) need of a low-cost method, owing to relatively low-grade ore; (b) desirability of allowing development, stope preparation, breaking, and drawing of ore to proceed concurrently; (*c*) tendency of ore to oxidize rapidly, adversely affecting mill recovery, favored method in which accumulations of broken ore could be minimized; (*d*) safety factor; (*e*) need of eliminating, as far as possible, features depending on judgment and skill of miners, due to the comparative inexperience of most miners available; (*f*) though laminated in structure, ore is hard and breaks in large blocks, thus making caving methods unsuitable.

Champion mine, Mich.   For sub-level stoping, with filling, at this mine, see Art 63.

44. SUMMARY OF OPEN-STOPE METHODS

Applications. Open stoping methods, described in Art 29–43, are designed for widely different conditions of dip, width of deposit, character of ground, and grade of ore.   Generalizations, applying to all types of open stoping, are difficult, but the following principles apply: (*a*) low-cost mining by open stoping is sometimes possible through sacrifice of part of the deposit in permanent pillars; then the method is applicable to low-grade orebodies not warranting higher-cost methods in any circumstances; (*b*) possibilities of selective mining vary; on steep dips they are usually limited to the leaving of low-grade areas as pillars; in thin deposits on flat dips a high degree of selectivity is possible; (*c*) underground sorting of ore is possible in flat deposits, but only to a limited extent on steep dips, especially where widths exceed economic length of stulls; (*d*) use of open stoping usually presupposes strong ore and strong walls, except in thin deposits of flat or moderate dip that can be worked by a retreating system, as at Calumet & Hecla (Art 39) and Pilgrim mines (Art 35); (*e*) methods are usually limited to tabular deposits with regular, well defined walls, but are sometimes used in large, massive deposits with irregular walls, as at Horne mine (Art 43).   The following comparison of underhand and overhand methods applies in part to breaking ground in any stoping method, and in part to open stopes in veins; it also draws attention to factors to be considered in planning open-stope methods in other types of deposit.

Underhand methods. ADVANTAGES: (*a*) all drill holes are down holes; this is advantageous for hand-drilling and permits efficient use of hand-held jackhammers, with resultant simplicity in drilling; (*b*) miners stand on ore while working, which may be safer than overhand stoping in narrow veins of weak ore with strong walls; (*c*) underhand methods, where applicable, require less timber than overhand; (*d*) in general, loss of fines is less in underhand than in overhand work.   DISADVANTAGES: (*a*) danger, because men work under inaccessible backs and walls, the height and area of which increase as stope is extended, and loose pieces may fall; (*b*) due to above conditions, the level interval must usually be smaller than for overhand methods; (*c*) facilities for storing waste in stopes are poor; (*d*) broken ore from face collects at a single point, which may interfere with economical handling.

Overhand methods. ADVANTAGES (not indicated above): (*a*) miners work near back of stope, where they can examine face carefully and take down loose ground, and are not exposed to danger from pieces falling from a height; (*b*) waste or ore is readily stored in stopes; (*c*) a greater variety of working plans is available than in underhand stopes and any type of machine drill may be used; (*d*) an open, overhand method may be changed to a square-setting, shrinkage, or filling method, far more readily than underhand stoping; (*e*) gravity aids in breaking ground; (*f*) broken ore slides down the dip under the impetus of blasting; this allows handling of ore to the level below without mechanical devices on flatter dips than is possible in underhand stopes.   DISADVANTAGES are largely the converse of advantages of underhand; in addition, support for men is necessary in overhand stopes on dips over about 40°, whether required by walls or not (Art 93).

TIMBERED STOPES

The term "timbered stope" is used here to denote stopes in which timbering is the dominant feature of the method. Stulled stopes (Art 38, 39) are types of timbered stope.

45. SQUARE-SET METHOD

Square-sets were first used in the U S in 1860 by Philip Deidesheimer, at Ophir mine, Comstock Lode, Nev.   In early days, the method was often called the Nevada square-set system.

Description. The stope faces are advanced by successive small excavations, each timbered before the next is begun. Timbers in adjoining sections are framed into and mutually support one another, forming a continuous structure of horiz FLOORS, composed

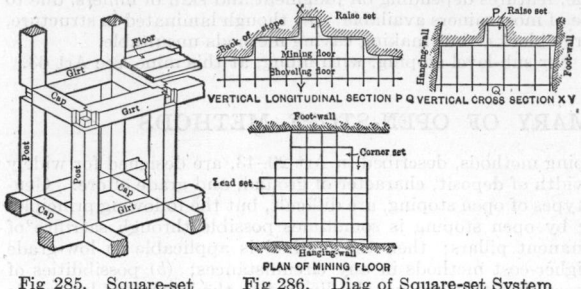

of rectangular frames supported at their corners by POSTS (Fig 285). One pair of parallel horiz timbers are CAPS, those at right-angles to caps being GIRTS (ties, braces or collar braces). Posts, about 7 ft high, are 5–6 ft apart c to c, both capwise and girtwise. Caps are often stronger than girts, the principal function of girts being to hold the posts in position. In veins, caps usually have their long dimension at right-angles to the strike; in masses, in the direction of max lateral pressure. Square-sets support men and broken ore, as well as the stope walls. Lowest floor of a stope is called the SILL FLOOR; this may be level with bottom of haulageway (Fig 287), or at a higher elev (Fig 289, 293). Highest working floor is the MINING FLOOR and next below is the SHOVELING FLOOR, made by laying planks across caps or girts (Fig 285). Above the sill are the 1ST FLOOR, 2ND FLOOR, etc. The first set erected on any floor is a RAISE SET; it has 4 posts, 2 caps and 2 girts. First set in a new row on a floor is a LEAD SET, requiring 2 posts, 2 girts and 1 cap, or 2 posts, 1 girt and 2 caps. In working alongside of sets in place, SIDE SETS or CORNER SETS are used, consisting of post, cap and girt. When a stope is well opened, nearly all sets added are corner sets (Fig 286). OPEN SQUARE-SET STOPES are those in which the sets alone are relied upon to support the walls; in FILLED SQUARE-SET STOPES, waste filling is used for added support.

Fig 285. Square-set Timbering   **Fig 286. Diag of Square-set System**

Breaking ground in square-set work follows general overhand practice (Art 26–28).

46. FORMS OF SQUARE-SET STOPES

General. Some stoping methods are based upon the use of square-sets, in others their use is incidental. When waste filling is used, the stope is the same as the corresponding form of untimbered filled stope (Art 60–65), except for the use of square-sets as temporary support before filling can begin. There is a similar correspondence between an unfilled square-set stope and an open stope of same form.

Occasionally square-sets are used in open overhand unfilled stopes, chiefly to provide working platforms; as at New Idria mine, Calif, where ore is over 10 ft wide, with steep dip. Nearly all square-set timber is reclaimed and reused until worn out (320).

Mining large, weak deposits by square-setting usually requires a division of the orebody, between any two levels, into stoping blocks of limited horiz area. Such stope work is called a BLOCK SYSTEM. Size of blocks is adjusted to strength of ground, so that work in any block is rapid enough to avoid excessive press. This sectionalizing is sometimes done by dividing orebody into alternate stope and pillar panels (see Frood mine, below), mining of pillars following completion of stope panels on both sides. In other cases, small blocks are stoped and filled; then corresponding blocks are mined alongside (Fig 287). Individual blocks may be mined by any form of square-set stope described below. DEVELOPMENT REQUIREMENTS vary with type of stope. A drift, either in wall or in orebody, is a prerequisite to opening the sill floor. In wide orebodies, there may be a grillage of drifts and crosscuts. At least one raise to the level above is usually necessary in each stope, for ventilation and handling timbers and filling.

a. Flat-back or Stepped-face Overhand Stope

Anaconda Copper Mining Co, Butte, Mont. Data from W. B. Daly, Mgr of Mines, in 1939. Copper ores occur in complicated vein systems; stoping widths, 4–100 ft, usually 10–30 ft; dips generally steep; country rock, commonly granite. Principal gangue mineral is quartz, with pyrite and blende. Numerous faults cause sloughing and squeezing of walls. Closely filled flat-back square-set stopes are used where square-set rill stopes or horiz (flat-back) cut-and-fill stopes (Art 60), or ordinary filled-rill stopes (Art 65) are not applicable.

In narrow veins the level interval is 100 ft or 200 ft; levels usually driven in the vein. Drifts are timbered with square-sets; offsets into footwall are usually made at every 5th and 6th set, to be used later for chutes and manways. When drift is far enough advanced, 2-compt raises to the level above are started in every 3d or 4th offset. When 2 adjacent

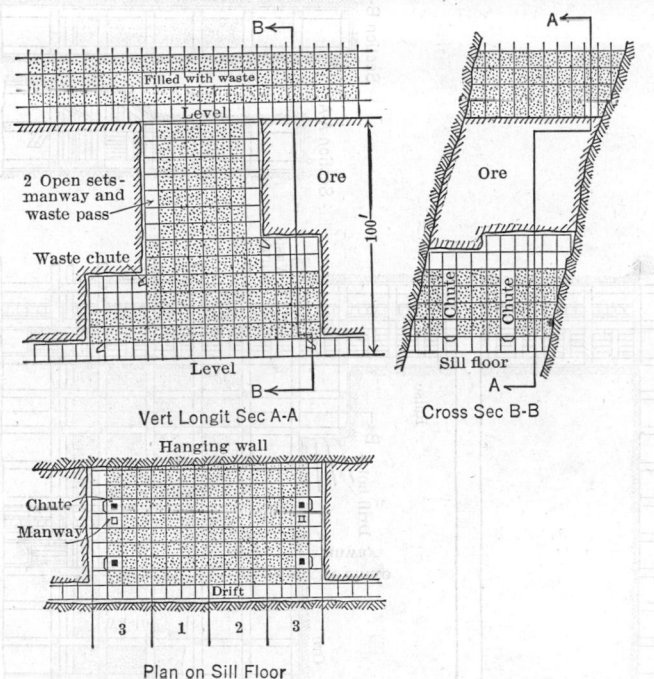

Fig 287. Block System (diagrammatic); numbers show order of mining blocks

raises are up far enough, the first 2 stope floors between them are mined and timbered, ore being handled through stop boards into cars on level. Sheeting of small stulls laid on sheeting caps is then placed over the drift caps, and a temporary floor of 3-in lagging is laid over caps of second floor; then intermediate chutes and manways are built. Stope is now carried up with a stepped face, a new floor being started when floor below passes a chute. Waste, from sorting in levels above and sometimes from inclined raises in footwall, is kept within 1 or 2 sets of back. Fig 288, from Gardner and Vanderburg (189), is a longit sec of a square-set stope in a narrow orebody at Butte. The mode of advancing the stope face typifies general practice in square-set stopes, applicable to wide orebodies as well as to narrow veins. Fig 288 shows the introduction of waste filling, but otherwise depicts open stoping with aid of square-sets; it would also represent a section of a transverse stope carried perpendicular to the strike in a wide orebody.

Argonaut mine, Calif. Fig 289 shows a narrow, square-set stope for which filling is obtained by mining wall rock. In such cases, raises to the level above would be unnecessary, but are advisable for ventilation and safety.

McIntyre mine, Schumacher, Ont (171). For description of geol features and mining by horiz cut-and-fill, see Art 60. Flat-back square-set stopes are used for mining heavy ground, especially where ore is wide. Sets are of cap-butting type, to resist side press. Posts are 10–11-in squared rounds, 8 ft long; caps, same size timber, 5.5 ft long; girts, 7 by 9-in squared, 4 ft 11 in long. In mining wide areas, timber cribs placed on the fill and blocked to back as auxiliary support are largely used. When blasting, sets are reinforced by diagonal timbers and added temporary posts under caps. Breast holes 10–12 ft deep are drilled, and blasted with max of 2–3 sticks of powder. Chutes are 50 ft apart and lined with 3-in plank; fill-raises, 300 ft apart. Ore and fill are handled in 1-ton cars on 16-lb sectionalized track, with turntables instead of switches.

Frood mine, Sudbury, Ont (49, 93). Data from H. J. Mutz, Supt of Mines, and others of staff of International Nickel Co of Canada, in 1930, 1937. Mining method here illustrates square-setting in large-scale work; a "block" system is used; individual stopes are flat-back overhand stopes. OREBODY is in a brecciated zone in altered sediments and

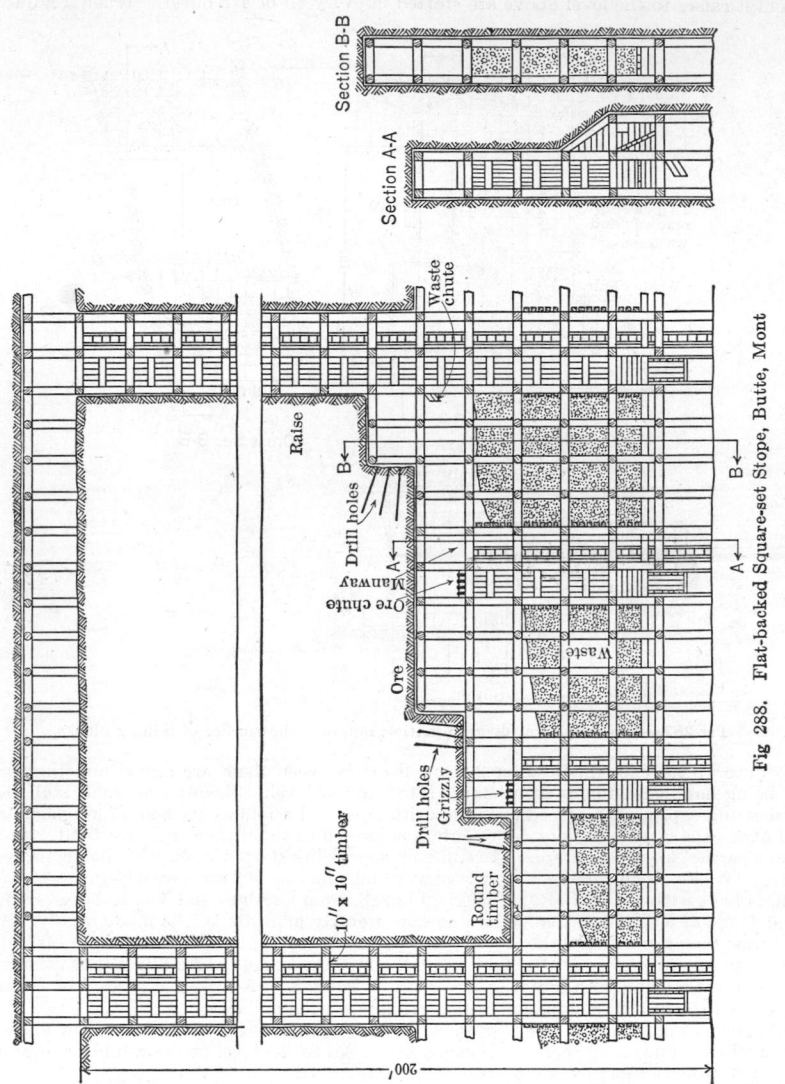

Fig 288. Flat-backed Square-set Stope, Butte, Mont

intrusives. Metallic minerals, chiefly pyrrhotite, pentlandite, and chalcopyrite. Outcrop extends more than a mile, and is over 600 ft wide in places. Mineralization is relatively weak in upper part of orebody, but intensifies at depth to massive sulphides, 40–200 ft wide. There are occasional lenses of quartz-diorite within the massive sulphide. Dip of ore averages 65°; walls, irregular. At depth of 2 000 ft and below, ore is rich enough to require a method allowing selective mining and high extraction. DEVELOPMENT. There are 2 vert shafts sunk from surface in footwall, and an inside vert shaft, to handle men and materials below the 2 800-ft level. Level interval above the 2 800-level is 200 ft; below it, 150 ft. On each level a main crosscut is driven through the orebody, and from it a 30-ft raise is put up in ore. At this point, a 4 by 6-ft drift is driven the full length of ore zone.

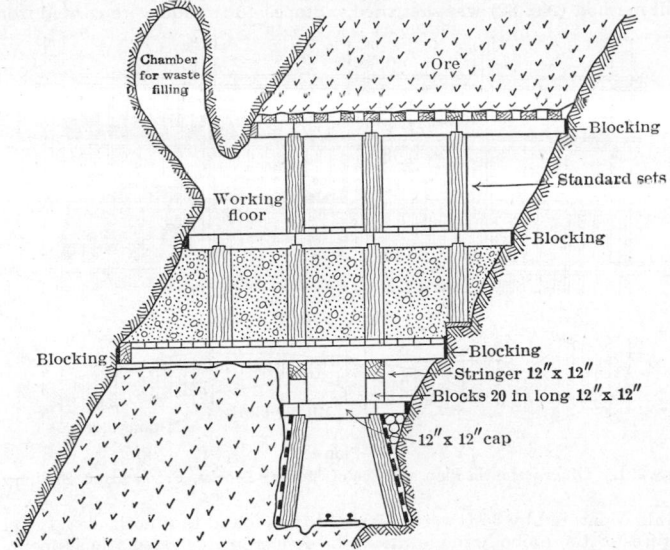

Fig 289.   Obtaining Waste Fill from Hanging Wall, Argonaut Mine, Calif

From this drift, at intervals of 80 ft, horiz diamond-drill holes are driven at right-angles to general strike, to determine the ore outline. Information thus gained permits careful planning of level development, which, as shown in Fig 290, comprises a main haulageway

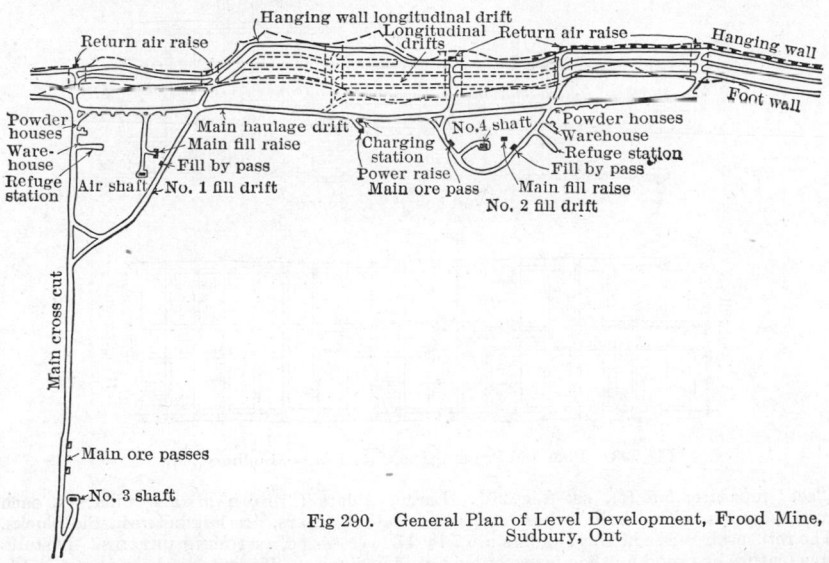

Fig 290.   General Plan of Level Development, Frood Mine,
Sudbury, Ont

in footwall, a series of longit drifts in ore, and connecting crosscuts about 485 ft apart. The longit (haulage) drifts are 44 ft apart to give proper chute spacing; their number depends on width of ore; they are driven 11 by 11 ft in cross-sec, timbered with 10 by 10-in fir sets, spaced 5.5-ft centers. Before stoping starts, back of drift is raised to height of 16 ft and a second floor, or "gangway," is timbered with square-sets having 10 by 10-in posts, 5 ft 10 in long. Chute pockets are built at gangway elevation; planking over drift sets provides footing for loaders. STOPING. Mining began below 2 000-level. Horiz cut-and-fill method (Art 62) was first tried. Stopes 45 ft wide were carried from foot to

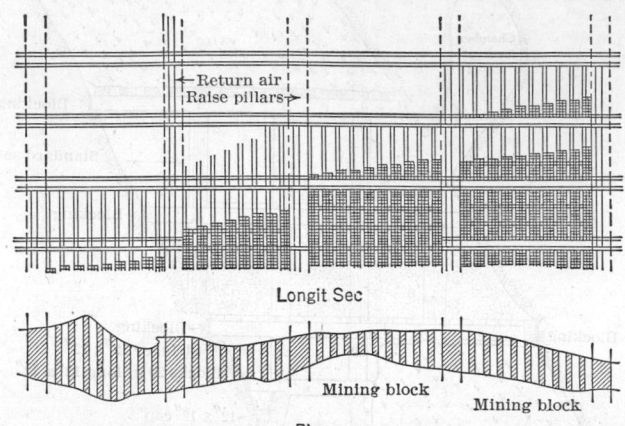

Fig 291.   Diagrammatic Plan and Sec of Stoping Blocks, Frood Mine, Sudbury, Ont

hanging wall, separated by 35-ft vert pillars. It was found that horiz cleavage planes and cross fractures in the orebody made the backs dangerous. Systematic support of backs, by cribbed bulkheads joined together by lagged stringers, was tried but proved unsatisfactory; then the present square-set system was adopted. New levels are laid out in mining blocks. In general, each block consists of 10 5-set stopes and 9 3-set pillars

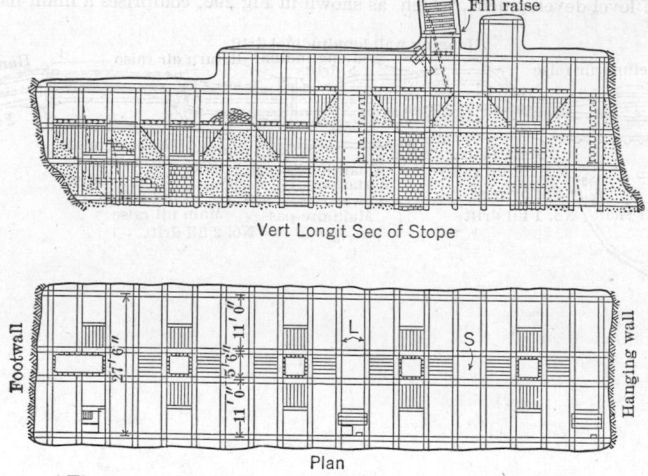

Fig 292.   Plan and Sec of Stope, Frood Mine, Sudbury, Ont

("set" measure, 5.5 ft), see Fig 291. Larger pillars ("return-air-raise pillars"), each corresponding in width to a 5-set stope and 2 3-set pillars, are left between the blocks. The return-air raises in these pillars are 7 by 17 ft cross-sec. STOPING DETAILS. Distinctive feature of Frood method is use of long girts in stopes. The standard square-set is 7 ft high and 5.5 ft square, c to c of posts. Girts run at right-angles to pillar lines, or in direction of strike. Long girts give a post-spacing of 11 ft, or twice that of standard sets. Fig 292 is a plan and section of a 5-set stope, timbered with sets S from foot to hanging through the center of the stope and flanked on both sides by long-girt sets *L*. Bottom of sill floor of stope is 7 ft above the rail in the haulage drifts. Cut starts by driving a 5 by 7-ft crosscut at this elevation, along center line of stope, from a gangway and extending to both walls. Ore is breasted with light drifters, drilling 9 to 11-ft holes 2.5 ft apart. Broken ore is scraped with 10-hp, double-drum hoists, directly into cars in haulage drift. First cut, about 8 ft high, is timbered with haulage-drift timbering, posts being 5 ft 8 in long. Where chutes are to be located, 10 by 10-in B C fir is used.

Sets are kept within 10–15 ft of face, lagged booms protecting workers at face. During silling operations, a waste raise near hanging-wall end of stope is driven to connect with the hanging-wall drift on level above; raise contains a cribbed manway, serving later for lowering supplies into stope, for a travelway, and for ventilation. Before first fill is introduced, bottom of first cut is floored with double layer of cedar plank, 2 by 10 in by 10 ft, laid on 4 by 10-in sills. Sets adjacent to pillars, on sill and all higher floors, are "gob-fenced" (lagged) before filling. Chutes are established in every fourth set, lengthwise of stope. Manways are carried up along one pillar line. Regular cycle of stoping operations commences as soon as sill floor is completed. Stope progresses upward by successive horiz slices 7 ft high as shown in Fig 293. Operating cycle is accomplished by dividing work into 3 shifts, known as drilling, timbering, and nipping shifts. Drilling-shift crew comprises 1 stope boss, 2 drillers, 1 timberman, 2 shovelers, and 1 wasteman. Two miners drill and blast the 5-set breast in 1 shift and also do any necessary blockholing. Light drifters are used; drill steel is in sets of 3-, 5-, and 7-ft lengths. From 35 to 50 holes are required for a 5-set blast; usual spacing is 1.5 ft vert and 3 ft horiz; upper row is inclined 15° upward. Explosive used is 40% gelatin; $2\frac{1}{2}$ to 3

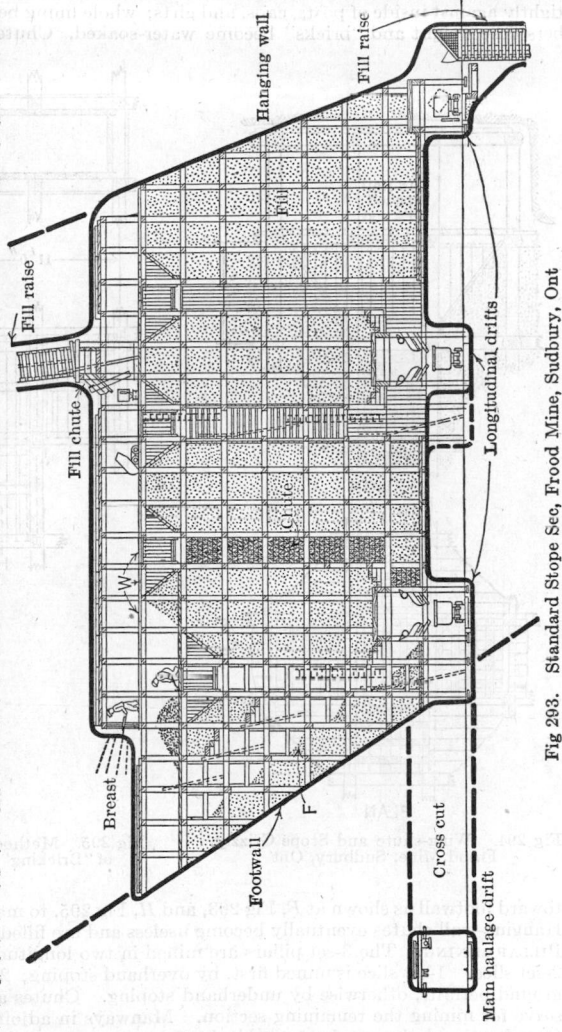

Fig 293. Standard Stope Sec, Frood Mine, Sudbury, Ont

sticks are required per hole; stemming of clay cartridges is used. Timberman on drilling-shift does miscellaneous timber work. Timbering-shift crew consists of 4 men: timberman, helper, blockholer, and shoveler. They re-blast any missed holes, stand and block new set, and, in general, put stope in shape for further drilling operations. On the nipping-shift a crew of 3 men, serving several stopes, deliver timber, steel, and other supplies to stopes in accordance with requisitions from shift bosses. ORE HANDLING. "Wing-chutes" *W*, Fig 293, 1 set high, are built over chute raises; a grizzly of 60-lb rails, spaced $14\frac{1}{4}$ in, covers 5 sets on the shoveling floor at top of winged chute; for detail see

Fig 294. This arrangement reduces shoveling to extent that bulk of broken ore is barred directly through grizzlies. FILLING. Waste fill is spread in 16-cu ft end-dump cars on 18-in sectionalized track; track sections, 11 ft long, are easily laid or dismantled by one man. Fill is usually kept within 3 sets of toe of broken-ore pile. CHUTE CONSTRUCTION. Vert chutes are spaced at 22-ft centers; sets are of 10 by 10-in B C fir. Plank lining has been replaced by "bricking." Timber blocks, 8 by 8 by 13 in, are placed so that butt ends project 3 in into chute opening, other ends resting against outer chute lagging. Each row is staggered in relation to rows above and below, see Fig 295; all rows are wedged tightly against inside of posts, caps, and girts; whole lining becomes tightly wedged as timbers take weight and "bricks" become water-soaked. Chutes nearest footwall are offset

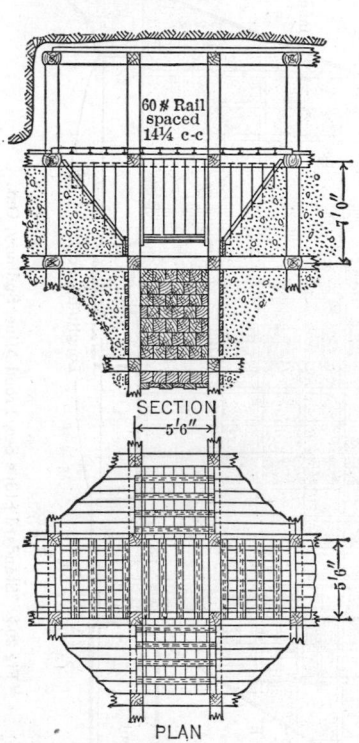

Fig 294. Wing-chute and Stope Grizzly, Frood Mine, Sudbury, Ont

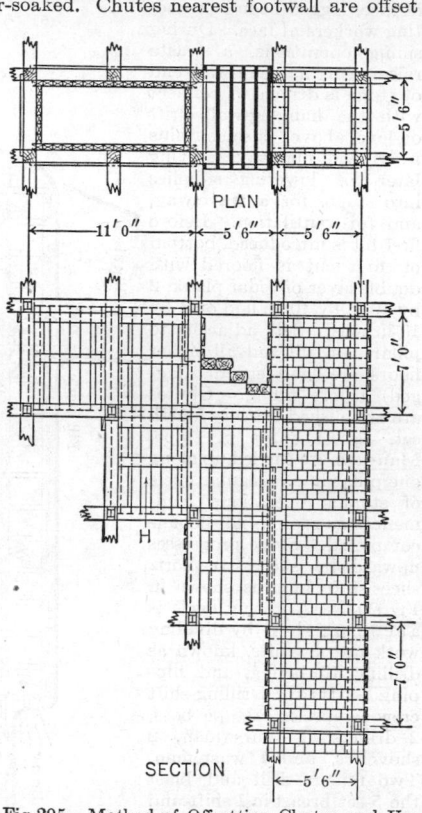

Fig 295. Method of Offsetting Chutes, and Use of "Bricking" as Lining, Frood Mine, Ont

toward footwall as shown at F, Fig 293, and H, Fig 295, to maintain efficient chute spacing. Hanging-wall chutes eventually become useless and are filled with waste on abandonment. PILLAR MINING. The 3-set pillars are mined in two longitudinal slices, a 1-set slice and a 2-set slice. 1-set slice is mined first, by overhand stoping; 2-set slice is mined overhand if ground permits, otherwise by underhand stoping. Chutes at 22-ft intervals in 1-set slice serve for mining the remaining section. Manways in adjoining stope serve as manways, fill passes, and airways for 1-set block; 2 open sets carried in this block serve same purposes for 2-set block.

b. Domed or Pyramid Stopes

Work is so arranged that the general outline of the stope back is dome-shaped or pyramidal. They are commonly open stopes, and have been used in massive orebodies of both strong and weak ore under strong hanging walls. The arched back is partly self-supporting and reduces pressure on timbers.

Fig 296 shows this method at CENTENNIAL-EUREKA mine, Tintic, Utah, for mining an irregular chimney, 350 by 100 ft in cross-sec, dipping 45°, and over 800 ft deep. Walls were fairly strong limestone, but in many places ore could be mined with a pick. Level interval was 100 ft vert, with raises between levels near one end of orebody. Sets were of 8 by 8-in timber, with sills 2 sets long laid parallel to long dimension of orebody. Work on sill floor started at the raise, and when a square, 3 sets on a side, was completed, a 1st floor set was placed in the raise. Sill and 1st floor were then widened simultaneously; when the 1st floor was 3 sets square, the 2nd floor was begun, and so on. Crib bulkheads were necessary to keep stopes from caving (Art 51) (210).

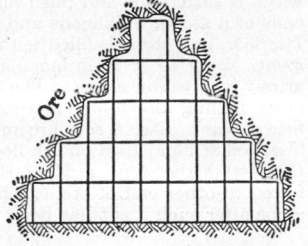

Fig 296. Domed Stope, Cross-sec

L. S. Cates describes similar work at BINGHAM, Utah, in irregular replacement orebodies (211). Ore was in shoots, 50–200 ft wide, 100–300 ft long, and in places 600 ft deep; dip, 0°–90°. Open pyramid stopes were used only where ore was solid and hanging wall firm. Space for only one set was excavated in advance of timbering; hence, sills were 1 set long. From a drift near middle of orebody, a row of lead sets (Art 45) was extended longit through it. Sill floor was opened from these sets to a width of 4–5 sets, then a row of lead sets was begun on 1st floor, directly over those on sill floor. Widening on any floor might begin 4–5 sets behind the lead set. Each floor was kept 2, or better 4 sets, wider than that above; extra width aided in keeping broken ore on the floors.

c. Rill Stope

This form is designed primarily for use with waste filling. The stope back on any floor is 1 or more sets ahead of that on floor below; hence, general slope of stope face roughly parallels angle of repose of filling. The fill is distributed largely by gravity; planking is laid on the filling, and broken ore slides to chutes at the toe of fill. Except for the square-sets, the stope is same as a filled-rill or inclined cut-and-fill stope (Art 65). Examples:

Butte, Mont. For ore occurrence and development, see Flat-back stopes above. Fig 298 shows an ideal longit sec of a timbered rill stope, opened up as in Fig 297. Data

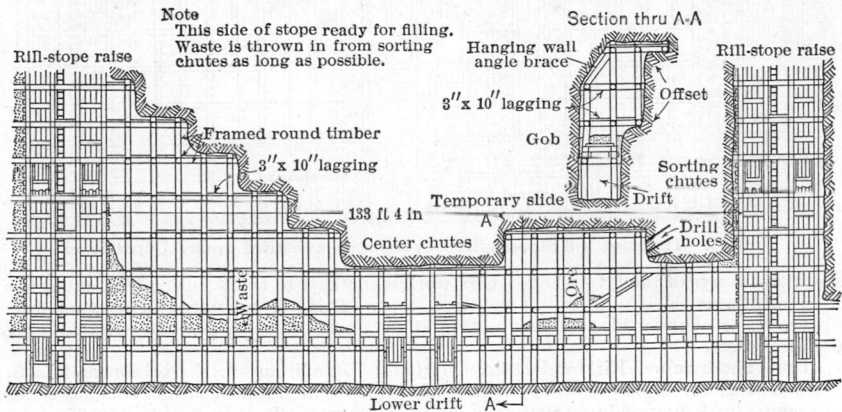

Fig 297. Preliminary Development of a Timbered Rill Stope

from H. L. Bicknell, W. B. Daly and others (534) in 1923, and checked in 1939 by officials of Anaconda Copper Mining Co.

Method is used in veins over 10 ft wide, where back and walls will not stand in a filled-rill stope (Art 65). Level interval, 200 ft; drifts timbered with square-sets; at intervals of 11 sets, offsets 1 set wide by 3 sets long are made in footwall for raises and chutes. Drifts are made 2 sets wide every 500 ft, for a distance of 10 sets, to provide space for switches. Alternate raises (stope raises, Fig 298), comprising a central manway with chute on each side, are carried up in ore to within 30–40 ft of level above, whence they turn vertical to hole through at least 15 ft in the hanging wall on level above. As a raise passes the 1st floor, one set on each side is mined and timbered. After raises are up 5 or 6 floors, the 1st floor is mined. All sets except those at chutes and manways are of round timber (Fig 337). Stopes 2 sets wide usually cover the width of vein. After completion of 2nd floor, "center" chutes are built in the offsets half-way between the stope raises and cribbed to 2nd floor, and sides of the stope-raise sets are lagged. Fig 297 shows right end of a stope in process of development to the form reached in left end. During development of the sloping stope faces, temporary slides convey ore to the 2nd floor; waste is sorted out and piled on the floors. When the rill face has been formed in both ends of a stope, bulkheads and chute gates (Fig 297) are built in the stope raises above 7th floor, and stope is filled with waste poured down the raises. This completes development. 2 by 10 or 12-in lagging is laid on top of the waste, so broken ore will slide to a grizzly over center chute. The 3d floor (7 sets long) is then mined and timbered. Thereafter, mining and filling proceed alternately in each end of a stope. Starting at stope face in each case, 4 sets are mined successively on 4th, 5th, 6th, and 7th floors, then 3 sets on 8th and 1 set on 9th floor. This completes a "cut"; the raises are then lagged; that end of the stope in which this work has been done is filled, and the miners are transferred to other end of stope, where the same operations are repeated. Fig 298 shows a stope after such a cut has been taken in each end. Mining proceeds until the top floors

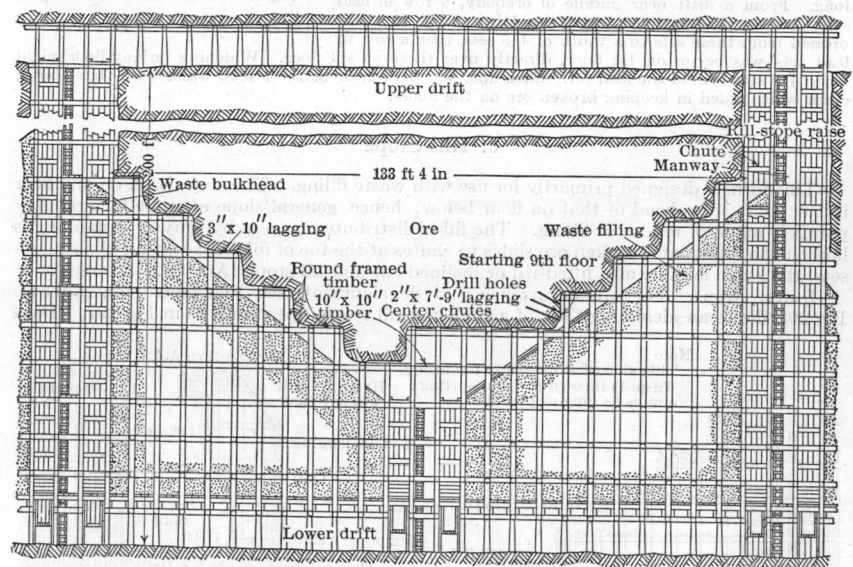

Fig 298. Timbered Rill Stopes after Development, as carried toward Upper Level

are within 5 sets of the level above; then work is confined to the V until a level-pillar has been left, 5 sets thick and the full length of stope. This pillar is mined later, when drift above can be abandoned. Sorting is done at the grizzly, one of the center chutes being used for waste.

Lake Shore mine, Kirkland Lake, Ont (95). Data from W. T. Robson and L. S. Weldon in 1936. Gold ore occurs in crushed and brecciated fault zones in complex series of syenitic intrusives and in a porphyry boss. Aver grade of ore in 1934 was 0.667 oz Au per ton. Ore zone on property is about 2 800 ft long. Mining reached depth of 4 500 ft in 1936. Aver stoping width is 15–16 ft, but widths to 70 ft have been mined. General dip from surface to 4 500-level is 82°, with local dips as low as 45°. Shrinkage stoping, first employed, was discarded because of excess dilution and ore left behind in local rolls or in parallel or branching leads; horiz and inclined cut-and-fill stopes were also tried; bad ground eventually led to square-set, flat-back and rill stopes. DEVELOPMENT is by 2 vert shafts, with levels 200 ft apart to 2 200-level and 125 ft apart below. Levels are developed by drifts in the veins. SQUARE-SET RILL STOPES. Drift is widened by slabbing to full width of ore for entire length of section to be mined. Back is taken down to height of 16–17 ft above rail. Sill floor is timbered as in Fig 299; distinctive feature of sill timbering is use of double caps, with longit stringers between them, which facilitate replacement of timbers broken by pressure and aid in holding the level open when stope below is being mined through; sill-floor timbering is designed to avoid breakage through pressure from walls. A centrally located, 3-compt raise (Fig 300) is driven to the level above, timbered with square-sets, 8 ft high and 5 ft 4 in c-c of posts; 10 by 10-in squared timber used for all members. Center compt of the raise is a manway; the outer ones are chutes. A double-rill stope is started from the raise, and carried to level above as a block 25 sets in length. Fill is introduced to each half of stope through the raise. A manway is carried at each end of the stope, next to stope chutes. On completing the first stoping block, successive single-rill sections, 12 sets long, are mined. The manway sets of the last completed section are used for conveying filling to the new section. Ground is broken by flat holes drilled by mounted drifters. A round consists of 12 6-ft holes, loaded with

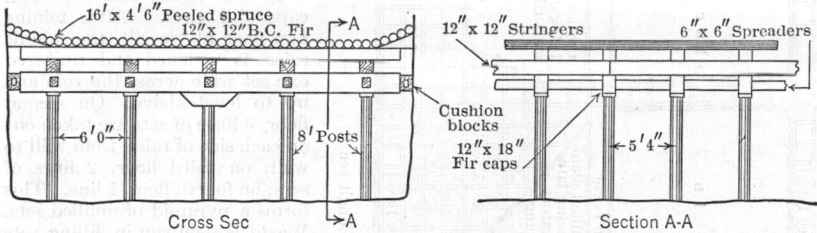

Fig 299. Sill-floor Timbering, Lake Shore Mine, Kirkland Lake, Ont

70% semi-gelatin dynamite. General practice is to advance the rill 2, or even 3, cuts before filling. Entire final face of a group of cuts is drilled, but not blasted until fill is introduced, thus permitting closer filling. Purchased sand is used for fill. Flooring over fill is spiked to caps, giving a slope of 56° to surface of fill. Crew of miner and helper do all work in a stope section; 20.11 tons are broken per machine-shift; powder consumption, 0.725 lb per ton.

Ground Hog mine, Vanadium, N M. Data from F. W. Richard (527) in 1930. Ore, Pb-Cu-Zn, occurs in irregular lenses in a fault fissure intruded by diorite porphyry and

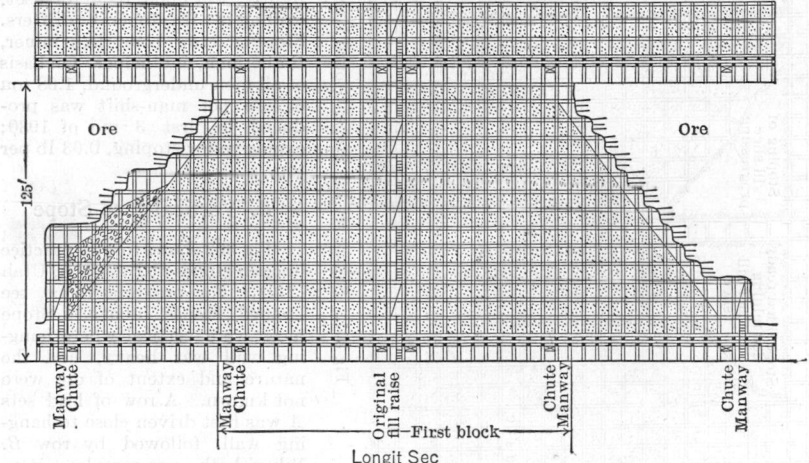

Fig 300. Square-set Rill Stope, Lake Shore Mine, Kirkland Lake, Ont

granodiorite dikes. As post-mineral faulting caused fracturing of ore and wall rocks, prompt support of ore and walls is necessary. Ore is usually massive sulphide; mill feed runs about 8% Pb, 3.5% Cu, 15% Zn, and 6.5 oz Ag per ton. Width of ore is 3–25 ft, normal to dip. Aver dip, about 60°. DEVELOPMENT is by vert shaft in hanging wall, intersecting vein at 300-level; inclined winze in vein from 400-level serves for mining below this horizon. Main levels are 100 ft apart vert; sub-levels half-way between main levels aid in distributing filling and make shorter lifts in raising. Stulled raises are 50 ft apart. STOPING. Rill stopes are used entirely. For ore widths less than 10 ft, filled rill stopes (Art 65) are used, with occasional timber support; for widths greater than 10 ft, square-set rills. Stoping blocks are 100 ft long, with a raise at each end and in the middle.

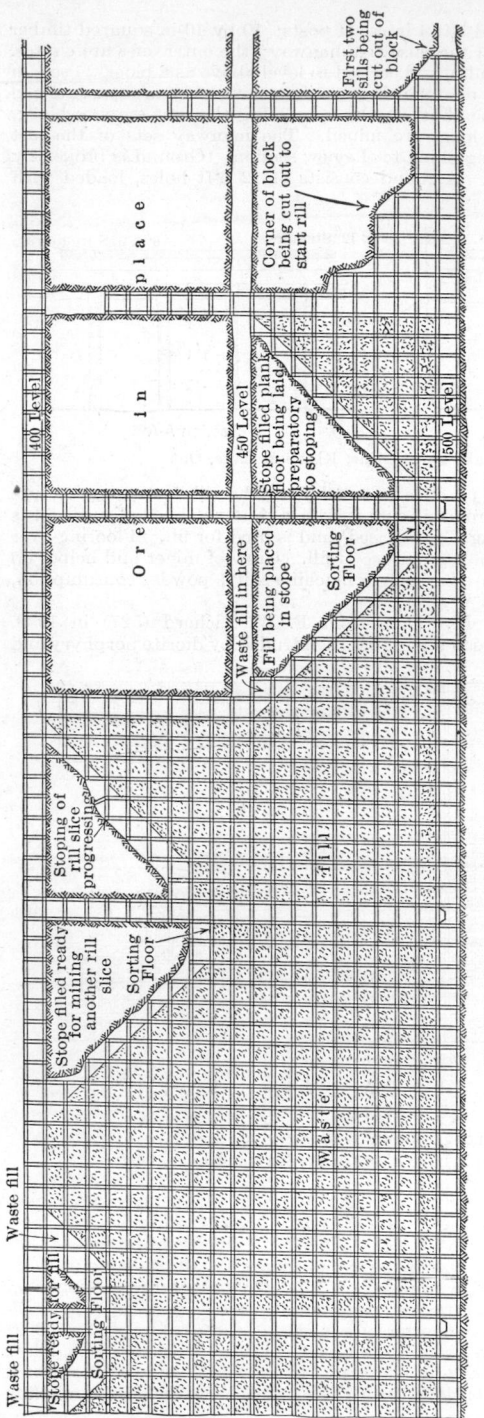

Fig 301. Square-set Rill Stope, Ground Hog Mine, Vanadium, N. M. Longit sec

Stoping starts by breasting to full width of ore on a main level. Floor sills of 10 by 10-in timber run from wall to wall and are covered by double 2-in flooring. In ore over 10 ft wide, square-sets are placed on the sills. Sets, 5 ft sq and 7 ft high, consist of 8 by 8-in posts, and 6 by 8-in caps and girts. After mining first floor above sill, the middle raise is widened and timbered one set wide across the vein and up to level above. On second floor, 3 lines of sets are taken out on each side of raise, from wall to wall; on third floor, 2 lines of sets; on fourth floor, 1 line. This forms a pyramid of unfilled sets. Waste is then run in, filling sets close to the back; after which flooring is laid on fill. Stoping continues on either side of raise as desired until toe of rill is within 10 ft of next raise; 2 sets nearest the raise are carried flat to furnish shoveling and sorting platform. For method of stoping at the several stages, see Fig 301. A few drill holes, blasted lightly, will make room for a set; drilling is with stopers or drifters. Stoping crew comprises miner, timberman, and helper. On basis of all men underground, 1.68 ton of ore per man-shift was produced in first 3 mo of 1930; explosive for stoping, 0.63 lb per ton.

d. Vertical-face Stope

Fig 302 shows former practice in open stopes at BINGHAM, Utah (211). For ore occurrence, see Domed stopes, above. Stope faces were vertical where hanging wall was heavy, and the nature and extent of ore were not known. A row of lead sets A was first driven close to hanging wall, followed by row B. When both were complete, stoping began at B, and sets C were carried to hanging wall. Successive vert slices were taken until the stope was worked out, or, if the weight became great, the stope was caved and a new one started alongside. Sills and caps were at right-angles to strike. Advantages (L. S. Cates): (a) "There is always a solid breast of ore on one side of stope, which relieves press on timbers.

(b) Should stopes cave unexpectedly, only the ore on floors and in chutes is lost, for a new stope can be opened by driving a row of sets on the sill floor, next to the caved stope, and carrying them up to the hanging as before."

This method in filled stopes is illustrated at BUNKER HILL & SULLIVAN MINE, Idaho. Data here are retained from 1927 edn of Handbook. More recent data by U. E. Brown (212) in 1931 show no material change. Large irregular shoots of heavy galena ore, with little waste, occur in shattered quartzite; dip, about 40°. Stopes, 300–700 ft long

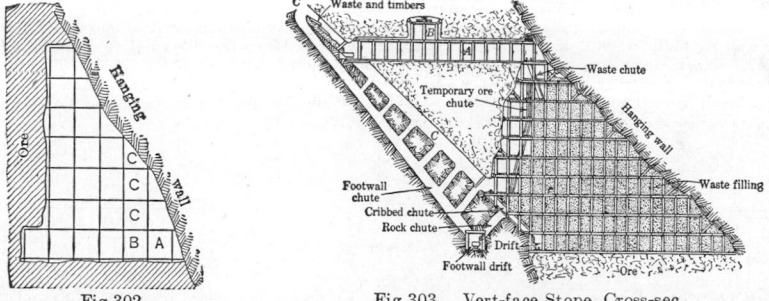

Fig 302   Fig 303.   Vert-face Stope, Cross-sec

and 40 ft wide, have been carried through lifts of 200 ft. Hanging wall and ore are heavy, and flat-back or stepped-face stopes expose areas of back too large for safety (214). Work begins on a level, Fig 303 (215); a vert slice, 3 or 4 sets wide, is carried up under hanging wall and filled. The face is then advanced toward footwall by mining vert slices 1 or 2 sets wide. Waste filling and timbers are dropped through footwall raise C, and trammed to top floor through crosscut A, 1 set wide. Waste is distributed in stope by temporary slides, as shown. A new crosscut B is driven directly over A to serve the next floor; crosscuts for lower floors are not shown, each being abandoned as a new floor

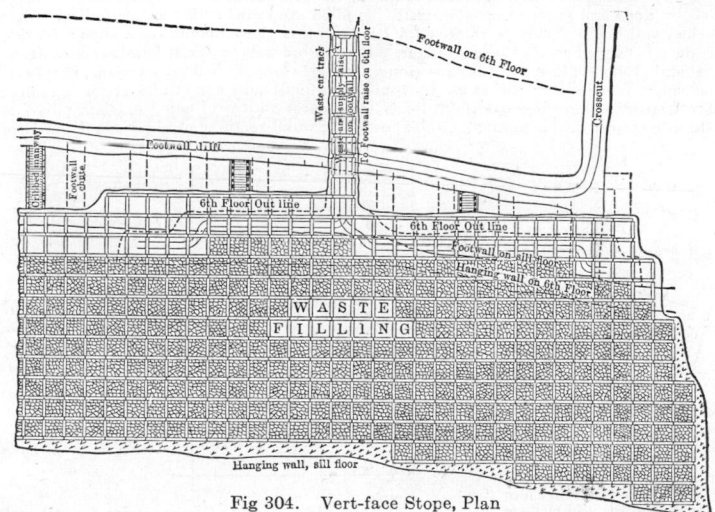

Fig 304.   Vert-face Stope, Plan

is opened. Fig 304 (S. A. Easton) is a plan of a narrower stope, worked up to 6th floor, showing the relation between work on top and lower floors, and arrangement of tracks for handling filling. In some stopes, filling is dumped through a raise along hanging wall; but a footwall raise is preferable in heavy ground. Rock chutes to footwall drift (Fig 303) are 15–20 ft apart, cribbed or lagged chutes being carried up from them through the filling as stope advances. On abandoning the sill floor, a raise from footwall side of rock drift is made, a little steeper than the footwall, and branched at intervals to intersect the ore at the upper floors. This raise serves as a chute when floors are advanced to footwall, and obviates necessity for transferring ore on an intermediate floor. This method is safe and provides prompt support for hanging wall. The sharp arch developed early in the stoping stage, and maintained until level above is reached, greatly increases strength of the ground. Most of the weight of ore is carried by footwall. See also Bib (575).

e. Underhand Square-set Stopes

Stopes of this type are unusual. Employed at BROKEN HILL SOUTH MINE, N S W, for mining chain pillars, 30 ft thick, under large filled stopes. Mining is done in vertical slices, 1 set wide, from wall to wall; when 2 or 3 adjacent slices are complete, they are filled before more ground is opened. Work starts from top of a winze, by an excavation for the set L (Fig 305). This undermines sets in a crosscut above, which are supported by a boom S. Set L is erected and caught up with a boom from the winze set (Fig 306). The 6 by 10-in crosspiece A supports the 2 caps and is

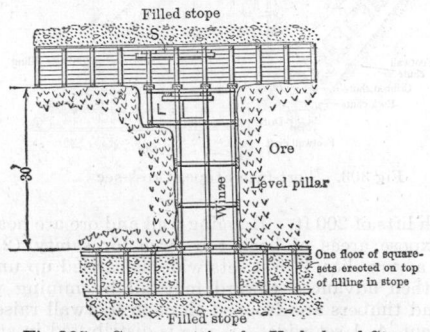

Fig 305.   Square-setting for Underhand Stope

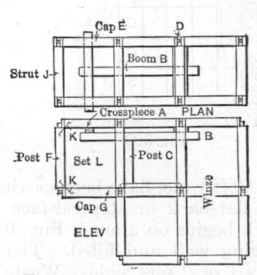

Fig 306.   Details of Underhand Square-setting

itself supported by boom B, which rests on C, its rear end being wedged under D. Dogs K tie posts F to caps and girts. After set L is blocked, the ground beneath is excavated, another set is suspended by dogs and process repeated until the filled stope below is reached. The bottom set is then blocked and boom B may be removed. By repeating these operations a slice 6 ft wide (1 set) and 30 ft deep is carried across the level pillar. Broken ore falls to and is handled on bottom floor of the underhand stope. Mining in the slice alongside starts from a lead set (Art 45), at one end of the top winze set. Work under old stope bottoms is difficult and sometimes requires spiling. It is found that timbers fail in slices over 60 ft long; for greater widths of lode the chain pillars are sliced in 2 sections. Object of this method is to expose only small sections of old stope floors at one time.

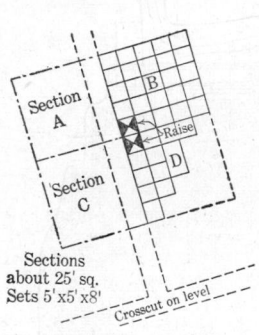

Fig 307.   Plan of 5th Floor of Underhand Square-set Stope, Briggs Mine

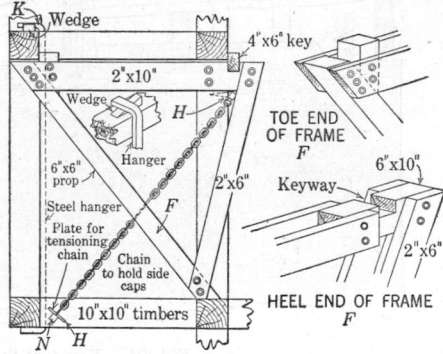

Fig 308.   Mode of Support for Underhand Square-sets, Briggs Mine

It is stated that, though slices are narrow, the 30-ft depth gives capacity and considerable economy. For details, see Bib (217).

Briggs mine, Bisbee, Arizona. Data from R. H. Dickson and G. J. Young in 1923 (579). Ore was copper and iron sulphides, overlain by irregular masses of barren sandy pyrite or brecciated quartzite. Overhand square-set stoping proved unsatisfactory, and the Briggs underhand method was evolved. Ore was blocked out by crosscuts and raises into sections from 10 by 20 ft to 25 by 35 ft horiz, and extending to height of ore or to level above. Square-sets were 5 by 5 ft by 7 ft 10 in high. The sections were mined in regular sequence around a central 2-compt raise (Fig 307). The 3 sets cornering on the raise at top of the ore were first mined and timbered with regular square-sets; mining then started on the floor below. When a set was undermined it was supported by the 2 triangular frames F (Fig 308, 309); by the 2 chains attached to dogs H, driven into the timbers and tightened by screwing up nuts N (Fig 308); and by light bent hangers K, tightened by wedges. These supports transmitted the wt to the raise sets, or to sets that had been blocked into place; they were removed and reused after the set had been blocked. Stoping on top and successive floors progressed downward (Fig 309), each floor being 1 set behind floor above; the ore fell to [chute below. When a section was finished it was waste-filled through a raise to level above before the adjoining section was mined.

A modified method of underhand square-setting, the Ratterree, used for mining small sections of sulphide ore adjoining worked-out filled square-set or cut-and-fill stopes, was also developed here (579). See also Art 57.

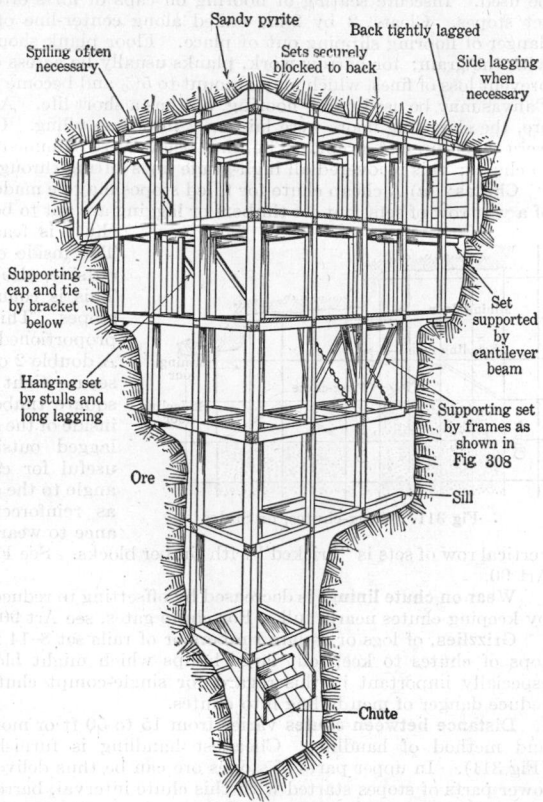

Fig 309. Briggs Method of Underhand Square-setting

47. HANDLING ORE, WASTE, AND TIMBER IN SQUARE-SET STOPES

Ore is handled in flat-back stopes by shoveling directly to chutes, by transfer to chutes in barrows or cars, or by slides. Use of slides is desirable, but may be impracticable if close filling is necessary or if careful sorting is important. Close spacing of chutes tends to low handling cost, but saving may be more than offset by added cost of timbering. A primary purpose of square-set rill stoping is to reduce ore-handling cost. Scrapers are sometimes used in square-set stopes; Fig 310 (189) shows one application, at Park Utah mine.

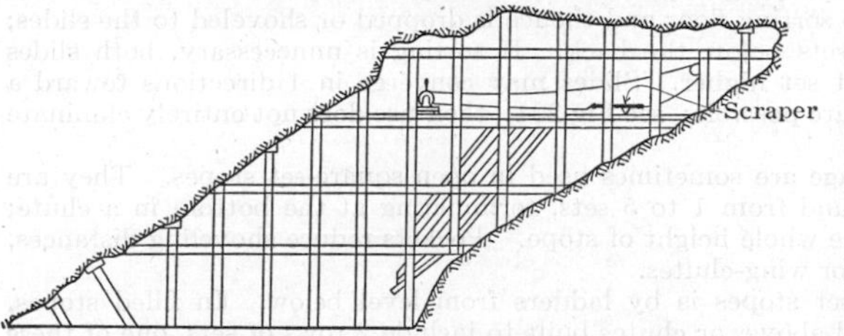

Fig 310. Use of Scraper in Square-set Stope, Park Utah Mine, Park City, Utah

Cross-Sec

Floors are of 2 to 5-in plank, long enough to cover 1 or 2 sets; the shorter length is more convenient; flooring is taken up and reused; 2-in plank is too weak to stand heavy blasting, and should be doubled, or protected by round lagging, or 3 or 4-in plank should be used. Insecure seating of flooring on caps or girts often causes accidents in square-set stopes. Cleats, 2 by 2-in, nailed along center-line of supporting members, reduce danger of flooring slipping out of place. Floor plank should be laid so that shoveling is with the grain; for barrow work, planks usually lie across caps. Over filling, tight floors prevent loss of fines, which may amount to 5% and become important with high-grade ore. Canvas may be used under flooring, but has a short life. At Goldfield, Nev, in high-grade ore, the shoveling floors were laid on 2 in of fine filling. On finishing a floor, the planks were taken up and swept. The fines below were skimmed off down to the caps and sent to chutes; this recovered all high-grade fines sifting through joints between planks (145).

Chutes: (a) A cheap chute for filled stopes may be made by simply lagging the outside of a vert row of sets, but set timbers or lagging are apt to be broken by falling ore; such a chute is feasible only with soft ore. (b) The inside of a row of sets (usually the outside, also) is lined with vertical planks. This is common in both open and filled stopes. Thickness of lining (2 to 4 in) is proportioned to wear during life of chute. A double 2 or 3-in lining may be used to secure tight joints. (c) Cribs of round or square timber, built independently or just inside of the sets, which may or may not be lagged outside. Independent chutes are useful for carrying through stopes at an angle to the sets. Chutes inside of sets act as reinforcement and offer strong resistance to wear and pressure of filling. (d) A vertical row of sets is "bricked" with timber blocks. See Fig 295; also, Black Rock mine, Art 90.

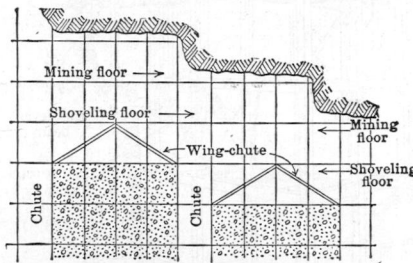

Fig 311. Wing-chutes, or Slides

Wear on chute linings is decreased by offsetting to reduce vert drop. It is also lessened by keeping chutes nearly full. For chute gates, see Art 90.

Grizzlies, of logs or square timbers or of rails 8–14 in apart, are often placed over tops of chutes to keep out large lumps which might block chute or gate. They are especially important in this regard for single-compt chutes in filled stopes; they also reduce danger of men falling into chutes.

Distance between chutes varies from 15 to 50 ft or more; it is closely related to cost and method of handling. Cheapest handling is furnished by slides or wing-chutes (Fig 311). In upper parts of stopes ore can be thus delivered to chutes 50 ft apart. In lower parts of stopes started with this chute interval, barrows are necessary.

In filled stopes, the closer the filling to back of stope, the smaller the area served by a slide. At Leonard mine, Butte, in flat-back stopes, 50 by 25 ft in horiz section, filling was kept 2 sets below the back; chute interval was 16 ft; about 50% of broken ore could be handled on slides (80). For economical handling, flat-back stopes usually require chutes closer together than those with inclined faces (see Rill stope, Art 46). Though barrows may be used with any chute interval, their handling cost is high, increasing rapidly with distance. It is best to use slides as much as possible, and to shovel remainder of ore to chutes. Shoveling distance should be kept down to 10 or 12 ft max, which requires chute intervals of 15 to 25 ft.

Wing-chutes (slides) are sloping floors of 3 to 4-in plank, spiked to the sets. In Fig 311 the ore falls 1 set to sorting floor and thence is dropped or shoveled to the slides; filling can thus be kept 3 sets below the back. If sorting is unnecessary, both slides and filling may be moved 1 set higher. Slides may converge in 4 directions toward a chute, and many variations are possible; see Fig 294; their use does not entirely eliminate shoveling.

Pockets or bins for storage are sometimes used in open square-set stopes. They are made by putting lining around from 1 to 5 sets, terminating at the bottom in a chute; they may extend through the whole height of stope. Pockets reduce shoveling distances, and may obviate necessity for wing-chutes.

Access to open square-set stopes is by ladders from level below. In filled stopes, there may be a raise to level above, or chutes built to include 2 rows of sets, one of these compartments being a MANWAY. In heavy ground, these are harder to keep open than single-compartment or "blind" chutes, but the manway is not only a traveling way through filled sets, but facilitates repairs to the ore chute and clearing it when it clogs.

Filling may be obtained in part from sorting, or from breaking waste or low-grade inclusions in the orebody; see also Fig 289, Argonaut mine. For running in filling from outside sources, a raise to the level above is necessary. In flat-back stopes, filling is distributed by shovels, barrows, or cars, depending on size of stope and distance between waste raises; in rill stopes, distribution is largely or entirely by gravity.

Timbers are handled most cheaply when lowered or dropped through a raise from level above; 1 compt of a waste raise may be used thus. Lacking access to stope from above, timbers are hoisted from below by a windlass, or electric or air hoist. In filled stopes, TIMBER CHUTES are sometimes kept open through the filling by lagging and lining a vertical row of sets next to a manway or ore-chute; or a timber slide may be built in a corner of manway.

48. DIMENSIONS OF SQUARE-SETS

Horizontal dimensions. Table 38 shows that practice favors sets about 5 by 5 ft in plan, with floors 7 to 8 ft apart.

C. T. Rice states (80): (a) Posts should be far enough apart to give shoveling room; to allow for right and left-hand shovelers, they should be equidistant capwise and girtwise. A clear space of 4.5 ft is about minimum for effic shoveling; hence with 10-in timbers, posts should be at least 5 ft 4 in centers. (b) Strength of ore limits max size of set, as the ground must stand unsupported over area of 1 set while timbers are being placed. Heavy press from weak ore may require smaller sets (see e). (c) Sets should be proportioned so that 1 round of holes breaks room for a new set, thus allowing prompt placing and blocking of sets. (d) Large sets are desirable in reducing amount of timber per ton of ore, but, in large sets, timbers are heavier and cost more to handle, and a stope started with a large post interval may become unmanageable if the ground suddenly becomes heavy. (e) Distance between posts and the area of stope floor are related factors. By working stopes rapidly in small sections, the pressure on timbers is reduced, thus allowing use of larger sets and smaller timbers. (f) A compromise between all the factors usually limits the max spacing of posts to 6.5 ft and minimum spacing to 5 ft.

Probably the distance between posts could often be increased without overloading timbers. In close-filled stopes, where the weight comes onto timbers from above and is transmitted to posts through lagging and caps, a comparison of relative strength and cost of sets of different size can be made.

Minimum height of sets for headroom is about 6.5 ft in the clear; in many mines, to allow for settlement, posts are cut to give a clear 7 ft. Length and cross-sec of post must also be adjusted to withstand pressures.

At Bisbee, Ariz, a reduction in pressure due to rapid work in small stopes allowed use of 8 by 8 and 10 by 10-in posts, instead of 12 by 12-in, and also an increase in height from 6 to 7.5 ft. Increasing length of posts effects no saving in timber, unless the increase is sufficient to save one or more complete floors in a lift. Long posts probably increase cost of placing caps, girts, and blocking, enough to counterbalance the saving in timber.

In 1914, the Ariz Copper Co lengthened posts from 6.5 to 9.5 ft; this increased the extraction per set from 170 to 250 cu ft of ore, and reduced total timbering cost 15%. Crushing strength of 6.5-ft posts is so much greater than transverse strength of cap and girt, that an increase in height of post does not materially reduce strength of set. It is difficult to prevent long posts from swinging when pressure comes from the side (178).

Size and strength of timber. As stated by E. D. Gardner and W. O. Vandenburg (189), it is difficult, or impossible, to estimate accurately the strength required of square-sets. Experience is the guide in selecting the kind and size of timber for given conditions. Where filling is used, requirements of strength are usually temporary, because pressures are eventually taken up by the fill. Hence, many mines use cheaper timber for square-sets than for use where more permanent strength is required, as in shafts or on main-level workings. Use of timber preservatives may be justified in the latter case, but not in the former. On the other hand, use of square-sets in stopes tends to give a false sense of security, and strength requirements should be judged accordingly; especially in blocky ground, where sets may be subjected to sudden and heavy shocks. Tight side and head blocking tends to reduce this danger.

49. FRAMING SQUARE-SETS

General. The two general types of framing are "post-butting" and "cap-butting." In either, variations in framing are theoretically without limit. Fig 312-337 show how widely practice has varied. Diversity of framing in early days was largely due to honest theorizing, but probably in part chargeable to desire for originality. Lack of standardization today is probably due to tendency to follow custom. As far as possible, symmetry and simplicity in framing should be sought.

Post-butting *vs* **cap-butting sets.** Early practice was about equally divided between these types. E. D. Gardner and W. O. Vanderburg (189) show that recent practice trends to more general use of cap-butting. Choice can not be based on theoretical grounds alone, because: (*a*) unit pressures in square-set stopes generally exceed safe bearing values used for ordinary timber structures and hence there is considerable crushing of the joints; (*b*) direction of pressure is rarely parallel to caps or to posts, and its exact amount is never known; (*c*) distribution of stress in different members of a set under eccentric loading can not be calculated, because joints are indeterminate and the members do not fit exactly.

Strength of timber under compression across the grain is from 10 to 20% of its compressive strength parallel to the grain. In framing post-butting sets, the area of the post tenons is made 12 to 44% of area of the joint; in cap-butting sets, the area of cap tenons is 10 to 66% of the area of the joint. Hence, under pressures within the limit of safe bearing values, square-set joints are strongest in the direction in which the tenons butt. For such conditions of loading, post-butting sets should be used where the direction of max press is vert; cap-butting sets, where direction of max pres is lateral. Where pressures exceed safe bearing values, joints are compressed. In cap-butting sets, ends of posts bear entirely on wood in cross grain, and under vert press the rate of compression is equal over whole area of joint. In post-butting sets, under heavy vert press, the post tenons or HORNS must fail before the crossgrain wood in caps and girts can aid in transmitting press to the post. As rate of compression is not the same in all parts of a joint, settlement in a stope is often irregular. C. T. Rice cites evidence (218) to show that settlement is greater and more irregular in post-butting than in cap-butting sets, and that more auxiliary timbers are needed in the former to keep floors level. Hence, many engineers prefer cap-butting sets for heavy vert press, and practice is almost uniform in using them for heavy lateral press also, though arguments like the above indicate the superiority of post-butting sets. But, in heavy ground, filling follows mining closely and takes most of the lateral press; the smaller and more uniform rate of vert settlement of cap-butting sets is a strong argument for their use in such ground.

Square-sets may also fail by "jack-knifing"; posts swing out of line and a girt or cap may drop, allowing adjacent sets to collapse. Hence, wide seats for girts and caps are desirable in cap-butting sets. In post-butting sets, wide seats are obtainable only by reducing size of the post horn. Long horns of small cross-sec are objectionable, as they break easily. With timbers over 10 by 10 in, post-butting sets with adequate shoulders and horns are readily framed. Sometimes, to give a wider bearing for either girt or cap, horns on posts are not of square section; they require a complicated framing machine. Girts are more apt to pull away from their seats under light than under heavy press.

Empirical rules proposed for framing details: (*a*) length of the post horn should be less than its least cross-sec dimension; (*b*) girts and caps should have a seat on the post not less than 2 in wide; a wider shoulder is desirable (218). SIMPLE FRAMING is best, especially for hand framing. Post-butting sets are generally simpler and cheaper to frame than cap-butting, but the difference is small when framing machines are used. Complicated joints resist distortion better, because of the numerous shoulders, but this advantage is doubtful, as corners are points of weakness at which crushing begins, and such joints are difficult to assemble if timbers have been even slightly crushed. SYMMETRICAL FRAMING is best; costs less to place timbers when posts can be set either end up; caps and girts should be so framed that either of two opposite faces may be placed upwards.

Examples. Fig 312–319 show post-butting sets; Fig 320–327, cap-butting. Some of the mines mentioned are no longer active. In Fig 313 the post is unsymmetrical, with a 6-in horn at top and 4-in at bottom; this secures a shallower mortise at top of set, which is easier to clean out and allows "flirting" the post (Art 52) if sets have swung out of line; long, slender horns make flirting of posts difficult. Another way to reduce length of horns of post-butting sets is to cut them of equal length and short enough to leave a "squeeze-space" between them. In early days one theory was that a squeeze-space allowed a certain "give" when press came upon sets (189); the practice has lost favor, because squeeze-spaces permitted excessive settlement. Set in Fig 314 is simple and symmetrical; post horns are short and strong; and dapped down on post, so that the horn takes only part of lateral thrust. Some examples show unframed girts, with narrow seat on post; bearing on post should be broad enough to avoid the dropping out of girts in case of general movement of sets; use of one unframed member of a set cheapens cost of framing, but, as sawed timbers vary in cross-sec, unframed ends must often be dressed in the stopes. Instances of use of narrow girts are shown (as in Fig 321); practicable where girtwise press is slight, but narrow girts provide smaller support for floor plank.

Combination sets contain both round and square timbers; they are planned to avoid the difficulties incident to framing sets entirely of round timber.

Fig 328 is a cap-butting set, with round posts and square caps and girts. It is well designed, full strength of post is obtained, all members are symmetrical and the set is easily stood and reinforced (152). A good shoveling floor may be laid either cap or girtwise. Fig 329 is a similar design,

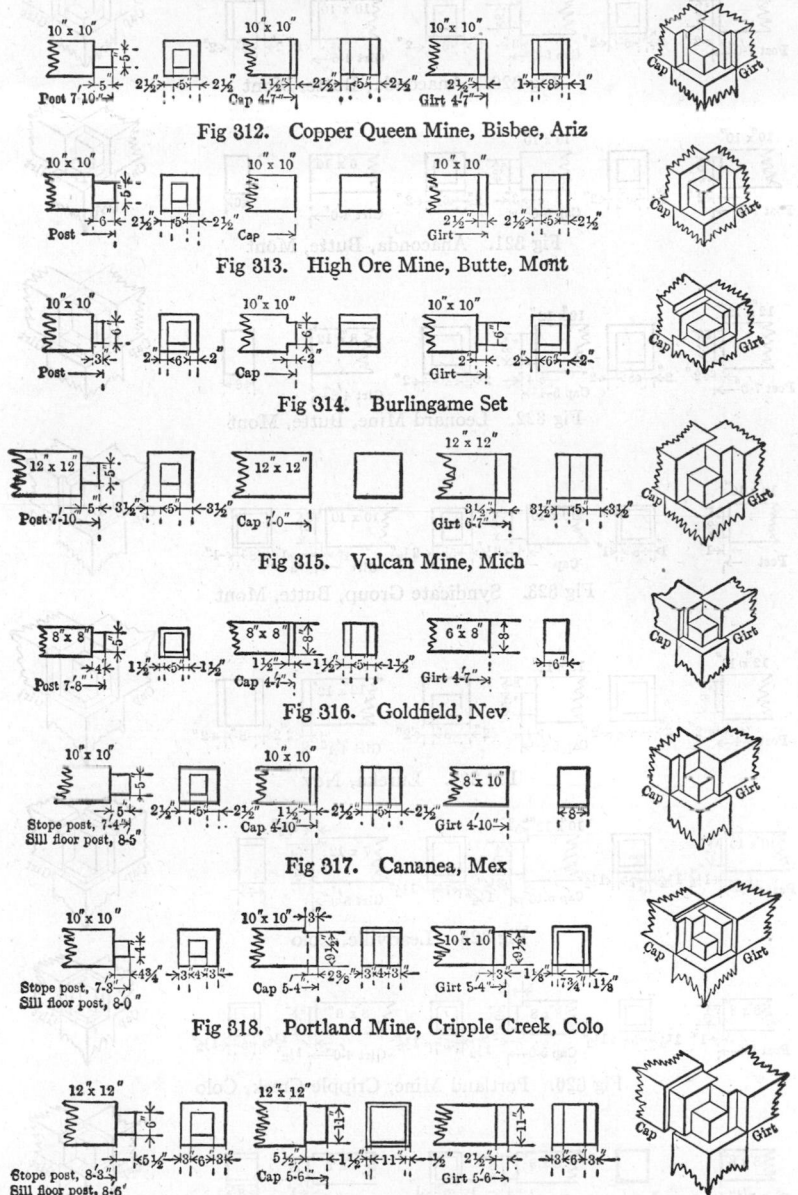

Fig 312. **Copper Queen Mine, Bisbee, Ariz**

Fig 313. **High Ore Mine, Butte, Mont**

Fig 314. **Burlingame Set**

Fig 315. **Vulcan Mine, Mich**

Fig 316. **Goldfield, Nev**

Fig 317. **Cananea, Mex**

Fig 318. **Portland Mine, Cripple Creek, Colo**

Fig 319. **Homestake Mine, S Dak**

but with posts butting; its weak point is the slender upper horn of post, the bottom horn being only 3-in; it affords good shoveling floors. Fig 330 is a cap-butting set, with round post and girt. The bottom post horn is only 1.5 in long, on the theory that it is easier and quicker to stand a post

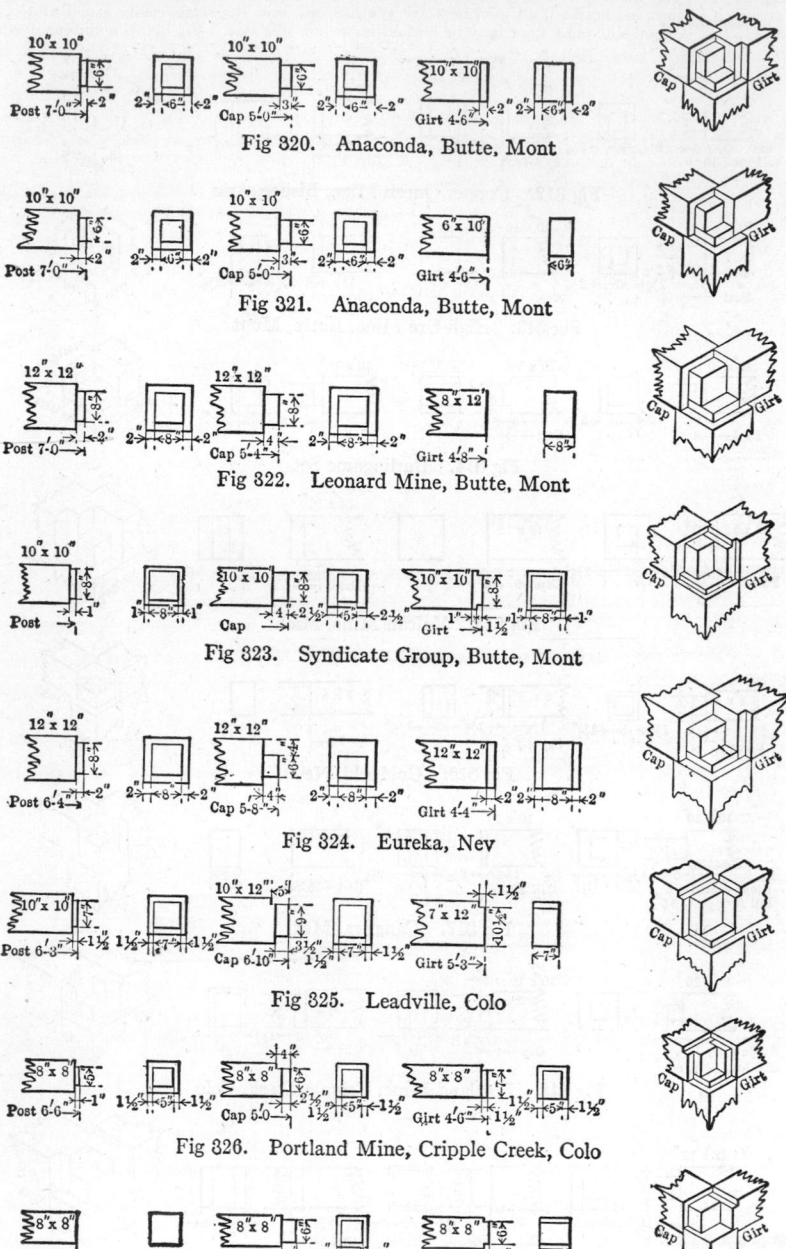

Fig 320. Anaconda, Butte, Mont

Fig 321. Anaconda, Butte, Mont

Fig 322. Leonard Mine, Butte, Mont

Fig 323. Syndicate Group, Butte, Mont

Fig 324. Eureka, Nev

Fig 325. Leadville, Colo

Fig 326. Portland Mine, Cripple Creek, Colo

Fig 327. Esperanza, Mex

with a short horn (219). It requires an unsymmetrical cap horn, and the small round girt of this set precludes use of a floor laid girtwise.

Round-timber sets. Simplest joint is made by first squaring the ends of timbers for a sufficient length to avoid interference of their cylindrical surfaces at the joint, which is then framed as with square timber. This saves cost of squaring the whole log, an important item in hand work. Disadvantages: the joint utilizes a max of only 60% of cross-sec of the timber, and round timber weighs at least 40% more than square of equal joint strength.

Fig 331, 332 show simple framings, open to the objections stated; also, they provide a poor seat for the bottom of the post. These sets can be framed in machines of the block type.

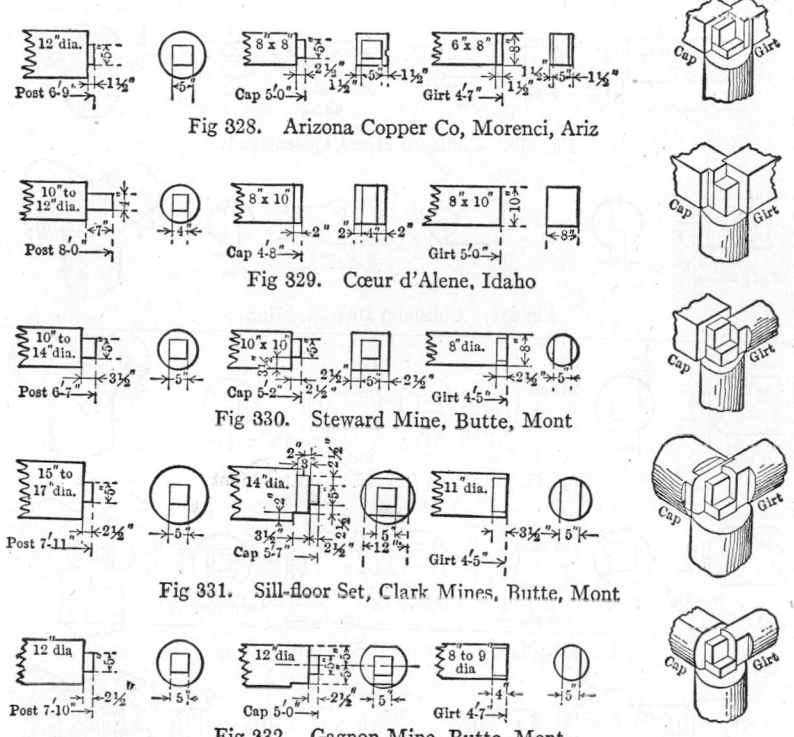

Fig 328.　Arizona Copper Co, Morenci, Ariz

Fig 329.　Cœur d'Alene, Idaho

Fig 330.　Steward Mine, Butte, Mont

Fig 331.　Sill-floor Set, Clark Mines, Butte, Mont

Fig 332.　Gagnon Mine, Butte, Mont

Bevel or miter framing (Fig 333–336) brings the entire area of members in contact at the joint. In general, the sets are hard to stand and block, and the bevels facilitate distortion under pressure if the sets once get out of line. Post, cap, and girt of a square-set must be firmly blocked when the other members are missing. Many miter joints require blocking on top before they can be blocked sidewise, or else simultaneous blocking in 2 directions. Either case increases expense and difficulty of placing. Fig 333 has a simple miter joint, to permit hand-framing of stunted, twisted timber; caps and girts are identical (209). Fig 334 is a hand-framed set, for heavy vert pressure; a 1-in squeeze-space is left between the post tenons, giving a cushioning effect said to prevent caps from splitting (221). It may be blocked in any direction, with some of the members missing. Fig 335 is a set designed by D. W. Brunton, in which end of post is beveled. It requires top blocking, to prevent riding of cap and girt, before it can be blocked sidewise. The square and bevel joint (Fig 336) is the best bevel framing for cap-butting round-timber sets. It is easily blocked, and the cap is the only member expensive to frame (222).

The best framing for round timbers is the STEP-DOWN SET (Fig 337). It is made possible by using the cutter-head saw, and costs little if any more than simpler types cut with block framers. Full strength of timbers is utilized, the square shoulders resist distortion and make for easy blocking, and ends of posts and caps are alike. A girt more than 10 in diam is seldom used (219). In general, better joints are obtained, in round-timber sets, if posts and caps are approx of equal diam. Upper side of large caps is slabbed off, to give a flat surface for flooring if laid capwise and to avoid interference with flooring laid girtwise.

Round *vs* square timber for square-sets. ROUND TIMBER is cheaper, has lower freight rates, and is stronger per sq in, because the outer fibers are uncut, but round timber is harder to handle and aline than square; caps must be slabbed to receive flooring, though cost of slabbing may be offset by value of slabs, if used for lagging. Reinforcement of round-timber sets is difficult and expensive. Sound fallen timber, and some trees of poor grade, or too small to go to the sawmill, often furnish adequate square-set timbers at reduced cost (219). SQUARE TIMBER is best for sills. In some round-timber stopes, square timber is used for the levels, manways, and chutes, to cheapen work of reinforcement.

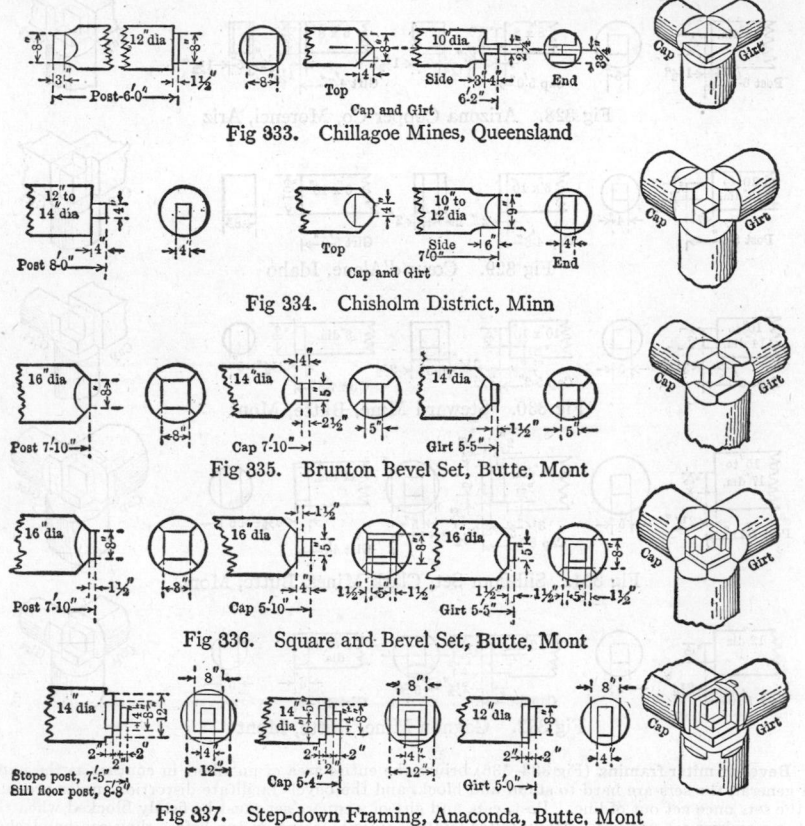

Fig 333.   Chillagoe Mines, Queensland

Fig 334.   Chisholm District, Minn

Fig 335.   Brunton Bevel Set, Butte, Mont

Fig 336.   Square and Bevel Set, Butte, Mont

Fig 337.   Step-down Framing, Anaconda, Butte, Mont

Square timber is preferred for chute-sets; it provides a flat face for spiking lining, and lasts longer in heavy ground than slabbed round timber.

P. B. Scotland states that round timber is stronger either with or across grain than square timber of same cross-sec and material. There are no data showing comparative strength of round and square timber of equal diam (*i e*, 10 in diam and 10 in square). A few transverse tests on 5-ft pieces of Texas pine at Morenci, Ariz, showed equal strength for pieces 8 in square and 8 in diam, but round timber deflected more and gave more warning of failure than square under same load. A safe estimate is that round timber between 6 and 16 in diam is as strong in both compression and bending as square timber 1 in smaller on the side. Nonobservance of this relation in substituting round for square timber destroys the saving effected by cheaper cost of the round.

Among 49 metal mines listed by Gardner and Vanderburg (189) in 1933, as employing the square-set system, 11 used round timber for all 3 members, and 10 others used round posts, with round girt or cap in 6 cases.

50. TIMBERING ON SILL FLOOR AND WALLS, SQUARE-SET STOPES

Sill-floor timbering (not always used) should be designed to give adequate foundation for the timbers above. Provision should be made for settlement, for reinforcing around traveling ways, for clearance between timbers at turnouts, and for supporting the timbering when the stope below breaks through. To meet these requirements practice varies with type of orebody, character of ore and walls, kind and size of stope, and speed of work.

Sills. Fig 338 shows a complete system, consisting of long sills (stringers), mortised at intervals to receive post tenons, and braced apart by sill-ties (girts, spreaders, or short sills). Long sills are also called 1-post, 2-post sills, etc, depending on number of posts they support. Sills are braced to stope walls by short pieces (butt-sills) cut to fit from sill-ties. Joints between long sills are usually made under posts, with butt or halved joints. For simpler framing, see Fig 339. Length of long

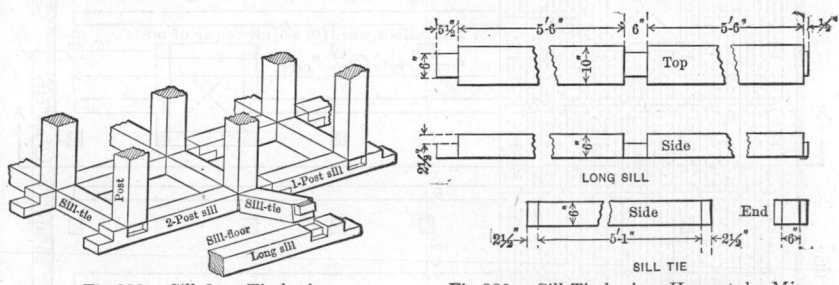

Fig 338. Sill-floor Timbering   Fig 339. Sill Timbering, Homestake Mine

sills depends on the ground; some ores will not stand unsupported over more than 1 set, thus requiring 1-post sills. In strong ground, convenience in handling determines max length, which usually covers 2 or 3 sets. Size of sills is from 5 by 10-in to 12 by 12-in or larger, depending on size of posts.

Long sills, firmly braced, are good in open stopes, where the floor is in ore. Sills extending over 2 or 3 sets will bridge a considerable opening, when the floor is subsequently mined, and are easily picked up on posts from stope timbering below. Framing for sill-ties (Fig 338) prevents them from dropping out when this work is going on. Wedging is relied upon to hold simpler framing (Fig 339).

Sills distribute pressure and reduce settlement on a soft floor. In open stopes, sills are covered with plank or poles for shoveling; in filled stopes, a floor prevents runs of filling into stope below. Attempts have been made to set sills in line with corresponding sills on level above, but it is unnecessary, as stope timbers may swing 1 or 2 ft out of alinement before the level above is reached. Size of stope and speed of work should be adjusted so that sills will not rot before stope from below breaks through. See Bib (224) for replacement of rotted sills. Simple

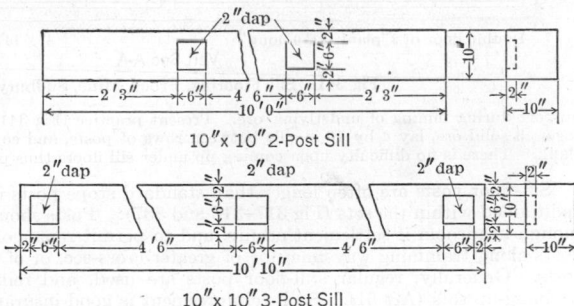

10″ x 10″ 2-Post Sill

10″ x 10″ 3-Post Sill

Fig 340. Details of Stope Sills, Bisbee, Ariz

forms of sill often suffice. A 3-post sill of 5 by 10 timber is common for 10 by 10 posts, which have flat bottoms and are braced capwise by 2-in plank spiked on top of sills; light sprags brace the post and sill girtwise.

Examples. Bisbee, Ariz (practice in 1939, contributed by H. M. Lavender). Timbering of sill-floor sets depends on nature of the ground. If floor is waste, flat-bottom posts are usual, resting on small blocks with 4 by 6-in spreaders between the posts. If floor is ore, to be mined from below, general practice is to use regular caps and girts; 2-, 3-, or 4-post caps, and posts supported on special "stope" or "mud" sills, of 10 by 10-in or 4 by 10-in timber, dapped 2 in deep to take the post's 6-in square horn. Length of sills is for 2, 3, or 4 posts, and 5- or 6-ft sets; Fig 340 shows sills for 2- and 3-post, 5-ft sets. In very soft ground, even though the floor is waste, regular caps and girts are used with the special sills, as they afford better foundation for the sets above. Goldfield, Nev. Sill-floor posts (10 by 10-in) have a flat bottom and stand on 8 by 10 sills; 2-in spreaders are spiked to sills between posts, but there are no braces between sills. Lateral bracing for feet of posts is furnished by a floor of 2 layers of 2-in plank spiked to top of sills (145). BUTTE, Mont. Amalgamated Copper Co often omits sills (80). Flat-bottom posts stand directly on stope floor, or on footblocks; 4 by 10 spreaders brace feet of posts capwise, 2-in braces, girtwise. This practice is largely due to time required to level off rough points on stope floor, for placing sills properly. In some camps, sills are bedded on a layer of muck for quicker placing and because the muck protects them when the floor is mined from below. Floor is sheathed with poles or old plank laid across the spreaders. Filling is well compacted by the time the stope comes up from below, and this type of sill floor is picked up as readily as if sills were used. Sills are omitted under round-timber posts also, though the latter are then difficult to aline. G. D. Moulthrop (219) states that, with round timbers, sills are often of 2-in plank, set to grade with a carpenter's level and alined by plumb-bobs from centers of caps already in place. SUDBURY, Ont. (Data from H. J. Mutz, in 1938.) International Nickel Co does not put framed sills under first-floor posts in Frood mine (Art 46). Where 4 by 10-in sills have been used under posts, they have been so badly squeezed as to offer no

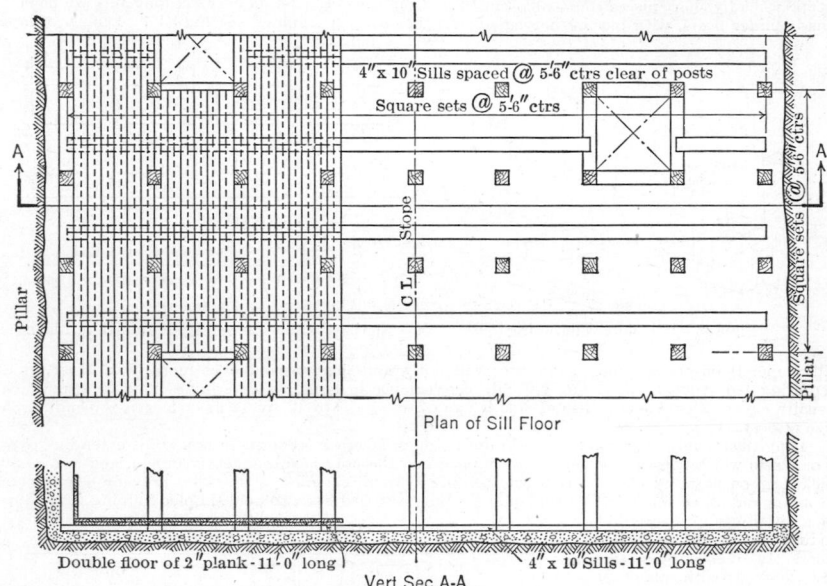

Fig 341. Sill Flooring, Frood Mine, Sudbury, Ont

support during mining of underlying ore. Present practice (Fig 341) is to stand square-bottomed posts on solid ore, lay 4 by 10-in sills between rows of posts, and cover these with 2 layers of 2-in plank. There is no difficulty upon coming up under sill floors thus prepared.

Sill-floor posts are often longer than standard stope posts if tramming ways are to be maintained within the sets (Fig 317–319 and 337). Posts should be long enough to afford enough headroom if settlement occurs, and to permit repair or reinforcement of timbers. Posts along tramming ways may be of greater cross-sec, or of stronger timber than stope posts. Generally, regular still-floor posts are used, and reinforced by added posts or doubling-up sets (Art 51). Such reinforcement is good insurance if there is possibility of excessive weight as stope progresses upward.

Drift sets with battered posts are sometimes used for sill floors in narrow or moderately wide veins, with heavy lateral press, as shown in Fig 342 (219). Posts are selected timbers, 14 to 23-in diam. The large batter (1 : 4) gives strength against side pressure and postpones repairs. False caps, placed over the set caps, receive sheeting on which the filling rests; space between sheeting and caps aids in repairing or replacing timbers.

At Leonard mine, Butte (Fig 343) (80), drifts, 1 set wide and sunk 1 set below stope floor, have been used. This simple plan reduces pressure on the level timbers, unless in very wide ore. Such stopes are somewhat harder to take up from below than those with flat floor. The level is called the sill floor, and the floor on which the stope is opened, the bedrock floor; sills are omitted on both. Sill-floor posts are 7 ft 11 in long and from 12-in diam up. Bedrock and stope posts are 7 ft 5 in long, 12 and 10-in diam, respectively. See also Argonaut mine, Fig 289.

Turnouts from main drifts into crosscuts require special timbering, to avoid short-radius track curves and for clearance between car and posts. At such points a double

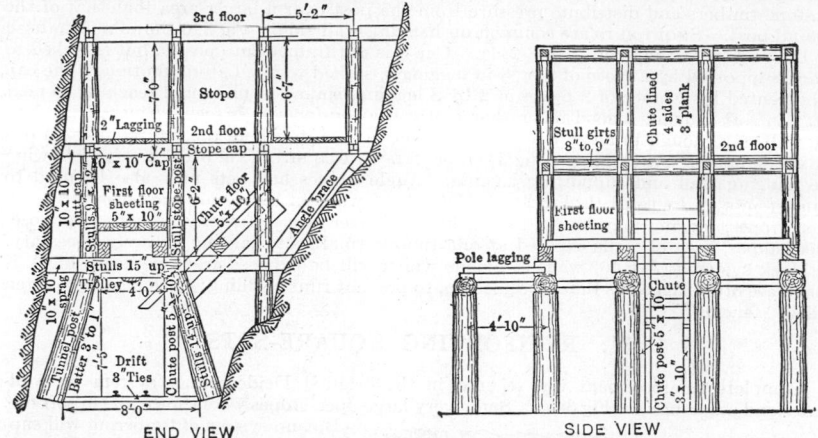

Fig 342. Sill-floor Timbering, Steward Mine

length cap (and sill) is used, with a flat-end post under its center. Later a truss set (Fig 356) may be built over the long cap and the post removed. At Bingham, Utah, an

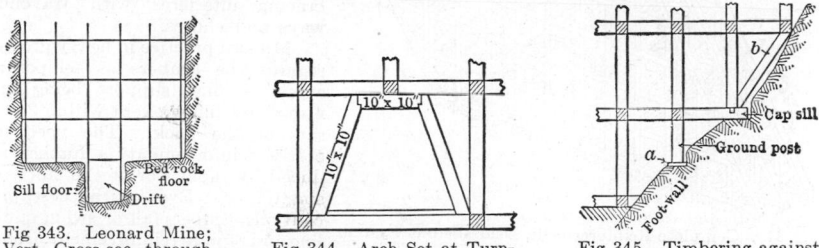

Fig 343. Leonard Mine; Vert Cross-sec through Stope

Fig 344. Arch Set at Turnout, Bingham, Utah

Fig 345. Timbering against Sloping Footwall

arch set (Fig 344), built on the sill floor, was used for reinforcing long caps (226). Its applicability depends on height and width of sets and size of car. Special timbering for turnouts is avoided by using turntables; most engineers prefer timbering.

Timbering on walls. Standard sets are often impossible in mining along irregular walls of dipping orebodies. Square-sets must have firm support on the footwall and follow the hanging closely enough to allow proper blocking of timbers.

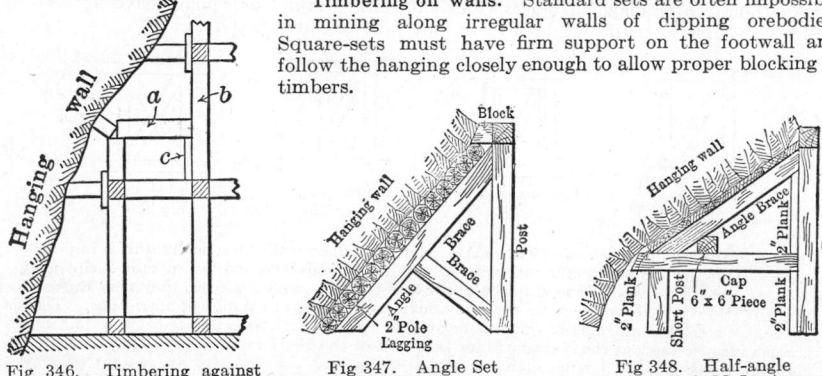

Fig 346. Timbering against Inclined Hanging Wall

Fig 347. Angle Set (E & M Jour)

Fig 348. Half-angle Set (E & M Jour)

In firm ground, short posts, caps, or girts are used along the walls, with their ends in hitches or wedged against the rock. Short posts on the footwall are GROUND POSTS

(Fig 345). Use of the bearing block a, and depth of hitch depend on character of ground. CAP-SILL (butt-cap or butt-brace) is used on flat dips or soft rock, to tie the foot of the post to stope timbers and distribute pressure from the post over a larger area than that of the ground post. SHORT SETS are common on hanging-wall side. Fig 346 shows a form used by L. S. Cates at Bingham, Utah (211). Cap a is not framed into post b, but is spiked to it and supported by a piece of 2 by 8-in lagging c, spiked to b. Lateral motion of the cap is prevented by a brace of 2 pieces of 2 by 8 lagging, spiked in place and reaching to next set. In soft ground, a good but rather costly bearing for sets is secured by cutting into the walls far enough to allow use of full-size sets at points where the dip requires an off-set in the floors. ANGLE SETS (Fig 347), or HALF-ANGLE SETS (Fig 348), are for following the hanging wall and supporting lagging. Angle braces and sets may also be used to support sets on footwall (b, Fig 345). Details of wall timbering are varied locally. In open stopes, lagging may be used on either wall over areas of shelly ground. In close-filled stopes, area of walls exposed at one time is small, and lagging is rarely necessary. In block systems (Art 46) walls of blocks which will be exposed when adjacent block is mined are often lagged as the stope goes up, to prevent runs of filling; such lagging is often called " fencing."

51. REINFORCING SQUARE-SETS

Complete reinforcement was secured in the original Deidesheimer system by wall-plates and angle-braces (Fig 349). Some very large open stopes were thus made in soft ore.

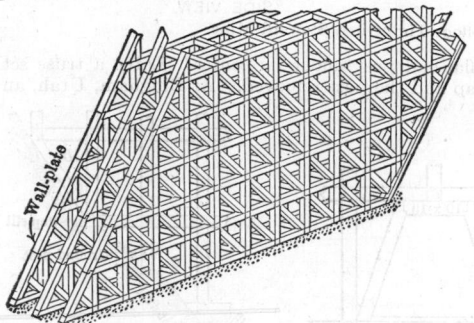

Fig 349. Complete Reinforcement, Deidesheimer System

But no system of timbering will support heavy rock pressures for any length of time. Wall-plates and complete angle-bracing have been discarded because of their cost; also, bracing interferes with traveling ways and chutes.

Modern practice in heavy ground regards the timbers as temporary supports, final support being furnished by filling, kept within 2 or 3 sets of the back. The need for costly reinforcement is further reduced by rapid working in stopes of small area. Even with these precautions, timbers fail or swing out of line and require reinforcement. Reinforcing timbers are common on sill floors, where haulageways must be kept open under heavy press from filling in stope above (Art 50). Reinforcement is used also in open square-set stopes in amounts varying widely with local conditions. When such stopes are in strong ground, the sets serve merely to support slabs, and as staging for miners and broken ore; in that case, no reinforcement may be needed.

Angle-braces or diagonal braces (Fig 350), either round or square, have no tenons; thin wedges may be used to tighten them, but a driving fit is better.

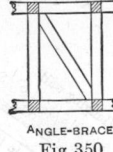

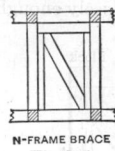

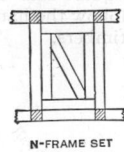

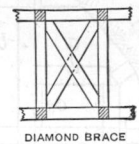

ANGLE-BRACE	N-FRAME BRACE	N-FRAME SET	DIAMOND BRACE
Fig 350	Fig 351	Fig 352	Fig 353

Theoretically, the brace should be at right-angles to hanging wall; practically, this is impossible. Angle-braces applied to sets tending to swing out of line are effective only in cases of incipient distortion and light pressures. If used in the upper sets of open or filled stopes, they may cause caps or girts to " ride " off the posts when the sets above are unblocked by mining operations. Tenons on posts at the ends of an angle-brace must be strong. When timbers or joints begin to fail, modified braces may be used, as the N-frame brace (Fig 351) or the N-frame set (Fig 352). The X-frame, or diamond brace (Fig 353) is uncommon. Angle-braces are also used to take weight off a post showing signs of failure (b, Fig 356); this is good for reinforcing drift posts on sill floors, as it does not decrease cross-sec of traveling way. The same bracing, with post b omitted, is placed over long caps at turnouts, or, with the post a omitted, it will take the weight of stope filling off center post of a haulageway. Sets thus braced are TRUSS-SETS; their use on the 1st floor to relieve sill-floor timbering is uncommon, as it involves keeping 1st-floor sets open. Truss-sets also support stope floors, where a post is removed to allow an angling chute to pass.

Reinforcing posts, stulls, or helpers (Fig 354) are convenient for picking up failing ends of caps and girts; they are round or square; size, from a 2-in plank to a post.

Doubling-up sets (false sets) are 3 or 4-piece reinforcing sets, like the N-brace (Fig 351) and N-frame (Fig 352), with angle braces omitted. The timbers are usually of same size as set timbers, but joints are not framed. They may be used to stop distortion, instead of angle-braces; like the latter, they are inadequate for heavy pressure or bad cases of swinging.

Cribs and bulkheads, next to rock filling, afford strongest reinforcement. Cribs, of round or square timber, are built between the posts of sets (Fig 355). They may be of timbers only, or filled with rock. Bulkheads, of criss-crossed timbers, skin to skin, are stronger than open cribs, but cost more. When used in open stopes to arrest

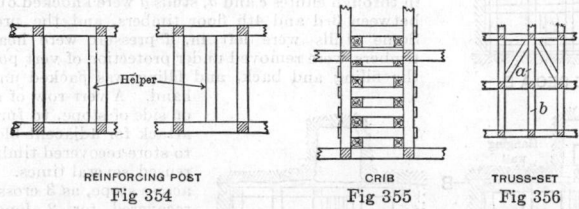

REINFORCING POST   CRIB   TRUSS-SET
Fig 354   **Fig 355**   **Fig 356**

swinging or crushing, or to prevent runs of filling, the bulkheads or cribs extend from wall to wall and from floor to back. In close-filled stopes, trouble from swinging sets may be stopped by building one or more cribs 4 sets square, on top of the filled sets and rarely more than 2 or 3 sets high. Each layer of the crib is of 6 pieces equal in length to 2 sets. At Centennial-Eureka mine, Utah, continuous cribs, 1 set wide, were built at intervals of 5 to 10 sets to support a domed stope (Art 46), about 100 ft wide by 350 ft long; they were of 8 by 8 timber and required about 1 300 bd ft per set.

52. MISCELLANEOUS DETAILS OF SQUARE-SETS

Fire protection. Some disastrous mine fires have started in square-set stopes. Careless use of open lights and discarding of cigarette ends are common causes of fire; some mines prohibit smoking entirely or place limitations. Use of elec miners' lamps reduces the hazard. Clean, orderly stopes are safer from fire than disorderly ones. Filling reduces danger of fire spreading through square-set areas; but fire sometimes travels along lines of posts, caps, or girts even though surrounded by fill. Frood mine (Art 46) provides fire breaks by removing entire lines of girts concurrently with filling. Ability to control ventilation is essential feature for fire-control in any timbered mine.

Crowning floors. Trouble from settling of timbers is not serious in low or narrow stopes, nor where the dip is such that sets are repeatedly offset along the footwall. In high, wide, vert stopes, timbers settle considerably, and faster in middle of stope than along walls. These troubles increase with height of lift. Small movements are often met by special posts, 1 or 2 in longer than regular stope posts and kept in readiness. At Morenci, Ariz, with block-system stoping, the sill floor of each block was arched or crowned to compensate settlement. Length of posts increased gradually towards middle of stope, where the posts were 2 in longer than those on the walls. Crowning was repeated in one of the upper floors as soon as the arch effect was lost.

Flirting posts. When sets are slightly distorted, a new post may sometimes be properly placed by cutting off part of the bottom horn, or cutting out the corresponding mortise; this is known as flirting posts. It is usually done more readily in cap-butting than in post-butting sets, because posts of the former have short horns (Art 49).

Blocking, if carefully done, materially reduces swinging of sets. It is also intended to crush under the initial creep of walls or back, thereby saving the main timbers. Sets should be blocked at joints, to avoid bending strains in timbers. If a long block (sprag) is necessary to reach a wall, it should have a headboard, so that the press will come onto the timbers through wood in cross grain. Good blocking is especially necessary over the posts at back of stope, as it alone holds the timbers when the side blocking is removed to make room for new sets. Sets on the floor alongside of an advancing face tend to " ride " toward the face, because the side blocking is blasted out on each round. Riding of sets is sometimes prevented by standing the posts with a slight pitch away from face; subsequent stoping tends to straighten them.

Recovery of square-set timber is rarely attempted. Where feasible, it points to the possibility of mining by some system requiring less timber. In New Idria mine, Cal (Art 46), timbers are usually recovered from unfilled square-set stopes after mining is completed. At Frood mine (Art 46) long girts are recovered after filling each floor; primary purpose here is reduction of fire hazard, but saving in timber also results. At Calumet & Arizona mine, Ariz, some timber was formerly recovered from stopes in flat orebodies, mined in small sections. Recovery took place during the filling period, which was delayed until a section was completed. Each section was carried up as a flat-back stope 4 sets wide, and of height and length of the orebody. When finished, 6-in stulls, unframed and held by wedges, were placed diagonally between the middle points of caps or girts on 1st and 2nd and 2nd and 3rd floors (*a* and *b*, Fig 357). The corner sets of a floor required 2 stulls, each being set off center to avoid interference. Under their support, sill-floor timbers were removed from 3 rows of sets, *X*, *Y*, and *Z*. A girt was first taken out, by sawing it in two; remaining pieces were pried out with a bar or by using a drill column as a jack. Then sets *V* were lagged, filling was poured in through chutes *c* and *d*, stulls *a* were knocked out and replaced between 3rd and 4th floor timbers, and the process repeated. Some stulls were left in, if pressure were heavy. Top-floor timbers were removed under protection of vert posts set between the filling and back, and filling was packed under the roof by hand. A vert row of sets *V* was left on side of stope, to furnish a point of attack for adjacent block and a place to store recovered timbers, which were reused several times. Caps were run across stope, as 3 cross members were recovered for 2 longitudinal ones. Haulageways, sometimes run as blind levels from a raise, were required on top and bottom floors. This method was found applicable in irregular orebodies.

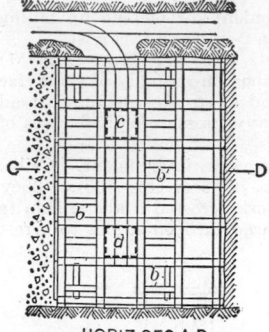

HORIZ SEC A B

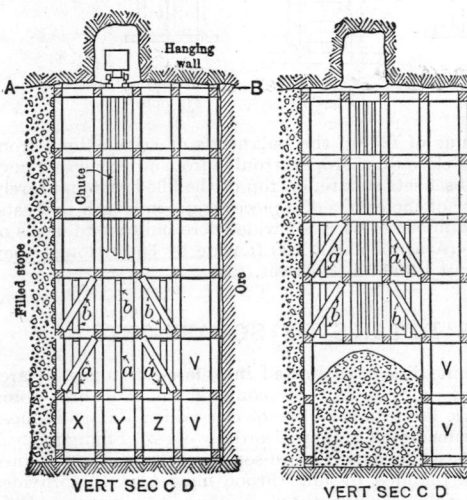

VERT SEC C D   VERT SEC C D

Fig 357. Recovering Timber from Square-set Stope

53. DATA ON SQUARE-SETS

To find total timber required in any stope, consider all sets as corner sets (1 post, 1 cap, 1 girt) and add posts, caps, and girts required along 1 wall and 1 end of the stope. Since amounts of timber used per ton vary with the specific gravity of the ore, figures per cu ft are better for making comparisons. Timber for floors, chutes, lagging, sill-floor sets, reinforcement, etc, is not included in Table 38; the amounts for these vary with size and form of stope. M. J. Elsing (213) estimates amount of timber for a set as stated in Table 37; posts 7 ft 2 in long, spaced 5 ft c-c both ways; aver number of pieces per set over a whole stope, 1.2 posts, 1.1 caps, 1.1 girts; size of posts and caps as stated; girts, 5 by 8 and 6 by 12 in; flooring used repeatedly. Elsing also records that square-set stopes in Copper Queen mine, in 1907, produced 565 600 tons of ore, required 31 400 sets, and consumed 8 950-000 cu ft of timber and 475 000 pcs of 5-ft lagging; or, 285 bd ft of timber and 15 bd ft of lagging per set yielding 18 tons of ore.

Table 37. Bd ft for a 5 by 5 by 7.17-ft Square-set

Size posts and caps	8″ by 8″	10″ by 10″	12″ by 12″
1.2 posts................	51	80	115
1.1 caps.................	27	42	59
1.1 girts.................	19	21	30
Stope lagging...........	18	18	18
Chute lining............	10	10	10
Blocking................	7	11	16
Flooring (aver over its life)	2	2	2
Misc, wedges, breakage...	9	11	13
Total bd ft...........	143	195	263

Examples following show wide variation, and indicate necessity for making liberal allowances in estimating total timber requirements. Morenci, Ariz. Approx total consumption was 15 bd ft per ton; a corner set, without reinforcement, took 8 bd ft per ton (178). At Cananea, Mex, a corner set requires about 8.4 bd ft per ton; total stope timber is 27 to 31 bd ft per ton. At Rossland, B C, about 100 bd ft of lumber was required per round-timber set for chutes, floors, ladders, and railings; aver diam of members, 16 in; a corner set contained 280 bd ft (209). BUTTE, Mont. W. B. Daly, in 1939, states that the amount of AUXILIARY TIMBER in a square-set stope depends on number of sets and width of stope. Where chutes and manways are 25 ft apart, general figures for the bd ft required for sets 5.33 ft square are: top lagging (3-in) for 1 set, 86; chute, 1 floor high (2-in lagging, 277; 3 by 10-in lumber, 84; 2 by 6-in lumber, 12), 400; manway, 1 floor high, 2-in lagging, 224; timber slide, 1 floor high, 53; total, 736 bd ft.

Table 38. Amounts of Timber Used in Square-sets

Fig No	Name of mine or set	Dimensions, c to c						Cu ft of ore per set	Bd ft per set *	Bd ft per cu ft of ore
		Height		Capwise		Girtwise				
		ft	in	ft	in	ft	in			
312	Copper Queen............	7	10	5	0	5	0	195.8	141.7	0.723
315	Vulcan, Mich.............	8	0	7	5	7	0	415.3	257.0	0.618
...	Broken Hill, N S W........	6	2	6	0	5	0	185.0	137.5	0.743
...	Savage, Nev.............	7	2	4	9	4	9	161.7	184.0	1.138
317	Cananea, Mex............	7	4	5	3	5	3	202.0	133.6	0.661
318	Portland, Colo............	7	3	5	8	5	8	233.0	149.3	0.641
319	Homestake, S Dak.........	8	3	6	0	6	0	296.9	238.5	0.804
320	Anaconda, Mont...........	7	6	5	0	5	0	187.5	137.5	0.773
321	Anaconda, Mont...........	7	6	5	0	5	0	187.5	122.5	0.653
322	Leonard, Mont............	7	8	5	4	5	4	217.6	185.3	0.815
324	Eureka, Nev.............	7	0	5	8	5	0	198.3	196.0	0.990
...	Bingham, Utah............	7	4	5	0	5	0	183.3	113.3	0.619
326	Portland, Colo............	7	0	5	0	4	11	172.0	85.3	0.496
327	Esperanza, Mex...........	8	0	5	0	5	0	200.0	90.7	0.453
316	Goldfield Consol, Nev......	7	8	5	0	5	0	191.7	83.6	0.436
325	Leadville, Colo...........	7	0	6	10	5	10	279.0	157.2	0.563
328	Morenci, Ariz.............	7	2	5	0	5	0	179.1	84.9†	0.474†
329	Cœur d'Alene, Ida.........	8	0	5	0	5	4	213.3	104.2†	0.489†
330	Steward, Mont............	7	0	5	2	4	10	174.8	93.5†	0.535†
332	Gagnon, Mont.............	8	3	5	0	5	0	206.2	89.3†	0.433†
334	Chisholm Dist, Minn.......	8	1	7	4	7	4	434.0	124.9†	0.288†
335	Brunton Bevel............	8	3	5	10	5	10	280.5	172.8†	0.616†
336	Square and Bevel..........	8	3	5	10	5	10	280.5	200.6†	0.715†
337	Step-down...............	7	9	5	4	5	4	220.4	132.0†	0.599†

  * These figures are for a corner set (1 post, 1 cap, and 1 girt). † Bd ft in round timber is computed by QUARTER-GIRTH RULE; area of cross-sec = 1.97 × square of radius, which gives cross-sec of largest square timber that can be sawed from a given log.

Data on framing. At ROSSLAND, B C, in 1903, round timbers averaging 16-in diam were framed by hand. Aver work for 1 carpenter per 9 hr was 21 posts, or 21 girts, or 16 caps. Cost per set was about 55¢ (wages, $3.50). Cost of same set, machine-framed, not over 30¢ (209). At HOMESTAKE MINE, So Dak, in 1903, some 12 by 12 timbers were framed by hand at 60¢ to 65¢ for a cap, girt, and post (wages, $3). Posts cost about 2¢ more than caps or girts. Costs indicate that 1 man framed 13 or 14 posts, or 14 to 16 caps or girts, per day (104). At SUDBURY, Ont, in 1938 (data from H. J. Mutz), 2 men with a single-end framer could make 170 posts, or 200 caps, or 300 girts in 8 hr. With a double-end framer, 3 men could frame 310 posts, or 500 girts, or 420 caps; while framing caps, 2 extra men were required for axe trimming.

Table 39. Machine Framing, Square-sets (Ibex Mine, Leadville, 1902)

Single-end, block-type machine, Denver Eng Wks	Posts 10 by 10-in, 6 ft long	Caps 10 by 10-in, 6 ft long	Drift posts 10 by 10-in, 6.5 ft long	Drift caps 10 by 12-in, 4 ft long	Sills, 6 by 8-in, 6 ft long	Raise cribbing, 4 by 8-in, 6 ft long	Wedges
No pieces framed..	1 158	20	144	97	48	1 156	16 800
Total hr..........	68.25	2	6.75	8.75	2.5	24.75	28.75
Cost per piece, ¢...	1.93	3.35	1.52	2.93	1.69	0.73	0.05

In a 166-hr run by above machine, delays were 0.75 hr. According to P. B. Scotland, a Denver Eng Wks double-end, block-type framer, used by Ariz Copper Co, run by 2 men, framed 160 round posts in 8 hr. Square caps and girts (Fig 328) were cut in a single-end framer; 2 men made 600 girts or 300 caps in 8 hr.
  Erecting sets. P. B. Scotland stated, concerning mines of Ariz Copper Co, that aver duty of 2 men in placing and lagging stope sets was 2 to 3 sets per 8 hr. B. H. Dunshee stated from Butte, that, if a stope were ready to be timbered, 2 miners would place 4 posts,

2 caps, and 2 girts, block down and cover the top with lagging in about 1 hr. Ordinarily this work took 2 hr or more, as loose ground often had to be picked down or poorly fitting timbers adjusted. In FROOD MINE, Sudbury, Ont (data from H. J. Mutz, in 1938), 2 men can stand a square-set (1 post, 1 cap, 1 girt) in 1 hr. In a standard stope (Art 46), where usual blasting makes space for 5 sets per shift, remainder of 8-hr timbering shift is spent in scaling, extending booms, blocking and lagging the back, and laying floor for the 5 sets.

Miscellaneous. Mining on sill floor costs 2 to 3 times as much as on upper floors, even for contract work. Breaking is by flat holes, the face is not undercut, and shoveling is on a rough rock floor. At Leonard mine, Butte, a standard crew consists of 2 machine men (stope-drills), 3 or 4 shovelers, 1 man on filling, and timbermen and blockers who look after several stopes. This crew carries up a 25 by 50-ft stope, 100 ft in 4 or 5 months, or in 1 year to a height of 200 ft, extra time being required in the 2nd 100 ft for repairing and reinforcing timbers and for crowning floors (80).

54. APPLICABILITY AND LIMITATIONS OF SQUARE-SETS

In early days, square-setting was almost standard for underground mining of large ore-bodies in the U S. Later, increasing cost of timber, and introduction of shrinkage, filling, and caving systems narrowed its field of use. Square-set stoping is a comparatively high-cost method and therefore best applicable to high-grade ores. It is used where ground conditions require closely spaced support of ore or walls, as in soft ground, or in harder ground which sloughs or slabs; and as an adjunct to methods for recovering pillars.

Open stopes. Experience shows that open sets do not afford permanent support for weak ground; timbers rot, or more often crush under pressure caused by the extension of stoped areas. This is serious, as the caving of large stopes may set up a slow crushing action (" creep "), which extends into adjacent unmined blocks and renders their extraction difficult and costly. The field for open square-sets is in orebodies too wide for stulls, and where the ground is strong, but requires prompt support to prevent slabs falling from back and walls. These conditions preclude use of shrinkage stoping; the alternative is a filling method, the choice being governed by relative advantages of these systems, as stated below and in Art 66, and by their relative costs.

Filled stopes. Conditions jointly justifying complete filling for square-sets are: (a) necessity for permanent support of the surface or of overlying ground containing other orebodies; (b) weak ore requiring complete and immediate support of stope backs.

If subsidence can be allowed, some caving method is often cheaper than and preferable to square-setting; but caving methods are limited to certain types of orebody (Art 82). If temporary cribs and stulls will support the stope back, straight filling is usually better than square-setting. Choice is further governed by the advantages and disadvantages outlined below; see Art 46 for advantages of different forms of square-set stope.

As auxiliary to other methods, square-sets have a wide field of use (Art 68).

Advantages of square-setting, not covered above: (a) reliability; properly applied, it is dependable for mining almost any kind of ground; (b) safety, since the area of ground open at any time may be adjusted to its strength; (c) flexibility; stopes can be expanded or contracted at will, irregular stringers followed into walls at any point, dikes or waste inclusions left unmined, and prospecting drifts driven from any floor; (d) good facilities for sorting in stopes; important where ore must be separated from waste, sulphide from oxide ore, or smelting from concentrating ore; (e) good facilities for handling ore and supporting men in the stopes; (f) good ventilation; (g) walls alongside of old stopes can be mined if desired.

Disadvantages of square-setting, not covered above: (a) high cost, due to use of much framed timber of good grade; (b) danger of fire, which has occurred in nearly all large districts where the method is used. Fire risk is greater in open than in filled stopes (see Fire prevention, Art 52).

Summary. Notwithstanding its cost, square-setting is necessary and useful for certain types of orebody, and as an adjunct to other mining systems. Following practice tends to reduce costs (P. B. Scotland): (a) use round timbers instead of square; (b) use second-class and smaller timbers where possible, instead of one size for all kinds of ground; (c) purchase logs partly seasoned, aver say 550 bd ft per ton; (d) accept mixed shipments, i e, ship as cut; (e) install slabbing saws and use slabs for lagging; (f) install mechanical devices for handling timbers on surface and underground; (g) frame at the lumber camp, thus reducing freight charges; (h) discard sills in all but soft, wet ground; (i) recognize the fact that accurate alinement of timbers is unnecessary, especially where filling closely follows mining.

55. MITCHELL SLICING SYSTEM (220, 228, 580)

This modification of square-setting was apparently first employed in mining soft hematite at Queen mine, Negaunee, Mich (136). It was further developed, in form described below, at Calumet & Arizona mine, Bisbee, Ariz, for mining flat, bedded bodies of heavy sulphide ore in limestone. Hanging wall was well defined and easily supported; orebodies contained little waste and rarely exceeded 50 or 60 ft thickness. Ordinary square-sets failed under the weight of soft, heavy ore. Mitchell system has also been successful at Magma mine, Superior, Ariz, in a steeply dipping sulphide vein, averaging 20–30 ft wide.

General plan is to mine by square-setting along the sides of a small block of ore; top of pillar thus formed is then mined, and hanging wall timbered. Under this protection, the rest of the pillar is sliced downward by underhand stoping.

Development. A main drift was driven, preferably along one wall of deposit; from it crosscuts (c, c, Fig 358), called slice-leads, were driven to opposite wall on 20-ft centers and timbered with sill-floor square-sets. A vert square-setted raise to level above, over first 2 sets of each slice-lead, served as a timber and manway, and later as a waste chute. On sill floor a small manway a gave access to manway side of raise on first floor. Small excavations, E, on sill-floor plan, were shot out at top of alternate sill-floor sets in slice-leads, and a chute built in each; these cuts were kept small and on same side of adjacent crosscuts, otherwise they weakened base of the pillar between 2 slice-leads. Cars could not always be run into slice-leads; if not, the first set alone served as a chute for loading cars in main drift. Two adjacent slice-leads were next carried to hanging wall, as flat-back square-set stopes, 1 set wide, called lead-stopes; broken ore formed its own slides to chutes; little mucking was necessary. This preliminary work cut out a pillar 15 ft wide; ordinary pillar lengths were 25 to 50 ft; greater lengths were mined as separate sections. Max vert height for safe mining was about 60 ft; heights of 100 ft were mined in two 50-ft sections, the upper one first (220).

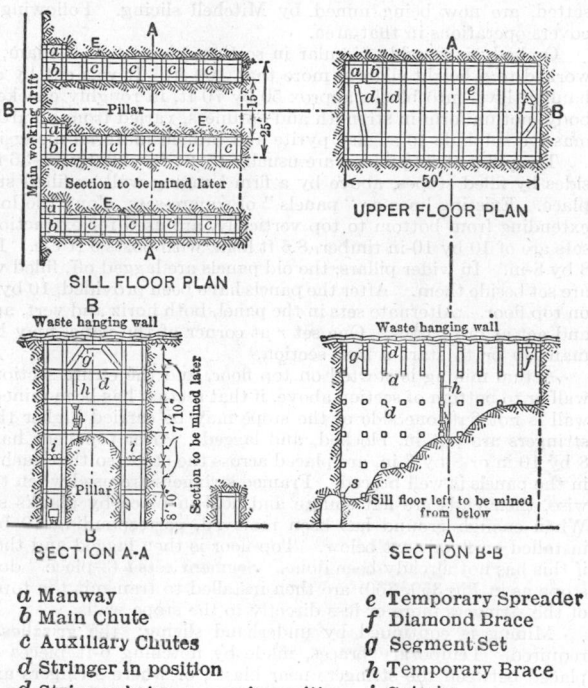

SILL FLOOR PLAN

UPPER FLOOR PLAN

SECTION A-A

SECTION B-B

a Manway
b Main Chute
c Auxiliary Chutes
d Stringer in position
d₁ Stringer being swung in position

e Temporary Spreader
f Diamond Brace
g Segment Set
h Temporary Brace
i Grizzly

Fig 358. Mitchell Slicing System

Slicing began from the end set on top floor of a lead-stope, by drifting across the pillar to the corresponding set in opposite stope, directly under the hanging wall. Ore ran out by gravity through an inclined drift from each lead-stope to center of pillar; successive drifts were run until the whole top of the pillar was cut off.

Stringers (d, Fig 358) were placed under hanging wall as soon as there was room, with enough lagging and blocking to secure back of stope and timbers. A cut must be made in a lead-stope cap or girt at one end of stringer, for swinging its tenon into place (B, Fig 360). Topmost stringers were supported temporarily by stulls resting on the pillar. When enough ore was broken to allow placing stringers between next lower run of square-sets, stulls were replaced by 3-piece segment sets gg, of 10 by 10 timber (see AA, Fig 358). This braced the sets in lead-stopes and transmitted to them pressure from hanging. Rest of pillar was stoped underhand in successive slices. Most of broken ore was thrown into lead-stopes and chutes, little mucking being necessary until 1st floor was reached. Slicing was continued to 1st floor, leaving sill floor to be mined from below. A plank floor was then laid on top of bottom stringers *s*, the inside of the square-sets in both lead-stopes was covered with 2-in lagging and the stope was filled with waste through the raises to the level above. This left lead-stopes open and ready for attacking adjacent blocks.

Campbell mine, Phelps Dodge Corp. Data on 1939 practice from H. M. Lavender. Mitchell slicing system at Bisbee, Ariz, is practically limited to the Junction, Campbell, and Cole mines, for recovering ore left in pillars between cut-and-fill or square-set stopes. It is confined to mining ores that are fairly dry, stand reasonably well, are uniform in composition (contain little waste that must be sorted out), are free from very heavy top or lateral press, and do not require heavy blasting. Special development work is usually unnecessary; ore is extracted through same drifts and crosscuts used for adjacent stopes worked previously, and fill is introduced through existing drifts and crosscuts on level above. The pillars in one area in Campbell mine, the original sections of which have been mined by inclined cut-and-fill methods (Art 65), except a small part that was square-setted, are now being mined by Mitchell slicing. Following description, see Fig 359, covers operations in that area.

Orebody is roughly circular in section, about 200 ft diam, and has been extensively worked to a height slightly more than 100 ft. It was cut by drifts and crosscuts on the haulage level into blocks approx 50 by 70 ft, in roughly checkerboard fashion. The ore-body, not uniform in strength and hardness, varied from a hard siliceous ore and siliceous massive sulphide to sugary pyrite and broken material alongside a weak porphyry wall.

The pillars being mined are usually 15–24 ft wide by 18–36 ft long; bounded on 3 or 4 sides by filled stopes, above by a firm hanging wall or filled stopes, and below by ore in place. Existing lines or " panels " of square-sets, along the long dimension of pillar and extending from bottom to top vertically, are used for extraction when possible. Square-sets are of 10 by 10-in timber, 8.5 ft high, with posts 6 ft c-c. In a few cases timbers were 8 by 8-in. In wider pillars, the old panels are lagged off, filled with waste, and new panels are set beside them. After the panels have been provided, 10 by 10-in grizzlies are installed on top floor. Alternate sets in the panel, both horiz and vert, are floored over (*p*, Fig 359), and act as ore passes. One set *r* at corner of the panel may be lagged off and left for a manway or to start a new section.

Actual mining is started on top floor, and the entire section is cut off to the hanging wall or to bottom of section above, if that section has been mined out. Where the hanging wall is not flat, one side of the stope may be carried higher than the other, and the top stringers are put in, blocked, and lagged. After top floor has been cut off, stringers *s*, 8 by 10 in or 8 by 8 in, are placed across the stope so that each corner of each exposed set in the panels is well braced. Framed stringers are used when they will fit the sets; otherwise, their ends are left square and held in place by planks scabbed to posts and caps. When enough ground has been removed, corresponding 10 by 10-in stringers are then installed on floor next below. Top floor is then lagged and the back secured by blocking if this has not already been done. Segment sets *t* (3-piece " doubling sets " framed in the stope as in Fig 359, 360) are then installed to transmit the top press from middle portion of the stringers more or less directly to the stope walls.

Mining is continued by underhand slicing; the grizzlies are moved downward as required. Temporary braces, made by notching 6-ft pieces of 2 by 12-in lagging, are placed between the stringers near blasts, or where stringers are bowing slightly, as at *b*, Fig 359. Bottom of stope is sloped toward the panels to minimize mucking, and, as shown, would also be sloped toward the manway, to give better support to the weaker end of the section next to the old filled stope. As mining descends, the solid end of the stope is lagged off vert outside of the end sets to protect men working below. It may be necessary to place angle braces *c* at either or both ends, to withstand the thrust of the adjoining filled stope or of ore in place. It is customary also to lag every third or fourth floor, as at *f*, for safety of men working below. If the stope should suddenly take weight, the entire stope may be waste-filled above the lagged floor, after which, mining is resumed with new segment sets. These operations continue down to first floor above the sill. Stringers, covered with lagging, are placed there, and waste-fill is introduced, at center of top floor, if possible, rather than from one end or corner. The panels are also filled with waste, unless they are to be used again. Most of the stringers and much flooring are salvaged as the stope is filled. The ground below the bottom stringers is left to be mined from below. In some cases the square-set below the segment set must be reinforced by a diagonal brace (*d* in Fig 359). If the wall is ore in place, instead of waste fill as shown, this diagonal may pass over the top of cap below, and rest in a hitch cut for it in the solid, which takes the weight independently of the lower square-set. Should a stope be shut down after being partially cut, it is important that the lowest stringers in place are not resting on the solid, as slight movement of the sets at either end will bend or break them.

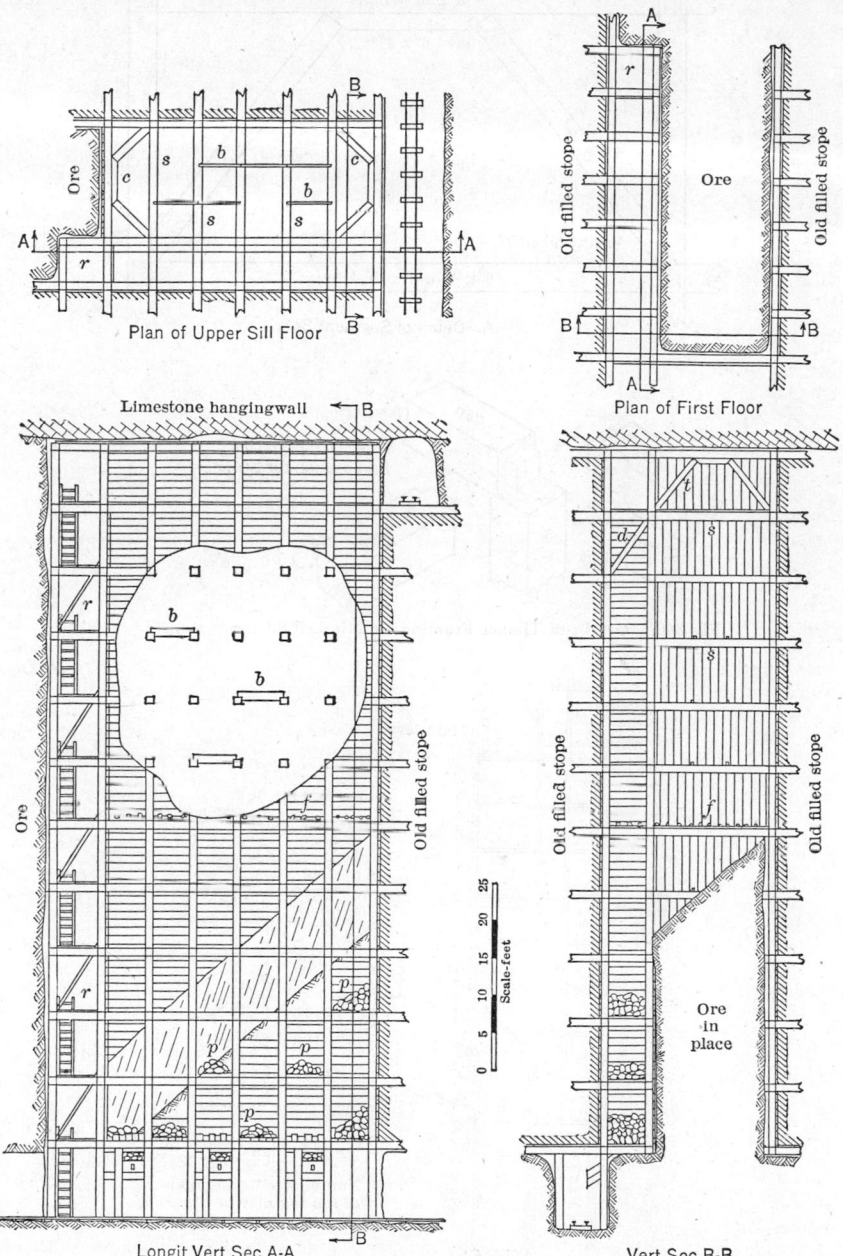

Plan of Upper Sill Floor

Plan of First Floor

Longit Vert Sec A-A

Vert Sec B-B

Fig 359. Mitchell Slicing System, Campbell Mine, Bisbee, Ariz

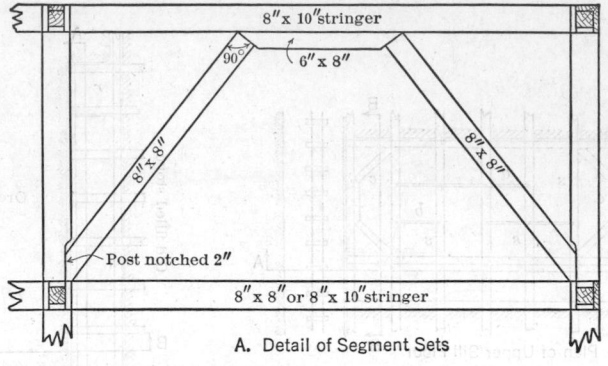

A. Detail of Segment Sets

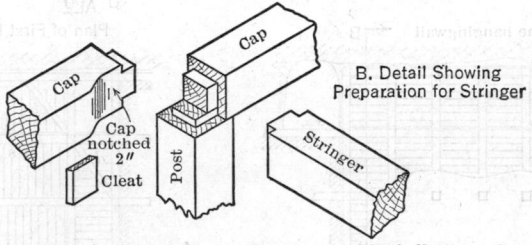

B. Detail Showing Preparation for Stringer

Fig 360.   Details of Timber Framing for Mitchell Slicing System

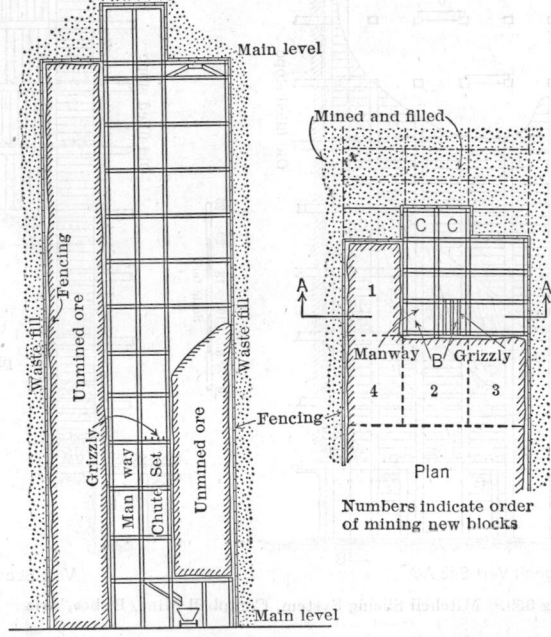

Vert Sec A-A

Fig 361.   Mitchell Slicing applied to Mining of Vert Pillars, United Verde Ext Mine, Jerome, Ariz

ADVANTAGES of the system, in general, are a saving in labor and timber as compared with square-sets. Special advantages are: obvious safety, rapidity of mining, and large tonnage per man-shift. The square-set panels at the side of a stope may be prepared in advance of actual mining needs. Direct STOPING COSTS, covering 25 000 tons from this area: labor, 44¢; explosives, 13¢; timber, 35¢; total 89¢ per ton. Output per man-shift, 14.44 tons. Wages for miners, $5.48, for muckers, $4.84. Comparisons between cost of mining by Mitchell slicing system and by square-setting are apt to be misleading, due to differing conditions under which the methods are used. However, recent direct costs of mining 17 000 tons by square-setting in the Bisbee mines were: labor, 65¢; explosives, 12¢; timber, 38¢; total, $1.15 per ton. Output per man-shift, 9.87 tons.

United Verde Ext mine, Jerome, Ariz. Mitchell system, as formerly applied to mining of vert pillars, was described by R. L. D'Arcy in 1930 (90). Orebody, now exhausted, was a large lens of high-grade copper sulphide ore; max length, 500 ft; max width, 300 ft. Level interval, generally 100 ft. Principal method of mining was a block system of square-setting, in which vert pillars, usually 6 sets wide, were left temporarily over main extraction drifts. These pillars were later found to be badly broken by movement, and so had to be mined in small sections. Fig 361 shows general plan. A small square-set section (2 sets wide and 3 sets long in Fig 361) was carried up to level above, the 2 end sets B, next to unmined ore, serving as chute and manway. Sets C are open sets of the adjacent previously mined square-set section. On completing a section, one of the outer sections alongside was removed by Mitchell slicing. Because of the broken nature of the pillar, the ore could frequently be barred down into the chute, without need of drilling or explosives. A series of 10 by 10-in stringers, braced as required, were placed between the square-sets and the old pillar fencing as mining progressed downward. The section was filled after completing mining, and the section on opposite side of the square-set stope was then mined and similarly filled. Thereafter all sets in the section were filled, except the chute and manway on the advancing side, these being kept open for access and introduction of fill to the next 3 sections (2, 3, and 4 in Fig 361).

56. MISCELLANEOUS TIMBERING SYSTEMS

Moore system (232) is a modification of square-setting, employed at one time in Tonopah Belmont mine, Nev, wherein the posts were replaced by diagonals in the vert plane

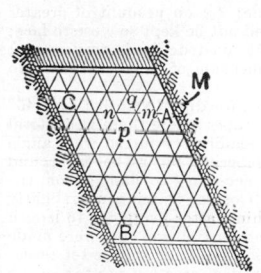

Fig 362. Diagram of Moore System

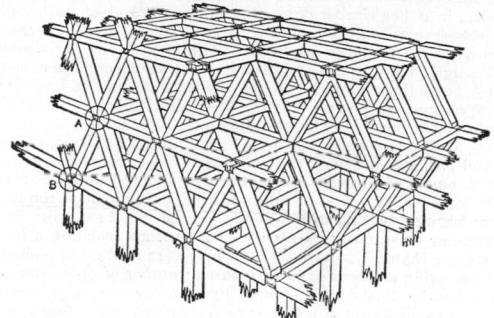

Fig 363. Moore System at Tonopah Belmont Mine

of the caps. This formed a series of triangular frames, placed parallel to direction of max pressure and braced apart by girts at the joints (Fig 363). In Fig 362, a force applied at M resolves into components along lines AC and AB. Sets were designed on the principle that if a member mn fails, the force acting through it is taken by diagonals mq and mp; a corresponding failure in ordinary square-sets might cause collapse of several sets.

F. S. Bradshaw furnished Fig 363 to 365, showing details. Sets were 8 ft high, 7.5 ft capwise, and 5 ft 11 in girtwise. Diagonals were inclined 65° (theoretical angle should be the dip of

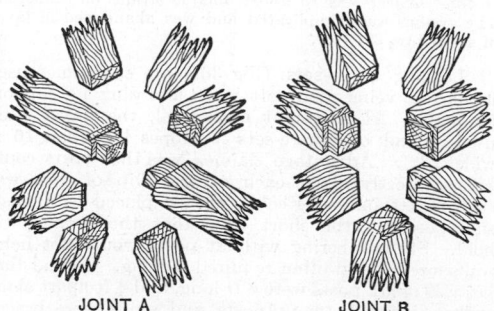

JOINT A   JOINT B

Fig 364. Details of Joints, Moore System

hanging wall, but is not practical; 65° is suitable for most cases). Fig 363 shows framing of triangular sets and their junction with ordinary square-sets. Fig 364 shows joints A and B, Fig 363.

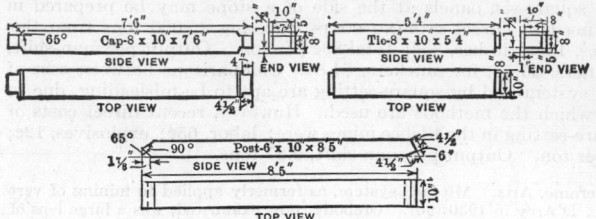

Fig 365. Details of Timbers, Moore System

All timbers were placed flatwise in the set; caps were butted for convenience in framing; it is needless to make joints stronger in one direction than another. Drift sets were formed by substituting 10 by 10 vert posts for 2 diagonals on sill floor. Along vertical end faces of stopes a half-cap was put in on alternate floors, supported at wall end by a 4 by 10 upright. On inclined walls, the angle of diagonals could be changed to fit, or in strong ground ends of caps might be set in hitches.

Table 40. Comparison of Corner Sets

Dimensions of set, center to center	Bd ft per corner set	Cu ft ore per set	Bd ft per cu ft	% timber across lode
Moore (cap, girt, 2 diags)..	7 ft 6 in by 5 ft 11 in by 8 ft	169.5	355	0.48	79
Square-set *.............	7 ft 6 in by 5 ft 11 in by 8 ft	161.1	355	0.45	78
Square-set †.............	5 ft 4 in by 5 ft 4 in by 7 ft 10 in	137.7	222	0.62	77

* Corresponding to Moore set. † Ordinary set, 10 by 10 post and cap, 8 by 10 girt.

Under direct vert or horiz pressure, the strength of a Moore set (of 8 by 10 and 6 by 10 timbers) is about the same as that of a square-set of same dimensions with 10 by 10 cap and post and 8 by 10 girt. Under oblique stress, it is stronger, due to the triangular panels, but, to utilize this strength, joints must be held from swinging girtwise. Moore set has no advantage over square-sets of equal size, in either timber consumption or amount of timber placed in cross-frames; but the timber in cross-frames is better placed to resist distortion. Advantages claimed: (a) greater strength than square-sets for same amount of timber; (b) lighter timbers to handle; (c) on account of greater strength, filling is not required in some stopes, or where required it need not be kept so close to face; (d) flexibility, since the angles of diagonals can be varied; (e) drift set construction is very strong; (f) chutes can be run diagonally or vertically; in latter case, one dimension of chute is limited to about 3 ft in sets of the size shown.

Moore sets were used with some success at Tonopah Belmont mine, for dip of vein between 45° and 75°, and width of 15 ft or more. They were not well adapted to stopes where there was lateral movement of one vein wall with respect to the other, as they were not readily reinforced with angle braces. They were not adapted to running ground requiring close timbering, but rather to ground which would stand over full width of stope, 1 set long; hence, it was necessary to change from triangular to square-sets about 2 sets before reaching a level above. Cost of framing was slightly greater than for square-sets. Caps were framed in a single-end machine, after being cut to length by a swing crosscut saw, with same number of operations as square-set caps; bevel cuts were made by hand. Posts were framed by a swing saw, with one less operation than for square-set posts. Girts required same framing as for square-sets. With skilled men, cost of erection per ton of ore was no greater than for square-sets.

Inclined square-sets. A modified square-set, with posts at right angles to hanging wall, was formerly used at Calumet & Hecla mine, Mich, on dips of 35° to 40°. Object was to avoid oblique strains on timbering. The system was complicated and was abandoned in favor of stulls (Art 39) (20).

Leaning stope-sets (Fig 366) are sometimes used in narrow veins with soft walls affording no support for stulls. At Argonaut mine, Cal, they have been used instead of square-sets in stopes less than 16 ft wide (230). Advantage claimed was that posts could be set directly above each other. Dip of vein was such that square-sets could not be placed with posts superposed in the short time that the ground will hold. Stull timbering without posts would not hold; walls swelled and often required lagging. Round timber was used; posts were 8 ft long, and 4 ft apart along strike; joints between posts and stulls were braced longitudinally by unframed sprags. Stope timbering started from 2 stringers, one on each

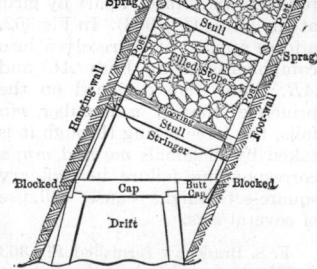

Fig 366. Leaning Stope-set, Cal

wall, blocked up from drift-set below, and separated by lagged stulls carrying filling. Swell of walls tightened timbers, so that they supported filling even when drift sets were destroyed by mining the chain pillar from stope below.

Stringer sets (formerly used in Ontario mine, Utah, in wide parts of a steep vein) consist of a horiz cap (STRINGER), from wall to wall, carried by posts 5 ft apart. Caps are braced by girts opposite posts. No framing was done, 60-d spikes being used at joints. Max length of stringer, 16 ft; for wider stopes, 2 stringers were butted, with a post under the joint. These sets suited the solid quartzite walls at Ontario mine, but gave trouble when tried in weaker ground elsewhere. They require nearly as much timber as square-sets, and as much labor, when latter are framed by machine.

Similar timbering, called STULL SETS, is used in the Cœur d'Alene district, Idaho. Fig 367 shows practice at MORNING MINE (231). Wall rock swells, causing side pressure great enough to broom out the ends of 24-in red fir caps, which are therefore protected by soft-wood blocking. At HECLA mine (data from C. H. Foreman in 1930), caps of stull sets are at 5-ft horiz and 9-ft vert intervals (223). Max length of cap that can be handled is 16 ft; sometimes 2, rarely 3, caps, placed end-to-end, are necessary to span stope. Head blocks are about 12 in thick, of 3-in by 5-ft boards of random width. For mode of recovering a caved stope at this mine, see Art 57.

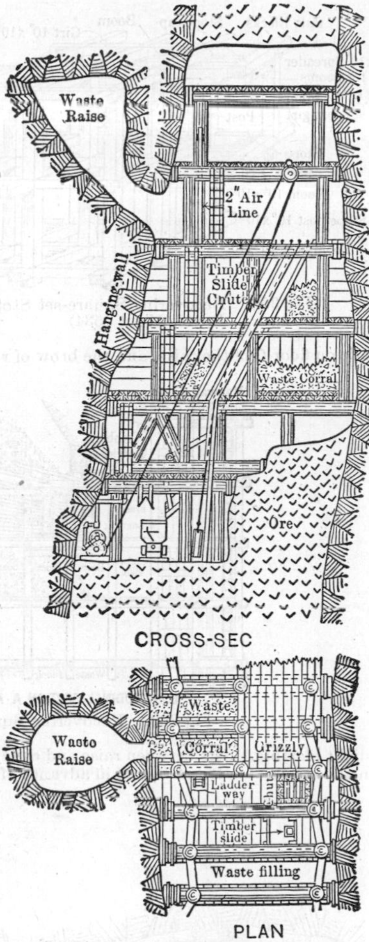

57. RECOVERY OF CAVED STOPES

General. Caving of stopes may be caused by: (*a*) attempting to mine blocks of too large an area; (*b*) failure to block sets properly, or reinforce them prior to blasting; (*c*) failure to keep fill close enough to back; (*d*) destruction of timber by fire; (*e*) abandonment of stope for a considerable time. After a cave, special timbering may be needed to reclaim the caved ore and so to control the stope that regular methods may be resumed.

Usual method of attack is to start at one side and, if possible, on top of the cave, placing supports under the solid back before removing the caved ground. Unnecessary breaking or shaking of the back should be avoided. Selection of mode of recovery depends on: (*a*) dimensions of stope; (*b*) normal method of mining; (*c*) manner in which the back is caved and amount of arching that has occurred (see Subsidence, Art 112–116).

Fig 367. Stope Timbering, Morning Mine, Idaho

Examples follow of practice in recovering square-set and stull-set stopes.

Butte, Mont. H. L. Bicknell in 1922 (534) gives method in wide square-set stopes. Where back over cave is approx horiz, underhand square-setting as in Art 46 (Fig 305, 306) is started from nearest open set on the floor just below the cave, but using 2 booms instead of one. Booms 10 by 10 or 12 in by 9.5 ft are placed below the caps and between the posts of the open set, and extended into caved area (Fig 368). The booms are supported by 2 posts under the lead cap, with 4-in blocks between booms and caps. Next to the 4-in blocks on forward end of the boom is laid 4 by 10-in lagging *L*, to support the 2 girts. Caps and girts are then placed and held in position by cross lacing to the sets already in. The back above the set is then steadied by sprags, blocking or cribbing. Enough caved ground is removed to repeat the operation in next set below, and posts between the 2 sets are placed and fastened to the existing sets. The sets are thus carried down the face of the cave to the standing sets below. Successive vert rows of sets alongside the first are then similarly worked down, until the entire face has advanced 1 set into the cave. This work continues until whole stope is recovered. The same general method is used in narrow square-set stopes.

Fig 369 shows a square-set where a cave left the solid back of vein sloping up at a steep angle from the undisturbed timbers. The caved ore was too high above the timber to start a boom-set until space was made ahead of the highest set C by spiling (Sec 6). The top spiling was driven first, then side spiling starting at the top; breast boards were placed between ends of side spiling, to prevent caved material from running into space below. Under protection of the spiling, the top booms were placed and blocked, also the upper caps and girts; top spiling was then blocked or cribbed to back. Part of the broken rock below was removed, and booms F were placed supporting the cap, girts, and posts on floor below. Fig 369 shows this work starting next to one of the walls; after 2 sets are in, those alongside were placed in order until opposite wall was reached. Meanwhile the posts between standing sets below and the sets resting on the booms were put in, and all timbers blocked to walls. Then a start was

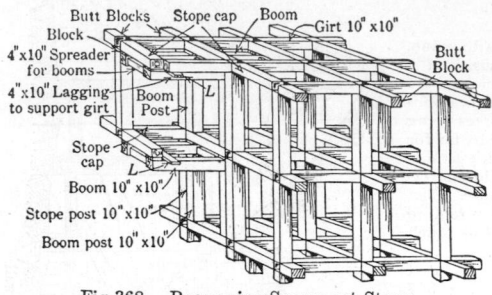

Fig 368. Recovering Square-set Stope, Butte, Mont (534)

made on floor G of the raise, and the brow of rock between raise and cave was removed by barring

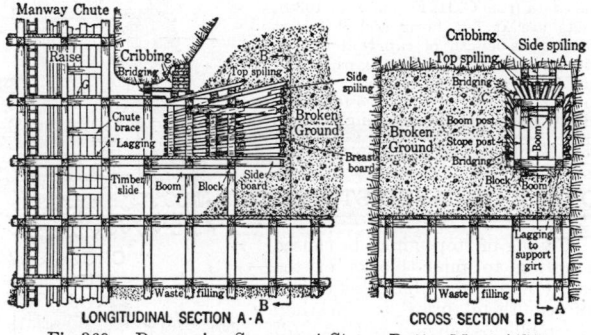

LONGITUDINAL SECTION A·A   CROSS SECTION B·B

Fig 369.   Recovering Square-set Stope, Butte, Mont (534)

or light blasting. Sets between raise and cave were timbered and blocked to the back above. Work continued over sets C and D, and in advance of them using spiling to make room for boom-sets.

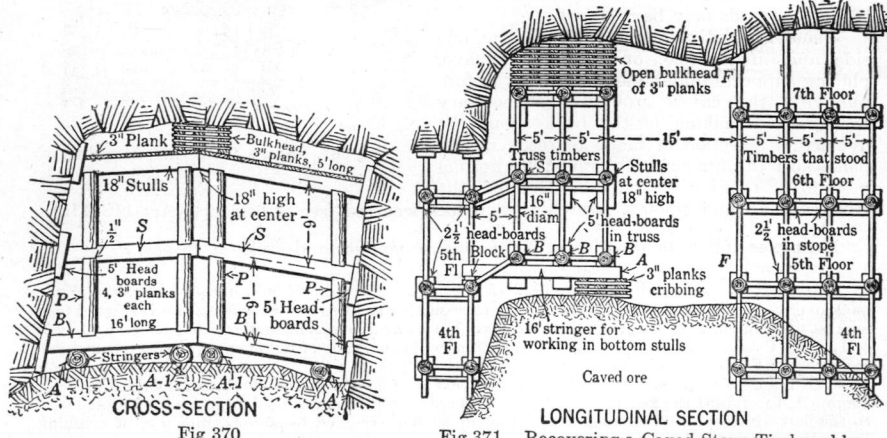

CROSS-SECTION
Fig 370

LONGITUDINAL SECTION
Fig 371.   Recovering a Caved Stope Timbered by Stull Sets, Hecla Mine, Idaho (581)

Hecla mine, Cœur d'Alene, Idaho. Data from C. T. Rice in 1918 (581). Stull sets are used for mining (Art 56). Caved stopes are recovered as shown in Fig 370 and 371. Work is started from highest standing timber; 4 stringers A (Fig 371) 16 ft long, slabbed top and bottom, are laid parallel to the walls, one end being supported by the standing stope timber, the other by the caved material. Stringers A–1 (Fig 370) are blocked up 6–18 in higher than the outside stringers A. Three pairs of stulls B are placed at 5-ft centers and 5 ft from last standing stull. The raised stringers A–1 make each pair of stulls form a flat saddleback (Art 38, Fig 229). Head-blocking of 3-in plank is used in each wall (Fig 370) and temporarily wedged. Posts P are then stood in 0.5-in daps cut into the stulls. A second series of stulls S is placed, blocked and braced girtwise to prevent swinging. Other stull sets are placed above, until the timbers are high enough to permit building a cribbed bulkhead between them and the back, after which the whole structure is tightened evenly with wedges. In the case in Fig 371, the remaining 15 ft of open stope was similarly timbered, starting from standing timbers F, F. The back was then picked down, ore drawn, stope filled with waste, and mining resumed (581).

58. PRESERVATIVE TREATMENT OF MINE TIMBER

General. Data from Bib (585, 586, 587, 588). Preservative treatment, by method most common at mines, adds about 30% to initial cost of timber; hence should be confined to that timber, estimated at 15–20% of all consumed, which is desired to outlast the normal life of untreated timber; latter may be as short as 1 yr; aver, 2–4 yr, rarely reaching 5–10 yr. Properly treated mine timber may be expected to resist decay for at least 15 yr; in a Penn anthracite mine, gangway posts treated with $ZnCl_2$ by open-tank method in 1906 were still sound and retained ample margin of protection in 1931, whereas adjacent untreated posts had all failed within 4 yr. Knowing the life of untreated timber under given conditions, and costs (in place) of timber treated and untreated, and estimating life required of treated timber, the respective annual charges (excluding cost of replacements, but providing for amortization of first cost) can be compared by applying the formula: $A = \dfrac{Pr(1 + r)^n}{(1 + r)^n - 1}$, where A = annual charge; P = initial cost, in place; r = interest rate, expressed as decimal; n = life, in years. CHIEF BENEFITS OF TREATMENT: (1) saving replacements, each of which usually costs 50–100% more than initial erection; some timber, as sill flooring and fencing in filled stopes of a block system (Art 46) can not be replaced and its failure causes trouble when mining adjoining blocks or pillars; (2) permits use of smaller timbers for a given load, since safety factor need make no allowance for loss of strength by decay (treatment itself has no effect on strength of timber); (3) a cheap, local wood of suitable strength, but prone to rot, may be substituted (after treatment) for more expensive timber; (4) where the mining method permits salvaging timber for re-use, resistance to rot is an obvious advantage. TIMBERS MOST ADVANTAGEOUSLY TREATED: (1) framed sets in shafts and haulageways required to stay open, say, 4 yr or more; (2) stringers supporting chute bottoms; (3) chutes and pockets, especially in dead ends; (4) cribbing in all permanent manways; (5) fence posts and lagging in filled stopes of block systems; (6) sills and flooring on sill floors in filled stopes above blocks of ore to be recovered later; (7) shaft guides (especially subject to rot at joints and bolt holes).

Cause and prevention of decay. Fungi causing decay grow inside of wood; visible parts are fruits, discharging spores which may be carried by air currents if not transmitted to adjoining timbers by direct contact. Growth is possible between about 40° and 100° F, is most vigorous at 70°–90° F, and is promoted by moisture; continuously dry or completely wet timber is immune; a post with one end in water is very susceptible. Wood can be sterilized by heat alone, at 150° F, but retention of a chemical antiseptic to depth of 0.5–2 in is required to prevent re-infection and the growth of fungi. Among numerous compounds and mixtures, $ZnCl_2$ has proved best adapted for treatment of mine timbers, its only drawback being possible leaching out of the wood in very wet places; usually this objection is slight. Minimum amount of $ZnCl_2$ is 0.35% by wt, or about 0.12 lb per cu ft for most woods; common specifications are 0.5–0.75 lb per cu ft, up to 1 lb for wet places. In Rand gold mines, $ZnSO_4$ (a cheap byproduct of cyanide plant refineries) is used, with addition of NaF and dinitrophenol. Large Nova Scotia coal mines submerge props in hot, strong solution of common salt; satisfactory results are probably due as much to the heating as to the salt. Creosoted timbers, though more lasting in resistance (also more expensive) and better suited for wet places, are nasty to handle; their added inflammability can be almost completely overcome by 6 mo seasoning after treatment, but fumes from burning creosote are dangerous, and its normal odor can arouse suspicion of a smouldering fire. Round timber must always be peeled, and framed or dimensioned timbers should be completely shaped, including bolt holes, if any, before treatment; new surfaces of any subsequent cutting may be painted with preservative with some slight advantage. Green timber is regularly treated, but results are best with timber seasoned as rapidly as possible without causing severe checking; the sooner the moisture in sapwood is reduced to below 20%, the less chance for infection before treatment.

Open-tank or hot- and cold-tank process is simplest and cheapest to install (a plant for $ZnCl_2$ treatment of 1 000 props per yr costs about $1 000), but is slower in operation and is best limited to round and seasoned timbers. In almost all woods, except hemlock and spruce, sapwood absorbs solution faster than heartwood, whence open-tank treatment may give a round stick all the penetration required. Wood is submerged in solution and heated to 175°–180° F (never over 200°) for 1–2 hr by direct heat of fire or steam coils. Expansion causes most of the air (of which dry wood may contain up to 50% by vol) to escape. Upon cooling while still submerged, either in same tank after withdrawing heat or in another tank filled with cold solution to which the wood is quickly transferred, solution is drawn into cells by contraction of air remaining in them. When cool, wood is stacked for drying. Suitable strengths of solution are same as for pressure treatment.

Pressure or closed-tank system is good for all sawn timber and, in general, whenever the desired output demands speed; pressure method gives the same or better results than open-tank in about $1/3$ the time. Green timber can be well treated only in closed tanks. Rate of treatment is slower with round than with squared timber, as a smaller volume of rounds can be packed into a given tank. A small pressure-tank plant, to treat 5 000 props per yr, costs $10 000–$15 000. Essential equipment includes: (*a*) horiz, cyl tank with hinged or removable door at one end, with gasket and bolts for tight closure; in small tanks, the wood may be inserted and withdrawn in individual pieces; larger tanks usually have rails for receiving trucks loaded with timber. Tank contains steam-heating coils, and inlets for live steam, comp-air, suction, and solution, and outlet for return of latter; also vents at top and bottom, controlled by valves; (*b*) tanks for mixing, storing, and measuring solution, latter equipped with some form of calibrated volume indicator; (*c*) air compressor, vacuum pump, and pumps for transferring and applying press to solution (which may be done by comp air); (*d*) steam boiler. Usual procedure: (1) admit live steam, avoiding temp above 250° F; with seasoned timber, this step may be omitted; for green timber, it is essential, and may require 1–4 hr; (2) drain tank and apply suction (20-in or better) for 0.5–1 hr; (3) admit solution, containing 3–5% $ZnCl_2$, and apply press of 150–180 lb per sq in, heating with steam coil, and continuing until the previously calculated vol of solution to give desired penetration or desired wt of $ZnCl_2$ per cu ft of timber (examples below) has been absorbed, as indicated by the measuring tank; (4) return solution to storage tank, by comp air or pump; (5) apply suction for 0.5 hr to extract excess solution; (6) remove timber and store for drying, preferably about 6 mo.

Examples. Inspiration mine, Ariz (586) consumes about 10 450 M bd ft of timber per yr, mainly sawn Douglas fir, on which freight constitutes over half the delivered cost. Plant for $ZnCl_2$ press treatment, designed and erected by mine employes, began operation in Jan, 1930, and in 11 mo treated 522 430 bd ft, working 1 shift with 1 operator and laborers for loading and unloading trucks. Typical charge of 162 cu ft was impregnated to depth of 2 in, or with 0.6 lb $ZnCl_2$ per cu ft (using sol of 4.7% strength) in 3 hr over all. In dry, summer weather, preliminary steaming and evacuation were omitted, without affecting results. Treated timber is given 6 mo to dry. United Verde mine, Jerome, Ariz (587), consuming 8 700 M bd ft of timber in 1929 (about 75% local pine, remainder Oregon pine), is generally well ventilated and decay is not excessive. Chief difficulties have occurred in fencing and flooring square-set filled stopes, some of which are not finished in less than 10 yr, and for which nearly half of all timber is used. Plant for $ZnCl_2$ press treatment of 1 000 M bd ft per yr was finished in May, 1929, at cost of $12 184, and in succeeding 7 mo treated 882.6 M bd ft (or 17% of all consumed in same period) at following cost, per M bd ft: labor (1 operator, 2 helpers), $3.980; power, $0.020; steam, $1.349; $ZnCl_2$ (@ $5.34 per cwt), $2.710; misc supplies, $0.394; repairs, $0.547; total, $9.00. Press tank, 5.5 ft diam by 32 ft long, takes aver charge of 3 700 bd ft in 8 hr (sometimes 3 charges in 2 shifts), never allowing more than 3 hr for impregnation at 180-lb press; sol contains 3% $ZnCl_2$; vol is calculated to give penetration of 0.75 in for heavy timbers, $3/8$ in for lagging and flooring, corresponding to aver 0.61 lb $ZnCl_2$ per cu ft. Hollinger mine, Timmins, Ont (588) finished $ZnCl_2$ press plant at mid-1934 and in next 6 mo treated 2 500 M bd ft, both green and seasoned, or all timber except lagging, track ties, and stulls. Consumption of $ZnCl_2$ (applied in 5% sol) averaged 0.53 lb per cu ft, with penetrations of 2–2.5 in at 150-lb press. Tank is 50 ft long and takes 700 cu ft of timber. Total time per charge: spruce, 4 hr; dry, sawn lumber, 2.5 hr; B C fir, 7–8 hr. Commercial treatment plants are located in many lumber centers and offer advantages to small mines not equipped to treat their own timber. Orders and specifications should be placed as long in advance as possible (say, 6 mo), to insure adequate seasoning before and after treatment. As a rule, specifications as to $ZnCl_2$ content and penetration for mine timbers may be less rigorous than for RR and structural timber, and price should be shaded accordingly. In southern Ill coal field in 1932, cost for treating with 0.5 lb $ZnCl_2$ per cu ft was 12¢ for sawn and 16¢ for round timber, per cu ft. For advice on this and related subjects, the Service Bureau of Amer Wood-Preservers' Assoc, Chicago, Ill, may be consulted.

FILLED STOPES

59. GENERAL

Definitions and general plan. FILLED STOPE, as term is used here, is one in which: (*a*) support for walls and men and, at times, for back of ore is furnished by waste rock, tailing or sand, which materials are called FILLING or GOB; (*b*) filling is an integral part of stoping; generally the orebody is excavated in small sections, filled wholly or in part before adjacent ground is attacked; (*c*) excepting the crosscut method (Art 64) use of timber, if any, is for temporary support of slabs or back and is not systematic as in square-set stopes (Art 46, 47). Most filled stoping is done in overhand flat-back, stepped-face or rill stopes (Art 38). Surface of fill is kept roughly parallel to stope back. As the stope progresses upward, chutes (usually of timber) are carried up through the fill, giving access to the stope and delivering broken ore to level below. Height of section mined before filling depends on character of ore and walls; details vary with size and shape of stope and source of filling; modes of arranging haulage ways and of mining level pillars vary with strength of walls and ore and width of orebody; for examples see following articles. In overhand filled stopes, the operations of breaking or cutting a slice from back of stope, and then filling the excavated area, have led to the wide use of the term CUT-AND-FILL. A flat-back filled stope is called a HORIZ CUT-AND-FILL STOPE; a filled rill stope, an INCLINED CUT-AND-FILL STOPE; these terms are used in the following articles. The term FILLED STOPE is also applied to a stope mined by some other method and then filled with waste to prevent caving or subsidence. This is DELAYED FILLING, and may be used in open, shrinkage, or timbered stopes after completion; such work is described by adding the words " with delayed filling " to name of stoping method used, for example SHRINKAGE STOPING WITH DELAYED FILLING. Examples of delayed filling in different forms of stope are: Hollinger, Wright-Hargreaves, Coronado, and Homestake mines, Art 68; Horne mine, Art 43; Calumet & Arizona, Art 52; New Jersey Zinc, Golden Queen, and Carson Hill mines, Art 87.

Source of filling. Usually, cheapest filling is waste rock, unavoidably broken with the ore, which is sorted out in the stope (Art 60); amounts of waste produced by sorting are usually insufficient, and must be supplemented by other material.

Excess filling may be supplied by: (*a*) Shooting down walls of lode; this obtains filling with little or no handling, and is feasible if wall rock is strong; in weak rock, such excavations expose a strip of unsafe ground alongside of ore in back of stope (see Resuing, Art 61). (*b*) Driving crosscuts into walls; the waste produced is distributed in stope by barrows, cars or scrapers (Sec 27). Inclined raises in walls serve same purpose, discharging filling into the stope by gravity (Nevada Wonder mine, Art 60). Crosscuts and raises serve to prospect the walls, and hence are preferable for obtaining filling where parallel stringers are apt to occur. Methods (*a*) and (*b*) are used mostly in flat-back stopes, for relatively small amounts

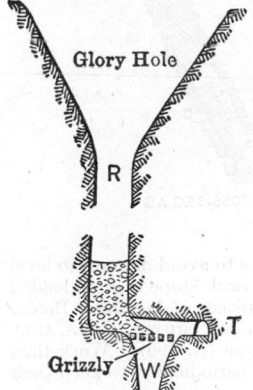

Fig 372

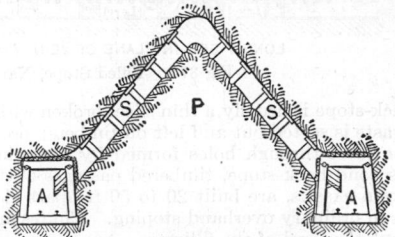

Fig 373. Caving for Waste. Diagrammatic Cross-sec

of filling required in excess of that from sorting. (*c*) Using waste brought from surface; it may consist of mill tailing, sand, or waste rock which can be broken cheaply in an open cut. Such filling, usually sent underground through FILLING or WASTE RAISES, is transported laterally along levels in cars (occasionally by belt conveyers) and dumped through raises into the stopes. Fig 372 shows mode of obtaining waste rock at LOS PILARES MINE, Nacozari, Mex (150). Glory-holes (Art 99) were opened in barren ground on the surface around raises *R*, which were 15 ft sq. Rock was broken with deep holes and heavy charges, and fell by gravity into the raise, at bottom of which was an offset connecting with drift *T*, and main waste raise *W*. Top of *W* was covered by a grizzly of heavy timbers 18 in apart, faced with steel, on which large boulders were broken. These raises terminated in bins, from which waste was distributed to stopes by electric haulage. There are many similar plans for obtaining waste for filling. Old dumps may sometimes be utilized by driving drifts and raises under them. (*d*) Utilizing waste from development work, thus saving or reducing cost of hoisting it; this is an important element in planning effic work in large-scale mining with numerous filled stopes and extensive exploratory and development work, as at Bisbee, Ariz. (*e*) "Caving for waste." Under proper conditions, this gives cheap filling. Two parallel timbered drifts *A* (Fig 373) are driven in country rock at a safe distance from the mine workings. Inclined stopes *S*, 3.5 to 4 ft wide and timbered with stulls, leave a V-shaped pillar *P* between the drifts. Chute gates (Art 90) are erected in drifts, say 6 or 8 ft apart. By blasting out the stulls, the back of *S* caves and the material is drawn as needed into cars. Obviously this method is feasible only in rock which will cave when thus undermined (259). Waste filling for Frood mine, Sudbury, Ont, is supplied by drawing caved hanging-wall rock from nearby Creighton mine (Art 68). At McIntyre mine, Schumacher, Ont (171), a large block of wall rock near the orebody is mined by sub-level stoping as source of waste supply (Art 43). (*f*) Drawing filling from upper stopes and reusing it in lower ones; feasible where it is unnecessary to support walls of orebody permanently. Allowance for swell of broken rock must be made in estimating cost and amount of filling material.

Other details as to filled stopes: see Art 60 to 65.

60. FILLED FLAT-BACK AND STEPPED-FACE OVERHAND STOPES OR HORIZONTAL CUT-AND-FILL STOPES, NARROW VEINS

Suitable orebodies are steep-dipping veins of strong ore, up to 15 or 20 ft wide; walls may be either weak or strong (Art 66).

Development follows practice in narrow veins (Art 14). If filling comes from outside sources, raises are necessary for delivering it into the stopes; main raises for passing filling to different levels should be continuous through successive lifts.

Breaking ground (see Overhand stopes, Art 26 to 28).

Stoping and filling. Fig 374 shows common practice in western metal mines. Stopes are started like open overhand stopes (Art 38). Ore from drift and cutting-out stope is sorted, and the waste used for filling other stopes. Level is timbered with lagged stulls or drift-sets (for choice, see Art 38).

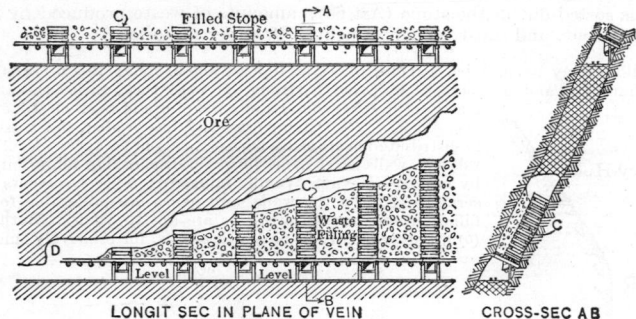

LONGIT SEC IN PLANE OF VEIN   CROSS-SEC **AB**

Fig 374. Filled Stope, Narrow Vein

First back-stope is usually a thin slice, broken with light shots to avoid damage to level timbers; waste is sorted out and left on timbers; ore from first back-stope is often loaded into cars on level through holes formed by removing 1 or 2 pieces of lagging. Before starting a second back-stope, timbered passages *C* (Fig 374), called CHUTES, MILLS, MILL HOLES, or ORE PASSES, are built 20 to 50 ft apart along the stope (Art 90). Work then proceeds as in ordinary overhand stoping. Chutes are built up periodically, to keep their tops at about the level of the filling.

Access to stope may be provided by timbered passages, like chutes; usually, manways are formed by putting ladders in one side of 2-compartment chutes. Openings *D* (Fig 374) serve as auxiliary entries during early work in stepped-face stopes. This description assumes that enough waste is rejected in sorting to fill the stope; if this be insufficient, excess filling is obtained as described in Art 59.

Sorting in stopes is usually possible only when ore minerals are easily recognized, where ore and waste differ markedly in appearance, or ore occurs in distinct bands or patches. Underground sorting is not feasible where fine breaking is required to separate ore from waste.

Sorting diminishes amount and increases grade of ore secured. This may reduce plant and operating costs for handling and milling an ore, and give more profit than is obtainable by treating entire contents of vein; it also reduces amount of outside waste required for filling. Sorting may result in a profit from ore of apparently too low a grade to work, as illustrated by following figures from a western silver mine. An 8-ft vein was mined as shown in Fig 374; about 40% of material broken, carrying $2 per ton, was left in stopes as waste; remainder was sorted and sent to a concentrating and cyanide plant; mill extraction, 90%; total cost of mining and treatment, about $9.90 per ton milled. Sorted ore had to assay $9.90 ÷ 0.9, or $11 per ton, to pay expenses; minimum aver value of vein

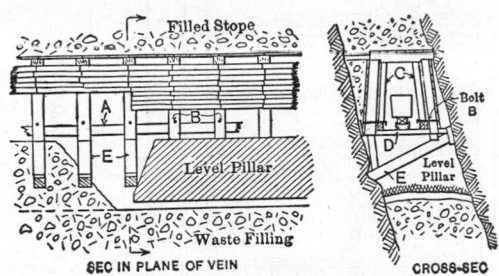
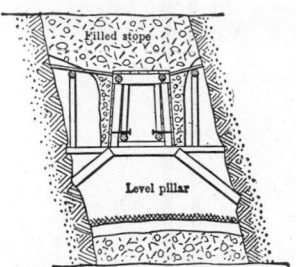

Fig 375. Mining Level-pillars, Waihi Mine, New Zealand

Fig 376. Mining Level-pillars, Vein widths 15-20 ft, Waihi Mine

matter which could be broken to produce sorted ore of this value was $(60 \times \$11) + (40 \times \$2) \div 100$, or $7.40 per ton. Calculations to determine advisability of sorting are similar to those given under Resuing, Art 61.

Mining level-pillars presents no difficulties if ore is strong, and if level is timbered with stulls to support filling in stope above. Work is same as that of breaking a back-stope with uppers; in weak ore, vertical posts or cribs, resting on filling, are required to support level-pillars, and prevent falls of ground as work progresses; such ground may be broken by holes drilled in floor of level above. If the level is required for haulage, etc, filling from outside source is necessary to replace ore in level-pillars.

Fig 375 shows method at Waihi mine, New Zealand, of mining pillars under timbered levels (233). Work begins by placing heavy stringers A, 15 to 20 ft long, on each side of track close to posts; 1.5-in bolts B are then driven into each post, their projecting ends resting on the stringer and supporting the posts when ground below is removed. Timbers C are wedged between bolts and caps; spreaders D are placed at each set. The underlying pillar is next broken down, each drift set laid bare being blocked up from stulls E. When 3 or 4 sets have been thus picked up, the open space is filled and stringers are moved on another length, their forward end always resting on solid ground. This method is used for vein widths up to 15 ft; for greater widths, stulls E would be too long to handle. Saddle-back sets (Fig 376) are used for widths of 15 to 20 ft. Fig 377 shows method at Nevada Wonder mine for supporting stull and post timbering; other variations are feasible. See also McIntyre Porcupine mine below.

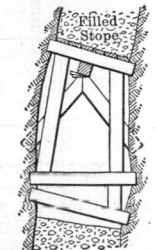

Fig 377. Support for Stull and Post Sets while mining Level-pillars, Nev Wonder Mine (Fig 379)

Examples of practice given below illustrate details of filled flat-back or stepped-face stopes in narrow veins; see also Resuing, Art 61.

Block P mine, St Joseph Lead Co, Hughesville, Mont. Data from W. O. Vanderburg (577) in 1931. Fissure vein carrying Pb-Ag ore occurs in large syenite chimney or stock, cut by rhyolite dikes. Vein has known length of 4 000 ft. Ore is 1–4 ft wide, but stopes aver 5 ft. Dip, 65°–88°. Mineralization is distributed in lenses throughout vein. Walls usually well defined and stand well for the short time they remain unsupported; occasional stulls used in blocky ground in rhyolite. Ore breaks well; about 95% broken in primary blasting will pass an 8-in grizzly. **Development.** Entry to deeper part of mine is through a 2-compt vert shaft, 1 200 ft deep (1931); first 350 ft was sunk in vein, next 300 ft in hanging wall, remaining 550 ft in footwall. Below 400 ft, level interval is 200 ft. Drifts run along vein in both directions from shaft; timbered with drift sets. Raises, 690 ft apart, are driven for exploration and ventilation. Length of stopes aver 400 ft, sometimes reaching 750 ft. Drift sets are 5 ft c-c, except every ninth set, where spacing is 6 ft to accommodate chute and manway. Stoping is started by removing lagging over drift sets and taking a 5-ft cut from back, the ore being shoveled into cars. Lagging is replaced, chutes built, and horiz cut-and-fill mining starts (Fig 378). Cuts, 5 ft high, are broken by uppers drilled with hand-rotated stopers; 1 miner drills about 15 holes per shift; blasted with 30% gelatin dynamite. Selective blasting and

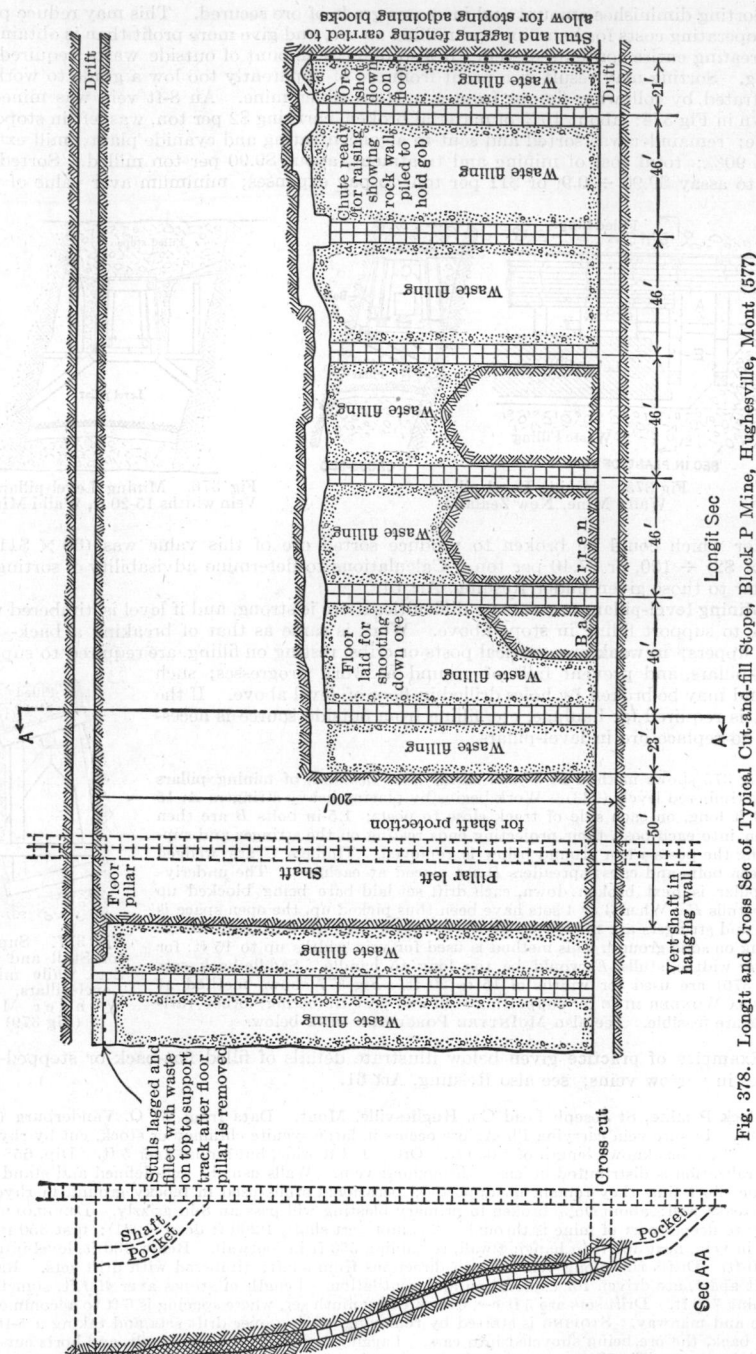

Fig. 378. Longit and Cross Sec of Typical Cut-and-fill Stope, Block P Mine, Hughesville, Mont (577)

hand sorting are used to obtain high-grade product and minimize loss of ore.   Amount of waste thus produced is more than enough for filling.   Following methods of breaking depend on ore occurrence: (1) where ore and waste are in alternate bands across the vein, they are blasted together and waste sorted by hand; (2) where ore occurs as single strong band, the waste is first blasted, then the ore; (3) where ore is weak and in one band, ore is first blasted and then the waste.   Before blasting, flooring is laid over fill to prevent mixing of ore and waste; flooring is of 3-in planks, 8 and 10 in wide, 5 ft long. Sorted ore is shoveled into chutes by hand.   Stope crew usually consists of miner and shoveler.   Chutes and manways are of framed sets of round timber and are built up periodically by timbering crews; chutes are lined with 3 by 10-in plank, 5 ft long, and are 26 in square inside lining; manways, 32 by 26 in.   Single-compt' chutes without adjoining manway were formerly used, but were unsatisfactory; repairing was difficult and it was dangerous to start ore running when hung up in chutes; manway gives safe and easy access to any point along chute.   At end of a stope section, fill is lagged off from unbroken ore by row of stulls 5 ft c-c, laced with pole lagging 3-5-in diam.   Horses of waste are left unmined (Fig 378). Stopes are carried through to level above.   About 5 ft below level, stulls are placed 5 ft c-c and lagged with poles.   Waste is run onto lagging to support track on the level.   If walls are weak, stulls are also placed under drift sets before floor pillar is removed. Vanderburg cites following advantages of cut-and-fill mining at this mine: (1) complete extraction of ore; (2) very little timber is required; (3) ore is not held in stopes for long periods; (4) decreased use of timber and use of waste for filling reduces traffic in shaft; (5) a high-grade product is obtained by careful hand sorting; (6) good ventilation is obtained; (7) safe working conditions; (8) fire hazard is small. Table 41 gives operating data for year 1929.

Table 41.   Operating Data, Block P Mine, Hughesville, Mont (577) Year 1929.   Tons hoisted, 106 242

	Development	Mining	Total
A. *Labor* (man-hr per ton):			
Breaking (drilling, blasting)	0.116	1.636	1.751
Shoveling	0.120	1.812	1.932
Timbering	0.048	0.508	0.556
Underground haulage	0.045	0.445	0.490
Pumping			0.096
Hoisting			0.165
Underground misc			0.175
Supervision			0.185
Total labor underground			5.350
Aver ton per man-shift underground			1.495
Surface haulage			0.072
Tool sharpening			0.082
Timber framing			0.094
Misc surface			0.221
Total labor on surface			0.469
B. *Power and supplies:*			
Explosives (lb per ton)	0.286	2.568	2.854
Detonators (number per ton)	0.114	1.963	2.077
Power (kw-hr per ton):			
Air compression			9.974
Hauling			0.676
Drainage			1.134
Hoisting			4.886
Tramway			0.175
Misc			0.610
Total power			17.455
Timber: Pole lagging (lin ft per ton, 3 to 6-in diam)			6.234
Stulls (lin ft per ton, 8 to 12-in diam)			1.304
Sawed stock (bd ft per ton)			
2 by 4-16 ft long			0.164
1 by 4-16 ft long			0.062
3 by 8-10 ft long			2.198
3 by 10-10 ft long			1.531
Total			3.955
C. Labor percentage of total cost			72.63
Power and supplies percentage of total cost			27.37

Nevada Wonder mine, Wonder, Nev (234).   Operations were suspended in 1919, but example illustrates present-day practice in many small mines and in portions of some large ones.   Gold-silver ore occurred in fissure vein 5-6 ft wide.   Ore was fractured; walls, weak. Following the cutting-out stope, level was timbered as in Fig 379, with 3-in plank lagging.   Chutes of 2-in plank (Art 90) were at 25-ft intervals.   A raise was then started in one wall, close to back of stope and at a pitch of 40° to 50°; enough waste was broken to cover timbers to depth of 2-3 ft.   Waste was leveled off and covered with a plat of 2 by 12-in plank, upon which ore from first back-stope fell; the plat aided shoveling and reduced loss of fines in filling.   Breaking ground began at one end of stope, 5-ft uppers being drilled with stope-drills.   Before removing all ore broken from first back-stope, holes were drilled for the second, but were not charged.   Ore was then cleaned up, some running to the chutes, the remainder being shoveled or handled in barrows.   Plat was removed, chutes and manways were built up and braced temporarily, and stope was filled by waste to within 3 or 4 ft of back.   Waste raises were driven alternately in foot and hanging walls between every 2 chutes; a raise served 2 or 3 back-stopes and was seldom over 30 to 40 ft high.

McIntyre Porcupine Mines, Schumacher, Ont.   Data from H. G. Skavlem and D. E. Keeley in 1933 (229, 171).   Gold ore occurs in quartz veins and in irregular replacement bodies. Wall rocks are generally lava-schists or porphyry; veins frequently along contact of these rocks. Aver width of ore is about 10 ft, but widths to 100 ft occur; length of ore varies, up to 1 200 ft. Dips, 60° to vert. In early years all stoping was by shrinkage; dilution from weak walls and need of sorting caused change to cut-and-fill and square-set methods. Mine is developed by vert shafts; levels, at 100-ft intervals to 1 000-ft level and at 125-ft intervals below. Raises for stope filling and ventilation are 250–300 ft apart. Fig 380 shows cut-and-fill practice. Chute-spacing at 35–150 ft was tried, but standard interval in 1933 was 50 ft, with manway alongside every third chute. Cuts are

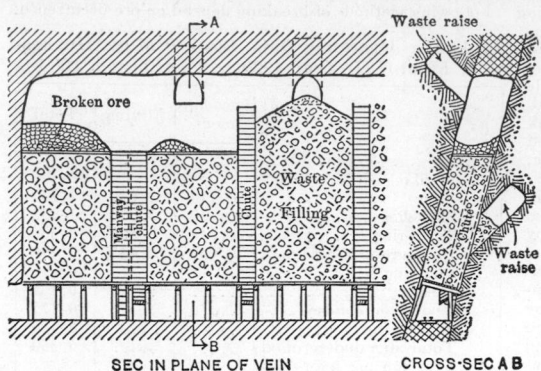

SEC IN PLANE OF VEIN   CROSS-SEC A B

Fig 379. Filled Flat-back Stope, Nevada Wonder Mine

8-ft high; breast is broken by mounted drifters drilling 10–12-ft flat holes. Powder con-

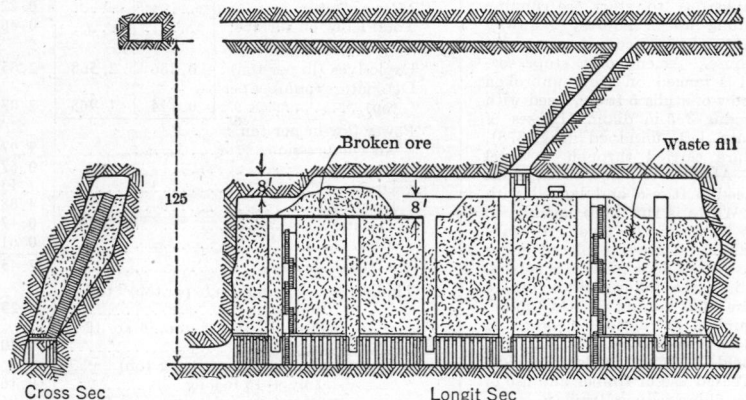

Fig 380. Horiz Cut-and-fill Stope, McIntyre Mine, Schumacher, Ont

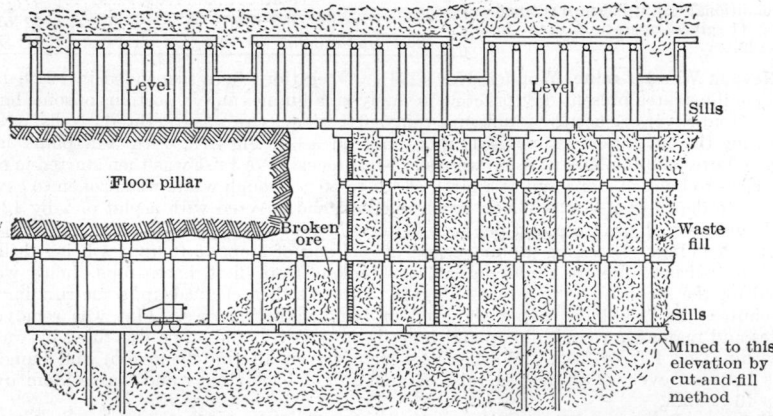

Fig 381. Longit Sec showing Method of Extracting Floor Sills, McIntyre Mine, Schumacher, Ont

sumption, about 1 lb dynamite per ton. In strong ground breast may be 50 ft or more ahead of muckers. In stopes under 12 ft, scaly backs are supported by stulls. Handling of ore to chutes is by hand shoveling, or scrapers with air-driven hoists. Where scrapers are not used, ore beyond shoveling distance from chutes is loaded into 1-ton cars and trammed to chutes. Same type of car is used for spreading waste; for handling ore and spreading waste, sectionalized track of 16-lb rail in 10-ft lengths is used. As stope approaches level above, cut-and-fill mining is stopped, to leave floor pillar of a thickness

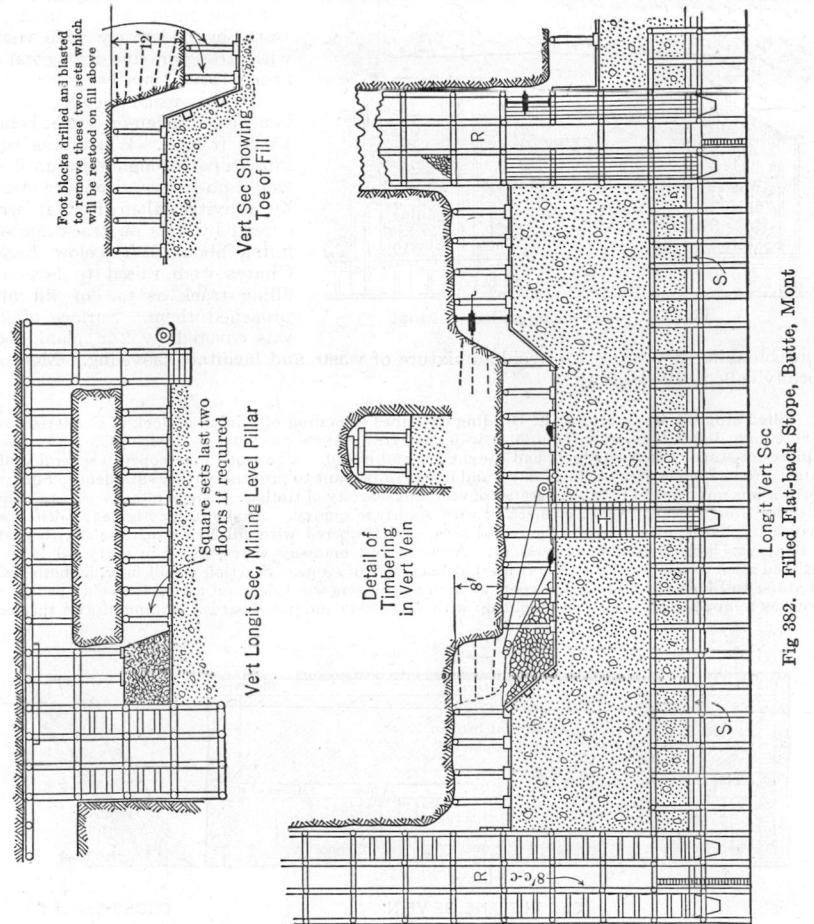

Fig 382. Filled Flat-back Stope, Butte, Mont

depending on width of vein and ground conditions; thickness of floor pillar rarely exceeds 20 ft. Level pillar is mined by square-setting, to preserve haulageway above (Fig 381). Sources of waste rock for filling are: (1) development and shaft sinking; (2) sorting in stopes; (3) old fill from finished stopes; (4) waste cross-cuts driven in walls of stopes; (5) regular waste stopes. Use of waste crosscuts is confined to stopes remote from waste passes. Mode of obtaining waste by sub-level caving is described in Art 43.

Anaconda Copper Mining Co, Butte, Mont. Data from J. A. O'Neill, Eng Research Dept, and J. J. Carrigan, Gen Supt, in 1939. For ore occurrences and development, see Art 46. Fig 382 shows detail of method. Through raise-chutes R to level above, driven 125–200 ft apart along the veins, are later used for supplying filling from crosscuts in levels above. Sheeting caps and sheeting S (pole lagging or small stulls) support filling over sill or haulage level. A chute and manway T is carried through filling for extracting broken ore from stope. One double-drum hoist scrapes both sides of stope into the chute, and also handles filling from through raise-chutes. Ore is shoveled on 2- or 3-in flooring on top of filling. Stulls with headboards support the walls when needed, and are salvaged before beginning each fill. In addition to low timber costs, the stope has the advantage of the good working conditions secured in all flat-back stopes, combined with close filling.

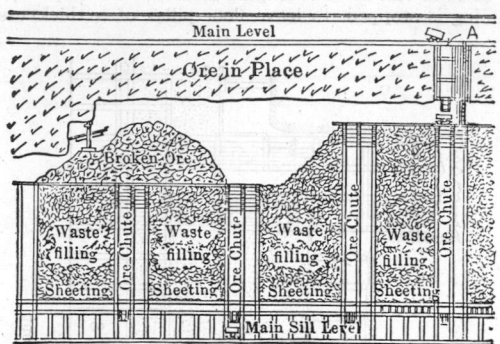

Fig 383. Back-filling at Butte, Mont

Butte, Mont (219). Fig 383, from B. H. Dunshee, shows a sometimes useful adaptation of flat-back filled stopes, used at Butte in moderately wide veins with strong ore and strong walls. Stope breast was carried about twice the usual height, in 2 benches, broken-ore pile being 15–20 ft high. Waste was run into stope through raise until it would no longer distribute itself by gravity; thereafter, it was spread by cars on track laid on filling about 6 ft below back. Chutes were raised to level of filling track as toe of fill approached them. Surface of fill was covered by 2-in plank before breaking down ore, to avoid admixture of waste and facilitate shoveling. Method locally called "Back filling."

Filled stope in weak ore. J. E. Harding describes a method of mining a block of shattered ore, 300 ft long, 100 ft high, and about 20 ft wide, at MINA SANTA FRANCISCA, Mexico (236). An open square-set stope, 4 to 6 sets high, had caught fire and caved. The stope was reopened several years later; ore had come down in huge slabs, and it was important to prevent surface subsidence. Square-setting was not deemed feasible, because of cost and scarcity of timber. Waste filling was obtainable cheaply from a nearby raise, connecting with a surface quarry. As shown by Fig 384, a drift was driven on 200-ft level through the caved area, and timbered with sill-floor square-sets with posts 4 ft apart; little spiling was necessary. A chute and manway were started in every 4th set; a cribbed raise A was put up to 100-ft level at each end of stope. Starting on sill floor, at both ends of stope and both sides of drift, a room as high as the sets was taken out across the vein; as fast as ore was removed, the back was caught up with vert posts and headboards. Filling, drawn through

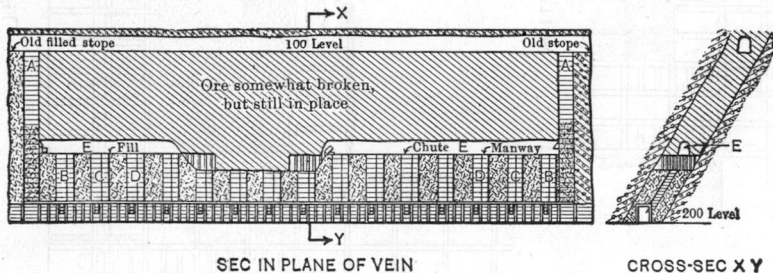

SEC IN PLANE OF VEIN   CROSS-SEC X Y

Fig 384. Filled Flat-back Stope in Weak Ore

raises A, was kept close to face and stowed close to back, the stulls being buried. Waste was trammed to advancing face of rooms through a small drift in the back directly over the sill-floor sets; cars were loaded from temporary gates built into raises A. When the sill floor was mined and filled, successive slices 10 ft high were similarly mined above. In any slice, rooms were started at the end chutes B, and connected with waste raises A; filling was drawn in and rooms advanced halfway to chutes C; chutes B were then built up, waste drifts E started, and the rooms completely filled. Rooms were then opened from tops of chutes C, carried halfway to chutes D and filled, the process being repeated until slice was removed. Distance between fill and face of a room never exceeded 10 ft; less in bad ground. Stulls for supporting back on sill-floor and upper slices were 10 ft long and 8-in butt diam, turned in a lathe and tapered to 6-in diam at other end; they were placed large end up, and were easily pulled out of filling with a hydraulic jack when uncovered in mining the slice above. This is a variant of the Crosscut method, Art 64.

61. RESUING (also called " Stripping ")

Field of use for resuing is in working very narrow veins or paystreaks.

General plan of work (Fig 385). *P* is a narrow high-grade streak, separated from a low-grade or barren portion *AB* by gouge *C*. A flat-back overhand stope of minimum width is first opened alongside of a portion of the paystreak, as at *AB*; the broken material is used for filling *F*. Exposed part of paystreak is then broken down clean and sent to level through chutes *M*, spaced 15 to 50 ft apart.

Alternative methods: (*a*) Mine the vein from wall to wall, and sort out as much waste as possible in the stope; this produces more ore and lower-grade ore than resuing (compare Art 60). (*b*) Carry a stope of minimum width (Art 27, 28), to include streak *P*; this gives amounts of ore intermediate between plan (*a*) and resuing. (*c*) Soft ore may be picked out before breaking to full stoping width. Choice of method depends on amount of sorting possible in stopes, and costs of breaking, handling, and treatment. Resuing often yields larger profit than any of these alternatives.

Requirements for the successful application of resuing: (*a*) A well defined plane of weakness, as a clay seam or slip on one side of paystreak. (*b*) Steep dips are desirable. (*c*) High-grade ore is necessary for mining narrow deposits with profit.

Cold Springs mine, Nederland, Boulder County, Colo. Data from W. O. Vanderburg (290) in 1932. Tungsten ore (tungstate of iron, $FeWO_4$) occurs as lenses in fissure veins; wall rock is chiefly granite, frequently gneissoid. Aver width of ore-streak mined, 8–10 in; aver length, 80 ft. Aver dip of veins, 70°. Walls tend to slough when exposed more than 6 ft along dip. Ore and waste are easily distinguished by visual inspection. Mine is developed by 2-compt shaft 40 ft in footwall and inclined about 71°; upper 3 levels are 50 ft apart, lower 3, 100 ft apart. No raises are driven in advance of stoping, but some timbered chutes and manways through old stope fills are maintained as openings between levels. Cribbed chutes are 25–30 ft apart; chutes at ends of stopes have manways alongside. Stope is advanced by successive cuts 4–6 ft high. Method of breaking ground varies with character of vein. Where ore occurs as a single band, resuing or " stripping " is used; waste is blasted first, usually on hanging-wall side, and leveled off by hand. A sheet-iron plat is then laid on the fill and exposed ore carefully blasted down with small charges of explosive, or taken down by hand moiling. Where ore and waste are too intimately associated for resuing, they are blasted down together and sorted by hand. Amount of waste thus obtained is more than enough for filling; excess is shoveled into chutes and hoisted to surface. In 8 mo of 1931, an aver of 0.445 ton of ore was recovered per man-shift of all labor; 4.48 lb of 40% dynamite were consumed per ton recovered.

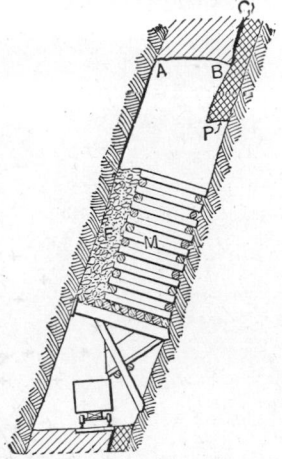

Fig 385. Resuing

Molybdenum Corp of America mine, Questa, N M. Data from J. B. Carman (492) in 1931. Veins carrying molybdenite (MoS_2) occur in zone of branching and interfingering fractures in porphyry. Width of mineralization varies from fraction of inch to 6 ft, but vein walls are sometimes 10 ft apart. Streaks of high-grade ore not over 6 in wide are commonly mined, but for whole mine aver width of material taken as ore is probably 12–18 in. Veins are commonly 200–500 ft long, extending down dip about one-third their horiz length. Average dip is 60°, but wide local variations occur. Both vein and wall rock drill and break easily; molybdenite is very friable and must be blasted carefully to avoid loss in fines. Ground usually requires support given by filling, but in places open stopes are used. Mine is developed by several tunnels at various elevations; level interval, 40–100 ft. No raises are driven for stoping only. Fig 386 gives a cross-sec of a typical stope, showing variation in width of ore and occurrence of included waste. Stopes are started by taking cut from back of drift, placing drift sets, and building chute-pockets 50 ft apart; manways are carried alongside of alternate chutes. Chutes and manways are of round cribbing or stulls laced with split lagging; chutes are 3 ft square inside; no grizzlies are used. Stopes are flat-back. Ground is broken by uppers, rarely over 3 ft deep. Both machine and hand drilling are employed; hand drilling favored in soft ground because recovery of ore is cleaner and more complete; hand-rotated stopers used for harder ground. Explosive is 40% gelatin dynamite. Method of breaking ore varies according to ore occurrence and is carefully supervised. Resuing is used where possible, waste portion of vein being mined before ore is broken down by picking or very light blasting. Plank flooring is sometimes laid on fill before breaking down ore, but usually fill is simply leveled off. Ore is shoveled directly to chutes without use of wheelbarrows, in spite of wide chute spacing. Double handling of ore is necessary in any case because of sorting. Enough material for filling is generally provided by waste necessarily broken and sorted out in stoping. In 1930, about 0.6 ton of ore was recovered per man-shift of all labor; explosive, about 3 lb per ton of ore.

City Deep mine, Johannesburg, So Africa. For data on resuing in this deep mine, see Art 33.

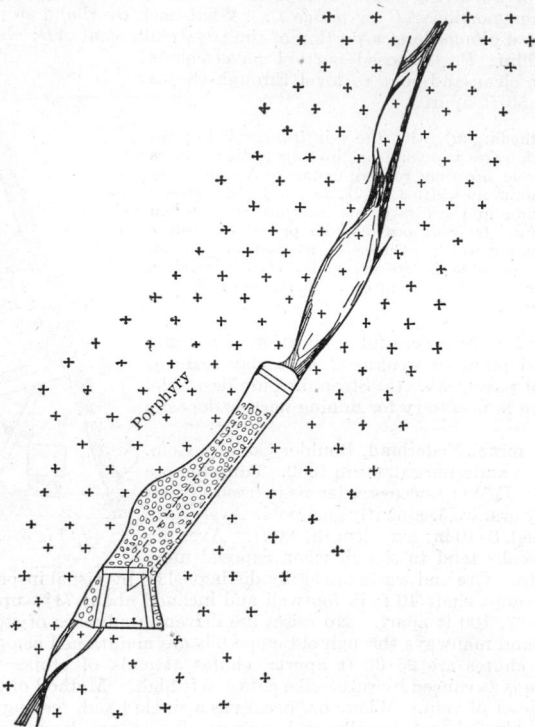

Fig 386. Vert Cross-sec through Typical Stope, Molybdenum
Corp of America, Questa, N M

Resuing *vs* other methods for mining a narrow, high-grade, gold-quartz vein; data from F. C. Roberts (238). In all examples, dip of vein is 85°, wall rocks contain no values, and as there is a clean slip on footwall, stoping can be done there without disturbing vein; general charges cover items of amortization, pumping, and general expense.

Example A	Tons	Cost per ton	Total
Mining............	104	$3.60	$374.40
Tramming.........	104	0.36	37.44
Hoisting...........	104	0.18	18.72
Milling............	100	1.44	144.00
General............			198.00
Total............			$772.56
Value of gold from 100 tons......			749.00
		Loss	$ 23.56

Example A. Width of vein, 6 in; value, $48 per ton. Vein and wall rock are broken together in a stope 30 in wide; broken material contains 20% ore and 80% waste; aver value, $9.60 per ton. 5% of the waste is sorted in stope; 5% of 80 = 4, hence 96% of tonnage of ore and waste broken is sent to mill, with a value of $9.99 per ton. Mill recovery, 75%, or $7.49 per ton. Cost per 100 tons milled is shown by accompanying statement.

Example B. Width and value of vein same as in Example A. Mining is done by resuing; a 30-in stope is carried in footwall and the vein broken down clean after about 3 600 sq ft are stripped; some waste from footwall stope had to be sent to surface. Mill recovery, 75% or $36 per ton. Statement shows cost per 100 tons milled.

Example C. Resuing a 12-in vein; value, $28.80 per ton. Mill recovery, 75% or $21.60 per ton. Method same as in Example B. Statement shows cost per 100 tons milled.

The same vein mined in a stope 30 in wide, where ore and waste are broken together, shows $124.38 profit per 100 tons milled, where 5% of the waste can be sorted in stopes; if 20% of the waste can be thus sorted, profit is $196.50.

Example B	Tons	Cost per ton	Total
Mining waste.....	500	$2.40	$1 200.00
Mining ore.......	100	3.60	360.00
Handling waste...	110	0.48	52.80
Tramming ore....	100	0.36	36.00
Hoisting waste...	110	0.18	19.80
Hoisting ore......	100	0.18	18.00
Milling ore.......	100	1.92	192.00
General.........	.....	......	252.00
Total.........	.....	......	$2 130.60
Value of gold from 100 tons....			3 600.00
		Profit	$1 469.40

Example C	Tons	Cost per ton	Total
Mining waste.....	250	$2.40	$ 600.00
Mining ore.......	100	3.60	360.00
Handling waste...	23	0.48	11.04
Handling ore.....	100	0.36	36.00
Hoisting ore......	100	0.18	18.00
Hoisting waste...	23	0.18	4.14
Milling ore.......	100	1.92	192.00
General.........	.....	......	240.00
Total.........	.....	......	$1 461.18
Value of gold from 100 tons....			2 160.00
		Profit	$ 698.82

62. FILLED FLAT-BACK STOPES OR HORIZONTAL CUT-AND-FILL STOPES, WIDE OREBODIES

Field of use. Ore should stand unsupported over back of stope or with no greater support than is afforded by posts or cribs resting on filling. Strong walls are not a requisite. General dip should be steep, but local variations in dip of foot- or hanging-wall contacts are not serious handicaps. For use of filling methods in weak ores, see Art 64.

General plan of work is same as for narrow veins (Art 60). Filling for wide stopes may be obtained in part from sorting or by breaking into walls, but generally it comes from outside sources and is delivered to stope through raises. Wide orebodies often call for more than one haulageway under stope to afford proper chute spacing. Rib pillars between stopes are usually necessary to limit size of stope; in wide orebodies, narrow

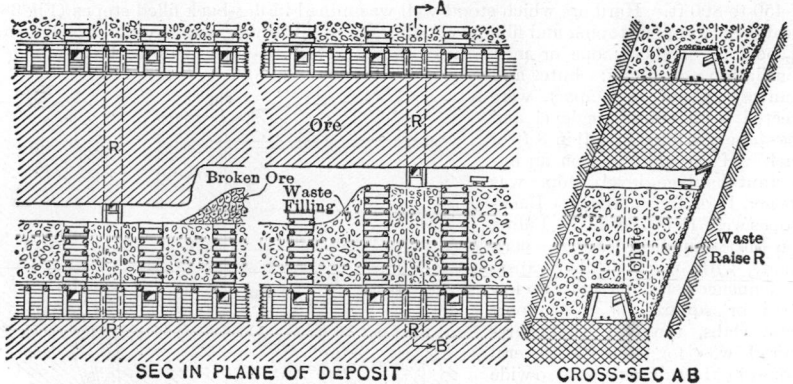

```
                              ┌─A
     SEC IN PLANE OF DEPOSIT              CROSS-SEC AB
```

Fig 387. Filled Flat-back Stope, Minnesota Iron Co, Soudan, Minn

dimension of stope is usually in direction of strike. Examples of practice are given below and in Art 63, 64.

Minnesota Iron Co, Soudan, Minn (35, 153, 183, 239). This is a classic example of early practice in U S. Orebodies were overlapping lenses of hematite, varying in length from 200 to 1 000 ft, in width from a pinch to over 100 ft, and in vert height from 250 to 500 ft; dip, 65° to 75°. Ore was very hard and strong; walls, weak and soft. METHOD OF MINING (Fig 387, 388). Overhand, flat-back stopes were carried with alternate ore-breaking and filling; timbered gangways were kept open through the filling; an occasional crib supported loose slabs in back of stope. Entry was by several inclined shafts in foot-wall; level interval, 80 ft. Levels were opened by driving wide crosscuts from shaft to hanging wall; a 7 by 8-ft drift was driven through center of lens, followed by a breast stope (Art 30), which took out full width of deposit to a height of 15 to 20 ft. Gangways, following advance of breast stope, consisted of 3-piece round-timber sets (Art 20), with 9-ft posts, 11-ft caps; the sets were 3 ft apart, close lagged and held in place with sway-braces. Fig 388 shows plan of gangway. At chutes, sets were of 20 to 24-in timber. Top lagging was 6 to 8-in diam, side lagging 3 to 5-in. Cribbed ladder-ways, 5 ft square, were built up on hanging-wall side of gangway at 50-ft intervals, and similar chutes every

25 ft along footwall side. When timbering was finished, stope was filled with waste to a depth of 12 to 15 ft; there should be at least 5 ft of fill above gangway sets. A 10-ft slice was then broken from back of stope, the ore being thrown into chutes; as stope advanced, chutes and manways were cribbed and a new layer of filling was put in, leaving a 6-ft space between fill and back of stope. Successive back-stopes about 15 ft high were taken as long as the back would stand safely under the filling in stope above; level-pillars were usually 6 to 10 ft thick (153). WASTE FOR FILLING was admitted through 6 by 6-ft raises R in the footwall, with one side following contact between rock and ore. Raises were about 100 ft apart and terminated in an open-cut at surface; the side exposed by stoping was timbered before filling was run into the

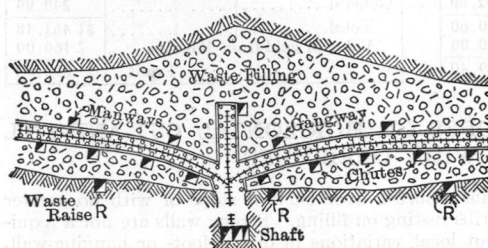

stope; this allowed filling to be drawn into stopes at any elevation and maintained raises for future service in lower lifts. Filling was distributed in small cars, loaded from temporary chute gates erected in raises. For upper lifts, filling was obtained by blasting walls of open-cut; the filling in exhausted upper lifts was drawn downward and used in lower stopes; in narrow parts of deposits, filling was done with lower handling costs by breaking down the walls.

Fig 388.   Plan of Part of Level, Minnesota Iron Co

Arizona Copper Co, Morenci, Ariz; data from P. B. Scotland (178, 152). Sulphide ores occur as disseminated deposits in quartz porphyry and as fault fissure veins in granite. Oreshoots to which this method was applied carried 2.5 to 2.8% Cu, and were irregular in outline; lengths, 450 to 1 750 ft; widths, 6 to 200 ft; commercial ore extended to depths of 450 to 800 ft. Hard ore which stood well was mined in flat-back filled stopes (Fig 389); locally called open stoping and filling. A slice, 15 to 20 ft high, was taken over whole area at bottom of shoot; one or more raises were driven to surface or to level above for ventilation and filling; chutes and manways, about 75 ft apart, were erected from tramming level and the stope was filled to within 8 ft of back. If orebody was on an important haulage level, stope was opened 10 or 15 ft above it. Back-stopes were 15 to 20 ft high. Filling was distributed in cars; experiments with mechanical scrapers were unsuccessful. Excepting a few cribs or square-sets to support loose slabs, the only timber required was for chutes. Several stopes in Metcalf mine were so wide (up to 300 ft) that pillars amounting to 5% of orebody were left to support walls and back. Danger from unsupported backs limited use of method to the firmest ground. Filling was obtained cheaply from surface quarries or glory-holes. (For other methods at Morenci, see Art 35, 46, 65, 68, 73.)

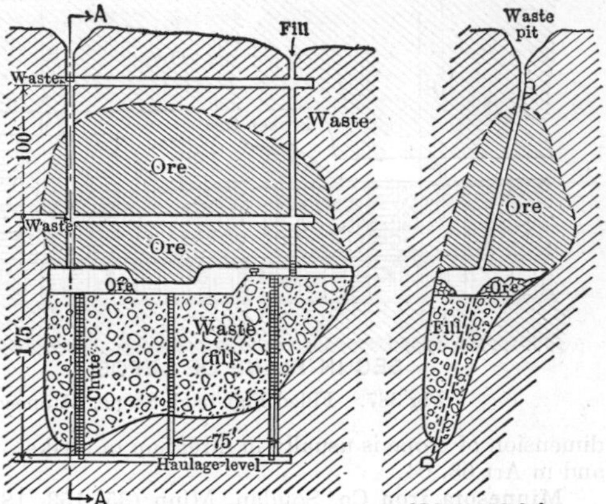

Fig 389.   Filled Flat-back Stope, Morenci, Ariz

United Verde mine, Jerome, Ariz. Data from T. W. Quayle (227) in 1931 and W. W. Lynch, formerly Mine Supt. Large body of pyrite occurs in a steeply dipping inverted trough, with diorite hanging wall, schist and porphyry footwall. Bodies of copper ore occur within the pyritic mass and usually extend into the footwall. The walls are generally commercial limits of massive sulphide on hanging-wall side and of schist or porphyry on footwall side. Main orebody is about 1 200 ft long, varying in width from a few ft to 200 ft. Except in some schist zones, ore is strong and stands over large areas without support except occasional cribs. Massive sulphide hanging wall is generally very strong. Footwalls of schist or porphyry usually require prompt support. Much ore is high enough in grade to be smelted without concentration and hence must be mined to give high extraction with little dilution from waste. These conditions, combined with irregularity of walls, were reasons for favoring horiz cut-and-fill method in the past, although some shrinkage and inclined cut-and-fill stoping were used. (Future plans call for wider use of inclined cut-and-fill. Author, 1939.) DEVELOPMENT. There are 3 vert footwall shafts, and 2 adits, on 500- and 1 000-ft levels. Level interval generally 150 ft. On each level a main crosscut intersects middle of orebody, and drifts near the sulphide-schist (or porphyry) contact determine the length of ore. Width, shape and characteristics of ore on a

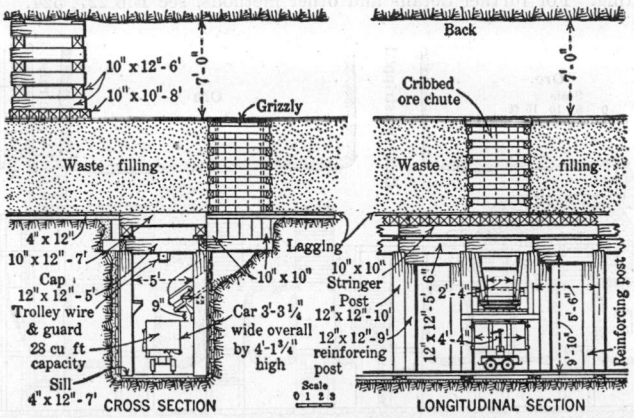

Fig 390. Chute and Gangway Timbering, United Verde Mine

level are determined largely by diamond drilling (Fig 48); these data guide the planning of stopes, additional haulageways and raises, and spacing of rib pillars. STOPING. Original practice in cut-and-fill work was to sill out stopes on levels and then establish timbered gangways, but gangway timbers required costly maintenance. In later practice, cutting-out floor was 13 ft above level, which also involved timbered gangways (Fig 390); timber maintenance was reduced, but still high. Still later practice was to sill the stope 21–25 ft above level, avoiding timbering of gangways altogether. Stopes were laid out to give max size consistent with safe mining; dimensions, 30–160 ft across the orebody and 60–200 ft along strike. Stope dimensions were also affected by necessity for maintaining regularity in the vert-pillar system. Raises were 6 by 11 ft, with a cribbed manway compt, the chute side being untimbered. For stopes 100 ft or more long, 2 waste raises were driven, one at one end and the other near center of stope; smaller stopes had only 1 fill raise. Where 2 fill raises were used, the timber was stripped from both; with only 1 raise, its timber was left in place to hold the raise open for ventilation. Silling operations were usually started from one waste raise 21–25 ft above rail; sill-floor cut, 7 ft high. Chute raises connected the haulageways with the stope at 16.5-ft intervals in massive sulphide, and 22-ft intervals in schist or porphyry. After sill reached pillar lines and ore limits, a second 7-ft cut was started from a waste raise. In stopes having 2 raises, the cut was started from the one near end of stope. Two rows of 7 to 8-ft flat holes were drilled by drifters; loaded with 50% gelatin dynamite. Before starting filling, sill flooring was laid, of 4 by 12-in, 5 ft 4 in c–c, and a

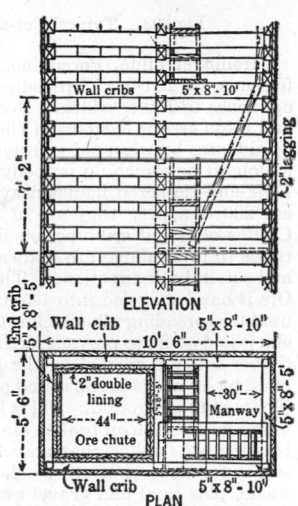

Fig 391. Cribbed Chute and Manway, United Verde Mine

double floor of 2-in planks, 10 ft 8 in long, placed to break joints; purpose of flooring on a solid floor was to aid level-pillar recovery. "Pillar fencing" was built along faces of the vert pillars, of 6 by 8-in posts 8 ft long, spaced 3 ft 7 in c–c and covered with 2-in plank 7 ft 2 in long, with staggered joints. Chutes were of 5 by 8-in cribbing, 5 ft 3 in long, lined with 4-in pine and sheathed outside with used 2-in flooring. Where manways adjoined chutes, construction was as in Fig 391. Grizzlies over chutes were of inverted

60-lb rails with 11-in openings. Waste was distributed from temporary chute pocket under waste raise by 18-cu ft scoop-body cars on 18-in gage sectional track. Track sections were of 8-ft straight lengths, curves of 9-ft radius, and standard switches; rails riveted to $^3/_8$ by 4-in steel-plate ties; sections connected by slip-joint tie and a spike; no bolts necessary. Fig 392 shows stope procedure. Stope continued upward by horiz cut-and-fill to within 20–30 ft of level above. Both floor and vert pillars were later mined by square-setting. For further details and other methods, see Bib 227, 524.

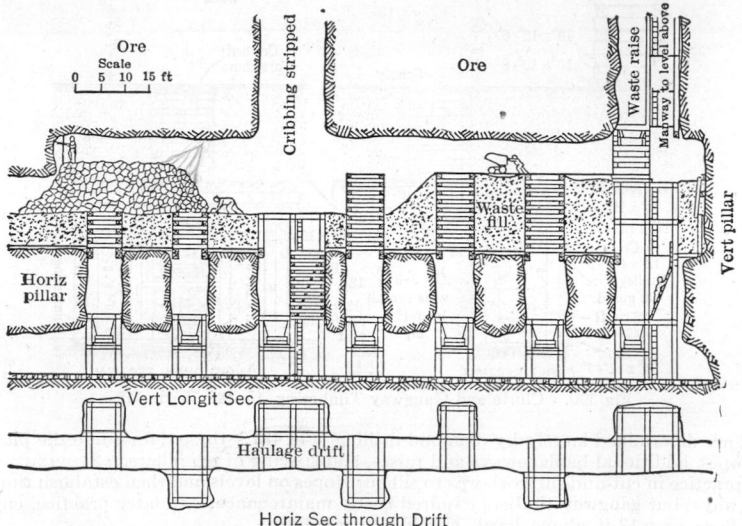

Fig 392.   Typical Cut-and-fill Stope, United Verde Mine, Jerome, Ariz (227)

Hollinger mine, Porcupine, Ont. Data from A. W. Young (306) in 1935. For geol features, see Art 68. Orebodies range from narrow single veins to groups of veins forming ore zones to 100 ft width. Horiz cut-and-fill method is used for wide orebodies, irregular and often erratic systems of closely spaced, branching and connecting veins, newly developed lenses between old stopes, and narrow veins having bad walls. Fig 393 shows application to a branching orebody. Level interval, 150 ft. Ore is silled out to height of 17 ft and timbered haulageway is built. Combination chutes and manways, 6 by 12 ft, are 200 ft apart; they are of cribbing, either 8-in round or 10 by 10-in sawed timber. Chutes of round cribbing are lined with 3-in plank; unlined if of squared timber. Fill raises to level above are midway between chutes; cuts 10 ft high are started from them and run in both directions. Three rows of flat 8-ft holes are drilled with mounted drifters. Ore is hand shoveled into 1-ton rocker-bottom cars and trammed to chute; same type car used for spreading fill, which is leveled off to within 10 ft of back; flooring of 3-in fir or 2-in elm is laid on fill to prevent mixing of ore and waste and aid shoveling. As breast advances, timber sets are erected on the new fill and kept close to working face; caps or stringers of 12 by 12-in are set on round posts resting on sills. Cribs of 12 by 12-in timber supplement the sets in bad ground. Fill is kept close to advancing breast and miners usually set up on filling rather than on broken ore. Nearly all stope timber is recovered and reused. Before blasting, sets below that may be broken are removed. Power-scraping is used in some stopes for delivering ore to chutes and distributing fill. Filling comprises development waste, plus sand and gravel excavated by dragline scraper from deposits about 3.5 miles distant and transported to mine by aerial tram (235). RECOVERY OF LEVEL PILLAR. Depth of this pillar depends on width of stope and nature of ground. Fig 394 shows a retreating method of removing a 20-ft pillar. Aver figures for all cut-and-fill stopes during 1934 are: tons broken per hole drilled, 3.613; direct stoping labor and explosive costs, per ton broken: breaking, 31.1¢; timbering, 10¢; filling, 12.2¢; mucking, 36.4¢; stope and sub-level develonment, 7.8¢; total labor, 97.5¢; explosives, 12.2¢; total, $1.097.

Creighton mine, Ont (93). Geol features and former mining by shrinkage are described in Art 68. As ground conditions are no longer suitable for shrinkage, recent (1937) methods are horiz cut-and-fill and square-set. Much of square-set operations is to recover level and rib pillars. Horiz cut-and-fill stopes, running longitudinally, are used where possible. "Silling" (cutting-out stope) is on the level or 30 ft above rail. A permanent flooring of cedar plank is laid on sill floor before fill is begun. Chutes at 22-ft centers are cribbed, have 4 in plank lining, and incline to conform with general dip of footwall. Grizzlies are of 60-lb rails, inverted and spaced for 11-in openings. Breast drilling is done

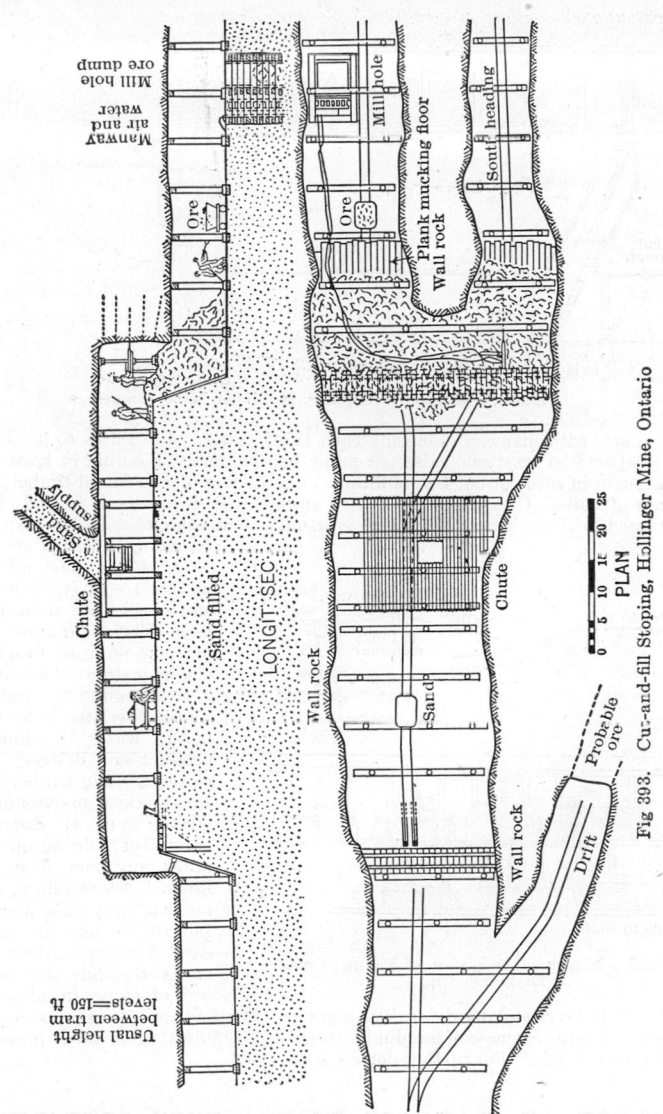

Fig 393. Cu-and-fill Stoping, Hollinger Mine, Ontario

from the ore pile. Flooring on top of fill for hand mucking is of 3-in plank. Fill is carried within 6–7 ft of back. Waste raises are 7 by 11 ft; cribbed manway used in driving raise serves for ventilation and handling supplies into stope.

Matahambre mine, Pinar del Rio, Cuba. Data from G. L. Richert (237) in 1929. Tabular bodies of ore, averaging 4.25% Cu in chalcopyrite associated with pyrite and quartz, occur in 1 prominent and 2 less important fracture zones across sediments, chiefly shale and metamorphosed sandstone. Dips, 42°–45°. Footwall, usually quartzite, stands well; hanging wall, usually shale, requires prompt support. Level interval has been increased from 100 ft to 150 ft. Development is by vert shaft; haulageways are drifts or crosscuts. Stoping is by horiz cut-and-fill; unusual feature is manner of filling with mill tailings. Bottom of sill-floor cut is 14 ft above rail; cut, 12 ft high. Chute raises

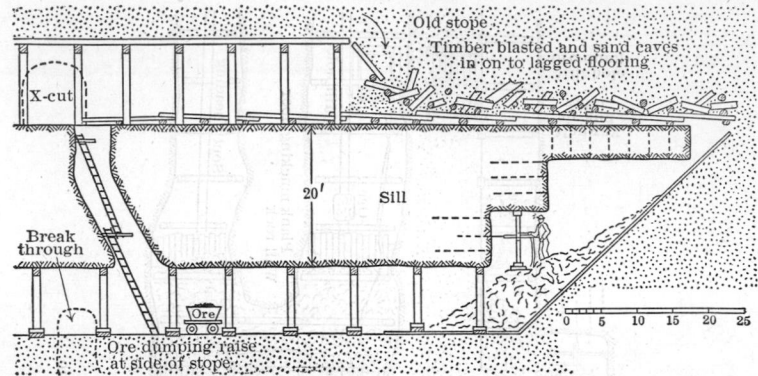

Fig 394. Mining Level-pillar, Hollinger Mine, Ontario

are 50 ft apart, with manway alongside each third chute. Fill raises to level above are 100–150 ft apart; at least one raise per stope has ladders. Flooring of hardwood slabs and poles is laid in sill-floor cut before filling. Chutes are of 8-in round timber, framed to obviate use of nails. Cuts are started with stoper drills in center or at end of the stope and continued with jackhammers. Ore is usually hand-shoveled to chutes; or wheel-barrows, if chutes are far apart.

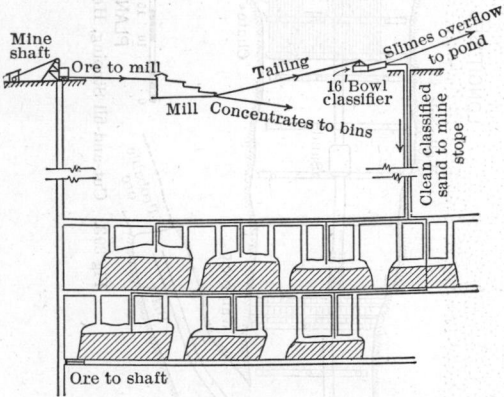

Fig 395. Matahambre System of Filling Stopes (Diagrammatic)

After stope has advanced to within 15–20 ft of level above, square-sets are used to remove level pillar. FILLING. Mill tailings are pumped to a 30-ft bowl classifier situated on surface near a raise leading to mine (Fig 395). Slime overflow goes to tailings pond; water is added to rake product and delivery to mine is through 2.5-in rubber-lined pipe. Pipeline system extends to stopes, where sand is distributed by hose. By building up small sand dams, any part of stope can be filled. Before filling, the chutes and manways are wrapped with burlap to prevent washing of sand through cribbing. Water seeps through the burlap and out of stope in about 12 hr; surface of fill is level and hard. Advantages of classified mill tailings over previously mined surface waste are: ease of handling; no spreading; flexibility; fewer raises required; better support of walls. For further details, see Art 92.

63. FILLED FLAT-BACK STOPES, WIDE OREBODIES
(Baltic Dry-wall Method)

Champion mine, Painesdale, Mich. Data from A. Mendelsohn (488) in 1931. Ore occurs largely in brecciated cappings of tilted lava flows, which dip at 30°–70°. Lode is nearly straight for long distances along strike. Hanging wall of a lode is the bottom of next succeeding lava flow; footwall is the trap lying under amygdaloidal top of flow.

In some places lodes outcrop; in others they are covered with glacial drift. Lode at Champion is in the brecciated top of "Baltic" flow; length on property, 8 000 ft; dip is uniform at 70° for 3 000 ft in depth, then flattens slightly. Aver width of ore mined in 1930 was 17 ft. Lode rock is very hard. Hanging wall is seamy lava requiring prompt support. Footwall is irregular and becomes more "trappy" at depth. Native copper occurs in irregular patches and must be sorted. Ore shipped in last 5 mo of 1930 ran 46 lb Cu per ton; before sorting, 25 lb per ton. DEVELOPMENT is by 4 inclined shafts in the lode. Main levels are 100 ft apart along dip. Drifts follow the ore as far as possible, but avoid sharp curves for haulage reasons; they serve to explore as well as to develop. STOPING. Recent mining is largely by a retreating system (see below); earlier method, the "Baltic Dry-wall," is still used in upper levels (1931). Distinctive features of "dry-wall" method, devised by F. W. Denton, are: (a) use of dry stone walls to maintain gang-ways and chutes through filling; (b) mode of mining level-pillars; (c) devices for distributing sand filling in stopes. According to A. Mendelsohn, Gen Supt, following description from earlier editions of the Handbook is correct as to current use of the method. Description based on notes by author in 1910, by C. W. Crispell, 1916, data by C. T. Rice (141) in 1912, and by W. H. Schacht (555) in 1923.

Dry-wall gangways; drawings from C. T. Rice (141). Copper rock (ore) from drift and cutting-out stope is sorted in the level, waste being thrown aside. Building of gang-

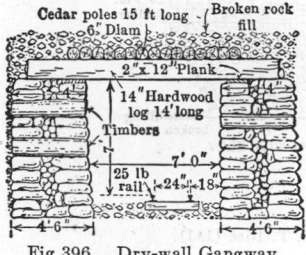

Fig 396. Dry-wall Gangway, Baltic Method

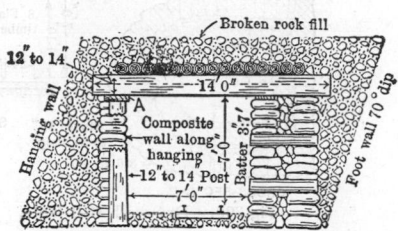

Fig 397. Gangway with One Composite Wall

ways follows at a convenient distance behind the sorters; Fig 396 shows type form and dimensions.

Stones for facing the walls are 14 to 30 in long; longer pieces when available, or old timbers, are used as ties between the faces. Face stones break joint, to avoid planes of weakness. Faces of walls next to drift are battered 3 to 4 in in height of 7 ft. Rock of Baltic lode tends to break into tabular forms, convenient for facing walls; stones are shaped by hammers necessary. Top of gangway is covered with lagging on caps (wall-pieces) spaced 3.5-ft centers; pressure from wall-pieces is distributed by a 2 by 12-in plank on top of wall. Fig 397 shows construction where lode is too narrow for two 4-ft walls; a wall of usual width is built along footwall, where heaviest pressure from filling occurs; hanging-wall ends of wall-pieces rest on a horiz timber A, 2 in or more in thickness, supported on posts under each wall-piece. Timber A is spiked to each post; a narrow stone wall is built between posts, and space behind filled with waste. Such composite walls are adequate along hanging wall of narrow parts of lode and cost less than those in Fig 396. Under wide stopes, a 4.5-ft or thicker wall is required to withstand side thrust of filling; 3.5 ft is the minimum width of a strong dry wall. Fig 398 shows gang-way construction where suitable waste is not available for walls like Fig 396; 3-sided cribs (pigsties) are built on each side and filled with waste. Such walls stand well, but fail when timbers rot; in these mines ventilation is good and timbers last 6 to 7 years. Dry walls

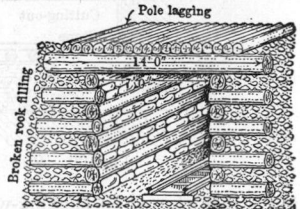

Fig 398. Cribbed Gangway

can be repaired by rebuilding small sections under protection of a false set which supports ends of wall-pieces over section under repair.

Dry-wall chutes (mills) are built at intervals of 30 to 70 ft; practice favors longer intervals and the use of cars in stopes for handling ore. CONSTRUCTION of such chutes is shown in Fig 399. The larger stones are used in inner walls to withstand wear of falling ore; outer wall takes most of thrust of filling; central core of loose stones allows outer wall to adjust itself somewhat to pressure, without disturbing inner wall. Walls are started from timbers, which are protected from wear by placing rocks above to overhang about 4 in.   Chutes are built in sections 5 ft high; walls of a new section are started 4.5 ft thick at level of the stope filling and taper to 3 ft thick at top.   Mouth of chute is about 4.33 ft wide by 3 ft high in the clear; timber E, about 8 ft long, is built into the gangway wall and serves as a lip-piece for fastening chute gate.   Vert chutes are easiest to build and maintain; where lode is narrow, some are vert for a few feet above the level and are then carried up parallel to the dip, but inclined chutes are avoided where possible.

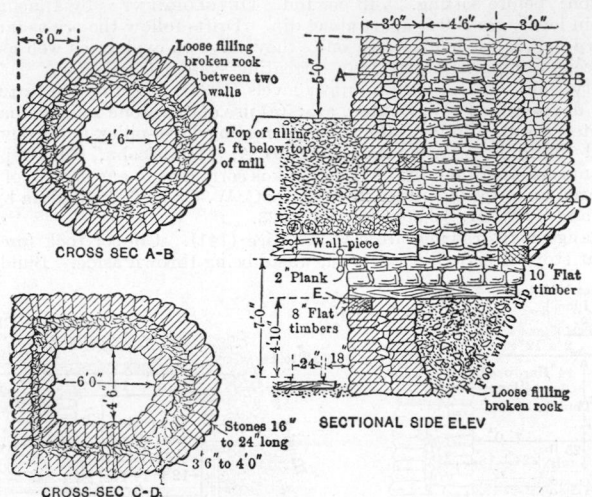

Fig 399.   Dry-wall Mill Hole.   After C. T. Rice (141)

Cost of dry-walling under suitable conditions compares favorably with that of timber to replace it, largely because of its greater strength and life, and consequent reduction of maintenance costs for gangways and chutes.   An incidental advantage of dry-walls is that, since less timber has to be lowered into the mine, more time is available in shafts for hoisting ore.

Stoping and filling methods vary in detail with local conditions.   Usually the drift and cutting-out stope furnish enough waste to fill spaces behind dry-walls before wall-pieces are put on; in case of shortage, the space on hanging-wall side of drift is filled; stop-

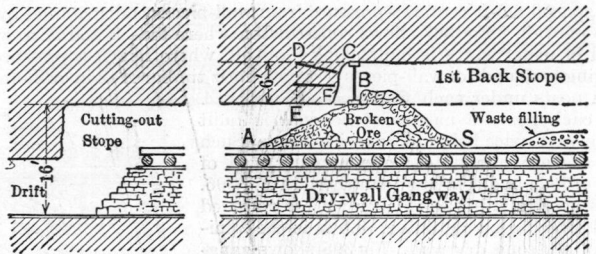

Fig 400.   Starting Stopes, Baltic Method; Longit Sec

ing is then started on hanging-wall side, and waste sorted out is used for filling space on footwall side of drift.

Fig 400 shows one way of starting a stope; first back-stope, 6 ft high, produces a pile of ore about 9 ft deep, the forward face of which, AB, protects lagging when the cut $CDEF$ is blasted.   Sorters at S work the ore through lagging into the level; waste is thrown back and to the sides.   Where feasible, lagging is covered with waste before stoping begins. Before starting a second back-stope, chutes are built up, and the stope filled to within 8 or 9 ft of the back (Fig 401).   Interval between chutes must be adjusted to strength and condition of walls, so that unsafe wall areas are not exposed between the fill and the pile of broken ore.   Sorting does not usually furnish enough waste for filling; excess filling is obtained through a raise from above, by shooting out footwall, by driving inclined raises into walls, or by sand filling (see below). W. H. Schacht states: of total fill used at Champion mine, in 1920–23, 43% came from sorting in stopes, 15% from footwall explorations, 15% from poor backs, none of which required handling. Filling requiring handling comprised: 12% from walls, 9% from development, 6% sand fill. Total fill, including sand, 60% of tons ore broken. Fig 401 shows second back-stope; a 1-ton car conveys ore to chute; waste is thrown back and aside; in higher back-stopes, waste may be trammed to a point like F (Fig 404). As stope face advances, mills serve alternately as chutes and

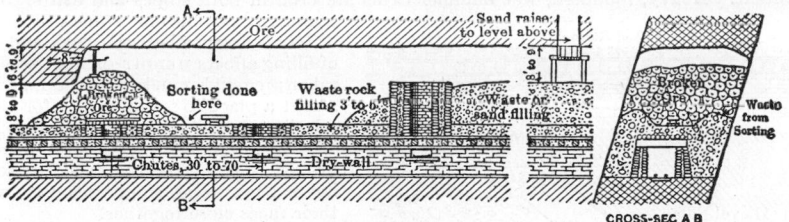

DIAGRAMMATIC SEC IN PLANE OF VEIN

CROSS-SEC A B

Fig 401.   Back Stoping and Filling, Baltic Method

ladderways. Successive back-stopes are carried to a height of 60 to 75 ft; questions of safety, cost, and economy of timber led to adoption of method in Fig 404 for mining the remaining level-pillar.

Irregular distribution of copper in lode requires operation of a large number of stopes to maintain regular output; individual stopes advance slowly; removal of level-pillar destroys gangway above. These conditions, combined with practice of mining outward from shafts, often require a level-pillar to stand untouched from 3 to 8 years, during which time ground becomes heavy, and unsuitable for flat-back stoping. It is proposed to apply Baltic method as a retreating system, to shorten time before level-pillars are mined; then a larger level interval might be possible, as well built stone chutes stand wear of falling ore for long periods. Width and dip of lode are also related factors influencing level interval, as chutes should be vert, if possible (Fig 404).

Sorting is done carefully by special men; rock showing even a speck of copper is sent to chutes. Large boulders are broken and the pieces examined; bosses decide whether fine rock, requiring shoveling, shall be classed as waste or ore. Few fines are produced in breaking, hence loss of fines in filling is small; a layer of fine waste, placed on top of the rock fills in stopes, eases work of shoveling; fines may be recovered by skimming off an inch or so of this when the stope is cleaned up. (See Mining level-pillars, below.)

Mechanical loaders, as used in stopes (482), are shown in Fig 402. The shovel (a) is a special Thew Electric, with a 20-hp motor and caterpillar tractor, loading into a hopper (b), which discharges

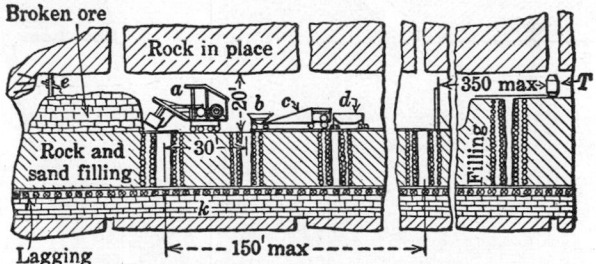

Fig 402.   Mechanical Loading, Champion Mine

onto an armored picking belt (c). Waste picked from belt is used for fill. Belt outfit weighs 16 tons; length, 24 ft, with 12 ft effective for picking; width, 4 ft; height at discharge end, 8 ft. Picking surface is of treated fir slats, 4 in thick, with cast shoes at ends, covered with 0.25-in steel plate and connected by links. Shoes run or slide without rollers on oiled angle-iron track. A shock platform at loading end cushions the impact of a dipper (5/8 cu yd) of rock. When in use, belt frame is anchored to track by 2 wheel-clamps; it is manned by 2–4 pickers; speed of travel, 6–8 ft per min; about 1/4 of rock broken is rejected. Belt delivers to a 4-ton, hopper-bottom dump car (d). This loader delivers lower-grade ore than hand loading; its use appears justified only during labor shortages. For details, see Bib (482), and Sec 27.

Breaking ground in flat-back stopes is done with breast holes 7 to 10 ft deep (Fig 400, 401). W. H. Schacht in 1923 (555) states that breaking ground is done in horiz slices 4–5 ft high. One row of flat holes is drilled across the back; distance between holes, 5 ft; depth, 7–10 ft. Drifts, of full width of lode (10–30 ft) and 10 ft high, are advanced by first blasting a cut at one side of the drift, then taking successive vert slices across the face. Slices are 18–24 in wide. Depth of holes, to 10 ft; 20–40 holes are required to square a cut, depending on width of drift, character of ground and copper content. Heavy, mounted, wet hammer drills are used in both stopes and drifts; 30%

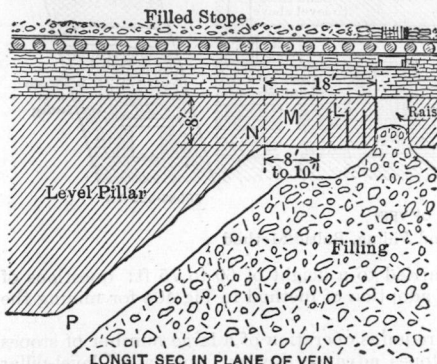

Fig 403. Mining Level-pillars, Baltic Method

ammonia powder in stopes, 40% in drifts. Distance between back and top of filling affects HEIGHT OF BACK-STOPES taken; enough muck must be made to afford a place to set up drills; for usual relations between these factors see Fig 401; if filling is low, a high pile of broken ore may be obtained by working 2 back-stopes simultaneously, with their faces close together.

Mining level-pillars (locally, "caving pillars"). Work begins at a raise at the boundary, or at a point midway between shafts, and retreats to shaft-pillars.

A rill stope (Art 38, 65) is started from bottom of the raise; cuts are inclined at angle of repose of filling, which is 40°; miners work on waste, which is dumped through raise as fast as ore is sorted and removed. Stope is enlarged to dimensions as in Fig 403; all broken ore is then cleaned up and portion L of the 8-ft pillar remaining under the level is shot down from wall to wall. This allows dry-walls and filling in old stope above to drop; projecting stub M of the 8-ft pillar keeps open a vert space 6 or 7 ft high along face PN. Rock-filled cribs are put in at toe of stope, when needed. Rest of level-pillar is mined as in Fig 404. Stope-drills are used, putting in 5 to 6 half-uppers, 6.5 to 7 ft deep per drill-

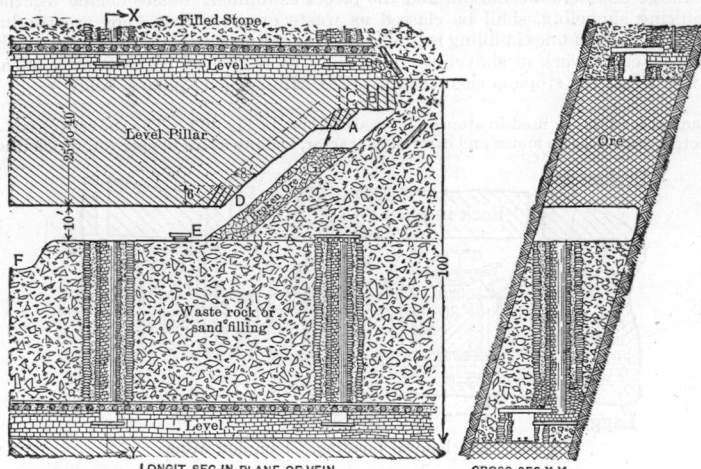

Fig 404. Mining Level-pillars, Baltic Method (Diagrammatic Sections)

shift. Usual crew, 2 machine-men and 2 sorters. After round at A is blasted, holes C are drilled. Then all broken ore in G is sorted out and removed; 3 men may take 1 or 2 weeks in cleaning up the stope. Next, round B is blasted; waste runs in from above; sloping face of stope is kept open by the stub of pillar left at C, and process is repeated. Holes at D for starting a new slice may be drilled before broken ore is removed and while the back there is easily accessible. Practice of drilling holes at C before they are needed is a safety precaution, as the stub must stand for a considerable time and the ground becomes dangerous to work under. In narrow parts of lode or in strong ground, rill stopes for mining level-pillars may be carried with stepped faces (Art 38). Ground is broken with breast holes, which are more effic than uppers in this lode, but barring down takes longer, and this method is not so safe as that in Fig 404.

Sorters work at *E*, and along face of pile of broken ore; waste rock may be piled at sides of stope or dumped at *F*. Two chutes must be kept open, one for ore and one for a ladderway. At the end of a stope, a mill is built close to the shaft-pillar and another about 25 ft away; when toe of fill covers the latter, stoping is stopped and the remaining piece of level-pillar is abandoned. Ore from

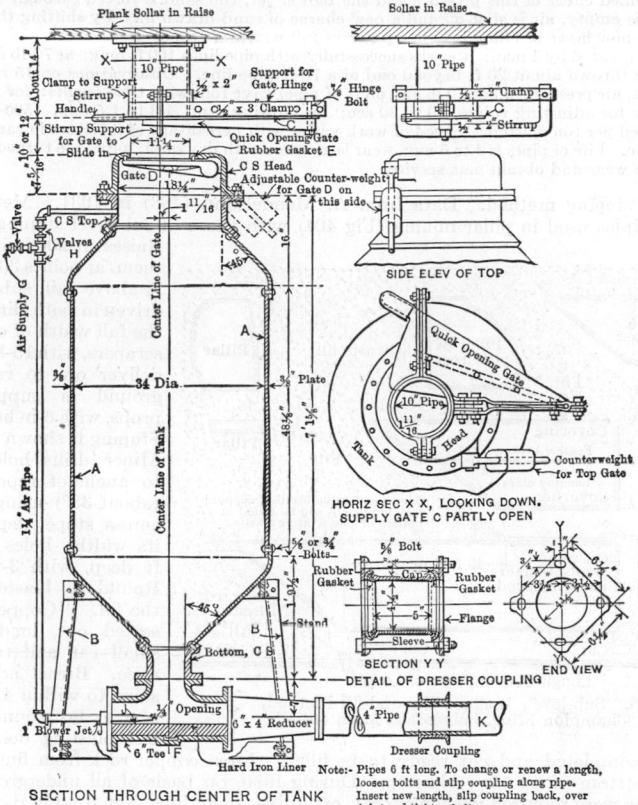

Fig 405. Sand-blowing Tank, Champion Mine, Mich (F. W. Denton)

stub ends of pillars *B* and *C* (Fig 404) mixes with waste, which rushes in from above when they are shot down; about 50% of this ore is lost in the filling. Filling drawn downward in mining level-pillars is replenished by waste from development, dumped into stopes at surface or from an upper level. Filling will readily work down through 5–9 levels; hence, at intervals, levels must be kept open for tramming waste in stopes below. Pillars under these levels are perforated by raises. Best height for level-pillars is about 35 ft; smaller heights do not take full advantage of low cost of ore from pillar-mining; if higher, the back may become bad before top cuts can be taken, and it is difficult to work broken ore down the longer slope of the filling to the sorters. If patches of unmined low-grade ore occur over a level-pillar during stoping, raises are carried up through such areas to tap the filling in stopes above.

Sand-filling. Mill tailing, called sand, is hauled back to the mine in 40-ton R R cars, to supply some of the excess filling required in flat-back parts of stopes.

At Champion mine, the sand is dumped at surface into a raise, roughly parallel to No 4 hoisting shaft and extending to 17th level. Sand is drawn at any desired level through chute-gates into 36-cu ft, bottom-dump, hopper cars, moved by electric haulage. Where sand-filling is practiced levels are connected to stopes below, at intervals of about 300 ft, by 4 by 4 to 4 by 5-ft raises, through which the sand is dumped. SAND-BLOWING TANKS, operated by compressed air, have been used to distribute the sand laterally in the stopes (Fig 405, from F. W. Denton). Cylindrical tank A, on a light angle-iron frame B, is set on top of fill under a raise, as at T, Fig 402. Bottom of raise is closed by a sollar, to which gate C is attached. Opening at top of tank has a counterweighted gate D, which makes an air-tight closure against gasket E. Tank terminates at bottom in a tee F, connected to a line of 4-in pipe K, laid on surface of completed fill and moved or extended as necessary. The Dresser coupling is important, in allowing the pipe line to be deflected slightly at each joint. A connection is made at G with air line supplying the drills; valves H admit air to top of tank and to blower jet J. OPERATION: A tank of sand (1.5 ton) is drawn from raise through gate C; compressed air is turned on, forcing gate D tight against its gasket and putting the sand in tank under pressure. Under combined effect of this pressure and the blower jet, the sand is forced through pipe line K. When tank is empty, air is shut off and a new charge of sand drawn in. By shifting the pipe line, the end of a new layer of filling is built up across full width of stope.

Tank is operated by 1 man; it works successfully with pipe lines 100 ft long; at 70-lb air pressure, some sand is thrown about 20 ft beyond end of a 70-ft pipe line. Observations on 15 runs (with a 28-cu ft tank, air pressure about 70 lb and 65 ft of pipe) gave following time results: for filling tank, 20 to 35 sec; for adjusting valves, 20 to 30 sec; for blowing sand, 1.3 to 1.5 min. 500–1 500 cu ft free air is used per ton of sand. Speed of work varies with percentage of moisture in sand and with length of pipe. Life of pipes is 4 to 6 mo; wear is greatest with dry sand; pipes are turned frequently to distribute wear and obtain max service.

Recent stoping method. Data from A. Mendelsohn (488) in 1931. Method combines principles used in pillar mining (Fig 404) with those of sub-level stoping (Art 43). Raises are 200 ft apart; from them, at points 33 ft and 67 ft above rail, sub-drifts are driven in both directions, at the full width of ore. Power scrapers, with 15-hp engines, deliver ore to raise; loose ground is supported on props, with 6-in headboards. Stoping is shown in Fig 406. Miner drills holes parallel to angle of repose of fill (about 38°) using 4–6 holes across stope, depending on its width; holes are 10–12 ft deep, with 3-ft burden. Round is blasted against the fill. "Copper rock" is sorted out, loaded into a small car and trammed to raise. Breast advances up slope to within 4 ft of waste above; last round is drilled, but blasting delayed until

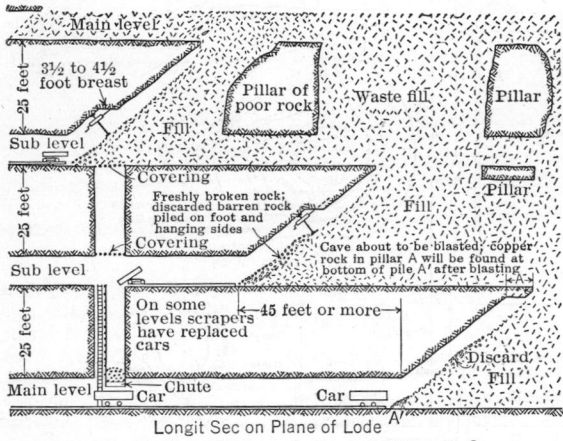

Fig 406. Sub-level, Inclined Cut-and-fill Method, Champion Mine, Painesdale, Mich (488)

sorting is completed and cut ready to be filled. Most copper rock from final round is found at bottom of fill after blasting. During 1930, on basis of all underground labor, 3.04 man-hr were required per ton of ore; explosive, including that used in development, was 1.3 lb per ton; exclusive of development, 0.8 lb per ton.

64.　CROSSCUT METHOD

Crosscut method is used for wide veins or masses, with weak walls and weak ore which will stand unsupported only over small openings. Ore is mined in horiz slices, in ascending or descending order and in small sections, each section being filled before the next is begun.

a. Slices Taken in Ascending Order

Development (see Fig 407) consists of footwall drifts D, crosscuts E, shaft F, and raises G to connect drifts at intervals of 40 to 60 ft. A slice is removed as in section XY. From D, crosscuts A are driven to hanging wall and filled through G with waste from level above. Crosscuts C are driven and filled; finally portions B are mined and filled. By breaking down the back of D, another footwall drift is then formed, from which a second slice is taken by driving and filling crosscuts, and so on to top of the lift. D is kept open by timbering or dry-walling for handling ore from lift above and filling to lift below; footwall drifts for upper slices are filled as soon as the slice they serve is mined. Broken ore from upper slices is handled to *D* through chutes *H*, built up through the filling as stoping proceeds. Several slices in a lift and several lifts may be worked simultaneously, provided workings in upper slices and lifts are kept in advance of those below.

Ore and filling are handled in crosscuts by shoveling, or in barrows or small cars; much of the filling must be shoveled into place in the crosscuts.

In some cases, successive crosscuts are contiguous instead of being driven in groups of 3 as in Fig 407; then, if ground does not require immediate support, waste may be sorted out in a crosscut and thrown back into the previous one (245).

Crosscuts are 6 to 8 ft high, and 6 to 10 ft wide, or as wide as strength of ore allows. Where necessary, they are timbered with light sets, or stulls and head boards, sidelagging being used to prevent runs of filling into adjacent workings.

Fig 408 shows timbering at the PROPRIETARY MINE, Broken Hill, N S W, where this method has had a limited use. 10 by 10-in struts *S*, running along the sides of crosscut, are supported by corbels on the posts; the back is carried by lagging on cross-pieces *D*; diagonals *E* are put in where required by pressure. Sets are about 6 ft apart; their size depends on character of ground and length of timber available. About 67% of the timber used is recovered

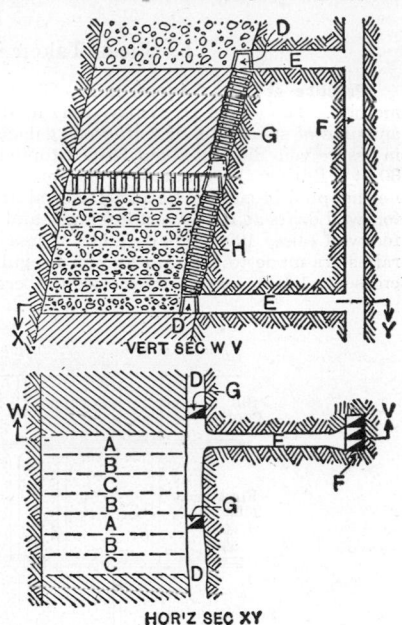

VERT SEC W V

HOR'Z SEC XY
Fig 407

on opening a new slice. The tapered shape of posts and the hole *H* (for inserting a piece of drill steel) aid in withdrawing them; or a chain and lever may be used (240).

Breaking ground. First openings in lowest slice of a lift are driven like drifts (Art 20); adjacent crosscuts cost less, as ore is free on at least one side. Upper slices are broken

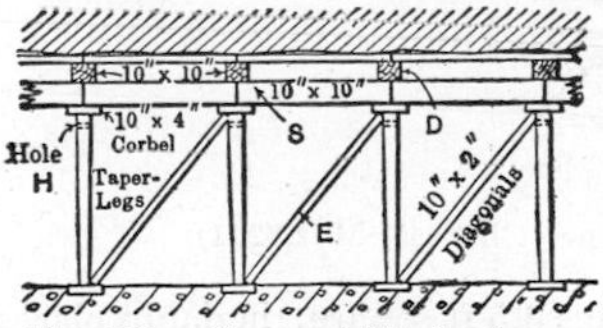

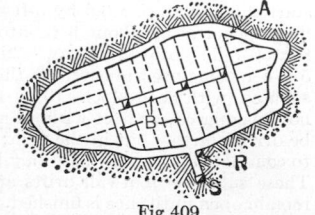

Fig 408. Crosscut Timbering, Broken Hill, N S W

cheaply, as the ore is always free on the bottom. At CABEZAS DEL PASTO MINE, Spain (248), contract price for mining the lowest slice averaged 50¢ per ton; for second slice, 25¢.

Mining topmost slice under overlying filled stopes requires care. Plank or lagging may be laid on floors of crosscuts in bottom slice, to prevent runs of filling when stope comes up from below; sometimes filling becomes so compact that this is unnecessary. Top crosscuts may be spiled under loose filling.

Level interval. The maximum is usually 65 to 70 ft (246). Filling can not be packed absolutely tight into crosscuts, and each layer settles somewhat under weight of the back. Successive subsidences cause ore above to crush, and increase difficulty and cost of mining upper slices; this effect increases with height of lift and weakness of ore.

At CHAPIN MINE, Mich, where this method was formerly used, settlements of 10 ft in a 100-ft lift are said to have occurred (247). At CABEZAS DEL PASTO MINE, Spain, the filling was coarse quartzite, quarried on surface, and so firm that no subsidence of surface was noticed (248). In some places subsidence occurs because the top slices of lifts are incompletely filled.

Several variations are possible. Haulage drifts *D* (Fig 407) need not be on footwall, but may be in any part of deposit or in wall rock. Crosscuts *A*, *B*, *C*, may run in any desired direction through deposit; large horses of waste may be left in place. Fig 409 shows application to an irregular

Fig 409

massive deposit, opened by shaft S. Usually first work on a level is to outline orebody with a closed drift A; then haulage drifts and crosscuts B can be placed in best position; one arrangement of crosscuts for slicing is indicated by dotted lines. At least one main waste raise R is desirable. For further detail and other variations, see Bib (240, 245–249).

b. Slices Taken in Descending Order

Practice at Tiro General mine, Charcas, Mex, illustrates this variation of crosscut method. Data from H. Willey (241) in 1930. Ores are complex sulphides with varying amounts of sphalerite, argentiferous galena, and chalcopyrite. Principal orebody occurs in fissure vein dipping about 70°. Stoping widths are from a few ft to 90 ft, aver about 30 ft. Both walls generally weak, and ore badly fractured. Top-slicing (Art 72) was not adopted because of necessity of maintaining upper levels. DEVELOPMENT consists of footwall drifts at 100-ft vert intervals, and 10–12 ft outside of vein, connected by 2-compt footwall raises 100 ft apart, and not less than 6 ft outside of vein; footwall drifts and raises are made to conform to vein irregularities by driving pilot drifts in the vein, with crosscuts 100 ft apart. Raises are timbered with 2 independent sets of cribbing of 10-in

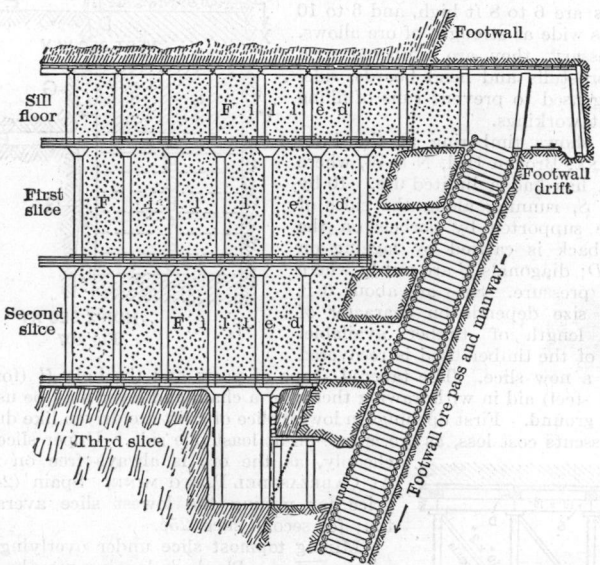

Fig 410. Sec through Ore Pass, Tiro General Mine, Charcas, Mex (241)

round timber, with 3-in plank lining, leaving clear openings 3.5 ft square; in damp places, this timber is creosoted. SILL FLOOR is developed by square-setting with 8-in round timber, 5 ft c–c. No sills are placed under the posts, but sills of two 3 by 10-in pine planks, best not less than 10 ft long and overlapping not less than 2 ft at joints, are laid from foot to hanging wall between the rows of posts, resting evenly on broken ore tamped under them. Space between sills is then leveled with broken ore, on which a floor of 2-in plank in 5-ft lengths is laid, their ends resting on the sills; gaps between posts are covered with short pieces. Square-sets are back-filled to within 2 sets of working face. SLICING. To start the first slice, a 6.5 by 5-ft crosscut is driven from the ore pass 12 ft vert below sill floor, penetrating about 6 ft into vein (Fig 410). From its end, narrow footwall drifts run 50 ft in both directions, taking the 12 ft of ore up to the sill floor, vert 10-in posts 5 ft c–c being used to catch up the sills above; these posts are 11 ft long, large end up and squared, with head-blocks 10 by 10 or 8 by 8-in; posts are wedged at bottom, which need not be squared, and set without sills or footboards. If footwall is slippery, the drift may be driven farther out in the vein; or if vein is so wide as to require more than usual time to complete a slice, the drift may be timbered with battered posts and caps, salvaged later. These sub-level footwall drifts are no larger than absolutely necessary, as they have to remain open until slice is finished. From one end of sub-level drift, a crosscut runs towards hanging wall, catching up the overhead sills with 11-ft posts and 10-in headblocks, 5 ft c–c.

As this crosscut nears completion, a second and adjoining crosscut is begun. The 10-ft space thus opened is floored with sills and plank as on the sill floor. Between the last 2 sets in the sub-level drift, 6 ft above the floor, a crosscut is driven into the footwall; from its inner end an inclined raise is put up to the side of footwall drift on main level, cribbed with 8-in round timber and lagged to give 2 independent chutes 3 ft 7 in by 2 ft 8 in clear; one is a manway, other a waste pass. Waste from this work is piled to depth of 6 ft on floor, supported at sides by 2-in bamboo poles (cheapest available material) laid against the posts. Successive 5-ft segments across the orebody then follow similarly. When one segment has been filled to 6 ft, back-filling to full height begins at hanging-wall end; space of one set nearest footwall is left open for handling waste in barrows to remainder of slice, this passageway being filled last when slice is finished. Meantime, similar extraction and filling has begun at other end of 100-ft block; one end of next lower slice can thus be started before upper slice is finished. Fig 411 shows stages of stoping.

Success of this method is due largely to avoidance of permanently open passageways through filling; uniform transfer of pressure to filling is also aided by deliberate lack of vert alinement of posts and absence of sills or stringers under them. Simplicity and routine operations are favorable features where labor is unskilled. Nearly all timber is lost, but is less in amount than by square-setting. Compared with former square-setting, saving in cost per ton by slicing method is estimated as follows: In new ore: labor, 10.6¢; explosives, 0.8¢; timber, 11.1¢; total saving, 52.5¢. In old workings: labor, 10.2¢; explosives, 1.1¢; timber, 27¢; total saving, 38.3¢.

Output per man-shift is about the same (1.44 ton in new ore, 1.34 ton in old workings) as with square-setting. Aver output (12 shifts per week) from a 100-ft block is about 1 000 tons per mo. Recovery is practically 100%, compared with 95% from square-setting.

c. Summary, Crosscut Method

Crosscut method allows safe and complete extraction of large, weak orebodies of almost any shape, without serious surface subsidence. Cost of development is high, owing to the small level interval and frequent necessity for driving haulageways and waste raises in country rock. Cost of shoveeling larg amounts of ore and filling is

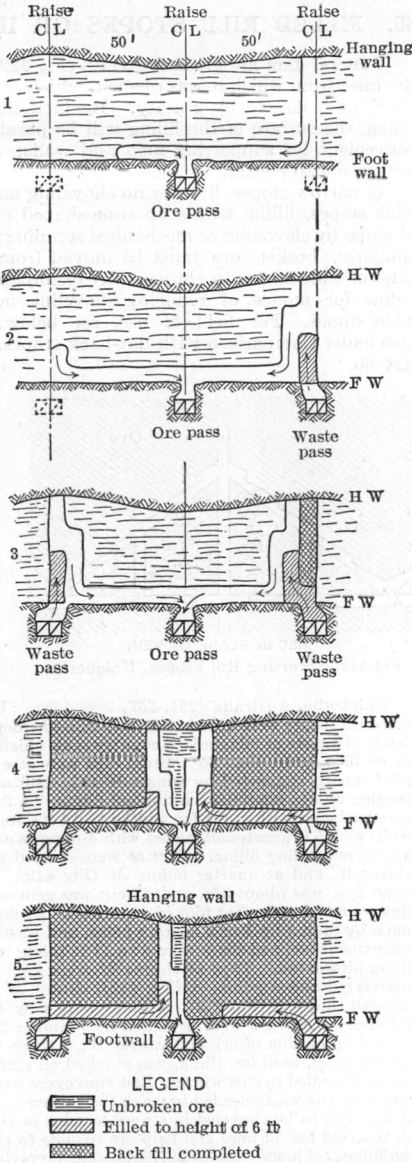

LEGEND

▤ Unbroken ore
▨ Filled to height of 6 ft
▩ Back fill completed

Fig 411. Tiro General Mine, Charcas, Mex (241). Plan of stope floor, showing 5 stages of mining

unfavorable to use of this method in the U S. Timber consumption is low, if ore will stand over back of a crosscut until it is filled; even in weaker ore, less timber is used than in top-slicing (Art 70–74) or filled square-sets (Art 46), which are alternative methods affording complete extraction; caving methods are preferable if surface need not be supported.

Crosscut method is sometimes advantageous for mining level-pillars in bad ground over filled flat-back stopes. At Rio Tinto, old pillar and chamber workings (Art 42) were re-mined by this method (549)

65. FILLED RILL STOPES OR INCLINED CUT-AND-FILL STOPES

General data are given in Art 38 (Fig 222, 223). Filling is run into a rill stope through the raise from which it was opened, which enters the stope at its highest point. Filling is distributed largely by gravity. By inclining the stope backs at the angle of repose of filling, the surface of the filling will be parallel to back of stope (Fig 412), and therefore convenient for supporting men and walls; a sloping surface of fill also aids in moving broken ore to chutes.

In narrow stopes, little or no shoveling may be required for handling filling or ore. In wide stopes, filling builds up cone-shaped under the raise and must be moved to sides of stope by shoveling or mechanical scraping; similarly, broken ore must be moved from sides of wide stopes to chutes. See examples below for modes of reducing shoveling in wide stopes. For field of use, see below; also under Comparison with flat-back stopes, Art 66.

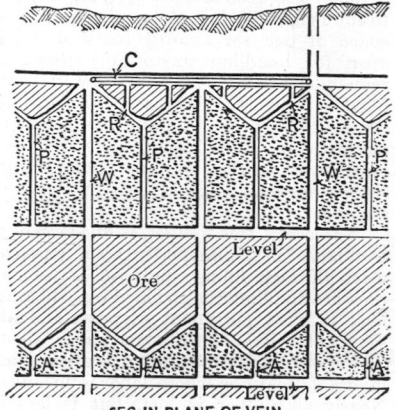

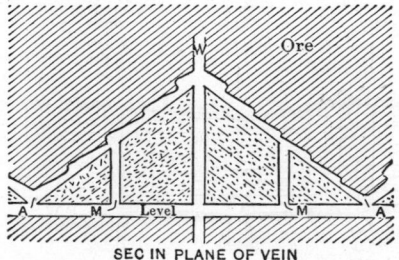

SEC IN PLANE OF VEIN
Fig 412. Starting Rill Stopes, Kalgoorlie

SEC IN PLANE OF VEIN
Fig 413. Rill Stopes, Kalgoorlie

Kalgoorlie, Australia (251, 257, 258, 146). This is an old but classic example of this method. Filled rill stopes were used in narrow, vein-like deposits of gold telluride ores, occurring as lenticular shoots of quartz or mineralized country rock, chiefly in amphibolite schist. Method was not applicable on dips flatter than 35°; usual dips were steep. DEVELOPMENT. Ideal plan was to run levels 200 ft apart, connected by winzes W (Fig 413) at intervals of 150 to 200 ft; winzes were sunk on hanging wall to minimize handling of filling. A flat cutting-out stope, 7 ft high, was taken. Levels were timbered with stulls for widths to 14 ft; for greater widths, with saddle-back stulls (Art 38). Stulls were 5 ft apart, and lagged with 4-in poles covered with old filter cloth, pieces of cyanide cases, etc, to retain fine filling. Chutes were started about 50 ft apart, at points A, midway between winzes W, and at quarter points M (Fig 412). STOPING AND FILLING (Fig 412, 413). Slope of stope face was about 37°, and rill cut was generally adopted (Fig 223, Art 38). Stopes 10 to 14 ft high were first opened at foot of winzes W. Broken ore was loaded into cars in level, through spaces made by taking up 1 or 2 lagging poles, and waste was dumped in through winze from level above. Subsequent inclined slices were 8 to 11 ft thick; operations of stoping, cleaning up broken ore, and filling alternated. Tops of chutes M were kept level with filling. When adjacent stopes finally intersected above points A (Fig 412), chutes M were abandoned and all broken ore was handled through chutes P (Fig 413). Chutes were 4 by 4 ft clear, usually cribbed with 7-in round timber; occasional manways were provided by building 2-compartment chutes. Cribbed chutes were also carried up on line of original winzes W, if these were used for running filling to lift below. Sand (mill tailing), used for filling, was stacked on surface until moisture content was less than 25%; if wetter it tended to clog winzes. Belt conveyers were often used to distribute filling, as at C (Fig 413); then only one winze needed to reach the surface. Even with winzes on the hanging wall, some filling always had to be shoveled in stopes to edge of rill. In rich ore, plank floors were laid on faces of fill to avoid loss of fines and help ore to slide to chutes; old filter cloths were sometimes laid under the floors. Floors were usually omitted, involving the removal of a few inches of filling with the ore from each slice (83). Stopes near top of lift could not be filled through original winzes W; auxiliary raises R (Fig 413) were put up to handle filling.

Park City Consol Mines Co, Park City, Utah. Data from G. M. Wiles (244) in 1936. Fissure veins in quartzite carry high-grade silver ore, with small amounts of Au, Pb, and Zn. Vein gangue is largely massive and sugar quartz, or uncemented conglomerate-like rock. Walls vary in strength from blocky quartzite to a shattered gravel-like material.

Dips, 50°–75°. Vert shaft was sunk to 400 level; from which 2 inclines follow separate veins to 900- and 1 000-ft levels respectively (1936). Level interval, 100 ft. Original stoping was by shrinkage (Art 68); change to inclined cut-and-fill was made because of serious dilution and loss of ore in shrinkage mining.

Open stulled stopes are occasionally used in narrow veins. Drifts under stopes are timbered as in Fig 414; timbers, set in hitches, permit recovery of level pillar below without disturbing the drift. Inclined cut-and-fill stopes are opened by driving, at 100-ft centers, 3-compt raises, middle compt being a manway. Chute-pockets in drift sets are 15 ft c-c. Stoping cuts start from raises and are carried on a slope of 50° (Fig 415). Drilling is with hand-rotated stopers; holes are usually short, but may be 8 ft deep where walls are firm. Explosive, 30% gelatin dynamite. Before starting new cuts, waste is run into stope to within about 2 ft of back; 2-in flooring is laid on the waste before breaking new cut. Height of cut is 6–12 ft, depending on strength of walls. On completing a cut, floors are swept and taken up before another run of waste is added. Stoping labor is about 1.44 man-hr per ton; explosive consumption, 0.55 lb per ton.

Wright-Hargreaves mine, Kirkland Lake, Ont. Data from L. B. Smith (176) in 1934. For geol features and other data, see Art 39. Inclined cut-and-fill method has been used on both North and South veins. Level interval, 150 ft. Raises *R* (Fig 416) are 300 ft

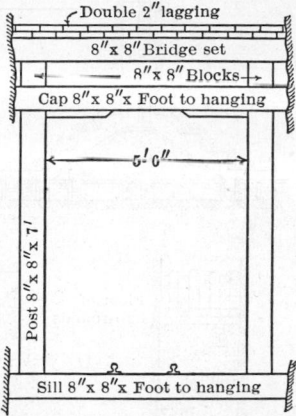

Fig 414. Gangway Timbering, Park City Consol Mine, Park City, Utah

apart. Backs of drifts are first taken down, and sill timbers placed (Art 39). Chute-pockets *P* are 15 ft apart. Stoping starts on each side of raises; face is in steps 8 ft high and 10–12 ft long, giving general slope of about 40°. Waste filling is brought to within 4

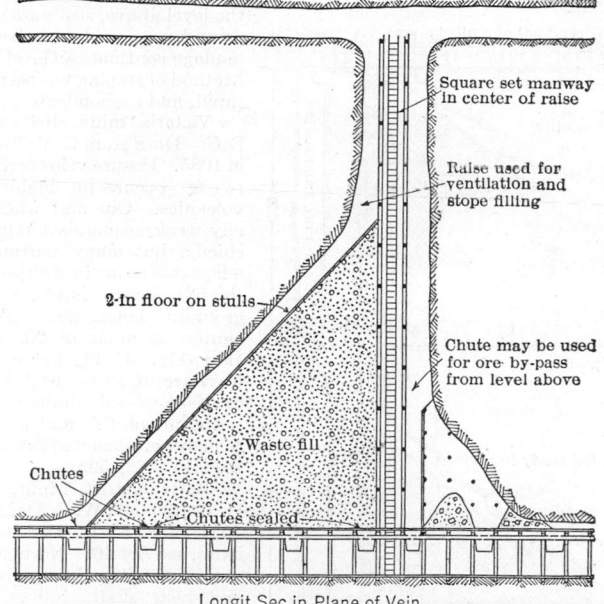

Longit Sec in Plane of Vein

Fig 415. Rill Stope, Park City Consol Mines Co, Park City, Utah (244)

or 5 ft of edge of cut. Flooring of half-rounds is laid on the fill. Miner starts on lowest bench, takes 2 rounds ahead and moves up to next bench. When raise is reached, the cut is complete; broken ore is then drawn and roof scaled. Flooring is lifted and stored on stulls

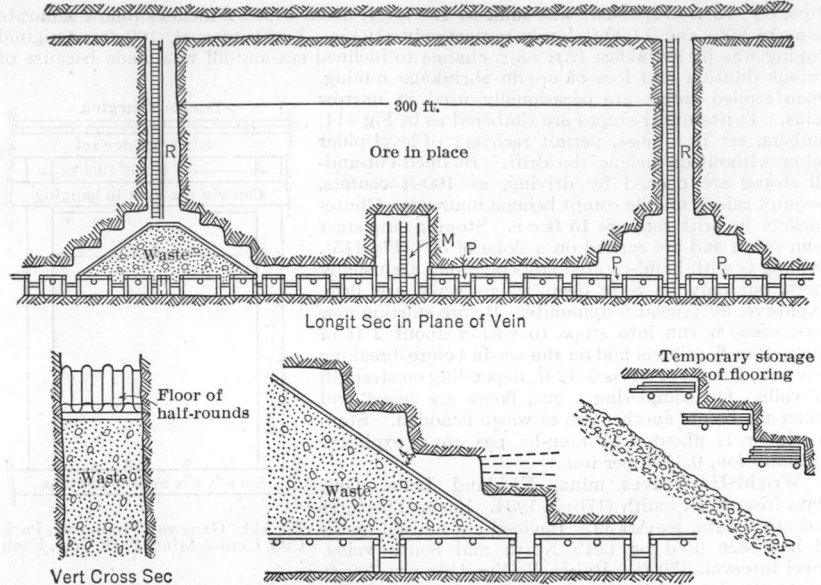

Longit Sec in Plane of Vein

Fig 416. Filled Rill Stope, Wright-Hargreaves Mine, Kirkland Lake, Ontario

close under the back, until ready to be relaid on new fill. When cuts from adjacent raises meet, manway M is maintained, with a chute on each side. When the stope breaks into the level above, stulls are used to support haulage-way timbers; normal haulage continues on level broken into. Method of stoping has been found safe, rapid, and economical.

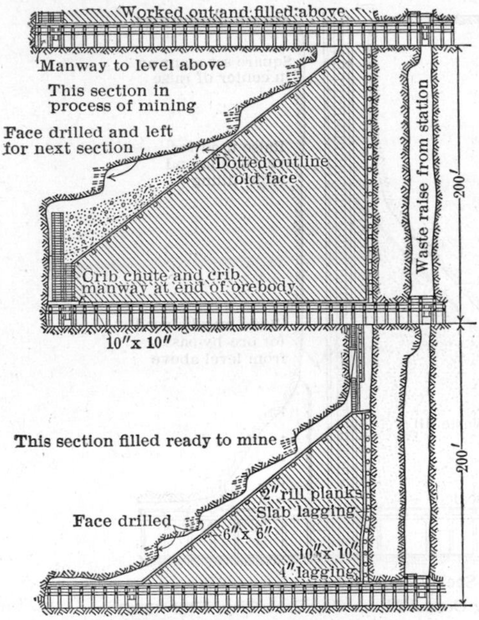

Victoria mine, Britannia Beach, B C. Data from C. V. Brennan (498) in 1935. Fissure veins carrying chalcopyrite occur in highly fractured volcanics. Ore and walls are generally weak; square-set mining is used chiefly, but many narrow veins are adaptable to inclined cut-and-fill. Distinctive feature is mode of breaking ground; holes are drilled toward chutes, at angle of 20° below horiz (Fig 417). Cribbed chutes and manways are of 10 by 10-in timber. Fig 418 shows sill timbering. For descriptions of this and other methods (chiefly shrinkage) at Britannia Beach, see Bib (562, 592).

Butte district, Mont. Data from H. L. Bicknell, W. B. Daly and others, 1921–1923 (534). For ore characteristics, see Art 46. Normal level interval is 200 ft; when orebody is wide and near shaft, 100 ft. Filled rill stopes used in narrow veins, where ore and walls require no immediate support. Fig 419 shows mode of starting a rill face by taking 3 successive 8-ft slices X, Y and Z, each starting at the raise and advancing toward middle

Fig 417. Ideal Longit Sec of Rill Stopes, Victoria Mine, Britannia Beach, B C (498)

chute (Fig 420). Slices are 6, 4 and 2 sets long respectively. Ore from these is handled through stop boards laid on caps of sill sets. Then sheeting S (Fig 419) of 4 by 10-in plank is placed 30 in above sill-set caps and supported by 10 by 10-in posts, caps, and stringers; this protects sill timbers from wt of the fill, and permits repairs without interfering with tramming. Lagging is nailed to stope side of raise, a bulkhead is put in raise near peak of stope, and waste is run into stope to within about 5 ft of the back. Fig 420 shows a stope fully opened, with the middle chute built up; two methods of breaking ground are indicated. Fill is covered with 2-in plank laid on cross pieces of 2-in lagging before blasting. Ore is sorted on grizzlies over the chutes; for details see Art 90. When upper ends of rill stope reach to within 5 sets of level above, the remaining V is usually mined as a square-set rill stope (Art 46). Square-sets stand on sills laid across the stope; sills are embedded in the waste, and held from sliding down the sloping face by girtwise braces and blocking to the walls. By similar methods a stope can be changed at any elevation into a square-set rill stope, if weak ore or walls are encountered. The level-pillar, 5 sets high, at top of stope is mined by ordinary square setting.

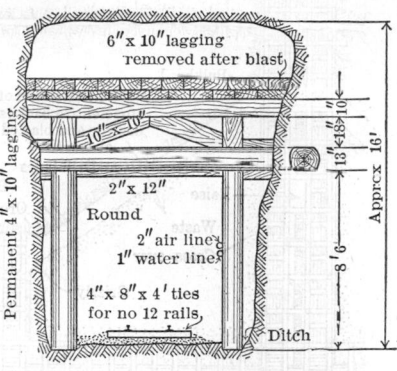

Fig 418. Typical Sill Timbering, Victoria Mine, Britannia Beach, B C

Parral, Chihuahua, Mex. Data from A. H. Hubbell (194) in 1936. Lead-zinc ore occurs in fissure veins in andesite. Width of ore, 10–125 ft. Shrinkage is used where possible, but inclined cut-and-fill where ore is wide and walls are bad. Fig 421 shows novel application of latter method. Chute raises 15 meters apart are driven from drift in ore near hanging wall, or from crosscuts, as in Fig 421; ore is silled out above level, leaving a pillar 3.5 meters thick. First cut is 8 ft high; second, 6–8 ft; ore is scraped to chutes. Fill raises R, 30 ft apart, are driven from back of cut to level above, being located midway across the stope width or near hanging wall. A footwall drift D is driven on the level 2–3 meters in footwall and footwall raises F from this drift connect the levels at 30-meter intervals, midway between the fill raises. From raises F, branch chute-raises B are driven to the stope, starting just above back of footwall drift. After fill has been run into the initial stope cut, lines of square-sets are started on the fill opposite each chute raise from the footwall drift. Each line of square-sets forms a trench, the top of which is always at bottom of the rills. Ore broken from faces of inclined slices runs to the trenches, where it is diverted to footwall chutes. Grizzlies at top of the trenches restrict the size of boulders

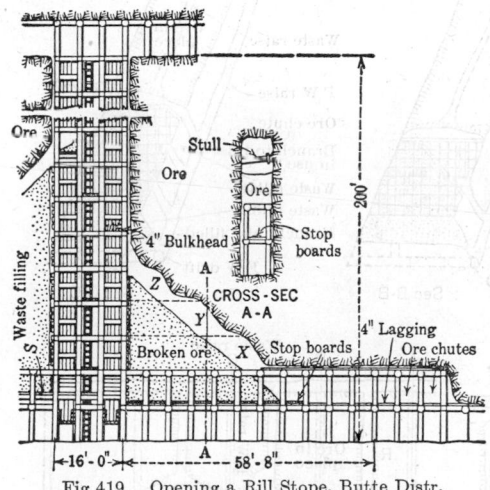

Fig 419. Opening a Rill Stope, Butte Distr, Mont (534)

delivered to chutes. As stope advances upward, the initial footwall chutes are replaced by others driven successively at higher points from main footwall raises, as in Fig 421, Sec C–C.

Campbell orebody, Phelps Dodge Corp, Warren, Ariz. Data from H. M. Lavender (91) in 1930, and from Robert Lenon of Co's Copper Queen Branch in 1938. Orebody is a massive-sulphide replacement deposit in limestone; ore minerals, chiefly chalcopyrite and bornite; gangue, limestone, silica, and pyrite. On 1 600-, 1 700-, and 1 800-levels, orebody is about 500 ft long; width, 50–250 ft; continuous from 1 400- to below 2 300-levels. Dip is generally steep, but varies locally from 25° to 90°. Footwall usually well defined; hanging wall, subject to greater irregularity, varies from an economic limit of low-copper content to a sharply defined limit conforming with local bedding planes. Grade of ore is

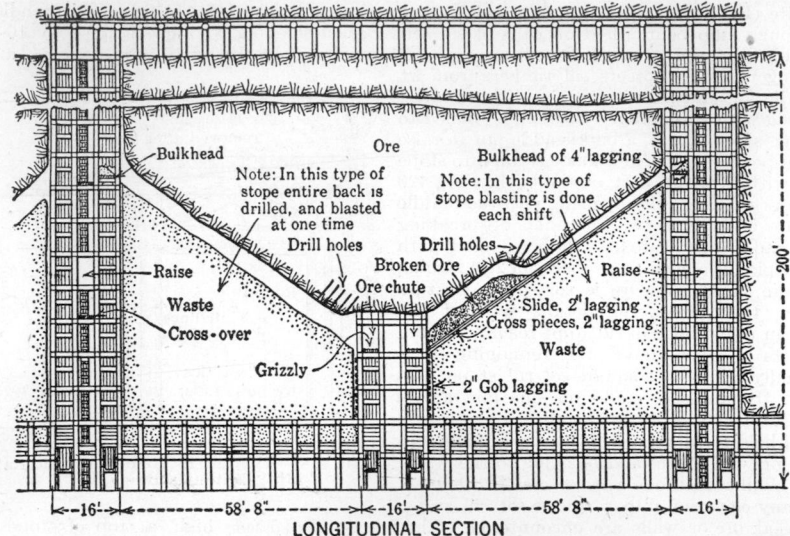

LONGITUDINAL SECTION

Fig 420.   Filled Rill Stope, Butte Distr, Mont. (534)

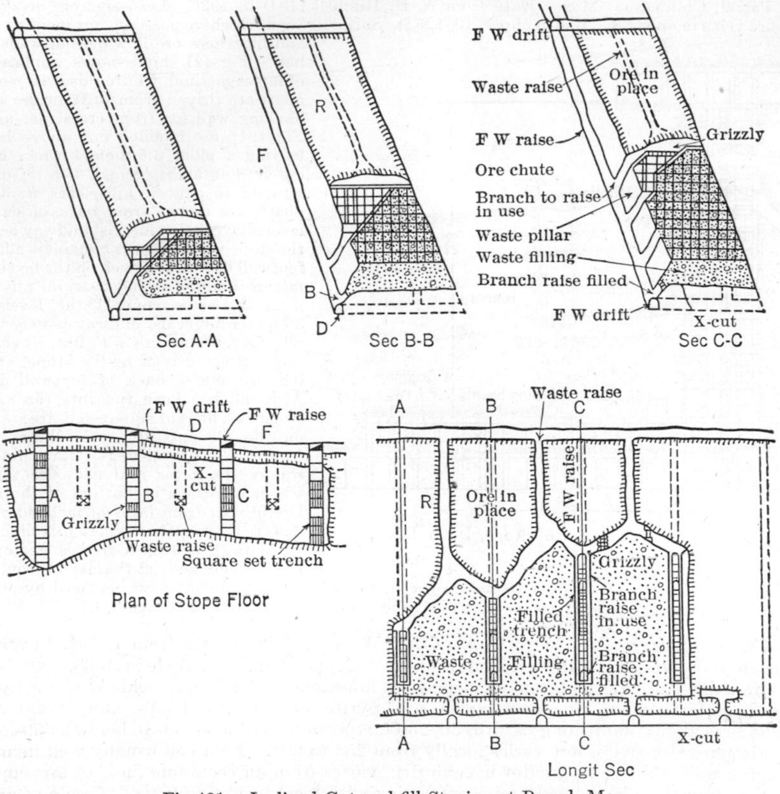

Sec A-A   Sec B-B   Sec C-C

Plan of Stope Floor

Longit Sec

Fig 421.   Inclined Cut-and-fill Stoping at Parral, Mex

relatively high and calls for mining method giving high extraction. Homogeneous nature of deposit obviates need of sorting. Both ore and walls are strong. The hard ore requires heavy blasting, to avoid making too many boulders. DEVELOPMENT. There are 2 vert hoisting shafts, and 2 ventilation upcasts. Level interval is about 100 ft; alternate levels are equipped for trolley haulage. Haulage-level drifts and crosscuts, 6 by 8 ft to 7 by 9 ft, have 4-ft gage track of 25-lb rail, with curves of 22.5 to 30-ft radius.

Intermediate-level drifts and crosscuts, formerly 5 by 7 ft, are now 6 by 8 ft, with 16-lb rail. Level development depends on size, shape, and dip of orebody, in accordance with stoping plans. GENERAL PLAN OF STOPING. Orebody is divided along the strike into stoping and pillar sections; the former mined by inclined cut-and-fill; pillars usually recovered by Mitchell slicing (Art 55). Until recently, the orebody was divided into 2 adjoining stope sections, each 45–50 ft wide, separated from the next 2 sections by a 45-ft pillar (Fig 422 A), the Mitchell slices in pillar mining running strikewise. More recently, orebody is divided longit into alternate stope and pillar sections of 36–48 ft (6–8 sets) and 18 or 30 ft, respectively (Fig 422 B); 18-ft pillars are mined by full-width slices as far as practicable; 30-ft pillars are to be split by a row of "single-leads" (square sets), the resulting 12-ft pillars mined by Mitchell slices. Stopes are usually mined in lifts of 200 ft, from one haulage level to next above, with pillars one above another. Stopes

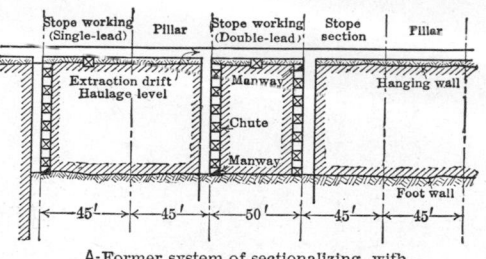

A-Former system of sectionalizing, with two types of stope development

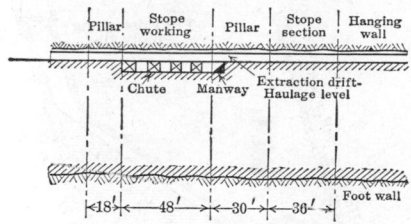

B-Present system of sectionalizing, with development for stoping

Fig 422. Systems of Dividing Orebody into Stope and Pillar Sections, Campbell Orebody, Warren, Ariz

are mined as single sections from wall to wall, where width of ore does not exceed about 75 ft. Where, as above the 1 600-level, width of orebody is greater (to 250 ft), stopes are sectionalized crosswise, the sections separated by a vert plane running strikewise.

Double-lead stoping. This method, employed prior to the more general use of scrapers, required more timbering than present method to avoid hand shoveling to chutes. From a hanging-wall drift, crosscuts were driven along the outside of the 2 section lines forming the strikewise stope limits (Fig 423). These crosscuts were then enlarged for standard sets ("stringer sets"). Posts were 9 ft 2 in long, their faces being 30 in from center line of track. Bottoms of posts were 6 in below rail. Crush blocks, 6 by 10 in and 20 in long, were placed on top of posts, and over these was laid a 10 by 12-in cap-like stringer, about 13 ft long, with the greater dimension vert. This gave a distance of 9 ft 2 in from rail to stringer. Sets were 5 ft c–c, with chutes in alternate sets. Silling started slightly above tops of stringers. During initial cutting-out between lead sets and shaping the back for initial fill, ore was allowed to pile up to form a natural slide toward each lead. The stope back was arched transversely and inclined upward from hanging to footwall. Initial stoping included driving a fill raise along footwall and on center line of the stope section, the raise holing to the intermediate level above and often extending to next haulage level. Before the first fill, lead sets were started along the stope boundaries. Posts, 10 by 10-in and 7 ft 4 in long, were placed along the outside of each row of sets; posts on the inside row were also 10 by 10 in, but 7 ft 7 in long. The difference of 3 in in length allowed for settlement in the rows next to the fill. Before filling, the stope bottom was covered with a mat of scrap timber, sometimes laid on sills. "Lead sets" were lagged on the fill side with split lagging 3–4 in apart, or 2 by 12-in planks edge to edge. An advantage of the latter was that the gob, in settling, tended to slide along the smooth surface and thus reduce vert pres on the sets. As the stope advanced upward, the lead sets served as chutes. Fig 423 shows a separate chute carried from hanging-wall drift to supplement the chutes formed by the lead sets. Grizzlies of 10 by 10-in timber, spaced 10 in apart, were placed across the lead sets at elevations corresponding approx with the intersection of sloping surface of the fill and the lead sets. With the filling of subsequent cuts and raising the lead sets, these grizzlies, unless badly worn, were moved to the grizzly floor above. Occasional sets within the leads were left covered with worn grizzly timbers, or 4-in flooring, and broken ore was allowed to remain thereon to prevent a direct fall of ore through the sets, thereby reducing wear on the timbers. On completing a given cut, waste was dropped through the fill raise and assumed its natural angle of repose (about 37°), the stope back approx following this angle. The fill was brought within 2–3 ft of the stope back and covered with 2 by 10-in or 2 by 12-in flooring laid on 2 by 10-in sills placed flush with surface of fill. Flooring usually began 10 ft above lower edge of fill and continued to the top. Spillage of waste from flooring operations rolled to bottom or unfloored section, which was finally floored. Cuts, started at bottom of the incline, were carried up as in Fig 423; they were about 12 ft high and drilled with mounted drifters. Holes 7–8 ft deep were drilled parallel to the floor, with a burden of about 2 ft each. Broken ore was

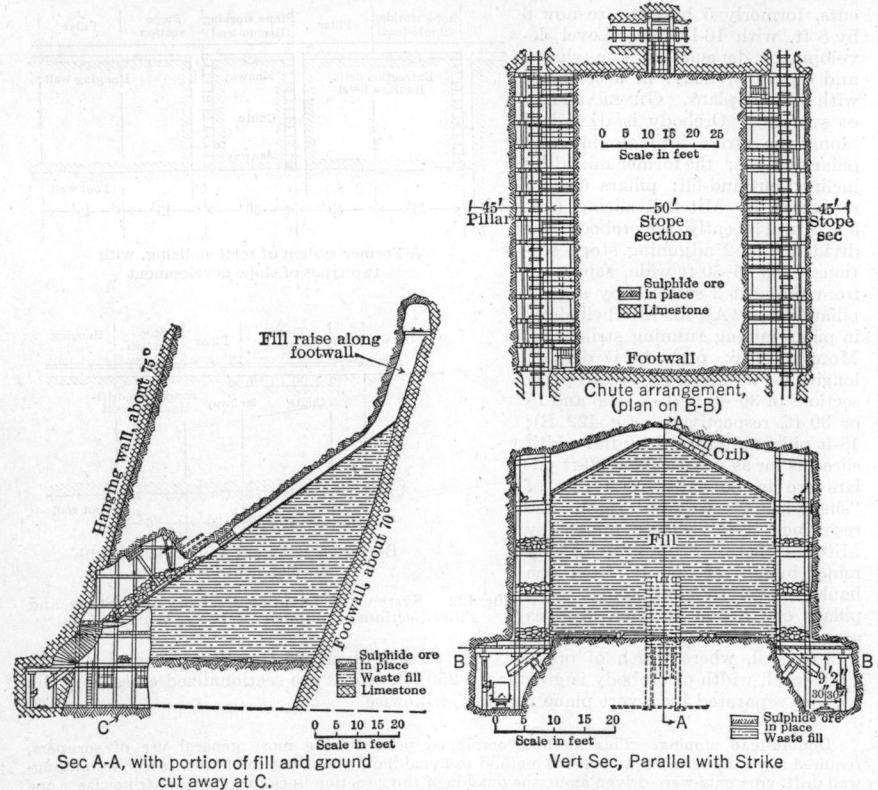

Sec A-A, with portion of fill and ground cut away at C.

Vert Sec, Parallel with Strike

Fig 423. Inclined Cut-and-fill Stope, showing former use of double-leads running parallel with Section Lines, Campbell Orebody, Warren, Ariz (91)

drawn concurrently with mining, but enough from each round was left temporarily to permit back to be reached for barring-down and setting-up for the next round. This undrawn ore protected the flooring during blasting. On completing a cut, the flooring was swept clean of fines, and taken up to be used again in the next cut. Following filling, lead sets were raised and lagged, flooring was re-laid and the new cut started. During mining stages, boulders were "plugged" (block-holed) with jackhammers, usually on the mining floor, although, when necessary, on the grizzlies.

Single-lead stopes. Use of scrapers later permitted modification of the double-lead method. Only one row of lead sets was used (Fig 424). The line of posts and caps was carried up along the opposite section line and lagged to form a gob fence, thus obviating the need of more than one extraction crosscut. In single-lead stopes, the fill raise was driven along the section line opposite the lead sets. As in Fig 424, the raise is outside the section line, for the purpose of serving both stope sections. With this exception, the work in the single-lead stopes was done as in double-lead stopes.

Recent practice. The extraction crosscuts and transverse lead sets have been eliminated. Drifts are run along hanging-wall side of stope section, and from these a longit line of lead sets is carried up (Fig 425). Extraction drift is on hanging-wall side of the leads, so that the drift timbers have a protecting brow of solid ground, thus avoiding direct wt of the waste fill on stringers over the posts. As in Fig 425, inclined cut-and-fill mining is now used in most of a pillar section between 2 completed stopes, where the lead sets run strikewise. One side of the section is bounded by gob fencing; the other, by solid ground. Drift timbering is virtually the same as for extraction crosscuts in double-lead stoping; but posts are 9 ft 6 in long, instead of 9 ft 2 in, and stringers over 15 ft long. Chutes are still built in alternate sets. Cutting-out starts by driving a heading, 10 by 15 ft or more in cross-sec, to footwall limit of stope, which may be the footwall itself (Fig 425), or a vert section line previously established. After the heading reaches such limit, a fill raise is driven, unless already made by open sets left for this purpose in a previously mined footwall section. In Fig 425 a raise has been driven along footwall to the level above. Such a raise has no chute at the bottom, the broken ore being scraped away to allow access to the raise. On completing the fill raise and widening the heading to full stope width, the stope back is blasted and sloped upward toward footwall, preparatory to filling and establishment of an inclined floor and back. This preparatory mining is done by shrinkage. Ore broken in the heading, the raise, and making the initial cut, is scraped into one of the chutes by a power scraper set over the drift. When preparatory mining has advanced sufficiently, "single-leads sets" and "gob-fence sets" are started along the stope boundary lines. Standard 10 by 10-in square-sets are used for all single-

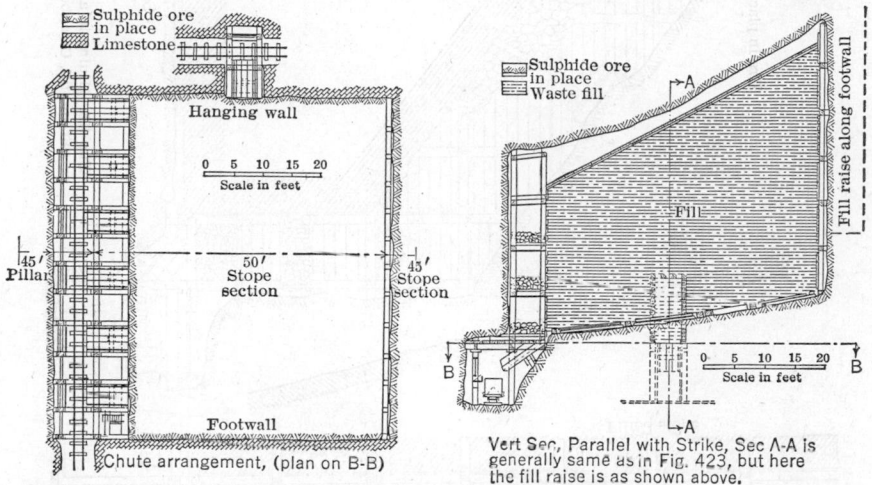

Fig 424. Inclined Cut-and-fill Stope, showing former use of Single Lead running parallel with Section Lines, Campbell Orebody, Warren, Ariz (91)

leads; occasionally, 8 by 8-in timber for the gob fence. All sets are cap-butting and framed to make sets 8.5 ft high and 6 ft by 6 ft c–c of posts. A novel feature is the use of 12-ft caps, so that each rests on 3 posts instead of 2. These "double-caps" give added strength and better alinement. A manway set is carried up with the single-leads, sometimes inside the stope-section line, but generally outside, to provide a sound open set from which to begin mining the adjoining section.

Before beginning filling, the stope bottom is covered with a mat of old timber, or 2-in flooring nailed to sills of doubled 2 by 12-in planks laid on the solid on 5- or 6-ft centers. Flooring is laid parallel to the direction in which the stope below will be mined, and covered with a mat of scrap timber laid parallel with flooring. Other timbering details, and the general procedure of mining and filling, are about the same as for double-lead stoping. Power scrapers are now standard equipment, their hoists being moved from floor to floor as stope advances (Fig 425). In employing strikewise leads, the entire row of leads may reach the hanging wall before the stope has progressed far upward. If so, another row of leads, nearer the footwall, is started on a bench cut into the waste fill, and is connected with original leads by an ore-slide steep enough to eliminate need for a scraper. Fig 426 shows timbering details for this case. A footwall section of a stope 48 ft wide has been previously mined, and mining the hanging-wall section is nearing completion. Two open sets in leads A of the old footwall section are being used as a fill hole for the new or hanging-wall section. The full height of section being mined is shown by height of line of sets B (about 100 ft). The section above has been mined out, the flooring of upper section being shown at C.

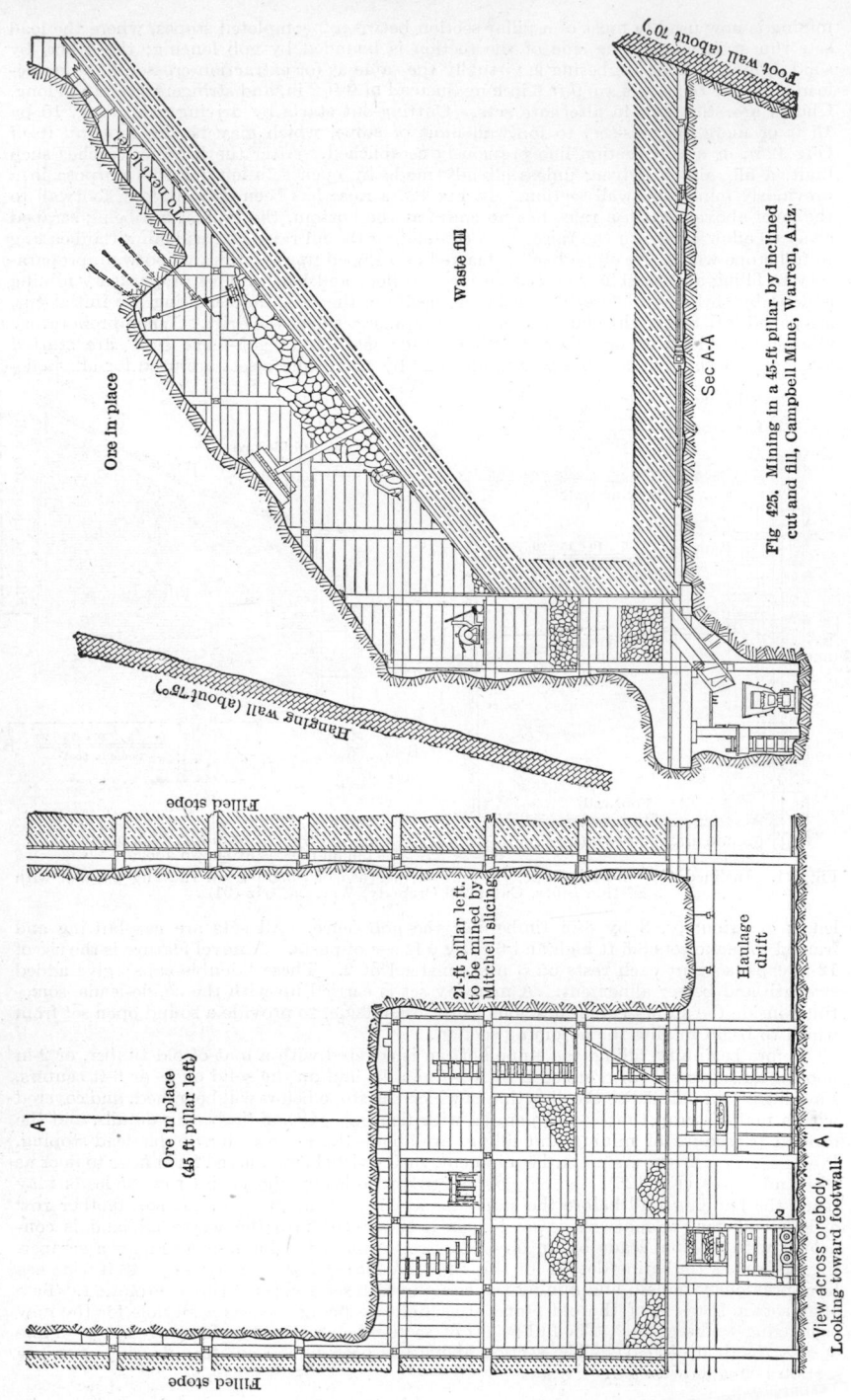

Fig 425, Mining in a 45-ft pillar by inclined cut and fill, Campbell Mine, Warren, Ariz

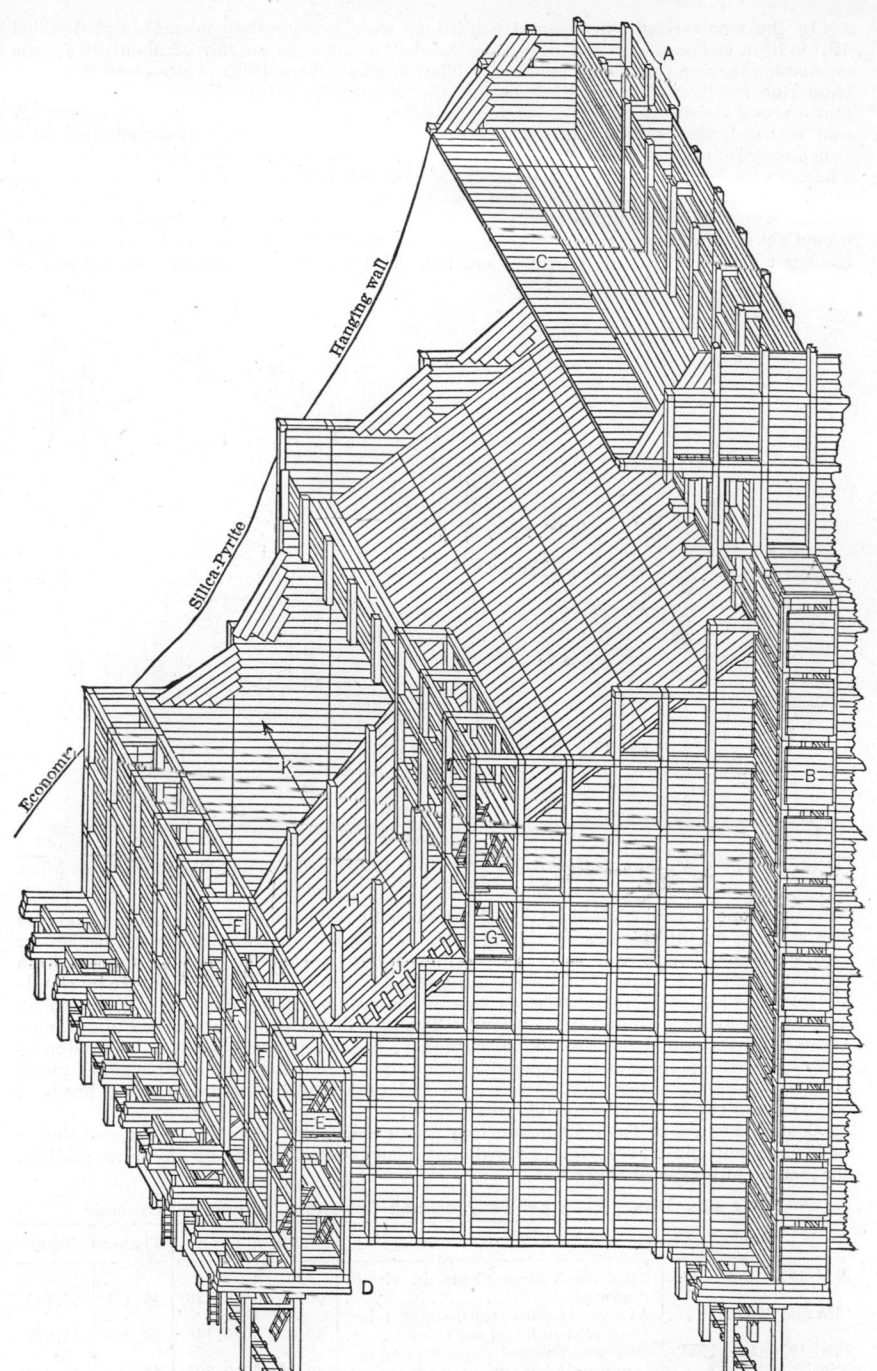

Fig 426. Mining a 48-ft Section under a Filled Stope by Inclined
Cut-and-fill, Campbell Mine, Warren, Ariz

In the new section, the ground conditions were heavier than normal, and doubled 10 by 10-in stringers D were used over the drift posts. At an elev of about 40 ft, the economic hanging wall was reached. The original single-leads were cleaned down, lagged on inside, and waste-filled, except the manway set E, outside the stope section, and 3 sets F inside the section, which were left open for an orepass to chutes below. A new row of leads was then started at G, these being stood on 3 by 10-in sills laid on a bench cut into the waste fill. Two leads were used as ore-passes; the third, as a manway. The ore slide connecting the new single-leads with the original ones is at H; the manway, at J. The part of the stope between ore-slide and gob fence K was completely waste filled. Top row of sets in the newly placed leads were floored L, as a "rakeway." Ore mined above, gravitating to this rakeway, was scraped to the chute-sets. When the stope reaches a height where the crown of ore beneath the mined-out section above becomes

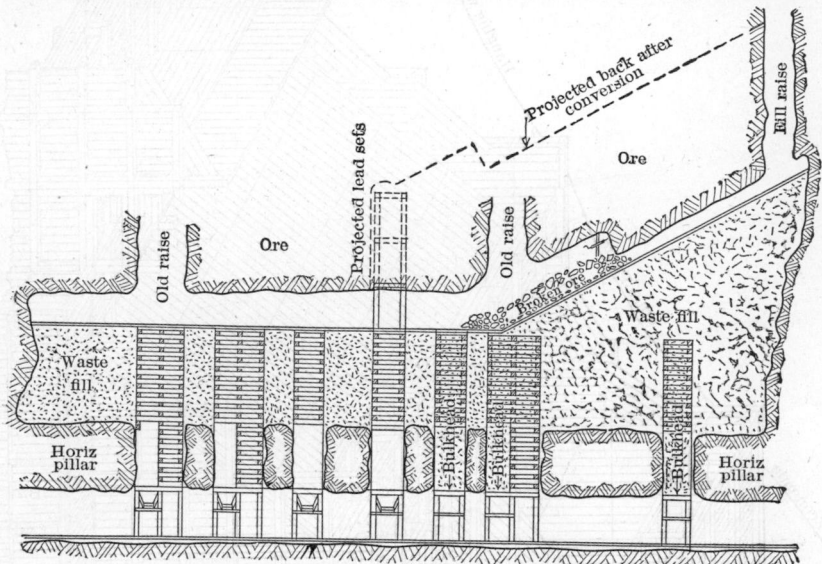

Fig 427. Typical Sec showing Conversion from Horiz to Inclined Cut-and-fill, United Verde Mine, Jerome, Ariz

thin, the stope is sectionalized into 10–12-ft slices at right-angles to the leads. The first slice is taken on the side nearest the fill hole, and the mat or flooring above is caught up with stulls and headboards as it is undermined. After this slice has been taken from hanging wall to the old section, the resulting hole is timbered off from the pillar by single-cap sets, and from the ore on the stope side by building a gob fence of lagged stulls, which are 8 by 8 or 10 by 10 in and 10–18 ft long. The tops of the stulls may be tied to deadmen in the fill of the completed slice, or to the single-cap sets opposite, by strands of old mine rope. The slice is filled as far as possible by dumping from the level and backfilled under the mat by hand. Successive slices are similarly taken until the entire crown has been removed and the section completely waste filled.

Costs. Figures in Table 42 include only direct charges of labor, explosives, and timber for inclined cut-and-fill stoping. They do not reflect cost of mining by any other method, nor include any general charges.

Table 42. Direct Costs per Ton, Inclined Cut-and-fill, Campbell Orebody

Period	General Conditions	Labor	Explos	Timber	Total
1934–1937, incl.......	Aver for 2 large stopes in virgin ground.........................	$0.457	$0.120	$0.158	$0.735
1936 and 1937.......	Aver for 3 medium-sized stopes, mining next to fill on one side........	$0.678	$0.140	$0.206	$1.024
July, 1936–Apr, 1938, incl..............	One medium-sized stope, coming up under timber mat..............	$0.791	$0.207	$0.203	$1.201
First Quarter, 1937...	All inclined cut-and-fill stopes.......	$0.704	$0.142	$0.226	$1.072

United Verde mine, Jerome, Ariz. Data from J. B. Pullen, of United Verde Branch, Phelps Dodge Corp, in 1938. For description of orebody and of former mining by horiz cut-and-fill, see Art 62. Underground mining was suspended from 1931 to 1937. When resumed, it was decided to adopt inclined cut-and-fill as principal method and to convert the former flat-backed stopes accordingly. The latter were 10-160 ft wide and to 200 ft long, but new stope sections are limited to a max of 60 by 100 ft in sulphide ores and 30 by 50 ft in schist and porphyry ores. Fig 427 shows the longit sec of a typical sulphide stope in process of conversion. As flat-backed stopes had been mined and filled for several floors, old chutes had to be used to deliver ore to haulage level. For each inclined cut-and-fill section, there are at least 2 such chutes. Over them, square-sets are built across the width of stope to serve as extraction chutes, manways, and supply entrances. All other old chutes within the section were bulkheaded, and filled from a raise to the level above. The stope back was then sloped upward from the line of square-sets to the fill raise at an angle of 37° (approx angle of repose of the waste filling). Then 8-ft successive cuts were made, from the square-sets toward the fill raise. Stopes are filled after each cut and floored with 2-in planks; square-sets, 6 ft sq and 8 ft high, of 10 by 10-in timber, follow each cut. Movement of broken ore to chutes and spreading of waste are aided by a scraper, the hoist of which is easily moved along the sets, for reaching the entire stope (see Sec 27). Gob fences along pillar and section lines consist of a single line of square-set posts and caps.

Calamon mine, Posadas, Spain; data from C. P. C. Sullivan (255). A form of filled rill stope is used in a vein of silver-lead-zinc ore in schist; ore and hanging wall are weak and require close support. Aver stoping width, 6.5 ft; dip, about 80°. Levels, 98 ft apart, are connected by 2-compartment raises at intervals of 98 ft. In Fig 428, triangular areas *DEF* and *GHI* are first mined by driving 3 superposed drifts *A*, *B*, and *C*, from raises *R*. The drifts, 8 ft high and the full width of stope, are timbered with close-lagged sets. Each drift is filled before starting the one above; much timber is recovered from

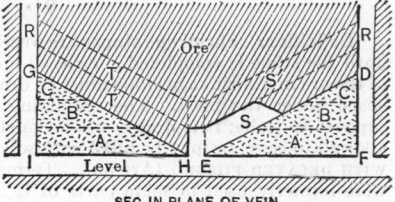

SEC IN PLANE OF VEIN

Fig 428. Rill Stope in Weak Ore, Calamon Mine, Spain

fill when exposed by work above. Faces *DE* and *GH* usually slope 28°, which is less than angle of repose of filling. A chute gate is next erected at *HE*, and the ground above broken down to a height of 8 ft; an 8-ft slice *S* is then taken off face *DE*, the work resembling the driving of a flat raise; back and walls of slice are supported by lagged drift-sets. Slice *S* is filled after holing into raise *R*; during filling, the opposite slice *T* is mined. Rest of lift is similarly mined, chute *HE* being built up after each pair of slices *S*, *T*, etc, have been excavated. Broken ore is pulled down the floors of inclined slices with hoes. Filling for horiz slices *A*, *B*, and *C* must be distributed largely by hand. Raises *R* are abandoned as the stopes go up; temporary chute gates are built in them, as required, for distributing filling to inclined slices by a stream of water; filling is waste from old workings or mill tailing.

The deposit was formerly mined by driving and filling horiz superposed drifts between raises (compare with Leaning stope sets, Art 56). The present method reduced timber consumption 50%, more than doubled output per man-day and reduced total costs about 35%. For detail, see Bib (255).

66. SUMMARY, FILLED STOPES

General. Contemporaneous filling methods usually entail higher costs per ton of ore than shrinkage (Art 67-69) or open-stope mining (Art 35-43), but compete with the latter in certain circumstances. Filling is preferable if factors of safety or dilution demand prompt support of walls; it also affords better opportunity for occasional timber support of ore that is not very strong. In general, filling methods afford a higher degree of selectivity than shrinkage or open-stoping, and hence are better suited where ore is spotty or walls are irregular. Horiz cut-and-fill is advantageous where sorting is needed. In recent years a number of mines formerly using open-stopes or shrinkage have turned to filling methods, reflecting a tendency toward safer mining, and higher and cleaner extraction in the richer orebodies.

Filled flat-back *vs* **filled rill stopes.** SAFETY. Principal danger in both types is from falls of ground. The sloping fill in rill stopes may cause rocks falling from walls or back (or from surface of fill) to roll down the slope and injure men; this risk is increased where fill is covered with plank. As cribbed bulkheads are less easily built in rill than in flat-back stopes, they are avoided when possible; footing for them is less secure when built on inclined surface of waste, and they may be dislodged by moving broken ore or fill. On the other hand, the arching effect of rill stopes may reduce hazard from falling ground. Cost. When applicable, rill stoping is usually cheaper per ton than horiz stoping; gravity aids movement of both ore and filling; fewer chutes are required. These advantages in rill stopes are partly offset by better working conditions in horiz stopes; flat floor affords better footing to men than inclined floor, thus facilitating handling drills, steel, and timber. Where weak ground requires close spacing of bulkheads, advantages of rill stopes may be lost. Flexibility. Opportunity for varying mining procedure is greater in flat-back stopes; area of stope may be extended or reduced at any horizon; prospect openings are easily run into walls, and waste from them used for filling; horses or low-grade ore can be left unmined; in rill stopes, faces must advance uniformly; their output usually ceases while filling; in a flat-back stope, mining may often proceed in one part while filling another. Sorting. Flat-back stopes offer better opportunity than rill stopes for effic sorting.

SHRINKAGE STOPES

67. GENERAL

Definition. Shrinkage stopes are overhand stopes in which the broken ore accumulates until the stope is completed. As rock increases in bulk when broken, from 30% to 50% of the ore in a shrinkage stope must be drawn out as the stope advances, to leave a working space under the back. The remaining ore supports the miners and gives temporary support to walls; it is drawn when the stope is finished. Stopes may be left empty and allowed to cave, or may be filled with waste; latter procedure is called SHRINKAGE STOPING WITH DELAYED FILLING (Art 59). Terms BACK-STOPING and OVERHAND STOPING ON ORE were formerly used in some parts of U S to denote shrinkage stoping; other names are "lay system" (English) and "magazine mining" (Swedish).

Field of use for shrinkage stopes is in steep-dipping deposits of strong ore with strong walls; for limitations of method, see Art 69.

In narrow veins, this method allows practically complete extraction, though level-pillars must sometimes be abandoned to prevent premature caves. Masses or wide veins can rarely be completely mined by shrinkage methods; size of stopes is limited by the area of ore or wall rock which will safely stand unsupported. In large orebodies, permanent pillars may be left for support between adjacent stopes, as at Alaska Treadwell mine (Art 68); this is a form of pillar and chamber work (Art 42). Pillars may sometimes be blasted after completing shrinkage mining, but before final drawing of ore, in which case caving may also be involved (Creighton mine, Art 68). High-grade orebodies usually warrant filling of shrinkage stopes and recovery of pillars by square-setting (Art 46), Mitchell slicing (Art 55), or top-slicing (Art 72, 73). See also Combined methods (Art 83–87).

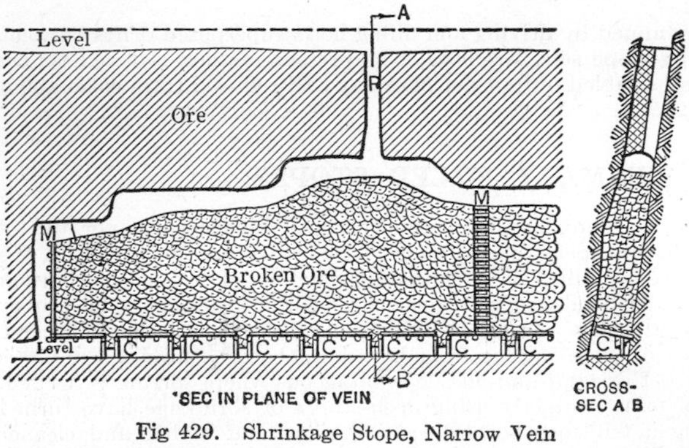

Fig 429. Shrinkage Stope, Narrow Vein

General plan. Fig 429 shows a stope in a narrow vein, opened from raise R as an ordinary overhand stope (Art 38). Ore from the cutting-out stope falls to the drift; that from succeeding back-stopes collects on top of level timbers, the excess due to swell being withdrawn through chute-gates C (Art 90). Ventilation and access to stope are afforded by raise R and manways, M. Procedure in wide stopes is similar (see below, and Art 68).

Chutes for shrinkage stopes are sometimes built up at regular intervals like those in waste-filled stopes (Art 60); they are then used for passing excess ore to the level. As the fill of broken ore in such a stope is stable, a weak back may be supported on cribs, but this practice involves much shoveling, which is obviated in typical shrinkage stopes (Fig 429). Chutes may also be justified by the presence of high-grade ore, which can be sorted in stopes and kept separate for special treatment (see Sorting, below). Chutes are sometimes used to handle small patches of waste, which would otherwise mix with the ore. Shrinkage stopes with built-up chutes are relatively unimportant.

Development for shrinkage stopes in narrow veins follows general lines laid down in Art 14. Level interval may be greater than in filled stopes (Art 59), because there are no chutes to maintain. Raises may be far apart, long stopes being opened from a single raise in the middle, or from a raise at each end. Blind oreshoots may even be mined without any raise to level above, ventilation and access being obtained through timbered manways at ends of stope. Development practice in wide orebodies is largely a question of arranging openings for drawing ore economically from the stopes (examples, Art 68).

Shape of stope-face. Both wide and narrow shrinkage stopes commonly have a flat back, under which, in drawing excess broken ore, it is easier to maintain a working space of uniform height than where the back is inclined or irregular. The advantages of a level working floor (Art 66) also apply here. Fig 444 shows a stepped-face shrinkage stope.

The shrinkage principle may also be applied in rill stopes of moderate width; these allow use of down holes, which alone should determine the angle of rill. Steep slopes, on which broken ore will roll, are a pronounced disadvantage in shrinkage stopes. Fig 430, from O. B. Ward (260), shows a

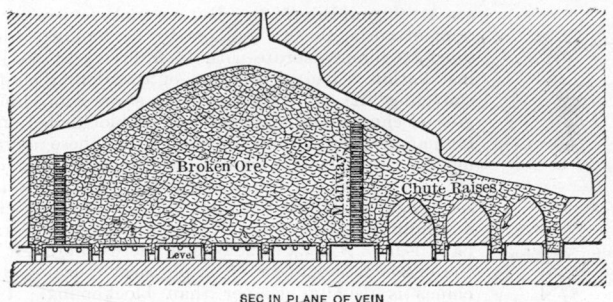

SEC IN PLANE OF VEIN

Fig 430. Shrinkage Stope, Lake View Consols Mine, Kalgoorlie, Australia

rill stope for steep-dipping oreshoots up to 25 ft wide in Lake View Consols mine (for ore occurrence at Kalgoorlie, W Australia, see Art 65). Level interval is 200 ft; inclination of the back is just sufficient (say 18° to 25°) for holes at top of stope to hold water.

Breaking ground. Practice is the same as in other overhand stopes (Art 26 to 28; note Fig 172, and accompanying text, also remarks on blockholing, Art 26; see Ariz Copper Co, Art 68).

Arrangements for protecting levels and drawing ore under shrinkage stopes are more or less interdependent; general considerations are:

(a) Protection for levels must be strong, to carry weight of broken ore, part of which is supported by footwall in inclined stopes and by friction between ore and walls in narrow vertical stopes; constant drawing of ore destroys any arching effect which might tend to make broken ore self-supporting, and may throw heavy shock loads on timber or other level protection. The walls may also exert heavy lateral pressure when the ore is being drawn (20).

(b) Method of protecting levels obviously depends on width of stope. In narrow deposits, simple or saddle-back stulls, stulls and posts, drift-sets, or level-pillars are adequate; choice is based on the same factors as for open stopes (Art 38); square-sets (Art 45) are often used for convenience instead of drift-sets. In wide stopes, 4 arrangements are common: (1) One or more timbered or dry-wall gangways, like those used in filled stopes (Art 64), may be built on stope floor; for example, see Homestake mine (Art 68), also Bib (243). (2) Entire sill-floor may be timbered with square-sets; those sets needed for haulageways and chute-gates are kept open by lagging (see Cresson mine, Art 68). (3) Floor of stope may be opened 10 to 20 ft above the level, leaving a level-pillar, through which CHUTE RAISES are made at frequent intervals to draw off ore; see Nevada-Massachusetts and Rosiclare mines, Art 68. (4) Floor of stope may be opened on the level, with no attempt to maintain haulageways through broken ore; ore is drawn off by shovelers working in numerous crosscuts, which connect edges of stope with haulageways driven nearby in walls of deposit or in pillars between stopes (King mine, Art 68; also Fig 451). CHOICE OF METHOD is based on a comparison beween first cost of opening stopes and subsequent cost of handling broken ore; these costs vary with size and character of orebody, wages and efficiency of labor, and supply costs; no two mines present exactly the same problem. For variations, see Art 68.

(c) The way in which ore breaks (or is broken) should be considered in planning for handling broken ore at the levels. Large slabs clog ordinary chute-raises and gates and require blasting to dislodge them; this work is costly and often damages chutes; if slabs are numerous, the delays soon destroy the advantages of chute-gates for cheap loading.

Trouble from last-named source is rarely serious in narrow stopes in small mines; drill holes are shallow, and the few slabs produced may be cheaply blockholed or spalled in the stopes. In such mines ore must be broken fine, for handling in small cars or skips. Under these conditions broken ore may be drawn through simple chute-gates, the installation of which does not materially increase first cost of opening stopes. Such gates are usually for handling pieces of ore not larger than 8 or 10 in.

In wide stopes of large mines, deep holes and heavy blasts are desirable to secure cheap breaking. Ores thus blasted rarely break fine, but contain slabs varying in number and size with structural characteristics of orebody. Cost of blockholing or spalling large slabs to 8 or 10-in size is high; amount of labor and explosive required may equal or exceed that needed for initial breaking. There are special chutes and gates for handling large slabs; bulldozing chambers with grizzlies over levels facilitate breaking up boulders;

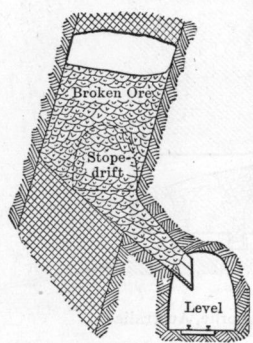

Fig 431.   Cross-sec (after Hoover)

see Art 90 and Bib (562). But, as such devices increase development costs, the ore tonnage to be handled through them must be commensurate with their first cost to justify their installation. The alternative of abandoning chute-gates and shoveling the ore into cars from stope floor eliminates clogging of chutes, and slabs need to be blockholed only to a size for handling by 2 men; in the U S, these advantages are usually overbalanced by cost of shoveling, and chute gates, etc, are in general use. For detail of various alternatives, see Examples of practice, Art 68. To prevent clogging, the minimum cross-section of chute-gates or of chute-raises should be at least $3 \times$ max dimension of pieces of ore. At large mines, the crushers should be of ample size; crushing in large machines is usually cheaper than blockholing. Underground crushers are sometimes advantageous.

(d) For convenience in mining level-pillars at top of stopes, haulageways are sometimes placed in the walls of the deposit (Fig 431). Stope is then opened from a stope-drift, as indicated by dotted lines; this device secures strong protection for levels, but is limited to deposits of moderate width; haulageways may be driven in walls on both sides of stope (Ariz Copper Co, Art 68).

(e) Haulageways and chute-gates should be located with reference to effect produced on the surface of broken ore at top of stope by drawing off below. In vert stopes, 25 to 30 ft wide, the best location for a single row of chute-gates is in middle of stope; if placed along one wall, the surface of broken ore above tends to pitch toward that wall and shoveling or staging is required to reach the stope-back on that side for drilling. In inclined stopes, ore tends to draw down on hanging-wall side, regardless of position of drawing points; some gates are placed on footwall, for drawing off ore there when stope is to be emptied.

Chute-gates suitable for shrinkage stopes are described in Art 90. DISTANCE BETWEEN GATES should be small, to reduce amount of ore remaining between them when the stope is finally drawn, as empty stopes are often too dangerous for shovelers to enter. Close spacing also allows more even drawing of broken ore. Gates are usually 12 to 25 ft apart; use of A-shaped pillars (Fig 438) between gates allows larger intervals. Where levels are stulled, ore remaining between gates may be recovered by cutting out lagging and dropping the ore on the level (260).

Access to shrinkage stopes is as follows: (a) Timbered manways are built up through broken ore; timbered, in narrow stopes, with 2 rows of lagged stulls; cribbed manways are used in wider stopes. For greater security, manways are often at ends of stope; if elsewhere, cribbed manways should be midway between 2 chute gates, and preferably on footwall, where they are least affected by movement of broken ore during drawing.

(b) Raises are driven in walls, or in pillars between stopes, and connected with stopes at vertical intervals of 15 to 30 ft by short drifts. This is common in wide stopes and affords strong protection for traveling and air-ways (see examples, Art 68). (c) Raises through back of stope to level above. Access is then usually supplementary to forms (a) or (b), primary purpose being that of ventilation.

Sorting in shrinkage stopes is not ordinarily feasible. (For exceptions, see Cobalt, Ontario, and Kennecott mine, Art 68.)

Support of back and walls. Shrinkage methods are primarily for use where the back will stand unsupported and walls will stand while stope is being emptied (Art 69). For support of the back in shrinkage stopes with chutes, see Chutes, p. 275. Loose slabs in stopes without chutes (Fig 429) may be supported temporarily by stulls, preferably tapered and set with their big ends up to facilitate recovery from above; this is practically the only form of support feasible during stoping. Occasionally the back and walls of stopes of moderate width are timbered while ore is being drawn, to protect men in the stope or to prevent contamination of ore by slabs from walls (Ariz Copper Co, Art 68).

H. H. Hodgkinson states in this connection (261): Timbering consists of lagging supported by transverse sets or frames spaced 4.5 to 8 ft apart. Fig 432 shows a good set for a highly arched back; a hitch is required at each end of the horiz timber. Fig 433 shows support for a weak wall at A. Unsymmetrical sets of this kind are feasible where peak of arch is not in center of stope. Fig 434 shows a rafter set for a stope with a flat back and poor wall at B. Timbers should be framed to conform to shape of back, a space of at least 10 in being left above the sets, for placing lagging and blocking; more space adds expense for extra blocking. Arched backs in general throw less weight on timbers and allow more space between sets than flat backs. Fig 435 shows extension of same general plan to the complete timbering of walls; successive stulls, uprights. and lagging are placed as ore is drawn. (Such work is costly and rarely justified in shrinkage stopes. Author.)

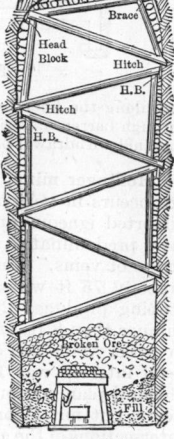

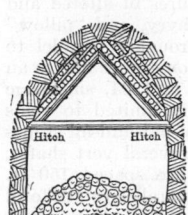 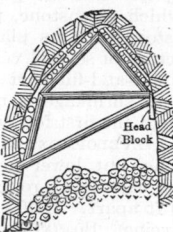 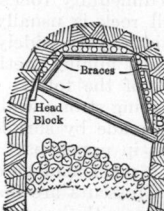

| Fig 432 | Fig 433 | Fig 434 | Fig 435 |

W. W. Lynch states that at United Verde mine, Ariz, shrinkage stoping was employed in 1927 to mine a block about 100 ft long and 50 ft wide. After carrying stope to full height of 100 ft, the back tended to slough on exposure to air. Before final drawing of ore, the entire back was gunited after arching. Result was satisfactory in protecting men working at bottom of stope after drawing of ore and prior to filling. Procedure was one of expediency to meet an unforeseen condition.

Waste filling is the only means of supporting permanently the walls of empty stopes. Filling is dumped in through numerous raises put up to level above through the level-pillar at top of stope. Delayed filling operations of this kind are always cheaper than contemporaneous filling (Art 59), because stopes are open and much of the filling runs into place by gravity; shoveling is required only at top of stope. In long stopes, the length of wall left unsupported during drawing may be reduced by drawing all the ore possible from each chute-gate in succession, starting at one end of stope. As room is obtained, filling is dumped into the empty end of stope from level above; toe of fill advances as the toe of ore pile recedes towards the other end of stope. Attempts made to draw ore uniformly over entire area of stope, and dump waste into the top at the same rate that ore is withdrawn, always result in loss of some ore and serious contamination with waste. See Ariz Copper Co, Art 68; Inspiration mine, Art 80; and Bib (262, 263). Further details of shrinkage stopes are given in Art 68, 84–87.

68. EXAMPLES OF PRACTICE, SHRINKAGE STOPES

Cobalt, Ontario (264, 265). District was formerly a famous silver producer. Native silver, with arsenides of Co and Ni, occurs in vert fissures in conglomerate, graywacke, and quartzite. Width of veins, rarely over 6 in; assays up to 3 000 oz Ag per ton were sometimes obtained; values often extended into wall rocks, forming 3 to 6 ft of milling ore on each side of vein. Entry was by vert shafts, generally following the vein; level interval, 50 to 75 ft; shrinkage stopes were usual; a few veins were mined in open stulled stopes (Art 39). Practice at BUFFALO MINE was typical of shrinkage methods with flat-back stopes. The hard, compact ore was broken with 5-ft uppers, placed fairly close together to avoid need for spalling or blockholing. Before stoping began, 6 by 7-ft drifts were driven to the limits of ore; levels were timbered with lagged stulls after the cutting-out and first back stope had enlarged the drift to a height of 13 to 15 ft. Ore from these openings collected in drift and supported miners while drilling holes for a second back stope. Chute-gates were 20 ft apart, and a cribbed manway was built at each end of stope. About 33% of ore broken was drawn during stoping, a 6-ft open space being kept under the back. In stoping, low-grade ore on one side of vein was first blasted. The high-grade streak was then broken with light shots, the ore being sorted, sacked, and sent direct to smelter. The remaining low-grade ore on opposite side was then broken (compare with Resuing, Art 61). At some mines no sorting was done in stopes. Fig 436 is a section through 2 levels of CONIAGAS MINE, showing method of dealing with oreshoots with so flat a pitch that ore would not

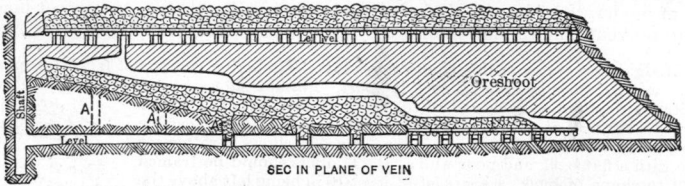

Fig 436.   Shrinkage Stope, Coniagas Mine, Cobalt, Ont

run along the floor by gravity. Chute-raises A, with funneled tops, were put up from the level through barren material; they permitted control of the surface of broken ore during stoping and of the final withdrawal of ore.

Hollinger mine, Porcupine, Canada.   Data from A. W. Young (306) in 1935.   Gold ore occurs in vert or steeply-dipping quartz-pyrite veins, along fractures in altered and distorted igneous and sedimentary rocks, in which greenstone, porphyry, and "pillow" lava predominate. Wall rock is usually schistose with its planes roughly parallel to strike of veins. Vein widths vary widely; juncture of several veins sometimes makes an orebody 75 ft wide. Chief mining method is cut-and-fill (Art 62); in 1934, shrinkage stoping produced 27.4% of the total. As such, shrinkage is usually limited to veins thinner than 8 ft, and having strong walls, though the first few cuts of cut-and-fill stopes in wider veins are often made by shrinkage. DEVELOPMENT is by several vert shafts; level interval was 100 ft in upper part of mine, but lower levels are spaced 150 ft. General plan comprises a main haulage drift on each level, roughly parallel to strike of veins, but not in ore. Crosscuts are 350–400 ft apart. Drifts are turned off in ore at intersections of the crosscuts with the numerous veins. SHRINKAGE STOPING. Preparation consists of silling out vein to full width of ore and to 17 ft above rail. Sill timbering usually consists of 12 by 18-in stulls, 7 ft c-c, set in hitches and at slight angle to horiz; stulls are reinforced by one or more 9-in min-diam round posts. Where vein is too low-grade to be workable at the level, but good ore is known to exist above, raises are driven from the drift to bottom of this ore before stoping starts. Chute pockets are in alternate sets, intermediate sets being lagged with 5-in poles. Stoping is in horiz slices 6–7 ft high. Holes 8 ft deep, burden of 18 in, are drilled at 70°–80° from horiz with wet stopers. Drillers work on contract and aver about 10 holes per shift. Contract rates vary according to width of vein and are graded in a manner that discourages miners from overbreaking. As stope advances upward, a stulled or cribbed manway is carried at one end. After stope reaches a height of about 50 ft, a raise is driven to level above for ventilation and service. Level pillars are left at top of stope, their depth depending on width of ore and nature of ground. Stope is scaled down during final drawing of ore, and weak walls are supported by stulls. On completing drawing ore, stope is filled to within 6–8 ft of back. COSTS. Following data apply to year 1934 and are aver for all shrinkage mining of that year: tons ore broken per hole, 2.55; direct stoping labor cost per ton broken: breaking, $0.423; timbering, $0.085; filling, $0.068; scaling, $0.137; stope development, $0.032; total labor, $0.745; explosives, $0.160; total direct labor and explosives, $0.905.

Wright-Hargreaves mine, Kirkland Lake, Ont.   Data from L. B. Smith (176) in 1934. Gold ore occurs in fissure veins in porphyry. For geol details see Art 39. Shrinkage stoping is used occasionally where ore is 6 ft wide or more, and walls are strong. Level interval, 150 ft; drifts are in ore. Shrinkage stoping starts by taking down back of drift to height of 15–16 ft above rails. After broken ore is removed by shoveling, haulageway is established by use of stulls (Fig 429 C). Stulls are 5 ft c-c, and set at right-angles to dip except where vein is vert; in latter case stulls are given sufficient pitch to hold firmly. Chutes are built in alternate sets, or 10 ft c-c. Manways are at 90-ft centers. In stopes under

10 ft wide, manways are 'of 2 lines of lagged stulls. If width exceeds 10 ft, cribbed manways are built against the footwall and fastened to it by eye-bolts and a piece of 16-lb rail (Fig 437). Stopes are flat-back, with breasts 8 ft high; drilling is by mounted hammer drills; holes flat and 6–7 ft deep. Stopes are worked through to level above without leaving sill pillars; stulls used instead. After stope is drawn, it is filled with waste.

Nevada-Massachusetts Co, Mill City, Nev. Data from O. F. Heizer (196) in 1930. Tungsten ore with about 1% WO_3 occurs chiefly in thin limestone beds dipping 70°–75°. Most productive bed averages 4.5 ft wide; walls stand with moderate amount of support and ore breaks well. DEVELOPMENT. Two main veins are developed by inclined shafts, 730 and 800 ft deep in 1924. Levels are 100 ft apart; drifts untimbered. STOPING. All mining is by shrinkage stoping without filling except that waste from development is dumped into empty stopes. After exposing ore by drifting, a ventilation raise, which is also a manway, is driven to level above. Meantime, chute raises are driven to height of 6 ft above back of drift, and belled out to connect with each other. Chute spacing is 20 ft if ore is dry and draws easily; otherwise the interval is 15 ft. Manways are at 80-ft intervals with 20-ft chute spacing; with 15-ft spacing, manways are 75 ft apart. Stope back is advanced as in Fig 438, one miner starting at ventilation raise and another at the manway. Holes are horiz if

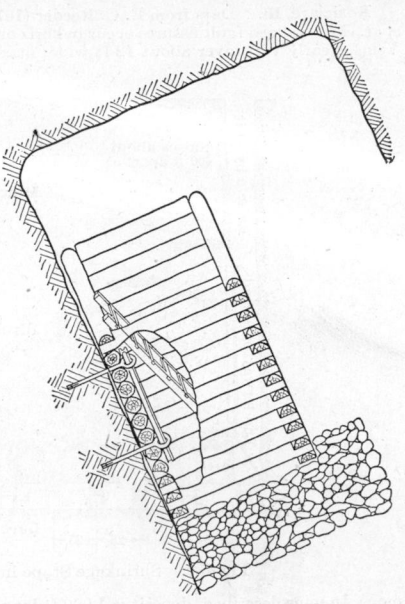

Fig 437. Cribbed Manway pinned to Wall by Eye-bolt and Rail, Wright-Hargreaves Mine, Kirkland Lake, Ont

ground is hard; otherwise vert, by hand-rotated stopers. As stope advances, excess broken ore is drawn, to leave about 6 ft between top of ore pile and back of stope. Weak spots in

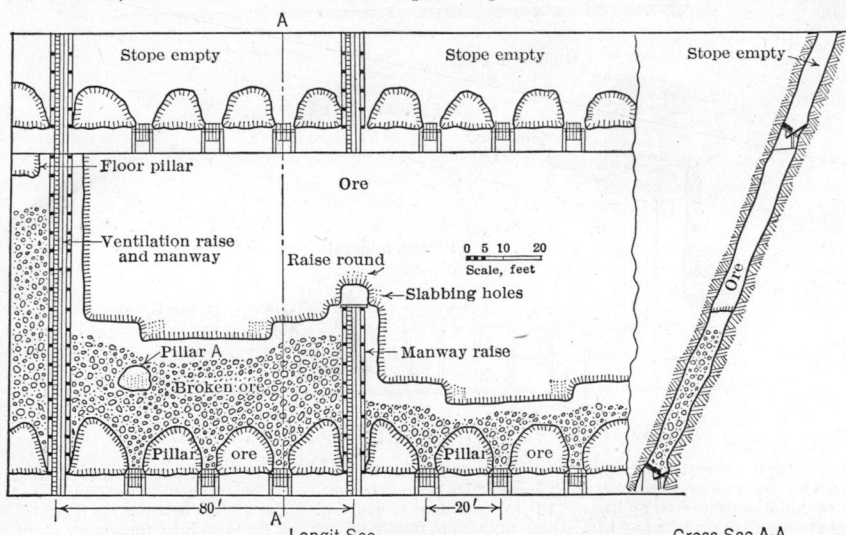

Fig 438. Shrinkage Stope in Nevada-Massachusetts Mine, Mill City, Nev

hanging wall are supported by stulls or pillars of ore. If grade of ore is low, pillars are left permanently; otherwise they are blasted out after stope is completed. Floor pillars,

6 ft thick, are finally removed by underhand mining. In 1928, average output per man-shift chargeable to underground work was 2.62 tons.

Rosiclare, Ill. Data from E. C. Reeder (197) in 1930. Shrinkage method is used in mining fluorspar. Mineralized fault fissures occur in horiz or flat-dipping beds of limestone, sandstone, and shale. Veins, nearly vert, aver about 12 ft wide; max width is about 34 ft, and 18-20-ft widths are com-

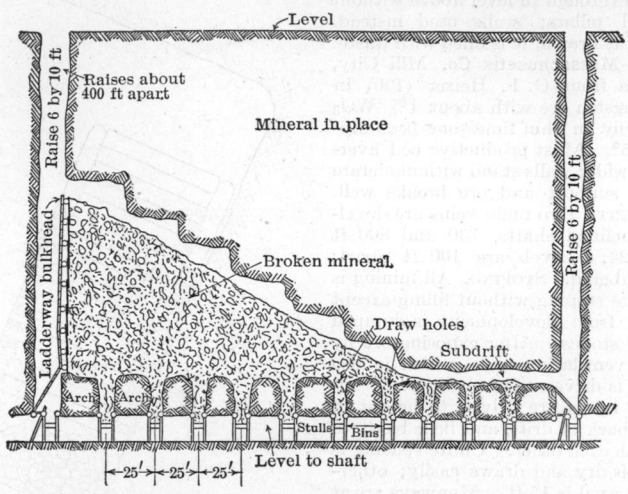

Fig 439. Shrinkage Stope in Wider Veins, Rosiclare, Ill (197)

mon. In mine described, deposit is 1 900 ft long; developed by vert shaft starting in footwall about 70 ft from vein and near longit center of deposit. Levels are opened at 100-ft vert intervals by crosscuts from shaft and drifts in vein. For the wider veins, chute raises are 25 ft apart and driven high enough for a sub-drift to be driven for connecting tops of raises; sub-drifts are slabbed to full width of vein (Fig 439). In narrow veins, stoping starts just above drift timbers, as in Fig 440. Stopes vary

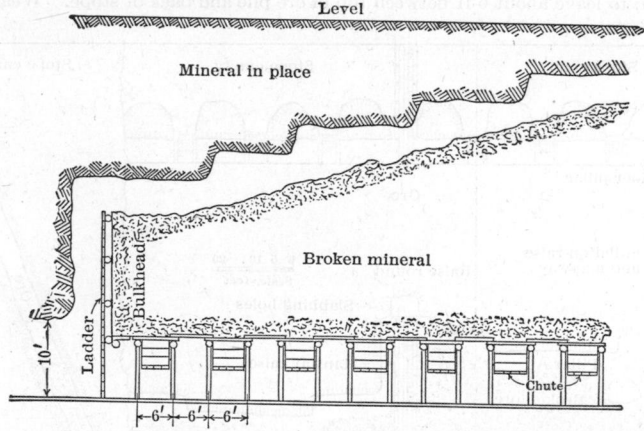

Fig 440. Shrinkage Stope, Narrow Veins, Rosiclare, Ill (197)

from 100 to several hundred ft long. The stope back is carried in benches, usually drilled with uppers; sometimes, 12 to 15-ft flat holes. Top of ore pile is kept 6-7 ft below back. The thickness of level pillar is computed on basis of 1 ft for each foot in width of stope, up to a depth of 15 ft, which serves for stope widths to 34 ft. These pillars are finally mined and dropped into the empty stope below. Production per man-shift in 1930 averaged 2.93 tons for all men underground.

Arizona Copper Co, Metcalf, Ariz (152). Methods once used at King and Coronado mines, studied together, illustrate advancement in shrinkage practice. Fig 441 shows method applied at King mine to orebodies 500 to 700 ft long, with max width of 30 ft, occurring in a fault fissure in porphyry; walls were strong and well defined; dip, about 70°. On each level, haulageways were driven in walls, the vein was crosscut at 25-ft intervals, and the entire sill floor of shoot excavated as a breast stope (Art 30), the ore being shoveled into cars. Stope was then carried up as a flat-back shrinkage stope, 33% of broken ore being drawn through crosscuts by shoveling. Access to stope was through raises, at 100-ft intervals, to level above. Back-stopes were 10 to 15 ft high, miners working towards each other from adjacent raises; at some point the belly of ore between 2 parties generally broke off, and the block was blockholed if necessary. Occasionally, parts of vein were too weak to allow safe overhand stoping. Then 2 raises, between which soft ore occurred, were connected by a drift 20 to 30 ft above the back. Ore in the pillar so formed was broken by holes in floor of

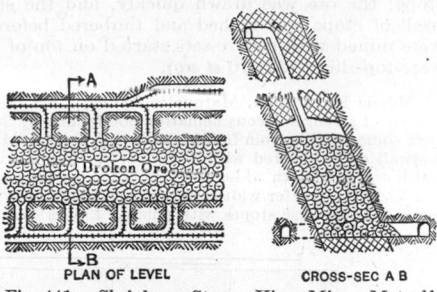

PLAN OF LEVEL   CROSS-SEC A B

Fig 441. Shrinkage Stope, King Mine, Metcalf, Ariz

drift, beginning midway between raises and retreating towards them; similar underhand methods were employed on approaching an upper level.

Above method was later modified to allow use of CHUTES FOR LOADING CARS. Fig 442

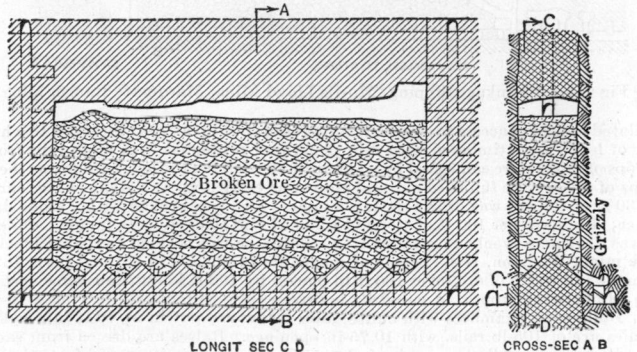

LONGIT SEC C D   CROSS-SEC A B

Fig 442. Shrinkage Stope, Coronado Mine, Metcalf, Ariz

shows its application at CORONADO MINE, for an oreshoot 1 750 ft long, with a vert dip and aver width of 35 ft. Walls and ore were strong; ore broke large and could not be run direct to cars without much blockholing in chutes. Stopes were 150 ft long, separated by 30-ft pillars; raises in centers of pillars, and connected with stopes at vert intervals of 25 ft, furnished ventilation and access. Chute-raises were 25-ft apart, those from hanging-wall drift being half-way between those from footwall drift. Floor of stope was opened 15 to 20 ft above level. Over each chute was a grizzly, on which shovelers broke up large pieces. Fig 443 shows another method permitting gravity loading of cars, and giving opportunity for breaking boulders without blasting in chutes. A level 2 sets high in middle of vein was square-setted. Inclined funnel-shaped raises, alternating to right and left from the sides of upper sets, communicated with the stope floor 20 ft above level. Ore collected on lagging of lower sets, where it was spalled or blockholed, and loaded into cars. Cost of preparatory work was less in this system than in that shown in Fig 442, but final drawing of stope was subject to more delays. "Stopes at the top of orebody can generally be carried to cap rock, and then be drawn quickly without difficulty. Danger of an air blast from sudden caving of an empty stope makes subsequent filling always

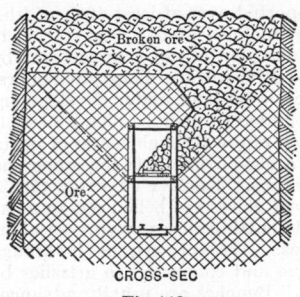

CROSS-SEC

Fig 443

desirable." In one place, an attempt was made to cave overlying waste on a heavy mat of timber laid on the broken ore, and then to draw the ore below, but if the mat descended more than 30 ft, it broke up enough to cause a serious admixture of waste. In deeper parts of oreshoots, shrinkage stopes were stopped 25 to 30 below bottom of the overlying stope; the ore was drawn quickly, and the stope filled with waste. In weak ground, back of stope was arched and timbered before ore was drawn (Art 67). Level-pillars were mined with square-sets started on top of waste fill; then the pillars between stopes were top-sliced (Art 70 *et seq*).

Morris Lloyd mine, Marquette Range, Mich (184). Shrinkage stopes were used for mining a deposit of strong siliceous hematite, 500 ft long by 25 to 75 ft wide; dip, 70° to 85°; hanging wall gave some trouble from falling slabs. Level interval, 150 ft; main haulage drifts were driven near footwall and timbered with 3-piece sets. Deposit was crosscut at 100-ft intervals, to determine width and grade; in wider portions, a second drift was driven later near hanging wall. Max stope width, 40 ft; greater widths were mined in 2 stopes parallel to walls, with a pillar between, or in a series of transverse stopes with pillars. Levels were connected by untimbered raises 100 ft apart,

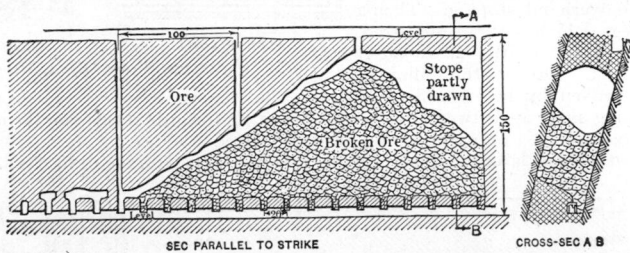

Fig 444. Shrinkage Stoping, Morris Lloyd Mine, Marquette Range, Mich

which ventilated and gave access to stopes. Chute-raises, put up at 20-ft intervals to a height of 10 ft above back of level, were timbered with 3-in plank and protected with 40-lb rails from injury by blasting. Tops of raises were connected by a sub-drift 15 ft above the level, stope was then widened to full size, tops of raises were funneled out and stope was carried up as a stepped-face shrinkage stope (Fig 444); 30% of the ore was drawn during mining. Ore was broken with 2 stope drills per 50-ft length of face; 1 laborer per 100 ft of stope blockholed and sledged large lumps. On completion of stope, ore was drawn as evenly as possible from chutes, as this seemed to reduce blocking.

Replogle mine, Wharton, N J. Lenses of magnetite in gneiss dip 55° and pitch 18°. Shrinkage stopes are made full width of ore (over 100 ft in places) by 400 ft long; transverse vert pillars 50–80 ft thick are left between stopes. A sub-drift is driven close to footwall, leaving a 10-ft pillar over main level. Bulldozing chambers with chute gates below are put in at 40-ft intervals on the sub-level; grizzlies are of 105-lb rails, with 10.75-in openings. Raises are driven from each bulldozing chamber to the hanging wall at an angle of about 40°. Stope floor is opened from the raises in form of a series of transverse V-shaped ridges. Access to stope is through manways in the transverse end pillars. Data from A. H. Hubbell in 1920 (582).

Mt Hope mine, N J. Data from J. R. Sweet (529) in 1932. Magnetite occurs in tabular orebodies dipping 60°–80°, and pitching 14° from horiz. Stoping widths, from a few feet to 40 ft. Height of orebodies along dip is 150–400 ft; length exceeds 7 500 ft. In main body the ore is hard and tough, standing unsupported over at least 40-ft widths. Wall rock is hard, granitoid gneiss. Main 1 000-ft shaft, inclined at 64°, was started in footwall, but cut through orebody below 250 ft. Former plan of development was by levels at intervals up to 260 ft. More recent practice is to drive inclines along pitch of orebody and 25–30 ft beneath it, thus permitting high extraction without undue development cost. Stoping blocks are usually 340 ft long. Stopes are bounded by inclined pillars 30–40 ft wide (Fig 445). Access to stope is by manway raise to top of ore through center of pillar, and connected by short drifts to parallel raises forming a cut-off line between stope and pillars. Inclining of pillars permits low-cost driving of raises. RECENT PRACTICE (1932) is to provide each stope with 4 chutes, 81 ft apart. Chute raises are belled out to make room for grizzly chambers. From ends of grizzlies, undercutting raises are driven along strike at 45°, as in Fig 445, leaving pillars over the grizzlies. Access to grizzlies is through a sub-incline in the hanging wall, parallel to main incline and connected to grizzlies by short crosscuts. Stope face finally becomes flat-backed. Benches are usually advanced from each end toward the middle. Height of benches is 6–15 ft, generally inversely to ore width. They are broken with 14-ft flat holes, drilled by jackhammer fitted with stoper leg and lying horiz on a 12 by 2-in plank, 12–16 ft long, the outer end of which rests on a rung of a ladder leaning against the back. Foot of drill extension leg is held in place by an eye pin inserted in 0.5-in holes bored along center line of plank, the pin being moved forward as required. This novel drilling method is effective. Burden on holes, 3–6 ft. Explosive is 40% dynamite. The 14-ft holes are loaded by first tamping in 12–15 cartridges, and distributing the remainder along full length of hole by alternating sticks of dynamite and wood. Some blockholing is done in the stope; the rest on grizzlies. This mining method does not permit economic recovery of pillars; 90% extraction is expected. Following stoping data are for year 1930: tons broken per machine-shift, 82.53; tons per man-shift chargeable to stoping, 57.59; av tons per man-shift underground, 7.09; av tons per man-shift on property, 4.52; tons broken per ft of hole, 2.58; powder per ton broken, 0.384 lb. For methods at other magnetite mines in same district, see Bib (494, 633).

Walker mine, Walkermine, Plumas Co, Calif (subsidiary of Anaconda Copper Mining Co). Following data, from J. F. Dugan, Gen Supt Mines, Int Smelt and Ref Co, cover practice in 1939. Orebodies are fissure veins of quartz, carrying copper sulphides associated with pyrite, pyrrhotite, and magnetite. Veins are 600–1 400 ft long, 10–60 ft wide, and dip 30°–85°; both walls are metamorphosed sediments and igneous flows.

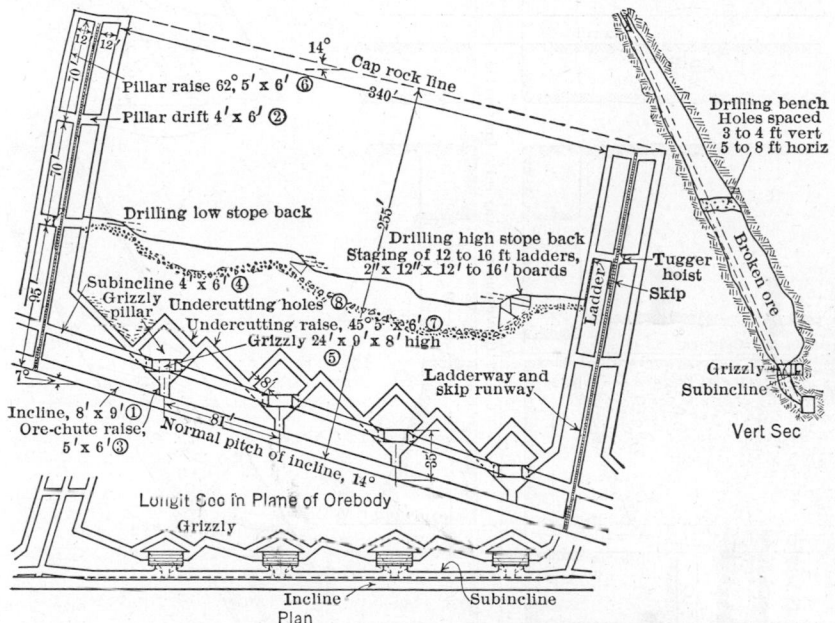

Fig 445. Shrinkage Stope Development and Mining, Mt Hope Mine, Mt Hope, N J (529). Numbers in circles indicate successive development steps

Mine is opened by a 2-mile adit on 700-ft level, 2 inclined shafts to 1 000-ft level and one to 1 200-ft level. The 700 and 1 000 are haulage levels, from which stopes are started (Fig 446). A sub-level A is driven 30 ft above haulage level B, and two 6 by 10-ft ore chutes C are raised 50 ft apart to bulldozing chambers D, connected with the sub-level by crosscuts E. Top of each raise is covered by 90-lb grizzly rails with 10-in openings. Above, and with enough brow to keep the grizzly from flooding, short finger raises F are milled out into a stope. Pillar raises G are driven to level above at 150-ft intervals, and from them are service drifts H every 30 ft vert, starting 50 ft above sub-level. Thus, stopes 110 ft long are separated by 40-ft pillars, which are robbed by drilling from the service drifts. Depending on character of ground, pillar-raise center lines may be shortened or lengthened 50 ft, cutting out or adding one chute. This would leave stopes 60 or 160 ft long, separated by 40-ft pillars. Through the level-pillars are mill holes from tops of finished stopes to the level above. These are covered with grizzly rails and then other stopes are opened directly above. Level interval is 100–300 ft vert, depending on the ground, and lifts of as many levels as desired may be opened from one haulage level. Pillar robbing starts at the far end of top level, retreating toward the shaft.

In the Piute orebody, the vein below the 700 adit is flatter than 45° and most broken ore must be scraped to the level (Fig 447). Large chute mouths O are 70 ft apart, with a 7 by 18-ft raise P driven from every third chute to level above. Service drifts Q are driven every 30 ft vert, starting 35 ft above the track, and then the raise is enlarged as a stope. Service, air, and water pipes supply 3 stopes and are brought through the raise

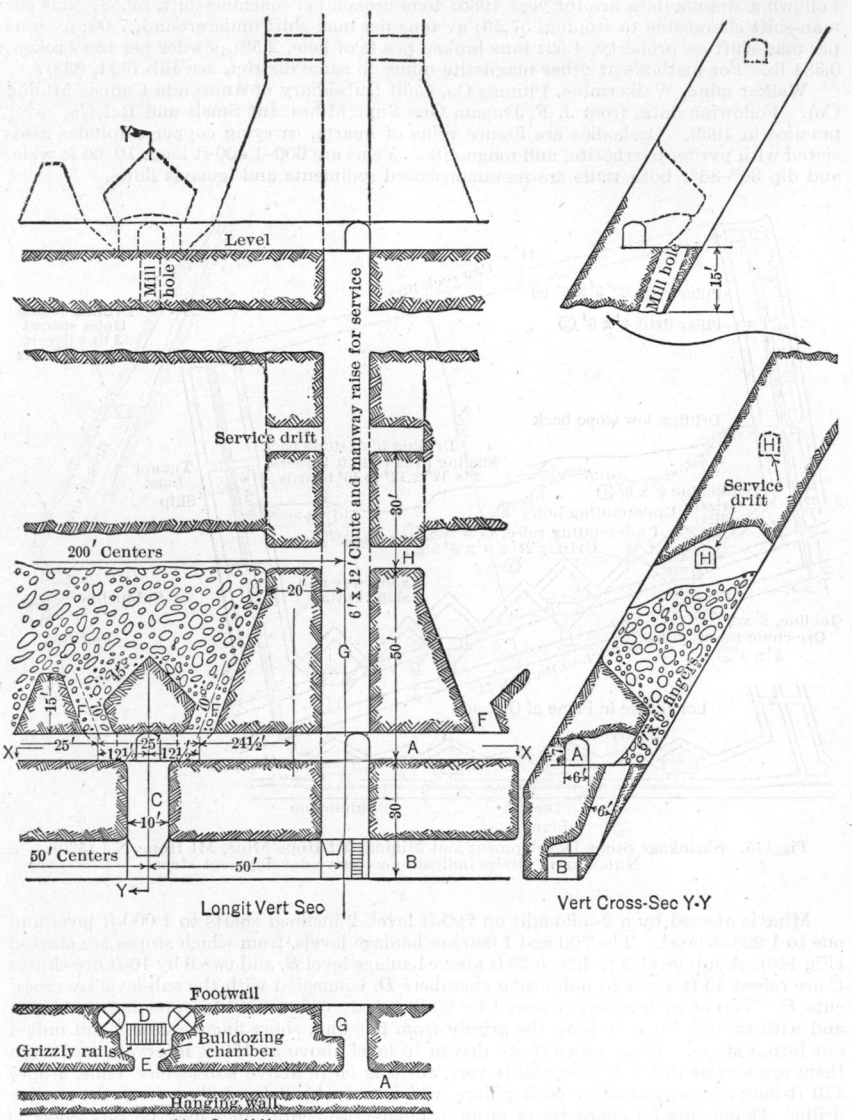

Fig 446. Shrinkage Stoping, Walker Mine (ideal sections)

from level above. Pillars are robbed from the service drifts. This method is locally called "semi-shrinkage" stoping. Most stope drilling is done with 3.5-in Leyners, mounted on 4-in bars and arms, but heavy rotating stopers are used in raises and narrower stopes. Bits are detachable; hot-milled, and tempered in an elec furnace. Aver break per machine-shift is 29 tons, with 1.9 sticks of powder per ton; 45% Gelemite is used to blast simultaneously large numbers of 6–12-ft holes.

Application of shrinkage stoping to large deposits is shown by following examples. Excepting Creighton and Homestake, the mines described have low-grade orebodies and methods used are designed to give cheap handling, large output per man stoping, and to require little timber; all essential for cheap mining. The methods are similar, but differ

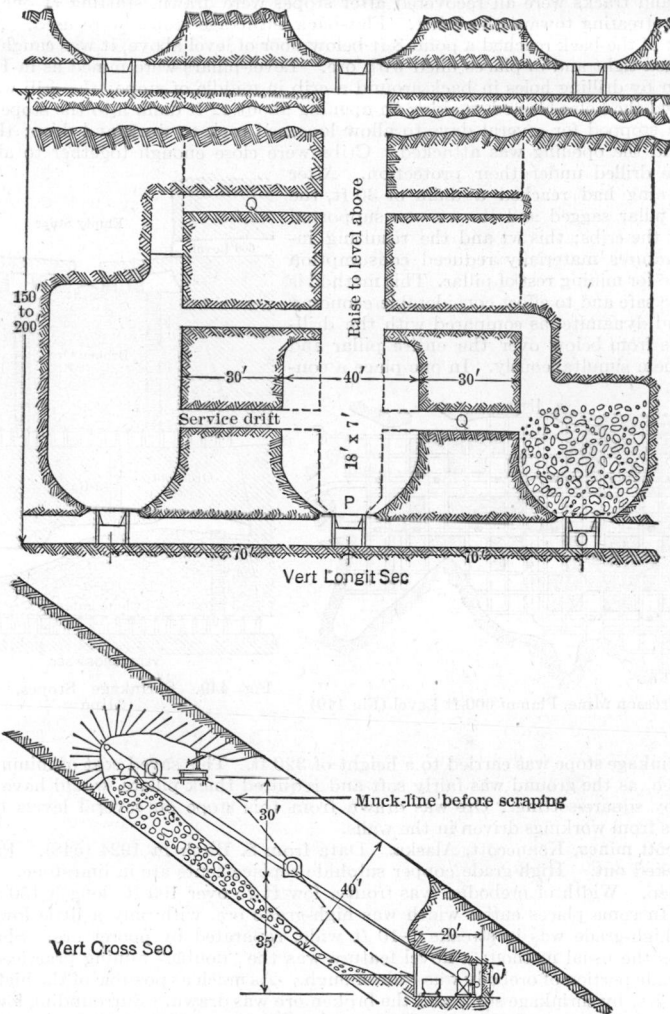

Fig 447. "Semi-shrinkage" Stoping, Walker Mine (ideal sections)

in percentage of orebody extracted, methods and control of ore breaking, and the handling of large slabs that must be broken. Some of these examples might be classed under Combined Methods, Art 83; some have been wrongly classed in Bib (530) as Caving Methods, because the modes of breaking ground may involve caving part of the stope backs.

Cresson mine, Cripple Cr, Colo. Data from R. L. Herrick (151) in 1911. Country rock is granite; gold telluride ores occur either in massive shoots in fissured zones, or in replacement veins in well defined sheeted zones alongside of or near basic dikes.

Fig 448 and 449 show method of mining an oreshoot on 600-ft level, which was 280 ft high and 60 by 120 ft in horiz sec. On each level, a breast stope (Art 30), 10 ft high, was carried over whole area of shoot, in which square-sets were erected, as in Fig 448, which also shows track layout and chute-gates. Open square-sets, which were inadequate to support the broken ore after stope had reached some height, were strengthened by lagging the sides of certain sets and then filling them with ore by shooting down the lagging overhead; sets behind chute-gates were left open for access in making repairs. Level timbering and tracks were all recovered after stopes were drawn, starting at one end of stope and retreating toward the other. Flat-back shrinkage stopes were used. As soon as any part of the back reached a point 8 ft below floor of level above, it was caught up on cribs, wedged tight and in places filled with ore. Level-pillars were mined as in Fig 449; work began by drilling holes in back around a crib in middle of stope; the crib was then removed and the holes blasted, making an opening about 12 ft diam into the stope above. Work then stopped for several days to allow loosened rock to work and drop; then the back around the opening was attacked. Cribs were close enough together to allow all holes to be drilled under their protection. After center opening had reached a diam of 30 ft, the remaining pillar sagged and its wt was supported entirely by the cribs; this wt and the resulting incipient fractures materially reduced consumption of explosive for mining rest of pillar. This method is stated to be safe and to effect considerable economy in labor and dynamite, as compared with the drilling of holes from below over the entire pillar and shooting them simultaneously. In one place a con-

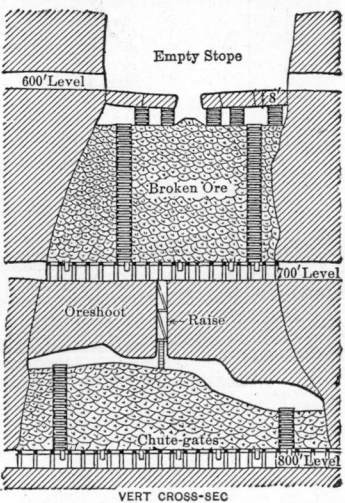

VERT CROSS-SEC

Fig 449. Shrinkage Stopes, Cresson Mine

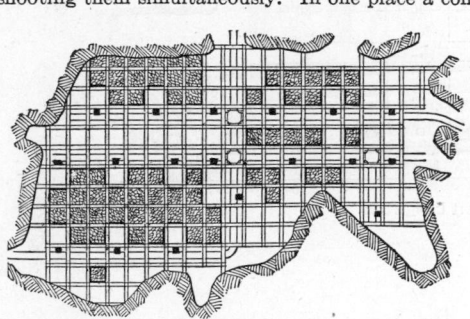

Fig 448. Cresson Mine, Plan of 600-ft Level (Fig 449)

tinuous shrinkage stope was carried to a height of 320 ft. This saved cost of mining level-pillars which, as the ground was fairly soft and required thick pillars, would have had to be mined by square-setting. Ore was drawn from this stope on several levels through chute raises from workings driven in the walls.

Kennecott mines, Kennecott, Alaska. Data from S. Birch in 1924 (548). Property is now worked out. High-grade copper sulphide replacements are in limestone. Dip is usually steep. Width of orebodies was from a few ft to over 100 ft; length 150 to over 1 000 ft. In some places entire width was high-grade ore, with only a little low-grade. In others high-grade was in streaks 1–10 ft wide, separated by poorer ore. Shrinkage stoping was the usual method; a novel feature was the "double" mining practiced when the high-grade portion of orebody was wide enough. As much as possible of the high-grade was mined first by shrinkage stope and the broken ore was drawn. Surrounding low-grade ore was then mined by ordinary shrinkage stope; if lenses of high-grade occurred in this second stope, they were broken with the mill ore. Care was taken not to overlook ore that made along bedding planes, or on faults or cross fissures away from main body. Generally, as a stope was drawn, it was safe to follow and recover ore in the walls that might have been missed in stoping. Recovery of level-pillars was usually delayed, so that drifts could be maintained for mining oreshoots that often came from below into what was thought to be barren ground. Waste from development was dumped into old stopes. Where possible, development drifts were kept in high-grade ore. Chute raises 25–35 ft apart and 20–25 ft high were put up from the level; they were connected, leaving V-shaped pillars over the level. If ore in a drift became lean, the stope above was carried ahead from the last chute raise to determine the direction in which the drift should be driven. Where ore was wide, 2 or more parallel drifts were driven on the level.

Alaska Treadwell mine, Douglas Island, Alaska, now flooded and abandoned, was formerly an outstanding example of large-scale shrinkage mining in U S, and many details of present practice elsewhere have been developed from work done there. Ore was low-grade, gold quartz, in a mineralized dike of irregular shape, 0–420 ft wide; dip, 50°–65°. Limits of ore were commercial rather than structural; aver assay as mined, $2–$3 per ton. Ore was strong; footwall weak, but supported by leaving on it a strip of unmined ore; hanging wall hard and strong. Profitable mining was done in transverse shrinkage stopes, separated by vert pillars 100 ft apart c–c and 18–25 ft thick, which were continuous through successive lifts and left as permanent support for the walls; horiz pillars were left below alternate levels. Level interval, 200 ft. Stopes were opened 18 ft above

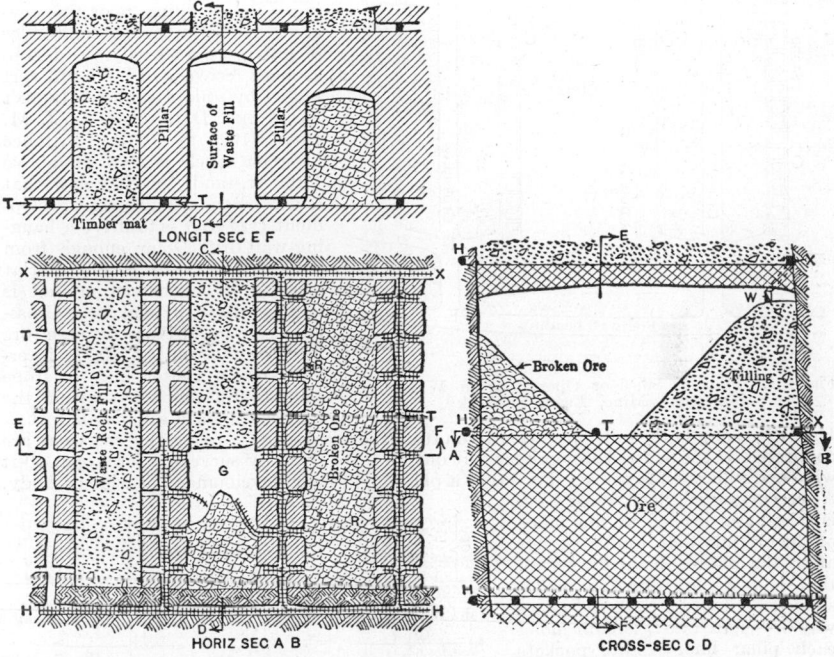

Fig 450. Shrinkage Stope, Homestake Mine, So Dak (former method)

levels from tops of inclined chute raises driven 15–30 ft apart along underlying drifts and crosscuts. About 20% of orebody was left in rib pillars. For full detail, see Bib (105, 273).

Homestake mine, Lead, S Dak (104, 271, 272, 199). Production has been practically continuous since 1878. The mine is notable for large-scale shrinkage mining applied to massive orebodies. Orebodies carrying moderate gold values occur as huge lenses in an intensely folded formation of chloritic schist within a series of garnet-mica schists, quartzites, and slates. Individual "ledges" are 50–150 ft thick, but squeezing and folding in places have resulted in orebodies over 300 ft wide; dips, generally steep. Ore is hard, tough, and extremely abrasive, breaking in large pieces unless drill holes are spaced closely. Tendency to break large inspired in early days a method of shrinkage in which all ore gravitated to sill floor and was mucked into cars. A. J. M. Ross states that under this system one "blockholer" was usually required to drill and break large boulders for every 2 muckers. Fig 450 shows general stoping method prior to 1917, as applied to ore wider than 80 ft. Transverse stopes were carried 60 ft wide, separated by 42-ft pillars. Level interval was 100–150 ft. Main haulageways H were driven in footwall about 20 ft from ore. Crosscuts were on center lines of pillars. Short drifts T ("break-throughs") ran each way at 30-ft intervals from crosscuts to pillar lines. Sill floor was then breasted out 8–10 ft high. Where deposit was very wide, a timbered gangway X was erected near hanging wall. At end of break-throughs, shoveling platforms with sheet-steel covering were built, height being that of a mine car. Stope was then carried up as a flat-back shrinkage stope, leaving an arched level-pillar above, about 20 ft thick at crown. Entrance to stopes was through raises to level above or through manways R. Final drawing of ore began at one end of stope. As shoveling platforms became useless, they were removed and track was extended into stope (as at G). Filling with waste closely followed final drawing. Before filling, floor was covered with a timber mat and sides of pillars were lagged to aid subsequent recovery of level and vert pillars by square-setting. RECENT PRACTICE. Data from A. J. M. Ross (199) in 1931. Distance between levels is 100 ft above 1 100 ft, and 150 ft below that level. Standard plan of development (Fig 451) is to drive a hanging-wall drift D far enough from ore to make almost certain that at least 30 ft of barren ground is between the drift and ore. Crosscuts X are driven through ore into the footwall at 102-ft intervals, or on center lines of stope pillars, and connected within the footwall to form a footwall drift E.

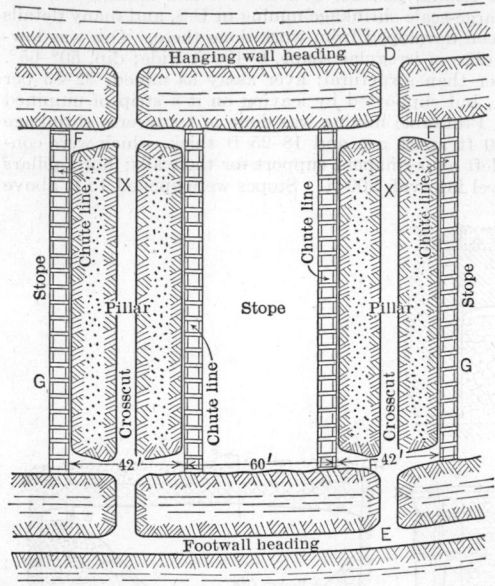

Fig 451. Plan of Sill-floor Operations in Wide Ore, Homestake Mine, Lead, So Dak

Drifts F, along both walls, are also driven from these crosscuts. After the crosscuts are connected by the drifts, sill floors are cut out on lines given by surveyors for stopes 60 ft wide and pillars 42 ft thick. Fig 451 is a plan of sill floor development in wide orebody.

After cutting sill floor, stope back is raised and arched in the shape of the ore pile that would be left after the chutes have drawn all that is possible. Broken ore is shoveled out and a timbered gangway G ("chute line") is built along each pillar line. Chute pockets are built within the sets for later use in drawing shrinkage ore. The stope floor between chute lines is covered with timber mat, and waste fill is run in through inclined raises R (Fig 452). Shrinkage mining now starts and continues to within about 25 ft of level above. Access to stope is gained through drifts from pillar raises. Ground is broken with flat holes, and benches are kept shallow to avoid burying large pieces. All block-holing is done on top of ore pile. After final drawing of ore, stope is filled as soon as possible. Crown (level-pillar) is removed by square-setting. Fig 453 shows cross-sec through stope in narrower ledges.

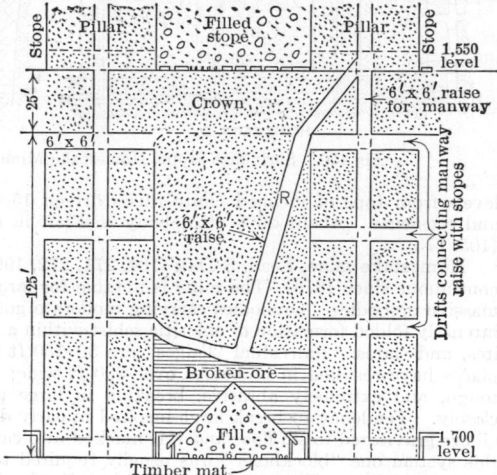

Fig 452. Longit Sec showing Principal Stoping Method, Homestake Mine, Lead, So Dak

Where width is less than 60 ft, stopes are carried longit, some measuring 100 ft along walls. Dividing pillars are then 25 ft thick and one chute line, along footwall, suffices.

Creighton mine, Ont. Data from O. Hall and R. D. Parker (216) in 1930. Large lenticular deposits, chiefly of massive chalcopyrite and nickeliferous pyrrhotite, occur in shear zones in norite and granite at or near contact; norite is on hanging-wall side. Aver dip of main orebody, 45°; of others, 35°–60°. Orebodies reach 1 000 ft in length; width to max of 300 ft. Entry is by inclined shafts in footwall. Level interval 120 ft in upper workings, 180 ft in lower. For many years, mining was principally by shrinkage method; more recently, by cut-and-fill and square-sets. For shrinkage mining, level development consisted of a footwall drift from which crosscuts were turned at 75-ft intervals along center lines of pillars.

In WIDE OREBODIES stopes 50 ft wide extended across orebody from foot to hanging and were separated by 25-ft pillars. Intermediate crosscuts were sometimes run under center lines of stopes to permit closer chute spacing (Fig 454). Footwall raises along contact and on center lines of pillars served for manways and ventilation. Other raises within footwall were ore and waste passes (Fig 455); ore passes delivered from the levels to underground crushers above skip pockets. Inclined chute raises, 15 ft apart on alternate sides of main crosscut, reached cutting-out floor of stope along pillar lines (Fig 454). If intermediate crosscuts were driven, there were also chute raises along

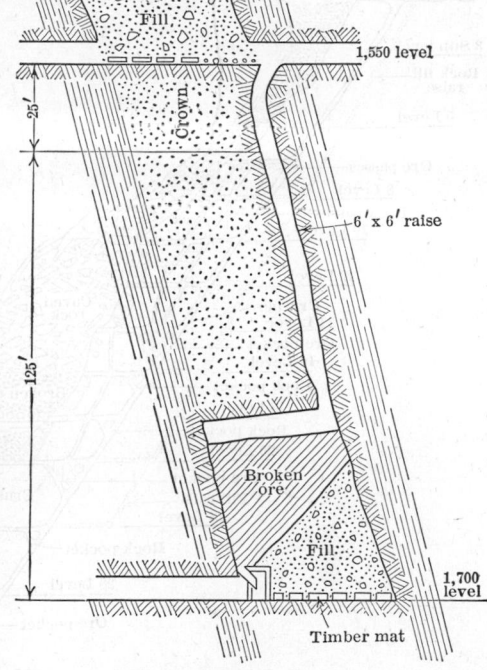

Fig 453. Cross-sec through Stope in Narrow Ledge, Homestake Mine, Lead, So Dak

center line of stope. Floor cutting, 25 ft above level, started by driving headings along pillar lines to connect chute raises. Headings were then slabbed on sides away from pillars and breast stoping continued until floor was completed. Stope was then carried by flat-back shrinkage stoping to within about 25 ft of level above. Floor pillar (crown) was broken through at hanging wall and mined by retreating toward footwall, using deep vert holes. Recovery of vert pillars consisted of driving raises 30 ft apart along center lines of pillars to within 10 ft of level above. At intervals in each raise, drift rounds were taken toward stopes, and along length of pillar to honeycomb it. Large sections of pillars, or whole pillars, were then drilled and blasted electrically (Fig 456). Breaking vert pillars and final drawing of ore retreated from hanging wall and far ends of a level. Hanging wall caved in large blocks and followed down on broken ore in drawing. Chutes were drawn until waste appeared.

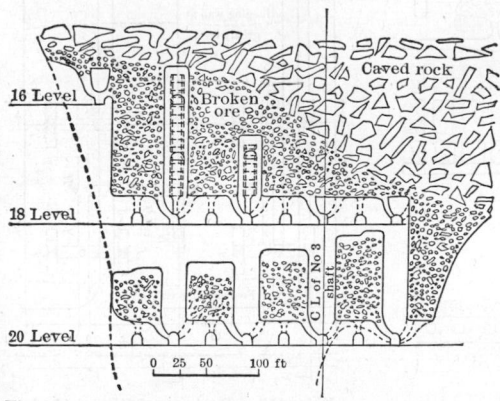

Fig 454. Longit Sec showing Crosscut and Chute-raise Arrangement, Creighton Mine, Ont

In NARROW OREBODIES, shrinkage stopes were carried longit and crosscuts from footwall drift were omitted. Length of stopes was limited by leaving 30-ft rib pillars at intervals, as required. Footwall raises served same purpose as outlined for wide orebodies.

Beatson mine, Kennecott Copper Corp, Latouche, Alaska. (All mining at this property was abandoned in 1930). Data furnished in 1927 by J. L. Fozard, F. M. Radel and J. A. Richards, who

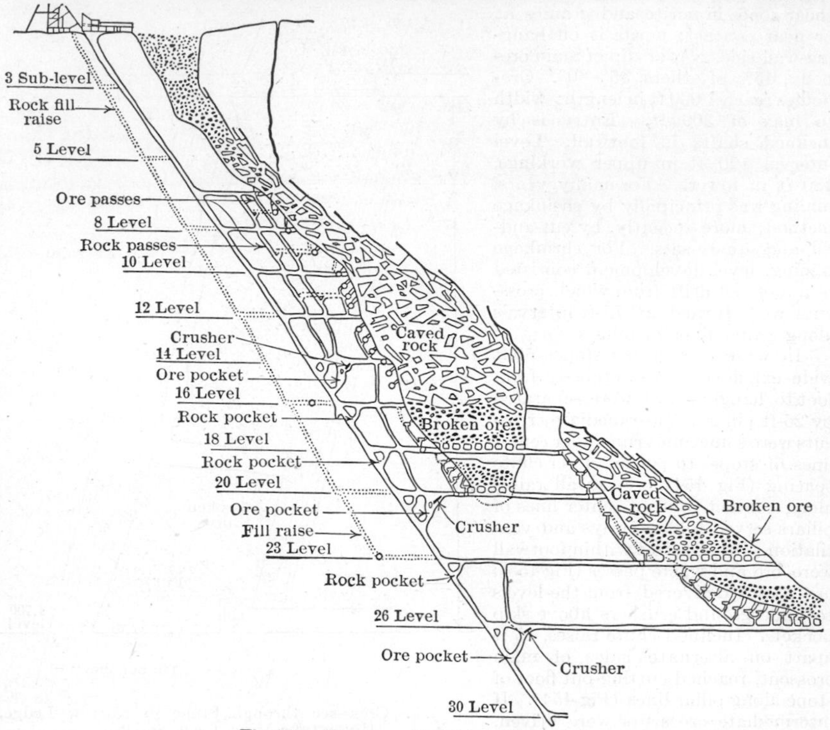

3 Sub-level

Rock fill
    raise

5 Level

Ore passes

8 Level

Rock passes

10 Level

12 Level

Crusher
14 Level

Ore pocket

16 Level

Rock pocket

18 Level

Rock pocket

20 Level

Caved rock

Broken ore

Ore pocket

Fill raise

23 Level

Caved rock

Broken ore

Crusher

Rock pocket

26 Level

Ore pocket

Crusher

30 Level

Fig 455.   Cross-sec Creighton Mine, Ont

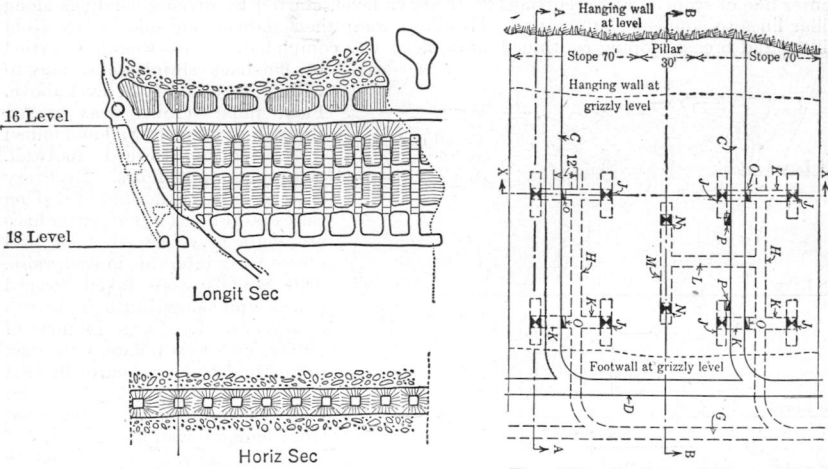

16 Level

18 Level

Longit Sec

Horiz Sec

Fig 456. Sec through Pillar, showing Raises and
Drill Holes, Creighton Mine, Ont

Hanging wall
at level

Pillar
30'

Stope 70'

Stope 70'

Hanging wall at
grizzly level

Footwall at grizzly level

Fig 457. Beatson Mine, Alaska.
(Diagram of main and grizzly levels;
latter shown by dotted lines)

devised the mining method. Orebody is a low-grade lenticular deposit of disseminated chalcopyrite in graywacke, containing mineralized bands of chert and slate; length of lens, 600 ft; max width, 250 ft; ore aver, 1.6% Cu. Hanging wall is a fault dipping 40°–60°; there is 1–10 ft of gouge, associated with a massive pyrrhotite body, 1–12 ft thick. Footwall is a commercial one; it roughly parallels the hanging. GENERAL PLAN. Prior to 1920, mining was mostly opencut. Some underground mining was done in transverse flat-back shrinkage stopes; max safe width of such stopes was found to be 20 ft; production in them averaged 20 tons per machine drill-shift. Chief requirements for profitable mining of lower lifts: large output; safety; cheap breaking (large tonnage per drill-shift); controlled breaking, to minimize dilution by waste; prompt support of walls; cheap handling. The method adopted (locally called the Beatson method) was suggested by results from enlarging raises. It

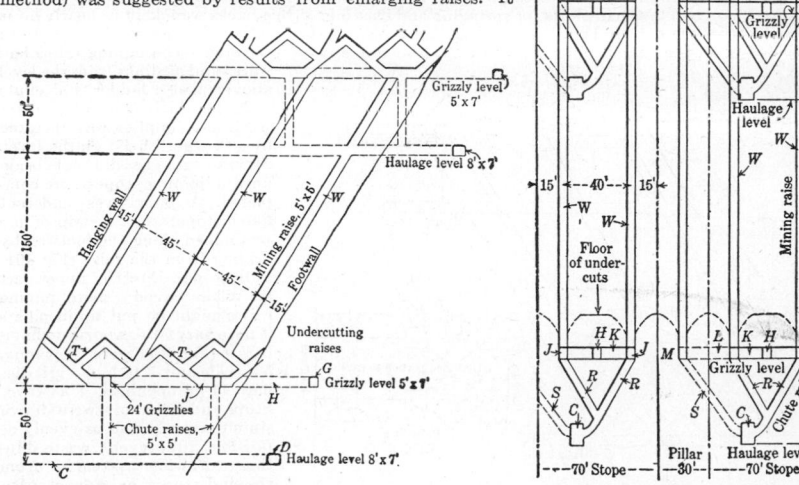

Fig 458. Beatson Mine, Alaska. (Vert sec AA, Fig 457, first stage)

Fig 459. Beatson Mine, Alaska. (Vert sec XX, Fig 457)

comprised a series of 70-ft transverse shrinkage stopes, separated by 30-ft rib pillars; ore was broken by blasting in deep holes drilled from raises put up through the area to be stoped, so that miners need not work in a stope after it was undercut. Pillars were partly mined and partly caved; broken ore was drawn through bulldozing chambers into chute raises. DEVELOPMENT. Entry was by a vert shaft in the hanging wall, about 1 200 ft from the orebody; an 8 by 7-ft crosscut was driven through the orebody on each level; level interval, 200 ft. Fig 457–460 show development preparatory to stoping. Haulage drift D was parallel to footwall and about 40 ft from it; crosscuts C were driven to hanging wall at 100-ft intervals; these constituted the main haulage openings and were equipped for motor haulage. An intermediate level ("grizzly level") was opened 50 ft above main level; this comprised: drift G, about 50 ft from footwall, with crosscuts H, 100 ft apart on center lines of stopes; drifts K, 23 ft long, giving access to grizzlies (bulldozing chambers) J; and drift L, connecting with crosscut M, which was on center line of the pillar and contained 2 grizzlies N. Grizzlies J were 40 ft apart along the strike and 60 ft apart across the deposit, starting 15–20 ft from footwall; this arrangement proved satisfactory for a 70-ft stope, where the ore was 100–250 ft wide (Fig 458). From the haulage crosscuts C, 5 by 5-ft chute raises R were put up to the grizzlies (Fig 459); as the raises branched, each chute gate O served a pair of grizzlies J. Chute gates P (Fig 457) were connected by raises S (Fig 459) with grizzlies N and served to draw the pillar ore. Development was completed by driving the 5 by 5-ft undercutting raises T (Fig 458) from ends of grizzly cham-

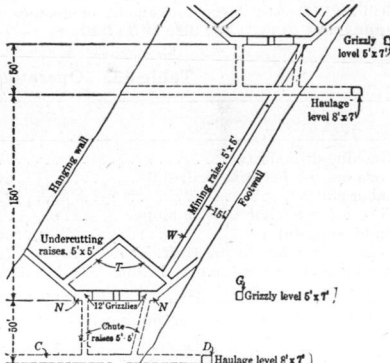

Fig 460. Beatson Mine, Alaska. (Vert sec BB, Fig 457)

bers J, and connecting them above; 5 by 5-ft mining raises W were then put up to level above. In the example shown, mining raises were 45 ft apart, starting 15 ft from footwall; spacing was varied to suit character of ground and width of stope. Fig 460 shows similar openings driven from grizzly chambers N (Fig 457) on center lines of pillars. STOPING. Stope floor was first cut out 5 ft high; work started from the undercutting raises; drilling with stope drills. After undercutting was finished, miners did not work in the stope again; all drilling and blasting was done in the mining raises, to which access was gained from level above. Fig 461 shows mode of breaking ground. Drilling was done with heavy jackhammers. Starting 15–23 ft above the stope back, 6–8 holes, about 8 ft deep, were drilled downward from sides and corners of the raise; holes were pointed to bottom on the boundaries of a 15-ft square, with the raise in center. They broke a chamber A, which gave room for handling steel up to 20 ft long; the ledges L formed supports for a plank platform from which subsequent drilling was done. About 20 holes, 12–20 ft deep, were drilled from each chamber (Fig 461); they were located to break to the pillar lines and cover an area about 30 ft by 35 ft. About 10 ft of ground was left between bottoms of holes drilled from adjacent raises; this ground usually caved, but might be drilled if necessary. Each round drilled from a raise required about 12 manshifts by 1 man and 2–4 man-shifts for springing and blasting. Stope backs were kept as nearly horiz as possible; broken ore was kept close to stope back to support the walls; drilling did not need to be completed in all the chambers on a given horizon before any were blasted. The mining raises had

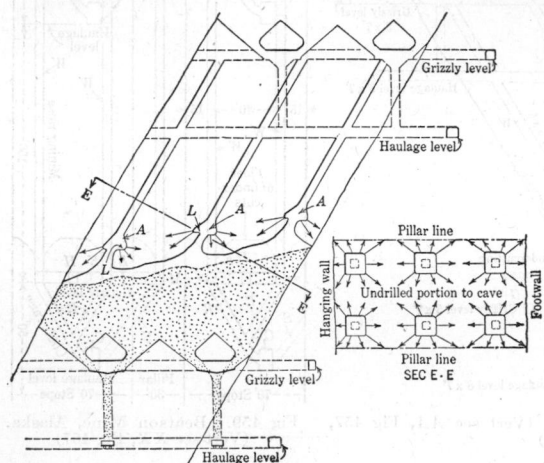

water and air lines from the level above; also a ladder and chute slide, in which a small skip for steel and supplies was operated by a "tugger" hoist on the level. MINING PILLARS did not begin until adjoining stopes were completed. A pillar was undercut like a stope; then a strip of ore was mined along the footwall by drilling from the raise (Fig 461) as in stopes. Most of upper part of pillar caved; more mining raises might be put up in pillars if necessary. BULLDOZING chambers J (Fig 457) were 24 ft long, 5 ft wide and 7 ft high; grizzlies had 11-in openings. DRAWING. Stope and pillar ore were drawn simultaneously and as evenly as possible to prevent waste dilution; drawing retreated from the end stopes on a level. AD-VANTAGES OF THIS METHOD of breaking ground compared with ordinary practice in flat-back

Fig 461. Beatson Mine, Alaska. (Vert sec AA, Fig 457, later stage)

shrinkage stopes: (a) Since danger from falls from stope back is eliminated, it permits wider

stopes and a greater ratio between stope and pillar widths. (b) Drilling is efficient; all holes are wet. (c) Many delays eliminated, as, setting up and tearing down, barring down backs, packing steel, breakage of hose. (d) Uninterrupted drilling for 6 out of 7 or 8 shifts increases footage drilled per shift and hence output per man-shift. (e) Drawing broken ore does not interfere with drilling. (f) Any large movement of ground shows itself in the mining raises. Table 43 gives OPERATING DATA. See also Bib (198).

Table 43. Operating Data, Beatson Mine (a)

	Stope	Pillar	Total and aver
Machine-drill shifts.	7 814	1 047	8 861
Tons ore per machine-drill shift.	172	218	188
Labor shifts.	12 733	2 606	15 339
Tons ore per labor shift in stope.	110	131	113
Bulldozing shifts.	14 507	3 603	18 110
Tons ore per bulldozing shift.	59	70	61
Pounds powder per ton ore, drilling.	0.27	0.16	0.24
Pounds powder per ton ore, bulldozing.	0.18	0.16	0.17

(a) Based on mining 1 672 888 tons by Beatson method, to Jan 1, 1926.

Alaska Juneau mine, Juneau, Alaska. Data from P. R. Bradley (584) in 1929, and L. H. Metzgar (564) in 1932. Mining here might be classified as caving, but shrinkage principles are also involved. It represents efficient underground mining of gold ore averaging only about 90¢ per ton. Values occur in quartz stringers and gash veins in slate containing numerous dikes and sills of metagabbro. Limits of ore are commercial; values are distributed irregularly in 4 ill-defined bands aggregating 755 ft wide, which, with intervening country rock, occupy an area 1 300–1 600 ft wide by 2 400 ft long. A cross fault divides the mine into 2 parts, and a strike fault dipping 55°–60° practically marks the footwall of the ore being mined. Presence of sulphides in the ore indicates values and makes sorting possible. DEVELOPMENT. Topography is very rough; entry is by main haulage adit (No 4 level) about 2 miles long and 950 ft below surface in the main orebody. Levels above, at 250-ft vert intervals, are connected with haulage adit by ore-transfer raises (Fig 462). Bulldozing chambers may be on main or sub-levels. STOPING. Stope preparation consists of driving branch raises from ore transfers, to connect with bull-

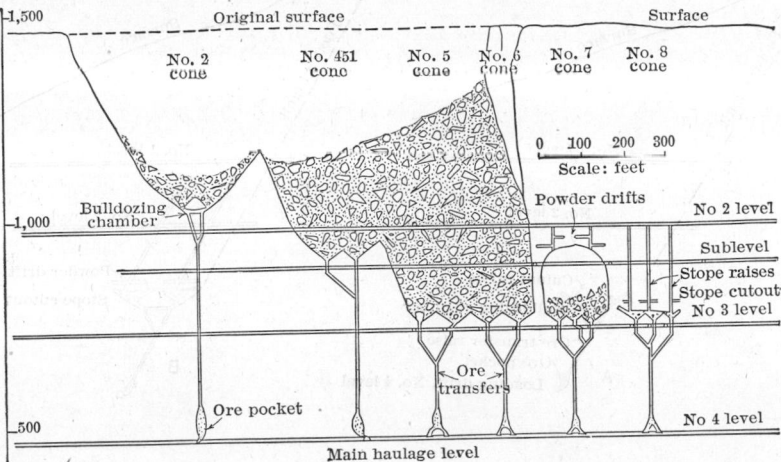

Fig 462. Development, Alaska Juneau Mine

dozing level at 75-ft intervals along strike and 100-ft intervals across strike. Thus, grizzlies are set at corners of a rectangle and serve a stope "cut-out" 130 ft along strike and 180 ft across it. Grizzlies with 25-in openings are of 15-in I-beams or H-beams, with 1-in wearing plates and separated by wooden spacing-blocks; they are set on slope of 1.25 in per ft. After placing grizzly, a 7 by 8-ft raise ("drawhole") is driven from upper end of grizzly at angle of 38° (Fig 463). After extending raise 18 ft, 4 branch raises ("cut-out raises") (Fig 464, A) are driven on a slope of 38°, diverging at 90° from each other. Two branches extend to limits of the area to be undermined. The others connect with corresponding raises from adjoining grizzlies. Thus, the "cut-out" is outlined both across and along strike by a set of raises having form of a large letter W (Fig 464, B). Cutting-out begins just above each drawhole and proceeds at a slope of 38° until the resultant 4 adjacent funnels meet at "peak" and outer limits of "cut-out" are reached. Cut-out miners work on contract basis at 35–38¢ per sq ft (1932), measured on the 38° slope; height of cut, 7 ft. Mounted drifters are used, miner averaging 8 7-ft holes per shift; 45 sq ft per machine-shift is aver break. During cutting-out, stope-raises (Fig 462), about 100 ft apart, are driven to level above. Upper level then serves as supply level and means of access to "powder drifts" below. When stope area is completely undercut, mining proceeds by large-scale blasting. Powder drifts (Fig 462, 464), 4 by 3 ft cross-sec, are driven radially from stope raises and loaded with enough powder to break down into

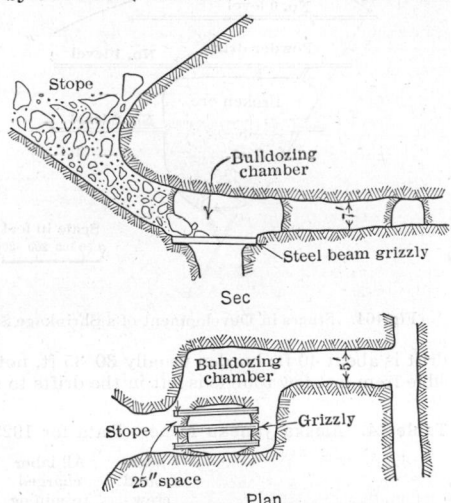

Fig 463. Bulldozing Chamber and Grizzly, Alaska Juneau Mine

the opening below the block of ground beneath the powder drifts, which are carefully planned as to depth, direction and burden, according to local conditions. Length of

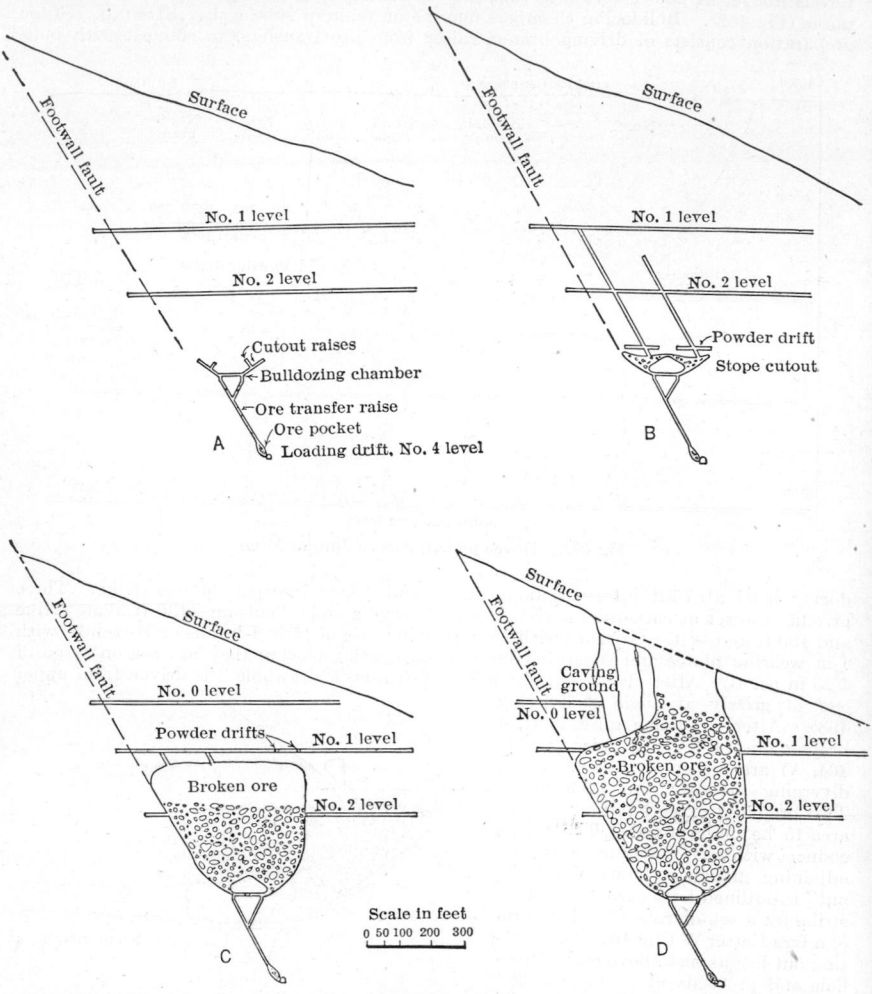

Fig 464. Stages in Development of a Shrinkage Stope, Alaska Juneau Mine, Juneau, Alaska

drift is about 40 ft; burden usually 30–35 ft, not exceeding 50 ft. As much muck as possible from last few rounds is left in the drifts to serve as stemming. Amount and spacing

Table 44. Alaska Juneau Mine. Data for 1928, Units of Labor, Power and Explosives

	Underground crew	All labor charged to mining		Underground crew
Labor (man-hr per ton of ore)			Explosives (lb per ton of ore)	
Development............	0.030	0.048	Development..............	0.06
Stoping.................	0.001	0.003	Stoping...................	0.05
Bulldozing..............	0.064	0.083	Bulldozing................	0.29
Tramming..............	0.064	0.132	Total...................	0.40
Total.................	0.159	0.266	Power, kw-hr per ton........	1.61
Tons per man-shift........	50.10	30.10		

of powder vary according to experience. Fig 465 shows typical powder-drift layout and distribution of charge. Explosive is 40% ammonia dynamite; it is fired by Cordeau-Bickford fuse, which is detonated by No 8 caps and two 30-ft lengths of safety fuse Through 1928, aver break in powder-drift blasts was 20 tons of ore per lb of explosive; for secondary breaking, powder consumption is 1 lb per 4.2 tons of ore. As stope progresses upward, the area is increased; powder drifts are driven alongside open-ing to enlarge stope and to induce caving. Grizzlies below are worked actively, so that ore broken by powder-drift blasts will fall consider-able distance and break further by impact on ore pile. Mining con-tinues thus until back attains such height and area that blasting begins (Fig 464 D). Table 44 summarizes costs for 1928. Of total cost, development accounted for 20.6%, and mining, 79.4%.

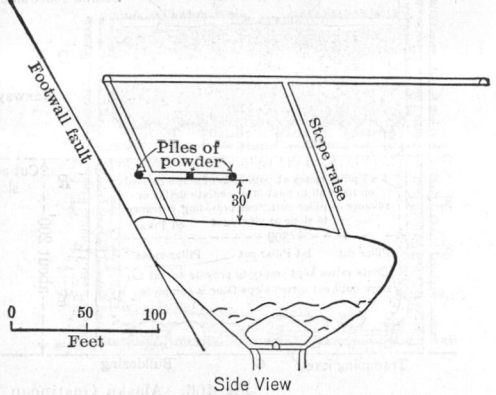

Alaska Gastineau mine, Juneau, Alaska. Operations ceased in 1921. Data, relating to former mining, from G. T. Jackson in 1920 (530). Orebody is an extension of the adjoining Alaska Juneau, described above. The ore bands are in schist as well as in slate and metagabbro, near a contact with green-stone. There is a well marked shear zone along footwall, particularly in slate. Dip, about 60°. GENERAL PLAN. Mining was by large shrinkage stopes separated by permanent rib pillars. Stopes were first undercut. In schist areas, ordinary flat-back shrinkage stopes were carried; all ore broken by drilling and blasting. In slate areas, narrow flat-back stopes were carried up the footwall and across ends of stope; rest of the back caved by its own weight. P. R. Bradley (598) states that the method assumed continuous and uni-form ore bands and that caving could be confined to a single band. Neither assumption was correct, and the com-bined effect of irregularly distributed values and dilution from waste pro-duced ore too low in grade to mill profitably. DEVELOPMENT. From a vert

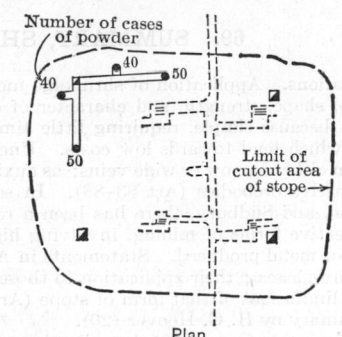

Fig 465. Typical "Powder Drift" Shot, Alaska Juneau Mine

shaft there was an adit haulage tunnel about 2 miles long. Level interval, 200 ft; there were 2 main ore passes in footwall connecting with the adit. Fig 466 shows the development for opening a stope; manway raises R, cross-sec 5 by 8 ft, were in the footwall opposite center lines of rib-pillars; short drifts D, driven to the pillar lines, gave access later to the stopes. Main levels were in footwall; chute raises, 35 ft apart. Bulldozing chambers were reached through small vert raises and crosscuts indi-cated by dotted lines at B; these openings were sampled half-way between 2 chute raises and connected to bulldozing chambers by short drifts. Tops of chute raises were connected on footwall by small raises run upward at 40°. Some chute raises, continued across the orebody on a 40° angle, were points of attack for cutting out the stopes; they were sampled to determine stope width. A small raise was driven at each end of stope to connect with first breakthrough from manway raise. STOPES in slate were 200–300 ft long; in schist, to 400 ft; rib pillars, 40 ft thick; width of stopes, 40–120 ft. Cut-ting-out stope was about 7 ft high. IN SLATE, stope floor was cut out about 20 ft narrower than width of ore shown by assays in the raises; machines started at each end of stope and took a cut 7 ft high by 12 ft wide along footwall (Fig 466); then the same size cut was taken across each end of stope. These cuts weakened the ore so that it began to cave over the rest of the back. Men worked in the footwall cut while caving went on; very few accidents from falls of ground occurred. Successive cuts were taken until the back was 40–50 ft below a worked-out stope above; then work ceased and the stope caved through to level above. IN SCHIST, ore did not cave readily or caved in blocks too large to handle. Slices about 7 ft high were blasted from the back, starting at footwall and working toward hanging. Backs were safe to work under if care was taken to keep them perpendicular to dip. About 125 tons of ore were broken per machine-shift in slate and 45 tons in schist; costs for labor, explosives, supplies, and general expense in slate stopes were about half those in schist. Aver costs (¢ per ton) for 1915–1918, inclusive, during which period about 6 500 000 tons were delivered to mill were: ore breaking, 16.17; bulldozing, 7.46; tramming, 6.66; oreways and chutes, 1.01; ore transportation, 3.56; preparing stopes, 8.0; development, 5.0; total, 47.86¢.

Limestone quarries. For application of shrinkage stoping underground, see Bib (562, 563).

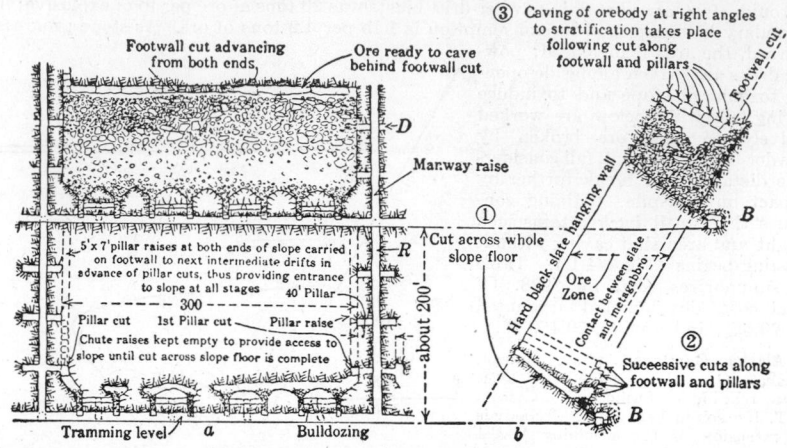

Fig 466. Alaska Gastineau Mine (530)

69. SUMMARY, SHRINKAGE STOPES

Limitations. Application of shrinkage methods is limited by their rigid requirements as to dip, shape, strength, and character of orebody and its walls. These are desirable methods, because simple, requiring little timber and practically no shoveling in stopes, features which tend towards low costs. Under proper conditions, shrinkage stopes may be used in either narrow or wide veins; as auxiliaries to other methods they are also used in large, massive orebodies (Art 83–88). In some districts in Canada, as Kirkland Lake, Porcupine, and Sudbury, there has been a recent tendency to change from shrinkage to more selective forms of mining, involving higher costs per ton, but possibly lower costs per unit of metal produced. Statements in Art 69 concern only shrinkage stopes without chutes (ore-passes); their application to those with chutes is obvious if read in connection with the limitations of that form of stope (Art 67). Following discussion is based largely on a summary by H. C. Hoover (20).

Requirements for successful application of shrinkage methods: (*a*) Dip of stope walls should generally exceed 60°, for ore to settle freely; tendency of broken ore to draw down first on hanging-wall side decreases as dip steepens. (*b*) Orebody should be regular in shape, otherwise loose ore will lodge on footwall. Empty or partly drawn stopes are often too dangerous for shovelers to enter. Walls of narrow stopes may be timbered during drawing (Art 67), but this is costly and suggests possibility of using open stulled stopes (Art 38, 39). Irregular oreshoots are difficult to mine in shrinkage stopes, even if in steep-dipping veins with regular walls; sudden flattening of a shoot necessitates either a sub-level or else long chute-raises through unpayable ground (see Coniagas mine, Fig 436, Art 68). Regular and fairly continuous orebodies are essential, because shrinkage stoping must be carried on considerably in advance of output requirements. (*c*) In overhand shrinkage stopes, ore should be strong enough to stand over back of stope, occasional slabs being stulled. Possible width of stope in a given orebody may be increased by working underhand, as in Beatson method or at Alaska Juneau (Art 68), where miners do not work in stopes after finishing undercutting. Conversely, weaker ores may be mined in stopes of given width by underhand than by overhand. But consistently weak ore cannot be mined in shrinkage stopes. (*d*) Ideally, the ore should be of uniform value; at least payable throughout. Except in narrow stopes, patches of waste can not be left unbroken, and sorting in stopes is rarely feasible (note exceptional conditions at Cobalt, and at Kennecott mines, Art 68). (*e*) Walls should stand without crushing or spalling off into the broken ore when stopes are drawn. Friction between ore and walls during drawing increases any natural tendency of walls to slab off; the hanging wall especially should be strong. (*f*) Prospecting openings can not be run in the walls of shrinkage stopes, hence limits of orebody should be well defined. (g) Physical or mineralogical peculiarities of ore may prohibit shrinkage stoping, for example: Some broken ores tend to "pack" in stopes, and must be blasted out; ordinarily this occurs only when stopes are left undrawn for a considerable time; frequent drawing prevents packing. Packing may be due to pressure or to cementing action of mine waters on pyritic ores; it may be controlled if size of stopes and plan of work can be regulated for drawing stopes promptly. Pyritic ores may oxidize so rapidly that heating occurs in shrinkage stopes; danger of fire may preclude use of shrinkage in such cases. More often, oxidation is less rapid, but may affect recovery in flotation process.

Advantages of shrinkage stopes: (a) Cost of development is usually low. (b) No shoveling or tramming is required in working space at top of stope; if ore can be drawn through chute-gates, there is no shoveling (see Art 67 for conditions justifying shoveling in drawing off ore). (c) Little timber is used; staging for miners and shoveling plats are unnecessary; timber for manways is recovered when stope is drawn. (d) Ventilation can usually be maintained at little expense. (e) Compared with filled stopes, shrinkage stopes sometimes wholly save cost of filling; filling an empty stope in one operation is always cheaper than contemporaneous filling. Shrinkage stopes avoid loss of fines in filling, and cost of ore-passes, and of shoveling ore to them. (f) In narrow veins, shrinkage stopes compete with stulled stopes (Art 38, 39), and are preferable for wide veins and heavy walls. They furnish firm working floor for miners; timber staging may reduce effic by causing feeling of insecurity. (See Art 43 for comparison with sub-level stoping.) (g) Shrinkage stopes afford large reserve of broken ore, but see disadvantage (d) below.

Disadvantages of shrinkage stopes: (a) If chute-gates are used, fine breaking is required; some large pieces may be buried in broken ore, and make trouble in chute-raises and gates. For alternative mode of dealing with this problem see Arrangements for protecting levels, Art 67. (b) Some spalling of waste from walls into ore always occurs; a given amount reduces aver value of broken ore more in narrow than in wide stopes. Much ore is lost if walls crush. (c) Ore can not be selected from different stope faces, for maintaining a uniform grade. (d) Ore left in stopes until they are finished ties up a considerable investment for labor, explosives, etc, to break it, and added working capital is necessary. At a given mine, tonnage of broken ore eventually reaches a fairly constant max. Interest on money required to break this tonnage is an operating charge against shrinkage methods; it represents cost of utilizing broken ore for support. H. C. Hoover cites an example where, on 250 000 tons annual production, the interest (5%) on capital represented by broken ore amounts to 7¢ per ton treated (20). A large reserve of broken ore is advantageous in insuring a regular output; but, only the ore in completed stopes is available for this purpose. In the few Lake Superior iron mines using shrinkage stopes, this storage feature may be availed of to save cost of stock-piling and reloading 60%–70% of the ore mined while navigation is closed. (e) Shrinkage systems are not flexible. When once started, they are difficult to alter, owing to lack of frequent raises; especially true if filling is the only alternative. Change of method may be required by change in dip, or in character of ore or walls in depth. (f) Walls of shrinkage stopes, unless very strong, can be re-stoped for lower-grade ore only when stopes are filled promptly and filling is left undisturbed; walls often crush when filling is drawn for use in lower stopes.

CAVING METHODS

Caving methods, strictly, are those in which ore is first undercut and then broken down by its own weight, or by weight of overlying rock, or by a combination of both. But, as a result of custom, operations involving caving of the material overlying an ore-body, as a systematic and essential part of the work, are also classed as caving methods, though practically all the ore is broken by drilling and blasting. Three distinct methods, SUB-LEVEL CAVING, BLOCK-CAVING, and TOP-SLICING, result from this classification, each having many modifications. For comparison, see Art 82 and 83.

70. TOP-SLICING

General. Top-slicing practice in the U S was developed from the "North of England Caving Method," used in certain English iron mines. Term top-slicing is sometimes erroneously applied (270) to sub-level caving (Art 75). Descriptive terms "Top-slicing and Cover-caving" and "Top-slicing and Partial Ore-caving" (286) have been proposed to describe the two methods accurately, but have not been generally used. Top-slicing method is also called simply "Slicing."

Field of use is in wide veins, masses, or thick beds of weak ore, where clean mining and high extraction are desired and where the overlying surface need not be supported; for its limitations and conditions, see Art 74.

General plan. Ore is mined in horiz floors or slices, taken in descending order from top of the deposit. Each floor is mined in small sections, the roof of each being allowed or forced to cave before an adjacent one is attacked. Work on each floor retreats from limits of ore toward points of entry; all ore is broken by blasting. The principle is illustrated by

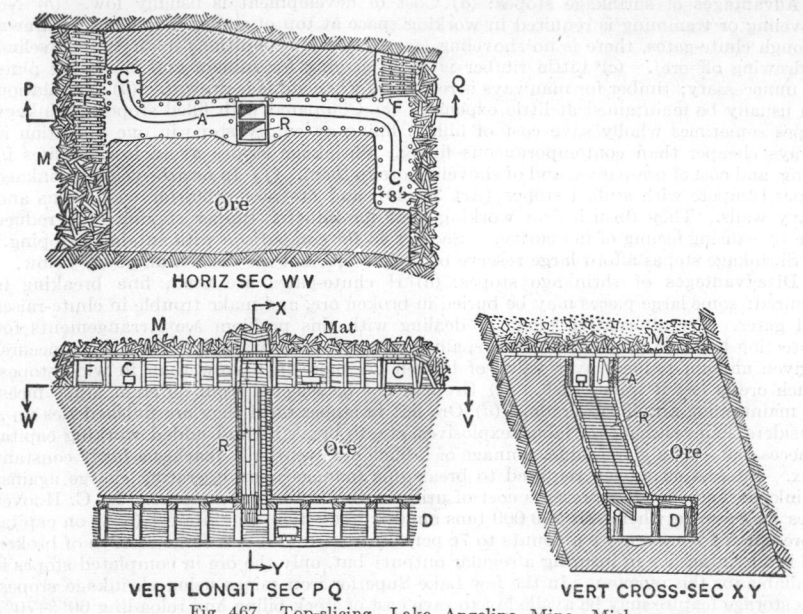

HORIZ SEC W V

VERT LONGIT SEC P Q

VERT CROSS-SEC X Y

Fig 467. Top-slicing, Lake Angeline Mine, Mich

Fig 467, showing top-slicing at Lake Angeline mine, Mich, 1894; J. P. Channing describes it as follows (287).

Ore was soft hematite, averaging about 75 ft wide and overlain by glacial drift. First level was opened 75 ft below top of orebody by driving a drift D about midway between walls; 2-compartment, cribbed raises R were put up to the overburden at 100-ft intervals. From top of each raise a 7 by 8-ft drift A was driven 50 ft each way, meeting caved ground, as shown, or a drift from the next raise. Drifts were timbered with 3-piece sets and were advanced by spiling, where necessary, as under loose overburden at top of deposit. Slicing began by driving 7 by 8-ft crosscuts C to the walls, at points half-way between raises or at ends of drifts alongside caved ground, as shown. Crosscuts were timbered with 3-piece sets of 6 to 10-in round timber, spaced 2 to 4 ft apart. Ore was shoveled into cars holding 1 500 lb and trammed to chute compartment of raise. When a crosscut was finished, its floor was covered with split lagging F, laid close together on 3 8-in round stringers. The crosscut sets were then blasted down, allowing overburden to drop. Contiguous crosscuts were driven and caved in succession, working back toward each raise until a slice 8 or 9 ft high had been removed from top of orebody. Other slices of same height were successively mined below the first. After taking several slices, the work assumed the form shown by Fig 467. A mass of twisted timber M, the MAT, collects at the top, its thickness increasing as work descends. The mat forms an artificial roof between ore and overburden; its subsidence may be controlled and it is easily picked up on timbers of the slice below it. Slicing usually begins on a new floor as soon as it will not interfere with work on floor above, and before the latter is finished; this maintains steady output. Simultaneous work on several floors is shown in Fig 489 and 491, Art 72. Openings like drifts (A, Fig 467), driven on each floor as a preliminary to actual slicing, are called SUB-LEVELS. They are designated by number, No 1 being highest on each lift. Term SLICE means a horiz layer of the orebody; also an opening driven for removing blocks of ore outlined by sub-level development. Thus, crosscuts C, Fig 467, are slices; exact meaning of the word depends upon the context.

Modifications. All top-slicing resembles in general Fig 467, but details vary widely in different orebodies. Variations in timbering of slices give rise to terms DRIFT-SLICING,

PROP-SLICING, and SQUARE-SET SLICING, denoting work in which slices are timbered with drift-sets, stulls, and square-sets respectively. Drift-slices may be driven 2 or 3 sets wide, or square-set slices may be 2 sets wide and 2-4 sets high, if conditions allow. Such excavations are called ROOMS, this work being sometimes termed "top-slicing by rooms" to distinguish it from "top-slicing by drifts" (or crosscuts), as in Fig 467 (286). Other modifications are to secure cheaper loading; thus, effic use of mechanical loaders (usually scrapers) in slices modifies the layout of raises and slices. In some cases, slices are made with sloping floors, for loading by gravity; called INCLINED TOP-SLICING (Art 73). Art 71-73 show details of modifications of top-slicing.

Development. ENTRY. Shafts must be located where they will not be affected by caving. If the position of property lines compels sinking in ground overlying the orebody, pillars of ore must be left for shaft protection, and these are not minable unless they can be reached from adjoining property. On Mesabi Range, Minn, auxiliary shafts for handling timber are sunk at points over the orebody, the shaft pillars being mined last; even then, much ore may be lost through wearing away of the outside of pillars as the mat descends around them. LEVEL INTERVAL. Table 45 summarizes practice at mines described in Art 71-73; levels are usually 50 to 100 ft apart. The intervals must be smaller in wide deposits and in heavy soft ore than in narrow orebodies or stronger ore. In most ores soft enough for top-slicing the maintenance cost for levels and raises is an appreciable expense tending toward a small level interval; cost of hoisting slice timbers in raises also increases with height of lift. In some districts, a balance is struck between these costs and that of driving and equipping haulage levels, as follows: Levels for mechanical haulage are spaced 100 to 300 ft apart vertically, or, where conditions allow, only one such level is driven at bottom of deposit. Intermediate hand-tramming levels are then opened as required, 35 to 50 ft apart vertically; they are often connected with a shaft in the country rock, through which timbers are lowered. LATERAL DEVELOPMENT. Levels may consist of a single drift (Fig 467), but in orebodies of large horiz section a rectangular system of drifts and crosscuts is often driven, arranged to allow proper spacing of raises for handling ore from slices. Layout of intermediate levels, where used, follows the latter plan, tramming distances being then determined by location of raises connecting with main level; even in wide orebodies short trams can be secured with relatively few raises put up from a haulage level consisting of 1 or 2 drifts (Fig 491); similar factors determine the most effic layout where loading in slices is done with scrapers (Fig 486). RAISES should be so located as to strike an economic balance between cost of handling ore in slices and cost of development; close spacing cheapens the former but increases the latter. Table 45 indicates that the commonest raise interval is 50 ft, but this does not indicate the distance that ore is trammed or "slushed," or scraped and trammed in slices, unless taken in connection with area of orebody and design of raises. Raises often provide the only means of entrance and of handling timber to slices, and then must have 2 compartments. SUB-LEVELS. Where slices are 11-12 ft high or more and ore is strong enough, sub-levels may be driven as untimbered drifts, say 6 ft high, instead of full height of slice, as in Fig 467. This increases speed of sub-level development; the sub-level is then enlarged at entrance of each slice, just before starting the latter. Usually sub-levels opened long before they are needed are costly to maintain, as caving of the mat on the overlying slice throws great pressure upon them. See Fig 489 for one method allowing simultaneous work on several floors, without opening sub-levels until caved ground above has come to rest. Development plans should be as simple as possible.

Breaking ground in drift-slicing is a form of breast-stoping (Art 30). In high square-set slices, some ore is broken overhand. For examples, see Fig 475, 477, 478, 490.

Timbering in slices supports comparatively small areas of mat for only a short time, hence light timbers of poor grade are adequate; to cheapen costs, round timber is used wherever possible.

Three-piece DRIFT-SETS with vert posts and simple framing are most used for slices, because: (a) they are generally strong enough; (b) floors laid without sills are easily picked up on the caps in the underlying slice; (c) in working alongside of caved ground, posts of sets are lagged along the solid side before the slice is caved, to keep back the gob. SQUARE-SETS have the same advantages, but require more timber. They are used in ground too heavy for drift-sets, or in high slices where single drift-sets would require posts of unmanageable length and superposed drift-sets would not support the side pressure of caved ground. PROPS (vert stulls) are employed where floors are laid on sills, the latter taking the place of the cap of a drift-set. Props are also used in slicing under rock capping at top of an orebody, and under peculiar conditions in Minnesota iron mines (Art 71). For light pressures and under a thick mat, "tee-pieces" (i e, stulls with head boards of two 2 by 12-in plank, 4-5 ft long) form cheap and satisfactory supports for plank floors laid without sills (66). See Art 71-73 for details of timbering.

Table 45. Top-slicing Details

Mine or district	Interval in ft between			Method of timbering slices	Height of slices, ft	Width of slices, ft	Details in Art No
	Haulage levels	Intermediate levels	Raises				
Mesabi Range, thick ore-bodies................	(a)	(c)	50 (b)	ds (a)	12–18	8–10	71
Mesabi, thin bodies, Hibbing-Chisholm Dist.....	......	(n)	(n)	ds	3–18	10	71
Utica (hand).............	......	26	50	ds	11–12	8	71
Caspian................	50–75 (i)	(n)	40	ds	10	8	71
Menominee Range, Iron River Dist...........	150	75	60–100	ds	12.5–14.5	......	71
Marquette Range........	100–125	(n)	50–65	ds	13–14	9	71
Negaunee...............	100	(n)	60	ds	11	......	71
Blueberry..............	100	(n)	100	ds	11	9	71
Armour No 2...........	......	......	30	ds	10	......	71
Low Moor..............	......	(n)	50	ds	12	12	71
Morenci................	(d)	50–100	25–40	ds	7–15 (e)	6–10	72
Copper Queen..........	......	......	50	sq (k)	11	7	72
Miami.................	150	50	50	ds & bh	10	7–12	72
Judge.................	200	33	50	str	7	3–20 (f)	72
United Verde...........	150	(n)	35	pr	11	35	72
Oceanic...............	50–70	(n)	35–40	pr (h)	8–10	15–40	72
Calumet & Ariz.........	100 (g)	(n)	45	pr (h)	8–10.5	5–6	73
Coronado..............	......	55 (l)	50	pr (h)	11	10	73
Humboldt..............	55	(n)	15	pr (h)	10	10	73

(a) See Art 71. (b) For parallel slicing; may be greater for radial slicing. (c) Not required until thickness of orebody approaches 100 ft, when 1 intermediate may be driven; for greater thicknesses, spacing of intermediates averages 60 ft. (d) See Art 72. (e) Economic height 11 ft. (f) Aver 10 ft. (g) Max. (h) Sills are laid under floors and caught up on props in slice below. (i) Approx. (k) Sub-gangway method. (l) Or other multiple of 11 ft. (n) Not used. ds = drift sets, 3-piece. sq = square-sets. bh = bulkheads. str = stringer sets. pr = props or stulls.
Note.—Before using this table consult details of work in Art 71–73.

Floors may be of lagging or plank. Plank is best, because it may be laid with tight joints to keep out fine waste; it is also easier to lay and to block up from below than round lagging. Usually, one layer of 2 by 10 or 2 by 12 plank, in 10 to 16-ft lengths, makes a good floor; double layers may be needed in a few slices at top of orebody; on Mesabi Range, single layers of $5/8$-in resawed or 1-in hardwood boards have been found adequate; wire fencing laid on poles is now in common use (see Art 71).

Sills under plank floors are generally omitted in horiz slices, but are used in inclined slicing, Art 73. On the Mesabi, 3-in poles 8–16 ft long are sometimes laid 1–2 ft apart to help support the boards when they become the back of the slice below. To avoid breakage, the plank should lie directly on ore, hence sills must either be sunk in the floor or embedded in a layer of broken ore supporting the plank. Cutting grooves for sills is slow and costly, and, as it is practically impossible to have slices on successive sub-levels directly under one another, there may be trouble in picking up sills from below. Sills allow use of props instead of drift-sets in slices, but this is not a compensating advantage, as it saves little timber. Occasional omission of floors on certain sub-levels is possible only under a thick mat, and is not feasible in high-grade ore. It was successful at Miami; at Cananea it increased costs in spite of saving timber.

Handling timber. In top-slicing, as in Fig 467, all timber for slices must be hoisted up the ladderways of raises; column-mounted, air-operated hoists (tuggers) may be used; where scrapers are used for moving ore, scraper hoists often serve also for hoisting timber. See Mesabi practice and that of Iron River Distr, Menominee Range (Art 71) for modes of arranging work so that timbers may be dropped to sub-levels.

Blasting down timbers in slices to force mat to cave is done by simultaneous firing of small charges of dynamite in holes bored in the posts. Holes are usually near the middle of posts, and are 4 to 6 in deep; in large-scale work, much time can be saved by having 1 or 2 men bore all holes with air-driven augers. Half a stick of dynamite or less is used per post; it is often unnecessary to blast all the posts in a slice.

Some engineers hold that mat settles in better shape if the supporting timbers are allowed to fail by pressure than if they are blasted down; some blasting is almost always required. Top-slicing is possible only when the mat caves promptly and rests solidly on top of slice; this condition is apt to be met when posts in slices are shot down. For handling small areas of mat which "hang up," see Morenci-Metcalf district, Art 72.

Recovery of timber is rarely attempted in top-slicing, largely because cheap timber is used, which will not stand removal and reuse. But, possibilities of salvage are indicated by following statement from P. B. Scotland, Gen Supt Ariz Copper Co, Morenci, in 1914.

"In mining coal by longwall method (Art 108), 25 to 50% of the stulls supporting the roof are recovered. When mat becomes thicker in our top-slice stopes, a similar saving might be made. At present, the mat is often penetrated and broken by vertical stulls, which would not occur if they were removed. In longwall working, it is . . . more economical to timber closely and make large recovery of stulls than to reduce the number of supports and lose all of them."

Height of slices. (*a*) Height of drift-slices and of those where sills of the floor above are picked up on stulls is limited by max length of post that can be handled; this is determined partly by size of openings through which timbers must pass and partly by comparative costs of handling and erecting timbers of different lengths. Usual height of drift-slices is 10 to 12 ft (Table 45), which represents an economic mean of all the factors. Art 71 gives examples of high drift- and prop-slices, and reasons for their use. (*b*) In very heavy ground, height of slice is generally reduced to avoid need for heavier posts, which cost more to handle and often more per bd ft than the 6 to 10-in diam commonly used. Long posts also tend to fail by "swinging" under heavy pressure. (*c*) Mode of timbering influences possible height of slices. Square-set slices may be several floors high; slices 17 to 20 ft high are sometimes timbered with 2 superposed tiers of drift-sets. Lateral pressure from caved ground limits use and height of such slices (278). (*d*) Higher slices are possible under a thick strong mat than under a poor one. Low slices are often taken at top of orebody until mat is well formed, then the height is increased to its economic maximum. (*e*) Character of ore may limit height of slice. At Miami (Art 72), ore sloughed off the top of faces higher than 10 ft faster than it could be mucked out and the bottom shot; this caused mat to cave prematurely (285). (*f*) Height of slices should be the economic max, to reduce the number of sub-levels and amount of flooring timber.

Hand loading. In horiz top-slicing, all ore broken in slices is shoveled. This is a disadvantage of the method and shoveling plats should be used. Ore is shoveled direct to raises or into barrows or small cars. Direct shoveling is cheapest, but requires raises spaced 25–30 ft apart throughout the orebody. Factors involved in choice between barrows and cars, for transport to raises, are illustrated by the following extreme examples:

At Bingham, Utah, ground was very heavy, slices were narrow and timbers required much reinforcement. Barrows holding 350 lb were used on sub-levels. 1 000-lb cars were found unsatisfactory; they could not make the short turns required, nor reach far corners of stopes, nor pass distorted timbers in narrow runways. It was found that leads for barrow work should not exceed 75 ft (66). Before the general use of radial slicing and scrapers on Mesabi Range, Minn (Art 71), ore was handled in cars at much lower cost than in barrows; sub-levels were straight and usually stood without timbering; slices were wide and laid out systematically; tramming distances on sub-levels reached 300 ft.

Mechanical loading (Sec 27). Scrapers or other mechanical loaders usually reduce cost of handling ore broken in slices. Scraping is usually called SLUSHING in Lake Superior district when done with a single-drum hoist. Ore may be scraped directly into raises (Fig 481), or up a slide into cars for tramming to raises (Fig 469), or there may be 2 scraping operations: (*a*) to get the ore out of the slice; (*b*) to scrape it to a raise (see Copper Queen mine, Art 72; Utica Extension mine, Art 71). In Lake Superior iron districts, ore in slices is now handled almost entirely by scrapers with double-drum hoists.

Gravity loading. In high square-set slices, ore from upper floors is handled through chute-gates (Fig 479). In inclined top-slicing methods (Art 73) the floors of slices are driven on an upward slope of 30°–33°; causing broken ore to slide out of the slice into funneled chute raises, or into a narrow square-set or shrinkage stope opened as part of the development preparatory to slicing.

Ore-storage. Chute-compartments of raises provide for this, which aids in maintaining steady output. Storage capac decreases as slicing approaches a level. Close cooperation between miners and trammers on levels is then necessary to avoid delays. "Hanging chutes" sometimes provide storage, while slicing on lowest sub-level of a lift (Art 90).

Sorting. Waste unavoidably broken is thrown back and becomes a part of the mat; top-slicing is not adapted to ores requiring systematic underground sorting.

Formation of mat. Slicing may begin directly at the top of orebodies overlain by SOFT GROUND, using spiling, where necessary, to advance sub-levels or slices. In heavy ground, this work is slow and costly, and causes unavoidable mixture of ore and waste. An alternative, which may be cheaper in spite of the ore sacrificed, is to start slicing 5 or 10 ft below top of orebody. Pillars thus left cave on the floors in highest sub-level, and aid in holding back fine waste during first stages of work.

Top-slicing is used also for mining orebodies overlain by a ROCK CAPPING; contacts between ore and capping are often irregular. It is then essential that the capping shall cave and not hang up over large areas, which may give way suddenly with disastrous results; a flat surface under which to begin slicing is also necessary. Hence, irregular tops of orebodies are usually mined as open square-set stopes (Art 45). Following are examples of practice (see also Mesabi square-set slicing, Art 71).

At Detroit Copper Co's mines, Morenci, Ariz (Art 72), tops of highest raises were connected by drifts and crosscuts, from which an open square-set stope, usually 10 to 20 ft high, was carried to capping. Stringers of ore extending into capping were followed by raises, which also weakened the back. Stope floor was covered with 2 layers of 2-in plank, at right-angles to each other. Deep uppers were drilled at short intervals in back of stope; holes were also drilled in posts of square-sets; all holes blasted simultaneously (279).

At Ariz Copper Co's mines, tops of orebodies were mined by open stopes, square-set stopes, or sub-level caving (Art 75). A double floor of 2-in plank was laid; overburden was caved either to surface or sufficiently high to make it safe to work under the mat (178).

At Cananea, Mex, tops of orebodies were mined with square-sets. Flooring was of 2-in plank laid on 5 by 10-in sills, 10 ft long. Capping sometimes stood long enough to allow salvage of some timber. When capping hung up, sets were not blasted down, but filled with waste to form a cushion above the mat on which large slabs might fall without endangering work in slices below (282).

In this work a continuous square-set stope over whole area of orebody is unnecessary. As 1 or 2 floors of caved sets sufficiently protect the slices, stopes of this height are opened at different elevations in different parts of the deposit, as required by irregularities in lower surface of capping. This avoids high square-set stopes of large area, and does not interfere with slicing. Where contact between ore and capping is regular, simpler methods of starting a mat are feasible. If capping is very soft, slicing begins at top of orebody, usually with double floors in first few sub-levels to build up mat quickly. In harder ground, a breast stope 8 or 10 ft high is carried across top of deposit, with stulls and headboards to support the back. After laying a floor, the timbers are shot down. Foregoing operations are also preliminary to other caving methods in which weight of caved ground above the workings is an essential.

Ventilation is generally poor in top-slicing unless fans are used. Slices often form "dead ends"; decaying timbers in mat give off heat and some CO. For example of artificial ventilation, see Miami, Art 72, where the installation of blowers caused marked increase in effic of labor (285).

Percentage extraction by top-slicing is high; usually only 5–10% of total ore is lost. Further details are given in Art 71–73.

71. TOP-SLICING IN IRON MINES

Mesabi Range, Minn, thicker deposits. In essentials, the following data on top-slicing (contributed anonymously in 1938 by one of the Mesabi mining companies) apply to, and are typical of, any underground mine on the Mesabi Range, when the orebody is thicker than can be mined by one slice. Drilling and blasting are done in timbered slice-drifts, extending to the predetermined limit of the orebody, and retreating toward main haulage drifts.

Conditions affecting choice of method. Orebodies of the Mesabi Range are flat-lying deposits in shallow troughs, of great lateral extent as compared to depth; usually overlain by slate, taconite (ferruginous chert) and glacial drift, in places, by glacial drift alone. The orebodies are generally less than 200 ft thick, max 400 ft. Overburden varies from a few ft to over 300 ft. Underground mining is adopted when open-pit methods are not physically or economically applicable. Such factors as form and dip of orebodies, variations in strength of ore and wall rock with depth, and structural irregularities, as faults, slips, fissures and fracture zones, have little influence in the choice of mining methods, as they are of minor importance on the Mesabi Range.

Main development. SHAFT LOCATION. When the size, shape, and depth of an orebody to be mined underground has been determined, the shaft is located in rock near deepest part of orebody, so that as much ore as possible will be tributary to it, and the deposit will be completely drained by it. Shaft pillars in ore are avoided; possible disturbance by subsidence receives careful attention. On surface, consideration must be given to topography, adequate space for plant, timber storage, stockpile ground, railway connections; also to adjoining operations, present or future. MAIN HAULAGE LEVEL. In many Mesabi Range mines, it is possible to develop the mine with only 1 main haulage level, which is located in ore, on or near the bottom rock. If the tonnage is large and a long life assured, economy of upkeep and repairs favors the driving of main drifts in the bottom rock. If the orebody is 100 ft or more thick, 1 or more tramming levels are driven to avoid choking of ore in long chutes, and facilitate movement of timber and supplies. The plan of the main level conforms with the shape of orebody and contour of bottom rock. A system of parallel drifts in direction of the long axis of the orebody, connected at intervals by cross drifts, is desirable because it promotes ventilation, more rapid drainage, permits a greater number of chutes, and the routing of traffic in one direction. The main haulage drifts are usually 8 by 8 ft (inside) if timbered, or 9 ft wide and 8 ft high in rock. In timbered drifts, sets are 5 ft c-c, the back lagged with round 3–6-in timber; sides are lagged when necessary. These drifts are generally on a 0.5% grade, in favor of load.

Sub-level development. The top sub-level is located to provide a height of ore of 12–14 ft above its floor. Vert cribbed raises, 5 by 5 ft if to serve as chutes, are driven on one side of main haulage drifts, are usually 50 ft apart, and are carried to top of the ore. From these raises, 8 by 8-ft crosscuts, usually timbered, are driven at right-angles to main-level drifts, at the elev of the sub-level, until the extreme edge of the orebody or property line is reached. If the bottom rock is encountered, the drifts are continued at a higher elev, involving a transfer of ore from beyond the rise. At intervals, the sub-level drifts are connected by crosscuts, for ventilation.

Mining by parallel slicing. Slice-drifts are started at the far end of each crosscut from the chutes, by blasting out the full height of ore and erecting an "opening" 3-piece set of timber (No 1, Fig 468). Caps are lengthwise of the crosscut, and the slice-drifts are driven at right-angles. Set No 2 is next placed, as opening set for the second slice. Sets 3–9, on approx 6-ft centers, are then mined, the breast of the slice-drift now being within 2 sets of the corresponding sub-level drift to be driven from the adjoining crosscut. Sets 10–16, and 17–20 are then removed, in order. The room thus opened is now 2 sets wide and, if under

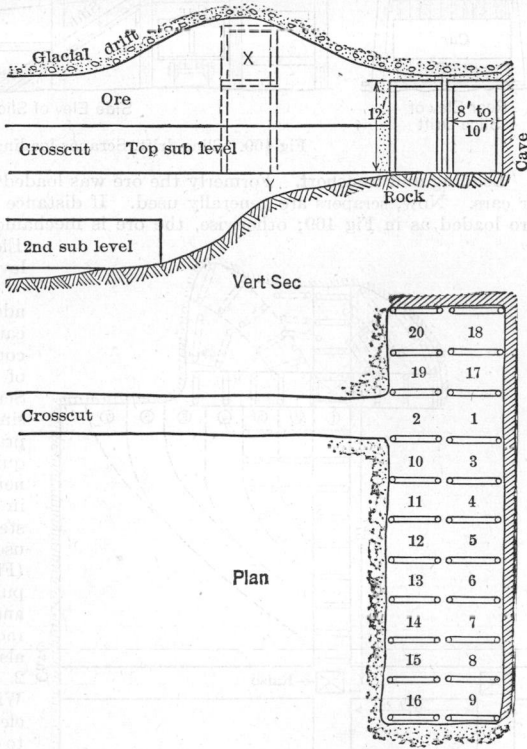

Fig 468. Details of Top-slicing, Mesabi Range, Minn

a loose back, it carries considerable weight. If so, poles are laid on the floor in longit rows at 24-in centers, and covered with 42-in diamond-mesh wire fencing. Sides of the rooms next to solid ore are also covered with fencing, stapled to the posts. The inside posts and caps are then blasted out, allowing the room to fill with waste from above. The fencing prevents intermingling of waste and ore, and protects the miner when working underneath or alongside the caved room. If the back is of sand and gravel, as wire fencing will not prevent contamination, $3/8$- to $7/8$-in hardwood boards are used; sometimes with wire mesh to reinforce the boards. This operation is repeated until entire sub-level is mined. Meantime, the second sub-level, 12–14 ft below, is developed so that mining can begin there under the cave when the work above has retreated far enough to mine safely. The order of removing the slices, as described, may be varied to meet local conditions. If the ground above is heavy, the order in the second slice-drift might be No 15, 16, 14–11, leaving No 10 to support the entrance until 19 and 20 are removed. In very heavy ground, a slice-drift is dropped as soon as completed. The upper surface of the orebody is often very uneven. Should the ore extend higher above the sub-level than can be mined by 1 slice, a second slice-drift superimposed upon the first is driven, dropping the ore down to the floor of the first (X, Fig 468). Near the boundaries, some ore usually remains between the sub-level floor and the bottom rock; as its thickness is not great enough for slicing from the sub below, this ore is recovered by stoping up the bottom before caving (Y, Fig 468).

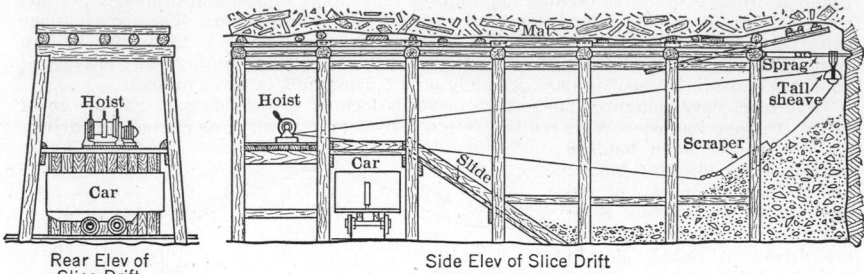

Rear Elev of
Slice Drift

Side Elev of Slice Drift

Fig 469. Slice-drift, Scraper-loading to Car

Loading and transport. Formerly the ore was loaded by hand shoveling into barrows or cars. Now, scrapers are generally used. If distance to chute is great, sub-level cars are loaded as in Fig 469; otherwise, the ore is mechanically scraped to chute (Art 91). Elec haulage is general on main levels.

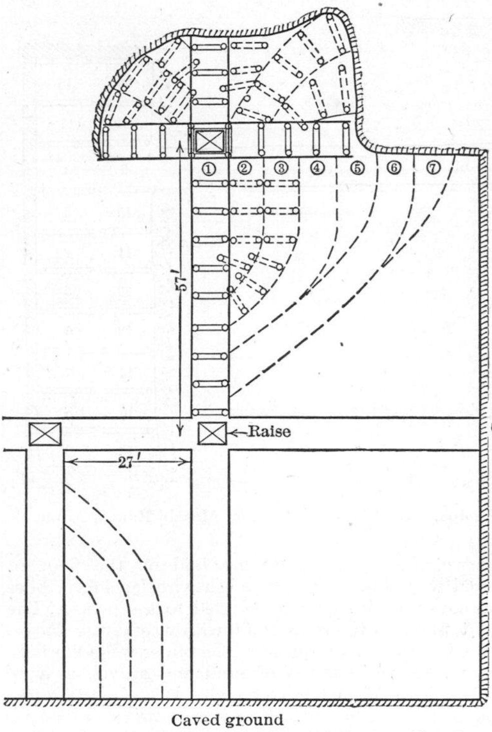

Mining by radial slicing. The adoption of power loaders has caused a change, under certain conditions, from the usual methods of top slicing to "radial" slicing. Scraping to cars or chutes with single-drum air hoists, as early practiced in parallel slicing, required snatch blocks to turn corners, or else the movement of ore in 2 or more operations. The first step towards radial slicing was the use of more chutes, 20–33 ft apart (Fig 481). This permitted a direct pull from the slice-drift at right-angles to the chute and from drifts radiating from either side; and also the blasting of ore in the first 2 sets directly into the chute. With the adoption of double-drum elec hoists, returning the scraper to the working face mechanically, the length of slice-drifts was increased to as much as 100 ft, 60–70 ft being common, and close spacing of chutes became unnecessary. By starting a new slice-drift from the side of a completed slice, and lengthening the caps as the distance from the chute increases, a fan-shaped area is mined with the chute at its apex. Advantages of radial over parallel slicing are: (*a*) high production per miner; (*b*) unnecessary to maintain a cross-cut for a considerable time; (*c*) reduced wear on ropes and snatch-blocks; (*d*) hoist operator has full view of scraper most of the time. Fig 470 shows successive stages in mining by radial slices; Fig 471, 472 show variations in method. There is no standard plan, because after preliminary development the mode of attack depends largely upon character of the ground, and weight and movement of the cave above.

Fig 470. Radial Slicing, Mesabi Range, showing Successive Stages of Removal

Timber. Top-slicing requires relatively cheap timber and lagging, such as round green timber with the bark left on. Caps are 8–10 ft long and 10 in min diam; posts up to 18 ft, 7-in top diam. Lagging in main drifts is 6–8 ft long, with 3-in top, live tamarack being best; in the slices, split cedar with 3.5-in min diam. Timber consumption per ton of ore depends on: the sub-level interval, whether bottom and sides of slices are covered by boards or wire fencing, and height, width, and spacing of sets in slice-drifts. Aver consumption in the mines of one large Mesabi company is approx 3.50 bd ft of round timber and 0.0046 cord of 6-ft lagging per ton of ore. EXPLOSIVE is a semi-gelatin 45%– 60% dynamite; consumption is about 0.5 lb per ton of ore. OUTPUT PER MAN-SHIFT underground is from 8.25 tons in multi-sub-level operations to 13 tons in thin one-slice mines.

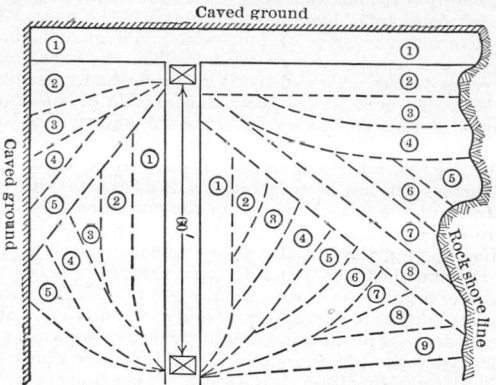

Fig 471. Radial Slicing, Mesabi Range, showing Variations in Plan

Mesabi Range, Minn, thin deposits. Data from J. V. Claypool in 1937 (267) and 1938 refer to slicing of deposits averaging about 16 ft thick in the Hibbing-Chisholm

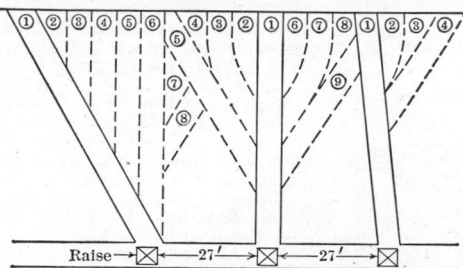

Fig 472. Radial Slicing, Mesabi Range, showing Variations in Plan

district. Capping is usually a bedded, ferruginous, slaty paint rock. Total overburden is 70–240 ft deep, of which glacial drift may compose 70–100 ft. Nature of capping is such that mining becomes dangerous unless done under skilled supervision and in accord with practice based on experience. Orebody is divided into slicing panels ("pillars") 100 ft wide, through the center of each of which an 8 by 10- or 10 by 10-ft timbered drift A (Fig 473), preferably at right-angles to haulage drift, extends to the ore limit, a distance of 400–700 ft. Slicing starts at the outer end and runs 50 ft each way from the entry drift. Slices are 10 ft wide and from 3 ft high on boundaries ("shorelines") to 18 ft in the main orebody. Drift sets are 6 ft 4 in c-c, with round tamarack sprags of 3 to 6-in

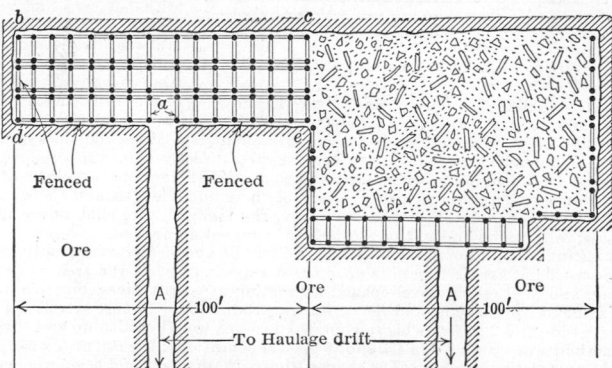

Fig 473. Parallel Slicing, Hibbing-Chisholm Distr, Minn. If *b-c* is a shore line, the 2 caps *a* and all posts except those along *b-d* and *d-e* are blasted; if *b-c* is a face of minable ore, this side also is wire-fenced and its posts are not blasted

diam. For safety, TIMBER used is of good quality. Posts are of green Norway, jack, or white pine, with 7–12-in top diam; caps, of same material, are 10–14-in. Caps were formerly 8 ft long, but experience showed that 10-ft caps afford better control of caving. Back poles are of live tamarack, 8 and 10 ft long and 3–5 in at small diam. Split lagging, of live white-cedar, is 7 ft long, with min diam of 3.5 in. For lagging above the back poles, ⁵⁄₈-in hardwood boards are used. When starting SLICING in a new "pillar" of solid ground, a room 3 slices wide and 100 ft long can usually be opened before the wt warrants blasting down. A room should show considerable press before attempting to cave it. When a room is ready for caving, its sides and ends next to unmined ore are covered from top to bottom with 42-in diamond-mesh fencing. Strips of fencing overlap a little, so that openings do not occur when press is exerted by debris following blasting of the timber. After a room has been fenced, the inside posts (all except those against solid ore) and the caps a of the 2 opening sets in the outermost slice are bored and blasted. Best results are when posts and caps of the 2 opening sets, next to the room entrance, are fired first. After caving the initial 3-slice room in a given "pillar," the following rooms are only 1 slice in width. Wt and diagonal press are usually troublesome in the second and third slice of a group, as the capping is strong enough to hold together until the third slice is blasted down; it then shears off and comes down completely. Retreat in one pillar usually precedes that in the adjoining pillar by 3 or 4 slices, or more if the back is hard to control. Slicing stops at 50 ft from haulage drift, after which the pillars of that drift are similarly sliced, retreating towards the shaft. Transfer of ore from the breast into chutes (as required when irregular bottom makes a footwall haulage drift desirable), or into cars for transport to shaft, is done with power scrapers. Slices are well lighted with 100-w flood lamps, so that miners can see the back at all times from a safe distance. Output per man-shift underground averages 13 long tons. Explosive, 60% semi-gelatin, 0.5 lb per ton. Timber, 2.5 bd ft per ton.

Miscellaneous data on Mesabi practice. Following notes are based on data published in 1912, 1913, and 1924, by C. E. van Barneveld (35, 482); W. Bayliss, E. D. McNeil, and J. S. Lutes (275); L. D. Davenport (276); A. L. Gerry (277). The descriptions apply chiefly to hand loading, now largely displaced by power scrapers, but are suggestive in showing variations in slicing details used to meet special conditions. DRIFT-SLICING AT EDGE OR "SHORE LINE" OF DEPOSIT. Fig 474 shows method; 3 by 3-ft test raises R were first put up 50 ft apart, to determine height of ore over the sub-level. At C, where ore was about 7 ft high, crosscut DE was driven, 7 ft wide and full height of ore; first slice EF was then taken. Crosscut and slices were timbered with 3-piece sets, with 7-ft caps and vert posts of a length to suit height of ore. Slice EF was advanced until ore became too thin to work; posts of last sets were usually 24 to 30 in. Other

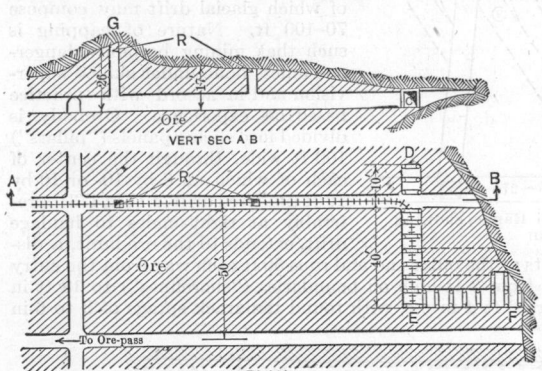

Fig 474. Starting Slices at Edge of Deposit, Mesabi

slices were driven alongside (see dotted lines). Ore was shoveled or wheeled to a car in crosscut DE. As the rock at shore line usually rose at a steep angle, it did not pay to turn the track into the slice. For this kind of work, sets are best placed with their caps along the sides of DE, instead of across it (Fig 475). Though slicing could have been started directly from the sub-level drift, a distinct gain resulted from driving a preliminary crosscut, and slicing up the slope of the bottom rock; ore came down grade, posts of slice-sets were of about equal length, and the whole layout was more flexible. When ground in slices became heavy, the timbers were shot down and new slices started alongside; all ground to right of DE was thus mined and caved.

Square-set slicing. Top of orebody is usually rolling, height of crests frequently reaching 30 or 40 ft. Square-set slicing has been used in such cases, especially when the area was small. Raises could be put up, and another sub-level opened for mining in 2 drift-slices, but this involves costly development, difficult ventilation, and delay in ore production. Square-set slicing was done in rooms 2 or 3 sets wide and 2 to 4 sets high; completed rooms were boarded up and caved as in drift-slicing. The method was elastic. Fig 474 shows typical conditions; the roll at G was 26 ft high, and would be sliced from existing sub-level. The change from drift-slicing would begin where ore was about 17 ft high. The first square-set slice was taken in the solid, leaving 1 set of ore standing between it and last caved drift-slice, to insure that the square-sets were in line and at right-angles to sub-level drift. This slice, 2 sets high, was timbered as it advanced; the pillar between it and the drift-slice was then mined, the order of removing sets depending on weight of ground. In succeeding square-set rooms, the first slice was taken alongside the cave, the caps connecting with the timbers on wall of previous room. Chisholm set (Fig 334, Art 49) illustrates size and type of square-set used. Fig 476 shows a room next to the cave; ground was first excavated for set A, which was firmly blocked; top was lagged, except a space 18 in wide across the set, which was covered with cross-boards, and served as a chute-gate for loading ore broken above. Ground over A was then broken into with a hole as in Fig 477, and excavation was squared up to take set B; set C was then raised, broken ore

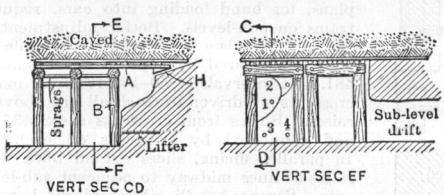

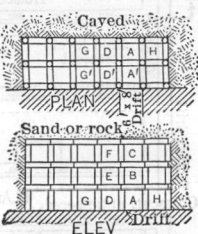

Fig 475. Breaking Ground in Drift-slicing, Mesabi

Fig 476. Square-set Slicing, Mesabi

falling to lagging on set A. Other sets were placed over C until top of ore was reached; back of highest set was blocked and lagged; side lagging was rarely necessary. Set D was mined next (Fig 478); its top was covered with lagging and short boards, but the lagging ran at right-angles to that

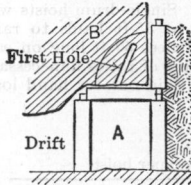

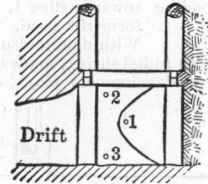

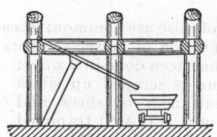

Fig 477. First Hole for B Set, Fig 476

Fig 478. First Hole for D Set, Fig 476

Fig 479. Chute for Square-set Slicing, Mesabi

on set A, so that the long dimension of chute opening would be parallel to the track turning from A into D. Sets E and F were then mined, from sets B and C. Work was resumed on sill-floor in set G, and continued until a slice 1 set wide had been mined along the cave side of room; set H and those over it were taken last. Second slice was taken in same way, starting with set A' (Fig 476); ground in sets over A', D', G', etc, was attacked from open sets over A, D, G, etc. Track was run into the first slice only; ore from upper sets of second slice was handled to cars through rough chute-gates (Fig 479). Usual length of rooms was 51.67 ft, which took 7 sets, including set in sub-level drift, caps of odd length were used at ends of connecting rooms. Square-set slices rarely exceeded 4 sets high; if higher, the side pressure from caved ground made it difficult to prevent timbers from swinging. On finishing a room, all lagging was dropped to sill-floor, and used for boarding up posts along the solid side and end (Fig 480). In upper sets, posts next to ore were boarded with horiz 1-in boards, and the room floor covered with the same. Holes were then drilled in some of the timbers and charged; entrance to room was boarded up and timbers were shot down. Rooms might be blasted with or without system; Fig 480 shows a systematic method; timbers marked by arrows were blasted; caps and posts at A, B, and C were expected to act as props and allow room to cave without disturbing timbers against solid ore. Some foremen shot down posts next to cave, 1 or 2 center posts and a few caps, claiming it caused better settling and left timber in better shape for working adjacent slice. Some timbers on the ore side of room often fell when the cave occurred; they were replaced as ground was timbered in taking the slice alongside.

Prop-slicing. In extensive areas where ore was overlain by considerable thickness of firm taconite, slice at top of deposit has been taken out with props spaced as required; max length of prop, 20 ft. Some orebodies 5–18 ft thick lay between 2 layers of taconite, the roof layer being 40–50 ft thick and tough and caving only when a large area was mined out. Such ground was developed by a main haulage road, from which drifts were run 50 ft apart to the "shore line"; pillars were then mined in 10-ft slices. Drifts were timbered with

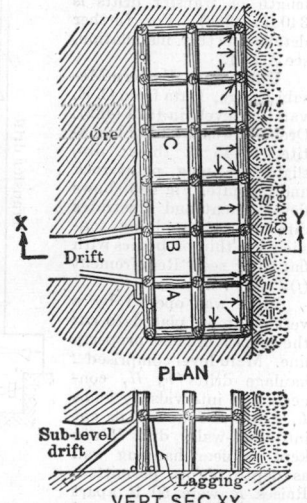

Fig 480. Boarding-up Rooms and Blasting Timbers, Mesabi Square-set Slicing

3-piece sets; slices, with 10 to 18-in props, placed 3–6 ft apart on cave side of slice. Where height of ore exceeded 12 ft, 1 floor of square-sets was erected and 2 props were set on each cap. This form of prop-slice is an open, stulled stope; it gave cheap ore and left large rooms which were not caved unless roof required it; the roof came in large blocks when it caved.

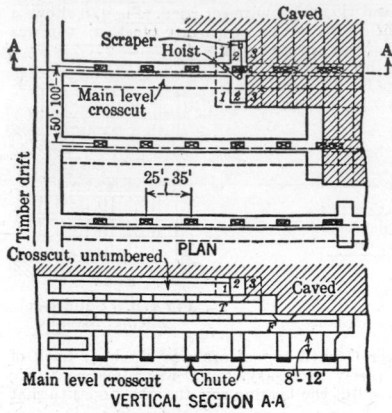

Fig 481. Drift Slicing, Scraper Loading (diagrammatic)

Scraping into raises. Early development plans, for hand loading into cars, required long trams on sub-levels. Better adjustment between these and haulage by elec loco or mule on main level was secured by type of development in Fig 481. At intervals of 50–100 ft along main drifts, crosscuts are driven to reach all ore above by vert raises. Raises from crosscuts are 25–35 ft apart, and connected by crosscuts on each sub-level. In parallel slicing, slices extend both ways from raises to lines midway to adjacent sub-level crosscuts. Scraper handling has replaced hand loading. Each raise serves slices 1, 2, 3. Top of raise is funneled toward slice 3 (T, Sec AA, Fig 481), and the corners of slice 2 are removed near crosscut to allow ore from slice 3 to be scraped into the raise. After slice 2 is mined, the raise is funneled towards slice 1, as at F. Single-drum hoists were formerly used, with 25- to 35-ft hauls to raise. With double-drum hoists, slices 50 ft long on each side of raise are common; these hoists, with radial slicing, made close spacing of raises unnecessary. Adaptation of power scrapers (Sec 27) to development plans, originally laid out for hand loading, has been done in 2 ways: (a) ore is scraped up slides at entrances of slices and into cars (Fig 469) trammed by hand to raises; (b) ore is scraped out of slices to the entry or "transfer" drift, and thence to the raises by another scraper. Fig 482 shows general plan of such an installation, where aver length of transfer drifts is 340 ft (268). For further details of this installation, see Art 91.

Utica mine, Eastern Mesabi Range. Data from C. E. van Barneveld in 1924 (482). Orebody was a bed of hematite, 10–45 ft thick; dip, slight; capping, paint rock and taconite. Fig 483 shows development and illustrates difficulty of applying top-slicing in thin orebodies with flat dip; see "Requirement (f)," Art 74.

Mine was opened by a vert shaft V, placed to cut the deepest ore near property line. Main level comprised 2 haulage drifts F, H, connected at intervals by loops L. Drift F followed or cut into foot-wall; drift H was kept as near hanging wall as depth of ore permitted. Raises R were 50 ft apart along main drifts. Sub-level interval, 13 ft; sub-level development comprised a series of parallel crosscuts from the raises, connected by timber drifts T (See A A, Fig 483). To meet problem of

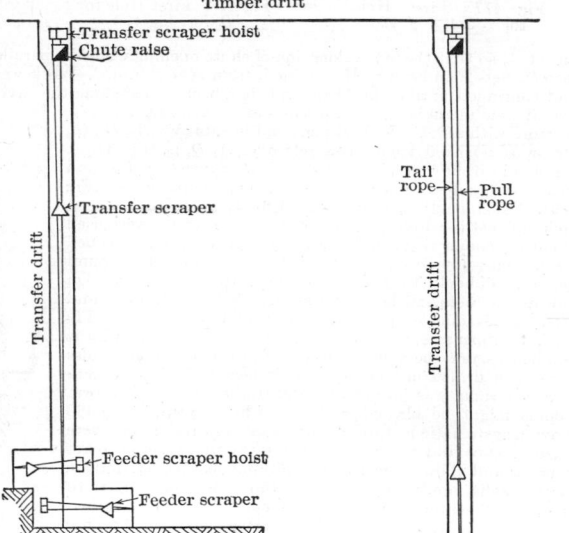

Fig 482. Use of Scrapers in Top-slicing, Utica Ext Mine, Mesabi Range, Minn

handling ore to the shaft from top sub-level (52 ft), the 26-ft sub-level was developed as an intermediate motor-haulage level, consisting of 2 drifts D, E, connected by crosscut X with a transfer chute C leading to a shaft pocket on main level. Raises B were put up 50 ft apart from drifts D, E, and from them crosscuts were driven to limits of ore on the 39-ft and 52-ft sub-levels. Sub-level crosscuts were timbered with 6-ft posts and 7-ft caps. Development on lower sub-levels was not undertaken far in advance of the time when it was needed. SLICING began at top of orebody, as indicated at S. Drift-slices timbered with 11 to 12-ft posts and 8-ft caps were run half way to adjoining crosscuts. Entire breast was drilled and blasted at one time. Before caving, poles 16 ft long were laid lengthwise on floor of slice and covered with boards laid crosswise. In working under hanging wall, some areas required slices 2 sets high. TIMBER CONSUMPTION per ton of ore; lumber, 1.413 lin ft; poles, 1.868 ft; plank, 2.963 ft; lagging, 0.00278 cord. Development as in Fig 483 was planned for hand-loading; length of slices could have been increased for scraper work. Some ore was scraped into cars with slip scrapers and single-drum hoists; sometimes low headroom under

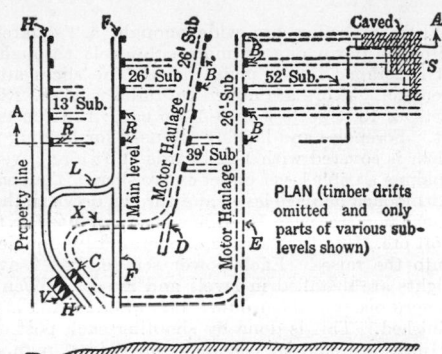

PLAN (timber drifts omitted and only parts of various sub-levels shown)

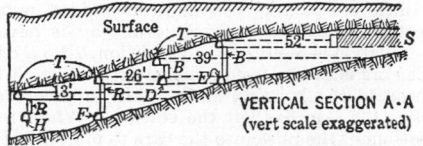

VERTICAL SECTION A-A (vert scale exaggerated)

Fig 483.   Top-slicing, Utica Mine, Minn (diagrammatic)

hanging wall interfered with free dumping of scraper and increased loading time.

Iron River District, Menominee Range. Data contributed in 1938 by C. D. Bailey, District Engr, Pickands Mather & Co. Fig 484 shows present methods of top-slicing. Ore is massive hematite; it stands unsupported in most sub-level drifts and raises, though some of these and parts of the main levels require timbering. Orebodies being top-sliced either extend up to the overlying sand or have weak hanging wall. DEVELOPMENT. Entry is by vert shafts; usually of 3 compts, for 2 ore skips in balance and a man cage. Main haulage levels are 150 ft apart. When a new level is opened, it is customary to drive the intermediate sub-level (Fig 484) at such elev as to halve the length of the main raises. The sub-level interval is 12.5 ft, increased to 14.5 ft when possible. Single raises are used as ore passes, with additional ones for ladder roads, timber ways or handling machinery. The raises are rarely cribbed. Main ore raises are 60–100 ft apart. MINING.

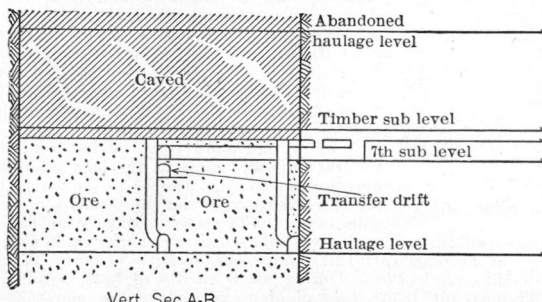

Radial slicing

Square slicing

Ladder

Timber rse

Plan of 7th Sub Level

Abandoned haulage level

Timber sub level

7th sub level

Transfer drift

Haulage level

Vert Sec A-B

Fig 484.   Top-slicing, Iron River Distr, Menominee Range

Where orebodies are wide enough, a "square" system of slicing is used. The ore is dropped down one or more sub-levels through small raises, to a transfer drift where it is scraped into a main raise. The slices are parallel and 60–100 ft long. Irregular remnants of ore are mined by radial slicing. Slices are timbered with 3-piece hardwood sets, of 10-ft posts with 8–10-in caps; 12-ft posts are used where the mining height is 14.5 ft. Forepoles and lagging are used for holding the back. When a slice is advanced 5 ft, floor is covered with 1-in boards 16 ft long, overlapping floor in 2 preceding sections and making a triple layer under entire slice. Timber, lagging, and boards are trucked in on the abandoned haulage level, and thrown down to the sub-level where they are to be used. Wet jackhammers, with $7/8$-in hex steel, are used in the harder ground; dry auger machines in soft ore. Hoe-type scrapers, operated by double-drum a-c motor hoists, move broken ore into the raises. Each power scraper has 2 extension elec light cords, and permanent lights are installed in levels and raises. When starting a new place, 2 slices are driven before blasting them down, but when slicing alongside a cave, each slice is blasted when finished. This is done by shooting each post on the caved side of the slice in 2 places. Miners are paid by contract, on basis of number of cars of ore produced, or number of feet of development driven; the pay is never less than the district flat rate. Forced ventilation is required. In addition, 2-hp a-c fans, with ventubing, are used for each slice. The ore is drawn from main ore raises into 3-ton rocker-dump cars, hauled by d-c trolley locos to the hoisting shaft. Air gates prevent sticky ore from sliding into the shaft after the skip has left the station. Where main ore raises are wet, ore is scraped from bottom of the raise into the cars to minimize the danger from rushes of soft ore and water. GENERAL OPERATING DATA (aver for district). Production per miner, 22–25 tons per day. Explosive, 0.6 lb per ton; boards, 1.87 bd ft per ton; timber and lagging (variable), 3.7 lin ft per ton aver.

Caspian mine, Menominee Range, Mich. Data from W. A. McEachern in 1911 (288). Early work at this mine is of interest in showing application of top-slicing under difficult conditions. Orebody was massive hematite, overlain by 130 ft of drift containing much water. Entry was by vert shafts sunk in walls. First level was 25 to 30 ft below overburden; level interval was 50 to 75 ft; lateral development on each level comprised a crosscut from shaft, and a drift along deposit from which crosscuts were run to walls at 50-ft intervals. Ore at top of deposit could not be mined until overlying sand had been drained, which was done as follows: 48 small raises were put up from 1st level (sub-level C, Fig 485), at different points. In each raise a 12-ft test hole was drilled ahead, then a round of 6-ft holes was blasted; 1 round was blasted after test hole reached sand, leaving 5 to 6 ft of ore at top of raise; 3 more holes were drilled through this pillar to hasten drainage, which took over a year. Prior to and during drainage operations, production was begun by opening shrinkage stopes between 2nd and 3rd levels; ore was strong enough to stand in stopes 25 ft wide, 100 ft long and 50 ft high, with 25-ft pillars. SLIC- ING (Fig 485). Cribbed, 2-compartment raises R were put up from sub-level C, about 40 ft apart. Sub-level A was opened about 5 ft below top of ore by driving drifts and crosscuts, as shown on plan of sub-level B. Crosscut E was driven to No 2 shaft for ventilation and han- dling timber. Blocks between crosscuts were mined in drift-slices, 8 ft wide by 10 ft high. No attempt was made to recover the 5 ft of ore left over sub-level A; it aided timbers in forming a mat to prevent sand from mixing with ore. Central drift and crosscut to shaft were kept open for transport of timber to the 2 succeed- ing sub-levels, by leaving 10-ft pillars on each side. Lower sub-levels were similarly mined. As pillars between shrinkage stopes were sliced, ore was drawn from stopes to let mat settle evenly. Method resembles "panel slicing" at Morenci (Art 72). Scrapers of reversible hoe type (Sec 27) were introduced here in 1922 for loading ore in slices. During last 6 months of 1923, output per man-shift scraping averaged 12.53 tons, for 18 826 tons of ore; aver output per man-shift in hand-loading 94 900 tons during same period was 7.41 tons (482).

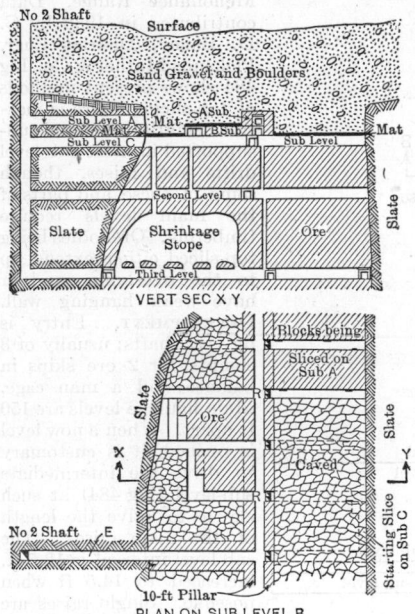

Fig 485. Top-slicing, Caspian Mine, Mich

Marquette Range, Mich. Data contributed in 1938 by Carl Brewer, Chief Engr, Cleveland-Cliffs Iron Co. Orebodies of soft hematite occur generally in flat-dipping (15°) troughs; width to 1 000 ft; thickness, 20–50 ft along the edges, to 300 ft in the center;

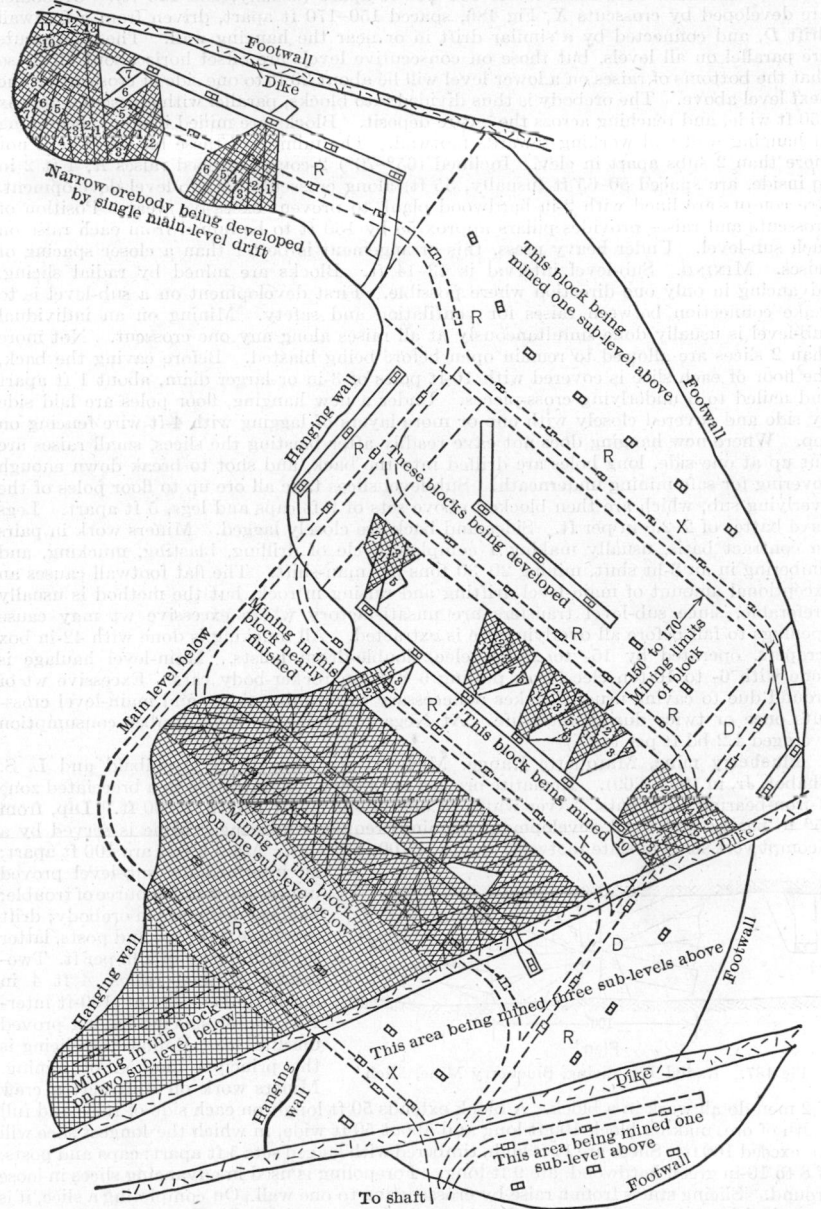

Fig 486.   Top-slicing in Negaunee Distr, Marquette Range, Mich.   Typical Plan.   Small numbers indicate sequence of slices. Hatched areas are caved

length, 2 000 ft or more.   The troughs are of 2 characters: (a) synclines intersected longitudinally by vert intrusive dikes; (b) V-shaped troughs between nearly vert dikes and flatter footwalls. Footwalls are slate or jasper. Hanging-wall cappings are usually a leached ore formation (jasper) which, on caving, breaks into gravelly aggregate, requiring careful mining to prevent contamination of ore. DEVELOPMENT. Entry is by vert shafts in footwall, with main levels 100–200 ft apart (usually, 100–125 ft). Orebodies are developed by crosscuts X, Fig 486, spaced 150–170 ft apart, driven from a footwall drift D, and connected by a similar drift in or near the hanging wall. These crosscuts are parallel on all levels, but those on consecutive levels are offset horiz about 30 ft, so that the bottoms of raises on a lower level will lie about 30 ft to one side of crosscut on the next level above. The orebody is thus divided into blocks, parallel with crosscuts, approx 150 ft wide, and reaching across the entire deposit. Blocks are mined in steps, beginning at hanging wall and working towards footwall. The mining of these blocks is kept not more than 2 subs apart in elev. Inclined (65°–70°) 2-compt cribbed raises R, 4 ft 2 in sq inside, are spaced 50–65 ft (usually, 55 ft) along crosscuts for sub-level development. Ore compts are lined with 2-in hardwood plank to prevent excessive wear. Position of crosscuts and raises provides pillars approx 55 by 150 ft to be mined from each raise on each sub-level. Under heavy press, this arrangement is better than a closer spacing of raises. MINING. Sub-level interval is 13–14 ft. Blocks are mined by radial slicing, advancing in only one direction where possible. First development on a sub-level is to make connection between raises for ventilation and safety. Mining on an individual sub-level is usually done simultaneously at all raises along any one crosscut. Not more than 2 slices are allowed to remain open before being blasted. Before caving the back, the floor of each slice is covered with 10-ft poles of 3-in or larger diam, about 1 ft apart and nailed to 3 underlying cross-pieces. Under a new hanging, floor poles are laid side by side and covered closely with one or more layers of lagging with 4-ft wire fencing on top. Where new hanging does not cave readily after blasting the slices, small raises are put up at one side, long holes are drilled into the back, and shot to break down enough covering for safe mining underneath. Sub-level slices take all ore up to floor poles of the overlying sub, which are then blocked above sets of 9-ft caps and legs, 5 ft apart. Legs have batter of 2–2.5 in per ft. Sides and back are closely lagged. Miners work in pairs on contract basis, usually making 1 complete cycle of drilling, blasting, mucking, and timbering in an 8-hr shift, mining 20–30 tons per man-shift. The flat footwall causes an exceptional amount of main-level drifting and raising in rock, but the method is usually preferable, since sub-level transfers are unsatisfactory where excessive wt may cause openings to fail before all overlying ore is extracted. All mucking is done with 42-in box scrapers, operated by 15- to 25-hp, elec, double-drum hoists. Main-level haulage is done with 6- to 10-ton elec locos, pulling 6–8 4-ton rocker-body cars. Excessive wt of ground due to caving usually makes it necessary to retimber raises and main-level cross-cuts once or twice during their life. At Negaunee mine in 1937, timber consumption averaged 1.2 bd ft per ton.

Blueberry mine, Marquette Range, Mich. Data from R. S. Archibald and L. S. Chabot, Jr, in 1935 (269). Hematite ore is a secondary concentration in a brecciated zone of iron-bearing sediments. Aver width of ore, about 50 ft; length, 2 000 ft. Dip, from 75° to nearly vert. All development openings require timbering. Mine is served by a 5-compt vert shaft in slate footwall; depth, 1 100 ft (1935). Main levels are 100 ft apart; an intermediate sub-level proved unnecessary and a source of trouble; haulage drifts are in orebody; drift sets have 9-ft caps and posts, latter set with batter of 1 in per ft. Two-compt, cribbed raises, 4 ft 4 in inside timbers, are at 100-ft intervals, closer spacing having proved unsuitable. Radial top-slicing is the principal method of mining. Miners work on contract; a crew

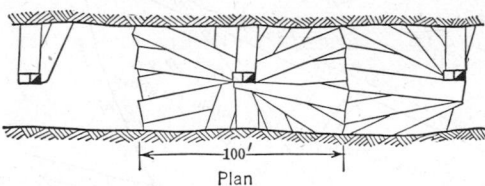

|← 100' →|

Plan

Fig 487.   Radial Top-slicing, Blueberry Mine, Mich

of 2 men do all work in a block. A block extends 50 ft longit on each side of raise and full width of ore, making block 100 ft long and about 50 ft wide, in which the longest slice will not exceed 100 ft. Slices are 11 ft high, timbered with lagged sets 5 ft apart; caps and posts, of 8 to 10-in green hardwood, are 9 ft long. Forepoling is used in advancing slices in loose ground. Slicing starts from a raise by crosscutting to one wall. On completing a slice, it is floored with 9.5-ft 3 to 4-in tamarack poles, spiked to cross pieces; bottom and solid side are then covered with wire netting. Posts are bored and blasted down before next slice is driven; the ground is too heavy to allow 2 adjoining slices to remain open. Slicing proceeds radially from raise (Fig 487). Broken ore is handled to raise by 42-in scrapers.

Inland Steel Co, Cuyuna Range. In Armour No 2 mine, Crosby, Minn, idle since 1932, a deposit of hematite was formerly mined by top-slicing. Development was similar to Fig 481; sub-level interval, 10 ft. Crosscuts were spaced 70-ft centers, with raises 30-ft centers. As Cuyuna ore is harder than Mesabi, hand-loading was preferred for handling broken ore containing much material over 4-in size; elsewhere loading was done with single-drum hoist and slip scrapers. In older development, raises were 70 ft apart and scrapers were used to load cars trammed to raises. H. T. Middlebrook, in 1938, states that most recent practice on Cuyuna Range adopts radial slicing and use of double-drum hoists with box scrapers. Aver output per shift per miner working in slices ranges from 16 to 20 tons.

Low Moor mines, Va. Data from C. Dixon in 1912 (291). Shallow, veinlike deposits of soft brown hematite were top-sliced; irregular and sudden changes in both dip and strike are common. Country rocks are soft and cave readily.

Fig 488 shows work in a deposit about 12 ft wide. Entry was by shaft in footwall or by adits. A main level was driven 7 ft high in the clear and 6 ft wide at top; timbered with 3-piece sets, 4 ft apart. Lagging was required on top of sets and usually on sides. Cribbed, 2-compt raises were driven on footwall at 50-ft intervals; 1 raise was holed through to surface as quickly as possible. Sub-levels were driven from raises at 12-ft intervals; they averaged 1 ft less in dimension all around than main level. Slicing (locally, robbing) started on the top sub-level, when it reached the ore limit; back and sides of sub-level were shot down and sets with 12-ft posts erected. As work retreated, floor was covered with 8-ft lagging laid on cross-sills of round timber 12 ft long, spaced 4 to 6 ft apart. Sets were blasted down after a section 50 to 75 ft long had been robbed; then robbing could begin at end of next lower sub-level; sills were picked up on 12-ft posts in sub-level below. Drilling was done with 2.25-in piston-drills. Sub-levels were so crooked that barrows had to be used to transport ore to raises. This method, which extracts about 95% of orebody,

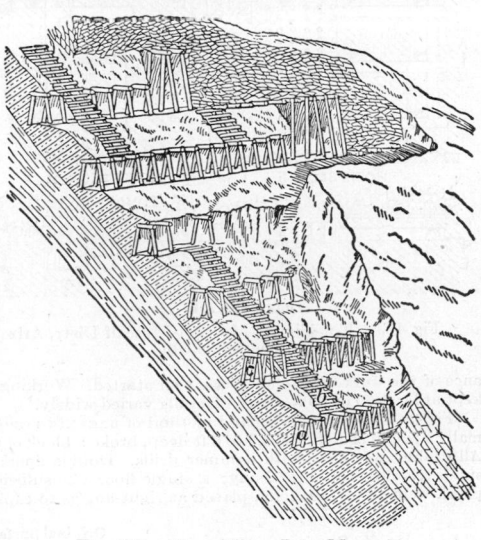

Fig 488. Top-slicing, Low Moor, Va

is open to the objection that all sub-levels must be driven to boundaries before robbing begins, and much retimbering is necessary for their maintenance.

72. TOP-SLICING IN NON-FERROUS MINES

Morenci-Metcalf district, Ariz. The properties mentioned here are now owned by the Phelps Dodge Corp; the work described stopped about 1923. Data from P. B. Scotland (152, 178), J. R. McLean (279), W. L. Tovote (280), and notes by L. Johnson in 1915. OREBODIES, usually carrying 2–4% Cu, are disseminated deposits in porphyry or fissure veins in granite. Top-slicing was formerly used for shoots of soft ore, some of them very large; thus, the Humboldt orebodies were 80 by 600 ft and 200 by 700 ft in horiz sec. Disseminated deposits are overlain by leached porphyry capping; oreshoots rarely exceed 300 ft in vert dimension. DEVELOPMENT. A haulage-drift for electric or mule haulage was driven near bottom of shoot; intermediate hand-tramming levels were opened above as required at vert intervals of 50–100 ft (Fig 491). Raises connecting with main level were spaced to limit tramming distance to 150 ft. Tramming levels consisted of a rectangular system of drifts and crosscuts which proved shape of deposit and allowed raises to be spaced over whole area on corners of rectangles usually 25 by 30 or 40 ft. This might be done by raising at 25-ft intervals along crosscuts 30 ft apart, or, where deposit was wide, by parallel drifts 30–40 ft apart with raises along them. Raises had a 4 by 4 or 5 by 5-ft chute compartment and 1.5-ft ladderway; they were spaced so that ore could be shoveled direct to chutes, and alined accurately to obviate necessity for constant surveying in slices. Inclined slicing was also used (Art 73).

Slicing. Irregular tops of oreshoots were square-setted (Art 70). Height of slices, 7 to 15 ft; economic height, 11 ft. Slices were timbered with 3-piece, unframed sets. Ariz Copper Co used round caps and posts, both 10 ft long and 7.5 to 9.5-in diam; Detroit Copper Co used similar posts, with an 8 by 8-in cap 6 ft long; slice-sets were about 5 ft apart. Raises at end of oreshoot were connected by a crosscut L, timbered with slice-sets (Fig 489). Drifts K, connecting with adjacent raises, might be as in Fig 489, or else carried full height of slice and timbered with sets to support mat; they provided exits in case of a sudden cave. Ore on right side of L was then mined; the direction of slice-drifts here would depend largely on shape and extent of this area. When this work was completed, slicing began at left of crosscut L, and was carried to other end of deposit; the face was advanced by slicing 6 to 10 ft wide across orebody, as indicated by dotted lines MN. Sec EF shows appear-

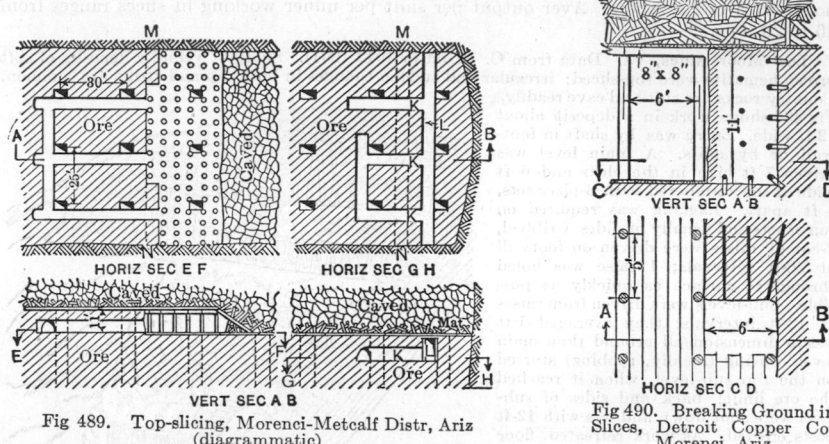

Fig 489.   Top-slicing, Morenci-Metcalf Distr, Ariz
(diagrammatic)

Fig 490.   Breaking Ground in
Slices, Detroit Copper Co,
Morenci, Ariz

ance of the work after a slice was well started. Working faces on adjacent sub-levels were usually kept at least 50 or 60 ft apart. Details varied widely.

Fig 490 shows timbering and method of BREAKING GROUND at mines of Detroit Copper Co. Normally a round of 10 holes, 5.5 to 6 ft deep, broke a block of ore 11 ft high, 6 ft wide, by about 5 ft deep. All drilling was done with hammer drills. A single floor was sufficient after a good mat was formed. Floor-plank were 10 to 15 ft long, placed at right-angles to caps of slice-sets. Posts were blasted down as

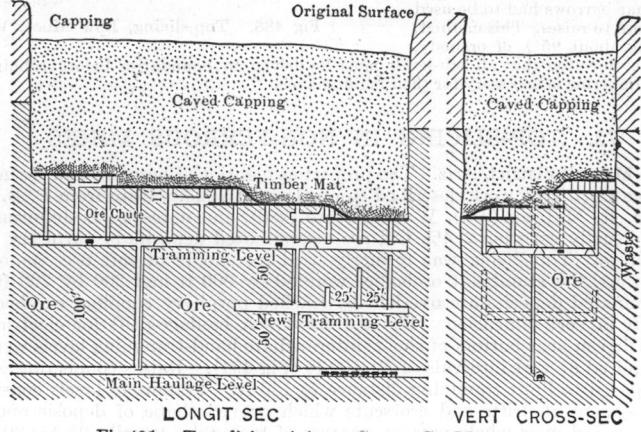

Fig 491.   Top-slicing, Arizona Copper Co, Morenci, Ariz

slice advanced, only enough space being kept open for shoveling to raises. Some barrow work was necessary in workings arranged as in Fig 489; to avoid this, Ariz Copper Co used the following modification: When the face had advanced so that direct shoveling was not feasible, miners were transferred to the next raises, where a new breast was opened and worked back to old one. This obviated barrow work, if raises were spaced so that each served an area not exceeding 25 by 30 ft. If orebody widened it was followed into the walls by square-setting, and a mat formed over the new area like that at the top of the deposit. Patches of waste were broken, thrown back from breast and left on floor. If the mat caved close up to breast, a crosscut was driven parallel to the old face and about 10 ft from it; when the new breast was under way, the 10-ft pillar was shot down and drawn. Should mat come down over a large area before floor was laid, or in case it hung up, the succeeding slice was started 15 ft below; 7 or 8 ft of this slice was mined and a floor laid; the overlying ore was broken with uppers, starting at end of area and retreating towards face of new slice; the broken ore from each round was shoveled away until waste appeared. The weight of mat in wide shoots was controlled by taking each slice in sections (Fig 491); slices were 30 to 40 ft wide; tramming levels, 55 ft apart. Slicing directly over a tramming level caused crosscuts and drifts there to crush; this was avoided by mining ore on and over the level in a slice of double height, timbered with 2 floors of square-sets. Following plan was used by Detroit Copper Co: Ends of 2 adjacent crosscuts on tramming level were connected by a breast stope, timbered with 1 floor of square-sets, 2–3 sets wide. The back of ore remaining over the sets and below the mat was then blasted with long uppers; broken ore filled the sets and was shoveled out, allowing the mat to settle gradually on the set timbers. While one section was being shoveled out, another was opened and timbered; posts of sets in first section were then shot down, and the procedure was repeated. PANEL SLICING. Fig 492 shows a method devised by Ariz Copper Co to eliminate the heavy expense of driving and maintaining raises 25 ft apart. On each slice a central main drift passed lengthwise through the oreshoot, and crosscuts were turned off at 40-ft intervals. The main drift, and crosscuts for 20 ft on each side of it, were timbered with 3-piece sets, 6.5 ft high; elsewhere, crosscuts were opened to mat above and timbered with slice-sets. Slices 40 ft wide were then worked from the walls back toward main drift, leaving a central pillar 40 ft wide which was sliced back from end of orebody after slices on each side of it were finished. Ore was shoveled into cars and trammed to raises spaced at 80-ft intervals along main drift and connecting with haulage level below. While one floor or panel was being worked, the next, 11 ft below, was in preparation. This system dispensed with need for tramming levels. Compare Fig 485.

Operating data. ARIZ COPPER CO. P. B. Scotland states that timber consumption in top-slicing, including chutes, ladders and reinforcements, was about 9 bd ft per ton of ore; most of it was round Texas pine and squared Oregon fir, but much cheap cull lumber was also used in top-slicing (178). DETROIT COPPER CO. J. R. McLean gives following data for Jan, 1914 (279): 124 088 bd ft of round and 322 661 bd ft of square timber were used. Table 46 shows details. Figures in Table 47 do not include 498 tons of

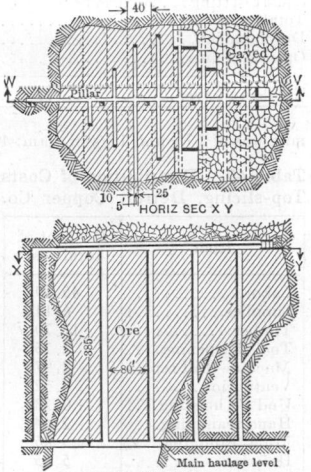

Fig 492.   Panel Slicing, Arizona Copper Co (faces under attack shown thus: ➡)

Table 46.   Timber Consumption, Top-slicing, Detroit Copper Co

Kind of work	Tons of ore mined	Round timber		Sq timber, bd ft per ton	Total timber, bd ft per ton
		Linear ft per ton	Bd ft * per ton		
Top-slicing..........................	45 395	0.5240	2.4933	5.5022	7.9955
Square-setting......................	1 294	0.6576	3.1236	6.3833	9.5069
Development in mines...............	1 353	0.4205	1.9974	33.3924	35.3898
Outside development................	498	0.3373	1.6024	20.6104	22.2128
Repairs, etc.........................	....	0.0146	0.0693	0.1894	0.2587
Totals and averages................	48 540	0.5382	2.5564	6.6473	9.2037

* On basis that 1 linear ft of timber = 4.75 bd ft.

Table 47.   Duty of Underground Labor, Top-slicing, Detroit Copper Co

Mine	Total output, tons	Number of men working		Output, tons per shift	
		Total	Stoping	Per man	Per man stoping
Ryerson..............................	24 017	305	184	3.03	4.98
Yankee..............................	8 394	182	87	1.77	3.26
Copper Mountain....................	12 025	169	134	2.73	3.40
Ariz Central........................	3 606	80	44	1.72	3.14
Totals and aver....................	48 042	736	449	2.54	3.99

ore from outside properties. Shifts were nominally 8 hr, actually 7.5 hr; 26 working days per month. Output per man-shift underground and on surface, including outside properties, 1.85 tons. Dyna-

Table 48. Explosive Consumption, Detroit Copper Co

Kind of work	Tons ore mined	Lb dynamite per ton	Ft fuse per ton	No caps per ton
Slicing	45 395	0.435	1.729	0.361
Square-setting	1 294	1.043	3.091	0.772
Totals and aver	46 689	0.451	1.767	0.372
Development	1 353	4.820	16.038	4.175
Outside claims	498	24.299	58.433	12.319
Totals and aver	48 540	0.818	2.746	0.601

mite was of 1 7/8 and 1 1/8-in diam; 40% dynamite was used wherever possible; 60% was required to break some ground. Blasting in slices was done with 5-X caps and double taped fuse. Table 49 covers the mining of 48 042 tons of ore at the 4 mines in Table 47. Mines were comparatively dry; there was little artificial ventilation; underground hoisting item includes cost of hoisting timbers from tramming levels to slices with small tugger hoists.

Table 49. Distribution of Costs Top-slicing, Detroit Copper Co.

Item	Per cent of total cost
Labor	45.19
Supplies	6.11
Timber	17.70
Tool sharpening	2.25
Machine-drill reps	2.97
Ventilation	0.52
Und'g'd hoisting	0.28
Hand tramming	2.64
Mule tramming	5.45
Hoisting	5.85
Und'g'd repairs	3.51
Mine drainage	0.70
Miscellaneous	6.83
	100.00

Copper Queen mine, Bisbee, Ariz. Data from G. J. Young in 1926 (593), and C. E. van Barneveld, 1924 (482). Some areas were top-sliced and the ore scraped into a drift or crosscut ("sub-gangway"), which connected raises on the floor below the slices (Fig 493). DEVELOPMENT. Two-compt raises from the levels were preferably on corners of 50-ft squares and connected by sub-gangways. SLICING began at the ore limits, or next to caved ground. In Fig 493, the first slice, 1, would start from top of raise *B*; broken ore was scraped directly to the raise by a hoe-type scraper operated by a double-drum hoist on floor of slice near the raise. In places, it might be possible to leave part of slice 1 open, while slice 2 was being taken; if not, slice 2 was started by raising from the sub-gangway. Ore from slice 2 might be scraped into raise *B*, and from slices 3, 4, etc, into the sub-gangway; then the hoist was turned 90° and the ore re-scraped to raise *C*. This was locally called the Scott system. SLICES were 7 ft wide by 11 ft high, timbered with 10 by 10-in square-sets; caps 7 ft, girts 5 ft. Sets in sub-gangway were 3.5 ft c-c. Output per man-shift reached 10 tons where slices could be laid out 50 ft long, as in Fig 493, but decreased to 6.5 tons in shorter slices.

Southeast Extension mine, Phelps Dodge Corp, Bisbee, Ariz. Data from H. M. Lavender in 1939. Top-slicing is used only in some small high-grade areas in this orebody that are not suited to block-caving. The ore is a secondarily enriched porphyry; soft and easy to drill; quite wet, but otherwise ideal for the method. The orebody had been developed for block-caving on the 1 000, 1 100 and 1 200 levels and, wherever possible, this work was utilized in the top-slicing areas.

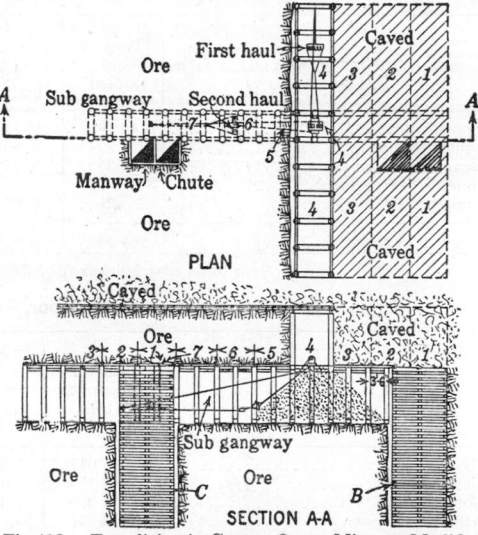

Fig 493. Top-slicing in Copper Queen Mine, as Modified for Scraper Loading

Fig 494 shows one section of the 1 000 level. Two 2-compt raises *A*, from the 1 200 main haulage level, were extended to the 1 000 level. Connections were made between the raises, and to existing work on the level, for ventilation, supplies, and access to the top-slice stope. From raises *A* on the 1 000 level, 2 transfer "scram-drifts" *B* were driven to the ore limits and timbered with 5-ft sq-sets with 8-ft posts; all timbers, 10 by 10 in. From the scram-drifts, two 2-compt raises *C*, 40 ft apart, were driven to top of the ore, where 2 drifts or "leads" *D* were driven to the ore limits. The raises were lined with 6 by 8-in cribbing; compts, 4 by 4 ft in the clear; the leads were square-setted, with 9-ft posts, 10 by 10-in caps, and 4 by 6-in girts 4 ft 2 in long.

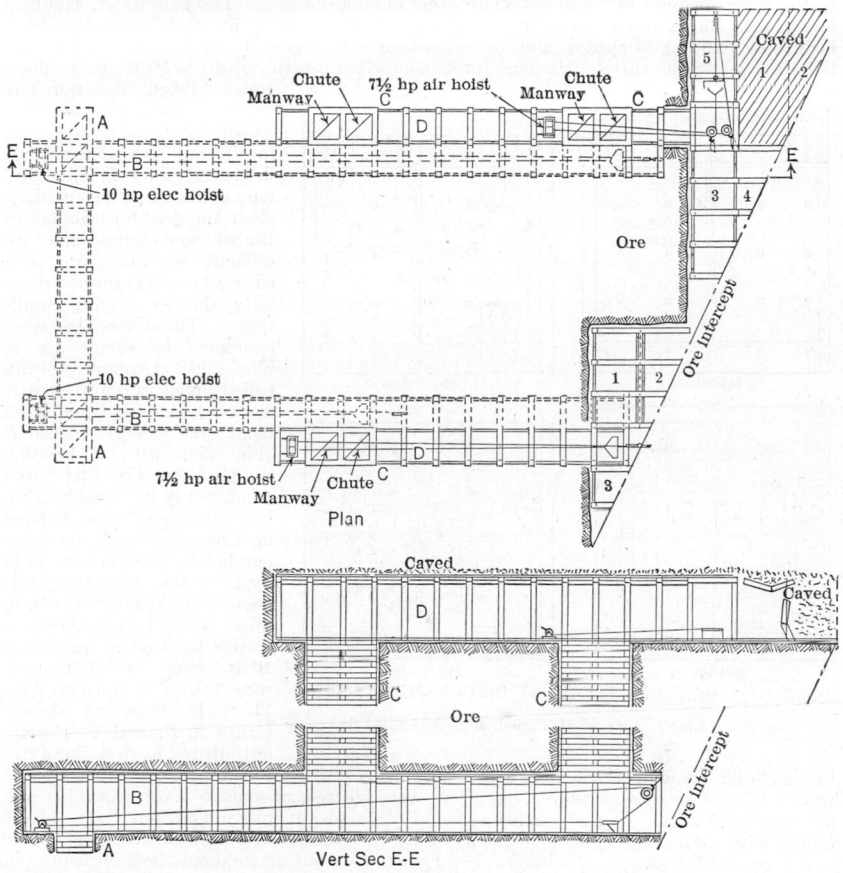

Fig 494.   Top-slicing, Bisbee, Ariz

Slicing starts near edge of orebody; slice-drifts are driven at right-angles to leads *D*. Drilling is done with pluggers and the slice-drift is carried to the ore limits, or to a section line.   Slice-drifts are square-setted with 10 by 10-in timber, 8-ft caps and 9-ft posts spaced 5 ft c–c.   After the first slice-drift reaches the limit of the section, work starts at that point in an adjoining drift and retreats by slabbing successive sets to the main leads *D*.   The areas sliced before caving occurs may be 1, 2, or sometimes 3 sets wide.   Sequence of work is indicated by numbers in Fig 494.   When a section is cleaned out, it is floored with 2 by 12-in plank, 10 ft long and parallel to length of slice-drifts; then the section is allowed to cave.   A slice rarely has to be shot down; with the length of cap and post used, the section usually caves soon after the ore is mined.   Broken ore is scraped to leads *D* by 7.5-hp air hoists; when enough ore has accumulated in the leads, the hoist headblocks are shifted for scraping ore into chutes *C*, in which it drops into scram drift *B*.   Here it is scraped into transfer raises *A* by 10-hp elec hoists, and falls to haulage level.   When slicing reaches the first raise *C*, the air-hoist is moved to the next raise. OPERATING DATA: output per man-shift, 12.57 tons. Direct costs per dry ton: labor, 52¢; explosive, 8¢; timber, 14¢; total, 74¢. Wages: miners, $5.48; muckers, $4.84.

Miami Copper Co, Miami, Ariz. Data from E. G. Deane in 1916 (285). Orebody is a large disseminated deposit of chalcocite in schist, overlain by a leached capping about 200 ft thick (Art 10-b). Top-slicing was employed in an area about 800 ft square, in which the ore was soft but considerably harder than the siliceous capping, which breaks into fine particles and runs like sand. These conditions, and the fact that ore in this section was richer than usual, led to adoption of top-slicing, which was partly preparatory to other methods for the lower lifts (see Art 80 for other mining systems). DEVELOPMENT. Haulage levels were 150 ft apart vertically, with 2 sub-levels between at 50-ft intervals, which facilitated building of chutes, and, in connection with artificial ventilation, aided in distributing air to the slices. Haulage levels comprised a series of drifts 50 ft apart, along which cribbed raises were put up on 50-ft centers. SLICING. Attempts to carry a slicing face from 50 to several hundred feet long failed; the long drifts from an auxiliary shaft, required for bringing in timber and supplies, were difficult to maintain, and slicing faces advanced irregularly, due to varying conditions. These troubles were overcome by slicing ore in blocks 250 ft square; locally called BLOCK METHOD OF TOP-SLICING. At middle of each block was a supply raise *R* (Fig 495) with a hoisting compartment 4 by 4.33 ft and a ladderway 2.5 ft wide; timber, steel, etc, were hoisted up this raise by a stretcher-bar hoist. Station sets of 12 by 12 timber with 9 or 10-ft posts were erected at top of raise, which was further protected by timber bulkheads 10 ft high; two bulkheads were 7 by 7 ft and two 7 by 11 ft in plan, as shown. Drifts *A*, *B*, and *C*, usually untimbered at first, were run

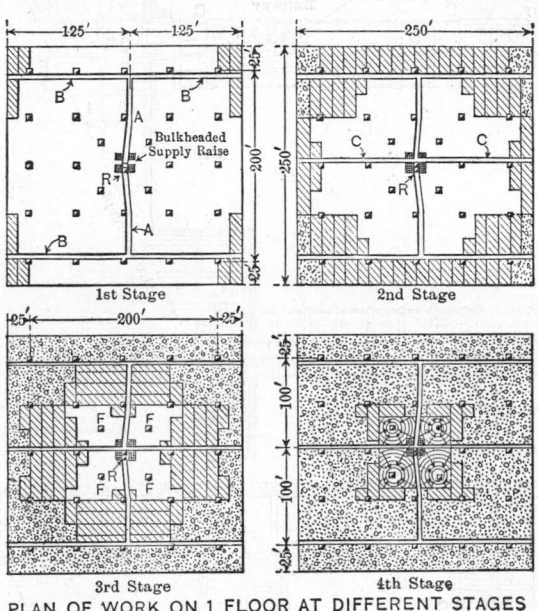

1st Stage   2nd Stage

3rd Stage   4th Stage

PLAN OF WORK ON 1 FLOOR AT DIFFERENT STAGES

Fig 495. Block Method of Top-slicing, Miami, Ariz

in the order named. Slicing began at end of *B* and *C*; Fig 495 shows 4 successive stages of work in same block. New slices were started as soon as those alongside had advanced a few ft. As many men as could work to advantage were put on; ore was mined with greatest possible speed, until only 4 central pillars around the supply raise remained (see 3rd stage). Inclined raises *F* were then put up to about the middle of each pillar; crosscuts (not shown) were driven to raises *F* from drifts *A* and *C*; slicing then continued, working from outside of pillars back to bulkheads, which by this time had squeezed down to a height of 4 to 6 ft. On completing this work, the last of the stope was caved; it was found best to let ground settle several weeks before starting another floor. Slices were 10 ft high, timbered, according to the ground, either with single sets, of 2 8-ft posts and a 12-ft cap, or with double sets, of 3 8-ft posts and 2 7-ft caps, all round timber. No floor was laid if mat was thick enough to prevent runs of capping; elsewhere a 2-in floor was spiked to 2 by 10-in sills; 5 by 10 and 4 by 8 sills were tried, but seemed to be no stronger than 2 by 10-in, after subjection to the heat and pressure of a completed slice. Bulkheads of old timber were built where necessary to aid slice-sets; the posts were shot down as soon as possible. All drilling was by plugger-drills, using a water spray. Ore in slices was shoveled to raises or handled in barrows. This method gave good results; weight on timbers did not get beyond control during the time that slices had to be kept open. It was found that pressure on central pillars was not intensified by caving around them. But ore in pillars was fractured, so that lifters were the only holes needed to break it. This fact, combined with the handling facilities provided by raises F, made pillar-ore cost less than that from outside slices. VENTILATION of the blocks was important; without it the heat from mat was excessive and reduced efficiency of labor. Air from a 60 000-cu ft fan was taken to the sub-level below the slicing floor and forced through raises into the slices as desired. Production per shoveler was 20 tons and per total manshift, 10 tons, these figures being about double those obtained in slicing on long faces without artificial ventilation.

Judge mine, Park City, Utah. Data from G. S. Krueger and E. A. Hewitt (147) in 1938. Ag-Pb-Zn ore occurs as bedded limestone replacements and as fissure veins cutting a series of folded and faulted shales, limestones, and quartzites. Bedded deposits dip about 20°, undulating in conformity with bedding planes; they are 2–20 ft or more thick; width, from a few to 100 ft or more; length, as much as 6 000 ft; hanging walls, usually firm limestone, do not require top-slice methods. Fissure veins dip 38°–60°; thickness, normal to walls, about 10 ft. Walls of the fissures are usually limestone, but one important vein has a weak shale hanging wall, wet and heavy. DEVELOPMENT comprises 2 vert shafts, 2 100 and 1 600 ft deep, and 2

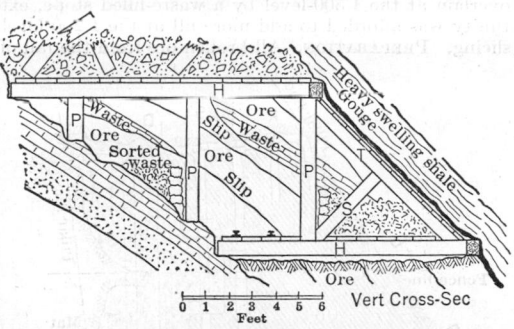

Fig 496. Top-slice Stope, Judge Mine, Park City, Utah
(Looking at face of stope)

tunnels. Main-level interval is generally 200 ft; numerous local intermediate levels are driven as required. Drifts and crosscuts are 5 by 7 ft, timbered with 8-in sets. STOPING. Overhand stopes, timbered with stringer sets, are generally used where walls are strong. Top-slicing is adopted where hanging wall is heavy, and is most effective on the flatter dips; widths of 3–20 ft (aver 10 ft) have been top-sliced successfully. Fig 496 shows ground conditions of a typical top-slice stope in a fissure vein. Fig 497 shows general plan of stope development and order in which slices are taken. In this case, orebody is developed by main-level drifts D at 100-ft vert intervals, with 2 sub-level drifts E at 33.3 and 66.7 ft above main levels. Double-compt raises R, 5 by 11 ft, timbered with 8 by 8-in sets spaced at 5 ft, are 50 ft apart. General plan of retreat is from both ends of orebody toward a central main raise. Individual slice sections, except at ends of orebody, extend from raise to raise. Face of a slice is advanced by a pilot heading, broken by a drift-round with back holes omitted; slabbing rounds complete breaking the face. Where waste inclusions are large or numerous, a pilot heading, best along hanging wall, is carried to end of block being mined. Slice is com-

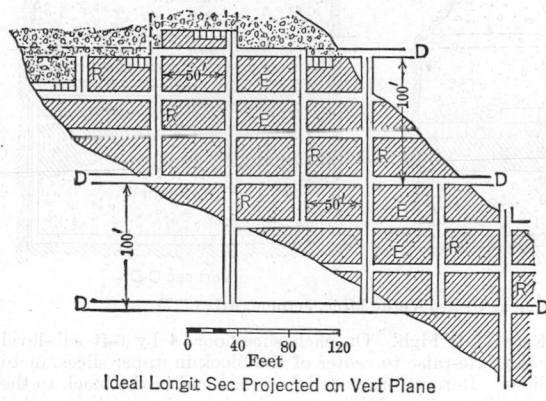

Ideal Longit Sec Projected on Vert Plane

Fig 497. Top-slicing in Judge Mine, Park City, Utah

pleted by slabbing on retreat, thus affording space for storing hand-sorted waste. Slices are timbered (Fig 496) with stringer sets 5 ft apart. Sills H, 8 by 8-in, are laid at right-angles to strike, and covered with 2-in lagging. Posts P are round timber, 8-in diam by 6 ft long. Sills become caps for the next lower slice. Sloping timbers T, faced with 2-in lagging and sometimes reinforced by angle stulls S, hold hanging wall where it is weak. Scrapers were tried for moving ore to chutes, but as sorting could not be well done, they were abandoned. Ore is shoveled into 0.5-ton cars and trammed to chutes. Caving usually follows without blasting of posts, promoted by fact that hanging-wall press is diagonal to sets. Operations are at such depth that subsidence has not reached surface.

United Verde mine, Jerome, Ariz (227). Data from T. W. Quayle in 1931, and from W. W. Lynch, formerly mine supt. For geol features and general description of orebody, see Art 62. Mining underground was generally by horiz cut-and-fill, lately changed to inclined cut-and-fill, as in Art 65. Top-slicing was used only in a special instance. An attempt had been made to mine as a single horiz cut-and-fill stope a block about 200 ft square, starting at 1 650-level. After the stope had been carried up several cuts, a large block of ground, over nearly the entire horiz area of the stope, fell from the back. This left the stope back in the shape of an arch (Fig 498, vert sec *C D*). Continuance of cut-and-fill was deemed unsafe, and top-slicing was substituted. The block in question was overlain at the 1 500-level by a waste-filled stope, extending to the 1 200-level. Opportunity was afforded to add more fill at the 1 200-level, as the filling dropped due to top-slicing. PREPARATION. All broken ore from the fall of ground was first removed. Then, before starting top-slicing, as firm a foundation as possible was established beneath the unmined block by complete back-filling of the open space with waste. It was realized that, as the block was thinned by slicing, it would eventually fall. But, with filling tightly packed against the old stope back, settlement occurred gradually, causing no accident to men, nor much interference with slicing. DEVELOPMENT. Raises *R*, Fig 498, for disposing of stoped ore were driven in ore from the 1 650-level on 35-ft centers near both hanging- and foot-walls. Service raises *S* within both walls and connected to each slice by short crosscuts were used to bring in timber and other supplies from the

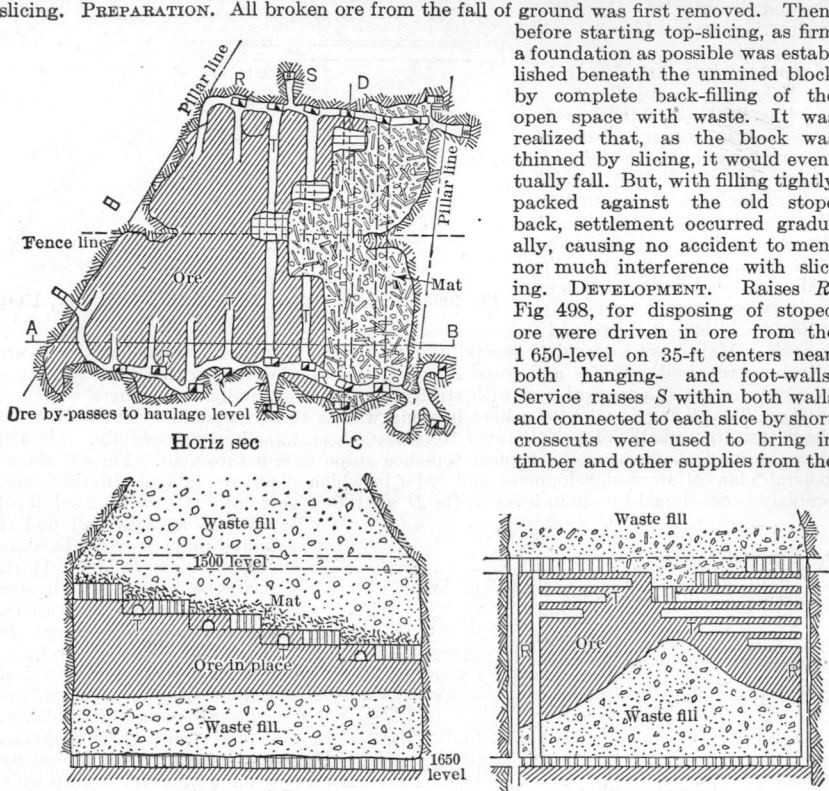

Fig 498. Top-slicing at United Verde Mine, Jerome, Ariz (227)

1 500-level. STOPING. Slices were 11 ft high. On each slice-floor, 4 by 6-ft sub-level crosscuts *T* were driven from each chute-raise to center of the block in upper slices, or to the edge of filling in the lower slices. Retreat proceeded from one end of the block to the other, and from a middle line to the walls. Mining was by breasting with mounted drifters. The broken ore was hand-shoveled and delivered to raises *R* in 18-cu ft scoop-body cars, running on sectional 16-lb rails. A double flooring of 2-in plank was laid on 4 by 12-in sills, set 5 ft 4 in apart at right angles to the sub-level crosscuts *T*. Posts of 10–14-in native pine, unpeeled, with 6 by 12-in headblocks, were placed 5 ft 4 in c-c directly under sills of the floor above; bottoms of posts rested on the ore, sills and flooring being laid after standing the posts. Generally, 3 lines of posts, lengthwise of sub-level crosscuts, were stood before blasting the posts. Posts were bored with air-driven augers; to minimize fire hazard, they were blasted with permissible explosive and elec caps. Top-slicing here proved more advantageous than square-setting, as to both cost and speed of mining. During first 10 mos of 1929, powder consumption was 0.71 lb per ton; timber,

9.91 bd ft per ton. Duty of labor was as follows, in man-hr per ton: breaking, 0.383; mucking, 0.651; timbering, 0.837; haulage and hoisting, 0.234; supervision, 0.120; general, 1.020; total, 3.245.

Oceanic quicksilver mine, Cambria, Calif. Data from A. W. Frolli (266) in 1937. Cinnabar occurs disseminated in sandstone. Main orebody is about 600 ft long by 15–40 ft wide; dip, nearly vert. Walls are not well defined; ore and walls are highly fractured and hence weak. In early work, surface ore was mined by open-cut; underground mining was by square-setting, with and without filling. Top-slice method was adopted because broken condition of orebody and walls made most other systems unsafe. DEVELOPMENT. As topography is steep, entry to mine is by tunnels; main haulage tunnel is about 350 ft below outcrop; from it a vert shaft was sunk to 750 ft. Level interval is generally 70 ft in upper workings, 50 ft in lower. STOPING. Two-compt cribbed raises R (chute and manway) are driven 35–40 ft apart (Fig 499). Slices are horiz and are usually 10 ft high; sometimes, in bad ground, 8 ft. In starting new slice, a drift, usually the

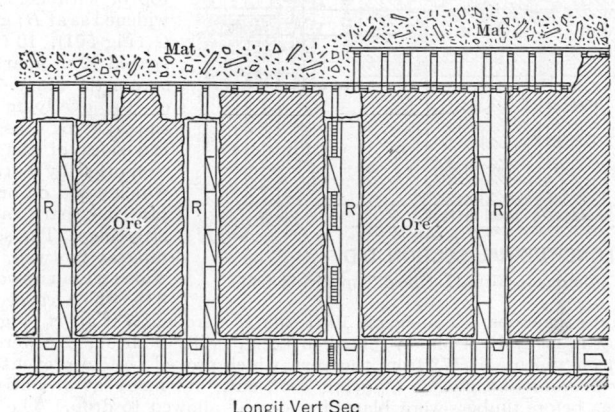

Longit Vert Sec

Fig 499. Top-slice Stope, Oceanic Quicksilver Mine, Cambria, Calif (266)

height of slice, is driven from the last raise to end of the ore. Stoping begins by widening the end of the drift to the ore limits. General plan is to retreat from one end of orebody to the other. Sills, of 2 pieces of No 2 common rough Oregon pine, 2 by 10-in and 12 ft long, are laid crosswise of the stope on 6-ft centers. On these, and lengthwise of the stope, single sills are laid for flooring. Silling and flooring closely follow the removal of ore, to prevent dilution from sloughing of walls. Roof or mat is supported by pine stulls, 8-in diam, placed 6 ft apart and directly under sills of slice above. When possible, raise cribbing and stulls are salvaged for reuse. When stoping has advanced about 30 ft, or to a point where timbers show wt, timbers are bored with 1.25-in holes 4–6 in deep, about 4 ft from the floor. Holes are loaded with half a stick of dynamite, both instantaneous and delay elec caps being used for better control of caving. Drilling is generally by breast-holing with jackhammers; due to broken nature of ground no systematic round is used. Explosive is 30% dynamite. In 1935, with miners' wages at $4 and muckers' wages $3.50 per 8-hr shift, mining costs per ton, excluding development, were: labor, $1.43; explosives, $0.08; timber, $0.14; other supplies, $0.08; power, $0.08; compensation insurance, $0.12; total, $1.93.

73. INCLINED TOP-SLICING

In this modification of top-slicing, the ore is mined in blocks or panels, and the slice floors, instead of being horiz, are driven on a slope sufficient for broken ore to slide or roll, either to narrow stopes or funneled chute raises on edge of the block. The method was designed to reduce cost of shoveling. It has had a limited use in the Morenci-Metcalf district, Ariz; attempts to use it at Bisbee, by Calumet & Ariz Mining Co, were unsuccessful. Following are examples.

Coronado mine, Metcalf, Ariz. Work suspended about 1923. Data from W. G. Scott in 1918 and P. B. Scotland in 1917 (595). Inclined top-slicing was used in a vein 20–40 ft wide (Fig 500). Ore was mined in blocks 50 ft long, separated by narrow shrinkage stopes

through which the ore broken in slices was handled. DEVELOPMENT. Sub-level drifts
Y were driven 55 ft apart vertically (or other multiple of height of slice, 11 ft); raises R,
at 50-ft intervals, connected sub-levels and main haulage levels Z. Crosscuts S, timbered
with square-sets, were run to walls or limits of ore at 50-ft intervals along sub-levels;
they extended into hanging wall far enough to leave 5-ft pillars between manway and
timberway raises X, which reached sub-level above. Breakthroughs B, 11 ft apart, gave
access to the shrinkage stope as it went up and to the slices as they descended. Vert
shrinkage stopes 4 ft wide were opened from the back of each crosscut S to top of
the ore or to the mat above. Chute gates and slides, in crosscuts S, delivered broken
ore to raises R; 2 gates sufficed for a stope 40 ft wide.

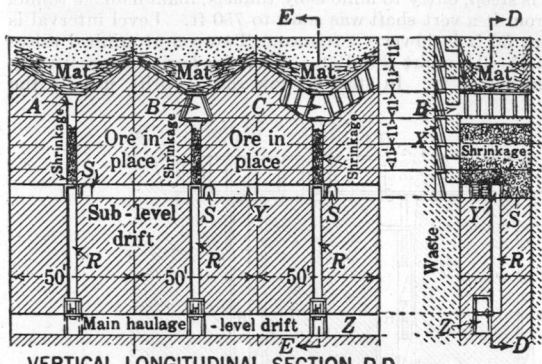

VERTICAL LONGITUDINAL SECTION D-D

Fig 500.   Coronado Mine, Inclined Top-slicing (595)

SLICING. Ore in shrinkage
stope was drawn down 11 ft,
as at A, Fig 500; then the
top of shrinkage stope was
widened as at B; grizzly stulls
G (Fig 501), 10 ft long and
spaced 12 in apart, were laid
across the stope. The stulls
of the overlying slice were
caught up by caps, paralleling
the sides of the stope and
supported by battered posts,
which stood on ore and were
braced apart at top by
stretchers. The slices, beginning at footwall, were 10 ft
wide and ran upward at about
33°, which caused the ore to
roll or slide into the stope. Transverse 10-ft sills M were laid 5 ft apart (Fig 501), with
a floor of 2 by 12-in by 12-ft plank, spiked to them. Sills of slice above were supported
by posts, set on the ore at 17° from the vert, which proved best to prevent them from
riding and with minimum chance of being shot out. As many as 3 contiguous slices
might be taken before timbers were blasted and mat allowed to drop. The method, as
applied here, requires ore strong enough to
stand in the shrinkage stopes; in weaker ore,
close-spaced chute raises may replace shrinkage stopes between blocks (see Humboldt
mine, below). OPERATING DATA. Production
from blocks 50 ft long in a 40-ft vein width
averaged over 2 000 tons per month, with 3
men per shift, 2 shifts per day. The stope
crew drew ore from shrinkage stope as required, hoisted its timber and did all other
work. Output per man-shift in inclined slicing in mining 29 000 tons in 1917 was 11.2
tons, compared with 4.64 tons for flat-slicing
25 600 tons in 1916; material costs for the 2
methods were about equal. From 1918 to
1923, a number of fires in the mats caused abandonment of top-slicing in favor of block-
caving and a combined method described in Art 87 (599).

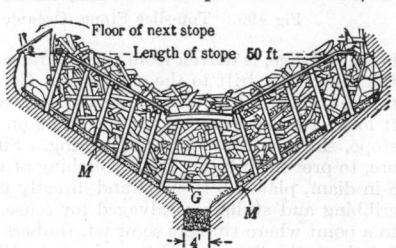

Fig 501.   Coronado Mine, Ariz, Longit Sec
through Slice

Humboldt mine, Phelps Dodge Corp, Morenci, Ariz. Operations at this property
were suspended in 1932. Data from J. P. Hodgson and J. Kiddie in 1922 (594). Inclined
top-slicing was used for some large shoots of soft ore; see Art 73 for ore occurrence.
Method was similar to that at Coronado mine (see above), but with chute raises instead
of shrinkage stopes between blocks. Ore was mined in blocks 50–60 ft long and full
width of deposit. In one shoot, 230 by 750 ft horiz sec, a main haulageway was driven
in one wall and from it parallel untimbered crosscuts were driven through the deposit
at 50-ft intervals, which brought them on center lines of blocks. From each crosscut, at 15-ft intervals, vert untimbered chute-raises were put up to the mat above
(44 or 55 ft); in the walls at ends of each crosscut were raises for handling timber and men.
Fig 502 is a vert sec through part of a crosscut L. First work on a sub-level was to
connect tops of raises with heading M, starting at far side of the ore; tops of raises were
belled out (see sec, Fig 502, and plan, Fig 503); 10-ft cross sills were set in hitches on
2.5-ft centers across floor of heading. The mat was picked up on posts and stringers

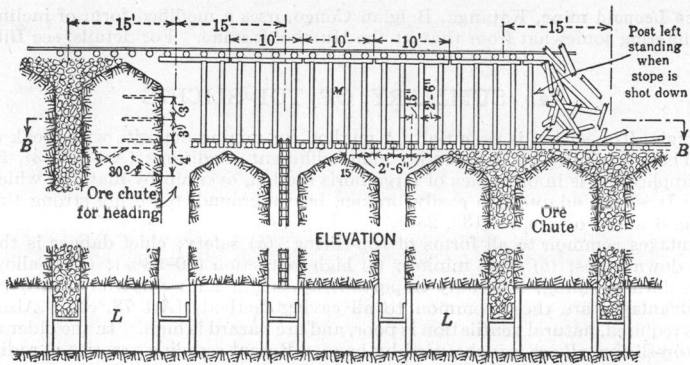

Fig 502. Humboldt Mine, Ariz, Inclined Top-slicing. Sec A-A, Fig 503

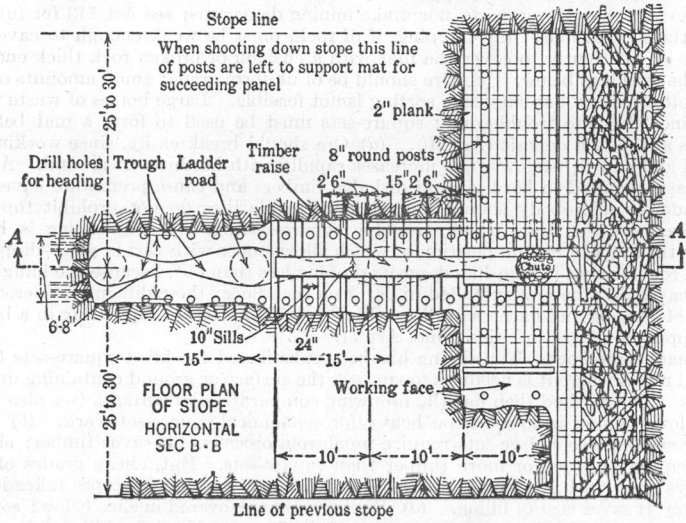

Fig 503. Humboldt Mine, Ariz, Inclined Top-slicing

(Fig 504), as at Coronado. After heading had advanced about 50 ft, slicing could begin. Slices were 10 ft wide, carried upward from heading at 33° until they reached caved ground or the limit of the block.

A comparison covering 4 years showed a reduction in costs of 15% in favor of inclined slicing over horiz slicing. Timber consumption, 1918–1921 incl, for all inclined slicing was 9 bd ft per ton, as against 7.9 bd ft for 1915–1921, all flat slicing. In another stope, 285 by 420 ft, crosscuts were 60 ft apart instead of 50 ft, with less satisfactory results. Inclined slicing at Humboldt mine was replaced (600) by another caving method (Art 87).

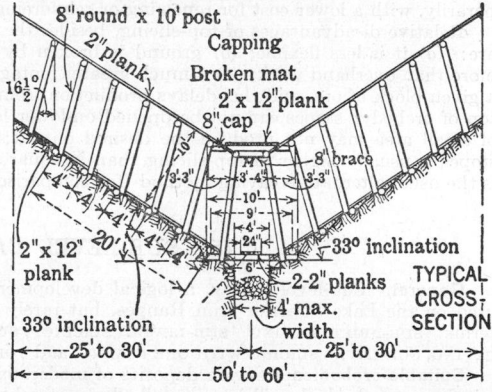

Fig 504. Humboldt Mine, Cross-sec through Wings of Stope

Prince Leopold mine, Katanga, Belgian Congo, uses a modified form of inclined top-slicing, differing somewhat from that at the Humboldt mine. For details, see Bib (274).

74. SUMMARY OF TOP-SLICING

General. Top-slicing is essentially a method for mining deposits with weak ore and walls. Though it may be used under many different conditions (Art 70–73), its commonest application is in orebodies of large horiz section, overlain by material which caves readily. It is well adapted to easily broken, heavy ground, requiring strong timbering and filling if mined overhand (132, 286).

Advantages common to all forms of top-slicing: (a) safety; chief danger is that men may fall down raises; (b) clean mining; (c) high extraction (90–98%); (d) it allows close sampling during mining; especially important in certain Lake Superior iron deposits.

Disadvantages are those common to all caving methods (Art 78, 82). Also, much timber is required, natural ventilation is poor, and fire hazard is high. In the older applications of top-slicing, all ore was shoveled by hand. Recent scraping practice in radial slices largely overcomes this disadvantage.

Requirements for successful application: (a) Subsidence of overlying ground must neither destroy valuable property nor make mining dangerous; see Art 113 for full statement of these conditions. (b) Capping, if of rock, must be weak enough to cave either to surface or sufficiently to cover the mat with a cushion of broken rock thick enough to protect the workings below. (c) Ore should be of uniform grade; small amounts of waste may be left on floors, but extensive sorting is not feasible. Large horses of waste may be left unmined, but are troublesome; square-sets must be used to form a mat below the horses, as at top of a deposit (Art 70). (d) Ore should break easily, since working faces are small and cost of narrow work increases rapidly with hardness of ground. Also, the heavy blasts required in hard ground dislodge timbers and cause premature caves (284). (e) Boundaries of orebody should be regular; irregularities do not prohibit top-slicing, but increase cost, as they usually involve square-setting. (f) Top-slicing is best for orebodies the shape, size, and position of which allow stopes with vert or steep-dipping side walls. Trouble arises in vein-like deposits dipping less than 60°, because the hanging wall must be caved and the mat extended under it on each floor; these difficulties increase with strength of hanging and flatness of dip. See Bib (277) for use of top-slicing in a bed 36 ft thick, dipping 9–12°; also Utica mine, Art 71.

Alternative methods. Top-slicing has been substituted for filled square-sets (Art 45) at several mines where it is needless to support the surface or ground containing unworked orebodies. The method then has the following comparative advantages (see also Art 54): (a) It allows mining in ground too heavy for economical square-set work. (b) In very heavy ground, where square-sets require much reinforcement, it saves timber; elsewhere it may require as much or more timber than square-sets. But, cheap grades of timber are always used, with less and simpler framing, and its erection in stopes takes less time (132). (c) It saves cost of filling. (d) Rich fines are recovered in slice below; some fines are always lost in filled square-set stopes (Art 47). (e) More unskilled labor can be employed; more shovelers and fewer timbermen are needed. (f) Stoping may stop temporarily, with a lower cost for renewing or reinforcing timbers.

Relative disadvantages of top-slicing, besides the general disadvantages stated above, are: (a) it is less flexible; (b) ground is broken by breast stoping, which usually costs more than overhand work; (c) a much greater footage of drifts, raises, etc, is required for a given block of ore, and this delays production from any area; (d) mining is confined to top of orebody; stopes can not be opened on lower levels; hence, top-slicing in orebodies of small area may not produce the desired output; (e) cost of bringing timber into the stopes is usually higher in top-slicing than in square-setting (Art 47). Sub-level caving is the usual alternative caving method (for comparison, see Art 78).

75. SUB-LEVEL CAVING

General. Sub-level caving, a logical development of top-slicing (Art 70), is largely used on the Lake Superior Iron Ranges, but rarely elsewhere in the U S. Other local terms: SUB-DRIFT CAVING, SUB-LEVEL SLICING, SUB-SLICING, SUBBING, SLICING AND CAVING, SUB-LEVEL SLICING WITH ORE CAVING, and TOP-SLICING WITH PARTIAL ORE CAVING.

Suitable orebodies are wide deposits of moderately soft or moderately firm ore, overlain by ground which will cave readily but coarsely, to form a capping which will arch and support itself temporarily over small openings. Latter condition is neither necessary nor desirable in top-slicing. For limitations and requirements of sub-level caving, see Art 78.

General plan. The method resembles top-slicing in that the ore is mined in horiz slices in descending order, so that the overburden, or capping, will break up and subside as the ore beneath is removed. Fundamental difference is that the height of slices in sub-level caving is usually 15–25 ft, as against 10–12 ft in top-slicing. Timbered slice-drifts are driven as in top-slicing, but a back of ore.7–15 ft thick is left between top of the sets and bottom of the mat, this back of ore being removed by mining and caving, starting at

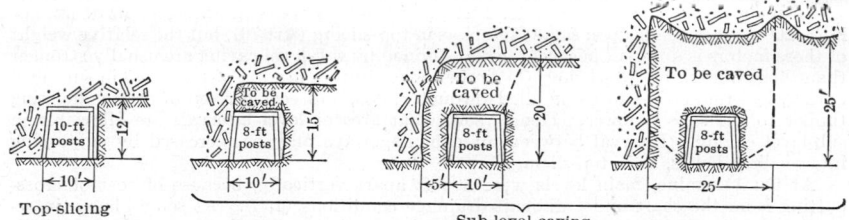

Fig 505. Diagrammatic Vert Cross-secs through Slice-drifts, comparing Top-slicing with Various Methods of Sub-level Caving

far end of the slice-drift and retreating toward the entrance. The slice-drifts are often 18–25 ft apart horizontally, the "caving-back" operation in a given slice-drift then reaching out on each side to lines midway between adjacent drifts. Fig 505 indicates the similarity between top-slicing and sub-level caving, and shows progressive variations in amount of ground taken per slice in the latter method.

Fig 506 also shows the resemblance to top-slicing in general plan of development, formation of mat, and the manner of retreat in a wide vein. MAIN LEVELS consist of drifts *D* and crosscuts *C*, planned to facilitate haulage and for proper spacing of raises *R*. SUB-LEVELS ("subs"), opened from raises as needed, consist of timbered drifts *S* and crosscuts *T*, cutting the ore into pillars (Fig 517, Art 76). This development work leaves pillars *P* between the back of one sub-level and floor of that above (Fig 506).

Mining begins on the highest sub-level, the end pillars being attacked first; work retreats toward some central point, as in the longit sec *VW*, Fig 506.

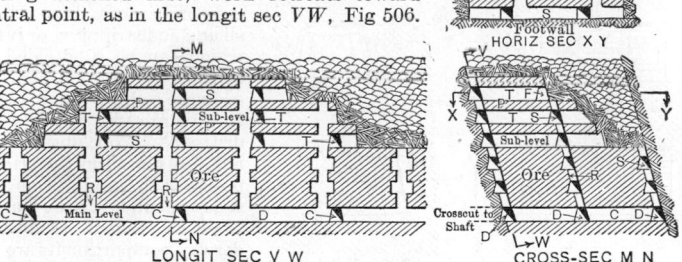

Fig 506. Sub-level Caving in Wide Vein (diagrammatic)

Work on individual pillars may begin at the hanging wall and retreat toward footwall (cross-sec *MN*), or may retreat from both hanging and foot to raises in middle of vein, or may retreat in a direction parallel to the strike.

In Fig 506, a slice-drift or slice *FF* is driven from crosscut *T*, next to caved ground and half-way across adjacent pillars; it is timbered with drift-sets and usually floored with lagging or plank. The overlying ore is caved into the slice-drift in small sections, from points *F* (horiz sec *XY*), and retreats to crosscut *T*. Ore is shoveled into either barrows or small cars and trammed to raise, or loaded mechanically into cars, or scraped direct to raises. Scraping has largely supplanted other means of handling ore. Contiguous slices are successively driven and caved in retreat. Mining of ore alongside and over slice-drifts is called "stoping back," "caving back," or "stripping." Fig 508–512 show details of different modes. Set-timbers and flooring are not recovered; as work descends, a mat of timber and waste (GOB) accumulates above. Method requires that gob shall hang temporarily over small excavations, long enough for safe removal of caved ore. Sub-level drifts and crosscuts connecting the raises divide the ore into blocks or panels, which are usually mined one at a time. Several blocks may be mined simultaneously by keeping adjacent working faces in advance of one another (Sec *XY*, Fig 506). In the same way, slicing and stripping may proceed simultaneously on several sub-levels. Main levels are mined like subs, the ore passing through raises to next lower main level.

Variations. Above plan may be adapted to orebodies of various shapes and sizes and to ores of different character by modifying layout of subs, raises, and main levels, the interval between subs, and the details of slicing and stripping (see below; also Art 76, 77).

Development. ENTRY (see under Entry, Art 70). INTERVAL BETWEEN MAIN LEVELS is 75–200 ft; it depends upon same factors as in top-slicing (Art 70), but the relative weight of these factors is different because: (*a*) ores mined by sub-level caving are usually stronger than those worked by top-slicing; (*b*) timber consumption per ton of ore is less in sub-level caving, less timber has to be handled through raises, and cost per ton of ore for hoisting timber to the subs is lower. Hence, somewhat greater level intervals are allowable in sub-level caving. Interval between main haulageways may be increased by employing intermediate levels, as in top-slicing.

At CHAPIN mine, main levels were 200 ft apart vertically, because of cost of cross-cutting from the shaft under difficult drainage conditions (153). At some places, intermediate levels were opened 50 ft apart; at others, raises were offset at 50-ft intervals to break the fall of ore and avoid excessive wear in chutes. Layout of main levels at this mine favored mechanical haulage. Oblique crosscuts allowed easy curves into crosscuts. Cars were hand-trammed in most of the crosscuts; only a few contained trolley wires. The disadvantage of oblique crosscuts is that some diamond-shaped pillars are formed on main levels, and also on subs, if these are directly over the main drifts. Slicing and caving are more difficult in diamond-shaped than in rectangular pillars, especially on reaching a stage where a triangular area remains to be mined. Also, ore is apt to be forgotten and lost when drifts and crosscuts are at oblique angles (183).

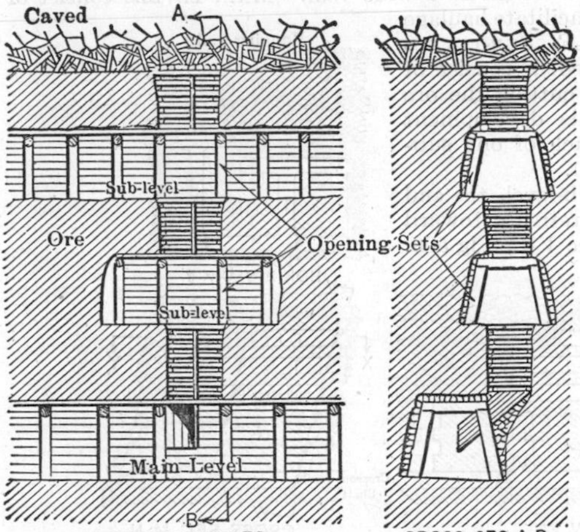

Fig 507. Timbering for Raises, Sub-level Caving

Main levels are planned to facilitate haulage and allow proper spacing of raises for handling ore on sub-levels. In very narrow orebodies, development often comprises a single drift; in wider orebodies, 1 or more drifts parallel to strike, often with crosscuts at 50- to 100-ft intervals; for examples, see Art 76. Original layout should cut ore into pillars suitable for slicing and stripping, or into pillars which can be subdivided systematically for this purpose by subordinate drifts and crosscuts. RAISES are usually close-cribbed; drift-sets ("opening-sets"), Fig 507, are placed in the cribbing opposite each sub-level as the raise goes up; sub-levels are started from these as needed. Chute and ladderway compartments are required in nearly all raises. Raises are usually put up from main-level drifts at intervals of 30–50 ft; branched raises are sometimes used to secure close spacing for hand and scraper loading; see Art 76 for various arrangements. Factors governing raise interval are like those for top-slicing (Art 70); see also below under Sub-levels.

Sub-levels. (*a*) Plan of sub-level development depends on shape, size, and nature of orebody, and character of capping; sub-level plans should guide main-level development rather than *vice versa*. (*b*) To facilitate slicing, sub-level drifts and crosscuts should intersect at right-angles, the pillars thus formed being rectangular. This practice is followed even where slice-drifts are oblique, as in Radial slicing, Art 76. (*c*) Regardless of method of loading, max length of slice-drifts for economical driving and stripping is about 100 ft. Economic length of slice-drifts also obviously influences interval between raises. See Art 76, 77, for various sub-level layouts.

Sub-levels should not be opened far in advance of mining requirements; to maintain them for long periods may require extensive renewals of timbering. New sub-levels can generally be developed quickly, as raises furnish numerous points of attack; but, when the ore from sub-level development is needed to maintain a certain output, the subs are run as soon as they are reached in the raises (76, 270). Drifts on a sub-level are sometimes crushed by pressure caused by mining on the sub above, especially when drifts on adjacent subs are directly over one another, instead of being staggered.

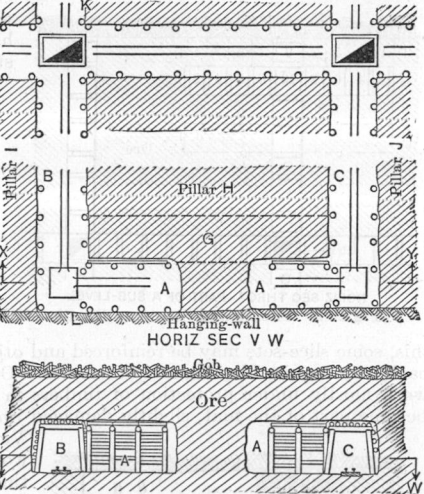

Vert interval between sub-levels is 12–25 ft; in a given orebody it is a compromise between following factors: (a) a large interval increases proportion of ore broken by caving and hence reduces aver cost of breaking ore for the whole deposit; (b) small intervals allow closer control, cleaner mining, and higher extraction; (c) max possible interval is a function of strength of ore, pressure of the gob, and time required to open and mine a sub-level. Depending on relative weight of these factors, the normal interval of 15–18 ft between subs is increased where possible and decreased if necessary. For unusual case where interval is 50 ft, see Montreal mine, Art 76.

Methods of slicing and stripping pillars formed by sub-level development vary with character of ore, pressure from caved ground, and thickness and strength of mat; local custom also influences the choice (270, 76, 293, 153, 482).

Fig 508 shows a plan suited to HEAVY GROUND which, in narrow excavations, can be supported temporarily by timber. A slice-drift A is driven across pillar H, and timbered with lagged drift-sets; when

Fig 508. Slicing and Stripping Details

completed, floor F of lagging or old timber is laid. Stripping begins by removing top lagging from sets at center of pillar and allowing the ore to run into the drift; the mat follows the ore down as indicated. Stripping retreats each way to crosscuts B and C, and the process is repeated in continuous slice-drifts until the pillar is mined out. Ore in back of crosscuts B and C, at D and E, may be broken as a final step in stripping each slice-drift, or when the adjacent pillars I and J are mined. The latter plan preserves crosscuts B and C, so that slice-drifts in pillars I and J can be driven from both ends. This increases speed of mining and shortens distance between working faces and crosscuts, but the cost of maintaining crosscuts may be prohibitive. An arrangement which avoids this difficulty is shown in Fig 506. If ground to left of KL (Fig 508) had been mined and caved, slice-drifts in pillar H could be driven from one end only, that is from crosscut C; stripping would then begin at inner end of slice.

In Fig 508, lagging on sides of the slice-sets holds back the gob while slice-drifts are being driven and stripped. Fig 509 shows a method permitting CLOSE CONTROL of both lateral and vertical pressure. A slice-drift AA is driven as shown, leaving a 6 or 8-ft pillar of ore PP next to gob. Work of removing pillar and stripping the slice begins at A and proceeds as follows: crosscuts 1 are driven through pillar PP and ore over 1 is caved; ore over 2 is then caved, and crosscuts 3 are driven and stripped; then ore over 4 is caved, and so on. The back of sub-level crosscut C, at 10, is stripped last; the next slice-drift is driven at FF and process is repeated. Fig 510 shows a systematic method sometimes used on Gogebic Range for stripping pillars and slices (482). Sub-level interval is 18 ft; slice-drifts, on 15-ft centers, are 10 ft wide at bottom, 7 ft at top, and 8 ft high. Starting at face of slice-drift S, a section of the pillar 1 is broken, usually by blasting; then cuts 2 and 3 are taken by blasting or barring. Without removing the top lagging, holes are drilled in the back of the slice-drift, and cut 4 and the lagging are blasted down; cut 5 is blasted or barred down as conditions require. This work is done in small sections, retreating toward entrance to slice-drift.

Fig 511 shows work in STRONGER GROUND under a strong mat. Drift A is a sub-level at end of orebody; slice-drifts B and C are driven in turn alongside of it. By the time slice B is completed, or possibly not until slice C is started, timbers in A begin to crush. If ore overlying A does not come down, timbers at far end of A are shot out, and caving is begun there by blasting down the back with light charges. The ideal condition is to have caving start at end of A and progress steadily back to crosscut D; to accomplish

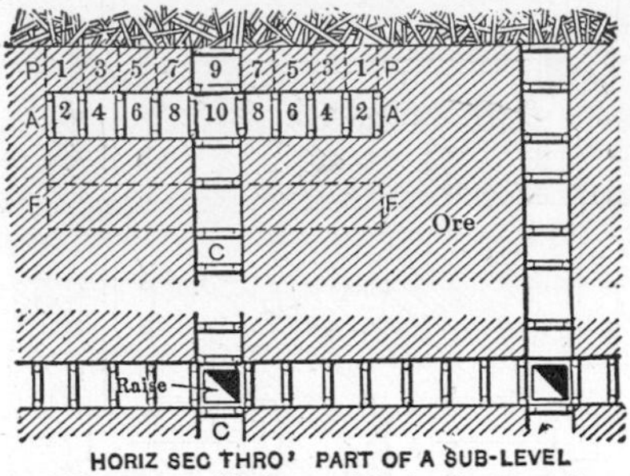

Fig 509. Slicing and Stripping Details

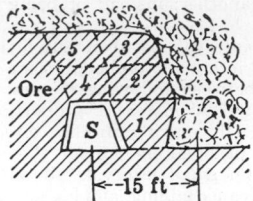

Fig 510. Cross-sec through Slice-drift

this, some slice-sets may be reinforced and others shot down; similarly, some parts of the back may require blasting and others not. Ore caving into slice A is loaded by men who work mostly under protection of timbers in B. Broken timbers are thrown back and become part of the mat; slightly damaged timber may be used for reinforcing weak sets.

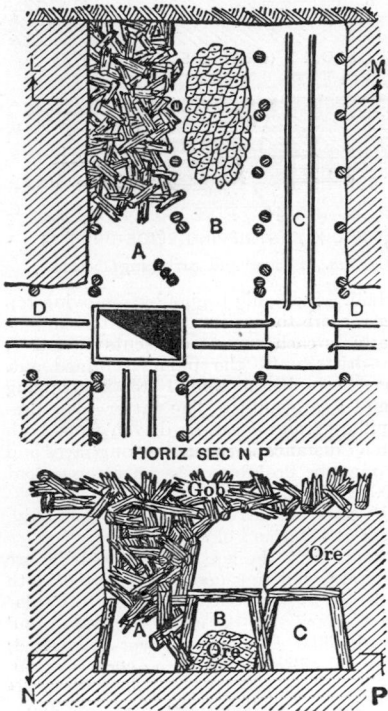

HORIZ SEC N P

VERT SEC L M

Fig 511. Slicing and Stripping Details

Vert sec LM, from B. W. Vallat (76), shows work while stripping is going on in slice B. A thick mat will often hang up until stripping is completed; P. S. Williams states that, on the Gogebic Range, Mich, the gob sometimes takes a week to close in (270). Obviously, details may be greatly varied. If parts of pillars crush before they can be mined out systematically, drifts are driven to the crushed area, and ore is drawn as long as it will run. Some of the ore which can not thus be recovered is obtained in stripping the sub-level below; such work is necessarily irregular.

Sometimes work is planned so that the weight of gob will crush part of the ore in sub-level pillars. Fig 512 shows this method of CHANDLER mine, Ely, Minn (see Art 76 for description of orebody). Stripping on any sub-level retreats from the ends of the deposit. Drifts D cut ore on the sub-levels into pillars say 10 ft square. Weight of the caved ground above breaks down ore in the back, and splinters the pillars so that they can be mined with pick and bar, without blasting. Where necessary, long props with head-boards support the mat temporarily, as at C.

For more recent practice on Gogebic Range, see Art 76.

Breaking ground in slice-drifts is similar to that in top-slicing (Art 70), except that there is no free face at the top; slices like those in Fig 509 are driven as ordinary drifts (Art 20).

Timbering. Cheap timber is used for same reasons as in top-slicing. Simply framed 3-piece sets are nearly always employed for slices. When slicing under a thick mat, FLOORS are often omitted.

P. S. Williams, commenting on GOGEBIC RANGE practice in 1910, indicated a growing tendency to cover floors of slices with boards, even where gob is compact enough to allow good extraction without them. Use of floor-boards sets a definite limit for men to work to in stripping and helps to prevent mixing waste with ore (270). HANDLING TIMBER.

Much slice timber must be hoisted up raises. Where sub-levels are opened in advance of mining requirements, timbers for sub-level drifts and crosscuts can be lowered from main level above. When a pillar of ore is left opposite a hoisting shaft in the footwall, raises can be maintained in the pillar, through which timber for development and slicing is lowered to sub-levels (270). SALVAGE OF TIMBER is not feasible.

Handling ore. Problems resemble those in top-slicing (Art 70). With hand loading, all ore broken must be shoveled. Barrows, or cars of 0.5–1.5 ton, are used on sub-levels. Some direct shoveling to raises is possible. Mechanical loading (usually with scrapers), is cheaper, increases duty of labor, and shortens time for slicing and stripping. Most of the loading in nearly all Lake Superior iron mines is now (1938) done mechanically, even where original development was planned for hand loading. For examples, see Art 76, 91. Small amounts of waste can be sorted out and left in the slices; floors should be laid where this is done, otherwise, the same waste will appear when slice below is stripped. Extensive sorting is not feasible.

Mat is started at top of orebody by one of the methods described in Art 70; see also Fig 518, Art 76, and accompanying text.

Ventilation problems in sub-level caving are like those in top-slicing. For efficient mining, powder smoke, and the heat and gases from decaying

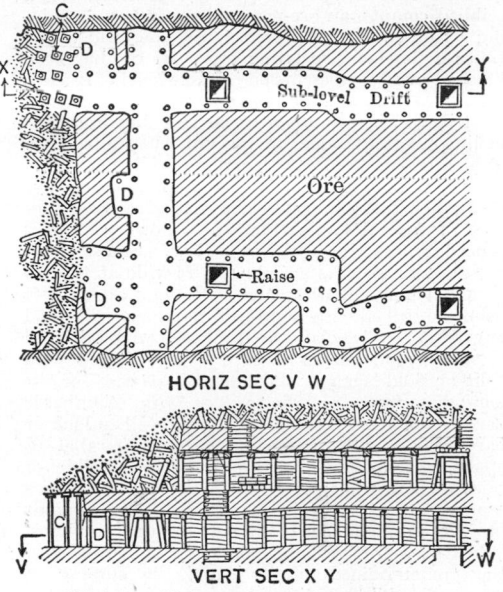

HORIZ SEC V W

VERT SEC X Y

Fig 512.   Slicing and Stripping Details

timber in gob, must be swept from the working places. Doors and brattices (Sec 14) are used to control natural air currents; working places which can not be thus ventilated have motor-driven pressure fans. Sub-levels are kept connected with main level above as long as possible, to facilitate handling timber; these connections and those with the timber-raises in shaft pillars greatly aid natural ventilation. For full discussion of ventilating problems in Lake Superior iron mines, see Bib (298).

Extraction. Some ore is lost in the gob, especially near top of orebody. Loss is materially reduced by using floor boards; it becomes less after some thickness of gob has been formed. Pillars crushing prematurely can not always be entirely recovered; such caving may cause further loss by preventing access to other pillars. Different engineers estimate that 5–20% of ore is lost in sub-level caving; no accurate data available.

76. SUB-LEVEL CAVING ON LAKE SUPERIOR IRON RANGES

Gogebic Range, Mich and Wis. Data from C. F. Jackson (281) in 1931. Orebodies occur in several productive horizons in cherty and slaty beds, dipping 55°–75°, as concentrations of hematite in V-shaped pitching troughs formed by intersection of dikes with footwall quartzite or impervious slates (Fig 513). Deposits, irregular in shape, vary from a few ft to several hundred ft in width and thickness, and from several hundred to several thousand ft in length. Hanging-wall capping usually consists of bands of slate and partly leached, cherty iron formation. On caving, hanging wall breaks into blocks or slabs tending to interlock and arch over openings of moderate size. DEVELOPMENT. Entry is by inclined or vert shaft in footwall (Fig 513); recent practice favors vert shafts. Main levels, 110–300 ft apart measured on dip of formation. Orebodies of the smaller widths are developed on main levels by drifts parallel to strike (Fig 514); wide orebodies, by longit drift near footwall, with crosscuts about 100 ft apart (Fig 514). Sub-level vert interval is usually 18–25 ft, sometimes greater; at Montreal mine, 50 ft. Sub-levels are developed from a series of raises from haulage drifts. Where haulage level comprises one or more longit drifts, the raises are on lines parallel to strike; slices usually run across orebody, with raises 18–20 ft apart at the sub-levels, to provide for direct scraping from slices. In very narrow orebodies slices generally run strikewise, with raises sometimes 200 ft apart. Where longit haulage drifts are used, raises are at same inclination as footwall; generally of 2 cribbed compts, an ore-pass and a manway containing a timber slide, compressed-air line, and sometimes a flexible ventilating pipe. If ore has been blocked out by crosscuts on haulage level (Fig 514), raises are crosswise of orebody, and slices parallel to strike. These raises may be vert, but are often inclined at right-angles to the crosscut and driven at an angle of 65°–70°. Regardless of haulage-level layout, raises are often 50 ft apart in starting, but are branched at some point above to give spacing of 18–25 ft at sub-levels (Fig 515). For exceptional procedure, see Montreal mine below. SLICING AND CAVING. Slice-drifts are about 8 ft wide at top, 10 ft at bottom, and 10 ft high. Rounds about 5 ft deep are drilled with hand-held hammer drills and auger bits. Slice-drifts are timbered with battered sets of round timber 5 or 6 ft c–c, lagged with split or pole lagging. Posts and caps are 7 or 8 ft long; diam from 8 or 10 in to 12 or 15 in. Timber is usually unpeeled tamarack; sometimes hemlock or hard wood. Where line of raises is parallel to strike, slice-drifts are driven from center line of raise to both walls; if crosswise of orebody, slices are parallel to strike in both directions to point halfway through block of ore between the raise lines. When slice-drift reaches hanging or footwall or to the predetermined mining limit, the stoping or "caving-back" operation starts at end of drift (Fig 515). A side cut is first taken next to caved ground, followed by several others, the last cut being always

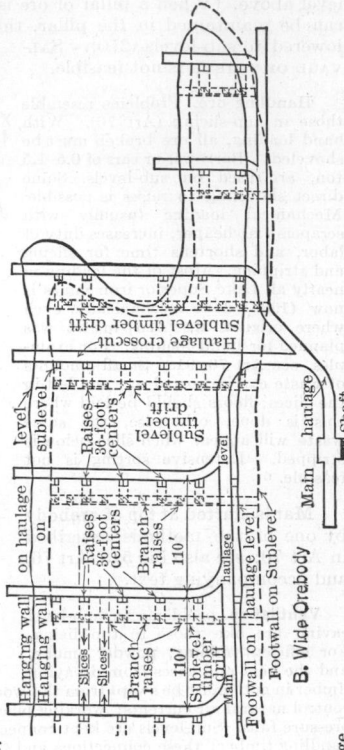

B. Wide Orebody

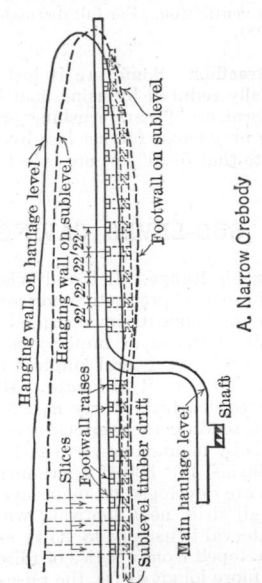

A. Narrow Orebody

Fig 514.   Main- and Sub-level Development, Gogebic Range

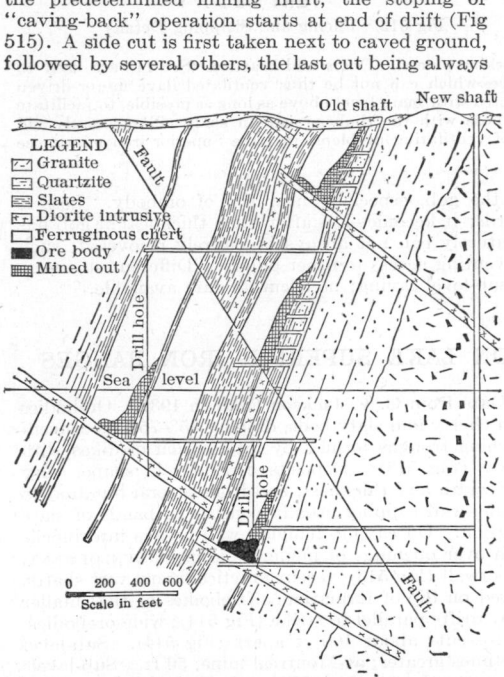

LEGEND
Granite
Quartzite
Slates
Diorite intrusive
Ferruginous chert
Ore body
Mined out

Old shaft   New shaft

Fault

Sea level

Drill hole

Drill hole

Fault

0   200   400   600
Scale in feet

Fig 513.   Typical Cross-sec of a Gogebic Range Mine, showing Scheme of Development

over the back of the drift. In making these cuts, lagging is removed from 1 or 2 sets, as required, to permit drilling. The side cuts are at an angle of 45°–50° from horiz; in blasting them, care is taken not to injure the pillar over back of drift. In starting the caving-back work, it may be necessary to mine several sets before the gob will come down. During advance of the slice-drifts and the caving-back operations, the ore is scraped by power scrapers into the raises. Floors are not covered as carefully as in top-slicing before caving of gob, but some covering, often old timber, is usual. The "hog-back" between slices may be blasted before caving the gob; if it is not mucked out, a mat (poles covered with wire fencing) is laid over it to prevent its mixing with gob. Caving-back operations are repeated, retreating to the raise, or to within about 8 ft of it if slicing is to be done on opposite side of the raise. Work is usually planned so that while a slice is being caved back, the adjacent slice is advancing. Miners work in pairs, on contract, usually producing, in caving back, 40–60 tons per man-shift, sometimes 80 or more tons. One mine reports an aver of 40 tons per man-shift for slicing and caving back combined. Caving back is carried on rapidly to minimize timber repair; slice-drifts are driven only in accordance with production requirements. Power scraping has virtually eliminated hand shoveling on Gogebic Range; usual equipment is commonly 15–25-hp elec double-drum hoists, with hoe or box scrapers. At Montreal mine, below, use of scrapers has eliminated loading chutes on haulage levels.

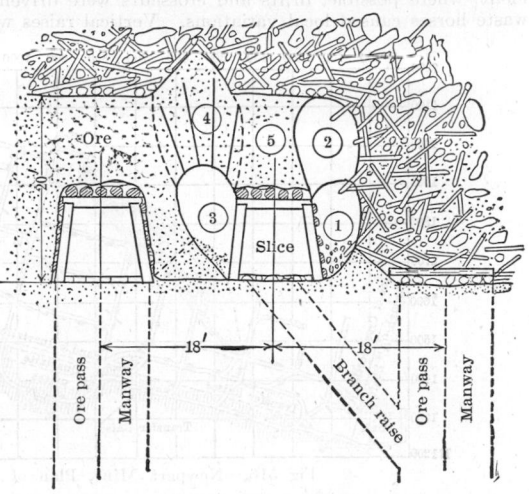

Fig 515.   Caving Back

Eureka-Asteroid mine, Gogebic Range, Mich. Data from O. M. Schaus (499) in 1930. Geological features are typical of district (see above). Types of orebodies: (a) the usual one consists of masses of triangular cross-section, lying at intersections of diorite dikes with the footwall; (b) blankets 5–20 ft wide lying on the footwall. Ore is soft hematite requiring timbering of all openings. Hanging-wall capping is cherty iron formation. DEVELOPMENT. Main shaft is vert, in footwall midway between property lines; depth (1930), 3 275 ft; at 2 000 ft it is 1 000 ft from footwall. Haulage levels are at 200-ft vert intervals. Level development depends on size and shape of the orebody, but usually comprises one or more drifts parallel to strike. Drifts in ore are 9 by 11 ft outside timber; battered sets of 8-ft posts and caps are 5 ft c–c. Untimbered drifts and crosscuts in footwall are 8 by 10 ft. Where ore is in narrow veins or blankets, raises are as much as 200 ft apart; they have 2 cribbed compts, ore-pass and manway. Ore-passes are lined with 1.5-in hardwood plank to aid passage of sticky ore and prevent wear on cribbing. In orebodies 100 ft or more wide, main raises may be 50 ft apart, branch raises splitting the intervening pillar. Inclination of raises is 55°–90°; 65° slope has been found best for ore-passes. Vert spacing of sub-levels is 18–25 ft. Orebodies 5–50 ft wide are opened on sub-levels by drifts; wider bodies, by crosscuts 25 ft apart, with a connecting drift along line of raises. MINING. Slice-drifts are 8 by 9 ft; timbered with 7-ft posts and caps. Scrapers are used both in advancing slice-drifts and in caving-back work. In narrow orebodies, caving starts midway between raises, max economical scraping distance being 100 ft. If ore is no wider than the drift, back lagging is removed between 2 sets of timber and a 6-ft round drilled in the back. After blasting, miners stand on the broken ore to drill next cut, which is fanned out parallel to drift. Before this is blasted, 3 or 4 back-lagging poles are replaced to prevent premature runs of gob. When second cut reaches the caved sub-level above, ore from both cuts is scraped out. In wide ore-bodies, slices run across them, sub-levels being spaced vert on 18-ft centers and horiz on 25-ft centers. Caving-back follows typical Gogebic practice (Fig 515). Miners work on contract; when slicing, rates are lower in wide orebodies, higher in narrow ones. In 1929, production averaged 5.71 tons per man-shift underground; dynamite consumption (60% in development, 40% in stoping) was 0.71 lb per ton; timber, 3.35 bd ft per ton.

Newport mine, Ironwood, Mich. Data from B. W. Vallat in 1911 (76). This example, though old, is retained to show variations in main-level development, sub-levels arranged for hand shoveling, and work at top of orebody. Entry was by inclined shafts in country rock, parallel to footwall dipping 68°. Fig 516 shows usual main-level development; where possible, drifts and crosscuts were driven on sides of 100-ft squares, but waste horses caused local variations. Vertical raises were 50 ft apart along drifts and

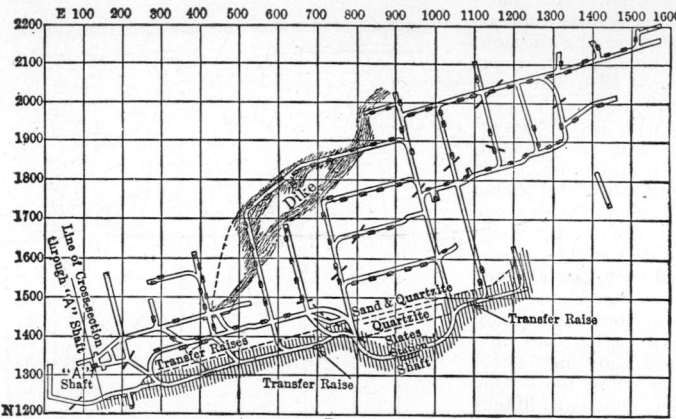

Fig 516. Newport Mine, Plan of 17th Level

crosscuts. Sub-levels were 15 ft apart, beginning 18 ft above main level, where a thicker pillar was left to protect haulageways. Sub-levels were opened by connecting the raises with drifts and crosscuts; the 100-ft pillars so formed were subdivided into 50-ft pillars, just before mining began in any area (Fig 517).

Slicing and caving were carried on in sections 300 to 400 ft long by full width of deposit. The contact between ore and rock at top of orebody pitched eastward. The first work on any sub-level started at its eastern end; an area 300 ft long was subdivided into 50-ft pillars (Fig 517). Slice-drifts (crosscuts) *A* and *B* (Fig 518) were driven in succession across a pillar on hanging-wall side. Men working under protection of the timbers in *B* drilled short holes in the ore above *A*, to break it clean without disturbing the capping; the sets were left to stand if they would. The floor of *A* was then covered with old lagging, blocking, etc, which, with the slice-sets, started the mat, on which

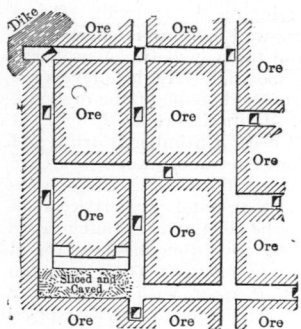

Fig 517. Newport Mine, Plan of Part of a Sub-level

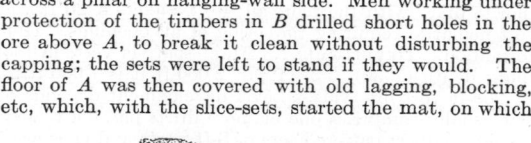
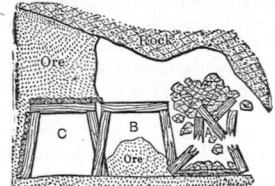

Fig 518. Newport Mine, Slicing and Stripping under Capping

the unsupported capping kept shelling off. Slice *C* was then driven, the ore over *B* was taken down, and so on over the whole area of sub-level. Meanwhile, areas 300 ft long to the west on same sub-level and 300 ft long to the east under the capping on next lower sub-level were developed (Fig 519). Slicing and stripping under gob proceeded as in Fig 511. On sub-levels, ore which could not be shoveled to raises was handled in 0.5-ton cars ("buggies") on 8-lb rails, with turn-sheets at intersections of drfts. In 1910, Newport mine produced 1 074 800 tons in 307 days, using 0.608 linear ft of round timber and 0.0049 cord of lagging per ton.

Montreal mine, Gogebic Range, Wis. Data from R. A. Bowen, Asst Supt (292) in 1938. Ore occurs as concentrations of hematite in pitching V-shaped troughs formed by intersection of dikes with quartzite or slaty sedimentary formation. Formation dips about 62° N; dikes, 45° S; troughs pitch about 16°. Orebodies up to 180 ft wide and 1 400 ft long are scattered along 2 miles of formation. Ore is "soft," of claylike consistency which is quite strong and permits relatively large openings. Capping is weakened longit by interlaminated ore seams, and transversely by cross-jointing planes; otherwise it is strong and hard, and breaks without producing very large blocks or much fines, tending to arch and hang in cav-

ing. The part of capping in direct contact with ore is high enough in iron to permit some ore dilution without destroying commercial value. DEVELOPMENT. Entry is by vert shaft in footwall. Haulage levels are 150 ft apart; sub-level interval, 50 ft. Haulage levels are developed by a drift D (Fig 520) within footwall, from which crosscuts X are turned off to cross orebody at 300-ft intervals. Main-

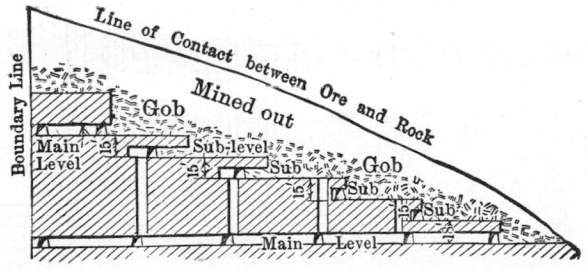

Fig 519. Newport Mine, Relation between Work on Sub-levels. (Vert longit sec, vert scale exaggerated)

level entries are either gunited or timbered with battered sets, 5 ft c–c, with 8-ft posts and caps, 11–13 in diam. Near the footwall, a "loading drift" E, about 50 ft long, is driven in one direction from each crosscut, elevated 4.5 ft above rail in crosscut. Opposite the entrance to each loading drift a short drift runs in the other direction to accommodate a scraper hoist. From each loading drift a double-compt cribbed "mining" raise R, 4 by 4 ft inside each compt, without chute pocket, is driven at the footwall inclination to the second sub-level, 100 ft above. All ore from the mining raises is scraped through the loading drifts to cars in the crosscuts. Nearer the center of the orebody, from drifts similar

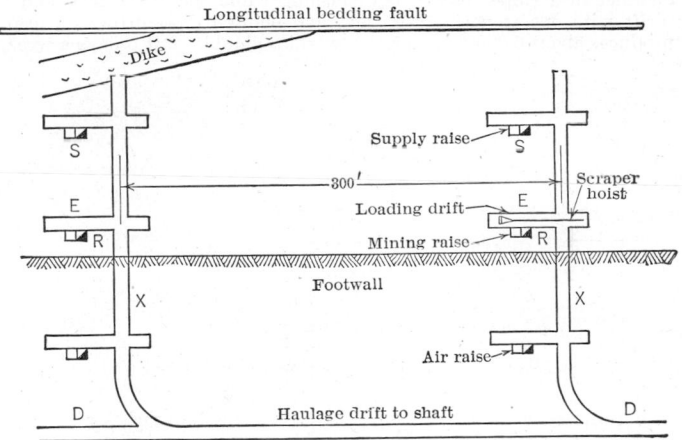

Fig 520. Montreal Mine, Generalized Plan of Haulage Level

to the loading drifts, a second raise S is driven to handle materials and serve as travelway and airway. Other raises within the footwall connect the main levels for ventilation. On the sub-levels, a "slushing" drift T connects the mining raises (Fig 521); crosscuts U connect the various raises serving each main crosscut. The ore is blocked out in 50-ft pillars along the strike, formed by 2 crosscuts V at 25 ft c–c, each 12.5 ft from the center line of pillar. Sub-level entries are timbered with battered sets 5.5 ft c–c, with 8-ft posts and caps. STOPING AND CAVING. Mining starts in a pillar midway between 2 mining raises, developed by the 2 crosscuts V. A manway is raised midway between crosscuts to a point 25 ft above the sub-level and a small, untimbered sub-crosscut Y is driven to the ore limit (Fig 522). Beginning near the ore limit, openings W from the inside of each crosscut are carried up, enlarging as they progress, until they hole through to one another and connect with the manway. Thereafter the "stope" is enlarged by narrow benches. As "slice" holes are blasted in the sides, the back caves down until it arches over the added width of opening created. The operation is thus carried on until the protecting shell of ore around the stope is very thin. The gob is usually exposed in several places before the stope begins to show weight. At this stage, any supporting ribs are cut, and caving or

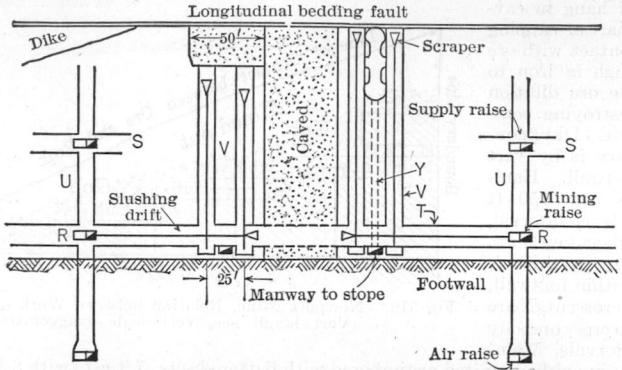

Fig 521. Montreal Mine, Generalized Plan of Sub-level

"dropping" starts. Caving is gradual and may continue for several shifts. By successive mining and caving, the pillar is mined back to the "slushing" drift T, and any ore on the footwall side is also stoped. The drift is well propped for passage of air after mining is finished. In sub-level work, a "task" for 2 men in advancing a heading is 5.5 ft per shift; for driving 2-compt raise, 4.5 ft per shift. In stoping, the task is 40 tons per man-shift, including slushing. Bonus is paid for work exceeding "tasks." Miners work in pairs; 2 pairs together in a stope (pillar), one slushing while the other drills and blasts. A slushing drift with one stope in operation, and enough crosscutting to keep ahead of mining, produces about 6 000 tons per mo, working double shift 5 days a week.

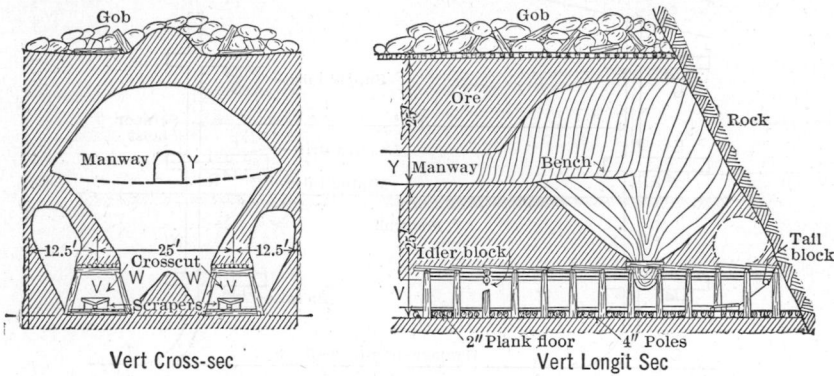

Vert Cross-sec   Vert Longit Sec

Fig 522. Stoping Procedure, Montreal Mine

Chandler mine, Vermilion Range, Minn (153, 183, 287). Orebody occurs in a flat-dipping trough (Fig 106, Art 14) capped by jasper. Ore is hard hematite, though shattered and broken, and machine-drills are often needed in driving main levels. Fig 106 shows mode of entry and position of levels and subs. Down to 8th level, main levels were 50 to 75 ft apart; sub-levels, 12.5 to 15 ft apart. Ore in the legs of the trough was about 70 ft thick; main levels usually comprised 2 drifts, near the walls and connected at intervals by crosscuts. Raises were spaced 50 ft apart along drifts. Sub-levels were opened, sliced and stripped, as described in text accompanying Fig 512, Art 75. Sets in sub- and main-levels were 3 to 4 ft apart; top lagging was used in all drifts; little side lagging was needed. No floors were laid in slices. Barrows or small cars (buggies) were used on sub-levels. Below the 8th level, shaft stations were cut at 20-ft vertical intervals; intermediate levels were of same size as main levels (Fig 106). Ore on each intermediate level was cut into pillars by drifts and crosscuts, and mined as on upper levels. This saved many raises and allowed greater use of cars instead of barrows.

Scraping in mines developed for hand loading (482) involves use of slides for loading cars (Sec 27), or right-angle turns in scraper leads due to spacing of raises. Fig 523 shows a plan to overcome these difficulties in heavy ground. Level interval is 110 ft; main levels comprise parallel drifts 50–75 ft apart, from which 2-compt raises C are put up 33 ft apart; sub-level interval, 18 ft; bottom sub, 20 ft above main level. Short branch raises B are put up to each sub-level from chute compartments of main raises. Branch raises start from horizon of next lower sub-level. The drift-slices are on 11-ft centers (see dotted lines); each has a raise opposite its entrance, into which broken ore is scraped. Fig 524 shows a variation of this plan, used in firm ground where the sub-level drift E may be driven before slicing starts on the sub above. Vert raises R are put up to the upper sub opposite each slice-drift, and timber slides S convey broken ore to main raises C. In

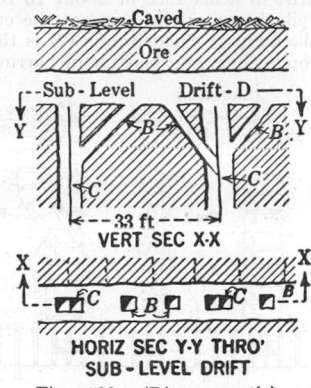

Fig 523. (Diagrammatic)

another variation, main raises are 50 ft apart and branched as in Fig 523, to come out on the mining sub at intervals of about 17 ft. Slice-drifts (10 ft wide at bottom) are started opposite raises; half the pillar on each side of a slice is drawn when slice is stripped. In these variations, the scraping hoist is located at the raise and broken ore is scraped directly into it. Such direct scraping gives outputs loaded per contract crew from 75 to 100% greater than in hand-loading contracts.

Fig 525 shows a more elaborate system of branched raises, to permit use of scraper loading in sub-level caving of a large orebody, originally developed for hand loading. Main levels, 110 ft apart, comprise parallel drifts L on 65-ft centers; raises R are inclined 65° and 33 ft apart. On third sub, 56 ft above the main level, the raises are connected by drifts D, parallel to drifts L. From alternate raises along drift D, 2-compt raises E, also inclined 65°, are put up to top sub; 4 by 4-ft branches F are driven from the horizon of the sub below to top one. A greater width of ore may require an extra drift as at G, and the raises H. On top sub-level, crosscuts C, 66 ft apart, are driven to connect tops of the raises. Slices 33 ft long are driven from crosscuts, as at S; intervening pillars are drawn as slices are stripped. Added raises are put up to serve lower sub-levels, as shown by dotted lines in Sec XY. This provides short straight hauls for scrapers; it requires a large footage of raises and drifts. Width served by a given set of main raises decreases on successive subs; on lowest subs in a lift, other methods must be used for handling part of the ore.

Radial slicing, developed by Oliver Mining Co on Vermilion and Gogebic Ranges, avoids 90° turns in scraping and also branched or other closely spaced raises. Double-compt, 4 by 8-ft raises, on 33-ft centers, are put up from main level drifts, which are 65 ft apart; sub-level interval, 18 ft. On each sub-level the raises are connected by drifts and crosscuts, dividing the ore into blocks about 25 by 55 ft in horiz sec. Successive operations in each block are shown in sketches A to F, Fig 526. A is the first slice-drift. Without removing timbers, the left half of the back of last 3 sets included in shaded area

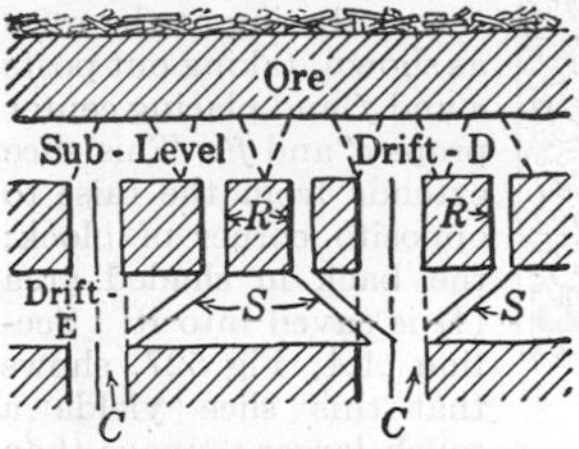

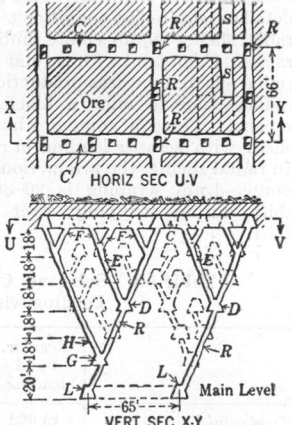

Fig 524. Vert Sec through Sub-level Drift (diagrammatic)

Fig 525. Sub-level Caving. Branched Raises (diagrammatic)

(1) is then caved. In B, posts a and b are removed and the caps supported by center props a' and b'. From this opening a diagonal or radial slice is started, which clears first slice-drift in a distance of about 15 ft and then continues parallel to it. Rail or plank are spiked to inside of posts at the curve, about 6 in from bottom, to guide scraper around the corner. Shaded area (2) is then stripped, 1 set at a time, by removing a few side or top lagging, and blasting or barring down the back. In stripping, only the ore which can

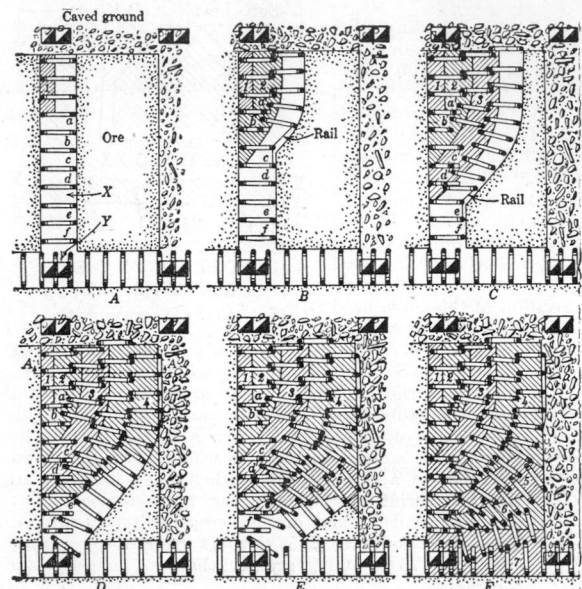

not be reached from the succeeding slice is taken; as much solid ground as possible is left over the miners. The back is usually caved for 2–2.5 ft from left end of cap. Broken timber and rock from the cave are thrown into first slice-drift and help keep posts from moving. In C, a 2nd diagonal slice is started by taking out posts c and d and putting in center props as before. The back in shaded area (3) is caved into this slice. In D, a 3rd diagonal slice is started by changing the timbering at the raise as shown, taking out posts e and f and placing center props e' and f'. This slice extends from the raise to opposite corner of block; the back in shaded area (4) is caved into it. Section AA, Fig 527, shows that this slice yields a much larger tonnage than

Fig 526.   Radial Slicing (diagrammatic)

the others. In E, the 4th diagonal slice again requires changes in timbering as indicated; the back, shaded area (5), is caved into this slice. In F, the last diagonal slice is started by making the changes indicated in drift timbering, and the back included in shaded area (6) is caved. Remainder of the back, shaded area (7), is caved into the crosscut. This general plan is modified in detail as required by conditions. Some operators state that radial slicing requires more timber than work with branch raises. Compared with regular slicing and hand loading, radial slicing increases production per man 75–100% and reduces time to mine a block, hence decreases timber repairs. Table 50 compares hand loading in rectangular slices with scraper loading in radial slices at same mine. In radial slicing, the production of a 2-man contract with

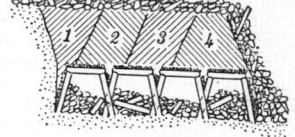

Fig 527.   Vert Sec AA, of Fig 526 D

double-drum scraping is 20–30 tons per shift during slicing-in, and 30–100 tons per shift during stripping; aver output for both slicing and caving, 30–40 tons per shift.

Table 50.   Sub-level Caving.   Comparison of Regular Slicing and Hand Loading with Radial Slicing and Scraper Loading

	Regular, hand loading	Radial, scraping		Regular, hand loading	Radial, scraping
Tons mined.............	10 992	14 886	Tons per timber set......	76.87	66.75
Man-shifts.............	1 344	820	Tons per prop..........	112.16	323.6
Timber sets............	143	223	Sets per 100 tons........	1.30	1.5
Props.................	98	46	Props per 100 tons.......	0.89	0.31
Tons per man-shift.....	8.18	18.5	Lagging per set.........	1/4 cord	3/16 cord

Miscellaneous examples. Fig 528 shows application of scraper loading in mining one leg of a trough-shaped deposit. The ore, about 15 ft thick, lies on a dike dipping about 25°. A tramming drift A was driven; back of drift was cut out at intervals of 25 ft, and from these openings inclined slice-drifts B, 7.5 ft high by 8 ft wide, were run to limits of the ore. Stripping retreats from upper end of slice-drift; the back and half the pillar on each side of the slice-drift are caved into it; broken ore is scraped to a chute, which loads a car on the tramming level A. Aver output per man-shift, 18 tons.

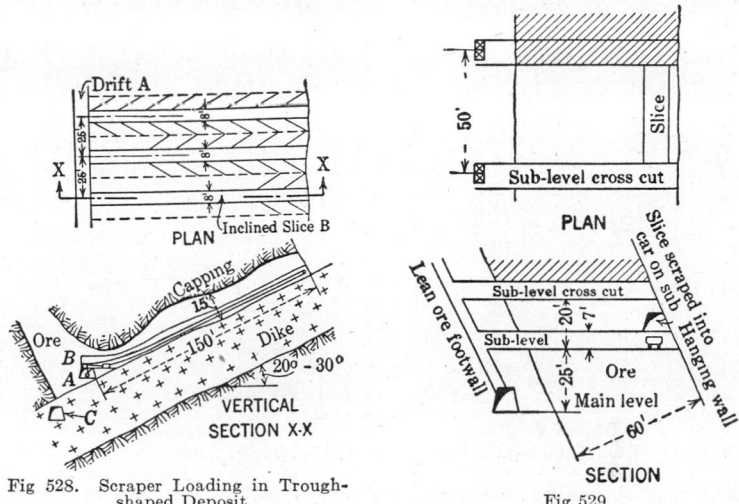

Fig 528.   Scraper Loading in Trough-shaped Deposit

SECTION
Fig 529

Method shown in Fig 529 was used to mine an orebody 60 ft wide. Main levels and raises from them were in footwall, which was lean ore (35% Fe). Sub-level interval, 20 ft; sub-level development comprised crosscuts 50 ft apart, run from each raise to hanging wall. Slicing started at hanging wall; the back of crosscut was cut out and a slice-drift was driven from the crosscut. Broken ore was scraped from slice-drift into a car standing in the crosscut. (Compare with sub-gangway used in top-slicing at Copper Queen mine, Art 70).

77. SUB-LEVEL CAVING IN UTAH AND ARIZONA

Mercur, Utah. Orebodies are low-grade gold and silver-bearing replacement deposits in tough, hard limestone, underlying sheets of porphyry which follow the limestone bedding planes on both strike and dip. There are several sheets of porphyry, and in places corresponding parallel orebodies overlying each other. Deposits are 4 to 70 ft thick; dip, 0° to 30°. Ore is usually soft, sometimes like clay; drilling is done single-hand or with augers; 30% dynamite is used. The porphyry hanging wall is blocky and generally caves readily. Practice of Consol Mercur Gold Mines Co is described below; this company suspended operations in 1913. Development. Entry was by a compound shaft (Art 16), the lower part being vertical; at each level a crosscut was run through the orebodies, with a drift along each body. Inclines were often sunk in ore from main levels and drifts turned off from them alternately to right and left at 50 ft apart, measured on dip. Thin beds (less than 20 ft thick; description by G. H. Dern, Bib 295). Fig 530 shows part of an oreshoot cut off on one side by a fault. Crosscut C was driven to footwall and a raise R followed the footwall to level above. Sub-levels, 4 by 6-ft, driven on footwall to the fault at 15-ft intervals, were timbered with 3-piece sets and lagged. An area thus opened was allowed to stand sometimes 2 or 3 months, so that pillars between subs would crush and become well broken; during this period, sub-levels were kept open by easing timbers where necessary. Mining began at fault on sub No 1, by pulling out a set of timber; as the ore caved it was shoveled into a car and trammed to raise R, or to special chutes provided for this purpose. A little blasting was required, to bring down ore and to blockhole boulders. When waste rock appeared, the miner retreated one set and repeated operation. When sub No 1 had been drawn back 10 or 12 ft, work started in same way in sub No 2, and so on in lower sub-levels. If two orebodies occurred, the upper one was mined first. Advantages claimed for the method were: small timber and powder consumption, safety, high extraction, clean mining. It was not applicable to deposits over 15 to 20 ft thick. THICK BEDS could be mined in 15-ft layers or slices parallel to hanging wall, by methods described above. Hanging-wall slice was taken first, followed by lower

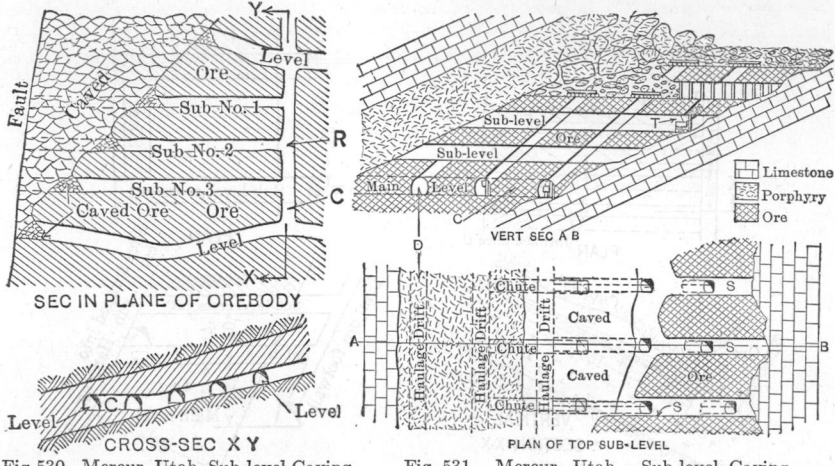

Fig 530. Mercur, Utah. Sub-level Caving   Fig 531. Mercur, Utah. Sub-level Caving

slices as ground above them was worked out and caved; eventually mining proceeded simultaneously in all slices (190).

Fig 531, from R. H. Allen (296), shows another form of sub-level caving, for beds up to 70 ft thick. Main levels consisted of parallel drifts D, connected by crosscuts C, 25 to 50 ft apart. Raises were driven between crosscuts. As the minimum angle on which ore will slide is greater than the dip, new raises had to be started on footwall side of higher sub-levels, as at T. Raises nearest footwall had chute and ladderway compartments; others had a single chute-compartment. Sub-levels were 14 ft apart vertically; sub-level development consisted of driving crosscuts S from each raise to foot and hanging walls. Mining began on the highest sub-level; ends of crosscuts next to hanging wall were widened out until two or more crosscuts were connected, the roof of excavation being temporarily supported by stulls. To start caving, a few holes were drilled in the back next to the hanging wall. Pillars between crosscuts were worked back toward footwall by driving successive slice-drifts, 6 or 7 ft high, across them; slices were timbered with 3-piece sets. Ore was hand-led to chutes in barrows. Shoveling along face of cave was stopped when much waste appeared, and a new section of the back was allowed or forced to cave, a safe working place being kept open along faces of pillars. Drilling was all done by hand, no heavy blasts were fired, and light timbers were adequate. Caving was not started in any area until the sub-level above had been worked back to footwall; by mining ore in blocks, caving could be carried on simultaneously on several sub-levels at different points along the strike. Thickness of ore caved on each sub-level was 4–7 ft; thus, 30 to 50% of orebody was broken by caving; remainder was obtained in drifts and slices. Results of work indicated that a

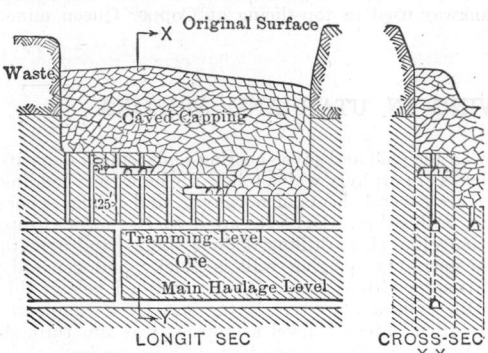

Fig 532. Arizona Copper Co. Sub-level Caving

12-ft interval between sub-levels might be better; a 4-ft back could be kept under better control and gave higher extraction than a 7-ft back. It was difficult to extract all ore along footwall, especially where dip was flat. Where this method was used, ore was fairly firm, hanging wall weak. Timber and powder consumption were low; labor cost, high. Daily output, 700–800 tons; output per 8-hr man-shift underground, about 2.5 tons.

Arizona Copper Co, Morenci, Ariz. Fig 532 (P. B. Scotland, 1915) shows a method once employed in upper part of an orebody preparatory to top-slicing. Sub-levels were 20 ft apart vertically; intermediate hand-tramming levels, about 75 ft apart. Interval between raises, 20 ft; ground was mined in blocks 40 ft wide. No mat was used; grade of ore recovered was seriously decreased by mixture with waste (178). Van Barneveld (482) cites use of a similar variation of sub-level caving on Gogebic Range, using branched raises to reduce handling costs.

78. SUMMARY, SUB-LEVEL CAVING

General. Sub-level caving is adapted to large-scale work in large, weak orebodies (see Suitable orebodies, Art 75). It is safe, and when properly conducted will yield a high extraction and produce clean ore. Disadvantages are in general the same as for top-slicing (Art 74); see comparison below.

Requirements (a), (b), (d) and (f) for top-slicing (Art 74) apply directly to sub-level caving; other essentials for the successful application of sub-level caving are: (a) Weight of caved ground is necessary on top of workings, and orebody must be wide enough to permit free descent of gob. (b) Waste, if in large amounts, prohibits sub-level caving, as it can not be stowed underground. Waste horses must be broken unless large enough to divide the deposit into sections which can be worked independently. Some grading of iron ore is possible. (c) Boundaries of orebodies should be fairly regular.

Sub-level caving vs top-slicing (Art 74). Relative ADVANTAGES of sub-level caving: (a) Cost of breaking ground is lower. (b) Less timber is required. (c) Larger daily output is possible from a given area. (d) Natural ventilation is generally better, and there is less timber to be hoisted to working places; local conditions and plan of work determine whether sub-level caving has any superiority in these respects. Relative DISADVANTAGES of sub-level caving: (a) Percentage extraction is slightly less, and there is always a greater chance of losing ore. (b) Mining is not so clean; more waste is mixed with ore. (c) Less sorting is possible in slices; grading of ore is more difficult. (d) Caving of overlying ground is not under such close control.

Factors of relative cost, percentage extraction, clean mining, and control predominate in making a choice. Top-slicing is better in very soft ground. It is used where its higher extraction produces ore rich enough to offset its higher cost, and where admixture of waste would lower the metal content of ore sufficiently to impair its market value. Under other conditions, sub-level caving is preferable. Block-caving is a possible alternative for sub-level caving (Art 82).

79. BLOCK-CAVING

General. Large sections (blocks) of the orebody, sometimes to a height of 400 ft or more, are successively undercut and allowed to slough and cave above the undercut portion. Drawing off the caved ore causes further caving, often aided and controlled as to its lateral extent by weakening the boundaries of the block by narrow shrinkage stopes or superimposed cut-off drifts. The ore caves and crushes by its own weight and weight of overlying capping into pieces of suitable size for handling. Caving usually extends eventually to the surface, the overburden settling as support of the underlying ore is removed. Drawing continues until appearance of overburden material at drawpoints indicates exhaustion of the ore. This method is a natural development of sub-level caving (Art 75–78), through gradual increase in height of ore caved in one operation. Some pillar-caving methods (Art 84–87) may be considered as varieties of block-caving. Following paragraphs presuppose a knowledge of details obtainable from Art 80.

Suitable orebodies are wide veins, thick beds, or massive deposits of homogeneous ore, overlain by ground which will cave readily. The ore must be such that it can be supported while blocks are developed and undercut, and will break up when caved. For other requirements and limitations, see Art 81. The chief field of use in the U S is in the Lake Superior iron districts and the "porphyry" copper mines.

Varieties of block-caving. There are 3 distinct forms: (a) Dividing horiz area of orebody into rectangular or nearly rectangular blocks, often square, drawing evenly over entire area to maintain an approx horiz plane of contact between broken ore and caved capping. (b) Dividing horiz area of orebody into panels, either crosswise or lengthwise of orebody, retreating from one end of panel to the other and maintaining inclined plane of contact between broken ore and caved capping. (c) No division of horiz area of orebody into definite blocks or panels; undercutting may be from wall to wall, with retreat from one end of orebody to the other, maintaining inclined plane of contact between broken ore and caved capping.

Under (a), the Pewabic (Art 80) was the first used and is the type form from which other varieties of block-caving have been developed. Blocks were undercut on main levels and ore was handled by shoveling in drifts driven through the caved mass. Present practice in all forms of block-caving is to undercut on a sub-level, and draw caved ore through vert or branched chute-raises to tramway level below; these methods are called "block-caving into chutes."

Development must be suited to the characteristics of the orebody and form of block-caving used; typical examples are given in Art 80. Remarks in Art 70, 75, on modes of entry, and layout of main and sub-levels, for top-slicing and sub-level caving, apply in general to block-caving.

Size of blocks. (See Table 51). Ratio of ore broken by caving and by blasting depends chiefly on height of block; hence, high blocks are desirable; they also reduce cost of development per ton of ore. Max practical height depends on thickness of deposit, dip of orebody, and character of ore and capping; best guide is experience elsewhere under similar conditions. Among "porphyry" copper mines using block-caving, height of blocks has increased from less than 100 ft to over 300 ft in some cases; King (asbestos) mine, Quebec, has caved successfully blocks 400 ft high. As to horiz area, tendency of Miami Copper Co has been to reduce size of individual blocks; original practice of undercutting from wall to wall and retreating from one end of orebody to other was gradually modified to mining of blocks 150 ft square, largely to reduce maintenance of development openings. F. W. McClennan states (283) that size of block should be large enough to cause the ground to cave freely when undercut and small enough not to throw excessive wt on the extraction openings below; that is, it is a compromise between free caving and low maintenance cost. Such compromise is sought at some mines by caving in panels, where width of block may be 75–200 ft, but length determined by length or width of orebody.

Table 51. Size of Blocks in Block-caving (Details in Art 80)

Mine	Width, ft	Length, ft	Height, ft	Mine	Width, ft	Length, ft	Height, ft
Pewabic................	200 (a)	200–250	100–125	Miami....	150	150	300+
Menominee Range (b)...	250	250	100	Inspiration	100 (j)	100 (j)	200 (f)
Tobin (Menom R) (c)...	100	200	125	Ray......	200	200	150–300
Mowry................	65 (a)	180 (d)	150	King......	160	160	400
Humboldt (above 350 ft)	150	(e)	30–100	Andes.....	110	132	175–250
Humboldt (below 350 ft)	112	200–400	100–180	Climax....	......	......	400–600

(a) Width of orebody. (b) One mine. (c) Largest block caved up to 1912. (d) Length of orebody. (e) See Art 80. (f) Aver; varies 70–300 ft. (j) Usual size; for exceptions, see Art 80.

Timber mats for separating capping from caved ore are rarely feasible in block-caving. They may be formed as described in Art 70, but can not be built up nor repaired after caving begins (Detroit Copper Co, Art 80). Miami Copper Co tried block-caving under a heavy timber mat formed in mining upper part of an orebody by top-slicing (Art 70). The timbers reached the chutes before all the ore was drawn to surface; many timbers were blasted out of the chutes (601).

Extraction. Figures of percentage extraction attained in block-caving are necessarily based on estimates of original tonnage, assay value, and metal content in the caved area (collectively called the EXPECTANCY); hence, the accuracy of extraction estimates depends in part on accuracy in expectancy estimates.

See Sec 25 for methods of estimating tonnage and value of ore in place. In porphyry copper mines, drill holes (Art 10-b) and (or) underground workings supply data for sections from which expectancy estimates are made. At Miami, tonnage estimates are made from vert sections 25 ft apart and parallel to direction of the drawing operations; ore limits on these sections are obtained from sampling the final drift and raise development, of which there is an aver of 1 ft per 47 tons of ore in place. Assay value calculated from samples is reduced 10%, based on previous experience in checking actual against sampling values when mining large tonnages by top-slicing, where there was no dilution by waste (601). Practice elsewhere is similar.

There is less chance of error in determining actual tonnage extracted and its assay, as these figures are usually obtained by mechanical samplers and weighing devices at mills, and are accurate in total even if the distribution of tonnage to individual blocks or chutes is in error. Careful records of amounts drawn from chutes are essential, to permit calculations of position of the caved overburden and control its subsidence; for practice, see Humboldt mine below, Art 80.

Figures for tonnage, grade (assay), and metal extraction are all required to give a clear picture of extraction. TONNAGE EXTRACTION is usually larger than tonnage expectancy, because in block-caving there is always some dilution by waste; for same reason, GRADE EXTRACTION is usually lower than grade expectancy. METAL EXTRACTION is the total metal in ore extracted, if the capping or walls of orebody are partially mineralized, metal extraction may be higher than expectancy, in which case grade extraction will be lower than expectancy. Correct figures for extraction by block-caving can not be obtained until sufficient area has been mined to give proper weight to clean ore from development openings and temporary pillars left over main and sub-levels, etc; in the porphyry coppers, final extraction is not determined until a section of the deposit has been bottomed.

Extraction results. Table 52 shows range of tonnage and grade extraction as experienced at Miami mine. From F. W. McClennan in 1930 (283).

Table 52. **Extraction Results at Miami Mine (See Art 80 for conditions)**

	Expectancy		Mined		Per cent extraction		
	Tons	Cu %	Tons	Cu %	Tonnage %	Grade %	Metal %
Total of 13 completed stopes..............	11 038 070	1.0260	12 710 378	0.9124	115.15	88.93	102.40
Best original stope......	998 016	1.0388	1 210 424	1.0091	121.28	97.14	117.81
Best pillar stope........	319 560	1.0640	387 827	0.9348	121.36	87.86	106.63
Poorest original stope...	1 071 535	0.8701	1 053 153	0.7786	98.28	89.48	87.94
Poorest pillar stope.....	1 098 313	1.1067	1 025 032	0.8995	93.33	81.28	75.86

Note. Poorest pillar stope was 150 by 300 ft in plan; best pillar stope, 150 by 150 ft. Tonnage expectancy figures do not include narrow "partitions" between certain blocks. At the Ruth mine, Ely, Nev, the results of drawing 10 000 000 tons of ore show a metal extraction of about 87%, with a tonnage extraction of 104%; (data from Co officials in 1938.)

Ore drawing. Chief cause of poor extraction is dilution by waste during drawing; dilution depends largely on: (a) nature of ore, walls and capping; (b) spacing of draw points; (c) experience and care in drawing; (d) extent to which gob is consolidated in adjacent mined-out blocks. F. W. McClennan (283) gives following 2 principal objectives in drawing, saying that in practice a compromise between them is reached: (1) To draw a max ore tonnage with minimum dilution by waste capping, the ore should be drawn evenly, so that the contact between broken ore and broken capping will be an even plane, preferably horiz. (2) To regulate the drawing so as to avoid or relieve damaging weight on extraction openings below the broken ore, thus reducing maintenance and ore-drawing costs and interference with the predetermined order of ore drawing.

Theoretically, closely spaced chutes, from which ore is drawn carefully and evenly over a large area under a high block, should give min dilution and max extraction. In practice, the difficulty and cost of keeping drifts and chutes open in large drawing areas under caving ground generally precludes such plan. In block-caving in panels it is customary to undercut the ore in small sections, retreating from one end of a block to the other. The drawing area is bounded by the line across the block on which undercutting is being done, by the sides of the block, and by a line of chutes across the block on which the ore has been drawn to capping, or to the minimum allowable grade of diluted ore. Working thus, the contact between top of caved ore and overlying caved waste is kept as nearly a plane as possible, but the plane is inclined, not horiz, sloping at 30°–60°. Factors influencing slope are summarized by M. Mosier and J. Martin for HUMBOLDT MINE, Morenci, Ariz, as follows (600): A horiz contact is desirable to maintain a flow of clean ore through chutes with minimum dilution, but requires maintenance of a large area of tramming level to produce a given output, also large working capital. A nearly vert slope would minimize wt on drifts and cost of maintenance, but would increase dilution to an impossible max. Between these limits is an angle, which, while allowing moderate dilution, permits a caving area large enough to furnish the scheduled daily tonnage without excessive repair costs. Factors influencing choice of angle are: character of ground, method of caving, thickness of pillars between drawing points, grade and character of overburden, output required, and size of drawing area.

An aver slope of 60° was found best for conditions at Humboldt mine; if wt on workings grew excessive, the drawing area was reduced at times by steepening the slope to 70° (Art 87) Slope of contact between broken ore and waste ("angle of retreat") was calculated on the assumptions: (a) that during drawing, ore and waste traveled on vert lines; (b) that the relative sp gr of solid and broken ore measured the relative space occupied by each. In this case, the ratio between space occupied by solid and broken ore was 12:20. Vert sections were made through each line of drawing points at right-angles to line of retreat; the theoretical results of drawing were plotted on these and the angle of retreat was measured. Position of capping or waste was known before undercutting and caving began. As undercutting proceeded and ore was drawn, room was made for the expansion of solid ore from 12 to 20 cu ft per ton; as drawing proceeded, this expansion reached the top of the ore. Further drawing caused the waste to move downward; assuming the movement to be vert, the amount of ore drawn from a line of chutes measured the distance through which the contact between ore and waste dropped. Experience at Humboldt mine proved that the "draw charts" so made were fairly accurate; waste appeared at the chutes very close to the expected time.

The drawing area in a block of given width is determined by distance between the toe of the waste-ore contact A (Fig 533) and the point B, at which undercutting is completed. If ore caves from the brow BC as fast as broken ore is drawn beneath it, the angle of the brow may also be controlled through regulated drawing. The brow may be vert or as flat as 30°, depending on character of ground and overburden and relative speeds of drawing and undercutting. A long overhanging brow may throw wt on adjacent workings; this is relieved, without decreasing the broken ore available, by driving a transverse shrinkage stope S (Fig 533) at front edge of the undercut area. If chutes under the brow are drawn more rapidly than ore will cave from the brow, an opening is formed through which waste flows from above. At Humboldt mine it was found that the sloping contact between broken

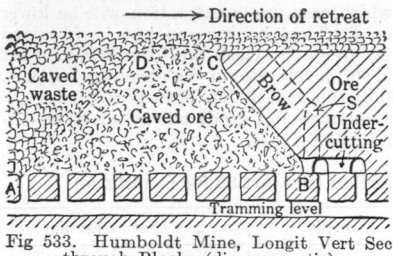

Fig 533. Humboldt Mine, Longit Vert Sec through Blocks (diagrammatic)

ore and waste should not intersect the overhanging brow, else some ore at upper end of brow would be lost; depending on height of block caved, the distance CD should be 20–50 ft.

Models may aid in determining best methods of drawing; for tests made in 1913–14 for this purpose at Inspiration mine, see Bib (262). In general, a capping that breaks into fine particles gives lower extraction than one caving in large slabs. Finely crushed ore may give trouble by packing (especially if moist), or by channeling through to capping. For further detail, see Examples of practice, Art 80, 81.

80. EXAMPLES OF BLOCK-CAVING PRACTICE

Pewabic mine, Menominee Range, Mich. Data from E. F. Brown (299) in 1898 and R. B. Brinsmade (153) in 1911. This form of block-caving was the first attempted. Method was crude as to ore handling, but principles of caving apply in present practice.

A lens of hard siliceous hematite, about 2 000 ft long by 200 ft wide, and dipping 76° to 90°, was overlain by hard, horizontally bedded sandstone; walls were of slate. Block-caving was used in low-grade ore, constituting most of the deposit; blocks 200 to 250 ft long, 100 to 125 ft high and full width of the deposit were caved in one operation.

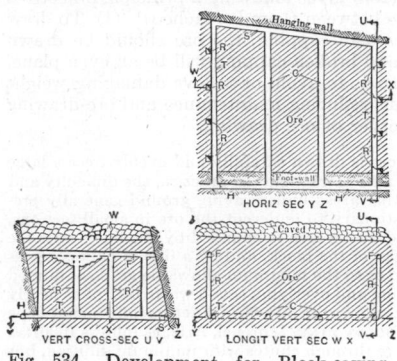

Fig. 534. Development for Block-caving, Pewabic Mine

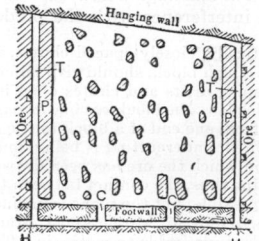

Fig 535. Pillars under a Block

The level interval was 100 to 125 ft. A main haulage-drift H (Fig 534) was driven in the footwall about 20 ft from the orebody. Crosscuts T ran to the hanging wall at the ends of the block to be caved; usually 2 intermediate and equidistant crosscuts C were run in a 250-ft block. The hanging-wall drift S aided ventilation. At 50-ft intervals along crosscuts T, raises R reached to within 20 ft of the level above, with crosscuts F connecting their tops. From crosscuts F, underhand stopes, 8 ft wide, were then opened from wall to wall and were carried down to crosscuts T. Thus both ends of a block to be caved were cut loose from the adjacent ore, except for a height of 20 ft at the top of the block.

Meanwhile, a breast stope 7 ft high was carried across the bottom of the block from cross-cuts C. Strong pillars P (Fig 535) were left alongside crosscuts T; elsewhere the block was supported on irregular pillars, made as small as was consistent with safety. None of the above work required timbering. Pillars were drilled with numerous holes and blasted out in sections. The block of ore was then free at the top and bottom, and was practically unsupported at its ends. A block took several weeks to settle 7 ft, after which the caved mass continued to "work" and crush itself; in 6 or 8 months, 80% of the ore would pass a 3-in ring.

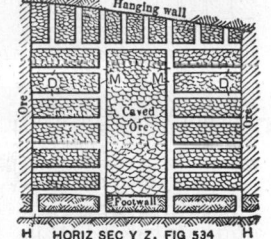

Fig 536. Extraction Drifts

After the ore was sufficiently crushed, timbered cross-cuts M (Fig 536) were driven by spiling to the hanging wall from the stub ends of crosscuts C; drifts D were turned off from M, every 25 ft. Short crosscuts might also be driven at 25-ft intervals from nearest drift to hanging wall. Plats were laid at ends of drifts, ore was allowed to run in and was shoveled into cars. When waste appeared, a set or two of timber was blasted down and drawing resumed. Work retreated from the ends of the block to crosscuts M, which were kept open. Caved ore remaining between drifts D was recovered by driving and drawing a second set of drifts half-way between D; caved ore between crosscuts was drawn last. The work of developing and caving blocks was done chiefly during the winter months, when Lake navigation is closed; much ore was drawn from caved blocks during the summer.

Variations of Pewabic method differ mainly in details of undercutting the blocks and in the mode of isolating stopes. These features are indicated by practice in a large low-grade hematite deposit on the Menominee Range, as described by R. Meeks in 1907 (300).

Main levels, 100 ft apart, were driven in the footwall. Ore was caved in blocks about 250 ft square by 100 ft high. The ore under a block was cut into pillars 30 ft square by drifts and crosscuts, 7 ft wide by 8 ft high. A narrow overhand stope was carried to the level above along both foot and hanging walls. Pillars were then removed in slices 8 ft wide, parallel to the strike. This work started in the pillars along the hanging wall and retreated to footwall; the back of each slice was allowed to cave before starting another. Caved ore was extracted as at the Pewabic mine.

This variation would be used where ore does not separate readily from the walls, or where the walls are irregular; more isolating stopes might be necessary at ends of blocks. Both open and shrinkage stopes have been used for isolating blocks; the former are preferred in the Lake Superior districts (286). This mode of undercutting blocks allows the use of timber for temporary support of ore too soft to stand when undercut, as in Fig 535.

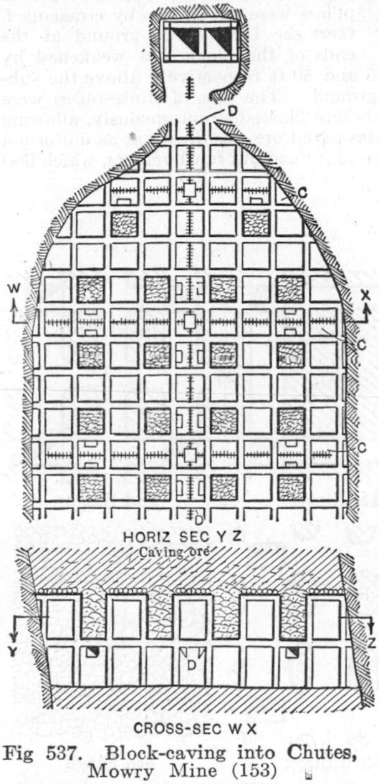

Mowry mine, Ariz. Data from R. B. Brinsmade in 1907 (153). Argentiferous lead carbonate ores occurred in irregular steep-dipping pipes or shoots, on a granite-limestone contact. The ore was mostly soft and crumbly, with much clay, Fe_2O_3 and MnO_2. Fig 537 shows method of mining a shoot about 65 by 180 ft in horiz section. A vert shaft was sunk at each end of the shoot; at vert intervals of 150 ft, the shafts were connected by drifts D, from which crosscuts C, 25 ft apart, were driven to the walls. A square-set stope (Art 45), 2 sets high, was then opened over the entire area of the deposit. Tops of 1st-floor sets were lagged, numerous chute-gates were built in the sill-floor sets, and the sides of the 1st-floor sets over the chutes were lagged with 2-in plank. The lagging over the chute-sets was then removed and the overlying ore caved into them. By drawing from all chutes uniformly, the ore was caused to settle vertically, and distortion of the sets was avoided; some sets always required reinforcement (Art 51). Boulders which clogged chutes were blasted; occasional areas of siliceous ore, too hard to cave, were removed by carrying square-sets up to the soft ore above; 80% of the ore was caved. This is the simplest form of block-caving into chutes. It has a narrow

HORIZ SEC Y Z
Caving ore

CROSS-SEC W X

Fig 537. Block-caving into Chutes, Mowry Mine (153)

field of use, under rare conditions of ore occurrence. Mining is confined to one lift, though a new level can be prepared while caving the ore over the level above.

Tobin mine, Menominee Range, Mich. Data from F. C. Roberts in 1911 (208). A large, vein-like deposit of soft non-bessemer hematite was mined by block-caving into chutes, as shown diagrammatically by Fig 538 (see also Art 43). Level interval, 125 ft. A main haulageway H was driven close to the hanging wall, and crosscuts C were run 24 ft apart to the footwall under the block to be caved. A small ventilating drift D was driven along footwall. Chute-raises R (Art 67) were put up from alternate sides of crosscuts C at intervals of 15 ft to a sub-level, which was opened from them 25 ft above the back of the main level. Sub-level development consisted of the drift M, about 15 ft from the hanging wall, the crosscuts N, driven to footwall directly over crosscuts C, and a drift S, along the footwall. Raises T were put up at 45° from M to the hanging wall, and opposite each crosscut; they caused the ore to cave along a plane passed through them, thereby leaving an added thickness of solid ore to protect the main haulageway H (cross-sec YZ). The tops of chute-raises were then connected by drifts P, cutting the ore on the sub-level into pillars 10 by 16 ft; in strong ore, these pillars were cut in two by crosscuts L (vert sec UV). The ground at the ends of the block was weakened by

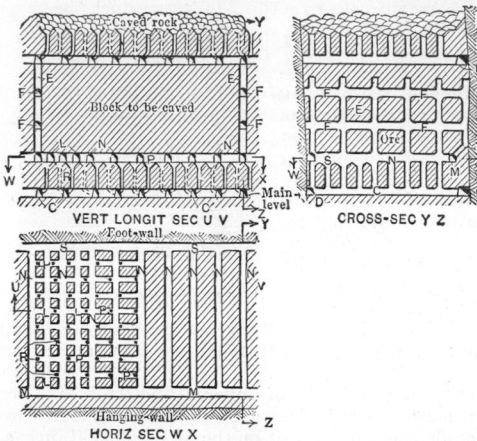

Fig 538. Block-caving into Chutes, Tobin Mine

raises E, from crosscuts N. Crosscuts F were driven 25 and 50 ft respectively above the sub-level. The number of raises E varied according to the ground. The tops of chute-raises were funneled, and numerous holes were then drilled in the pillars and blasted simultaneously, allowing block of ore above to drop. Through the chute-raise gates caved ore was drawn at as uniform a rate as possible over whole area of the block. Caved ore here contained but few boulders, which had

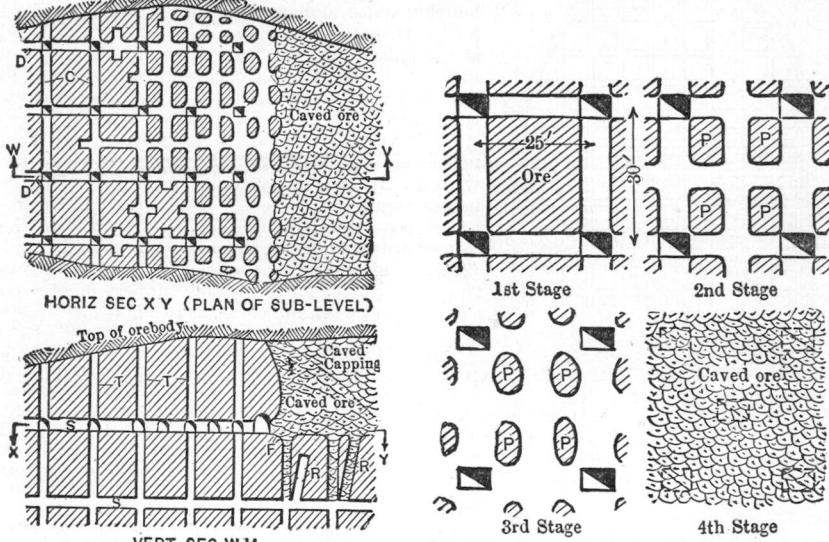

Fig 539. Block-caving, Morenci

Fig 540. Stages of Work in Undercutting Sub-level Pillars, Morenci

to be blasted in chutes. Pillars between sub- and main levels were caved with the block below. Up to 1912, the largest block caved was 100 by 200 ft in horiz section. Very little timber was required. Main haulage-drifts were timbered with 3-piece sets; posts, 8 ft long and 12 to 15 in diam; caps, 10 to 12 ft long and 12 or 13 in diam. In crosscuts, 8-ft posts and 5-ft caps of 10 to 12-in round timber were used (301).

Detroit Copper Co, Morenci, Ariz. (Part of Phelps Dodge Corp, in which work was suspended about 1923). Data from W. L. Tovote in 1910 (280). DEVELOPMENT. Main haulageways and intermediate hand-tramming levels were opened as for top-slicing (Art 73). Two-compartment raises, put up to the capping from the highest intermediate level, were 4 by 6 or 5 by 7 ft in section, and were at the corners of 30-ft squares or 25 by 30-ft rectangles. Sub-levels S, Fig 539, were opened as needed, by driving drifts D and crosscuts C. The vert interval between sub-levels depended on the ease and regularity with which the ore broke; it varied from 20 to 35 ft. CAVING began at one end of the orebody on the highest sub-level. Fig 540 shows the successive operations in any area. Drifts and crosscuts, driven through the pillars formed by sub-level development, subdivided each pillar into 4 small ones P, the sides of which were cut away as much as was safe. Ore in the sub-level floor was blasted out around the raises to a funnel shape as at F, Fig 539. Numerous holes were drilled in pillars P, and 8 to 10-ft holes, 2 to 5 ft apart, in the backs of all drifts. Timbers were removed from the raises overlying a section of a sub-level thus prepared, and all holes fired simultaneously. CAVED ORE WAS DRAWN through the original raises, and through inclined raises R, Fig 539, called "jigger-chutes";

these were usually untimbered, and the round that broke a jigger-chute through to caved ore was arranged to flare out its top. Some ore was shoveled on the sub-level to raises near the edge of the caved area. Drawing continued until a chute ran mostly waste. Occasionally boulders blocked the chutes and had to be blasted. GENERAL. Fig 539 shows block-caving on a sub-level 25 to 30 ft below the capping. Raises T would have been unnecessary if the contact between ore and capping could have been determined otherwise, but they were useful in weakening the ore before caving. At times (279) the top of an orebody was top-sliced (Art 73), until a heavy timber mat had been established. To secure the advantage of a mat in separating ore from waste, a large area had to be caved on a sub-level before any ore was drawn off, and drawing was done uniformly from all chutes. Even then the mat sooner or later broke up and timbers from it often clogged the chutes.

Humboldt mine, Morenci, Ariz. (Part of Phelps Dodge Corp; work suspended in 1932). Data from M. Mosier and J. Martin in 1925 (600), and M. Mosier and G. Sherman (99) in 1929. Ore is chalcocite in porphyry, carrying about 1.9% Cu in area formerly mined by block-cav-

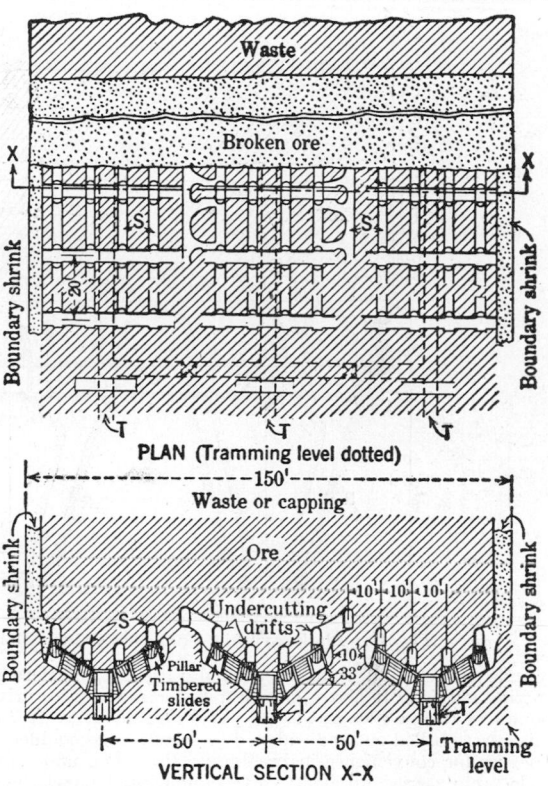

PLAN (Tramming level dotted)

VERTICAL SECTION X-X

Fig 541. Block-caving, Humboldt Mine, Morenci, Ariz

ing; orebody, 2 000 ft long, with max width of 600 ft and vert range of 1 000 ft. Ore is highly fractured in all directions, with fracture planes 2–18 in apart and recemented with quartz and pyrite; fracturing makes ground suitable for block-caving; permanent drifts and raises require timbering, but temporary workings usually stand well without timber. See Art 73 for other methods formerly used. Block-caving in panels, 150 ft wide by 30–100 ft high, was used in upper 350 ft of the deposit (Fig 541). Hand-tramming drifts T were driven under the panel on 40 or 50-ft centers; from them, at 20-ft intervals, raises sloping 33° ("timbered slides") were put up, leaving a 10-ft pillar of ore between tops of slices driven from adjacent drifts (Sec X X, Fig 541). For detail of slide timbering, see Bib (600). Next, shrinkage stopes, at least 6 ft wide, were carried up on the ends and along sides of panel, except along boundaries next to worked-out ground. These were rill-face stopes, extending to about 8 ft below top of block to be caved; entry to them was from the ends of stope. UNDERCUTTING retreated from one end of the panel; drifts S were driven on 10-ft centers across backs of the slides; 8-ft holes were drilled in backs of drifts S; the 5-ft pillars between drifts were drilled; pillar and back holes in any section were fired simultaneously. DRAWING. Practice was to draw so that the slope of the contact between broken ore and waste was about 60° (see Art 79 for detail). BLOCK-CAVING INTO BRANCHED CHUTES was used later for lifts greater than 100 ft (Fig 542). Panels, 112 ft wide, extended 200–400 ft along the strike, each served by 2 haulage drifts D, 10 by 10 ft and 56 ft apart, running parallel with long axis of panel. From both sides of haulage drifts, chute raises, R, 28 ft apart, were driven at 75° to intersect the grizzly level, 50 ft above rail, at points 14 ft from center lines of haulage drifts. Grizzly drifts G, 4 by 6 ft, were at right-angles to haulage drifts, directly over and connecting tops of raises R. Grizzlies were symmetrically but unevenly spaced, certain pairs being 14 ft c–c, others 21 ft c–c. Alternate chute raises were funneled lengthwise of grizzly drifts, to accommodate 2 grizzlies 14 ft c–c, as at H. On opposite sides of each grizzly, 4 by 6-ft drift

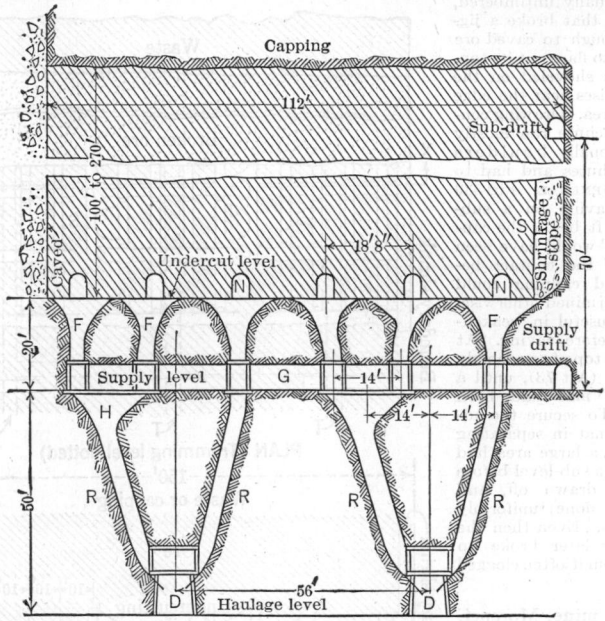

Fig 542. Block-caving into Branched Chutes, Morenci, Ariz (vert sec)

rounds were cut and, from these, small raises F, "finger raises," were driven to the under-cutting level, 20 ft above grizzlies; finger raises were driven at angles to provide draw points 14 ft apart lengthwise of panel and about 19 ft apart crosswise. Tops of finger raises were belled out and widened to permit large boulders to be drawn well down toward grizzlies for convenience in breaking. Preceding undercutting, shrinkage stopes S, 6 ft wide, were carried up along vert boundaries of panels high enough to cut ore free from adjoining ground and guide the line of shearing; extent of shrinkage stoping accorded with judgment of operating staff in each case. Undercutting drifts N ("dog holes"), 4 by 6 ft, connected tops of finger raises laterally and longit, forming a grid of drifts and leaving rectangular pillars about 10 by 14 ft. Final step of undercutting consisted of drilling and blasting pillars and backs of undercutting drifts. In opening a new panel, it was

Table 53. Operating Data in Block-caving, Morenci, Ariz

| Year | Tons mined | Tons per man-shift | | | Powder per ton, lb | Bd ft timber per ton |
		Stoping (a)	Mine pay-roll (b)	Overall (c)		
1927	1 136 339	40.35	10.00	9.07	0.24	0.23
1928	1 483 984	62.76	11.84	10.45	0.19	0.25

(a) Includes: (1) boundary shrinkage stopes; (2) undercutting; (3) belling finger raises; (4) chute tapping; (5) stope repairs; but excludes all development. (b) All shifts on payroll, including men on salaries. (c) Shifts charged to mining, including all labor, as mechanical, electrical, carpen-ter, and other surface departments occupied on work chargeable to mining.

necessary to undercut a length of 84–196 ft to start caving freely, even though the new panel might be against caved waste in a completed section. A distinctive feature of Morenci practice was use of 16-in grizzly openings instead of customary 10–12-in spacing; wider spacing was necessary because ore broke coarsely. Chute tappers wore safety belts as protection against falling through grizzlies. Blasting boulders at grizzlies and starting hung-up raises by blasting were done electrically for safety and to eliminate smoke from fuse. Chute-tapping effic was about 120 tons per man-shift. During initial stages of drawing, angle of retreat was about 60°; as stope extended, this angle was decreased to 50°, or to even less if weight did not interfere. Following rules were based on experience: (1) ore must be completely undercut; even small unbroken areas act as pillars causing excessive press at the grizzly level; (2) enough ground must be cut through in boundary shrinkage stopes to permit blocks to begin caving without delay after undercutting, but not enough to cause entire collapse; (3) press on grizzly level is resisted best by leaving as much unbroken ground as possible around grizzly drifts; this is done by making these drifts small and reducing number of finger raises to a minimum; spacing of finger raises is a compromise between requirements for good drawing, which prescribe close spacing, and need for controlling wt on development openings; (4) grizzly-bar spacing should be as wide as conditions of haulage and hoisting permit; chute-tapping labor is thus reduced and speed of drawing increased; (5) haulage raises should have enough storage capac to make ore drawing and haulage independent of one another. Table 53 shows results for 1927 and 1928.

Miami Copper Co, Ariz. Data from J. H. Hensley, Jr, in 1923 (601), G. W. Young in 1926 (593), and F. W. McClennan in 1930 (283). Mineralization consists of complete or partial replacement of primary cupriferous pyrite by chalcocite, usually occurring in seams and to a lesser extent disseminated through altered schist. Tenor is about 1% Cu. Orebody is a flat-lying massive deposit, with an area of about 50 acres and an aver thickness of about 200 ft, overlain by barren capping, 320 ft thick aver. GENERAL PLAN OF MINING. Early mining was by top-slicing, replaced later by shrinkage stoping with sub-level caving of pillars. Present method is block-caving. Caving practice at first involved undercutting and caving orebody across entire width (500–600 ft), starting at one end and retreating along length; drawing was plannned to maintain plane of contact between broken ore and capping at angle of 40°–60° from horiz. This proved unsuccessful,

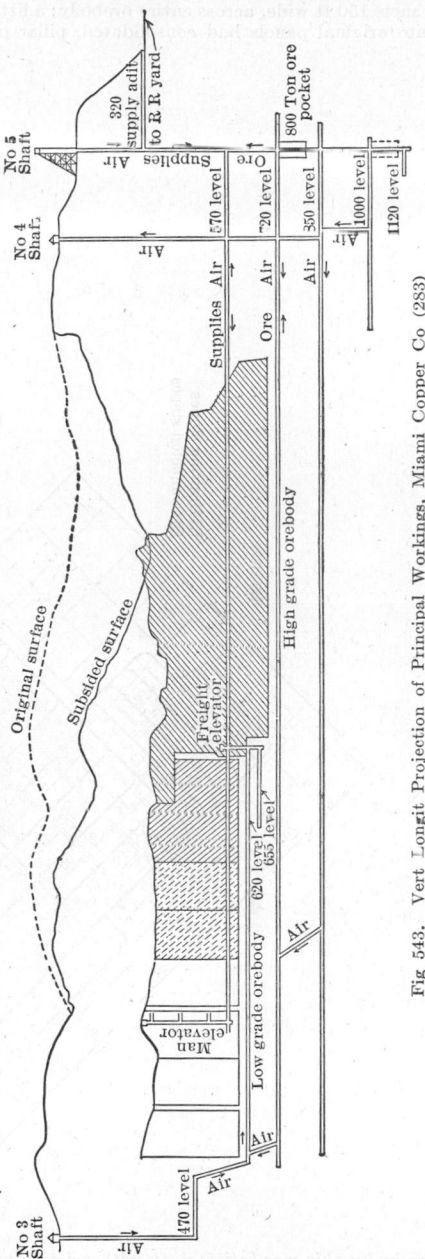

Fig 543. Vert Longit Projection of Principal Workings, Miami Copper Co (283)

because excessive wt was thrown on extraction openings, causing heavy maintenance costs and interference with orderly drawing. Later practice was to cave and draw alternate panels 150 ft wide, across entire orebody; a little later, when waste rock which had settled into original panels had consolidated, pillar panels were caved and drawn back across

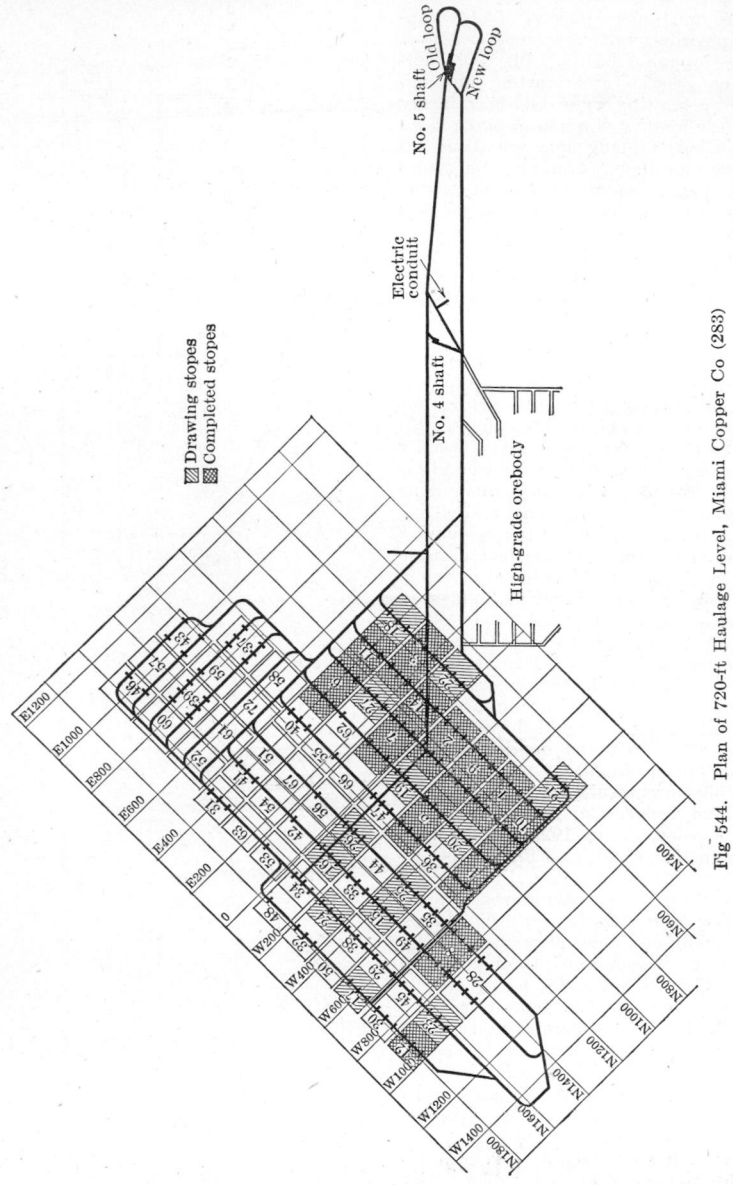

Fig 544. Plan of 720-ft Haulage Level, Miami Copper Co (283)

orebody; this was satisfactory with existing moderate thickness of ore, but was modified to caving on smaller blocks where thickness of ore was 300 ft or more. Original blocks were 150 by 300 ft, but experience indicated that blocks 150 by 150 ft gave best results, and this was made standard. Order of mining blocks is such that adjacent blocks are not

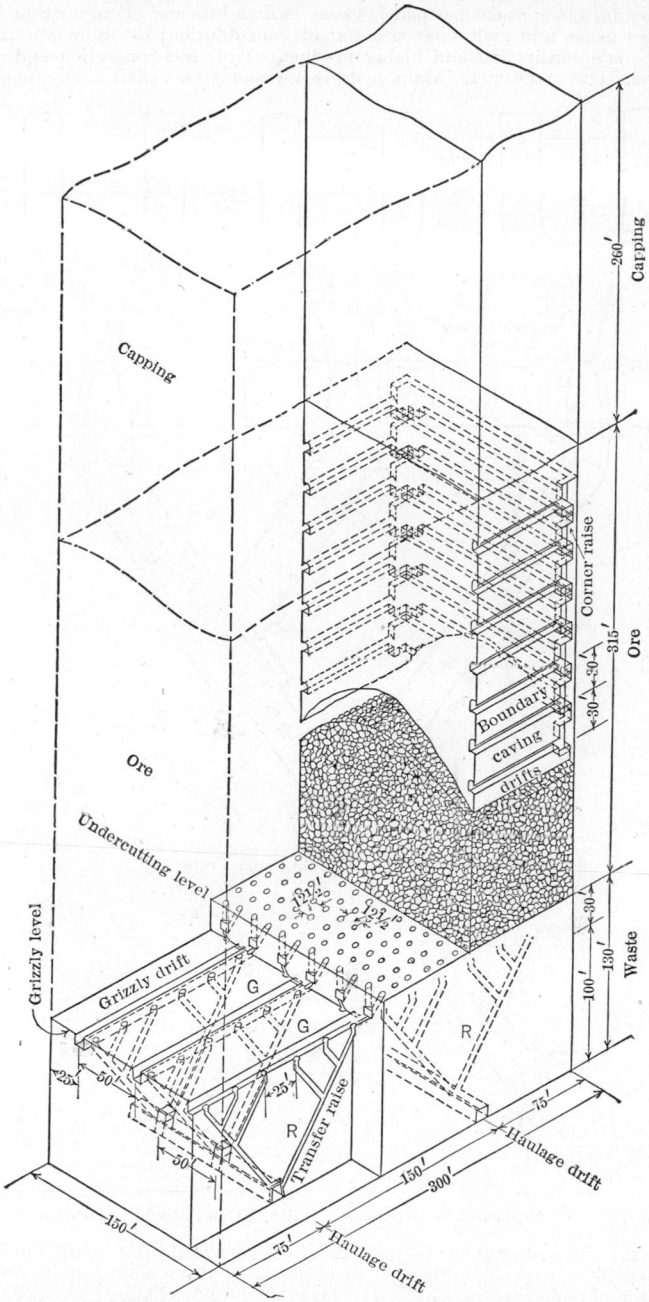

Fig 545. Isometric Drawing of Stope 150 by 300 Ft, Miami Copper Co

mined until waste fill along any boundary has consolidated for several months. Advantages claimed for block as against panel system in high lifts are: (1) min wt on extraction openings and hence min maintenance costs; (2) min dilution; (3) more working places, hence better standardization and higher production; (4) less congestion and delays on haulage level. DEVELOPMENT. Main entry is a 4-compt vert shaft sunk outside of ore-

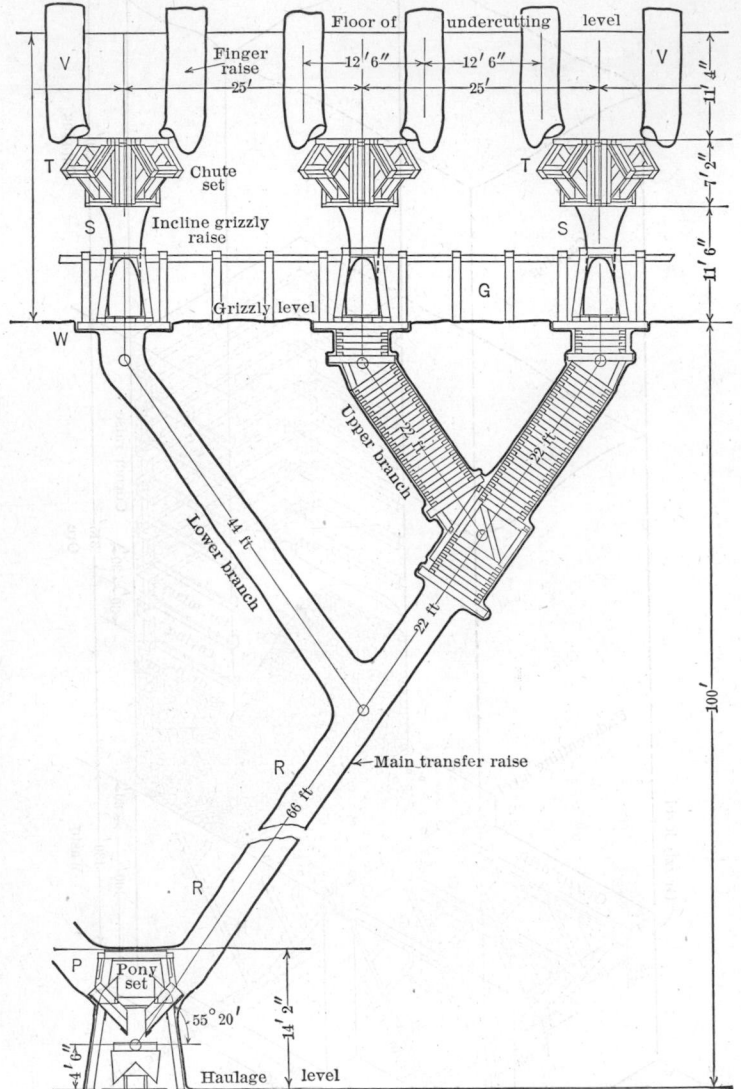

Fig 546. Vert Projection of Ore-transfer Raise System, Miami Copper Co (283)

body; 2 other shafts, beyond opposite ends of ore area, serve for ventilation. Fig 543 shows the shafts and spacing of levels. Ideal plan is to drive main haulage levels 130 ft below horizon of undercutting, with grizzly level 100 ft above haulage level. Grizzly level serves also as main supply level and ordinarily is connected to shaft. This procedure was modified above 720-level (Fig 543) only to take advantage of existing workings. Fig 544 shows development of 720-haulage level; in general, drifts are 150 ft c–c, timbered with

3-piece sets of 10 by 10-in, 6.25 ft c–c. Fig 545, 546 show development above haulage level. Sequence in preparing a stope 150 by 150 ft: Pony sets and chutes P (Fig 546) are installed at 3 points over the haulage drift, the middle one directly under center of the block; the others 50 ft on each side. Six transfer raises R, inclined at 55° 20′ above horiz, are driven at right-angles to haulage drift from both sides of the pony sets. At same time, 3 grizzly drifts G are driven at an elev 100 ft above and at right-angles to the haulage drifts, and vert over the transfer raises. Following the connection of the tops of transfer raises with grizzly drifts, grizzlies are installed over the raises. To avoid a large opening at tops of branch raises, a one-round vert winze cut W is taken from the drift bottom at the point where the raise will break through and a long drill steel is left projecting from center of the winze as a

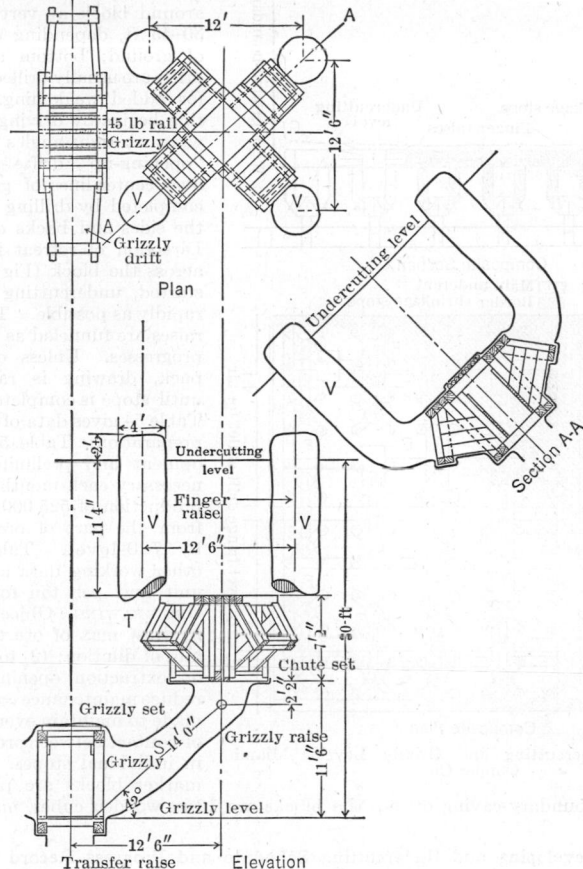

Fig 547. Location and Orientation of Chute Set, Miami Copper Co

guide in making the connection. Grizzlies are of 45-lb rails, placed crosswise of the drift and 12 in apart, supported on 10 by 10-in stringers. From the sides of each grizzly, a 3.5 by 3.5-ft raise S is driven at right-angles to the grizzly drift, inclined at 42° for a distance of 14 ft and thence vert for 10 ft (Fig 547). At the proper elevation, room is made for "chute set" T, which is carefully alined to assure proper spacing of the draw points above; chute sets are oriented at 45° with grizzly sets. Four finger raises V, 4 ft diam, are driven from the chute openings, inclined to a point 8.85 ft horiz from center of the set and thence vert to the undercutting level, 30 ft above the grizzly level. Drawholes are thus established 12.5 c–c over the entire horiz area of the block (Fig 545). UNDER-CUTTING. Fig 548 shows procedure. Chute sets are numbered 1 to 36 and draw points lettered. Undercutting level is opened by driving 4 drifts E of small cross-sec, parallel to grizzly drifts through every third line of drawpoints, 37.5 ft apart and equidistant each side of the central grizzly drift. These drifts are connected along both ends by "fringe" drifts F. In conjunction with undercutting, a narrow, vert shrinkage stope G is carried up 2 or 3 rounds along one end-boundary line (Fig 548) and usually advancing along the sides and other end of the block as undercutting progresses. To assist caving further and confine it to boundaries of the block, vert raises are driven at the 4 corners, and "boundary caving" drifts H are driven completely around block at vert intervals of 30–45 ft, depending on character of ground; bottom and back of drifts are usually drilled and blasted for added weakening. Undercutting begins by driving drifts J, 8 ft wide, at right-angles to the small "opening-up" drifts and directly over center-lines of grizzlies; it is completed by drilling and blasting the sides and backs of the drifts. Direction of retreat is diagonally across the block (Fig 548). Once started, undercutting proceeds as rapidly as possible. Tops of finger raises are funneled as undercutting progresses. Unless ore tends to pack, drawing is rarely started until stope is completely undercut. Table 54 gives data of typical stope preparation; Table 55, the development and preliminary stoping necessary each month to maintain production of 525 000 tons per mo from the part of orebody served by 720-level. Table 56 gives other working data and costs per unit and per ton for 1925–1928. ORE DRAWING. Objectives are: (1) to draw max of ore tonnage with min of dilution; (2) to minimize wt on extraction openings and thus reduce maintenance costs. Effort is made to maintain even, horiz plane of contact between ore and capping in individual stopes. As a guide, marker blocks are planted 25 ft apart in all boundary-caving drifts; the blocks are 12-in wooden cubes, marked with a

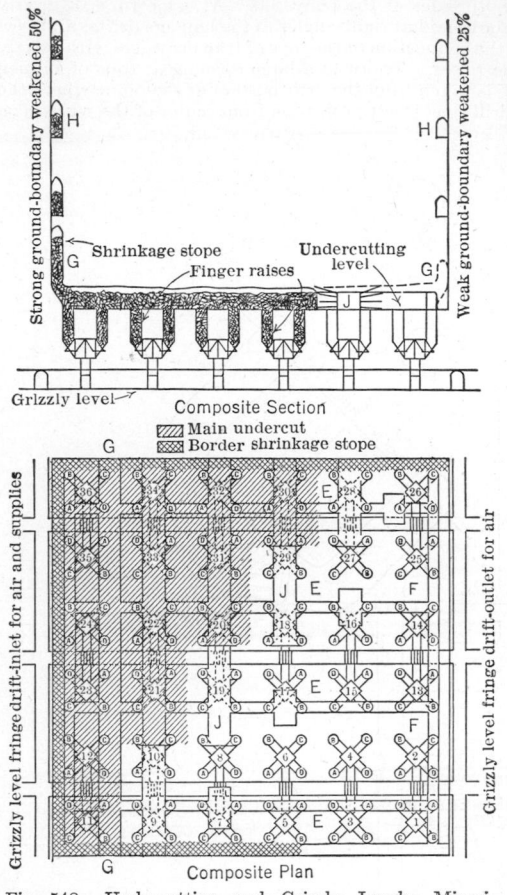

Fig 548. Undercutting and Grizzly Levels, Miami Copper Co

Table 54. Developing and Undercutting Schedule and Progress Record of a Typical Stope, Miami Copper Co

	Scheduled to start	Started	25 % complete	50 % complete	75 % complete	Complete	Scheduled to complete
Transfer raises	1- 1-29	12- 2-28	12-29-28	1-28-29	2-28-29	5-15-29	6- 1-29
Grizzly-level drifts	4- 1-29	3-20-29	4- 6-29	4-23-29	5- 7-29	5-25-29	6- 1-29
Grizzly raises	5- 1-29	5- 5-29	5-15-29	5-21-29	5-29-29	6- 9-29	6-15-29
Chute sets	6- 1-29	6-10-29	6-25-29	7- 8-29	7-25-29	8- 5-29	8- 1-29
Finger raises	7- 1-29	7- 5-29	7-21-29	7-29-29	8- 8-29	8-20-29	9- 1-29
Undercutting-level drifts	8- 1-29	8- 3-29	8-23-29	9- 8-29	9-22-29	10- 4-29	10- 1-29
Undercutting-level drifts	10- 1-29	10-14-29	10-25-29	11- 4-29	11-12-29	11-18-29	11-15-29

NOTE: Numbers indicate dates.

Table 55. Development and Preliminary Stoping per Month, Miami Copper Co.

CLASSIFICATION	UNITS
Haulage-level drifts, ft...............................	345.8
Haulage-level chute sets...............................	3.5
Transfer raises, ft....................................	1 105.3
Grizzly-level drifts, ft................................	688.1
Grizzly-level raises and chute sets, sets.................	37.7
Boundary caving drifts, ft.............................	2 292.6
Boundary caving corner raises, ft......................	299.3
Finger raises...	150.6
Undercutting-level drifts, ft...........................	897.4
Undercutting-level drilling and blasting in, sq ft..........	23 528.9
Boundary caving drifts drilling and blasting in, sq ft......	2 292.6
Boundary caving raises drilling and blasting in, raises.....	7.6

Table 56. Development and Preliminary Stoping Requirements and Costs for Orebody Served by 720-ft Haulage Level, Miami Copper Co. Expectancy, 39 968 411 Tons

	Aver est tons served per unit	Cost per unit 1925–28 incl	Cost per aver est ton in place, based on 1925–28 costs
Haulage level, per ft...........................	1 518	$19.950	$0.01315
Haulage-level chute sets, per set..................	148 031	325.606	0.00220
Transfer raises, per ft...........................	475	8.496	0.01789
Grizzly-level drifts, per ft.......................	763	10.700	0.01402
Grizzly-level raises and chute sets, per set..........	13 917	336.701	0.02419
Boundary caving drifts, per ft....................	229	7.033	0.03071
Boundary caving corner raises, per ft..............	1 754	3.528	0.00201
Total development...........................			$0.10417(a)
Finger raises, per raise..........................	3 486	32.789	0.00941
Undercutting-level drifts, per ft..................	585	2.996	0.00512
Undercutting-level mining, per sq ft..............	22.3	0.308	0.01378
Drilling and blasting boundary caving drifts, per ft..	229	1.119	0.00489
Drilling and blasting boundary, caving corner raises, per raise...................................	68 439	87.407	0.00128
Total stoping...............................			$0.03448(a)

(a) Based on extraction of 12 710 378 tons from stopes completed to late 1929, equivalent to 115.15% of tonnage estimated, the cost for development and stoping per ton of ore extracted would be reduced to $0.0905 and $0.0299 respectively.

countersunk copper tag, which shows the original elev of the block and the number of the chute over which it was placed. The blocks are large enough to be caught on the grizzly and their arrival shows the position from which the accompanying ore has come; also that the stope is caving to its boundary. Stope engineers inspect stopes daily and issue drawing orders. Tapping crew (blaster and helper) usually draws 12–15 finger raises per shift, blasting 5–8 times and drawing about 400 tons. Chute blasting is by elec caps and hand batteries. General plan is to draw chutes in rotation, but variation in routine may be required by: appearance of capping in a given chute; necessity of repairs; need of relieving wt on timbers; requirements as to grade of ore; need of proper distribution for economic operation of trains on haulage level. Drawing continues until grade drops below economic limit. Care is taken in measuring and recording tonnage from each finger raise. Measurement is by count of cars on haulage level, but accuracy requires close coordination between tapping of finger raises and drawing of transfer raises. To maintain daily production of 18 000 tons, 13 or 14 stopes must be in drawing stage, but production from stopes in initial or final stage of drawing is relatively small. EXTRACTION. Table 52 gives tonnage, grade and copper extraction from 13 completed stopes; terms "best" and "poorest" refer to relative combined results. COST DATA. Over 4-yr period, Oct 1, 1925 to Sep 30, 1929, aver tons produced per man-shift underground was about 27; timber consumed per ton, 1.045 bd ft; explosive (40% gelatin), 0.2225 lb per ton; for drawing alone, 19.7 tons of ore were drawn per lb of powder used; power consumed in mining department was 1.9 kw-hr per ton of ore. Mining costs per ton during same period were: development, $0.100; stoping, $0.136; electric haulage, $0.053; hoisting, $0.033; ventilation, etc, $0.021; general underground, $0.011; engineering and sampling, $0.014; mine surface, $0.020; mine accident, $0.011; total, $0.399.

Inspiration mine, Ariz. Data from A. C. Stoddard (642) and G. J. Young (655) in 1929; revised in 1939 by Co officials. Orebody is a large, irregular deposit of low-grade copper ore in fractured schist and granite. Ore minerals are chalcocite, azurite, malachite, and chrysocolla, largely distributed along fracture planes, but occasionally disseminated through ground mass. Length of mineable ore was given in 1929 as about 8 000 ft; aver thickness, 200 ft. Thickness of capping varies from nil to 500 ft. Since beginning operations all mining has been by caving. A method using a so-called "square-set control" was formerly employed (later practiced by Miami Copper Co). Procedure varied but following description of practice in 1919 illustrates general method. DEVELOPMENT. Haulage drifts were on 100-ft centers; as at present, they were 7.5 ft high, 9 ft wide at rail and 7.5 ft wide at cap, inside of timbers. Pony sets with chute pockets on both sides were placed 25 ft apart; from them inclined raises were driven to floor of grizzly level, 30–35 ft above. If untimbered, raises were from 3 by 3 ft to 5 by 7 ft; if timbered, 3 by 3 ft to 4 by 4 ft inside cribbing. Grizzly drifts were parallel to and 25 ft on both sides of center line of haulage drift. When untimbered, grizzly drifts were 4 by 6 ft to 5 by 7 ft; if timbered, sets had 7-ft posts and a cap to give 3.5-ft width at top. Grizzlies, of rails 10 in apart, were placed over each raise. From each grizzly, 2 raises were driven, one in each direction at right-angles to the drift. For the first 18 ft, these raises sloped 40°–42°; then turned vert to accommodate a 4-post square-set. From the square-set, 4 finger raises were driven to the undercutting level, 30 ft above the grizzly level, resulting in a spacing of one drawpoint for each 156 sq ft of area. UNDERCUTTING consisted of driving small drifts on 25-ft centers on undercutting level, with eventual drilling and blasting of intervening pillars. Above-described practice was often modified as to spacing of grizzly drifts and drawpoints; for example, in 1925, grizzly drifts were 42.5 ft c–c, each drawpoint controlling an area of about 133 sq ft. A disadvantage in the so-called "square-set" system of control was that men had to go above the level into the square-set to draw ore, making supervision of drawing difficult; also, maintenance costs were high. "GRIZZLY CONTROL" system was introduced to correct these faults and is still in use throughout the mine. Unit blocks are usually kept small, about 100 ft square, though some are 85 ft wide by 133 ft long, others 170 ft wide by 100 ft long. Spacing of the haulage drifts is a function of the distance from drifts to bottom of the ore; the less this distance the closer the spacing of haulage drifts. Length of block is determined by the area which, it is judged, will cave readily. A block may have 1 or 2 haulage drifts beneath it, each serving an area of which the width is a multiple of 16.6 or 17 ft, where capping overlies the ore. Where there is no capping, and a block to be drawn reaches to surface, there is no fixed multiple. Pony sets and chutes are installed 25 or 33.3 ft apart along the haulage drifts. Each of these distances is a multiple of a mine-car length, and allows cars to be loaded from one or more chutes with one spotting of train; the smaller interval is used where careful control of drawing is necessary, the larger, where careful control is unnecessary. From the pony sets, and on both sides of a drift, inclined raises R (Fig 549, 550), with branches, reach to the grizzly-level drifts D. The latter are 35–70 ft above and at right-angles to haulage drifts, and spaced to correspond with the raise interval along them. Grizzly interval along the grizzly drift is 16.6 or 17 ft, sometimes 21.25 ft, depending on the care demanded in control. From opposite sides of each grizzly, raises S are driven to a vert height of 18 ft above the grizzly level. At this elev, the tops of the raises are spaced at the grizzly interval in one direction; while at right-angles the spacing is alternately 14 ft and 11 ft, when the grizzly drifts are 25 ft c–c; increased proportionately when these drifts are farther apart. The lesser distance is always between the tops of the 2 lines of raises in the pillar between 2 grizzly drifts. Undercutting drifts T are driven at right-angles to the grizzly drifts and over the line of raises from them. Their spacing is therefore the same as that of the grizzlies, and the pillar between adjacent drifts is approx 5 ft narrower. Crosscuts V are driven as necessary. Undercutting is started from the corner of a block, if possible from a corner having unbroken sides, and is finished at whatever point may be safest. It is done as rapidly as possible, and is carried horiz in the plane of the undercutting drifts. Drawing is controlled at the grizzly level, the raises being drawn equally to bring the caved ore mass down evenly. During 1938, ore was mined at rate of 21.86 tons per man-shift chargeable to mining. Timber consumption, 1.164 bd ft per ton; powder, 0.128 lb per ton.

Ray mine, Ariz. Data from R. W. Thomas (294) in 1929, confirmed by Company officials as substantially representing practice in 1938. Orebody is a disseminated-copper deposit in quartz-sericite schist; chalcocite is the predominant ore mineral. Shape is irregular in plan and section; length, about 7 000 ft; aver width, 1 500 ft; thickness, 40–400 ft. Capping is 40–600 ft thick, aver about 250 ft. In caving, ore breaks coarser than at most mines using caving system. Timbering is required for all permanent openings. DEVELOPMENT comprises 2 vert ore-hoisting shafts, 2 inclined shafts for supplies and waste, and 1 vert shaft for men. There are 4 main haulage levels, 150 ft apart, as made necessary by shape and dip of orebody. MINING METHODS. Ray mine was first in the Southwest to use large-scale caving. Recent practice is the result of evolution from original shrinkage-stope and pillar-caving (Art 85). Fig 551 shows block caving, as used

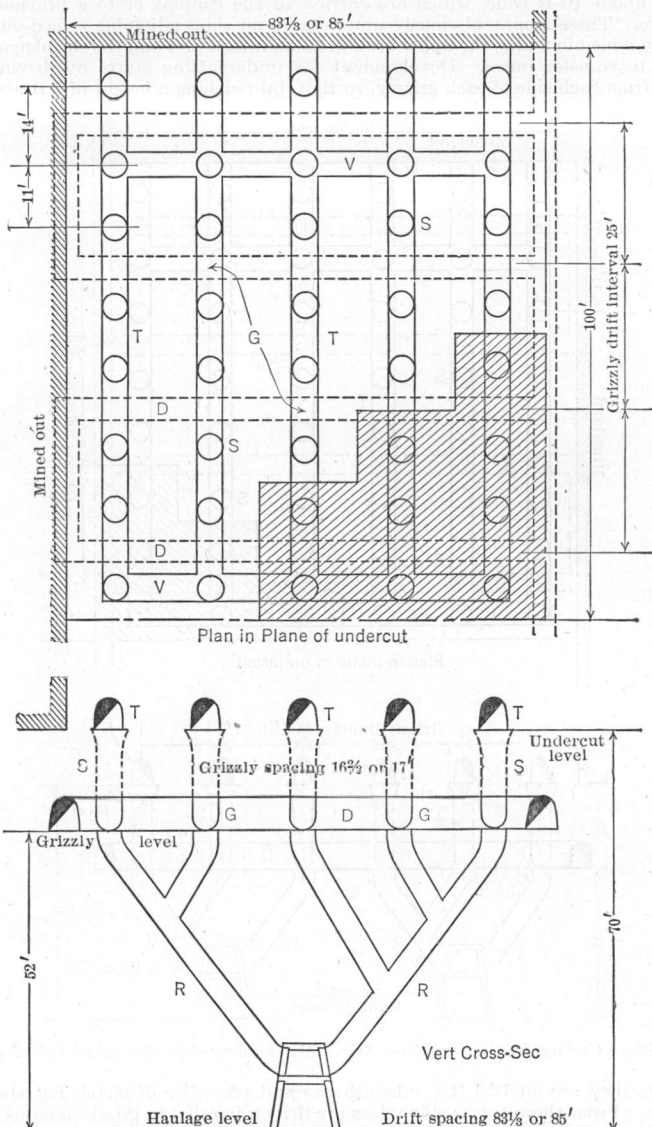

Fig. 549. Block Caving, Inspiration Mine, Ariz. Max haulage-drift spacing for highest ore horizon

where height of ore is 150 ft or more above haulage level. Panels, 200 ft wide, are developed by 4 motor-haulage drifts D, 50 ft c–c. These drifts are 7 ft high by 7.5 ft wide, inside timbers. From each side of them, chute raises R are driven 25 ft apart to grizzly level, 40 ft above rail. The raises are inclined so that grizzlies will be 25 ft apart, crosswise of panel, but staggered symmetrically as to those in adjacent drifts; they are

4 by 4 ft if untimbered, or 4 by 4 ft inside cribbing if timbered. Grizzly drifts G ("laterals"), 3.5 by 5 ft, are run over center lines of chute-raises at right-angles to haulage drifts. Grizzly bars have 13-in openings. "Fringe" drifts connect the laterals along panel boundaries. The ends and sides of a stoping block are "cut off" by shrinkage stopes S, about 10 ft wide, which are carried to the capping or to a previously mined area above. These stopes, obviously unnecessary on sides adjoining mined-out sections, are usually mined in 2 lifts, the upper section being mined first and the shrinkage ore hand-trammed to transfer raises. Development for undercutting starts by driving "throat raises" T from each side of each grizzly, so that, on reaching a height of 7 ft above top of

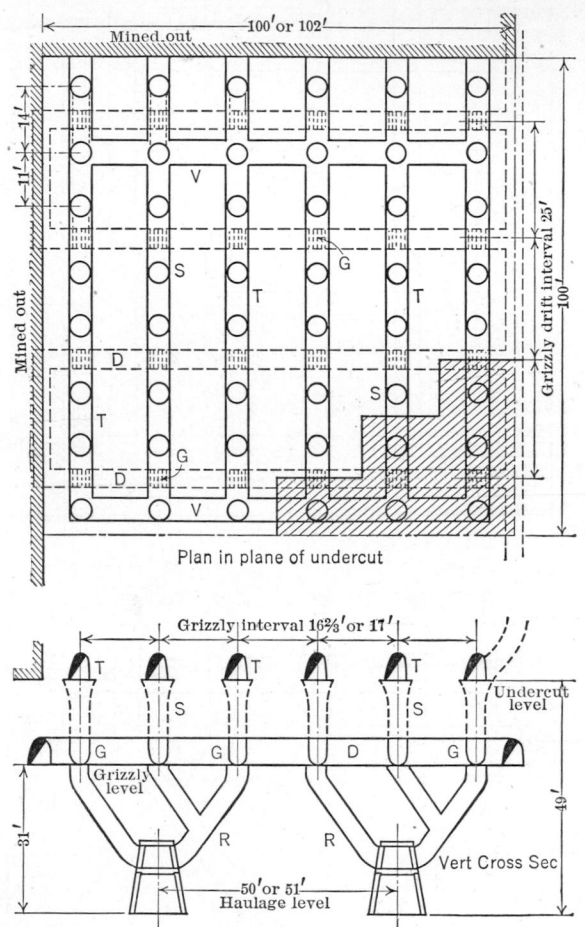

Fig 550. Block Caving, Inspiration Mine, Ariz. Min haulage-drift spacing for lowest ore horizon

grizzly set, they are on 12.5 ft c–c lengthwise and crosswise of panel, but staggered as in Fig 551. From these points, 45° raises are driven parallel to grizzly laterals until connected with similar raises starting from tops of adjacent throat raises. Ground between diverging raises and above throat raises is blasted down to give a flat-backed, saw-tooth slot W, 4 ft wide, across the entire block; the center line of each slot becomes the center line of a shrinkage stope. Alternate stopes are termed "undercut stopes" U and "pillar stopes" P; the former are carried to height of 40 ft above tops of grizzly sets; the latter, to 32 ft. Stopes U are widened toward top, so that the final round, breaking a width of about 18 ft, completes the undercut between stopes U and P. Undercutting is carried on progressively from one end of block to the other, followed by drawing on a limited scale. This gradually removes support from under the main mass of ore and sets up cantilever action, causing ore to slough and break up. Uniform drawing starts after block is completely undercut.

Ruth mine, Nevada Consol Copper Corp, Ruth, Nev.   Data kindly furnished by W. S. Larsh, Asst Gen Mgr, in 1938.   Orebody of disseminated chalcocite and chalcopyrite in monzonite porphyry is oval in plan; major axis, 2 400 ft; minor axis, 1 200 ft; aver

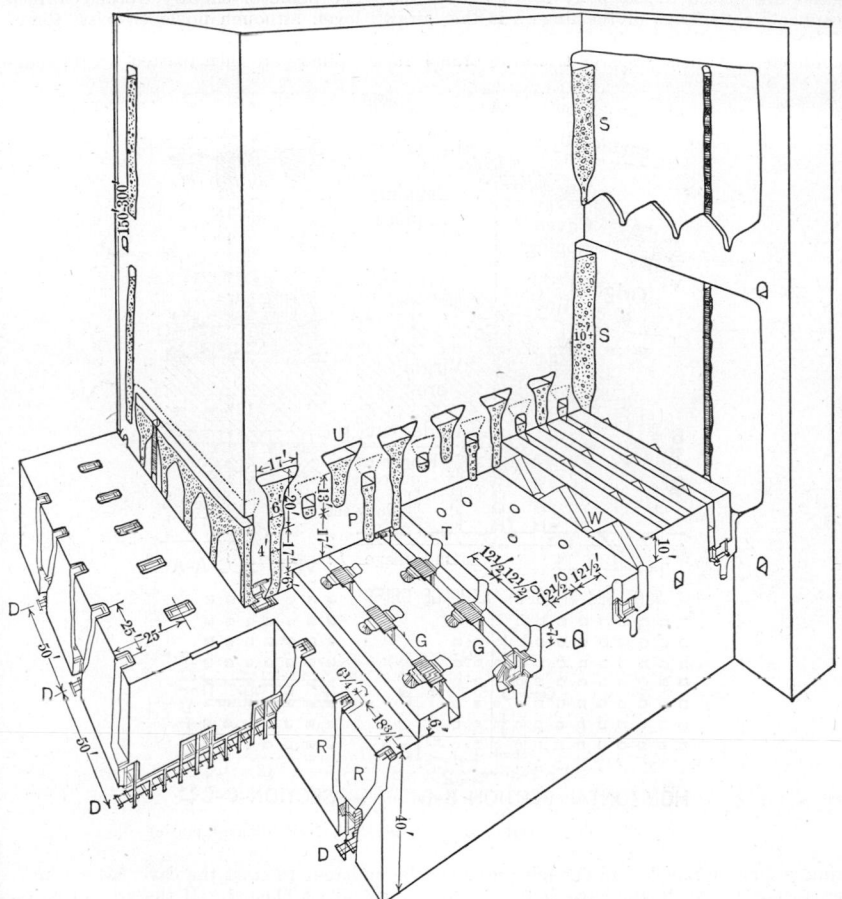

Fig 551.   Sublevel Undercut Caving Method, Ray Mine, Ariz (294)

thickness, 190 ft; aver dip 15°.   Formations overlying orebody, some of them oxidized capping, are 110 to 1 000 ft thick.   Ore and inclosing sedimentary rocks close to the contact are soft and heavy; some swelling ground.   After trying several methods, a form of block-caving, known locally as "BRANCH-RAISE CAVING," was adopted.   DEVELOP-MENT.   Haulage drifts are driven below the orebody at such intervals that 50° inclined raises from them will reach bottom of orebody at an aver of 60 ft vert above the level floor (min distance, 40 ft; max, 80 ft), which has been found the most economical height. The raise systems are spaced 25 ft apart along the haulageways and run at right-angles to them.   Branches from the main raise are designed to reach bottom of orebody at 12.5-ft intervals (Fig 552).   To start a raise, pony sets P, Fig 553, 5 by 6 ft and 6.5 ft apart, are erected over the drift.   From them the main legs of raises R, and the branches from them, are driven on a 50°–65° incline.   Near top of main raise and its branches, a curve brings them to the vert when they are finished. Raises have 2 by 3-ft manways and 3 by 3.5-ft chutes, with 4-in dividers; cribbed with 4 by 12-in or 6 by 12-in timber, with about a 2-in spacing. A square-set, *S* Fig 553, is erected at top of each branch and 2 finger raises *T*, Fig 554, are put up from each square-set at right-angles to the plane of the main raise, their tops being spaced 12.5 ft c–c. Finger raises are 3.5 ft square inside 6 by 12-in cribbing. Plank gates are put in the square-sets; a grizzly *G* of old rail is laid with 10-in spacing in each square-set over the chute compt of each main raise; steel arc-gates are placed in the pony sets at the level. The plane or slightly warped surface connecting the tops of the fingers is the "draw" level, although no level exists there. CAVING. Small drifts *D* (Fig 552, Sec *B-B*) are driven over the tops of finger raises and connected by crosscuts over alternate branch raises; pillars are then blasted. Undercut-

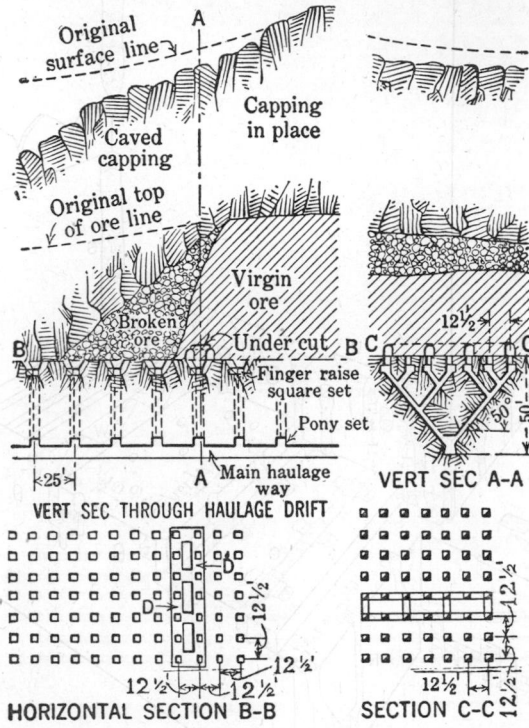

Fig 552. Block-caving, Ruth Mine, Ely, Nev (diagrammatic)

ting is done in panels and enough area must be undercut to start the cave; after which, crosscuts are run to the cave, and the intervening pillars blasted. If the ground is too heavy to permit undercutting drifts, as much of the work as possible is done from tops of the finger raises. After the draw from the fingers is about half completed, board gates are put in the other 2 sides of the square-set, but no finger raises are driven. DRAWING is done carefully; the "expectancy" of each draw set is charted and a model made showing the estimated position of the capping. The amount to be drawn from each finger raise is determined by the engineering staff, which furnishes "draw sheets" to each shift. Drawing is calculated to keep the contact between broken ore and capping on a 30°–40° slope. Chute tappers and draw bosses estimate the amount drawn from each finger; these estimates, reported to the stope engineer, are adjusted to balance against the number of motor-hauled cars drawn from main raises; adjusted figures are applied to charts and model daily. The ore drawn from each finger raise can not be measured precisely, but differences between estimates and actual number of cars loaded are not great and tend to compensate. The chute tappers become adept in making the estimates, being materially aided by the standard size of the raise cribbing. EXTRACTION. Figures on about 10 000 000 tons are about 87% of the copper and 104% of the tonnage. The draw level is placed at the bottom of the ore as nearly as possible, and the whole orebody taken in one lift. Better results in extraction are obtained in drawing over a fairly large area than in a high narrow orebody, as the ore has a better chance to cave. Drawing too rapidly causes chimneys (channels) to run through to the capping (always to be avoided).

King mine, Quebec. Data from J. G. Ross and others of Co staff (250) in 1934 and 1936. Asbestos occurs in a large mass of highly fractured serpentinized peridotite and also in small veins or as fibrous development on slippage planes. Original mining was by open-cut (Art 96). First underground mining was by shrinkage, later replaced by sub-level stoping. Block-caving was finally and successfully adopted. There are 2 unusual features: (a)

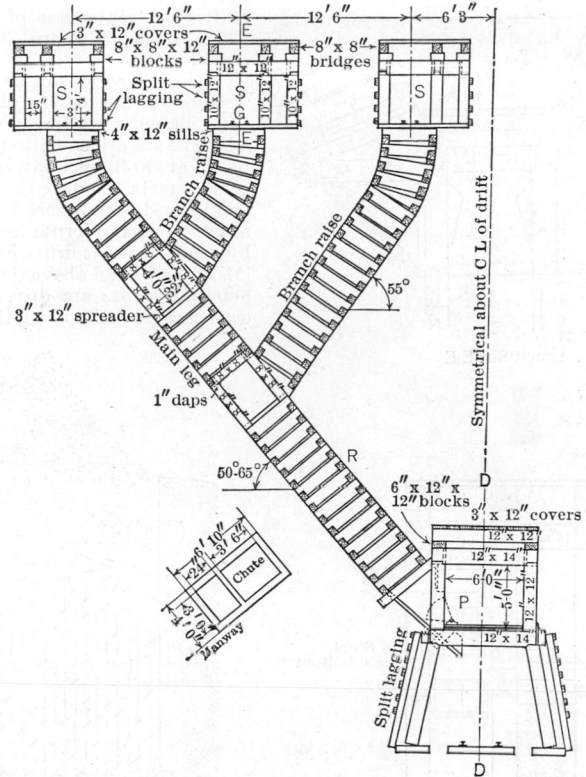

Fig 553. Raise-chute System, Ruth Mine, Nev

proximity of property boundaries, R Rs, and buildings requires avoidance of subsidence in the area surrounding the ground being mined; (b) detrimental effect of wood fiber in final product precludes use in mine of wood in any form. Subsidence problem is solved by mining in blocks (160 by 160 ft) rather than panels (see Miami Copper Co, above), and keeping subsided area filled with dry mill tailings, of which much had been accumulated nearby (Fig 555). Following methods avoid use of wood: (1) 6-in and 8-in H-beams are used for drift sets, with steel plate or old rails for lagging; (2) steel track-ties; (3) ore chutes and ladders are all-steel; (4) head blocks for drill columns are of strips of rubber belting clamped or riveted together; (5) wedges are of a composition of hard rubber and asbestos; (6) tamping sticks are copper tubing with copper plug in one end; (7) picks and shovels have metal handles; (8) metal survey plugs; (9) workmen are supplied with lighters, no matches being allowed in the mine; (10) dynamite is transported into mine in waterproof canvas sacks. DEVELOPMENT. Haulage drifts are on the 500-ft level. Each block, 160 by 160 ft, is served by 2 parallel 8 by 9-ft drifts, each 40 ft from center line of block (Fig 556). Grizzly level is 45 ft above haulage level; undercutting level, 20 ft above grizzly. Grizzly drifts are parallel to haulage drifts, on 40-ft centers, spaced symmetrically with haulage drifts. Grizzly drifts are lined with sets of 6-in H-beams, 2.5 ft c–c, lagged with scrap rails 1 ft apart. Whole structure is concreted flush with inside faces of posts and caps, leaving a section 6 ft high, 3.5 ft wide at bottom, and 2 ft at top. From each side of haulage drift 4 chute raises are driven 40 ft apart and inclined at 55°. At a point 20 ft from chute, each raise branches 2 ways, to cut grizzly drifts at 20-ft intervals. Thus, grizzlies are 20 ft c–c in direction of drifts and 40 ft c–c at right-angles to drifts. Grizzlies are of 80-lb rails on 6-in steel H-beam sills, with 16-in slots 4 ft long across the grizzly drift. From each side of the 32 grizzlies in a block, a raise is driven to a point 20 ft above grizzly level and 10 ft from center line of grizzly drift. Thus, draw-points are 20 ft c–c in 2 directions over entire area of block. At each of 4 corners of block, 6 by 6-ft vert raises are driven almost to surface. Boundary-caving or cut-off drifts, 4 by 6 ft, are driven entirely around the block at 40-ft vert intervals. Before caving starts, the drift backs are drilled and blasted with 3 vert 7-ft holes 4 ft apart. UNDERCUTTING level is opened by eight 7 by 7-ft drifts parallel to the grizzly drifts and above the draw raises; 8 by 8-ft drifts are driven across the ends of these drifts, along the 2 opposite

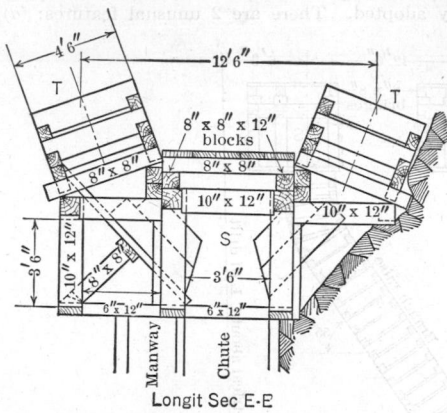

Longit Sec E-E

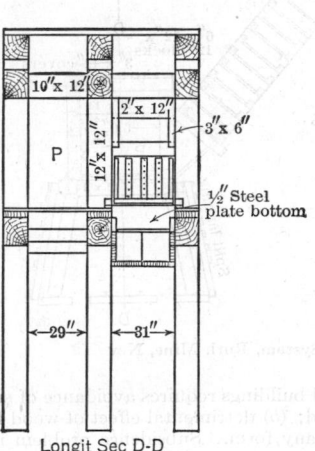

Longit Sec D-D

Fig 554. Details of Raise Timbering, Ruth Mine, Nev

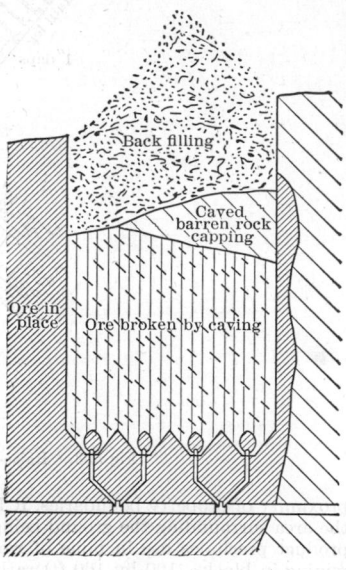

Fig 555. Use of Back-filling in Block-caving, King Mine, Quebec

sides of the block at right-angles to the grizzly drifts. Backs and walls of undercutting drifts are drilled with fan-shaped rings of 7-ft holes, 3 ft apart. Each underlying draw raise is drilled so that, on blasting, it will be cup-shaped rather than conical; this permits large boulders to settle nearer grizzlies, where they are more readily drilled and blasted. Starting in a corner of the block, undercut drifts and underlying raises are blasted in areas 40 by 40 ft, in diagonal retreat toward opposite corner. Drawing starts after finishing undercutting. Before caving starts, markers (numbered steel plates) are distributed at regular intervals in the fringe drifts. As these are recovered in drawing, the dates and positions are recorded, to serve as a guide to determine how close to the proper limits the caving action has reached. Caving follows fringe drifts closely, and back-filling keeps subsidence within anticipated limits. It is stated that it would seem practicable to cave from a depth of at least 600 ft within 20 ft of a property boundary without disturbing the area beyond it, provided backfilling is adequately supplied.

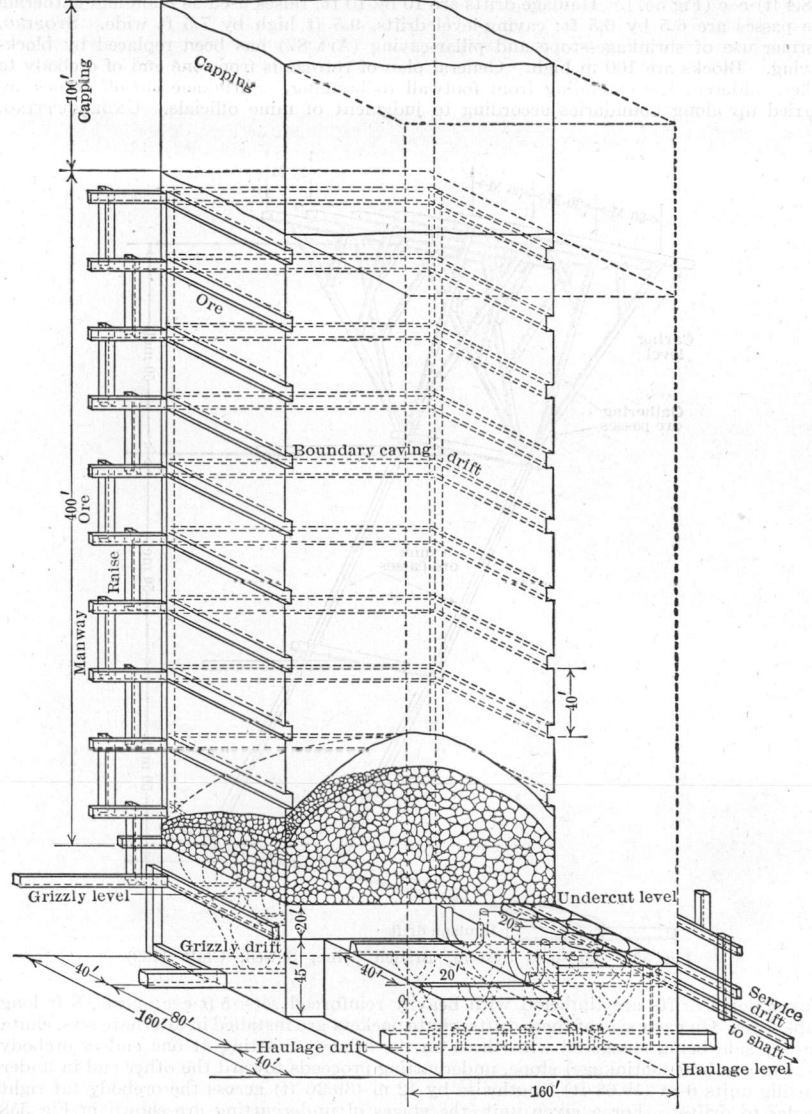

Fig 556.   Isometric Drawing of Stope Block, King Mine, Quebec

Braden mine, Sewell, Chile. Data from J. S. Webb and T. W. Skinner (289) in 1932; additional data from management in 1938. Large, irregular, crescent-shaped deposits, carrying chalcocite and chalcopyrite, occur in highly fractured zones in andesite, around a neck of volcanic tuff. Ore dips steeply; tuff contact forms hanging wall; footwall is commercial limit of workable ore in andesite. Width of ore zone, 328–1 968 ft; oxidized capping extends 164–328 ft below surface. DEVELOPMENT. Topography is steep and main entry to mine is by adit below operating levels, to which ore is delivered through ore passes for haulage to mill bins. Level interval was formerly 50 m (164 ft), but present development has 100-m (328-ft) lifts. Parallel drifts are driven on caving level 12 m (39.4 ft) apart. Gathering raises cut the bottoms of these drifts to provide dumps 30 m (98.4 ft) c–c (Fig 557). Haulage drifts are 10 by 10 ft; raises used as main and gathering ore passes are 6.5 by 6.5 ft; caving-level drifts, 9.5 ft high by 7.5 ft wide. STOPING. Former use of shrinkage-stope and pillar-caving (Art 87) has been replaced by block-caving. Blocks are 100 m high. General plan of retreat is from one end of orebody to other, undercutting extending from footwall to hanging. Shrinkage cut-off stopes are carried up along boundaries according to judgment of mine officials. UNDERCUTTING.

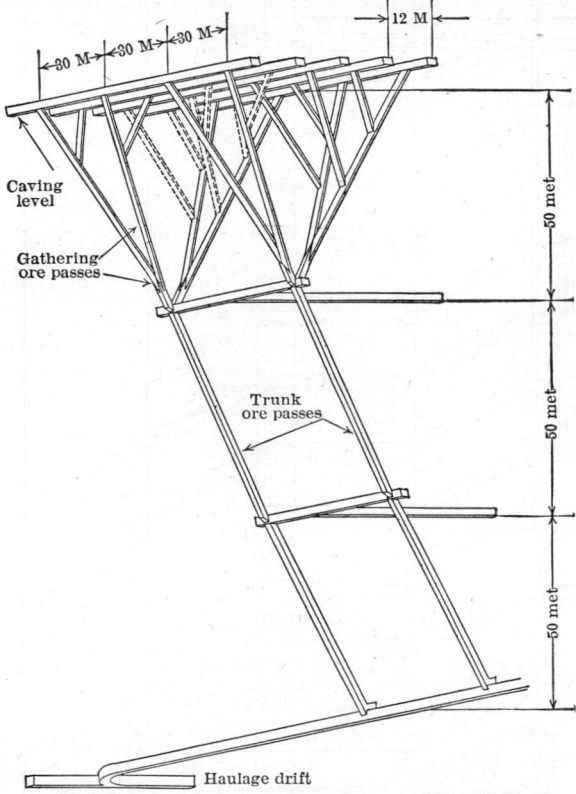

Fig 557. Ore-pass System, Braden Mine, Sewell, Chile (289)

Caving-level drifts are timbered with heavily reinforced sets, 5 ft c–c; posts, 8 ft long; caps, 7 ft. On each side of these drifts, chute pockets are installed in alternate sets, chutes on one side being staggered with those on the other. Starting at one end of orebody, next to a cut-off (shrinkage) stope, undercutting proceeds toward the other end in under-cutting units 6 m (19.68 ft) lengthwise by 12 m (39.36 ft) across the orebody (at right-angles to drifts). For a given unit, the stages of undercutting are shown in Fig 558. Along a 6-m section of drift a 6-ft fan-shaped round is drilled and blasted (Fig 558, A). The ore thus broken is drawn out through the chutes, leaving an open stope about 7 ft high above the drift timbers. Before the initial blast, a small manway raise M, from the next drift to center line of the intervening pillar, is driven on a slope of 48°, and at an angle of 8° 30' from the perpendicular to the drift, to meet a similar raise N, driven from the last chute in the undercut stope. This connection is completed before making the second widening blast in the undercut stope, thus providing safe entrance and exit. Three more undercutting rounds are drilled and blasted successively (Fig 558, B, C, D), forming a small shrinkage stope. The ground usually shows signs of weakening after the third blast, but to assure safety to the miners, the back is stulled after each blast. The final blast breaks to the adjacent caved area. Before regular drawing is started, undercutting continues in adjacent drifts until sufficient area is weakened to produce a continuous caving action. An undercut crew consists of 3 miners, who work on contract basis of

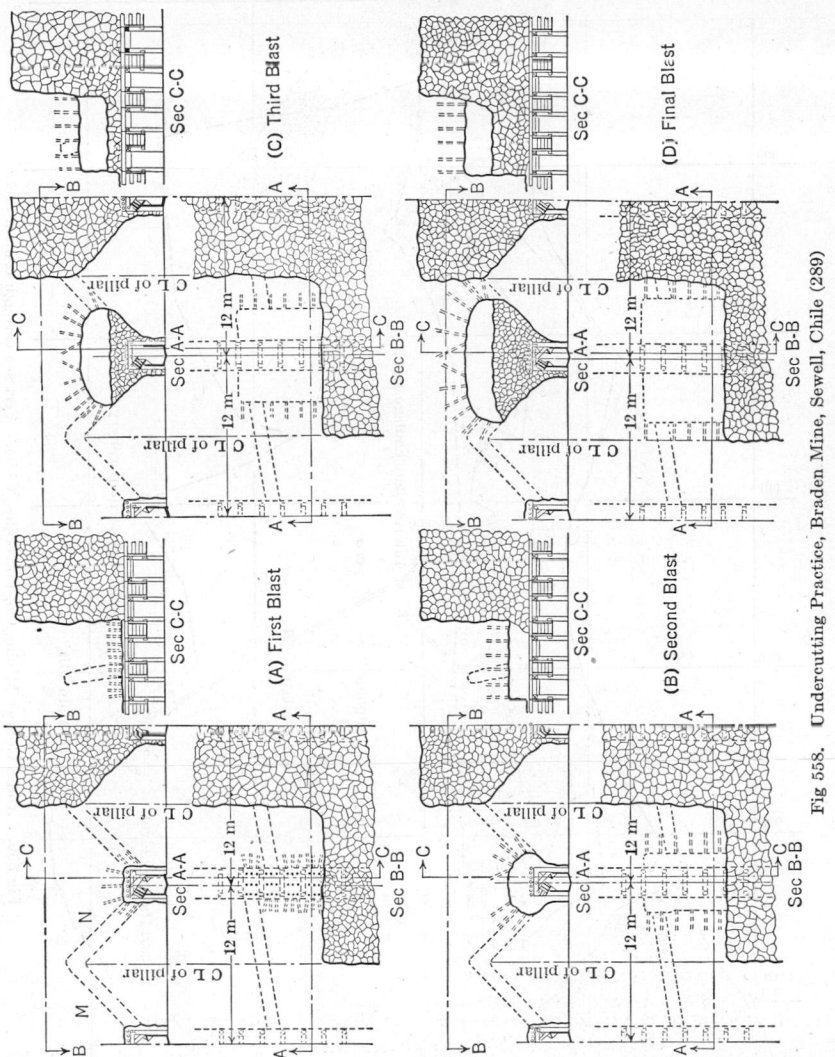

Fig 558. Undercutting Practice, Braden Mine, Sewell, Chile (289)

lineal meterage undercut. Stoper drills are used. On caving level, ore is drawn into 1-ton cars and trammed to tops of gathering raises. Each trammer is assigned a minimum of 10 chutes. With dumps 30 m (98.4 ft) c–c, max tram is 15 m (49.2 ft). Trammer receives daily orders as to number of cars to be drawn from each chute, and record of tonnage drawn is kept. Trammers are paid according to number of cars, with guarantee of base wage. Accurate count of cars is obtained by an automatic counter on each car. Trammer must load a full ton into car and dump it before the counter registers. Counters

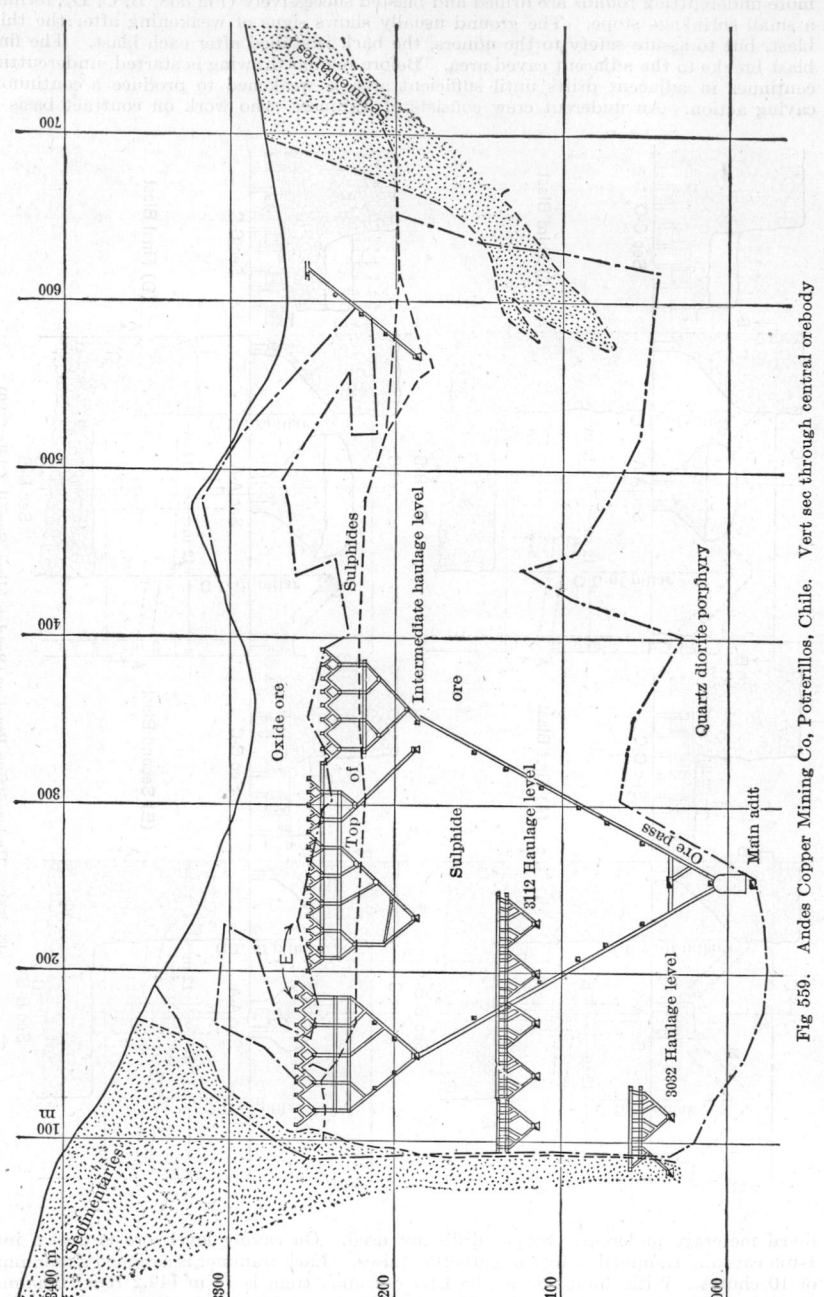

Fig 559. Andes Copper Mining Co, Potrerillos, Chile. Vert sec through central orebody

on each car are read at beginning and end of each shift, and at intervals during the shift.

Andes Copper Mining Co (Anaconda Copper Co), Potrerillos, Chile. Data from I. L. Greninger, Asst Gen Mgr, in 1939. Copper minerals, chiefly chalcocite and chalcopyrite, are disseminated in porphyry, forming a large, massive orebody. Porphyry intrusion has left enclosing sediments tilted at 50°–60°. Orebodies within intrusive generally have same dip as sedimentaries. DEVELOPMENT. As topography is steep, entry is by adits; main adit is at elev of 2 974 m (9 754 ft) and is 4 787.82 m (2.97 miles) long. Ore passes

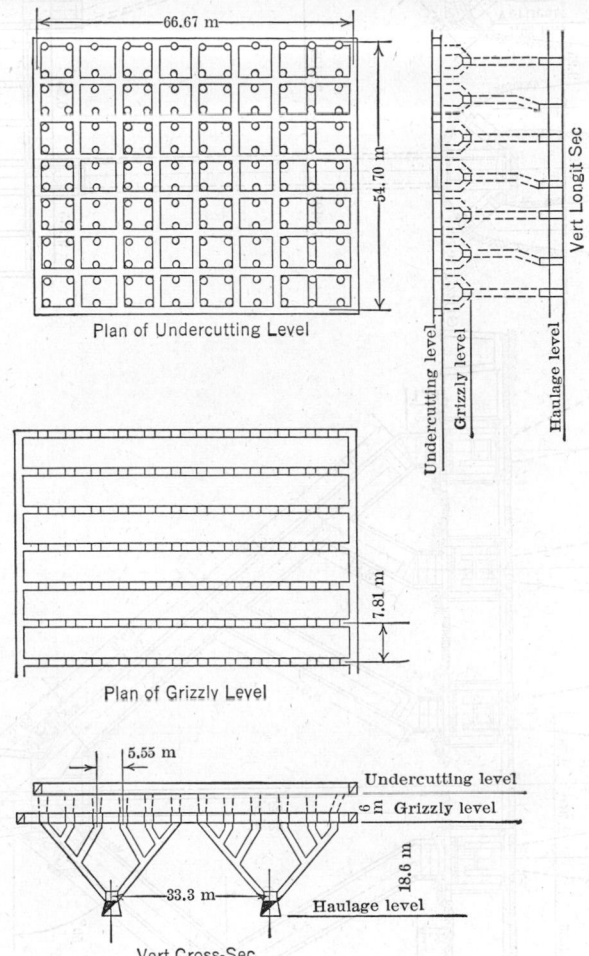

Fig 560. Plans and Secs of Typical Block, Andes Copper Mining Co

extend from main adit to 3 intermediate haulage levels at 3 032, 3 112, and 3 184 m. On each intermediate level, parallel haulage drifts are driven, 30–33 m c–c. Development above the haulage levels, to prepare for undercutting, is shown in Fig 559, which is a vert section through the central orebody. Fig 560 shows details of a typical block. This method was developed at the Inspiration mine, Ariz. Fig 561 shows the raise system. Control in drawing is maintained at the grizzly, whereas in earlier practice at Andes (see E, Fig 559), "control sets" were placed between the grizzly and undercutting levels; the control set was a 4-post square-set, from which 4 finger raises were driven to the undercutting level above; each finger raise was controlled by a chute gate at the control set. For details see Bib (643). HAULAGE DRIFTS are timbered with sets of 10 by 10-in Oregon

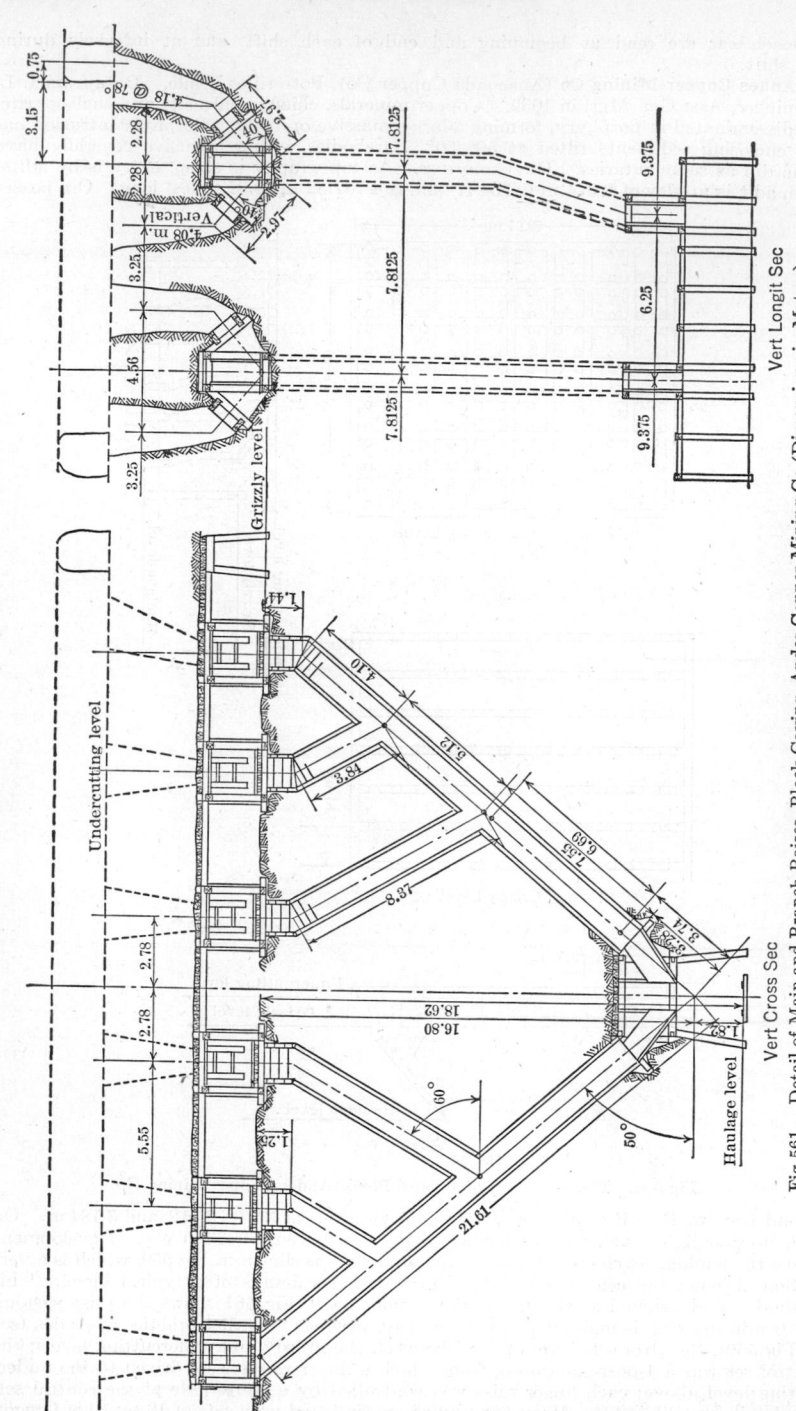

Fig 561.   Detail of Main and Branch Raises, Block Caving, Andes Copper Mining Co (Dimensions in Meters)

pine, 8.5 ft wide at the cap, with 9-ft posts battered 1 in per ft. Grizzly drifts, formerly lined with masonry (643), are now timbered as in Fig 562. Main raises are lined with 6 by 12-in cribbing skin to skin, each piece protected by a 3 by 3 by $^3/_8$-in angle iron at its upper edge. Fig 560 shows undercutting details. Area to be undercut is divided by 6.25 by 6.25-m pillars, which are shot out successively, retreating from one corner of the block to the diag opposite corner. Blocks are now 50 by 60 m in horiz sec. ORE DRAWING is in accordance with written orders, a close check being kept on tonnage and grade drawn from each branch raise. Main raises are calibrated by successive filling and

drawing off. A check is obtained by counting the cars drawn from each chute. Data on tonnage drawn from branch raises are posted daily on office stope sheets, from which graphic charts are made, and copies carried by underground foremen and bosses. In 1939, for direct labor underground, production was 40–45 tons per man.

Climax, Colo. Data from W. J. Coulter (303) in 1929 and W. E. Romig (304) in 1937. Molybdenite occurs in disseminated form; also in veinlets along fracture planes in altered schist and granite. Ore area lies concentrically around a large dome of silicified and sparsely mineralized granite. Wall limits are determined by assay values; dips are steep; horiz width of ore is 300–700 ft. Former mining was by shrinkage-stope and pillar-caving; now by block-caving, with lifts of 400–600 ft. First practice in block-caving involved use of grizzlies, 60 ft above haulage level, 50 ft c–c, both lengthwise and crosswise of orebody, from which finger raises extended to stope bottom. Difficulty in maintaining grizzly chambers, due to blockiness of ground, led to a novel system, in which scrapers eliminate need for grizzly levels.

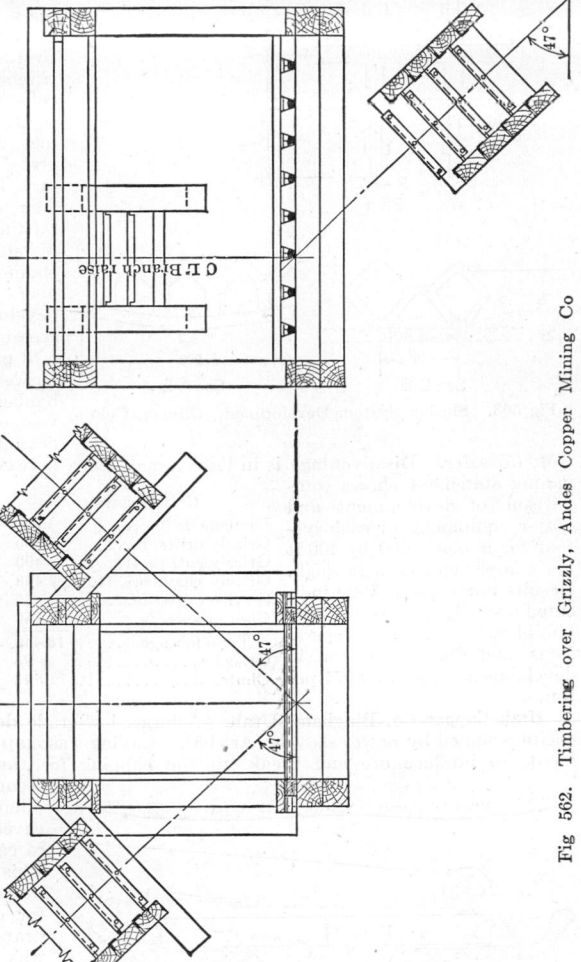

Fig 562. Timbering over Grizzly, Andes Copper Mining Co

DEVELOPMENT. Present (1937) vert interval between haulage levels is 465 ft, but 500-ft lifts are proposed for future. Level development comprises parallel haulage drifts, 11 ft high by 13 ft wide, and 200 ft c–c. At intervals of 75 ft, "slushing drifts" extend from both sides of and at right-angles to haulage drifts (Fig 563). At intersection with haulage drift, bottom of slushing drift is 8 ft above rail, or 1 ft above top of cars, thus allowing ore to be scraped directly into cars. Slushing drifts usually extend 100 ft on each side of haulage drift, and are driven on a +15% grade. At 50-ft intervals along these drifts, chute raises are driven as in Fig 563. Undercutting is done by slabbing the sides of the upper branches of these raises, pillars being left temporarily as required. Undercutting is completed by drilling and blasting simultaneously a number of pillars. Thereafter, ore caves by its own wt, and drops through the chute raises to the slushing drifts, whence it is scraped into hoppers discharging directly into cars in haulage drift. Scraper hoists have double drums, and 150-hp motors; 72-in, hoe-type scrapers are manganese-steel; rope is 1⅛-in, plow-steel. Hoppers over haulage drifts

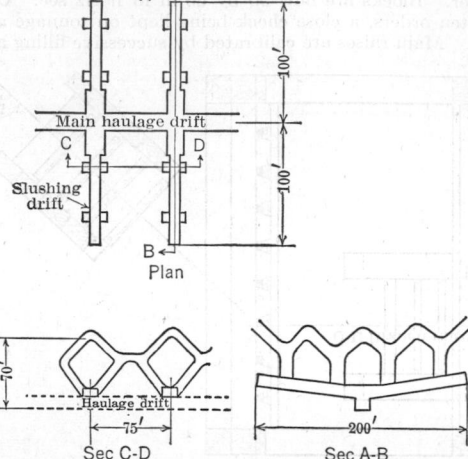

Fig 563. Slusher System Development, Climax, Colo

(Fig 564) are of structural steel, 34 ft long by 10 ft wide, with sides 3 ft high; bottom slopes up on 15% grade from a 4 by 7-ft discharge hole in center. A 24-in log is placed across slushing drift at each end of hopper. Planks, 3 by 12 in, are dapped into logs and extend to discharge hole; 60-lb rails, with heads up, are fastened to these planks and bent over the logs, ends of rails being set in concrete. Scraper hoist is mounted on a frame which can be moved from end to end of hopper, permitting scraping from either branch of slushing drift. Advantages claimed for the " slushing system " over " grizzly system " are: (1) less development, hence lower cost and greater speed in bringing blocks into production; (2) less distance between undercutting level and haulage level, hence more ore developed for a given lift; (3) greater flexibility; (4) better draw control; (5) safer. Disadvantage is in less storage space between stope and cars. Accompaning statement shows comparison of development and major equipment for each system for a block 600 by 400 ft horiz area and 410 ft high. Results obtained in 1929 indicated a saving by slushing system of $0.027 per ton in operations and $0.044 per ton in development; total, $0.071 per ton.

Grizzly system	
Haulage drifts, ft.....	3 800
Grizzly drifts, ft.....	3 000
Grizzly entries, ft.....	2 400
Grizzly chambers, ft..	2 400
Service raises, ft.....	80
Chute raises, ft.......	6 760
Total footage.......	18 440
Grizzlies.............	96
Chutes..............	48

Slushing system	
Haulage drifts, ft...	2 050
Slushing drifts, ft...	3 600
Total footage.....	5 650
Loading platforms...	18
Hoists.............	18

Utah Copper Co, Bingham, Utah. A large, low-grade deposit of disseminated chalcocite is mined by power shovels (Art 96). Caving was employed in the earlier development, to produce ore and break up the capping for the shovels without blasting.

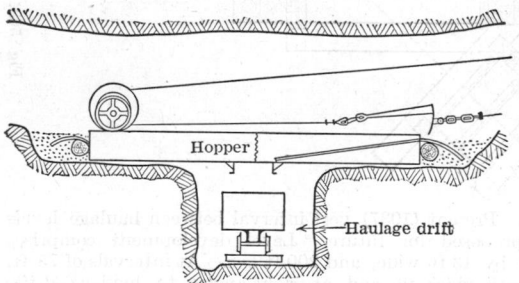

Fig 564. Vert Cross-sec through Haulage Drift, showing Slusher Platform, Climax, Colo

Rooms were opened; then the pillars were weakened until they caved, and the ore was handled in cars or barrows to the chutes. This plan was modified later by putting up raises to caved areas for drawing off ore. Finally a branched-raise caving method was developed. Fig 565 shows the development. Two main levels were opened from tunnels 200 ft apart vertically. The ore on lowest or main haulage-level was cut up by drifts and crosscuts into pillars about 75 ft square. Main raises were inclined at 50° to 60°, each serving an area 70 to 75 ft square. Sub-levels were at vertical intervals of 17 ft; later this was increased to 25 ft and then to 33 ft, which was the largest at which caving could be controlled. Numerous branch and sub-branch raises (not shown in Fig 565) were driven from main raises between subs. The collars of branch raises on subs were approx on corners of 15-ft squares. A block of ore was caved by enlarging the tops of all raises under it, and finally mining the remaining pillars; for further detail, see Bib (114, 190, 305). Loss of ore by mixing with capping was high.

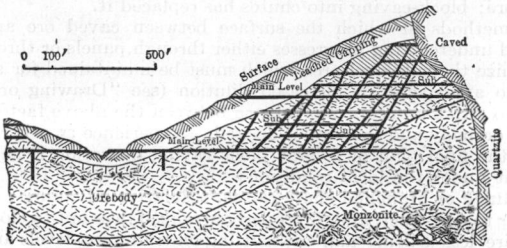

Fig 565. Utah Copper Co. Cross-sec through Part of Orebody

81. SUMMARY. BLOCK-CAVING

General. Block-caving, where applicable, gives a lower mining cost per ton than any other underground method. It requires relatively large capital expenditure for preliminary development, and is essentially for large-scale work. In its different forms (Art 79, 80), it is applicable to deposits of various shape and to ores of various strength, but has rigid requirements and limitations. In unsuitable deposits, or where carelessly conducted, the loss of ore may exceed that of any other method; systematic work, careful supervision and good judgment are essential to success.

Requirements, besides those common to all caving methods (Art 82), are: SUITABLE OREBODIES. For general applicability of method see Art 79. Orebodies must have enough horiz area to cave freely and without excessive dilution by waste rock from side walls. Large massive deposits meet these conditions. Vein-like deposits must be wide, and dip over 65°; ideal conditions are strong walls from which ore parts easily; isolating stopes may be used to free ore from walls if their cost is justified by ore tonnage so released. Block-caving may be used in flat beds if thick enough to warrant cost of development; usually minimum thickness is 70–80 ft. Block caving is not a selective method; as underground sorting is not feasible, a fairly uniform distribution of values in the orebody is necessary. Outlines of the orebody should be fairly regular; small extensions of ore into walls are not recovered and tongues of wall rock jutting into the ore can not be left unmined. Some dilution and loss of ore are inevitable in block-caving; their amounts affect the economic min and max grades of ore to which the method is applicable. PHYSICAL CHARACTERISTICS OF ORE which will break up under block-caving have not been exactly defined; some ore successfully mined by block-caving contains numerous small veinlets or other planes of weakness; behaviour of a given ore is determined by trial. Block-caving is adapted to moderately soft or moderately hard, but not to very soft or tough ores. CAPPING must cave when underlying ore is dropped; wt of overburden is essential to aid in crushing the ore. The most favorable capping breaks into large pieces; soft, brittle capping decreases extraction by breaking fine and sifting into the ore, or by "channeling" through to the chutes. Capping differing in appearance from ore is desirable, for ready detection at chutes at end of drawing operations.

Advantages of block-caving: (a) Safety. (b) Cheap mining, since but little drilling, blasting and timbering are done per ton of ore; amount of development is relatively small. (c) Production is centralized, allowing efficient supervision. After caving begins, a large and easily varied output is obtained from one level. (d) Natural ventilation is good, compared to that in other caving methods.

Disadvantages of block-caving: (a) Preparing the blocks for caving requires time and large expense. (b) Cost of maintaining drifts in drawing area is high and this work interferes with production. (c) Variation in rate of production to meet changes in demand for product is difficult. Stoppage of drawing for a considerable time may result in complete loss of the development openings in the area involved. (d) Extraction is sometimes low, and there is constant danger of losing large amounts of ore. (e) Method is inflexible; once started, a change to another underground method is difficult.

Choice between different forms of block-caving (Art 79). Dilution with waste is least when surface between caved ore and capping is kept approx horiz by even drawing from chutes. To accomplish this, the ore area must be divided into blocks, mined successively; maintenance of sub-levels under caving ground of large horiz area is difficult and costly, hence trend is toward use of smaller blocks where sub-level block-caving is used. The Pewabic method is practically obsolete under modern conditions in the U S, due to necessity for driving and maintaining extraction openings through the caved ore and for shoveling all the ore; block-caving into chutes has replaced it.

Block-caving methods in which the surface between caved ore and capping is an inclined plane, and undercutting progresses either through panels or through entire length of orebody, minimize the sub-level area which must be maintained for a given daily production, but do so at expense of increased dilution (see "Drawing ore," Art 79). An attempt is made to strike an economic balance between the above factors as modified by size and nature of orebody and the output desired. Experience at other properties guides initial work, but the final plan of a large block-caving operation is generally the result of long experiment under the local conditions.

Vertical vs inclined or branched chute-raises. Relative advantages of inclined chute-raises: (*a*) Easier to construct, and, if properly arranged, less apt to clog. (*b*) For given spacing they require less drifting and crosscutting on tramming-levels and subs where ore is undercut. Conversely, for a given first cost of lateral development, they may be spaced closer than vert chutes, which is essential for uniform drawing. (*c*) They are applicable in softer ground, since with vert chutes the ore must stand practically unsupported while tops of raises are funneled out and sides of sub-level pillars are cut away. (*d*) They collect ore as drawn at comparatively few points on the sub-level below the caved block. Grizzlies may be installed at such points and large lumps spalled before entering the chutes to main haulageways. With vert raises, ore must be collected and trammed from many different points. (*e*) Gates can be operated in branch-raises a few feet below floor of the sub where the ore is undercut; hence, when drawing is finished, the capping is drawn down only a short distance into the chutes.

Block-caving into branched chutes is limited to orebodies of large horiz area; one disadvantage is that branch and finger-raises are complicated and must be set by survey to come out at proper intervals on the undercutting floor.

Block vs sub-level caving (Art 78). Relative advantages of block-caving: It is cheaper, gives larger daily output from a given area, requires less development per ton of ore, natural ventilation is better, and, by caving into chutes, shoveling is eliminated. Sub-level caving is possible in softer ore and smaller orebodies; caving is better controlled, and yields cleaner ore, with a higher percentage extraction. These factors may outweigh the advantages of block-caving.

82. SUMMARY OF CAVING METHODS (See also Art 74, 78, 81)

General conditions leading to use of caving methods: (*a*) large-scale work; (*b*) orebodies of large horiz area, as wide veins, thick beds, or masses, usually overlain by a capping varying from glacial drift to firm rock; (*c*) ore which is weak or which, if hard, is thoroughly fractured; (*d*) deposits of cheap minerals or low-grade ore, in which loss of ore or contamination with waste is less serious than for high-grade ore (Table 57).

Requirements for top-slicing, sub-level caving and block-caving are stated in Art 74, 78, and 81. Absolute requirements common to all caving methods: (*a*) The overburden must cave and "follow down," as the ore beneath is removed. A method requiring weight on top of the workings is useless unless that weight is obtainable from the overburden. The capping need not always cave to the surface, but it should cave sufficiently to protect the workings and furnish the necessary crushing force. Capping which hangs up and then drops suddenly over considerable areas is very dangerous; both the workings and the men may be destroyed. (*b*) Surface subsidence must not injure valuable property nor make underground work dangerous. This precludes caving under structures which can not be moved to a safe place, or under streams

Table 57. Comparison of Caving Methods

From the standpoint of	Usual order of merit		
	1	2	3
Cheap mining costs......	BC	SC	TS
Clean mining..........	TS	SC	BC
Percentage extraction....	TS	SC	BC
Close grading of ore.....	TS	SC	BC
Flexibility..............	TS	SC	BC
Chance of losing ore.....	TS	SC	BC
% of ore won by caving..	BC	SC	TS
Timber consumption (*a*)..	BC	SC	TS
Natural ventilation......	BC	SC	TS
Control of caving........	TS	SC	BC
Large output from given area.................	BC	SC	TS

BC = Block-caving. SC = Sub-level caving. TS = Top-slicing. (*a*) Fire hazard varies directly as timber consumption.

which can not be diverted, or under lakes, swamps, etc, which can not be drained. Presence of known orebodies, or of virgin ground likely to contain ore, prohibits caving in an underlying deposit.

Orebodies specifically unsuited to caving (P. B. Scotland): (a) Those which are flat and thin, or small and high-grade, or very irregular in shape. (b) Deposits containing much waste which must be sorted underground. (c) Deposits containing mixed sulphide and oxide ores, or milling and smelting ores, which must be kept separate for treatment.

General comparison. Note, in addition to the summary in Table 57, that top-slicing is best adapted to very soft, heavy ores; sub-level and block-caving, to stronger ores. A weak, friable capping favors top-slicing; strong capping which breaks large favors block-caving. Sub-level caving always occupies a position intermediate between top-slicing and block-caving. Where a choice exists, it usually lies either between top-slicing and sub-level caving, or between sub-level and some form of block-caving; for detailed comparisons, see Art 78, 81.

COMBINED METHODS

83. GENERAL

Term "**Combined method**" designates here a group of mining methods involving a concurrent and systematic use or combination of two or more of the methods described in Art 29–82. Such methods vary widely and are difficult to classify specifically. They are employed chiefly in mining large bodies of soft or hard ore; in general, they are for large-scale work and aim at a high extraction. The term does not apply to cases in which a minor portion of an orebody is mined by methods other than that applied to the major portion of the orebody, even though the use of 2 or more methods may be systematic.

Combinations used generally involve subdivision of the orebody into a series of alternating pillars and stopes; stopes are usually shrinkage stopes, with various methods for mining pillars (see Table 58). Combinations of shrinkage stopes and block-caving are also known as "Shrinkage Stope and Pillar-caving," or more simply as "Pillar-caving."

Table 58. Combined Methods

Mine	Method of mining		For details see Art
	In stopes	In pillars	
Ray Consol Cop Co, Ariz..............	Shrinkage	Block-caving	85
Miami Copper Co, Ariz..............	Shrinkage	{ Shrinkage stoping and } { sub-level caving }	86
Braden Copper Co, Chile..............	Shrinkage	Block-caving	87
Duluth, Cananea, Mex................	Shrinkage	Block-caving and top-slicing	87
Coronado, Ariz.....................	Shrinkage	Block-caving	87
Humboldt, Ariz....................	Shrinkage	Block-caving	87
Silver Dyke, Mont.................	Shrinkage	Block-caving	87
Magma, Ariz......................	Filled rill	Timbered stope	87
Loretto mine.....................	Square-sets (a)	Top-slicing	(b)
N J Zinc Co......................	Shrinkage (a)	Top-slicing	87
Golden Queen, Cal.................	Open sq-set	Shrinkage, or cut-and-fill, or sq-set	87

(a) With delayed filling, Art 67.   (b) Not described here, see Bib (604).

South African diamond mines use combined shrinkage stoping and sub-level caving (Art 88), differing entirely in principle from pillar-caving. Methods at Creighton and Beatson mines, Art 68, may also be classed as shrinkage-stope and pillar-caving systems.

84. PRACTICE AT BOSTON CONSOL MINE

General. SHRINKAGE STOPES AND PILLAR-CAVING were used for about 5 years by Boston Consol Co, but were abandoned in 1914 after the property had been acquired by Utah Copper Co, which it adjoins. This company extended its opencut (Art 96) into Boston ground and ceased underground mining there. Early method at Ray (Art 85) was developed directly from the Boston method; its evolution illustrates many essential points in mining large, low-grade orebodies by shrinkage stopes and pillar-caving. There are two variations, based wholly on differences in mode of handling ore: (a) HAND-TRAMMING SYSTEM, in which stopes are opened directly over the drift sets on the levels and ore is handled there in small cars to chutes connecting with a haulage level below; (b) SUB-LEVEL or MOTOR-HAULAGE SYSTEM, in which stoping begins from a sub-level above a motor-haulage level and ore is drawn down to latter through chute-raises; the sub-level is a stoping base only. OREBODY is a large, low-grade, disseminated copper deposit, in monzonite porphyry, overlain by leached capping. It was opened by 2 adit levels, 150 ft apart vertically, the upper reaching a max depth of 200 ft below capping (114). Following data are by L. A. Blackner in 1915 (61).

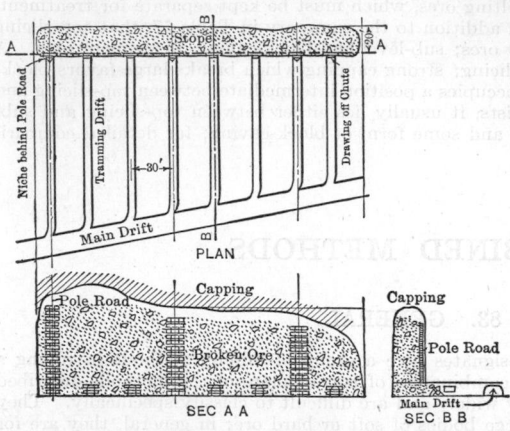

Fig 566. Boston Mine, Hand-tramming System; Chutes at One Side of Stope

Hand-tramming system. In the early stages, the plan shown in Fig 566 was tried. A drift on the center line of the stope nearest the ore boundary was widened to 20 ft. From it was carried up a shrinkage stope, access to which was through "pole roads" (Art 88) at the ends of alternate tramming drifts. At first, excess ore was shoveled at the ends of the drifts; later, chute-gates were erected in each drift to eliminate shoveling. DISADVANTAGES: (a) max output was limited to that which could be produced from one stope; (b) the broken ore in the stope drew down on one side, making it difficult for machinemen to work; (c) as cars had to be loaded at the end instead of the side, they slopped over, and much shoveling was required to clean the tracks; (d) the widening of the stope floor on the level wasted time and money, as the space so formed was filled with unrecoverable ore; (e) final extraction was low, as ore in rear of stope could not be re-covered.

Fig 567 shows a later plan. Chute-gates, 30 ft apart on each side of the stope, made it possible to draw the swell of the broken ore more evenly, and to secure higher final extraction; also several stopes could be worked simultaneously. But, with the chute-gates so arranged, the miners had to work at times in the middle of the stope, where the back was continually sloughing off, and in starting a stope some ore had to be shoveled from the middle to the sides. Ventilation was poor, the pole roads gave trouble, and the other disadvantages of the plan in Fig 566 persisted. Moreover, the large openings caused by placing the crosscuts from the tramming drifts opposite each other weakened the bases of the pillars, making it difficult to maintain the tramming drifts.

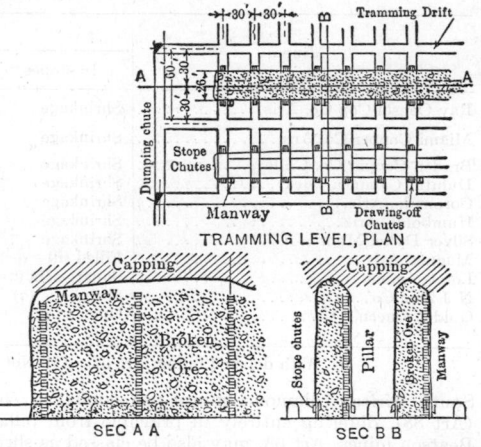

Fig 567. Boston Mine, Hand-tramming System; Chutes on Both Sides of Stope

Fig 568 shows the final stage of the hand-tramming system, before underground mining ceased. The development work was halved by running tramming drifts in alternate pillars only; crosscuts were staggered, reducing the size of opening at their entrance to a minimum. Two chute sets were erected in each crosscut at the stope center, to provide gates under the stope instead of at the sides. The stope floors were above the level and consisted of a series of funnels apexing at the chutes. This important improvement did away with expensive drifting and widening on the stope floor and made it possible to recover all the broken ore. Manway raises were put up in alternate pillars at 60-ft

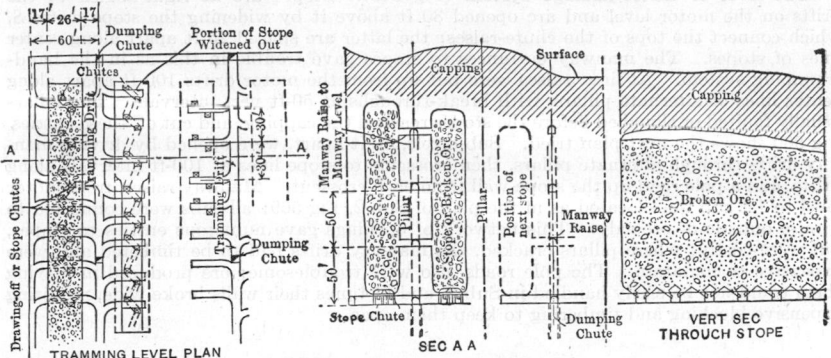

Fig 568. Boston Mine, Hand-tramming System; Chutes in Middle of Stope

intervals along tramming drifts, small crosscuts from them furnishing access to stopes. This mode of entry was later replaced by manway pillar drifts (Fig 569), because the pillars

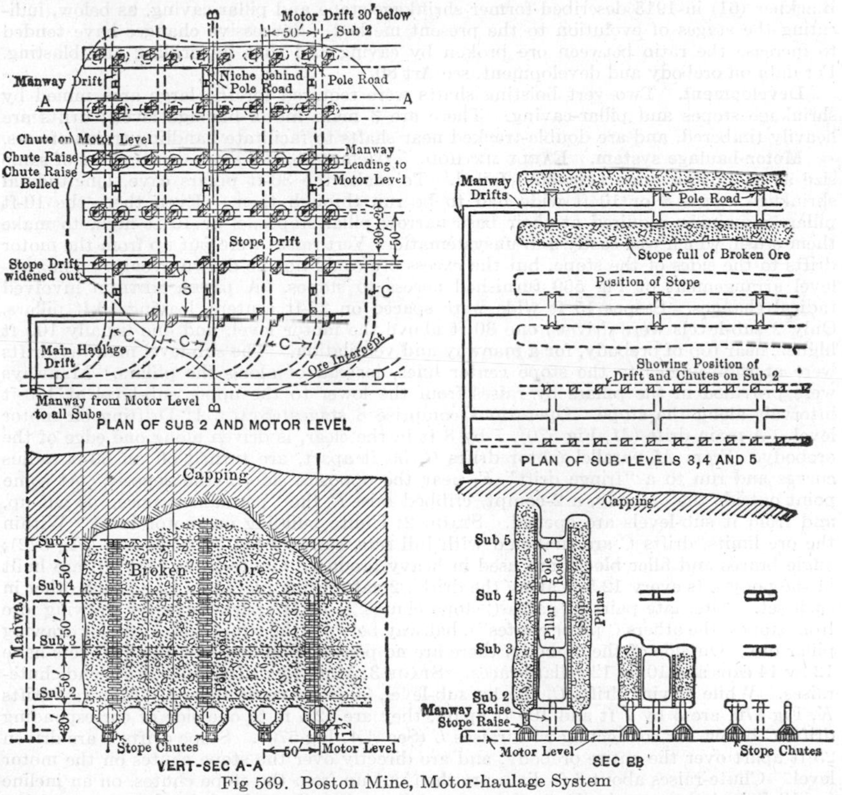

Fig 569. Boston Mine, Motor-haulage System

cracked and the raises became unsafe. Manway drifts were good in hard ground, but in presence of seams and faults they caved; also the drifts and crosscuts on the level required much retimbering. The arrangement of chutes in Fig 568 required a tram uneconomically long for hand work. The detail of caving pillars and drawing ore was not worked out; added drifts would have been needed on the levels to extract the pillar ore.

Sub-level or motor-haulage system (Fig 569). Stopes are at right-angles to the drifts on the motor level and are opened 30 ft above it by widening the stope drifts S, which connect the tops of the chute-raises; the latter are spaced 25 ft apart along center lines of stopes. The manway entrances to stopes gave trouble in this as in the hand-tramming system. At first, raises were put up from the motor drifts 100 ft apart along center lines of alternate pillars, with break-throughs at 50-ft vert intervals. The pillars usually faulted or sloughed before the stopes reached the capping, and cut off these entries, Fig 569 shows the next plan tried. Sub-levels, 50 ft apart, were opened by driving manway drifts through alternate pillars, then crosscuts to stope lines at 100-ft intervals along drifts, and a pole road up the stope wall from each crosscut. Manway raises, from motor level to 1st sub were located as in the plan of Sub 2, Fig 569; all subs were connected to a raise outside of orebody. This network of openings gave numerous entries to stopes, but were costly; where pillars cracked, the manway drifts had to be timbered and were expensive to maintain. The pole roads also were troublesome; ore produced in driving them could not be easily handled in Sub 2, and at times their walls broke wide, requiring expensive blocking and timbering to keep them open.

85. PRACTICE AT RAY MINE, ARIZ

General. Present method at Ray is usually classified as block-caving (see Art 80), although some shrinkage stoping is still done in connection with caving operations. L. A. Blackner (61) in 1915 described former shrinkage-stope and pillar-caving, as below, indicating the stages of evolution to the present method. Successive changes have tended to increase the ratio between ore broken by caving and that by drilling and blasting. For data on orebody and development, see Art 80.

Development. Two vert hoisting shafts were required for the large area mined by shrinkage stopes and pillar-caving. There are 3 main motor-haulage levels; drifts are heavily timbered, and are double-tracked near shafts to facilitate handling trains of cars.

Motor-haulage system. Early method. Attempts to use stopes and pillars of same size as at Boston mine (Fig 569) failed. To make the 30-ft pillars cave, longitudinal shrinkage stopes 8 or 10 ft wide had to be run through them. Even then, the 10-ft pillars remaining required at their base narrow pillar-stopes, 8 or 10 ft high, to make them crush, which was costly and unsystematic. Vert raises were put up from the motor drifts to the sides of the stope, but the excess ore could not be drawn evenly. The sub-level arrangement of Fig 569 furnished access to stopes. A later method involved radical changes. Stopes 15 ft wide were spaced on 25-ft centers, leaving 10-ft pillars. Only 2 sub-levels were driven; one 30 ft above the motor level, and one usually 100 ft higher, near top of orebody, for a manway and ventilation. The sub-level manway drifts were at right-angles to the stope center lines, instead of along the pillars. Manways were provided in the pillars by raises from the lower to the upper sub-level at 100-ft intervals along the stope. Operations comprise 8 stages: Stage 1: Drifting on motor level. A main drift (M, Fig 570), 7 by 8 ft in the clear, is driven along one edge of the orebody. From M parallel motor drifts C, 50 ft apart, are turned off on 60-ft radius curves and run to a "fringe drift" F, near the opposite side of the deposit. At some point outside the orebody, a 2-compt, cribbed raise R, the "permanent raise," is put up, and from it sub-levels are opened. Stage 2: Chute building on motor level. Within the ore limits, drifts C are timbered with full sets, surmounted by pony-sets (Fig 572); angle braces and filler blocks are used in heavy ground. Chute-gates (Art 90) are built in the pony sets every 12.5 ft along the drifts, 2 gates being placed opposite each other in each set. Alternate pairs of gates ("stope chutes"), 25 ft apart, serve for drawing ore from stopes; the others ("pillar chutes"), halfway between the stope chutes, are for drawing pillar ore. Outside of the orebody, there are no pony sets in drifts C; the drift sets have 12 by 14 caps and 10 by 12 collar braces. Stage 3: Manway drifts, stope drifts and chute-raises. While driving drifts C, the 1st sub-level, 30 ft above, is opened. Manway drifts K, Fig 570, are 5 by 7 ft and 100 ft apart; they are 12.5 ft to one side of corresponding drifts C below, for connecting with raises L (See AA, Fig 570). Stope drifts S are driven 25 ft apart over the entire orebody, and are directly over the stope chutes on the motor level. Chute-raises about 6 ft diam are then put up from the stope chutes, on an incline for 10 ft and then vertically to the stope drifts. On the 2nd sub-level, manway drifts N are driven directly over drifts K. Stage 4: Manway raises, belling out chute-raises, widening stope drifts, building manway sets. Manway raises are put up to drifts N at 25-ft intervals along drifts K; as their centers are 7.5 ft from centers of stope drifts S, they are bisected by the stope wall; chain ladders are hung in these raises. The tops of the chute-raises are funneled while driving manway raises; this is done with stope-drills putting in uppers. Stopes are started by drilling a line of holes slanting into the sides of the stope drift; these holes and those drilled in belling the chute-raises widen the stope drift to 15 ft. Manway sets are erected in the drifts *K*, directly under the manway raises, as soon as the stope drifts are widened; the manway sets consist of driftsets, standing on 8 by 8-in stringers projecting into the stopes; 3 by 3-ft cribbed manways are built up from these sets through the broken ore as the stopes advance. STAGE 5 consists of mining the stopes to the capping. For mode of breaking ground, see Fig 174. The broken ore swells about 33%. The cribbed manways are abandoned when the stope is halfway to the 2nd sub, after which the miners pass through the manway raises. In hard ground, stopes are 15 to 20 ft wide; in soft, sloughing ore, 10 to 15 ft wide. STAGE 6: Before drawing

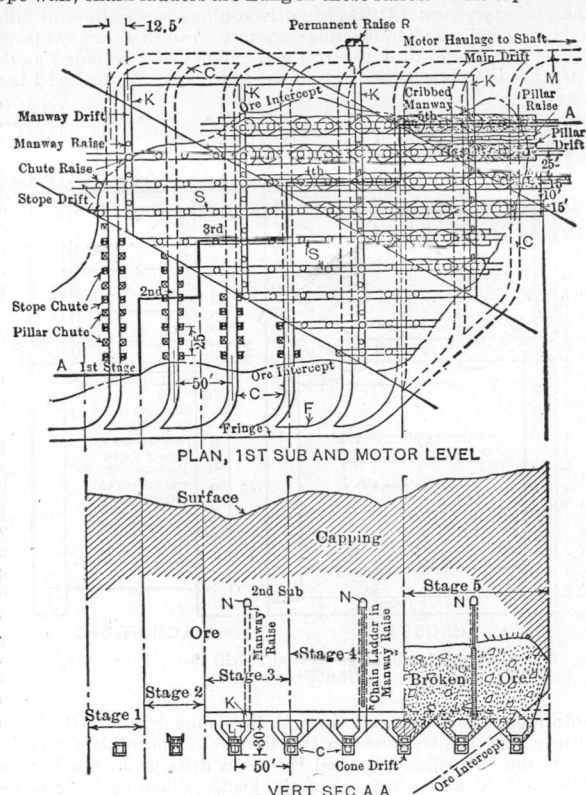

Fig 570. Ray Motor-haulage System (showing 5 stages of work)

the stopes, the pillars are undermined by one of the following methods. Method 1 (Fig 573), used in hard ground where stopes are 15 to 20 ft wide, leaves narrow pillars easily under-

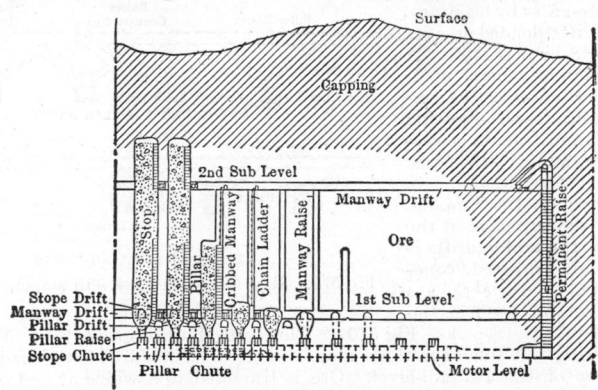

Fig 571. Ray Motor-haulage System

mined. Pillar raises, run from the pillar chutes (2nd stage), start in the pillar nearest fringe drift *F* (Fig 570). After connecting the raises along a pillar, they are widened, lined with deep holes and blasted. This is repeated in successive pillars, retreating towards main drift *M*. Method 2 (Fig 573) is used in soft ground, where pillars are wide and stopes narrow. Drifts are driven along center lines of pillars, 22 ft above the motor level (Fig 571), and chute-raises are put up to them on flat inclines from the pillar chutes. Raises are funneled at the top and pillar drifts widened as desired. The backs of the drifts are then blasted with deep holes (Fig 573). Method 1 is cheaper and is used wherever pillars are narrow enough to allow it. STAGE 7: Drawing ore ("reserve drawing"). Generally the orebody and capping are fractured, so that when the pillars in a stoped area are caved and the ore drawn, the capping breaks to the surface along a nearly vert plane at the edge of the area. In areas where haulage drifts are to be abandoned, the chutes near the fringe drift are drawn faster than the others, so that the capping assumes a slight incline toward this drift; by the time the drifts take weight, all the ore beyond is drawn, which avoids expense for retimbering. Only a few cars of ore are drawn at a time, to induce gradual settling of the capping, with minimum loss and dilution of ore.

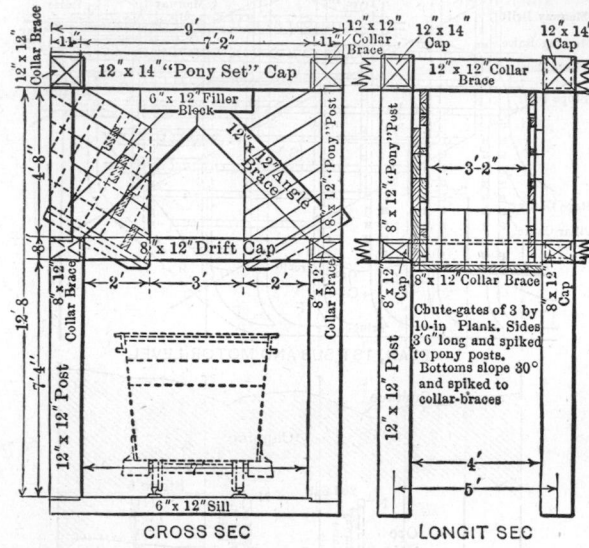

Fig 572. Ray Motor-haulage System, Drift Sets, Pony Sets, and Chute-gates

When drawing chutes, the motorman runs empty cars through the fringe drift into the back ends of drifts *C*, Fig 570, whence they are trammed to the chute. A chute blaster or loader loads the car, and one trammer pushes it toward the main drift while another spots an empty. All drifts have a 0.25% grade in favor of the load. When an 8- or 12-car train is loaded, a motor hauls it through the main drift, returning the empties to the back end of the motor drift. The highest efficiency results when only 2 trammers and 1 loader are used in a drift. In one case 6 trammers, 3 loaders, 2 machinemen (for blasting boulders in chutes), 1 mucker and 1 timberman (for repairing damage to chute-gates by blasting), working in 4 drifts, loaded an aver of 150 tons per 8-hr man-shift. A boss, a timberman on general repair work and a car checker are employed in each reserve-drawing section. (See Hand-tramming system for further detail.) STAGE 8: Cone-drifting. After all chutes in a block are drawn to the capping, the ore below the sub-level in the pillars between the motor drifts is recovered. Small, timbered "cone-drifts," parallel to drifts *C*, are driven on the motor level in the

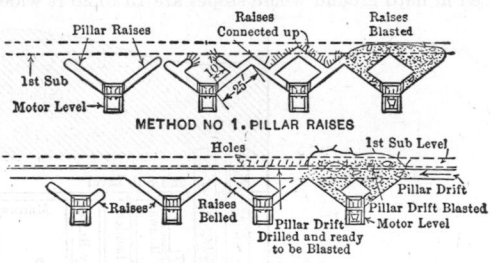

Fig 573. Ray Motor-haulage (6th stage), Undermining Pillars

enters of the pillars (Sec *AA*, Fig 570). Chutes are built opposite each other in every set along the drifts. A small shrinkage stope directly over the drift is widened and carried to the sill floor of the 1st sub-level. Ore is trammed to a winze at end of drift, and dumped to the motor level. When all the cone-drift chutes are drawn to the capping, the remaining pillars are mined by slicing. Thus, all ore above the motor-haulage floor is eventually recovered.

Hand-tramming system (Fig 574, 575). DEVELOPMENT on tramming levels comprises parallel drifts *D*, 25 ft apart and connected with fringe drifts *F*, near edge of the ore.

Drifts are timbered as in Fig 576, using angle braces only in heavy ground. Caps are lagged with 4 by 10-in plank; posts with 2 by 8-in, placed as indicated. Stope chutes are 25 ft apart along tramming drifts. A permanent raise R is put up as in the motor-haulage system, and a sub-level opened 75 to 100 ft above the tramming level. The sub-level consists of manway or ventilation drifts, 75 ft apart and directly over every 3rd tramming drift D; manway drifts are turned off from a drift overlying one of the drifts F. Vert raises, with chain ladders, are put up from D to the manway drifts, as in the plan, Fig 574, and in Fig 575. Stopes, 15–18 ft wide and 25 ft apart, run at right-angles to D, and are started from the stope chutes by driving inclined chute-raises, 2 sets (10 ft) wide, to meet raises from adjacent drifts and form hogbacks in stope floor (Fig 574). Tops of these raises are widened and stope carried up as in motor-haulage system; 3 by 3-ft cribbed manways through broken ore directly under manway raises give access to stopes. Undermining the pillars (Fig 577). Pillar chutes are built in drifts D, Fig 574, between the stope chutes. Raises in Fig 577 are driven from the pillar chutes, widened and blasted; remaining ore in the block (about 80% of total) is then ready to be drawn. Some ore packs in cones over the hogbacks between tramming drifts; in the higher-grade ore it is recovered by cone-drifting, as in motor-haulage system; in low-grade ore, cones and hogbacks are caved with the lift below. Dumping chutes, connecting with a motor-haulage level, are built at ends of each drift D, Fig 574.

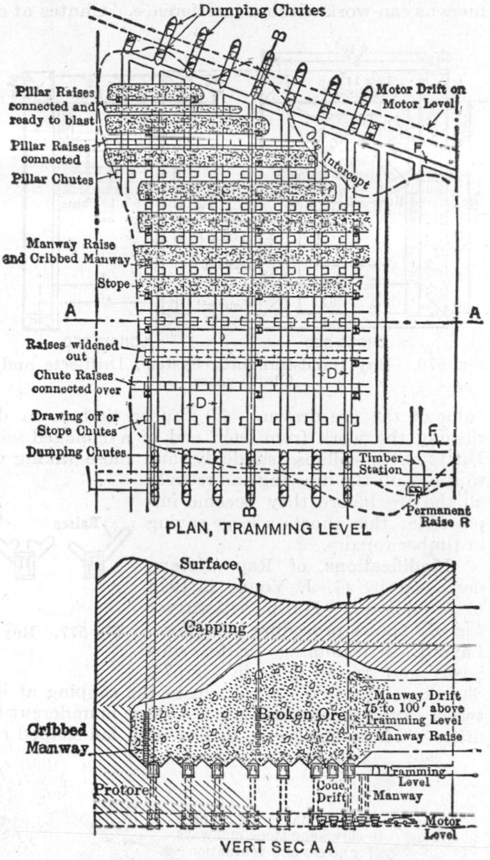

PLAN, TRAMMING LEVEL

Dumping Chutes

Pillar Raises connected and ready to blast

Pillar Raises connected

Pillar Chutes

Motor Drift on Motor Level

Intercept

Manway Raise and Cribbed Manway

Stope

Raises widened out

Chute Raises connected over

Drawing off or Stope Chutes

Dumping Chutes

Timber Station

Permanent Raise R

VERT SEC A A

Surface

Capping

Broken Ore

Cribbed Manway

Protore

Manway Drift 75 to 100' above Tramming Level

Manway Raise

Cone Drift

Tramming Level Manway

Motor Level

Fig 574. Ray Hand-tramming System

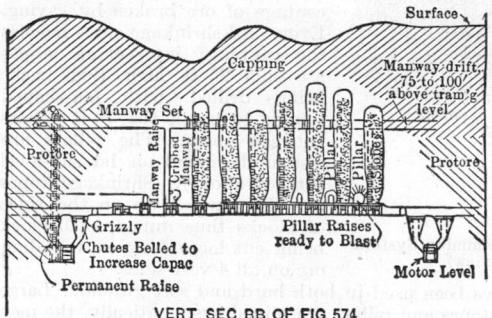

Surface

Capping

Manway drift 75 to 100' above tram'g level

Manway Set

Protore

Manway Raise

Cribbed Manway

Pillar

Pillar

Protore

Grizzly

Chutes Belled to Increase Capac

Permanent Raise

Pillar Raises ready to Blast

Motor Level

VERT SEC BB OF FIG 574

Fig 575. Ray Hand-tramming System

Drawing ore differs from drawing in the motor-haulage system, because the pillar over drifts D is too small to take the weight off them. This difficulty is met as follows: (a) If large blocks are drawn evenly over their entire area, great pressure is brought upon the tramming drifts and timber repairs are excessive. Hence a "receding method" of drawing is adopted. The 2 pillars farthest from the permanent raise are caved first, and the chutes farthest from the permanent raise are drawn fastest. As soon as the first row of chutes runs capping, the next pillar is undermined and caved. Thus, no area greater than 50 to 75 ft wide is crushing at one time. A steep slope is maintained between caved ore and waste. (b) Rapid drawing is advisable, as it usually allows the ore from an undermined area to be recovered without timber repairs. To secure fast work and low costs, the number of trammers and muckers must be properly proportioned to the non-producers (timbermen and chute-blasters). There should be as many trammers as can work without interference. Chutes at each end of the tramming drifts facilitate rapid handling; other chutes in the middle of each drift weaken the drifts and make them crush. In one section, with chutes as in Fig 575, 8 trammers handled 97 tons aver per 8-hr shift. (c) Drawing operations are systematized. Owing to the large number of chutes being drawn at one time, a continuous record must be kept of each, to know constantly the tons remaining and the assay. The car checker notifies the boss which chutes are ore and which waste, so that he can place his men advantageously and know when to undermine the next pillar. The boss is responsible for a steady output, the car checker for the assay

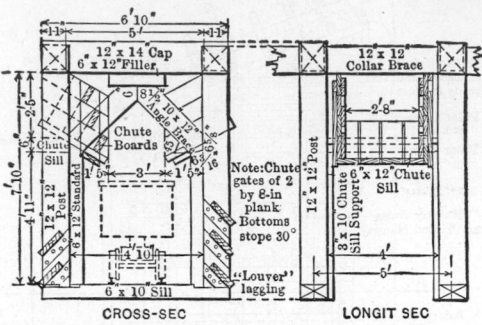

Fig 576.   Ray Hand-tramming System, Drift-sets and Chute-gates

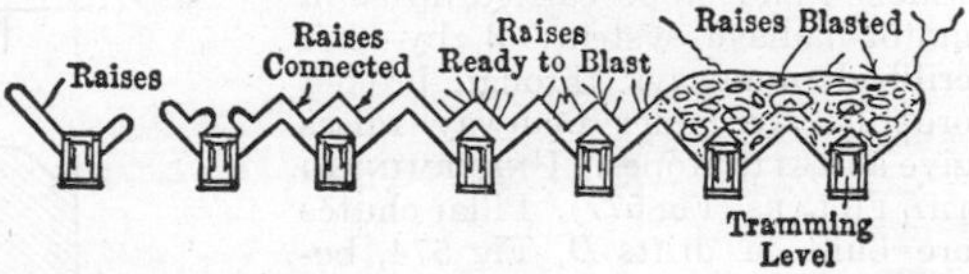

value of the ore drawn. (d) Broken timbers in drift sets are repaired promptly, by rushing the work from each end of a damaged section; neglected repairs mean lost ore. Drifts never collapse suddenly, and those taking weight are generally detected in time to speed up the drawing and recover all the ore before they become impassable; this effects a large saving in timber repairs.

Modifications of Ray system, described by G. J. Young in 1926 (593) follow.   HAND TRAMMING. Fig 578 shows procedure in soft ore. Layout of tramming drifts, sublevels and raises is as in Fig 574.

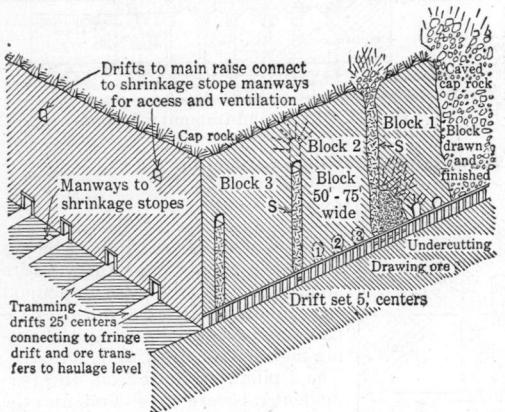

Fig 577.   Ray Hand-tramming System, Undermining Pillars

Shrinkage stopes S are put up to the capping at intervals of 50–75 ft. The block between caved ground and nearest stope is undercut from raises 15 ft c–c along tramming drifts. These blocks are drilled with fan-shaped rounds and blasted successively, starting next to stope and working toward the cave. Drawing chutes are built in each set in the tramming drifts. When a block is completely undercut, drawing retreats from the cave to next block. This plan lessens dilution by waste. MOTOR-HAULAGE is also modified in soft ground, to increase percentage of ore broken by caving. Every 3rd shrinkage stope reaches the capping; intervening stopes are only 25 ft high, their backs being drilled with fan-shaped rounds to break the 10-ft pillars between them. The pillars are also undermined on 1st sub-level (Stage 6 above). Shrinkage stopes are also carried up on the sides of blocks thus mined, each block being cut loose from surrounding ore on all 4 vert sides.

Fig 578.   Modification of Ray Hand-tramming System for Soft Ground. (Perspective view)

Summary. The Ray systems have been used in both hard and soft ground. Large tonnages are produced per man; as stopes and pillars are mined systematically, the men soon become proficient. Timber consumption is relatively small; the amount of raising and drifting compares favorably with that of other methods in similar orebodies. The systems are flexible as to output; practically any number of men may be used during active operations and a corresponding tonnage produced.

Motor haulage is applicable only to orebodies of large area and of a height exceeding 100 ft; otherwise the cost of driving and timbering the stope laterals and of equipping and maintaining the haulage levels is not justified, and HAND TRAMMING is more economical. ADVANTAGE OF MOTOR HAULAGE: it is suited to large outputs, especially during reserve drawing, when the output is limited only by the efficiency of the haulage and hoisting plants. ADVANTAGES OF HAND TRAMMING in smaller and thinner orebodies: (a) lower initial development cost; (b) less timber required; (c) higher extraction, as chutes can be built in every set in both the original drifts and cone-drifts. With motor haulage, the pillar between the sub and motor level is dangerously weakened if chute-raises are spaced too close; (d) blocks of ore can be opened and production started sooner. DISADVANTAGE OF THE RAY SYSTEM is that a large amount of capital is tied up in the broken ore for a considerable time. This is a drawback of all shrinkage-stope and pillar-caving methods (compare with disadvantage d, Art 69).

86. PRACTICE AT MIAMI COPPER MINE, ARIZ

Orebody (Art 80). System described below was applied from 1910 to 1916, incl, to a block of relatively hard ground in the western end of the property containing 2 300 000 tons. See Art 72, 80, for methods used in other parts of orebody.

General plan. Shrinkage stopes and pillar-caving were used; stopes, 50 ft wide and 200 to 500 ft long; pillars, 50 ft wide. Originally the pillars were to be mined by sub-level stoping (Art 43), leaving broken ore in the stope, but it was difficult to drill "down"

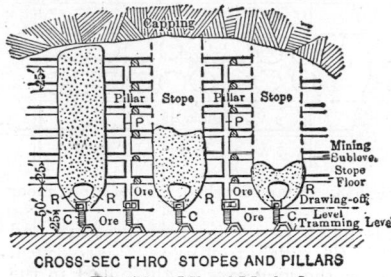

CROSS-SEC THRO STOPES AND PILLARS

Fig 579. Miami Method

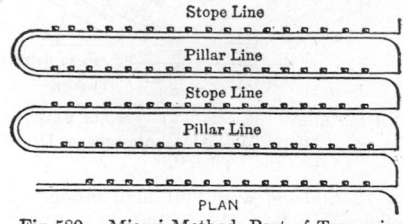

PLAN

Fig 580. Miami Method, Part of Tramming Level

holes, and a shrinkage-stoping and sub-level caving method, similar to that at Kimberley (Art 88), was finally adopted. Ore was drawn simultaneously from both shrinkage and pillar stopes, to make the capping settle evenly. This was called locally the WIDE STOPE AND PILLAR SYSTEM. Following data are from D. B. Scott in 1916 (154).

Development comprised a haulage level, a drawing-off level, the sub-levels for stoping, and raises for handling ore and for access to stopes (Fig 579). Added sub-level drifting was necessary to determine the boundaries of the orebody; its general outline was found by churn drilling (Art 10-b). HAULAGE LEVEL was 50 ft below the stopes. By drifting under the long axes of both stopes and pillars (Fig 580), trains of cars could be loaded along an entire stope without uncoupling; this allowed the rapid drawing of excess ore so desirable during stoping. Also with chutes 25 ft apart, this plan required a minimum amount of development. 10 by 10-in timber was used in haulage drifts, with 9-ft posts and 8-ft caps; sets, 6.25 ft apart (Fig 634, Art 90). DRAWING-OFF LEVEL, a distinctive feature of this method, was 25 ft above the haulage level; it consisted of drifts parallel to those on the haulage level, with a fringe drift at each end for entry and ventilation (Fig 581). Drifts were on center lines of stopes to secure a symmetrical arrangement of raises for drawing ore (Fig 579). For convenience in putting up vert development raises in the pillars, the pillar drifts were 5 ft off the pillar axes; this arrangement was later modified so that symmetrical drawing raises were possible also in the pillars. The drawing-off level drifts were timbered with 10 by 10-in sets 5 ft apart, using 8-ft posts and 7-ft caps. In some drifts, these sets were almost intact after nearly 2 years. Experience showed that a min amount of lagging should be used on these sets, that it should be light (2-in) and spaced 2 or 3 in apart. (For timbering at chutes, see Fig 582, 584).

RAISES. Chute-raises C, Fig 579 ("pocket chutes"), were 25 ft apart. They were 5 ft square, each holding 15 tons; for cribbing, 8 by 8-in timber proved most economical, a representative group of chutes showing a cribbing life of 12 430 tons each. Grizzlies with 18-in sq openings were placed on the drawing-off level; they were set several inches above the collars of the raises, to permit easy working when the grizzlies blocked. Inclined raises *R*, Fig 579 ("stope raises"), were driven from the drifts to the stope floors at points over the pocket-chutes. Originally, vert raises were run from the back of drift to center line of stope; they proved difficult and awkward to draw. Stope raises (untimbered) were 6 ft sq at the bottom and funneled at the top. Development raises *P*, Fig 579, were 50 ft apart along center lines of pillars. During pillar-mining, intermediate raises reduced the interval to 25 ft. Raises (not shown in Fig 579) similar to the stope raises were put up under the pillars from the drawing-off level. In earlier work they were in the plane of the stope raises (Fig 581);

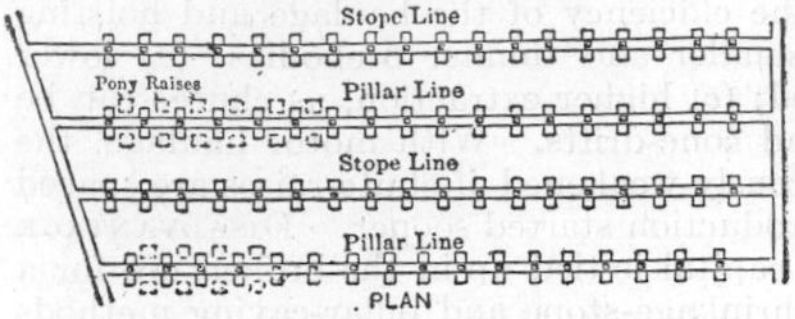

Fig 581. Miami Method, Part of Drawing-off Level, Directly over Fig 580

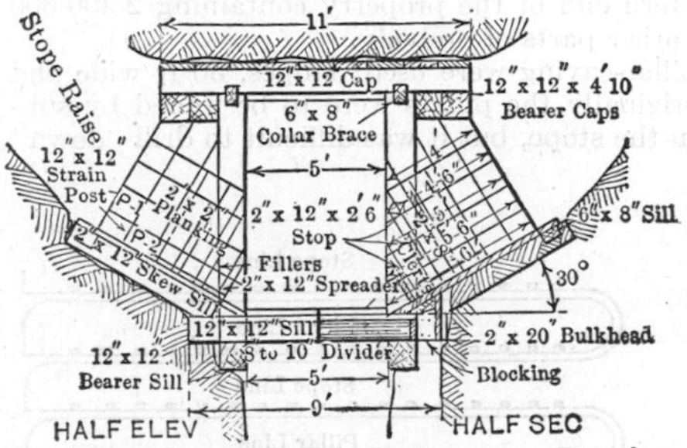

later, in planes halfway between the latter (Fig 583), an arrangement probably more effective in drawing ore. "Pony raises," largely used in drawing pillar ore, and located midway between the regular raises (Fig 581), were put up from "pony sets" (Fig 584). This allowed ore from pony raises to run on slides to the pocket chutes, and doubled the number of openings into the floor of the pillar. The pony sets, of 12

Fig 582. Miami Method, Chute-sets on Drawing-off Level

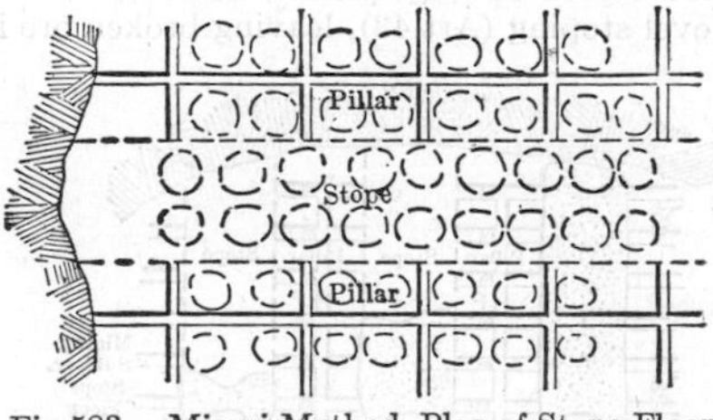

Fig 583. Miami Method, Plan of Stope Floor

by 12 timbers, were 8 ft high inside, which was found better for both drawing and repairs then 6-ft sets. SUB-LEVELS were opened in the pillars from raises *P*, at vertical intervals of 25 ft (Fig 579). Drifts were driven on the long axes of the pillars to the

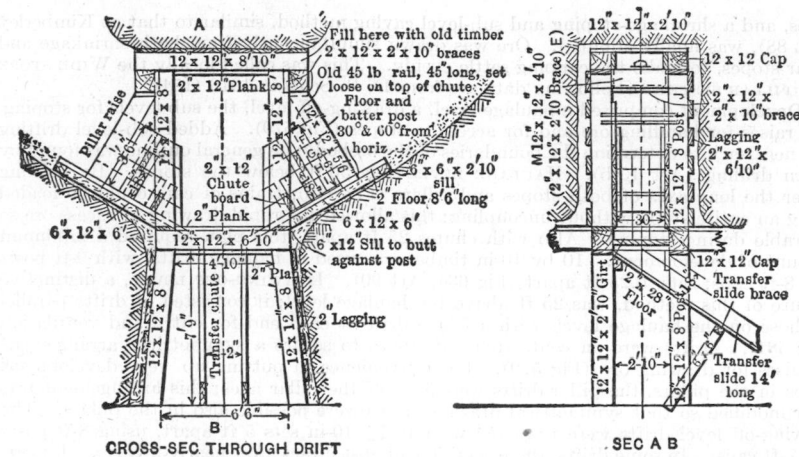

Fig 584. Miami Method, Pony Sets, Chute-gates and Transfer Slides in Pillars

ore limits, with crosscuts 50 ft apart to the stope boundaries. This plan was selected as best, after trying several others. As originally planned, the Miami method called for continuation of the crosscuts across the stopes, but they were abandoned on finding that they could not be economically used as points of attack. DEVELOPMENT RATIO.

Including all openings in stopes and pillars, 45 tons of ore were developed per ft of drift and crosscut, and 200 tons per ft of raise.

Shrinkage stopes were started by funneling the raises to a top diam of 15 to 20 ft; their rims practically touched over the whole stope (Fig 583). Funneling was done by uppers drilled from a set-up in the raise; down holes around the collar were unsuccessfully tried. The sides of the stope (50 ft wide) were next squared up, and stubs between funnels blasted out. This excavation connected with the pillar crosscuts on the 1st sub-level, which served as entries to the stope. Fig 585 and 586 show steps in the mode of breaking ground. Drilling began along the stope sides, as in Fig 174, Art 28. The swell of broken ore was 39%; enough was drawn to keep a 6 to 8-ft space under the back. Max height of stopes, 125 ft; in most cases, ore was broken to the capping, completed stopes being left full.

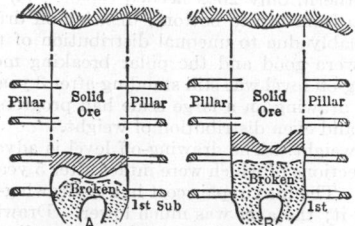

Fig 585.   Miami Method, Successive
Steps in Breaking Ground

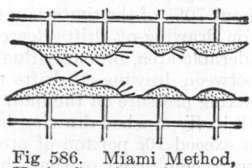

Fig 586.   Miami Method,
Horiz Sec through Stope,
showing Drill Holes

Pillar-mining began at the edge of the ore on the top sub, and progressed downward and along the pillar (Fig 587), to provide a safe exit and insure even settlement of capping (compare Kimberley method, Art 88). As pillars took weight when the capping over them was dislodged, they had to be mined quickly. Hence 3 or 4 sub-levels were attacked simultaneously, the working faces on adjacent subs being kept 100 ft apart. In mining pillars, crosscuts were driven halfway between the original ones, to furnish more drilling faces. After crosscutting was well advanced on the top sub, the end of the pillar was undercut by uppers drilled outward from the faces of the central drift and the end crosscut. Enough shoveling was done for setting up drills on the broken ore, and long holes were put in the back. Usually, no ore was broken on the highest sub nearer than 10 ft to the capping. Similar working faces sloping about 45° (Fig 587) were opened successively at the end of the pillar in lower subs. Fig 588 shows routine of drilling in retreating

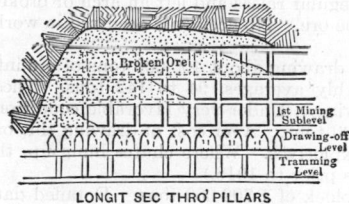

LONGIT SEC THRO' PILLARS
Fig 587.   Miami Method, Mining
Pillars

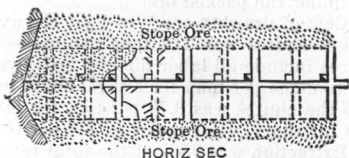

HORIZ SEC
Fig 588.   Miami Method, Drill Holes in
Pillars

along a sub. The first round from the drift and crosscuts broke to about 12 ft above the sub; the 2nd round, for which long bits could be used, increased this height to 20 ft. Holes were often drilled to the broken ore above, but the remaining 5-ft arch usually caved. Attempts were made to drill 5-ft holes in the floor of the sub, to assist subsequent caving of this arch, but the ground "raveled" so badly that the collars of these holes had to be cased with 3-in pipe to prevent fitchering. These holes broke poorly and were given up. Excess ore was shoveled to raises P, Fig 579, and to intermediate raises in the pillars. Just before each raise was abandoned and covered by broken ore, lagged stulls were placed in it about 5 ft below the sub-level. This is important in pillar-mining; if raises were not covered, the capping would "pipe" down through them and prevent proper breaking. As each raise was reached in mining on the next lower sub, a similar stull platform was built, and the stulls above were blasted out. Mining on the lowest sub, or sill-floor of the pillars, was subject to modifications imposed by the pony raises, which halved the distance between the regular 25-ft drawing raises. All raises were funneled in retreating from the end of the pillar. Funneling was not carried more than 25 ft ahead of pillar breaking, because it undercut the entire width of pillar. To protect drillers in case broken ore settled suddenly in the raise, machines for drilling the back were set on 10-in stringers across the funnels.

Drawing broken ore systematically began on completion of about 70% of all stope and pillar-mining; no drawing was permitted within 100 ft of any active mining. Drawing of a stope next to a pillar in process of being broken was tried, and caused the pillar to crush and sway. The weight on the drawing-off level during the drawing period varied greatly at different points; at first, some ground was very heavy, with apparently no weight in other places. Probable causes: (a) Combined height of capping and ore in northern part of section mined was 465 ft; in southern part, 350 ft. In the northern section, some drifts required complete retimbering; in the southern, only 20% needed repair. (b) In one small section, the pillars could not be broken from top to bottom; drawing-off drifts below unbroken blocks were always heavy, probably due to unequal distribution of the weight. In a large area, where all conditions were good and the pillar breaking most complete, about 70% of the timber on the drawing-off level was still standing after 3 years. (c) Weight on drawing-off drifts decreased after drawing on a large scale had progressed over a considerable area, probably due to a wide and even distribution of weight.

Pillars between drawing-off drifts took little weight. The drawing-off level is advantageous in taking pressure off the haulage level, sections of which were intact after 5 years, even beneath badly crushed drawing-level drifts. The max repair cost in any drawing-off drift did not exceed 10¢ per ton of ore drawn on it; the aver was much lower. Drawing operations were conducted so that the surface between broken ore and capping dipped about 15° W. Hence the final stages were reached first at western boundary and retreated eastward. Drawing was planned to cause even settlement of the capping. The ore ran most freely when drawn from a series of chutes in a plane at 90° to the direction of retreat, or crosswise instead of along a stope or pillar. In some stopes, the ore packed tightly in the chutes in the long time elapsing between stoping and drawing. To start such chutes, pony-set raises were sometimes put up from the drawing-off level halfway between the drawing raises. Inclined raises 15 ft long were driven on each side of the drift to broken ore on the stope floor. The tops of the raises were funneled just before they broke into the stope; blasting of funneling rounds loosened the broken ore above and usually that in the adjacent drawing raises. This method had the disadvantage that the pony sets took weight and were expensive to maintain. To start the flow of ore in packed chutes without extra raises, the back of packed ore over the drawing raises was temporarily supported by heavy stulls. Small drifts were then driven in solid ground, parallel to the long axis of the stope and about 15 ft above the drawing-off level. These drifts connected a series of hung-up raises. Starting at the end of the drift, vert and horiz holes were drilled across the stope; these blasted out the legs between the regular raises and left an arch of broken ore which always collapsed, bringing down the stope ore. No accidents occurred in working under the packed ore.

Cost of drawing ore. In 1 yr, the aver rate of drawing about 400 000 tons of ore into pocket chutes was 118 tons per man-shift; monthly averages, 94 to 142 tons. These figures include all labor directly employed in drawing. Under very favorable conditions the tonnage per man for several shifts exceeded 200 tons. Aver cost of drawing this ore into the chutes was 3.7¢ per ton, for labor and explosives. Where chutes hung up, the cost for short periods reached 15¢ per ton. (Costs prior to 1916.)

Extraction was 95% of the total tonnage in a block of 1 700 000 tons. Detailed data showed the recovery from stopes was about 10% greater than from pillars; some pillar ore was undoubtedly drawn through the stope-chutes and *vice-versa*. Extraction and ease of drawing improved with the hardness of the ore; soft ores were more apt to pack. In a few chutes where the ore was tightly packed, drawing removed a cylindrical mass of ore about 14 ft in diam, extending to the capping. This tendency of chutes to "ravel" to the capping without drawing from the sides is greatest in soft ores which are compressed by pressure; raveling may contaminate large tonnages of ore with capping. These facts suggest that many raises per unit of area tend to a higher extraction than fewer with large funneled mouths.

Secondary recovery of ore. After finishing drawing, some broken ore remained in wedges over the drifts and along boundaries of stopes and pillars. Ore above the drawing drifts was recovered by shooting down their backs, retreating from the ends of the drifts. In this work, the output per man-day averaged 40 tons. To recover ore along old pillar lines, intermediate drifts were driven between the original drawing-off drifts. Chute- and supply-raises at 200-ft intervals were put up to these drifts from crosscuts in the tramming level. The drifts were supported by 12 by 12-in sets, 4.16 ft apart. Chute-gates were built in each set. A shrinkage stope 20 ft wide was then carried above the drifts until loose ground was met or caving occurred. The ore was trammed in small cars to the raises, the max tram being 100 ft.

Undercut caving with hand-tramming later replaced above-described method; for details, see Bib (601). For more recent applications of block-caving, see Art 80.

87. MISCELLANEOUS EXAMPLES OF PRACTICE

Braden mine, Sewell, Chile. Data from J. S. Webb and T. W. Skinner (289) in 1932. For geol features and block-caving, see Art 80. SHRINKAGE-STOPE AND PILLAR-CAVING, closely resembling Ray system (Art 85), was used prior to block-caving. Original stopes, normal to strike, were 7 m (22.95 ft) wide, separated by 10-m (32.8-ft) pillars, and were

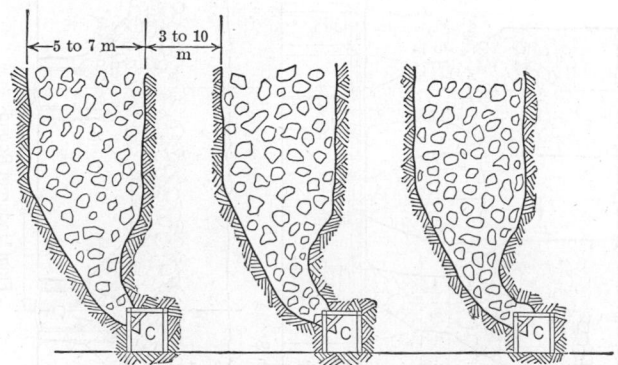

Fig 589. Original Development by Crosscuts, Braden Mine, Sewell, Chile

carried to a vert height of 100 m (328 ft). As these pillars tended to arch and failed to cave properly, their thickness was reduced to 5 m, stope width being kept at 7 m. Caving of pillars still proving unsuccessful, their width was reduced to 3 m, and the stope width to 5 m, with satisfactory results. DEVELOPMENT. Stopes and pillars were originally developed by crosscuts *C* (Fig 589), at intervals depending on stope and pillar dimensions. Each crosscut served 1 stope and the pillar in which the crosscut was driven.

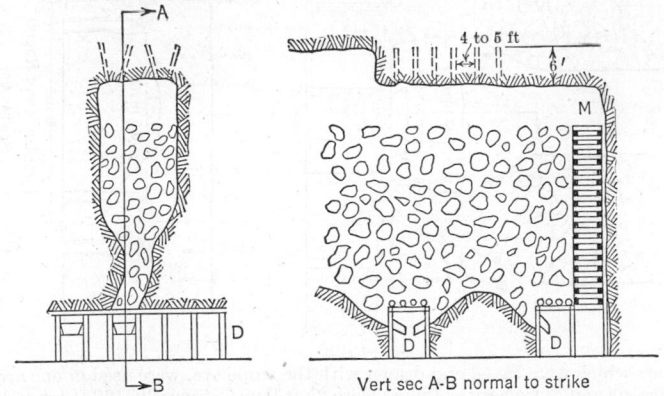

Fig 590. Spacing of Drill Holes in Shrinkage Stope, Braden Mine, Sewell, Chile

Difficulty in maintaining crosscuts during pillar-caving led to replacement of crosscuts by drifts *D* (Fig 590) on 8 or 12-m centers, direction of stopes and pillars remaining normal to strike. SHRINKAGE STOPING. Access was by cribbed manways *M* at each end of stope. In shrinkage operations, miners worked in pairs, drilling per shift a section of back about 10 m long. Stoper-drill holes, 6 ft deep, were spaced 1–1.25 m apart longit, and in sets of 4 (Fig 590), 2 cut and 2 side holes; 15–20 holes were drilled per machine-shift, breaking an aver of 70 tons, of which about 28 tons could be drawn. PILLAR CAVING began by driving a 2 by 2-m sub-crosscut C (Fig 591) along center line of pillar just above the drift sets. Starting at the hanging wall, the tops and sides of sub-crosscuts were drilled and blasted in 6-m sections until the entire pillar base was weakened. Subsequent drawing caused complete breaking up of the pillar.

Coronado mine, Clifton, Ariz (599); part of Phelps Dodge Corp; work in this property stopped about 1923. Cu ore occurred in a steep fissure. Shrinkage stopes, with inter-

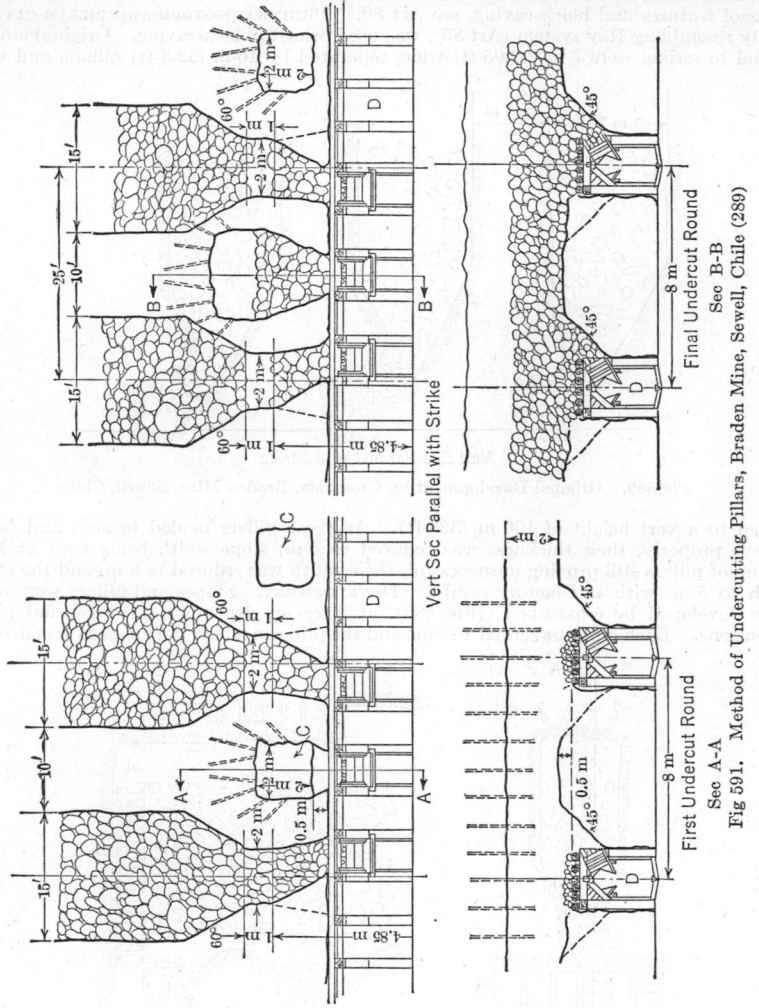

Fig 591. Method of Undercutting Pillars, Braden Mine, Sewell, Chile (289)

vening pillars which were caved and drawn with the stope ore, were used in one area where ore was siliceous and quite hard. Pillars were 25 ft long; stopes 40–160 ft long; height of lift, 100–150 ft; width of vein, to 40 ft. Branched raises were put up from a haulage level to a drawing-off level 45 ft above; their tops were connected by timbered crosscuts, from which stopes were opened; access to stopes was by manway raises and breakthroughs in the pillars. Before drawing, the pillars were undercut and also cut free on top; pillar ore was drawn at same time as the stopes. Output, about 14.5 tons per man-shift.

Humboldt mine, Phelps Dodge Corp, Morenci, Ariz; operations suspended in 1932. Data from M. Mosier and J. Martin in 1925 (600). Orebody is large and carries about

2% Cu; ground harder than in most "porphyry" mines; Art 73, 80 give details and other methods used. The timbered-slide method (Art 80) was used above the 350-ft level to "base-level" the deposit there. Following method, locally called "Morenci block-caving," used on lower levels, combined shrinkage-stope with pillar-caving, somewhat like the Ray (Art 85) and the Inspiration (Art 80); where ore was weak enough, it was modified to straight block-caving into chutes (Art 79). DEVELOPMENT. Levels comprised haulage drifts 56 ft apart. At first, branched raises sloping 60° (Fig 592) were put up from the drifts at 28-ft intervals to a grizzly level 45 ft above; these proved too flat, and caused

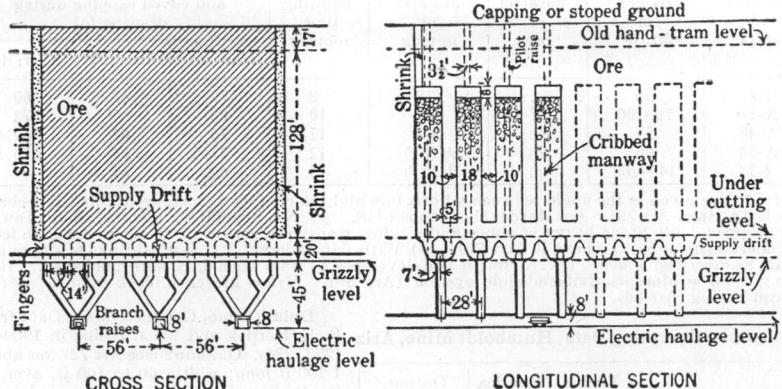

CROSS SECTION   LONGITUDINAL SECTION

Fig 592. Pillar-caving, Humboldt Mine, Ariz (600)

clogging. Later practice (Fig 593) was satisfactory in reducing total footage of raises 40% and their cost 50%. Two grizzlies, of 50-lb rail with 10-in openings, were placed over each raise, with 2 finger raises from each grizzly to the undercutting level 20 ft above; this spaced the finger raises on the undercutting level on corners of 14-ft squares. Height of lift (Fig 592), 145 ft; later increased to 200 ft. STOPES were in panels or blocks. First step was to put up, on sides of panel, boundary shrinkage stopes, 8 ft wide, to a height 10 ft below top of block. Next, transverse shrinkage stopes, 18 ft wide and at least 70 ft high, were driven successively, leaving 10-ft pillars. These stopes were opened from

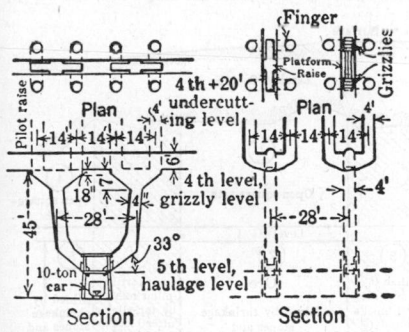

Section   Section

Fig 593. Haulage-level Raises, showing Fingers and Grizzly Stations, Humboldt Mine

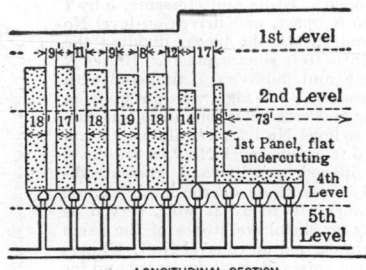

LONGITUDINAL SECTION

Fig 594. Change from Shrinkage Stopes and Pillar-caving to Straight Block-caving, Humboldt Mine

drifts and crosscuts connecting tops of finger raises. Access to stopes was by small pilot raises to the level above. UNDERCUTTING. A pillar was undercut when stopes on both sides were completed. DRAWING. See Art 79 for percent extraction and detail of practice in block-caving, which applies also here. Table 59 gives slope of contact between waste and ore in stopes during drawing. In drawing a stope with a high lift, a wedge of broken ore was left on sides of the block next to future stopes; slope of such wedges was steepened to 70°, to minimize amount of ore tied up; wedge was drawn with ore from the later stopes. Fig 594 shows MODIFICATIONS of stope and pillar widths to suit strength of ore; in softer ground, ore would cave if cut loose by boundary stopes and undercut; method then became straight block-caving. In such cases, horiz undercutting was done by connecting tops of finger raises by drifts and occasional crosscuts, belling tops of finger raises, and shooting pillars simultaneously in areas 56 by 14 ft. OPERATING DATA in Table 60. For further details see Bib (99, 600).

Table 59.   Slope of Contact Between Caved Ore and Waste During Drawing, Humboldt Mine, Ariz

Number of stope	Height of lift, ft	Character of ore	Method of mining	Drawing time, months	Slope of contact between caved ore and caved capping during drawing (a)		
					Max, deg	Min, deg	Aver, deg
1-48	55	. . . .	TS	8	70	47	60
A-38	70–100	H	TS	10	88	55	72
A-48	55	(b)	MI	12(c)	76	62	69.5
A-54	90	(d)	MB(e)	12	77.5	66	70.5
4-34	140–200	(g)	MB(f)	5	62	61	61

(a) Slope given is the angle between a horiz line and the contact as measured from draw-charts (see Extraction, Art 79). (b) Harder than stope 1-48. (c) Not including 2 months, when drawing was stopped. (d) Stope heavy at times and shallow transverse shrinkage stopes were run in front of undercutting area to relieve it (Art 79). (e) With flat undercut. (f) With shrinkage stopes and pillars as described above. (g) No weight had developed to time when data were published. H = heavy. TS = Morenci timbered-slide system (Art 80). MB = Morenci block-caving. MI = Miami caving (Art 86).

Table 60.   Operating Data, Humboldt Mine, Ariz

Year	Tons mined	Timber, bd ft per ton	Powder, lb per ton	Output, tons per man-shift
1924	125 743	1.60	0.54	12.39
1925(a)	357 626	0.81	0.33	21.80
1927	1 136 339	0.23	0.24	40.35
1928	1 483 984	0.25	0.19	62.76

(a) Eight months.

was employed (Fig 595). Open square-sets (Art 45) were used where possible above level No 1, as the ore near the capping was the richest in the mine were employed in the larger blocks (Fig 596). On completing the square-set stope over the block, the timbers were removed and the stope left open. Drifts and crosscuts, 5 by 7 ft, 45 ft apart, were driven on level No 2, underneath the block, dividing the ore into 40-ft square pillars. Raises R (chute and ladderway), timbered with square-sets 2 sets high, were put up from drifts and crosscuts; one raise was carried to level No 1 for ventilation. From R, 16 ft above level No 2, a sub-level was opened by drifts and crosscuts directly over those on the level. These openings, 10 to 15 ft wide, served as floors for shrinkage stopes of the same width, carried up to level No 1. Chutes C, over raises R, were for entry and for handling the excess ore. Chutes were lined with 3-in plank set on edge, with ends beveled at 45°. These stopes cut the block into 6 pillars P, 25 to 30 ft sq and 85 ft high, free at the top and supported on the sides by the broken ore. The tops of raises R were funneled (Fig 596) and the ore was drawn. The chute lining came down with the ore; end pieces and dividers and about half the side pieces were recovered. PILLAR-CAVING. The ore often contained small

Duluth mine, Cananea, Mex. Data from R. L. Herrick and M. J. Elsing in 1909–10 (282, 284). OREBODY (see Art 72) was about 1 100 ft long; width, 60 to 100 ft, aver, 75 ft; it dipped steeply and was overlain by 40 to 150 ft of leached capping. The ore was hard and brittle; ore and capping broke well and stood over large openings. The mine is no longer active. GENERAL PLAN. Top-slicing was used in the eastern part of the orebody, in lenses separated by porphyry horses (Art 72). In the western end, where there were no horses and the ore was fairly uniform, a combined method of SHRINKAGE STOPING AND PILLAR-CAVING

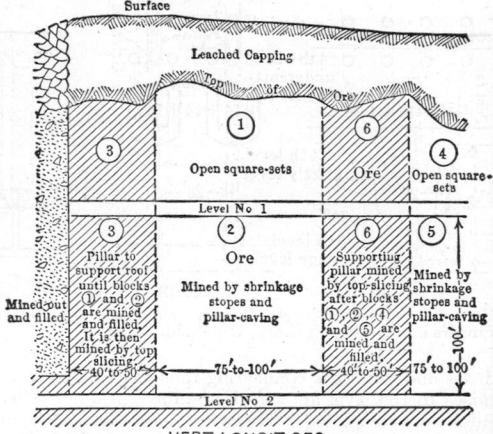

Fig 595.   Duluth Mine, Diagram of Sequence of Operations

fractures, causing pillars P to break and fall into the stopes during drawing. If it were known that the pillars would not break, they were undercut before drawing. Drifts and crosscuts on the sub-level floor divided the base of the pillar into small units, which were blasted out before drawing began. Broken pillar ore was drawn through inclined raises to the sub-level floor from the openings on level No 2. If a pillar had not been undercut and did not break down during drawing, a drift was run below it on level No 2 and raise S was put up (Fig 596). The base of pillar could then be blasted by holes drilled from the raise, or in drifts and crosscuts driven from it. ADVANTAGES of shrinkage stoping and pillar-caving as practiced in Duluth mine: (a) it is cheap, because of the mode of breaking ground and of its small timber consumption; (b) ventilation is good; (c) it is safe if properly applied. REQUIREMENTS for this application of shrinkage stope and pillar-caving: (a) orebodies of large area; (b) orebodies with definite boundaries; (c) ore that will stand unsupported in the stope backs; (d) ore of fairly uniform grade, little sorting being possible underground; (e) ore which will not pack; (f) capping that will stand unsupported while mining the blocks. These requirements being evidently rigid, the method in this form has a limited application.

Magma mine, Ariz. Data from W. C. Browning and F. W. Snow in 1925 (574) and from Snow (77) in 1929. Orebody is a steep-dipping fault-fissure, carrying in places 6% Cu, with some Au and Ag; width, to 45 ft. For some areas requiring close timbering, rill stopes are used; in firmer ground, a combined method (Fig 597), which comprises transverse filled-rill stopes, separated by pillars mined later by a modification of Mitchell slicing (Art 55). STOPES are usually 16 ft wide along the strike and separated by 14-ft pillars; but, in vein-widths of 10–15 ft, stopes are longit and distance between pillars reaches 45 ft. Experience indicates that 16 ft is max safe width of open stopes. Level intervals of 100–300 ft have been tried, but 200 ft has proved best. Level development

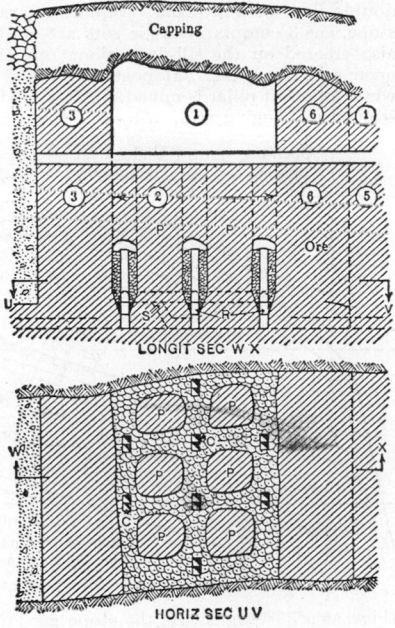

Fig 596. Duluth Mine, Pillar-caving in Block No 2, Fig 595

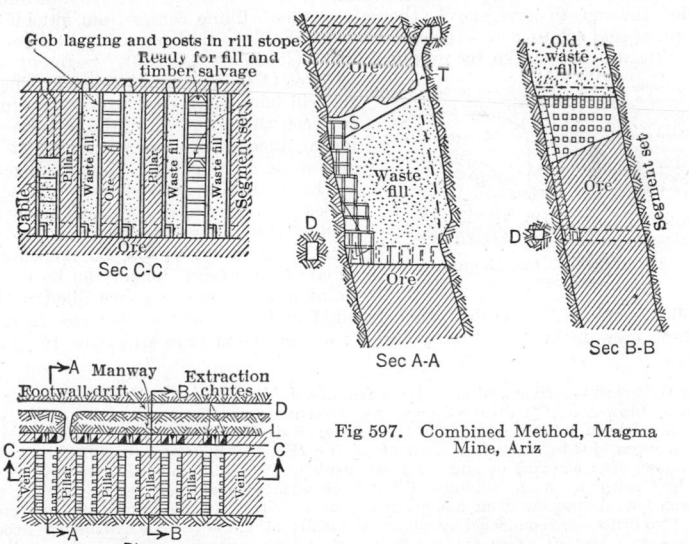

Fig 597. Combined Method, Magma Mine, Ariz

comprises: drift D in footwall, with crosscuts to orebody about 150 ft apart; extraction drift L in ore along footwall; and crosscuts 30 ft c-c, on center lines of stope sections, driven to hanging wall. Sill-floor of stope is cut by widening crosscut to 8 ft on each side of center line and raising the back to height of 10–12 ft. Stringers, 10 by 10 in by 16 ft long, are placed on sill-floor, parallel to strike, at 5-ft centers, and covered with a double floor of 2-in plank. Square-set raise S, started at footwall and carried up with stope, has 3 compts; outside sets are chutes, the center set a manway. Square-sets are also erected on the sill-floor along one side of stope; square-sets are lagged and held open as a crosscut; 8-ft posts are stood along other side and lagged, to retain waste when adjacent pillar is mined. After sill-floor timbering is placed, a small waste raise T is started in hanging wall. Stope is then carried up as a filled-rill stope, taking slices 7 ft

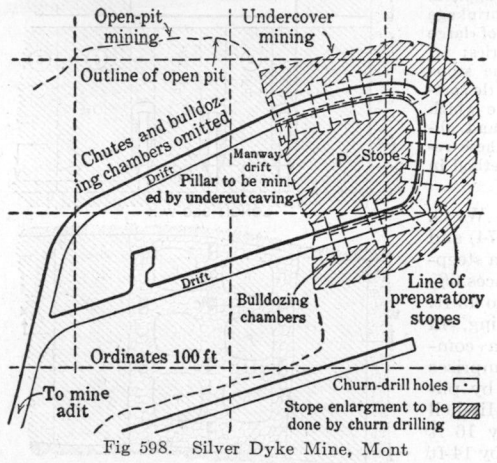

Fig 598. Silver Dyke Mine, Mont

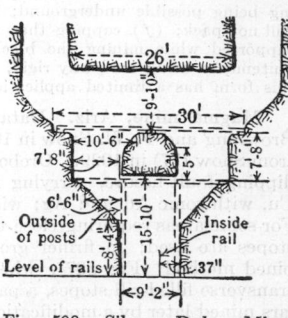

Fig 599. Silver Dyke Mine. Rock Limits of Double-pocket Chute and Bulldozing Chamber

thick at a 35° angle. As the stope goes up, a "gob line" is established along each pillar by standing posts on those below and lagging them. Ends of posts are halved into each other; before a layer of filling is run in, a strand of old cable is tied around each joint and to the joint between corresponding posts on opposite side of stope. Stope backs are arched to the hanging wall; when highest point of stope is about 35 ft above sill-floor, raise T is holed through to level above; thereafter, waste filling comes from outside sources. Filled square-sets are used to extract ore under the floor timbers of filled stopes on level above. PILLARS ARE MINED by modified Mitchell slicing (Art 55). Segment sets (Fig

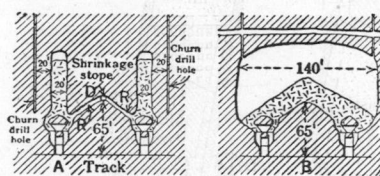

Fig 600. Silver Dyke Mine, Diagrammatic Vert Secs.

597, sec C–C) are placed at top of pillar, under the sill-floor timber of overlying stope, and between the posts set in the gob lines of adjacent filled stopes. Work starts at footwall and stope floor is kept sloping (Fig 597, sec B–B), so that ore will slide to the square-set raises that were used for the stopes on each side of the pillar. Another line of segment sets is put in for safety, 50 ft below top of pillar; if necessary, a floor can be laid at this point and the space above filled with waste. After pillar is mined, the entire space is filled and 75% of the stringers is recovered. Pillar-stope crew includes 2 miners and 1 mucker; good crew will mine 16–25 tons per man-shift.

Silver Dyke mine, Neihart, Mont. Data from G. J. Young in 1927 (603). OREBODY is a massive deposit of low-grade Cu, Pb and Zn ore, in altered quartz porphyry and gneiss; roughly elliptical in plan; max length, 600 ft; width, 400 ft; developed depth, 250–300 ft. Mine has been inactive for several years (1938). GENERAL PLAN of mining (Fig 598–600) was to undercut a block from inclined raises, after carrying up and drawing shrinkage stopes around the periphery. Stopes were widened by blasting of churn-drill holes drilled from surface; eventually the whole block caved and was drawn. DEVELOPMENT. Mine was opened by adits. From the lower one drifts were run at 80-ft centers. Two drifts were connected by a loop (Fig 598); others were to be extended as needed. Vert chute-raises were at 25-ft intervals along drifts; chutes were either single or double, well timbered, and contained a small ore pocket under a grizzly for bulldozing. Fig 599 shows rock limits of a double chute. ISOLATING STOPES (Fig 598, 600). From top of each chute raise, two 45° raises connected above the center of drift. Shrinkage stopes, 20 ft wide by 50–60 ft long, were put up from these raises

60 ft above each drift. Stopes were widened to 40 ft by blasting bottoms of the churn-drill holes drilled from surface as shown; ore was drawn after each blast. Narrow pillars between stopes were then broken by churn-drilling, leaving a horseshoe-shaped open stope isolating a central pillar *P* (Fig 598), about 60 ft thick. UNDERCUTTING. Drift *D* (Fig 600) was driven about 40 ft above grizzly level, and connected to each chute by inclined raise *R*. Undercutting started at inner sides of open stope, which were drilled and blasted from bottoms of raises *R*; work retreated upward to drift *D*. Complete undercutting produced condition shown in *B*, Fig 600. It was expected that caving would extend to surface, the resulting pit to be enlarged as an open-cut, if desired, by churn-drilling. Aver cost of mining for 8 mos in 1926 was 42¢ per ton, including overhead, plus about 30¢ per ton for development. Production, 700 tons per day.

New Jersey Zinc Co, Franklin, N J. Data from C. M. Haight and B. F. Tillson in 1917 (522) and R. B. Paul in 1938. OREBODY is trough-shaped, of franklinite, willemite,

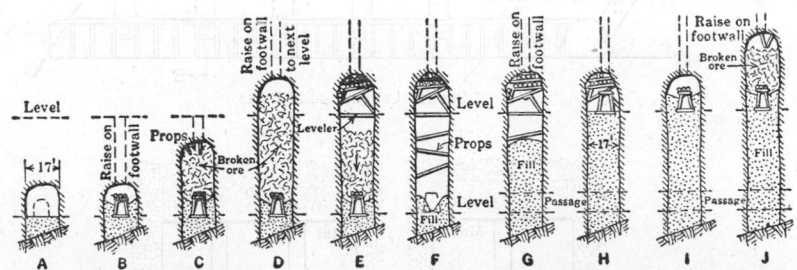

A. Drift widened, bottom filled. B. Sets on fill, footwall raises. C. Stope being carried up. D. Stope finished, 15 ft or more above level. E. Pulling stope, back taken up, levelers placed. F. Stope finished, with props to hold sides. G. Stope being filled, with passage on lower level. H. Stope filled, sets erected, ready to take out timber. I. Fill behind sets, ready for mining. J. Stope going up to repeat cycle.

Fig 601. Transverse Stope, N J Zinc Co, Transverse Secs (522)

zincite and calcite, in crystalline limestone; it has sides of unequal height and pitches at a gentle angle. The ore in the legs of trough is 12 to over 100 ft thick, compact and tough, but not very hard (307, 98). GENERAL PLAN OF MINING. Entry is by a 1 500-ft inclined hoisting shaft and 2 inclined service shafts. Level interval, 50 ft. In wide parts of deposit, a combination of shrinkage-stoping and top-slicing is employed; ore is high-grade, hence the method is planned to give complete extraction. SHRINKAGE STOPES, 17–18 ft wide, are run from wall to wall, leaving 20–60-ft (aver, 35-ft) pillars. On completing and drawing a 50-ft lift, stopes are filled with waste from surface, and lift above is

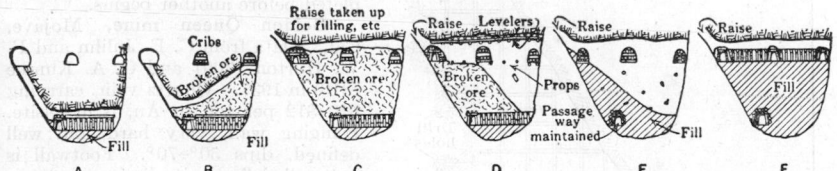

A. Bottom filled, sets placed, raise carried up. B. Stope in progress. C. Stope finished. D. Drawing down stope, back timbered. E. Stope emptied, fill started. F. Fill finished, with sets ready for another lift.

Fig 602. Transverse Stope, N J Zinc Co, Longit Secs

started. Fig 601, 602 show mining and filling operations in transverse stopes; novel features are: (*a*) only one cutting-out stope is required, that is, at bottom of the deposit; before ore is drawn, stopes are carried from one level to a height 15–18 ft above next higher level; a timbered gangway is built on the fill to serve the lift above; (*b*) stope backs are timbered prior to drawing, for safety and to support a track on which waste fill is trammed into the stope. MINING OF PILLARS is started from top downward, after the stopes at one end of orebody are completed. Fig 603 shows one method of mining pillars. Crosscut *A* is driven from wall to wall on center line of pillar; entrance raise *R* is put up in footwall; chute-raises *S* are vert except the one at footwall contact; they are 20–30 ft apart, and each has a chute *C* at its bottom; in wide pillars, 2 lines of raises are driven, as in Sec *A–B* (2) of Fig 603. Three 4 by 6-ft sub-level drifts *D* are driven in each 50-ft lift. In opening a slice, "center drift" *E* is advanced to hanging wall, at full height of slice.

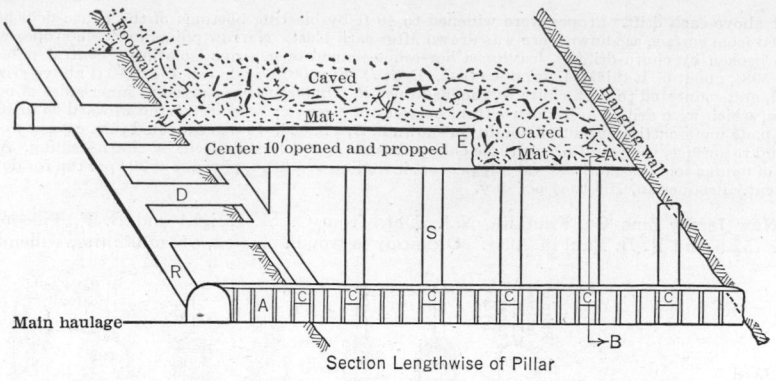

Section Lengthwise of Pillar

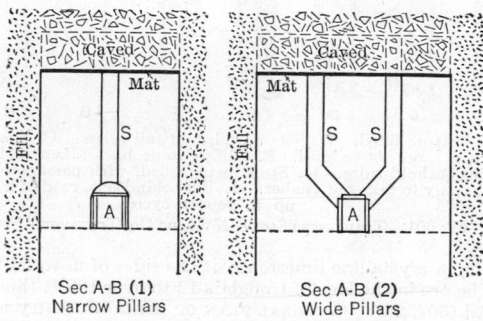

Sec A-B (1)
Narrow Pillars

Sec A-B (2)
Wide Pillars

Fig 603. Top-slicing Pillars, N J Zinc Co

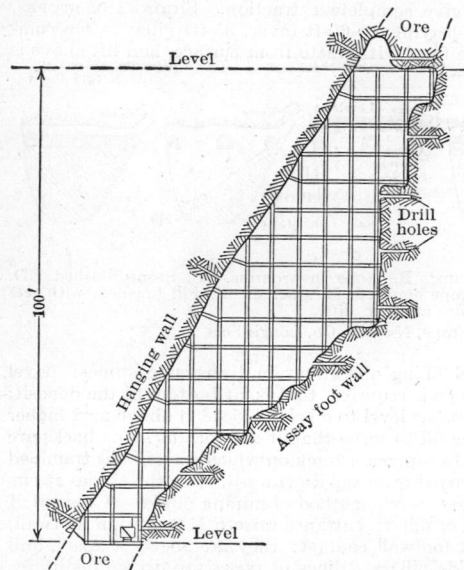

Fig 604. Prospecting Walls by Drill Holes in Mining "Slot," Golden Queen Mine (310)

Slicing to sides of pillar begins at hanging wall, retreating to footwall; stope fill is breasted back with lagging. Except in long pillars, each slice is completed before another begins.

Golden Queen mine, Mojave, Cal. Data from C. E. Julihn and F. W. Horton (309) and C. A. Kumke (310) in 1937. Quartz vein, carrying $10–$12 per ton in Au, is in felsite. Hanging wall, very hard and well defined, dips 50°–70°. Footwall is not well defined; its limits are determined by assays. Width of ore is 10–40 ft. Vein is fractured, but can be mined by ordinary shrinkage where narrow; difficulties met in shrinkage mining, when ore widened unexpectedly, led to a novel method known locally as "slot" system, combining square-setting with shrinkage or cut-and-fill methods. DEVELOPMENT. As topography is steep, entry is by adits at 200-ft vert intervals, with intermediate levels halfway between. Drifts are driven along footwall and sometimes also along hanging. STOPING. In the "slot" system, square-set stopes, 1 set wide and without fill, are

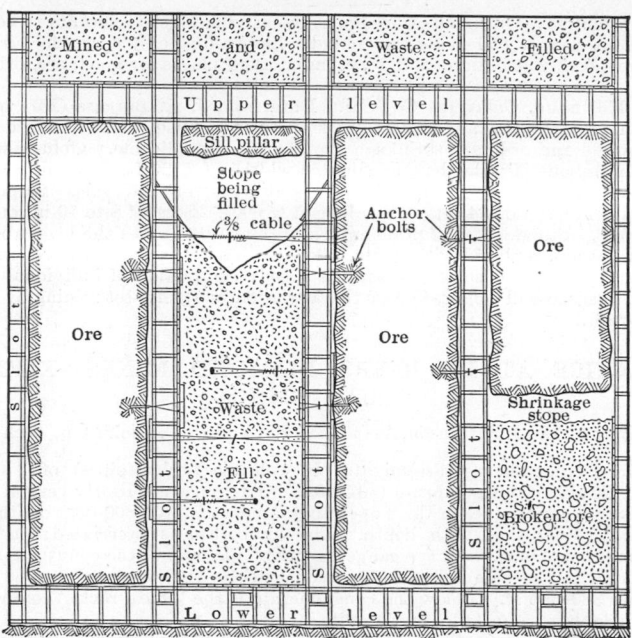

Fig 605. Method of Mining Pillars between Slots, and Tying Slot Timbers, Golden Queen Mine (310)

carried up from level to level, these slots being separated by pillars 25–35 ft long. As the slots advance upward, the footwall is explored by test holes to assure that footwall ore limit has been reached (Fig 604). When 2 adjacent slots have been completed to level above, the intervening pillar is usually mined by shrinkage (Fig 605). If ground becomes bad, the shrinkage stope can be changed readily to horiz cut-and-fill, by drawing out broken ore and filling with waste through adjoining slots. Then the slots are used also for chutes and manways for cut-and-fill operations. To avoid necessity for men to work under bad ground, scrapers distribute the fill, hoists being placed within the squaresets. If, after changing to cut-and-fill, the back gives too much trouble, it is easy to change to straight square-setting. These methods have proved flex-

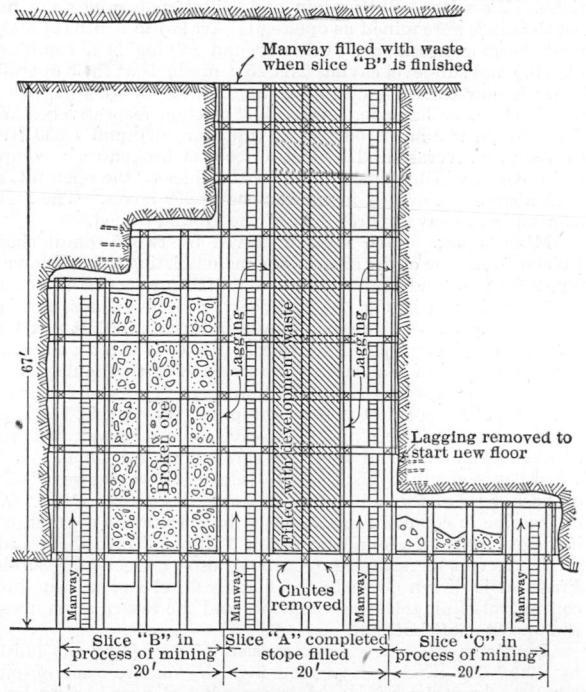

Fig 606. Square-set Shrinkage Stopes with subsequent Filling, Carson Hill Mine, Melones, Calif (297)

ible and satisfactory. Outlining of ore limits in carrying up slots permits rapid mining of pillars without danger of leaving ore behind. Slots afford easy access for air and water lines, assure good ventilation, and serve as storage places for machines, drill steel and hose.

Carson Hill mine, Calaveras Co, Cal. Data from J. A. Burgess (297) in 1937. A combination of shrinkage and square-set stoping is applied where prompt support of walls is required and ordinary shrinkage stopes are not applicable. Gold-bearing quartz veins, dipping about 60° and having minable widths of 5–20 ft, occur in a belt of soft, talcy schist. Development is by drifts in ore at 75-ft vert intervals. Stopes, 1–4 sets wide, are mined in sections 4 sets (20 ft) long (Fig 606). Sets, of 8 to 10-in round timber, are 5 by 6.5 ft. Stope is kept full of broken ore until it reaches the level above; ore is then drawn out and replaced with waste, after which an adjacent 4-set section is started. Use of short sections and small lift permits speedy completion of individual stopes and contributes to successful application of this variation of square-set mining by a "block" system (Art 46).

88. PRACTICE AT DE BEERS DIAMOND MINES, KIMBERLEY, SOUTH AFRICA

(Contributed by L. J. Parkinson, Ass't Gen Mgr, and H. T. Dickinson, Tech Dir, 1938.)

General. Diamonds are disseminated in volcanic necks (pipes) of "kimberlite," a serpentine derived from peridotite (307, 252). The pipes are nearly vert, of circular or ellip cross-sec; diam of pipes in the 3 operating mines is approx 800 ft at depth of 1 000 ft and gradually diminishes with depth. The kimberlite is brecciated; locally called "blue ground" or "blue." A typical geol section (Fig 607) of the country rock in which the pipes occur is: surface debris 0–10 ft, dolerite 10–110 ft, shale 110–380 ft, Dwyka conglomerate 380–385 ft. Below the conglomerate is the "hard rock" contact, beneath which are melaphyre, quartzite, and granite.

The Kimberley mine was allowed to flood in 1914, when the bottom level was at 3 650 ft. The De Beers mine has been idle since 1908, though pumping and maintenance work continue. Wesselton, Bultfontein and Dutoitspan mines are now (1938) being exploited. All the pipes were mined as open-cuts (Art 95) to depths of 300–500 ft before underground work became necessary. Underground mining is a combination of shrinkage stoping (Art 67) and sub-level caving (Art 75); methods at the 3 operating mines are standardized. Work is now carried on at moderate depths, the depths, below surface, of top sublevels and bottom, or haulage, levels (1938) being, respectively: Wesselton, 980 and 1 600 ft; Bultfontein, 960 and 1 600 ft; Dutoitspan, 670 and 1 350 ft. The solid blue ground is overlain by several hundred feet of loose or broken rock, composed of a mixture of shales and dolerite which has sloughed off the sides of the open pit, and blue ground which has been abandoned or lost in mining the upper levels. The method utilizes the wt of this overburden to cave approx half of the ground mined.

Mine layout. Each mine is served by two 5-compt shafts in country rock, about 1 000 ft from edge of the pipe. The main hoisting shaft is downcast; 2 compts are for hoisting, 2 for men and material, and the fifth for service lines and ladderway. The second shaft (not shown in Fig 607) is upcast, with an exhaust fan at the collar; it is used as an emergency exit. Two main 17 by 8-ft tunnels, 600 ft apart vert, run from the hoisting shaft to the pipe. The upper one *A* (Fig 607) is a traveling way, waiting place for shift, and for storage of material. The lower *B* is the haulage way, the deepest level of the mine. A 3-compt service shaft ("prospect") *F* is sunk in country rock just off the main tunnels and approx 100 ft from the pipe. From this, stations and connections *T* to the workings are 40 ft vert apart, to serve each sub-level; this shaft is used for distribution of men, explosives and material throughout the mine. Added communication is provided between sub-levels by 2 or 3 sets of 32° "stepways" *G* (Fig 608), in country rock on both sides of the mine. Six or more vert passes *P* (Fig 608), located around the rim of the pipe in country rock, 50–75 ft back from the contact, connect the sub-levels to the haulage level; all ground broken is "tipped" into them and drawn off on the haulage level. A vert air shaft *M* (Fig 608) also connects the sub-levels to the haulage level. Fresh air is drawn down to the haulage level and upcast through this shaft; regulators control vol of air taken by each sub, and the return air is upcast through the stepways to the upcast shaft bottom.

Development. New work consists of deepening the hoisting shaft and "prospect" by 600–1 000 ft, depth varying inversely as cross-sec of pipe. Shaft station and ore handling arrangements are then provided at new bottom level, and a haulage tunnel is driven from the hoisting shaft past "prospect" *F* through approx center line of pipe and beyond. As the " prospect " is sunk, stations are cut 200 ft apart and tunnels driven in country rock to the new vert " tipping " passes. From these points of attack, passes are raised 150 ft and winzed 50 ft until holed. Closed " tip doors " (grizzlies) are installed at each tipping point, to limit size of lumps to 12-in diam. Subs are developed by first driving a single tunnel T (Fig 609-A) across the pipe from the " prospect," at 0.75% up-grade. Simultaneously, 2 parallel crosscuts C are driven in " blue " at right-angles to this, on a line approx $2/3$ the distance across the pipe from the prospect. These are 67.5 ft c-c and, by connecting " splits " S, 90 ft apart, ventilation is provided. Secondary development consists of cutting subs into blocks U which are multiples of 22.5 ft, usually

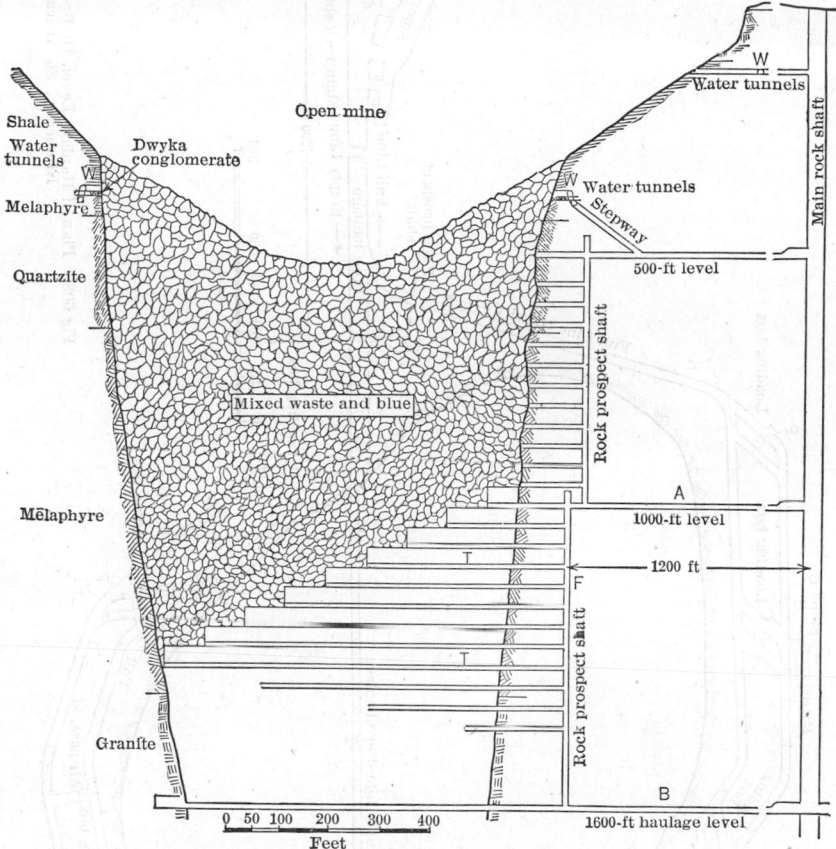

Fig 607. Vert Cross-sec showing General Development, De Beers Diamond Mine, Kimberley, So Africa

67.5 by 90 ft (Fig 609 B and C). This work is done only as the advance of stoping requires it, since the blue ground does not stand well and weathers rapidly on exposure. As stoping (chambering) advances, the blocks are finally reduced to 22.5 by 22.5-ft centers, as at V (Fig 609-C). Normal section of all " blue " tunnels and crosscuts is 7 by 4.5 ft. Crosscuts on each sub are offset one-half block (11.25 ft) from those of the sub next above, to provide for eventual undercutting of back pillars (Fig 610). In general, little timbering is required, as openings are narrow and only driven as required. Where ground is heavy, 3-piece sets of 10-in round timber are used and lagged with old rails or 3-in plank. If opening must stand a long time, but ground is not heavy, 5 by 4-in lagged steel sets are used to prevent sloughing.

Stoping. Approx 50% of the ground is broken in shrinkage stopes; the rest comes from back pillars which are caved. Stoping begins on each sub on side of mine opposite

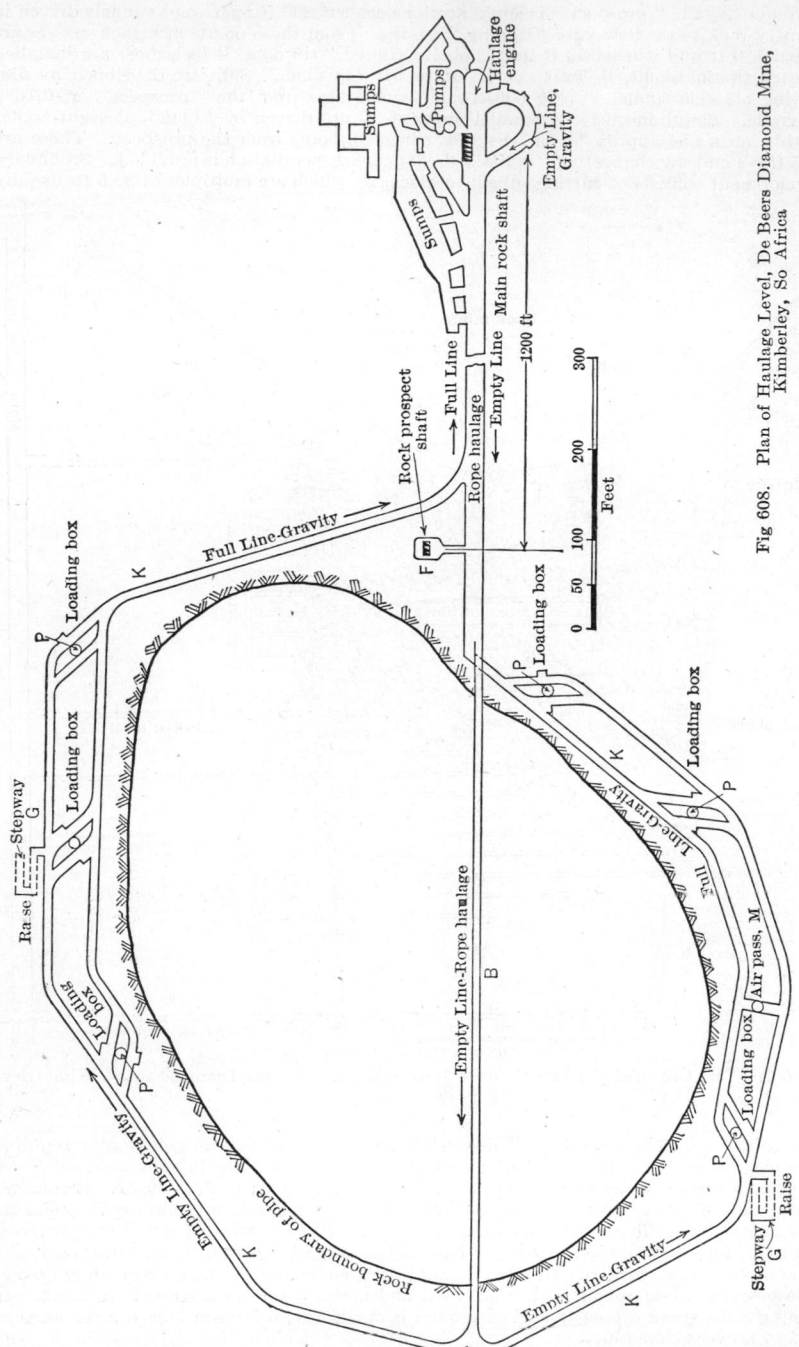

Fig 608. Plan of Haulage Level, De Beers Diamond Mine, Kimberley, So Africa

prospect shaft. From the nearest crosscut, short drifts D (Fig 609-B) are put through to rim rock. A crosscut E is driven along the line on which the stope is to advance. This is widened to 10–12 ft when raising of back begins. Raising is so done that a face lying 25° to the horiz is developed (Fig 611), and extended until the top is holed through into loose ground left on level above. All holes are drilled dry and inclined 20° from the vert. The face is then advanced until it reaches rim rock at the opposite side. On completing the first stope cut, 2 stopes are started on the next cut, on opposite sides of the pipe and advanced

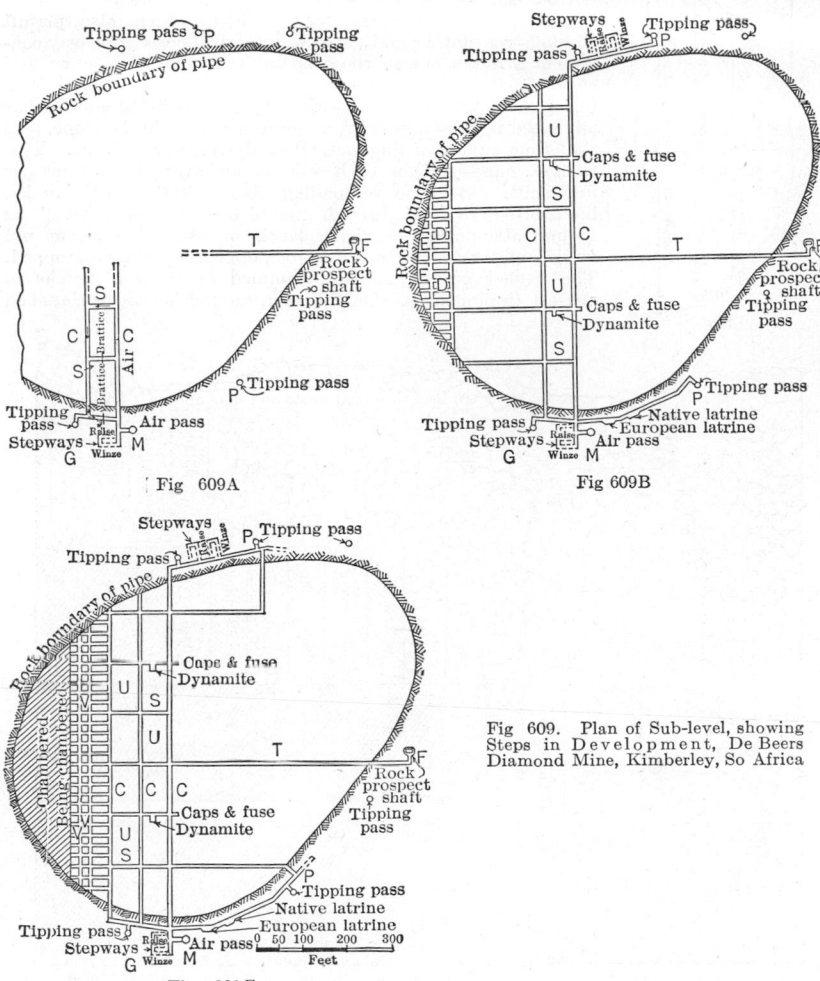

Fig 609A

Fig 609B

Fig 609C

Fig 609. Plan of Sub-level, showing Steps in Development, De Beers Diamond Mine, Kimberley, So Africa

until their bottom ends meet, usually near center line of the pipe. The remaining triangular-shaped block of ground is then " squared-up " by shortening the face, and by a succession of horiz slices which advance the face upwards until a final round is drilled and the area holes into the level above. For this concluding stage of a cut, ventilation and access are provided by a poleway and " pass poleway," the latter being cut in solid ground (Fig 611, 612). Stope faces advance along the line of crosscuts and at right-angles to the original blue tunnel T (Fig 609-B). By a succession of cuts, the face gradually retreats along the line of the tunnel towards the prospect shaft. When the stoping line on any sub has advanced 600–800 ft, 4 stopes may be started on the one sub; 2 begin at opposite contacts and 2 in the center. The stoping line on each sub is 3 or 4 blocks (67.5 or 90 ft) behind that of the sub above (Fig 610). Standard width of stoping blocks is 22.5 ft, of which a width of 8–12 ft, depending on condition of hanging, is mined by shrinkage. The remainder is left as a " back pillar," which is recovered by caving when undercut later by a stope or chamber on next sub below (Fig 610). Blue ground from shrinkage stopes is removed as required to provide working room at the face, and amounts to 30–35 tons per stope-shift. Ground broken per stope-shift, including back pillar caved, averages 150 tons. Usual access to stopes is from the bottom end; added access and escape ways are provided by "poleways" above every second drift, which also permit through ventilation and entry way for drill hose. Poleway consists of a notch cut in the solid in front side of a stope and covered with poles and old rails to prevent loose ground from filling the cut. When the top end or high-point of a stope has advanced beyond any drift, all ground broken in the stope, plus that from caving of the back pillar above, is loaded out. Two natives hand-load in each sub at an aver of 15 tons per man-shift. Aver life of loading places, 40–45 shifts; added life is often obtained through ground from "other sources," as ground abandoned on higher levels or left behind from old mining methods. When waste rock appears, loading is stopped. The loaded ground is hand-trammed in 16-cu ft trucks to nearest tipping pass. On the aver, ground hoisted is classified

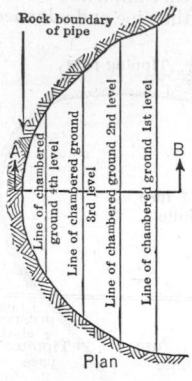

Plan

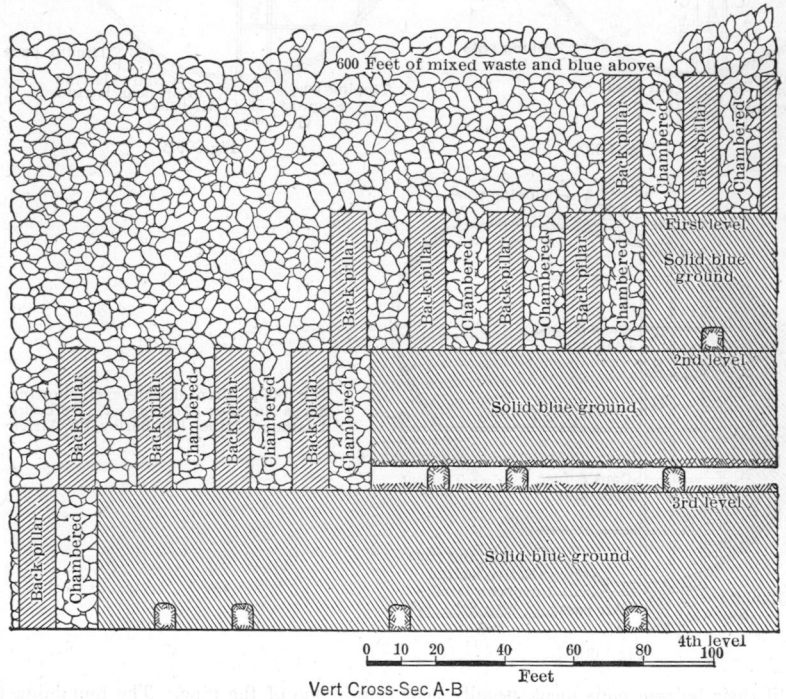

Vert Cross-Sec A-B

Fig 610. Stoping in De Beers Diamond Mine, Kimberley, So Africa. Showing back pillars left in place, and method of undercutting them from next level below

according to source, as: development, 3%; broken in stopes and back pillars, 75–80%; other sources, 22–17%, which includes some admixture of waste rock.

Eight to 10 subs are worked simultaneously, to give the required 5 000 tons per 8-hr shift. From 1 to 4 stopes are worked on each sub, as a total of 24–26 are required. Present stope back is 40 ft, but 50-ft backs are being introduced. Extraction is difficult to determine, but is estimated under present system to be above 90%.

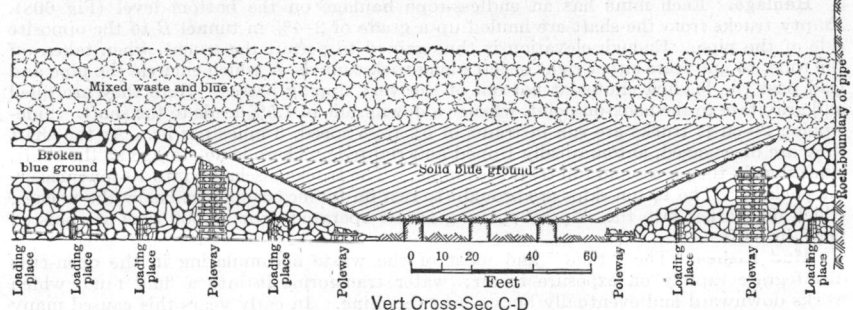

Fig 611.   System of Chambering, De Beers Diamond Mine, Kimberley, So Africa

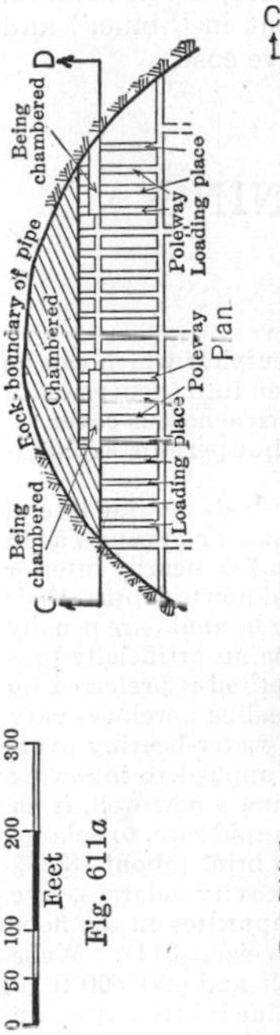

Fig. 611a

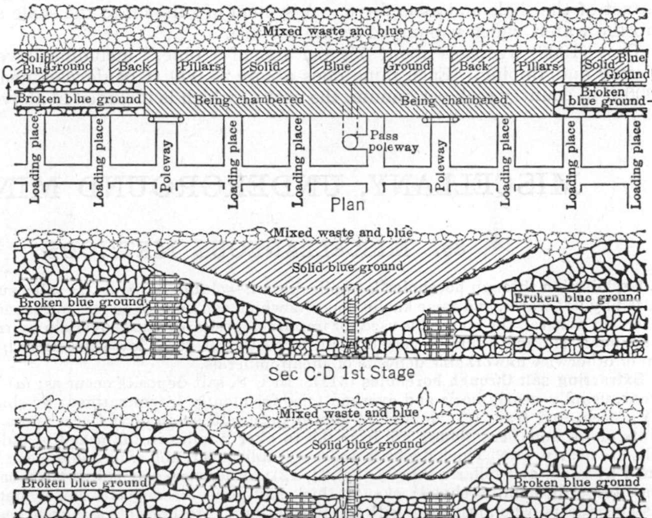

Plan

Sec C-D 1st Stage

Sec C-D 2nd Stage

Sec C-D 3rd Stage

Sec C-D Final Stage

Fig 612.   Method of Completing Chamber, De Beers Diamond Mine, Kimberley, So Africa

Haulage. Each mine has an endless-rope haulage on the bottom level (Fig 608). Empty trucks from the shaft are hauled up a grade of 2–4% in tunnel B to the opposite side of the pipe. Enough elevation is thus gained to permit the trucks, when taken off the rope, to gravitate either right or left along rock tunnels K which encircle the pipe and lead past the loading chutes at bottom of the vert tipping passes. Here they are filled and gravitate to the hook-on point, whence a downgrade of 1.5% leads to the shaft. Side-tipping 20-cu ft trucks are run in trains of 5; rope speed, 3 miles per hr. At the shaft they are disengaged, automatically tipped and righted. There is no storage at the shaft, since that in the passes and full trucks is ample. The trucks discharge into 10-ton measuring pockets. The 10-ton skips are brought to rest on buffer beams just below the pocket, which discharges into the skip by opening an air-operated door; 5 000 tons are hoisted per 8-hr shift.

Mud rushes. The "blue" and most of the waste accumulating in the open-cuts disintegrate rapidly on exposure to air; water transforms it into a fluid mud, which works downward and eventually bursts into the mine. In early years this caused many fatalities and great expense for cleaning out workings. The water comes from the softer formations within 400 ft of the surface. Formerly this seeped into the open-cut, but the problem was solved by driving ring tunnels W (Fig 607) around the pipes just below the contact of the shale and melaphyre. A system of raises into the shale and drifts along it trap the water, which is pumped to the surface.

Cost (1938) averages about 55¢ per ton of "blue," including development, mining, hoisting and tipping. Each mine does about 25 000 ft of development in "blue," and 2 000 ft in country rock per annum, the cost of which is included in above cost.

MISCELLANY, UNDERGROUND MINING

89. MISCELLANEOUS METHODS

Exploitation through boreholes is applicable to: soluble minerals, as salt; sulphur which can be melted by hot water, and some kaolin deposits which can be broken by, and taken into suspension in water. In general, the method is used for impure deposits, or those overlain by treacherous cover, or where shaft sinking would be very difficult or costly; it gives low extraction, but permits exploitation of otherwise unworkable deposits of cheap minerals.

Extracting salt through boreholes (311). In U S, salt deposits occur as: (a) beds of wide lateral extent, usually nearly horiz and overlain (also frequently interstratified) by shale or gypsum, as in N Y, Mich, and Kan; (b) "domes" of almost pure salt, as on Gulf Coast and a few nearby interior points of La and Tex; domes are from 0.5 to over 2 miles in diam and of unknown depth; their walls are nearly vert. Thick deposits under suitable cover, and where shafts can be sunk, are usually mined by room-and-pillar methods (Art 34, 42); otherwise, salt is extracted as an artificially produced brine through boreholes; even in thick and mineable deposits, latter method is preferred by alkali producers, who must work with salt in solution. Methods of casing and sealing boreholes vary with geol and operating conditions. Fresh water may be supplied (a) from water-bearing overlying strata, or (b) through pipes from surface. Brine is lifted by: (a) press applied to inflowing fresh water from surface; (b) air-lift; (c) deep-well pumps (Sec 44). On starting a new well, fresh water is supplied, and a necessarily weak brine (often wasted) is extracted, at a rapid rate, to enlarge the walls of bottom cavity; thereafter, flow is retarded to yield nearly saturated brine (about 18.5% NaCl in N Y, 23% in Kan) to reduce subsequent cost of evaporation; as the cavity enlarges, rate of delivering saturated brine may be increased, unless a blanket of insoluble impurities on the floor interferes with solution. GULF COAST METHODS (Fig 613, 614), from W. M. Weigel (311). Wells of Morton Salt Co, Grand Saline, Tex (Fig 613), are about 265 ft to top of salt and 400–500 ft in total depth. Casing is sealed above an overlying water-bearing stratum, and brine is lifted by comp air through a 4-in pipe reaching nearly to bottom of well. Fig 614 is typical of the deeper wells on domes worked by alkali producers. Casing is sealed at top of salt, 670–850 ft below surface, and hole continued 600–1 000 ft downward into salt; fresh water is delivered through a pipe nearly to bottom of hole, at a press sufficient to lift brine to surface. CENTRAL N Y METHOD. Salt is interstratified with shale, limestone, and gypsum, in a laminated formation (max thickness, 470 ft) 800–2 250 ft below surface. Starting with 10-in drive pipe to bedrock, a drill hole to bottom of salt is cased with 6-in pipe and sealed at a level below all sources of water. A 3-in pipe is lowered in the casing nearly to bottom. At start, water is pumped down the 3-in pipe, and weak brine rises; after about 6 weeks, direction of flow is reversed (Fig 615-A). As explained by E. N. Trump (308), by these means the cavity becomes funnel-shaped because (a) fresh water tends to float on brine, and (b) rate of solution is faster in water than in brine. Ultimately, the floor of cavity flattens enough to retain a blanket of insoluble residue, and solution is then confined to edges. Caving usually occurs when a cavity reaches 150 ft diam; in a thin bed, this happens about twice a year (perhaps once a year in a thick bed), usually causing abandonment of the hole and drilling a new one. If the roof, usually shale, contains layers of salt, connections may open between adjacent cavities, after which air-lifting or pumping must be adopted. MICHIGAN METHOD (also that of

Kan) is like that at the deeper Gulf Coast wells (Fig 614); water is pumped continuously down the central pipe and brine rises around it. In this case, as shown in Fig 615-*B*, the cavity first assumes a barrel-shape, then approaches a sphere, and finally attains about the same shape as in Fig 615-*A*. According to Trump (308) saturated brine can not be recovered by this procedure in a thin bed, because the fresh water, being lighter and more mobile than brine, tends to rise close alongside the central pipe and dilutes the brine issuing from the cavity; in a bed 150 ft thick or more, the water has better opportunity to diffuse into the brine and assist the dissolving of salt. TRUMP METHOD

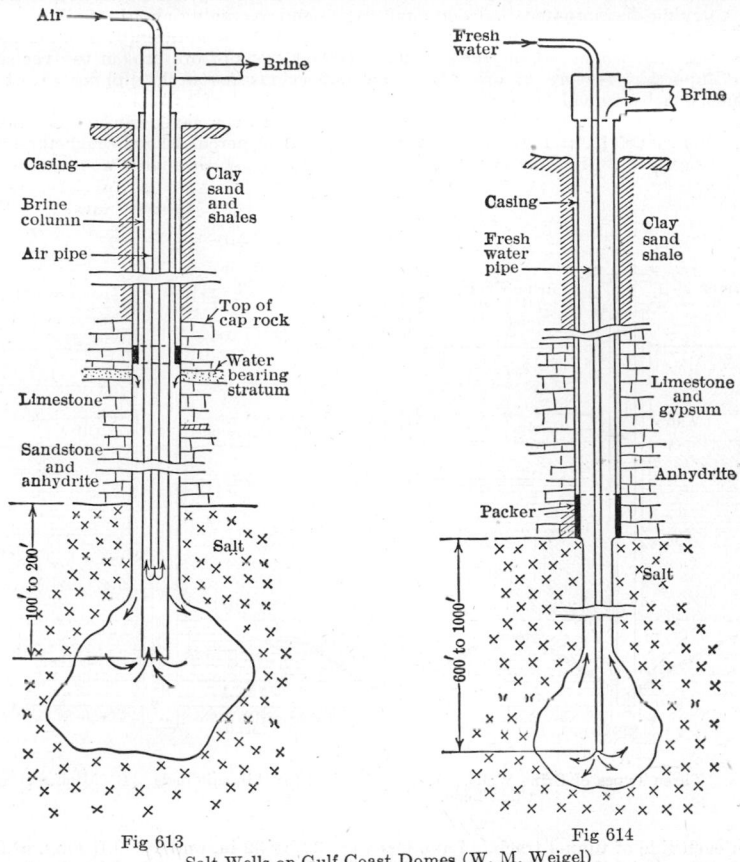

Fig 613   Fig 614
Salt Wells on Gulf Coast Domes (W. M. Weigel)

(308) is designed to produce a cavity from which saturated brine can be withdrawn with minimum delay (that is, with least waste of weak brine) after completing the drill hole. As shown in Fig 615-*C*, a bed is dissolved in circular, horiz slices, each about 10 ft thick, beginning with a 5-ft under-cut at bottom. At start, action is confined to perimeter of undercut by maintaining a pocket of comp air above the brine; an undercut 4 ft high can be extended to 300-ft diam in 12 mos, delivering 175 gal brine per min. On reducing air press by about 5 lb per sq in, the level of brine rises about 10 ft and begins dissolving the next slice, the entire bottom area of which is now exposed to solution. To provide an equivalent area of spherical surface (that is, to yield same flow of brine of same density) would require dissolving of 13 times as much salt.

Leaching copper ore in place. Recovery of "cement" (metallic) copper by precipitation on iron from waters containing $CuSO_4$ is an old practice in many regions, such waters usually being only those naturally met in underground workings, or surface water which has percolated through mine dumps. Application of same principles by artificial distribution of water over ore still remaining in place, is practicable under certain favorable conditions, of which the most important are: (*a*) presence of iron sulphides (preferably pyrrhotite) in amount sufficient to provide ferric sulphate as solvent for copper; (*b*) geol structure (such as an impervious footwall, Ohio Copper mine, below), permitting the copper-bearing water to be collected without excessive loss, or to be impounded without excessive cost to avoid interfering with mining at lower levels (as at Ray mine, below); (c) ore of such physical character that water can penetrate to the copper minerals without causing excessive disintegration or collapse of the ore fragments (a firm, siliceous ore mineralized along seams is most favorable); (d) adequate supply of water, and cheap scrap iron.   Details of 2 successful operations follow.   OHIO COPPER Co, Bingham, Utah.   Orebody is a large tabular deposit of shattered quartzite and monzonite carrying disseminated chalcocite and pyrite and averaging about 0.88% Cu (302). Fig 616 shows the underground development in an unprofitable attempt to mine the ore by block-caving, which left in place about 38 000 000 tons of ore broken to aver size of 4 in.   Important feature of orebody is an impervious footwall, dipping about 55°. Entrance was by tunnel from surface, which avoided need of special pumps and water columns.   In 1925, water was pumped and distributed over caved surface of orebody, about 1 400 by 600 ft, at 1 200–1 400 gal per min.   After percolating through the broken ore, it was caught at the Mascotte tunnel and allowed to flow through 2 wooden launders,

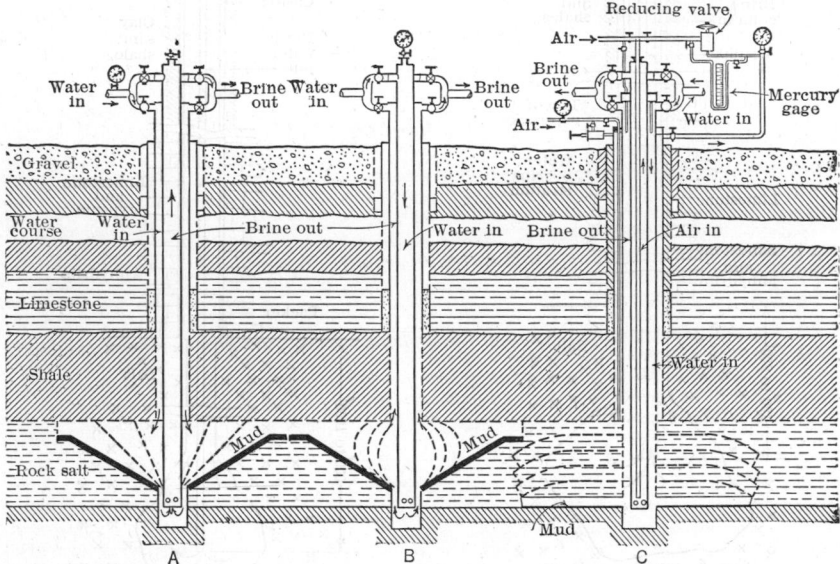

Fig 615.   Three Types of Brine Wells.   A. N Y Method for thin salt beds.   B. Mich method for thick beds.   C. Trump system

one on each side of tunnel track.   Launders were 32 by 32 in, and 1 600 ft long, at 0.5% grade, with sectional false bottoms, 17 in above floor, in form of wooden lattice with 0.25-in sq openings, on which detinned iron scrap was distributed.   Copper precipitate collecting underneath was removed at intervals of 6–30 days, shoveled into cars, trammed to surface, and shipped to smelter.   Water entering launders carried (aver) 0.204% Cu; recovery in precipitate, 97%.   Of total precipitate, about $3/4$ averaged over 90% Cu, and $1/4$ (that from lowest launders) ran over 70% Cu.   In 32 mos (1922–1925) output was 17 000 000 lb of copper, at operating cost of 3.846¢, and smelting charge of 2.477¢ per lb.   RAY MINES, of Kennecott Copper Corp, Ariz, began leaching in western portion of its orebody in Jan, 1937, and produced 10 201 364 lb of copper by that method during the following 17 mos (525).   In this 10-acre area, the ore was unusually high in pyrite, and averaged about 1% Cu; above it was an unaltered zone 125 ft thick averaging 0.6% Cu surmounted by a leached zone 50 ft thick.   Total copper recoverable by leaching in this area down to third level was estimated at 50 000 000 lb.   Preparatory work underground included driving drainage drifts, building several concrete dams, and a concrete ditch (500 gal per min), with sump and pump station on third level, to prevent escape of water to lower workings in adjoining areas.   Copper-bearing water is pumped to surface by 2 centrifugal pumps made of Duraloy, with combined capac of 500 gal per min, through 8-in lead-lined pipe.   Fresh water is pumped by 4-stage centrifugal pump at 340 gal per min, and distributed over surface of leaching area by pipe lines and sprinklers, which are shifted whenever copper content of recovered water drops to 0.4%. On returning the sprays to a previously treated area after an interval of about 2 mos, the percolated water resumes its normal content of nearly 1% Cu. Settlement of caved ground, apparently resulting from the leaching, interfered at times with maintenance of pipe lines and sprinklers; uniformity in distribution of water is essential to good extraction. Occasional shortage of fresh water will be met by utilizing the discharge solution from the precipitation plant, after oxidizing its ferrous sulphate to ferric, and eliminating the objectionable colloidal basic sulphates thereby produced. Precipitation plant, on surface, has 2 units, each of 5 cells, 10 ft-8 in wide by 40 ft long, with 8-in partitions down their middles, thus forming the equivalent of a launder 5 ft wide and 400 ft long for each unit. Preferred form of scrap iron is coarsely shredded detinned cans, from San Francisco; this is charged twice a day, by crane and clamshell bucket, and rests on a wooden grill false bottom, openings $3/8$ by 0.5 in. Accumulated precipitate (10–12.5 tons per cell) is periodically washed through the grill (by-passing the flow meanwhile), and flows by gravity through tile pipes to 6 draining cells; there it is handled twice, from cell to cell, by another crane and clamshell bucket, before loading into RR cars; the aver 22.8% moisture in the shipped product could be reduced by added handling. Entire

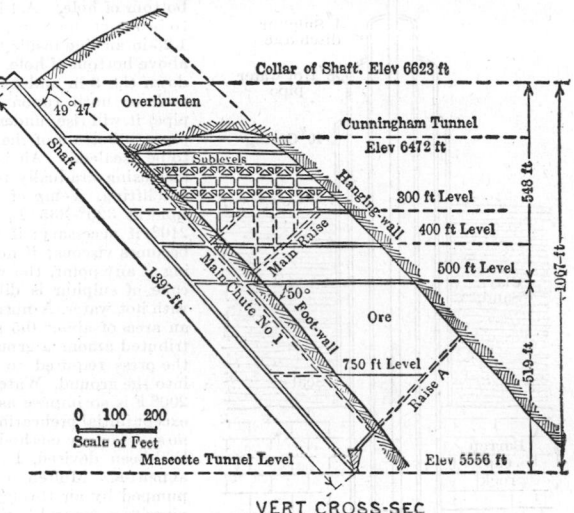

Fig 616. Development Work, Ohio Copper Co

operation is conducted by a crane operator and 2 helpers, working day-shift only. Aver results to July 1, 1938: Cu in leach sol, 0.923%; Cu in tail sol, 0.0079%; indicated recovery, 99.14%; ratio Fe consumed to Cu produced, 1.15; Cu in precipitate (dry), 87.27%. All cells are of concrete; for structural details, see Bib (525). PHELPS DODGE CORP, Morenci, Ariz, is now (1939) leaching caved areas over old workings by methods similar to those at Ray.

Frasch process for sulphur. Sulphur occurs as disseminations and occasional pocket-masses in beds of porous limestone and gypsum, associated with some salt domes on the Gulf Coast of La and Tex. Of 200 known domes (1935), 9 have produced sulphur commercially, operated by 4 companies, all using improved forms of the original Frasch process. The sulphur-bearing beds lie under 400–2 000 ft of unconsolidated or porous strata carrying large volumes of water impregnated with H_2S, which has defeated all attempts at shaft-sinking. Some deposits, lying under marsh land or open water, have been developed by floating equipment. Some are capped by barren rock, and a bed of anhydrite is usually at bottom of the sulphur horizon. The process consists of sinking and casing drill holes to bottom of sulphur bed, introducing water at 320°–335° F, and recovering molten sulphur by air-lift. Chief difficulty and expense are involved in securing, treating, heating, and distributing suitable water. Modern plants have central stations equipped to heat 5–10 million gal per day to 340° F, distributing it through insulated pipe lines to the several wells. Following data from W. A. Cunningham (312) in 1935 refer to Freeport Sulphur Co's operations at Hoskins Mound, Tex, begun in 1925 and recently enlarged.

Water-heating boiler plant of 12 units develops 16 000–18 000 bhp. Fuel is natural gas, but oil can be substituted in 5 min (unfailing supply of hot water is essential to operations once begun). Of 7 500 000 gal water required daily (from surface reservoir and deep wells), 2 750 000 gal go into boilers and 4 750 000 gal are heated indirectly for distribution to sulphur wells. Boiler feed-water is softened by lime-soda-sodium aluminate method, settled for 3 days, and filtered; it is then preheated in 2 stages: first in exchangers supplied with "bleeder water" (see below) at 180°–200° F; next by exhaust steam from engines and pumps. Mine water for the sulphur wells is treated cold with soda-lime (also $FeSO_4$, if necessary), sedimented for 3 days, but not filtered. It is heated in 3 stages: first to about 135° F by direct contact with flue-gas, next to about 212° F by exhaust steam and boiler blow-off (amounting to 25–30% of boiler feed), finally to 325°–340° by direct contact with live steam. It is then distributed to wells through insulated 10-in pipe lines. Besides 63 pumps and various power generators, the plant includes 3 low-press and 5 high-press compressors, with combined capac of 4 500 cu ft free air per min to 1 000-lb press, to supply air-lifts at wells. WELL OPERATION. A 10-in casing is sunk through unconsolidated material (1 000–1 600 ft at Hoskins) and seated with cement in the cap rock over the sulphur horizon (Fig 617).

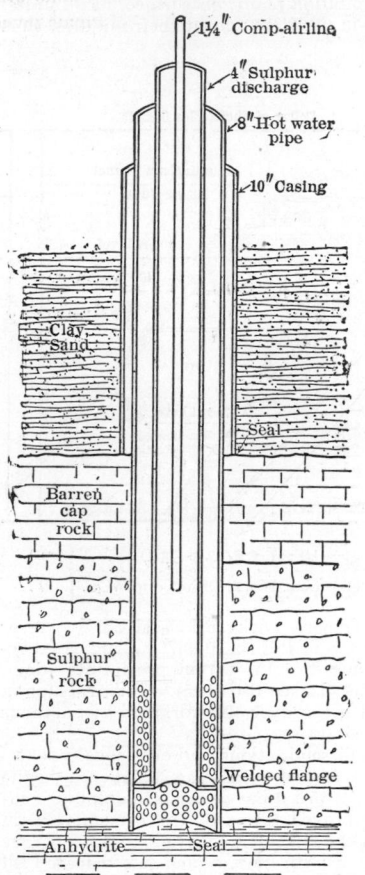

Hole for 8-in casing is continued downward with standard rotary oil-well drill to bottom of sulphur and into underlying anhydrite. The 8-in casing, its lower 35 ft perforated, is seated and cemented at bottom of hole. A 4-in pipe rests on a flange welded to inside of the 8-in pipe just above its bottom. A 1.25-in air line inside the 4-in pipe ends about 200 ft above bottom of hole. At start, hot water is pumped down the 8-in and 4-in pipes; molten sulphur accumulates until (upon stopping flow down the 4-in pipe) it will rise, under hydrostatic press in the 8-in pipe, to bottom of the air line; the well is then said to be "sealed." Air is then admitted, slowly at first, increasing gradually to equalize the rates of melting and lifting. Temp of water is held as closely as possible at 320°–335° F, adding "tempering" water at 210° if necessary; if water is too hot, the sulphur becomes viscous; if not hot enough to prevent freezing at any point, the well may be lost, since a solid cake of sulphur is difficult or impossible to remelt with hot water. A normal well extracts sulphur from an area of about 0.5 acre. "Bleeder" wells are distributed among a group of producing wells to relieve the press required to force large volumes of water into the ground. Water returning from them at 180°–200° F is so impure as to be useless for any purpose except initial preheating of boiler feed, by exchangers; no satisfactory method for purifying "bleeder" water has been devised. PURIFICATION AND SHIPMENT OF SULPHUR. Molten sulphur from a group of wells is pumped by air through insulated and steam-heated pipes to a central "relay" station, where subsequent manipulation includes: (a) elimination of air and other gases in steam-jacketed separator; (b) collection in a steam-heated, constant-level, flow tank; (c) delivery through orifice meter into steam-heated, cast-iron "relay" pit; (d) transfer from a full pit, by submerged centrifugal pump, to final storage vat. Latter is a rectangular wooden enclosure 800–1 000 ft long, 200 ft wide, with walls erected only 3–4 ft above rising level of sulphur, until final height reaches 40–60 ft; such a block contains 400 000 to 750 000 tons of sulphur, analyzing 99.5–99.95% S. After 6–12 mo for cooling, the walls are removed, standard-gage tracks laid alongside, and face of block is bored with mechanical augers and blasted with dynamite to lumps which can be loaded by clam-shell bucket or steam shovel.

Fig 617. Arrangement at Bottom of Frasch Sulphur Well. (Diagrammatic sec, not to scale)

Mining kaolin through boreholes, West Cornwall, Conn (313). Kaolin occurs in vein-like residual deposits, dipping 50° and intercalated with seams of broken quartz, feldspar, and mica. As the mixed material could not be mined by ordinary methods and the kaolin washed out at a profit, boreholes were used. Holes were cased with 4-in pipe to within a few ft of the footwall of the deposit. Inside the 4-in pipe was placed a 2-in pipe, terminating in a cap with several nozzle-like openings. Water under 40 to 60 lb pressure was forced down the 2-in pipe, the bottom of which was allowed to sink to the footwall as the surrounding material was broken by the jets and washed up the annular space between the pipes. Depth of wells, 50 to 198 ft. The vein matter contained 20% kaolin; the overflow of the wells carried 5 to 10% solids, averaging 60 to 75% kaolin. The percentage of pure kaolin in the solids was inversely proportional to the velocity of the water current.

Mining gilsonite. When heated to a certain temperature, gilsonite flakes off without melting, a property utilized for mining this mineral in overhand stopes. Steam or hot air jets are turned against the face under attack, and, as the gilsonite flakes off, it is caught in a hopper and loaded by gravity to cars below (U S Patent 950 363, Feb 22, 1910).

90. CHUTES AND CHUTE-GATES

Chutes (mills, mill-holes, ore-chutes or ore-passes) are used chiefly in filled and shrinkage stopes, Art 59, 67; also in square-set stopes, Art 47.   They are vert or inclined passages through the stopes, for handling ore or waste.   The term also designates chute-raises (Art 67), chute-compartments of raises, and chute-gates.

Requisites of a chute: (*a*) a life at least equal to that of the stope it serves; (*b*) minimum tendency to clog; (*c*) a cost small in proportion to total tonnage passed; (*d*) low maintenance cost; (*e*) suitability to the stoping conditions.   Details of construction are important as they affect the life of the chute, which often limits the max allowable level interval.   The chute's life depends on the amount and character of ore passing through it, and the pressure due to the stope filling.   The tonnage passed is a function of the stope width, interval between chutes, and distance between levels.   Spacing of chutes is affected by the cost of handling ore in stopes and the development work required for a given spacing (Art 47, 60–66; also Raises, Art 70).   These factors should be considered in connection with the initial and maintenance costs of chutes for a given stope.

Vertical vs inclined chutes.   The former are preferable, as they are easier to construct and maintain, and will pass a larger tonnage for a given amount of wear.   Inclined chutes are necessary in narrow, pitching veins, or near an inclined hanging wall in wide deposits; if provided with a ladderway, they are easier to climb.

Types.   The commonest chute has a rectangular cross-sec, and is built of cribbing or plank; it often has a ladderway, and sometimes a slide for hoisting timbers, drills and steel.   In veins less than 6 ft wide, chutes are sometimes built by lagging vert rows of stulls.   Circular chutes of dry stone walls are used at the Baltic mine, Mich (Art 63); circular wooden and steel chutes have been used at Broken Hill, Australia, and circular chutes walled with pre-cast concrete segments, at Ashanti, W Africa.

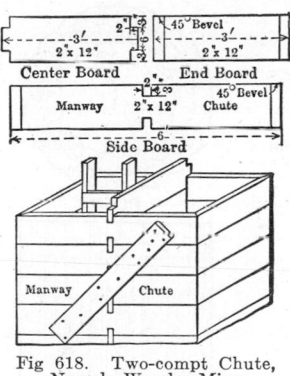

Fig 618.   Two-compt Chute,
Nevada Wonder Mine

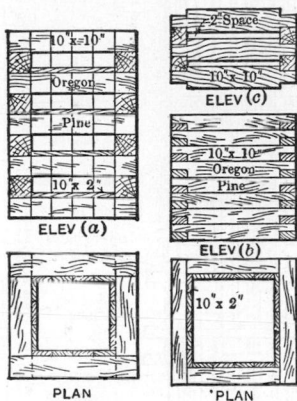

Fig 619.   Cribbed Chutes

Size.   To prevent clogging by the arching of broken ore, the min cross-sectional dimension should be at least 3 × max diam of the largest piece of ore, and preferably more.   Single-compt chutes are usually 4 by 4 ft to 5 by 5 ft.   The min width for a ladderway is about 2 ft; better, 2.5 ft.   In mines having a large level interval, the chute and ladderway should be of equal size, so that the compartments can be interchanged when the chute is worn out.   In filled stopes, manways are usually provided only in every 2nd or 3rd chute.   Manways are advantageous for ready access to chutes when they clog or need repairs.   See below and Art 63 for sizes of circular chutes.

Rectangular plank chutes cost less than others;   the type form is shown in Fig 618 (see also Art 60);   the ladderway is sometimes omitted.   The first few cribs above the stulls at the level are of 3-in plank.   The edges of the planks are toe-nailed together. While filling is being placed around them, the planks are held in position by diagonal cleats, as shown.   The planks are cut, notched and beveled by a swinging circular saw (234).   Corners, instead of being mitered as in Fig 618, are often notched and dovetailed, end and center boards then being interchangeable.   Planks can be spaced close or semi-open by adjusting depth of notches.   Plank chutes serve for small tonnages, as in narrow veins, or where ore is sorted and only a small amount is saved;   they will not withstand heavy pressures from filling in stopes with weak walls.

Cribbed chutes are in general use in the U S for large tonnages, and for supporting heavy pressures in filled stopes. Fig 619 (*a*) shows open cribbing; 2-in spreaders hold the timbers in place; the lining is of vert plank. Fig 619 (*b*) and (*c*) show close and semi-open cribbing, which may or may not be lined.

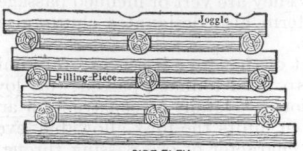

SIDE ELEV

Fig 620.   Round-timber Cribbed Chute, Sec 16 Mine, Ishpeming, Mich

Timbers with grain at right-angles to the direction of falling ore wear faster than when the grain is parallel to the flow. Unlined chutes must be heavy enough to last as long as the chute is needed, because they are difficult to repair or replace. Fig 620 shows round cribbing, for chutes 5.33 ft sq, either single or double compartment. Crib timbers are 10 to 18-in diam, and have an aver life of 3 months, on 2-shift work, 6 days a week; hemlock is preferred, because of its toughness. The lower 20 ft of worn chutes are lined with 0.25-in steel plate; above that, with 3-in plank (209).

Though round timber is cheaper, chutes built of it are harder to erect and to line tightly.

Square-set chutes. In square-set stopes, chutes and manways may be made by lagging vert rows of sets. Fig 621 shows a SORTING CHUTE in filled rill stopes at Butte, Mont (see Art 65). For a height of 5 sets above sill floor, the chute is 3 sets long by 2 sets wide; above that, 1 set wide. Middle sets form a manway; outer ones are ore pockets above the level. Gates and grizzlies are placed over the pockets. While ore is drawn

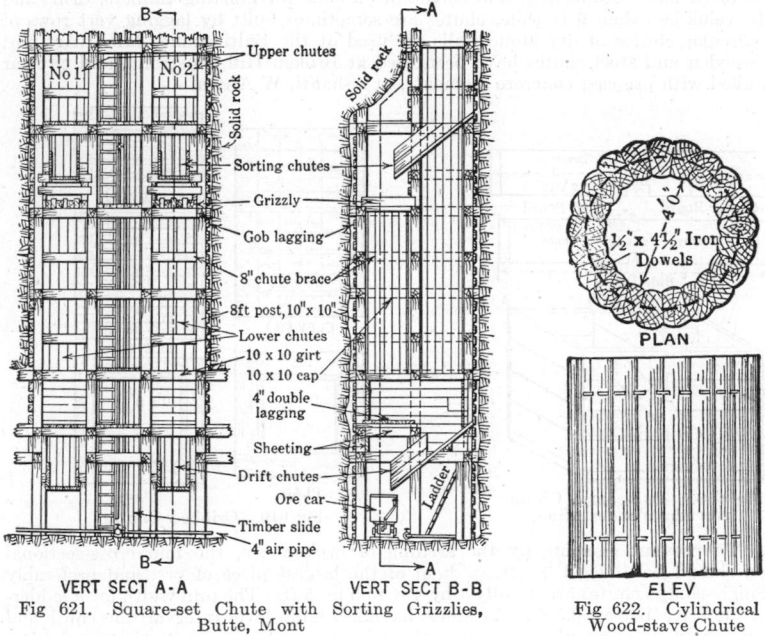

VERT SECT A·A   VERT SECT B-B   ELEV
Fig 621. Square-set Chute with Sorting Grizzlies,   Fig 622.   Cylindrical
                  Butte, Mont   Wood-stave Chute

from upper chute No 1, waste is sorted on the grizzly and thrown into lower chute No 2, and *vice-versa*.

Cylindrical wood-stave chutes (Fig 622) are preferred to cribbed chutes in large filled stopes at Broken Hill South mine, N S W (314). The level interval is 150 ft. In cribbed chutes (Fig 619), the lining cut out rapidly; the spikes holding it also failed and the planks ripped off. Repairs were excessive and even 4-in lining was inadequate. Cylindrical chutes worked better. They are built in 4-ft sections, of beveled staves. Since the grain of the staves is vert, the cutting action of falling ore is minimized. The staves are bound with wire hoops while filling is being placed around them.

There are 4 types of chute in this mine: (*a*) chute of 4-ft internal diam, with 10-in staves; (*b*) 3-ft chute with 10-in staves; (*c*) 3-ft chute with 6-in staves; (*d*) 3-ft chute with 5-in staves; 5-in thickness is the minimum for sufficient bearing between staves and for resistance to collapse. Type (*a*) is used for the lower 35 ft of both vert and inclined chutes (its large diam minimizes clogging); type (b) is for vert chutes, for the sections from 35 to 70 ft, when the lift is 150 ft; type (c) is used from 70 to 120 ft on 150-ft lifts, and from 35 to 70 ft on 100-ft lifts; type (d) is for repairing rectangular chutes which have failed. The upper 30 ft of these stopes is mined by underhand square-setting (Art 46), and hence chutes are not required. Staves are of eucalyptus, sawed from round or square timbers. At first, dowels, as in Fig 622, were used to hold the staves together until they could be wired, but as this construction was too slow small dogs (cramps), of 0.5-in iron, were employed. Successive lengths of chute are simply stood one upon another, as they do not tend to move laterally after being enclosed with filling. Fig 623 shows an inclined stave chute. Fig 624 shows a connection between vert and inclined chutes; the loosely hanging rails yield to every blow and take wear at the turn.

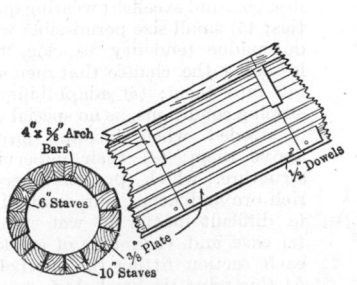

Fig 623. Inclined Cylindrical Chute

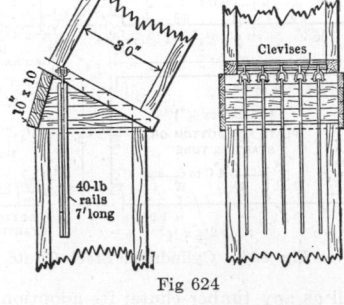

Fig 624

Stave chutes are marked by low first cost and good wearing qualities; they may be withdrawn on finishing a stope. They are serviceable for lining raises and passes for handling filling. E. J. Horwood stated in 1916 that an essential condition for their satisfactory use is that the pressure be approx equal on all sides; hence they are not applicable in stopes having a heavy hanging wall (242). Table 61 shows relative costs of stave and rectangular cribbed chutes at Broken Hill South mine. Eucalyptus costs $56.40 per M bd ft; 10 by 10-in Oregon pine, $45.60; 2 by 10-in Oregon pine, $48 per M. See Bib (314) for details.

Table 61. Cost of Chutes, Broken Hill South Mine, Australia

Type of Chute	Cost per linear foot			
	Material	Labor	Total	
4-ft chute, 10-in staves........................	$9.35	$0.75	$10.10	
3-ft chute, 10-in staves........................	7.35	0.75	8.10	
3-ft chute, 6-in staves.........................	4.40	0.35	4.75	
3-ft chute, 5-in staves.........................	3.70	0.35	4.05	OP = Oregon pine
3-ft inclined chute, Fig 623....................	8.60	1.00	9.60	SB = Eucalyptus
Close-cribbed chute (Fig 619b) 10 by 10-in OP......	11.80	0.20	12.00	("Stringy Bark")
Cribbed chute (Fig 619) 10 by 10-in OP, 2 by 10-in OP spreaders, 2-in SB lining....................	10.00	1.00	11.00	
Cribbed chute (Fig 619c) 10 by 10-in OP..........	9.50	0.20	9.70	

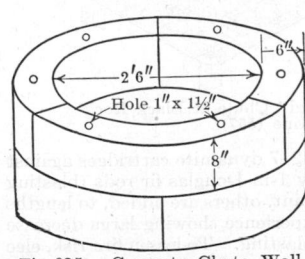

Fig 625. Concrete Chute Wall, Ashanti Goldfields

Cylindrical concrete chutes. Ashanti Goldfields, W Africa, in working exceptionally loose and slippery ore of Obuasi reef by flat-back, square-set and closely filled stopes, has found pre-cast concrete segments cheaper than timber for walling single-compt ore passes (537). Segments, 3 to a ring, are 8 in high, 6 in thick, with inside radius of 1.25 ft (Fig 625). Each segment has 2 holes, top and bottom, 1-in diam and 1.5 in deep, for inserting iron pegs, 6 per ring, equidistantly spaced to allow staggering of vert joints.

Cylindrical steel chutes were successful at the South Blocks mine, Broken Hill, Australia (315). A diam of 30 in is the minimum size to prevent frequent clogging.

Joints with rivet heads projecting inside were a source of weakness, as the heads wore off; this led to the construction in Fig 626.   Chutes are of $^3/_8$-in plate for the first 60 ft above the level, $^5/_{16}$-in for the next 50 ft and $^1/_4$-in for the remainder.   Some chutes, carried to 140 ft above the level, have passed 15 000 tons without repairs.   Repairs were difficult, but unnecessary if sharp bends were avoided, if chutes were properly spaced, and if blasting in clogged chutes was prohibited. Clogged chutes were loosened by a "cannon," made by boring a 2-in hole in a piece of 5-in shafting and using gunpowder to fire a projectile at the hung-up ore.   ADVANTAGES of cylindrical chutes: (a) moderate first cost and excellent wearing qualities; (b) small size permissible without undue tendency to clog, thus lessening the chance that men may fall into them; (c) adaptability to stoping conditions, as no special care is needed when blasting ground above them; (d) their impervious structure, which prevents loss of rich ore and keeps out sand filling (a difficult matter in wet mines); (e) ease and cheapness of erection, each section fitting the one below. At this mine the steel chute worked as well as any timber chute; its adoption in any case depends largely on the relative cost of steel and timber.

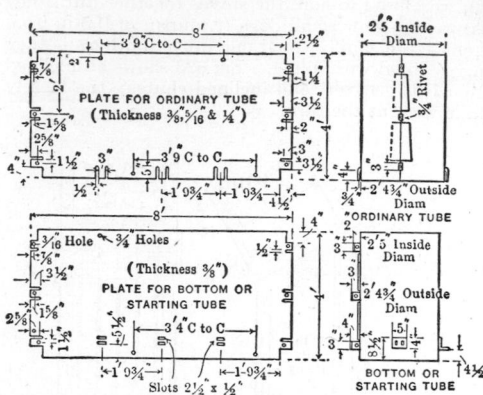

Fig 626. Cylindrical Steel Chute

Rectangular steel chutes (14 by 14.5 in) have been used in filled square-set stopes at Centennial Eureka mine, Utah, for handling high-grade ore without loss of fines.   They are of $^3/_{16}$-in plate, bolted to 1.5 by 1.5 by 0.25-in angles at the corners and on the outside.

Clogged chutes may be started: (a) by climbing up the chute and placing a light shot to unkey the clog (dangerous work, which should be prohibited); (b) if there is a manway, by breaking into the chute; (c) by using a "cannon" (see Steel chutes); not always

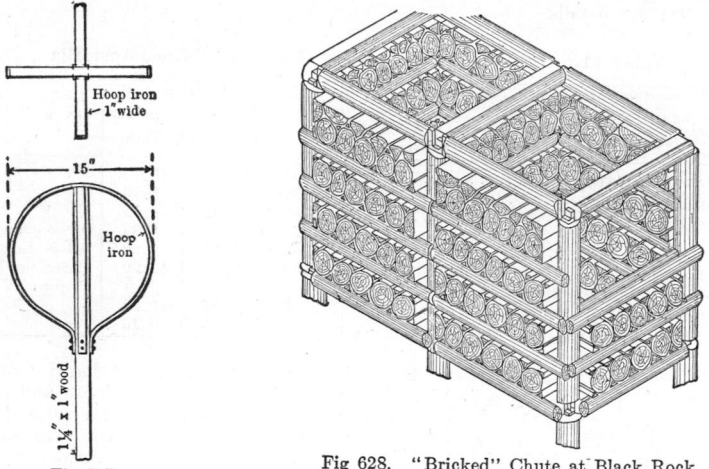

Fig 627

Fig 628. "Bricked" Chute at Black Rock Mine (557)

effective and causes delay; (d) by exploding " bombs " of 2–7 dynamite cartridges against the hanging ore.   At Miami mine, bombs are tied to 1 by 1-in Douglas fir rods (blasting sticks) 10 ft long; if one stick will not reach the clogged point, others are added, to lengths of 50–60 ft.   Miami uses electric detonators for firing, experience showing large decrease in chute-blasting accidents compared with fuse and cap blasting.   To lessen fire risk, elec detonators are also desirable in blasting timbered chutes.   See Bib (619) for details of blasting clogged chutes in southwestern U S.   Fig 627 shows a similar device, of a 1 by

1.25-in hardwood rod, with flat iron hoops on one end. Extra lengths of rod are lashed on as required. The hoops prevent the rod from catching. The hanging ore is poked until it falls, or a stick of dynamite is fastened to the rod and exploded at the clogged point. This device can be used to a height of 100 ft (316).

Wear. Ore falling freely in a high empty chute is very destructive. Chutes should always be kept nearly full; the wear on the lining then depends on the velocity with which the ore moves and hence varies with the cross-sec. Long chutes may be constructed in segments of convenient height (usually not exceeding 50 ft), offset from one another; a gate may be inserted at bottom of each segment to retard or control flow of ore. Wear on chute lining in square-set stopes can be reduced by substituting short wooden blocks, laid horiz, for the customary vert planking. Fig 628 shows this method of " bricking " at Black Rock mine, Butte (557); blocks are 20 in long and held in place by round poles spiked to outside of posts. Similar method, but using blocks of squared timber, is used at Frood mine (Art 46, Fig 295). Such blocking has additional advantage of stiffening the square-sets.

Chute-gates, at bottoms of chutes, raises, etc, control the flow of ore in loading into cars. Their design and details vary widely. Following general points are important: (a) The cheapest chute-gate that will do the work without undue maintenance cost and

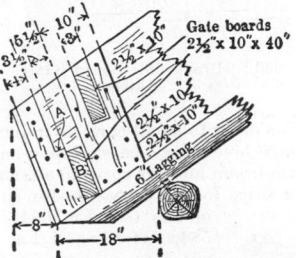

Fig 629. Chute-gate, Homestake Mine

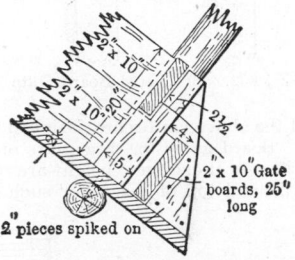

Fig 630. Chute-gate, Dives Pelican Mine, Colo

delays due to clogging is the best. First cost should be considered in connection with the total tonnage passed; elaborate designs are warranted only by large tonnages. (b) Gates must be suited to the size of the ore. Simple board gates serve for fine ore; other forms are necessary for handling large lumps. (c) For rapid loading, mechanically operated gates are sometimes required. (d) Strength is essential, as wear is heavy and gates must often withstand blasting of boulders in or above them. (e) Clearances must be ample, to provide room for barring, to allow for settlement of supporting timbers, and to prevent men from being injured by getting pinched between chutes and cars. Following examples are of types found good under different conditions; see also Bib (317).

Simple chute-gates (Fig 629). The gate-boards are held by side cleats; small chutes may have only 1 board, but 2 give better control of the flow of ore and facilitate removal of large lumps (Fig 576, Art 85, shows a larger chute with 3 boards). For small-size material the lower board B, Fig 629, is pried up with a pinch-bar; notch A is a convenient resting place for board B when the chute is running freely. Instead of inside cleats, brackets of round or strap iron or rails may be used to hold gate-boards (Fig 632); these, being outside of chute, do

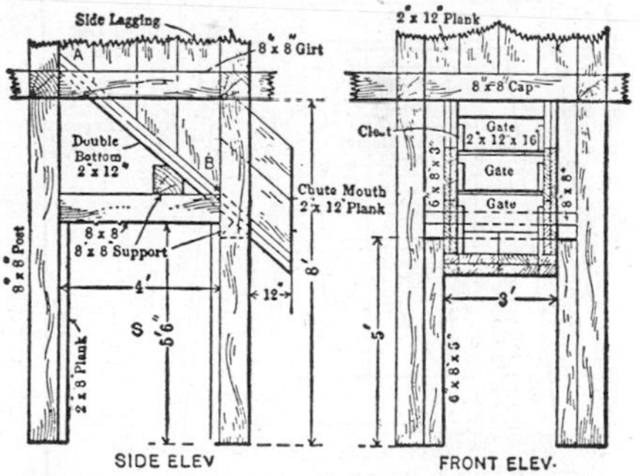

Fig 631. Chute-gate in Square-sets, Bingham, Utah

not obstruct flow of ore and are not damaged by it. Modes of attaching such brackets, other than that in Fig 632, are obvious; as brackets of bent angle-iron, used at Noranda (Fig 633); the drop boards are 2 by 10-in; inside width of chute, 4 ft. Fig 630 shows a simple chute supported on stulls, under a narrow shrinkage stope; chutes for mill holes in filled stopes are similarly supported. Fig 631 is a chute for square-set stopes (66). The bottom of such chutes is cut out rapidly, especially by hard siliceous ore, when the chute is not kept full. Linings of plank, old rails or steel plate, are useful. Wear is reduced by offsetting chute (Fig 634), so that solid rock forms chute bottom. In square-sets same result is obtainable by lagging chute sets on level and omitting bottom boards AB, Fig 631; space S then fills with broken ore, which stands at its angle of repose above chute lip and takes the wear.

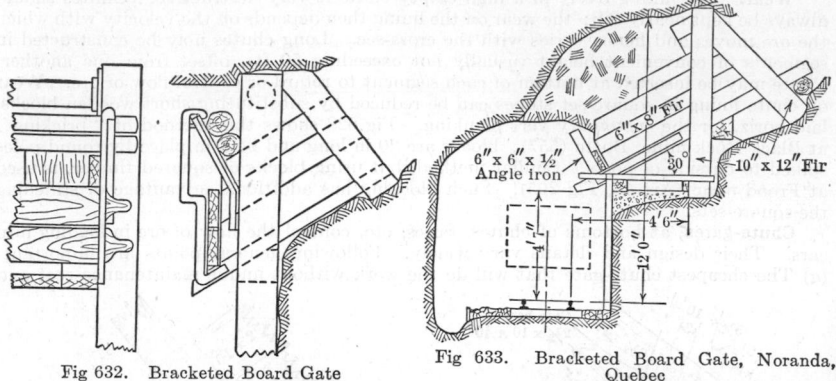

Fig 632.   Bracketed Board Gate

Fig 633.   Bracketed Board Gate, Noranda, Quebec

All the above chutes are designed for loading fine ore into small cars, as in hand tramming. Board gates for large cars on motor-haulage levels may be similarly supported, but drift sets of excessive height are required for headroom and for clearance between the chute lip and top of car.   For such conditions practice favors pony-sets for supporting chutes (see Fig 634; also Fig 584, Art 86, and Fig 572, Art 85).

Sliding steel gate. Fig 634 shows chute equipped with such gate in the Miami mine on motor-haulage levels for pocket chutes C, Fig 579, Art 86. The gate ("guillotine" type) is a steel plate, sliding nearly vertically in guides bolted to the pony-set posts, and operated by a hand lever. The ore is rarely as large as 10-in diam; fine ore is quickly loaded (154). Gates of guillotine type are best adapted to fine or medium-coarse ore, and require mountings free from distortion. They may be operated by levers, rack and pinion, or by direct connection to air or hydraulic cylinders.

Chinaman chutes (Fig 635) are for shrinkage stopes in narrow veins. By omitting lagging between adjacent stulls over the level, an opening is left from wall to wall and of width equal to the interval between stulls. Under this is a platform, 20 to 30 ft long, of

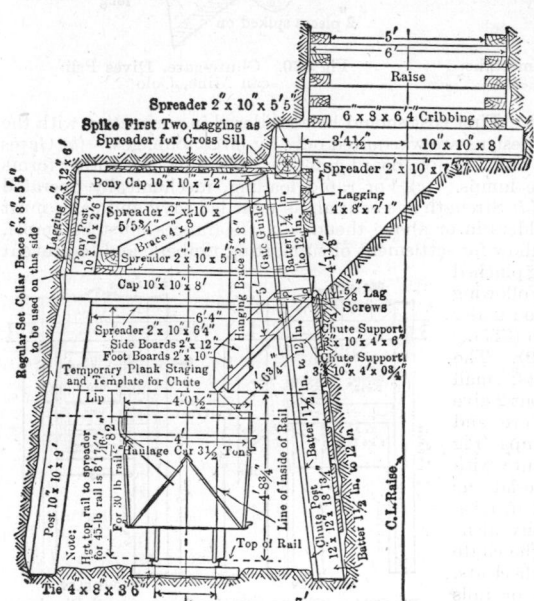

Fig 634.   Chute-gate, Miami Copper Co, Ariz

horiz stulls in hitches about 5 ft above the track.   The stulls are lagged, leaving an open space about 15 in wide over the track for the whole length of the platform.   Short 2-in planks A, placed across the open space, serve as gates. Broken ore from the stope runs down in a wedge-shaped pile on the platform. For loading cars, a few of the boards A close to toe of pile, at either or both ends, are removed; ore from the sides is shoveled to the central opening. ADVANTAGES: (a) the wide opening between stulls prevents clogging; (b) large pieces may be sledged or blasted on the platform without damaging timbers; (c) the ore settles evenly, as it is drawn over the whole width of the stope instead of from one side; (d) rapid drawing is possible, as several cars may be filled simultaneously. DISADVANTAGES: (a) higher cost; (b) the platform is only 5 ft above the rails, thus reducing headroom for trammers; (c) level timbering must be higher above the track, which involves more shoveling in opening a stope.

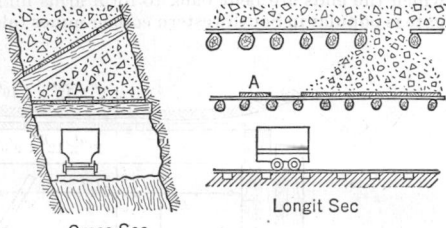

Fig 635. Simple Form of Chinaman Chute

Fig 636 shows a Chinaman chute-gate, with a bulldozing chamber in rock, used by Tennessee Copper Co (data from L. Bregy). This gate is cheaper and requires less dead work in the pillar above main haulage levels than other types of bulldozing chute used there. The 4 20-in sq grizzly openings (double hatched) are protected by 2 angles over inner edges of stringers S, and by U-shape steel plates dropped over filler pieces V, and bolted below caps T. Grizzlies not in use are covered by planks. Loaders enter chamber by ladder at E. Large pieces are blockholed on the grizzly. Except the grizzly openings and entrance, floor of chamber is lagged. One or more chute-gates, with raises 30 ft or more apart, are built on a turnout.

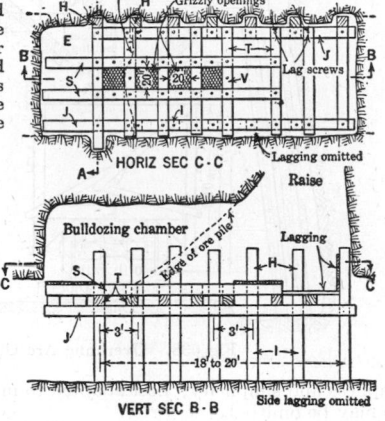

Fig 636. Chinaman Chute with Bulldozing Chamber, Tenn Copper Co

" **Bulldozing** " chutes and chambers are used for large-scale shrinkage stopes (Art 68), where blockholing can not be done in the stopes and where large slabs would clog the gates. For examples, see Alaska Gastineau, Beatson, and Alaska Juneau mines (Art 68). Bulldozing is also a necessary step at some mines using block-caving (Art 80). For other details of a few installations, see Bib (562).

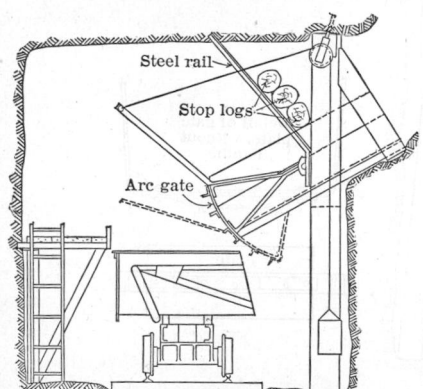

Fig 637. Underswung Arc Gate, Northern Ontario

Arc gates, often used for moderately fine ore, may be operated by hand levers, or compressed-air cylinders; cost not justified by small tonnages. UNDERSWUNG GATE (Fig 637), closed by lifting through the stream of ore, is generally preferable to those which cut down through the ore; it is more easily controlled and less apt to jam or allow sudden rushes into the drift. OVERHUNG ARC GATE (Fig 638) is not well adapted to coarse ore, due to difficulty of closing it quickly and tightly in presence of large lumps. If the axis of rotation is placed slightly lower than the level at which edge of arc meets bottom of chute, the gate can be operated with less effort.

Fig 639 shows an "overcut" gate made of a flat steel plate, reinforced by a strap of which the ends are bent back to form arms hinged to posts at both sides of chute. This gate is popular in Southwestern copper mines (also used at Frood mine), having advantages

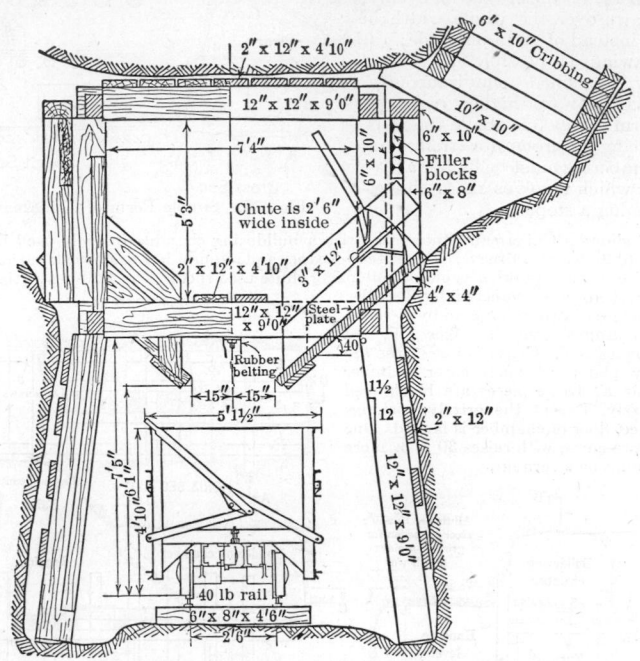

Fig 638.   Overhung Arc Gate, Inspiration Mine

of cheapness and simplicity; best adapted to moderately coarse ore. On small gates, the handle may be omitted.

Butterfly gate (Fig 640), originating in So Africa, used widely in Europe and at some Lake Superior iron mines, is simple and easily operated, but not well adapted to coarse

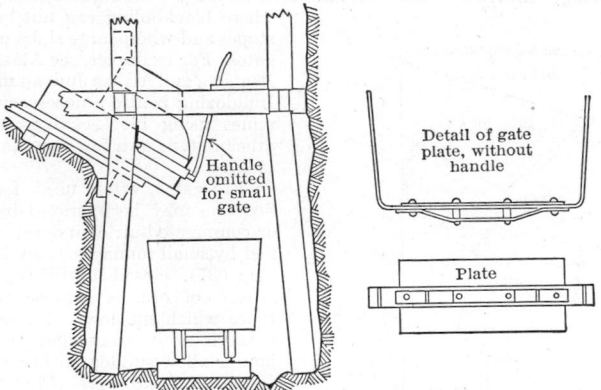

Fig 639.   Flat-plate Overcut Gate

ore. A flat steel plate is hinged along its center line so as to rotate on a horiz bar h, of which the ends are supported on sides of chute. A pin p, inserted from outside through a hole in side of chute, holds the gate shut; on withdrawing pin, pressure of ore opens the gate. Flow is stopped by inserting pin and raising lower edge of plate until upper edge digs into the ore stream, thus rotating and closing the gate.

Finger chutes. Fig 641 shows a chute (105) for handling large amounts of relatively coarse, dry ore. The fingers, held in place by the weight of an arm *B*, are separately hung from rod *CC* so that they move independently. Short ropes from the arms join a main rope, passing over a roller to a small windlass. To draw ore, the fingers are raised high enough for it to pass; when drawing is completed the fingers fall by gravity. If a large piece catches on the lip, it holds up only 1 or 2 fingers, the others dropping to normal position. To prevent leakage when chute is not in use, a tail board is placed across the lip in angle irons *D*. Advantages of finger chutes: quick loading, freedom from clogging and from spilling ore on tracks. Their cost is prohibitive except for large tonnages; in two Alaska Treadwell mines, they were replaced by simple chute-gates. Fingers made of bent rails have been found satisfactory by Tenn Copper Co (317) and several other mines.

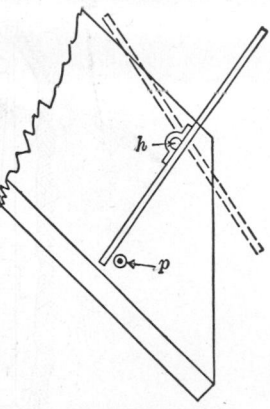

Fig 640. Butterfly Gate

Ball-and-chain, or curtain gate (Fig 642) a patented device invented by D. L. Cramp, and used at Lake Shore Gold Mines and elsewhere, is well adapted for chutes passing ore of widely divergent mixed sizes (597), since large lumps can be barred through without causing a run of fines. It acts to hold stationary the upper layer of a bank of ore standing only slightly steeper than its natural angle of repose. Size and wt of balls and chains are proportioned to sizes of ore and chute; a chute 32 in wide would need 5 6-in balls. Each ball is connected by a short, light-weight chain to a bridle bar, which is raised and lowered by rope, pulley, and windlass.

Keating chute (Fig 643) was adopted at Creighton mine, Sudbury, Ont, for heavy ore from shrinkage stopes, after trying numerous other forms. The ore contained many boulders, requiring blasting in the chutes. The gate consists of round lagging *A*, held in place by 2 bent rails. The I-beams across the tops of the posts protect the miner when working at a blocked chute; the inside I-beam may be omitted without danger (317).

Baltic gate. Fig 644 shows gate used at the bottom of dry-wall mill holes in upper parts of the Champion mine, Mich. It is operated by lever *A*, and rests on the edge of the car when loading. It is inexpensive and well adapted to the Baltic method of mining (Art 63),

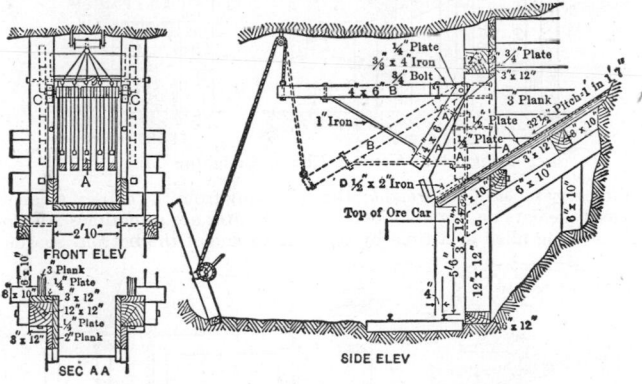

Fig 641. Finger Chute, Alaska Treadwell Mine

because, as mill holes are used alternately as chutes and ladderways, the gates must be dismantled or installed when the change is made. Same type of gate has been retained under different mining system for loading 5-ton cars on lower levels; lever bar is sometimes placed on opposite side of drift, and connected to pan by rope passing over 2 overhead pulleys.

Hanging chutes (Fig 645) are used on Mesabi Range while mining the lowest sub-level in top-slicing (Art 70, 71). They have the advantage of holding several cars of ore in a short vert distance, and so avoid interference between miners on the sub and trammers on the main level. The sub-level track is carried on short drift-sets, which also support the chute sides; the bottom, of loose boards, rests on 30-lb rails, which run lengthwise of

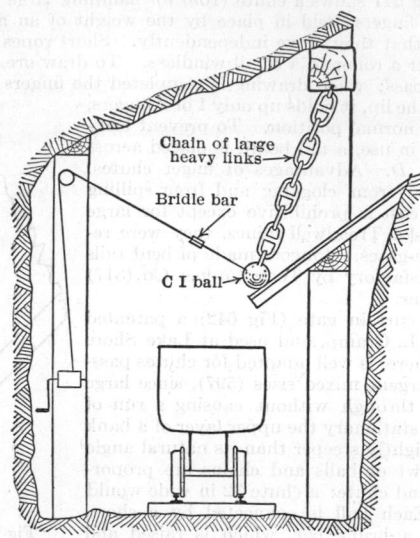

Fig 642. Cramp Chain Gate

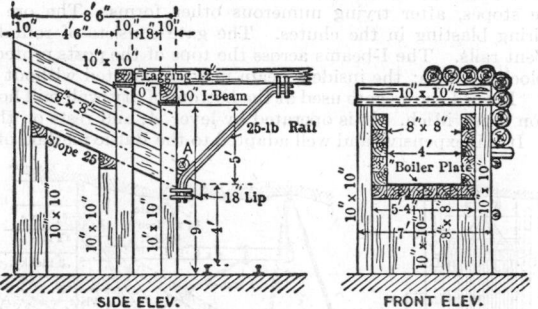

Fig 643. Keating Chute, Creighton Mine

the chute and carry most of the weight; the rails hang from the caps of small sets just high enough to clear the cars on the main level. The chutes are sometimes 20 ft or more long, 1 or more cars being filled at a time by removing some of the bottom boards (35).

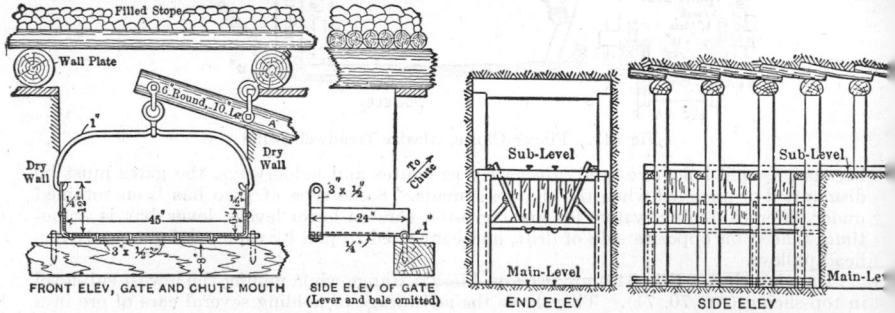

Fig 644. Chute-gate, Baltic Mine, Mich   Fig 645. Hanging Chute-gate, Mesabi Range, Minn

91. MECHANICAL HANDLING IN STOPES (See also Sec 27)

General. Mechanical devices may be used in stopes solely for transport or solely for loading, or for a combination of these purposes. Herein is first described the use of certain equipment for transport; then misc examples of mechanical loading or transport or both. Other examples of mechanical handling are given under open stopes (Art 31-34), top-slicing (Art 71, 72), and sub-level caving (Art 76, 77); for use of scrapers for distributing filling in stopes, see Art 62; for scrapers and loaders in headings, see Art 20. For construction and operation of the numerous machines in use for underground loading and handling, see Sec 27. Development of these machines has been rapid during recent years, with a corresponding increase in their application. In many mines, former stoping methods have been modified to allow the use or increase the effic of mechanical handling; in other more recent ones, the development of stopes has been planned for such equipment as an essential feature. In general, mechanical handling is most advantageous for fairly large-scale operations, where the savings effected apply to sufficient tonnages to warrant the first cost and maintenance of the equipment.

Besides savings in direct cost of loading and transport, there are often collateral or indirect economies connected with mechanical handling: (a) increased rate of output from a given area, of special importance under a weak or heavy roof; (b) reduction in footage of narrow work required to develop given stoping areas; (c) employment of more

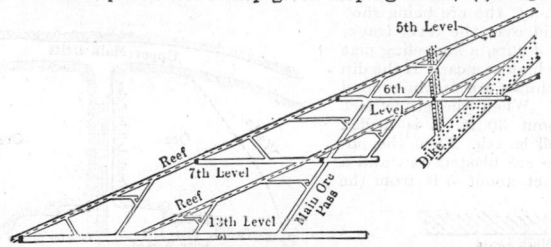

Fig 646. Development at Crown Mines, Transvaal (*E & M Jl*)

skilled and semi-skilled labor and less dependence on lower-grade labor (though natives of So Africa and Nor Rhodesia have proved quickly adaptable as scraper operators); (d) in flat or slightly dipping stopes, a saving in installation, maintenance, and moving of stope trackage; (e) under treacherous roof, or while drawing pillars, scrapers reduce danger to workers by making it unnecessary for them to remain continuously in the stope.

Transport in stopes on flat dips. Deposits dipping 10°-35° present a problem of obtaining cheap transport from stope faces to levels. On steeper dips, ore slides to the levels. Minimum dip for sliding by gravity is 33°-45°, depending on character of ore and footwall; on dips flatter than 10°, cars may run directly to stope faces. On intermediate dips, ore must be transported to the levels. Some form of scraper is usually the best and simplest means of stope transport, if scale of work and other conditions justify its installation (see Sec 27, and below, under Scrapers).

Other methods of stope transport, used prior to modern scraping methods, and still used alone or as auxiliaries to scraping are: (a) By costly shoveling along footwall. Ore from upper parts of a lift may require several handlings before reaching the level; this limits the level interval (Art 19) and increases development costs. In general, it is justified only for small work in high-grade ores. (b) By intermediate levels and raises, to which ore is shoveled or scraped. Lateral transport on intermediate levels may be in barrows, cars, or scrapers. Fig 646 shows an elaborate system at Crown Mines, Ltd, Transvaal, for hand shoveling in stopes (73). Main haulage levels were about 300 ft apart; chute-raises (ore-passes) sloped 55°, and were arranged for a max shoveling distance of 100 ft; 20-cu ft cars trammed to chute-raises; their tracks were on footwall parallel to strike, and level with collars of raises. Such systems, of which many variations are possible, are expensive in non-productive development; they do not eliminate shoveling and wheelbarrow work, but reduce its distance. Hoover (20), in discussing this general method, says: "In some flat deposits, crosscuts into the walls or even levels under the orebody are justifiable. The more numerous the ore-passes, the less the lateral shoveling, but as passes cost money for construction and for repairs, there is a nice economic balance in their frequency." Obviously, scrapers may be used in similar systems of intermediate levels and raises (compare development for top-slicing, Art 70, 71). (c) By tracks laid on footwall at an angle to the dip, so that cars can be run to stope faces (Fig 202, Art 34).

This is feasible in deposits of large area, with regular footwall, and dip less than 10°, but not in short, irregular oreshoots. (*d*) By breast stoping to the dip (Art 31). (*e*) By gravity planes, stationary or shaking chutes, or other stope conveyers described below. These aids to stope transport are limited to open stopes in regular deposits; not applicable where hanging wall is heavy, requiring close support, nor to deposits of very irregular shape and dip.

Self-acting (gravity) planes, Empire mine, Grass Valley, Cal. Ore occurrence resembles that at North Star mine (see below); dip is about 30°.

From a raise *R* (Fig 647), near middle of oreshoot, intermediate drifts are driven 75 to 100 ft apart. At *A*, just above the highest drift, are placed 2 drums with a brake. One drum has a friction clutch for regulating the length of rope to suit the different levels. The raise is double-tracked, with turnsheets at the intersections with drifts. Cars lowered from the turnsheets by gravity dump automatically into chutes at the main level (336). To give room for loading, there must be a minimum clearance of 18 in between top of car and hanging wall; hence planes are not applicable in veins less than say 4.5 ft thick. For details of gravity planes, see Sec 11. For use of planes operated by hoists, see Rand practice, Art 33.

"Go-devil" planes, North Star mine, Cal. Aver dip of vein, 23°. L. O. Kellogg (337) gives following data. Main levels are 333 ft apart; from them, stopes are opened in a series of lifts (Fig 648, 649, and Art 39). Beginning at a level, the first stope is carried toward the raise and to the limit of the oreshoot, the ore being shot down on plats laid over the level track. After making 2 or 3 cuts, a shoveling plat is built, at least as high as a car. If the dip is steep enough, chutes are put in to load cars by gravity. When the stope face has advanced about 30 ft, it is drilled throughout its full length. Then the pillars next to chute are blasted out, and a row of stulls is set about 5 ft from the

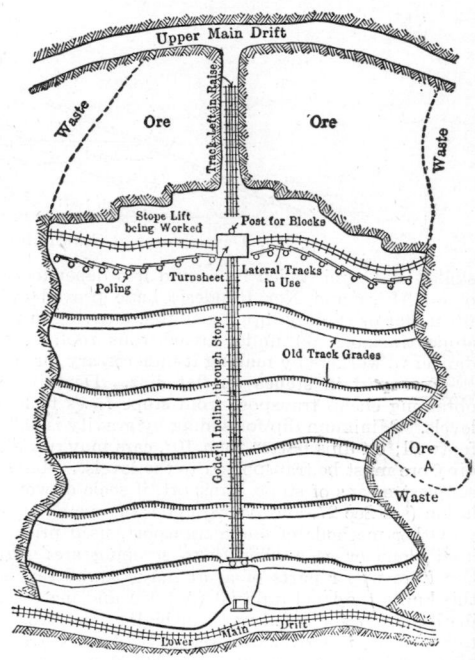

Fig 648. North Star Mine (Stope showing successive lifts)

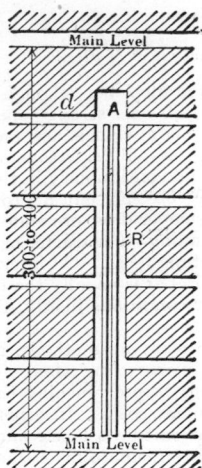

Fig 647. Gravity Plane, Empire Mine

face. These are lagged to retain the broken ore. When space is made, the first intermediate track is laid (Fig 649) and the 2nd lift begun. (Fig 648 shows work at the 6th lift.)

The ore, stoped in successive lifts, is lowered to the main level by double-track planes ("go-devils"). The headblock (Fig 650) comprises 3 sheaves, with a triangular brake block between them, applied by the lever to all three sheaves. The headblock is suspended at the top of the plane by a bolt through a post. A ⅝-in rope is used for 16-cu ft cars. The trammer fills a car on a lateral track, trams it to a turnsheet at the intersection with the plane, hooks on the rope, pushes the car over the edge of the turnsheet on to the go-devil track, and grasps the brake lever. The descending loaded car pulls up the empty. The track is 20-in gage, of 12-lb rails on 4 by 6-in ties. Three cars in a stope handle the product of 4 or 5 drills, from 10 to 15 go-devils supplying a daily production of 350 tons.

Stationary chutes are open steel-plate troughs, of curved or rectangular cross-sec, laid on the stope floor, or on waste rock or small timber bents. Ore is shoveled into the chutes at the face, or wheeled to them in barrows. On the Rand (Art 33) semi-circular chutes convey dry ore on dips over 30°, which is about the minimum angle at which ore will slide. Flatter dips are possible if the ore is thrown or dumped into the chute, thus having an initial momentum. These chutes are in 10-ft sections, 18 in wide, of ⅛-in plate. Rectangular chutes, 20 in wide by 5 in deep, and pitching 31° to 34°, were used at Golden Cross mine, Cal, for dips of about 30°. Similar chutes have been used for cleaning up stopes at Mohawk copper mine, Mich (Art 41). Stationary chutes are cheapest and simplest. During blasting they may be protected by piling ore on each side. In a few cases on the Rand, a small stream of water has been used to assist movement of ore, when chutes are nearly at the critical angle.

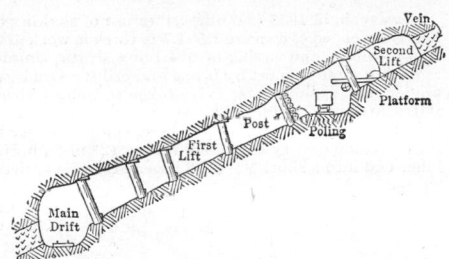

Fig 649. North Star Mine (Sec through stope, showing 1st track)

Shaking chutes have been used widely in flat stopes on the Rand, though lately often replaced by scrapers. They are shallow, sheet-iron troughs, of curved cross sec,

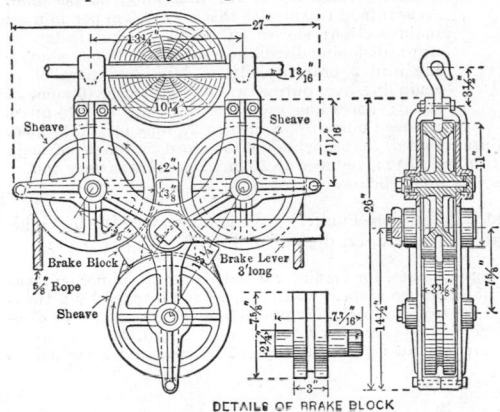

Fig 650. "Go-devil" Sheaves

hung by chains from eyebolts in holes in the hanging-wall, or better from a taut wire rope and turnbuckle (Fig 651). The chute is suspended in an inclined position, and the ore shoveled into it while it is swung longitudinally by one or more Kafirs. At each backward swing the ore moves by its inertia down the chute a few inches to a foot or so, and discharges almost continuously. In large, flat stopes, ore is thus conveyed considerable distances by two or more chutes in series; also, the successive lengths may be placed at angles to one another. These chutes are inexpensive, with large capacity and low operating cost. Disadvantages of suspending chutes from eyebolts: (a) difficulty, with irregular hanging-wall, of drilling holes in line and at proper intervals, and adjusting the chains so that chute swings freely and some chains do not work against others; (b) new holes must be drilled each time chute is moved. If hung from a rope (Fig 651), the chains are easily shifted. The rope supports may be 30 ft or more apart; closer, in narrow stopes. Clips are fastened on the rope at intervals equal to the chute lengths. As the rope remains in place during blasting, the chute is readily shifted. A few holes can be drilled on a new line, the upper end of the rope moved over and the rope tautened. Chutes deliver directly into the pocket or car (187). On the Rand, chute segments are 8 ft long by 18 in wide, of ⅛-in plate. Lower end of any segment slips into upper end of the next one, and is fastened by 2 bolts fitting loosely in slots, to allow flexibility. As the stope face advances, the chute is lengthened, to keep within shoveling

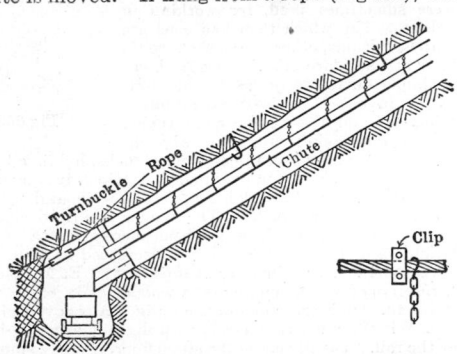

Fig 651. Mode of Support for Shaking Chutes

distance. Fig 652 shows a chute of ¼-in plate, reinforced by straps. On slopes less than 8° or 10°, ore will not move forward efficiently. It is advantageous to have stope faces parallel to the dip, so that chutes may be set at the max possible slope. Long chutes may be swung by air or electric motor mounted on a drill column and provided with reciprocating mechanism. For data on shaking chutes in Randfontein Estates, see paper by H. Clark (556).

L. Jacob, in 1935 (547) describes use of shaking chutes at OTTANGE 2 MINE, Moselle, France. A nearly level bed of iron ore 1.5–1.7 m thick is worked by room-and-pillar methods, followed by extraction of pillars and caving of overlying strata; immediate roof is a bed of blue marl 0.75 m thick, requiring some support by props and cribs. Ore is wet and contains about 50% of fines with strong tendency to agglomerate; it is broken to room width of 14 m by L O X explosive in slabbing rounds, retreating on both sides of a previously advanced heading 4 m wide. The conveyer comprises 3 sections: (1) discharge end, 12.5 m long, sloping upward from floor to load into a car 1.4 m high, standing on haulage entry outside of room; (2) main horiz section, to max length of 30 m, dividing at its inner end into a short Y; (3) 2 inner extensions, max length 30 m, each joined to a branch of the Y

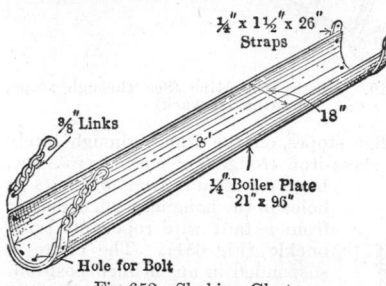

¼" x 1½" x 26" Straps

⅜" Links

18"

¼" Boiler Plate 21" x 96"

Hole for Bolt

Fig 652. Shaking Chute

by adjustable connections permitting the extensions to be spread apart at any angle to max of 30°. Troughs are of 3- and 4-mm Mn-steel plate; rectangular sec area of main trough is 750 sq cm; of branch troughs, 530 sq cm. All sections are rigidly joined, mounted on roller bearings resting on floor, and oscillated (with accelerating forward stroke and quick return) by mechanism placed under discharge end and driven by a 19-kw, squirrel-cage motor; strokes about 175 mm long, 82 per min. Aver rate of travel with this ore, 13.5 m per min on main section; slower on branches, and faster on upward-sloping discharge end. With 8 men shoveling into 2 branches, 18 m long and parallel to main line, aver output was 36 tons per hr (6 men, 28 tons); spreading the same branches to 30° apart reduced output of 8 men to 27 tons per hr (6 men, 22 tons). It was found advisable (to maintain speed) for branches not to exceed the length of main section, limiting over-all length of room to about 70 m, reduced to 55 m when ore was very wet.

For another example of shaking chutes, see Boleo, below.

Aerial ropeways (see Sec 26). One (Henderson-Tucker) gave good service in the Geldenhuis mine (Rand), in stopes averaging 7 ft wide, on dips of 5° to 10°.

The standing rope terminated over a small pocket, for loading cars on the level; upper end was fastened to a drill column at any desired point in the stope, and the rope was tautened by a turnbuckle. The trolley and bucket descended by gravity, and were pulled back by a small air or electric hoist on the drill column. This device was suitable for stopes of any length, but, for spans exceeding 100 ft, the rope had to be supported at an intermediate point by a clamp attached to the arm of a drill column. The bucket dumped automatically. The rig could be dismantled in 15 to 20 min, and erected in about 30 min, irrespective of the length. Moving the column at the upper end took 10 to 15 min. During blasting the bucket was removed and rope slackened (256). Two track-cables were sometimes used, for working in balance. The winch then had separate clutched drums, otherwise buckets could load at one place only. Fig 653 shows a simple device to overcome this difficulty, invented at New Kleinfontein mine. X and Y were the main ropes; Z was a swinging stop, to take up shocks. M and N were side-tipping trucks, holding 4 to 10 cu ft. Haulage rope O passed around 2 grooved wheels W and over pulley A, which traversed rope BC and so varied working length of O. This conveyer would work in a reef 45 in wide, and on dips of 15°–35° (546).

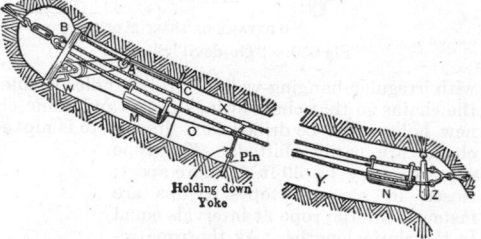

Fig 653. Aerial Ropeway for Stope Transport

Monorails and trucks. The Wager Bradford elevated system, proposed for levels and very flat stopes on the Rand, has not been successful. Difficulties in supporting the rail and cost of installation offset the advantages due to decreased friction. BARROWS WITH GROOVED WHEELS ON MONORAILS (554). For thin veins at dips to 25°, E. M. Weston used a 2-cu ft wooden Cornish barrow, with grooved wheel running on a wooden rail; or for regular dips to 18°, a 3-cu ft steel barrow on steel rail. Under rear end of the body is a grooved block, for guiding the barrow in sliding on the rail. Wheel is a hardwood disk, with slightly larger 1/8-in steel disks on each side, forming a groove to fit the rail. It will run on the stope floor, if fairly smooth. Several barrows may operate on 1 rail, an empty being tipped off the rail on meeting a loaded barrow.

Belt conveyers underground. Belt conveyers have been installed underground both for transport exclusively and also to afford opportunity for hand-sorting of ore in transit. Usually, the conveyer delivers to loading pockets or final disposal, not into mine cars.

For examples of simple transport, see Mesabi (Art 96); also Tri-State district, Grand Saline salt mine, and Boleo (below). Other examples follow.

New Idria quicksilver mine, Cal. A belt conveyer, installed in an adit 300 ft lower than original outcrop, is used both to dispose of stripped waste and to permit hand-sorting of ore from glory-hole workings. At bottom of glory-hole chute, boulders are bulldozed to pass a grizzly of 4-in round steel bars spaced at 14-in centers; material is delivered to conveyer by apron feeder and a chute punched with 1-in holes, to allow fines to cushion large pieces; usual rate of feed, 350 tons (capac, 1 000 tons) per hr. Belt, 42 in wide; length, c–c of pulleys, 1 250 ft, of which 670 ft is inside and 580 outside of adit; belt speed, 310 ft per min when discharging open-pit strippings, 45 ft per min when sorting ore (320).

East Geduld No 1, So Africa. Recent installation of a belt conveyer at the loading pocket near bottom of the 3 225-ft vert shaft (195) was a new development in Rand practice. Coarse ore from a grizzly is hand-picked, and waste returned (by cars) for stope filling. Method offers advantages to deep mines where filling is needed, other means of sorting are inapplicable, and shaft facilities could be fully occupied with hoisting of ore.

Tri-State district. C. W. Nicolson (191) records in 1938 that 2 new mines have installed belt conveyers, 500 ft and 700 ft long, both intended to be lengthened, for moving ore received from scrapers to skip-loading pockets at shaft. Before falling on belt, the ore passes over a 10-in grizzly, but large slabs frequently pass through. Extremely abrasive character of ore entailed special design of belts. At 200 ft per min, 24-in belt carries 100 tons per hr; labor cost, 0.9¢ per ton. For operation at one of these mines, see D. C. & E. mine, Art 31.

Cie du Boleo (552). After experiments in 1927, conveyers, both shaking troughs and belts, have almost completely replaced the 0.5-ton cars formerly used. Pay ore, disseminated chalcocite, occurs in a seam about 60 cm thick in a bed of wet clay about 2 m thick, dipping 9°, under heavy and weak roof. Straight-faced breast stopes are advanced in direction of strike, working both up and down dip from sub-levels about 60 m apart (on slope). Mining is by hand; a miner usually extracts a block 2 m high, 2.2 m wide, and 1.1 m advance in 4.5 hr, including 1.5 hr on timbering. At a face to the rise, ore is thrown into a motor-driven shaking chute (Fig 654, A) 30 m long (in 3-m sections)

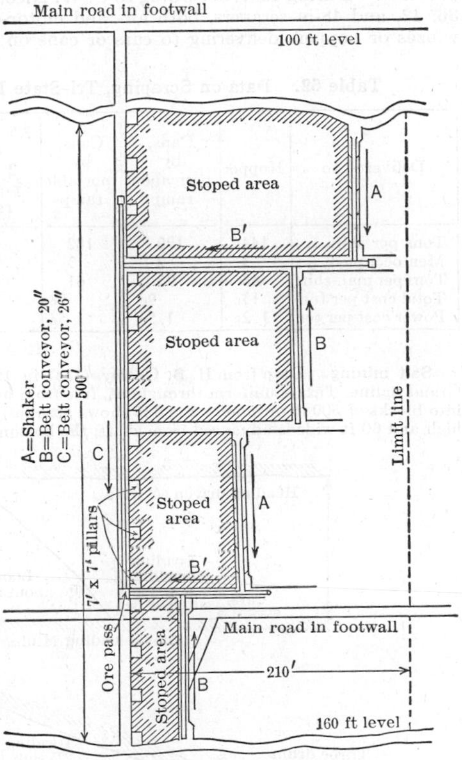

Fig 654. Stoping with Shaking Chutes and Belt Conveyers, Boleo Mines

either suspended from roof or supported on rollers; 3 men can move such a shaker in 2 hr. At a face down dip, a 20-in belt conveyer B, of 18-in overall height, carries ore upgrade. Both face conveyers deliver to a 20-in belt B′ on the sub-level, of which the max length is 60 m; this delivers to a 26-in belt C, in an incline at edge of stoping area, from which the ore is dropped through chute to main haulage level 6 m below, in the footwall. Adoption of conveyers increased output per man-shift from 1.352 met ton in 1927 to 2.126 tons in 1931. An incidental advantage, especially important under the difficult roof conditions, was that a given area could be stoped more quickly, with larger sub-level intervals, and at less expense for drift maintenance. Further details in Bib (552).

Scrapers in stopes. Scrapers, usually operated by double-drum hoists (occasionally 3-drum, as at El Potosí, below), are widely applied in nearly all forms of stoping, though most often in stopes at inclinations where ore will not roll or slide unassisted. In some cases, they serve only for transport, as distributing waste in filled-back stopes (Art 62), or working ore downward over irregular footwall, as in Golden Messenger mine (Art 40, and below), but their chief function is loading ore, directly into cars by a ramp or slide, or into loading chutes in bottom or lower edge of a stope, or at end of a special scraper drift. They have been particularly useful in top-slicing and sub-level caving systems of Lake Superior iron-ore mines. In some mines, as Flin Flon (Art 43), Utica Extension (Art 71), and Climax (Art 87), the whole development and extraction plan has been devised to include scraping as its chief feature; in Tri-State District (Art 31), Michigan amygdaloid mines (Art 41), Rand gold mines (Art 33), and many others, scrapers have been adapted to former practice (sometimes slightly modified) to economize in labor. Following examples illustrate other scraper applications.

Tri-State district. Ore is hoisted almost exclusively in cans 30 to 32-in diam and same height, holding 1 100 to 1 400 lb; for movement underground, can is mounted on a low truck, and then requires vert clearance of 54 in. An aver shoveler ($5.25) loads 25 tons per shift. During 1937, according to C. W. Nicolson (191) several of larger mines adopted 36, 42, and 48-in scrapers, both air- and motor-driven, for 3 purposes: (*a*) scraping to winzes or hoppers delivering to cars or cans on a slightly lower level; (*b*) scraping into cars or cans on same level, via ramp or slide, permanent or portable; (*c*) scraping to a conveyer belt delivering to shaft pocket. Data in Table 62 include some experimental installations and hence are subject to improvement. For data on scrapers in 3 mines of the Commerce Mining & Royalty Co, see Bib (583).

Table 62. Data on Scraping, Tri-State District

Delivered to	Hopper	Cans, by permanent ramp	Cans, by portable ramp	2.5-ton cars with 2 semi-portable ramps	Belt conveyer
Tons per shift....	144	190	182	123	200
Men occupied....	3	2	3	2	2
Tons per man-shift	48	95	61	61	100
Total cost per ton	13¢	9¢	9¢	10¢	8¢
Power cost per ton	1.2¢	1.5¢	1.5¢	1.5¢	1.2¢

Salt mining. Data from H. B. Cooley (553) in 1932. Salt bed, lying 700 ft below surface, Grand Saline, Tex, is uniform throughout, free from horiz seams or vert cleavages, and may break into blocks of 500 lb or more. Fig 655 shows alternative methods of mining; in both, a room 60 ft high and 60 ft wide is advanced from shaft, the bottom of which is far enough below room level to

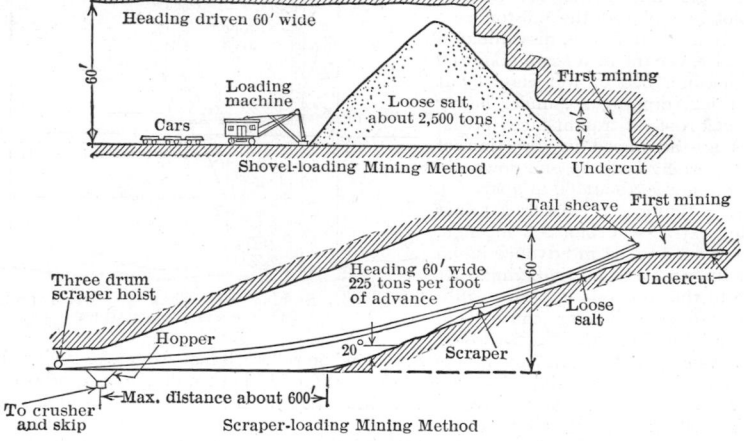

Fig 655. Salt Mining at Grand Saline, Tex

accommodate a crusher and skip-loading pocket. The shovel-loading method, a variation of shrinkage stoping, has advantage of permitting a large reserve of broken salt during periods of slack shipments. In the scraper method, an inclined heading 60 ft wide is driven up a 20° slope from near the shaft pocket; on reaching a height of 60 ft it is continued horiz. Inclined underhand slices are broken with vert 6-ft holes, 3 ft apart. Broken salt is scraped to shaft pocket by a V-scoop of 2-ton capac, operated by 3-drum hoist. Max effic distance from shaft to bottom of inclined face is about 600 ft. When the room, producing about 75 000 tons of salt, has advanced that distance, a similar room is turned at a right-angle about 120 ft from shaft, the scraper hoist is moved opposite to it, and a belt conveyer is installed in the first room to transfer salt to shaft. A corresponding room can then be turned in opposite direction and worked without shifting hoist or extending conveyer; the 2 rooms maintain production for about 2 yr before moving equipment again.

N'Kana mine, N Rhodesia. Scrapers are used in sub-level open stopes, when the dip is less than 50°, and in connection with rock chutes delivering ore by gravity to footwall haulage tunnels (528). Stope widths, in direction of strike, are 35 ft (under weak roof) to 80 ft; length on dip, up to 150 ft; scraper drifts are usually at 125-ft vert intervals. For details, see Bib (528, Dec, 1935). Hoe-type scrapers are 60 in wide and weigh 2 400 or 2 800 lb; respectively operated by 50- and 100-hp motor hoists. A bracket bolted outside of one end aids in righting scraper if it overturns. Tail-rope blocks, 14-in diam, are fastened: (a) by 2 or 3 eyebolts wedged into holes and connected by chain from which the block is suspended; (b) by a piece of $3/4$-in wire rope, clamped around a thimble, and its ends wedged and cemented into 2 holes 4 in apart and 2.5 ft deep; a row of such slings is connected by chain across top of stope and tail block attached where needed. Scraping may be continuous, or on 2 shifts; a 35-ft stope may yield 6 000 tons a month; larger ones, 10 000 tons. Blasting of boulders facilitates scraping and passing through the grizzly with 22-in openings. A scraper crew, working 2 or 3 stopes, comprises 1 European and 12-15 natives. Cost of scraping during a 6-mo period, 7.2 d per ton, including labor, explosives, supplies and power. See also Roan Antelope mine, Art 43.

Pickands Mather & Co. Study of slicing with scraper-loading into 60-cu ft hand-trammed cars, at the Bennett mine on the Mesabi Range, showed that loading and tramming consumed 30% of the time for a complete cycle, the slices being 50 ft long, 10 ft wide, 12 ft high (268). Substituting a scraper for cars in the transfer drift (terminating at a chute delivering to main haulage-way in footwall) and working 2 slices at once from opposite sides of this drift (3 men taking the place of previous 4), increased man-shift output from 27 to 30.8 tons where transfer drift was 150 ft long, and from 24.5 to 30.7 tons in a 200-ft drift, an increase of 25% in latter case. Necessity for building and moving scraper slides was also eliminated. Same Company's UTICA EXTENSION MINE (Art 71) was thereupon developed for scraper handling exclusively; ore bed, 10-12 ft thick, is nearly horiz but slightly undulating. Transfer drifts, 6 by 6 ft, were driven from tops of footwall loading chutes along bottom of ore to boundary of the block to be mined; these drifts averaged about 340 ft long and required no uniformity of grade (an added economy over car transport). Slices were started on both sides and at right-angles to end of transfer-drift, and staggered by width of one slice (Fig 482). Each slice was worked with a box scraper 42 in wide, 18 in high, and of 10 cu ft capac; this proved better than a higher 14-cu ft scraper. Scraper speeds were 7.5-15 hp, with 440-v motors. Transfer drifts were floored about 4 ft wide with 2-in plank; the box scraper used here was 48 in wide and 30 in high; normal capac, 24 cu ft, but actual vol dragged over floor was about 29 cu ft. A scraper 60 in wide had less loading effic. Pull rope diam, 0.5 in; speed, 450 ft per min; tail rope, $3/8$-in diam; speed, 550 ft; return tail rope was carried on 6-in sheaves along drift. Operation and reversing of the 35-hp hoist at chute end of drift was entirely automatic, though under control from either end of scraper-road; speed was retarded within an adjustable distance (usually 25 ft) from each end; overwinding at either end was also prevented automatically. By this plan, 1 miner could watch the transfer scraper and operate the feeder scraper in 1 slice while 2 others were drilling or timbering in opposite slice; output of 23.7 tons per man-shift was thus attained.

Woodward Iron Co. The upper bench (10-12 ft thick) of the "Big Seam" hematite at Bessemer, Ala, is worked by a room and pillar method (Art 40), loading cars almost entirely by scrapers (177). Dip is gentle but variable. Main haulage-ways are 12 ft wide, but widened for double-track opposite bottom of each room. These are turned 12 ft wide up the rise at 75-ft intervals, beginning at property line, and driven for 25 ft with hand loading. Scraper slide, then installed, is mainly of 12-in, 25-lb channels, 16 ft long; bottom requires 12 channels, flat side up, bolted together, and supported by trestle near outer ends. Double-drum, 55-hp hoist, on a self-propelling truck, serves 3-5 rooms alternately, standing on side track opposite the slide. Beyond its neck, a room advances 30 ft wide, to the next higher haulage-way, usually 220 ft (sometimes 300 ft) and is then stripped 10 ft on each side, making 50-ft rooms and 25-ft pillars. A round of 14-18 8-ft holes, by 2 or 3 tripod drills, breaks 100-125 tons per drill-shift. Box-type, 3 100-lb scraper loads out 2 rooms while a third is being drilled and blasted, and 2 others are being started. Including a slice finally taken from wall of haulage-way, first mining yields about 65% recovery, increased to 75% by splitting the pillars.

Flin Flon sulphide ore is excessively hard, and breaks into large, angular pieces; it is mined by sub-level open stoping (Art 43) and as the surface equipment includes a 42-in crusher, no effort is made to break ore in stopes smaller than 36 in (565). A stope 300 ft long (dip 70°) discharges through 8 untimbered raise chutes, 40 ft apart, into a "scram" drift, each end of which connects through a grizzly raise with main haulage crosscuts 12 ft below (Fig 279).   The chutes are inclined at 50° and offset to footwall side of drift, so that broken ore rolls onto the floor and is bulldozed if necessary.   At each end of scram drift, and beyond the grizzly, a 75-hp, double-drum hoist operates a scraper, dragging ore from the nearest 4 chutes, or 150 ft max travel.   Scraper is of arc-hoe type, 6.75 ft wide, weighs 2 800 lb, and delivers about 5 tons per trip, or 500 tons in 8 hr.   Haul rope $^7/_8$-in, tail rope, $^3/_4$-in, passing over 24-in sheaves.   Floor of drift is laid with longit 40-lb rails, 2 ft apart, to reduce scraper friction.

El Potosí mine, Chihuahua, Mex (see Art 37).   Scrapers are utilized in the glory-holes in chimneys and thick mantos (when the benched area becomes too wide for gravity discharge to central chute) and especially in open stopes in thinner mantos, opened through raises from haulage drifts in footwall (174).   In 1933, scrapers handled 154 750 tons, or

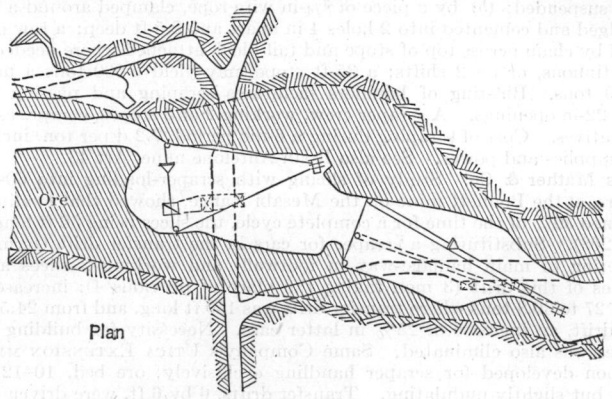

Fig 656.   Scraping in El Potosí Mine, Mex

34% of total output.   When suitable, scraping saves 10–30¢ (U S) per ton over hand shoveling, due to increased output per man-shift; it has also permitted working of numerous otherwise unprofitable orebodies.   Hoe scraper, made in Co shops, is 3 ft wide and 15.5 in high; back plate is curved to 16-in radius, and has replaceable edge; ropes are strands from discarded 1.25-in shaft-hoisting rope.   Preferred hoist has 3 drums, with 15-hp motor; as compared with a double-drum, this hoist can scrape a larger area from one set-up, and with less frequent shifting of tail-rope sheaves.   Scraping distance is normally 100–125 ft; occasionally 150 ft, with some loss of effic unless a higher-speed motor is warranted.   Fig 656 shows scraper installations in a typical manto stope, worked by underhand benches to height of 40–65 ft above a nearly horiz floor.   (See also Sec 27.)

Golden Messenger mine, York, Mont.   Scrapers move nearly all the ore from stopes, about 125 tons a day (Art 40).   Veins, 4–10 ft wide, dip 30°–60° (aver 40°), and are often interrupted by step faults of small throw; these produce an irregular footwall, and require numerous pillars (Fig 245).   Stopes are worked both over- and underhand, through drift chutes 15–30 ft apart.   At chutes 60–75 ft apart, scraper hoists with 7.5-hp motors are mounted on top of drift sets.   By adjusting snatch blocks, ore can be scraped into chutes 40 ft on either side, as well as into the hoist chute.   Due to small capac of chutes at this low dip, ore is often drawn into stock piles at points where it can be reached quickly when chute is being drawn.   Drag of 125 ft is about the limit for these hoists, using 36-in box scrapers.   Similar scrapers are installed inside of the stopes, aiding flow of ore over high spots in floor, through openings between pillars, and to within reach of chute scrapers (69).

Witwatersrand.   Data from C. L. Butlin (559) in 1930.   Adoption of single-hole benches drilled by jackhammer, together with reduction in stoping widths, greatly increased the area from which ore had to be removed to maintain the output.   At MODDERFONTEIN MINE, for example, in 1923 each 100 ft of stoping face produced 23 tons per shift; in 1928, the aver was only 10 tons.   Experience with shrinkage stoping (Art 33) and scraper loading has shown the most favorable conditions for such work to be: (a) stope face straight and nearly parallel to dip; (b) absence of faults, and of roof supports in scraper path; (c) scraper pull not longer than 200 ft, sometimes requiring a subdivision by intermediate haulage levels.   Breaking and scraping are conducted alternately in adjoining panels, the scraper removing about 40% of ore broken and thrown back from face; rest remains in shrinkage pile for subsequent disposal by another scraper (Fig 196).

Comp-air, 10-hp motors were usual; now replaced by larger elec motors. Rope speeds, 60–100 ft per min under load, and 100–180 ft empty. Scrapers could handle 12–15 tons per hr; actual performance, about 37 tons per scraper-shift, employing 6 or 7 natives for entire work. Aver of 5.5 tons per man-shift compares favorably with effic of former hand shoveling in wider stopes. Advantages of scrapers used in shrinkage stopes, as proved at Modderfontein, are: (a) ability to work with good effic in thin reefs (36 in or less); (b) saving in labor by eliminating hand shoveling under adverse conditions; (c) reduction by 85% of car trackage required in hand-loading stopes. For further details of scraper practice, see papers by H. Clark and R. B. Smart (556).

Power-shovels in stopes. The utility of these shovels in stopes, as contrasted with headings (Art 20), is limited to nearly flat orebodies with height of at least 9 ft, worked in wide, open stopes, as in S E and S W Mo. Under these conditions, a caterpillar shovel has following advantages over a scraper: (a) greater flexibility, as it can move freely in stope, and from one stope to another; (b) ability to load cars without need for a slide, and at any place to which cars can be brought; (c) does a completer job, leaving less ore to be cleaned up by hand. Examples follow.

Hartley mine, Tri-State District. A caterpillar-mounted, elec-driven, dipper shovel in 1932 loaded part of output of this mine into 32 by 32-in cans, standing on trucks 13 in high above rail. Motor, 15-hp, chain-drive, has enough power to move boulders several tons in wt. Dipper is specially designed for loading cans. Shovel can work in a room 9 ft high. During a test period of 127 working days, the shovel loaded 16 565 tons (24 516 cans) at following cost per ton: Connected energy charge, 0.382¢; power consumed, 0.946¢; depreciation and repairs, 3.070¢; interest, 0.776¢; labor (1 operator, 1 helper, 1 extra trammer), 7.830¢; total, 13.004¢. At same time, hand loading by contract (averaging 35 tons per man-shift) cost 21.202¢ per ton, plus 0.167¢ for wear of tools; total 21.369¢ per ton (323).

Barr mine, Tri-State District. In 1929, 30% of the output was loaded with dipper-type (10-cu ft), elec-driven (25-hp) caterpillar shovels into 1.5-ton cars hoisted on self-dumping cage (unusual in this district). Cars were loaded alternately on both sides of shovel. Usual duty was about 100 cars per shift of 3 men, or 49 tons per man-shift. Contract price for hand-loading from plank floor was 38 to 41.5¢ per car (25–28¢ per ton); aver duty, 24.9 tons per man-shift. Shovel thus doubled output per man, and reduced labor cost per ton (shovel crew totaling $13 per shift) to about one-third that of contract hand loading (143).

St Joseph Lead Co, S E Mo. This Co has made extensive use of the Thew shovel, modified in some details. It is elec-driven, has caterpillar traction, but is transported from stope to stope by climbing onto a truck hauled by loco. At Mine La Motte, the shovel is rarely moved into a stope until 400–500 tons of broken ore has accumulated, which it then loads into 48-cu ft (2.7-ton) cars, 42 in high, at rate of 160–300 tons per shift. Cars are moved by cable-reel loco. Shovel needs min headroom of 6 ft 2 in (560).

92. "SAND FILLING" OF STOPES IN METAL MINES (See also Art 110)

General. Sand or similar granular material has following advantages as mine filling: (a) rapidly and cheaply transported by air, water, or both; (b) spaces can be filled solidly and completely, and in places inaccessible or costly to reach by other means of transport; (c) when well placed and drained it has greater compressive resistance than any other material except concrete; (d) at any mine equipped with a nearby concentrator or cyanide plant, abundance of suitable sand is usually assured; (e) ultimately, when well settled and not violently disturbed, sand will stand unsupported in an almost vert face; if it contains iron sulphides, it may become, through oxidation, almost as firm as rock; at Horne mine (Art 43), pyrrhotite mill tailings are added to coarser filling for this reason; (f) solidly placed sand, being almost impervious to air, prevents short-circuiting of ventilating currents through stopes thus filled. Sand and even coarsely crushed material (max size about one-third diam of conducting pipe) has been conveyed by low-press air in some European coal mines, and sand $3/8$-in max size by high-press air, at Champion mine, Mich (Art 63); but water is commonest transporting agent, as in following examples (note use of air jets in conjunction with water at Hodbarrow mine). The gold mines of So Africa have widely employed sand filling, utilizing the leached residues from cyanide plants. Method was first applied to reinforcing shaft pillars and important underground stations; later to support of heavy ground in general, especially to aid extraction of pillars and other remnants, or recovery of ore temporarily used as filling for "pig-styes." In some mines, sand filling has been placed close to faces of active stopes. According to R. S. G. Stokes in 1936 (195), sand filling has been abandoned in mines of Central Rand, though still advantageously employed in some deep mines of Far Eastern Rand, as where parallel gold-bearing "leaders" have been found in hanging wall of main reef; in such cases, sand serves as footwall for further developments. When a suitably situated shaft is not available, special boreholes, 7–11 in diam, are shot-drilled, at cost of about $4 per ft, for dropping sand. A large mine usually needs at least 2 such holes; New Modder has used 8 holes to distribute 3 000 tons of pulp per day; Simmer & Jack had 2 boreholes besides pipe lines in inclined shafts. Government Gold Mining Areas has 2 holes 1 000 ft apart and drops 4 000 tons of sand (dry wt) in 8 hr (576, 630).

Details of So African practice. Following notes are from papers by E. Pam, W. A. Caldecott, O. P. Powell, B. C. Gullachsen, R. E. Sawyer, and others, on practice between 1910 and 1916 (251, 329); more recent data are fragmentary (576, 589, 630). PREPARATION OF STOPES. Fig 657 shows typical filling operations. Barricades are erected in box-holes between level-pillars, and along the sides of areas to be filled; where possible, work is so arranged that faults, dikes or shaft-pillars are utilized to retain filling. On flat dips, the sand is sometimes shoveled up to make a dam along the side of area being filled (AB, Fig 657); to do this, the pulp must be very thick. Construction of BARRICADES depends on their position and length of time they are expected to stand without rotting. After draining and taking

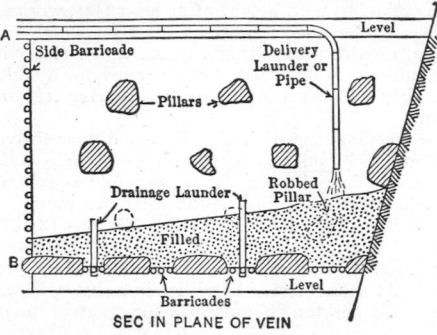

Fig 657. Sand Filling, Transvaal Gold Mines

weight from the hanging, sand compacts so that a free face of fill will stand without support. Hence, barricades may only be needed for the period of filling and draining, though for safety they are best kept unbroken during the life of the level. If there is danger of running water entering the stope, the barricades must be strong and permanent; the water should be isolated and piped off through the fill; otherwise, it may develop a disastrous hydrostatic pressure. The types of barricade in Fig 658 have been successful; (a) and (c) are common at bottom of open stopes; (b) is built in box-holes; (d), less expensive, is used on sides of filled area; woven wire, 6 by 18-in mesh, is sometimes used instead of split lagging for support of cocoa matting. At Simmer & Jack, cost of such barriers, 6 ft high, is 7 sh per lin ft. TREATMENT OF SANDS. Cyanide salts break up in tailing lying on the edges of old dumps, exposed to air and sun; such material may be sent underground without danger. But, to save cost of rehandling, tailing direct from the cyanide vats ("current tailing") is most frequently utilized. Current tailing requires oxidizing treatment to destroy cyanide salts. $KMnO_4$ and bleaching powder are commonly used, the amount depending on strength of the last cyanide solution used, and on moisture content of the sand from the vats. At Simmer & Jack mine, the tailing contains 12% moisture, carrying up to 0.02% total cyanide. From 0.2 to 0.25 lb of $KMnO_4$ is used (5% solution) per ton of sand. Frequent moisture tests are made on the pulp entering the borehole, which has never contained more than 0.0025% total cyanide, and no traces of HCN have been found in stopes being filled. As Rand sands contain H_2SO_4 from decomposing pyrite, some alkali (as lime) is added to prevent generation of HCN. At East Rand Proprietary mine, in 1916, ashes from coal were found to contain enough CaO and $CaCO_3$ for this purpose. Slime should be removed from sand to be used as filling, since it retards drainage through barriers; this is done by classification in the mill or in cones erected usually close to point of discharge to underground. Govt Gold Min Areas has a battery of 16 cones, 9 by 9 ft, at each of its 2 boreholes, receiving 1 : 1 pulp through pump and pipeline from mill 2 miles away. In former years, Rand tailings were mainly coarser than 100-mesh; later tendency towards finer grinding has diminished somewhat the pro-

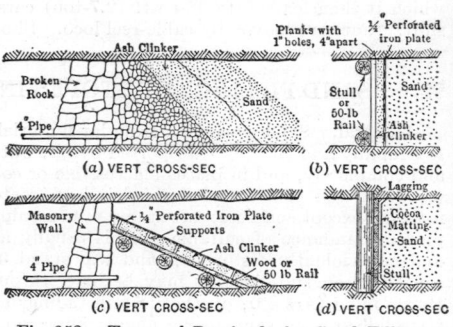

Fig 658. Types of Barricade for Sand Filling on the Rand

portion of sand most suitable for filling. PASSING SAND TO STOPES. Boreholes for this purpose, 7 to 11-in diam and uncased, are so located as to minimize cost of lateral handling. Their up-keep is nil. Clogged holes are easily reopened by running into them a small stream of water. Sand may also be conveyed through pipes in a shaft ladderway (note use of a wooden box for fairly dry sand in Cinderella shaft, below). As delivered to bore-holes, thickened and de-slimed pulp usually has about 70% solids, by wt, requiring a slope of 30% (17°) for satisfactory flow in such launders as may be needed on surface. Underground, the pulp, usually diluted to about 1 : 1, is carried laterally to the stopes from the borehole or shaft in pipes or open launders. Launders are best if the requisite grade is obtainable. Fig 659 published by W. A. Caldecott in 1914 (329), shows the launder grades for carrying Rand tailings in pulps of different fluidity; it is platted from following formulas:

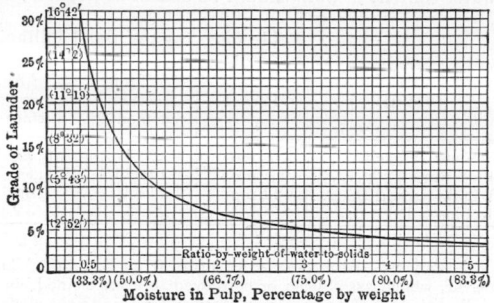

Fig 659. Launder Grades for Sand Pulp (Rand)

$$W = \frac{12}{G - 1} = \frac{P}{100 - P}; \quad P = \frac{100\,W}{W + 1} = \frac{1\,200}{G + 11}; \quad G = 1 + \frac{12}{W} = \frac{1\,200}{P} - 11$$

where W = ratio of water to solids, by wt; P = per cent of water, by wt; G = grade of launder, per cent. These formulas are based on observations (within the limits platted) upon flow of pulp under large-scale working conditions; they refer to ordinary mill sands, containing about 4% pyrite; as much as 10% of the solids are retained on a 0.01-in aperture screen. The exact grade varies with many factors. "In general, the conditions tending to require increased launder grade or higher water ratio are: small volume of pulp, frequent sharp curves in launder, wrong shape and rough internal surface of launder, unevenness of grade, large size of sand particles and high percentage of pyrite. Conversely, a large volume of pulp flowing in a well designed and laid launder without curves, and con-

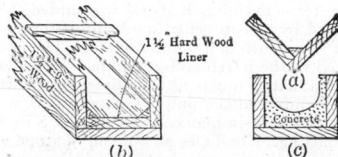

Fig 660. Launders for Handling Sand Underground (Rand)

Fig 661. Drainage Launder for Sand Filling (Rand)

taining much slime and few coarse or pyritic particles, requires less grade than is usually needed for sand pulp. In installing a launder, it is desirable to increase the grade by say 20% around curves, as well as for some distance at the head of the launder, to overcome the initial inertia of the pulp" (Caldecott). Fig 660 shows FORMS OF LAUNDER. The simple V launder (a), with hardwood liner, is good and easily shifted. Type (c), with concrete liners 3-ft long, has been used in the Robinson mine. Launders are laid on the floor of the level or hung from the roof; they may terminate near the top of the stope or be carried down the dip (Fig 657). PIPES, required for moving sand horizontally along levels, wear fast and are turned frequently to distribute wear. Ordinary C-I, steel, and wood-lined pipe, and some with porcelain lining, have been used; wood-lined pipe was popular at first, but gave trouble and is now little used. Steel pipe is preferable to that with special linings and in flat places has a long life; at Village Main Reef mine, an unlined pipe passed 75 000 tons of sand before the wear was considerable; vertical pipe wears fastest. After stopping and before starting the sand, clear water is run through the pipes for a few minutes, to prevent clogging. If the depth is great and the flow in a vert pipe too rapid, hoppers may be inserted every 300 ft. See Art 110 and examples below for data on the horiz length of pipe through which sand may be forced by the head in a vert pipe. DRAINING SAND IN STOPES. Water runs off from the sand through pipes or filter beds or barricades at the sides and bottom of filled areas. Drainage launders (Fig 661), laid on the footwall and extending through the barriers, were formerly widely used, but have lately been largely eliminated. COST OF SAND FILLING (Table 63.) In 1931, costs at Witwatersrand Deep and Simmer & Jack mines were reported as 15¢, and at Modder Deep Levels, as 13¢ per ton of sand (576). Filling operations should be continuous rather than intermittent. If current tailing is used, the cost of rehandling at dump is avoided; the water content of pulp should be as low as possible, to reduce pumping cost.

Table 63.   Cost of Sand Filling, Witwatersrand

Mine	Period	Aver tons lowered per month	Aver cost per ton, cents			Per cent of cost on surface
			Surface	Underg'd	Total	
Simmer & Jack......	9 mo	19 171	6.73	13.11	19.84	33.9
East Rand Prop......	Aver mo	19 490	4.64	9.22	13.86	33.5
Witwatersrand Deep..	12 mo	27 387	7.64	7.48	15.12	50.5
Robinson Deep.......	4 mo	25 815	3.55	15.29	18.84	18.8

Examples. ROBINSON MINE (data from E. Pam). The plant handled 200 tons of dump sand per hr, which was sluiced or conveyed to a brick lined bin (500 to 600 tons capacity) near hoisting shaft. A 6 by 8-ft tunnel ran from side of bin to the shaft; bin sloped 30% toward the tunnel and discharged through 30 by 18-in holes into which water was sprayed; the launder in the tunnel sloped 20%; sluicing water at 50-lb pressure was supplied to launder through 2 by 1/8-in nozzles, the mixture in launder being 35 to 40% water by weight. At the shaft, the sand flowed down a 5 or 6-in unlined pipe, with loose flanged joints so that sections could be readily turned or replaced. Pulp was distributed laterally to stopes in pipes; on the 2 000-ft level, a 600-ft length of horiz pipe was used successfully. Stopes were prepared (Fig 657) with bulkheads composed of stulls and lagged with 1.5-in plank, which fitted close to floor and roof, all crevices being calked with hay. Excess water ran off top of filling through 12-in apertures in the side barriers; these openings were blocked up as the sand level rose. Area to be filled should be as long as possible, to reduce pressure on barriers and give free overflow for water. It was planned to fill working stopes, as well as old ones. Barriers impervious to water require greater strength, since, due to its incompressibility, any water left in sand transforms roof pressure into lateral pressure; such barriers were not used elsewhere (see below). ROBINSON DEEP MINE (Caldecott and Powell). Current tailing in form of thick pulp was run by a small stream of water containing $KMnO_4$ through a tunnel and borehole to the stopes. Tunnel was 4.5 by 6 ft, 1 125 ft long, and ran from sand plant at 36.4% grade, intersecting the borehole 390 ft below surface; it had a vert grizzly across it. The borehole was 10 in diam at surface and 7 in at 1 729 ft depth. The sand in borehole contained 28% water. Underground handling was like that at the SIMMER & JACK MINE (Caldecott and Powell, A. R. Hughes). Sand was trammed from cyanide vats to a mixing box 10 by 5 by 4 ft, where water containing $KMnO_4$ was added. The pulp (3.5 parts water to 1 part sand by wt) was pumped by a 4-in centrifugal pump through a 6-in pipe, 900 ft to diaphragm cones erected on surface at the mouth of a 6-in borehole. The underflow of the cones, containing 30% moisture, was delivered to the borehole by launders with a 30% grade. Two 8-ft cones, handling 200 tons per 10 hr, eliminated much of the slime. At bottom of the borehole a wooden launder, 9 by 7 in, sloping 15°, conducted the pulp to stopes, more water being added. In 1910, bulkheads at sides of stopes were of 3 by 9-in plank, supported by 8 by 8-in stulls; planks were perforated and covered with cocoa matting. Box-holes at bottom of stope were blocked by building a dry wall across them, through which a 6-in pipe projected into the stope. A wooden drain launder (Fig 661) ran from the pipe to a point 2 to 12 ft above top of sand; upper side of launder was covered with cocoa-matting filter frames. Later barriers had an ash-clinker filter bed (Fig 658). CINDERELLA CONSOL MINE (R. E. Sawyer). Sand from edges of old dump was conveyed to shaft by mechanical haulage and dumped into a vert wooden conduit, 12 by 11-in crosssec. The conduit gave no trouble from wear or clogging when sand contained less than 5 to 6% moisture; wetter sand collected on the sides and gradually choked it. The conduit, 3 900 ft long, discharged on a steeply inclined plate, from which a stream of water washed the sand into a launder; thence, after mixing, it was delivered to the stopes by pipes or launders. Capacity of plant, 400 tons per shift. Filling actually reduced pumping, as sand sent down averaged 3% moisture, while that in stopes retained 10%. This system is stated to be cheaper than flushing from the surface, as the plant is small and pumping is reduced by sending down dry sand. WITWATERSRAND DEEP MINE. 12 000 tons per month of current sand was sent underground, part down a borehole and part down a winze; practice was similar to that at Simmer & Jack. Filling entering mine contained 28% moisture; pillars and hitherto inaccessible ore were mined under its protection.

Matahambre, Cuba. Data from D. D. Homer in 1938; see also Bib (237, 590) and Art 62. Conveying mill tailing to stopes through rubber-lined steel pipe has been successful since July, 1927; special advantages: (1) reduction in cost of placing fill to about 29¢ per ton, against 55¢ for surface material (shale) previously used; (2) an increase of about 33% in rate of output from a given stoping area, due to more rapid filling. Total economy estimated at $1 per ton mined, at 1930 wages and normal 30 000 tons per month. Current mill tailing (quartzite and shale), or as much as needed, is de-slimed in 2 Dorr bowl classifiers, each set close to top of a raise connecting with underground; one, 7 by 29 ft with 21-ft bowl, is 200 ft higher than foot of mill and, supplying a few upper levels of mine, is fed by a Wilfley pump; the other, 6 by 27 ft with 16-ft bowl, fed by gravity, supplies lower levels; either can treat whole flow of tailing. As received, tailings aver 49% finer than 200-mesh; as discharged, sands are 49% coarser than 65-mesh and 97% coarser than 200-mesh; about half the mill tailings is thus available for filling, and supplies 60% of all material required (remainder coming about equally from ore sorting and rock development). Such sand compresses 11.2% by vol at 1 530 lb per sq in, and 18.2% at

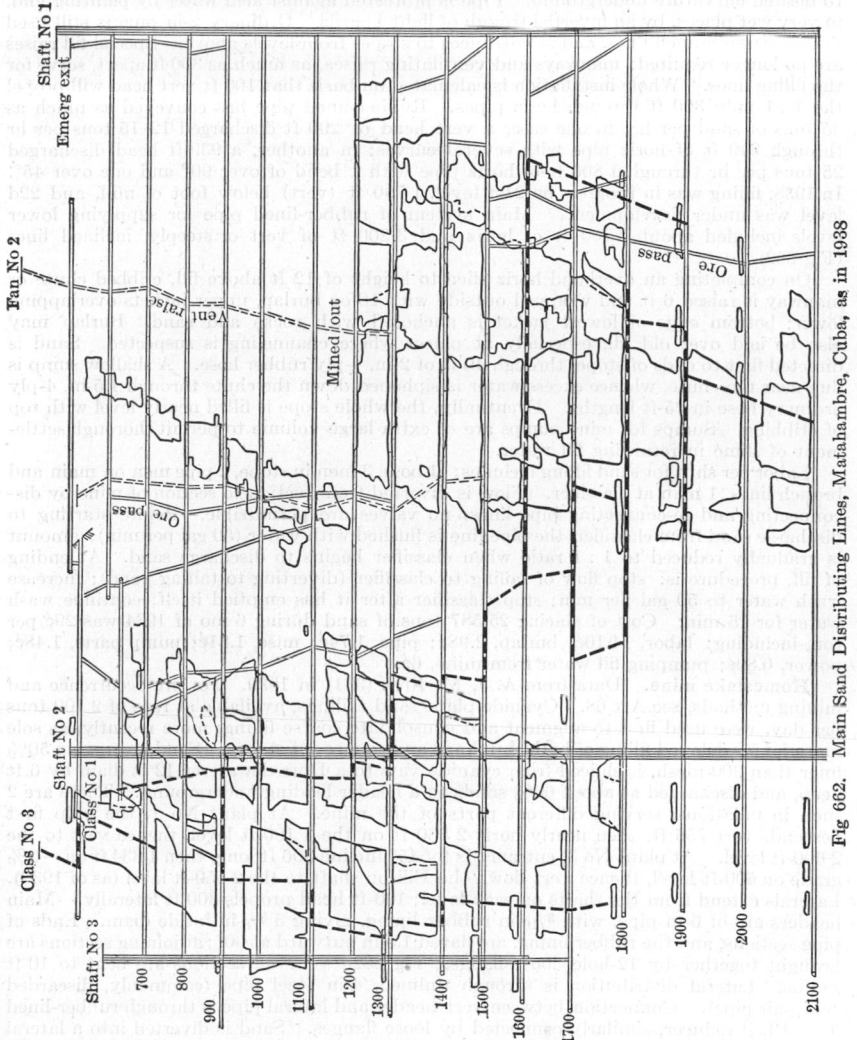

Fig 662. Main Sand Distributing Lines, Matahambre, Cuba, as in 1938

3 060 lb; slime, unless removed, tends to filter out of stopes into drainage ditches and sumps. Classifier rakes discharge into a screen-covered hopper, where water is added, by a spray above and a 0.75-in hose below it, to make a pulp of about equal parts water and solids, by wt (sometimes 50% excess water). Outlet from hopper has a belled, bronze bushing, flanged to delivery pipe. When not in use, it is plugged to avoid trickling of dry sand into the pipe.

Early experience proved that, in main lines, ordinary steel pipe lasted only about 2 weeks; extra-heavy pipe, 3 weeks. All main lines were then installed with rubber-lined pipe, 3.5-in outside, 2.5-in diam inside of 0.25-in rubber wall. Pipe is in 12-ft lengths, with 7.5-in, 4-hole flanges; rubber is flared outward over face of flange to diam of 4.75 in, forming a gasket permitting some angular deflection at joints and preventing access of sand behind the rubber. After passing 500 000 tons of sand in 7 years, no piece of straight pipe has had to be replaced because of wear; corrosion and some wear at curves have required replacements. Branches are at angles of 15° and 30°, also flanged, and always placed where flow is not retarded by a curve. Pipe is bent cold, to match an iron rod bent to desired curvature underground. Pipe is protected against acid water by painting and, in very wet places, by an inverted trough of light boards. Ordinary 2-in pipe is still used in less active branch lines, and at entrances to stopes from levels above. Special fill raises are no longer required; manways and ventilating raises, as much as 300 ft apart, serve for the filling lines. Whole installation is calculated on basis that 100 ft vert head will propel the 1 : 1 pulp 300 ft through horiz pipes. Rubber-lined pipe has conveyed as much as 35 tons of sand per hr; in one case, a vert head of 290 ft discharged 12–15 tons per hr through 940 ft of horiz pipe with several curves; in another, a 939-ft head discharged 25 tons per hr through 1 800 ft of horiz pipe with 1 bend of over 90° and one over 45°. In 1938, filling was in progress on 21st level, 1 790 ft (vert) below foot of mill, and 22d level was under development. Main system of rubber-lined pipe for supplying lower levels included about 3 700 ft of horiz and 3 200 ft of vert or steeply inclined lines (Fig 662).

On completing an overhand horiz slice to height of 12 ft above fill, cribbed chute or manway is raised 6 ft and wrapped outside with 10-oz burlap, upper jackets overlapping lower; bottom edge of lowest jacket is anchored with rocks and sand. Burlap may also be laid over old fill, especially at places where channeling is suspected. Sand is directed first to ends of stope, through 40 ft of 2-in, 4-ply rubber hose. A shallow sump is dug near the chute, whence excess water is siphoned down the chute through 1.5-in, 4-ply ordinary hose in 25-ft lengths. Eventually, the whole stope is filled nearly level with top of cribbing. Sumps for mine pumps are of extra large volume to permit thorough settlement of slime in returning fill water.

Labor per shift for sand filling includes: 1 boss, 3 men in stope, 2 pipe men on main and branch lines, 1 man at classifier. Flow is diverted from section to section of mine by disconnecting and re-connecting pipe lines; no valves are permissible. Before starting to discharge sand from classifier, the pipe line is flushed with water (50 gal per min); amount is gradually reduced to 1 : 1 ratio when classifier begins to discharge sand. At ending of fill, procedure is: stop flow of tailing to classifier (diverting to tailing pond); increase wash water to 50 gal per min; stop classifier after it has emptied itself; continue wash water for 15 min. Cost of placing 25 587 tons of sand during 6 mo of 1934 was 29¢ per ton, including: labor, 14.10¢; burlap, 2.98¢; pipe, 1.74¢; misc, 1.81¢; pump parts, 1.48¢; power, 0.89¢; pumping fill water from mine, 6¢.

Homestake mine. Data from A. J. M. Ross (331) in 1939. For ore occurrence and mining methods, see Art 68. Cyanide-plant sand tailings, available at rate of 2 100 tons per day, were used first to augment and consolidate coarse filling; more recently, as sole material for delayed filling of both shrinkage and square-set stopes. Sand, averaging 50% finer than 200-mesh, is sluiced from cyanide vats to a Dorr dewaterer 12 ft diam by 6 ft deep, and discharged at about 60% solids to a header leading underground. There are 2 such installations, serving different parts of the mine. At plant No 1, the pulp first descends vert 756 ft, then nearly horiz 2 560 ft on the 1 100-ft level, thence vert to the 2 600-ft level. At plant No 3, entrance is by 45° incline 306 ft long, then 1 334 ft on −2% grade on 500-ft level, thence vert down the Ellison shaft to the 2 150-ft level (as of 1939). Laterals extend from the shafts on each level; 100-ft head propels 300 ft laterally. Main headers are of 6-in pipe, with $^3/_{16}$-in rubber lining, giving 5 $^5/_8$-in inside diam. Ends of pipe sections, and the rubber lining, are flared 1.5 in outward at 90°; adjoining sections are brought together by 12-hole, loose flanges, Fig 662a; curved sections are bent to 10-ft radius. Lateral distribution is through unlined, 4-in steel pipe (commonly, discarded comp-air pipe). Connection between vert header and lateral pipe is through rubber-lined T and bell reducer, similarly connected by loose flanges. Sand is diverted into a lateral pipe by inserting a rubber-covered blind disk, $^1/_2$ in thick, with bolt holes bored to correspond with flanges, between lower leg of T and the next lower section of header. Laterals above the one momentarily in use are similarly closed by blind disks on the side legs of the Ts. Since both the T and bell reducer on the 4-in pipe are fixed, a "dummy" disk, of same thickness, but having a 5.5-in central hole, is also inserted at all T-joints through which flow is to be maintained. Reversing the disks at a T requires about 40 min. Standard valves, at first used, proved too expensive to maintain.

Preparatory to filling an emptied SHRINKAGE STOPE, some of which are more than 150 ft high, all drifts or crosscuts, leading to drawholes, except one, and any other openings from sublevels, are bulkheaded with 2 layers of 12 by 12-in timbers, 0.25 in apart, and covered inside with 12-oz burlap, Fig 662a. Ends of all timbers are cemented into hitches in walls, floor, and roof of the drawhole drift. Just inside the one unclosed drawhole, a square-set raise, lagged and burlaped on 3 sides, is started close to the stope wall, and continued upward a little in advance of the rising level of sand (compare Matahambre, above); this raise later serves as air and manway, when the pillar is to be mined. Wherever possible, sand is delivered into the stope through an opening from level above; occasionally by a riser from the stope level. Filling a SQUARE-SET STOPE, which is usually 7 sets long by 3 sets wide (the 6 by 6-ft sets having 9-ft posts on sill floor, 8-ft posts elsewhere), involves close lagging on all sides with 3-in plank, burlaped on inside; floor boards are then removed. A manway (middle set on one side of stope) is similarly lagged, except that each piece of lagging, 8–12 in wide, on the side facing the middle of the stope, has a 2 by 12-in slot, which, as sand builds up, are successively closed by wedges, surplus water overflowing through the next higher slot. Sand is delivered through a riser in the manway, terminating at top in a horiz pipe discharging as far as possible from the manway. This method has worked successfully with 1 400 ft of pipe in the drift and a 75-ft riser. An aver square-set stope can be filled in 8 hr on each of 3 successive days, which allows time for each run, of about 700 tons, to drain and settle before the next addition of sand. A sill-floor set takes about 15 tons; other sets, 12 tons each. It formerly took more than 2 weeks to fill such a stope with coarse waste.

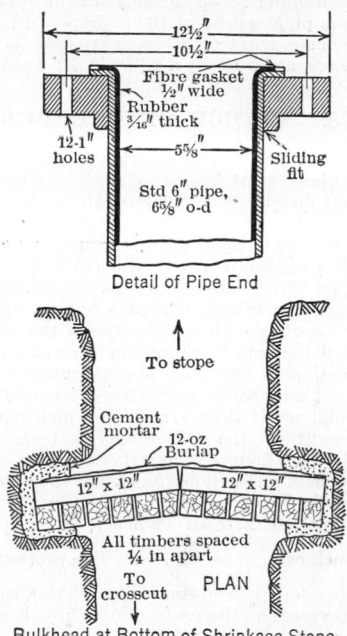

Detail of Pipe End

To stope

PLAN

Bulkhead at Bottom of Shrinkage Stope

Fig 662a. Details of Sand Filling, Homestake Mine

Hodbarrow mine, England, applied sand filling to recover 1 000 000 tons of hematite in 2 widely separated remnants of a thick, almost horiz bed, of which about 90% had been removed by top-slicing (591). One area was covered with glacial clay and gravel; other had limestone roof, and lay under surface reclaimed from ocean. At both places, dune sand in a bed 15 ft deep was available close by. In the first area, fill was flushed down an 8-in steel pipe in a 240-ft shaft; at other, down 2 bore-holes (a third in reserve) 350 ft deep, cased with 7.5 and 9-in pipe. At each hole, about 17 100 cu yd of sand (enough to replace 57 700 tons of ore) was obtained within a radius of 170 ft by flushing through a launder on 5° slope; top of casing pipe was cut off in successive segments until 1 ft below top of clay underlying the sand, and covered by plate with 0.75-in holes. Subsequently here, and from start at shaft location, sand was delivered by loco with 7-cu yd, side-dump cars loaded by 3-ton crane. Three men delivered 250 cu yd in 8 hr, replacing 850 tons of ore. Each borehole required 100 gal water per min; at shaft, sand was dumped into a brick-walled pit, from which it was flushed to column pipe with 2 water jets from 3-in pipe; pulp averaged about 1 : 1 ratio, by vol. DISTRIBUTION at bottom was through 4-in iron pipe. At first, pipe lines were laid to grade of −1° or more; later, use of air-jets, through a 1/8-in orifice bored on center line of 90° elbow with 14-in radius, greatly accelerated flow and permitted parts of a line to be laid on an up-grade. Longest line (to May, 1930) was 900 ft, including many bends and 300 ft of +1% grade; it had 3 air jets about evenly spaced and supplied at 60–70 lb press.

Usual slices in the mine were 50 ft long, 10 ft high, 10 ft wide; bottom and one side were previously placed sand; top, end, and other side were ore. Before filling, all ore exposed on wall was curtained with brattice cloth hung loosely on a row of stulls; entrance to slice was dammed with plank only 2 or 3 high at start, and every possible leak was stuffed with hay. Filling was then run in at rate of 112 cu ft (6 tons) of sand, per hr. Allowing for delays, a slice could be filled about 25 times faster than it could be mined by hand, or 11 times faster than when machine-mined. By careful blasting, adjoining ore in next slice could be removed without serious inflow of sand from the filled slice; when drained, the fill was very firm; surface subsidence over filled area was estimated at not over 5% the height of ore removed. Costs for filling only, per ton (8 cu ft) of ore removed (min wages, Apl, 1932, 6s 5d per shift) were estimated (at 1d = 2¢): Wages, surface and underground, 12¢; fuel and lubricants, 8¢; brattice cloth, 3.5¢; overhead, 4¢; total, 27.5¢. Timber consumption was reduced about 30% below that required by former top-slicing.

Australia. For use of sand tailings as contemporaneous filling for stopes at Kalgoorlie, W Australia, see Art 65.

Extinguishing fires. Sand purposely containing a large proportion of slime has successfully controlled and extinguished mine fires; notably at Butte, Mont (543) and

Jerome, Ariz (544).   At Butte, thickened mill tailings, 50% finer than 200-mesh, in pulp containing 18–30% solids. was dropped through 8-in c-i pipe and distributed laterally in 4-in pipe; a head of 100 ft propelled pulp 800 ft horiz.   Launders required 2% grade.   At Jerome, surface rock was crushed 35% finer than 100-mesh and dropped through boreholes, at 65 tons per shift, in 1 : 1 pulp.

93.   CHOICE OF UNDERGROUND METAL-MINING METHOD

General. The selection of a method of mining for a given orebody is aided by making an inverted statement of the limitations and applications of the methods already described, but no concise statement can be framed to cover all the variations that occur in nature. Usually several methods are more or less adapted to the grade, size, shape, and attitude of the orebody, and the strength of its ore and wall rocks; from these a choice may be made or a method evolved which will best suit the geological, economic, and local conditions (Art 25).   Table 64 groups the mining methods for this purpose; it is intended merely to suggest methods available under ordinary conditions, each of which may be studied in connection with peculiarities of the orebody in question.   The ideal method provides safe and humane working conditions and yields the greatest ultimate profit, but a mining method is generally a compromise between conflicting factors.

Under some conditions, a low-cost method yielding a low extraction may give greater total profit than a method which recovers a larger proportion of orebody; under other conditions, the reverse may be true.   Following equations (H. L. Smyth) show relations between factors involved: Let Q = total tons of ore recoverable by the method yielding highest extraction; X = tons abandoned by another method; p = profit per ton by method Q; p' = profit per ton by the other method; $p' - p$ = saving per ton effected by the other method.   When $p'(Q - X) = Qp$, the 2 methods are equally desirable and, in such case, $\dfrac{X}{Q} = \dfrac{p' - p}{p'}$.   The proportion of the deposit which may properly be sacrificed therefore depends on ratio of saving to the profit per ton by the other method.   This ratio increases as the profit diminishes; hence, for a given saving, more ore of low than of high value may be sacrificed (172).   Calculations like the above may be elaborated by varying the milling, freight, and smelter charges on ores of different values; in such cases, the effect of the variables and the point of max profit may be determined graphically (Fig 99 and Bib 330).

Table 64.   Application of Underground Metal-mining Methods

Type of Orebody	Dip	Strength of ore	Strength of walls	Possible methods of mining	For details See Art No
Thin beds	Flt	Stg	Stg	Breast stoping.................. Systematic room and pillar........ Open overhand stopes........... Coal mining methods.............	30–33 34 39–41, 91 102–111
		Wk or Stg	Wk	Top-slicing.....................	70–72
Thick beds	Flt	Stg	Stg	Breast and bench............... Systematic room and pillar........	30–32 34
		Wk or Stg	Wk	Top-slicing..................... Sub-level caving.................	70–72 75–77
		Wk or Stg	Stg	Underhand glory-holing........... Mitchell slicing system...........	37 55
Very thick beds	....	....	....	Same as for masses...............	......
Very narrow veins	Stp	Stg or Wk	Stg or Wk	Resuing......................	61
Narrow veins (Widths up to economic length of stull, Art 38)	Flt	....	....	Same as for thin beds............	......
	Stp	Stg	Stg	Open underhand stopes.......... Open overhand stopes........... Shrinkage stopes................ Filled flat-back stopes........... Filled rill stopes................	35 38–41, 91 67–69 60 65

Table 64. Application of Underground Metal-mining Methods (*Continued*)

Type of Orebody	Dip	Strength of ore	Strength of walls	Possible methods of mining	For details See Art No
Narrow veins—*Continued*	Stp	Stg	Wk	Filled flat-back stopes............ Filled rill stopes............... Square-set stopes................	60 65 45–54
	Stp	Wk	Stg	Open underhand stopes.......... Square-set stopes...............	35 45–54
	Stp	Wk	Wk	Square-set stopes................ Top-slicing..................... Crosscut method................	45–54 70–74 64
	Flt	......	......	Same as for thick beds or masses...	......
Wide veins	Stp	Stg	Stg	Open underhand stopes.......... Underground glory-hole.......... Shrinkage stopes................ Sub-level stoping............... Filled flat-back stopes........... Filled rill stopes............... Square-set stopes............... Combined methods...............	36 37 67–69 43 62 65 45–54 83–87
	Stp	Stg	Wk	Filled flat-back stopes........... Filled rill stopes............... Square-set stopes............... Top-slicing..................... Sub-level caving................ Combined methods...............	62, 63, 67 65, 66 45–54 70–74 75–78 83–87
	Stp	Wk	Stg	Open underhand stopes.......... Square-set stopes............... Top-slicing..................... Sub-level caving................ Mitchell slicing system.......... Block-caving.................... Combined methods...............	36 45–54 70–74 75–78 55 79–81 83–88
	Stp	Wk	Wk	Square-set stopes............... Crosscut method................ Top-slicing..................... Sub-level caving................ Combined methods...............	45–54 64 70–74, 82 75–78, 82 83–88
Masses		Stg	Stg	Underhand glory-hole........... Shrinkage stopes................ Pillar and chamber workings...... Sub-level stoping............... Filled flat-back stopes........... Filled rill stopes............... Combined methods...............	37 67–69 42 43 62, 63, 67 65 83–87
		Wk	Wk or Stg	Square-set stopes............... Crosscut method................ Top-slicing..................... Sub-level caving................ Block-caving.................... Combined methods...............	45–54 64 70–74, 82 75–78, 82 79–81 83–88

Wk = Weak   Stg = Strong   Flt = Flat   Stp = Steep

Safety. Table 65 gives averages for 7 years 1931–1937, from data on metal-mine accidents published by Bur of Mines; no more recent data were at hand at end of 1940. Choice of method should be based on assumption that no method need be unduly hazardous if properly applied. For more detailed analysis of accidents during 1930–1931 and 1935–1937, by causes as well as by mining methods, see Bur Mines *Bull* 362, 422, 428. See Sec 23 for other data.

Table 65.   Accident and Fatality Rates in U S Metal Mines

Aver for Years 1931–1937, incl (658)

Mining method	Aver No of mines considered (a)	Aver man-hr worked per year, all mines	Rate per 1 000 000 man-hr	
			Fatalities	Injuries (b)
Open-stope (incl room and pillar, and sub-level)...	112	21 654 513	1.31	79.34
Shrinkage..............	24	3 654 363	2.15	133.42
Cut-and-fill............	19	6 564 339	1.96	91.38
Square-set.............	35	12 345 777	1.68	127.44
Block-caving...........	7	2 903 065	2.02	138.18
Sub-level caving........	16	3 190 170	1.03	29.06
Top-slicing.............	22	5 120 783	0.78	22.21
Open-cut (power-loading)	49	10 551 978	0.37	17.83
Open-cut (hand-loading)..	5	358 950	1.19	52.92
Average...........	...	66 343 938	1.31	78.28

(a) Incl no mine employing fewer than 25 men.
(b) Entailing loss of 1 day's work, or more.

OPEN-CUT MINING

94. GENERAL

Open cuts ("Open workings," "Open pits," "Open casts") are surface excavations; in connection with coal mining they are called STRIPPINGS. (For quarries, see Sec 5.)

Field of use is in mining deposits that outcrop or lie under shallow cover. The upper parts of narrow, rich veins may be thus mined, with small equipment and no expense for development; this is a favorite "poor man's" mode of obtaining capital for subsequent work, regardless of ultimate economy. Large open cuts, involving extensive development and equipment, are often made on outcrops of wide, veinlike orebodies, because they produce ore cheaper than is possible with underground methods. Veins can be worked by open cuts only to a limited depth, chiefly because of danger of falls of wall rock; weak walls and flat dips decrease possible working depth. Open cutting is the only profitable method of mining thin, flat beds, with shallow cover (Art 96, 97, 98). Large bed-like masses, covered by rock or alluvium, may often be mined cheaper by open cuts than by underground methods (see Mesabi, Ajo, Nevada Consol, Art 96). Large orebodies that can be excavated in a series of hillside benches are well adapted to open cutting (Art 95). An orebody can seldom be entirely mined by open cut; underground work is usually required in depth, and in some cases to mine the ore around edges of deposit.

General plan. Open-cut methods are combinations of loosening, loading, and transporting earth and rock in surface excavations (Sec 3, 5).

The combination selected depends on shape, size, and depth of pit, local topography, and output required. Output and method should be adjusted to size of deposit, to secure minimum cost of production, including interest and amortization on capital for equipment and removal ("stripping") of waste overburden. STRIPPING may be completed before beginning mining, or mining and stripping may proceed simultaneously, after a sufficient area has been uncovered to avoid interference between the two operations; the latter plan is best, as it reduces the initial investment required before production begins. Stripping may be done in one or more slices, depending on the depth; stripped material must be disposable within a reasonable distance, and at points where dumps will not embarrass subsequent mining. BREAKING GROUND. Open-cut faces are usually worked in benches (for details, see Art 95–101). Hydraulicking (Art 98 and Sec 3) may be used for breaking down unconsolidated material. In general, ground is broken cheaper in open cuts than in stopes, because of the large faces and use of heavy blasts. LOADING is by hand or mechanical excavators, depending on the scale of operations; where glory-holes (Art 99) are feasible, chute-gates are used. TRANSPORT (see Sec 3, 5). An underground haulage system may aid in handling output from an open-pit, material being dropped through chute raises in bottom of open workings.

Classification. An arbitrary grouping of open-cut methods, based on modes of loading, is used in Art 95–99 for presenting details. For small-scale work, with pick and shovel or plow and scraper, see Sec 3. See also under placers, Art 117 *et seq.* For elaborate suggested classification of surface-mining methods, see Bib (181).

95. OPEN-CUT WORK WITH HAND LOADING OF ORE

Field of use: (*a*) in small pits, where total tonnage does not warrant the first cost nor permit efficient use of mechanical excavators (Art 96, 97); (*b*) in large pits, the shape, location, or other features of which (such as erratic mineralization and need for selective mining and sorting) make mechanical loading or glory-hole methods (Art 99) inadvisable; (*c*) in large-scale work, where labor is cheap.

Plans of work. Faces are generally carried in benches (Fig 663, 664), the height of which depends on factors outlined in Sec 5. With several benches, the width of each should be sufficient to provide room for road or tracks, and to catch loose rocks falling from above. Some foreign laws specify minimum width of 10 ft for safety; this is usually exceeded. (See Bib 470.)

Ground is broken as in broken-stone quarries (Sec 5), or in large underhand stopes (Art 27, 28). Holes are usually drilled by hand or by machine drills, since deep churndrill holes and gopher or tunnel blasts (Sec 5) are apt to break large masses, requiring excessive blockholing for hand loading. Ore is shoveled, forked or lifted into cars, trucks, buckets, or stone-skips at the foot of the benches. Transport methods from pit to surface vary with the shape, size, and depth of pit, and topography. Typical practice follows:

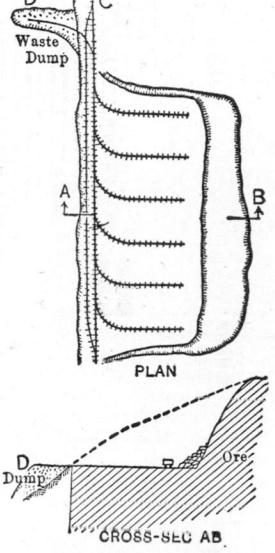

Fig 663. Open-cut on Hillside, Hand-loading

Narrow veins. The outcrops are often mined underhand (Art 35). Ore may be hoisted in buckets on skids on the footwall, or dropped through a winze to a haulage drift (Fig 206). At Cobalt (Art 68) many veins were thus worked to depths of 50 to 100 ft. Stulls support loose slabs of wall rock, as in open stopes (Art 38).

Large orebodies outcropping on hillsides are easily worked by open cuts. Fig 663 shows one method. A long face is advanced as a single bench, ore being shoveled into small cars. The track layout facilitates hand-tramming or horse-haulage of loaded and empty cars, without delays or interference. Track *C* may lead to mill or shipping bins, to loading bins of an aerial tramway, or to a gravity plane for delivering to bins below. Hillside topography usually furnishes nearby locations for waste dumps, as at *D*. The height of face, as in Fig 663, soon exceeds the economic max for breaking ground; chances of injury to workmen from falls of rock also increase rapidly with height of face. Hence the face may be divided into benches, with tracks on each for transport; this involves the problem of collecting the ore from successive benches; inclined wooden chute is a simple means for doing this. Automotive trucks are being used in increasing numbers (with both hand and machine loading); compared with track systems, they have advantage of allowing steep grades and sharp turns, while avoiding cost of laying and shifting track.

Examples. Puertocitos, Cananea, Mex. In 1910 there were 3 benches, each 80 to 100 ft high. Ore was loaded into 0.5-ton cars; the track layout was like that in Fig 663, but with a single fringe-track connecting the loading tracks. Ore from the lowest bench was dumped down a raise to an adit leading to bins at the R R. Ore from the highest bench was dumped down a raise from a tunnel driven into the face at the 2nd bench, which was connected with the R R bins by aerial tramway (282). Arizona Copper Co (Art 62) mined oxidized ores in open cuts. Benches were up to 30 ft high; the faces were kept at max length, to afford numerous points of attack and a steady output. Ore from all benches was dumped through raises to a haulage tunnel driven in connection with underground operations. If ore could not be shoveled direct to raises, it was trammed in 25-cu ft cars. An aver man in 9 hr loaded about 13 cu yd and trammed it 50 ft (178). At Eisenerz and Erzberg, Styria (333, 659), a conical mountain of limestone partly replaced by siderite and ankerite is attacked on 60 benches to a height of 2 326 ft (Fig 664); total length of benches, 16.75 miles in 1936; width, 33–39.5 ft; aver height, 39 ft; 18 benches are combined in pairs for part of their length, for more economical operation of power shovels which are used mainly for moving waste on lower benches. Max annual tonnage (1929) was 5 500 000 tons, of which about 2/3 was waste; approx same ratio since maintained; min shipping grade of 30% Fe requires some hand sorting on belts after crushing and screening. Erratic mineralization and need for close sorting on benches favor hand loading; in 1929, about half of all material was thus loaded. Group of 4–6 men works 130 ft of face, drilling with jackhammers; explosive (ammonite and dynamite), 0.068–0.082 lb per short ton; holes fired singly, with fuse, 5 times a day. Hand-loaded cars are hauled outside by steam locos, or by elec locos through inside connections (one for each bench) to vert raises delivering ore to 3 main haulage levels at different elevations. Underground haulage system (also serving some underground min-

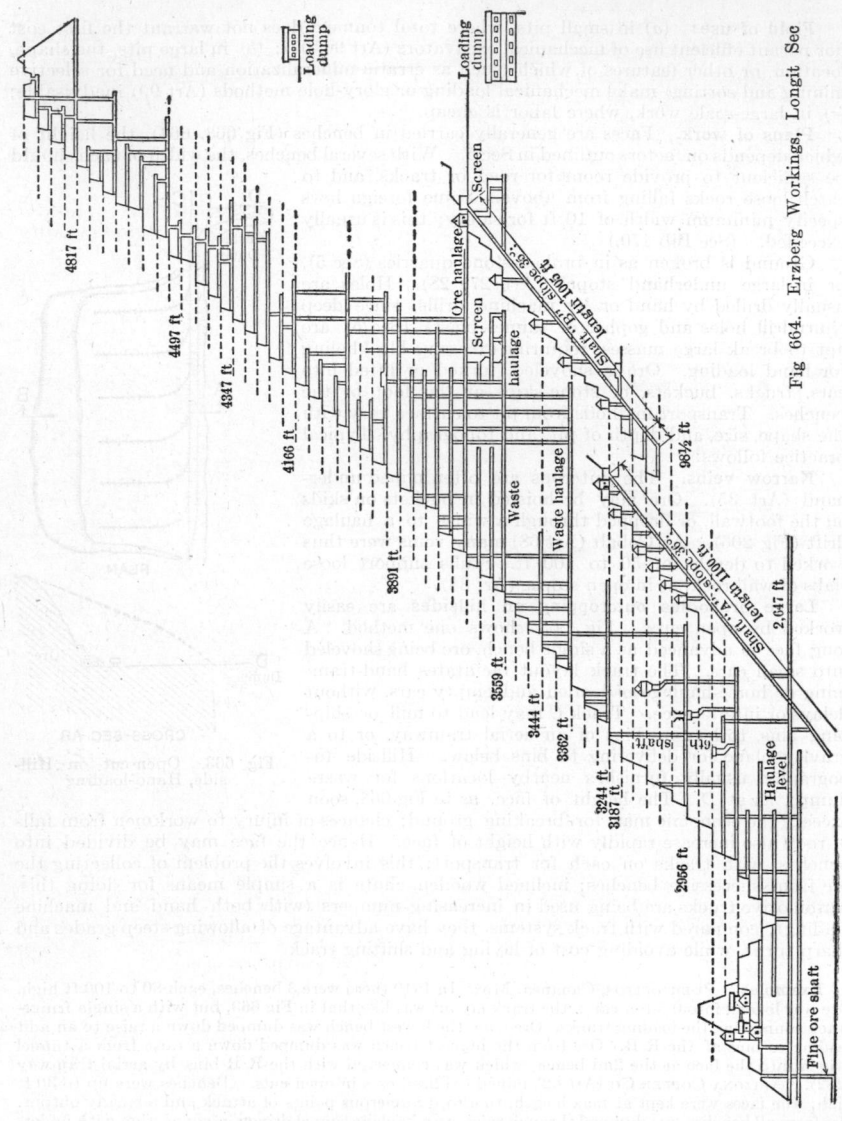

Fig 664. Erzberg Workings, Longit Sec

ing) has 46.6 miles of narrow-gage track. Inclined planes, both inside and out, rack roads for elec locos, and underground belt conveyers, all assist in movement of ore. FRESNILLO MINE, Zacatecas, Mex. Data from D. B. McAllister in 1921 and T. C. Baker in 1923 (640). Orebody is a stockwork in graywacke; area 1 200 by 400 ft; estimated content, 5–6 million tons, assaying 5.25 oz Ag and 20¢ in Au. Surface quarrying by hand work was carried on intermittently from 1910 to 1920. Benches, 20 ft high; holes, 20 ft deep, 6–10 ft apart and 6–10 ft from face of bench; first 5 ft of a hole were drilled double-hand, the rest with jumpers. Holes were sprung, then loaded with split charges of 40% dynamite. Ore was blockholed or sledged to 8-in size on quarry floor, loaded into 26-cu ft cars, each trammed by 2 men to mill bins. Monthly tonnage, 15 800; tons per man-shift breaking, 5.5; tons per man-shift for all operations, 2.39. Explosives per ton: 0.122 lb; 0.091 cap; 0.333 ft fuse. Orebody was later mined by a glory-hole method (Art 99). BLUE DIAMOND GYPSUM deposit, Arden Nev. Data from W. G. Bradley (193) in 1932. The outcrop of a horiz bed of gypsum 16 ft thick is quarried on hillside until overburden (removed by gasolene shovel and scraper) reaches same depth; deeper parts are mined with rooms and pillars (Art 34). Space 20 ft wide by 100 ft long (to yield about 2 300 tons) having been cleaned, vert holes 15–16 ft deep are drilled by jackhammer at rate of 10 holes per 8 hr. Spacing of holes is half the depth of face. Holes are sprung first with 5 8-in sticks of 30% gelatin dynamite, again with 8 or 9 sticks; after cooling for 24 hr, holes are loaded with 25–30 lb of black powder in the chambers and 10–20 sticks of Hercomite No 6 above; chamber is primed with 1 stick of 30% gelatin dynamite. Up to 25 holes are fired at a time by elec. This method entails considerable blockholing of lumps over 3 ft diam. Explosives per ton, 0.25 lb for primary and 0.13 lb for secondary blasting. Tons broken per ft of hole, 3.68. Track is parallel with and 10–16 ft from working face, with sidings for 10 cars, of 2.5-ton capac; all haulage by 4-ton Plymouth gasolene loco, pulling 7 cars 1 000 ft to crusher. Duty of labor in hand loading, 20 tons per man-shift.

Deep pits of small area require hoisting apparatus. ENGINE PLANES (Sec 11) may be built on one wall of the pit. Cars serve for dips less than 30°; above that, skips are better. SHAFTS may be sunk near the pit and connected with it by crosscuts. Fig 665 shows early work of this kind at Creighton mine, Sudbury, Ontario. The shaft dipped 60° and had 2 skipways. Double-track crosscuts were run to the orebody at the 60- and 160-ft levels, with raises between levels and to the surface. The pit was started as a glory-hole (Art 99); on reaching a level, the pit bottom was kept flat, and radiating tracks were laid from the crosscut tracks. Blasted ore fell to the pit floor, where it was loaded into 1.5-ton cars. In 1908, this pit was about 350 ft diam by 160 ft deep (354). CABLEWAYS AND DER-

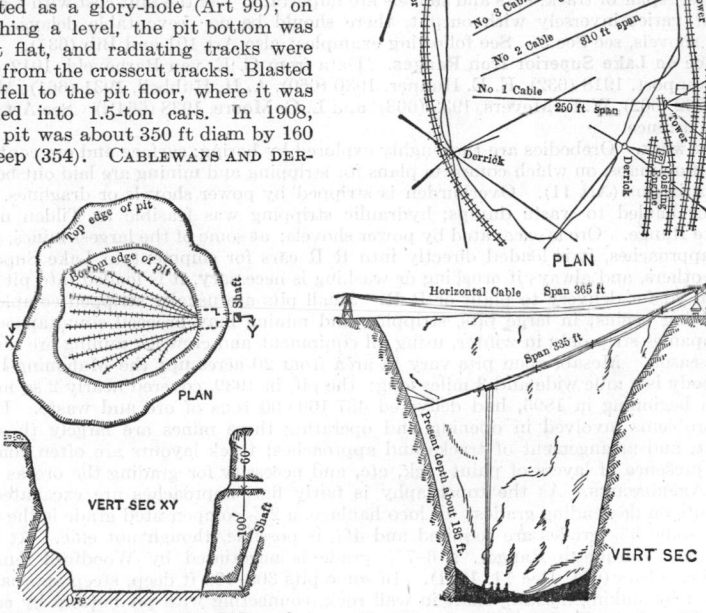

Fig 665. Open-cut, Creighton Mine, Ont   Fig 666.   Open Pit, Tilly Foster Iron Mine, N Y

RICKS allow extraction of ore from deep pits without preliminary underground development. Fig 666 shows their application in an open cut 450 ft long, 300 ft wide and over 200 ft deep (Art 42). Ore or waste was loaded by hand on the pit floor into 1.1-cu yd stone-skips, which were picked up by cableways or long-boom derricks and placed on trucks on surface tracks near rim of pit (353).

Large-scale work, cheap labor. PREMIER DIAMOND MINE, Transvaal, So Africa (332). A kimberlite "pipe" (Art 88), about 0.5 mile long by 0.33 mile wide, was mined in 50-ft benches. The faces were kept steep, and were broken in steps by vert holes drilled with jumper drills. The material was shoveled into 20-cu ft cars at the foot of the benches. Tracks were in loops 200 to 300 ft long, paralleling the faces and connecting with main haulage tracks. The layout in Fig 663 was impracticable, because of enormous tonnage and length of benches necessary to produce it. Endless-rope haulage (Sec 11) was used on main tracks, and on inclines to surface. In 1912, 11 000 natives were employed in the pit, in 2 11.5-hr shifts; 2 100 per shift were drilling on the main benches, 700 in development cuts for opening lower benches, 600 blockholing and spalling, and over 1 300 on tramming. Monthly output, 1 000 000 16-cu ft loads of "blue ground" and 87 000 loads of waste. Aver cost of mining and haulage was slightly less than 30¢ per load, including waste. The pit in 1912 was 200 ft deep. Underground methods (Art 88) are now used.

96. OPEN-CUT MINING WITH POWER SHOVELS

Field of use: (a) removing shallow overburden from coal, iron ore, phosphates, etc, which are then mined by other open-cut methods; (b) stripping and mining deposits of large area and tonnage, which are fairly uniform in character and lie near the surface, and may or may not be covered by overburden.

General. Power-shovel methods involve large capital outlay, for equipment and preliminary stripping; hence they are limited to work in deposits large enough to return this outlay plus interest during life of mine; properly applied, they yield enormous outputs at low unit costs.

The general features of power-shovel mining appear simple; but good management, close attention to details and systematic work are essential. Shape and position of orebody must be predetermined, to allow intelligent planning of approaches and track layouts, for minimizing delays and handling max amount of material by the shovels; maintenance and repair of track, cars and shovels are important. As the unit cost with a given equipment varies inversely with output, there should be no preventable delays. For details of shovels, see Sec 3. See following examples; also Art 101 and Bib (631).

Practice on Lake Superior Iron Ranges. Data from C. E. van Barneveld, 1912 (35), L. D. Davenport, 1918 (632), E. E. Hunner, 1930 (660), A. H. Hubbell, 1931 (661), M. H. Barber, 1932 (662), W. R. Meyers, 1932 (663), and L. C. Moore, 1938 (664).)   See Art 10-b for ore occurrence.

Plan of work. Orebodies are thoroughly explored by boring; surface and ore contours are platted on maps, on which complete plans for stripping and mining are laid out before excavation begins (Art 11). Overburden is stripped by power shovels or draglines, and dragged or hauled to waste dumps; hydraulic stripping was feasible at Tilden mine, Marquette Range. Ore is excavated by power shovels; at some of the largest mines, with suitable approaches, it is loaded directly into R R cars for shipment to Lake Superior ports; at others, and always if crushing or washing is necessary, it is loaded into pit cars of 4–30 cu yd for delivery to plant or R R. Small pits are usually stripped completely before mining begins; in large pits, stripping and mining may proceed simultaneously; some companies strip only in winter, using all equipment and crew for mining ore during shipping season. Mesabi open pits vary in area from 20 acres up; the Mahoning-Hull-Rust orebody is a mile wide and 3 miles long; the pit, in 1939, covered nearly 2 sq miles, and, from beginning in 1895, had delivered 487 100 000 tons of ore and waste. Engineering problems involved in opening and operating these mines are largely those of equipment, and arrangement of tracks and approaches; track layouts are often complicated by presence of layers of paint rock, etc, and necessity for grading the ore as it is loaded. APPROACHES. As the topography is fairly flat, approaches are excavated as through cuts on descending grades; for loco haulage, a 2% compensated grade is the max desirable; some 3% grades are required and 4% is possible, though not effic. At Volunteer mine (Marquette Range), a 6–7% grade is negotiated by Woodford remote-controlled elec cars (661, Dec 14, 1931). In some pits 300–400 ft deep, steep approaches are avoided by sinking hoisting shaft in wall rock, connecting with pit bottom by crosscuts, which may also serve for drainage. Belt conveyers in inclined shafts serve similar purpose at some deep open-pits. Motor trucks (Sec 27) can climb 10% grades with 20-ton loads. Sometimes separate approaches are cut for stripping and mining; for stripping, they are located to minimize the haul to waste dumps; for mining, there must be a track or road system which will reach the max amount of ore without unduly steep grades.

Stripping faces usually have a 1 : 1 slope (Art 113) with a 20-ft berm at bottom of bank. In deep overburden, the banks are broken at least every 75 ft vertically with a 25–30 ft berm. Stripping is so arranged that shovels work against a 25–35-ft bank. Stripping is done with side cuts just as wide areas are graded in R R work. Regular stripping stops 6–8 ft above the orebody; remaining cover is removed by a smaller "clean-up" shovel, with a crew of 6–8 laborers. As the top surface of orebodies is uneven, final cleaning is done by scrapers; small revolving shovels have also proved useful. Overburden is mostly glacial drift, containing boulders 2–12 ft diam; large boulders are "chained out" when uncovered, and blockholed. Overburden is often loosened ahead of the shovel by blasting. STRIPPING EQUIPMENT varies widely; much stripping is done by contractors who furnish plant. Common equipment includes a revolving, caterpillar power shovel, with 8–10-cu yd dipper; reach, to 95 ft; lift, to 56 ft. Such a shovel often has interchangeable dragline boom 100–150 ft long, using 4–6-cu yd scraper (Sec 27). R R type of shovel is nearly obsolete, and steam is rapidly giving way to elec power, both for shovels and haulage. Small shovels, 1.5–3 cu yd, for cleaning and other shallow work, are sometimes driven by gasolene or gas-elec power. Chief advantage of long-reach shovel for stripping is that it can make a through cut in one operation, loading cars on the surface, which would require several successive cuts with accompanying track work, if dug with smaller shovels. STRIPPING DUMPS are located on barren ground, or where open cuts are impossible. A low area, sloping away from initial dumping point and offering a downhill haul, is ideal. Dumps are started by dumping alternate cars on opposite sides of the track, and gradually jacking up the track until the dump reaches required height. After this, the dump is "fanned out" by moving the track sidewise. Usually, dumps are started from trestles, 20–25 ft high and strong enough for the empty, but not the loaded, train. Desirable lengths of dumps are 1 200–1 400 ft; heights, 20–40 ft, preferably the latter; 60-ft dumps are excessive, as the tracks settle badly. Straight dumps are best; curved tracks are hard to shift. The muskeg swamps of Mesabi Range are unsatisfactory locations for dumps; dumps settle, and the muskeg bulges on each side; but swamps may be employed with advantage in winter.

Mining ore. Amount of loosening required varies widely with compactness of ore. Former practice of chambering small holes, drilled by wagon-mounted drifters and finished at 1-in diam at about 26-ft depth, entailed excessive blockholing besides so loosening adjoining ore that subsequent blasts lost some effectiveness. Present practice on Mesabi adopts 6-in holes, churn-drilled to about 40 ft, or 5 or 6 ft below bottom of bench, loaded to half-depth with 60 and 80% Gelamite, and fired (as many as 100 at a time) with Cordeau; smaller blasts may be fired electrically. In harder ores of Marquette Range, 6-in holes are churn-drilled to depths up to 110 ft (aver 45 ft at Volunteer and 68 ft at Tilden mine), spaced about 15 ft in a row 13–20 ft back of face. Usual explosive is 40, 60, or 80% gelatin or Gelamite, column loaded. Volunteer mine fired 535 holes in 1 blast, breaking 630 000 tons; Tilden mine, with 2 blasts in 1930, broke 450 000 tons with 129 550 lb of 60% and 80% explosive in 225 holes; 24.3 tons per ft of hole, or 3.48 tons per lb of explosive. Faces of benches in ore are sloped 0.5 : 1 on the Mesabi, or down to 1 : 1 on the Gogebic and Cuyuna Ranges (Art 113). A 1 : 1 slope is allowed on faces carrying a series of tracks and switchbacks. Ore is mined in side cuts; benches, 25–30 ft high on the Mesabi, or higher in the harder ores of Marquette Range. Popular shovel is elec operated, full-revolving, caterpillar-mounted, with 2–5-cu yd dipper (Sec 27); its maintenance costs about 25% that of a steam shovel.

Track haulage. As example of steam haulage, the Hull-Rust-Mahoning pit uses 120-ton locos for trains of 12 30-cu yd cars up 1.5% grade, returning empties on grades not exceeding 5%. At pits where R R cars are inadmissible, side-dump pit cars of 20–30-cu yd capac are common. Recent tendency has been towards elec haulage, with 60–75-ton trolley locos. A 60-ton loco, with 600 hp in 4 d-c, 600-v motors, exerts a starting pull of 30 000 lb, and can haul a gross load (including loco) of 340 tons up a straight 3% grade at 7.5 miles per hr (see Sec 11). A 75-ton elec loco hauls 6 loaded 75-ton cars up 2% grade at 10 miles per hr, while a steam loco of same wt can haul only 5 such cars, on same grade, at 8 miles per hr. L. C. Moore, basing his computation on a typical Western Mesabi wash-ore pit yielding 700 000 long tons of concentrate from 1 050 000 long tons of crude ore, and moving 500 000 cu yd of stripping per season, estimates a saving of 6.58¢ per ton of concentrate in favor of elec over steam haulage, including fixed charges in both cases. Haul involves a rise of 260 ft in a run of 4.4 miles, with trains of 4 30-cu yd (55-long ton) cars. For details, see Bib (664). "DIFFERENTIAL" SYSTEM has been adopted by Susquehanna, Wakefield, and Richmond pits; at Susquehanna, a train of 6 4.5-yd (8-ton) cars is hauled through a tunnel on −0.5% grade to shaft by a 190-hp motor-car carrying same load of ore; such a train weighs less by 10% when loaded and by 18% when empty than a 7-car train hauled by elec loco (660). The empty motor-car has enough tractive force to pull an empty train, while its 8-ton load adds enough tractive force to draw the loaded train. TRACKS AND LAYOUTS. 80–90-lb rail, well graded and ballasted, is used on large-scale work. Temporary tracks are lighter and laid with less care. Grades of main tracks should be below 2% or at most 3%; short stretches of 5% grade may be unavoidable. Special tracks on 5–6% grades are sometimes laid for short-cuts for quick return of empties to pit. 7.5° curves are the max desirable, and 15° the max allowable, but 50° curves are required and operated successfully in some cases. Fig 667, 668 show general layouts; they are variously modified. Switchbacks are also used ¡to connect benches in small pits or in deeper parts of large pits. The SPIRAL SYSTEM (Fig 667) is ideal. It permits easy grades, curves, and turnouts, and requires few switchbacks, but is limited to large pits of regular outline.

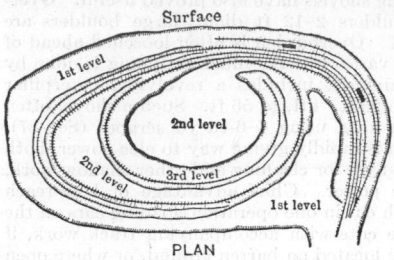

Fig 667. Spiral Track Layout, Mesabi Range

Truck and tractor haulage (Sec 27) was adopted experimentally on the Mesabi about 1936 (664, 665) and quite widely in 1937–8 among smaller and deeper mines on Mesabi and Cuyuna Ranges. Side- or end-dumping trucks to 15- and 20-ton capac, and tractor-drawn, crawler-mounted, side- or bottom-dump wagons to 15- and 18-ton capac are used.

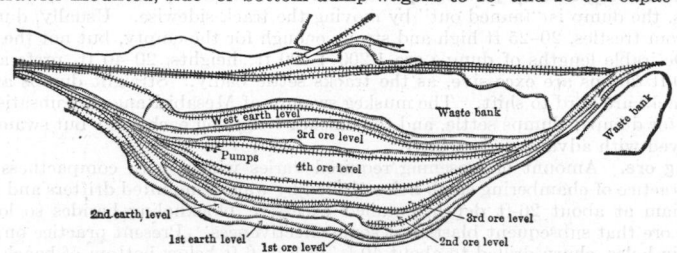

Fig 668.   Track Layout, Mountain Iron Mine, Mesabi Range

The larger trucks, with 125- to 150-hp Diesel engines, come out of pits on (max) 10% grade at 5 miles per hr and return down 14%–20% at high but safe speed. Trucks are used also for dumping into raises on pit floor, but their chief advantage over the slower tractor-wagon is seen on hauls of 800–1 000 ft or more (665, 667). R. W. Whitney and G. J. Holt (667) offer following data ¡in 1939, based on 2 years' experience with 15-ton trucks on Cuyuna and Mesabi Ranges, hauling from pit bottom to surface dump; 6-wheel type, with dual rear wheels, is preferred to the 10-wheel (with 2 sets of dual rear wheels) because: (*a*) can turn sharper curves (20-ft rad); (*b*) more economical of tires; (*c*) saves time for servicing (0.5 hr against 1 hr); (*d*) lower maintenance. Diesel engines consume less fuel than gasolene; under 3 gal of fuel oil per hr against 5.75 gal of gasolene; over-speeding of Diesel engines is checked by recording tachometers. Life of closely inspected tires is approx 4 000 hr.

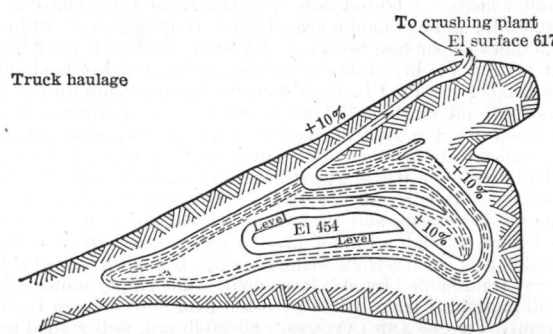

Fig 669.   Two Haulage Systems, Louise Pit, Cuyuna Range

equivalent to 16 000–20 000 miles on a highway. Life of truck estimated at 10 000 hr. In ore, two 4-yd dippers make a load of 15.4–18.2 (aver, 15.7) long tons; on stripping, sideboards are added, and load is then 3 dippers. Road grades of 8–10% are feasible for loads, and on return 20% is permissible. In Louise pit (Fig 669) 214 ft deep, 3 185 ft of road at 10% replaced 8 500 ft of R R at 2.6% grade, and 3 trucks displaced 2 locos serving same shovel. Truck speeds with loads are (miles per hr): level, 10; up 5%, 8; up 7%, 6; up 10%, 5. For other data, see Table 66. At another Mesabi pit, stripping during mid-winter at a partly frozen bank, largely of clay and 20–25 ft high, loading with 4-yd shovel, 15-ton trucks hauled 1 mile over nearly level road on snow, making round trip in 6.7 min; loading, 1.4 min; delays, 1.2 min.

Table 66. Data on Truck Haulage out of Lake Superior Iron-ore Pits (667)

	Cuyuna	Mesabi	Mesabi
Total haul for loads, ft.........	3 185	4 200– 4 600	1 925
of which, up 7.5–10% grade...	2 135	1 800	1 200
Return road, total length, ft....	same road	1 600– 1 800	1 075
of which, down 19–20% grade.......		800	450
Vert lift, ft...............	214	155	100
No of 15-ton trucks in service...	3	8	6
Dipper of loading shovel, cu yd..	1.75	4	4
Digging conditions...............		var	good
Aver time cycle, min:			
Truck waiting at shovel......		0.8	0.3
Interval between trucks......		(b)0.3	(b)0.3
Loading....................	(a)3.0	0.9	0.9
Travel, shovel to dump........	8.0	4.4	3.6
Dumping...................	1.0	0.8	0.8
Return travel...............	2.5	1.5	1.2
Delay at shovel or dump.....		0.9	
Total time per truck.....	14.5	9.6	7.1

(a) Incl delays. (b) Not counted a delay, since shovel was picking up a load during this interval.

Belt conveyers (Sec 27), receiving ore directly from shovels or through pocket or chute with regulating pan conveyer at bottom, have recently been installed at several Mesabi mines, notably La Rue, Canisteo, St Paul, and Spruce. At St Paul, the 30-in conveyer is 854 ft long, in 3 equal sections, on 19° incline; max capac, 300 tons per hr at 350 ft per min; it is fed through a 1 500-ton pocket with gate 40 ft below present pit bottom; pocket is centrally situated in ore, so that aver haul for tractor-wagons is 600 ft (max, 1 200 ft). Spruce mine, in 1937, installed a 30-in conveyer in 9 zig-zagging sections, totaling 4 481 ft and rising by non-uniform grades (max 25.6%) 386 ft from its lowest point to top of R R loading bin. Aver capac at 500 ft per min, 500 tons per hr. It is fed with crushed ore through 10 by 10-ft raises at 3 points in pit bottom, 2 supplied with ore by tower excavators with 600-ft radii, and 1 by a 2.25-yd shovel and four 20-ton trucks. For details at Spruce mine, see Bib (664, 665, 666).

Drainage. Many Lake Superior pits make from 0.5–1.5 million gal of water per day. As the topography usually prevents opening self-draining pits, drifts are run under the pit to collect water and lead it to a shaft near the pit edge, whence it is pumped to surface. For economic limit of stripping depth, see Art 101.

Nevada Consol Copper Co, Ruth, Nev. Following data are contributed by courtesy of D. C. Jackling and W. F. Boyd in 1938. Copper Flat orebody was originally a fairly flat, massive deposit of monzonite porphyry containing disseminated chalcocite and chalcopyrite and having a leached capping aver 110 ft thick (307). Ore averaged 500 ft thick. Mining has always been done with power shovels on benches 50–100 ft wide, and at approx 50-ft vert intervals. Tracks on each bench form a closed loop with a spiral approach; favorable for handling trains (Fig 670). Grades of main approaches are 2.5% max; loading tracks, level. Slopes between benches are 45°–80° from horiz, depending on character of rock. On reaching final pit limits, benches are consolidated 3 into 1, making final slope of banks 45° in hard, and 40° in soft, material. Both ore and waste require blasting; 9-in holes are drilled with Bucyrus-Armstrong, 29-T, elec churn-drills (5 in service) to 10 ft below the next lower level. Holes are 18–21 ft apart and usually placed 10 ft from edge; this puts 35–40 ft of burden on hole at the toe; they are sprung with 40% stick powder. Wet holes are loaded with stick and dry holes with 70% bag powder. Over 5 tons broken per lb powder. Equipment comprises 5 Bucyrus-Erie, 120-B, full-revolving elec shovels with 4-yd dippers, and one Marion elec, with 1.5-yd dipper. Motive power for haulage is 4 saddle-tank and 12 side-tank, 80-ton, 0–3–1 steam locos.

Table 67. Operating Data, Nevada Consol Copper Co, Ruth, Nev

	1936	1937	1938
Tons per shovel-shift (ore and waste) .	5 030	4 513	4 661
Tons per loco-shift (" " ") .	1 443	1 284	1 718
Feet of hole per drill-shift............	73.72	75.54	68.62
Tons broken per lb of explosive.......	5.73	5.39	6.05

Waste is handled in 20-, 25-, and 30-cu yd side-dump cars, and ore in 70- and 80-ton cars, dumped in a tipple at the mill. Other equipment: Jordan spreader, caterpillar bull-dozers, trackshifters, service cars. Rail on the main lines is 90-lb and that on the loading and dump tracks is 75-lb. (See Table 67).

Chino mine, Nevada Consol Copper Co, Santa Rita, N M. Data from H. A. Thorne (63) in 1931, revised 1939 by Co officials. Orebody is a disseminated chalcocite, in porphyry and adjoining silicified sedimentary rocks; most ore is hard and tough and breaks large, involving much blockholing. Ore ranges 0.70–2.00% Cu; grade of reserves estimated

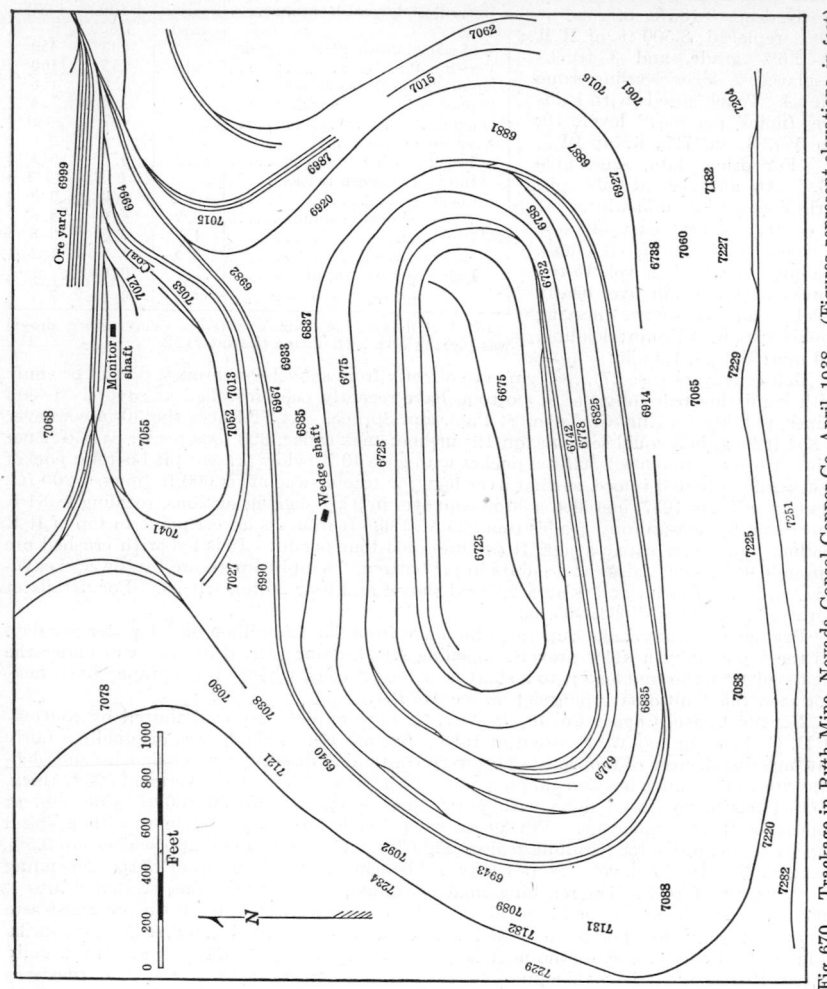

Fig 670. Trackage in Ruth Mine, Nevada Consol Copper Co, April, 1938. (Figures represent elevations, in feet)

(1938) at 1.17% Cu. Leached capping is 0–150 ft thick; orebody is irregular, both top and bottom, up to 600 ft thick. Pit (Fig 671) is elliptical, 5 000 by 4 000 ft, with large mass of unprofitable rock near its center, on which principal mine plant is situated. Topography is favorable for easy disposal of stripping, but a stream had to be diverted and confined in concreted flume 7 500 ft long, around N edge of pit. Parts of orebody were extensively developed by old workings; remainder tested by churn-drills (Art 10-b) to aver 900-ft depth. Shovel benches 42 ft high have proved most economical; face of a bench will stand nearly vert for years, and a 25-ft berm assures safety from casual falls; aver slope, top to bottom of pit, 45°. BREAKING GROUND. Vert top holes and inclined toe holes are used. Former are spaced 18–25 ft in a row approx 10 ft from crest, and drilled 5–10 ft below bench grade, for breaking to bottom, or 30 ft deep for trimming face; these 6-in holes are drilled by elec, self-propelling churn-drill rigs. The 6-in tools are to be replaced by 9-in. In Aug, 1938, 12 such rigs drilled 10 459 ft of hole in 1 108 machine-hr (9.44 ft per hr, incl 9.2% delays). Toe holes, 22 ft deep, inclined about 30° to reach 5 ft below grade, and spaced 15 ft apart, are drilled by heavy air-hammers, starting at 3.75 and finishing at 1.375-in diam. Aver speed in toe holes, 5.8 ft per hr, total time. All holes are sprung at least once, using 40% gelatin, with water for stemming. Blasting charge in vert holes is 35% and 50% bulk powder, if dry; gelatin, if wet, stemmed with screened

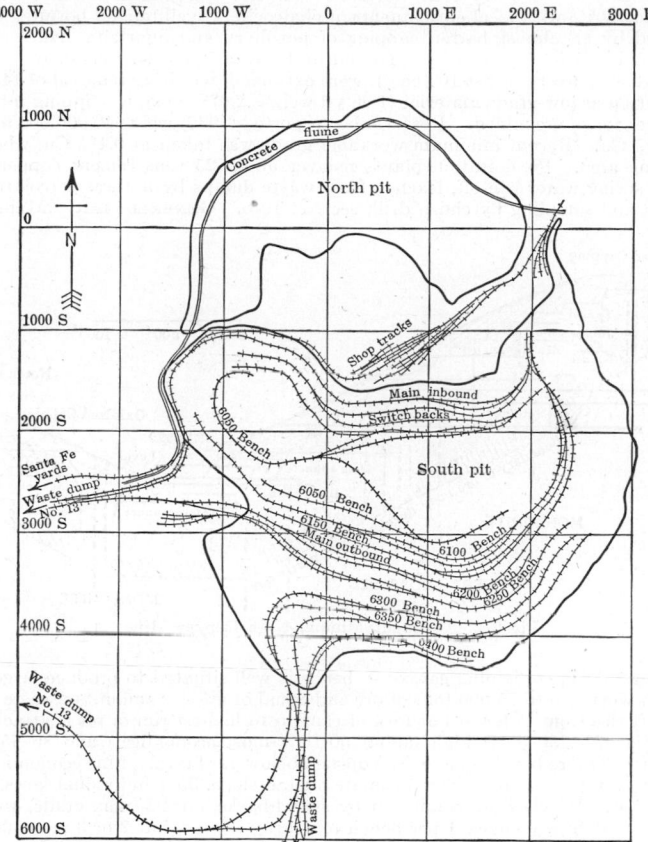

Fig 671. Pit Outline and Track Layout, Chino Mine, Santa Rita, N M, as of Jan, 1939

dirt. Charge in toe holes, 40% or 60% ammonia dynamite if dry, gelatin if wet, unstemmed. Blasts are fired with Primacord wherever possible; otherwise by elec detonators, not over 10 holes at a time. Powder for secondary blasting, for 9 mos in 1938, averaged 5% of total consumption. Including secondary blasting, aver for entire pit is 6.43 tons of material broken per lb explosive. LOADING. Equipment includes 8 R R-type elec shovels on caterpillars, with 4-yd dippers; 2 full-revolving elec shovels on caterpillars, with 4.97-yd dippers; and 1 truck-mounted elec shovel, with 8-yd dipper and 80-ft boom, which can make a through cut 80 ft wide at bottom and load into cars on track 42 ft above it. Power consumption by the 4-yd shovels is 0.76 kw-hr; by the 4.97-yd shovels, 0.72 kw-hr; and by the 8-yd shovel, 1.41 kw-hr, per cu yd loaded. Crew on 8-yd shovel consists of 4 men; on the others, 2 men. HAULAGE. In 1938, Chino mine had 26.7 miles of std-gage trackage, plan of which is shown in Fig 671. All main lines are 85-lb rail; bench tracks, 85- and 75-lb; latter is being replaced with 85-lb. Dump tracks, 75-lb rail, are also to be replaced with 85-lb. Aver haul for both ore and waste is 2.23 miles. Curvature of tracks is kept under 20°, and grades do not exceed 2.5%, compensated. Motive power includes 11 American, 6-wheel, 90-ton; 6 Baldwin, 6-wheel, 85-ton; and one 4-wheel Porter, 42.5-ton, locos; the latter for switching only. Air-dump, 20- and 30-cu yd, cars are used. Trains of 200 cu yd are hauled on level or down grade; 140-cu yd trains on adverse grades.

    Utah Copper mine (Kennecott Copper Corp), Bingham, Utah. Data from A. Soderberg (119) in 1930, revised in 1938 by Co officials. Orebody, a trough-shaped mass of monzonite porphyry about 6 000 ft long, 4 000 ft (max) wide, 2 000 ft (max) deep, contained originally 800 000 000 tons workable ore, carrying disseminated Cu sulphides, chiefly chalcopyrite with local enrichments of chalcocite, covellite, and bornite. Orebody is blanketed by an almost barren capping of porphyry and quartzite, averaging 115 ft thick, but only 20–50 ft in places. To end of 1937, 265 706 395 tons of ore, averaging 1.13% Cu (0.98% aver for last 10 years), were extracted, requiring removal of 145 604 780 cu yd of barren or low-grade material (1 cu yd weighs 2.077 tons), a stripping ratio of 1.14 ton waste per ton of ore mined. Reserves last reported (1930) were 640 000 000 tons, averaging 1.07% Cu. Recent minimum workable grade was taken at 0.4% Cu, when within the stripping area. Precipitation plants recover about 25 tons cement copper per day during the spring water run-off, leached from waste dumps by natural percolation. For prospecting and sampling by churn drill, see Art 10-b. GENERAL PLAN. Main orebody

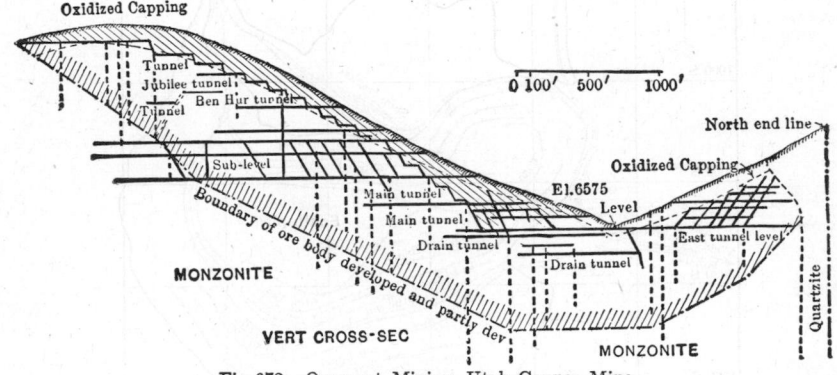

Fig 672. Open-cut Mining, Utah Copper Mine

lies between 2 deep, conjoining canyons; hence is well situated to produce large tonnage by open-pit work (up to 75 000 tons of ore and equal or greater amount of waste per day). The 1 500-ft rise from R R yard at fork of canyon to highest rim of pit is attacked on 23 benches (Fig 672), 50–80 ft high (about 50 ft is most economical) and 30–450 ft wide (aver, 100 ft); 3 more benches have been opened below yard level. Max economical overall working slope, top to bottom, 28°; ultimate overall slope, 35°; individual faces, variable, but about 50°. Benches are connected by switchbacks, on 4% max grade, with extensions to waste dumps (usually 1 per bench to nearby dumps, but 2 or 3 are combined for the longer hauls) in canyons outside of orebody. In 1937, there were about 85 miles of std-gage track; rail distance, yard to remotest shovel, about 7 miles; aver haul, 2.6 miles. Trains of 10–14 cars, 80–90 tons per car, are collected at yard and hauled thence in 50-car trains, by steam locos, 18 miles to concentrators. Waste cars, holding 30 cu yd, are in 4 to 9-car trains. BREAKING GROUND. Early practice of heavy blasting with coyote holes proved destructive of benches. Fig 673 shows present method. Holes averaging 22 ft deep are drilled by reciprocating drills; hammer drills are unsuitable, because continuous water supply can not be distributed in winter. Driller and 2 helpers average 45 ft of hole per shift, besides blasting and trimming; 1 set of steel makes 4–5 holes before losing gage. Toe holes, spaced 15 ft, start 3–5 ft above floor, and pitch 5°–15° downward to bottom on grade; mid-face holes (not always required) are horiz but pointed backward towards advancing shovel; vert top-holes are rarely needed in higher benches. Progress requires 2 drill crews per shovel. Toe holes are sprung, usually 4 times, with 7, 15, 30, and 50 sticks, stemmed with water. Final charge is 150–250 lb of low-freezing ammonium nitrate powder, 60% Ngl for dry holes, and semi-plastic for wet holes, fired by fuse in such sequence (usually 18 per round) that each shot is partly blanketed by its predecessor, to reduce throwing. Breakage beyond 21-ft reach of shovel is avoided, to save delay in setting up for next row of toe holes. Mid-face holes are drilled from top of pile produced by toe-hole blast, but are not fired, and then only 1 or 2 at a time, until shovel has made space for their broken ore to fall. Top holes, if needed, are fired after shovel has passed by. Some bulldozing and blockholing is necessary. Powder consumption averages 1/8 lb per ton broken, of which 16% is for chambering, 69% for main blasts, 15% for secondary blasting, mainly trimming. Drilling averages 0.022 ft per ton broken. Tests proved that vert holes were less effic, more costly, and left hard digging at toe of bank. LOADING. In 1937, mine had 22 elec, caterpillar shovels, with 4.5-yd dippers and 30 ft booms swinging 190°; also 7 full-revolving elec shovels, with 5-yd dippers. All types work about 25% faster in ore than in waste (longer trains of larger cars), overall aver being 4 136 tons per shovel-shift. Aver per shovel-shift (Oct, 1938) was 6 000 tons in ore and 4 600 tons in

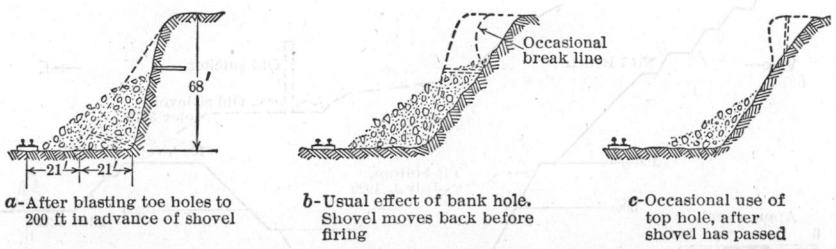

| a-After blasting toe holes to 200 ft in advance of shovel | b-Usual effect of bank hole. Shovel moves back before firing | c-Occasional use of top hole, after shovel has passed |

Fig 673. Blasting at Utah Copper Mine

waste. Loading averages for full-revolving shovels are about 15% higher than for the others. Power at 5 500 volts for shovels is carried on benches by portable 25-ft steel towers, which also support trolley wire. HAULAGE. At end of 1937, 75 miles of pit track had been electrified for 75-ton trolley locos (ballasted to 85 tons), of which 2 serve each shovel; each hauls 12 empty cars (252 tons plus its own wt) up 4% grade at 12 miles per hr. A few combination trolley and storage-battery locos have been used. The others carry a reel with 2 000 ft of cable for use beyond electrified track; recent purchases are without reels. Loading an ore train takes 1.25–1.5 hr; round trip from yard to most remote shovel, about 1.25 hr. PERFORMANCE DATA (see Table 68).

Table 68. Performance Data, Utah Copper Mine, 1937

Tons ore mined.........../..........	23 134 450	Electric power consumption per ton material (ore and waste) removed, kw-hr per ton:	
Tons waste removed...............	28 292 292		
Total tons material moved.........	51 426 742		
Stripping ratio—waste to ore.......	1.22	Electric shovels.................	0.2018
Aver daily tonnage, all material......	143 650	Electric locomotives.............	.3958
Tons removed per lb explosive.......	9.20*	Compressors....................	.1686
Tons moved per man-shift..........	84.07	Shops..........................	.0111
Aver tons (dry) loaded per shovel-shift:		Misc...........................	.0109
		Total..................	0.7882
Ore............................	4 910	Aver ore haul, miles.............	2.58
Waste..........................	3 664	Aver waste haul, miles...........	1.44
Aver (weighted)................	4 136	Ton-miles per kw-hr.............	4.80

* High, due to removal of fill material.

United Verde mine, Jerome, Ariz.

Data from E. M. J. Alenius in 1930 (544, 656), with additions by J. R. Bloom in 1939. For description of orebody, see Art 62. Open-cut mining was adopted to recover ore in upper levels, mining of which by underground methods was interrupted in earlier years by mine fires, which spread to the sulphide orebody itself and prevented further underground work in this area. Major problems in open-cut mining involved: (1) stripping about 11 000 000 cu yd of waste, chiefly hard, blocky diorite; (2) mining extremely hot sulphide ground; (3) maintaining high degree of selectivity in mining and handling smelting ore, concentrating ore, converter flux, and waste; (4) operating in a deep pit of relatively small diam. Fig 674 shows the geol conditions and relationship between orebody and stripping requirements. Original plan proposed mining by glory-hole after completing major stripping; decision to use small elec shovels and automobile trucks came after stripping proved need for selective mining.

Stripping. Method and equipment used above 160-level were distinct from those below that level. Major stripping consisted of carrying back, at a proper slope, a face of diorite about 600 ft high. For this, steam shovels, steam locos, standard-gage track, 25-cu yd air-dump cars, and complementary equipment were used. Waste disposal and access to benches involved construction of more than 5 miles of switch-back R R line; waste was mostly placed

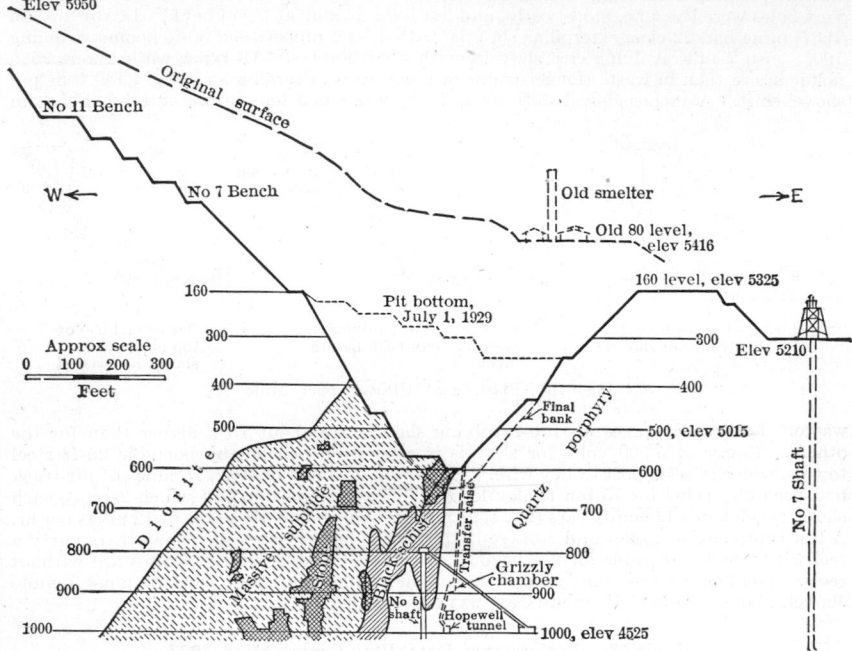

Fig 674. Typical Section of United Verde Pit, Jerome, Ariz, as of Jan 1, 1939 (looking north)

in nearby gulches. TRACKS, semi-permanent, were of 90-lb rail; bench tracks and upper switch-backs, 75-lb rail; 60-lb rail on dumps. Loaded cars usually moved to dumps on a max down grade of 3%; where material had to be moved upgrade, the grade was reduced to 2%. All curves were tapered and grade was compensated. Table 69 lists the HEAVY EQUIPMENT. The 8-cu yd, full-revolving shovel operated entirely on the 160-level, against a bank which, during the major stripping, varied in height from 110–315 ft. It was mounted on traction wheels running on 130-lb rail. The 4-cu yd, R R-type shovels excavated the upper benches, generally 50 ft high; originally operating on rails, they

Table 69. Heavy Equipment for First Major Stripping, United Verde Mine, Jerome, Ariz

No	Item	Type	Wt, size, or capac
1	Steam shovel	Full-revolving	8-cu yd dipper
2	" "	Standard	4- " " "
1	" "	Full-revolving	0.75- " " "
5	Steam locos	Switch	82.5 tons
2	" "	"	53.5 "
30	Cars	Air-dump	25-cu yd
1	Spreader	....	14-ft spread
1	Locomotive crane	....	100 tons
2	Track shifters	Peterson	
6	Gondolas	F B composite	50-ton
6	Flat cars	....	50-ton
1	Tank car	....	50-ton, 10 000 gal

were later equipped with caterpillar traction. The 0.75-cu yd caterpillar shovel was used for excavation on switchbacks and roads. Shovels and locos originally burned coal; later equipped for oil. The 82.5-ton locos hauled 6 loaded cars; the 53.5-ton locos, 4 cars. HOLE DRILLING AND BLASTING. Churn drills, used at first, did well in weathered diorite. On 50-ft benches, holes were spaced 35–40 ft lengthwise of bench and 5–10 ft back from edge; they were drilled 12.5% deeper than height of bank and loaded with 10–12 boxes of 35% gelatin powder; toe holes were sometimes needed for removing hard ribs. On the 110-ft bench, churn-drill holes, cased with 6-in pipe in loose ground, were placed close to edge of bank and 30–50 ft apart; they were drilled 10–15 ft deeper than height of bank; distance from bottom of hole to toe of bank, 55–95 ft; this distance and the character of ground governed the powder charge, which was 4 000–8 000 lb; drilling speed, 5–30 ft per shift. Beneath zone of weathering, diorite was too hard and blocky for churn drills, which were replaced on the 50-ft benches by air drills. Combination of toe-holing with jackhammers and drilling vert holes with tripod drifters (Fig 675) was found best for the conditions. Toe holes were 6–15 ft apart; vert holes, 12.5 ft apart. Powder charge for toe holes, 100–250 lb; for vert holes, 75–150 lb. Holes, 20–30 at a time, were blasted electrically from a 440-v line. COYOTE BLASTING. To equalize progress of 8-cu yd shovel with that of 4-cu yd on upper benches, some lower benches were consolidated, in a bank over 300 ft high at one end of pit. Due to height of bank and difficulty of churn-drilling in fresh diorite, coyote blasting was thereafter used on the bottom bench. Six such blasts were made, breaking a total of 793 000 cu yd; largest single blast, 259 000 cu yd. Procedure was to drive a 4.5 by 6-ft drift parallel with and 75–135 ft behind the face, and, at 30-ft intervals along the drift, to sink 5 by 5-ft winzes to depth 20–30 ft below the pit grade (Fig 676). A case of gelatin dynamite with 4 No 8 elec caps was placed in bottom of each pocket.

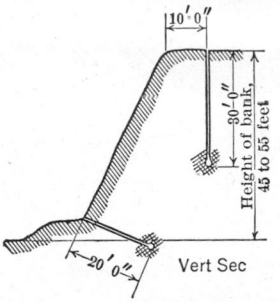

Fig 675. Arrangement of Blast Holes on Upper Benches, United Verde Open-pit

Powder for main charge was unloaded at the tunnel mouth and transported to the pockets on special wooden cars. Black powder was used in first 3 blasts; for greater shattering effect, " Quarry Special " in the next 3, with addition of 60% ammonia dynamite in the last 2 blasts. The powder was covered with paper and sand tamping, and the tunnel back-filled. Table 70 gives data on these blasts.

Table 70. Coyote Blasting Data, United Verde Mine, Jerome, Ariz (544) [1]

Blast No	1	2	3	4	5	6
Number of pockets...................	7	6	14	10	5	13
Aver distance between pockets, ft........	30	30	30	30	30	30
Total development drifting and sinking, ft	410	485	910	686	225	800
Aver distance of pocket to toe of bank, ft..	78	100	133	65	61	100
Aver vert height above pocket, ft........	121	167	189	146	120	120
Average height of bank, ft..............	a	a	a	a	100	100
Aver burden on each pocket, cu yd.......	5 000	7 800	9 800	6 000	5 230	9 240
Black powder, lb......................	100 000	95 400	250 000			
Quarry Special No 6, lb................				91 700		200 000
Quarry Special No 4, lb................					45 000	
60% ammonia dynamite, lb.............					5 000	30 000
50% gelatin dynamite, lb..............	13 050	3 500	9 900	11 650		3 250
35% gelatin dynamite, lb..............					4 000	
Total powder, lb................	113 050	98 900	259 900	103 150	54 000	233 250
Cu yd broken.......................	140 000	135 000	259 000	105 000	54 000	200 000
Cu yd per lb of explosives.............	1.24	1.36	1.00	1.02	1.00	0.86
Cu yd per ft developed...............	394	278	285	153	240	250
Costs per cu yd:						
Development, labor and supplies.......	$0.0850	$0.0827	$0.0502	$0.1297	$0.1400	$0.0407
Explosives.........................	0.0783	0.0697	0.0915	0.1065	0.1360	0.1272
Total...................	$0.1633	$0.1524	$0.1418	$0.2362	$0.2760	$0.1679

(a) Pockets under slope only.

Pit slope. Original stripping was based on assumption that a 0.5 : 1 slope would be safe in the dense, unaltered diorite of hanging wall, and a 1 : 1 slope in the softer footwall. Stripping was completed in 1927; no difficulties as to pit slope occurred until late 1929, when a subsidence, originating from underground stoping, fractured the high, steep diorite bank on hanging-wall side. A subsequent large slide, Mch, 1931, proved that a slope as steep as 0.5 : 1 was no longer practicable, and it was decided to flatten the diorite side of pit to a 1 : 1 slope. This involved removal of 4 000 000 cu yd of waste besides the original estimate of 7 000 000 cu yd.

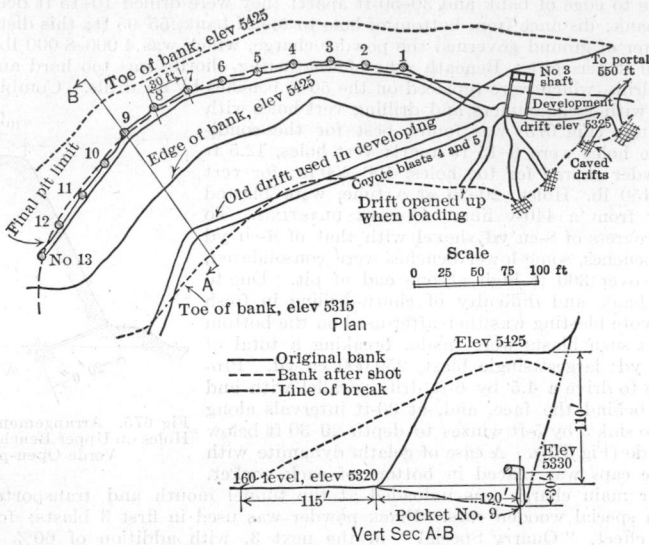

Fig 676. Development for Coyote Blast No 6, United Verde Open-pit

Operating data, original stripping. Table 71 gives data on operations during 1925.

Table 71. Stripping at United Verde Mine, 1925

	4-cu yd shovels	8-cu yd shovel
Cu yd per shovel-shift............	784	1 001
Cu yd per bbl fuel oil............	64.7	50.8
% of time loading...............	46.4	49.1
Cu yd per loco-shift..............	358	
Cu yd per bbl fuel oil to locos.....	46.7	
Lb explosive per cu yd broken....	0.648	
Cu yd per man-shift..............	11.8	

Mining in lower pit before 1931. Work below 160-level (Fig 674) has been mostly confined to main orebody. Required flexibility and selectivity led to choice of low benches and small equipment. Benches were 25–33 ft high. Major equipment included 1.75-cu yd elec shovels, 10-ton automobile trucks, service trucks, elec churn drills, air drills, gasolene crane, and road scraper (bulldozer). Automobile trucks delivered to transfer raises extending to pit from main haulage tunnel on 1 000-level (Fig 674). Drilling was chiefly by churn drills, but air drills were used in places not easily accessible for churn drills. Churn-drill holes were close to edge of bank, generally 10–12 ft apart, and 5 ft deeper than height of bank. In hot ground, where use of powder was limited, spacing might be 4–5 ft. Holes were usually sprung, and loaded with 150–250 lb 35% or 50% gelatin dynamite; blasted electrically. Holes in hot ground were cooled to 120° F or less, before loading, by running in water for 1–24 hr, or using wet sand. For sand, holes were chambered to hold both sand and explosive. Using a little water, the sand was washed into crevices, sealing off hot gases. For holes that could not be cooled, charge was in form of a torpedo. For a 6-in churn-drill hole, a 4-in paper tube, 6–8 ft long and 0.5-in wall, was used (Fig 677). Bottom of tube was sealed by a wooden plug to which a wire was fastened for lowering into the hole. Charge and detonators were placed in the tube and covered with sand. When shooting a round of hot holes, torpedoes were first wired together electrically; when blasting signal was given, they were then lowered into the holes and detonated. Such holes were not chambered, nor stemmed. For toe holes in hot ground, torpedoes were ordinary mailing tubes filled with gelatin dynamite. OPERATING DATA during 1929 are in Table 72.

Table 72. Pit Mining, United Verde, 1929

Cu yd per shovel-shift............	390
Power, kw-hr per cu yd.........	0.966
Cu yd per truck-shift............	131
Truck-shifts per shovel-shift......	2.97
Cu yd per gal gasolene to trucks...	7.65
Explosive, lb per cu yd..........	0.436
Cu yd per man-shift.............	13.69
Tons per man-shift..............	29.66

Operations since 1931. Ore production at United Verde was suspended in 1931 and resumed in 1935, when the mine was acquired by Phelps Dodge Corp. Removal of waste

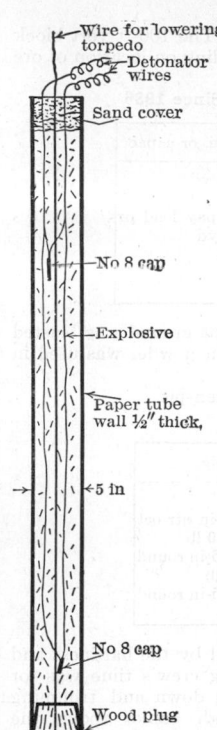

Wire for lowering torpedo

Detonator wires

Sand cover

No 8 cap

Explosive

Paper tube wall ½" thick,

5 in

No 8 cap

Wood plug

Fig 677. Sec of Torpedo for Blasting Hot Holes, United Verde Open-pit

from the open-pit, largely due to a slide in Mch, 1931, continued during the interval. J. R. Bloom, Pit Foreman, contributes following data in 1939 on work since 1931. To end of 1935, 5 282 000 cu yd of waste was removed. Stripping consisted in cutting back the diorite bank to a 1 : 1 slope above the 160-level and maintaining a 0.5 : 1 slope below. Benches were left at various intervals above the 160-level. All material was hauled by locos to waste dumps about at same elev as the loading. In 1935, dump space was no longer easily accessible, requiring longer hauls on heavy grades. The 4-cu yd, full-revolving, crawler

Table 73.   Major Equipment for Later Stripping at United Verde Open-pit, 1931–1935

No	Item	Type	Wt, size, or capac
2	D-c elec shovel	Full-revolv crawler	4-cu yd dipper
1	D-c elec shovel	" " "	2.5-cu yd dipper
4	A-c elec shovel	" " "	1.75-cu yd dipper
3	Steam locos	Switch 0–6–0	82.5 tons
2	Steam locos	Switch 0–4–0	53.5 tons
1	Gasolene loco	Switch 0–4–0	30.0 tons
1	Gasolene loco	Switch 0–6–0	30.0 tons
20	Air-dump cars	Lift-door	25 cu yd
8	Air-dump cars	Drop-door	25 cu yd
1	Locomotive crane	Full-revolv, 7-lever	100 tons
1	Dump dozer	Comp-air	42-in blade
2	Track shifters	Peterson	
	Gondolas, flat cars, and tank car		

shovel proved far more satisfactory than the R R-type steam shovels used earlier. The smaller elec shovels were used mostly as alternate units. BLASTING PRACTICE resembled that employed on the original stripping; coyote blasting was unsuited to maintain a safe final bank. Four elec churn drills, with jackhammer and Leyner air drills, were used; explosive, 35% and 60% quarry powder, 35% and 60% gelatin stick.

Table 74.   Data on Stripping, United Verde Open-pit, 1931–1935

Caved waste removed, cu yd	820 000		
Solid waste removed, cu yd	4 462 000		
Total (cu yd in place)	5 282 000		
	4-cu yd shovels	2.5-cu yd shovel	1.75-cu yd shovels
Cu yd per shovel-shift	1 000	650	475
Cu yd per kw-hr	1.7	1.5	0.9
Cu yd per loco-shift (steam)	500 @ ¾ mile		
Cu yd per bbl fuel oil	62.0 @ ¾ mile		
Cu yd per loco-shift (gasolene)	250 @ ½ mile		
Cu yd per gal gasolene	9.5 @ ½ mile		
Lb explosive per cu yd broken	0.412		
Lb explosive per cu yd removed (a)	0.348		
Cu yd per man-shift	20		

(a) Includes caved material.

Ore mining in lower pit was resumed Jan, 1935, and continued that year in conjunction with stripping. Since 1936, stripping has been confined to waste from within the orebody, and caved material from the banks. For proper classification of material loaded, the smaller shovels were best. Three classes of ore, direct-smelting, concentrating, and converter, and waste material, were dumped into separate transfer raises. After passing through the 900-level grizzly chamber, they were hauled out the 1 000-level haulage tunnel to outside transfer bins. Blockholing of large pieces was required on 900-level to pass the material through the 15-in grizzly. BREAKING GROUND. The 100-ft vert block between mine levels was removed in 3 cuts from 27 to 37 ft, depending on location of ore

Table 75. Major Equipment, United Verde Open-pit, Since 1936

No	Item	Type	Wt, size, or capac
1	D-c elec shovel	Full-revolv crawler	2 1/2 cu yd
4	A-c elec shovels	" " "	1 3/4 cu yd
4	10-wheel, 11.25 × 24-in pneumatic-tire trucks	Double dual rear drive, 2-way hyd side dump	20-ton pay load or 9 cu yd
2	Linn tractor trucks	2-way hyd side dump	8 cu yd
1	Caterpillar No 75 tractor	Bulldozer	

pillars beneath. Drilling was similar to that described above. Hot ground was blasted with same precautions, but 4 by 4-in wrapped 35% blasting gelatin powder was used in

**Table 76. Drilling Equipment at United Verde Open-pit
Since 1936**

Items	Type	Size or weight
3 Churn drills	Spudding	6-in holes
25 Jackhammers	Wet-head	2.5-in cyl; 7/8-in qtr oct steel. 45–50 lb
5 Tripod-mounted drifters	Auto-feed Leyner	3.5-in cyl; 1.25-in round steel. 156 lb
3 Wagon drills	Gravity-feed Leyner	3.5-in cyl; 1.25-in round steel

churn-drill holes at temp to 120° F. Type of drill was determined by the hardness and broken or solid character of the ground. Approx 20% of mining crew's time was for barring down and trimming the high banks above the lower pit; this had to be done when falling rock would not endanger shovel and churn-drill operators below. Table 77 gives data when all material was passed through transfer raises and haulage tunnel. CONCLUSION: It is estimated that the completed United Verde pit (Fig 674) will have a vert depth of 1 100 ft; area within the excavated outline, 60 acres; area of lowest level, 0.9 acre. A total of 19 200 000 cu yd (in place) will have been removed, representing 10 200 000 tons of ore and approx 31 000 000 tons of waste.

Table 77. Data on United Verde Open-pit Mining, 1937–1938

	2.5-cu yd shovel	1.75-cu yd shovel
Waste, cu yd		698 000
Ore, cu yd		465 000
Total removed (cu yd in place)		1 163 000
Cu yd per shovel-shift	450	450
Cu yd per kw-hr	0.9	1.1
Cu yd per truck-shift	210	
Cu yd per gal gasolene	12	
Ft of hole per churn-drill-shift	13.0	
Lb explosive per cu yd broken (a)	0.499	
Lb explosive per cu yd removed (b)	0.508	
Cu yd per man-shift (c)	9.8	

(a) Does not include caved yardage, nor explosives for bulldozing on grizzlies. (b) Includes explosives for bulldozing. (c) Includes labor for final disposal to smelter cars or waste dumps.

New Cornelia mine, Phelps Dodge Corp, Ajo, Ariz. Data contributed through courtesy of H. M. Lavender, Gen Mgr of Mines, in 1939; see also Bib (100). Copper minerals, chiefly chalcopyrite, occur in fracture planes and disseminated in quartz monzonite, also to a lesser extent in adjacent diorite and rhyolite, and form a large orebody mined by open pit. Deposit was overlain by an oxidized zone from which 17 000 000 tons of carbonate ores, averaging 1.38% Cu, were mined and treated by leaching. Operations now confined to underlying sulphide ores. Orebody is about 4 800 ft long and 2 700 ft wide; aver original thickness, 425 ft; max thickness about 1 000 ft; it pitches under waste covering at one end, where pit limits are determined by economic depth of stripping. Ore reserves at Jan 1, 1937, were estimated from the pit layout then planned as approx 155 000 000 tons, averaging about 1% Cu; added tonnage lies outside of pit limits. Much of the ore area is hard and siliceous, breaking into large boulders; overburden generally softer than ore.

Exploration involved 270 diamond-drill and 15 churn-drill holes, totalling 146 569 ft (Art 10-b). MINING CARBONATE CAPPING involved removal of 3 mineralized hills; elevations, 115–165 ft above general surface. These were mined in a single lift (without benches). Banks higher than 45 ft were broken by "coyote" or tunnel blasting; lower banks, by churn and air drills. Ore was loaded by steam shovels into 20-cu yd air-dump cars and

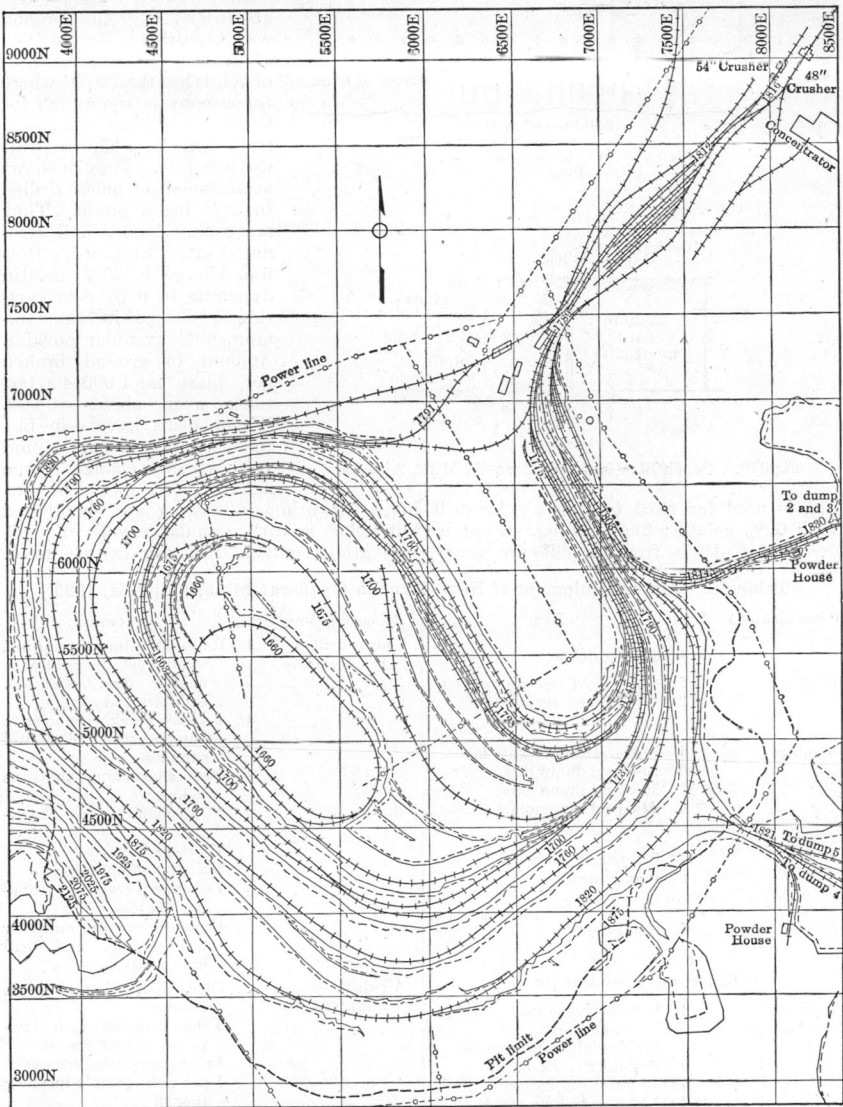

Fig 678. New Cornelia Open-pit, Ajo, Ariz, as of Jan 1, 1939

hauled by steam locos to crushing plant; aver haul, 1 mile. After carbonate hills had been leveled, remainder of oxidized ore was mined by 30-ft benches. MINING SULPHIDES. Fig 678 shows lay-out of present pit. Entry is through an approach cut starting 2 000 ft from the crushing plant, and roughly paralleling the E side of pit; track in bottom of approach is on 2% adverse grade. Near entrance, branch lines extend E to waste dumps. At Jan 1,

1939, bottom of pit was 465 ft below topmost level, and 175 ft below aver elev of the rim. Aver height of banks, 50 ft. Bench tracks are kept level and make a complete loop within the pit; 5% grade is used on ramps; 90-lb rail on approach and 70- and 90-lb on pit tracks.

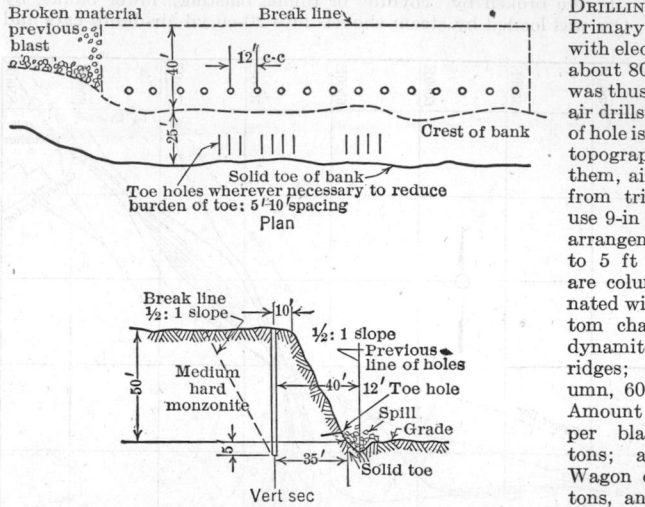

Fig 679. Bench Blasting, New Cornelia Mine, Ajo, Ariz

DRILLING AND BLASTING. Primary drilling is chiefly with elec churn drills; in 1938 about 80% of ground broken was thus drilled. Wagon-type air drills are used where depth of hole is less than 20 ft; where topography is too rough for them, air drills are suspended from tripods. Churn drills use 9-in bits. Fig 679 shows arrangement of holes, drilled to 5 ft below grade. They are column-loaded and detonated with Primacord. Bottom charge is 40% gelatin dynamite in 6 by 8-in cartridges; charge in the column, 60% granular powder. Amount of ground broken per blast is 1 000–400 000 tons; aver about 40 000. Wagon drills have 4-in pistons, and use $1\frac{1}{4}$-in round steel, with 4-ft changes. Same machine, with special mounting, is used for hard toe holes. Air-drill holes for primary blasting are chambered with 60% gelatin; final loading, except in wet holes, is with granular powder of 60% or 70%. Cuttings from all holes are sampled for grade control. LOADING AND HAULING.

Table 78. Major Equipment of New Cornelia Open-cut Mine, Ajo, Ariz, 1939

Classification	Units	Item
Primary Operations		
Loading	5	$4\frac{1}{2}$-cu yd electric shovels
	2	4-cu yd electric shovels
Haulage	15	70-ton oil-fired steam locos
	60	20-cu yd dump cars
	31	30-cu yd dump cars
	4	22-cu yd automobile trucks
Drilling	13	Electric churn drills
	8	Wagon drills
Miscel	4	Bulldozers
Service and Maintenance		
Haulage servicing	1	Locomotive crane
	3	Track-shifters
	1	Service lubrication truck
	1	Sprinkler truck
	1	$1\frac{1}{2}$-ton supply truck
	1	$1\frac{1}{2}$-ton pick-up truck
	3	Railroad motor cars, one equipped with first-aid equipment
	7	Railroad trailer cars
	1	Garage with an overhead crane, fully equipped with tools and supplies

Classification	Units	Item
Churn-drill maintenance	1	Railroad motor car equipped with hoist on trailer to handle distribution of drill bits and supplies
	1	$1\frac{1}{2}$-ton truck with hoist to handle drill bits and supplies
	1	Drill sharpening shop as follows:
	3	mechanical-elec sharpeners
	4	fuel-oil furnaces
	3	bit-tempering tubs
	1	overhead crane for transporting bits
	1	complete welding outfit for drill repairs and drill casing salvage
Air-drill maintenance	1	Drill sharpening shop as follows:
	3	bit grinders with low-press exhaust system
	3	elec tempering furnaces
	1	pot and crucible furnace; fuel oil
	1	oil tempering bath
	1	salt bath
	1	threading machine
	1	bit sharpener
	1	power hacksaw
	5	air compressors
Blasting equipment	2	Powderhouses

Ore and waste are loaded by 4.5-cu yd elec shovels into 20- and 30-cu yd side-dump cars, hauled to the coarse crushing plant by oil-fired steam locos. Stripping on upper benches is facilitated by 22-cu yd dump trucks. Bulldozers are used to build ramps and roadways, to clear areas for drills to operate, and to grade benches for laying tracks. EQUIPMENT. Table 78 lists main items in use in 1938; OPERATING DATA are shown in Table 79. From the beginning of operation to Jan 1, 1939, a total of approx 55 000 000 tons of ore (carbonate and sulphide) and 30 000 000 tons of waste had been mined. Production in 1938 was 4 974 893 tons ore and 5 825 004 tons waste.

Table 79. Operating Data, New Cornelia Mine, Ajo, Ariz, Year 1938

Aver tons mined per shovel-shift in ore. .	3 116	Ft drilled per drill-shift; churn drills....	49
Aver tons mined per shovel-shift in waste..........................	3 473	Tons ore and waste broken per lb powder used........................	4.38
Aver tons per haulage shift, locomotives.	1 552	Tons ore produced per man-shift......	30.5
Aver tons per haulage shift, trucks.....	1 159	Tons ore and waste produced per man-	
Aver haul in miles, ore and waste......	1.7	shift............................	66.1
Ft drilled per drill-shift; wagon drills...	122	Power, kw-hr per ton (electric shovels	
Ft drilled per drill-shift; tripod drills...	83	only)...........................	0.2319

Arkansas Mountain stripping. Overburden is being stripped from a hill at S W side of the New Cornelia pit, with elec shoveling and truck haulage. The steep slopes and limited space for tracks prevented rail haulage, and the short haul to available dumping space was favorable for truck haulage. Shoveling started Mch, 1937, and to Jan 1, 1939, approx 3 000 000 tons were stripped. A 4.5-cu yd elec shovel, and 4 22-cu yd dump trucks were used. Benches were at 50-ft vert intervals, progressing upwards from bottom of the slope to top level, 300 ft above uppermost level in main pit. These levels are now being worked back to their final limits, by progressing from the topmost downwards. The shovels, trucks, drills, and other equipment were shifted over ramps with grades up to 28%. Air drills were used on the steep slopes; churn drills, when the benches were established.

Table 80. Truck Haulage, Arkansas Mt, Ajo, Ariz, 1938

Total number of trucks in service.................	4
Tons hauled.................................	2 320 738
Number of truck-shifts........................	2 001.6
Tons hauled per truck-shift....................	1 159
Length of haul, miles.........................	0.28
Aver ratio of truck-shifts to shovel-shifts........	3

Morenci, Ariz (Phelps Dodge Corp). W. C. Lawson in 1938 described the preliminary stripping operations begun in 1934 (668). Orebody is a large, low-grade deposit of copper minerals, chiefly chalcocite, disseminated in porphyry. Exploration by diamond drilling and underground openings indicated total reserve of 284 000 000 tons, assaying 1.036% Cu, with small amounts of Au and Ag. Pit limits are planned to extract 230 000 000 tons, having 1.06% Cu; reduction from the total represents establishment of grade cut-off limits, excluding portions of orebody carrying high stripping ratios. Aver thickness of

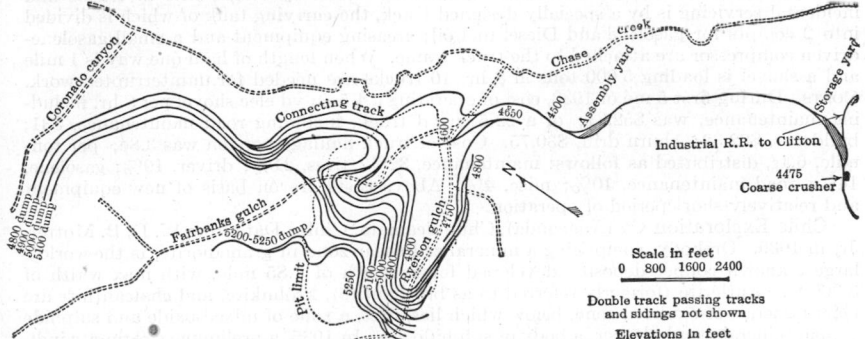

Fig 680. Layout of Pit, Morenci, Ariz

capping, 216 ft; max, 500 ft; estimated stripping ratio, 1.04 ton of waste to 1 of ore. Ultimate pit depth of 1 300 ft, below highest point of capping, and over-all slopes of 45° are planned. Character of capping varies, but drilling conditions are generally good, though occasional ribs of high-quartz material break with difficulty. GENERAL PLAN comprises uncovering an area nearest the millsite, and developing the pit for rail haulage, including switchbacks to upper benches and waste dumps and roadbeds to the mill, 3 1/3 miles by rail from the pit (Fig 680). Banks will be 50 ft high, with 100-ft bench widths.

For many years, grades for both ore and waste haulage will be favorable. Aver haul between pit and assembly yard will be about 2 miles; from the yard, haul to crushing plant will be $1^1/_3$ miles, on 0.4% grade. Upper benches will be reached by 4 switchbacks over a ruling grade of 4%; tracks to main dumps, on 0.2% grade. About half of total stripping will move in direction opposite to ore movement; remainder will go to dumps over same tracks as ore. Longest waste haul, about 3 miles. Extreme roughness of topography led to choice of automobile trucks for haulage during preliminary stripping. Trucks proved highly flexible, disposing of waste in canyons to be crossed by rail. PREPARATION. First work was building about 6 miles of service and truck-haulage roads. About 75% of all roads required drilling hillside slopes with large jackhammers suspended from tripods with block and tackle. Drills were chucked for 1.25-in round steel; all holes drilled dry, with detachable bits. Some through-cuts were made with a 1-cu yd Diesel shovel, and 5-cu yd trucks with wheel-base of only 121 in, permitting short-radius turns. Other preparatory work included extension of water, air, and power lines to pit, building shops, and grading for a new townsite. DRILLING AND BLASTING. For all primary drilling in stripping, elec churn drills with 9-in bits are standard. Holes are drilled 8–10 ft below grade and column-loaded with bag powder, with 1 case of gelatin in each hole as a primer, detonated by Cordeau or Primacord. Easily accessible holes are stemmed with mill tailings, using 1 line of wire-bound fuse; other holes are stemmed with rock screenings, using 2 lines of double-countered fuse, because the coarser stemming may injure the fuse. Aver advance per churn-drill shift, 85 ft. Drill bits aver 55 ft per sharpening. In blacksmith shop, 3 men with mechanical sharpener can sharpen and temper 22 bits per 8 hr. LOADING. In 1938, 4 full-revolving, Ward-Leonard control, elec shovels were in service; 3 had 4.5-cu yd, manganese-steel dippers; the fourth, a 5.5-cu yd, alloy-steel dipper, which weighed, plus full load, less than the loaded 4.5-cu yd dipper. Shovels receive power at 2 300 v through trail cable. Automatic water sprays are located ahead of the shovel to control dust. During first few months of 1938, about 5 000 tons were loaded per 8-hr shovel-shift. On a 2-shift basis, delays to shovels in waiting for trucks and in repairs were only 8% of total possible loading time. Power consumption averaged 0.186 kw-hr per ton loaded. HAULAGE. Equipment (1938) consists of 18 22.5-cu yd, end-dump, 6-wheeled, gasolene trucks, each of the 4 rear wheels having 2 13.5 by 24-in pneumatic tires; pay load, about 35 tons. Bench widths permit a truck to be spotted on each side of shovel; this minimizes arc of shovel swing, and an empty can be backed into position while shovel is loading truck on opposite side. A bulldozer at each shovel keeps surface smooth. Aver haul (1938) is 0.6 mile; max, 1 mile. On favorable roads, grades to 15% can be negotiated at very slow speed; max grade of 10% is set where possible; for long stretches, 6 or 7% grade is preferable. Top speed on slightly favorable or level grades, loaded or empty, is 15 miles per hr. Sprinkler trucks control dust on roads. While mining is suspended on "graveyard" shift, half the trucks go to repair shop for servicing; hence, each truck is serviced after 32 hr operation. There is a complete tire-repair shop, including vulcanizing equipment. Delivery of gasolene to trucks and incidental servicing is by a specially designed truck, the carrying tank of which is divided into 2 compts for gasolene and Diesel fuel oil; greasing equipment and a small gasolene-driven compressor are attached to the truck frame. When length of haul one way is 1 mile and a shovel is loading 5 000 tons in 8 hr, 10 trucks are needed for uninterrupted work. COSTS. During first 5 mo of 1938, cost of operating a 4.5-cu yd elec shovel per 8 hr, including maintenance, was $52.81; of a 22.5-cu yd truck, including road maintenance, $31; bulldozer, $22.32; churn drill, $30.75. Cost of truck haulage per ton was 3.8¢; per ton-mile, 6.1¢, distributed as follows: maintenance, 32%; tires, 21%; driver, 19%; gasolene, 14%; road maintenance, 10%; misc, 4%. Above costs are on basis of new equipment and relatively short period of operation.

Chile Exploration Co (Anaconda), Chuquicamata, Chile. Data from W. D. B. Motter, Jr, in 1939. Orebody, comprising a mineralized shear-zone in granodiorite, is the world's largest known copper deposit; developed for a length of 1.85 mile, with max width of 3 300 ft. Antlerite (formerly referred to as brochantite), kröhnkite, and chalcanthite are chief minerals of oxidized zone, below which lies, first, a zone of mixed oxide and sulphide copper minerals, and, deeper, a body of sulphide ore. In 1935, a preliminary estimate indicated reserves of approx 360 000 000 tons of oxidized ore, aver 1.75% Cu; 100 000 000 tons of mixed oxides and sulphides, aver 2.87% Cu; and 575 000 000 tons of sulphide ore, aver 2.27% Cu; total, 1 035 000 000 tons, aver 2.15% Cu. Some areas are overlain by waste capping. Ore is moderately hard and, due to soft mineralized seams, breaks coarsely in blasting; gyratories at coarse-crushing plant have 60-in openings, thus reducing block-holing in the pit. Topography permits long working faces, for many shovels and ore trains. In Jan, 1939, 15 benches had been opened and 11 were being worked, with 13.6 miles of bench faces. Upper benches are 37–64 ft high; lower benches, all 40 ft. The pit has produced as much as 59 142 tons of ore and 33 510 tons of waste in 3 8-hr shifts. PIT EQUIPMENT comprises (Mar, 1939): two 8-cu yd full-revolving elec shovels on R R trucks, one mainly for development, the other held in reserve; six 4-cu yd caterpillar elec shovels; six 4-cu yd

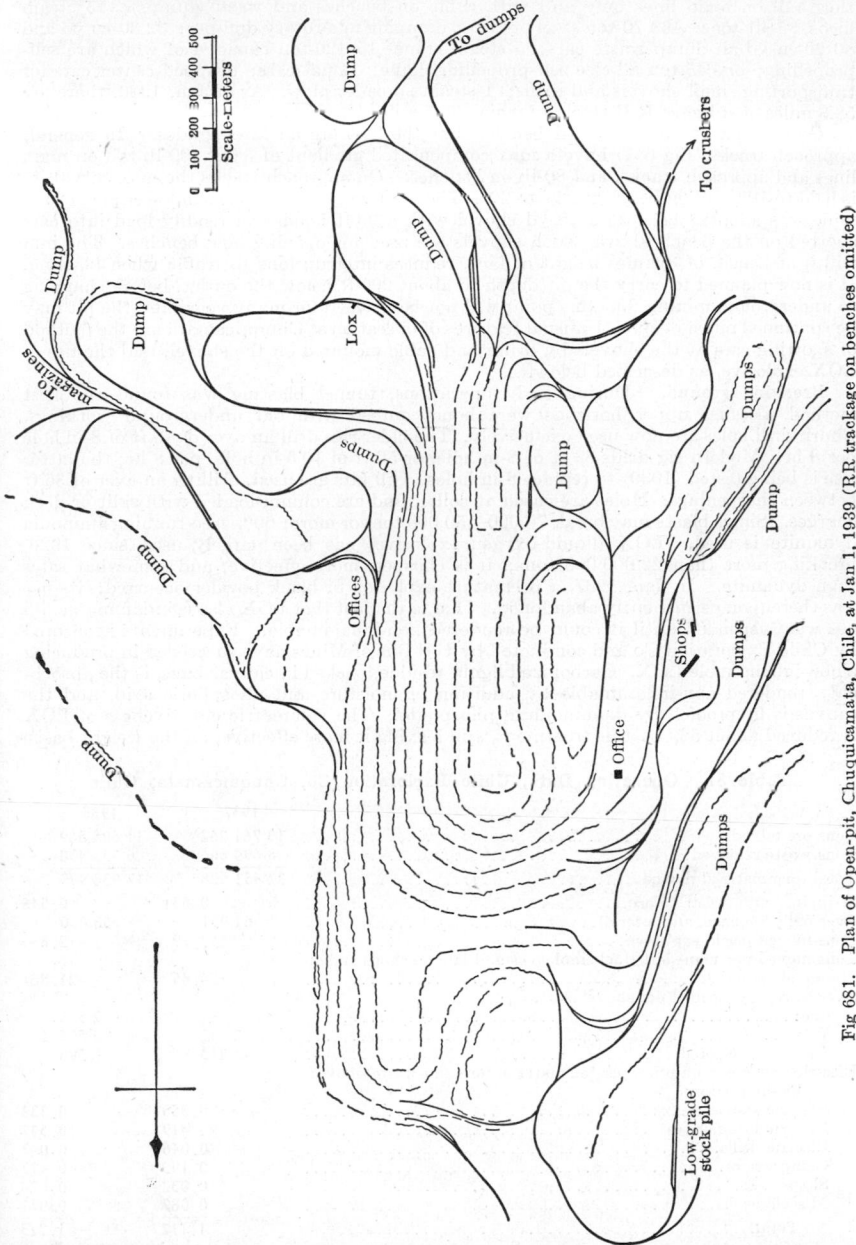

Fig 681. Plan of Open-pit, Chuquicamata, Chile, at Jan 1, 1939 (RR trackage on benches omitted)

R R-type caterpillar elec shovels (all of the above, except one 8-yd shovel, are Ward-Leonard control); seven 4-cu yd R R-type caterpillar elec shovels with a-c motors; total, 21 shovels, all equipped with cable-drums for spotting cars while loading, thus relieving the locos; three 0.75-yd Diesel shovels on caterpillars for misc clean-up work; 2 road graders; 3

Nordberg track shifters; 93 Cyclone elec churn drills; one 29-T Bucyrus-Erie drill; 19 elec locos, 75–87 tons, combination cable-reel, third-rail, and some with trolley (operating on third-rail on main lines only and with cable on benches and waste dumps); 15 steam locos, 85–91-tons; 460 70-ton steel ore cars, dumping in a rotary dumper; 32 30-cu yd and 80 20-cu yd air-dump waste cars; 5 steam cranes 15–120-ton capac, 4 of which are self-propelling; one 45-ton all-elec self-propelling crane; 14 flat cars; dropped-center cars for transporting small shovels and drills; 1 steam spreader plow. As of Jan, 1939, there are 58.8 miles of std-gage R R track, of which 38.7 miles are electrified.

General pit operations. All benches but the first are on level grades. In general, approach tracks (Fig 681) have a max compensated gradient of 3%; 100-lb rail on main lines and approach tracks, and 80-lb on benches. On approach tracks the max curvature is held to 10°, and on bench tracks to 20°. The 40-ft height for benches in lower part of the mine was adopted because an 8-yd shovel with a 90-ft boom can readily load into cars spotted on the bench above; such shovels are used for opening new benches. The min width of bench, of 3 times height of face, reduces interruptions to traffic when blasting. It is now planned to carry the pit depth to about 200 ft below the outlet, before changing to underground mining, but this point will not be reached for many years and the pit may be continued much deeper. Unusual features of operation at Chuquicamata are the method of spotting cars at the shovels by drum and cable mounted on the shovel, and the use of LOX explosive, as described below.

Breaking ground. During early operations, tunnel blasting was found the best method, because upper horizons were honeycombed with old underground workings. Churn-drill holes are now used exclusively. The older rigs drill an aver of 46 ft of 8-in hole per 8 hr. Modern rig drills 88 ft of 8-in hole, or 56 ft of 10.5-in hole, per 8 hr; the latter size is being tested (1939) to replace 8-in holes. Gill bits are used, drilling an aver of 35 ft between sharpenings. Holes are cased at collar, and are column-loaded with split or deck charges. Single blasts may break 70 000–150 000 tons or more; 60% free-running ammonia dynamite is used. LOX (liquid-oxygen explosive) has been largely used since 1926, breaking more than 22 000 000 tons; it is cheaper, more effective, and somewhat safer than dynamite. In Jan, 1937, a premature explosion of black powder occurred; its use was thereupon permanently abandoned. Due to the fact that LOX also is inflammable, its use was suspended until it could be rendered non-inflammable. Experiments sponsored by Chile Exploration Co and conducted by U S Bur of Mines have succeeded in producing a non-inflammable LOX. Carbonized lignin residue, packed in canvas bags, is the absorbent; rendered non-inflammable by addition of moisture and phosphoric acid, and the canvas is fireproofed by diammonium phosphate. The volumetric effectiveness of LOX is reduced about 5% by this treatment, still leaving it more effective, on the weight basis,

Table 81. Operating Data, Chile Exploration Co, Chuquicamata, Chile

	1937	1938
Tons ore mined	13 761 262	11 605 569
Tons waste removed	8 690 366	6 333 430
Total tons material moved	22 451 628	17 938 999
Stripping ratio, waste to ore	0.631	0.546
Aver daily tonnage, all material	69 931	58 030
Tons moved per lb explosive	2.79	2.83
Tons moved per man-shift (incl employees and labor—shops and all outside labor)	24.45	21.98
Aver tons (dry) loaded per shovel-shift:		
Ore	2 331	2 588
Waste	2 052	2 595
Average (weighted)	2 213	2 590
Electric power consumption per ton material (ore and waste) moved, kw-hr per ton:		
Electric shovels	0.355	0.333
Electric locomotives*	*0.419	*0.537
Electric drills	0.046	0.047
Compressors	0.193	0.197
Shops	0.032	0.038
Miscellaneous	0.067	0.071
Total	1.112	1.223
Aver ore haul, miles	2.96	2.52
Aver waste haul, miles	1.73	1.69
Ton-miles per kw-hr	4.60	3.63

* Some material handled by steam locos; consumption by electric locos alone was, in the respective years, 0.523 and 0.592 kw-hr.

than the 60% dynamite. Substitution of LOX for dynamite entails no change in depth, chambering, or spacing of drill holes, but an 8 5/8 or 10 1/2-in hole is better for LOX than an 8-in, to concentrate this less dense explosive at the bottom. The Co makes its own liquid oxygen in a plant with a capac of 250 liters per hr. LOX blasts are fired within 1 hr after beginning charging. All blasts, except secondary shots, are detonated with Primacord, which has replaced Cordeau. Considering a typical single-row blast (multiple rows are occasionally used) in a 40-ft bank, 8-in holes would be spaced 13 ft c–c, 23 ft back from toe of bank or about 6 ft from the rim, resulting in a burden of 850 tons per hole; with 20% overbreak, the broken ground is 1 020 tons per hole. For data on earlier practice at Chuquicamata, see Bib (638).

Flin Flon open-cut. Data from M. A. Roche (669) in 1933 and 1935. Orebody is a steeply dipping lens of hard pyrite, banded with greenstone ledges and fringed on one side by softer disseminated ore. Outcrop is 2 600 ft long and 450 ft wide at middle, tapering out completely at ends. All but about 600 ft at its mid-length lay under 12–15 ft of water (an arm of Flin Flon Lake) and 15–90 ft (aver 20 ft) of mud and clay. After building 2 dams from shores to a conveniently situated island, an area enclosing all the submerged outcrop was emptied of about 4 million gal in 2 mos by 2 Morris 10-in dredging pumps, against aver head of 50 ft; mud and part of the clay was dragged to the pumps by 3 V-scrapers with 35-hp slusher hoists, aided by high-press water jets. Another scraper handled boulders. In 3 summer seasons, 789 300 tons of material were thus removed, costing 15¢ per ton; remaining 288 500 tons of bottom clay was removed later by power shovels and Shay loco. Only the upper 300 ft of orebody will be mined by open-cut (see Art 43 for underground methods), involving about 1 000 000 tons of overburden, 5 000 000 tons of ore, and 2 000 000 tons of waste rock. In late 1933, the pit was 150 ft deep and 1 300 ft long; approached by through cut on 6% grade from narrow north end, track being laid on hanging-wall (greenstone), with switchbacks near opposite schistose wall. BREAKING GROUND. During 3 yr, 8 No 29 Armstrong elec drills (550-v, a-c), caterpillar mounted, averaged 15–17 ft of 6-in hole per 10-hr drill-shift, mainly in hard sulphide and greenstone. Holes, usually 50 ft or deeper, to about 5 ft below grade, are 16–20 ft apart, and staggered in rows 20 ft apart; first row about 20 ft from edge. They are chambered by successive charges of 50% gelatin, stemmed with water; then loaded with about 700 lb gelatin in 5 by 16-in cartridges, to about 20 ft from bottom, and stemmed with 10 ft of sand; above this, a "deck" charge about 15 ft high is confined by sand to top of hole. Owing to conductivity of sulphides if in contact with wires, a defective circuit can not be detected by galvanometer; enameled lead wires are therefore laid into grooves along opposite edges of a wooden strip and taped in place; primers are also attached to this stick. Besides the main blast holes, a row of unchambered rim holes, spaced 5–10 ft, is loaded with alternating top and bottom charges only sufficient to break hole to hole. As much track must be moved before blasting in this narrow pit, large blasts are made at long intervals; the ore is also better broken by firing many holes simultaneously. In a blast of Nov 23, 1932, 639 holes, averaging 44.43 ft deep (which took 1 930 8-hr rig-shifts to drill and 16 050 lb explosive to chamber) and containing 239 650 lb of 50% gelatin, broke 443 153 tons, of which 292 484 tons were ore. Blast of Sep 13, 1933, broke an area 700 ft long by 150 ft wide with 232 main holes and 175 rim holes (aver 30 ft deep) along foot and hanging walls, affording 471 980 tons of ore and 33 613 tons of waste; explosive (50% gelatin), 15 850 lb for chambering and 246 000 lb in blast. Aver consumption of explosive since beginning this work has been 0.351 lb per ton broken, incl 0.031 lb for chambering. LOADING AND HAULING. Each of 2 Marion 4 160 elec, 150-ton, full-revolving, caterpillar-mounted shovels, with 4-yd dippers and 29.5-ft booms, loads 1 000–1 500 tons in 10 hr, dumping 20 ft above grade with 37-ft reach. Cars (23 in service) are 22.5-yd (60-ton), drop-door, side-dumped by air. Motive power includes 2 General Electric 85-ton locos, and several 20-ton size for spotting. The large locos haul 2 60-ton cars from pit on 6% grade; they have hauled up to 3 000–3 500 tons 2 miles in 10 hr; usual aver is a little over 1 000 tons per loco. When pit reaches its full proposed extent, it will have about 8 000 ft of track (85-lb rail), besides that in yards and waste dumps.

Asbestos mining in Quebec. Data from W. A. Rukeyser (670) in 1932. In scattered places in a long serpentine belt, fractured rock carries chrysotile in seams to max of 3-in width, usually much narrower. Rock containing as little as 2% asbestos has been mined; general aver, 5.25%. Fiber 0.75-in and longer commands premium, and has commonly been hand-sorted for special treatment, remainder going to crushing and separating mills. Where sorting and loading is by hand, requiring rock to be broken small, benches are usually blasted with 10 to 16-ft vert holes, drilled by light hammer drills at cost of 3–17¢ per ton broken; sorted material, incl waste, is shoveled into steel boxes holding 2.5 tons, which are dumped by crane into 10-ton cars, hauled out of pit as described below. Recent trend, induced by diminishing proportion of long fiber and its smaller premium, is towards mechanical loading direct into cars, with only such sorting of waste as a shovel can accomplish. Of rock mined in 1929, 30% was waste compared with 13% in 1919. Power shovels permit heavier blasting with deeper holes and higher benches. BREAKING ROCK. Vert holes 32–40 ft deep (75 ft at one mine), 10–25 ft back from face, and spaced 5 ft or less, are made with heavy hammer drills on portable derricks, starting at 3.375 in, finishing at 1.125 in. Toe holes are drilled by same machines, differently mounted. Lower third of hole is loaded with 75% gelatin; remainder of charge, 30–50 lb of 40% dynamite; about 20 holes are elec fired at a time; some blockholing is needed. Aver break, 8 tons per lb explosive; cost of explosive, 4–7¢ per ton. LOADING AND HAULING. Caterpillar steam shovels with 2.5-yd dippers have been commonest; gradually replaced, since 1929, by elec shovels of same or 4-yd size. Side-dump, 10-ton cars are usual; one large mine has air-dumped, 30-ton cars. In pit bottoms, steam, gas-elec, and elec locos of trolley, battery. and cable-reel types, have all been used. At Jeffrey mine, a circular pit 2 000 ft across and 200 ft deep, developed by spiral benches with 6.5 miles of track, trains of 30-ton cars are hauled by 60-ton elec locos from pit bottom to mill. In smaller and deeper pits, locos deliver cars at bottom of an inclined tunnel, up which the cars are hoisted, 2 at a time, to or near the mill; 3 such tunnels are 967, 1 045, and 1 100 ft long; grades from 10 to 37%. King mine, with a pit 1 200 by 1 000 ft and 400 ft deep, retained suspension cableways (1 400-ft spans) after they had generally been abandoned at other large mines, using them to hoist 10-ton loads hauled into pit from underground shrinkage stopes on 300-ft level. For method of block-caving at King mine, see Art 80.

    Gasolene shovels in open-pits. According to W. R. Moorehead (320) NEW IDRIA mine, Calif, in 1931 produced daily about 750 tons of low-grade ore (0.085% Hg), in a fractured sandstone with seams of cinnabar, from open-pit workings at outcrop of a steeply dipping lens (max 800 by 180 ft), from which richer portions had previously been extracted; material was dropped through a central raise to grizzly and conveyer belt in adit 200 ft below bottom of pit (Art 91). Hanging-wall stripping was glory-holed through another raise to same adit. Elliptical pit was worked by 2 benches at opposite ends. Dry jackhammers drilled vert holes 15–20 ft deep, spaced 8–15 ft, and 6–12 ft back of crest; after chambering with 40% gelatin, each hole was loaded with 50 lb black powder, primed with gelatin. Of 4 caterpillar-mounted, gasolene shovels, 2 had 1-yd, and 2 had 3/8-yd dippers. They loaded into end-dump auto trucks of 5.25–6.25-ton capac; aver haul, 300 ft. On basis of 21 516 tons in Sep, 1930, unit expenses included, in man-hr per ton: drilling and blasting, 0.343; shoveling, 0.368; trucking, 0.053. Explosives: gelatin (40 and 35%), 0.829 lb; black powder, 0.589 lb. CARSON HILL mine, Calif. Data from J. A. Burgess (297) in 1937. Gold ore is mined in 2 outcrop workings on or adjoining the Bull and Calaveras veins. In Union pit a soft schist orebody, 400 by 50–150 ft, is mined in 20-ft benches. Holes 20 ft deep, spaced 8 ft in rows 12 ft apart, are sprung once with 5 sticks of 40% gelatin, then loaded with 50–100 lb black powder, and fired elec, 1 row at a time. Cost for explosives, 2.2¢ per ton. One gasolene shovel with 1-yd dipper loads into 3 3-ton trucks; aver haul to ore-pass, 600–900 ft. Crew, shovel runner, 3 drivers, 1 or 2 drillers, averages 500 tons per day. Calaveras pit is in a long steeply dipping band of soft schist 50–100 ft wide, and has raise connection with underground workings. Vert holes, 20 ft deep, spaced 8 ft in rows 12 ft apart, are drilled from wagon mounting, sprung first with 1 or 2, then 8 or 10, sticks of 40% gelatin dynamite, loaded with 75–100 lb of black powder, and fired elec, 3 rows at a time. Cost for explosives, 6.9¢ per ton. About 1 ton of hanging-wall and other waste is moved for 4 tons of ore.

97. OPEN-CUT MINING WITH DRAGLINE EXCAVATORS

    General. For structural details of draglines, see Sec 3, 27. Chief ADVANTAGES of dragline over the power shovel, in suitable material: (a) can dig deeper below its own level; max depth 20–25 ft for small machines with 50-ft booms to 85–125 ft for those with 185–200-ft booms; (b) can discharge at higher elev; max dumping height above base of machine, at boom angles of 25°–40°, is 25 ft for small, to 100 ft for largest draglines; aver for most draglines is 30–40 ft, with booms from 65 to 110 ft; (c) longer reach for both digging and dumping; max dumping radius, at lowest position of boom, may slightly exceed boom length (due to momentum of loaded bucket), but is usually 5–10 ft less than boom length on medium-size draglines; max digging radius exceeds dumping radius by 13–15 ft with the smallest, to 50 ft with the largest draglines, and depends upon operator's skill in "throwing" the bucket; this added distance is $1/3$–$1/2$ the dumping height. Compared with shovels, chief DEFICIENCIES of the dragline are: (a) except in easy digging (Table 82), bucket load is 5–10% less than that of a shovel dipper of same capac, due to lack of "crowding" effect; (b) loads can not be so accurately discharged into a vehicle; hence a hopper or chute is usual for such loading (for exception, see Shiras pit, below); (c) bucket effic (% of capac actually filled) diminishes more rapidly with less suitable material (Table 82), and almost disappears in materials offering only slight difficulty to a shovel; (d) dragline works to less advantage on rough footwall or bedrock, and does a poorer job in cleaning up corners; (e) less selectivity is possible, unless the valuable and worthless portions of a deposit are stratified or clearly segregated. WIDEST FIELDS for draglines thus appear to be: (a) stripping wide areas over fairly level deposits, as coal, phosphate beds, iron ores like those of the Mesabi Range, and where the overburden requires no added transport; (b) mining soft ores in wide and shallow bodies fairly uniform in composition and free from irregularities in structure. For special applications to coal stripping, see Art 100.

Bucket effic of draglines varies with nature of material, and depends chiefly upon percentage of voids in the load. Table 82 gives a classification according to suitability for draglining, and the effic factor applicable to each class. In very easy digging, as the overburden of Fla phosphate deposits (Art 98), the factor may reach 108%, due to heaping the loads. When working under water (see Art 129), the factor will be less than with dry material, due to spillage.

Table 82. Bucket Efficiencies* of Draglines in Various Materials

Easy digging factor, 95–100%	Medium digging factor, 80–90%	Medium-hard digging factor, 65–75%	Hard digging factor, 40–65%
Sand and small gravel, dry or moist Loam and loose earth Muck Sandy clay Loose clay-gravel Cinders and ashes Bituminous coal Well loosened material	Materials not hard to dig without blasting, but breaking with large voids Clay, wet or dry Coarse gravel Clay-gravel, packed Packed earth Anthracite	Materials requiring light blasting; bulky and not easily penetrated by bucket Well broken limestone, sandstone, shale, etc Ores not massive in character Heavy, wet, sticky clay Gravel with large boulders Cemented gravel	Blasted rock with large voids, difficult to enter Hard, tough shale All hard rocks "Caliche" Mixtures of coarse and fine broken material Tough, rubbery clay which shaves from bank

* % of bucket capacity actually filled

Power requirements. Bucyrus-Erie Co states that elec draglines with Ward-Leonard control require 0.40–0.75 kw-hr per cu yd, on machines of all types and sizes. On those driven by a-c motors, consumption is 0.30–0.85 kw-hr per cu yd, highest for the largest draglines. Table 83 gives consumption of fuel and lubricant by Diesel-driven draglines of the walking type.

Mayari iron mines, Cuba (54). See Art 10-a for ore occurrence. The large area of ore-bodies, their softness, and freedom from overburden, favor use of mechanical excavators. Draglines are used for ore 20 ft thick or less, when both surface and bedrock are irregular; steam shovels, tried first, could not clean bedrock without digging it up, and their small radius of action necessitated frequent moves. In 1916, 2 draglines, with 2-cu yd Page buckets, handled 1 000 tons per day (1 shift) (346). The excavator worked from the original surface, the bucket swung in a radius of 60 ft and readily removed all ore to bedrock for a width of about 100 ft; projecting hummocks of bedrock, stumps, etc, were discarded. Ore was loaded into 50-ton, side-dump, steel cars, on tracks on surface. Crew: 1 operator, 1 fireman and 3 pitmen.

Balkan mine, Menominee Range, Mich. Data from C. E. Lawrence in 1915 (347). Draglines were used for stripping and mining a hematite deposit overlain by swamp, quicksand, clay, hardpan, and boulder gravel. Before

Table 83. Oil Consumption of Walking-type Draglines Operated by Diesels

Boom ft	Bucket cu yd	Engine cylinders		Fuel oil, gal per hr	Lubric oil, gal per hr
		No	size, in		
60 70	2 1 1/2	2	12×15	3.5–5.5	0.07
60 70 80	3 1/2 3 2 1/2	2	14×17	5–7	0.10
80 90	2 1/2 2	5	8 3/4×10 1/2	7–9	0.12
80 100 120	5 4 3	3	14×17	7–9	0.15
		5	10×12 1/2	8–10	0.12
85 105 125	6 5 4	5	10 1/2×12 1/2	10–12	0.14
110 125 140	7 6 5	4	14×17	10.5–12.5	0.20
140 160 175	7 6 5	5	12×15	13–15	0.24
165 185 200	11 9 8	5	14×17	15–20	0.26

beginning work a stream crossing the property was diverted, and a shaft sunk outside the deposit, with drifts and raises for draining the overburden. Fig 682 shows the pit, about 1 150 ft long by 900 ft wide; the spiral tracks (Art 96) had a grade of 2.6%; depth of stripping, 60 to 108 ft. Slopes of banks were 2 : 1 in fine sand near surface, and 1 : 1 in underlying gravel and clay; slopes could have been steeper in dry material. The stripping (1.2 million cu yd) was contracted. Two draglines had 85-ft booms, 4-cu yd buckets, and 24-ft turntables; they were mounted on hardwood rollers, running on 4-in plank; working wt, 150 tons. Output per machine, 2 000 cu yd per 10 hr, loaded through a hopper into 4-cu yd Western dump cars; 15-ton locomotives hauled 10-car trains 0.5 mile to a dump. Height of bench taken in one cut was limited to 30 ft by the flat angle of repose of the soft material. At a depth of 60 ft, some clay banks began to cave, which was stopped by dressing them with evergreen boughs or pit gravel. After cleaning the surface of the ore, the banks were protected by gravel-filled cribs; water was kept out by a ditch in ore completely around the workings; a 20-ft berm was left to maintain the ditch and cribbing. The excavators then mined the ore, which was first shaken up by blasting with 20 to 30-ft churn-drill holes. The

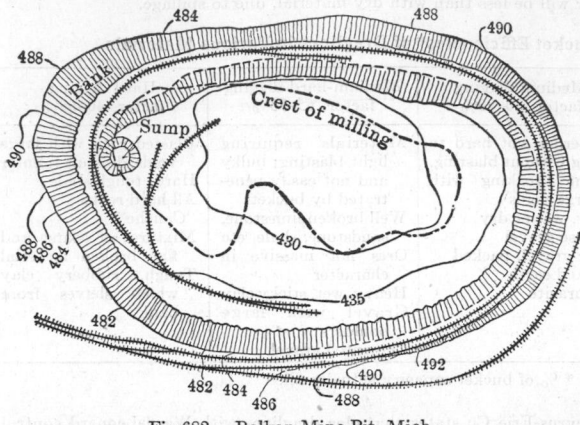

Fig 682. Balkan Mine Pit, Mich

2 machines loaded about 5 000 tons per day. Draglines were adopted chiefly because of the wet, mushy overburden, which would not support a steam shovel in the pit bottom; they worked successfully in the ore also, which was medium hard.

Shiras pit, Mesabi Range, Buhl, Minn. According to E. E. Hunner (660) a revolving elec shovel equipped as dragline (Sec 27), with 150-ft boom and 5-cu yd Page bucket, was used to strip and remove ore from a long, narrow, irregular orebody. Overburden, 25–30 ft deep; ore, 40 ft deep, 125–200 ft wide, 1 500 ft long. Starting at one end, the dragline advanced on surface along one side, overcasting spoil from about 2/3 proposed width of pit; on return along other side, remaining 1/3 was similarly overcast, except what was needed for grading a loading track along edge of pit; same machine, moved to pit bottom, then loaded ore into 50- and 75-ton cars on this track, with lift of 80 ft from bottom of ore to top of car. Crew, excluding rock pickers: 1 operator, 1 oiler, 1 pitman, 2 car trimmers and brakemen. Aver output, 1 250 tons per 10-hr day.

Cuban Mining Co, Cristo, Oriente Prov, Cuba. Data contributed in 1939 by F. S. Norcross, Jr, Gen Mgr. The orebody, which occurs as a persistent bed of manganese oxides of variable thickness, is overlain by 2–40 ft of tuffs, covered in turn by argillaceous limestone. General dip of the formations is 14° N, but with steep asymmetrical folds, and normal and reverse faults with throws to 40 ft. Principal working mine is an open pit, now 2 600 ft long by 1 000 ft wide (Fig 683). Orebody outcrops to S, and dips under heavy overburden to N W. Original STRIPPING was done by train haulage; now generally superseded by the dragline. Overburden now being removed is chiefly along the N and W boundaries of the pit, where stripping may reach a depth of 120 ft, with a Bucyrus-Monighan walking dragline having a 4-cu yd bucket and 120-ft boom. To early 1939, this machine has removed 90 ft of overburden along N wall and stacked the waste in a 55-ft bank (Fig 683). To provide dump area for deeper cuts, the previous spoil will be moved back by dragline recasting or a tower cableway, making a final bank say 600 ft wide and 55 ft high. At a depth of 90 ft, pit slopes are 1 : 1 in the limestone series and 1 : 1.2 in the softer tuffs. The overburden requires little blasting; where necessary, 5 20-ft jackhammer holes are shot with 40–60% dynamite. Operating data for the dragline per 8-hr shift are: output, 1 000 cu yd when digging overburden to 90-ft depth, 1 500 cu yd when recasting an average of 200 ft back; crew, 1 operator, 1 oiler, 2 pitmen; power consumption, 500 kw-hr; maintenance and repairs, $6. Secondary stripping inside of pit limits, or where overburden is shallow, is done by a 2.25-cu yd dragline, casting into adjacent mined areas. ORE PRODUCTION (1 000 to 2 000 tons per 8-hr shift) is handled by a 2-cu yd shovel and a 2.25-cu yd dragline with 60-ft boom. The 2 units work in combination so as: (1) to maintain aver grade by mixing ores; (2) to adapt advantages of each machine to the varying conditions. The shovel is used where the ore lies quite flat; it can dig harder ore (thus saving in blasting) than the dragline, which is used in irregular areas due to its greater flexibility and reach. Ratio of shovel to dragline tonnage varies between about the limits of 2 : 1 and 1 : 2, depending on extraction areas. Ore is blasted with lines of 2-in holes (to 22 ft depth) drilled by jackhammers using chisel bits. The holes are shot with

60% dynamite or *rompe roca*, depending on hardness of ore. Ore is hauled 1.3 miles to mill in 4-cu yd dump cars. Gear-driven steam locos pull 9-car trains. Temporary pit tracks have grades to 6%; main entrance track to pit, a 4% grade. Operating data per 8-hr shift: for 2-cu yd shovel; aver output, 600 tons; power consumption, 470 kw-hr; maintenance and repairs, $7; for the dragline, aver 500 tons; power consumption, 480 kw-hr; maintenance and repairs, $5.

Stripping coal with draglines having buckets to 12-cu yd capac has been successful in the Middle West, although most work is still done by shovels, with dippers to 35-cu yd capac. Draglines have also replaced shovels at many anthracite strippings, especially on pitching outcrops. For stripping both kinds of coal, see Art 100.

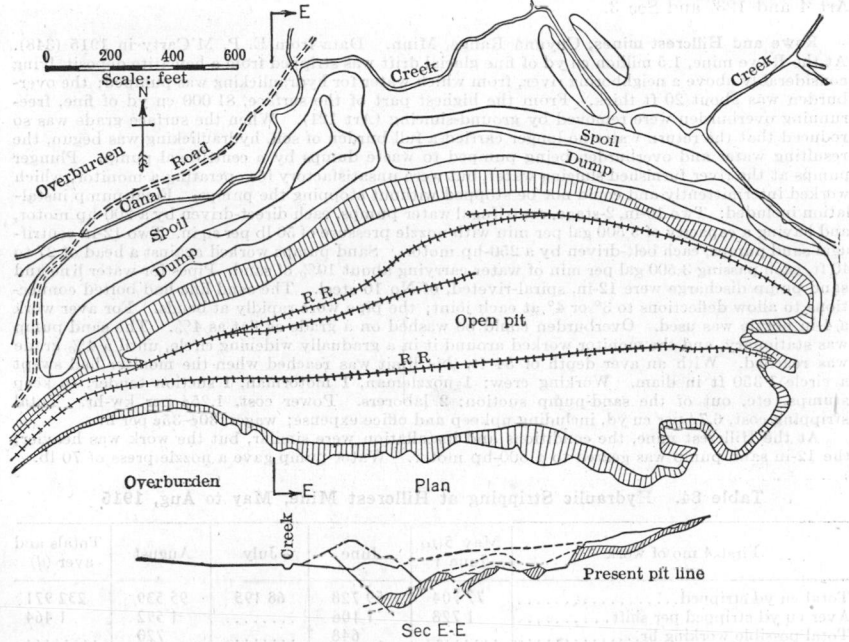

Fig 683. Open-pit Mining with Dragline, Cristo, Cuba

Tennessee brown phosphate. Data from P. M. Tyler and H. R. Mosley (338) in 1939. For prospecting, see Art 6, 10-a. "Brown rock," the most productive of phosphates mined in Tenn, is an enriched residual product from weathering of nearly horiz beds of phosphatic limestone. In the bed of clay matrix, 2–20 ft or more thick, phosphate occurs in platy slabs, to 24 in thick, and in lumps and grains down to microscopic size. Overburden of clay and low-grade matrix ranges to 20 ft or more, with few boulders. Where matrix is rich, 6 ft of overburden is profitably removed per ft of matrix; for lower-grade deposits, ratio is 3 : 1. Irregular pinnacles of unweathered rock sometimes project to surface; or, weathering enrichment may follow deeply into the original rock along joint planes. Under these conditions, considerable hand mining is entailed. In early days of hand mining exclusively, pieces smaller than about 1 in were discarded; now, with washers and flotation process, overall recovery from a matrix carrying 50–60% bone phosphate is 70–85% of phosphate content. Most STRIPPING AND MINING is now done by draglines of 1.5–4-yd capac, with 45 to 115-ft booms; shovels proved unsuitable (due to short reach) and all hydraulicking has been abandoned. Except where bedrock is fairly even, the smaller scrapers are best. Caterpillar mounting is commonest, but "walking" draglines are being introduced. A cut is usually made across the minable area, the excavator standing on the stripped matrix and loading cars on the same level or on bedrock, if it is fairly even. Stripping from next adjacent cut is then dropped into the space previously occupied by matrix. When hand work is required around pinnacles or in bedrock cavities, the material may be shoveled into steel boxes to be picked up and emptied by the excavator, but it is usually thrown into piles within reach of the scraper. HAULAGE is usually by 4-yd (3.75 dry long ton) Western side-dump cars, in trains of 12–20, hauled by coal-fired locos. At one important mine, producing 2 grades of matrix for delivery to different destinations, bottom-dump, 12-yd (12-ton) tractor trucks, on 18 by 24-in tires, have proved suitable; they are loaded by 4-yd walking dragline, standing at top of bank. COSTS. Mechanization of Tenn mines has been less rapid than in the larger deposits in Florida (Art 98) but is now nearly complete. Output of phosphate per man-yr was 575 tons in 1937, 543 tons in 1929, 312 tons in 1919, and 207 tons in 1909, by which year the richer, hand-worked deposits were largely exhausted. Costs vary widely, even at the same plant; following ranges, per dry long ton of cleaned product (aver 73% bone phos) are typical: stripping, 15–25¢; mining matrix, 20–40¢; transport to mill, 15–30¢; washing (excluding flotation), 50–75¢; drying, 50¢. Wages (1938) per hr: common labor, 30–40¢; dragline operators, 70–85¢; loco engineers, 50–60¢.

98. HYDRAULIC STRIPPING AND MINING

General. Where feasible, hydraulicking is cheap and rapid for stripping alluvium, or for mining unconsolidated deposits. It requires large volumes of cheap water; see Art 4 and 123, and Sec 3.

Rowe and Hillcrest mines, Cuyuna Range, Minn. Data from E. P. M'Carty in 1915 (348). At the Rowe mine, 1.5 million cu yd of fine glacial drift was stripped from a hematite deposit, lying considerably above a neighboring river, from which water for hydraulicking was pumped; the overburden was about 20 ft thick. From the highest part of the surface, 81 000 cu yd of fine, free-running overburden were removed by ground-sluicing (Art 121). When the surface grade was so reduced that the return water no longer carried a full burden of soil, hydraulicking was begun, the resulting water and overburden being pumped to waste dumps by a centrifugal pump. Plunger pumps at the river furnished sluicing water, but were unsatisfactory for operating a monitor, which worked intermittently and could not be stopped without stopping the pumps. Final pump installation included: Two 10-in, 2-stage, centrifugal water pumps, each direct-driven by a 200-hp motor, and having a capacity of 3 500 gal per min with nozzle pressure of 50 lb per sq in. Two 12-in centrifugal sand pumps, each belt-driven by a 250-hp motor. Sand pumps worked against a head of 27 to 40 ft, each passing 3 500 gal per min of water carrying about 10% of sand. Pipes for water line and sand pump discharge were 12-in, spiral-riveted, of No 16 steel. The sand line had bolted connections to allow deflections to 3° or 4° at each joint; the pipe wore rapidly at bends. For aver work a 4-in nozzle was used. Overburden could be washed on a grade as flat as 4%. The sand pump was stationary, and the monitor worked around it in a gradually widening circle, until a 4% grade was reached. With an aver depth of 54 ft, this limit was reached when the monitor had swept a circle 1 350 ft in diam. Working crew: 1 nozzleman, 1 motorman, 1 suction tender, to keep stumps, etc, out of the sand-pump suction; 2 laborers. Power cost, 1.25¢ per kw-hr. Total stripping cost, 6.7¢ per cu yd, including upkeep and office expense; wages, 30¢–35¢ per hr.

At the Hillcrest mine, the conditions and installation were similar, but the work was heavier; the 12-in sand pump was geared to a 300-hp motor. Water pump gave a nozzle press of 70 lb.

Table 84. Hydraulic Stripping at Hillcrest Mine, May to Aug, 1915

First 4 mo of work	May 5 to June 1	June	July	August	Totals and aver (d)
Total cu yd stripped...................	77 704	59 728	68 195	95 539	232 971
Aver cu yd stripped per shift..........	1 728	1 106	....	1 592	1 464
Total possible working hr..............	....	648	....	720	....
Total hr worked......................	442.90	497.75	550.50	639.83	1 580.48
Aver working hr per 12-hr shift........	9.85	9.20	....	10.65	9.94
Water used (a) { gal per min..........	3 606	2 740	3 240	3 580	3 330
{ miner's in (b)........	322	244	289	480	297
Duty of water (e).....................	10.7	9.07	....	6.64	9.86
% solids in sand-pump discharge.......	16.4	14.8	13.0(c)	13.2(c)	....

(a) For actual working time.   (b) 1 miner's in = 1.5 cu ft per min.   (c) Allowing for 200 gal per min seepage into the pit.   (d) Omitting July.   (e) Cu yd per miner's inch per 24 hr.

Table 85. Causes of Delays and Shutdowns (referring to Table 84)

Note. Delays are in hours	May 5 to June 1	June	July (c)	August	Total (d)	% of total (d)
Work on pipe line.........	12.78	54.42	57.25	50.25	117.45	36.8
Repairing pump............	29.33	72.67	30.58	11.00	113.00	35.4
Hot thrust-bearing.........	36.48	3.42	0.50	....	39.90	12.6
Setting up pumps..........	....	....	....	10.83	10.83	3.4
Power off.................	4.50	....	....	8.08	12.58	3.9
Miscellaneous.............	5.42(a)	19.75(b)	1.50	....	25.17	7.9
Total.................	88.51	150.26	....	80.16	318.93	100.0

(a) Includes packing pump, 2 hr; inspection and changing pump runner, 3.33 hr.   (b) Includes 16 hr lowering scow.   (c) Delay record incomplete.   (d) Omitting July.

The above work showed the economic limit for profitable hydraulic stripping to be sharply defined; operations can easily be carried to a point where the labor required over-balances the cheapness of the method. At the Rowe mine, a 6 to 8-ft layer of tough clay, sand, and boulders was left on top of the ore, to be cleaned up by steam shovels. Hydraulic stripping in this district saves considerable in original investment. Disadvantages, as compared with power shovel work (Art 96) : (a) stripping must be completed, at least over a large area, before mining can begin; (b) the equipment is useless for subsequent mining; (c) operations must stop in very cold weather (349).

Florida pebble phosphates. Data contributed in 1926 by K. C. Browne, with revisions by C. A. Fulton (148) in 1935; see also Bib (350). The nodules, from microscopic grains to 1 in diam, occur in flat beds in a clay-sand matrix. Thickness of deposits, max 40 ft, rarely over 25 ft; minimum workable, 6 ft; area, to several hundred acres; they lie on a clay bed, and are covered by 1 to 50 ft (aver 20) of sand and alluvium containing limestone boulders. The nodules form 15 25% of the phosphate matrix. STRIPPING, formerly with steam shovels, later by hydraulicking, is now wholly by draglines. These are usually elec driven; bucket, 4–9 yd; boom, 100 ft or more; caterpillar mounting is commonest, but "walking" type and wheel trucks are also used. The cut is usually 210 ft wide, and may be 0.5 mile long; an 8-yd machine digs about 600 cu yd per hr, dumping into exhausted adjoining cut, and moves 60 ft backward after about 3 shifts. Dragline also digs 30–40% of stripped matrix, from side nearest spoil bank, dumping it on top of undisturbed bed. During 1934, an 8-yd dragline, working 4 168 hr out of a possible 8 760 hr, moved 2 471 781 cu yd at cost of: 0.74¢ labor, 0.45¢ power (0.555 kw-hr), 0.64¢ supplies; total, 1.83¢ per cu yd. MINING. At 200–400 ft behind stripping face, matrix bed is hydraulicked by monitors through bedrock ditches to a sump, whence it is pumped by centrifugals to washing plant. Water is supplied to monitors, through 12- and 8-in spiral-welded pipe, by turbines, usually 1 pump to 2 monitors. Pumps are 2-stage, direct-connected to 400–1 000-hp motors, and deliver 2 000–6 000 gal per min at 175 to 225-lb press. Large units use 3-phase, 60-cycle, 2 300-volt ac. Nozzles are 1.75–2.5 in diam. A monitor with 2-in nozzle, at 200-lb press, discharges about 2 000 gal and moves 2 cu yd of matrix per min. When distance to face reaches 125–175 ft (in about 6 shifts) monitors are moved within 25 ft of face; a move of entire equipment, including blasting new sump and bedrock ditches (holes previously drilled and loaded), takes 1–1.5 hr. Bedrock ditches have grades of about 3 in per ft; at which, to prevent clogs, there must be 5 or 6 of water to 1 of matrix (by wt). At sump, a 10 to 12-in volute centrif, with 12-in suction pipe, is direct-connected to 150 to 300-hp, variable-speed motor, running 300–600 rpm. C-I pump runners, 30–38-in diam, have life of about 250 000 cu yd; steel discharge lines are 10 to 14-in outside diam. If distance to washing plant exceeds 1 500 ft, one or more relay pumps are connected to discharge line, increasing cost of operation by about 1¢ per cu yd for each relay. Practice tends toward large pits and fewer washers; pulp has been moved 0.75 mile by 3 pumps in line. One large mine in 1934, working 4 413 hr out of a possible 8 760 hr, mined and pumped 1 025 000 cu yd of matrix an aver distance of 3 000 ft at cost of: 4.72¢ for labor, 4.62¢ power, 1.75¢ supplies, 0.99¢ misc; total, 12.08¢ per cu yd. Matrix bed averaged 8.46 ft thick. Following data (657) are aver for 1925 to 1935 inclusive, from 4 companies together producing half the total output of State since 1925: cu yd overburden per cu yd matrix, 1.78; cu yd matrix per long ton phosphate, including that recovered by flotation, 4.10.

Golden Ridges mine, New Guinea. Data from E. B. Jensen (333) in 1935. Orebody is a blanket formation lying on volcanic breccia and overlain by (max) 05 ft of decomposed porphyry; ratio of overburden to ore, about 3 : 1; top surface of ore is very irregular. Overburden is loosened by blasting and removed by hydraulicking; ore is then carried at vert face and scraper-hoisted to mill bin. Blast holes are 5 in diam and 44 ft deep (for aver 40 ft of overburden), spaced 20 ft in a row 25 ft from edge, and drilled by hand-actuated (6 natives) spudding bit and stem weighing 286 lb, at aver speed of 3 ft per hr. Holes, sometimes chambered, are loaded with rack-a-rock (potassium chlorate saturated with nitrobenzol just before loading), about 1 lb per 5 cu yd, esti-mating back break of 12 ft behind holes, and fired with Cordeau, usually 5 at a time, breaking about 6 720 cu yd. Sluicing water, via ditch, flume, and tunnel, is conducted to any one of 3 monitors through 300 ft of 10-in and 300 ft of 8-in, spiral-riveted pipe with stove-pipe joints. Section lengths are 10 ft on straight lines, 5 ft on curves. Static head at monitor, about 130 ft; 2-in nozzle, deliv-ering 1.5 cu ft per sec, is best; with sluice grade of 1 : 5, that amount of water will move 50 cu yd per hr of freshly loosened overburden. To save excessive wear in sluice boxes, sluicing is best done over the rock bottom.

99. GLORY-HOLES (See also Art 37)

General. Fig 684 shows glory-hole work in a wide vein. Drift D is 50 to 100 ft below the surface, with raises R to the surface. The ore around each raise is "milled" into it, forming a funnel-shaped pit F, and is loaded through chute-gates into cars on level D. These pits are GLORY-HOLES, MILLS or MILLHOLES, and the method is called MILLING in some districts, as on the Lake Superior iron ranges (see Mesabi, below). The sides of glory-holes are kept steep enough for ore to slide to the raise. Ground is broken underhand; faces may be carried in benches, for convenience in setting up drills. When broken ore will no longer slide, due to flattening of the pit wall, a new cut is begun at the raise.

Unsystematic breaking of ground may result in very steep slopes, difficult and danger-ous to work. When working on steep slopes, drillers should be supported by ropes and safety belts; jackhammers are practically the only drilling machines for such conditions.

Adjacent glory-holes intersect as they are deepened. The ridges remaining between the holes when the level is reached may be milled through short raises put up in them, or they may be quarried and loaded out by hand. Raises often clog, causing costly delays. Grizzlies of timber or old rails are sometimes placed near their tops, to catch boulders to be broken (compare Fig 372, Art 59; see also Mesabi and Fresnillo, below). The proper interval between raises depends on their height, the shape and size of orebody, and the angle on which broken ore will slide; raises should be spaced so as to balance their first cost against cost of removing the ore in the ridges between the holes. Raises 30 to 50 ft high give less trouble from clogging than higher ones.

Limitations. Glory-holes may be adapted to masses or thick beds (see examples below). The ore should slide on moderate slopes and not pack in the raises. Bad weather seriously hinders the work; wet ore and water give trouble in raises; snow and ice make work on steep slopes doubly dangerous. Sur-

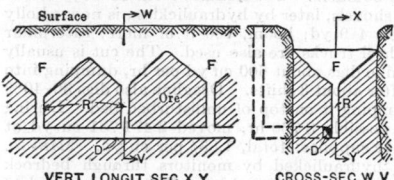

VERT LONGIT SEC X Y   CROSS-SEC W V
Fig 684.   Glory-hole Method (Diagrammatic)

face water must be kept out by ditching. The work is dangerous in veins (Fig 684), unless the walls are strong; loose slabs are barred down before they become inaccessible, but their menace always limits the depth of the glory-holes. This danger and trouble with hung-up raises are the chief DISADVANTAGES. The great ADVANTAGE is in providing cheap handling and loading, in connection with the cheap breaking common to open-cut work.

Alaska Treadwell mine (105). For ore occurrence and underground methods, see Art 68. In the first 6 years of its life (1890–1896), the entire production was from glory-holes; the resulting excavation was 1 700 ft long, 450 ft deep, with a max width of 420 ft. This work was stopped in 1906, because of a large slide of rock from the footwall and the necessity of leaving a pillar of ore to protect projected lower workings from surface water; the great depth made the danger from falling rock excessive. Glory-holes were started by a raise from an intermediate level, generally directly over a chute-raise. A stope, 20 to 30 ft high and covering 3 chute-raises, was opened around the bottom of the raise, for storage and to serve as a bulldozing chamber for breaking boulders which would block the chute-raises. The glory-hole faces were opened in a series of benches around the raise; so far as possible, large boulders were sledged in the pit. Piston drills, 3.25-in, made 12-ft holes. In small pits, where setting-up was easy, from 150 to 200 tons were broken per 10-hr drill-shift. As the pits grew larger and the sides steeper, setting up was more difficult and the output decreased to about 70 tons per 10-hr drill-shift.

Copper Queen mine, Bisbee, Ariz. Data from G. J. Young (341) in 1930. Ore remaining in bottom of Sacramento open pit, when depth became uneconomical for mechanical loading and loco haulage, was recovered by glory-holing through raises to grizzly and bulldozing chambers 130–145 ft below; pockets under grizzlies discharged through arc-gate chutes to main haulage level, 93 ft lower. For details of grizzly chambers, see Bib (341). Floor of pit, 400 by 450 ft, was divided among 11 vert raises, 10 by 10 ft, in 2 concentric circles (Fig 685). Drills employed: (a) Cyclone, gasolene-driven churn drills, working at top of bench and only far enough back from edge to insure firm footing; 6-in holes, 60 ft deep, spaced 18–23 ft; chambered 3–5 times, to take final charge of 400–500 lb of 40% gelatin (in wet holes), or No 2 quarry special; stemmed to depth of 25–35 ft; (b) tripod-mounted, Sullivan T3, working in niches on 45° slopes of pit; holes 18–25 ft deep, starting at 2.5 in; (c) jackhammers for blockholing and cutting niches, drilling holes to 16 ft deep. All holes fired elec. Heavy blasting did not entail excessive blockholing, due to fractured condition of ore. Max output, 2 500 tons per day; aver, 100 tons per man-shift. Crew: 6 drillers, 6 helpers, 4 blasters, 1 nipper, 1 pipefitter, and foreman.

Mesabi Range, Minn (35, 183, 275, 351). See Art 10-b, 71, 96. The MILLING SYSTEM is used here in deposits which can be profitably stripped, but are too small to warrant the investment for power shovels, or are so situated or shaped that power shovels and locomotive haulage are impracticable. Milling is also used to recover ore from deep portions of power-shovel pits, inaccessible by R R tracks on economical grades. PLAN OF WORK. A shaft is sunk outside of the orebody, with levels 50 to 100 ft apart; the 1st level is usually 50 to 70 ft below the top of the ore. Fig 686 shows a favorable layout of levels for deposits of large area. The elliptical main haulageway H facilitates motor-haulage; crosscuts C are 40 to 50 ft apart. Untimbered raises R, 4 by 4 ft to 5 by 5 ft, are put up to the surface every 40 to 50 ft, with chute-gate at the bottom of each. Another plan is to drive on each level a rectangular system of drifts, connecting with a main haulageway. In vein-like deposits, a central drift is driven with crosscuts to walls at 50 to 100-ft intervals, from which raises are put up.

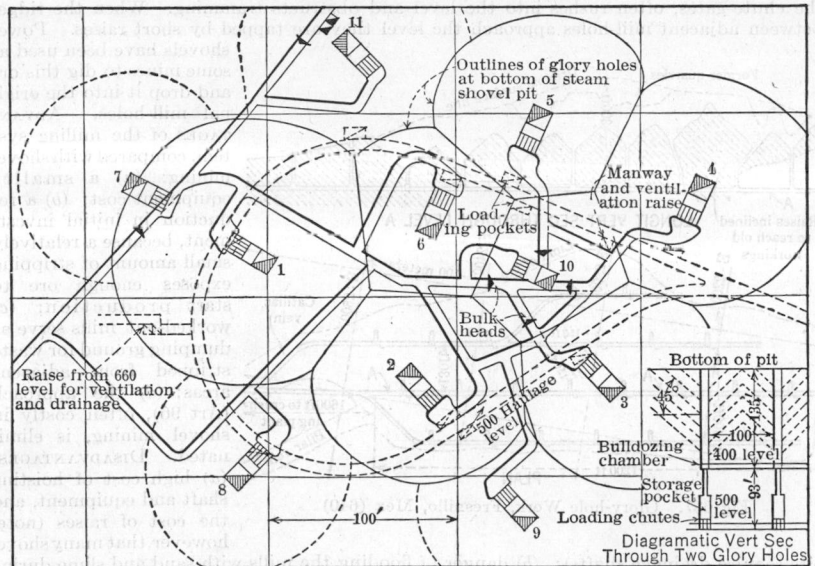

Fig 685. Distribution of Glory-holes, Copper Queen Mine

Several mill-holes are opened simultaneously, to provide numerous working places. After starting a mill-hole, the sloping faces are attacked first at the raise; alternate blasting and picking-down proceed up the slopes; when the ore will no longer run to the raise, a new cut is started. Mesabi ores break small, and run readily on 45° slopes; in dry weather, on 38°. Slabs are barred down after each blast, by men supported by ropes; ropes are also left hanging in mill-holes for men to grasp in case of a sudden slide of ore into the raise. Effic of milling increases with size of the mill-holes. Raises often hang up, especially when starting mill-holes. Clogs are lessened by breaking large boulders before they reach the raise, and by drawing the ore down frequently before it has time to pack. At Monroe mine, sub-drifts were driven above the haulage level, connecting all raises and giving opportunity for barring down clogs; main-level drifts are sometimes 2 sets high at raises, to facilitate barring. At the Iroquois mine, a chain or wire rope hanging in each raise was raised by a small hoist and pulled down by men on the level, in case of a clog. High raises are more apt to clog than shorter ones; at the Jordan mine, a decrease in height from 85 to 30 or 40 ft materially reduced delays. Tapering raises have been tried, but it is difficult to design chute-gates that will prevent ore from collecting on the sides of the raise and destroying its taper. Production from milling is usually irregular, being influenced largely by the weather. Heavy rain stops work and washes out gullies on the sides of the mill, which must be filled by broken ore before resuming regular operation. Rains also block the raises with fine ore and water, which, on opening

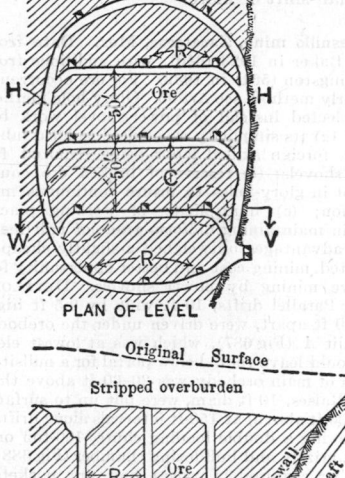

PLAN OF LEVEL

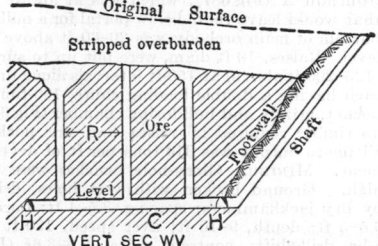

VERT SEC WV

Fig 686. Milling System, Mesabi Range (Diagrammatic)

the chute-gates, often rushes into the level and obstructs tramming. When the ridges between adjacent mill-holes approach the level they are tapped by short raises. Power shovels have been used at some mines to dig this ore and drop it into the original mill-holes. ADVANTAGES of the milling system, compared with shovel mining: (*a*) a smaller equipment cost; (*b*) a reduction in initial investment, because a relatively small amount of stripping exposes enough ore to start production; (*c*) worked-out mills serve as dumping ground for waste stripped from adjacent areas; (*d*) the approach (Art 96), often costly in shovel mining, is eliminated. DISADVANTAGES: (*a*) high cost of hoisting shaft and equipment, and the cost of raises (note, however, that many shovel

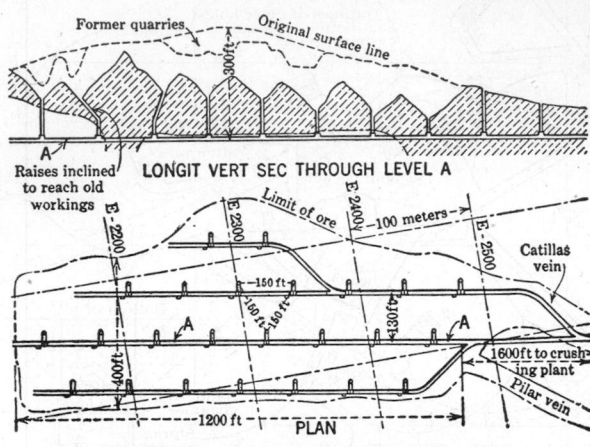

Fig 687. Glory-hole Work, Fresnillo, Mex (640)

pits require drainage shafts); (*b*) danger of flooding the mills with sand and slime during storms; partly controllable by surface ditching. COST of mining ore by miling is higher per ton than from shovel pits of reasonable capac, and lower than from top-slicing (Art 71). Duty of labor is high, up to 25–30 tons per man-shift or more.

Fresnillo mine, Zacatecas, Mex. Data from T. C. Baker in 1923 (640), with additions from A. Livingston (561) in 1932. For ore occurrence and early method, see Art 95. Glory-hole method was selected instead of power-shovel work because: (*a*) its simplicity was suited to local labor supply, foreign skilled labor being required for power shovels; (*b*) reserve of broken ore could be kept in glory-holes to insure continuous mill operation; (*c*) multiplicity of working places aided in maintaining uniform grade of mill feed. These advantages outweighed a slightly cheaper estimated mining cost and better opportunity for selective mining by power shovels. DEVELOPMENT. Parallel drifts, 10 ft wide by 9.5 ft high and 130 ft apart, were driven under the orebody from adit *A* (Fig 687), which was at lowest elev that would leave room below portal for a millsite; bottom of main orebody was 20–60 ft above this level. Raises, 10 ft diam, were put up to surface (125–200 ft above) at 150-ft intervals along drifts, each having a double loading chute, 100-ton ore pocket, grizzly and bulldozing chamber (Fig 688); no timber required in raises and ore pockets. Ultimate output was 313 tons per ft of development. MINING. Glory-hole benches were 9 ft high. Ground broken with vert holes, drilled by dry jackhammers; spacing, 3.5–4 ft; burden, 3.5–5 ft; depth, 9–10 ft; aver speed, 120 ft per 8-hr drill-shift; contract price, 2.8–3.6¢ (U S) per ft. Aver charge per hole, 1.5 lb "Durox." About 6 tons of ore were broken per lb explosive; 0.107 cap and 1.2 ft of fuse used per ton. Comparatively close spacing and shallow depth of hole proved cheaper in total cost (including blockholing, clogged raises, etc) than deep holes and heavy charges. Best slope for sides of glory holes

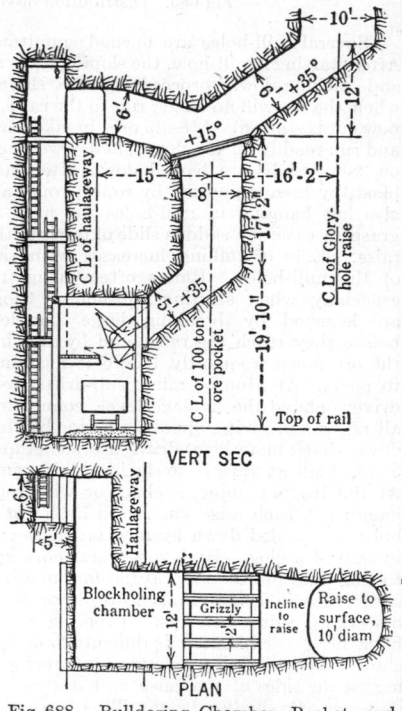

Fig 688. Bulldozing Chamber, Pocket, and Chute, Fresnillo, Mex (640)

found to be 50°–60°; ore remaining between bottoms of glory-holes, when slope decreased to 35°, was removed in horiz benches with barrows. Aver output, over whole operation, 130 tons per drill-shift, or 8 000–10 000 tons per grizzly per mo (3 shifts). HAULAGE was by elec loco, in 9-car trains of 10-cu yd cars. For mining waste, the raise affected was emptied of ore; waste was loaded from chute-gates into smaller cars. Total cost of equipment (much of it bought during high-price post-war period), and buildings for producing 3 500 tons per day was approx $140 000; this shows comparatively low initial investment for glory-hole work. See Bib (640) for comprehensive data on details.

Table 86.   Aver Data, Fresnillo Glory-hole Pit, 1921–1925

Man-hr per ton ore:	
Breaking............	0.332
Secondary blasting...	.129
Transportation......	.129
General and surface..	.037
	0.627
Power, kw-hr per ton...	2.010
Explosives, lb per ton..	0.217
Timber, bd-ft per ton..	0.070

Mt Isa, Queensland.   Data from J. Kruttschnitt and V. I. Mann (500) in 1937.   For ore occurrence, see Art 43.   Upper and oxidized portion of Black Star lode, glory-holed to 150-ft depth, was 1 100 ft long by 200 ft wide at middle of lens, which dipped 55°–60°; narrow ridge of high ground on hanging-wall side was leveled off first.   Outcrop length was about evenly divided among 7 raises, each connecting through grizzly chamber and ore pass with main haulage level on footwall 400 ft lower (Fig 689).   Benching around top of

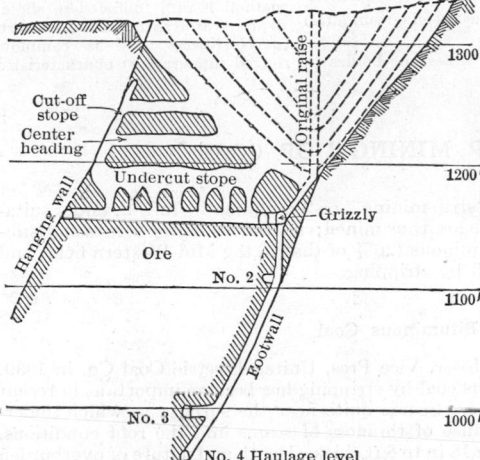

Fig 689.   **Vert Cross-sec through Glory-hole, Mt Isa, Queensland** (500)

raise was done with jackhammers, holes 6–16 ft deep; miners, on day shift only, had to wear safety belts; ladders provided for access. Aver slope of walls, 50°. All holes chambered; explosive producing best fragmentation was slow-acting, 25% ammonia-base dynamite. Triangular remnants between bottoms of glory-holes were mined (Fig 689) by transverse sub-level open stopes with ring-drilled pillars like those later adopted in wider parts of the sulphide orebody at lower levels (Art 43). The 15-ft pillars between stopes 30 ft wide proved inadequate to support hanging wall (weakened by undisclosed fractures) and caving occurred when about 60% of the remnant ore had been removed; drawing of crushed ore was continued until dilution by wall rock became excessive. Cost of glory-holing 270 063 tons in first half of 1933 was: labor and supervision (mining 51%, transport, 39%), 32.9¢; drills, steel, and comp air, 5.1¢; other power (mainly transp), 5.2¢; explosives, 7.4¢; timber and other supplies, 3.2¢; total, 53.8¢ per short ton.

Round Valley tungsten mine, Bishop, Cal.   Example of small-scale work described by W. O. Vanderburg (637) in 1935.   Deposit of contact-metamorphic limestone, containing scheelite and averaging 0.5% WO₃, is 125 by 200 ft in area.   Working level, at bottom of 75° inclined shaft 100 ft deep, has 7 raises, 5 by 6 ft, up to pit bottom.   Drilling with dry jackhammers; blasting with 40% gelatin and fuse.   Raises are kept full of broken ore, to hold back large blocks until they can be bulldozed; some hand shoveling required.   Ore from chutes is trammed by hand and hoisted by skip.   Crew of 11 men produce 120 tons per single-shift day, at total working cost of 76.3¢ per ton. Unit costs per ton: all labor (40% on breaking), 0.799 man-hr; power (@1.5¢), 1.9 kw-hr; explosives, 0.33 lb.

Tunnel method.   Data from D. T. Farnham in 1914 (352).   This is a variant of glory-hole work, for securing cheap loading costs in open cuts without putting up raises.   A shale quarry at Renton, Wash, is illustrative (Fig 690).

The quarry face was 700 ft long by 150 ft high; output, about 700 tons per day; small output and high working face rendered power-shovel work inapplicable.   Heavily timbered tunnels *T* were driven from the quarry floor into the face, and 6 by 12-in timbers, 8 in apart, were placed on the caps to form a grizzly.   Hopper gates (Art 90) were built between sets.   The tunnels were about 25 ft long, 5 sets being kept in the solid, and 7 or 8 sets erected outside.   About 20 tunnels were driven 20 ft apart along the face. The bank was then blasted down, the grizzlies being first covered with 3 by 12-in plank and a 2 or 3-ft layer of shale; from 2 000 to 3 000 tons were shot down in 1 blast on a group of 3 tunnels. The planks were then removed from the grizzlies, 1 or 2 at a time, starting at the outermost set; the broken shale was bulldozed as necessary and worked through into cars below. The ridges of shale between the tunnels were loaded by hand. A 3-man crew loaded 2.3-ton cars and trammed them 200 ft at an aver rate of 1.9 cars per man per hr in summer and 1.7 per hr in winter, or 4.37 tons per man-hr. Before using tunnels the duty of labor, in loading 2-ton cars by hand from the quarry floor on a 100-ft tram, was 2 tons per man-hr. Same method is still followed in shale deposits at Renton and elsewhere in Northwest, and is common practice in the steeply pitching lenticular limestone bodies (in rugged topography) characteristic of the region.

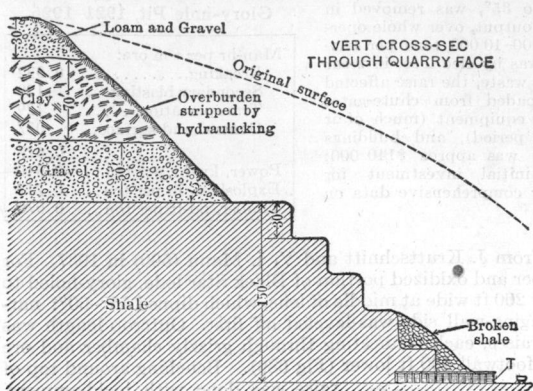

Fig 690. Tunnel Method, Renton, Wash (Diagrammatic)

100. "STRIP MINING" OF COAL

Open-cut mining of coal is termed "strip mining," or "stripping." In U S, under suitable conditions, both hard and soft coals are thus mined; in 1937, U S Bur Mines statistics show that 7.1% of total output of bituminous (26% of that in the Mid-Western field) and 11% of Penn anthracite were obtained by stripping.

(a) Bituminous Coal

Data kindly supplied by M. M. Moser, Vice Pres, United Electric Coal Co, in 1939.

General. Production of bituminous coal by stripping has become important in recent years, especially in Mid-Western fields. Seams quite near the surface, to which underground methods are inapplicable because of thinness of seams and the roof conditions, are successfully stripped; they are from 18 in to 8 ft thick. Depth and nature of overburden are variable, but depths to 90 ft have been profitably removed. Topography of stripping areas and the coal seams are both generally fairly level. In spite of the apparent simplicity of stripping, systematic prospecting, familiarity with technique, long-range planning, proper equipment and well trained mechanical organization are essential. Quality and thickness of coal, character and depth of overburden, distance from pit to preparation plant, and freight rates to markets, are important. Costs vary widely, depending chiefly upon character of overburden and thickness of coal. In some areas, hard limestone, requiring blasting, overlies the coal; in others, overburden is mainly alluvium. The economic ratio in Mid-West fields is about 10 ft of overburden per ft of coal. Proper drainage is important in a strip mine, which is often 60–70 ft deep; heavy rainfalls can cause serious damage to equipment and completely paralyze operations.

Stripping methods. In 1939, 3 systems of stripping were practiced in Mid-West coal fields. Fig 691 shows a mine employing a SINGLE STRIPPING SHOVEL, advancing in direction of the arrow, and removing overburden A which, if of rock or shale, has been loosened by blasting. The shovel crawlers rest on the cleaned coal seam. Stripped material goes to a waste bank B, piled in the cut from which the coal has been taken. The toe of waste bank rests against edge of coal seam, and its far side lies on bank C of the previous cut. The cross-sec in Fig 691 shows the relation between depth of overburden A, width of coal seam D, height and slope of waste banks B and C. The largest shovel in use in 1939 has a 32-cu yd dipper; boom lengths, up to 125 ft. Stripping by shovel (as of 1939) is limited to depths of about 60 ft, depending on lengths of boom and dipper handle. Volume handled by a large 30-cu yd shovel is about 1 250 cu yd per hr. The uncovered coal is blasted and loaded by smaller shovels (0.5–6 cu yd) into trucks or R R cars.

Fig 692 shows working positions of machines in a TANDEM STRIPPING operation, using a shovel in conjunction with a dragline; the crawlers of both rest on exposed coal. Work progresses in direction of the arrow, shovel E removing block C, the top of which has been previously benched by dragline D. The dragline benches the cut B, preparing it for next trip of the shovel; the material is earth, clay, or shale. The 2 machines handle

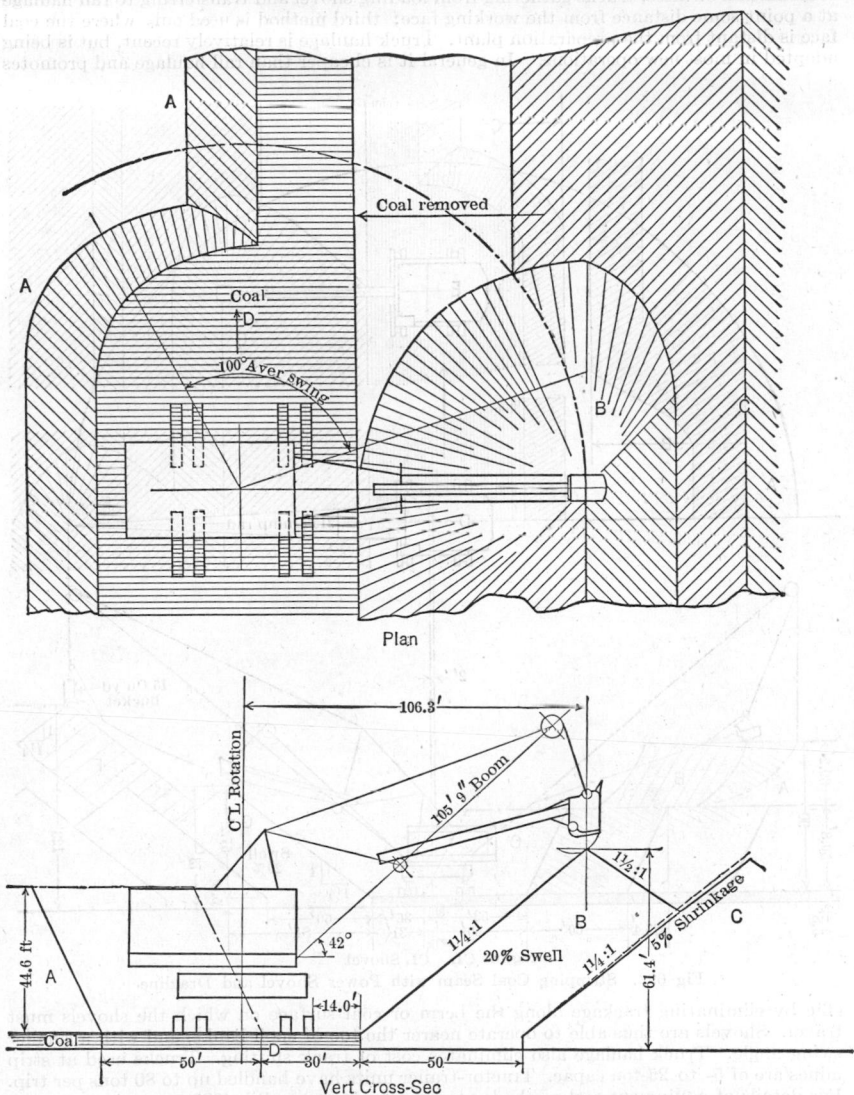

Plan

Vert Cross-Sec

Fig 691. Stripping Coal Seam with Power Shovel Alone

nearly equal amounts of overburden. That of the dragline is piled in a windrow F behind and above the rock G, which has been stacked by the shovel (Fig 692). The draglines have buckets up to 14 cu yd, with 160-ft booms. Overburden 90 ft deep has thus been well handled. Fig 693 shows a SINGLE DRAGLINE on a bench about one-third the depth from surface to the coal. A walking dragline is preferred because more manageable on poor footing. The loading shovel follows the dragline, as shown. When stripping bench *F*, the dragline works along lines *A–B* and *C–D*; the lower material is usually the firmer and hence is put into the base of spoil bank. In stripping bench *G*, the dragline works along line *C–D* only, placing the material in the nearest windrow, as at *E*. Easy digging is a requisite, and bucket capac must be sacrificed to the reach required for success.

Haulage from the loading face to tipple or preparation plant is by trucks, rail, or a combination of these, trucks gathering from loading shovel and transferring to rail haulage at a point some distance from the working face; third method is used only where the coal face is distant from the preparation plant. Truck haulage is relatively recent, but is being adopted in most new operations. In general it is cheaper than rail haulage and promotes

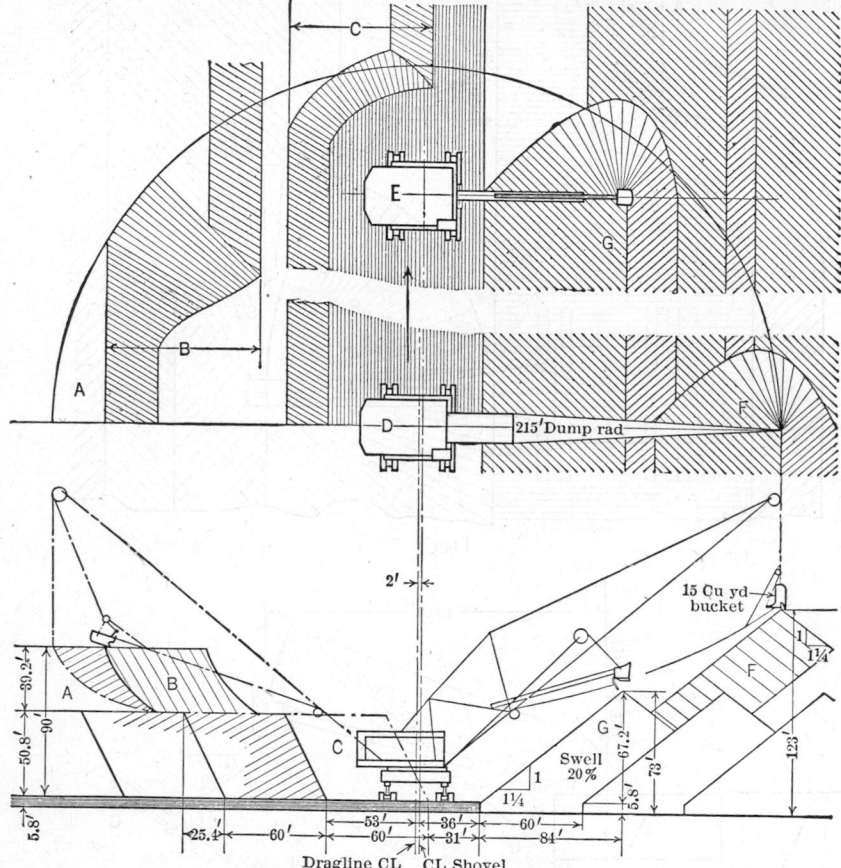

Fig 692. Stripping Coal Seam with Power Shovel and Dragline

effic by eliminating trackage along the berm or coal surface on which the shovels must travel. Shovels are thus able to operate nearer the toe of spoil banks, and with a smaller swing angle. Truck haulage also eliminates cost of track shifting. Trucks used at strip mines are of 5- to 25-ton capac. Tractor-trailer units have handled up to 80 tons per trip. For details of equipment and methods at several mines, see Bib (680).

(b) Anthracite Coal

Data from H. H. Otto in 1931, R. D. Hall in 1935, H. N. Eavenson in 1936, and others (671).

General. Strip-mining in anthracite fields has recently advanced notably in tonnage, area of individual strippings, and depth of cover removed; it is applied both to virgin coal and to outcrops where much of the coal has previously been mined from below. When steam-shovels were first applied, in 1881, max economic limit of overburden was held to be 1 ft per ft of coal; by 1911, the ratio (with 60% rock in overburden) had reached 3 : 1; in 1936, ratios were 7 : 1. Crystal Ridge stripping (begun 1925 and finished 1934), 2 700 ft long, 500 ft wide, 165 ft deep, moved 5 200 000 cu yd of overburden to recover 665 000 tons of coal; Summit Hill stripping (begun 1925) moved 7 300 000 cu yd of overburden and marketed 2 200 000 tons of coal during its first 10 yr, and will eventually have moved a total of 13 000 000 cu yd to recover 4 600 000 tons of coal.

Increase in the profitable ratio of overburden to coal has been due to cheaper excavation by draglines and power shovels, automotive haulage, and the abandonment of inclined planes for hoisting. In nearly flat seams, back-filling similar to that used in bituminous beds is practicable (see Clinton colliery, below). In steeply pitching seams, involving

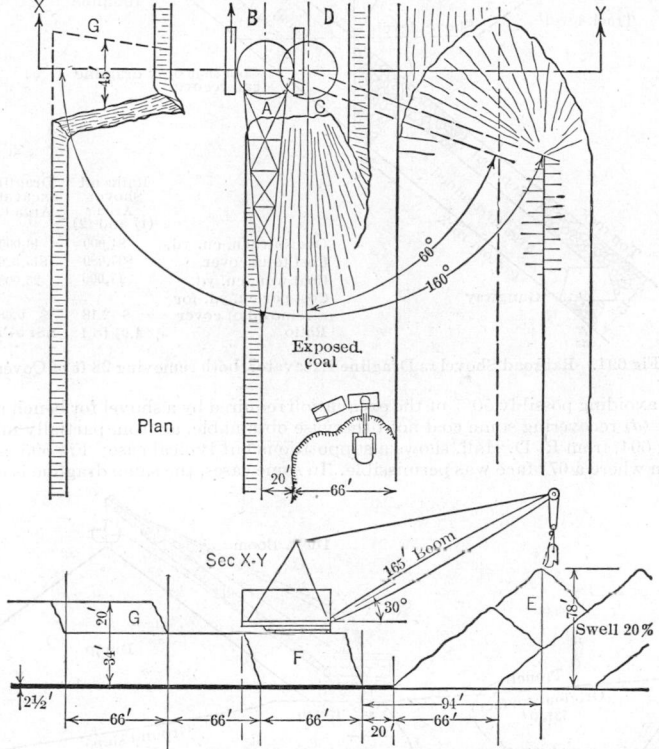

Fig 693. Stripping Coal Seam with Dragline Alone

deep and narrow strippings, back-filling is rarely possible, except where overburden from one end can be dumped at the other end with some saving in haulage. Dragline excavators have been less rapidly adopted in the northern field, where the wider strippings make haulage of some kind unavoidable, and shovel loading more generally applicable.

Flat seams. Clinton colliery, in the northern field, has a nearly flat bed 65 in thick containing 50 in of coal, under aver 25 ft of overburden (half sandstone, and half earth). Stripping area, 28.3 acres; overburden, 1 112 000 cu yd; coal, 174 000 tons. A Monighan, Diesel-driven, 375-ton walking dragline excavator, with 160-ft boom and 6-yd bucket, first uncovered the outcrop by a trench 130 ft wide at top, 75 ft at bottom, depositing spoil, without other handling, in a pile 55 ft high and 70 ft back from edge. Rock was broken with jackhammer holes staggered at 8-ft spacing in parallel rows, loaded with 40% gelatin (0.5 lb per cu yd) and fired elec, 100 at a blast; broken rock removed by same excavator. Coal was loosened with black powder, and loaded into mine cars by Diesel, 50-ton Bucyrus shovel with 1.25-yd dipper. Haulage by 20-ton gasolene locos out of pit; thence by mine locos to tipple. After extracting coal from first trench, another slice was taken, depositing spoil in space just made.   Max operating force (excavator working 2 shifts), 27 men, of whom 9 were on part-time. In 2 mos of 1931, 163 700 cu yd (about 1/3 rock) were moved; delays, 5% of working time; while swinging 180°, aver time was 1.5 min per cycle.

Pitching seams. For these, draglines with buckets of 5 to 12 cu yd have advantages of: (*a*) long casting reach; (*b*) permitting steep banks, since only the bucket is endangered by

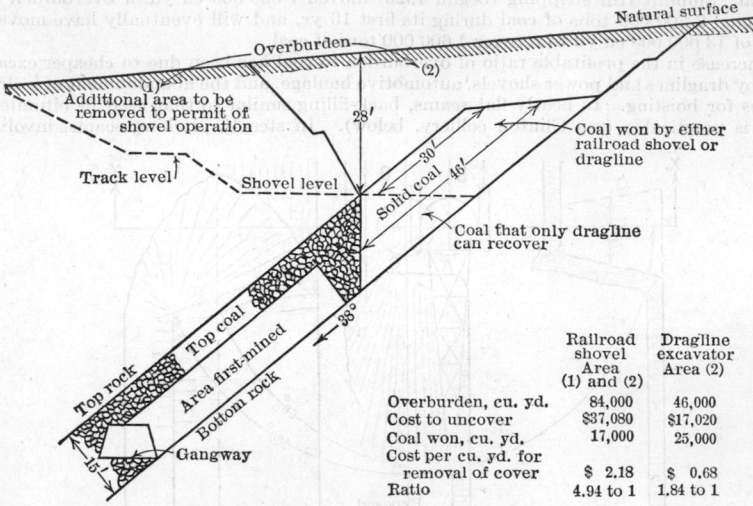

	Railroad shovel Area (1) and (2)	Dragline excavator Area (2)
Overburden, cu. yd.	84,000	46,000
Cost to uncover	$37,080	$17,020
Coal won, cu. yd.	17,000	25,000
Cost per cu. yd. for removal of cover	$ 2.18	$ 0.68
Ratio	4.94 to 1	1.84 to 1

Fig 694.   Railroad Shovel *vs* Dragline Excavator, both removing 28 ft of Cover

slides; (*c*) avoiding possibly 50% of the excavation required by a shovel for bench and loading roads; (*d*) recovering some coal not otherwise obtainable, as from partially mined outcrops. Fig 694, from R. D. Hall, shows a suppositious but typical case; Fig 695, a dragline installation where a 67° face was permissible. In some cases, the same dragline is employed

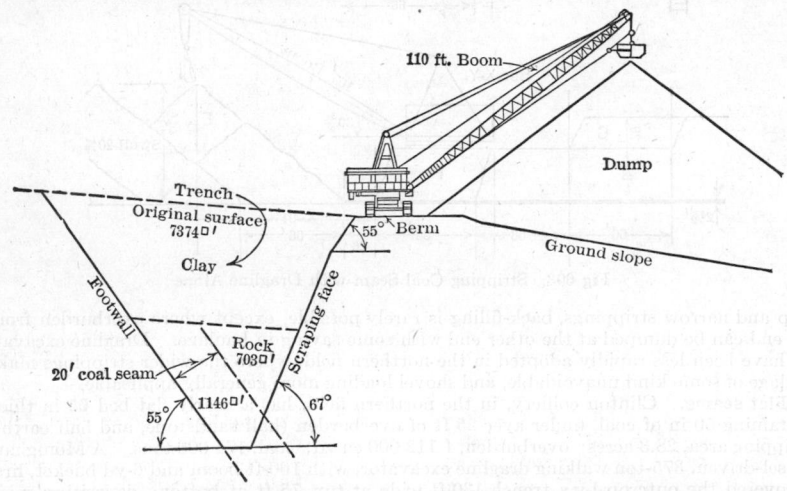

Fig 695.   Dragline Excavation at Merriam Stripping

on both overburden and coal; in others, coal is loaded by shovel or another dragline. Rock is generally broken with unchambered, 6-in, churn-drill holes; above a previously mined bed, holes are usually placed only over pillars. For transport, tractor-trailers, and trucks, have largely replaced locos and cars, due to (*a*) saving in track laying, moving, and maintenance; roads are quickly prepared by bulldozers, and 1 man at dump replaces a track-moving gang; (b) smaller capital cost; in rush seasons, trucks can be rented; (c) steeper grades (to 15 or 20%) and sharper turns permissible; (d) less working space required around loader; (e) more continuous loading is usually possible; (f) automotives easily shifted from one job to another. Following examples illustrate strippings on pitching coal.

Summit Hill. For yardage and tonnage, see above. Coal 50–400 ft thick, latter due to folding; only upper part will be stripped. Equipment: for overburden, 1 Bucyrus 320B, elec shovel, 7.5-yd, and 2 Bucyrus 120B, elec shovels, 4-yd; for coal, 1 Link-Belt K55, gas-elec dragline, 2-yd, and 1 Marion 37, elec, convertible shovel-dragline, 1.75 and 1.5-yd; 19 6-in churn drills, 12 elec, 7 gasolene driven; 2 wagon drills; 35 standard-gage, 30-yd, side-dump cars for spoil; 10 geared locos, 50–65-ton; 5 rod locos, 38–55 ton. Coal loaded into R R cars on track at 3% max grade.

Crystal Ridge (Mammoth seam). For yardage and tonnage, see above. Stripped with Bucyrus 7.5-yd, elec shovel; waste hauled 5 900 ft up 3.5% grade to dump in 30-yd cars; coal loaded with 3-yd elec shovel. Same stripping later extended 70 ft, with dragline having 3.5-yd bucket for clay, 4-yd for rock, casting and re-casting into old pit. Totals: 27 300 cu yd clay, 73 500 yd rock, 13 500 yd caved material from old rooms, to yield 46 200 cu yd coal loaded by shovel into trucks.

Hell's Kitchen. Primrose virgin coal, 30 ft thick, dipping 30°; removing 1 300 000 cu yd overburden uncovered 514 000 tons coal. Stripped with 2 Bucyrus 70C steam shovels loading 4-yd, side-dump cars; hauled up 3% grade by 20-ton steam locos. Coal loaded by one of the above shovels, or a 1.5-yd gasolene shovel, into mine cars.

Lansford. Mammoth seam, 55 ft thick, dipping 60°, previously mined. Outcrop exposed for 6 000 ft; stripped to 65 ft deep, both walls sloping 60°. Shovels, 2.5-yd in rock, 1.5-yd in coal, load Mack trucks dumping into tops of old rooms connecting with haulage level 360 ft below.

Richards. Synclinal fold with dips of 43° and 64°; pit 130 ft deep in 1934, expecting to reach 184 ft. Coal in 3 splits, with slate and sandstone partings 4–5 and 10 ft thick. Marion 490 shovel loads trucks which climb ramps along sides and across ends of stripping.

Wm Penn, at Shenandoah. Mammoth seam in 2 splits; parting widens from 40 to 180 ft within length of stripping. As dip is in same direction as slope of hill, outcrop of top split, 14.5 ft thick, lies downhill from that of bottom split, 17.5 ft thick, and its stripping advances ahead of the other. Both strippings are overcast downhill by Bucyrus dragline with 2-yd buckets.

101. MISCELLANEOUS DATA, OPEN-CUT MINING

Economic limit of depth. Open cutting loses its advantage of cheapness where the stripping cost per ton of ore exposed exceeds the difference in cost between open-cut and underground mining. For large, flat deposits, with fairly uniform cover of moderate depth, the problem is simple, as the cost per ton of ore for excess stripping to provide safe slopes around the pit is so small that errors in its estimation are unimportant. But, on small areas and for deep overburden, the cost of stripping slopes is important. In dipping deposits, where one or both walls must often be cut back to safe slopes, the amount of stripping is not a simple function of the depth, and this complicates calculations of the economic limit of open cutting. In districts where enough underground and surface mining have been done to establish fairly accurate unit costs, close estimates can be made from borings or other data, to determine the feasibility or limits of open cuts. The max depth of profitable stripping is often expressed in terms of a ratio of cu yd of stripping per ton or cu yd of ore (or ft of overburden per ft of ore). These ratios are useful if applied intelligently; ratios applicable in a well known district may be incorrect in a new region.

Mesabi estimates (35). Sometimes a choice of method can be made by inspecting the ore estimate (Art 11). Relative costs of underground and open-pit mining are usually calculated by applying unit costs to a column 1 yd sq. EXAMPLE: a drill hole shows 50 ft of drift and paint rock, 15 ft hard taconite, and 36 ft merchantable ore; general conditions allow use of either method. Comparison of costs, using 1912 unit costs (641) which, though old, illustrate method of calculation:

Underground mining. Cost of mining a volume of ore 1 yd sq by 36 ft high
@ 75¢ per ton (1 cu yd = 2 tons)..................................... $18.00
Open-pit mining. Stripping a column of overburden 1 yd sq by 50 ft
deep @ 30¢ per cu yd....................................... $5.00
Stripping 15 ft of taconite = 5 cu yd @ $1 per yd............... 5.00
Steam-shovel mining of 36 ft of ore = 24 tons @ 15¢ per ton...... 3.60   13.60

Saving by open-pit work per sq yd of area............................ $4.40

Similar calculations are made for other drill holes, and all are combined in proportion to the tonnage represented by each. This preliminary estimate is supplemented by more exact figures when necessary. Questions of adverse topography, dumping facilities, presence of swamps, quicksand, etc, are local factors which do not permit generalization.

Pennsylvania anthracite stripping (345) (see also Art 100) is generally undertaken when it is cheaper than underground mining. But strippings yield higher extraction, cleaner coal and a higher percentage of prepared sizes (Sec 34), and allow close adjustment of output to demand; these factors may be decisive in making a choice. Strippings are often opened to recover coal otherwise not minable. EXAMPLES in determining the economic limit of depth and area of strippings: Fig 696 shows a stripping based on a ratio of 2.75 cu yd of overburden removed per ton of coal uncovered. But on resolving the operation into its component parts (see areas A, B, C, etc), it is found that area A is the lowest one within this ratio. For areas B and C the ratios are 3 : 1 and 3.5 : 1 respectively; that is, they are removed at a loss, even though a considerable profit comes from areas D and E. Hence, to justify this operation, marked advantages must be gained by removing B and C. Fig 697 shows a crop stripping common in the southern anthracite fields; either the cover must be removed, or a thick chain pillar of coal left, as shown. The coal below the pillar is minable at as low a UNIT COST for cutting and loading as could be realized by mining the entire upper 250 ft of seam from gangway W after stripping the overburden. By the latter method, DEVELOPMENT COSTS would be less by a few cents per ton. But, comparing the results with the case in Fig 696, the ratio here is 4 cu yd stripping per ton of coal in the chain pillar, or a ratio of 1 : 1 based on the total coal above gangway W. Hence, the coal strictly classed as stripping coal is mined at a loss (345).

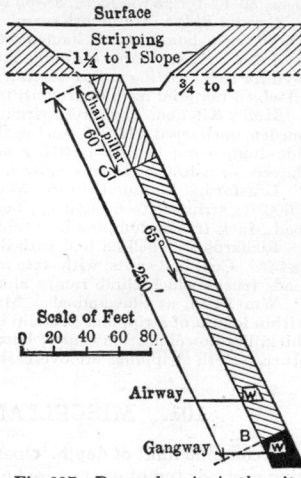

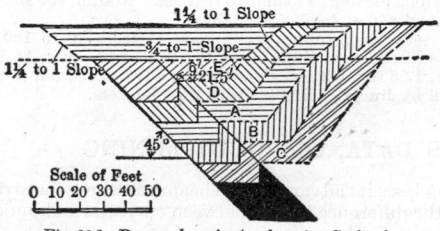

Fig 696. Pennsylvania Anthracite Stripping

Fig 697. Pennsylvania Anthracite Stripping

Porphyry coppers. Estimates of economic stripping limits at these mines often involve problems arising from fluctuating metal prices, varying smelter contracts, differences in milling costs and recoveries, and freight rates. Parts of the overburden often contain a little copper, and when this must be mined and loaded in any case, it may sometimes be more profitable to send it to mill than to dumps. The factors involved in these problems are shown in the following formula, used at Chino mine to ascertain the lowest grade of rock that may be called minable ore (340); all costs, and the copper price, are in dollars or fractions, and percentages are expressed as decimals:

$$\frac{M + F_0 + m}{A\,2\,000pC} + \frac{f_c + S}{D\,2\,000p} + R + E + c = B\frac{100}{105}$$

transposing and simplifying:

$$A = \frac{M + F_0 + m}{2\,000pC\left[\dfrac{100B}{105} - \dfrac{f_c + S}{2\,000pD} - (R + E + c)\right]} \qquad \text{where}$$

M = mining cost per dry ton ore
F_0 = freight per dry ton, mine to mill
m = milling cost per dry ton
f_c = freight per dry ton of concentrates, mill to smelter
S = smelting charges per dry ton of concentrates
R = refining and delivery charges per lb Cu

E = export freight and insurance per lb Cu
c = commissions, per lb Cu
p = % Cu contents paid for by smelter
B = assumed price per lb Cu
C = % recovery at mill
D = % Cu in concentrates
A = % Cu in material in question

The above formula includes an unusual refinement in using the factor $100 \div 105$, which allows 5% interest for the period (estimated as 5 mos) between mining the ore and sale of its contained copper. For further detail, see Bib (340).

Slopes of faces in power-shovel mining. Following data from E. E. Barker in 1911 (339) are based on experience at the Nevada Consol (Art 96).

The slope at which a bank will stand depends on the depth to be excavated, as well as character of the material; hence no general rule can be formulated. Slopes steeper than

1 : 1 will not stand in the leached porphyry and fractured schist of the disseminated copper deposits. Blasting shatters harder rocks, so that banks will not stand much steeper than 0.66 horiz: 1 vert. Faults, if present, may necessitate flatter slopes. Experience with rock "flows," in deep excavations in soft rock on the Panama canal, shows that slopes suitable for ordinary work may not stand on great depths. These statements indicate the wisdom of using generous slope allowances for both estimates and operation. (See Sec 3 and 5 for data on angles of repose and safe slopes.)

The slope of a working face as a whole is affected by the height and width of benches, number of benches, and slope of each face (Fig 698). For benches of equal size, the general slope is given by: $S = \dfrac{a + (n - 1)\, b}{nc}$, where S = general slope ratio, a = base of the bottom slope triangle, b and c = width and height of bench, n = number of benches. Fig 698 shows a layout suited to economical power-shovel work in soft porphyry ore; that is, the benches have the minimum economic width and the max economic height and slope; 50-ft benches are safe, and the shovel is seldom in danger of being buried. Width b depends largely on the slope of the broken ore which ordinarily will repose on a slope of

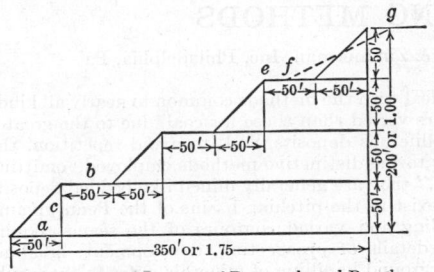

Fig 698. Ideal Layout of Power-shovel Benches, Nevada Consol Copper Co

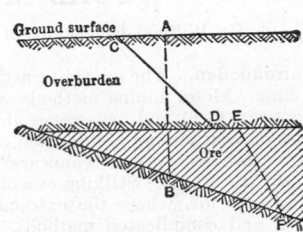

Fig 699. Limits of Power-shovel Pits, Mesabi (G. J. Young)

about 1.5 : 1, but the impetus given in blasting flattens the slope to about 2 : 1. Churn-drill holes for blasting are started about 10 ft from the edge of the bank, and loosen the ground for about 10 ft back; the position of the broken ore face is indicated by dotted line *fg*. The remaining clear space *ef* (about 20 ft wide) gives ample room for the loading track, without danger of its being buried by the blasts. The general slope of the 4 benches is 1.75 : 1; a larger or smaller number of benches would increase or decrease the ratio, in accordance with the formula.

Examples of practice as to overall slopes in open-cuts under different conditions are given in Art 95-97. See also remarks on pit slopes in Art 113.

Pit limits for power-shovel mining in orebodies which feather out at their edges are determined as in Fig 699 (286). *AB* is the line along which the unit cost of underground mining equals that of power-shovel work plus stripping. Line *CD*, on a slope equal to the angle of repose of the overburden, fixes the crest and toe of the stripping. The top of the pit in ore is determined by width of the berm *DE*, usually 20 to 30 ft. Through *E* a line *EF* on a slope suited to the character of ore marks the limit of power-shovel operations; ore to the left of *EF* would be mined by some underground method, as top-slicing (called "scramming" on the Mesabi, Art 71). See also Fig 97, Art 11.

Advantages of open-cut mining; (*a*) Properly applied, it gives large outputs at a lower unit cost than by any other method. (*b*) After a pit is well opened, its output can be varied greatly. In self-draining pits, work may be stopped and started without trouble, though with a loss of interest on investment. (*c*) Mineral within the pit limits is completely extracted. (*d*) The large working faces allow ore to be broken with minimum drilling and explosives. (*e*) Effective sorting of ore is possible in connection with hand loading. When loading with large power shovels into dump cars, sorting is limited to concentrated areas of waste (or some particular grade or kind of ore to be kept separate), large enough to fill one or more trains; otherwise delays due to switching or breaking up trains may offset saving effected by sorting. Closer sorting is possible with small power shovels loading into automobile trucks; at United Verde pit (Art 96) such equipment handles waste, smelting ores, and milling ores separately. A close determination of values over relatively small areas is usually possible in open-pits by sampling cuttings from blast holes, especially if churn drills are used. Sorting is impossible in glory-holes. (*f*) No timbering or filling are needed, artificial lights are unnecessary for day work, and supervision is easier. Hygenic conditions are generally better than underground; open cuts also eliminate dangers peculiar to underground mining (see Table 65). Duty of labor is higher, and usually a larger daily output can be produced from a given area than by underground mining.

Disadvantages of open-cut mining: (a) The surface is destroyed for other purposes, though in shallow, back-filled pits, the soil may be restored for farming. (b) Surface rights of way and room for dumps must often be purchased. (c) Large-scale work, especially that involving extensive stripping, requires large capital outlay before any return is secured. (d) Open cuts are limited to relatively small depths. (e) The plant is often composed of a number of scattered units. (f) Work is stopped or seriously hindered by bad weather. (g) An open pit collects snow and rain, and tends to drain water from the surrounding surface. This may add a serious expense for pumping to the cost of subsequent mining at depth, but may be partially met by surface ditching; note also trouble with mud-rushes at the Kimberley diamond mines, Art 88. Great care must be taken in scaling loose slabs from working faces to p rotectmen at the base of the faces from injury. (h) Horses of waste must be mined and handled.

COAL MINING METHODS

By William Emery, Jr, of Day & Zimmerman, Inc, Philadelphia, Pa

Introduction. The preceding articles deal with the methods common to nearly all kinds of mining. Metal mining methods are more varied than those for coal, due to the greater diversity in form and occurrence of metalliferous deposits, and, to avoid repetition, the articles on coal mining are devoted chiefly to the distinctive methods employed, omitting minor variations. As coal seams are "beds," they are generally mined like bedded deposits (Art 30, 31, 32, 42). Striking exceptions exist in the pitching basins of the Pennsylvania anthracite fields, where the extreme folding and varied contours of the seams require original and complicated methods. For details of prospecting, development, breaking ground, support of excavations, and underground handling of minerals, refer to these subjects in Art 1 to 93.

102. CLASSIFICATION, DEFINITIONS, AND GENERAL CONSIDERATIONS

A distinction is sometimes made between the methods of mining anthracite and bituminous coals, but for a given case the proper method depends much less on the kind of coal than on the physical characteristics of the seam, roof, and floor. For example, similar methods are employed in the flat seams of the northern anthracite field of Penna and in the bituminous mines of the same state; likewise, some of the "pitch-mining" methods of Penna resemble those used in the pitching bituminous seams of Colo. Standard underground methods, with their modifications, fall into two groups:

Pillar methods (Art 105, 106), known as room-and-pillar, pillar-and-breast, pillar-and-stall, bord-and-pillar, are those in which, from haulageways (gangways, roads, entries, or headings), comparatively wide openings (breasts, rooms, stalls, chambers, or bords) are driven. These openings correspond to stopes of metal mines. PILLARS, between rooms and other openings, support the roof. Nearly all coal in the U S is mined by room-and-pillar. Aver recovery in FIRST MINING, that is, with no attempt to rob pillars, is 30%–50%. Final ROBBING increases the yield. U S Bur of Mines in 1923 stated extraction in U S anthracite mines was 49–69%, aver 65%; in 10 states, producing 90% of the bituminous coal, extraction was 55–92%, aver 65%. J. D. Sisler in 1931 (620) estimated total losses in mining bituminous coal at: 40% in Ohio, 27% in Penna, and 22% in W Va; or approx same losses as in 1922.

Longwall methods (Art 108), divided into ADVANCING and RETREATING longwall, are used extensively abroad, but, until recently, have found little favor in the U S. Instead of opening rooms, with intervening pillars, coal is mined from a continuous face. As work advances or retreats, the roof is allowed to cave, haulageways and airways being kept open by packwalls of waste (gob). Recovery is approx 100%.

Development openings, corresponding to the levels and drifts in metal mines, are locally called ENTRIES, HEADINGS, or ROADS (bituminous mines, U S), or GANGWAYS (anthracite mines). Openings for ventilation are termed AIRWAYS or AIR COURSES, also MONKEYS or MONKEY WAYS in anthracite mines. The mode of entry, by tunnels, drifts, or vertical or inclined shafts (slopes), depends primarily on the conditions governing the development of any mineral deposit, viz: topography, together with the pitch and physical characteristics of the seam (Art 14–20). For modifications in development to provide the special ventilation needed in coal mining, see Art 104, 108.

Stripping (open-cut mining) is sometimes adopted for coal seams, or parts of seams, near the surface (Art 100).

103. CHOICE OF METHOD

The best method in any case is that which will yield a max recovery at a min cost per ton, in the best marketable condition, and with least danger to the miner.

General factors influencing choice and details of method are as follows: ROOF PRESSURE is an indeterminate quantity varying with thickness of overburden. In longwall mining, a roof that hangs over moderate areas and settles gradually may help break down the face, but in general, where longwall is used, a roof that breaks "clean" at a moderate distance from the face is of greater advantage, as it relieves the pressure and simplifies roof control. Much attention is now being given to roof control in connection with long faces and mechanical loading, and much of the success so far obtained from mechanical loading and the methods devised for it is attributable to control of the roof and roof pressure. In pillar-mining in general, heavy roof pressure requires larger pillars and smaller openings; this is especially true in thick seams, or in soft, friable coal. Failure to recognize roof pressure in working out a room-and-pillar system may cause a squeeze or general crushing of pillars, and loss of coal over large areas. This may occur during first mining, but oftener during robbing, where removal of even one pillar may transfer to adjacent pillars a wt exceeding their supporting power. Pillar methods are used in most American mines, under all conditions of roof pressure in both flat and pitching seams; but greater attention is now given to the adaptability of longwall and modified longwall methods to flat seams, where heretofore roof pressure and other conditions were considered unfavorable. CHARACTER OF ROOF AND FLOOR. The roof is the stratum directly above the seam. A good roof is self-supporting over moderate areas; other conditions being favorable, a greater recovery may be obtained in the first mining and less timber is required. These advantages disappear when the roof is self-supporting over large areas, because during robbing excessive pressure may be transmitted to pillars. The roof may be weak, as in the case of draw slate, with a stronger stratum above. If the weak stratum is thick enough to choke the room when it falls, equalization of press may be obtained, which is advantageous during robbing. Control of such a roof is difficult and dangerous, requiring much timber. In some regions, roof conditions are greatly improved by leaving a thin layer of coal unmined under the roof stratum; especially true where air and moisture cause flaking and disintegration. Character of floor also influences size of openings. Soft bottom requires narrow openings and large pillars, especially where firm coal is mined under strong roof. Pressure on pillars tends to force them into the floor, causing floor to bulge, known as "heaving bottom." A firm floor is always desirable. CHARACTER OF COAL. Strong coal may be mined by pillar or longwall. Mining soft, friable coal is always difficult, and in pillar methods requires large pillars. Flat seams of friable coal under heavy cover are best mined by longwall, if character of roof permits. INCLINATION AND THICKNESS OF SEAM. In general, the max allowable size of opening decreases with increasing pitch and thickness of seam. Friable coal in a pitching seam sometimes tends to run; this emphasizes the requirement of large pillars and small openings. Practice abroad favors longwall for pitching seams of moderate thickness; in U S practically all pitch-mining is done by pillar methods. PRESENCE OF EXPLOSIVE GAS AND DUST indirectly influences choice of method, but has a direct effect on details of all methods. Advancing longwall in a gassy seam involves constant danger of gob fires; hence, retreating longwall is preferable. In pitching seams containing occluded gas, coal often tends to break away from face and pillars (called "bumpy" coal), and requires narrow openings and large pillars (for discussion of this subject, see Sec 23). If there is danger from explosions of gas or more especially of dust, it is best to use a panel system (Fig 722), to confine explosions to small areas. Explosive dust also makes low-velocity air currents desirable and influences cross-section of airways (see Sec 23). PRODUCT DESIRED. Generally, the best method is that which will produce largest amount of lump coal; coal for coking is an exception (see Sec 34, 35). Wide faces produce the most lump coal; from this point of view under favorable conditions longwall methods are best. Excessive use of explosives should be avoided, and systems of loading and haulage carefully designed to avoid breakage. LABOR AND MARKET. In longwall, there must be a steady market and a steady class of labor; even a short stoppage may result in serious damage to the working face. In pillar methods, this is less important. ESTABLISHED WAGE SCALES AND WORKING CONDITIONS. Where, by agreement or custom, extra pay is required for certain types of work, as yardage for narrow work in entries or rooms less than

10 ft wide, brushing (breaking down) of top or lifting of bottom, gobbing (packing) of waste in the seam, or of draw-slate above the seam, timbering, and other items generally mentioned in wage agreements, it may not be possible to adopt the method most suitable for the physical conditions on account of its excessive cost. FREIGHT RATES. R R rates (and more recently trucking rates) are generally the factors governing shipments into market zones (except for special-purpose coals). These rates may directly affect choice of method; a mine having a favorable freight rate to a given market may be able to use a method giving greater recovery per acre than a competing mine without this advantage. SPECIFICATION PURCHASES. Large tonnages are purchased on certain standards of ash, sulphur, volatile matter, ash fusion, and Btu content. A system designed for mechanical loading, without auxiliary cleaning, may so alter the quality of shipped product, as compared with hand loading without auxiliary cleaning, as to eliminate the coal from a desirable market. SIZE OF PROPERTY (its available tonnage) may bear directly on choice of method, by limiting the equipment investment. Thus, a relatively small property, physically capable of development by a system employing mechanical loading, may be unable to employ the system if, to produce a marketable product, additional investment in a cleaning plant is required (Sec 34, 35).

104.　ROOM-AND-PILLAR METHODS

General. Because of the frequent presence of explosive dust and gas (Sec 14), thorough ventilation is more important for coal than for metal mines. This requires driving DEVELOPMENT OPENINGS IN SETS. Fresh air enters by one or more openings, the INTAKE, and after passing through the workings the foul air leaves the mine by other openings, the RETURN.

Development in flat or slightly pitching seams. SINGLE-ENTRY (rarely used, see Sec 14). A single opening is driven, from which rooms are turned off in one or both directions (Fig 700). The entry acts both as a main haulageway and an intake airway. The ventilating current circulates as shown. A fall of roof may cut off the flow of air. Fig 701 shows a typical DOUBLE-ENTRY layout. Main entries are driven from the shaft, or from the surface; from these, cross or butt entries are opened. Rooms are turned off the cross entries. The cut shows the split system of exhaust ventilation (Sec 14), the main haulageways being intakes. Advantages: (a) in case of accident in one entry, the other affords an escape; (b) the mine is divided into separately ventilated sections, so that a fall of roof or complete closure of any pair of butt entries will not affect ventilation in other parts of the mine; (c) main or cross entries may be driven ahead as far as desired and ventilation maintained without turning off rooms. Fig 702 shows TRIPLE-ENTRY applied to main entries, with double-entry in cross entries. The middle entry is the main intake and haulageway; the outer ones form the return. While involving more narrow work than double-entry, this system is well adapted to gaseous mines of large working area; it is also used where local conditions (bad roof, etc) prohibit driving a single entry of sufficient width for double-track haulage; the middle entry is then used as the return and the outer entries as intakes and haulageways. In QUADRUPLE-ENTRY, 4 main entries are driven in parallel (Fig 703), each side of the mine being served by a separate intake and return. One intake entry may be used as a traveling way, and the other as a haulageway, or both as haulageways. This system facilitates circulation of large volumes of air and is well adapted to high-speed endless-rope haulage (Sec 11). By leaving the center pillar intact, i e, eliminating the BREAK-THROUGHS B, the two sides of the mine become wholly independent of each other, and may be considered as distinct mines, each opened by double-entry. QUINTUPLE-ENTRY is the same as the preceding, with addition of one more entry, used as a traveling way.

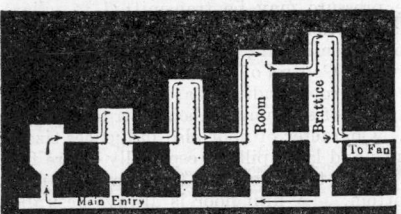

Fig 700.　Single-entry System in Flat Seam

Entries in flat or slightly pitching seams. SIZE of entry depends on two factors: (a) Entries must be large enough to insure adequate ventilation. State laws prescribe a minimum quantity of fresh air per man or animal, and a max velocity of current (Sec 14). Airways should have the min perimeter for a given sectional area; a square entry is preferable to a rectangular one. In haulageways, height and width are influenced by size of car and mode of haulage. (b) Cost of maintaining wide openings may be prohibitive if roof is bad, or the floor has a tendency to heave, or the coal is friable or easily crushed; in such cases, narrow entries, while costly to drive, are in the end an economy. In seams containing more or less waste, or in thin seams, where floor or roof must be blasted to secure headroom, entries are usually driven 16 to 20 ft wide and then narrowed to 6 to 10 ft by building the waste into a packwall along one of the RIBS (Fig 704). (Rib is the face of solid coal along the side of a working.) Extra cost of driving is partly or wholly paid for by the coal taken out and transport of waste is eliminated. DIS-TANCE BETWEEN ENTRIES. Main entries in flat seams are commonly driven on 30–60-ft centers, leaving, for a 10-ft entry, a 20–50-ft pillar. Large pillars are required to protect main entries during life of mine. Cross entries need not remain open after the area served is exhausted; they are on about 30-ft centers, leaving a 20-ft pillar for 10-ft entry. For economy in driving, entries should be as close together as possible to

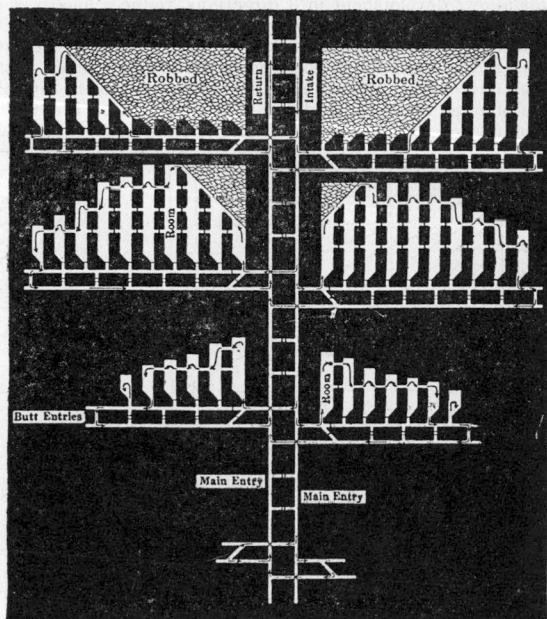

Fig 701. Double-entry System in Flat Seam (U S)

reduce cost of breakthroughs. Distance between sets of

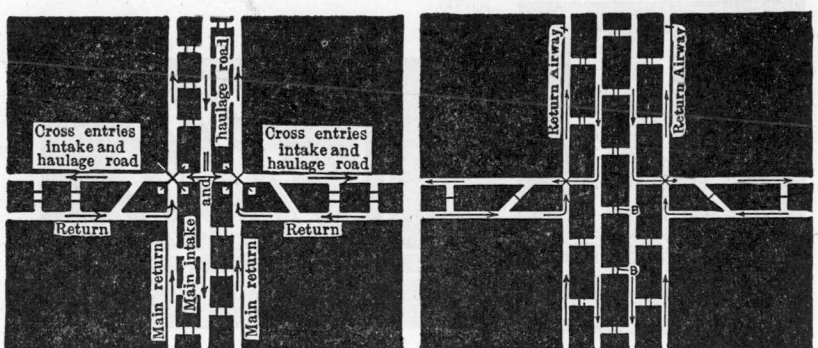

Fig 702. Triple-entry System (Coal Miners' Pocketbook

Fig 703. Quadruple-entry System

cross entries depends on length of room and method of mining; length of room depends on character of roof, floor, and coal, system of haulage and ventilation. Rooms are commonly 300–350 ft long and, where turned in one direction only, give a gross entry spacing of 350–400 ft. Where turned in both directions, spacing of cross entries is 700–800 ft, or twice the length of rooms, plus suitable pillars if desired. DIRECTION AND LOCATION depend largely on size and shape of the property, surface conditions, cleavage or CLEAT of the coal (in bituminous mines), dip, amount of water, etc.

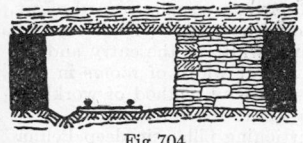

Fig 704.

Main entries should be located approx to bisect the property.   In mines opened by drifts, this allows development in 3 directions, reduces length of cross entries and permits final robbing at an earlier date, decreases cost of protracted maintenance of long haulageways, facilitates haulage, and permits material increase in output on shorter notice.   To favor haulage and drainage in slightly pitching seams, main entries are driven directly on the pitch and cross entries approx parallel to strike.   In bituminous coal, the cleat may alter this plan, as the cost of driving is often increased if entries are not parallel to one of the pronounced cleavage planes.   ALINEMENT AND GRADE should be uniform.   Curves

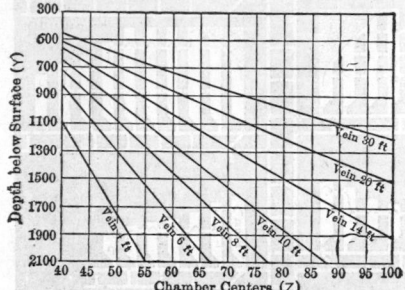

Fig 705.   Relation between Depths and Room Centers for Different Thicknesses of Seam for 20-ft Rooms

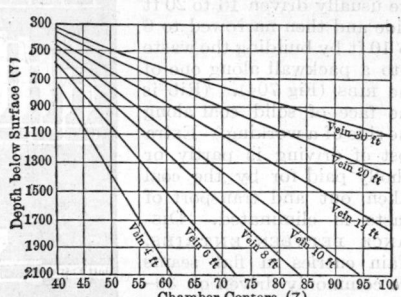

Fig 705a.   Relation between Depths and Room Centers for Different Thicknesses of Seam for 24-ft Rooms

increase frictional resistance and wear and tear on track and rolling stock.   Bends in airways increase friction and hence reduce efficiency of ventilation.   Uniform grade is essential for efficient haulage and drainage.   Cross-entry haulageways usually have a slight grade (0.75 to 1.5%) favoring the load.   To obtain this it may be necessary to blast top or bottom rock and to fill local depressions.   Cross entries in slightly pitching seams may be driven at an angle to the strike to secure any desired grade.   The following formula (355) is useful: $sin\ A = tan\ X \div tan\ Y$, where A = angle between cross entry or rooms (if on a grade) and strike line; X and Y = pitches of cross entry and seam, degrees

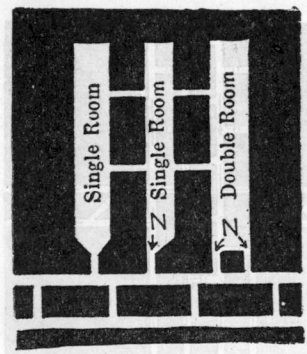

Fig 706

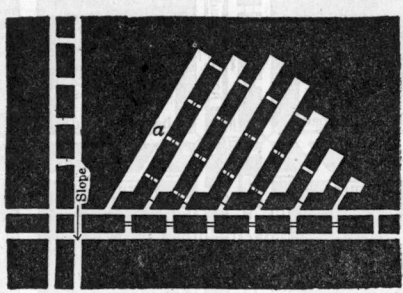

Fig 707

(Tables 88, 89).   Angle between rooms and cross entry = angle between rooms and strike line + angle between main entry and strike line.   Sharp curves from main to cross entries should be avoided; sometimes done by driving diagonal CUT-OFFS.

Rooms and pillars in flat or slightly pitching seams.   Rooms are usually turned off at right-angles to the entry in one or both directions, depending on system of mining and dip of seam.   From the NECK N, Fig 706, of about the same width as the entry and 10 to 30 ft long, the room is widened on one or both sides.   Aver width of rooms in the U S is 24 ft; their length varies with local conditions, custom, and method of working.   Table 89 (355) is useful in laying out rooms driven at an angle to the entry.

D. Bunting (368) gives the following formula for proportioning pillars in deep Penna anthracite seams of flat pitch: $yz = 1\,000 \times \left(0.70 + 0.30\dfrac{b}{h} \right) b$, where y = depth below surface, ft; z = distance center to center of rooms, ft; b = width of pillar, ft; h = total thickness of seam, ft.   It is assumed that the weight of the overlying strata is 144 lb per cu ft and that the safe load on a cube of anthracite is 1 000 lb per sq in.   Fig 705, 705a, platted from this formula, gives results corresponding with practice in Penna.

Bunting states that, in the application of any formula to the calculation of the size of pillars necessary to resist the press of overlying strata, consideration must be given to the nature of the seam and its contiguous strata, and to the dip.   Moreover, the proper factor of safety varies with local conditions, such as the relative location and extent of workings, and the seriousness of possible disturbance to the overlying strata and surface.

Where conditions permit wide openings, DOUBLE ROOMS may be used; they have 2 necks and are usually served by a track on each rib, gob being stored in the middle.   Fig 706 shows types of single and double rooms.   Haulage in rooms, unless mechanical, becomes difficult on pitches of 6° to 8°; rooms may then be turned off obliquely (Fig 707); this means of reducing haulage grades in rooms is feasible in seams pitching to 12°; calculations for grade are made as for oblique entries (see above). This practice increases the difficulty of robbing pillars.

Table 87.   Dimensions of Rooms and Pillars in Flat Seams (U S)

Ex No	Location	Rooms		Room necks		Pillars
		Width, ft	Length, ft	Width, ft	Length, ft	Width, ft
1	Pittsburgh Seam.	21				12
2	" "	24				15
3	Southern Colorado.	20	200	8	30	20
4	Dawson, N M.	24	350	6	20	20
5	Oklahoma.	20–25	200–275	8–10		
6	Hisylvania, Hocking Valley, O.	30	250		21	12
7	Saline County Coal Co, Ill.	20	300–350	6		14
8	Michigan.	30	150			8–16
9	Primero, Colo.	18	300	8		22
10	Loup Creek, W Va.	25	400			35
11	Whitwell, Tenn.	42	200	6	21	36
12	Franklin, Ill.	21		10		16
13	Steubenville, O.	22	250			20
14	J. K. Dering Coal Co, Ind.	22	150			13
15	Castle Valley, Utah.	22	400	12	20	51
16	Stearns County, Ky.	40				20
17	" " "	24				16
18	Tennessee.	30	215	10	21	21
19	Melcher, Ia.	60		10		30
20	Kaylor, Pa.	42		12	21	
21	Gary, W Va.	20		12		40

Influence of cleat.   Bituminous coals usually contain two cleavage planes or cleats, running approx at right-angles to each other.   Advantage is taken of them to facilitate breaking down the coal and to release occluded gas by driving the rooms at different angles to the more pronounced cleat.   FACE CLEATS are longer and more regular than END CLEATS.   Fig 708 shows methods of driving.   In driving FACE-ON, the face of the room is parallel to the face cleats.   This is the general method where conditions permit; it requires less powder and undercutting than the others, and yields more lump coal.   In LONG-HORN work, the room face makes an angle less than 45° with the face cleats.   Coal breaks in long slabs and with well placed shots there is a fair yield of lump coal.   In HALF-ON work, the room face is at 45° to the cleats; adapted to coals breaking equally well on face and end cleats.   In SHORT-HORN work, the room face is between 45° and 90° to the face cleats;

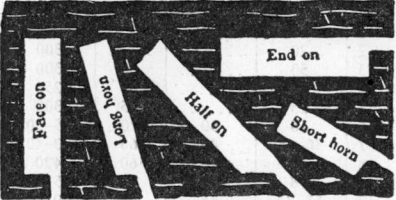

Fig 708. (Coal Miners' Pocketbook)

adapted to cases where pronounced end cleats require that added support be given to the coal face and bears the same relation to end-on work that long-horn does to face-on. In END-ON work, the room face is parallel to the end cleats; this, with short-horn, is adapted to withstand strong roof pressures, but yields less lump coal than other methods. In coals containing occluded gas at high pressure, face-on methods may cause violent outbursts of gas, whereas end-on rooms cut the face cleats and allow gas to escape gradually. Under these conditions, by using long-horn or short-horn methods, the pressure of gas may be controlled and utilized to assist in breaking down the face.

Table 88. Dimensions of Rooms and Pillars (356)

Ex No	Location	Rooms		Room pillars, width, ft	Cross-cuts, c to c, ft	Thickness of coal, ft	Pitch of bed, deg
		Length, ft	Width, ft				
1	Alabama (Pratt seam)	300	25	10–20	50	4–6	2–40
2	" (Thin seam)	100–300	20	10–20	20–50	2–4	2–20
3	" (Blue Creek)	300	25	25	50	8	0–15
4	" (Blocton)	250	25	25	50	5–6	0–10
5	" (Flat Top)	250	25	25	50	10	2–4
6	Ark (Sebastian Coll'y)	150–250	18–30	12	40	3–9	4–12
7	Illinois (Springfield)	150–200	30	15–20	60	5	0
8	" (Staunton)	200	40	20	60	5–6	0
9	Oklahoma	100–300	18–30	10–12	40	3.5–6	8–40
10	Iowa	180–210	21–30	9–15	60	3.5–7.5	0
11	Maryland (Georges Creek)	150–300	......	40	105	12–14	0–10
12	Penna (Connellsville)	250	12	32	105	6–9	5–12
13	" "	250	12	72	105	6–9	5–12
14	" (Pittsburgh)	250	21–24	12–18	75–100	4.5–7	nearly flat
15	" (Clearfield)	180–200	21	15	75	2.7–6.3	0–3
16	W Va (Fairmont)	250	25	18–20	65	7–11	0–5

Ex No	Character of coal	Direction of rooms	Character of roof	Roof faults or slips	Character of bottom	Depth of cover, ft	Time of drawing pillars
1	B	OF	Sl	(b)	FC	100–600	R
2	A	OF	Ss	N	H	50–300	R
3	B	WG	Ss	N	H, FC	50–400	(c)
4	B	NC	Sh (d)	N	H, FC	50–600	(c)
5	B	OF	Sl (e)	N	H, FC	50–200	(c)
6	B, F	UP	Sl (e)	ST	H, FC	50–400	ND
7	A (f)	(g)	Sl (h)	(i)	H, FC	200–400	ND
8	A	(j)	Sl (h)	N	H, FC	400–500	ND
9	A	UP	Sl	ST	H, FC	50–700	ND
10	A	(k)	Sh, Ss, Ls	(l)	FC	200–300	(c)
11	B	WG	Ss (d)	(m)	FC or Sh	50–300	(c)
12	B	OF	Ss	N	FC or Sl	20–350	R
13	B	OF	Ss	N	FC or Sl	350†	R
14	A	OF	H, Sl	N	FC + Ls	50–350	R
15	A	NC	Sl	(n)	N	FC	20–300	R
16	A	OF	(n)	N	FC	50–750	R

Ex No	Entry stump pillar width, ft	Coal left in first working, %	Total coal recover'd, %	Cross headings c to c, ft	Entries width, ft	Pillar width, ft (o)
1	21	......	....	326	8	10
2	20	......	....	300	8	10
3	50	......	85	300	8	12
4	25	......	80	250	8	12
5	25	......	85	300	8	12
6	18	30	70	175–300	8	18
7	30–35	40	60	300–400	12–20	40
8	40	40	60	420	20	40
9	18	30	70	125–300	8	18
10	18–24	35	90	360–400	8	(p)
11	250	......	90	1200	8	.....
12	30	60	95	300	8–9	52
13	30	80	90	300	9	52
14	21–40	40	85–95	480–500	8	30–40
15	20	......	....	......	8	15
16	25	......	95	560	10	20–30

B = Soft. A = Hard. N = None. F = Not Friable. ST = Sometimes. ND = Not drawn. OF = Face-on. WG = With grade. NC = No cleats. UP = Up pitch. Sl = Slate. Ss = Sandstone. Sh = Shale. Ls = Limestone. FC = Fireclay. H = Hard. R = Retreating. (b) Draw slate 2 to 10 in. (c) As soon as room is driven. (d) Soft. (e) Sandy. (f) Some cleat. (g) End-on. (h) Blocky. (i) Horse backs. (j) Parallel to main cleat. (k) Across cleats. (l) Local slips. (m) Small slips. (n) Heavy draw slate. (o) Betw entry & air course. (p) Main, 25–50 ft; cross, 12–25 ft.

Table 89. Distance from Center to Center of Rooms or Breasts,
Measured on Entry or Gangway

Angle between room and entry, deg	Width of room + thickness of pillar, ft											
	20	25	30	35	40	45	50	55	60	65	70	75
	Distance measured on entry, ft											
90	20.0	25.0	30.0	35.0	40.0	45.0	50.0	55.0	60.0	65.0	70.0	75.0
85	20.0	25.1	30.1	35.1	40.2	45.2	50.2	55.2	60.2	65.3	70.3	75.3
80	20.3	25.4	30.5	35.5	40.6	45.7	50.8	55.8	60.9	66.0	71.1	76.2
75	20.7	25.9	31.1	36.2	41.4	46.6	51.8	56.9	62.1	67.3	72.5	77.7
70	21.3	26.6	31.9	37.2	42.6	47.9	53.2	58.5	63.9	69.2	74.5	79.8
65	22.1	27.6	33.1	38.6	44.1	49.6	55.2	60.7	66.2	71.7	77.2	82.8
60	23.1	28.9	34.6	40.4	46.2	52.0	57.7	63.5	69.3	75.1	80.8	86.6
55	24.4	30.5	36.6	42.7	48.8	54.9	61.0	67.1	73.3	79.4	85.5	91.6
50	26.1	32.6	39.2	45.7	52.2	58.7	65.3	71.8	78.3	84.9	91.4	97.9
45	28.3	35.4	42.4	49.5	56.6	63.6	70.7	77.8	84.9	91.9	99.0	106.1
40	31.1	38.9	46.7	54.5	62.2	70.0	77.8	85.6	93.3	101.1	109.0	116.7
35	34.9	43.6	52.3	61.0	69.7	78.5	87.2	95.9	104.6	113.4	122.1	130.8
30	40.0	50.0	60.0	70.0	80.0	90.0	100.0	110.0	120.0	130.0	140.0	150.0
25	47.3	59.2	71.0	82.8	94.6	106.5	118.3	130.1	142.0	153.8	165.6	177.5
20	58.5	73.1	87.7	102.3	117.0	131.6	146.2	160.8	175.5	190.1	204.7	219.3
15	77.3	96.6	115.9	135.2	154.5	173.9	193.2	212.5	231.9	251.2	270.5	289.8
10	115.2	144.0	172.8	201.6	230.4	259.2	287.9	316.7	345.5	374.3	403.1	432.0
5	229.5	286.9	344.2	401.6	459.0	516.3	573.7	631.1	688.4	745.8	803.2	860.5

Development in pitching seams. The following notes describe Penna anthracite practice, which may be considered standard for the U S. As in flat mining, development openings are driven in pairs, consisting of a haulageway or GANGWAY, and an airway or MONKEY. These openings are connected by CHUTES, corresponding to the breakthroughs of flat mining. In thick, gassy seams, an extra monkey may be added, to provide a

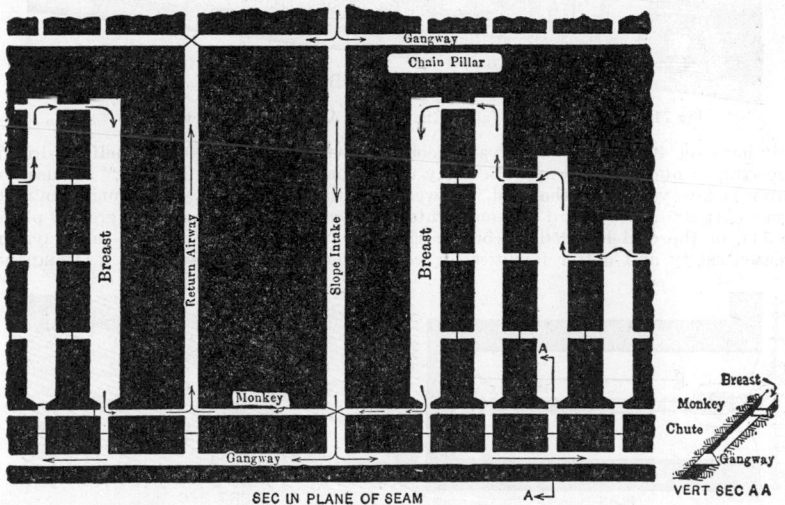

Fig 709. Typical Development of a Pitching Anthracite Seam, Penna

separate split of air in each working place. Fig 709 shows typical development for moderately thick seams; for variations, see Art 106. SIZE OF GANGWAYS depends more on size of car and method of haulage than on character of coal, roof, or floor, and thickness of seam. Gangways for mule haulage are commonly 7 ft high by 10 to 12 ft wide in the clear. For mechanical haulage the height may be less, though good practice leaves at least 2 ft clearance above top of car. DIMENSIONS OF MONKEYS depend primarily on air requirements (Sec 14); thus, if an area of 36 sq ft is required to pass the air needed in a split without undue friction, a monkey in a 6-ft seam would be 6 ft high. DISTANCE BETWEEN DEVELOPMENT OPENINGS. In Penna, the distance between gangway and monkey in moderately thick seams is commonly 30 ft. In thick seams, this distance depends largely on whether the monkey and gangway are on the same or opposite walls of the seam. It is customary to space gangways 300 ft apart along the pitch, leaving a CHAIN PILLAR 20 to 50 ft wide (along the pitch) underneath each gangway (Fig 709). This allows a breast length, including the chute, of 250 to 280 ft. In thick-seam mining,

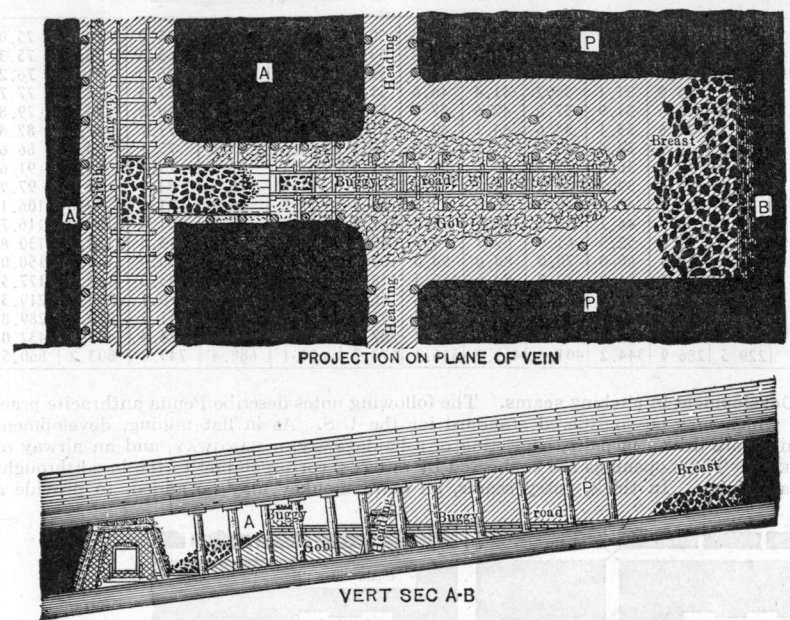

Fig 710. Buggy Breast (after Chance, Vol AC, 2nd Geol Surv Penna)

on pitches over 40°, it may be advantageous to divide a lift of 300 ft in half by driving a COUNTER or BUGGY gangway. In many cases small mine cars, "buggies," are used on counter gangways; if so, the coal is lowered to the main gangway through COUNTER CHUTES (Art 106). Standard cars on counter gangways may be lowered by gravity planes (Sec 11), or the coal handled in counter chutes. Advantages of counter gangways are increased safety and better facilities for ventilation and handling timber. DIRECTION,

Fig 711. Buggy Breast (Coal Miners' Pocketbook. Pitch exaggerated)

LOCATION, AND GRADE OF GANGWAYS. Gangways are driven in the seam, following its contours along one wall, and are on a grade of 0.75 to 1.5% in favor of loaded cars; they are usually turned in both directions from the main openings. BREASTS correspond to rooms in flat mining. Experience shows that moderately thick seams may be worked most economically by driving breasts 24 ft wide, on 50-ft centers, and not exceeding 300 ft long. Variations in dimensions, due to character of roof and floor, and texture and thickness of coal, are much the same as in flat seams. Friable coal in a pitching seam is apt to break away from the face and ribs, causing a "run-away" with more or less disastrous results; in such coal, narrow, well timbered breasts are essential.

Classification of breasts according to their pitch. WAGON BREASTS correspond to rooms in flat mining and are used where pitch is less than 12°.   Full-size mine cars are run to the face and loaded by hand or conveyers; shaking chutes or scrapers may be used to transport coal from the face to cars placed on the gangway.   BUGGY BREASTS (Fig 710, 711) dip

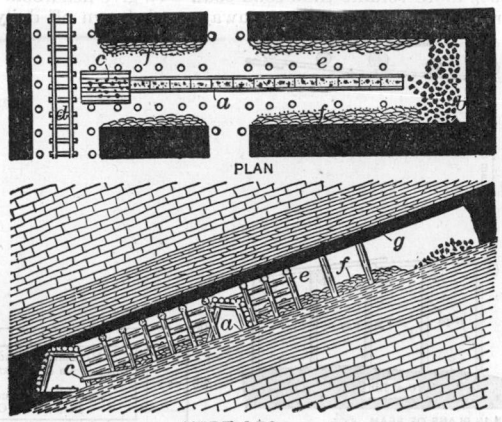

PLAN

Fig 712.   Chute Breast (Coal Miners' Pocketbook).   *a*, Sheet-iron chute. *c*, Loading platform. *e*, Props. *f*, Gob. *g*, Top coal

10°–18°; small cars (buggies) transport coal from face to cars on the gangway.   Buggies have been largely replaced by conveyers, shaking chutes, or scrapers (Sec 27).   CHUTE BREASTS.   For pitches over 15° and less than 30° to 35°, a chute lined with sheet iron (usually No 16 gage) conveys coal from the face to a loading platform at the gangway (Fig 712).   On dips less than 20°, the coal must be pushed along the chute, or mechanical

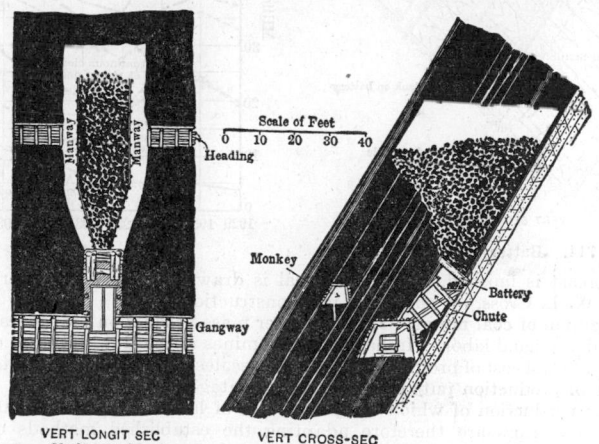

Fig 713.   Battery Breast, Mammoth Seam, Hazleton, Penna (after Chance)

drags may be used.   Rock and refuse are gobbed on the sides of the chute.   When the pitch exceeds 35°, coal will generally slide on the bottom rock; the sheet iron is then eliminated and planks set against the two rows of props guide the coal to gangway.   STEEP BREASTS WORKED EMPTY.   As the dip increases, the working of empty breasts becomes increasingly difficult and dangerous, and the breakage of coal a serious item.   Dips of 40° to 45° are probably the limit for safe and economical empty work.   Breasts pitching

55° to 60° have been worked by a staggered battery method (Art 106), but the practice is bad and should be avoided. BATTERY BREASTS, used in steep pitching seams, resemble shrinkage stopes in metal mines (Art 68). At the head of the chute (Fig 713) is a battery or gate, consisting of props heavily lagged or planked. From this point the breast is widened as required; manways are carried up each side and the broken coal is retained in the middle by lagged or planked props. The broken coal supports the miners; it occupies approx 50% more volume than solid coal. To give headroom at the face, excess broken coal is thrown down one of the manways and drawn off daily at the gangway.

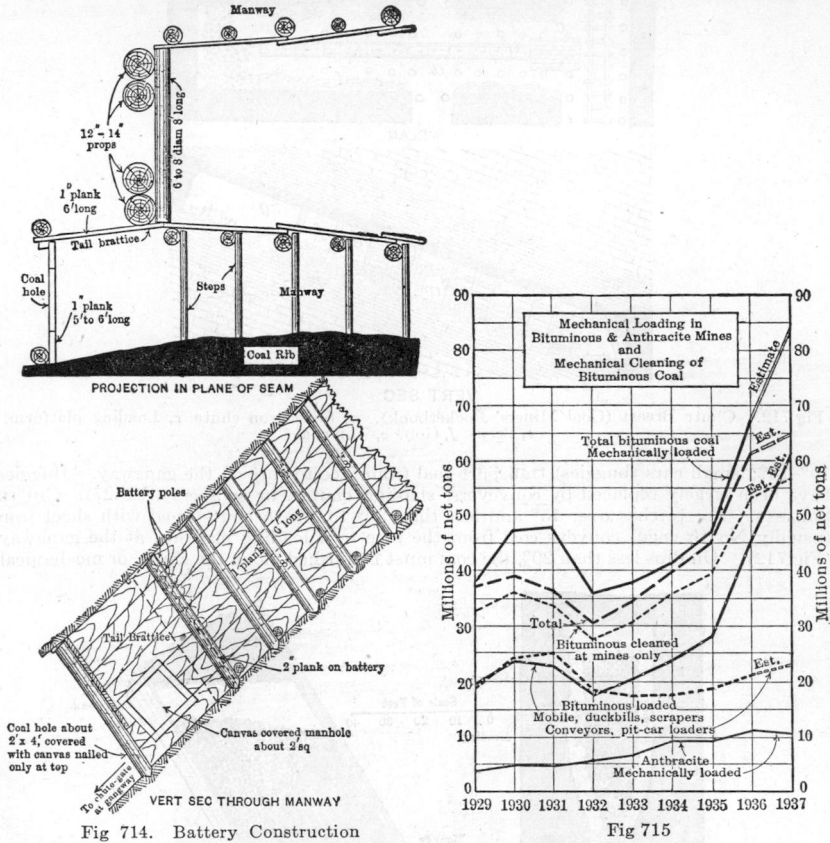

Fig 714. Battery Construction   Fig 715

When the breast is finished, the broken coal is drawn through the battery as desired. Fig 714, by W. L. Cross, Jr, shows typical construction.

Mechanization of coal mines. Like all other mass-production industries, coal mining seeks to eliminate hand labor. In hand-loading mines in the U S, the labor cost probably exceeds 60% of total cost of production. As wage scales increase, this percentage increases, and the cost of production puts coal at a disadvantage compared with oil, gas, and elec power, in the production of which the percentage of labor cost to the total is relatively small. Coal operators are therefore adapting the established methods of room-and-pillar, panel, longwall and modified longwall, to the use of mobile loaders, conveyors, shaking chutes, and scrapers (Sec 27). Besides mechanical loaders, elec coal drills, hand-held, post- or track-mounted, and track-mounted cutting and shearing machines of large capac are being installed.

From statistics of the National Bituminous Coal Comm (672) Fig 715 shows tonnage of anthracite and bituminous coal mechanically loaded in U S mines from 1929 to 1937, and tonnages of bituminous coal mechanically cleaned in the same period. Table 90 shows equipment used in bituminous mines in 1936. N B C C estimates percentage of U S coal production mechanically loaded at 12% in 1933 and 16.4% in 1936, exclusive of coal from strippings.

Table 90. Tonnage of Bituminous Coal Mechanically Loaded Underground in 1936

	Net tons	Percent
Loaded by machine:		
Mobile loading machines..........	40 961 321	90.1
Scraper loaders........	1 272 466	2.8
Conveyers equipped with duckbills		
and other self-loading devices	3 240 411	7.1
Total loaded by machine........	45 474 198	100.0
Handled by conveyers:		
Conveyers equipped with duckbills		
and other self-loading devices..	3 240 411	13.1
Pit-car loaders..................	10 537 707	42.6
Hand-loaded conveyers..........	10 949 943	44.3
Total handled by conveyers.....	24 728 061	100.0
Recapitulation, less duplications:		
Mobile loading machines..........	40 961 321	61.2
Scraper loaders.................	1 272 466	1.9
Conveyers equipped with duckbills		
and other self-loading devices..	3 240 411	4.8
Pit-car loaders..................	10 537 707	15.7
Hand-loaded conveyers..........	10 949 943	16.4
Grand total loaded mechanically..	66 961 848	100.0

105. EXAMPLES OF ROOM-AND-PILLAR MINING IN FLAT SEAMS
(See also Tables 87, 88)

Georges Creek district, Md. Data from H. V. Hesse in 1909 (357). Fig 716 shows unsystematic methods employed in 1850 for a bituminous seam 6–9 ft thick. All workings were at random, with no attempt to recover pillars; 55% of total coal, not including top coal left standing for a roof, remains and makes reworking or robbing difficult and costly. This old example shows necessity for systematic mining to secure max recovery. In this

Fig 716. Unsystematic Mining, Georges Creek, Md

seam, narrow rooms and wide pillars are required by the character of roof and coal. Fig 717 shows a recent systematic plan of working, evolved after numerous experiments. Most of the coal is obtained by robbing (Art 107); total recovery of 94% is claimed.

Pittsburgh region. Data from F. Z. Schellenberg in 1910 (358) and Pittsburgh District Committee on Coal, of the A I M E, in 1926 (606). Seams are regular, permitting systematic development; a pronounced cleat in the Pittsburgh seam is an important factor in laying out workings. Where pillars are not drawn, rooms are 20–25 ft wide and 200–300 ft long, with 8 to 10-ft pillars. Rooms are often turned off butt entries, and driven with their faces on the face cleats. With pillar-drawing, panel systems are used, most of the faces being at right-angles to the butt face cleats. Standard length of rooms, 200–300 ft; width, 10–20 ft; headings, 8-10 ft wide, are 2 to 6 in number, spaced 35–50-ft centers, according to the ventilation and haulage requirements, the overburden, and life of the entry in question.

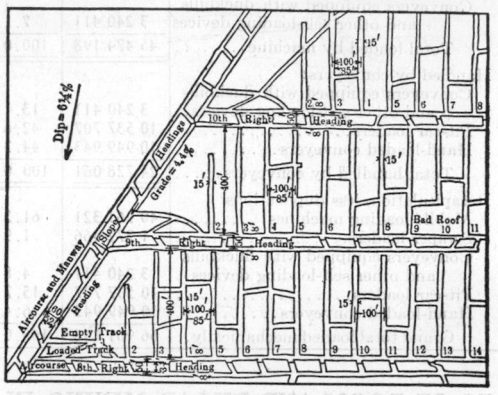

Fig 717. Systematic Mining, Georges Creek, Md

Pittsburgh seam throughout this district is 4.5–9 ft thick; dip, 0°–6°; recoveries from mining, 55–90%. Fig 718 shows standard method in the Connellsville region; Fig 719, Fairmont district, northern W Va; Fig 720, Pittsburgh Coal Co; Fig 721, 722, general method of Monongahela River Consol Coal and Coke Co. Panels are 500–600 ft wide by 1 400 ft long; rooms are usually turned in both directions from the butt entries. Pillars are robbed during either advance or retreat; faces of robbing operations are at 45° to the butt entries.

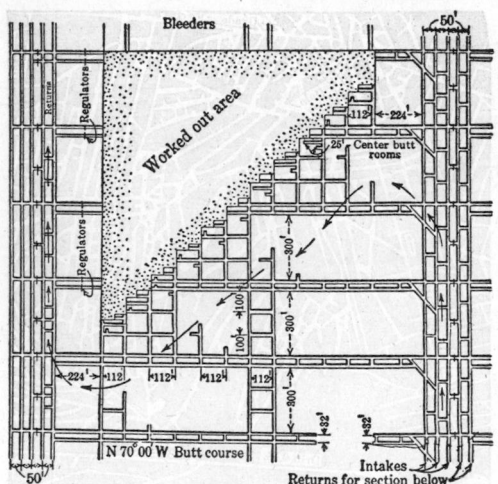

Fig 718. Standard Mining Method of Advancing and Retreating, Pittsburgh Seam, Connellsville Region, Penna (606)

West Virginia. Due to the regularity of the seams, definite systems of mining are planned and carried out with only slight variations to meet local conditions. Main entries are triple or quadruple; section entries, triple or double; cross entries, double. Panel systems are common. Usual dimensions are as follows, with exceptions noted below. Main and section entries are at 40–60-ft centers and 8–12 ft wide; cross entries, 30–50-ft centers, 8–12 ft wide; interval between pairs of cross entries, 400–600 ft; rooms, on 40–80-ft centers, are 15–30 ft wide and 200–400 ft long; interval

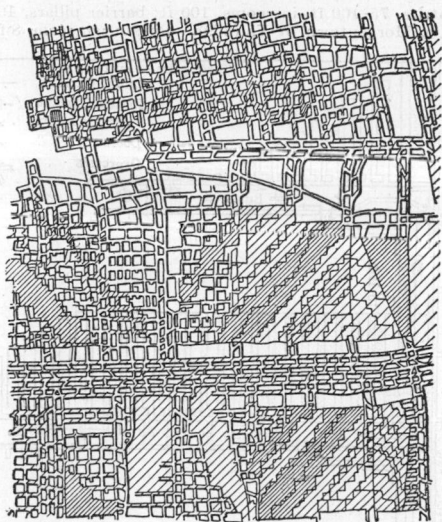

Fig 719. Mining in Fairmont District, W Va

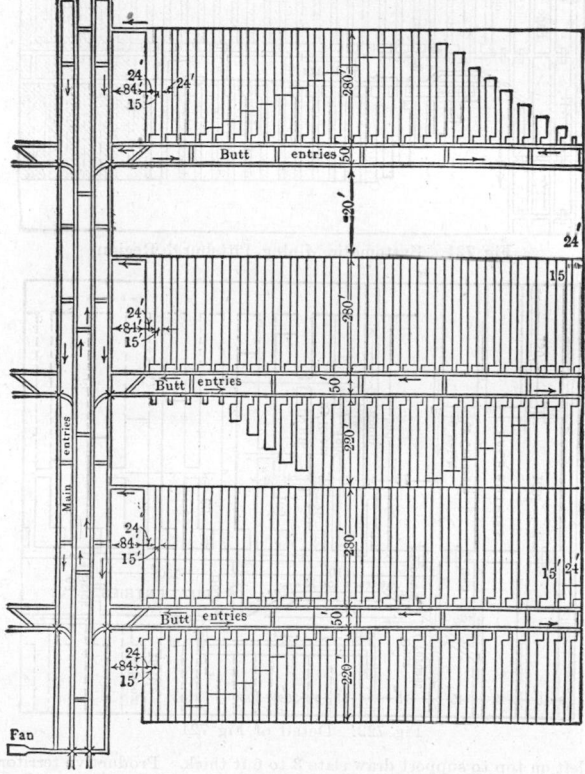

Fig 720. Systematic Mining, Pittsburgh Seam

between crosscuts in entries, 75–100 ft, in rooms, 100 ft; barrier pillars, 100–200 ft wide. MONA MINE, Arkwright Coal Co, Morgantown, W Va (359). Pittsburgh seam, 8 ft thick, of which 7 ft is

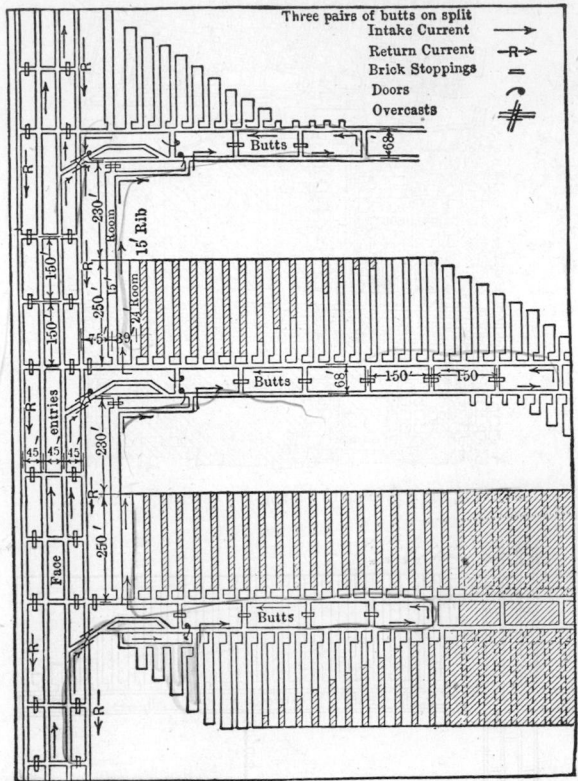

Fig 721. Systematic Mining, Pittsburgh Region

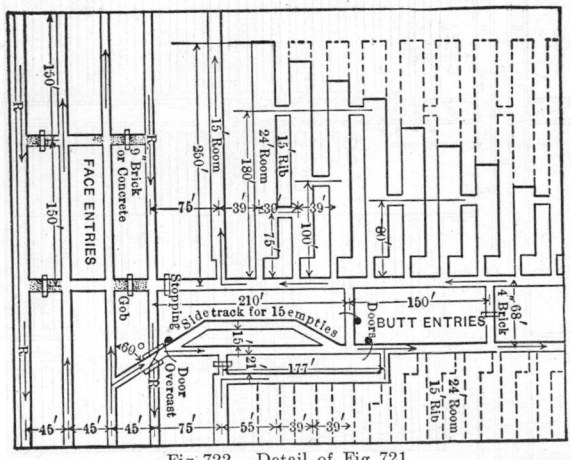

Fig 722. Detail of Fig 721

mined and 1 ft left on top to support draw slate 3 to 6 ft thick. Productive territory is developed by pairs of butt entries on 60-ft centers, at intervals of 300 ft. Butt entries, 11 ft wide, are driven

950 ft to accommodate 14 rooms on 60-ft centers, leaving a 150-ft barrier pillar between face entries and first room. Rooms are turned off the inby butt entry only, and are driven to the outby entry of the next pair of butt entries; rooms 11 ft wide; pillars, 49 ft. Most of tonnage is recovered on

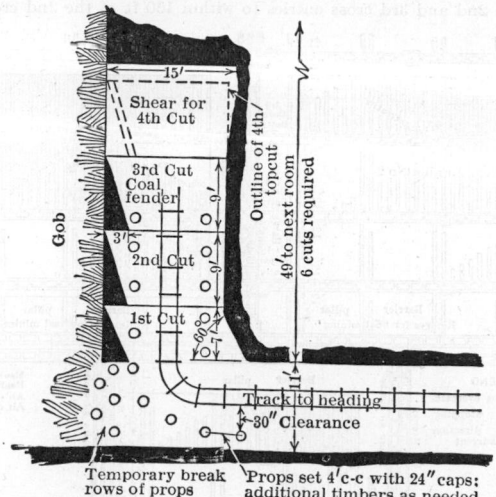

Fig 723. Mining of Room Pillars, Mona Mine

retreat, and roof control is successfully accomplished by maintaining a 45° pillar line. Coal faces, both on advance and retreat, are top-cut and sheared by a Universal-type, track-mounted machine cutting a 6-in kerf. Drilling is by track-mounted, elec auger drill; loading by a track-mounted,

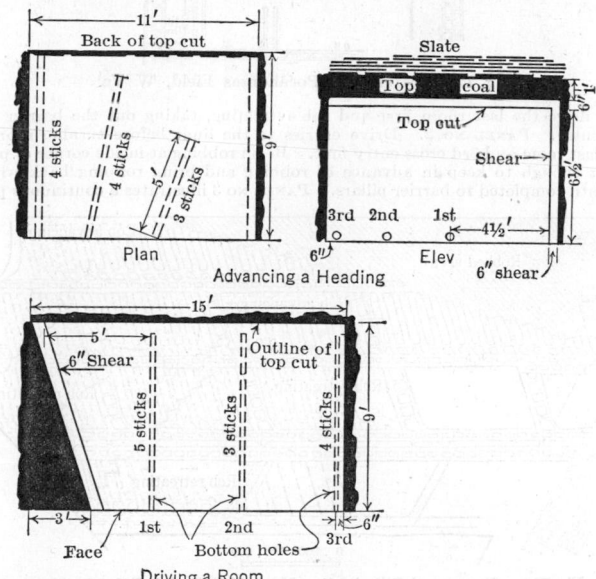

Fig 724. Breaking Ground, Mona Mine

elec loader. In retreat, room pillars are extracted by a series of 15-ft cuts, leaving small "fender" blocks of coal next to the gob (Fig 723), which keep the gob from rolling into the fall of coal. Fig 724 shows method of breaking ground in advance and retreat. POCAHONTAS FIELD. Seams, 3 to 10 ft thick. Fig 725 shows the general development plan of the Pocahontas Coal and Coke Co,

I—27

providing for quadruple main entries, triple cross entries, and double panel entries; alternative methods are shown in panels 1, 2, 3. The following directions, issued by the company, indicate the distinctions between these methods. PANEL NO 1. Drive the rooms on the 3rd cross entry as soon as they are reached. Begin robbing (Art 107) when the second room is completed, and rob advancing on the 2nd and 3rd cross entries to within 100 ft of the 2nd cross entry. On the

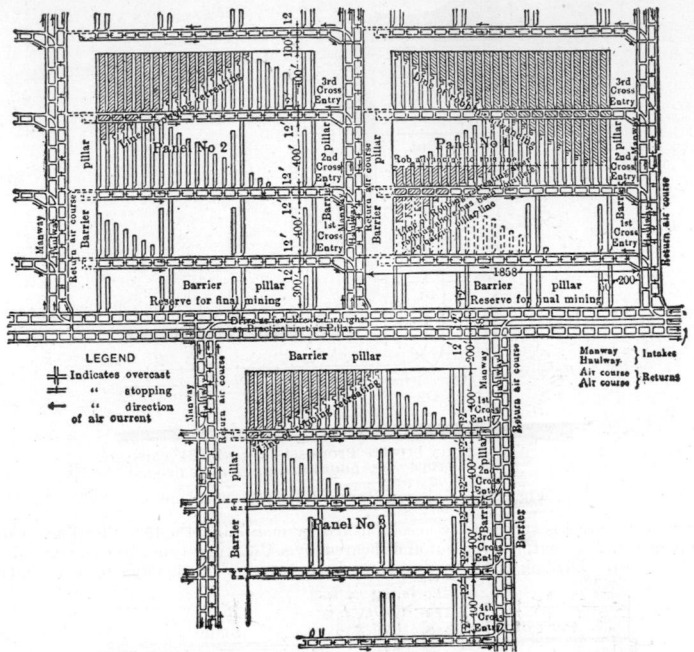

Fig 725.　Mining in Pocahontas Field, W Va

1st cross entry drive the last room first and rob retreating, taking out the barrier pillar left on the 2nd cross entry. PANEL NO 2. Drive entries to the limit before turning rooms, except as shown. Turn last room and 3rd cross entry first. Begin robbing at inside corner of panel; develop rooms only fast enough to keep in advance of robbing and bring robbing back with a uniform "break-line," until completed to barrier pillars. PANEL NO 3 illustrates a continuous panel. Drive

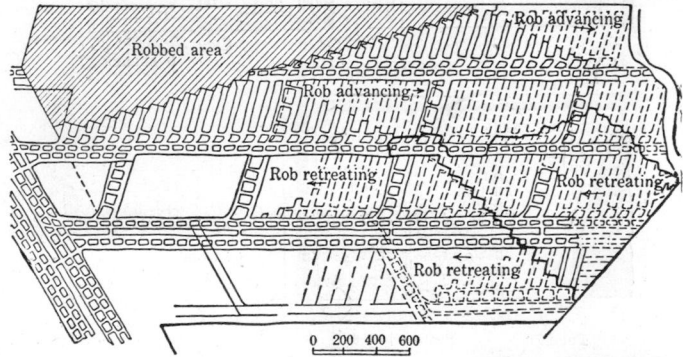

Fig 726.　Room and Pillar, Mine No 6, U S Coal & Coke Co (607)

entries to the limit before turning rooms, except as shown. Turn last room on 1st cross entry first, and begin robbing as soon as the second room is completed. Develop rooms only fast enough to keep in advance of robbing, and bring robbing back with a uniform break-line until the limit of mining is reached. With uniform conditions, such plans can be quite closely followed (360). MINE No 6, U S COAL AND COKE CO. Data from E. O'Toole in 1923 (607). The method (Fig 726) is

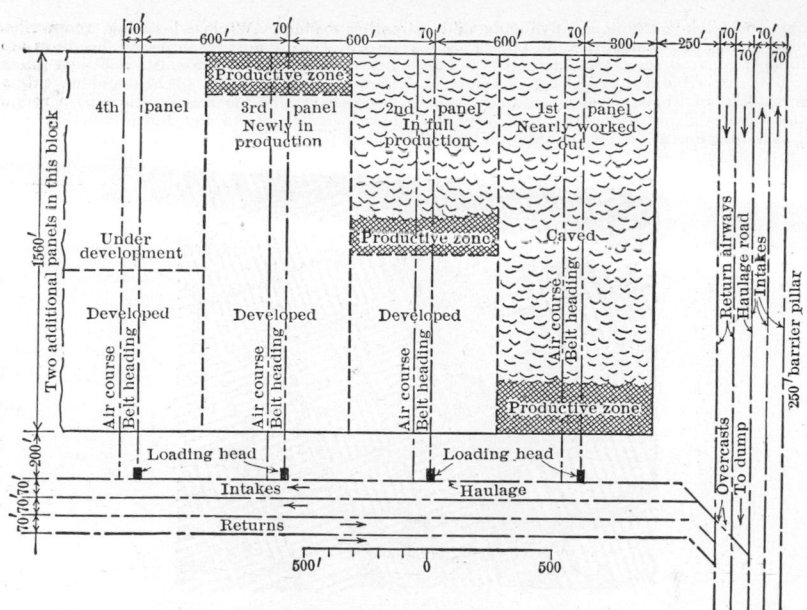

Fig 727. Mining System, MacAlpin Coal Co (490)

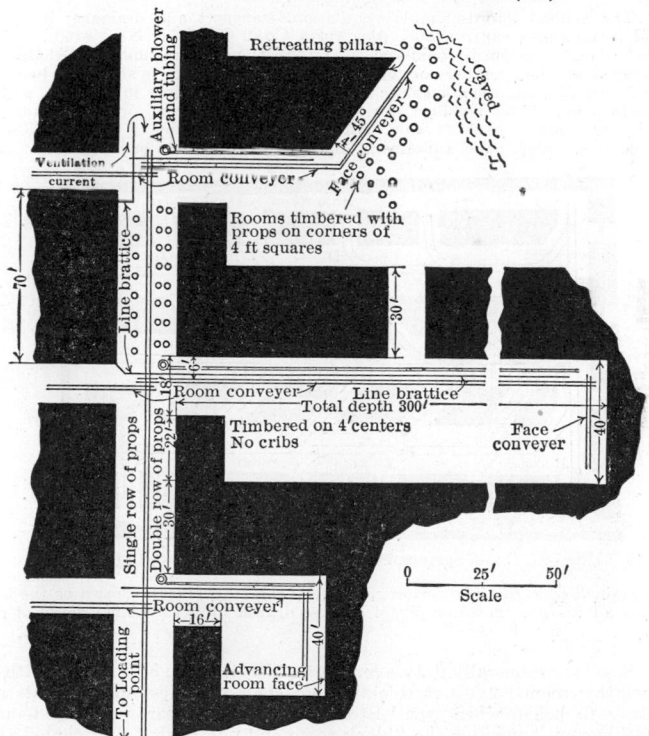

Fig 728. Typical Room Diagram, MacAlpin Coal Co (490)

a room-and-pillar continuous advancing and retreating system. While advancing, room ribs, heading stumps and heading chain pillars are extracted. During advancing period, headings are continually progressing, rooms being driven on the inby side. When the rooms reach their limits the pillars are withdrawn, resulting in complete extraction of the section. When robbing cuts a cross heading off from the main headings, haulage proceeds to another heading through a room. Each section is planned for 1 000 tons per shift. This method aims to give full production soon after beginning operations and maintain it until the mine is practically exhausted. Life of a section

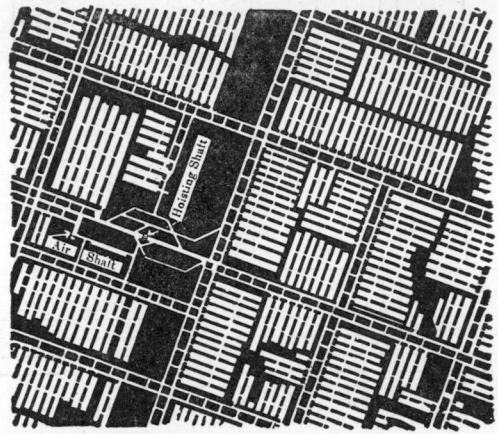

Fig 729. Block Room-and-pillar System, Ill

is 10–40 yr. The method affords simple ventilation, transport and drainage; it concentrates operations and permits max supervision. MacAlpin Coal Co, Mine No 4 (490). Pocahontas No 4 seam, 3 ft thick. System is room-and-pillar retreat; pillar drawing using chain-flight face and room conveyers and belt mother conveyers on panel entries; cars to slope and belt conveyers to tipple. As in Fig 727, main headings are in sets of 5; cross headings in sets of 4, and panel or room headings in pairs. Cross headings are on 2 200-ft centers; panel or room headings, 600-ft centers. All headings are 16 to 20 ft wide. Room necks, 18 ft wide, 16 ft deep. Rooms, 40 ft wide on 70-ft centers. Each panel contains 40 rooms, 20 driven from each heading. A cycle of

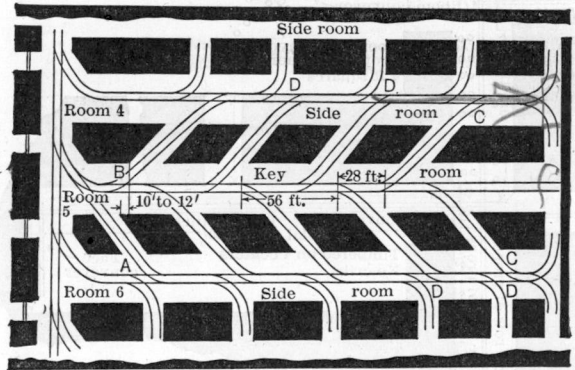

Fig 730. Room System, Peabody Coal Co Mine No 8, Ill (491)

mining is maintained on each panel heading, whereby the inby pillar is drawn as the 2 adjacent outby rooms are advancing. Heading pillars are also drawn. Fig 728 shows detail of room and pillar mining.

Illinois. Seams are generally flat; aver depth, 200 ft. The coal is firm, with partings of varying widths; seams, 2.5–9 ft thick. Roof characteristics vary; floor is generally fire clay, likely to heave when wet. Straight room-and-pillar, panel systems, and a modified panel system known as the "block room-and-pillar" or "semi-panel" (Fig 729), are all in use. For dimensions of openings see Table 91 (361). Some longwall mining is also done (Art 108). PEABODY COAL Co, Mine No 8, Christian County, Ill (491). No 6 seam, 6 to 7.5 ft thick; 370 ft of overburden. Panel system of 30-ft rooms at 50-ft centers, 256 ft long. Panel entries are in pairs 12 to 14 ft wide on 42-ft centers; 21 to 37 rooms are turned from each pair of panel entries, every 7th room being omitted, to leave

Table 91. Illinois Room-and-pillar Practice

Ex No	System of mining	Entry width, ft			Entry pillar width, ft		
		Main	Cross	Room	Main	Cross	Room
1	Room-and-pillar................	6†	......	......	......	......	......
2	Panel (a).....................	21*	21*	21*	35	35	......
3	Room-and-pillar................	7	6†	......	16	12†	......
4	Room-and-pillar................	8	8	......	12†	12†	......
5	Room-and-pillar................	12	12	......	42	15	......
6	Panel.........................	12	12	12	60*	60*	......
7	Semi-panel....................	8	8	8†	25	20	8
8	Semi-panel....................	8	8	8†	35	35	30
9	Room-and-pillar................	12	12	......	40	40	......
10	Panel.........................	14	14	14	50	50	......
11	Room-and-pillar................	9	9	......	25	21	......
12	Room-and-pillar................	7	7	......	35	30	......
13	Panel.........................	21*	21*	21*	40	40	......
14	Panel.........................	9	9	......	20	20	......
15	Room-and-pillar................	14	21	......	42	42	......
16	Room-and-pillar................	8	10	......	30	34	......
17	Panel.........................	12	12	12	50	50	......

Ex No	Barrier pillar width, ft		Room		Width of room-pillar, ft	Room necks		Dist from entry to full room width, ft	Distance between rooms, centers
	Main	Cross	Width, ft	Length, ft		Width, ft	Length, ft		
1	......	......	15†	250	15	6†	15	25	30
2	35	35	27	600*	43*	21	12	24	70*
3	17†	......	24	240	6	9	9	......	30
4	20	......	24	150†	18	8	10	20	42
5	36	......	26	200+500	19	8	7	12†	45
6	50	50	30	265	30	12	12	30	60
7	40	20†	24	180	10	8	10	15	34
8	60	50	26	200	9	8	9	27	35
9	150*	......	30	300	30	12	20	50*	60
10	100	100*	30	250	25	22*	22	28	55
11	40	......	43*	200	4	9	19	......	47
12	60	......	24	240	3†	9	18	......	27†
13	110	75	30	300	40	21	25*	50*	70*
14	30	......	24	250	20	9	4†	20	44
15	60	......	40	250	40	21	18	36	80
16	38	......	28	180	10	10	9	30	38
17	50	50	35	250	19	9	9	25	54

Ex No	No of rooms on room entry	Crosscuts width, ft	Dist from entry to 1st crosscut, ft	Width of room stump, ft	% of coal recovered	
1	....	15	....	24	45	
2	12†	21	60	49	50	
3	....	9	....	21	81	
4	....	8	....	34	44	
5	....	12	....	37	96*	
6	14	12	50†	48	50	
7	18	8	....	26	54	
8	14	8	....	27	56	
9	....	20	60	48	58	
10	40*	21	65	33	63	
11	....	5	....	38	55	
12	....	9	....	18†	68	
13	....	21	50†	49	56	
14	....	9	....	35	55	
15	....	30*	50†	59*	63	
16	....	4†	....	28	42†	
17	25	12	70*	45	55	

† Minimum for district. * Maximum for district. * Max for district-and-pillar. (a) Small section, worked by room-and-pillar.

a 70-ft pillar for roof control. Track-mounted horiz cutting machines and caterpillar loaders are used. To facilitate car change and loading, every third room is driven as a "key" room. As shown in Fig 730, the first crosscut in the key room is driven through into the side room, making sure there is enough pillar left between entry and crosscut *A*. Then the first crosscut to the left from key room is turned when the outside rib of crosscut is 10 or 12 ft past the inside rib of opposite crosscut *B*. This procedure, which staggers the crosscuts for roof protection, is carried out until the room is nearly finished. The last crosscuts are driven from the side rooms *C*, because the back switches in the side rooms make the car change much quicker. Each back switch has a switch directly behind it, *D*, to speed up the car change. Crosscuts in the key rooms aver about 56-ft centers, with 40-ft pillars. This makes the switches 56 ft apart on each side, but only 28 ft from switch to switch, counting both sides. MINE No 57, of same company, uses nearly the same system of panel mining and "key" rooms, but shear-cuts room faces and advances them as in Fig 731. Increased yield of lump is claimed. MOFFAT

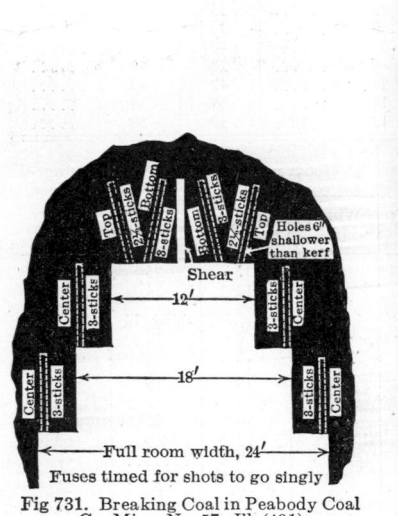

Fig 731. Breaking Coal in Peabody Coal Co Mine No 57, Ill (491)

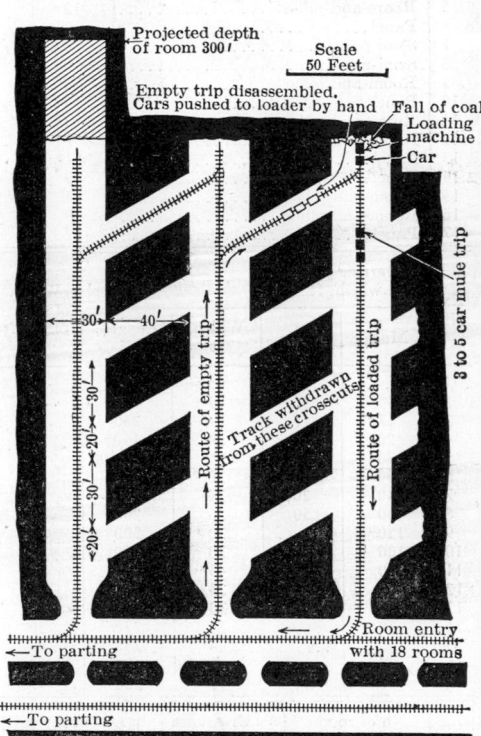

Fig 732. Mine-car Gathering Cycle, Moffat Mine, Ill (634)

MINE, Moffat Coal Co, Sparta, Ill (634), is in the No 6 seam and was originally developed for hand loading. Rooms are 30 ft wide on 70-ft centers, with max length of 300 ft; breakthroughs on 50-ft centers. Gathering was first done by mules. Later, caterpillar loading machines were installed, as in Fig 732. The system was further modified, as in Fig 733, by using tractor-trailer (storage-battery) gathering units mounted on rubber tires. These are of 5-ton capac, bottom-dumping, and are run directly over the conveyer hopper when discharging. Another modification is planned, as follows: The 300-ft rooms will be lengthened indefinitely. Every 300 ft, 3 lines of crosscuts will be driven across a panel of 18 rooms, for haulage and air, with a line of stoppings outby the first line of crosscuts to advance the air supply. Each 18-room panel will have a hopper-conveyer unit, located centrally along the tractor-trailer haulageway. This will limit the max gathering haul to about 1 000 ft, and the aver haul to less than 600 ft. As two gathering units can then serve a loading machine, the territory will be subdivided into

2 sections, of 9 rooms each, on each side of the hopper-conveyer. Each section will have
a loading machine, with auxiliary equipment. Thus the single conveyer will serve 2
loading machines and 4 tractor-trailers. Panel entries, parallel to the rooms, will be
advanced by gang work as usual. Fig 735 shows the proposed method; Fig 734, the
method of timbering.

Indiana. Panel systems of room-and-pillar work with double-entry development are
in universal use. The following figures of practice of the Brazil Block Coal Co are fairly

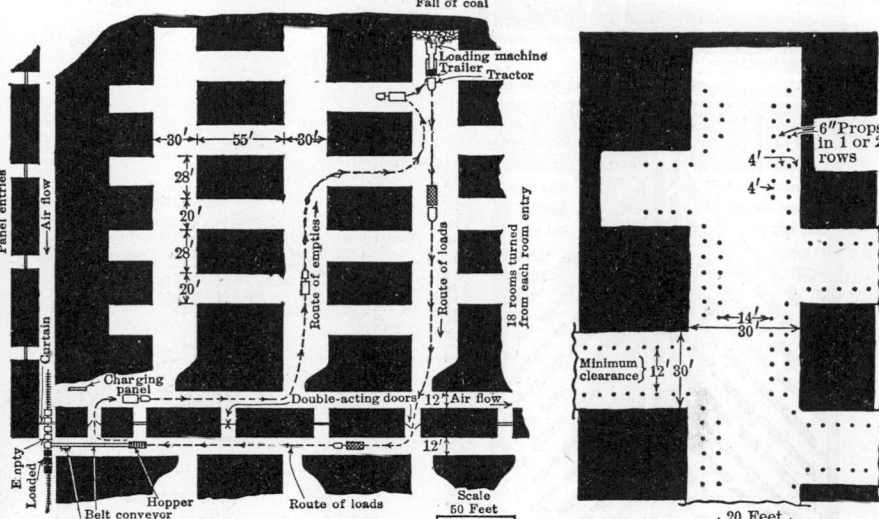

Fig 733. Tractor-trailer Cycle, Moffat   Fig 734.   Timbering Diagram,
Mine, Ill (634)   Moffat Mine, Ill (634)

representative; seams are 4.7–10 ft thick; depths, 80–600 ft. Roof is sandstone or shale;
floor, fire clay. Rooms, 18–30 ft wide, usually 21 ft; necks, commonly 9 ft wide and
12–20 ft long. Width of main-entry pillars, 18–40 ft; cross-entry pillars, 15–30 ft; room
pillars, usually 9 or 10 ft wide, occasionally, 20 ft (362). SAXTON MINE, Saxton Coal
Mining Co, Terre Haute, Ind (635). Seam No IV, 5 ft thick. Fig 736 shows typical
production panel. Main entries are 11 ft wide, on 33-ft centers; room entries, 11 ft
wide, 25-ft centers. While panel entries are advancing, the middle entry serves as

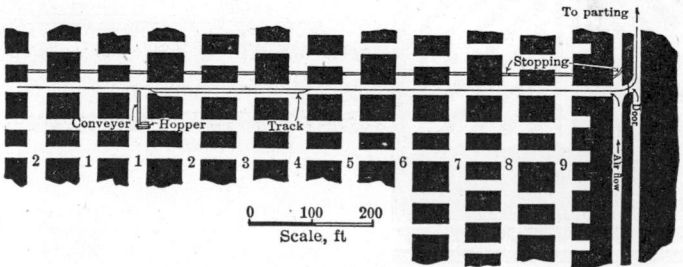

Fig 735.   Mining System, Moffat Mine, Ill (634)

haulageway; when a panel has been driven full distance, track is removed from middle
entry, which then serves as return airway only. In each panel, 24 rooms are turned at
45° along each side entry. Rooms are 21 ft wide on 33-ft centers, and are driven to max
length of 350 ft. Six subsidiary rooms are turned at 45° from the first room. Room
panels, 594 ft wide, are separated from one another by barrier pillars 25 to 50 ft wide,
thus making room-panel entries on 619 to 644-ft centers. By using wide rooms and narrow
pillars, a recovery of approx 66% is claimed. In development work, the coal face is

undercut its entire width and sheared from top to bottom above the right-hand rail. Depth of cut, 8.5 ft with 6-in kerf. Fig 737 shows mode of cutting and placing shots in rooms. Equipment includes track-mounted cutting and shearing machines, elec post-mounted auger drills, track-mounted shovel loaders in development entries, and track-mounted flight loading machines.

Ohio. WHEELING TOWNSHIP COAL MINING CO, Mine No 2, Adena, Ohio (639). Pittsburgh No 8 seam, 54–60 in thick. Draw slate, 11 to 14-in, is taken down, leaving

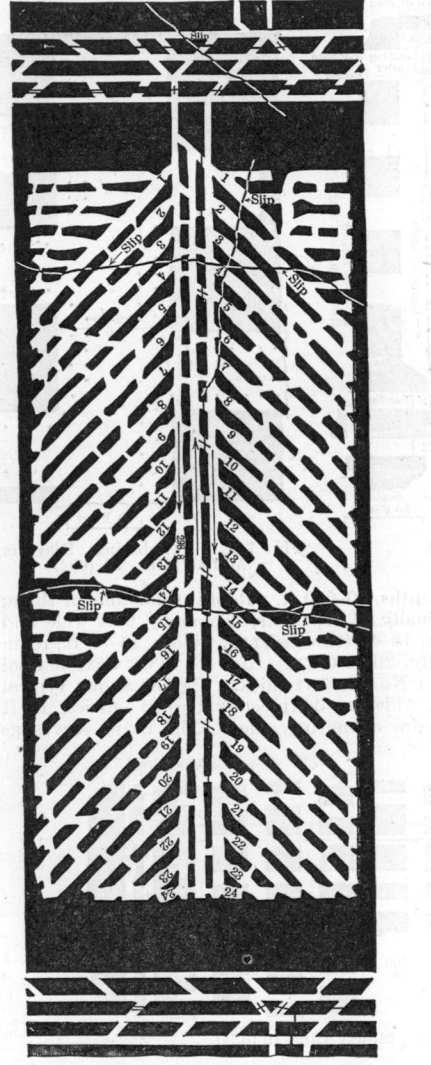

Fig 736. Panel in Saxton Mine, Ind (635)

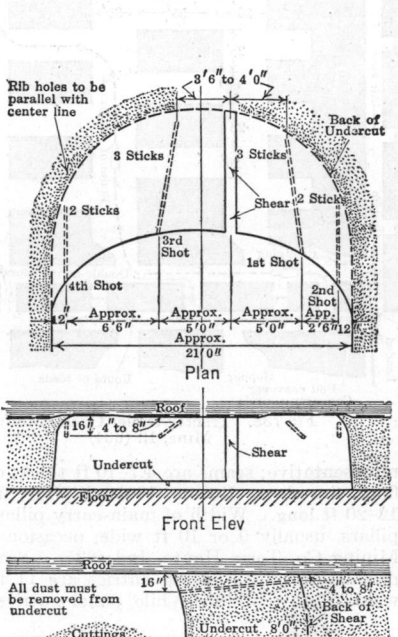

Fig 737. Breaking Coal in Rooms, Saxton Mine, Ind (635)

a 12-in seam of coal as roof. Mine opened by drift under cover of 30 to 260 ft. Quadruple main and face entries are driven as 2 pairs, connected for haulage purposes every 600 ft. One pair serves as intake, other as return. Butt entries 8.5 ft wide are in pairs on 32-ft centers, turned on 484-ft centers at right-angles to face entries. Driving butt entries 1 635 ft allows for turning of 48 rooms 26 ft wide, 225 ft deep, on 34-ft centers, leaving a 136-ft pillar between first room and the face entry. Room necks are turned off butt entries at 55° and deflected to full 90° after 4 cuts. Necks are 12 ft wide to accommodate track-mounted cutting and loading machines. Every eighth room is omitted, giving 7-room panels separated by 42-ft pillars to control roof. After the butt entries have been driven the required 1 635 ft, production is obtained by simultaneously advancing blocks of 7 rooms off each entry. These rooms are completed before production starts on the next 2 blocks of 7 rooms each. No pillar recovery is attempted. Coal is loaded by caterpillar loading machines directly into 3-ton cars. Room face is undercut and sheared near its center by track-mounted cutting machine, making a 9-ft cut, 6 in wide. Four holes are drilled in the face with post-mounted elec auger drill of 1.5-in diam; 1 hole on each rib and 1 hole between each rib and the shear cut; all holes are horiz and

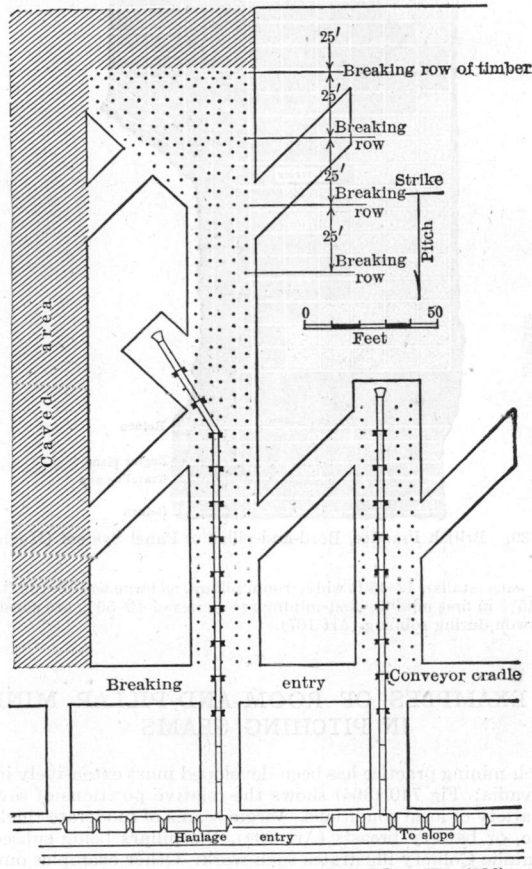

Fig 738. Room Work, D. O. Clark Mine, Wyo(636)

6 in below the draw slate. The hole to left of the shear cut is shot first and the broken coal loaded out; then the left rib hole is fired, and its coal loaded; same system is repeated on the right side. Pellet powder is used; 3 sticks per shot. Draw slate is shot down after coal has been loaded out. Entries are undercut and sheared on both ribs. One 1.5-in hole is drilled with hand-held elec auger in the center and 6 in below the draw slate and loaded with 2.5 sticks of pellet powder. Crew of 6 men, working a pair of entries, under normal conditions makes seven 9-ft cuts per shift, or about 30 ft advance in each heading. Standard room timbering comprises a row of road posts on 3-ft centers 4 ft to the left of center line of room; another row on 3-ft centers 4.5 ft to right of center line (extra 6 in to allow clearance for loading-machine operator); 2 rows of gob posts on 6-ft centers, between road posts and ribs. All posts are hardwood, in lengths of 5.5 or 6 ft, secured by sawed wedges driven between roof and top of post.

Wyoming. Fig 738 shows typical room-and-pillar operation in the D. O. Clark mine of the Union Pacific Coal Co, Sou Wyo, where self-loading shaking conveyers (duckbills) are in use (636). Distinguishing feature is that one pillar is being mined on retreat while an adjacent room is advancing.

British practice. Room-and-pillar methods in England (bord-and-pillar, post-and-stall, pillar-and-stall), and in Scotland (stoop-and-room), resemble those in the U S, except in dimensions of openings and percentage of recovery on first mining (Fig 739). Common dimensions (363): entries

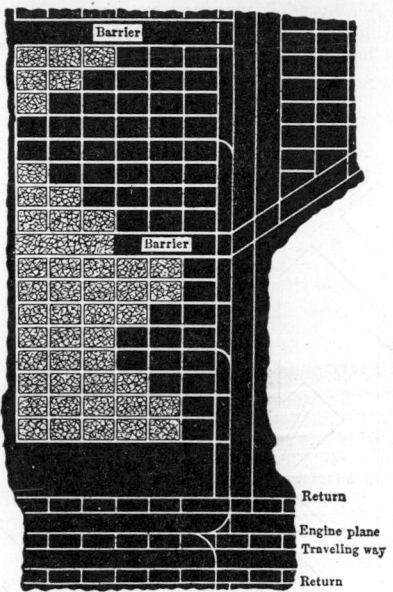

Fig 739. British Practice, Bord-and-pillar or Panel System (Hughes)

(walls), 6 ft wide; rooms (stalls), 12–15 ft wide; room pillars, as large as 132–198 ft square. Recoveries are about 30–35% in first mining; first-mining recoveries of 40–50% are considered dangerous. Most of the coal is won during robbing (Art 107).

106. EXAMPLES OF ROOM-AND-PILLAR MINING IN PITCHING SEAMS

General. Pitch-mining practice has been developed most extensively in the anthracite basins of Pennsylvania; Fig 740 (364) shows the relative positions of several seams and indicates a wide variety of local conditions. Virgin seams of moderate thickness are mined with buggy, chute, or battery breasts (Art 104), the pillars being subsequently robbed (Art 107); the Natalie Colliery illustrates such work. Other examples outline more complex methods for special conditions.

Natalie Colliery, Western Middle field, Penna. The Lykens seam occurs here in 2 splits, separated by 60–80 ft hard conglomerate. Seams are very irregular; pinches, faults, and sudden changes in the texture of the coal are common. The underlying split (Lykens No 1) averages about 4 ft of shelly, friable, badly crushed coal, with bands of slate and dirt to 1 ft thick; it contains a little gas. Roof and floor are hard conglomerate. The overlying split (Lykens No 2) averages 4–5 ft of very hard clean coal, with no gas; roof and floor, conglomerate. Aver pitch of both splits, 25°; vert depth of workings, 410 ft. Main opening is a double-track slope, driven on pitch in Lykens No 1, cars hoisted to surface. Gangways, 7 by 12 ft and about 300 ft apart along the pitch, are driven on the strike against the top rock, on grade of 0.75% favoring the load. The monkey, 30 ft above the gangway, has an area of 36 sq ft, dimensions varying with thickness of seam. Chutes, 6–8 ft wide by thickness of seam, are turned off at right-angles to the gangway on 50-ft centers. Breasts are 24 ft wide and 270–290 ft long, leaving a 10 to 30-ft chain pillar to support the gangway above. Headings, turned on 60-ft centers, have an area of 36 sq ft. Coal is conveyed from

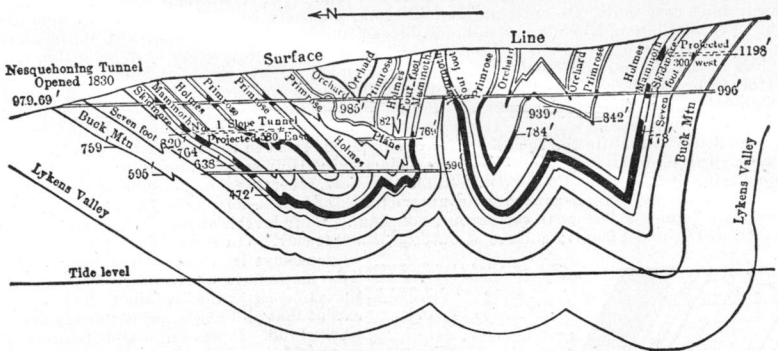

Fig 740. Workings from Nesquehoning Tunnel, Southern Anthracite Field (Whildin)

the face to the gangway by sheet-iron chutes. Lykens No 2, opened by a tunnel from No 1, is mined similarly. Forced ventilation is used; interruptions of air current, due to opening of doors for gangway traffic, are not serious because of small quantity of gas.

Staggered battery breasts. At a mine in the Middle Western anthracite field of Penna, the seams have an aver dip of 20°. Coal is firm and hard and 5 ft thick; roof and floor, good. Breasts are 24 ft wide on 50-ft centers and worked with sheet-iron chutes. Coal is paid for by the car, miners doing their own loading. As the faces of the breasts advanced in one section, the dip increased gradually from 20° to 60°. Due to the small area in which this occurred, and because the whole mine was worked on a car basis of payment, it was deemed inadvisable to drive a counter gangway and work battery breasts from it. Instead, and to provide safety and support for the miners and decrease breakage of coal, staggered batteries were used when the pitch reached 40° (Fig 741). This shows poor mining, but illustrates variations of practice to meet local economic and geological conditions. Many other variations are in use.

Rock-holes (rock-chutes) are widely employed in mining contiguous seams. Development openings are driven in the underlying seam and rock-holes (inclined raises similar to chute-raises, Art 67) are driven to the overlying seam from the gangways or breasts, or both. Breasts may be opened in the overlying seam directly from the rock-holes, or from small gangways driven to connect tops of rock-holes. This often effects large economies in development; especially in reworking the thick Mammoth seam, which contains large amounts of coal left by crude early methods. Reopening old gangways in Mammoth seam is dangerous and costly; it is often impossible even to drive new gangways near worked-over areas.

One or more contiguous seams may be opened by tunnels run across the strata from a main haulageway in one seam. This presupposes possibility of driving and maintaining gangways in the other seams. Where a series of short tunnels is driven to reach an adjacent seam they are known as SECTIONAL TUNNELS, and are spaced at intervals depending on their length, speed of development desired, and condition of the seam to be opened. They avoid breakage of coal in rock-holes, provide numerous working faces and hence allow rapid development. Examples follow.

Lawrence Colliery, Schuylkill region, Penna (H. H. Morris). Holmes seam, averaging 8–10 ft of firm coal, is mined by rock-holes from development openings and breasts in the Four-Foot seam; the seams are separated by about 10 ft of rock; pitch, about 60°. Gangways and monkeys are driven

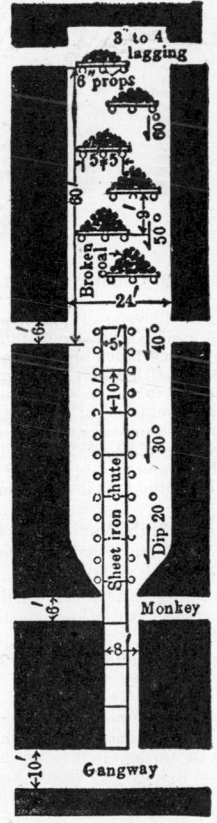

Fig 741. Staggered Batteries

on 30-ft centers in the Four-Foot seam, with chutes on 50-ft centers. A few feet above high side of the monkey, a battery is built, and enough coal blasted to allow a 6 by 8-ft rock-hole to be driven at about 40° through the top-rock to Holmes seam. The rock-hole is partitioned to make a manway and a coal chute. On entering Holmes seam, a battery breast is driven 24 ft wide up the pitch. For ventilation, 2 or more rock-holes, breasts and headings must be opened in the Holmes; a split of air from the Four-Foot monkey is carried up the manway of one rock-hole, through the workings in the Holmes and down another rock-hole manway into the Four-Foot monkey. After the Holmes breasts have been driven and drawn, breasts of same width are driven in Four-Foot seam directly under those in the Holmes. Pillars must all be of same size. Sometimes the mined coal in the Holmes breasts is held in reserve and not drawn when a breast is finished, in which case an extra battery is built in the rock-hole, for opening the breast in the Four-Foot. In this part of the mine, surface conditions prohibit robbing; pillars in the Holmes seam, however, could be robbed before driving breasts in the Four-Foot. In another part, several seams, pitching 65° and 1.5–30 ft thick, are mined by counter-gangways, counter-chutes and rock-holes (Fig 742). The colliery is opened by a "gun-boat" slope in the Seven-Foot seam. Main level is at 634 ft elev; counter-levels at 820 ft, 920 ft, and 1 000 ft; surface at outcrop, 1 200 ft elev. (In Penna anthracite mines, elev of gangways is given in ft above sea level.)

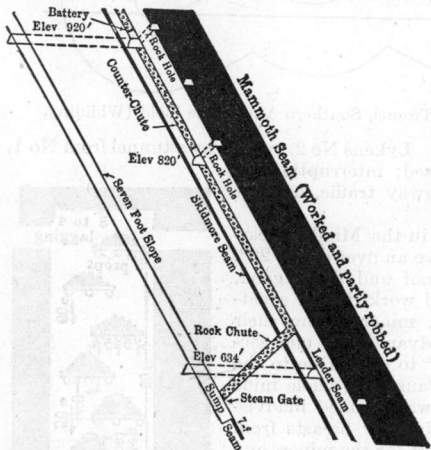

Fig 742. Counter-chute Method (Lawrence Colliery)

The method in the thinner seams is about the same as at the Natalie Colliery (above), except that all breasts are of battery type and worked full. It was impossible to drive gangways in Mammoth seam, due to condition of its old workings; hence, rock-holes (6 by 6 ft) are driven from Skidmore or Leader seam at 60-ft centers on the gangways and 60-ft centers on the pitch from Skidmore breasts. Distance between Skidmore and Mammoth seams, 20–60 ft. All coal mined on the counter-levels goes to a counter-chute in Leader seam (a 12 to 18-in split of Mammoth appearing at irregular intervals between the Skidmore and Mammoth). This counter-chute extends in the Leader from the 1 000-ft counter-gangway to a point above the 634-ft level, where a rock-chute is turned back to the loading pit slightly below 634-ft level. Batteries are built in the counter-chute above each counter-gangway, to regulate the flow of coal and maintain dump room on the gangways. Breakage is minimized by keeping the chute as full as possible and by careful drawing; this gives a "prepared yield" (Sec 34) as high as 60%. A successful rock-hole system, more elaborate than the above, is used by the Lehigh Navigation Coal Co; for this, and for details of various intricate methods of re-working the Mammoth seam, see Bib (364).

Rock-holes and buggy gangways are used at one mine in the Southern field for working the Mammoth seam; development openings are driven in the underlying Skidmore seam, which is 90 to 100 ft away. Rock-holes are driven at intervals of 300 to 600 ft from the Skidmore gangways and connected at their tops by buggy gangways in the Mammoth. Breasts are then turned off the buggy gangways, and the coal is mined and dumped down the rock-holes, which in reality are rock counter-chutes. By driving buggy gangways in both directions, the haul is halved and speed of development doubled. The rock-holes furnish convenient points to which to retreat in robbing; the method avoids maintenance of expensive main gangways in the Mammoth.

Lehigh Navigation Coal Co, Lansford, Penna. Data from W. G. Whildin in 1914 (364). Battery breasts and "cut-backs" are used for mining the Mammoth seam. Where the pitch is 60° to 90°, gangways and airways are driven along the top rock, so that the loading chutes can be driven back on a 30° pitch; this provides a safe working place for loaders, and allows better control in drawing broken coal. In flatter seams, gangways are driven on bottom-rock, and airways either along the bottom or top rock; distance between gangway and monkey, 20–50 ft. The larger interval results in a lower maintenance cost of gangways.

The method of opening a breast is shown in Fig 743, 744. Chutes 6 by 6 ft, partitioned to make a manway and a loading chute, are driven from the gangway on a slope of 22° to the bottom rock and then up the pitch to the height for opening the stump heading. Here a jugular battery is put in and a 4 by 6-ft stump heading driven to the next chute. This is used both for ventilation and access, and is known as the "bottom-breast crosscut." From it, a "front" manway (dog-hole) is driven on one side of the breast 20 ft up the pitch, and a "back" manway on the other side. The breast is started 10 ft wide by 8 ft high next to the back manway and is gradually widened to 18 ft at top of the dog-hole, leaving a stump pillar (Fig 743). Mining then proceeds by advancing a battery breast, 18 ft wide by 15 ft high, on the bottom rock for a distance of 21 ft above the bottom-breast crosscut. At this point a cut-back, 10 ft wide along the pitch, is carried up to the top rock from rib to rib. After the first cut-back is finished, the breast is driven 30 ft farther up the pitch, where a second cut-back is made. Where the pitch is 45°, the loose coal does not fill the whole space, in which case the miners carry a "path" along each rib of the cut-back. Two miners blast the coal, each traveling his own path, until the top rock is reached and all the coal taken out between

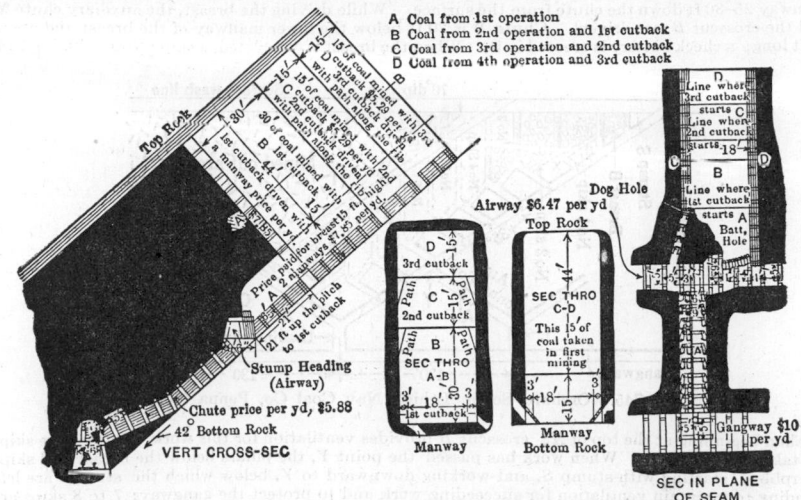

A Coal from 1st operation
B Coal from 2nd operation and 1st cutback
C Coal from 3rd operation and 2nd cutback
D Coal from 4th operation and 3rd cutback

Fig 743. Cut-back in Breast 62, E Mammoth Seam, No 10 Shaft, L N C Co

the cut-backs. The breast is again driven up the pitch 15 ft, where a third cut-back is made. If the breast does not run away, or the top coal does not fall, a cut-back is made every 15 ft to the limit of the breast. In steep-pitching veins, no paths are necessary, the miners standing on the loose coal. For further detail, see Bib (364). Note that prices quoted in Fig 743 are as of 1914.

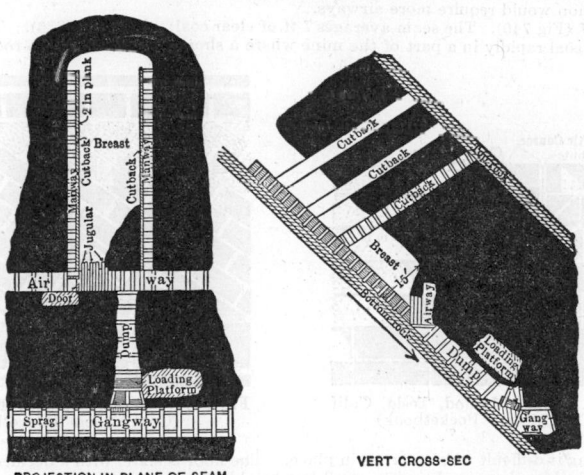

Fig 744. Cut-back System, Mammoth Seam, Penna

Orchard seam, Nesquehoning District, Penna. Data from J. S. Miller in 1925 (609). Dip, 65°–70°; coal is hard; roof fairly strong; width at surface 8 ft, increasing to 15 ft at first gangway. Fig 745 shows method used by Lehigh Nav Coal Co, instead of the usual battery-breast and pillar method, with subsequent robbing by one of the plans in Fig 750, 751 and 752. Mining is done from a series of main chutes *C* (Fig 745), driven at an angle to the dip on a slope of 30°–35°. Loading chutes *L* are first put up from the gangway at 130-ft centers; air connections *A* are next driven and then the main chutes. Until the latter hole through to surface they are ventilated by an elec fan. Main chutes, 300 ft long, require little upkeep compared with a chute driven up the pitch.

Mining starts near top of a main chute; a breast B, about 50 ft long is opened, with its upper manway 25–30 ft down the chute from the surface. While driving the breast, the auxiliary chute X, and the crosscut B, are driven. Chute X is 20 ft below the lower manway of the breast and about 25 ft long; a check battery is erected in it. When the breast is completed, a skip (No 1 skip, Fig 745)

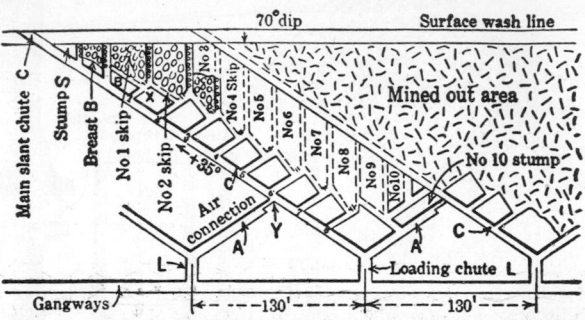

Fig 745. Orchard Seam, Lehigh Nav Coal Co, Penna (609)

is taken beginning at the top of X; crosscut B provides ventilation for this work. Successive skips are taken in same way. When work has passed the point Y, the pillars below the breast and skips are robbed, starting with stump S, and working downward to Y, below which the stumps are left standing to maintain ventilation for succeeding work and to protect the gangway; 7 to 8 skips are taken on each main chute and usually 2 skips and a stump on each airway A.

Driving and robbing a main chute takes 11–12 months; 4 or 5 chutes are worked simultaneously. The method extracts 68% of the coal; gives a high percent of prepared sizes; concentrates the area of operations for a given output as compared with pillar and breast work; eliminates objectionable features of pillar-breast, pillar-skip, and pillar-chute robbing (Art 107). In this property, the method increased output 40–90 cars per day and about halved the cost per car. As the seam is free from gas and the workings reach the surface, natural ventilation is used. Deeper work with forced ventilation would require more airways.

Tesla, Calif (Fig 746). The seam averages 7 ft of clear coal; pitch, 60° (376). The system was devised to get coal rapidly in a part of the mine where a short-grained, slate cap rock came in over

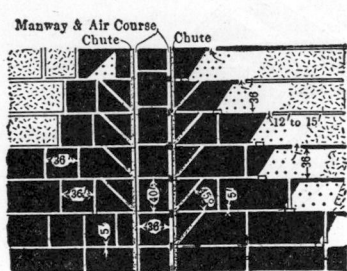

Fig 746. Mining Method, Tesla, Calif
(Coal Miners' Pocketbook)

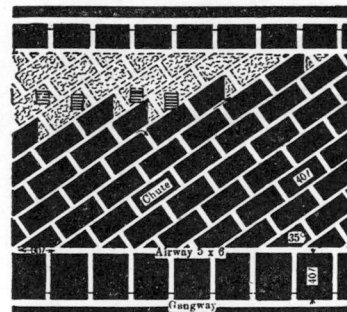

Fig 747. Mining Method, Tesla, Calif
(Coal Miners' Pocketbook)

the coal, making it difficult to keep props in place. The floor is slate, with a decided heaving tendency; roof is good sandstone; there is a small but troublesome amount of gas. Two double-compt chutes are driven up the pitch and connected by crosscuts. Small gangways are driven from chutes parallel to main gangways at intervals of 36 ft along the pitch. These are continued 300 ft from each chute if conditions warrant. The end of pillar between the highest small gangways is then attacked, the coal being worked on the cleavage planes. Resulting breast consists of a 36-ft face, including the drift or gangway through which the coal is carried to the chutes. A 2 or 3-ft pillar is left between breasts to keep rocks from falling on breast below. Working face in each breast, 45–48 ft. Light iron chutes, to load coal into cars on the small gangways, are moved along as the face advances; loading is cheap, loss from breakage, small. Coal is dumped from cars into angle chutes, connecting with main chutes on slopes of about 45°; these keep main chute full, so that each breast can deliver coal continuously, and so reduce breakage. The breast gangways are 5 ft wide, untimbered.   The small pillar left over the tops of breasts is maintained until the face has advanced 12–15 ft, when it is cut out.   The roof caves and fills the opening.   Ventilation at faces is by chutes driven between gangways at 36-ft intervals.

Fig 747 shows another system in a 7-ft seam.   As roof is shelly and breaks quickly, mining must proceed rapidly.   A gangway and airway, 40 ft apart, are connected by chutes every 30 ft, which are driven up the pitch at about 35°; they are connected by crosscuts 40 ft apart.   This divides the seam into pillars, which are then worked out from top downward.   Rows of cogs are built about 80 ft apart, to delay roof settlement and prevent remaining pillars from crushing; little other timber is required.

Pierce County, Wash.   Data from S. H. Ash in 1925 (610).   Steeply pitching seams are 3–25 ft thick; coal often gassy; roof and floor bad, precluding wide breasts; hence mining is by a chute-and-pillar system.   Fig 748 shows general plan on pitches to 65°; in steeper seams, slant chutes are driven on pitches of 45°–60°.   Gangways are 200 ft apart.

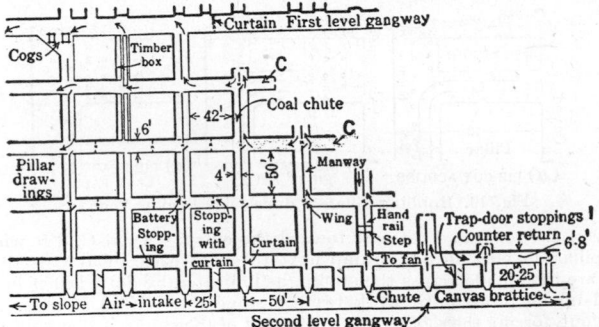

Fig 748. Development by Chute-and-pillar, with Ventilation Details, Pierce County, Wash (610)

A counter gangway (monkey or airway in Penna mines) is driven 20–25 ft above the gangway. Chutes are on 50-ft centers; 6 ft wide between gangway and counter gangway, above which they are 8–10 ft wide.   Half chutes, for traveling ways, are put up to the counter-gangway between alternate main chutes.   Crosscuts C (Fig 748) vary from a small hole to 6 ft wide.   This work comprises the first mining (see Art 107 for pillar robbing).   Brattices are carried through the chutes; the inby compartment is used as a manway, the outby as a coal chute.   Fig 748 shows path of air currents.

107. ROBBING PILLARS

General.   Robbing or drawing pillars consists in removing the coal left for roof support after first-mining has been completed.   The character of roof and floor, texture of coal, thickness and dip of seam, presence of gas and other local conditions, all influence the method of work and the time at which it should be done.

Systems of robbing.   There are 2 general systems: robbing during the ADVANCE and robbing on the RETREAT.   A further distinction may be made between PRELIMINARY and COMPLETE or FINAL robbing.

Advance system.   Fig 701 shows its application in a flat seam with rooms turned in one direction only.   First-mining is followed closely by preliminary robbing, which removes the room pillars; stump pillars are left to support the haulageways, and, with the entry pillars, are removed on the retreat system after first-mining and preliminary robbing are completed to the limit of the entry and the section abandoned.   Pillars must be drawn uniformly, keeping working faces in a straight line; this avoids throwing excessive press on any one pillar and secures a uniform line of break in the roof.   Direction of line of re-treat depends chiefly on character of roof, which should break as robbing proceeds; otherwise the press on stump, entry, and remaining room pillars may crush them or cause a general squeeze.   ADVANTAGES: (a) max production per unit area of development; (b) reduction of loss caused by deterioration of pillar coal on long exposure to air; (c) increased yield of lump coal in soft or friable seams, because pillars are removed before roof press can cause extensive crushing; (d) improved ventilation in non-gaseous mines; (e) room pillars are smaller, due to short life and limited area of support.   DISADVANTAGES: (a) gas is apt to accumulate in caved areas, which can not be ventilated, and there is always danger from fire; (b) where roof strata are water-bearing, breakage of the roof increases amount of inflow; (c) comparatively large stump and entry pillars are necessary to prevent squeezes and avoid excessive cost of maintenance of entries.

Retreat system is the reverse of the advance. Development entries are driven to their limit, rooms turned, and first-mining is completed throughout the entire area before robbing begins. Robbing is begun at the inside limit of the area and retreats toward the main or sectional entries; robbing is complete, *i e*, room, stump, and entry pillars are extracted in one operation. A combination system known as ADVANCE AND RETREAT is sometimes used where rooms are turned in both directions (Fig 721). Rooms are turned in one direction only as the development entries advance, and room-pillar robbing is carried on during advance. When the limit of the entry is reached, rooms are turned in opposite direction and work retreats toward main entries, final robbing being carried on during retreat.

Examples of American practice. Details vary widely with underground and surface conditions and quality of labor; many cases require special methods. CONNELLSVILLE REGION, Penna. Fig 749 shows pillar-drawing in flat seams. Robbing in any pillar

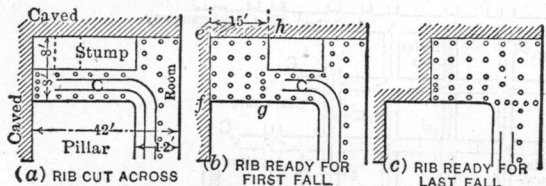

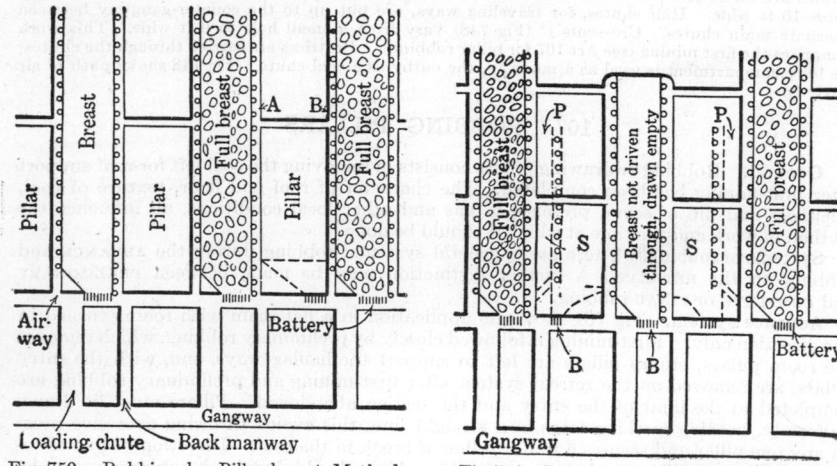

Fig 749. Robbing Pillars, Connellsville Region, Penna

begins at face of the room and retreats toward the entry. A cut *C*, 8 ft wide, is driven through the pillar, leaving an 8-ft stump next to caved area. Cut *C* is timbered with props. Cuts are then made across the stump, as indicated by dotted lines in (*a*), and the roof is picked up by props until work reaches stage (*b*). Props in area *efgh* are next drawn or shot out, forcing the roof to fall. The rest of the stump is then mined and caved, and the process repeated until the whole pillar is drawn back to the entry pillars, which are removed by similar methods (358). This plan, with modifications of detail, is in universal use in the U S for drawing pillars in flat seams. Loading may be done mechanically with

Fig 750. Robbing by Pillar-breast Method (609)

Fig 751. Robbing by Pillar-skipping Method (609)

scrapers (Sec 27). ANTHRACITE MINES, Penna. Methods are unsystematic and often left to the miners. In flat or slightly pitching seams, pillars are usually robbed by taking slices ("skips") off the ribs, the roof being temporarily supported by props. In steep-pitching seams one of the following methods is used, with variations to suit local conditions: (*A*) Pillar-breast (Fig 750). A battery is placed at one corner of the pillar; manways on each side of pillar are connected at intervals, as at *AB*; pillar is then mined as a breast. This method, though practically abandoned, is used to some extent in modified form by leaving wider pillars on first-mining. Then a full-width breast is driven in middle of the pillar, and the remaining narrow ribs are drilled full of holes and blasted in one operation (609). (*B*) Pillar-skipping (Fig 751). Middle breast of a group of 3 is not driven through; it is drawn empty; the 2 adjacent breasts are left full of broken coal. A skip *S* is taken off the inside of each pillar, much of the coal being blasted into the central empty breast. Small pillars *P* are left between skip manways and full breasts; they are drilled and blasted after the skips are completed (609). (*C*) Pillar-chute method (Fig 752) is most used, either of necessity or because of its safety. The pillar is first split by a chute *P*, 4-6 ft wide, driven from the gangway. Robbing begins at the top and is carried

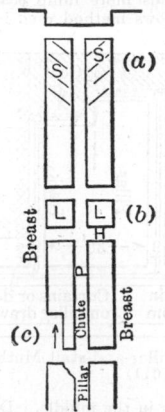

Fig 752. Robbing Pillars, Thick Steeply Pitching Seams

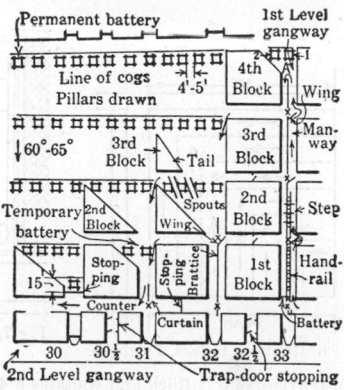

Fig 753. Pillar Drawing in Chute-and-pillar System, Pierce County, Wash (610)

on by inclined skips (*a*), or by driving heading *H* and then blasting out the small pillars *L* with long shots (*b*), or by running skips up the pitch from a heading (*c*). Only experienced miners should be employed for robbing; danger increases with steepness of pitch and thickness of seam. Liberal use of props is essential to support "flakes" of roof-rock, and give warning of impending falls. No props are drawn; they crush down as the roof comes in, and aid in keeping rocks from rolling onto the working face. PIERCE COUNTY, WASH. Data from S. H. Ash in 1925 (610). First-mining by chute-and-pillar system is shown in Fig 748. Three adjacent pillars formed by 4 chutes and 2 gangways are usually drawn in one operation (Fig 753), in which robbing is starting at the upper inby corner of pillar No 33; work is finished in pillar 30 and is in intermediate stages in pillars 31, 32. Sequence of operations: crosscuts in the pillars to be robbed are well timbered.

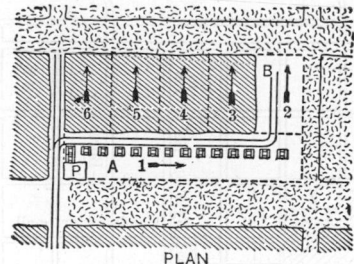

Fig 754. Robbing Pillars, Northumberland

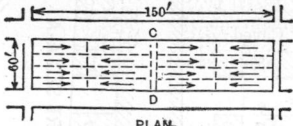

Fig 755. Robbing Pillars, West Durham

A cog (1 in pillar 30) is built under the upper gangway as close as possible to the inby rib of the chute. A corner pillar 30 is then worked off until space is gained to build another cog 4 or 5 ft from the first. A temporary battery of props above this cog protects men from injury by falls from above and provides a traveling way on the gangway. Work proceeds by "taking off the angles," until half the top block of pillar 33 is mined; remainder of block is the "tail." The upper inby corner of 3rd block in pillar 33 is next robbed in same way, and the tail of 4th block is then drawn. Broken coal from the tails is run out through spouts between the cogs below (see 3rd block of pillar 32), after which a permanent battery is built above the cogs. Pillars are drawn back to the 1st block, as in pillar 30, and a permanent cog stopping placed in the chute neck. Roof breaks above the cog lines and broken material is held on the pitch by the cogs. With a good roof 90% of the coal is often recovered.

Foreign practice. H. F. Bulman and R. A. S. Redmayne give the following examples in England (365). SEATON BURN COLLIERY, Northumberland. Fig 754 shows robbing in a flat seam, averaging 4 ft thick, at a depth of 360 ft; pillars are 30 yd long, 16 yd wide. A "way" *A* (skip) is driven 6 yd wide the length of the pillar. A small pillar *P* 2 yd square (a "stook") is left to support the haulageway; a track is run along the solid rib and cogs are built on the open or caved side 3 ft apart. When the "way" has been driven the length of the pillar, a "lift" *B*, 6 yd wide, is driven across the pillar. Five lifts complete the robbing of the pillar. This seam yields more lump coal when worked end-on. MARLEY HILL COLLIERY, West Durham. Fig 755 shows method used in a flat

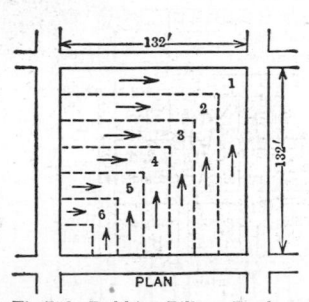

Fig 756. Robbing Pillars, Durham

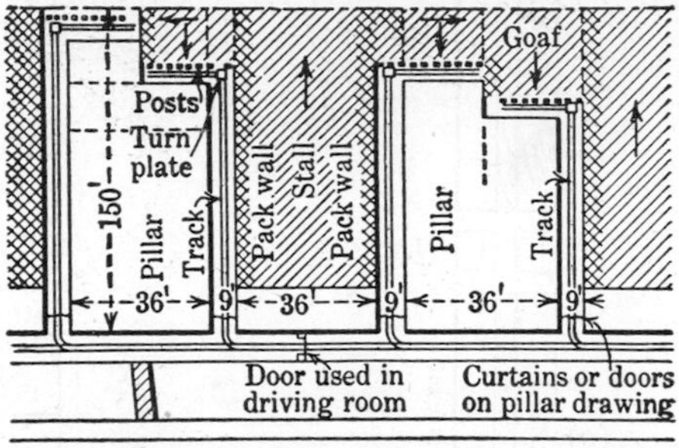

Fig 757. Robbing Pillars, Pillar-and-stall Method, Wales (611)

seam, which averages 5 ft thick and contains a 4-in and a 1.5-in parting in the middle. Depth of seam, 432 ft. Pillars are 50 by 20 yd. The pillar is first split on its short dimension by a "sliding-over" or "half-pillar wall" *CD*. From this and from the haulageways 5-yd lifts are turned and the work completed as at Seaton Burn colliery. MURTON COLLIERY, Durham. Fig 756 shows the method in a 46-in flat seam, at depth of 1 470 ft. Lifts 6 yd wide are driven at right-angles to and toward each other, in sequence shown. This retains the square shape of pillar, considered best for withstanding heavy press, throughout the entire operation.

G. S. Rice in 1921 gave following examples of foreign practice (611). PILLAR AND DOUBLE STALL (Fig 757) was formerly used in Scotland, and in 1911 in a Welsh anthracite bed 7–8.5 ft thick. Stalls are 42–48 ft wide, with 2 entrances and tracks along each rib; area between tracks is gobbed; pillars, 36–42 ft wide. When a stall reaches next entry, it is widened on either side and the adjacent pillar robbed retreating by taking cross slices 10–18 ft wide (Fig 757). Sometimes a thin pillar is

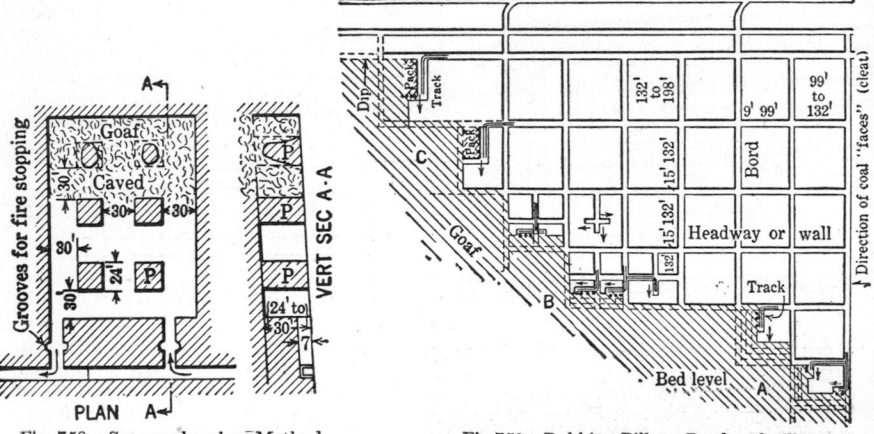

Fig 758. Square-chamber Method, South Staffordshire

Fig 759. Robbing Pillars, Bord-and-pillar Method (611)

left between stalls; if so, this pillar is not recovered. A recovery of 90% is claimed; the method is being supplanted by longwall (Art 108). SQUARE-CHAMBER METHOD, South Staffordshire. Fig 758 shows its use in a nearly flat seam, 24–30 ft thick. Chambers, separated by thick pillars, are 46 yd wide and 200 ft long; they are opened off the level with 2 narrow gate roads connected by a "lane"

10 yd wide. Stalls, 10 yd wide, are driven 8 yd apart from the lane; cross lanes, 10 yd wide, connect stalls every 8 yd, leaving 4-6 pillars, 8 yd square, in a chamber. This work is done in the bottom bench, 7-8 ft thick. After the chamber is formed, the top coal is taken down in sections, by cutting vert grooves in it 6 ft apart, separated by "spurns," or narrow webs, which are reduced by pick and finally knocked out with a "picker" (like a boathook). The mass falls as a whole, and is loaded out. On reaching the roof, the internal pillars are sliced as much as possible before the roof falls. Some coal is necessarily buried. Pillars between chambers are mined after the ground has settled. This method requires skilled work. BORD-AND-PILLAR or STOOP-AND-ROOM (Fig 759) is the most important European pillar system. It is considered especially applicable where: (a) coal bed is

horiz or not dipping over 1 in 3; (b) bed is 4-10 ft thick; (c) roof is strong, not flexible or bending; (d) bed free from thick partings. LONGWALL has supplanted it where: (a) roof is weak or flexible; (b) bed is under 4 ft thick; (c) seam is thick, but has a soft underlying clay; (d) bed has thick partings suitable for packwalls. In typical bord-and-pillar, narrow openings are driven at right-angles to each other, forming rectangular pillars which are extracted when workings reach the boundary; it is essentially longwall retreating (Art 108). In a typical application, Eppleton Colliery, Durham, England, there are 3 horiz seams, 3.7-7.3 ft thick, at depths of 1 008-1 170 ft. Pillars are 33 by 44 yd to 66 yd square. "Headways" or walls (driven on the butts) are 3 yd wide; bords at right-angles, 5 yd wide. In forming the pillars only 10-17% of the coal is extracted. Generally, on reaching the boundaries, pillar-robbing retreats along a stepped diagonal line (Fig 759). Pillars to be drawn are split by a headway and a narrow bord into 4 small pillars, which are either split again or successively sliced off on the goaf side; or, where the roof breaks short, sides of the headings are sliced, working toward the goaf.

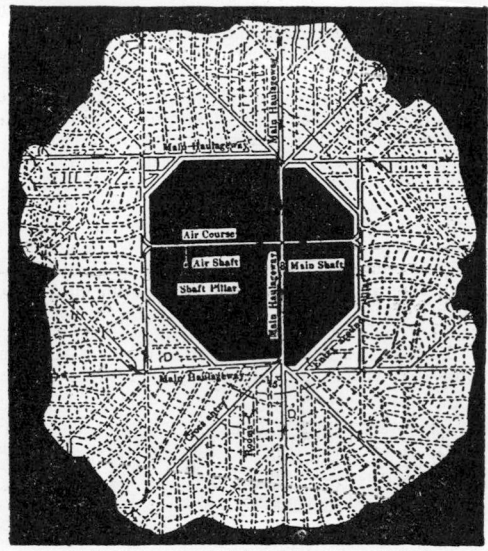

Fig 760. Longwall Advancing (after Swift)

Small corner stumps, left for protection under a poor roof, are sometimes lost. Most timber used in mining pillars is recovered. Total recovery of coal, 95%. Objections to method: large amount of costly, narrow first work, which produces much small coal. For further detail, see Bib (611).

108. LONGWALL METHODS

The fundamental principle is the complete removal of the entire seam in one operation, by carrying a continuous working face (hence the name longwall), leaving no pillars and allowing the roof to cave behind the face.

General plan of work in a flat seam is shown by Fig 760 (366). A large pillar maintains the hoisting and air shafts; successive positions of the face, as advanced outward from the shaft pillar, are indicated by dotted lines. As face or breast is advanced, the roof between it and the shaft pillar caves. Packwalls on each side of the numerous haulageways must be maintained through the caved area (GOB or GOAF) to reach and ventilate the working

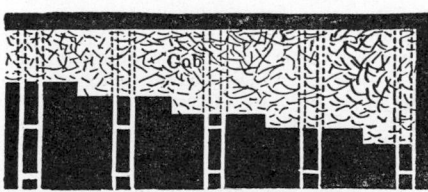

Fig 761. Longwall Retreating

face. Weight of roof often causes the packwalls to settle; headroom is maintained by breaking down (brushing) the roof over haulageways; the waste thus produced, with that from mining, is utilized in packwalls, the excess being thrown back into the gob. Haulage roads are known as MAIN and BRANCH or CROSS ROADS, haulageways or entries (Fig 760). From branch roads, short openings called STALL ROADS or ROOMS are kept open at intervals; they are approx perpendicular to the face. As the face advances, new branch and stall roads are started and old ones abandoned; this keeps the stall roads short and saves maintenance. Haulage tracks may be turned from the stall roads and run along the face, so that coal may be shoveled directly into cars; various forms of conveyer and scraper (Sec 27) may also be used for transporting coal along the face (369).

This plan of work is known as LONGWALL ADVANCING or LONGWALL WORKING OUTWARD. Fig 761 shows another form called LONGWALL RETREATING, in which the seam is first developed by a series of haulage and airways, which are driven to the property lines before any mining is done. The ends of these openings are then joined, forming a long face which is worked back toward the shaft; the roads and airways are in solid coal and the mined-out area is allowed to cave a short distance back from the face.

Advancing vs retreating systems. CAPITAL OUTLAY. Longwall advancing requires smaller outlay for development than any other coal mining method. Narrow work in driving haulage and airways is eliminated, with the exception of the development openings in shaft pillars, etc. The mine begins to produce coal in a relatively short time. Longwall retreating requires a larger initial outlay with no immediate return. Extensive development openings must be maintained during life of the mine; capital requirements are in direct proportion to area of the property. In advancing systems, MAINTENANCE of haulage and airways is an increasing deadwork charge; these openings pass through caved ground and the packwalls supporting them often give trouble from settlement. Longwall retreating entirely avoids cost of building and maintaining packwalls; all haulage and airways are in solid ground. VENTILATION is more efficient in retreating than in the advancing system. Caved or gobbed areas are difficult to ventilate. Gas if present may accumulate in the gob, and cause explosions and gob fires seriously affecting the active workings. Retreating systems eliminate the necessity for ventilating the gob. Nevertheless, longwall retreating is rarely used, chiefly because of the large investment required; what follows refers to longwall advancing.

Longwall vs room-and-pillar methods. ADVANTAGES of longwall, aside from those connected with investment and quick return: (a) smaller powder consumption and greater

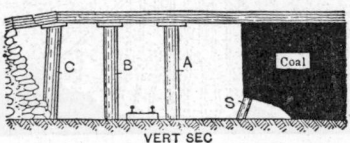   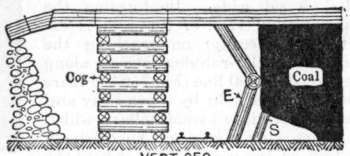

Fig 762. Longwall Face   Fig 763. Longwall Face

yield of lump coal; (b) ample storage underground for waste; (c) fewer roadways per unit length of face, thus reducing first and maintenance costs; (d) easier and cheaper ventilation; (e) less liability to accident from roof falls; (f) requires less timber; (g) surface subsidence is more uniform and causes less damage; (h) duty of labor is greater; supervision is easier. DISADVANTAGES of longwall: (a) labor must be experienced; (b) market demand must permit uniform production at all times (Art 103); (c) danger from gob fires in advancing systems; it is difficult to divide working places into small districts to localize effects of gas or dust explosions; (d) cost of packwalls; (e) requirements for successful application of longwall are quite rigid. Roof must come down gradually behind the face; a very strong roof or one that breaks short at the face prohibits use of longwall. Faulty ground makes it difficult to maintain a continuous working face. Waste for packwalls must be cheap, whether obtained from the seam or by brushing the roof or floor (see Art 103).

Work at the face. The pressure caused by settling of the roof is utilized in breaking coal at the face. Fig 762, 763 show sections through typical faces. The roof between gob and face is supported partly by props on about 5-ft centers along the face and partly by the stall-road packwalls; the distance between gob and face is commonly 10 to 12 ft. With bad roof, collars are placed between props A and B, or every 3rd or 4th prop B may be replaced by a timber crib 3 to 4 ft sq (cog or chock). The face is undercut by hand or machine, and is generally supported by sprags S, set on 4 to 6-ft centers. Sometimes lateral support in the form of " cockermegs " E, Fig 763, is also required. When undercutting is completed, the sprags are knocked out and the face is allowed to fall. Under ideal conditions the roof pressure breaks the coal down; frequently the coal must be wedged or blasted. The broken coal is then loaded, the fresh face dressed, a new row of props set near the new face, packwalls are extended, the excess waste is gobbed, and the tracks are shifted. Props C are pulled if possible and if sound are reused. For further detail, see Practice in Illinois, below.

Distance between stall roads is from 36 to 150 ft. Hughes (363) summarizes the factors determining this dimension as follows: (a) the face between 2 stall roads must be advanced regularly and rapidly, which is difficult with very long faces; (b) stall roads spaced too closely involve excessive first and maintenance costs; (c) seams too thin for cars to run along the face require close spacing of stall roads; (d) the number of stall roads depends somewhat on the output required; only 2 cars at a time can be run into a section of working face between 2 roads, i e, one from each end; (e) number of men working at one section determines its length and hence the distance between stall roads.

Modifications of longwall for inclined seams are chiefly to secure a working face and haulage roads, directions of which allow convenient handling of coal. On DIPS TO 5° the stall roads are run to the rise, the working face being parallel to the strike and therefore horiz. On DIPS OF 5° TO 12° OR 15° the roads may be at an angle to the dip, thus keeping grades within the limit of hand tramming. Pitches to 30° are sometimes worked to the dip instead of to the rise; cars run down the stall roads by gravity, pulling a hoisting rope after them. The limit for such work is about 30°, where packwalls begin to slide. ON STEEP DIPS, filled flatback (longwall) or stepped-face stopes may be used (Art 60); stall-roads then become chutes or mill-holes. See also Miller mine near end of this Art. See Bib (355, 363, 367, 370) for details and variations of foreign longwall practice.

Practice in Illinois. Data from S. O. Andros in 1914 (366). This is one of the few American regions where longwall has been successful. Table 92 shows size and characteristics of the seams and dimensions of workings in 11 mines.

Table 92. Data on Illinois Longwall Mines

Mine No	Depth of shaft, ft	Thickness of bed, in	Size of shaft pillar, ft	Distance between cross entries, ft	Angle betw cross and main entry = angle betw room* and cross entry, deg	Distance between room centers at face, ft	Width of roadways, ft		Width of packwalls on road-sides, ft
							Main and cross	Room	
1	413	39	400×600	225	45	42	9	8	12
2	465	44	250×250	225	45	42	9	9	9
3	398	42	550×550	240	45	42	9	9	9
4	546	40	(b)	200	70	42	10	10	12
5	135	36	360×560	275	45	42	7	7	12
6	100	36	150×300	225	45	42	7	7	9
7	200	37	350×450	.....	45	42	8	8	9
8	300	40	....	225	45	42	9	8	12
9	(a)	42	....	320	30	40	8	5	9
10	480	42	500×500	225	45	42	9	7.5	12
11	530	34	600×3600 (c)	225	45	49	8	8	12

(a) Slope. (b) No pillar. (c) Protects 3 hoisting shafts. * Stall roads.

Note.—Immediate roof is shale, except for small areas of mine No 5, where roof is sandstone. Floor is fireclay, hard, sandy or soft. Mine No 1 has sandstone floor grading into fireclay; in mine No 3 a hard sandy shale underlies coal in places. Coal in all mines contains lenses or bands of clay, pyrite, or sulphur balls, 2 to 21 in thick.

All of the mines are worked by longwall advancing and with one exception have vert shafts. The greatest difficulty in starting operations is to form the shaft pillar and establish the working face. Usually in this district, after the hoisting shaft and air shaft have reached coal, a main entry is driven about 225 ft from each side of the hoisting shaft. From the air shaft 2 entries are driven in opposite directions at right-angles to the main entry, to the edges of the proposed shaft pillar. The latter is usually blocked out by driving around it a 9-ft entry E (Fig 764), called the "entry-around-pillar" (Fig 760). Large pillars are desirable, to protect the shaft and provide a long working face. Another 9-ft entry is then driven around the shaft pillar, parallel to E, leaving a 15-ft pillar between the two; breakthroughs between the entries are about 42 ft apart. Fig 765 shows an alternative method, used where the coal in the shaft pillar spalls off; the pillar face is protected by a 15-ft packwall; the 15-ft space between the 2 entries of Fig 764 is also packed with gob. Sometimes an entry 27 ft wide is driven around the pillar and 2 packwalls are built as the entry advances. One packwall 12 ft wide is built alongside the shaft pillar, and one 6 ft wide on the future longwall face, leaving a haulage road 9 ft wide between the two walls and the necessary openings through them for haulage.

The subsidence following the first break of the roof, as the workings extend outward from the shaft pillar, is very violent and will destroy the entry-around-pillar unless the latter is well protected. Seven to 10 months are required for driving entries through the shaft pillar and blocking it out after the hoisting and air shafts reach the coal. Actual mining is rarely begun until the entries-around-pillar are connected and direct ventilation

established. In some older mines, no pillar was left to support the roof around the shaft;
the coal was extracted, allowing the roof to settle gradually till it rested on the floor. In
such case, the shaft timbers are supported on soft-wood 12 by 12-in posts, and the coal is
removed from all sides of the shaft. The space thus left is filled with soft-wood cogs
(shanties), and with packs of brushing and mining rock. Through the gob a 7-ft roadway

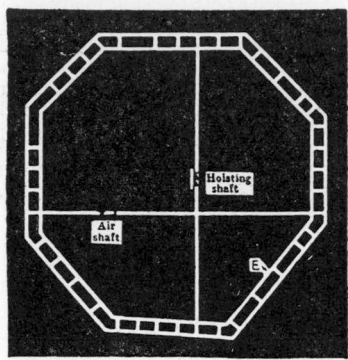

Fig 764. Blocking-out Shaft Pillar, Ill

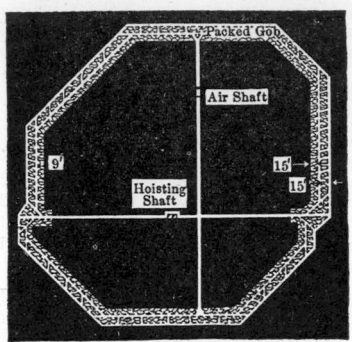

Fig 765

is opened from each side and end of the shaft. As the roof settles the packs are compressed and squeezed into the fireclay bottom till roof and floor meet. The shaft bottom
is then widened and timbered. Advantages claimed: the expense of timbering the shaft
bottom is reduced, and the roof weight begins sooner to ride on the working face. Operators using shaft pillars state that these advantages are offset by the uncertainty of being

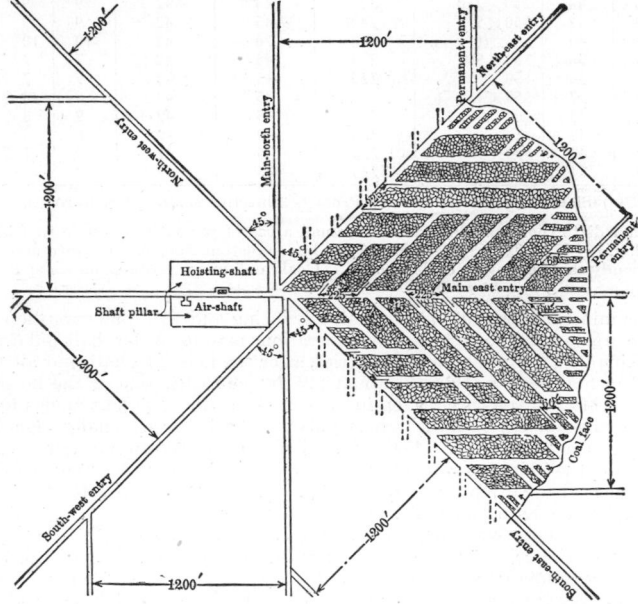

Fig 766. Longwall Mine

able to control subsidence sufficiently to prevent the shaft from being thrown out of plumb.
Fig 760 and Table 92 show the usual arrangement of entries and stall roads. For an
alternative arrangement used in 1 mine see Fig 766. In pitching seams of La Salle anticline (dips to 50°), working faces are kept parallel to the dip and coal is handled to an entry
below in light sheet-iron chutes.

Fig 767 shows a flat working face. The " places " are 42 ft long; their limits are marked by " march props," as shown. Due to scarcity of labor, about 50% of the " places " are worked by 1 miner; the rest by 2 miners. The crew on a " place " is responsible for building packwalls and for gobbing as well as for mining. Where possible, an undercut 8–12 in high and 2–2.5 ft deep is made by picking in the fireclay floor. Sprags are 6–8 ft apart; props are set 2–5 ft from the face and 6–8 ft apart. With an aver depth of undermining, a good miner can undercut about 20 ft of face a day when working in soft clay 8–12 in thick. For loading a car, that portion of the coal is taken which has been standing longest on sprags. These are knocked out, and if the gob has been properly filled, so that the roof weight rides on the face, the coal breaks from the roof and is ready for loading, otherwise, the coal is wedged down. Under fairly good conditions about 80% of the coal exceeds 1.25-in size.

If the floor is sandstone, or if the fireclay is much over 18 in thick, undercutting is done in the coal itself; this produces much slack and increases the number of gob fires, because more fine coal goes into the gob with the waste. To save time and labor the miner often neglects to support the coal on sprags until the usual 2 ft of undermining is completed; instead, he makes a cut 4–8 in deep and pries down the coal. This

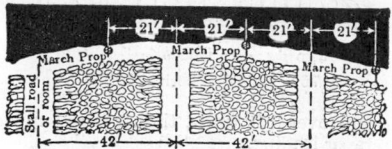

Fig 767. A Longwall Face (Plan)

does not utilize the slow breaking power of the roof; more accidents occur, and more slack and smaller coal result than when full undermining is insisted upon. For blasting, black powder is used where necessary. Practically all undercutting is done by hand.

The rock obtained from brushing the roof, that remaining after building the packwalls, and the clay obtained from undermining the coal, are piled in the gob area between the packwalls lining the roads, to help support the roof and control its pressure on the face. After the first break at the shaft pillar and face, if the gob area has been properly filled, so that the roof weight " rides " on the coal, subsequent roof breaks occur every 2 to 6 ft; they parallel the face and extend upward and backward from it at angles of 50° or more; cracks are more nearly vert on faces which are worked slowly. The distance between breaks depends chiefly upon the character of roof and the packing of the gob; with proper packing it should correspond to the width of coal brought down. The distance to which breaks extend into the roof rarely exceeds 15 ft. Squeezes which fill a working place with roof material occur when a room is driven ahead of adjacent rooms, or more commonly when packwalls are defective and the gob area is not sufficiently filled. There should be enough filling for the roof to come down gradually without breaking off short at the face of packwalls, but not so much that insufficient weight is thrown on the face of coal. The better the gob is packed, the better the coal "works." When part of the working face squeezes, the face is usually diverted to pass around the squeezed area, sometimes leaving a small block of coal in the gob.

The necessity for artificial humidification to prevent coal-dust explosions has not been apparent in these mines. Since all the coal is removed from the seam as the face advances and the excavation is filled with waste rock, the only sources of dust are the working face and the spillings from cars. Dust from the face is covered with shale and clay within a few days after it is made and does not accumulate. As the aver temp of the air in these mines is higher than in room-and-pillar mines, the relative humidity is decreased and moisture is absorbed from the dust of ribs and roads. In a few mines, the haulage ways are sprinkled at intervals of 1 week to 3 months (Sec 23).

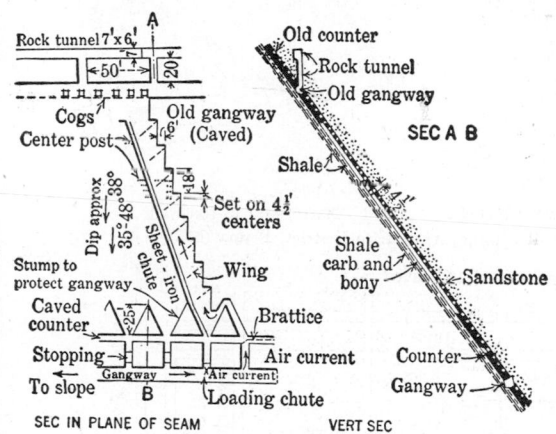

Fig 768. Longwall Mining, Miller Mine, Wash (610).

Miller mine, Wash.

Data from S. H. Ash in 1925. A modified longwall method was substituted for breast-and-pillar and chute-and-pillar systems (see Pierce County, Wash, Art 106, 107) in a seam 4–4.5 ft thick; aver dip 38°, which is considered slightly flat for best results. Fig 768 (diagrammatic) shows general plan of work. The coal is worked in 6-ft "skips," about 18 ft apart. On one face, 500 ft long, 30 miners produced 250 short tons per 8 hr. Coal is loaded to a sheet-iron chute, never more than 24 ft from the face; a wing, kept under each miner, protects man below from falling objects and guides coal to the chute. Fig 769 shows timbering; props are on 4.5-ft centers along the pitch. Bib (610) gives more detail.

Anthracite district, Pa. Use of longwall has increased with development of mechanical loading (Sec 27) and need for mining thin seams. H. D. Kynor, in 1921, describes method for flat or slightly pitching seams, Fig 770 (612). Gangways are 200 ft apart. A chamber is driven from lower to upper gangway; a line of "break props" is set; lines of timber cogs are built parallel to face and 10–16 ft apart; cogs in a line are 6–8 ft apart. In seams under 30 in thick, rock-packed roads 10 ft wide are made parallel to gangways and 60 ft apart; 2–3 ft of top rock broken down supplies rock for 12-ft walls on each side of road. In seams over 3 ft thick, timber cogs support the roof. Fig 770 indicates ease of applying scraper loading.

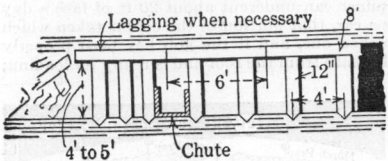

Fig 769. Face Timbering, Miller Mine

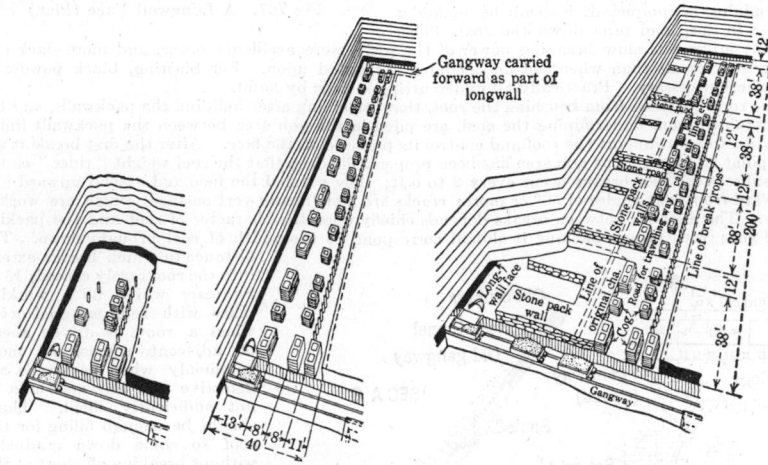

START OF CHAMBER   CHAMBER COMPLETED   DEVELOPMENT OF LONGWALL

Fig 770. Longwall Mining, Anthracite District, Penna (612)

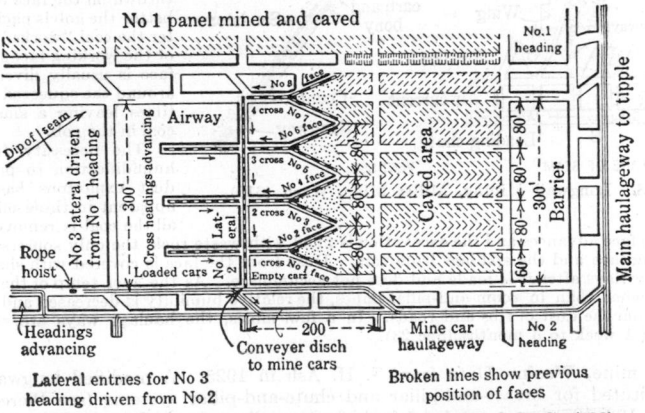

Lateral entries for No 3   Broken lines show previous
heading driven from No 2   position of faces

Fig 771. "V" System, Norton Mine, West Va Coal & Coke Co (608)

"V" system, Norton mine, West Va. Data from G. B. Southward in 1924 (608). Modified longwall is used under roof conditions prohibiting regular longwall. It is applied in Lower Kittanning seam; aver thickness, 6 ft; roof is slate and shale 20–30 ft thick, overlain by a sandstone bed 40 ft or more thick; total cover, 25–250 ft. Seam is worked in panels 300 ft wide (Fig 771); face is a series of V's, with sides 85 ft long and points 80 ft apart; angle of V, 45°. Roof over each V is considered as a beam supported by the coal; hence character of roof determines max length of span, and depth of cover determines amount of coal necessary for support, which in turn fixes the angle of the V. Panel development comprises lateral entries 200 ft apart, with cross entries 80 ft c-c. Slab cuts are made on the faces; machine cuts are taken to keep the V-angles constant and the points in line. Advance cross entries are driven at same speed as faces retreat; hence, when face reaches a lateral entry, cross entries have reached the next lateral, through which coal goes to haulageway. Only a small amount of advance work is required in this combination of longwall advancing and retreating.

Coal is loaded by hand to elec-driven, steel-pan, belt conveyers, which parallel the faces (see heavy dotted lines in Fig 771); similar conveyers take coal without rehandling through cross and lateral entries into cars in the haulageway. Props, set behind the face conveyers after each cut, and in the area between faces, support the slate; at intervals, timbers are removed near caved area and the roof falls. Aver production from 8 faces, besides coal from development, is about 750 tons per day of 2 8-hr shifts, by an aver of 60 men between faces and tipple. The method gives a 600-ft working face in a 300-ft panel; it simplifies supervision, drainage and ventilation; accidents few and output per man high (608).

109. BREAKING GROUND IN COAL MINES

General. Breaking ground (Art 26) is, in coal mines, sometimes called CUTTING COAL. Principles are the same as those of breaking ore or rock, except that coal is relatively soft and brittle, and, as a lump product is generally desired, the explosives are of low power and number of holes in a given face a minimum. No definite rules can be laid down as to location of drill holes and charge of explosive, for the following reasons: WIDELY VARYING LOCAL CONDITIONS occur in different seams, or successive cuts in the same seam. Slate partings, "blowing benches," pinches or faults, rolls, slips, cleat, and character of the coal itself, demand experience for properly locating and charging holes. CONTRACT WORK is usual, miners being paid by the car of coal or yard driven; they purchase their tools, explosives, fuse and caps, and pay their laborers. Since a misplaced or improperly charged hole will reduce his earnings, both by increasing his supply account and decreasing output, the miner is prompted to take advantage of every possible condition which will break most coal with least effort and explosive.

For example, miners applying for work in the Southern Anthracite Field of Penna often state that they are Mammoth, Buck Mountain, or Lykens miners, as the case may be. Observing their work, it is apparent that they have studied their particular seam and in locating a drill hole are quick to recognize advantages or disadvantages which no rules can cover. Men must work for some time as helpers and pass a state examination before becoming miners and allowed to "cut coal."

Drilling. The miner plans his work to suit the conditions and keep his laborers busy. Drilling is done chiefly with hand or power augers, mounted on bars or posts. The various small and light jackhammer drills (Sec 15) have been successful in driving gangways, especially in the Southern Anthracite Field, where work in thin seams requires the breaking of considerable top or bottom rock. To facilitate blasting and obtain a max lump product, coal cutters (Sec 16) are widely used in bituminous mining and to some extent in the Northern Anthracite Field. Chain machines are limited to pitches less than 20° to 25°; those of the "post-puncher" type are successful in the semi-bituminous coals of Washington on pitches up to 38° (371, 612).

Explosives used are black powder, low-power Ngl or ammonia dynamites, and, in gaseous or dusty mines, the permissible explosives (Sec 4). The rending effect required to produce a large proportion of lump coal is secured by black powder or 15% to 20% dynamite; practice tends toward the latter. For modes of charging and firing, see Sec 4.

Examples of practice. SOUTHERN ANTHRACITE FIELD, Penna. W. L. Cross, Jr, furnishes following data on driving gangways, monkeys, chutes, headings, and breasts, in Skidmore and Buck Mountain seams at Buck Run Colliery. Fig 772, 773 show methods of driving gangways. Holes in coal are drilled and fired first, the broken coal is removed and the face dressed. Then the rock holes are fired, bottom rock being lifted in each case. Aver advance per round, 5 ft, with an aver consumption of 25 lb of 35% dynamite. Fig 774 shows driving a monkey in firm and hard coal, drilling with hand augers. When near the chute an advance of 1 cut or 5 ft is made in 8 hr. As distance from chute increases, advance is slower, because the coal must be reshoveled. Fig 775

Table 93. Data on Breaking Ground in Anthracite and Bituminous Coal Mines

Summarized from data by T. Marvin, published in *Explosives Engineer*, Oct-Dec, 1926 (613)

Example No*	Seam or district	Character of coal	Height of seam ft	Height of seam in	Width of face, ft	Method of relieving and depth of cut, ft	No of horiz rows	No of holes per row, beginning at top	Holes Total No of holes	Depth of holes, ft	Total depth of holes, ft	Explosive Kind	Charge per hole (IN = inches, $*$ = lb, CA = cartridges)	Charge per round	Kind of tamping	Method of firing †	Sequence of firing
									BITUMINOUS COAL								
1	West Virginia	A	4	0	20	UC6	1	3	3	6	18	PE	3CA	9CA	FC	EL	(a)
2	West Virginia	B	6	6	15	TC6		3	3	6.5	19.5	PE	3&4CA	10CA	FC	EL	(a)
3	West Virginia	C	8	9	16	MC	2	3-3	6	6	33.5	PE	0.75-2CA	9.25CA		SQ	(b)
4	Sewell seam		3	8	40	SO		4	4	4.5-6.5	20	PE	3&4CA	14CA(c)			(h)
5	Pittsburgh No 8 seam	D	3	8	24	UC6(d)		4	4	6	23.7	PE	1&1.5*	5*		SQ	(l)
10	Pennsylvania	I	4	0	28	UC6		4	4	6	20	BP	20IN	80IN(g)			(a)
11	Western Pennsylvania	J	3	1	21	UC6		5		5.5	11	BP	3CA	36IN			(m)
12	Centre County	K	3	7	25	UC6	2	4-2	6	5.5	27.5	BP	6&8IN	6CA		SQ	(a)
13	(o)	L	3	6	20	UC6		2		5.5	18	PE(n)	1&1.5*	3.5*			(q)
14	Indiana (p)	M	5	7	28	UC6	2	3-2	6	5.5	33	PE	1.5-2.5CA	12CA			(a)
15		N	6	6	13.5	UC7		2	2	6.5	13	PE	3CA	6CA			(a)
16	Pittsburgh Nine-foot seam	O	5	6	12	UC6	2	2-2	5	5	16.5	PE	12&26IN	50IN			(r)
17	(l)	P	7	6	21	SN	2	4-3	5	5	25	PE(n)	1&1.5*	6.5*		EL	(s)
18	Michigan (p)	Q	5	7	40	UC6	2		7	5	22	BP	1&1.5*	5*		EL	(u)
19	North Carolina	R	4	6	30	SO		8	8	5	35	PE	1&1.5CA	9.5CA	FC		(w)
20	Tyson seam, Md.	S	3	3	18	SN(w)		6	8	4	16	PE	3&3.5CA	27CA			(x)
21	Mary Lee seam, Ala.	T	4	4	40	UC5			6	5.5	33	PE	4CA	24CA			(a)
22	Kentucky	U	5	3	28	UC5			6	5	15	BP	0.5 & 0.75CA	2.75CA			(a)
23	Cherokee seam, Kan.	V	3	2	24	UC3.5(w)		3-3-3	2	4	8	BP	12 & 15IN	39IN			(a)
24	Kentucky	W	7	8	18	UC6	3		9	6.5	58.5	PE	3*	6*	RD	EL	(z)
25	Oklahoma	X	3	8	22	UC5.5		4	3	6.25 & 6.7	15	PE	1-6CA	22CA	CD		(a)
26	Alabama	Y	4	0	28.8	UC6.5	2	4	8	6.5	51.7	PE	1CA	3CA	FC		(aa)
27	Illinois (p)	Z	6	0	28	UC6(cc)		3	6	5.5	33	PE	3CA	24CA			(bb) (a)
28	No 6 seam, Ill (p)	Z	7	0	28	UC6(dd)	2	3	6	5.5	16.5	PE	1.5CA	4.5CA			(cc)
29	No 6 seam, Ill.	Z	5	6	30	UC6		3	4	5.5	24	PE	2&3CA	14CA	CD	EL	(a)
30	Utah	AA	6	0	22	UC6		4	3	6	19.5	PE	2&3CA	8CA	AD	EL	(ee)
31	Utah		9	0	20	TC7	1	3-2	5	5.5	27.5	PE	2CA	9CA	CD	EL	(ff)
32	Utah	BB	8	0	12	UC6	2	3-5	11	5.5	55	PE	2&3CA	12CA		EL	(gg)
33	Utah	CC	9	6	22	UC5	2					PE	1&2CA	15CA			
34	Wyoming		9	6	37	UC7	1	4	4	6.5	26	PE	2.5 & 3.5CA	13CA			(hh)
									ANTHRACITE COAL								
6		E	7	8	24	SO	5	2-2-1-3	11(e)	6	66	PE	4-6CA	54CA			(i)
7		F	9	6	12	SO	2	3-2	5	6 & 6.5	30.5	PE	4&5CA	23CA			(j)
8		G	7	0	20	SO	2	2-5	7	5-6.5	40.5	PE	2-6CA	26CA			(j)
9		H	8	0	24	SO	2	6-3	9	6.5	54	PE	4-6CA	41CA			(k)

NOTES TO ACCOMPANY TABLE 93

* Numbers are same as diagram numbers in Bib (613). † Where not stated, method is probably elec blasting. # Lb. AD = Adobe. BP = Black powder FFF in Ex 5, fine grained in Ex 12. CD = Clay dummies put in loosely. CA = Cartridges. EL = Elec blasting. FC = Fire clay. IN = Inches. MC = Center-cut. PE = Permissible 11/4-in by 8-in cartridges. SN = Snubbed. SO = Shot from solid. SQ = Squibs. TC = Top cut. U/C = Undercut. A = Soft, high volatile, low sulphur and ash. Definite cleavage, but coal tends to stick to roof. Contains 1/4-in sticker near bottom and 2-in binder near middle. B = Semi-bit coal, limestone bottom, roof of soapstone 1-18 in thick and coal underlying limestone; 1-in black band and 2-in copper rock in lower part of face. D = Semibit coal, 31/2 ft slate, 3 ft of coal at top, 45° pitch. F = 5 ft of coal, 4 in slate and 3 ft 4 in of coal on top, lower coal hard. E = 1 ft 4 in coal, 5 in slate, 1 ft coal, 2 in dirt, 8 in coal on top. Bottom bench medium hard with slips. Slate seams brittle or soft. G = 2 ft 6 in coal, 3 in slate, 2 ft 7 in coal, 3 in bony coal near middle. I = 6 in bony coal near middle. J = 11 in of tough bone and bony coal near middle. Top 8 in of seam is hard. H = Medium hard with many slips, parting 4.5 ft from floor. L = 7 in bony coal near middle of face, cannel coal at top. M = 7-in sulphur band near bottom. N = Soft, high-volatile dry seam. Holes 1 ft from ribs and 6 in from top. O = 1 ft of draw slate left in roof, 1-in slate band near bottom. P = Coal soft but firm. 1/2-in binder near middle. Q = 4-in clay band about one-third from bottom. R = 6-8-in blue band about one-third up face. S = 1/2-in and 3/4-in slate band below center; 9 in of extra soft coal at top. T = Coal rather hard, elec drills. U = Sulphur bands in lower part. V = 3 ft 10 in-2.5 ft thick. Coal much cut by clay horsebacks. W = 28-in slate band near center requires heavy blasting. Y = Soft. X = 5 in bony coal near center. Z = Blue band below middle. AA = 12 in of draw slate above seam breaks with the coal if holes are too close. BB = Massive, no cleavage, sticks to top unless back holes are close to roof. CC = 2-in binder of bony near roof. (a) One at a time, middle hole first. (b) Row above slate fired and coal loaded, then others fired. Center holes fired first. (c) 6 times as much coal broken per lb powder when coal is undercut. (d) Occasionally coal is snubbed by a shot or picked. (e) Drilled with jack-hammer. (f) Top bench holes fired first. Center hole on each bench fired before rib. (g) Varied as thickness of bony coal changes. (h) Two center holes fired first. (i) 1, center hole in slate; 2, 3, 2-hole row just above slate; 4, 5, rib holes in top row; 6, center hole in row just below slate; 7, 8, rib holes in this row; 9, center hole in bottom row; 10, 11, rib holes in this row. (j) 3 middle holes in lower row fired before rib holes; 2 holes in upper row fired last. (k) 1, 2, center holes in top row; 3, 4, holes next outside; 5, 6, rib holes top row; 7, center hole below; 8, 9, rib holes in bottom row. (l) 1, left center hole above bony; 2, extreme left; 3, right center; 4, extreme right. (m) 1, 2, 3, central holes, right to left; 4, 5, outside holes. (n) About 6 oz per 11/4 by 8-in cartridge. (o) Method secures 56% lump coal over 1-in screen. (p) Found best for mechan loading. (q) 1, 2, snubbing holes just above sulphur band; 3, 4, 2 center holes in upper row; 5, 6, 2 rib holes in upper row. (r) 1, two rib holes in upper row; 3, center hole; 4, 5, two cut holes below binder. (s) Holes in 2 vert rows near rib, above band. Lower pair fired first. (t) 62-65% lump coal produced; aver 7 ton per lb explosive in room; 4 ton in entries. (u) 1, snubbing hole just above blue band; 2, upper row. (v) Holes are below center, collars of 2 cut holes 10 ft apart; toes, 4 ft. Fired in sequence, cuts first. (w) 9 in soft coal at top picked out. Holes placed in a row below lower slate band, inside pair fired first. (x) 1, 2, center holes; 3, 4, holes on either side; 5, 6, rib holes. (y) Coal also sheared by pick. 40% dynamite in horsebacks and for "brushing" roof. (z) 1 row below and 2 above slate band; 3 center holes fired first, then other 6 at one time. (aa) 1 row below, other above bony. 1, center holes below bony; 2, rib holes below; 3, center holes above; 4, rib holes above. (bb) 11 ft between center and rib holes; 255 tons per 50 lb explosive. (cc) Pick snubbed also, 2 rows above blue band. Holes fired singly, beginning with center hole in lower row, then rib holes, then center hole in upper row. (dd) Pick snubbed, 21/2-in holes. (ee) 1, 2 center holes; 2, 2 rib holes. (ff) Fired simultaneously. (gg) Lower row fired with instantaneous elec cap, center back hole with 1st delay, upper rib holes with 3rd delay. (hh) Top row above bony, 2nd row just below bony with a row of snubbing holes below. Snubbing holes fired first in order; then second row, beginning at center; this drops coal below binder. Binder is picked off and then top coal broken, beginning with center hole. 35% of coal is on a 3-in screen and 35% is minus 13/4-in slack.

shows driving a chute entirely in coal on a pitch of 40°–50°. Slightly more than 1 cut of 5 ft per shift is made; aver powder consumption per 30-ft chute, 50 lb. In driving a heading in Buck Mountain seam (Fig 776), the miner in one breast starts a blind heading through the pillar, a heading from the next breast being driven to meet it. Hole No 1 is charged with 4 sticks of dynamite, and the broken coal removed; then hole No 2 is drilled, charged with 3 sticks, and fired; the result-

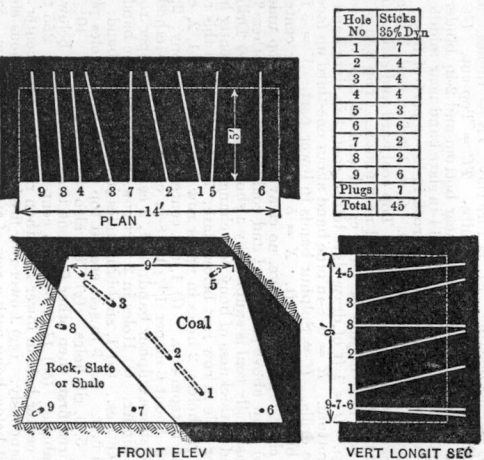

Hole No	Sticks 35% Dyn
1	7
2	4
3	4
4	4
5	3
6	6
7	2
8	2
9	6
Plugs	7
Total	45

Fig 772. Driving Gangway, Skidmore Seam

ing cut should be fairly square. A second cut is made by holes 3 and 4; then hole 5 is drilled and fired. If second cut breaks through to the blind heading, a second hole will be unnecessary, as the rib can be squared up with a pick. The blind heading is similarly driven, except that usually there are only 2 cuts. In Buck Mountain seam, breasts are driven as in Fig 777. All holes are drilled in bottom bench in the so-called " mining seam," viz, the portion most easily drilled and giving the best results on blasting, 2 cut and 2 rib holes making an aver round. Cut holes are charged with 5 sticks,

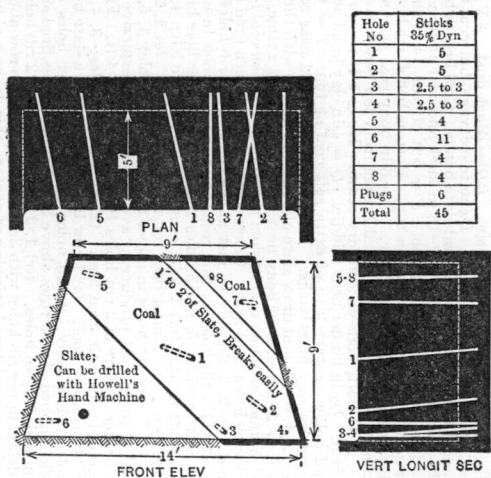

Hole No	Sticks 35% Dyn
1	5
2	5
3	2.5 to 3
4	2.5 to 3
5	4
6	11
7	4
8	4
Plugs	6
Total	45

Fig 773. Driving Gangway, Buck Mtn Seam

rib holes with 3 sticks, of 20% dynamite. If necessary to break the " middle stone," a 3-ft plug hole is charged with 1.5 sticks of 20% dynamite. Aver advance, one 5-ft cut per shift. ILLINOIS METHODS in bituminous coal (Table 94). In flat seams, the face is undercut before blasting. This reduces power consumption, minimizes danger from blow-outs and increases yield of lump coal. Fig 778, 779, 780, showing holes in faces undercut by hand or machine, are fairly typical of American practice. Table 93 summarizes data published by T. Marvin in 1926 (613).

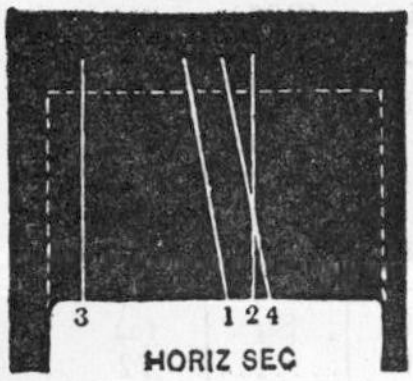

Hole No	Sticks 35% Dyn
1	4
2	3
3	2
4	2
Total	11

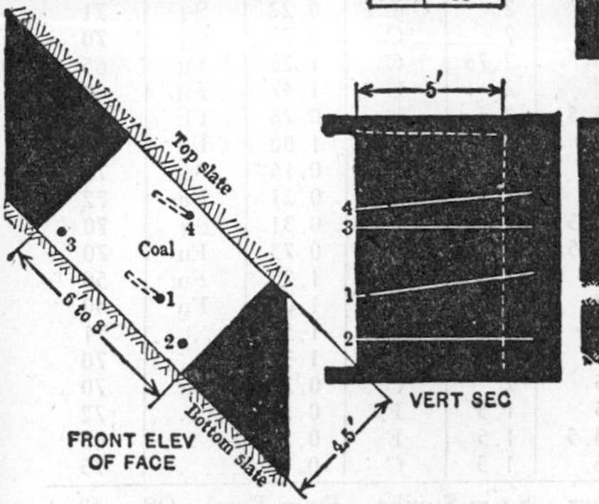

HORIZ SEC

PLAN

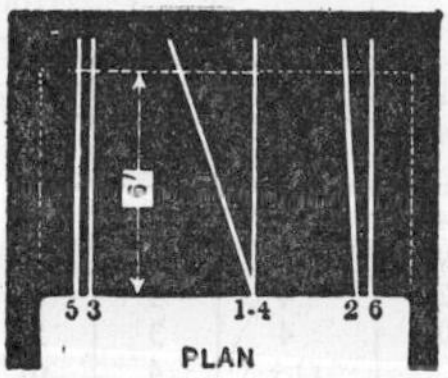

Hole No	Sticks 35% Dyn
1	6
2	3
3	2
4	2
5	2
6	2
Total	17

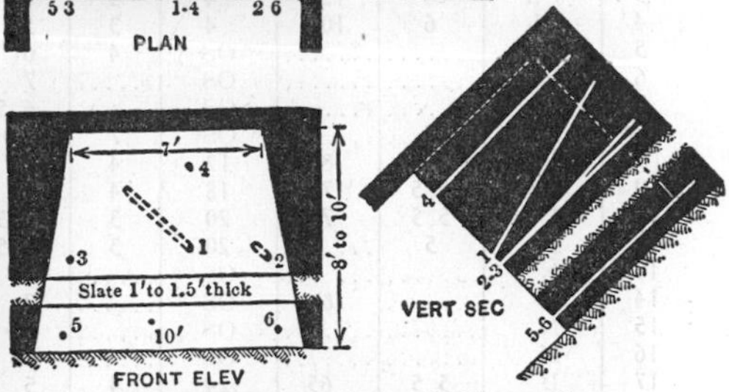

VERT SEC

Fig 775. Driving a Chute, Skidmore Seam

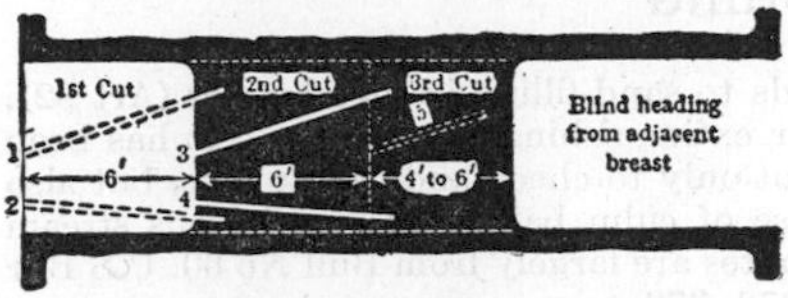

FRONT ELEV OF FACE

VERT SEC

Fig 774. Driving a Monkey, Skidmore Seam

Fig 776. Heading Driving, Buck Mtn Seam

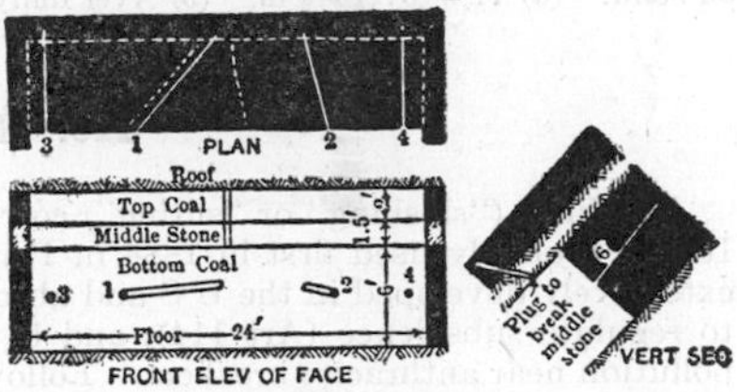

Fig 777. Driving Breast, Buck Mtn Seam

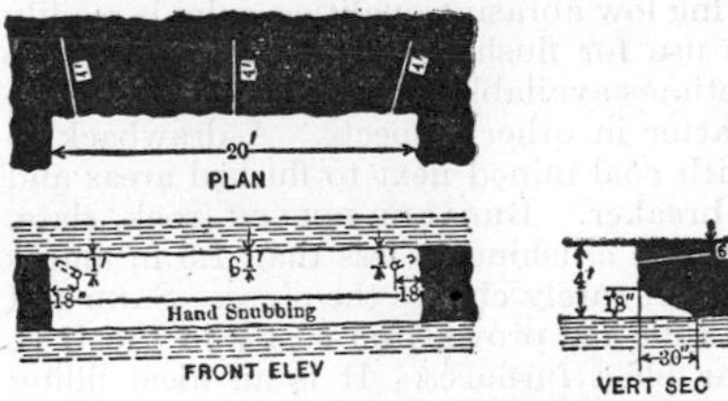

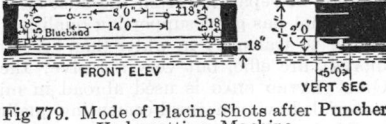

Fig 778. Mode of Placing Shots after Hand Snubbing

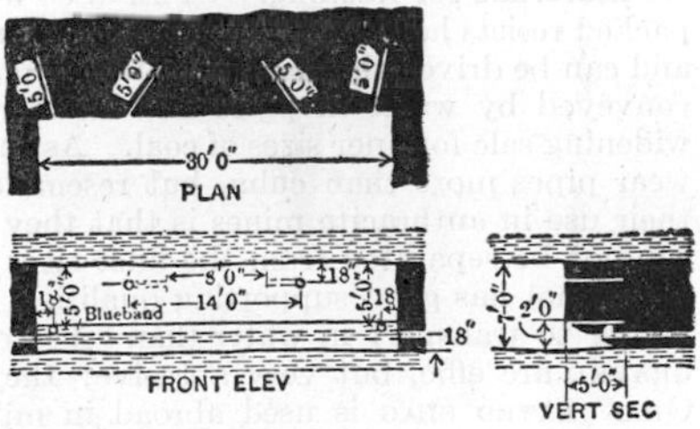

Fig 779. Mode of Placing Shots after Puncher Undercutting Machine

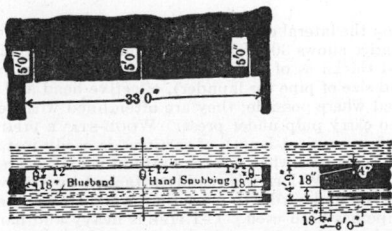

Fig 780. Mode of Placing Shots after Chain Undercutting Machine

Table 94. Data on Blasting in Illinois Room-and-pillar Mines (361)

Mine No	Type of under-cutting machine	Depth of cut, ft	Tons per ma-chine, per shift	Height of snub-bing, in	Holes No per round	Length, ft	Diam, in	Black powder Size of grain	Lb per ton of coal	Method of firing	Percent of coal over 1.25 in
1	Ch	7	140	30	3	7	2	F	0.14	Sq	(a)
2	Ch	7	195	....	3	6	2.25	C	0.13	....	72
3	Ch	6	120	4	3	6	2	C & F	0.22	Sq	71
4	Ch	6	100	4	3	5	2	C	0.25	Sq	70
5	N			OS	4	6	2.75	C	1.25	Fu	65
6	N			OS		7	2	C	1.47	Fu	60
7	N			OS		6.5	2.5	F	0.78	Fu	60
8	N			OS	7	8	2.5	C & CC	1.00	Fu	86
9	P	5.5	80	12	4	5	2	F	0.16	Sq	73
10	P	5.5	70	18	4	5	1.5	F	0.21	Fu	72
11	P	5.5	70	20	3	4.5	1.75	FF	0.31	Sq	70
12	P	5		20	3	4.5	2.25	F	0.73	Fu	70
13	N			OS		8	1.5	C	1.25	Fu	50
14	N		(b)	OS		7	2.5	C	1.00	Fu	40
15	N			OS		7	2	F	1.56		71
16	N			OS		7	2.5	CC	1.39		70
17	P	5.5	65	24	4	5	2	C	0.23	Sq	70
18	P	5.5	70	20		5	1.5	FF	0.22		72
19	Ch	6	130	20	2	4.5	1.5	F	0.50		65
20	Ch	7	127			6	1.5	C	0.19		75

Ch = Chain machine. N = None. P = Puncher. Sq = Squibs. Fu = Fuse. OS = Shot off solid. (a) 79% over 3/4 in. (b) Aver daily output per miner, 7 tons.

110. FLUSHING

Flushing ("slushing" or "silting") corresponds to sand-filling in metal mines (Art 92). It was probably used first in 1884 in Penna for extinguishing a mine fire. It has been extensively developed in the U S and abroad, not only to check and isolate fires, but also to regulate subsidence (Art 114), and to dispose of culm banks; its use lessens stream pollution near anthracite breakers. Following notes are largely from Bull No 60, U S Bur of Mines, by C. Enzian in 1913; see also Bib (372, 373).

Materials for flushing. CULM (Sec 34) is excellent; easily drained and when well packed resists heavy press. Compact culm will often stand in a vert face without timber, and can be driven through without spiling. Having low abrasive qualities, culm is readily conveyed by water in pipes and launders. Its use for flushing is decreasing with the widening sale for finer sizes of coal. ASHES, sometimes available at steam-operated mines, wear pipes more than culm, but resemble the latter in other respects. A drawback to their use in anthracite mines is that they mix with coal mined next to flushed areas and can not be separated from the finer sizes in the breaker. BREAKER REFUSE (rock, slate, and bone) has good supporting qualities. It requires crushing to less than 1.5 in and is harder to transport in water than ashes or culm, but rarely chokes the pipes. SAND and GRAVEL are effic, but very abrasive; they have thus far proved too costly in the U S. GRANULATED SLAG is used abroad in mines near blast furnaces. It is an ideal filling material, having natural cementing qualities and being strongly resistant to pressure.

Modes of handling filling material on the surface, between the surface and the mine, and underground, resemble those described in Art 92.

Few data are available on the lateral distance to which filling may be transported in pipes under a given head. Silesian practice allows 300 ft horiz for each 100 ft of available head; the distance is affected by size of pipe and thickness of pulp. Water in pulps varies from 40% to 90% of total vol, depending on grade and size of pipe (or launder), effective head and kind of filling. TROUGHS (launders) (Fig 660) are used where possible; they are often lined with cement, terracotta, or sheet iron. PIPES are required to carry pulp under press. WOOD-STAVE PIPE resists acid and abrasion, and, due to its lightness and convenient length of sections, is easily installed; but it is unsuited to high press, and dries out and collapses when not regularly in use; it wears unevenly and springs out of line; its life is short. STEEL OR W-I PIPE is readily attacked by acid water, and is more quickly abraded than wood; it is heavier and harder to place than wood-stave pipe and generally costs more. Abroad, wood-lined steel pipe has been used. C-I PIPE is heavy and hard to handle underground, but resists abrasion and acid water; its life is about 3 times that of W I and 5 times that of steel. Bell and spigot joints permit deflections. Location of mine with respect to a foundry determines whether this pipe is cheaper than others.   TERRACOTTA PIPE resists acid and stands wear until the glaze wears off, after which abrasion is rapid.   It is unsuited to high press and because of its brittleness must be handled carefully and protected from roof falls.   Its cost is comparatively low, but its life is short.   GLASS-LINED PIPE has been satisfactory in Europe, in an effort to reduce wear at bends and elbows; its high cost practically prohibits its use in the U S.   PORCELAIN-LINED PIPE is highly effic for small-size filling material, as it has exceptional wearing qualities, resists acid and has low frictional resistance; it is widely used in Europe, but is too costly in U S.   In Penna, wood-stave pipes are probably most used for low heads, C-I or steel pipes for higher heads; much flushing is done through unlined bore holes and troughs; the latter are preferable to pipes.

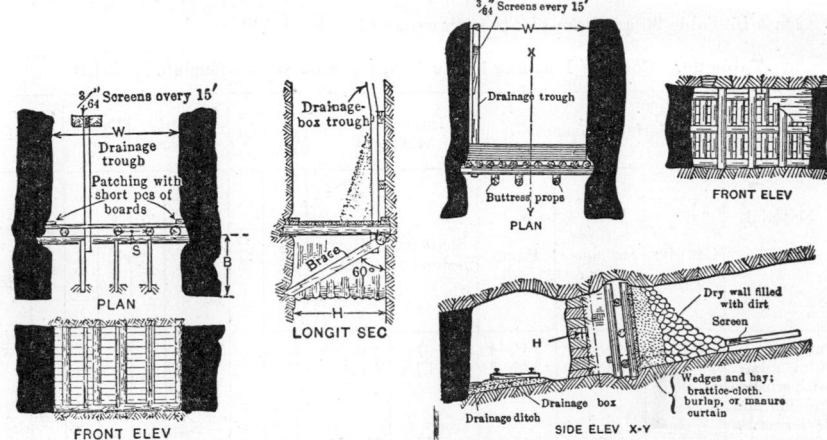

Fig 781. Bulkhead for Dips under 10°   Fig 782. Bulkheads for Dips of 10° to 25°

Bulkheads (barricades, Art 92).   Their design (Fig 781–784) varies with dip of seam. They are placed a short distance B (Fig 781), the haunch distance, above the lower end of the working to be flushed.   Table 95 gives empirical formulas.

Fig 781 shows construction for flat workings; leakage at the bottom is prevented by manure or dirt packing.   Props are lagged with 1 layer of 1.5-in plank, or 2 layers of 1-in.

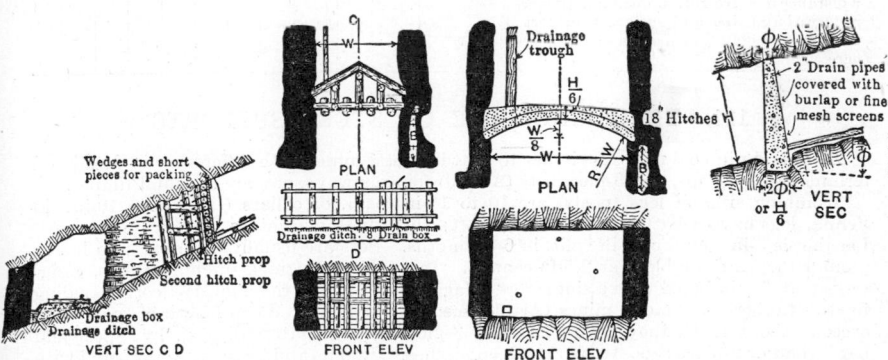

Fig 783. Bulkhead for Dips of 25° or More   Fig 784. Masonry Bulkhead

Bulkheads are made stronger on steeper pitches, and their drainage is carefully provided for, to avoid subjecting them to the full hydrostatic head of overlying water and culm. They are drained by troughs and screens (Fig 781, 782); or by filters of hay, straw, burlap, and dry-walling.   A trough returns the water for reuse if necessary more quickly than the other devices.   Fig 784 shows an arched concrete bulkhead; good for heavy press and where timber is costly.

Table 95. Size and Spacing of Props in Barricades

	D = diam of prop, in	S = spacing of props c to c, ft	B = haunch distance, ft
Flat workings, 0° to 10°	D = L	S = W ÷ H	W ÷ 2
Chute workings, 10° to 25°	D = 3 L ÷ 2	S = 2 W ÷ 3 H	W ÷ 2
Pitch workings, over 25°	D = 7 L ÷ 4	S = 4 W ÷ 7 H	2 W ÷ 3

W = width of opening, ft. H = height of opening, ft. L = length of prop, ft. Number of props required for a barricade = (W ÷ S) + 1.

Data in Table 96 are from plants with capac of at least 400 cu yd daily.

Table 96.   Costs of Flushing in the U S, ¢ per cu yd (C. Enzian, in 1913)

Material	Surface transport			Intermediate transport		Underground tr'sport		Distribution			Drainage		Total	
	Gravity	Scraper or conveyer	Pump	Shaft or slope	Bore hole	Trough	Pipe	Flat workings	Chute workings	Pitch workings	Incidental	Special	Minimum	Maximum
Culm	1–1 1/2	4 1/2–6	2 1/4–4	1/4–1/2	1/10–2/10									
Culm mixed with crushed breaker and boiler refuse	4–5 1/2	7 1/2–10	5 1/4–8	3/4–1 1/2	2/10–5/10	1/10–3/10	3/10–5/10	7 1/4–9	12 1/2–14 1/2	14–27 1/2	4/10–7/10	1 1/4–8	9 3/10	56 1/4
Local hydraulicked sand, loam, gravel, clay, etc	8–14	11 1/2–18 1/2	9 1/4–16 1/2	9/10–1 3/4	3/10–7/10									
Local crushed sand, loam, gravel, clay, etc	30–40	......	......	1–1 1/2	4/10–8/10									
Material from a distance in returning empty coal cars	Cost of material, loading, freight, unloading, preparing and surface transport			1–1 1/2	4/10–8/10	Add 25% to each cost specified								

111. TIMBERING. USE OF STEEL SUPPORTS

Timbering in coal mines is similar to that in metal mines with differences in detail and terminology. Props, and 3-piece sets (Art 20) for gangways, etc, are of round timber.

Common sizes of legs (posts) are 10 to 14-in diam, of collars (caps) 8 to 10-in; in Penna, legs have a batter of 2.5–3 in per ft; in bituminous mines they are often vert. Lagging is 3-in round or 6-in split, in 6-ft lengths. Sets are usually 5 ft apart; in heavy ground they are doubled, at 2.5-ft centers. In moderately thick pitching seams, gangways may be timbered with a single row of lagged props along the high side, corresponding to stull timbering in metal mines (Art 38, see also Fig 235). When length of such props exceeds about 12 ft, they are replaced by 3-piece sets on flatter dips, or by " post and bar " (half or 2-piece sets, Art 20) on steep pitches. Rooms and breasts are timbered with props set with a slight underlie (Art 38); their spacing depends on character of roof. Headboards are sometimes used; generally props are wedged against the roof. In flat rooms or moderately pitching breasts, where the roof tends to flake off, caps may be placed between props, at least over the track or chute (355).

Steel supports are increasingly used in both coal and metal mines, especially for wide openings and those of semi-permanent character, as haulageways, pumprooms and shaft stations. STEEL vs TIMBER. Steel lasts much longer, especially in moist, foul air. It is procurable in sizes that will carry heavier loads than any available timbers. Less excavation is required and cost of erection is usually less than for timber of equivalent strength.

Disadvantages of steel are its relatively high first cost (unless second-hand material is available), and that it can not be so readily cut and fitted underground, unless gas-oxygen torches are used. It may be required by heavy press regardless of other factors; its installation is often justified by saving in maintenance.

Proper size of steel for given service cannot be definitely computed, because it is impossible to measure the weight to be supported. Steel members for replacing timber are slightly heavier than required for equivalent strength. In a new region, their size is based on experience with wood or steel under similar conditions elsewhere.

Types. Props may be of standard H-sections, of old rails, or other available material. Wooden or steel base blocks and head boards are generally necessary, to prevent props from being forced into floor or roof. Fig 785, 786 show examples of gangway sets made by the Carnegie Steel Co in numerous forms and sections of leg and collar. Legs are commonly of H-section (Fig 786) or of 2 channels (Fig 785); collars of I-beams; joints

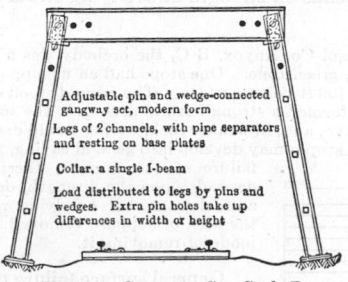

Adjustable pin and wedge-connected gangway set, modern form

Legs of 2 channels, with pipe separators and resting on base plates

Collar, a single I-beam

Load distributed to legs by pins and wedges. Extra pin holes take up differences in width or height

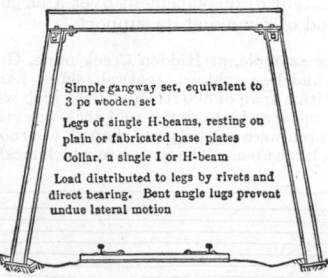

Simple gangway set, equivalent to 3 pc wooden set

Legs of single H-beams, resting on plain or fabricated base plates

Collar, a single I or H-beam

Load distributed to legs by rivets and direct bearing. Bent angle lugs prevent undue lateral motion

Fig 785. Gangway Set, Style B   Fig 786. Gangway Set, Style F

may be rigid or adjustable. Entry and gangway roofs are often supported by I-beams, H-sections or rails, resting on wooden legs, concrete pillars or walls, or in hitches in the coal ribs. Arches and cambered girders are widely used in British and Continental mines. Lagging may be of wood, or, for fireproof construction, of old rails, sheet steel or corrugated iron. Brick or concrete arches are sometimes turned between collars of adjacent sets. Concrete slabs, with light wire-mesh reinforcement, may be built over the collars in pumprooms. For examples of steel supports in shaft stations and pumprooms, see Sec 12 and 13 respectively. For further data, see Carnegie Steel Co catalogs and Bib (374, 375).

GROUND MOVEMENT AND SUBSIDENCE

The following Articles were written originally by Alan M. Bateman, Prof of Economic Geology, Yale Univ. Revised in 1926 by H. G. Moulton, Consulting Mining Engineer. Revised and enlarged in 1938 by Stephen Royce, Consulting Mining Engineer and Geologist, and Geologist for Pickands Mather & Co.

112. THEORIES AND PRINCIPLES

Status of information. While ground movement and subsidence have long been studied and many theories advanced, data are scanty and often conflicting.

In the U S, committees of the Am Inst of Min Engs are investigating the subject with reference to coal, non-ferrous metal and open-cut mining. Best current sources of information are: COAL MINING. Comm Rep, A I M E, 1926 (469), containing tabulations and data and Bib from 1913 to 1924. OPEN-CUT MINING (470, 471). GENERAL. Bull 91, Eng Exp Sta, Univ of Ill, by Young and Stoek, 1916 (465), contains an extended Bib. (See also Bib 472, 473, 621, 673, 674).

Economic features. Heretofore, the chief interest in subsidence has concerned surface damage, since ground under buildings must generally be supported to prevent injury from settlement. In general, subsidence must be prevented where towns are located over workings; where settlement would affect the grades of R Rs, sewers and piping; where water courses overlie mine workings and subsidence fractures might admit much water; and where, in case of large mines, surface effects would be too great to permit subsidence, except in areas containing no permanent improvements. Subsidence can sometimes be controlled to produce such uniform surface settlement that buildings are not seriously damaged; as in case of certain regular coal seams where the coal was completely extracted.

Possible subsidence affects choice of location of mine shafts and surface plant. Mills should be placed where they can be supported, or at points safe from settlement; otherwise foundations and machinery may be injured.

The problems of subsidence as affecting mining operations themselves are now usually more important than surface effects. In some mining methods, press caused by subsidence of overlying strata aids in breaking the mineral; in metal mines, control of subsidence reduces mining costs and dilution of ore. Coal-mining practice tends toward complete extraction of coal, accompanied or followed by uniform subsidence; this minimizes danger of loss from squeezes. Subsidence is sometimes desirable for filling voids, as when extracting sulphur from deep deposits by hot water.

General principles. Withdrawal of support caused by removal of minerals subjects the overlying rocks to 2 kinds of distortion: (*a*) local caving of stopes; (*b*) a general, widespread movement. The second type is, however, only an extension of the first. The extent of displacement over a large area depends on strength of overlying strata and method of removing its support.

For example, at Hidden Creek mine, Granby Consol Co, Anyox, B C, the orebody was a lens of Cu and Fe sulphides; footwall, slate; hanging wall, greenstone. One stope had an unsupported roof with a span of 300 ft; top of the arch was approx 400 ft below surface. The ground stood over this large area because the roof rock was strong, and formed a strong natural arch over the stope; if the arch were not properly shaped, the roof would cave, and, in weaker rock, caving would extend over a large area. The extent to which local caving in stopes may develop into general caving, with failure of the surface, therefore depends upon the strength, depth and character of overlying rock, the area of support removed and mode of removing it.

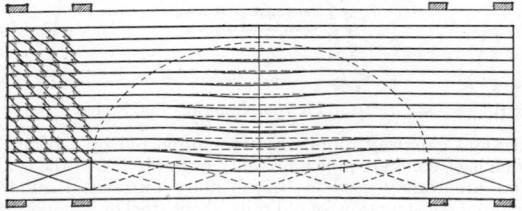

Fig 787. Fayol's Experimental Subsidence of Horiz Strata

General surface failure over a large area is of 2 kinds: (*a*) Usual type in coal mining consists of settlement of bedded rocks over worked-out seams, where beds are comparatively flat and thin; (*b*) in extracting ore from bodies underlying massive rocks, the action may be merely local spalling over stopes, but may extend to complete collapse of the surface. Subsidence of bedded rocks over coal mines appears to involve beam action to some extent; the strata bend and break, due to tensile stresses. Subsidence of massive rocks over metal mines involves failure from fracture by compression; as over stopes of the Miami copper mine (Art 86); surface cracks first appeared, followed by subsidence along vert breaks.

Early theories. From studies during latter half of last century in France, Belgium and Germany, many mathematical theories of subsidence were developed. Best known is that of H. Fayol in 1885 (467), based upon experiments with artificial beds of earth, sand, clay and plaster, in small boxes. The conclusion was that fracture of the ground would spread out in form of a dome, the increased vol of broken material filling the area affected, finally checking movement at some depth bearing a definite relation to thickness of mineral removed. In homogeneous, or in flat lying stratified rocks, these domes tend toward a semi-ellipsoidal form, with major axis vert, and the base of the half ellipsoid coinciding with the limits of mining (Fig 787). As mining is extended, laterally or in depth, new ellipsoidal domes develop, and the older, interior domes continue to show

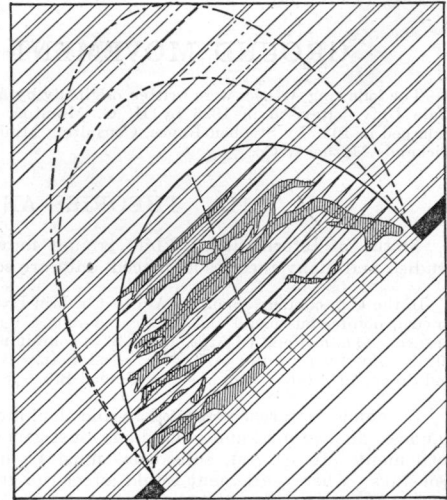

Fig 788. Fayol's Experimental Subsidence of Inclined Strata

increased movement along their surfaces as long as subsidence continues within and below them. These successive domes produce the phenomenon shown in workings over a mined orebody, where the ground is displaced downward in successively greater scarp movements as the center of mining is approached.   In case of inclined strata, the axis of doming tends to be warped toward the normal to the bedding, and lies between that direction and the vert (Fig 788); (205).   These reactions to subsidence are affected by fault planes or other planes of weakness in the terrane (Fig 789, 790).   For a historical study, see Bib (465).   Recent experiments in sand by W. J. Mead, of Mass Inst of Tech, have confirmed the mechanical principles of this type of movement, early developed by Fayol and elaborated by Goupillière.

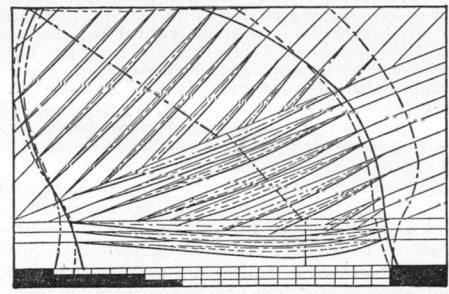

Fig 789. Fayol's Experiments with Uncomformable Beds

Recent theories.   Following discussion is abstracted from a paper by George S. Rice (472).   GROUND MOVEMENT, without some of which there can be no subsidence.   Small movements of hanging wall or roof are evident in every mine where falls occur or timbering is needed, and in deep mines by a flow of the rock that gradually closes openings.   Greater movements occur in orebodies mined by top-slicing or similar method, and in coal mines worked by longwall and pillar withdrawal.   The successive changes between these first movements underground and surface subsidence are veiled with uncertainty, even in nearly horiz bodies of homogeneous material.   The variables of dip of

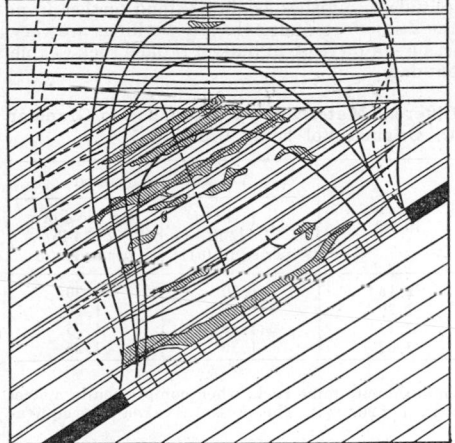

Fig 790. Fayol's Experimental Subsidence of Horiz over Inclined Beds. (Fig 787–790 from Goupillière, Vol 2)

strata, and their strength, possible faults, mining method, character and depth of overburden, and character of the underlying strata, add complexities.

(See also recent papers, in *Trans* A I M E and *E & M Jour*, by P. B. Bucky, Assoc Prof of Mining, Columbia School of Mines, detailing his experiments on strength of rock strata and pillars, and allowable span of roof over mine workings.—R. P.)

Effects of ground movement that seriously concern mining, from both safety and economic standpoints, are: (*a*) Simple falls of rock or ore. (*b*) "Bumps" (Sec 23).   In this case, gradual settlement of the immediate roof probably causes rigid strata above, comparable to beams under heavy load, to break successively when subsidence leaves a sufficiently wide unsupported space (622).   Such breaks cause a hammer-like blow on the lower rocks, transmitted as a shock wave to the mine roof; this, being elastic, does not collapse, but loose material is thrown down, timber smashed, and wind blasts produced. Firedamp outbursts may occur simultaneously.   (*c*) Squeezes in coal mines (Sec 23) may cause subsidence, but it is slight, as the pillars remain in place.   (*d*) Flow of rock, even of the granitic type, in mines 3 000–5 000 ft deep, as in the Lake Superior district, may slowly close shafts or other workings.   (*e*) Extensive falls of hanging wall in metal mines, and rock readjustments in deep mines, set up violent air blasts.   Such falls sometimes occur in thick coal beds, with high open chambers, as in India.   (*f*) Irregular subsidence and rupture of upper beds, in room-and-pillar mining.   If the beds are close together, mining the upper ones may be impracticable, due to difficulty and cost.   In longwall, or where workings are sand-filled, permanent damage is small.   (*g*) In ore veins that are thick, dip steeply, and have relatively weak walls, if sublevel-caving be used, the wall rock may slump in with the ore and lower its value.   (In Lake Superior iron mines and elsewhere, such dilution is controlled by flooring sub-levels with plank; Art 71.—Author.)

Mechanics of ground movement.   A commission, appointed in 1825, to investigate surface cracks in vicinity of the coal mines at Liège, Belgium, concluded there was no danger from subsidence over workings deeper than 300 ft.   In 1838, Gounot proposed his theory of the law of the normal, *i e*, planes normal to dip of the bed limit the fracturing from an excavation. A similar theory was advanced about 1838 by Trollez, of France. Later, Rucloux and Durmond, of Belgium, Callon, Culomb, and Goupillière, of France, Schulz, von Sparre, von Dechen and Hausse, of Germany, and Jicinsky and Rziha, of Austria, each developed theories. Schulz criticized the law of the normal, considering that the plane of fracture varied with the material and in shale was vertical.

Although Fayol is generally credited with the dome theory, Rziha apparently first proposed it, on theoretical grounds only, in 1881–82; he also believed that stratification of the beds had little effect on angle of break, and described a "falling space," approx a spheroid, the rocks within which dropped when the force of gravity exceeded cohesion. Surrounding the falling space, Rziha thought there was a "friability" or "tearing space"; also that, in very deep mining, the increase in vol of the broken rock may prevent surface disturbance, and proposed the formula: $h = M \div a$, in which h = harmless depth; a = coeff of increase of vol; M = vert height of excavation.

Fayol made extensive laboratory tests, as well as mine observations, and in 1885 summarized the contradictory opinions advanced to that time, as follows: 1. Extension of movement upwards: (*a*) movement is transmitted to surface, regardless of depth of workings; (*b*) the surface is not affected when workings exceed a certain depth. 2. Amplitude of movements: (*a*) subsidence extends to surface without sensible diminution; (*b*) movements become more feeble as they extend upwards. 3. Relative positions of surface subsidence and mine workings: (*a*) subsidence always takes place vert above the workings; (*b*) subsidence is limited to an area bounded by lines drawn from perimeter of the workings and perpendicular to the beds; (*c*) subsidence can not be referred to the excavation by either vert lines or lines normal to the beds, but only by lines at 45° to the horiz, by angle of repose of the material, or by some similar angle. 4. Influence of gobbing: (*a*) Use of packing protects the surface effectually; (*b*) packing merely reduces the effect of subsidence.

Fayol's conclusions were that ground movements are limited by a dome having for its base the excavation and that their amplitude diminishes as they extend farther from center of the area, this also being true of the vert effects; also that, if workings are very deep, there will be no surface subsidence, because of increase in bulk of broken rock (Table 97); this is not substantiated by more recent data.

Table 97.   Fayol's Tests on Volumes of Different Materials, when Crushed to Granular Size (20 mm) and Compressed; Original Vol being Unity (465)

(*a*) Corresponds to vert rock press at depth of 1 638 ft (*b*) Corresponds to vert rock press at depth of 3 276 ft	Increase in vol	Vol when compressed	
		By press of 1 422 lb per sq in (*a*)	By press of 2 844 lb per sq in (*b*)
Clay..................................	2.16	1.00	0.90
Shale.................................	2.29	1.28	1.16
Sandstone.............................	2.14	1.36	1.25
Coal..................................	2.02	1.30	1.25

U S Bur of Mines' tests on naturally broken anthracite mine rock, when compressed in a steel cylinder at 833 lb per sq in, showed a shrinkage in vol of 26.2%. This press was taken to be equivalent to rock press at 860 ft below surface.

Since Fayol's work, other enginers have advanced theories and empiric formulas regarding angle of break, angle of repose, probable vert subsidence, and its extent relative to the mining excavation. Rice found the assumptions for coefficients in the formulas are such as to destroy the practical value of the formulas, except for identical conditions. The possible combinations of factors are infinite. Factors include the various strengths of rock and earth strata; their relative dryness; their dip; shape of excavation and whether packed or not; and, most important, the method of mining.

The following diametrically opposed views are still held: (*A*) Surface subsidence always extends beyond the area of excavation, a view supported by British authorities, and by many instances in the U S. (*B*) Subsidence does not extend beyond the area of excavation. The mine subsidence committee of the Mining and Geol Inst of India recently reported, after making accurate observations at 24 collieries, that " Where no packing is done and pillars are taken out completely, the area of subsidence is less than the area of excavation; and in seams dipping less than 1 in 5, where no packing is done and pillars are completely removed, there is no draw." That is, the break does not extend beyond the vert plane extending from edge of the excavation; a view substantiated by data from mines in Penna and West Va (469). See also recent papers on model tests.

Rice's experience at the Ladd and Cardiff mines (longwall field of northern Ill) shows that there is always a draw in advancing longwall. In Great Britain, where this system is in general use, cracks opened in brick buildings ahead of the face, but they mostly closed when subsidence was complete a few years later. Survey monuments and time studies at other mines in the Spring Valley, Ill, longwall district, have established the fact of draw. But, experience in mines using room-and-pillar system and drawing pillars within panels, where surface subsidence was well within vert planes bounding the area of pillar withdrawal, confirms the views of the India subsidence committee. L. E. Young reports similar findings in Ill in 1916 (623).

In investigating ground movement, the arching stresses and strength of rock strata acting as beams have been much discussed, but their relative importance is difficult to determine. Where the rock stratum immediately over the excavation, acting as a beam or flat slab, has broken (and as each successive layer breaks), the beam stresses are transferred to an arch spanning the excavation and resting on the solid strata on each side (Fig 791). The doming effect is probably a fact, but when the dome reaches the surface

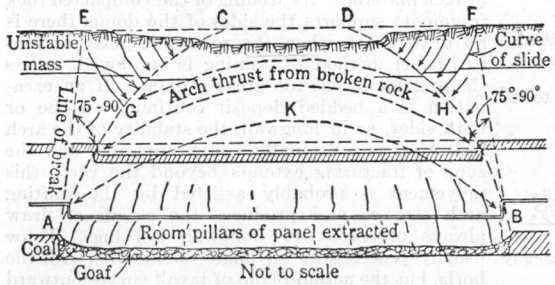

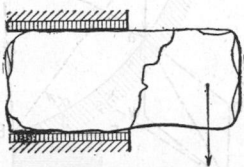

Fig 792. Rock Layer acting as a Fixed Beam, showing how doming effect may start in horiz strata at edge of excavated ground (465)

Fig 791. Suggested Mechanics of Room-and-pillar Caving (623)

its shape may have been modified greatly by the dip and strength of the rocks. Recent instances have repeatedly shown that shale, for example, breaks approx vertically, regardless of dip of its bedding planes. Break as shown (Fig 792) is usually nearly vert.

When an excavation is in a bedded deposit, or thick coal seam, not back-filled nor tightly packed, the overlying rock breaks when its span becomes too great for its strength as a beam. The overlying stratum acts as a beam fixed at one end projecting from the

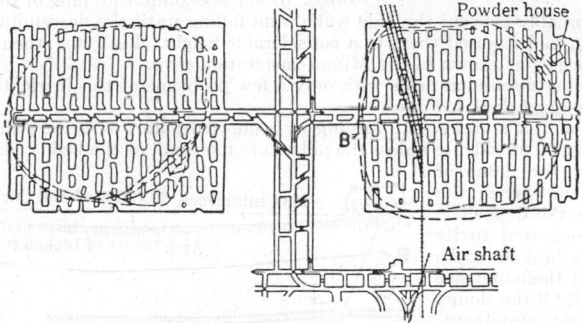

Fig 793. Effects of Subsidence in Panels of a Penna Coal Mine; dotted lines show cracks, 8–10 in wide at A, and 2 smaller ones at B (623)

solid; hence, on breaking near either support, the fracture usually inclines inward toward the excavation (Fig 792). Layers above break similarly, forming a flat dome increasing in height with the successive falls. The edges of such caved strata show a saucer-like shape of the initial breaks, if the ground is at all uniform (Fig 793). As the successive breaks occur, the space between the broken rock and the roof lessens; finally, if the depth of excavation is not too great, relative to its height and width, the dome breaks through to the surface. Meantime, the fragments falling from top and sides of the dome make a roughly conical pile, down which the fragments tend to roll and wedge against the dome walls. When the pile reaches a height greater than the width of excavation, Rice believes there will be an arch thrust through the mass of partly compacted broken rock, which tends to prevent further spalling of the sides of the dome or planes of break (Fig 794). Civil engineers have considered this in tunneling and trenching in earth and sand.

J. C. Meem's experiments (473) with dry sand in a cylinder are confirmed by the behavior of dry granular material in high bins; the wt on the bin bottom is independent of the height of the column of material above a moderate height compared to the bin diam. The wt of material above this height is carried by the bin walls (Sec 12).

Filling a stope with ore or waste prevents the walls from caving, due to the arching effect of the loose rock. Also, after the first load comes on the stulls under a shrinkage stope, added filling does not increase the load on the timbers (unless the horiz width and length of the stope are great.—Author). In tunneling under caved ground, although forepoling and heavy timber may be needed, the timber does not bear the full load of loose material above it, but only the part under the natural arch formed in the broken material. As arching of the compacted rock fragments supports the sides of the dome, there is no draw effect when the room-and-pillar or limited-panel method of mining is employed, unless the excavation has too great a diam. If an excavation in a bedded deposit continues on one or both sides, as in longwall, the stability of the arch buttresses is continually being impaired, and the zone of fracturing extends beyond the vert; this movement is probably assisted by the shifting arch stresses and produces the effects of draw always observed over longwall workings. Draw usually proceeds at an angle of 65°–75° with the horiz, but the actual plane of break curves outward from the excavation and is affected by the character of the ground (Fig 794, 795). In homogeneous rock, the plane of break may be the resultant of the vert wt component and an arch thrust from the broken rock, which would add to the load on the rock in place, giving the downward movement a disrupting effect. In a very thick orebody, lying at some depth and mined by caving, after the first general break to surface similar arching of the broken capping would probably prevent the side walls from falling until the descending capping, by further caving, had exposed them to a considerable height (Fig 796); then normal rock slides would occur, as shown in the Miami-Inspiration cave.

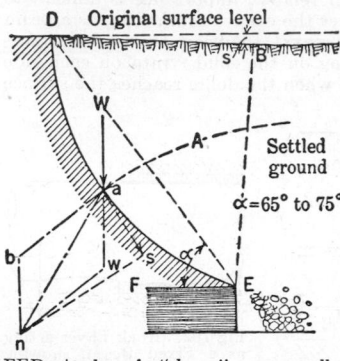

FED, Angle of "draw," as usually defined.
EaD, "Plane of stability"
EBD, Moving ground tending to slide
Aa, Thrust of arch from caved ground
Wa, Weight of strata
an, Resultant thrust
ns, Rubbing pressure on solid ground
as, Slide component
s, Subsidence

Fig 794. Theory of Stresses in Subsidence where using Longwall

The preceding discussion deals with only a few problems of this intricate subject, but touches on the most disputed ones.

Summary of Rice's views. 1. Mining by room-and-pillar, with the pillars left standing, may not cause subsidence unless the pillars are too small or the bed is near the surface. Conversely, the dome of breaking will not reach the surface unless the deposit is very thick, compared to its depth, as the broken rocks will wedge and their increase of volume will fill the dome. (Regarding this statement, allowance must be made for compressibility of the broken rocks, which is apt to be high where the depth is considerable.—Author.)

2. When pillars are partly or wholly extracted in a panel of moderate size, surface subsidence is ultimately inevitable.

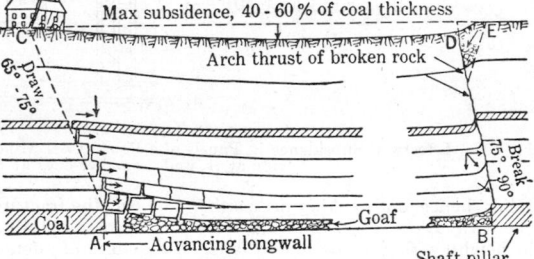

Fig 795. Suggested Mechanics of Longwall Subsidence

When a deposit is thick, compared to its depth, and the lateral width of deposit or panel is of moderate size and the area excavated surrounded by a barren pillar or solid mineral, surface subsidence rarely extends beyond the area of deposit or panel; that is, there will be no draw, because the arching thrusts of the broken rock buttress the walls (Fig 791). Vert subsidence will then approx the height of excavation, less amount of broken material left in place; provided the rock strata, after the first falls, tend to come down *en masse* and thus not greatly increase in volume.

3. Longwall, or equivalent method, inevitably causes surface subsidence, independent of depth of deposit, accompanied by a draw; that is, subsidence extends beyond the workings, and over the solid mineral to a line subtending an angle of 65°–75° from the horizon of the excavation. The angle will be modified by dip of the strata and by faults. In longwall, subsidence ranges from $1/2$ to $2/3$ of the thickness of the bed, varying with amount of packing. As long-wall is usually practiced only when the roof is shaly, the packs are so compressed that old ground when reopened is often as tight and hard as the original. Where hydraulic sand-filling is used, subsidence is negligible.

Rice's "plane of stability" differs from the angle of repose of loose material, because it refers to rock or dry earth in place. It is a warped plane extending from edge of the excavation to the surface, where it meets the theoretical line of draw; hence, the line of draw is a chord of the warped plane, below which the ground is not affected. Position of the warped plane, with respect to a straight plane, depends on the relations of the arch thrust of the broken ground, sliding movement beyond the vert, and resistance of the rocks to rupture under the combined stresses (Fig 794).

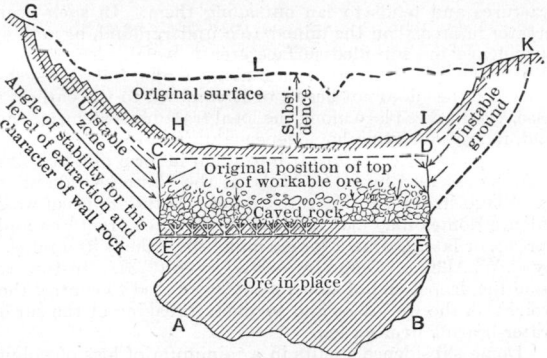

Fig 796. Suggested Mechanics of Subsidence in Block-caving of a Large Orebody

113. MISCELLANY, SUBSIDENCE

Effect of variations in rock structure. Subsidence is affected by homogeneity and strength of the overlying rock and by faults or other planes of weakness. Homogeneous material usually develops its normal lines of fracture and subsidence only at depths great enough to cause press exceeding the shearing strength of the rock. Hence, weak rocks fail in shear and show lines of fracture outside the area directly above the excavation at comparatively shallow depths; whereas strong rocks tend to break in vert planes, or form domes within the vert planes at shallower depths, and will not develop subsidence areas beyond the area of excavation until greater depths are reached.

No figures are available, from which an exact relation between strength of strata and depth causing complete failure can be determined, but empirical data may be obtained from observing particular cases; for examples, see Bib under "Status of Information" (beginning of Art 112). Fractures are often localized at a contact between a harder and a softer rock stratum. Presence of igneous intrusives in a sandstone or limestone formation modifies the lines of subsidence, unless the press resulting from depth of the excavation exceeds the shearing strength of these rocks. Similarly, planes of weakness (as faults) localize breakage of strata and affect subsidence.

W. R. Crane (673, 674) demonstrates the important effects of bedding, fault planes, and joint fracture systems, in controlling subsidence movement. He finds that the major yield takes place along a mean, or resultant, of the various fracture systems in all directions toward the mine openings, weighting them in order of prominence of occurrence as well as in proportion to their steepness of dip. The flattest inclined planes of weakness are given great weight in determining the ultimate limit of draw, but the actual displacement on these limiting planes is apt to be small in amplitude and long-delayed, unless such flat fractures greatly predominate in number over the steeper ones. Crane's work above cited was chiefly on the Lake Superior iron and copper ranges. A large predominance of flat fractures in controlling subsidence at Rio Tinto mines, Spain, is described by R. E. Palmer (675).

The effects of "natural shrinkage stoping" by local fragmentation of the overlying rocks in subsidence may lessen or prevent surface subsidence, where the rocks immediately over the workings are weak and fractured, where the rocks above these are physically strong and unfractured, where the total stresses are less than the shearing strength of the stronger overlying rocks, and where the volume of subsidence is small relative to the cross-section as a whole. Where the overlying rocks are not much affected by fractures and natural planes of weakness, but are too weak to resist the shearing stresses, ellipsoidal domes of subsidence are apt to develop above the zone of fragmentation. As the fragmental material is compressed under the weight of these domes, new domes develop of greater width and height until the surface is reached, being drawn in an area which is apt to be less than the mined area. Such a case, stopping just short of subsiding the surface, occurred at the Brier Hill shaft of West Vulcan iron mine, Norway, Mich (676).

Wherever subsidence domes intersect important fractures, the yield transfers to these fractures and tends to fan out along them. In such event, surface subsidence may be greater in area than the mined area underground, or may equal it; whereas in pure dome subsidence the subsided surface area is usually less than the mined area (Fig 791, 796). Where the mined orebodies are along major fracture systems, the ellipsoidal dome subsidence either does not occur, or is confined to the earliest stages of movement. In such case, yield takes place along the local fracture system, spreads to any intersecting fractures, and, in any overlying homogeneous unfractured rocks, is controlled by the angle of yield in such rocks, or else spreads into them in form of a new system of domes. A case of this kind is described by C. E. Mills, at the United Verde mine, Ariz (677).

Where strong vert fractures, dikes, or other zones of weakness enclose an orebody, subsidence domes may be confined within such fractures and work up to surface without spread, or lateral draw; for example, the Athens iron mine, Negaunee, Mich, as described by C. W. Allen (678) and by W. R. Crane (673). In this case, sub-level caving, retreating from the deeper end of the orebody, was used to control the progress of caving, lessen the weight on the workings, and to delay breaking of the surface and consequent tapping of water-bearing overburden.

Dome subsidence results in a minimum of loss of volume, as subsidence works up to surface; fragmentation produces a max loss of volume in subsidence. Compressibility of the fragmented material sometimes lessens its helpful effect. In shallow workings, the cantilever or beam action of very strong overlying strata, as limestone or quartzite, may arrest the upward progress of caving in workings of moderate volume. But such action is rarely long-lived at a depth over 500 ft, unless the span of subsidence is very small. Keying and arching may terminate "natural stope" caving at great depths if the dip is steep, or the width small compared to length. Natural stopes resulting from reduction of volume in concentrating iron orebodies naturally from the jasper in place have been found on the Gogebic Range, Mich, unfilled after very long periods.

Mud runs and air blasts occur when subsidence taps water-bearing overburden so as to bring it into contact with openings in the mine. Such dangers are encountered on the Lake Superior iron ranges, and sometimes result from tapping a mud- or water-filled natural cavity, a common condition in any limestone territory. Bulkheads are the only safeguard against these conditions, unless the water can be drained from the suspected source of the mud, as at the Kimberley diamond mines (Art 88).

The waterhammer effect, produced when masses of fast-moving quicksand strike a rigid obstacle, is enormous. If solid rock is available in a drift, a bulkhead 12 ft thick, of reinforced concrete and hitched 6 ft into the rock at top, bottom and sides, with steel rails in the concrete, will stop almost any run. It should be poured from a small sub-drift 10 ft above the back of the main drift. If the drift to be blocked is no longer used, some 30 ft of timber cribbing should be put in on the dangerous side before the bulkhead is poured; otherwise, steel plate and oak laminated doors, 2–3 ft thick, can be recessed in the bulkhead in a V-shape with the point toward the cave, hung on ball-bearing hinges like safe doors. The bulkhead is then provided with 4 or more extra-heavy, 12-in relief pipes with valves, which are left open, to be closed slowly when the mud run occurs. Such a bulkhead withstood over 2 500 lb per sq in at the Judson mine, Alpha, Mich, in 1919, and saved the main level, the mine, and the men underground. The site for the bulkhead must be prepared with a minimum of shattering, and checked over carefully before pouring. An 18-in seam of slaty paint rock was forced out under such a bulkhead in the Amasa Porter iron mine disaster, Mich, in Feb, 1918. Major disasters have also resulted from such mud runs at the Keel Ridge, Mansfield, Milford, and Barnes-Hecker iron mines in the Lake Superior region. Properly designed bulkheads have averted them at other mines, notably the Chapin and Judson.

Air blasts result from sudden collapse of large mined openings, which forces air under press through communicating workings. Bulkheads, or the blasting in of large volumes of ground to block access of air blasts, are the only preventives.

Accumulation of water in the gob above top-slicing or sub-level caving sometimes causes local mud runs. Drainage, blasting in of the hanging wall, and vigilance whenever a usual water flow lessens or suddenly ceases, are the chief precautions. Where subdrift caving starts beneath water-bearing surface, a back of ore must usually be sacrificed and much lagging and planking be used as the slices are taken out, to guard against mud runs. Bulkheads of timber with trap doors at strategic points are safeguards. They should be double, V-shaped, and well hitched to the rock or solid ore, and doors fitted to close on cutting a rope, with an axe hung to a chain and staple for this purpose only.   In reclaiming workings after a quicksand run, bulkheads are the chief protection.   Sometimes 3 or more will fail before a mud rush is stopped by a final bulkhead.

Spread, propagation, and detection of subsidence.   Whether subsidence is of the local fragmentation, or the dome type (as already described); or follows fracture systems in the rocks; or is communicated to surface material above; or is a combination of any of these movements, its periphery is always marked by a spreading halo of tension cracks, affecting the rocks or soil, and any drifts, shafts, structures, pavements, pipes, railroads, or other improvements in the affected zone.   The appearance of tension cracks is the advance notice, as their transformation into shearing movement is the first stage, of subsidence at any given locality.   Surface survey monuments should early be set in threatened areas and periodically checked to measure their movement, both horiz and vert.   Such observations, correlated with mining progress, and with geological conditions, make possible the forecasting of further damage in time to prepare for it.

Time-lag element in subsidence is a difficult phase of the problem.   There is always a lag between mining and the start of subsidence, and nearly always between cessation of mining and the end of subsidence.   Thirty to 40 million tons in a series of iron orebodies in a steeply-dipping formation at Ironwood, Mich, were mined by a caving system over 25 or 30 years before subsidence amounted to more than local caves at the outcrop. Regional subsidence has since been widespread.   Shafts and crosscuts underground suffered 4 or 5 years before the trouble reached surface.   Depths of mining ranged from surface to over 2 000 ft.   Changes in rate or location of mining are sluggishly registered at surface 1 or 2 years after they occur.   Movement is mostly on fracture systems.

A comparable amount of iron ore in folded hard iron formation, having great shearing strength, has been removed in certain areas of the Marquette Range of Mich over the past 75 years with no surface effect, at depths to 1 500 ft or more.   On the Menominee Range, a cave from mining about 1 500 000 tons took 9 years to reach surface, appearing along a steeply dipping fault whose outcrop nearly parallels the formation.   Mining was suspended during 1 month.   Surface monuments showed that subsidence ceased within a day of the stoppage of mining, and recommenced within a day of resumption.   Orebody top was about 500 ft below surface, current mining about 1 000 ft; formation dips 60° south; fault, 80° north.

At an Ariz copper mine, depth of orebody 1 000 to 1 700 ft, net voids 800 000 cu yd, subsidence took 5 years to reach surface along a fault zone of 50° dip; 10 years to reach surface by dome subsidence under incompetent malpais flows.   Lag after mining is several years.

Rules.   Subsidence transmits fastest along fault fractures;   the steeper the fracture the quicker the transmittal.   Doming is more deliberate.   Yield on multiple intersecting fracture systems is slowest and most widespread.   Large deep orebodies subside the surface later than shallow orebodies of less size.   Natural block-caving of a small area in steep-dipping soft slate worked up 1 000 ft without spread of area or decrease of volume in 1 year at a Menominee Range mine.   Keying and arching may indefinitely delay subsidence in moderate-sized orebodies in hard rock.   When such situations yield, the action is apt to be sudden, with little warning.

Topography in subsidence.   When surface movement has begun, its behavior may be controlled by topography more than by mining.   The Turtle Mountain slide and disaster, which wiped out part of the town of Frank, Alberta, in 1903 (476), was caused by the mining of a relatively thin seam of coal, dipping steeply into the base of the mountain.   A landslide on a mountain side was caused by a relatively slight disturbance.   In regional subsidence, a steep mountain side takes precedence over low-lying territory in a manner suggestive of hydraulic head, with most of the subsidence working up the mountain side.

Subsidence in open-pit mining (Art 96, 97) is confined to lateral draw.   Large-scale open-pit mining began in the great shallow orebodies of the Mesabi iron range, Minn, where ore stands successfully on a $1/2$: 1 slope, and rock on slopes of $1/4$: 1 to $1/2$: 1. This in a bedded formation with dip of 5° and under.   On the Gogebic Range, Mich, the same beds are open-pitted in 2 mines, the dip averaging 60°–70°.   Original practice was modeled on Mesabi lines, and serious slides resulted, as ore will not stand successfully at steeper than a 1 : 1 slope, diorite at 50°, and footwall slate and quartzite are being cut back to a 30° slope.   Experience shows that stripping dumps should not be close to the walls of such pits, or failure of the walls will be promoted by excess weight.   On the Cuyuna Range, Minn, ore banks standing at 53° failed, in part due to upsetting press from a mica schist footwall, which swelled on exposure to weather.   The slope after stability was restored is 40°–45°.   In exceptional cases ore will stand on a slope of $3/4$: 1, but 1 : 1 is about the best that can be expected.   These beds dip from 60° to nearly vert. Thus, flat-lying strata are more stable under open-pit conditions than steeply inclined beds. Surface material stands at angles of 1 : 1 for clay, hardpan, and boulders, 1 1/2 : 1 for sand and gravel, to 1.7 or even 2 : 1 for fine sand. All of these slopes flatten greatly if the pits contain water.

Effect of subsidence on surface structures. Injury is not caused by amount of subsidence but by its manner. Greatest damage results from irregular subsidence, or from a change in relation of subsided areas to adjacent areas.

For example, a church at Stassfurt, Germany, built of stone masonry about 400 yr ago, has sunk 21 ft (due to potash mining) without collapsing. Similar phenomena have been observed in the Penna anthracite district. But, a building standing at a junction between subsided and undisturbed ground will be damaged. The draw resulting from subsidence often causes tension cracks, having horiz without vert displacement, as in the foundation of a shaft house of Miami Copper Co (625). J. J. Rutledge in 1923 (624) cites damages to buildings from draw resulting from squeezes and pillar failure, in advance of completely robbed areas in Oklahoma coal mines. Other causes of foundation settlement may result in damage greater than those from subsidence in mining operations. Another kind of subsidence damage is due to a change in relation between subsided surface and adjacent surface, thereby affecting grade lines and drainage. Change in drainage may cause overlying land to become water-logged, depreciating its agricultural value. This matter is purely economic, relating to damage as compared to cost of preventing subsidence, including loss of mineral left in pillars.

An extreme type of violent surface dislocation, of earthquake intensity, from sudden subsidence of underground workings, often accompanied by air blasts underground, is well known in the Lake Superior copper country (see *Proc* Lake Superior Min Inst, Vol XII, p 58, with photographs). The disturbance originates usually from abandoned, inaccessible workings; details of the underground movements are therefore unknown. This explosive type of subsidence results from collapse of large areas of old workings in hard rock on pillars that ultimately fail.

114. CONTROL OF SUBSIDENCE

Subsidence may be checked by increase in vol of the subsiding area. If the excavation be filled wholly or in part by natural or artificial supports, subsidence may be controlled or prevented. If the control is incomplete, protective steps may be taken underground and on surface.

In narrow stopes, subsidence is localized chiefly in a caving upwards, continuing until the back arches itself and supports the overlying strata. Support is necessary only to sustain the ground between the excavation and the top of the arch. Timbering usually suffices, its chief purpose being to PREVENT THE STARTING OF CAVING. In large excavations of metalliferous deposits, having considerable vert thickness, and in coal and salt, subsidence is often more extensive and timbering ineffectual. In coal mines, the necessity of artificial support depends on method of mining, value of coal in pillars compared to cost of filling, and value of surface, or amount of possible damage if surface is not owned by the mine.

W. R. Crane (673) suggests minimizing surface effects by following means: (1) carry working face or long dimension of the workings parallel to the principal line of draw; (2) leave blocks of unmined ground to be removed later, if possible; (3) fill with waste rock in blocks between pillars; (4) fill surface caves at outcrop of ore with waste rock to support walls; (5) blast out hanging and footwall rock to fill the cave, if practicable.

Shaft-pillars. Young and Stoek (465) summarize rules from different authorities for calculating shaft-pillars in flat coal seams, as follows: MERIVALE. $S = 22 \sqrt{D} \div 50$, where S = length of side of pillar, yd; D = depth of shaft, fathoms. ANDRE. Area of pillar for a 450-ft shaft is 35 sq yd; area increases 5 sq yd per 75 ft increase in depth. DRON. Draw a line enclosing surface buildings. Leave shaft-pillars so that the extension of solid coal beyond this line = 1/3 depth of shaft. WARDLE. Pillars not less than 120 ft sq, increasing with depth of shaft. If the minimum be 120 ft sq for depth of 360 ft, add 30 ft for every added 120 ft of depth. HUGHES. Allow 1 ft breadth per ft of depth; hence, a 600-ft shaft should have a pillar of 300 ft radius. PAMELY. Up to 300 ft, make pillar 120 ft; for greater depths, add 1 ft for every 4 ft depth. FOSTER, R. J. Radius of pillar is $3 \sqrt{Dt}$, where D = depth shaft, t = thickness of seam. MINING ENGINEERING (London). For shallow shafts, allow a minimum of 60 ft radius; for deeper shafts, $R = 60 + (D \div 10) \sqrt{t \div 3}$, where R = radius of pillar, D = depth, t = thickness of seam, all in ft. ROBERTON, E. H. $R = (D \div 6) + 2 \sqrt{Dt}$, where R = radius of pillar, D = depth of shaft, t = thickness of seam, all in ft. CENTRAL COAL BASIN rule, Ill. Allow 100 sq ft of pillar for each ft of depth; if bottom is soft, increase by half; if coal is thicker than 5 to 6 ft, pillar should be larger.

The diversity of opinion regarding shaft-pillars is shown graphically in Fig 797. Fig 798 shows effect of a shaft-pillar (467); depth of seam 453 ft, thickness 60 ft, and on 2 sides of the pillar 25 ft of the thickness has been removed. Surface was affected to points C, D, and horiz masonry at C', D' became curved. To protect surface structures, Scotch engineers leave pillars $1/3$ to $1/5$ larger than floor plan of the structure. In flat seams at Connellsville, Pa, for depths of 150–300 ft, a margin of 25–30 ft of coal is left around a building. If the tract is large, 50–60% of the coal underlying is removed, remainder being left in pillars.

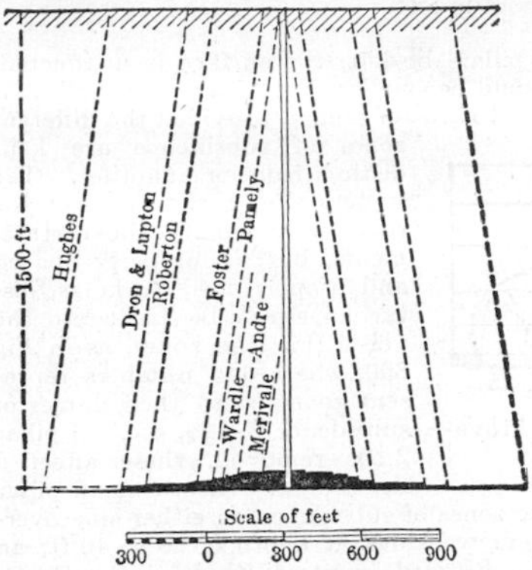

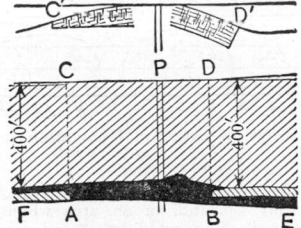

Fig 797. Sizes of Shaft Pillars, according to Different Formulas (Knox)

Fig 798. Effect of Shaft Pillar on Surface Subsidence (Fayol)

For dipping beds, relative positions of surface structure and pillar are shown in Fig 799 (474). Richardson (466) suggests " construction of a cross-sec showing the surface object and underlying orebodies; from each end of the object draw lines cutting the reefs toward the rise side and making an angle with a horiz plane equal to angle of fracture. The portion enclosed within these lines is the pillar required. Angle of fracture is taken as half way between the vert and normal to the planes of stratification.

The above data apply mainly to subsidence of relatively thin beds or seams, as in coal mining. In mining large, irregular-shaped orebodies at depth, experience shows that shaft pillars are rarely long-lived at a steeper angle than a 65° cone about the collar of the shaft. Conditions of weakness, fracture systems and faults, previously discussed, may greatly flatten this angle of safety.

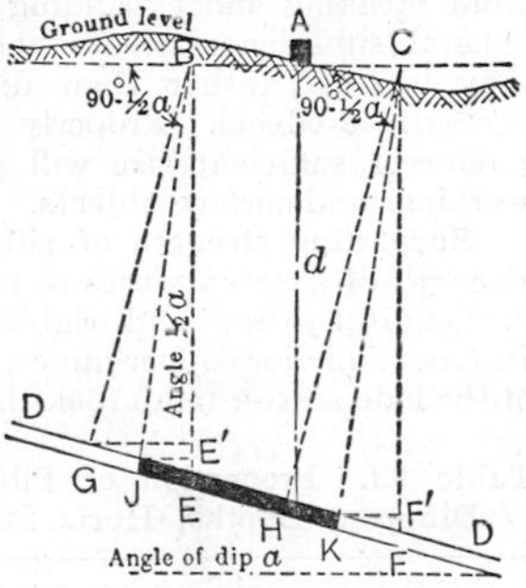

Effectiveness of filling. Vert movement is reduced in extent but not prevented. Ordinary filling is compressible (see tests below), and never fills excavations completely. When roof settles, the resistance of filling, weak at first, increases rapidly, and soon stops movement.

Fig 799. Position of Pillar with Respect to Surface Object (O'Donahue)

Belgian engineers believe the most careful packing gives no guarantee against damage to surface buildings; it only lessens subsidence (467). In the Westphalian mines, filling greatly reduces vert subsidence, but has little effect upon its lateral extent (465). A French engineer says: "In working by a system which permits the roof to fall, movement of strata gradually diminishes and stops at a certain level; with filled longwall, it is almost independent of depth; leaving sufficient pillars can alone insure safety of the surface " (467).

Fayol's observations at Commentry mines (467) are: (a) Certain seams, 3.25–6.5 ft thick, difficult to keep open without filling, have hardly required timbering from the time they were filled. (b) For soft rock, formerly used, a hard incompressible rock was substituted; haulageways became steady, roof settled much less, and cost of timbering decreased. (c) Some filling was done imperfectly; roof slabbed off and required much timber. Filling was then done carefully, leaving no spaces. Soon the press was hardly felt at the face, and all timbers could be saved. Fayol showed that in the same formation, in an excavation 39 in high, subsidence would reach a height of 658 ft if the roof sank without breaking; if roof broke, it would reach 541 ft; by filling, it would be reduced to 262 ft.

Summary of opinions: (a) filling greatly diminishes subsidence; (b) does not prevent it; (c) minimizing open spaces by careful packing is important. Fayol's figures are based on mine gob which undergoes fairly high compression; sands or crushed materials compress but little (see tests below), but their use is costly and may be impracticable. In narrow excavations, filling limits and usually prevents subsidence.

Effectiveness of pillars. In general, pillars are the only means of protecting shafts, important workings, or surface objects of value. In Belgian and English coal fields, they prevent surface damage, if about 50% of the coal is left.

Fayol stated respecting room work that, if enough pillars be left, the surface is unaffected; the mesh of the network of pillars and working places should be smaller as workings are shallower. As depth increases, workings can be enlarged in proportion to area of pillars, provided the different zones of subsidence are kept distinct from one another. The structure and character of the rocks may modify above statements, but, in properly spaced and proportioned workings, disturbance may be limited to the vol within the zones, as in Fig 800, where odd numbers represent rooms with their domes of subsidence Z_1, Z_3, etc. If pillar 2 be removed, these affect a larger area. Also, a small pillar may not effectively protect a surface object, because the zones of subsidence on either side overlap. In Clay Co, Ind, in an area which subsided from workings at depth of 20 to 40 ft, an outline of each pillar could be traced on the surface. Richardson states that on the Rand, when a pillar has been left, subsequent pull or draw on each side often causes more damage than if no pillar existed.

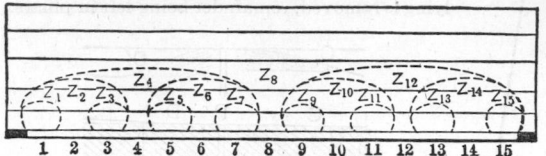

Fig 800. Effect of Extent of Excavation on Amount of Movement (Fayol)

General conclusions: Adequate pillars afford the only effective prevention of subsidence for coal mines, unless hydraulic filling (Art 110) is available. Timbering serves in small stopes of metal mines, when its strength exceeds the force exerted by the portion of the roof below the dome of equilibrium. It is held that in coal seams timbering prevents the overlying beds from breaking and expanding before general subsidence occurs; hence it may increase rather than diminish the surface effects. Properly spaced pillars of sufficient size will protect workings and surface objects.

Supporting strength of pillars has not been determined. Tests show the crushing strength of selected pieces of rocks and coals, but pillars are usually composed of layers varying in hardness and friability; laboratory tests do not apply to the pillar as a whole. In Lake Superior copper mines, rock pillars at 3 000-ft depth, amounting to 10% and more of the lode matter (trap rock) have failed by fracture or flowage of the wall rocks (679).

Table 98. Safe Unit Stresses for Stone (Douglas)

	Crushing, lb per sq in	Shear, lb per sq in	Tension, lb per sq in
Granite......	1 020	200	150
Limestone....	800	150	125
Sandstone....	700	150	75

In making computations, empirical formulas are necessary, aided by an approx estimate of strengths of the rocks based on tests. An aver of numerous tests of the Rand quartzite gives a mean ultimate crushing strength of 7 521 lb per sq in (466). Since tested cubes are weaker than the same area in a wide bed, Richardson thinks 10 000 lb is a probable figure; or, at great depths, even 15 000 lb. Taking sp gr of quartzite as 2.83, the above figures give 8 183 and 12 275 ft, respectively, as the depths at which quartzite will fail under its own weight (Table 99); for inclined strata, multiply the figures in the table by the cosine of the dip. Ultimate strength of trap rock forming pillars in Lake Superior copper mines is 16 666 lb per sq in (465). Tests of building stone (475) have little value in subsidence; rocks of the coal measures are unsuitable for building. Moisture lowers crushing strength of sandstone about 40% (Table 100).

Tests of crushing strength of Illinois coal gave an aver max of 1 486 lb per sq in; coal from the Pittsburgh seam, 3 155 lb (465). An aver of 45 tests by Daniels and Moore (478), upon different sized prisms of Penn anthracite,

Table 99. Proportion of Pillars for Different Depths, Horiz Strata

Depth, ft	Pressure, lb per sq in	Percentage of pillar area for crushing strengths of 10 000 lb	Percentage of pillar area for crushing strengths of 15 000 lb
1 000	1 222	12.2	8.1
2 000	2 444	24.4	16.3
3 000	3 676	36.8	24.5
4 000	4 888	48.9	32.6
5 000	6 110	61.1	40.7
6 000	7 332	73.3	48.9
7 000	8 554	85.5	57.0
8 000	9 776	97.8	65.2
9 000	10 998	....	73.3
10 000	12 220	....	81.4
11 000	13 442	....	89.6
12 000	14 664	....	97.7

with press applied parallel, normal and inclined to the bedding, shows a crushing strength of 1 926 lb per sq in (see also Table 101); 12 samples of bituminous coal gave 1 007 lb per sq in. On a clay floor, the bearing power of the pillar does not exceed that of the clay (Table 103).

Supporting strength of filling is greater with fine materials than with coarse. Though sands have a high percentage of voids, they are almost incompressible to the crushing point of the grains. Voids of broken rock are smaller in percentage, but larger in size; as pieces are in contact in few places, the angles and edges crush sooner and allow considerable compression. This crushing takes place under a press less than the crushing strength of a single piece. If voids of broken rock be filled with sand, its compressibility is lessened. Mixtures of large pieces of sandstone and shale, used for filling in coal mines, have about 40% voids. Fayol states that in workings 300–900 ft deep, such filling is compressed 30%, leaving a vol about 12% larger than the original material in place (467). The commission investigating the Frank slide, Alberta, concluded that under aver conditions settlement would be 5% of thickness of bed, if ordinary sand were used; an inappreciable amount, with granulated slag; 10–15% with loam, sandy clay, and ashes; 40–60% with dry packing (476). See Table 102.

Water should be kept out of partly subsided areas; it may loosen sands or clays and cause surface movement, resulting in further underground subsidence. Workings extending under watery strata or creeks may cause downward movement of water, which will loosen the rock and start subsidence. Streams flowing over excavated ground should be

Table 100.   Crushing Tests, North Carolina Sandstones (475)

Absorption, %	Conditions	Crushing strength, lb per sq in
4 2	Dry	10 736
4.2	Wet	6 399
3.71	Dry	11 741
3.71	Wet	6 174

Table 101.   Crushing Tests, Pennsylvania Anthracite Coal

Samples from Anthracite Fields	Height of sample, in	Aver per sq in First crack	Aver per sq in Max load	Number of tests
Northern	1	3 022	6 241	122
	2	2 025	4 087	116
	4	1 875	2 854	113
Eastern Middle	1	4 996	7 417	7
	2	3 343	3 857	6
	4	3 413	3 821	7
Western Middle	1	3 001	8 631	3
	2	788	3 499	3
	4	1 440	2 447	3
Southern	1	1 124	3 814	12
	2	1 099	2 377	12
	4	988	1 809	12

Table 102.   Supporting Strength of Dry Filling.   Griffith and Conner (477)

Kind of material in artificial supports	Approx depth, ft, of column of coal measure rock, 1 ft sq, necessary to compress artificial support					
Per cent of compression	1	3	5	10	20	30
Rectangular gob piers, ordinary construction		10	12	36	125	*306
Circular piers of mine rock, well constructed		46	75	146	292	*512
Timber cogs filled with gob, aver construction		8	68	182	270	*419
Loose pile of broken sandstone through 1 3/4-in ring, 40% voids			20	53	124	*298
Broken sandstone, 40% voids, filled with sand			21	53	186	*465
Loose pile large size broken sand rock, 45% voids		48	66	121	351	*492
Mine room filled with broken sandstone, 50% voids	12	27	45	117	434	a615
Room filled with broken sandstone, 40% voids		44	74	177	619	1 310
Room filled with broken sandstone, 40% voids filled with sand		46	77	325	6 000	b8 860
Room filled with dry coal ashes, 64% voids		13	25	70	143	332
Room filled with dry river sand	12	40	70	442	1 715	6 640
Room filled with river sand flushed in with water	111	522	891	2 310		c8 860
Room filled with coal culm flushed in	32	118	190	472	1 822	5 905
Concrete pier, 1 cement, 7 sand and gravel; 5 months old	117	1 092	(e)			
Resistance of flushed culm	1.0	1.0	1.0	1	1	†
Resistance of flushed sand	3.5	4.4	4.7	5	4	†
Concrete pier	3.6	9.0	(d)	(d)	(d)	†(d)

(a) 27% settlement.   (b) 23% settlement.   (c) 20.75% settlement.   (d) Worthless.   (e) Gradually cracked to pieces under continuous load equal to 600 ft of rock.   * Free to expand laterally.
† Comparative.

Table 103.   Bearing Power of Rocks, Clay and Sand

Safe bearing power, tons per sq ft, for different materials	Min	Max
Rock (hardest), thick layers native bed..	200.0	....
Rock equal to best ashlar masonry.....	25.0	30
Rock equal to best brick masonry......	15.0	20
Rock equal to poor brick masonry......	5.0	10
Clay in thick beds, always dry.........	6.0	8
Clay in thick beds, moderately dry.....	4.0	6
Clay in soft beds...................	1.0	2
Gravel and coarse sand, well cemented..	8.0	10
Sand, dry, compact, well cemented.....	4.0	6
Sand, clean, dry....................	2.0	4
Quicksand, alluvial soils..............	0.5	1

diverted, to prevent inrush of water and sand. Water in mine workings should be confined to drains, to prevent undermining or disintegration of pillars; if allowed to run through filled areas, it carries away the finer materials and reduces the vol of fill. In salt mines, the water menace is more serious. DISINTEGRATION OF MINE PILLARS due to oxidation, decomposition, slacking, or solution, can be prevented by coating them with concrete (gunite) or plaster.

115.   THE LAW AS TO SUBSIDENCE

Barring special enactment, or a reservation in the title, the surface owner in U S and in the British Empire is entitled under the common law to the subjacent and lateral support of his surface.   Lateral support applies to the natural land surface only, not when burdened with buildings; grant of surface for building purposes implies a grant of lateral support; its removal through flow of quicksand into adjacent excavations, with resulting damage to buildings on adjoining lands, was adjudged in favor of the building owner in Cabat *vs* Kingman (166 Mass, 403).   This American decision is surprising when compared with English precedent, where in the case of Popplewell *vs* Hodkinson (L. R. 4 Ct. Exch. 247), it was decided that water drained from subsurface by an adjacent excavation and causing subsidence damage to adjoining surface did not give the damaged surface owner cause for redress.   Again in contradiction is the case in England, subsequent to the Mass case, where a quicksand flow into an excavation was found cause for redress of an owner of adjoining subsided buildings (Jordesan *vs* Sutton, etc, Co. L. R. 1899, 2 Ch. Div. 217).

Trend seems to be that removal of lateral support is ground for damages in all cases of damage; in the case of buildings the decisions are not so uniform, except where negligence in mining can be shown.   Reservations or special agreements may modify rights to lateral support.   Subjacent support is a positive right of the surface owner in all cases where it has not been specifically waived.

Severance of mineral ownership from the surface ownership does not waive the right to support. (Victor, etc, Co *vs* Morning, etc, Co, 50 Mo. App, 525).   It is held that the mineral owner must so mine his mineral as not to disturb the surface.   This is true also where the mineral estate has been divided into two parts, one below another.   The Marquette Cement Co, at LaSalle, Ill, succeeded in enjoining the longwall coal mining operations of the Oglesby Coal Co, 300 ft below the former's limestone quarry, in court proceedings in 1917 and 1918.   See Charles H. Shamel: " Mining, Mineral, and Geological Law."   For recent British enactment and practice, as well as the Provincial, Dominion and Colonial laws of the British Empire, see Briggs: "Mining Subsidence."

116.   CONCLUSIONS AS TO SUBSIDENCE

Subsidence is the almost universal result of large-scale mining operations.   Foresight in the location of shafts, equipment, and townsites, outside the zone of probable subsidence of the orebody AND ANY LIKELY EXTENSION THEREOF would save the industry much expense and the loss of untold tonnages extending under cities, the replacement of which cannot be borne by the mining profit.

The natural laws governing subsidence are, in principle, clear.   The haphazard appearance of subsidence action is illusory, and is due to the interaction of these principles with varying local conditions.   Certain broad generalizations are possible, but are safe only where not contra-indicated by local conditions.   Deep-level, regional, large-scale, long-lived subsidence in rock has a tendency to develop an ultimate angle of draw of about 63°. Subsidence at Bisbee, Ariz; Ely, Minn; the footwall on the Gogebic Range, Mich; the Eastern Menominee Range, Mich; to name a few deep-level cases in widely divergent geol settings, all have angles of draw close to this figure.   Extreme depth, closing local fracture systems by simple pressure, tends to confine subsidence to the doming type, which in turn tends to maintain draw within about a $1/2 : 1$ slope.

The exact depth at which rock flowage exists in the undisturbed crust of the earth is unknown. Mining depths have already encountered rock flowage in pillars and other points where the unit stress is multiplied over that normal to undisturbed ground at the same depth. The sheared, schistose, sheeted, and jointed rocks of the Pre-Cambrian, often yield by a pseudo rock flowage at depths as shallow as 1 000 ft. Actual yielding takes place along the shear and joint planes with which these old rocks are scarred. Such yield is usually a slow, creeping process, rather than the violent and sudden collapse of younger and less scarred rocks. Experience emphasizes the wisdom of allowing ample margins of error for the safety of expensive shafts, equipment and buildings, town-sites, and other improvements, to guard against the appearance of unexpected local factors.

PLACER MINING METHODS

Revised, 1940, under Direction of O. B. PERRY, E.M.

Introductory. Classification: (*a*) Surface methods which are applications of open-cut work (Art 95–101), and of dredging (Art 128, 129). These are the most important and varied, since most placers occur at or near the surface. For a detailed classification of methods and equipment, see Bib (181). (*b*) Underground methods for deep or buried placers (Art 117) are known as Drift Mining or Drifting (Art 130).

Placer mining includes the work of excavating and transporting placer gravels, and of recovering their contained gold or other valuable mineral, which is usually done by concentrating or "washing" the gravel in running water. All the common methods of excavating and handling earth and rock (Sec 3, 5) are utilized where suitable. The term placer mining, as sometimes used, excludes hydraulicking (Art 123), dredging, and drift mining; general term "alluvial mining" then includes all methods of mining placers (286).

Exploration or prospecting of placers, to determine their value and yardage prior to exploitation, is done by drill holes or shafts (Sec 25).

117. PLACER DEPOSITS

Definition. Placers are deposits of sand, gravel, or other alluvium, containing particles of valuable minerals in workable amounts. Native gold is the most important placer mineral; a large part of the world's output of platinum and cassiterite (stream tin) is derived from gravels; other minerals for which alluvial deposits are regularly worked include monazite, columbite, ilmenite, zircon, diamond, sapphire, ruby, and other gems; native Ag, Bi and Cu, amalgam, palladium, cinnabar, occur occasionally in gravels; some phosphate deposits (Art 98) may be classed as placers. The terms "gravel deposit," "gold-bearing gravel," and "alluvial deposit" are used loosely instead of "placer" or "placer deposit." The following paragraphs deal chiefly with gold placers; their bearing on other placers is obvious.

Geology. "Three conditions operate to form placers: (*a*) Occurrence of gold in bedrock to which erosion has had access; (*b*) separation of gold from bedrock by weathering or abrasion; (*c*) transport, sorting, and deposition of auriferous material derived from erosion. Erosion, while operative in most cases, is not absolutely essential, as residual placers may be formed by the weathering in place of auriferous bedrock" (377). The primary SOURCE OF PLACER GOLD is almost always in auriferous veins, stringers or other orebodies. These deposits were not necessarily rich; they may have been entirely eroded, or their remnants may not be workable.

Gravel deposits are often concentrations of enormous volumes of rock, in which gold may have existed in stringers too small to mine. Thus, in the Klondike, no large orebodies have been found in connection with the placers; the prevailing country rock is schist, containing numerous unworkable quartz stringers sometimes showing gold. To produce the present placers, it is estimated that 136 cu miles of rock, averaging less than 2¢ in gold per ton, have been eroded and concentrated. Some gold may be deposited from solution in residual placers; this agency is unimportant in the deposition of gold or formation of nuggets in stream gravels (307, 378).

Weathering and erosion. Deep secular decay of gold-bearing rocks preceded the formation of most important placers; it can occur only in base-leveled regions of topographic maturity. Under such conditions, rocks break down into clay and fine particles, which are removed by wind and slow-moving water. This effects surface concentration of heavy and resistant minerals, and sometimes forms commercially important residual deposits, as the eolian placers of Australia. A subsequent uplift which rejuvenates the streams will cause rapid removal of the residual mantle and further concentration of its heavy minerals along water courses. Placers formed by the concentrating action of running water are called SORTED PLACERS. Rapid erosion of fresh rocks by swift streams rarely produces extensive placers. A geological history involving several cycles of base leveling and uplift favors the formation of rich placers, as deposits of one period may be reconcentrated in streams of a later cycle. Many rich placers in Alaska, California and Victoria were thus formed; they are called RESORTED PLACERS (377, 379, 307).

Distribution of gold in sorted and resorted placers is irregular; normally, but not invariably, heavy gold is concentrated on bedrock or within a few ft of it; coarse gold is sometimes scattered through the lower part of a deposit, but, except in minute quantities, gold is never distributed uniformly through a great thickness of gravel. In small

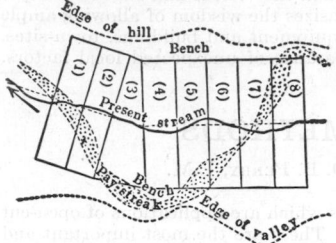

Fig 801. Meandering Paystreak

creeks, pay gravel may occupy the whole width of the stream bottom; in larger streams, there may be some gold at all points on bedrock, but most of it is usually concentrated along a narrower streak, known as the "paystreak," "pay-lead," "channel," "run of gold" (England), or "gutter" (Australia). Paystreaks often follow devious courses, bearing no apparent relation to that of the present stream; Fig 801 shows a case in point. Paystreaks may split or cut off suddenly; they may or may not occupy the deepest part of a stream channel; they may form at any elevation in a gravel deposit, on top of a stratum of clay or other impervious material, which is called a "false bedrock." Some placers have several paystreaks, thus formed and overlying each other (307).

Various hypotheses have been advanced to explain the formation and idiosyncrasies of paystreaks. J. B. Tyrrell holds that Klondike paystreaks occupy the bottoms of the original V-shaped gulches formed in the early period of stream action. Clay is the chief product of secular decay and is quickly removed by active erosion; hence, gold concentrated in such weathered material would be deposited in the bottom layer of the sediments laid down in a new stream. As the stream widened and meandered the paystreak would be covered. A later uplift might produce a new gulch at a lower elevation; depending on its location, the old paystreak might descend into it or remain in its original position (see Bench placers below). H. L. Smyth points out the fact that the whole contents of a stream bed must be in motion to allow concentration of heavy minerals; such motion occurs in young streams where gravels are shallow and floods occur. Lindgren ascribes paystreaks to the following causes: (a) partly to a natural "jig-like" movement in moderately deep, water-soaked gravels, during long conditions of fair balance between loading and erosive power of the overlying stream; (b) partly to a slow forward and downward movement of large bodies of stream gravels, which would allow heavy minerals to work downward; (c) largely to the fact that heavier gold particles entering a stream bed from an adjoining hillside are not carried out onto gravel flats of streams of gentle grade (the only ones that have extensive flood plains), but settle on the marginal bedrock of the gravel flat. As the flood plain widens, it covers the accessions of gold along its margin and the final result is a paystreak resting on bedrock and lying under barren or lean alluvium (380, 379, 377, 307). There is no essential disagreement between these statements; all the agencies noted probably act at different times.

Glacial gravels may contain gold; glaciers dissipate the gold which they pick up instead of concentrating it. Hence glacial gravels have little economic value unless they have been concentrated by post-glacial streams or have derived their gold from an unusually rich primary source.

Gradient of auriferous water courses varies between wide limits. Lindgren (307) states that the most favorable conditions for concentration of gold exist in streams of moderate grade, say 30 ft per mile. If sediment is deposited in an overloaded stream, concentration of coarse gold ceases; conditions for formation of rich placers are also less favorable where erosion is very rapid, unless the gold supply is unusually abundant. California streams in the Sierra Nevada have grades of 50 to 100 ft per mile; many in Alaska have grades of 100 to 150 ft per mile. Depressed or elevated ancient river beds may have been tilted and the original grades much modified.

Summary. A knowledge of local geology, regional geological history, and physiographic development is a distinct aid in placer mining; it furnishes an hypothesis on which to base prospecting, exploration, and mining. Further data on the geology of placers are given below and in Art 118; see also Bib (307, 377, 378, 379, 380) and U S Geol Surv *Bull* 337, 410, 498, 533, 534, 592, 739.

Placers may be classified according to their origin into residual, sorted and resorted placers, as above. From the mining standpoint the following grouping, based largely on form, is more useful: (a) RESIDUAL PLACERS, which, when formed directly over outcrops or on gentle slopes below them, are sometimes called "eluvial" placers. Residual placers are relatively unimportant; their valuable particles are not rounded by abrasion; concentration in them is superficial, the richest part being at or close to the surface (379). (b) HILLSIDE PLACERS occur on valley slopes; are not in well defined channels, but are somewhat sorted by water; a transitional type between residual and gulch gravels. (c) GULCH or CREEK PLACERS are gravel deposits in, adjacent to, and at the level of small streams (Fig 802); they are usually shallow. Gulch placer sometimes denotes gravel in gulches which are dry or carry intermittent streams. (d) BENCH PLACERS (terrace gravels) are fragments of old stream gravels partly removed by subsequent stream action which has cut deeper into bedrock. They may occur on the flanks of present valleys (Fig 802), or as remnants of a previous drainage system, the course of which has no direct relation to existing streams. The White Channel, in the Klondike, is of the latter type. (*e*) RIVER-BAR PLACERS occur in bars and gravel flats adjacent to large streams of gentle gradient; their surface often lies a few ft above normal water level. Fine gold is deposited by existing streams in bars at points where the velocity of the water is checked (Sec 2, Art 21). (*f*) GRAVEL-PLAIN PLACERS are formed in flood plains and deltas; the term is not strictly defined. The wide valley at Oroville, Cal, formed by meandering of the Feather River, is a gravel plain; also some of the tundra placers

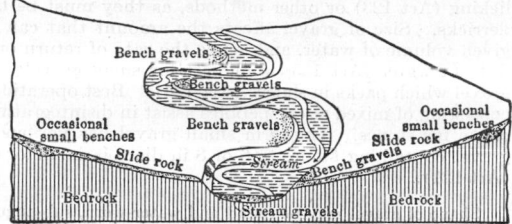

Fig 802.   Placer Deposits (U S Geol Surv)

of the coastal plain at Nome, Alaska (383). (*g*) BEACH PLACERS (marine placers) are formed by the concentrating action of waves on a sloping beach.

┌Gold in beach placers may come from a sea bluff of auriferous gravel, broken down and concentrated by the surf; some beaches are probably enriched by gold brought to the sea by nearby streams. Nome beach, a famous example, is 50 to 75 yd wide, slopes 4° to 5° and abuts an escarpment of gravel, muck and tundra 10 to 20 ft high (Fig 803); workable placers occupied 20 miles of beach. Fine gold is concentrated near the bottom of lenticular masses of garnet and magnetite sand, which are 5 to 9 ft thick and normally rest on a clay false bedrock. The lenses are rarely more than 100 ft long, and are not uniformly enriched over the width of the beach. The richest pay was usually in lenses 5 to 6 ft wide by 2 to 6 in thick (377, 381). Beach placers, consisting of surface concentrations of very finely divided gold in magnetite and garnet sands, occur on Kodiak and

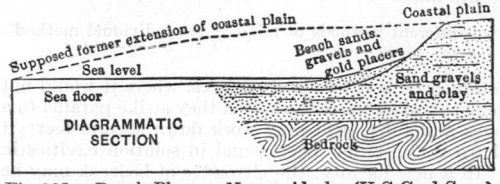

Fig 803.   Beach Placers, Nome, Alaska (U S Geol Surv)

Popoff Islands, Alaska, on the coast of Oregon and elsewhere. They are constantly shifting; in places, beaches are reworked annually or after storms. Beach deposits must usually be mined by simple hand methods (Art 119). Many disastrous attempts to work them on a larger scale failed to recognize that while individual thin layers may be rich, the aver value of any considerable depth of sand is very low. Wave action sorts beach material into equal-falling grains (Sec 28); where the gold is very fine and associated with fine magnetite and garnet sand, it is difficult or impossible to recover it by ordinary placer mining appliances (382).

Buried placers ("deep placers" or "deep leads," Australia) exist in many districts; any of the above deposits may be a buried placer, for example:

A general subsidence, or overloading of streams, may deeply bury the accumulated placers under barren alluvium. In the Fairbanks district, Alaska, deep placers, laid down as creek gravels in ancient water-courses which occupied the present valleys, are now buried under 20 to 300 ft of alluvium. Bedrock of the old streams was a little steeper than that of the present valley bottoms. Most of these channels are centrally located with reference to the bedrock slope of the present valleys; present streams occupy asymmetric depressions, one wall of which they follow closely. The gravels are covered with "muck" (Alaskan term for black humus, fine sand, clay and silt), derived partly from the valley slopes and deposited in part by sluggish streams. Near the headwaters of the creeks, the deep gravels merge with those of the present streams (383). The Tertiary stream placers of the Sierra Nevada, Cal, were covered by deposits of rhyolitic and andesitic tuffs and breccias in places 1 500 ft thick. The region was then elevated and a new stream system eroded the present canyons, some of which are 2 000 or 3 000 ft deep. Old gravels now rest as more or less connected remnants, on the summits between the modern canyons (307). Similar conditions, with basalt flows, occur in Victoria. Near Nome, 7 buried beach placers have been found in the coastal plain, indicating periods of subsidence or elevation which shifted the position of the coast line. The richest is the Third Beach, lying 20 to 124 ft deep and 3 miles inland from the present beach, which it roughly parallels; it has been traced 5 miles, and contains placers like those of the present beach (384).

Dry placers is a term applied to auriferous alluvials of various kinds, occurring in arid regions. They seldom lend themselves to large-scale work, but contribute a fairly consistent small output of gold from southwestern U S and Western Australia (Art 119). For description and for "dry-washers," see Bib (409, 452, 506).

118. CHARACTERISTICS OF PLACER GRAVELS

Size of gravel varies from fine sand to boulders of several tons. Numerous large boulders may prohibit methods like dredging (Art 128, 129); they increase cost of hydraulicking (Art 123) or other methods, as they must be broken by blasting or handled with derricks. Size of gravel affects the amount that can be washed or concentrated with a given volume of water, and hence the rate of return on invested capital. In general, the duty of water (Art 123) is highest for small gravel; duty may be reduced by very fine gravel which packs in sluices (Art 124). Best operating results are obtained with a gravel consisting of mixed sizes; pebbles assist in disintegrating clay, and sand increases carrying capac for stones. The term small gravel has various meanings in placer mining; thus, gravel containing stones to 6 or 8 in diam is small for dredging and large for shoveling-in (Art 121).

Shape of gravel may be round and water-worn, sub-angular, or angular. The duty of water in washing gravel is less with angular stones; also with those predominatingly flat.

Character of fine or cementing material. Some gravels consist entirely of rounded stones with a little sand; others, of stones embedded in a clay matrix. At times the fine material is so solidified by chemical action as to cement the stones together, forming CEMENTED GRAVELS. Loose gravel and sand are easily excavated and washed, but it may be difficult to hold the water in dredge ponds in such material. Values in deposits containing much sand are apt to be "spotty"; extensive sand layers are usually barren. Stiff clay increases cost of excavation; in dredging, it reduces output, increases repairs, and prevents free discharge of buckets. Some clays break up readily in water, others ("sluice robbers") form balls that roll through sluices and pick up gold or amalgam. Cemented gravel increases costs like stiff clay, but to a greater degree; it prohibits dredging if much is present; it can often be broken by blasting prior to washing. A few California drift mines (Art 130) crush cemented gravel in stamp mills.

Depth of gravel affects applicability of different methods of mining; see individual methods, Art 121–130.

Character of bedrock. Gold is retained on soft creviced surfaces, where it would not lodge on hard smooth surfaces. In schists and slates (especially if they strike parallel to a stream course), clay, clayey sandstones and tuffs, gold may work down several feet; it also settles into minute crevices in hard rock; it has been found in solution cavities in limestone to a depth of 50 ft (307). In a new locality, the character of bedrock may be inferred from surrounding geology; evidence from shafts or boreholes is more reliable than that from exposures in stream beds, in which decomposed rock would be eroded. Large boulders of adjacent country rock in the gravel usually indicate hard bedrock. Bedrocks of schist, granite, and some sandstone and porphyry, are usually decomposed to a depth sufficient to allow dredging. In one South American hydraulic mine, a granite bedrock is rotted to a depth of 5 or 10 ft; though barren, this material must be washed to recover the gold lying on it. In limestone and slate formations, bedrock is almost always hard and blocky, often with deep crevices. Creviced bedrock increases costs, as it must be taken up to recover the contained gold. In hydraulicking, hard bedrock increases cost of bedrock ditches. Bedrock of regular contour is desirable for all placer methods (385).

Character of gold. Placer gold ranges in size from large nuggets to minute specks called "colors." The size of colors is indicated by the number making 1¢ worth of gold; some gold in the Snake River, Idaho, runs 2 000 colors to 1¢. Gold usually occurs in flattened and rounded grains; angular pieces and crystallized gold, occasionally found, indicate nearness to the primary deposit. Fine gold is sometimes in thin scales, difficult to save; scaly gold and more rarely other forms may be coated with a film of SiO_2, MnO_2, or limonite, which hinders amalgamation. Fragments of quartz often adhere to gold, or form part of nuggets. Gold is commonly associated with particles of magnetite and ilmenite ("black sand"), garnet (ruby sand), zircon and other heavy rock minerals (307). If present in large amounts, black sand may pack in riffles of sluices (Art 125) and interfere with gold saving.

Lead in form of shot occurs in placer districts where much hunting has been done; it is caught by gold-saving devices and is separated at the time of clean-up; it generally pays to melt such metal and sell it as base bullion.

Placer gold varies in fineness (purity) from 500 to 999 (parts Au per 1 000); it is always alloyed with silver; sometimes copper is present; it is usually purer than that in veins of the same district; its purity increases with the distance transported and with the decreasing size of grains.

Distribution of values may be the determining factor in choosing the mining method. Thus, all the gold in a deposit 100 ft deep may be concentrated on bedrock in a 4 or 5-ft paystreak. A high-cost method like drifting (Art 130) may give more profit than cheaper open-cut work involving the handling of 95 ft of barren material.

Frozen gravels of Alaska, Yukon, and Siberia must often be thawed by artificial means before they can be worked (Art 128, 130, 131). Even if they could be mined like solid rock, thawing would usually still be necessary before sluicing.

Buried timber occurs in many places in the tropics, and in placers where one or more paystreaks have been previously drifted; it is a serious hindrance to and may prohibit dredging. It may be washed out of the bank in hydraulic mines and, if large, cut into pieces for hoisting by derricks. Standing timber increases cost of open-cut work by the cost of clearing, which, per cu yd, varies inversely with the depth of gravel (385).

Swell of gravel upon excavation is usually 20 to 30%, up to 50% for compact clayey gravel. Swell may vary in different parts of same deposit: its determination is important in all sampling work, to avoid errors in estimating values. Several excavations should be made and the resulting gravel measured loose in a wooden box holding 1 or 2 cu ft; the percentage of swell is computed from the volume of excavation.

Values in gravel are expressed in cents or dollars per cu yd, or per sq ft or sq yd of bedrock. Drift mines often report values per ton. Value per sq ft is the most convenient basis where most of the gold is in thin paystreaks. If 2 or more paystreaks overlie each other, total value per sq ft is obtained by adding values per sq ft of the separate paystreaks; this is simpler than estimates per cu yd. Value per sq ft $\times$ 27 $\div$ depth in ft = value per cu yd.

119. PAN, ROCKER, LONG TOM, "DRY" WASHERS

The pan and rocker are used by prospectors in searching for placers, by miners for washing gravel on a small scale, and by engineers for recovering gold from samples obtained in placer examinations.

Pan (gold-pan) is a circular dish with sloping sides; top diam, 10, 12.25, 16, or 16.25 in; depth, 2 to 2 3/8 in; side slopes, 35° to 40°. Fig 804 shows dimensions of the typical American pan, which weighs 1.5 to 2 lb; the Australian pan is larger.

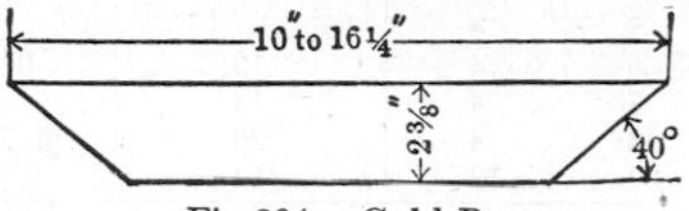

Pan should be light, but stiff enough to stand rough usage; inner surfaces must be smooth, bright, and free from grease and rust. If properly cared for, pans of polished steel meet these requirements, and are cheap. Agateware does not rust, but easily chips.

Fig 804. Gold Pan

Aluminum pans are light, do not rust, but lack stiffness. Pans of copper, or with copper bottom and steel rim, are sometimes used for fine gold which will amalgamate; the bottom is silver-plated and coated with mercury.

Operation of panning. The pan of gravel is placed in water, the gravel thoroughly wetted and stirred by hand to break up lumps of clay, and the larger stones are picked out. The pan, still under water, is then given a shaking or gyratory motion, which brings the light material to the surface and allows heavy particles to settle; at intervals the pan is tilted and the surface material washed off. These processes alternate until nothing but gold and a little heavy sand is left, which is dried and the gold separated by blowing, or by a magnet (for black sand), or mercury is added to collect the gold as amalgam. In experienced hands there is little or no loss of gold (Sec 31).

Field of use. Panning is slow, back-breaking work; as the only tools required are a pick, shovel and pan, it is a favorite poor-man's method and is a common temporary expedient in a new district. The pan is indispensable for testing gravel when prospecting and for cleaning-up rocker and other concentrates in large-scale sampling and mining operations (Sec 25, Art 7).

Duty of labor in panning. An experienced man can pan carefully about 100 pans of aver gravel in 10 hr; cemented gravel or sticky clay reduces this figure; duty increases with the percentage of coarse gravel, which need not be panned. A good panner rarely handles more than 1 cu yd aver gravel per 10 hr.

Number of pans per cu yd of gravel varies with the swell (Art 118) and character of the gravel, and the amount put into the pan.

On preliminary examinations the value of gravel is computed from number of pans washed and weight of gold recovered; a small error in the number of pans per cu yd may make a serious error in the estimate of value. Content of the ordinary pan of 16-in diam (Fig 804), computed as frustum of a cone, is 321 cu in. If swell of the gravel is 20%, 1 pan level full holds 321 ÷ 1.20 = 267 cu in of gravel in place; hence there are approx 6.5 pans (1 728 ÷ 267) in 1 cu ft, or 176 pans in 1 cu yd of gravel in place. If each pan is heaped 1.5 in at the center, there will be only 133 pans per cu yd. The number of pans taken as equivalent to 1 cu yd in different districts is usually between 130 and 150. At Fairbanks, Alaska, most miners compute values on the basis of 189 pans per cu yd; where this is done, 1 heaping load on a No 2 round-point shovel is considered a panful (386). Estimates based on panning are valueless unless made by a skilled panner, who is also competent to judge the effect of local conditions.

Batea is a flat conical pan, of wood or iron; its diam varies locally from 16 to 30 in. It is used in Mexico and South America (and in southwest U S for dry concentration of gravel); variations of it are employed by natives of India, Sumatra, Nigeria, etc (605).

Rocker (cradle). Fig 4, Sec 25, shows one design. Gravel is placed on the screen; water is poured over it from a dipper, and at the same time the machine is given a rocking motion. The water and undersize of the screen pass over the apron to the bottom of the rocker, and are discharged over the tail-piece. When the stones remaining on the screen are washed clean, they are removed and the process is repeated. Most of the gold is retained on the apron; some is caught on the bottom, which may have cross-riffles. Clean-ups are made at intervals, depending on richness and character of gravel.

For saving fine gold, the material on the floor of the rocker must be kept loose and free, and spread evenly; clayey gravel, or that containing much fine black sand, often packs behind riffles and tail-piece and requires frequent clean-ups. Before cleaning-up, the material back of the tail-piece is removed, dumped into the screen and re-rocked; the apron is then lifted out and its contents washed into a pan for final concentration; Chinamen are sometimes expert enough to use the apron itself as a vanning plaque. In sampling work, the rocker is thoroughly cleaned-up after each sample has been run through; the tailing must often be re-rocked to save fine gold. On large-scale sampling in clayey gravel, it pays to break up the clay in a puddling box ahead of the rocker. Wooden or galvanized iron pails are convenient for carrying samples to rockers.

Table 104. Dimensions of Rockers in Different Regions

Example No	Length of bottom, ft	Width of bottom, in	Height of tail-piece, in (a)	Screen			Slope of bottom (b)
				Size, in	Diam of holes, in	Pitch of holes, in	
1	5	14	1.5	18 by 18.25	0.25	1.0	1 : 12
2	5	18	1.5	24 by 21	0.25	0.5	1 : 12
3	6	19(c) to 15(d)	....	....	0.37–0.5	....	1 : 12
4	4	18	0.75	16 by 16	0.5	0.5	1 : 21
5	4	16(c) to 15(d)	1.75	20 by 21	0.5	2.0	1 : 11
6	4	15.5	0.75	23.5 by 15.5	0.37	1.0	....
7	4	14	....	13 by 13	....	....	1 : 8
8	4	20	0.75–1	12 by 24	0.25	0.5	1 : 12
9	12	14	1	36 by 12	0.25–0.63	....	....

(a) Height at center. Tail-piece is called "lower end-piece" in Fig 4, Sec 25. (b) Any desired slope is obtained by blocking up the frame on which the rocker rests. (c) At upper end of rocker. (d) At tail-piece.

Example 1. Rocker shown by Fig 4, Sec 25; recommended by Knox and Haley (385) for sampling, with the comment that most rockers are too high and short and therefore poor gold savers. **Ex. 2.** A Cal rocker, found by author to be heavy and clumsy; tail-piece unnecessarily high. **Ex. 3.** A large rocker used by miners (388). **Ex. 4.** From W. H. Storms (387). **Ex. 5.** A very satisfactory rocker, used by the author in sampling work. **Ex. 6.** From D. Waterman, *Min & Sci Pr*, Feb 20, 1909. **Ex. 7.** Design by S. O. Andros (389). A galvanized iron chute is used instead of an apron; gold saving is entirely by cross-riffles on the bottom. **Ex. 8.** A Cal rocker; screen set to cover only the upper part of apron, which is 18 in long; this forces all undersize of the screen to pass over the apron; reduction in screen area is compensated by the unusual width. **Ex. 9.** A Cal rocker, driven by a 1.5-hp distillate engine through an eccentric with a 1-in. throw. Capac, 5 cu yd or more per 8 hr (617).

Rockers should have tight joints, with corners strengthened by galvanized iron or zinc angles, placed outside; 2 or 3 light tie-bolts (Fig 4, Sec 25) aid in preventing shrinkage or swelling. Rockers are sometimes built to knock-down for easy transport (387). Bottom board should be in 1 piece, free from knots and cracks, and of lumber which will not "rough up" when scraped in cleaning-up. If good lumber is not obtainable, the floor may be covered with canvas fastened by quarter-round strips tacked in corners. Canvas makes an excellent surface for saving fine gold. Rocker bottoms may be covered with blanket, which is taken up at intervals and washed in a tub; blankets are good fine-gold savers, but are undesirable in sampling work because of the delay in cleaning-up. Aprons are of canvas, or rubber sheeting with canvas backing; their covering is not stretched tight; a sag is left at the bottom. High rockers are sometimes built with 2 or 3 aprons inclined in opposite directions and superposed, so that the tailing from one falls onto the upper end of the next; 1 apron is sufficient and more convenient for ordinary work. Some Chinese rockers are apronless; to save the fine gold they require expert operators. Screens are of galvanized or black sheet iron with round holes; 18-gage iron is heavy enough for small gravel; 10-gage better for coarse; Table 104 gives usual sizes and spacing of holes, which are slightly countersunk on under side to prevent clogging. Fig 805 shows excellent screen construction. Screen is picked up and dumped by the rocking handle *H* and small block *B*, both being fastened to the screen box. Very heavy rockers are undesirable; they are hard to transport, and, like those having a large roll, are difficult to rock properly. 1-in lumber, dressed to full 0.75 in, is usually heavy enough. Long rockers, if not too heavy, are more efficient than shorter ones for saving fine gold.

Grade of rocker should be adjusted to character of gravel. Too flat a grade causes packing and loss of fine colors; less grade is required for light alluvium than for that carrying much heavy black sand.

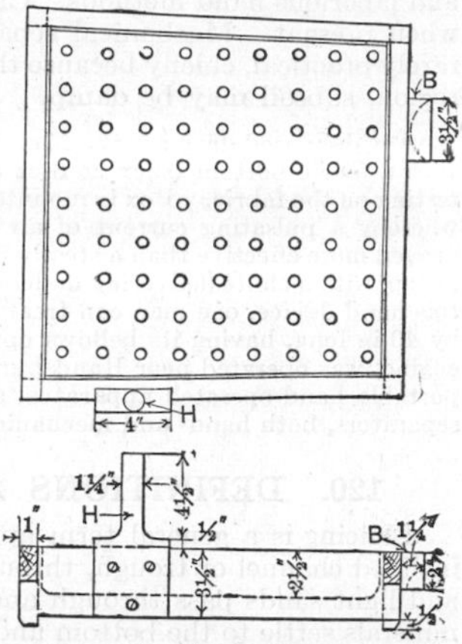

Water required. S. O. Andros found that a rocker required 4 to 6 barrels of water per day, in washing samples of dry gravel; the larger amount for loose sand (389). Water can be reused by digging settling pools connected by a shallow ditch, if the gravel does not contain too much clay.

Duty of labor. A rocker may be operated by 1 man, but 2 are better; they spell each other in rocking and handling gravel and tailing. Purington gives the duty of 2 men rocking steadily as 3 to 5 cu yd of gravel (place measure) per 10 hr (390). Duty on sampling work varies widely with size of samples and arrangements for feeding.

Field of use. For mining, the rocker is a prospector's tool, or is used prior to larger-scale operations; it will work small rich deposits in regions of scant water supply. It is invaluable for washing samples in prospecting and examination.

Fig 805. Screen for Rocker

Long Tom is an open box *L*, Fig 806, having at its lower end screen *S*, punched usually with 0.5-in holes. Dimensions vary; Fig 806 represents early California practice (391).

Running water is carried to the head end by a small flume *F*. Gravel is shoveled into the Tom or into the flume *F*; it is shoveled over in the Tom and large stones forked out; the fines are worked through the screen, and with the water fall into a wide "riffle-box" (sluice, Art 124), set on a flatter

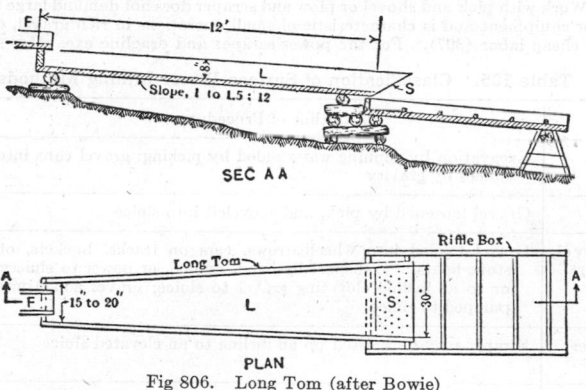

Fig 806. Long Tom (after Bowie)

grade than the Tom. The gold is caught behind the riffles, with or without aid of mercury. Capacity depends largely on the amount of gravel which can be shoveled into it; Wilson says that 2 men (1 shoveling to the Tom and 1 working on it) can wash 6 cu yd of ordinary gravel, or 3 to 4 cu yd of cemented gravel, in 10 hr (388). At times the Tom is operated by 4 men; 2 shoveling-in, 1 forking out stones, and 1 shoveling fine tailing away from the end of riffle box. Toms are now rarely used in the U S; where running water and grade are available, a simple sluice (Art 124) is as effective and requires less labor. A modified Tom 3–4 ft wide by 8-10 ft long, washed by surf, was used in beach mining at Nome (188). For crude washing devices of other countries, see Bib (392).

"Dry-washing" of placer gravel has contributed some gold from small-scale operations in districts where water is scarce, notably Western Australia, Queensland, and the desert areas of Sonora and southwestern U S. Gravels in these districts are largely (not exclusively) of residual origin or have been transported relatively short distances by torrential streams. Hence, the gold is comparatively coarse, and distributed erratically in both depth and area, though bedrock enrichments are not unknown. Requirements for dry-washing are that the gravel shall be thoroughly dry and disintegrated; cemented gravel has been worked, but only at added expense for disintegration, either mechanically or by slow and laborious hand methods. Clay is unworkable by dry-washing, and causes loss of gold when present. Mechanical separators, used in conjunction with power excavators, are rarely practical, chiefly because the gravel is dug faster than it can be dried; even in an arid region, subsoil may be damp.

A widely used device is the Mexican dry washer (444). It is a shallow box, about 18 by 36 in, with a fabric bottom (such as 8-oz canvas) supported on wire screen, and having 5–8 cross-riffles resting on the fabric. Box is mounted at slope of 15°–25° and forms the stationary top of a bellows, whereby a pulsating current of air is forced upward through the fabric. Pulsating current has proved more effective than a steady flow, as from a fan. A screen with 3/8–1/2-in holes is mounted at top, with a chute delivering undersize to upper end of separator, while oversize falls outside. With this hand device, one man can treat 0.5–1 cu yd per day. A similar machine, with box 11 in wide by 40 in long, having its bellows operated through pulley and crankshaft from a 0.75-hp gasolene engine, was operated near Randsburg, Cal, in 1932 (16) at capac of 0.8 cu yd per hr. For similar portable hand-operated apparatus, as used in W Australia, see Bib (452). For other varieties of separators, both hand- and mechanically operated, see Bib (444, 445, 446).

120. DEFINITIONS AND CLASSIFICATION OF METHODS

Sluicing is a general term applied to many forms of placer mining. A sluice is an inclined channel or trough, through which gravel is carried by a stream of water. Stones and light sands pass through and run to waste at the lower end; gold and other heavy minerals settle to the bottom and are caught in riffles. A riffle is a groove or interstice, or a cleat or block so placed as to produce the same effect, in the bottom of a sluice. Art 124, 125 give data on sluices and riffles. Wooden sluices (Fig 825) are sometimes called box-sluices; inclined ditches, in gravel or bedrock, are ground-sluices. Riffles in ground-sluices are formed by the natural irregularities of their bottoms.

Table 105 outlines the commoner combinations of excavating and transporting agencies used in open cuts for digging gravel and getting it into sluices. (For underground methods, see Art 130.) Of the methods outlined, dredging and hydraulicking are normally low-cost operations, suitable for large-scale mining of low-grade gravels and requiring large capital outlay. The others (excepting at times ground-sluicing) have comparatively high operating costs and require richer gravels to yield a profit. Work with pick and shovel or plow and scraper does not demand large initial expenditure for plant or equipment and is characteristic of small operations in rich gravel, or of mining in regions of very cheap labor (397). For the power scraper and dragline excavator see Art 122.

Table 105. Classification of Surface Placer Mining Methods

Method	Outline of Procedure	See Art
Ground-sluicing	Excavation by running water aided by picking; gravel runs into sluices by gravity	121
Shoveling-in	Gravel loosened by pick, and shoveled into sluice	121
Pick and shovel, with transport	Gravel loaded into wheelbarrows, cars on tracks, buckets, or stone-boats. Transport by hand, animal, or power to sluices, or to an incline elevating gravel to sluice; gravel sometimes pumped to sluice	121
Plow and scraper Power scraper	Scraper may be hoisted up an incline to an elevated sluice	122
Dragline	Dragline excavator delivers gravel to a sluice, or more elaborate washing plant mounted on skids, wheels or rollers, to keep it within reach of excavator	122
Hydraulicking	Water discharged under press from nozzles breaks gravel from bank and transports it to ground sluice; added water may be used to aid transport	123
Dredging	Mechanical excavator (usually chain-bucket type) delivers to screen, sluices, jigs, etc, all mounted on a boat	127 128
Dragline dredging	Mechanical excavator, usually a dragline, stands on shore of pond and delivers gravel to washer mounted on a boat	129

Note. Work with elevators is not included (see Art 126). For various forms of "River Mining," such as wing-damming, fluming, etc, see 9th Ann Rep, Cal State Mineralogist, 1889, p 263. For a more detailed classification, see Bib (181).

121. GROUND-SLUICING, SHOVELING-IN, HORSE-SCRAPING INTO SLUICES

Ground-sluicing. Fig 807 shows typical ground-sluicing in shallow creek gravels, where bedrock grade is steep enough to allow it. Sluice M is set at the lower end of the ground to be worked and a shallow trench T is dug, preferably on one side of the deposit. T is deepened to bedrock by turning a stream of water into it, and if necessary picking up the bottom, the material being washed through the sluice. On reaching bedrock the trench is widened by picking and caving its banks into the stream. Small plank or earth dams D, erected where necessary, throw the stream against the bank to aid in undercutting it and so minimizing labor; their skilful use forces a stream to do considerable work without supervision during a night shift. Coarse gold remains on bedrock, finer gold is caught by the sluice riffles. As the bank recedes, exposed bedrock is cleaned with shovels, hoes, hand scrapers, brushes, and wires for digging into crevices; profits may depend upon thoroughness of cleaning, since gold tends to remain on bedrock (in some cases, no other means of recovery is provided). The concentrates may be cleaned up in the same or in a special sluice (Art 125). Large stones are forked out and piled on cleaned bedrock, as at B.

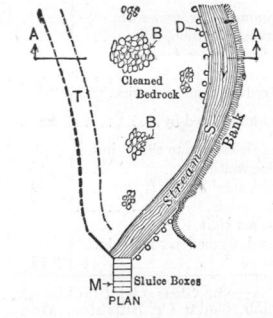

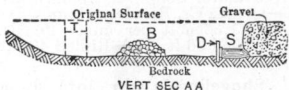

Fig 807. Ground-sluicing (diagrammatic)

Ground-sluicing has many variations. In Alaska, it is often used for cheaply stripping creek gravels covered by muck (Art 118). Tundra and brush are grubbed and burned; subsequent sluicing may be done as in Fig 807, or the water may be led through several channels into which intervening ridges eventually cave; spring floods are thus used to advantage. Also, small streams of water may be caused to trickle down the face of the bank, cutting vertical channels; the ground between caves or is blasted or pried off. Thus, in 1911, Granville Mining Co, Dominion Creek, Yukon, stripped frozen muck 18 ft thick, the bank receding 4–7 in per day; est'd cost, with high wages, 10¢ per cu yd of muck (393). Such work generally stops on reaching gravel. Ground-sluicing uses water as an excavating agent where pressure water for hydraulicking is not available.

Requirements for ground-sluicing: (*a*) Shallow gravel, rarely more than 6 to 8 ft deep. (*b*) Sufficient grade for the available water to carry the loosened soil. Data covering different conditions are lacking. Granville Co (see above) sluiced muck on grades of 17 to 25 ft per mile; grades for gravel are much steeper. (*c*) Plentiful water. Here again data are lacking. Longridge (394) states that it takes about 6 times as much water to move material in a ground-sluice as to do the same work in a box-sluice. Scanty water supply may sometimes be supplemented by pumping back from settling pools at end of sluice. (*d*) Dumproom for tailings at lower end of sluice may be provided by natural grade of bedrock or surface; drag-scrapers may move tailings from end of sluice.

Duty of water and labor. Mead estimates that 2 men can move 20–30 cu yd max of gravel per day by ground-sluicing (395). A native laborer in Swaziland handles up to 10 cu yd of light tin gravel per shift, where a good stream of water is available (396, 397). In Colombia, in gravel 5–15 ft deep, a stream of 135 miner's in (Art 120) moved only 50 cu yd per day (385). Purington gives following data on stripping muck (50–75% ice) in Alaska. On Anvil Cr, Nome, 400 miner's in of water; bank, 20 ft high; grade, 4.5 in to 12 ft; duty of water, 10 cu yd per in per 24 hr. Elsewhere on Anvil Cr, a 4.5-ft bank of muck was stripped with 100 in of water; grade, 3 in to 12 ft; duty of water, 3 cu yd per in per 24 hr. On Crooked Cr, near Council, 55 in of water; bank, 4 ft high; grade, 4.5 in to 12 ft; duty of water, 3.45 cu yd per in per 24 hr (390).

Table 106 gives data collected by E. D. Gardner and C. H. Johnson (16) at ground-sluicing operations in western U S in summer of 1932; at some, a small part of available water was applied through nozzles; greater effectiveness of booming (described below), as compared with continuous sluicing, is indicated. Besides labor cost, expense for supplies was estimated at 2–4¢ per cu yd.

Booming ("hushing") is applicable where the water supply is inadequate for steady work. Water is impounded above the diggings; and by releasing it at intervals it washes gravel through the ground-sluices. Booming is also used for stripping. Dams for booming usually have gates opening automatically when the reservoir is full. A vert or hinged gate is common, controlled by a lever carrying an open box at outer end. The reservoir when full overflows into the box; the added wt lifts the gate, and the box then empties itself. Gates must be so arranged that the dam will not be injured by the rushing water. Booming strips light overburden cheaply. In 1904, on American Cr, Alaska, an area 900 ft long by 25 ft wide was stripped of muck and gravel 5 ft thick in 3 weeks; costs, including dam and gate, did not exceed 7¢ per cu yd (394). See also (390, 391). According to Wimmler (188) in 1927, ground-sluicing and booming in Alaska cost 15–35¢ per cu yd; cost of equipment, $350–$1 500 (excl ditches), of which $250–$500 represented cost of dam with automatic gate. See also Table 106.

Table 106.   Examples of Ground-sluicing in 1932 (16)

	A	B	C	D	E	F	G	H	I	J
Depth of gravel, ft	5	6	15	8	18	20	10	15	22	20
Character	tight	med	easy	med	med	med	med	med	med	med
Boulders over 6-in, %	20	10	15	15	10	10	15	10	35	25
Bedrock	soft clay	soft clay	not reached	rough porph	not reached	not reached	soft l'stone	rough porph	soft	not reached
Aver water, miner's in (a)	70	60	80	60	100	70	70	10	300	500
Booming, times per day						4	2	6	24	14
Booming water, miner's in (a)						300	650	1 600	7 500	4 000
Booming duration, min						27	30	1.5	2.5	15
Auxiliary water, head, ft		6		27	15		60		22	
Nozzle diam, in		2		2	2		1		?	
Moved by hand or derrick, %	40	15	15	30	20	10	20	10	30	0
Boulders moved by	hand	hand	steam der'k	wheel barrow	drag-line	hand	hand	hand	hand der'k	
Max size stones to sluice, in	6	4	6	3	2	6	3	6	9	15
Sluice width, in	18	18	13	24	30	18	22	36	38	48
Sluice, total length, ft (b)	20	24	84	16	504(c)	600	36	36	192(d)	1 008(e)
Sluice grade, %	10	2.1	2.8	8.3	2.1	4.2	8.3	6.2	6.2	5
Men per shift	1	2	3	1	2	4	2	1	1	9
Gravel washed per man-shift, cu yd	2.75	12	9	3	18	4	18	17	32	7

A—On Clear Cr, Blackhawk, Colo.   B—Mouth of Kamloops Cr, Granite, Colo.   C—Calif Gulch, Cedar Cr, Superior, Mont.   D—On Clear Cr, Blackhawk, Colo.   E—Mouth of Kamloops Cr, Granite, Colo.   F—Willow Cr, Therma, N M.   G—Calif Gulch, Cedar Cr, Laurin, Mont. H—Quartz Cr, Rivulet, Mont.   I—Sauerkraut Cr, Lincoln, Mont.   J—Swauk Cr, Liberty, Wash.   (a) 1.5 cu ft per min.   (b) Riffled throughout, unless otherwise noted.   (c) Riffled 250 ft. (d) Riffled 96 ft.   (e) Riffled 400 ft.

Shoveling-in (i e, into sluices) has its simplest form in shallow creek gravels, where bedrock grade is steeper than is required for sluices (Fig 808).   Sluice S is on bedrock, with the lower end raised and flattened to give headroom for dump D.   Added dump-room is obtained as needed by extending lower end of sluice.

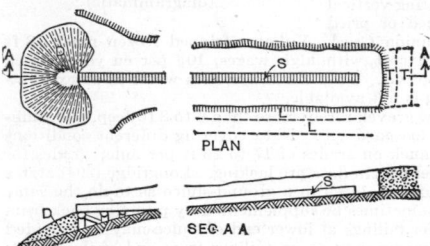

PLAN

SEC A A

Fig 808.   Simple Shoveling-in

Gravel is excavated in transverse cuts T, or more often in longitudinal cuts L.   Only the finer material goes through the sluice; large stones are piled on cleaned bedrock. Transverse cuts deliver all gravel at the head of the sluice, but require use of barrows for lateral transport in all but narrow pits; with longitudinal cuts the sluice must be shifted when the bank has receded about 12 ft from it, otherwise, shoveling cost becomes excessive.

In wide deposits, shifting may sometimes be avoided by feeding the main sluice from narrower and steeper radiating or lateral sluices.

Water is conducted to head of sluice in flumes, pipes, or canvas hose.   On Seward Peninsula, Alaska, "flume hose" is commonly 12 to 14 in diam, of 12 or 14-oz duck, sewed with 3 seams.   It is light and flexible, but begins to rot after about 4-mo service (398).   If a stream flows in the creek bed, water is dammed above the diggings.

Ideal conditions as in Fig 808 are rare.   The required grade must often be created artificially, by excavating under the sluice, or by mounting it on trestles (Fig 823).   The elevated sluice is erected cheaply and quickly; it is often the only means of obtaining dumproom; bedrock trenches facilitate shoveling, but are too costly if deep or in hard rock.   In ALASKA, wherever feasible, muck and top gravels are first removed by ground-sluicing; the underlying pay, rarely more than 5 or 6 ft thick, is then worked by shoveling-in.   Barren gravel often overlies the pay; where grades do not allow this to be ground-sluiced it is removed with barrows or scrapers; only the pay gravel is sluiced.

Sluices, riffles, grades, water, clean-ups (see Art 124, 125).

Drainage of pits.   Ideal condition is a self-draining pit (Fig 808).   Where grades are flat, dams are generally necessary, both above and below the area worked; they are built cheaply, of logs, earth, or brush (see Sec 43, Art 16).

Seepage is preferably removed by bedrock drains, on grades as flat as 1.5 in per 100 ft; they are started on the surface at the proper distance downstream to reach bedrock at the lower end of the pit and then continue on bedrock grade. Purington (390) gives following data on Alaskan practice, which is fairly typical. Drains are usually 2 ft sq, lagged with horiz poles held at 4-ft intervals by posts and caps. After the first cut in the pit is taken, the drain is covered with logs and moss laid on the caps. For small operations, 10 by 12-in box-drains of 1-in plank are adequate. A perforated standpipe should be placed over the drain at the lower end of the pit; drains may require flushing to keep them open. In the Fairbanks District an open unlagged drain, 3 ft deep by 3.5 ft wide, took 2 men 6 weeks to excavate. Lagged drains in hard ground may be costly. Seepage may be pumped out. The cheap homemade China pump, operated by an overshot waterwheel, can be used only when there is more water than is required for sluicing. Pumping costs more than drains.

Table 107. Duty of Labor Shoveling into Sluices in Alaska. Purington (390)

Location	Depth of gravel, ft	Height of lift, ft	Cu yd per man per 10 hr
Klondike (a)...........	2	9	3.5
Birch Cr (b)..........	4.41	(c)	5.0
American Cr..........	......	......	2.75 (d)
Fairbanks (e).........	3.0	......	7.5
Nome (f).............	5 to 7	......	5.76
Solomon River (g).....	3.0	......	3.75
Council Dist (h)......	3.5	......	6.63

(a) 2 men; platform used. (b) Aver of 12 operations. (c) Height of lift not over 6 ft. (d) Large boulders interfered with work. At one point, a 5-ft bank was shoveled at rate of 4 cu yd per man-shift. (e) Aver of 3 operations; lifts less than 5 ft; some bedrock taken up. (f) Aver figures; Pioneer Co, on Anvil Creek, 3-ft bank, obtained a duty of 9 cu yd. (g) High lift and irregular bedrock. (h) Aver figures, including one case where, on a limestone bedrock, with a double lift, duty was 3.5 cu yd; another where, with 8-hr shifts, 3-ft bank and 5-ft lift, duty was 12 cu yd.

Duty of labor in shoveling-in varies with height of bank and character of gravel and bedrock (Table 107). Shovelers can throw to heights of 6 to 8 ft (9 ft limit); for greater heights platforms must be built and the gravel re-shoveled from them. During boom years in central Alaska, 7–8 cu yd per shift was considered aver man's work. The time required for careful cleaning of a creviced bedrock materially reduces the shoveler's aver output. Table 108, from Gardner and Johnson (16), gives data on 6 shoveling-in operations in western U S active in summer of 1932.

Limitations and costs. Shoveling-in is adapted to shallow gravels. It is simple, does not involve large expenditure for plant and can be carried on in remote districts where cost of installing mechanical excavators would be prohibitive. In ALASKA, where labor and supply costs are high, the cost of plant, including dams, drain ditches, water ditch, and a string of 10 sluice boxes (Art 124), is from $500 to $2 000 (390). The method has the great advantage of allowing careful cleaning of bedrock. Operating costs vary widely with wages and duty of labor; only rich gravels can be worked at a profit. Wimmler (188) in 1927 quoted following cases from Alaska where overburden was removed by booming or ground-sluicing, and pay gravel worked by shoveling-in; all costs are per cu yd: (1) Hot Springs dist; cut 50 by 500 ft; frozen muck and some gravel boomed to depth of 25 ft for 7¢; shoveling-in of 2.5 ft of gravel and bedrock, $2.30; combined cost, 30¢. (2) Little Minook Cr, Rampart dist; cut 12 by 600 ft; 18 ft of muck and gravel boomed for 18¢; shoveling-in 2 ft of gravel and bedrock, containing 50% boulders, $2.20; combined cost, 38¢; this was a fourth cut and cost less than first. (3) Little Minook Cr; a first cut 12 by 1 000 ft boomed 7.5 ft deep for 22¢; shoveling-in 2 ft of gravel with 60% boulders, $2.80; combined cost, 77¢. (4) Greenstone Cr, Ruby dist; pit 60 by 200 ft; sod stripped by hand; muck and gravel ground-sluiced to 6-ft depth for 38¢; shoveling-in 2 ft of gravel, $1.65; combined cost, 70¢ (5) Greenstone Cr; bench deposit with favorable grade; ground-sluiced 10 ft of muck and gravel for 26¢; shoveling-in 1 ft of gravel for $2.56; combined cost, 47¢, incl deprec. Elsewhere, combined costs are 25¢–$1 per cu yd.

Table 108. Examples of Shoveling into Boxes, in 1932 (16)

	A	B	C	D	E	F
Depth worked, ft....	2	6	6	2.5	4.5	6
Character..........	loose	tight	tight	tight	loose	med
Boulders over 6-in, %	0	30	20	50	10	5
Bedrock............	none	clay	even	rough	none	even
Sluice, width, in......	8	8	12	12	10	8
" total length, ft	24	96	64	36	36	60
" riffled, ft......	12	8	64	12	12	28
" grade, in per ft	1	1	7/16	1/2	?	0.6
Men per shift........	2	4	4	2	2	2
Cu yd per man-shift..	10–15	6.25	5	1	3.25	4.75
Rehandled, %.......	5	10	0	50	0	0

A—On Feather River, Oroville, Cal. B—Mary Ann Cr, Oroville, Wash. C—Peshastin Cr, Blewett, Wash. D—Peshastin Cr, Blewett, Wash. E—No Clear Cr, Blackhawk, Colo. F—Bear Cr, Bearmouth, Mont.

Cars and barrows for loading sluices. Fig 809 shows radiating tracks for small mine cars (Sec 11). To use this method the head of sluice must be at or near the level of bedrock, which must have a fairly regular contour. Barrows may be used similarly and on rougher bedrock by laying plank runways.

Inclined barrow runways, for loading an elevated sluice, are usually at right-angles to the sluice, for working by longitudinal cuts (L, Fig 808). For cost of barrow and car work, see Sec 3, 5. An objection to them is that they dump large amounts at one time; this makes the flow in the sluice uneven, causes clogs and is not conducive to good gold saving. If the sluice can be loaded at a single point (Fig 809), a dump or "mud-box" (Fig 828) decreases these troubles and allows forking out of large stones.

Scraping into sluices, with drag or wheel scrapers, is possible in small gravel on soft rock; Sec 3 gives details and cost of scraping. Purington gives following data for Alaska (390): A 2-horse wheel scraper, working in small gravel on soft schist bedrock, handles 30–40 cu yd per 10 hr at about one-third the cost of shoveling-in; 1 plow loosens for 4 scrapers. Scrapers dump through a hatchway in a platform over head of sluice (Sec 3). Examples from western U S (18) in 1932. (1) Horseshoe Bend on Green River, below Vernal, Utah. Loose gravel 4 ft deep, no boulders over 8-in and no clay; gold very fine, black sand abundant. Man and 2 boys, with team of burros and 3.8-cu ft slip scraper handled 6.5 cu yd per day, loosening by hand and scraping 25 ft to hopper and screen at top of sluice 20 ft long; water pumped by 1.5-hp gasolene motor from nearby river. Est working cost, $1 per cu yd. (2) Tailings from Blue Channel drift mine Folsom, Cal; originally partially cemented, but disintegrated by several years' weathering; some clay but no coarse boulders; gold somewhat rusty. Tractor with 7-cu ft scraper dragged material 300 ft to screen and hopper; bucket elevator raised it 26 ft to head of 12-in sluice 110 ft long. Water pumped

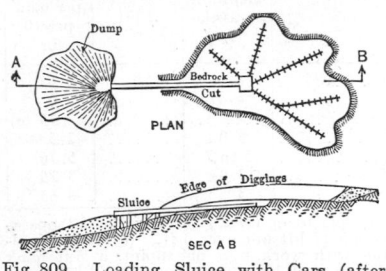

Fig 809. Loading Sluice with Cars (after Young)

from old shaft, 20-ft lift. Black-sand concentrates amalgamated in small concrete mixer; final recovery in a short sluice. Two men handled 20 cu yd per shift; total gasolene for tractor, elevator, pump, and amalgamator, 25 gal per shift; est total cost (labor @ 40¢ per hr), 62¢ per cu yd.

122. DERRICKS, CABLEWAYS, INCLINES, MECHANICAL EXCAVATORS

Except for certain applications of dragline excavator, these devices are now seldom used. They have been successful mechanically, but, as operating costs are high compared to dredging (Art 128), gravel must be richer to yield a profit. Many installations have failed financially, through failure to recognize this fact and ignorance of limitations of different types of equipment.

Derricks may be used in shallow open cuts in the following ways· (a) gravel is shoveled into barrows, wheeled to a fixed point and dumped into the derrick skip or bucket; (b) gravel is shoveled into stone skips, or buckets mounted on small trucks running on rails and pushed by hand to within reach of the derrick boom; (c) gravel is shoveled into buckets which are slid along skids by the derrick tackle. Plan (a) requires greatest amount of lateral handling; miners spend much time in wheeling and dumping instead of picking and shoveling. Plan (c) is the most efficient in this respect. Derricking is adaptable to shallow beds, where the gravel must be elevated to sluices and where excavation and cleaning of bedrock are necessarily done by hand.

Cableways (Sec 26) with self-dumping carriers (Art 130) are sometimes substituted for derricks. Operating cost is higher than for the derrick when used as above, because cableways involve tramming and dumping at a point under the cable. The automatic dumping carrier is of little advantage, since a man on the dump box is always necessary. For a large installation in Montana, see (409). Alaska. Data from N. L. Wimmler (188) in 1927. Method of shoveling gravel into barrows, wheeling to bucket, hoisting latter up an inclined cableway, and dumping it automatically into sluice, was still employed in 1924 at a few small mines in the interior district, where necessary sluice grades and dumproom were not otherwise obtainable. Such pits rarely exceeded 150 ft diam. Shoveler spent 1/4–1/3 of his time wheeling to central point, where bucket, holding 2–5 barrow loads, rested in a pit with its top level with runways. Shoveling duty of 7–9 cu yd per day was good work. Steam hoists were 5–15 hp. Examples: (a) On Ophir Cr, Innoko dist; overburden (18 ft of frozen muck and 4 ft barren gravel) was ground-sluiced for 16¢ per cu yd; 5 ft of gravel and bedrock was mined as above for $1.75 per cu yd; combined cost for 27-ft depth, 42¢ per cu yd. (b) On Chatham Cr, Fairbanks dist; 10 ft of overburden was ground-sluiced for 16¢, and 4 ft of gravel and bedrock mined as above for $1.25 per yd; combined cost for 14-ft depth, 48¢ per cu yd.

Inclines were sometimes used in Alaska for hoisting from a pit to head of an elevated sluice. From foot of incline, a system of radiating tracks was laid on floor of fairly level pit, over which cars loaded at edges of pit were trammed by hand; hoists were operated by steam. Fig 811 shows a similar method of hoisting in cars loaded by scraper.

Power scrapers (Sec 3, Art 6; see also Art 91, and Sec 27) are adapted for mining and elevating gravel from shallow placers; unsuited to hard or blocky bedrock; a soft, even bedrock may sometimes be cleaned with scrapers, but final hand cleaning is usually necessary. Power scrapers are also advantageous for removing tailings from ends of sluices. Large heavy scrapers are generally used; small drag or wheel scrapers are too light and too difficult to hold while loading when drawn by power. EXAMPLES follow.

Auburn, Calif. Gardner and Johnson (18) describe use in 1932 of a power scraper at Mammoth Bar. As in Fig 810, a 1 3/8-in track cable was stretched from top of a 64-ft mast (a spruce tree 24-in diam at bottom and guyed with 7/8-in ropes) to a bridle rope stretched across the river 700 ft downstream. The loaded 1-cu yd Page bucket was hauled at 300 ft per min by hoist with 95-hp gasolene engine and 1.25-in rope, returning empty by gravity at 1 200 ft per min. A grizzly at top of hopper was about 20 ft above ground. Most digging was under water; upon completing removal of the expected 100 000 cu yd, it was intended to pump out the pit and recover any missed gravel, while also cleaning bedrock by hand.

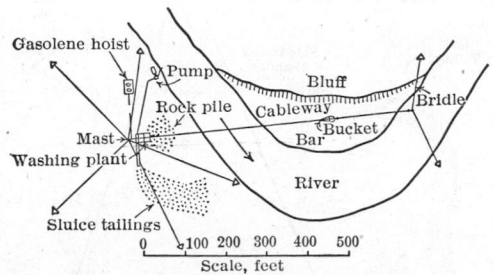

Fig 810. Placer Mining with Power Scraper, Auburn, Calif

Sierra Leone Goldfields, Ltd (448) was operating in 1932 in a narrow valley of the Pampana River, West Africa, at a point 12 miles from nearest motor road. Topsoil nearly barren; richness of gravel increased with depth, but main pay was in upper 2 ft of bedrock under gravel which required blasting; total depth excavated, 10–25 ft. Gold varied from small nuggets to almost dust. Sauerman slack-line cableway with 1-cu yd bucket (scraper), centered on one side of channel, excavated semicircular area with 600-ft radius, discharging into hopper about 50 ft above ground level; operation repeated after moving equipment 1 200 ft upstream. Sluice, of steel pans 12 ft long, 4 ft wide, 2 ft high, bolted together, was 200 ft long; riffles of steel rail rested on coarse wire screen. Natives raked the gravel down sluice; water flumed from intake 2 miles upstream. Heavy sands were collected every 10–15 days, rewashed on 12-in sluice, 15 ft long, and finally panned. Crew, about 50 natives.

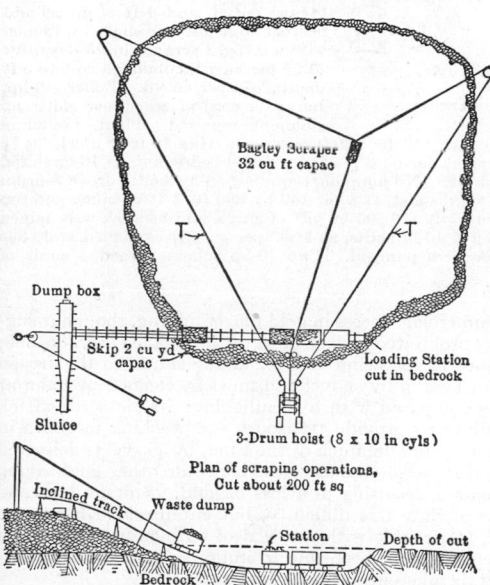

Fig 811. Bagley Scraper with Incline and Auxiliary Hoist

Alaska. Steam-driven scrapers were widely used in the interior districts, but by 1924, according to Wimmler (188), few remained in operation, due to diminishing aver value of deposits for which they were suitable. Conditions favorable for scrapers: (a) large areas of shallow gravel; (b) freedom from large boulders; (c) soft and relatively smooth bedrock, not too deeply fissured; (d) unfrozen gravel; (e) pit free from water, by natural drainage, bedrock ditches, or pumping; (f) requisite sluice grade and dumproom not otherwise obtainable. Scrapers were usually Bagley (bottomless) or slip.

Bagley scraper, at larger mines, dragged gravel to a central point, discharging into a 2.5–4-cu yd car at depressed loading station; car then hauled up incline and dumped automatically into head of sluice. Scrapers 3.5–5 ft wide, 1.25–2.5 cu yd capac, and weighing 3 100–4 125 lb, proved more suitable than larger ones. They were operated by 3-drum hoists driven by 2-cyl, 8 by 10-in to 10 by 12–in steam engines; ample power was essential for economical work. Under good conditions, scraper made 30–50 trips per hr; usual range 15–40 cu yd per hr into sluice. Fig 811 shows typical arrangement of larger mines in Fairbanks dist. Total depth worked, 15–35 ft, of which, pay gravel was 6–8 ft, and bedrock, 2–4 ft. Area of pits, 80 000–120 000 sq ft.

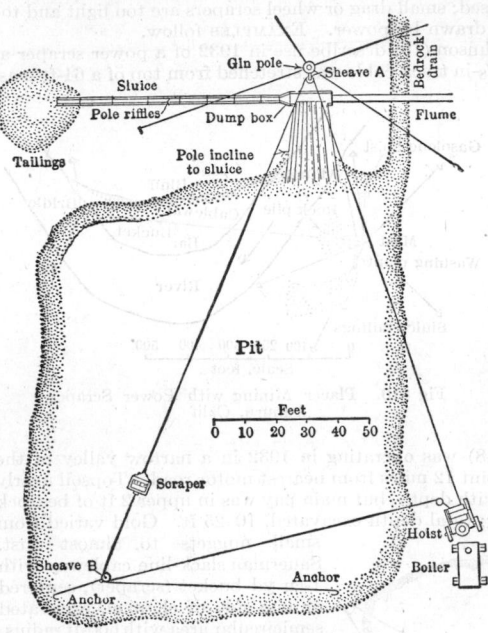

Fig 812.   Slip Scraper dragged up Incline

Crew on each of 2 10-hr shifts, 6–8 men. Power cost with 80–150-hp wood-fired boilers, 4.8¢ per hp-hr; with 180-hp coal-fired boiler, 2.4¢ per hp-hr. Cost of scraping and sluicing only, 45–90¢ per cu yd; total cost (incl stripping) to 15–35 ft depth, 40–60¢ per yd. Equipment investment, $15 000–$25 000.

Slip scraper is restricted to shallow deposits; other conditions as above. Usual capac, 0.75 and 1 cu yd, but load arriving at sluice is often only 0.5–0.75 of capac. In typical work (Fig 812) scraper requires 2 men at loading point, but discharges into sluice automatically at top of inclined runway. On completing a cut the width of scraper (4–4.5 ft) and about 1 ft deep, tail sheave B is shifted along the anchor cable, which is fastened to a row of deadmen across far end of pit; max length of pit, about 300 ft; width usually about half the length. With 150–300-ft haul, scraper can make 10–30 trips per hr; usual range, 50–125 cu yd delivered to sluice per 10-hr shift. At a 65 000-sq ft pit in INNOKO dist, 4 ft of overburden was ground-sluiced for 14¢ per cu yd, and 4 ft of gravel and bedrock were put into sluice by 13 men with a 0.75-yd scraper in 95 days, for $1.55 per cu yd; combined cost to 8 ft depth, 87¢ per cu yd. Boiler, 40-hp, burned a cord of wood per shift; no pumping required. Plant, excluding ditch, cost $6 500. At another pit in same dist, 150 by 230 ft, after removing 10 ft of muck for 7¢ per yd, crew of 6 men, with 0.75-yd scraper, moved 6 ft of gravel and bedrock in 74 10-hr shifts, at $1.35 per cu yd; combined cost, 54¢ per yd. No pumping required; 50-hp boiler drove 3-drum hoist; equipment cost $7 000. In HOT SPRINGS dist, at a pit 140 by 290 ft, 4 ft of muck and top gravel were ground-sluiced for 15¢ per yd; 7 ft (10 500 cu yd) of gravel and bedrock were mined and sluiced by 7 men and 1-yd scraper in 110 10-hr shifts, at $1.32 per cu yd; combined cost, 89¢ per cu yd. About 100 miner's in of water were pumped. Two 40-hp boilers burned 4 cords of wood per shift.

Power shovel has rarely been a commercial success in gold placer mining, though it suggests itself for use when hydraulicking is prohibited by lack of water and grade (165, 385, 390, 401, 402). Failure due to one or more of following causes: (a) attempts to dig frozen gravel; (b) hard bedrock which can not be dug by shovel and must be cleaned by hand at large expense; (c) lack of mobility, as compared with hydraulicking; a serious drawback which leads to costly delays; (d) failure to provide transport and washing facilities in proportion to its digging capac; it is therefore idle much of the time; (e) gravel is delivered from dipper or cars intermittently and in large amounts; the sluice or other gold-saving device is first over- and then underloaded, resulting in a loss of gold. Storage bins and automatic feeders ahead of the sluice obviate this difficulty, but entail added headroom and greater first and operating costs; (f) trouble with disposal of tailings from sluices or washing plants. Some of these difficulties have been due to improper management, but item (c), probably the most important, is inherent in the power shovel.

Shovel mining of placer tin in Nigeria. Data from W. E. Sinclair (449) in 1933. Cassiterite is commonly concentrated in a 3 to 4-ft bed of "wash," a hard, cemented gravel with streaks of tough clay, lying on bedrock of decomposed granite, and covered with up to 100 ft of tenacious clay, hard and tough when dry, sticky and treacherous when wet. These and other conditions (bedrock usually lower than natural drainage level, scarcity of water during 6 mos and lack of storage facilities, generally level topography) favor use of power shovels, with gravel pumps for lifting the tin-bearing material out of pits.

One successful operation employed a 300-ton, full-revolving steam shovel, with 6-yd dipper and 95-ft jib for stripping a through cut 60 ft wide at bottom, followed by a caterpillar-mounted steam shovel with 7/8-yd dipper; the latter took up only half the width of "wash" exposed, leaving other half as a bench for the return trip of stripping shovel. Thereafter, lateral stripping was dumped on the area previously occupied by "wash"; 17 cu yd of overburden had to be moved to expose 1 cu yd of wash. The small shovel loaded into 1-cu yd, side-dump cars, hauled by gasolene loco to end of cut, and dumped into a sluice leading to gravel-pump sump. An 8-in centrif gravel-pump, driven by 90-hp steam engine, raised the mixture 65 ft to sluice boxes at top of bank (Art 126). STRIPPING at 2 500 cu yd per day (not full capac) cost in pence per cu yd: fuel (coal @ £3 per ton, del'd), 2.49; white wages, 1.19; native, 0.75; oil and stores, 1.15; repairs and spares, 0.44; overhead, 0.38; total, 6.4d. MINING of "wash," pence per cu yd. breaking, loading and hauling (800 ft), 6.80; labor at gravel pump, 1.32; labor at sluice boxes, 1.90; white supervision, 5.14; coal, 5.72; oil, stores, and repairs, 2.36; management and misc, 1.99; total, 25.23d.

Inca Placers, Lumberton, Fort Steele Div, B C. H. Sargent (399) in 1938 described operations by Consol Min & Smelting Co, Palmer Bar Cr. The deposit of unsorted gravel, 400 ft wide and 1/2 mile long, parallel with stream and 5–30 ft above its level, is unusual in that gold (fairly coarse) is confined to upper 3–6 ft; of several drill holes to bedrock, the deepest showed 200 ft of underlying barren gravel. Boulders large and numerous, but barren overburden is absent. Water from a dam 0.5 mile upstream is flumed along upper edge of deposit.

Methods used: (a) Hand shoveling into sluices running downhill from the flume towards the creek; limited to small areas, and generally unprofitable, due to boulders. (b) Digging by Diesel-power shovel, discharging on belt-conveyer 70 ft long (gasolene-driven) which elevates gravel to upper end of a substantial line of sluice boxes; conveyer is mounted to permit shifting along the sluice. (c) Use of 2 auto-trucks to carry gravel from power shovel to foot of conveyer. Trucks are loaded from a movable pocket covered by grizzly with 6-in spacing; oversized boulders stacked by same shovel, but largest are not moved from the pit.

Dragline excavator (Art 97 and Sec 3) has recently attained considerable prominence in placer mining, both in deposits of dry gravel and in those of which part or nearly all is excavated from under water. The dragline has many of the drawbacks of the power shovel and can not dig as hard material, handle boulders so readily, nor work successfully on an irregular rock surface. But it is more mobile and has these distinct advantages: (a) it has a wider digging radius, hence less frequent moves are necessary; (b) it stands on the surface and dumps at a considerable elevation above its track; thus grade for sluices may be obtained without a separate elevating device, under conditions impossible for a power shovel standing on bedrock; (c) the operations of loading, tramming and elevating cars, common to many power-shovel operations, are rarely necessary; the long boom of the excavator enables it to do its own transporting and elevating. Dragline excavators can also mine small yardages of loose gravel which would not warrant installation of a dredge. Following examples illustrate applications of the dragline for excavating, transporting, and elevating gravel to movable sluices or washers. For use of dragline with floating washing plants (Dragline Dredging) see Art 129.

Atlantic City, Wyo. Data from C. L. Ross and E. D. Gardner (118) in 1935, on drag-line excavator and track-mounted washer operating in 1933–1934 along Rock Cr. Elev, 7 600 ft. Channel 100–250 ft (aver, 200 ft) wide. Well rounded and easy digging gravel, 9–12 ft (aver 10 ft) deep, containing few boulders; 65% of material washed was below 3/4-in in diam. Upper 3 ft was barren soil; bedrock, diorite schist decomposed to depth of 2–5 ft into tough blue clay, sloped 2° (not enough for sluicing). Most of the gold, rounded and relatively small, was in lowest 6 in of gravel; higher gravel carried 5¢ per yd; black sand not abundant. Excavator was a caterpillar-mounted dragline, with 60–ft boom and 1.25-yd bucket when using gasolene; 1.75-yd with 40° fuel oil. Hopper of washer was 27 ft above base of excavator. Washer (total wt 55 tons) moved on a pair of 90-lb rails, in 15-ft sections, spaced 15 ft 7 in apart; each rail rested on ties at top of a 4-ft embankment (above bedrock) placed for the purpose by the excavator. Washer was carried on 7 wheels on each rail, and was dragged ahead, 15 ft at a time (4 times in 24 hr) by the excavator. Washing equipment: (a) hopper holding 3 bucket-loads; (b) trommel, 4.5 ft diam, in 3 4-ft screening sections (5 ft blank at each end) punched with 0.25-, 1.5-, and 0.75 by 1.5-in holes; (c) 5 parallel sluice boxes, 28 in wide, 12 ft long, 19-in drop, with iron-capped riffles 1.75 in high spaced 1.25 in apart; (d) tailings sluice, 28 in wide, 72 ft long, with same riffling and grade as the boxes and discharging 8 ft above bottom of cut; (e) stacker, a 26-in rubber belt 40 ft long, with rise of 8 ft. Water (1.25 cu ft per sec) was drawn from creek at max distance of 1 200 ft from the washer, through 12-in slip-joint pipe in 15-ft sections, one of which was removed (or added) at each move of washer. Centrif pump, with 75-hp gasolene engine, gave a 50-ft head. Pump was carried forward, in 1 200-ft steps, by the excavator.

For OPERATING PLAN see Fig 813. Creek was first diverted into a ditch 50–100 ft outside the channel. Stripping to full width of channel was done on 2 trips in opposite directions. A drain ditch was dug 4 ft into the decomposed bedrock along each side of channel, its material being dumped on top of exposed gravel, while overburden was piled outside. Stripping was kept at least 50 ft ahead of gravel digging, normally by stripping during night shift and digging gravel the other 2 shifts; in Spring and Autumn, when freezing prevented washing, stripping might advance far enough to permit washing for a time on 3 shifts, when next resumed. Usual rate of stripping was 1 000–1 200 (aver 1 150) cu yd per 8 hr. Gravel removed in 15-ft cuts across full width of channel, the dragline standing alternately to right and left of washer. About 18–24 in of decomposed bedrock was taken up, with care to mix it with gravel to aid disintegration. During 240-day season of 1934, plant advanced 6 500 ft upstream, washing 420 000 cu yd (aver recovery, 23.75¢) at total cost (incl stripping) of 11.9¢ per yd, comprising: labor and supt, 4.5¢; fuel, 1.8¢; other supplies, 2.7¢; royalty, 1.7¢; deprec, taxes, insurance, etc, 1.1¢. Crew included 6 men each on AM and PM shifts, and 5 men at night; superintendence by owners.

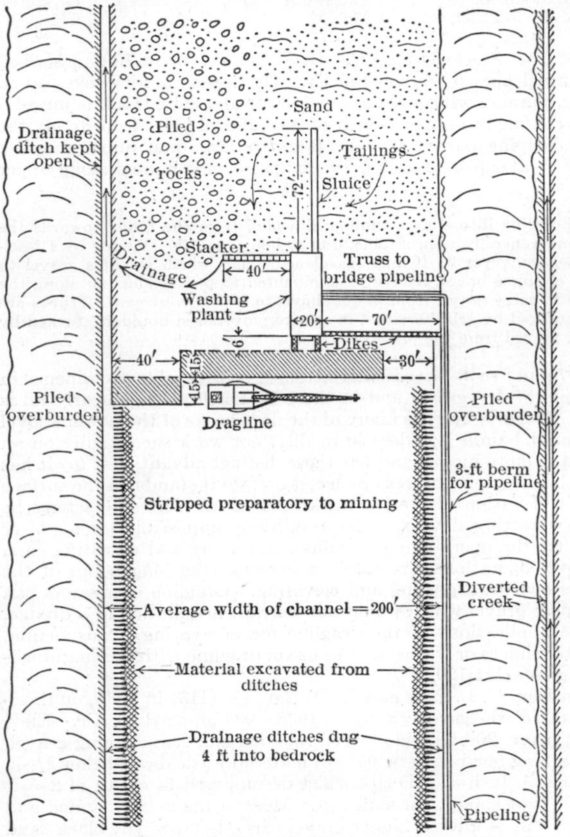

Fig 813. Dragline and Movable Washer, Atlantic City, Wyo (118)

Calaveras County, Cal. Data from S. R. Fox (166) in 1935. Lidgerwood dragline with 60-ft boom and 1.5-yd Page bucket made cut 120 ft wide, dumping into 14 by 14-ft hopper of a movable washer. Excavator had 60-hp boiler, fired with 1.5 cords of wood per 9-hr shift. Washer, mounted on rollers on a plank-track, had 4.5 by 22-ft trommel punched with $3/8$-in holes and a few 0.75-in holes at lower end to save occasional nuggets and provide coarser pebbles to counteract packing behind riffles. Total length of tables and sluices, 70 ft, of which 55 ft had Hungarian riffles (Art 125); riffles caught over 95% of total yield and about half of all the flour and flaky gold recovered; remaining 15 ft of sluice was floored with coconut matting under wire screen. Coarse tailings stacked by 24-in belt 40 ft long, disposal being aided at times by portable hydraulic giant. Water supplied by 10-in centrif pump, driven by water wheel under 300-ft head; same wheel drove 20-hp generator supplying 15-hp motor on trommel and stacker. A 30-ft move of dragline took 10 min; of washer (dragged by tackle from dragline), 20 min; total moving time of 3 hr was consumed mainly with water connections, using canvas tubing at elbows; with flexible and slip joints in metal pipe, total moving time probably would be about 1 hr. Total operating costs, 16.7¢ per cu yd.

Hillsboro dist, N M. Data from O. H. Metzger (450) in 1938. Area of about 1 200 acres in Dutch Flat was being worked by 2 dragline excavators with 1- and 1.25-yd buckets, and a transportable washer having four 36-in Ainlay bowls. One dragline was used for stripping 2–6 ft of soil, amounting to about half of total excavation; other dragline for gravel, at about 300 cu yd per 8 hr. Grizzly over washer hopper discarded boulders; gravel passed to trommel washer rejecting all over 0.25-in to stacker; undersize to Ainlay bowls, of which only 3 could be run when water was low. Tailings from bowls passed by Wilfley pump to coarse stacker, water being impounded for reuse. New water was pumped 4 miles from wells. Entire washing plant driven by 65-hp engine; fuel for this and all other equipment was gasolene. Washer, mounted on wheels, was moved by caterpillar tractor. Yield reported as 50–75¢ per yd; tailings, about 10¢. Costs: excavating (incl stripping) and washing, 16–20¢; pumping, etc, 4–5¢; total, 20–25¢ per yd, excl capital charges and royalty. One-shift work required 10 men at combined wages of $50.

Willow Cr, Iditarod dist, Alaska. One dragline installation described by N. L. Wimmler (188), operated for several years after 1916, working 4–6 ft of light gravel under 12 ft of frozen muck; bedrock, soft slate decomposed to sticky clay on top. Bucyrus dragline with 60-ft boom and 1.5-yd Page bucket (weighing 3 700 lb), driven by 60-hp boiler, was mounted on skids and rollers. It excavated 1 ft into bedrock, uncovering 100 000–150 000 sq ft per season, or about as much as could be cleared of overburden in that time by ground-sluicing. Aver pit, 110–120 ft wide by 150 ft long, required 5 positions of dragline, radiating about 65 ft from central dump box at head of sluice. Water, 160 miner's in. Labor cost (5 men), $57 per day; wood (1.25 cord), $25 per shift; no pumping required. In 1922 (good water supply) 130 000 sq ft (67 400 cu yd) of overburden was ground-sluiced for 9¢ per cu yd. In 52 10-hr shifts of 7 men, 24 100 cu yd of gravel and bedrock was treated for 28¢ per cu yd. Combined cost, to 19 ft depth, 16¢ per cu yd.

Circle dist, Alaska. J. B. Mertie, Jr (463) gives following data on 2 similar operations in 1936–37. MASTODON CR. Pay gravel in length of 0.75 mile varied 120–160 ft wide, 12–15 ft deep, with 4–5 ft of overlying muck; bedrock was fissured mica schist. Aver diam of gravel, 12 in, with numerous boulders to 4-ft diam. Gold, fairly coarse, was distributed through 5–6 ft depth of gravel (9 ft in some places) and sometimes penetrated 3–4 ft into bedrock, of which 1.5 ft was normally scraped. Caterpillar-mounted dragline with 55-ft boom and 1.25-yd bucket was operated by 120-hp, 6-cyl Diesel engine. A bulldozer was used to push gravel from margins of cut to within reach of dragline. Elevated sluice, completely enclosed and weighing about 30 tons, was mounted on 2 skids. Square dump box had rail grizzly discharging larger boulders over the side. Sluice, 80 ft long, 30 in wide, was of steel boxes lined with wood; grade, 13.5 in per 12 ft. Cross-riffles were of steel rail, heads up, and 0.5 in apart at base. Sluice water was supplied at 4 200 gal per min by 12-in pump, driven by 160-hp Diesel engine, and drawing from a dam downstream from workings. Under good conditions, 15 men could treat 1 000 cu yd per day. DEAD-WOOD CR. Pay gravel about 250 ft wide, 6 ft deep, covered with 5 ft of muck, and resting on fractured bedrock, of which 2–4 ft was scraped. Gravel was well rounded, mostly smaller than 10 in (aver, 5 in) with few boulders as large as 2 ft. Gold fine (5–6 mg) and flaky, and 85% of it was on or in bedrock. Caterpillar-mounted, Diesel-driven dragline had 55-ft boom and 1.5-yd bucket. A bulldozer was used as on Mastodon Cr. Elevated sluice, on skids, had dump-box 7 ft wide, 34 ft long, with block riffles, and 50 ft of steel boxes 34.5 in wide, with Mn-steel cross-riffles; grade, 1.4 in per ft. A No 1 giant with 4-in nozzle, working on gravel in dump box, was supplied with 4 000 gal per min by 10-in centrif pump driven by 97-hp Diesel engine; water came originally from a ditch, but within sufficient head. Crew of 17 men cleaned 3 000 sq ft of bedrock per day.

Power excavators in general. Modern types are often constructed to operate, after necessary but simple alterations, as either shovel or dragline; full-revolving machines are most flexible; those of walking type have an advantage over caterpillar-mounted on soft ground. For use of draglines delivering to floating washers, see Art 129. For sizes, capac, digging and dumping radii and lifts of shovels and draglines, see Sec 3, 27. For placer mining, dippers or buckets of less than 2-cu yd capac are usually preferred. For respective advantages of dragline and shovel, see paragraphs above. Table 109 gives data on 5 placer operations using power excavators reported by Gardner and Allsman (165) as operating in 1937. S. R. Fox (166) offers following advice relating to draglines: (a) Small, light, convertible shovel-draglines, with 35- to 40-ft booms and 1-yd or smaller buckets are not satisfactory for placer mining; their short reach entails too frequent moves, and the light bucket will not dig efficiently at depths below 20 ft. (b) A 60-ft boom and the heaviest model of 1.5-yd Page bucket make the smallest effic combination, which should have about same capac as a 2-cu ft chain-bucket dredge. (c) For estimating, not more than half the max rated capac should be assumed as attainable; best basis is record of actual performance over 30- or 60-day period. (d) Washer should be designed for capac 20% greater than that of excavator.

Table 109. Data on Five Placers Using Power Excavators in 1937 (165)

	I	II	III	IV	V
Aver depth gravel, ft.....	18–20	15	17	40	25
Digging character.......	easy	easy	easy	hard	hard
Boulders over 12-in diam..	none	many	none	5%	few
Clay....................	none	little	....	none	none
Bedrock................	granite	gran and sch	volc ash	serpentine	tuff
Excavator..............	dragline	2 drags, 1 shov	2 drags, 1 shov	shovel	shovel
Dipper or bucket capacity, cu yd................	1	2 1/2 and 1 1/4	2 1/2 and 1 3/4	1 1/4	3/4 ⎱
Excavator boom, ft......	50	50 and 22	drag, 50	21	....
Excavator power........	Diesel	gasolene	elec	gasolene	gasolene
Aver dug per hr, cu yd....	(a) 100	180	240	75	62
Hr per day digging.....	16	15	20	16	8
Transport by...........	⎱ movable	⎱ movable	⎱ movable	trucks	trucks
Length of haul, ft.......	⎰ washer	⎰ washer	⎰ washer	900	600
Trommel holes, in.......	1/4	1 1/8	1 1/8	1 1/2	5/8
Oversize disposed by.....	belt	belt	belt	truck	belt
Power for washer.......	elec	gasolene	elec	gasolene	elec
Sluices, width..........	⎱ 4 36″	8 @ 14″	12 @ 14″	48″ and 34″	⎱
	⎰ Ainlay	8 @ 20″			⎰ (f)
" total length, ft...	bowls	52	53	86	
" grade, in per ft...	....	1 1/4	1 1/4–1 1/2	1 1/4	1
Riffles.................	none	1 1/4″ angles and corduroy	1 1/4″ × 1 1/4″ angles	1 1/4″ × 1 1/4″ angles	1 1/4″ × 1 1/4″ angles on matting
Stacker belt............	18″ × 48′	36″ × 100′	48″ × 120′	none	24″ × 65′
Water consumed, miner's in....................	....	205	374	223	71
Water supplied by.......	10-hp pump	pumps	pump	pump	50-hp pump
Shifts per day..........	2 @ 9 hr	2 @ 10 hr	3 @ 8 hr	2 @ 9 hr	1 @ 8 hr
Men per day...........	7	(b) 22	(c) 24	(d) 22	(e) 4
Wages, ¢ per hr, weighted aver.................	71	(b) 70	(c) 89	....	72
Total cost of plant.......	(g) $12 000	$147 200	$264 795	....	(h) $30 000
Operating cost, ¢ per cu yd:					
Labor...............	....	....	4.4	13	4.6
Supervision...........	....	....	1.1	2	2.0
Power...............	....	....	1.9	7	2.4
Supplies.............	....	....	3.7	11	2.0
General.............	....	....	0.6	2	5.2
Total:..............	(k) (i) 8.0	25.0	(i) 11.7	(i) 35	(j) 16.2

I—Pantle Bros, Lincoln, Cal.   II—Humphreys Gold Corp, Clear Cr, Colo.   III—Humphreys Gold Corp, Virginia City, Mont.   IV—W. Von der Hellen, Siskiyou Co, Cal.   V—LaGrange, Cal.
(a) Incl stripping of 10–12 ft of overburden.   (b) Excl 2 supts, 1 foreman, 1 time-keeper.   (c) Excl 8 supts, foremen, and technicians.   (d) Incl 10 truck drivers, but excl 6 supts, mechanics, etc.   (e) Excl 1 foreman.   (f) 500 sq ft of area.   (g) Washing plant only.   (h) All new equipment.   (i) Excl depreciation.   (j) Incl depreciation.   (k) Based on total yardage, incl stripping.

123. HYDRAULIC MINING OR HYDRAULICKING (See also Art 98, 126)

Term " hydraulicking " is applied to excavation of gravel banks by streams of water under press from nozzles.   Method was invented in Calif, 1852, by E. E. Mattison; Bib (391) gives history of development.   In the U S, most deposits suitable for hydraulicking have been exhausted or, until recently, were unworkable due to legislative restrictions on disposal of tailings; recent governmental program of constructing debris dams has permitted some revival of hydraulicking in Calif (464); (see Dumproom, below).

General plan of work.   Water is impounded in reservoirs, or diverted from streams, and conducted in ditches, flumes, and pipes to an elevated point above the placer and thence to the working face through pipes.   Pipes terminate in GIANTS or MONITORS (Fig 819), which control direction of jet.   Gravel is broken partly by direct impact of jets, partly by undercutting and forcing banks to cave.   Water flows away from the face (usually in bedrock ditches), carrying gravel to a sluice leading to a dump; the giants often "pipe" fallen gravel into the sluice, and "bank water" (see below) is often supplied for same purpose. As the face is washed away, the bedrock cuts and sluices are advanced. Cemented gravel banks may require blasting before they can be disintegrated by water (Bank blasting, below). Gold is captured chiefly in the sluice.

Details of water supply and methods of opening and advancing working faces, arrangement of pipe lines, giants, sluices, etc, vary with local conditions; the accompanying cuts indicate diversity of practice (see also Fig 843). Fig 814 shows ideal conditions of grade and dumproom; Fig 815, layout for a bench placer; Fig 816, a mine on a small stream (404), where bedrock grade (2.35%)

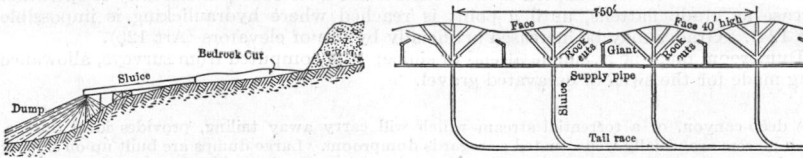

Fig 814. Simple Layout for Hydraulicking (after Young)

Fig 815. Layout for Hydraulicking Bench Gravel, Klondike (after Purington)

was insufficient to provide dumproom, and tailing had to be elevated; the pit itself was used for a dump as work proceeded upstream.

Tunnels are sometimes driven, to carry sluices to lower ground furnishing a gravity dump; also for opening placers, where local conditions prevent open-cut entry on bedrock. Thus, in Fig 817, tunnel T is driven on sluice-grade to the lowest point of the bedrock, and connected with surface by 1 or more shafts, S. Gravel is hydraulicked into the shaft, the timbers and protecting lining of which are removed as excavation is deepened. On reaching bedrock, the gravel bank is hydraulicked to the sluice in the tunnel. Bowie states that 300-ft shafts in Calif were readily operated in this way; their cross-sec was 3 by 3 ft to 4.5 by 9 ft; tunnels were 7.5 to 8 ft high and 2 to 3 ft wider than the sluice, to give room for construction and cleaning-up (391).

The principal problems of hydraulic mining are connected with water supply, sluice grades, and dumproom; the method appears simple, but has rigid limitations. Some small-scale hydraulicking is successful, but as a rule it is adapted to large outputs, it requires large initial investment, and skilled management and engineering.

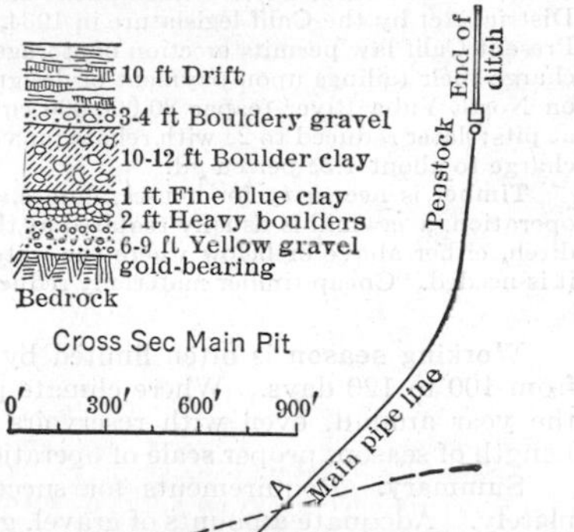

10 ft Drift
3-4 ft Bouldery gravel
10-12 ft Boulder clay
1 ft Fine blue clay
2 ft Heavy boulders
6-9 ft Yellow gravel gold-bearing
Bedrock

Cross Sec Main Pit

0'   300'   600'   900'

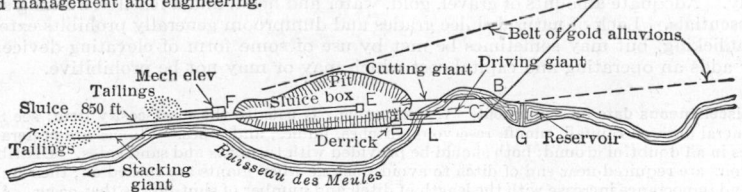

Fig 816. Hydraulic Mine near Beauceville, Quebec

Size and tenor of deposit must be such as will amortize the investment required for its exploitation and pay the profit desired. Minimum gold content that will yield a profit may vary with locality from 4 to 50¢ or more per cu yd, depending on capital invested, rate of working, life of property, working costs and gold recovery.

Character of gravel and bedrock (see Art 118).

Water supply must be ample for required output. Speed of working determines rate of return, and depends largely on amount of water available (see Duty of water, below), which is related to the press; a small amount under high press often breaks as much gravel as a larger amount under a lower press. But the output is often determined by the sluice

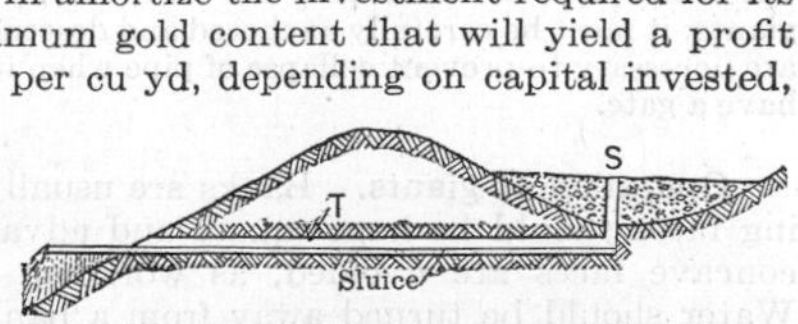

Fig 817. Hydraulic Mine opened by Tunnel (cross-sec)

capac (Art 124), instead of the cutting capac of the giants. Pressure must be sufficient to allow giants to be set at a safe distance from face and still do effective work. Giants usually operate under heads of 200 to 400 ft, occasionally 600 ft; less than 200 ft is apt to give a low duty. Shallow creek placers of Alaska are hydraulicked on a small scale with heads of 35 to 100 ft; danger of sudden caves and slides from high banks requires higher press, so that the giants may throw streams from a considerable distance. With heads over 600 ft, the requirements for heavy pipe, bracing, and anchorage become exacting (385). Numerous attempts made to pump water for hydraulicking have nearly all been commercial failures (390) (compare Art 98).

Grade for sluices best adapted to most cases is 4–5%. Cost and difficulty of operation increase as grade flattens, until a point is reached where hydraulicking is impossible (Art 124). Grades may be increased artificially by use of elevators (Art 126).

Dumproom must be available at end of sluice; it is computed from surveys, allowance being made for the swell of excavated gravel.

A deep canyon, or a torrential stream which will carry away tailing, provides ideal dumps. Bench placers are usually well situated as regards dumproom. Large dumps are built up on sloping ground by gradually extending lower end of the sluice (Fig 814); branch sluices are often installed and the dump widened (fanned-out) as well as lengthened. In either case, slope of the ground must be steeper than the sluice grade. Tailing must sometimes be impounded to prevent damage to low-lying mining or farming land. This condition may prohibit hydraulicking, due to impossibility or cost of installing and maintaining DEBRIS DAMS, especially for large-scale work. Hydraulicking in the Sacramento and San Joaquin drainage areas, Calif, practically ceased in 1893, when the Caminetti Act was passed, creating a Federal commission to regulate hydraulic mining and prevent further silting-up of these rivers. For details of this act, and for types and construction of debris dams, see Bib (405, 464). Amendment of the Caminetti Act, and passage of the Placer Mining District Act by the Calif legislature in 1934, encouraged renewal of hydraulic mining in that State. Present Calif law permits erection of storage dams behind which the mines of the district may discharge their tailings upon payment of designated fee. At the privately owned Bullard's Bar dam, on North Yuba River (capac 80 000 000 cu yd), storage fee was originally 3¢ per cu yd measured at pits; later reduced to 2¢ with rebate for volume of boulders stacked in pit, which reduced storage charge to about 1.5¢ per cu yd.

Timber is necessary for houses, flumes, trestles, sluices, riffles, sluice linings, etc. For a large operation, a sawmill is usually required at the start, located preferably near the head of the supply ditch, either above or below where the water is diverted. Timber is then floated to points where it is needed. Cheap timber materially reduces costs (385).

Working season is often limited by climate or water supply. Alaskan seasons vary from 100 to 120 days. Where climate permits continuous work, water is rarely available the year around, even with reservoirs for impounding flood waters and melting snow. Length of season, proper scale of operation, annual returns, and capital, are closely related.

Summary. Requirements for successful large-scale work are rarely satisfied completely. Adequate amounts of gravel, gold, water and head, and a feasible working season are essentials. Lack of natural sluice grades and dumproom generally prohibits extensive hydraulicking, but may sometimes be met by use of some form of elevating device; the latter adds an operating and capital cost which may or may not be prohibitive.

Miscellaneous data on equipment. WATER SUPPLY is usually the most costly item; see Sec 38 for general data on rainfall, runoff, reservoirs, ditches, flumes, and pipes. Flumes are preferable to ditches in all doubtful ground; both should be provided with turnouts and sand gates. Distributing reservoirs are required near end of ditch to avoid wastage when giants are turned off; their number, size, and importance increase with the length of ditch and number of shut-downs that occur. Almost any reasonable expenditure is justified for preventing breaks in the supply system; constant operation is essential to large output and low costs. A PRESSURE BOX (penstock) is necessary at upper end of pipe leading to giants, to catch floating leaves and sticks, settle fine sediment, and keep air out of the pipe; for details, see Bib (391, 406). A single PIPE LINE is desirable if it will supply all the giants; it must be carefully anchored and descend to the pit in as direct a line as possible. Air valves are necessary to prevent collapse of pipe when it is emptied. Each branch leading to a giant should have a gate.

Operation of giants. Banks are usually broken by undercutting and caving. Working faces should be kept square and advantage taken of corners. Narrow pits or deep concave faces are avoided, as workmen are constantly menaced by falling material. Water should be turned away from a bank that is about to cave, otherwise the rush of caved material may reach the giants and men. Water cuts fastest where thrown against a bank at an oblique angle. Banks shaped as in Fig 815, with giants placed opposite a nose, allow effective use of water and reduce danger from caves, as the latter fall outward at right-angles to face and not toward the giant. Some Alaskan operators work creek gravels 15–50 ft deep by setting the giant on top of the bank and piping downstream, but the duty of water thus obtained does not indicate a high effic (390). With 1 giant, part of the bank is caved, then with a larger nozzle the fallen gravel is washed to sluices. With 2 or more giants, their time is apportioned between caving and sluicing. BOOSTER GIANTS may be used to drive gravel across flat bedrock to sluices. Ruble elevator (Art 126), when used, requires a separate giant, and another is often used (sometimes only periodically) for spreading tailings piles.

Number of giants depends on size of working face, character of gravel, press and amount of water. Practice tends towards use of a small number of large giants, rather than a larger number of small ones; the former cut faster and save labor. Giants are placed to command as much of the face as possible, to work advantageously in a combined attack on one point, and as near the face as is safe (406). For best results, at least 2 giants and 2 working faces are required, so that hydraulicking may proceed on one face while boulders are being removed from the other (394).

Height of face for economical work is normally limited to a max of 150–200 ft; higher banks are usually worked in benches. Conditions allowing high benches are: high water press, compact gravel that does not "run" when caved, and a wide pit. Where the bottom layer of a high face is tough, the upper gravel may be piped off far enough to allow giants to be moved closer to the face and exert more force.

Bank-water (bank-head or bye-water) applies to streams brought to the pit in ditches, not under press. Bank-water is allowed to run over the face, aiding in disintegrating clayey gravel, thawing frozen ground, moving gravel to sluice, and maintaining a steady flow through it.

Bedrock cuts or ditches are a continual and sometimes serious source of expense in most hydraulic mines; in some early Calif mines, they reached 60 ft depth (391, 407); in case shown in Fig 815, 4 men were constantly employed in extending bedrock cuts (390). When much clay is present, more branching bedrock cuts are required than for fine sandy gravel (406); grade of bedrock also influences spacing of cuts. Drainage of pits is usually provided for by sluices; occasional bedrock drains are required.

Boulders too large to be piped to and through the sluice are removed by derricks or cableways or broken up. As derricks must be located behind the giants, they must have long booms and masts and are cumbersome to move. Cableways do not interfere with giants, but have restricted reach sidewise. Derricks and cableways may be operated by small water wheels; either is usually preferable to blasting where boulders are numerous, especially if sluice grades are flat (406). Sledging, if feasible, is generally the cheapest mode of breaking boulders if done by cheap labor and without delaying piping; "mud-capping" (Sec 5) usually costs more than blockholing. R. H. Ernest, Round Mountain Mining Co, Nev, states that for mud-capping 839 rhyolite boulders, many highly silicified, aver size 4 cu ft, 402 lb of 40% gelatin dynamite were used or 0.481 lb per boulder.

Bank blasting is sometimes necessary in cemented gravels before they can be broken down by giants. Small T-shaped tunnels (Fig 818) are usually driven at the foot of high banks. Drifts D are charged with explosive and drift E is tamped solid with the excavated material. Only enough explosive is used to shatter the ground; in some cases several cross drifts D are driven. A blast will usually shatter nearly twice the area of ground covered by the drifts. In some cases, where only the bottom layer is cemented, the top gravel is hydraulicked, and small shafts are sunk to bedrock, where the explosive is placed in small chambers. Bank blasting has seldom been employed in recent years.

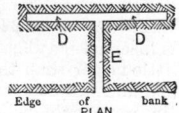

Fig 818. Bank Blasting

Miscellany. CLEANING BEDROCK is sometimes done by giants; hard creviced bedrock

Fig 819. Giant or Monitor

must be cleaned by hand at high cost. LIGHTING is necessary at night, since work is continuous; modern equipment usually includes a small hydroelectric plant. LABOR. Skilled men required are: nozzle [tenders, carpenters, blacksmith; sometimes a machinist and derrick winchman. For SLUICES, RIFFLES, etc, see Art 124, 125.

Table 110. Sizes and Weights of Hydraulic Giants
(Joshua Hendy Iron Works, San Francisco, 1939)

Giant No	Inlet diam, in	Butt diam, in	Std Nozzle diam, in	Heaviest Part, lb	Shipping weight, lb
1	7	4	2, 3	120	390
2	9	5	3, 4	150	520
3	11	6	3, 4	210	890
4	11	7	4, 5, 6	225	1 075
5	13	8	5, 6	335	1 475
6	15	9	6, 7	520	1 850
7	15	10	6, 7	520	2 100
8	18	10	7, 8	600	2 300
9	18	11	9, 10	690	2 450

Table 111. Water Discharged, Cu Ft per Min, by Hydraulic Giants (a)

Effective head, ft	100	200	300	400	500	600
Nozzle diam, in						
2	94	133	163	188	210	232
3	222	300	368	425	475	522
4	380	535	655	756	845	926
5	590	835	1 020	1 180	1 320	1 445
6	850	1 200	1 470	1 700	1 900	2 080
7	1 160	1 635	2 000	2 320	2 590	2 835
8	1 510	2 140	2 620	3 020	3 380	3 700
9	1 920	2 700	3 320	3 820	4 270	4 680
10	2 360	3 340	4 090	4 720	5 280	5 780

(a) From Joshua Hendy Iron Works, San Francisco, Cal, in 1939. Flow based on discharge coefficient of 0.90; see under "Discharge through nozzles"; also Sec 38.

Giants (monitors). Fig 819 shows a modern, double-jointed giant, connected to pipe line by a slip or a flanged joint. It can swing horizontally through a full circle about the joint J, and through a wide vertical angle about joint M. Weight of the spout is counterbalanced by lever S and weighted box P; lug L is bolted to a heavy timber, securely fastened and braced to bedrock; guide vanes are set inside the spout, to prevent rotary motion of the jet which destroys its solidity.

Details of construction vary. A vertical king-bolt K, to take the thrust as the water enters the giant, is common; top of the bolt should have a ball-bearing to reduce friction when the giant is swung. Some makers replace the king-bolt by a special ball-bearing joint at J, to avoid obstruction to the flow, but the king-bolt is a good safety precaution, and, with well designed pressure boxes, should give no trouble by catching stringy matter. Tables 110, 111 give data on Hendy giants; other makers build giants of similar size and wt.

Nozzles (N, Fig 819) of different makers are not interchangeable; nozzle of any size may be attached to a giant up to the max it will take. They must be carefully designed and highly finished, otherwise the jet is ragged and cannot be thrown as far without spraying. Grit cuts the nozzle, and destroys shape of jet.

Deflectors. Small giants, or those working under light heads, are pointed by hand; deflectors are required on large giants and in general where the head much exceeds 100 ft. Deflectors are of 2 kinds: (a) A short flexible coupling C, with ball joint and leather gasket, is inserted between nozzle N and end of spout P (Fig 820). (b) A short section of pipe, a little larger than the nozzle, is attached loosely to its end and projects over the jet; it may have a threaded tip, replaceable when worn. Both types turn freely on gimballed joints, and are controlled by a lever L (406). The reaction of the jet, when diverted by the deflector, forces the giant in the opposite direction; L is easily moved and gives a sensitive control. Type (b) is best for heads over 300 ft, but requires a

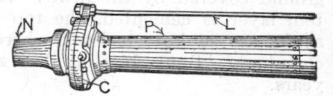

Fig 820. Deflector for Giant

separate deflector for each size of nozzle. A single deflector of type (a) will take any nozzle smaller than the max that can be used on the giant.

Discharge through nozzles (Sec 38, Art 9). Approx calculations may be made by the formula, $Q = Ca\sqrt{h}$, where Q = discharge, cu ft per min; a = cross-sec area of nozzle, sq in; h = head at nozzle, ft; C = constant depending on coeff of discharge.

For giants with inside vanes (see above) the coeff of discharge is put by Longridge (394) between 0.8 and 0.85; by J. J. Garrard (397) as 0.94. Corresponding values of C are 2.68, 2.84 and 3.14, respectively. Makers' tables usually give full theoretical discharge (C = 3.34) with no allowance for friction.

Miner's inch (Sec 38, Art 19), unless otherwise stated, is taken here as equivalent to a flow of 1.5 cu ft per min, corresponding to its legal definition in Calif and Mont (40 miner's in = 1 cu ft per sec). INCH-DAY is the volume (2 160 cu ft) delivered by 1 miner's in flowing 24 hr. Old records of the duty of water in hydraulicking require careful scrutiny; in Calif alone, the inch varied locally from 1.2 to 1.76 cu ft per min (391).

Duty of a miner's inch in hydraulicking is the cu yd of gravel which can be broken down and sent through sluices in 24 hr by 1 miner's in. It varies with height of bank, character of gravel and bedrock, grade of bedrock, amount and pressure of water, manner in which the water is utilized, and with all the factors influencing sluice capacity (Art 124). Published data rarely state completely all the factors involved. See Tables 112–117; also Art 124 and under examples below.

Table 112. Duty of the Miner's Inch at North Bloomfield and La Grange Mines, Calif
Bowie (391)

	Date	Cu yd gravel washed	Miner's in-days	Grade of sluices	Height of bank, ft	Duty per in-day, cu yd
North Bloomfield Mine (a)	1870–1874	3 250 000	710 987	....	100	4.6
	1875	1 858 000	386 972	6.5 in per 12 ft	100	4.8
	1876	2 919 700	700 000		200	4.17
	1877	2 993 930	595 000		265	3.86
	Total......	11 021 630	2 392 959	....	....	4.6
La Grange Mines (b)	1874–1876 (c)	676 968	624 745	4 in per 16 ft	10– 48	1.08
	1875–1876 (d)	683 244	375 155		60	1.82
	1874–1876 (e)	284 932	207 010.		50– 80	1.37
	1875–1878 (f)	459 570	302 960		40– 50	1.52
	1880–1881 (g)	329 120	203 325		10– 80	1.57
	Total......	2 433 834	1 713 195	....	....	1.42
	1908 (h)	....	....	8 in per 12 ft	100–200	7–10

Note. Duty of miner's in in early Calif work was estimated by State and U S Army engineers at 1 to 7.5 cu yd, aver about 3 cu yd. J. H. Hammond gave following data: At Hobson's mine, Placer Co, piping a 120-ft bank, using 500 in water at head of 360 ft, with sluices set on grade of 12 in per 12 ft and paved with rock riffles, duty of a miner's in was 24 cu yd in light free gravel and 10 cu yd in coarse cemented gravel. By increasing sluice grade to 18 in per 12 ft and using iron riffles, duty of one inch in light gravel increased to 36 cu yd. These figures are exceptionally high (407). (a) Larger part of material moved was top gravel. Sluices, 6 ft wide by 32 in deep. Block riffles used almost entirely; rock riffles in tail sluices. (b) Sluices previous to 1881 were 4 ft wide by 30 in deep, paved with blocks. (c) French Hill claims. (d) Light Claim. (e) Chesnau Claim. (f) Kelley Claim. (g) Vigno Hill. (h) Data from P. Bouery, Supt, pub by Joshua Hendy Iron Works, Bull No 111. Sluices, 6.33 ft wide by 47 in deep. Higher duty is due to steeper grades, higher banks, and improved riffles (Art 125), [and to use of water under heads of 400 to 600 ft.

Purington comments on Table 113 as follows: The high duty of the miner's inch in the Klondike (Ex 11–18) is due to well rounded gravel containing no large stones, heavy sluice grades, and use of block riffles. Low duties at Nome (Ex 21 27) are due partly to the fact that the gravel is flat and rough, partly to use of hydraulic elevators, which take 50 to 66% of the available water. Duties given are for both giant and elevator water (Art 126). Iron riffles are commonest, but have little effect on duty because the sluices are short. Dimensions and grades refer to bedrock sluices leading to the elevator. The figures are based on operators' statements and comparatively short runs.

Table 114 shows difficulties of starting large-scale hydraulicking, and close relation between costs and output. Frozen ground makes ditch construction hard; new ditches require constant repairs, but these lessen with time.

Table 115, from Wimmler (188), gives data on sluices and duty of water at Alaskan mines active within a few years prior to 1927; stated flow of water includes that from all sources, ground-sluicing water, in addition to cutting water, being required in all cases except at Little, Osborne, and Ophir Creeks, where hydraulic elevators were employed. The somewhat lower duties, as compared with Calif and Mont (Table 116), are explained by: (a) lower available grades on bed rock; (b) prevalence of flatter pebbles in some districts, and of heavy gravel in others; (c) large amount of ground-sluicing (or elevator) water required by above conditions; (b) frozen gravel in some localities.

Table 116, after Gardner and Johnson (17), gives duty of water in sluices at mines operating in western U S in 1932. For riffling of same sluices, see Table 120.

Cost and operating data. Hydraulicking costs from 4¢ per cu yd under very favorable conditions in Calif to 25¢ or more in Alaska. Unfavorable conditions, as frozen gravel, or necessity for elevating tailing or for pumping giant water, may increase cost to 60¢ or more. Records of cost usually include only operating expenses, omitting capital charges; the latter may be very high; thus, a number of Calif mines spent $200 000 to $500 000 in preparing for work; the equipment of 1 mine, including 290 miles of ditch and 8 miles of pipe, cost $2 000 000 (409). Following examples (see also Art 126) give costs under various conditions. Table 117 relates to 6 hydraulic mines active in 1932 in western U S.

Table 113. Duty of Miner's Inch, Alaskan and Yukon Districts
C. W. Purington, in 1905 (390)

Ex No	Location	Height of bank, ft	Charac-ter of material	Grade, in per 12 ft	Miner's in of water	Duty, cu yd per in-day	Sluices Width, in	Sluices Depth, in	Riffles
	Juneau:								
1	Windfall Cr.....	16	......	....	1 000	2.0	.....	.....	....
2	Gold Cr........	200	A	4.5	4 000	2.0	72	60	Bl
3	Silver Bow Basin	80	A	4.0	2 500	2.0	50	55	Bl
	Atlin:								
4	McKee Cr......	40	A	8.0	700	1.5	32	32	Ai + Bl
5	" "	85	A	8.0	1 200	3.0	32	40	Ai + Bl
6	Birch Cr........	25	A	5.25	1 200	0.5	30	30	Bl
7	Spruce Cr......	29	A	5.0	1 200	1.0	40	36	Bl
8	" "	20	A	5.5	900	0.5	48	32	Bl
9	Pine Cr........	20	A	3.0	700	0.6	36	36	Rl
10	" "	60	A	5.0	3 500	0.625	60	40	Bl
	Dawson, Yukon:								
11	Bonanza Cr.....	20	B	12.0	250	5.0	24	20	Bl
12	" "	25	C	12.0	125	4.0 (?)	20	16	Sp
13	" "	25	B (a)	11.0	150	10.0	24	24	Bl
14	" "	35	B	12.0	200	6.5	24	24	Bl
15	" "	75	B	12.0	266	8.0	24	30	Bl
16	Eldorado Cr.....	60	B	11.0	160	7.0	24 (?)	24	Bl + Hu
17	Last Chance....	46	B	12.0	230	7.0	24	18	Pi + Bl
18	" "	25	B	14.0	120	5.0	20	20	Pi
19	Hunker Cr......	15	B (b)	13.0	150	2.0	14	14	P + Bl
20	" "	8	B	12.0	125	2.6	17	14	Pi
	Nome:								
21	Anvil Cr........	30	D	4.5	500	1.4	33	18	Ai
22	" "	20	E	4.5	400	10.0	.....	.....	Ai
23	" "	12	......	9.0	100	....	16	14	Ai
24	Glacier Cr......	20	F	6.0	760	1.32 (c)	36	24	Aig
25	Dexter Cr......	40	G	6.5	100	2.0 (?)	16	16	Aig
26	Newton Cr......	8	H	7.0	150	3.33	24	24	P + Ai
27	Basin Cr........	20	I	8.0	250	0.6 (d)	18	18	Pi
	Council:								
28	Ophir Cr.......	12	I	10.0	600	1.5 (d)	24	16	Ra + Ai
29	" "	8	J	10.0	750	1.0 (e)	24	16	Ra + Ai
30	Solomon River..	5	K	10.0	600	0.8 (f)	37	24	Aig

A = heavy stones. B = "White Channel"; small round gravel, frozen. C = hillside, small gravel, frozen. D = heavy, partly frozen gravel, much flat schist. E = frozen earth or muck stripping. F = flat, semi-frozen gravel. G = heavy gravel, limestone bedrock. H = small coastal plain gravel. I = heavy gravel. J = slabs and clay. K = subangular gravel. (a) part tailings. (b) very little frozen. (c) 66% of the water used by an hydraulic elevator, 36-ft lift. (d) hydraulic elevator, 29-ft lift, used 60% of water. (e) hydraulic elevator, 28-ft lift, used 66% of water. (f) hydraulic elevator, 12-ft lift, used 50% of water. Bl = block-riffles. Ai = angle iron. Rl = long rails. Sp = sawed pole, iron-shod. Hu = Hungarian. Pi = pole, iron-shod. P = pole. Aig = angle-iron grates. Ra = rails.

Table 114. Hydraulic Mining, Yukon Gold Co. Twelve Mile River Water System (408)

Year	Period of operation, days	Percentage of possible time worked	Water supply, in-days	Cu yd gravel	Cost of operating and ditch mainte-nance	Cost per cu yd, omitting deprec on main ditch	Duty of water, cu yd per in-day
1910	....	....	371 206	1 656 020	$140 433	20.80¢	4.50
1911	....	....	482 580	2 125 750	135 710	15.50	5.40
1912	168	96.8	524 249	2 967 750	76 760	9.37	5.40
1913	150	93.28	406 135	2 875 952	73 054	9.70	6.60
1914	168	96.29	519 834	3 241 641	64 397	7.60	6.02

Table 115. Duty of Water in Alaskan Sluices (188)

Locality	Sluice box			Type of riffle	Water through sluice, miner's in	Duty, cu yd per in per day	Nature of gravel
	Width, in	Depth, in	Grade, in per 12 ft				
Seward Penin:							
Boulder Cr......	30	30	4	Mn-steel grate....	700	1.00	Unfrozen, med., much flat
Big Hurrah Cr...	36	18	5	Rails...........	900	1.20	Do, do.
Little Cr........	48	24	5–7	Angles & rails....	....	1.37	Partly frozen, med
Osborne Cr......	36	24	7	Blocks & rails.....	750	1.20	Partly frozen, heavy
Ophir Cr........	..	..	5	Blocks & rails.....	....	1.25	Partly frozen, med
Mt McKinley Dist:							
Moore Cr.......	24	20	6	Punched plate over matting & longit steel-shod.......	300	1.60	Unfrozen, med-round
Fairbanks Dist:							
Pedro Cr........	36	30	11	Blocks...........	350	1.20	Partly frozen, heavy
" "	36	30	5	Rails...........	400	0.80	Partly frozen, med
Circle Dist:							
Mastodon Cr....	30	24	8	Blocks...........	500	0.70	Partly frozen, med-round
Seventy Mile Dist:							
Crooked Cr......	30	24	8	Blocks...........	460	1.20	Partly frozen, light
Yentna Dist:							
Falls Cr........	36	30	8	Longit steel-shod...	500	0.90	Unfrozen, med; boulders
Nugget Cr.......	28	24	7	Longit steel-shod...	450	0.80	Do, do.
Peters Cr.......	30	24	6	Rails...........	800	0.80	Do, do.
Kenai Dist:							
Crow Cr........	52	36	6	Rails...........	2 600	0.50	Very coarse; many large boulders
Nizina Dist:							
Dan Cr.........	48	44	5	Rails, longit.......	....	0.32	Do, do.
Chititu Cr......	40	36	5 3/4	Rails, longit.......	2 200	0.42	Do, do; also heavy

Table 116. Duty of Water in Sluices at Hydraulic Mines, Western U S in 1932 (17)

Example	Location	Max diam of boulders to sluice, in	Water through sluice, miner's in	Duty, cu yd per in per day	Box width, in	Box depth, in	Sluice, total length, ft	Grade, in per 12 ft
1	Weaverville, Cal....	12	400	0.5	36	24	96	9
2	Douglas City, Cal..	18	500	3.7	48	36	48	9
3	Douglas City, Cal..	2	1 200	0.5	48	..	48	9
4	Junction City, Cal..	18	460	4.2	48	36	120	9
5	Wash. Camp, Cal...	18	1 500	2.7	48	36	1 700	6
6	Comptonville, Cal..	4	600	1.0	30	24	3 500	2.6
7	Helena, Cal......	12	1 300	1.0	48	40	168	12
8	Centerville, Idaho..	6	240	0.5	32	24	72	9
9	Centerville, Idaho..	7	400	0.4	30	..	96	9
10	Emigrant, Mont....	12	600	0.5	23	24	500	4
11	Virginia City, Mont.	6	85	1.4	14.5	18	180	5
12	Gold Creek, Mont..	10	600	2.0	22	24	120	9
13	Gold Creek, Mont..	8	150	4.0	22	24	120	9
14	Sheridan, Mont....	20	2 800	0.1	44	40	1 900	3.5
15	Superior, Mont.....	8	180	1.3	24	18	240	7
16	Townsend, Mont...	10	900	0.6	32	36	2 700	4
17	York, Mont.......	8	350	1.4	30	36	400	3
18	Baker, Oreg.......	6	150	2.6	26	20	180	15
19	Leland, Oreg......	0.75	900	0.7	48	..	32	5.25
20	O'Brien, Oreg......	8	650	0.9	32	..	304	4.5
21	Galice, Oreg.......	5	300	1.0	30	..	95	9

Salyer mine, Trinity county, Cal. Data from Gardner and Johnson (17) in 1934. Deposit of "blue" gravel about 40 ft thick, tight, containing many boulders, capped by clay, and covered by 60 ft of loose gravels and clays. Water system, with 5 000-in capac, included ditches, flumes, and siphons, but no reservoirs, and cost $300 000. Pit was supplied at 350-ft head through 2 16-in pipes with combined capac of 2 800 miner's in. Two giants, with nozzles of 8 to 5 in, according to available water, gave duty of 4.33 cu yd per in-day.

Sluicing required min of 1 500 miner's in. Sluice was 5 ft wide, 350 ft long, dropping 8 in per 12-ft box; wood-block riffles 18 in square, 12 in high, wore rapidly and were to be replaced by steel rails. About half the water and most of the sand passed to undercurrents, which caught about 10% of the yield. Mercury was used in sluice and undercurrents. Boulders in pit were handled by crane on a tractor. Aver crew at mine, 15 men. In 97-day season of 1932, 718 900 cu yd was moved at direct cost of 2.63¢ per yd, incl deprec of mine equipment, but excl depletion, administration, and deprec of water system and other permanent installations. Additional data in Col IV, Table 117.

Table 117. Data on on Western U S Hydraulic Mines Active in 1932 (17)

	I	II	III	IV	V	VI
Aver depth gravel, ft	9	45	65	100	12	14
Character of gravel	med	tight	med, cement	med to easy	med	easy
Boulders over 12″, %	8	8	5	....	2	5
Bedrock, kind	cement	schist	....	....	....	....
" surface	smooth	uneven	uneven	....	even	....
Gold, size	....	....	coarse	fine	....	....
Giant water, miner's in	1 200	1 300	1 300	2 800	(a) 900	60
Bank " " "	0	200	0	0	0	290
Total water	1 200	1 500	1 300	2 800	900	350
Ditches or flumes, miles	(f) 2.5	(d) 8 & 16	(f) 8 & 12	....	....	(b)
Pipe lines, diam, in	24–15	30–15	24–15	2 @ 16″	36–16	12
" " length, ft	3 000	1 800	1 500	....	5 000	500
Head at giants, ft	300	210	400	350	300	100
No of giants used	(c) 3	2	2	2	2	1
Nozzle diam, in	3 & 5	6	5 & 7	5–8	4.5 & 5	1.5 & 1.25
Elevator	Ruble, 25′	none	none	none	Ruble, 14′	none
Boulders handled by	blasting	blasting	blasting	crane & tractor	hand	hand
Duty of water (e)	0.5	2.7	1.0	4.3	0.7	1.4
Sluice, total length, ft	48	1 700	168	350	32	400
" size and grade, Table 116	Ex 3	Ex 5	Ex 7	60″ × 50″ @ 6.2%	Ex 19	Ex 17
Riffles, Table 120	Ex 3	Ex 5	Ex 7	wood blocks	Ex 19	Ex 17
Undercurrents, area	none	none	12′ × 20′	1 944 sq ft	none	12′ × 36′
Washed per day, cu yd	540	1 700	900	7 400	667	500
Shifts per day	3	1 @ 10 hr	2 @ 9 hr	....	2 @ 12 hr	3
Men in pit, per day	21	6	4	15	6	12
Wages per shift	$3.75	$4.00	$4.00	$4.00	$5.00	$3.50
Operating cost, ¢ per cu yd:						
Labor	13.5	2	3.0	....	4.5	9
Supervision	2.0	....	....	....	....	3
Supplies	3.5	2	1.5	....	1.5	(i) 17
Total	19.0	(g) 4	4.5	(h) 2.63	6.0	29

I—Redding Cr, Douglas City, Cal. II—Omega Hill, Washington Camp, Cal; data for 1931. III—North Fork, Helena, Cal. IV—Salyer, Cal. V—Browning property, Leland, Oreg. VI—Eldorado Bar, York, Mont. (a) Incl giant at Ruble elevator. (b) Water pumped 120 ft vert, and booster pump to give head of 100 ft. (c) Of which, 1 cutting and driving, 1 at Ruble elevator, 1 (3-in) used periodically for tailings disposal; only 2 giants used at a time. (d) Ditch. (e) Cu yd gravel per day per miner's inch of water. (f) Flume. (g) Excl supervision and ditch repairs. (h) Excl general administration. (i) Power, 15¢.

Omega Hill mine, Washington Camp, Cal. Data from Gardner and Johnson (17) in 1934. Ancient river gravel, 30–60 ft deep (lower 6–8 ft cemented) lying under 10–20 ft of volcanic ash. Water supply through 2 ditches: one 16 miles long, with numerous flume sections 6 ft wide; other 8 miles long; both delivered to reservoir 210 ft above pit. Two 6-in, or three 5-in giants were used. Sluice, 48 in wide, lay in bedrock cut and extended 1 700 ft outside, to gulch where tailings dam could be located. At end of sluice, a grizzly with 1-in spacing separated coarse gravel (used for making dam) from undersize, which was delivered behind the dam by another sluice. Previously prepared culvert in bottom of gulch assisted drainage of clean water from the tailings pond. When one pond was full, another dam was made farther down the gulch. Additional data in Col II, Table 117.

Eldorado Bar, York, Mont. Example of placering with pumped water from Gardner and Johnson (17); data refer to operations in 1931. Centrif pump driven by 250-hp motor lifted 4 000 gal per min (356 miner's in) 120 ft vert to head of the bar; suction pipe, 14-in; delivery pipe (500 ft long), 12-in diam. Booster pump at top, with 50-hp motor, developed press of 40 lb per sq in, and delivered about 60 miner's in through 6-in fire hose to 1.25- or 1.5-in nozzle for cutting, or (through same hose) to 1.5- or 2-in nozzle for sweeping; remainder of water pumped was used for bank water. The gravel worked easily; boulders moved by hand. For details of sluice, see Ex 17, Tables 116, 120; other data in Col VI, Table 117. Crew of 4 men on each of 3 shifts worked 500 cu yd per day. Power cost 0.9¢ per kw-hr, plus $1 per mo per hp of connected load, totaling about $75 per day.

Gold Hill mine, Idaho City, Idaho. Data from O. H. Metzger (428) in 1938. A bench deposit consisting of 4 beds of tight gravel alternating with hard clay, and including a bed of soft sandstone, varies in thickness from 25–50 ft at upper end of workings to 150 ft at lower end; the 2 areas, though contiguous, are worked practically independently, each with its own sluice and group of 3 giants, piping in one while clay and boulders are being removed from the other; little work is done where deposit is less than 35–45 ft thick. Bedrock is clay, sloping 8–15% towards Elk Cr. Water comes from 2 sources: from Moore's Cr (rights to 2 700 in) through 8 miles of ditch and 2 40-in siphons each more than 0.5 mile long, and from Elk Cr (rights to 2 300 in) through 10-mile ditch; flows unite at penstock 5 000 ft from and 225–325 ft above workings. Two 20-in pipes convey to header within 1 000 ft of workings; thence 3 18-in pipes run to valves distributing to 6 giants through 15-in pipes. Normal consumption (of 3 giants at a time), 3 000 miner's in (considerably reduced toward end of season); approx aver duty, 1.5–1.75 cu yd per in-day. Giants have 4- or 5-in nozzles; press, 90–110 lb per sq. in. Sluice boxes are 3 ft 7 in wide, inside of liners; drop per 12-ft box, 8 in for the longer, and 6 in for the shorter sluice. Riffles are 4 by 6-in crosspieces, spaced 2–3 ft, and covered with longit 30-lb rails, heads up. Hg is added at 3–5 oz per day to first 3 boxes. Boulders are cleared from ends of sluices by 1-yd, gasolene-driven dragline, which also builds tailings dam, working 3 shifts on the 2 jobs. Boulders in pit are drilled by jackhammer connected to portable compressor. Three-shift operation (June, 1937) required 34 men; total wages, $154.25. In 1937 season of about 70 days, 200 000 cu yd through sluices yielded 900 fine oz, or 15.75¢ per yd.

Salmon Cr, Baker, Ore. Data from Gardner and Johnson (17) in 1934. Unusual feature was use of 0.5-cu yd, gasolene-powered shovel for handling boulders, water supply being inadequate to move them and to loosen profitable yardage of gravel at same time. When not occupied with boulders, the shovel aided in loosening clay-bound gravel. Cutting was done by No 2 giant with 2.25-in nozzle under 150-ft head, using 90 miner's in; an additional 60 in of water came over the bank, about 25 ft high. Bottom 1 ft of gravel, containing most of the gold, was left on bedrock, and washed separately at end of a month's run. For data on sluices and riffles, see Ex 18, Tables 116, 120. Crew on each of 2 8-hr shifts: 1 piper, 1 shovel operator, 2 sluice tenders; foreman on day shift. Gasolene for shovel, 12.5 gal per shift. Est cost (@ 130 cu yd per shift), 20¢ per yd, plus shovel rental, interest, and amortization of plant.

Alaska. Data from N. L. Wimmler (188) in 1927. GENERAL. Most hydraulic mining areas in Alaska (except in southern dist and upper Yukon basin) are characterized by: (a) Relatively shallow (max, 25 ft) deposits, of both stream and bench types; latter usually only slightly above streams. (b) Pay streaks close to bedrock. (c) Cemented gravel rare; frozen gravel and overburden fairly common. (d) Aver stream grades, 25–150 ft per mile, or less than the 6 in per 12 ft desirable for economical sluicing. (e) Water adequate for economical mining obtainable only at high cost for ditches. (f) Water supply erratic, and usually under low head; reservoir sites of large capac are scarce. (g) Working season of only 90–120 days; as short as 30 days in some localities deficient in water. These conditions affect mining methods in following ways: (1) Use of much of available water for ground-sluicing or bank water; in some places, water thus used may be 3 times the vol of that for the giants. (2) Necessity for frequent moves may lose 40–60% of time available for hydraulicking; loss still greater if only 1 shift is worked. (3) Intermittent operation, pending accumulation of useful vol of water. (4) Frequent necessity for elevating gravel or tailing. (5) Occasional adoption of "piping over the side" of sluice boxes depressed in a bedrock cut (see Dan Cr, below) unusual elsewhere. (6) Operations are relatively small-scale, employing 2–8 men; often, with 50–500 miner's in of water under 35–200 ft head, season's work will be 2 000–30 000 cu yd; a few larger mines, with 500–2 500 in of water under 100–300 ft head, may move 30 000–100 000 cu yd; max, 1 000 cu yd per day. Examples (operating in 1924) follow.

Falls Cr, Yentna dist. Creek deposit of unfrozen, round gravel, aver 8 ft deep, with 10–15% of boulders up to 3-ft diam. Bedrock is clay, shale, and sandstone, easily cleaned. Total water, incl ground-sluice, 300–700 in. Usual pit, 80 ft wide, 125 ft long. Sluice, 36 in wide, 42–54 ft long, on 8-in per 12 ft grade, with steel-shod, 2 by 4-in riffles, set lengthwise. Two giants, 3-in nozzles and 100-ft head, stood on top of bank and alternated in washing gravel from one side of pit to top of sluice, while other side was being cleared of boulders. Tailings required a stacker giant. Crew of 4 men on each of 2 10-hr shifts, at time of max water, could clean about 1 000 sq ft in 2 shifts, or finish an aver pit in 8–9 days. Setup for new pit took 1 day.

Crow Cr, Girdwood dist. Creek deposit of unfrozen gravel 6–25 (aver 12 ft) deep, with 50% of boulders over 6-in diam, many of them large. Bedrock, tough clay, readily cleaned. Total water, incl stacker giant, 2 600 in, of which 1 000–1 400 in was ground-sluice water. Two parallel and adjoining pits, each 100–150 ft wide and 400–450 ft long, were worked alternately but in step, piping in one while clearing boulders from other. Each pit had its own sluice, 5 ft wide, 8–10 boxes long, at 6 in per 12 ft grade; first 2 boxes had transverse riffles of 40-lb rail; others, longit 25-lb rails. A No 7 giant with 6-in nozzle stood at top of bank on center line of each pit, piping to head of sluice; when reach exceeded effic distance, a smaller booster giant on bedrock at one side of pit assisted sluicing. Upon completing both pits, bank between them was washed in and bedrock cleaned by giants. One stacker giant, No 7 with 5-in nozzle, at 170-ft head, served both sluices. Boulders were drilled and blasted, and put through sluice. With crew of 12–18 men, 66 000 cu yd was mined in 1923 at 43¢ per cu yd.

Dan Cr, Nizina dist. Deposit 6–18 ft deep, of rounded gravel containing up to 75% of boulders over 8-in diam, some reaching 6–10 ft. Bedrock, slate of variable hardness, cut by occasional porphyry dikes causing irregularities. Gold, flat and 40–60% of it coarser than 0.25 in. Deposit worked in a chain of consecutive pits, each 500–700 ft long by 175–300 ft wide, progressing up-stream by steps, although working face of each pit retreated downstream. Assuming a completed pit, as

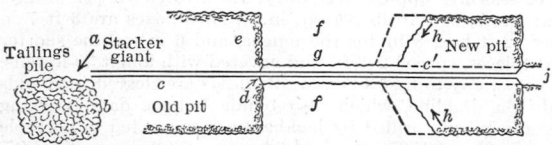

Fig 821. "Piping over Side," Dan Cr, Alaska (188)

a—Tailing stacker.   *b*—Tailing pile.   *c*—Sluice in old pit. *c'*—Sluice in new pit.   *d*—Wing dams.   *e*—Old pit.   *f*—New ground.   *g*—New bedrock ditch.   *h*—Giants.   *j*—Entrance for ground-sluice water.

at *e*, Fig 821, first step was to install a line usually of 16–20 (never fewer than 8) boxes, 48 in wide and riffled longitudinally with 20-lb rail, in the old bedrock ditch *c*, and erect a pair of short wing dams *d* at top of upper box. As early in the Spring as water was available, a central ditch *g*, the full length of proposed next adjoining pit, was cut through gravel and 5–6 ft into bedrock, using a giant with 4-in nozzle, smoothing the bottom (about 6 ft wide) with picks, to avoid fracturing. Max grade obtainable was 5–5.5 in per 12 ft, sometimes as flat as 3.5 in. Boxes, 48 in wide, 46.5 in deep (inside), riffled lengthwise with 20-lb rail, were then laid on bottom of entire ditch, connecting with the boxes in old pit at *d*. Ground-sluice water, about twice the vol delivered by a giant, was then turned into the sluice at *j*. After an initial cut to bedrock across the head of the new pit, 2 No 4 giants with 5-in nozzles and 275-ft head were set on bedrock, one on each side of the sluice and well out towards edge of pit, as at *h*. The 2 sides were then worked alternately, washing a slice 35–50 ft wide over the side of the depressed sluice on one side, while boulders were being handled on the other. On completing a slice, the giant was moved downstream a corresponding distance; process was repeated until the blocks *f* had been removed, along with 1–2 ft of bedrock. Tailings were stacked continuously by No 4 giant with 4-in nozzle under 310-ft head. Clean-up, usually not until after finishing a pit, involved removing first the sideboards and later the bottoms of the boxes and washing out gravel lodged between them and the walls and bottom of the cut. In 1923, an exceptionally favorable

year, 2 pits were completed, respectively 528 by 165 ft, and 480 by 170 ft; latter, averaging only 6 ft deep, took 9 days for set-up, 17.5 days for hydraulicking, and 10 days for clean-up. For the 2 pits, time required was: 22 days for set-up, 42 days (of 24 hr) hydraulicking, 26 10-hr shifts for clean-up. Total cost, $34 124.

Chititu Cr, Nizina dist. Stream deposit of coarse gravel 140–150 ft wide, 10–11 ft deep; bedrock, medium-soft slate. Method in

Sec A-A, Larger Scale

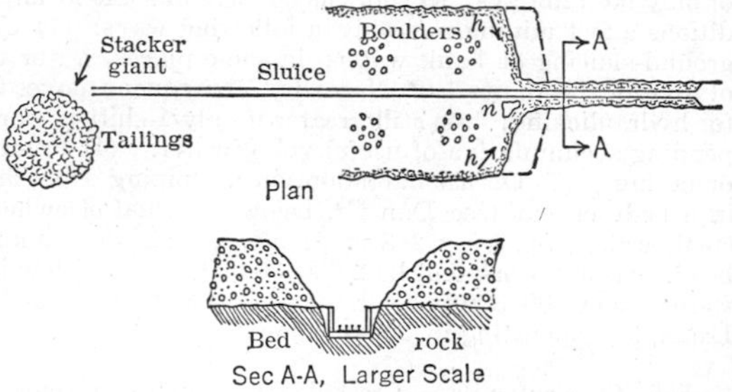

Fig 822. " Piping over Side " on Chititu Cr, Alaska (188)

1923–24 resembled that on Dan Cr, except that working face advanced upstream, as in Fig 822. Bottom of bedrock sluice, at grade of 5.5–6 in per 12 ft, was formed of 20-lb rail, laid longitudinally at 4-in centers, and spiked to crossties laid on slate bottom; only the sides of sluice, 3 by 3 ft, were boarded. Opposite sides of pit were worked alternately by giants at *h*; the small triangular block *n* was left till last, to protect men working at boulders on other side. Boulders were piled on clean bedrock by donkey engine and steel stoneboat. In 1923, one such pit, 460 ft long, 140 ft wide, 11 ft deep, yielded 23 323 cu yd in 44 20-hr days; cost of labor only, 21¢ per yd; in 1924, total operating cost was 51¢ per cu yd.

124. SLUICES

Construction. Sluices are in sections, usually 12 ft long; each section is called a SLUICE BOX. Fig 823 shows typical box for shoveling-in and other SMALL WORK (Art 121). Sides and bottom are 1-in by 12, 14 or 16-in boards, rough or planed on one side; the bottom is 2 in narrower at one end that at the other, so that adjoining boxes will telescope a few inches into each other. Sluices may rest on bedrock, or be set in ditches, or be elevated. They are braced laterally by struts *B*. On the side opposite each shoveler is a board *S*, against which the gravel is thrown, instead of being shoveled carefully into the sluice; this increases the duty of labor and prevents spilling. A collar placed at the

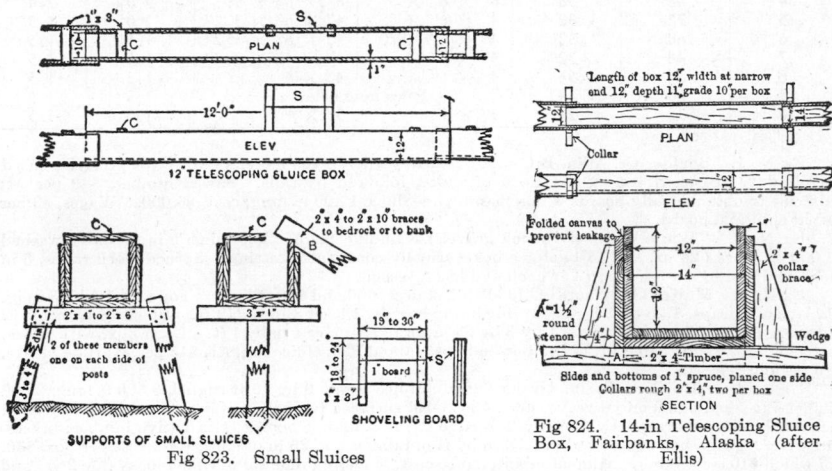

Fig 823. Small Sluices

Fig 824.   14-in Telescoping Sluice Box, Fairbanks, Alaska (after Ellis)

junction of each 2 boxes (Fig 824) eliminates braces *C*, Fig 823, which obstruct top of sluice and interfere slightly with cleaning-up. Small sluices may be made with flush joints, like a flume (Sec 38); some operators say this reduces clogs, but the telescoping box is most used because it is easily erected and moved (111). These sluices have a short life, but are cheap and well suited to small work. Worn-out boxes should be burned and the ashes rocked or sluiced to recover gold from cracks and joints.

Fig 825 shows LARGE SLUICES for hydraulicking; details vary widely (Table 118); 4 by 4-in sills suffice for sluices up to 4 ft wide; 4 by 6-in sills and 4 by 4 or 4 by 6 posts for wider ones. Sills are 3–4 ft apart; every 3rd or 4th post is supported by angle braces. Posts are dapped into sills, or fastened with cleats, or toe-nailed (Fig 825). Lumber need not be surfaced, but for sides and bottom

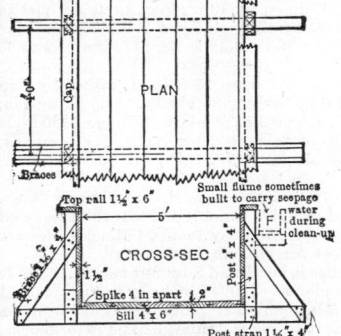

Fig 825. Sluice (riffles and side lining omitted)

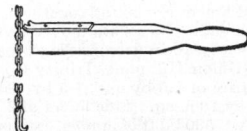

Fig 826.   Tightener for Bottom Boards (after Purington)

should be free from knots. To prevent loss of Hg and amalgam, bottom joints are made tight with tongue and groove lumber, splines, or outside battens; close fitting alone is often relied upon. Fig 826 shows a useful device for tightening bottom boards before spiking (390). Sills must have solid foundation to prevent settlement. As bottom of a new sluice may rise by water collecting under it, ends of sills should be weighted down (391, 406). Following data, referring to Table 118, while old, give elements of cost, which can be adjusted to present costs of labor and supplies.

Table 118. Details of Sluices for Hydraulicking

Example No	Width, in	Depth, in	Dimensions of		Thickness of	
			Sills	Posts	Bottom, in	Sides, in
1	24	....	$4'' \times 6''$	$4'' \times 6''$	1.5	1.25
2	24	20	$2'' \times 2''$	$2'' \times 2''$	2.0	1.5
3	29	38.5	$4'' \times 6'' \times 6'$	$4'' \times 4'' \times 3' \ 4''$	1.5	1.0
4	48	58	$6'' \times 6'' \times 5'$	$6'' \times 6'' \times 5'$	2.0	2.0
5	72	32	$4'' \times 6'' \times 8'$	$4'' \times 6'' \times 3' \ 2''$	2.0	1.5
6	60	32	$4'' \times 6'' \times 7'$	$4'' \times 6'' \times 3' \ 2''$	1.5	1.5
7	48	32	$4'' \times 6'' \times 7'$	$4'' \times 4'' \times 3' \ 2''$	1.5	1.5
8	54	54	$4'' \times 6''$	$4'' \times 4''$	1.5	1.5
9	60	54	See note below		1.5	1.5
10	32	24	$3'' \times 4''$	$3'' \times 4''$	1.5	1.5

Ex No 1. Boulder Cr, Atlin, B C (390). Heavy gravel, 400 miner's in of water; duty, 1 cu yd per in-day. Block riffles used at head of sluice, followed by rails. Sawed lumber, $40 per M; difficult to obtain locally boards wider than 8 in. Sluice 1 400 ft long; cost, $6 000. Wages, $3 per 10-hr shift and board.

Ex No 2. "White Channel" bench gravels, Klondike (390). 250 miner's in of water washed 1 000 cu yd per 24 hr. 12 to 14 sluice boxes usually constitute a string. Spruce block riffles, 5 in high and 9 in sq are used; cost 25¢ each and last 1 season.

Ex No 3. McKee Cr, Atlin, B C (390). 2 sluices, 600 and 700 ft long. Top rail, 1.5 by 8 in by 12 ft; post straps, 1.25 by 2 by 14 in; side lining boards, 1.5 by 8 in by 12 ft. Blocks 8 by 8 by 12 in are used for riffles; riffle strips, 1 by 3 by 28 in; braces, 1.5 by 4 in by 1 ft. Each box, with riffles, etc, contains about 540 bd ft of lumber and costs about $25; sluice lumber, $45 per M; riffle blocks, $6 per box-length.

Ex No 4. Silver Bow Basin, Alaska (390). Sluice is in a 9 by 10-ft tunnel, 3 300 ft long; 2 500 miner's in wash 5 000 cu yd gravel per 24 hr. All surfaced lumber. Riffles are 12 by 12 by 12-in spruce blocks, separated by 1 7/8 by 2-in riffle strips. Lining boards, 1-in native lumber; braces, 1 by 8 in. Each box contains about 1 100 bd ft of lumber and 25 lb of nails; total cost per box, $30, of which $10 is for labor. Annual maintenance cost, including renewal of riffle blocks (life 2 yr) and lining boards, $1 000.

Ex No 5. North Bloomfield tunnel sluice, Cal (391). 30d nails used for the bottoms, 20d nails for the sides. Side lining made of worn blocks, 3 in thick and 18 to 20 in deep. Braces, 2 by 4 in by 2 ft. Block riffles, 20.5 in sq and 13 in deep, riffle strips, 1.25 by 3 in by 5 ft 11.5 in long; aver of 19 blocks per 12-ft box. A flume for seepage water (F, Fig 825), 13 in wide, 14 in deep, of 1.5-in plank, was built along one side of sluice.

Ex No 6. Bedrock Claim, Cal (391). Boxes, 14 ft long. Top rails, 2 by 7 in by 14 ft. 1 by 0.5-in tongues were set in grooves between bottom planks. Side lining composed of blocks 3 in thick by 20 in sq. Braces, 1.5 by 4 in by 2 ft. 27 blocks, 17 in sq by 13 in deep, used as riffles in 1 box; riffle strips, 1.25 by 3 in by 5 ft. Cost per box, $30.86, as follows: 650 bd ft lumber and side lining @ $20 per M, $13; 704 bd ft blocks @ $14 per M, $9.86; 20 lb nails @ 5¢, $1; labor, $2 to $3 per day, $7.

Ex No 7. La Grange mine, Cal; sluice used in 1880 (391). Boxes, 16 ft long, with 4 by 6 in posts at ends. Top rails, 1.5 by 8 in by 16 ft; braces, 1 by 6 in by 3 ft; 36 blocks, 14 by 14 by 8 in, used in each box; riffle strips, 1.75 by 2 in by 4 ft; side lining, 1.5 in plank, 16 ft long. 420 bd ft of lumber required per 16-ft box, exclusive of riffles. 15 lb of nails used per box. Cost per box, $28.34, as follows: 420 ft lumber @ $30 per M, $12.60; 36 blocks @ 35¢ each, $12.60; 15 lb nails @ 4 1/4¢, $0.64; labor @ $1 to $2.50, $2.50.

Ex No 8. Lorenz mine, Trinity Co, Cal (415). 600 to 700 miner's in wash 500 cu yd in 10 hr. Posts, sills, and braces are bolted together; sills are mounted on skids running full length of box and beveled at each end. Boxes are moved under bedrock to new positions by teams. Block riffles are 11 in or 18 in sq by 10 in deep; riffle strips, 2 by 2 in. Cost per box, about $20.

Ex No 9. Union Hill mine, Trinity Co, Cal (415). Sluice is laid in an 8 by 8-ft tunnel, 1 300 ft long. Frames are of 1.5 by 6-in, 1.5 by 4-in, and 4 by 5-in pieces. Riffle blocks, 12 in deep and 11 by 11 in to 18 by 18 in sq. Side liners of 2 by 10 and 2 by 6-in plank last about 3 yr. Riffle sticks 2 by 2 in by 5 ft. 500 bd ft of lumber used per box for frames, bottoms and sides; 525 bd ft for blocks. Cost per box: lumber, $16; blocks, $9; construction, $10.

Ex No 10. River Bend mine, Siskiyou Co, Cal (416). Sluice is at head of an hydraulic elevator. Frames are 4 ft c-c. 12 in sq blocks used for riffles, also rails and transverse angle-iron riffles.

Steel sluices are used chiefly at the head of hydraulic elevators (Art 126). They are tight, have low frictional resistance and are easily bolted together; their cost is prohibitive in most districts (tail sluices for dredges (Art 127) are an exception).

Curves should be avoided if possible; they increase friction and wear, reduce velocity of the water, and if sharp cause splashing. Sluices are curved by making small deflections at successive joints. Brigham (406) says a 5-in "swing" is the max permissible for a 12-ft box; for a sharper turn, use a 4-in swing on a 6-ft box, or 3.5-in on a 4-ft box. Curves should be eased at both ends, and outer edge of boxes elevated 1/8 to 3/8 in per ft of sluice width. Grade of sluice should be steepened at curves; an increase of 15% is desirable on short turns. Bowie (391) gives data on curves, relative to turn-in and turn-out sluices. These work well on steep grades, but require careful design on flat grades at connections with main sluice; otherwise gravel collects above or below the junction. Fig 827 shows a TURN-IN SLUICE, carrying 1 000– 1 400 miner's in, adopted after many experiments. Radius of curvature, height of drop, width of opening at the junction, and grades as shown, were all at the limit on which the 2 sluices would run uniformly without depositing gravel.

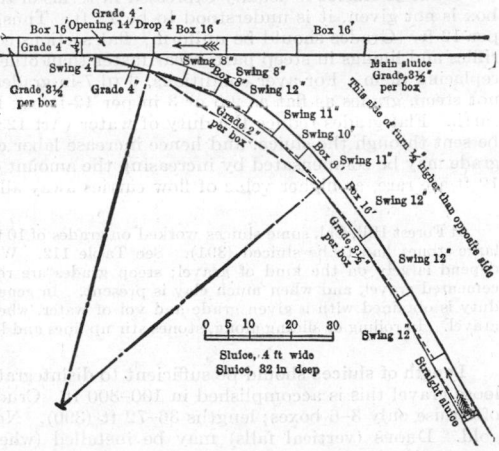

Fig 827.   Turn-in Sluice at Head of Tunnel, Delaney Claim, Patricksville, Cal (after Bowie)

TURN-OUT SLUICES, generally used for "fanning out" a dump, are harder to operate on light grades than turn-in sluices.

A 4-ft turnout was used at La Grange at a point where limited dumproom required sharp curves and grades were only 2.75–4 in per 16-ft box. Originally, the opening at point of divergence was 14 ft wide, with a 1.5-in drop between main and turn-out sluices, and the latter was swung 4 in per 16-ft box; it worked satisfactorily. On increasing the swing to 5 in, the boxes adjacent to the junction choked, and the discharge had to be widened to 24 ft. It was found here that, in a 200-ft swing on a 2% grade, the greatest possible swing per 16-ft box was 8 in for a 4-ft sluice; but the curve could be increased in proportion to the grade. At the turn-in and turn-out a board must be placed diagonally across main sluice, to concentrate discharge and prevent formation of bars.

Duplicate sluices are sometimes installed to avoid delays; one is cleaned-up while the the other is running; both usually empty into one tail sluice. In sluicing tin-bearing gravels, there may be enough concentrate to fill the riffles in a short time and require frequent clean-ups; in such cases, duplicate sluices allow continuous operation.

Bulkheads. Head end of a sluice for hydraulicking is usually flared out by building diverging bulkheads (wing dams) on each side; these aid in collecting gravel and water as they flow back from the face, and assist piping in fallen gravel.

H. L. Mead, in 1913, stated that the sluice mouth at La Grange, Cal, is 6 ft wide and 18 ft high; a heavy bulkhead of this height is built out from both sides. The giants generally work in pairs, first cutting down the bank and then swinging, following the fallen gravel toward the sluice and adding water to it; very heavy material may thus be washed into the sluice. The high bulkhead and high sides of sluice near its head allow gravel to build up and increase the grade; this, with the above method of washing, starts material down the sluice with a high veloc and increases its capac (395).

Mud box (Fig 828) has been used on small sluices in Alaska as a puddling or dump box; usually set at the sluice head; in late years it has become less common. In it, sticky clay and mud are broken up and large stones forked out; it may be installed for the latter purpose alone in shoveling-in, if sluice is too narrow to use a sluice fork effectively. Mud boxes have an apron 8 or 10 ft square at one side of the box, on a slope of 35 to 50°; gravel from cableway or derrick buckets, or from skips and power scrapers (Art 122), is dumped on the apron and slides into the box. Mud boxes are set on steeper grades (10 to 12 in per 12 ft) than sluices; they are paved with pole, block,

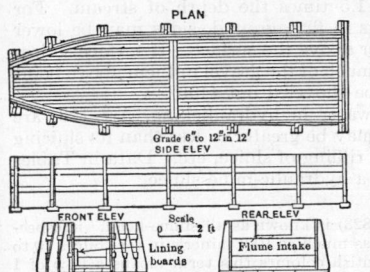

Fig 828.   Mud Box or Dump Box (after Purington)

or rail riffles, and collect much of the coarse gold. For sluices 12 to 16 in wide they vary in length from 16 to 24 ft and in width from 30 to 48 in.

Grade of sluices is usually expressed in terms of the fall in inches per box; if length of box is not given, it is understood to be 12 ft. Thus, a 5-in grade means a slope of 5 in per 12 ft. Grades should be uniform; flat sections control the capac of the whole sluice; riffles and linings in steep parts wear faster than others and the flow must be stopped for replacing them. For aver conditions, 6 to 7-in grades are satisfactory. If natural fall is not steep, grades as flat as 2.5 or 3 in per 12-ft box have been used for light gravel and earth. Flat grades reduce the duty of water (Art 123), limit max size of stones that can be sent through the sluice, and hence increase labor cost for handling boulders. Lack of grade may be compensated by increasing the amount of water. Grades over 13–14 in per 12 ft are rare, as higher veloc of flow carries away all but very coarse gold.

At Forest Hill, Cal, some sluices worked on grades of 10 to 24 in per 12 ft. Water was scarce and large stones had to be sluiced (391). See Table 112. Where the fall is unlimited, sluice grades depend largely on the kind of gravel; steep grades are required by coarse, flat, sub-angular, or cemented gravel, and when much clay is present. In general, grades may be flatter, and a larger duty is obtained with a given grade and vol of water, when sluicing a mixture of large and small gravel. In rolling or sliding along, stones stir up fines and keep them in suspension.

Length of sluices should be sufficient to disintegrate the gravel and free the gold. For loose gravel this is accomplished in 100–300 ft. Crude shoveling-in operations in Alaska often use only 3–6 boxes; lengths 36–72 ft (390). No attempt is made to save very fine gold. DROPS (vertical falls) may be installed (where topography allows) to break up cemented gravels and lessen sluice length. General practice is to lengthen a sluice so long as the yield from lower boxes exceeds cost of installing and operating them. Veloc of flow largely determines the minimum size of colors caught by riffles; hence, a greater length than needed to disintegrate the gravel is useless. Short sluices with drops and undercurrents (Art 125) are often more effic gold-savers than long sluices without them. Very long sluices may be needed to transport gravel to dumps; their lower parts are called TAIL-SLUICES. For examples see Tables 116, 117, 118 (notes); and under Cost and operating data, Art 123.

Cross-section of sluices is proportioned to amounts of water and gravel and to veloc of flow, which in turn depends on grade. For minimum first cost and wetted perimeter (hence for minimum frictional resistance and max discharge for a given cross-sec) the sluice width should be about twice the depth of stream, as in flumes (Sec 38, Art 15); it may be impossible to retain this ratio in large sluices. Depth of water should suffice to submerge the largest stones. Width of sluice is adjusted to depth and grade, for the required capac. Fine gravel containing fine gold should have very shallow, wide sluices, on steep grades (see Undercurrents, Art 125). The tendency for riffles to pack increases with depth of stream, which is usually 6–12 in.

Miner's inches of water	Width, in
200–300	24
400	30
600	36
1 000	40
1 500–2 000	48
3 000	60

W. A. Newman (618) gives accompanying data on aver Calif practice in medium gravel that could be washed at rate of 3 cu yd per miner's in per day; grade, 5–7 in per 12 ft; widths are inside of side boards, before inserting liners. To reduce first cost, and facilitate cleaning out and replacing riffles, the height of sides of a sluice should not exceed 1.3 to 1.5 times the depth of stream. For sluices in deep cuts in firm ground, sides may be lower than for those on or above the surface. If surface sluices clog and overflow, much of the gravel in them above point of overflow must be shoveled out (406).

Water required. Data given under Duty of water in hydraulicking, Art 123, are unsatisfactory, as the cutting capac of giant water may be greater or less than its sluicing capac, depending on character of gravel, grade and riffling of sluice, etc. Data in Tables 115, 116, 117 refer to duty of total water entering a hydraulic-mine sluice.

The water used in a small sluice for shoveling-in (Fig 823) is known as a "sluice-head," irrespective of its quantity; it varies from 30 to 60 (occasionally as much as 100) miner's in for sluices 10 to 14 in wide set on grades of 6–8 in per 12-ft box. In British colonies this term means a flow of 1 cu ft of water per sec (394).

Calculations of sluice grades, cross-sec, veloc of flow, etc, can not be made accurately, because the complex relationships between the factors are not wholly known, and few experiments have been made to determine the necessary empirical constants. Most authorities suggest some modification of Chazy's formula, Sec 38, as a basis. For examples see Bib (394, 388, 417).

The author's calculations of n in Kutter's formula (Sec 38), for a few sluices where all necessary data are available, show values from 0.027 to 0.04. Calculations should be checked against actual operations under similar conditions; Tables in Art 123, 124 are helpful. Geike gives the accompanying data on veloc of streams required to move materials of different sizes (418). Somewhat smaller velocities suffice for sluices.

Veloc, ft per min	
15	Begins to wear away fine clay
30	Just lifts fine sand
40	Carries sand as coarse as linseed
60	Moves fine gravel
120	Moves pebbles of 1 in diam
180	" " of egg size

Table 119. Capacity of Sluices

Sluice		Grade per 12-ft box, in	Miner's in of water	Bib No
Width, in	Height of side, in			
10 to 12	(a)	6	30	(286)
12 to 14	(b)	9	67	(286)
72	36	6 to 7	2 000 to 3 500	(391)
48	30	3	800 to 1 500	(391)
48	30	6	2 000	(391)
36	30	2.25	600 to 1 000	(391)
36	(c)	....	200 to 600	(406)
48	....	....	400 to 1 200	(406)
60	....	....	1 000 to 2 500	(406)
72	....	....	2 000 to 4 000	(406)
96	....	....	3 000 to 5 000	(406)
120	....	....	4 000 to 7 000	(406)

Van Wagenen (417) states that a veloc of 200 ft per min is necessary to move pebbles the size of an egg, 320 ft for stones of 3 to 4 in diam, 400 ft for boulders of 6 to 8 in diam, 600 ft for boulders 12 to 18 in diam. G. K. Gilbert's experiments on stream and flume traction are also suggestive, Bib (419).

(a) Depth of flow, 6 to 7 in.   (b) Depth of flow, 10 in.   (c) Height of side, in this and following examples, is 0.5 to 0.75 width of sluice; depth of flow, 0.33 to 0.5 of clear inside depth of sluice. Duty of water (Art 123) must be known or assumed in designing a sluice for a given amount of gravel.

Conversion factors for sluice calculations: Inches of fall per 12-ft box $\times$ 0.694 = % grade; inches per 16-ft box $\times$ 0.521 = % grade; fall in ft per mile $\times$ 0.027 = fall per 12-ft box, in; miner's in of water $\times$ 0.025 = cu ft per sec; cu yd of gravel per 24 hr $\times$ 0.000312 = cu ft of gravel per sec. If D = duty of 1 miner's in, in cu yd of gravel washed per 24 hr, and the flow of water and gravel is uniform, then 80 $\div$ D = ratio between cu ft of water per sec and cu ft of gravel per sec.

125. RIFFLES, UNDERCURRENTS, AND OTHER GOLD-SAVING DEVICES

Riffles have 3 chief functions: (a) to retard material moving over them and give it a chance to settle; (b) to form pockets to retain gold which settles into them; (c) to form eddies which roughly classify the material in the riffle spaces. Their exact operation is not well understood. Strength and shape of eddies (the "boil" of the riffle) is affected by shape and spacing of riffles, their position with respect to direction of flow, and the veloc of current. The boil must be strong enough to prevent riffles from filling with heavy sand (packing), and not too strong to prevent lodgment of gold.

Features of design of riffles, especially for large-scale hydraulicking, are stated by Bouery (420) as follows: (a) They should oppose minimum resistance to flow, in order to get high duty from the water. (b) They should resist wear, to reduce cost of replacing and maintaining them, and to preserve their gold-saving capacity. Effect of wear on gold-saving should be considered in design and choice of material. (c) They should be sufficient in number to save all the gold commercially recoverable. The ultimate economy of a high-cost material, as manganese or nickel steel, compared with cheaper structural steel, may be determined thus: Let A and X represent maker's cost of 2 materials a and b, and B the cost of transport for either. Assume that the life of the cheaper material (a) is 1 year, that of the high-priced material (b) is N years. For equal costs at the end of N years, $X + B = N (A + B)$, or $X = N (A + B) - B$. If this equality exists, or if X is greater than $N (A + B) - B$, there is no economy in purchasing high-grade material. If X is less than $N (A + B) - B$, the economy of high-grade material increases approx with N. Good material saves indirectly also, by reducing unit cost of labor and interruptions due to replacing worn riffles (420).

Riffles for small sluices. Fig 829 shows forms commonly used for shoveling-in (Art 121). The pole riffle (a) is a favorite in Alaska for coarse gold; (b) is the same form made of sawed lumber; (c) transverse (or "Hungarian") riffle offers greater frictional resistance, clogs more easily, and costs more than (a), but is a better saver of fine gold. In a string of boxes, both types are commonly used. Small riffles are fastened by nails driven into them through sides of sluice; as the nails are not driven home, they are easily pulled when riffles are removed for clean-ups. Wedges may be used instead of nails, but are troublesome.

Riffles for hydraulicking are of many kinds; their importance demands description in detail. In recent practice, the usual types are steel-shod Hungarian and longit riffles.

Cobble or rock riffles (Fig 830) are cheap and resist wear well if of hard rock; their life averages about 5 times that of wood blocks (406). As the surface is rough, they require steeper grades than other riffles. They are well adapted to tail sluices which are cleaned up infrequently, as they are difficult to take up and relay.

Block riffles (Fig 831), where timber is cheap, are often the most economical form for the upper parts of sluices, as they are quickly taken up and replaced. They make

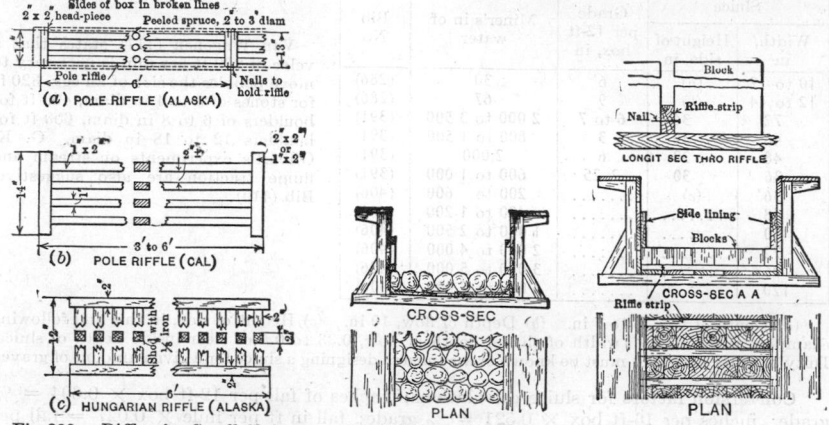

Fig 829. Riffles for Small Sluices   Fig 830. Cobble Riffles   Fig 831. Block Riffles

a smooth pavement on which stones may roll or slide, and work well. The blocks are 8–12 in deep, set in transverse rows separated by "riffle strips," and are square so that when worn they may be turned to give the smoothest surface; side of the square is an even divisor of sluice width. It is usual to set blocks in adjacent rows to break joints, because longit cracks enlarge quickly and force earlier renewals. At a few mines, better gold recovery is claimed for a pavement in which joints are broken as above, but longit spaces are also left between the blocks of each row (390).

Blocks are held in place by the side lining and riffle strips. Each strip is nailed to a row of blocks with headless wire nails, which are not driven home but project from 0.5 to 0.75 in. The adjacent blocks are driven against these nails until they rest solidly against the riffle strip. For dimensions, see examples following Table 118.

The objection to block riffles is their rapid wear under heavy service; their life depends on quality of wood, sluice grade, character and quantity of gravel, and amount of water. Long-grained wood, which "brooms up," is best; hard wood is not desirable. On a given grade, the larger the ratio of water to gravel, the less the wear (391). Blocks worn to a thickness of 4 or 5 in are discarded, or used for lining the sides of sluices. Bowie gives accompanying data from early California mines (391).

Locality	Width of sluice, ft	Grade, in per 12 ft	Depth of blocks, in	Life of blocks, in-days of water
North Bloomfield	6	6.5	13	175 000–200 000
Manzanita mine	5	7.0	13	100 000–150 000
La Grange	4	3.0	8	100 000–110 000

At Manzanita mine, and also at French Corral mine where similar figures were obtained, poorer timber was used for blocks than at North Bloomfield. P. Bouery, in 1913 (420), states that in 6-ft sluices at La Grange the life of 13-in blocks was 45 days to 3 mo; those in the higher boxes lasted longest. On increasing the duty of water 40%, the life of blocks decreased 60%, so that a clean-up was necessary every 17 days. Consequent delay and expense, and limited supply of pine blocks, led to use of manganese-steel riffles (Fig 836).

Longitudinal rail riffles (Fig 832) are of 20 to 40-lb RR rails, in lengths to 20 ft, usually set upside down and spaced 3 to 5 in or more apart by wooden or C-I spacers. On a given grade, rails will run as much fines and more boulders than blocks (406); they are largely used in the upper boxes of sluices, as they wear fairly well and are easily taken up.

Transverse rail riffles. Bouery's experiments at La Grange, Cal (see under Block riffles), published in 1913 (420), give valuable data on riffles for large hydraulic sluices: La Grange sluice is 6 ft wide, on a grade of 7 to 8 in per 12 ft; depth of water, 12 to 18 in.

Experiment showed that transverse were superior to longit riffles. A rock or a sand particle may remain in contact with and wear the web, flange or head of a longit rail throughout its entire length, but wears only the top of a transverse rail. Longit rails 8 in apart wore faster than those spaced 5 in. 40-lb longit rails, spaced 5 in, were discarded after passing 9 600 000 miner's in-days of water; 40-lb transverse rails, spaced 5 in, passed 14 400 000 miner's in. 5-in spacing (c to c) proved best; different spacing might

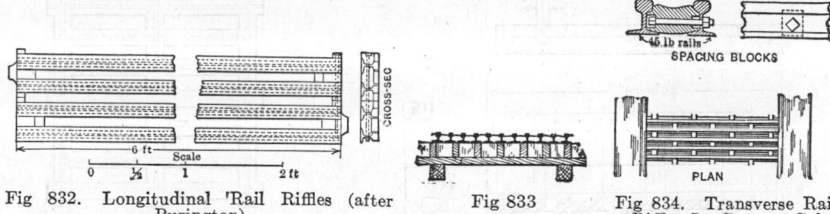

Fig 832. Longitudinal 'Rail Riffles (after Purington)

Fig 833

Fig 834. Transverse Rail Riffle, La Grange, Cal

be advantageous for other grades or depths of water, but Bouery puts the economic interval between 4 and 6 in; spacing less than 4 in increases first cost; spacing greater than 6 in interferes with free passage of boulders. 45-lb rail was selected for the first experiment; 16 and 25-lb rail were considered too light; 55-lb rail had too large a web and flange in proportion to its head; 40-lb rail was finally found to be the most economical. Rails were set on a series of 2 by 6-in wooden riffles, separated by blocks (Fig 833); rails alone do not form sufficiently deep pockets, and they allow eddies which wear the sluice bottom. This system proved much more efficient for catching gold than the previous block riffles, and the gravel never packed hard between the rails. 7 spacing blocks had to be set between each pair of rails (Fig 834). Wear is greater in center than at sides of sluice, and rails bend before wearing out, unless rigidly supported. By using 7 spacing blocks, rails could be used until they were 62.5% worn, instead of 37.5%, as was the case with 3 or 4 spacers. Ends of worn rails, utilized to protect the sides of sluices (Fig 835), were held in place by nails bent over the flange of top rail, and by a 2 by 6-in plank. Side rails did not increase the duty of water materially, but decreased cost of replacing the blocks formerly used; they last 5–7 years; duty, about 30 million cu yd of gravel.

Further experiments, with cast and alloy steels, showed manganese steel to be the most economical. Many forms of riffle were developed, aiming to lengthen their life and to utilize worn rails. Fig 836 shows a manganese-steel riffle considered by Bouery to have all the requisite qualities, viz: high gold-saving capac, slow wear, good setting, rigidity, and security against theft of gold. Some of them passed 52 800 000 miner's in-days of water and from 12–15 million cu yd of gravel before they were discarded. For further data, see Distribution of gold in sluices, and Bib (420).

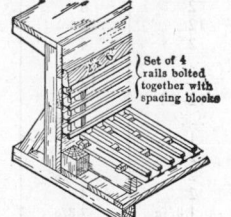

Fig 835. Rail Side Lining, La Grange, Cal

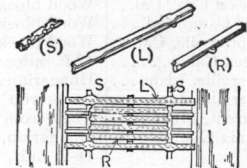

Fig 836. Bouery Manganese-steel Riffle

Wooden Hungarian riffles, shod with iron straps, similar to Fig 829, c, but made of 2 by 4-in or larger scantlings, may be used where rails are not available. They resemble rail riffles in respect of gold-saving, but have shorter life and are less convenient.

Angle-iron riffles (the Evans riffle) are of the Hungarian type. They have been used chiefly in hydraulic elevator sluices (Art 126), on tables and tail sluices of dredges (Art 127) and sometimes for small open-cut work (Table 113) and hydraulicking. Size of angles varies from 1.5 by 1.5 by 1/4 in for small-sized material, up to 2.5 by 2.5 by 3/8 in. Fig 837 shows one method of holding angles in place. They are set with the vertical leg on the upstream side; clear space between them, 0.25 to 3 in. Close spacing gives a weak eddy and the "dead water" space is said to be a good fine-gold saver, assuming that the current velocity allows such gold to settle on the riffles. T-iron may be used instead of angles.

C-I grate riffle (Fig 838) has worked well in small sluices on Seward Peninsula, Alaska. It is light, easily handled, and can be set so that the long dimension of slots is either transverse or longit; the latter setting is thought best (390).

High-carbon steel plates have effected important economies at several large mines, where used as riffles and as linings for tail-sluices. They reduce friction, compared with wood block or other

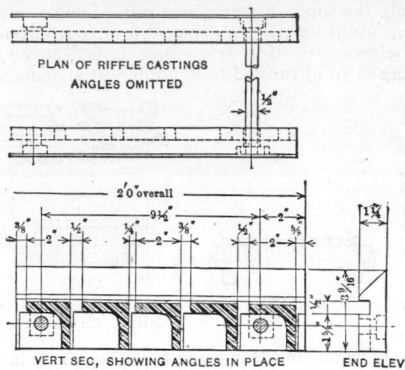

PLAN OF RIFFLE CASTINGS
ANGLES OMITTED

VERT SEC, SHOWING ANGLES IN PLACE   END ELEV

Fig 837.   Riffle Castings for 2 by 2-in Angles, $5/16$ or $3/8$ in thick

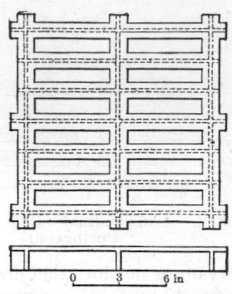

Fig 838.   C-I Riffle (after Purington)

pavements, and are especially useful on limited grades. The steel contains 0.8–1.2% carbon; in some cases it is found that the outside skin of the plate is more resistant to wear than the interior. Plates are commonly 0.5 in thick, of same width as sluice and of various lengths. Fig 839 shows modes of supporting plates 12 ft long. A 2-in space and a 0.5-in drop is left at end of each plate. Supports T are 6 to 8-in logs, 12 ft long, sawed flat on 2 sides and tapered from 3.5 in at upper end to 4 in at downstream end. Plates are held down by 3 by 10-in lining boards. This made a good riffle and increased the sluice capacity about 40%; angular blasted boulders 30 in long could be sluiced, as against 20-in pieces with block riffle (412). At Waldo, Oregon, plates 20 by 30 in were set on 2 by 4-in cross joists; the plates were 1.5 in apart; no drop was used (422). The Quesnelle Co, B C, used plates 58 in sq in a 6-ft sluice, separated

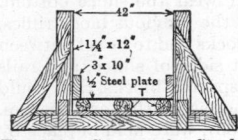

Fig 839.   Support for Steel Plate, Ruby Cr, B C

Table 120.   Riffles at Hydraulic Mines of Western U S in 1932 (17)

Example	Location	Type of Riffle	Width, in	Height, in	Spaced c-c, in
1	Weaverville, Cal....	Wood, cross..................	2	6	4
2	Douglas City, Cal....	Wood blocks.................	12	12	12
3	Douglas City, Cal...	Hungarian....................	2	4	4 1/2
4	Junction City, Cal...	Wood blocks.................	...	...	...
5	Wash. Camp, Cal....	Wood blocks.................	...	12	...
6	Comptonville, Cal...	Wood blocks.................	12–24	7	12
7	Helena, Cal.........	12-ft rails..................	...	3 1/2	4 1/4
8	Centerville, Idaho...	Hungarian....................	1	1 1/2	2 1/2
9	Centerville, Idaho...	Angle iron...................	2	2	4
10	Emigrant, Mont.....	Angle iron, 1/4-in...........	2	1 1/2	2 3/4
11	Virginia City, Mont.	Hungarian, 10 4-ft secs........	2	4	8
		16-lb rails, 1 12-ft length.......	1 3/16	2 3/8	3
		Poles, 4 6-ft lengths...........	4	4	5
12	Gold Cr, Mont......	Cast-iron bars, 4 ft long.......	3	1 1/4	5
13	Gold Cr, Mont......	" " " "	3	1 1/4	5
14	Sheridan, Mont.....	40-lb, 30-ft rails............	1 7/8	3 1/2	6 1/4
15	Superior, Mont.....	5 1/2-ft poles..................	4	4	...
16	Townsend, Mont....	6-ft poles...................	5	5	6 1/2
17	York, Mont........	16-ft strap iron (a)...........	3	1/2	4 1/2
		Wood blocks.................	4	4	4
18	Baker, Oreg........	10-ft rails, 2 lengths..........	2	2 1/2	4
		6-ft poles, 10 lengths..........	4	4	5
		Hungarian, last 100 ft........	1 1/2	1 1/2	3
19	Leland, Oreg.......	Wood, cross..................	2	4	...
20	O'Brien, Oreg.......	Wood blocks.................	...	6	...
		Angle iron...................	4	4	...
21	Galice, Oreg........	3-ft, 40-lb rails, lengthwise......	...	...	...

(a) Supported on 2 by 4-in wooden cross strips, spaced 4 ft.

by a 2-in space and a 0.5-in drop. A number of boxes at head of sluice were paved with manganese-steel rail riffles which extracted most of the gold (421). Table 120, from Gardner and Johnson (17), gives data on riffles installed in the same sluices (correspondingly numbered) as those for which other data are found in Table 116; lengths are stated only for longit riffles; width of sluice fixes length of cross-riffles.

For further data on riffles for fine material, see Undercurrents below, and Dredging (Art 127).

Side linings are required to protect the sides of large sluices; also they often furnish a means of holding riffles in place. Plank liners are common (Fig 831), 1-in for smaller sluices, 2 to 3-in for wide sluices with a high head of water. Where block riffles are used, worn blocks are placed on the sides; they serve for tail sluices, but are inconvenient where frequent clean-ups are necessary. See Fig 835 for rail linings. Height of side linings need not be more than 2 or 3 in above normal level of the stream of water and gravel.

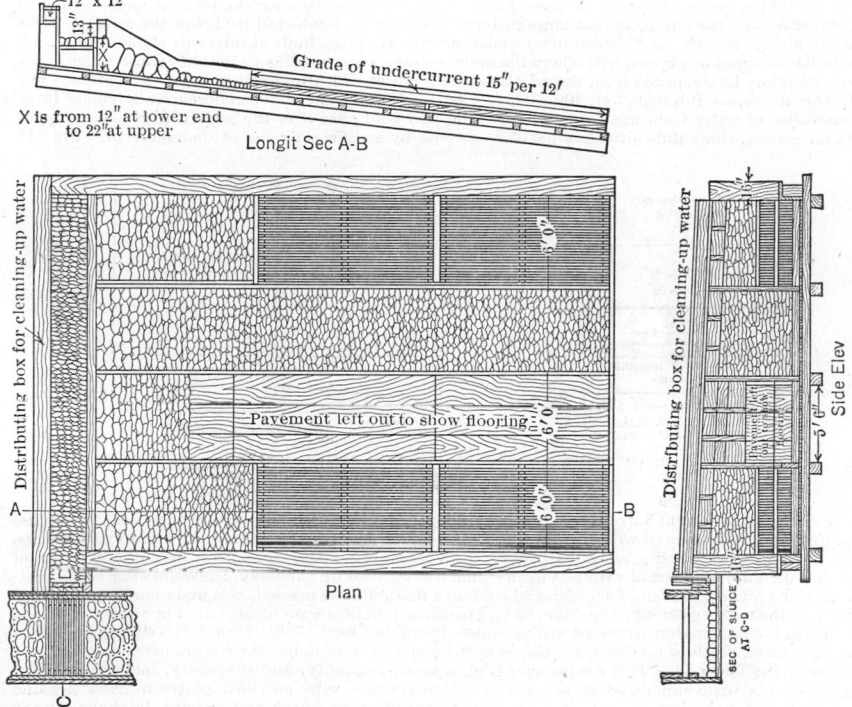

Fig 840. North Bloomfield Undercurrent (after Bowie)

Undercurrents are intended to save fine gold which will not settle in the sluice. Fig 840 shows the North Bloomfield undercurrent, fairly typical for large Calif sluices; it is a wide sluice, set on a heavy grade at one side of and below main sluice.

Bowie gives following details: Across the main sluice, at some point where a drop can be made, is placed a grizzly, over which coarse material and some water passes; the under-size falls into a spill box and runs thence through a distributing sluice (grade 2–3%) to the undercurrent proper. The latter is a shallow box, 20 to 50 ft wide and 40–50 ft long, divided into sections by vert partitions for convenience in placing riffles and cleaning-up, and to allow better control of the distribution of material. Undercurrents are paved with small wooden blocks, cobbles, or pole riffles shod with iron; grades required for these riffles are 14, 16 and 12 in per 12 ft, respectively. Depending on location of the under-current, its tailing and water are discharged directly or led back to the main sluice, which extends below the drop at which undercurrent is erected. Width of undercurrent, 8 to 10 × width of main sluice. A wide undercurrent costs slightly more to clean up than a narrow one, but is often more effic; at French Corral, with a 5-ft sluice, yield of first undercurrent (20 ft wide) was 20% of yield of all; 10 ft added width increased yield to 27% of total (391).

Modern undercurrents of this general type vary widely in detail. Grizzlies in sluices 20–36 in wide are made of 8 to 12-lb rail, 0.75-in round or octagonal steel, or steel flats; spaces between members, 0.25–1 in. In large sluices, grizzlies are usually of V-shaped steel bars, either stationary or so supported that they will rock under the impact of boulders; rails are also used; openings vary in width to 2 in. Space occupied by grizzly is full width of sluice bottom; its length in direction of flow ranges from a few to 18 in, usually found by trial. Grizzly bars transverse to sluice remove sand with less loss of water than longit bars. Grizzlies are placed on grades which may be flatter or steeper than the sluice grade. Any device that will slow up the current just ahead of a grizzly is desirable, as it gives sand and gravel a chance to settle and pass to the undercurrent.

Hungarian riffles of small angle iron, or of wood shod with iron, are also used for undercurrents. For saving very fine gold, carpet tufted with chicken wire, cocoa matting with expanded metal, and burlap tables, are employed at different mines. The ideal location for the form of undercurrent in Fig 840 is near the dump, so that large material need not be conducted far below the grizzly. This is not always feasible, and several other undercurrents are often built at intervals along a sluice. A min fall of about 5 ft is required where the undercurrent water returns to the sluice; the sluice grade can therefore be steepened from the grizzly to the point at which undercurrent water reenters. For further detail, see Bib (390, 391, 406, 394, 423, 424). Though the above undercurrents remove large quantities of water from main sluice, some sand and gold pass over the grizzly with oversize. In small sluices, these difficulties are partly overcome by a different type of undercurrent. Fig 841

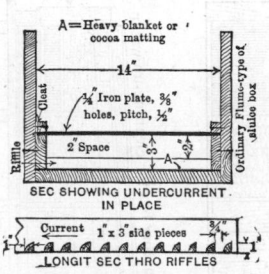

Fig 841. Undercurrent (after Ellis)

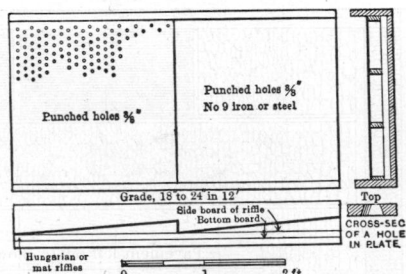

Fig 842. Caribou Undercurrent (after Purington)

shows an undercurrent introduced at Fairbanks, Alaska, in 1914. It greatly increased the saving of fine gold, as compared with the old type, but it was necessary to clean up the boxes every 2 days, since its effic decreased greatly thereafter. Two boxes of a string (passing a max of 150 cu yd of gravel per day) were fitted with this device; one was cleaned up each day, the blanket or cocoa matting being washed in a tub. On a claim where much fine gold was present, this undercurrent recovered 20% of the entire clean-up, and changed an operating loss into a profit (414). Fig 842 is a modified Caribou riffle or undercurrent regarding which Purington says (390): Hungarian riffles of wood or iron, carpets, plush or blankets, are placed in the sluice bottom under the screen, depending on character of the fine gold. This device affords cheapness, flexibility, and simplicity, but will not give good results with unpuddled clayey gravel. Experiments with punched plates in New Zealand showed that holes less than 3/8-in diam give too small a discharge and are apt to choke; 7/16-in holes passed too much water and material. These results were obtained in treating marine gravel containing fine shingle (425). Proper size of holes in any locality is a matter of experiment. On Snake River, Idaho, a different form of Caribou riffle and undercurrent has been used, in which the heaviest concentrates are drawn off continuously through holes in sluice bottom. This allows collection of black sand containing valuable minerals other than gold which require further treatment (426).

Bulowat Syndicate, New Guinea (458) in 1938 was working an alluvial deposit 12–30 ft deep, resting on clay and having 2/3 of its gold close thereto. Gold particles are flat, and 3/4 of output is of pin-head size. Deposit is ground-sluiced with 30 cu ft per sec (1 200 miner's in) of bank water at 300–700 cu yd per day, by 90 natives on 2 shifts. Sluice, 48 in wide, grade 0.6 in per ft, has 30 ft of angle-iron cross riffles spaced 3 in, and 50 ft of small riffles 0.75 in apart. Next 10 ft of sluice has 3/8-in slots from side to side, spaced 3 in, followed by 20 ft of 3/8-in plate drilled with 0.75-in holes on 1-in centers. These apertures drop about half the water to undercurrents, which are in duplicate, one on each side. Each is 30 ft wide by 18 ft long, composed of 15 tables 2 ft wide, sloping 0.125 in per ft. Riffles are wood, 1 by 1 in, set 1 in apart. Flow over the undercurrent is 4 ft per sec, compared with 9 ft per sec in the sluice. Use of undercurrent adds 25–30% to recovery of gold under the existing conditions.

Operators disagree as to the use and value of undercurrents. Where the gold is fine the weight of evidence is in their favor, if they are properly designed and cleaned up often enough to do effic work. At La Grange, Cal, after riffles like those in Fig 836 had been installed, undercurrents were discarded, as they clogged and the gold recovered did not pay cost of cleaning up (420). Of 39 placer mines in western U S described in (17) as operating in 1932, only 10 had undercurrents, and some were of doubtful advantage.

Use of mercury in riffles and undercurrents is quite general; amalgam is easier to handle in clean-ups than fine gold; some gold, otherwise lost, is always saved by amalgamation. Where much coarse gold occurs, mercury is omitted in a few boxes at the head of the sluice, to avoid the trouble and cost of retorting coarse gold amalgam.

When Hg is used, sluicing begins with a small head of water, until all cracks and leaks are stopped. The water is then shut off and riffles in upper part of sluice and undercurrents are charged with Hg. More is added from time to time, as needed to keep a clean surface of Hg exposed. Amounts of Hg vary; a common initial charge for large sluices is 2 to 3 flasks (76.5 lb each); for large undercurrents, 80 to 160 lb. Mercury must be clean and in charging all splashing or spattering should be avoided, otherwise minute globules are formed which float away. Loss of Hg is inevitable; it varies from 4 or 5% of the total amount used to 30% under poor conditions, averaging perhaps 10 to 15%; loss is least in well built, long sluices, provided with undercurrents (391, 394).

Cleaning-up consists in removing the riffles and collecting gold and amalgam. Interval between clean-ups is made as long as possible, to reduce the delay they cause; often the lower parts of a sluice are cleaned up only once in a season. Clean-ups are required when worn riffles must be replaced, and when much gold has collected, as in the first few boxes of a sluice handling rich gravel; danger of theft often influences frequency of clean-ups. Cleaning-up begins at the sluice head, by removing a few riffles and turning in a small flow of water. The concentrates are worked over with shovels or scoops; as they wash slowly down the sluice bottom, the gold and amalgam lags behind the black sand, etc, and is scooped up into pans or buckets. The process is repeated in next lower section. See Bib (17, 414, 391, 398).

Distribution of gold in sluices. Most gold is caught near the sluice head. Bowie estimates that an aver of 80% of total yield of large sluices is recovered in first 200 ft of length, according to results at several early Calif mines (391). In Alaskan shoveling-in or small open-cut work, the dump box and first 3 or 4 boxes below it retain most of the gold. Distribution depends upon nature of gravel, shape and size of gold, and amount of clay.

Table 121 shows results of experiments by Bouery, at La Grange, Cal, in 1910, to determine the distribution of gold of different sizes; the tests lasted 15 days (420). Value of the amalgam, $13.50

Table 121. Distribution of Gold in Sluice Boxes, La Grange, Cal

Box number	Total gold recovered, oz	Sizing test on gold recovered in different boxes					
		Mesh, per cent					
		+ 10	− 10 + 50	− 50 + 100	− 100 + 150	− 150 + 200	− 200
5	100	45.8	50.7	1.4	0.4	0.3	1.4
6 to 16(a)	831(b)	17.0	78.8	2.2	0.9	0.3	0.8
22	26.2	6.5	76.1	11.6	2.6	0.9	2.3
48	4.15	4.8	58.1	28.3	3.2	1.3	4.3
88	0.65	2.8	18.6	72.6	1.2	4.0	0.8
136	0.14	0	36.8	18.8	29.9	7.6	6.9

(a) Inclusive.   (b) 80, 69, 88, 68, 75, 108, 101, 100, 53, 46, 43 oz in these boxes.

per oz in the head boxes to $6 in box 136. Head boxes did not show the highest saving, as they were often blocked by boulders and sand (Bulkheads, Art 124). Such experiments permit accurate determination of the point beyond which the gold recovered does not repay construction and maintenance of added sluice length.

Loss of gold in sluices can not be accurately determined. The gold content of gravel treated is i. t known exactly, and there is no way to sample it or the sluice tailing during operation. In large low-grade placers, as at Oroville, Cal, ample opportunity is afforded to compare aver values computed from churn-drill exploration with actual recoveries on dredges, and empirical factors have been developed for discounting churn-drill samples. Such factors represent a combination of errors in sampling and losses in gold-saving apparatus, and can not be used in other localities. Drill and shaft samples in rich Alaskan creek placers often give results widely different from recoveries obtained later by hydraulicking or simple open-cut methods (447) (Sec 25).

Purington estimates that Alaskan shoveling-in recovers 80–90% of total gold (390). Different authorities place recovery with ordinary sluices and undercurrents at 60–85%; it must vary with character of gold, as well as that of the gold-saving devices.

Sluices act as runways for material ranging from large stones to fine sand. Veloc of current must suffice to sweep the coarse material along. Gold is separated from other heavy concentrate by the classifying action of irregular eddies set up by riffles; a strong "boil" is required to prevent riffles from packing. These conditions, combined with an irregular flow of water in hydraulicking and intermittent clean-ups, are not conducive to saving fine flaky or spongy gold and are responsible for losses. Undercurrents reduce this loss, if properly cared for, but no known device will force all of the fines to pass through a stationary grizzly on sluice bottom and leave enough water to carry on the oversize. Nearly all placers worked on a large scale have a very low gold content, and in spite of losses these simple gold-saving devices probably make nearly the max profit, in view of any recovery obtainable. This discussion does not apply to small gravel containing very fine gold only (as on the Snake River, Idaho, and in certain beach sands), nor to gravels containing valuable minerals besides metallic gold, which present problems still unsolved. Bib (390, 427, 424, 382).

126. ELEVATORS

Elevators of several types are employed to secure artificial dumproom at placers lacking natural facilities for disposal of tailing, and where conditions prohibit dredging.

Hydraulic elevators (Fig 843, 844) were formerly used widely; at present, they are

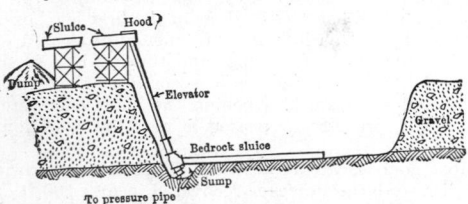

Fig 843. Elevator Pit (diagrammatic vert sec)

found mainly in isolated places where more effic power equipment can not be applied. The excavated gravel, with the giant water and seepage, is conducted in ground- or box-sluices to the foot of elevator, which delivers it to a sluice on surface leading to the dump (385, 394, 390, 397). The surface sluice is usually short, with or without undercurrents. FIELD OF USE is in flat placers lacking sluice grades and dumproom, but having ample cheap water under pressure. Depths of gravel range from a few ft to 90 ft; depths of 20–25 ft are favorable, as they allow much gravel to be mined from 1 set-up of elevator, without excessive lift. Boulders (or buried stumps and timber) too large to pass through the elevator increase operating cost, as they must be blasted or handled by derricks; if too numerous, they may prohibit elevator work. The elevator is inefficient and wasteful, but useful where necessary water is available.

Elevator CONSTRUCTION and OPERATION are shown by Fig 844. For dimensions, weights, and capacities, see makers' catalogues.

Water under press is discharged upwards through nozzle N; in passing through the throat area, T, it sucks in water, gravel, and air through intake opening O. The force of the jet elevates the aërated column of water and gravel through upcast pipe P, the upper end of which projects through bottom of first box of the surface sluice. To prevent spattering, this box is covered and is provided with a liner ("hood") which diverts the discharge laterally. The hood and throat take the most severe wear, and are usually of manganese steel; special steels may be used for other parts. The upcast may be a riveted or welded steel pipe, with slip or flanged joints, depending chiefly on height of lift. Evans elevator has an auxiliary suction opening on each side of the main intake, to allow air to enter the elevator if main

1 Flange of press pipe
2 Swivel elbows
4 Flanges
6 Nozzle butt
9 Ground section
10 Entrance section
11 Throat section
12 Outer section
13 Upcast pipe flange

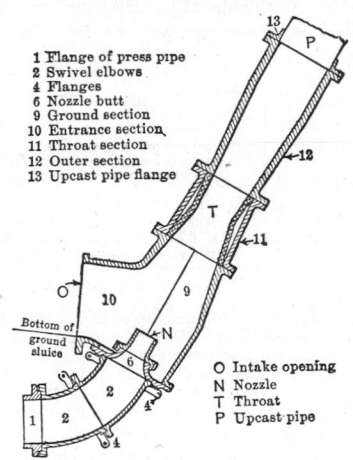

O Intake opening
N Nozzle
T Throat
P Upcast pipe

Fig 844. Hendy Hydraulic Elevator

intake clogs; suction openings may also be extended by pipes to low places on bedrock and used to suck out seepage water. The SUMP at foot of elevator is usually 10 or 15 ft sq and about 4 ft deep (385). Bedrock sluices may dump into the sump, or directly into the elevator intake; latter plan is best, as the suction head should be small. The UPCAST usually has a slope of 60°–70°; makers of the Evans elevator state that it works best at 80°. Elevators are sometimes set vertically, or on slopes as flat as 42° (394).

Water required. The elevator nozzle water will lift from 0.5 to 1 × its own vol of outside water. Hence, 50–66% of the pressure water available is assigned to the elevator, and the rest to the giants; the higher figure is conservative (note experience at Swaziland, below). Distribution of water between elevator and giants is controlled by size of nozzles used on each (see Flow through nozzles, Art 123).

Max height of lift for economical operation is about 17% of the effective head at elevator nozzle. High heads are proportionately more effective than low ones; the lift is also affected by size of gravel and slope of upcast (394). Ordinary range of lift is 10–20% of the head on the nozzle water. Higher lifts may be overcome by compound or step-lift elevators; 33% of the press water is then used in the bottom lift and 67% in the upper, which has a larger upcast. This requires abundant water supply, but approx doubles the lift obtainable with a single elevator. With cheap elec power or fuel supply, the natural press of the elevator nozzle water can also be boosted by stage centrifugal pumps. These devices are rarely used. MAX SIZE OF GRAVEL depends on the throat diam. To prevent serious clogs, a grizzly is necessary in the bedrock sluice; its bars are spaced at least 1 in closer than the throat diam.

Capacity of elevators. The gravel forms at most 5% (usually 2–3%) of the total wt lifted; hence, in estimating capacities, only the water needs to be considered.

There are no exact rules; the capac in a given case varies with the ratio of pressure head to lift, the effective head and vol, regularity of flow of gravel and water to the elevator, and also with the giant-water duty. The latter is a major factor in determining size of elevator. If there is much seepage water, which reduces the capac available for elevating giant water, a WATER LIFTER (practically a small elevator, with a suction pipe instead of an open intake) is often installed to drain the pit.

Efficiency of an elevator is expressed by: $E = H(62.4W + S) \div 62.4N(H_1 - H)$, where $E = \%$ effic; H = height of lift, ft; H_1 = effective head at nozzle; W = cu ft per min of giant, seepage, and bank water; S = wt of gravel elevated per min (placer gravel normally weighs about 3 000 lb per cu yd); N = water discharged through elevator nozzle, cu ft per min (397). Effic is usually only 10–20%. Longridge cites 12 elevators in N Z, operating on lifts of 13–67 ft with water under heads of 200–448 ft, the effic of which (omitting wt of gravel) was 20–33% (394).

Wild Goose Mining Co, Ophir Cr, Council District, Alaska. Data in Table 122, contributed by W. H. Lanagan and C. H. Munro, are retained from previous edn of this book, as representing former large-scale work in Alaska. For further detail, see 2nd edn, pp 924–926. Subsequent work of that kind on Ophir Cr has been in gravel 4–10 ft deep lying mostly on slabby limestone, irregular and difficult to clean (188). Such mining has been conducted only during those parts of the working season when men and water could be spared from the Co's dredges. From 1918 to 1921 incl, a total of 96 885 cu yd was worked by elevators at aver cost of 31.3¢ per yd, excluding deprec and management, but including proportionate share of ditch maintenance. In 1919 only 11 050 cu yd could be handled, at 73¢ per yd; in the other 3 yr, the range was 21.8–29.6¢ per yd.

Table 122. Hydraulic Elevator Work, Wild Goose Co, Alaska

		1908	1909	1910
	Area, sq ft....................	306 480	465 300	320 300
	Aver depth worked, ft...........	10.7	8.7	8.1
	Material handled, cu yd.........	121 960	150 637	95 960
Operating data	Number of pits working.....	12(a)	19(a)	9
	Piping: Number of days......	123.8	186.2	116.5
	Sq ft per day........	2 480	2 500	2 740
	Cu yd per day.......	986	809	825
	Cleaning bedrock, days.......	81.5	84.0	23.5
	Time lost, days.............	79.9	73.9(b)	10.3
	Total running time, days....	285.2	285.6	93.0(c)
	Sluiced per day, sq ft.......	1 075	1 630	3 420
	Sluiced per day, cu yd.......	428	528	1 030
Water used	Elevator water, in-days......	63 082	74 791	54 587
	Giant water, in-days........	18 368	26 788	27 451
	Pump water, in-days........	6 000	4 200	(d)
	Other water, in-days........	3 120	8 035	5 738
	Total water, in-days........	90 570	113 814	87 776
Water Duty	Elevator water, sqftperin-day	4.9	6.2	5.9
	" " cu yd per in-day.......	1.93	2.01	1.75
	Giant water, sq ft per in-day..	16.7	17.4	11.7
	" " cu yd per in-day.	6.6	5.6	3.5
	Total water, sq ft per in-day..	3.4	4.1	3.7
	" " cu yd per in-day .	1.35	1.32	1.1

(a) 2 more pits started, but not completed. (b) Short water, 15.5 days; no water, 53 days; other delays, 5.4 days. (c) Excluding time digging sumps. (d) Included in "other water."

Little Creek, Nome, Alaska. Data from N. L. Wimmler (188) in 1927. Former large operations using elevators are now being dredged. Deposits 15–40 ft deep of medium-sized gravel containing much clay, frozen and covered with moss and muck; latter, together with 2–10 ft of barren gravel, was first removed (often elevated) by giants.

Until 1923, during each season (June 10–Oct 15) elevator mining was usually conducted in 4 pits at a time, each having a final area of 3–5 acres. Total output per season, 350 000–550 000 cu yd, or 1 000–1 500 cu yd per day from each pit. Crew for each pit, 10–15 men with 2–4 horses, working 2 11-hr shifts. Water, 750–1 000 miner's inches under 290- to 310-ft head, supplied 2 giants (3–3.5-in nozzles) and an elevator for each pit. Elevator lifts were 30–55 ft; nozzles, 4.5 in for lifts to 40 ft, larger for higher lifts; usual water consumed, 450–550 in. Tailings were stacked at intervals by a 3-in giant; boulders were hauled on stoneboats. Head box, 12 ft long, 4 ft wide, had drop of 5 in; other boxes, to total length of 150–180 ft, were of steel, 8 ft long, 4 ft wide, at grade of 0.5–0.6 in per ft; usual riffles were angles and longit 16-lb rail. Sinking of pit through gravel and 8–10 ft into bedrock, and installing elevator, took 4 days. Usual life of replaceable manganese-steel throat on elevator, about 3 mo, or 100 000 cu yd. In 1921, 4 pits yielded 550 000 cu yd at working cost of 35¢ per yd, incl 3.5¢ for ditch maintenance. Aver duty (for all water) was 1–1.25 cu yd in frozen, or 1.25–1.75 cu yd in partly frozen ground.

Inmachuck River, Alaska. Data from N. L. Wimmler (188) in 1927. Frozen deposit 20–25 ft deep, of which about half was muck, removed in advance. Elevator with 9-in throat, 4-in nozzle, 37-ft lift, under 350-ft head, handled washings from 2 or 3 giants with 3-in nozzles; stacker giant was also needed. Crew: 6 men on day (10-hr) and 3 men on night shift; 6 men on ditch. In 64 days of 1924, a pit 315 by 460 ft cost 17.2¢ per sq ft, delivering 53 000 cu yd of gravel and bedrock at 47¢ per cu yd. Aver season, 85–90 days.

Swaziland, So Af; data from J. J. Garrard in 1917 (397). Tin-bearing gravels, averaging about 18 ft deep, have been worked. Records for 12 months' operation in 1913 show that 4 elevators, with an aver lift of 23.3 ft, took an aver of 73% of the water available, leaving 27% for the giants. Best month's work showed 60% elevator to 40% giant water; the worst, 84% elevator to 16% giant water; effic of elevator, 16.58%. As the water supply was ample, its inefficient use was allowable.

Box elevator. Knox and Haley (385) describe a home-made elevator used successfully by the North Fork Salmon River Mining Co, Cal. It consisted of a steel-lined box about 18 in sq, sloping about 50°, with a 5-in jet at the bottom and 0.5-in steel striking-plate at the top, immediately over the sluice. Height of lift, 30 ft; operating head, 250 ft. Water supply was excellent; about 700 miner's in were required for elevator. Boulders to 11 or 12 in diam were handled; there was no throat, everything being lifted directly by the jet. Capac, about 1 000 yd per day.

Ruble or grizzly elevator consists of a chute inclined at about 17° and having a 10-ft apron to make connection with bedrock. The apron fits closely between the walls of the main chute, which is 60–90 ft long. The chute and apron are lined with 0.25-in steel side and ³/₈-in bottom plates. Chute is about 8 ft wide, its walls tapering from 12 ft high at the bottom to about 4 ft at the top. For the first 20 ft of the incline, the bottom is solid; remainder of incline is bottomed with transverse grizzly bars, 2.5 in apart, made of 2 by 6-in timbers covered with 0.5-in steel straps. Underneath the grizzly is a steel-lined false bottom, sloping from upper end of elevator to a sluice box, set at right-angles to elevator and directly under lower end of grizzly. The sluice, about 60 ft long and supported on light trestles, is paved with Hungarian and pole riffles, consisting of 2 by 4-in timbers shod with steel. The elevator is supported on 3 heavy stringers resting on trestle bents, which are mounted in turn on skids. It is moved by winch and cable.

Operation: The elevator giant is alined with the center line of the elevator and about 80 ft away from it. Wings, about 10 ft high and lined with scrap timber, are built out on each side, 1 wing extending to the bank; they are supported on portable frames. The cutting giant works behind the elevator giant and drives the fallen gravel along the bank to the elevator wing, where it is picked up by the elevator giant and washed in small quantities at a time up the solid portion of the incline. Care is taken to "boil out" the fines over the lower portion of the grizzly; otherwise, gold would be washed over the elevator top. When heavy stones are clean, they are washed up and over upper end of the incline. The fine tailing is piped from end of sluice by the elevator giant about once an hour. An extra tailing giant may be set up for stacking tailings when the water is not being used by other giants. When the boulder dump reaches the end of grizzly, a platform is laid on it extending outward and upward from the elevator. Thus the dump can be piled much higher than the elevator itself. These tailings are piped down periodically by the tailing giant. If the water pressure is high, a large amount of material can be worked with 1 set-up of the elevator, but the elevator must be moved to a new position when the driving limit of the cutting giant is reached, or dump room is exhausted; 5 or 6 days are required per move. This delay can be obviated only by using 2 or 3 elevators, and changing the water from one to another. At one property, such an elevator used 600–1 200 in of water under 450-ft head. The gravel was heavy, with nests of boulders weighing 1–5 tons; depth of bank, 20–25 ft. Capac of the elevator, 1 000–2 000 cu yd per 24 hr; 100 000 cu yd of gravel were washed in 4 months; total operating cost, including ditch maintenance, 6¢ per cu yd. First cost of elevator, $3 400; the mine was 90 miles from a railway. For further details, see Bib (385, 453). Two other examples follow.

Redding Creek, Douglas City, Cal. Data from Gardner and Johnson (17) in 1934. Deposit of stream gravel about 9 ft deep and 120 ft wide; insufficient natural grade for sluices (0.83%) required use of Ruble elevator. Water under 300-ft head came through 3 000 ft of 24-in pipe and supplied (through 15-in pipes) 2 giants with 5-in nozzles; one cut and swept gravel to foot of Ruble, the other driving oversize up the slope. A third giant, with 3-in nozzle, leveled off tailings pile at intervals. Ruble was 8 ft wide, 60 ft long, with lift of 25 ft; grizzly bars (iron-clad, 3 by 6-in plank laid on edge, crosswise) were spaced 2 in apart. Sluice, receiving undersize and most of the water, was 48 in wide, 48 ft long (see Ex 3, Tables 116, 120). Shallowness of gravel required Ruble and sluice to be moved 3 times during 105-day season of 1932; each move took a week for 7 men and a caterpillar tractor. Boulders were bulldozed, consuming 2 000 lb of 40% gelatin in season. For other data, see Table 117, Col I; cost of 19¢ per yd did not include ditch work, construction, interest, deprec, or amortization.

Gallia mine, Sawyer Bar, Cal, illustrates combination of Ruble elevator for discharging coarse tailings, and hydraulic elevator for fine. Data from Gardner and Johnson (17) in 1934. Gravel, 33 ft deep, contained 10% of boulders over 12 in; bedrock fairly even. Water at 265-ft head, through 2 000 ft of 36- to 15-in pipe, supplied a 3.5 or 4-in giant in pit, a 4.5-in giant at Ruble, and an elevator with 20-in intake, 30-ft lift, and 4-in nozzle. Pit giant worked intermittently, to avoid congesting the Ruble; other giant and elevator worked continuously. Ruble, 4 ft wide, elevating 25 ft, had grizzly of 90-lb rails, spaced 2.5 in, and set lengthwise. Sluice from Ruble to elevator was 120 ft long, 24 in wide, grade 4.5 in per box, and riffled with 2 by 2-in angles and longit rails. Ruble had to be moved every 3 weeks to gain dumproom, taking a week's time of 3 men. Boulders too large to go up Ruble were moved by derrick; those uncovered in cutting, by donkey engine. In 60 days of 1932 (incl moving of Ruble), crew of 3 men on each of 2 12-hr shifts treated 12 000 cu yd at cost of 17¢ per yd; pit giant could move 50–60 cu yd per hr.

Advantages of the Ruble elevator: low first cost, the fact that it can be made on the ground, and its capacity for handling heavy boulders. It is adapted to flat placers unsuitable for dredging, less than 50 ft deep, where water is available for hydraulicking. It is not suited to rough or very uneven bedrock, owing to difficulty in moving.

Use of giants for stacking tailing is possible where dumproom is ample in area but deficient in grade, and where the water will run off by gravity (406). The North Columbia Gold Mining Co, Atlin, B C, stacked coarser tailing to heights of 25 and 35 ft with giants working under heads of 110 and 140 ft (411). Where this device is used, the stacking giant can often be operated intermittently. See Bib (415).

Ellis describes an INCLINED SLUICE used in connection with giants in California, Oregon, and in Alaska for stacking tailing at the end of a sluice. On Mastodon Cr, Circle, Alaska, a 9-ft gravel bank was hydraulicked with 2 No 1 giants into a sluice delivering tailing to a sump. From this the tailing was easily driven up an inclined sluice to a height of 35 ft. A No 2 giant under a head of 100 ft was used for stacking; duty of the total water for hydraulicking and stacking was 2.5 cu yd per miner's in per 20 hr. Fairly heavy slabs of bedrock were raised by the giant. It is stated that this device used less water than would be required by an hydraulic elevator, and that it is better suited than the latter for small installations (413). INCLINES and giants have also been used in Alaska for FEEDING SLUICES which must be elevated a short distance above bedrock. A vert steel-lined backstop is built directly behind the sluice, and gravel is banked up in front of it forming an incline leading to bedrock. Material is then piped up this incline against the back-stop, from which it drops into the sluice. No details are available (429).

Gravel pumps have been used successfully in Swaziland and Nigeria, for elevating tin-bearing gravel; elsewhere, occasionally and less successfully, for gold placering.

Swaziland. Data from J. J. Garrard (397). 8-in centrifugal pumps, with renewable impellers and linings, are direct-connected to 50-hp motors, running at 485 r p m, and deliver water and gravel to a total height of 40 ft. Pump is mounted on a pontoon resting on bedrock in the pit. The gravel is hydraulicked and washed to a sump, whence it is pumped to an elevated sluice. Suction pipe of the pump is sometimes 300 ft long; delivery pipe slopes 45°. During year ended June 30, 1915, 3 gravel pumps ran 70.9% of the time that power was available, elevating 420 423 cu yd of gravel at an aver rate of 24 cu yd per hr. Amount of water pumped, 190–230 cu ft per min; aver height of lift, 38.6 ft. Aver running cost per hr of the 3 pumps was 42.2¢, of which 23¢ was for power (cost 0.733¢ per kw-hr), 10.6¢ for renewals, 8.6¢ for repairs. This gives a cost of about 1.8¢ per cu yd. Aver effic (output ÷ input) for the 3 pumps, 27.35%.

Nigeria. Data from W. E. Sinclair (626) in 1933. For geol occurrence of tin-bearing gravels, see Art 122. Standard suction-pipe diams of centrif pumps are 6, 8, 10, 12 in;

max lifts, 65–85 ft; 6-in pump lifts 10 cu yd gravel and 6 000 gal water per hr, under aver head; 12-in pump, 40 cu yd gravel and 24 000 gal water per hr; intermediate sizes directly proportional. Pump casings or liners are of manganese steel. Fig 845 gives power requirements of 6-, 8-, and 10-in pumps under varying heads. Pumps are mounted: (a) on bedrock, at lowest accessible point of deposit; (b) on pontoon, normally resting on bottom, while at work, but moved from place to place by temporarily flooding the pit to necessary depth; (c) 2 pumps, preferably of equal capac, in tandem, permitting use of smaller and lighter pumps for a given head. Max effic and min abrasion are obtained when delivery pipe slopes 40°–50°. By whatever method the gravel is broken, it is delivered to pump sump through a bedrock sluice carrying enough water to make a mixture con-

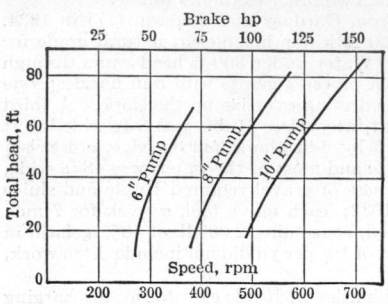

Fig 845. Recommended Speeds and Powers for Gravel Pumps under varying Heads, Nigerian Tin Fields

taining about 20% solids; close control of pulp consistency is desirable. In these tin fields, ground is broken by:
(a) ground sluicing, of soft or medium-hard ground;
(b) shoveling-in, by hand;
(c) digging and tramming by hand; (d) steam-shovel and loco haulage (see Art 122); (e) hydraulicking, limited to rich or unusually extensive deposits justifying large initial outlay. Table 123 gives aver cost data prior to 1933, in pence per cu yd washed, under the conditions noted; up to that time, coal at £3 per ton was usual source of power, since largely replaced by hydro-generated elec. With weekly adjustment, pump delivered 45 200 cu yd of aver gravel before requiring replacement of liners or runners. An inci-

Table 123. Cost of Mining, Pumping and Washing Tin Gravel in Nigeria (Pence per cu yd; prior to 1933)

	I	II	III	IV	V
Breaking and tramming wages...............	2.20	6.91	9.96	6.80	4.04
Pumping: wages				1.32	2.21
Fuel (coal)............	3.10	3.54	3.60	5.05	3.79
Renewals and maint....	1.47	1.75	1.87	1.50	1.36
Lubricating oil........	....	.....	.....	0.86	1.02
Sluicing and washing.....	(a)	(a)	(a)	1.19	1.40
White supervision........	2.21	2.60	2.76	5.14	3.47
Overhead and general....	0.86	0.65	0.85	1.99	1.46
Total..............	9.84	15.45	19.04	23.85	18.75

I—Ground-sluicing (no tramming). II—Shoveling-in (no tramming); breaking ground alone varied 3–10 pence, depending on distance shoveled. III—Breaking and tramming by hand. IV—Aver based on 40 846 cu yd pumped from same position in 9 mos; 8-in pump, 90-hp steam engine; total head, 65 ft; aver suction lift, 12 ft; tramming distance, 50–750 ft; cost includes pumping surplus water. V—Based on 9 090 cu yd washed in 480 hr (Nov, 1930) of which 216 hr pumping gravel; 10-in pump, 90-hp steam engine consuming 60 tons coal; total head, 79 ft; delivery pipe 90 ft long, sloping 70°; gravel, 7 ft deep, averaged 10.12 lb of 70% Sn conc per cu yd. (a) Not included in total.

dental advantage of the centrifugal pump, especially important in this tin field (see p 546), is its ability to disintegrate clay and even cemented gravel without assistance from puddler or log washer.

Boe mine, Quesnel division, B C. Data from 1932 Ann Rep of B C Minister of Mines. Mine operated profitably for several years in spite of adverse conditions. Gravel, 15–20 ft deep, contained much glacial clay and required blasting. Water, from seepage only, and sufficient for only 10-hr work a day, was supplied at 45-lb press through 10-in centrif pump (steam-driven from 2 60-hp wood-fired boilers) to a giant with 3-in nozzle, at 1 800 imperial gal per min (192 miner's in). Gravel pumped to sluice from sump, protected by screen with 4 by 5-in openings, by 8-in centrif pump driven by 25-hp gasolene engine. Sluice water was impounded, settled, and returned to giant. Capac of outfit, 300 cu yd per 10-hr day. Daily expense: labor (5 men), $20; 3 cords wood, $15; 40 gal gasolene, $14.80; 2 kegs powder, $6; misc, incl amortization, $27.90; total, $83.70, or 28¢ per cu yd.

Mechanical elevators usually consist of an endless chain-bucket excavator, supported on a tower and delivering to an elevated sluice. The buckets handle only gravel; a centrif pump is also required. These elevators have been used at several mines to raise gravel mined by hydraulicking, but have failed due to: (a) high first and operating cost; (b) pump troubles; (c) complicated machinery, requiring services of a machine shop; (d) lack of mobility. Bib (385, 409, 430).

127. CHAIN-BUCKET OR BUCKET-LADDER DREDGES

By F. M. BLANCHARD and C. M. ROMANOWITZ

Introductory. A placer mining dredge comprises a mechanical excavator and a screening and washing plant, both mounted on a floating hull. Dredge performs 4 functions: (a) Excavates the placer material. (b) Screens the material into 2 or more sizes, usually with a revolving screen; undersizes, usually all below 0.5 or 0.75 in, go through recovery devices, the oversize to reject. (c) Treats the fines to recover their metallic or other heavy components, usually on tables or jigs, or a combination of the two. (d) Deposits the fines from the treating unit, and the coarse rejects from the screen, to rear of dredge.

The dredge floats in an artificial pond often supplied from an outside source, by gravity through ditches or by pumping. The dredge digs at its bow and deposits washed tailings at its stern, thus carrying the pond with it as it advances. Dams may be needed to raise the water level, and it is sometimes necessary to seal the dredge tailings with sand and slimes. The chain-bucket dredge is the only type described here, as it has practically superseded all other forms, such as dipper and suction dredges, for placer mining. (For dragline dredging, see Art 129). The bucket-elevator dredge is also used for recovering platinum and tin ore, with modifications in the treatment plant to meet requirements. Size of the dredge is designated by the capac, in cu ft, of its individual bucket.

The New Zealand type of dredge, with open-connected buckets, was introduced to the U S in the late 1890's. It was successful in loose river gravels, but found unsuitable for digging "inland" where the gravel was more compacted. Development of the modern dredge began 1901 in Calif. Since then, improvements in the effic of the machines have led to their wider use, both on shallow and very deep placers. The most important improvements have been in digging capac and the treatment plant; also in the design of deep-digging dredges, and the sectionalizing of hull, superstructure, and machinery for transport by trucks and airplanes, and to facilitate rapid field erection. For notable example of dredge transport by airplane, see Bulolo, Art 128.

Factors affecting operation. Successful outcome of dredging demands (aside from sufficiency of profitable gravel): (a) correct and adequate prospecting; (b) selection of equipment best suited to the conditions; (c) effic management and an experienced crew. SELECTION OF EQUIPMENT is guided by: (1) Max and min depths of gravel and overburden. (2) Total yardage. (3) Amount, distribution, and character of valuable metal or mineral; its size, shape, or other features (for example, "rusty" gold) affecting its recovery. (4) Formation; tight, loose, clay, sand, cement, boulder sizes, buried timber, reefs, dykes, etc. (5) Bedrock conditions and its grade. (6) Surface contours. (7) Availability of water. (8) Special conditions to be met, as leveling, resoiling, leaving water ways, control of muddy water, etc. (9) Flood conditions. (10) Frost, frozen ground, or other conditions found in extreme North. (11) Climatic conditions, and length of working season. (12) Transport facilities and remoteness of property. (13) Class of labor available. (14) Labor and material costs. (15) Taxes and royalties. (16) Special laws to be considered. (17) Funds available.

Bucket-elevator dredge. Commonest, or "California," type is equipped with screen, tables or jigs, and a stacker to dispose of the oversize reject from the screen. Certain VARIATIONS have proved useful for small placers and shallow creek deposits, as in Alaska; also for mining tin ore. (a) Substitution, on tin dredges, of a rock chute for a stacker to convey oversize from the screen. This simplifies the mechanical equipment and is used where proportion of oversize material is not large. (b) Flume dredge equipped with a screen. The screen rejects are usually larger than 6-in diam, and are passed to stern of the dredge by stacker or rock chute. Material below 6 in is delivered to a flume or sluice, 5 or 6 ft wide, carrying large volumes of water, like the sluice in a hydraulic mine (Art 124). The sluice usually has large-sized Hungarian or rail riffles. (c) In flume dredge without screen, all material goes directly into a sluice. This design is suitable for creeks where gravel is small in size and gold is coarse. In some cases, rocks too large to go through the flume are sorted out by a grizzly at upper end of flume and rejected into the pond, at side of the dredge.

Fig 846 is a plan, and Fig 847 a side elev of a 6-cu ft California-type dredge, for digging at 38 ft below water. Such a dredge, in 1 272 days, digging at aver depth of 26 ft and under difficult conditions, averaged 155 000 cu yd per mo; under easier conditions, a similar dredge has dug 200 000 cu yd per mo. Fig 848 is a side elev of a 3-cu ft dredge, designed for 16-ft depth; in actual performance it averaged 64 000 cu yd per mo. For an 18-cu ft, deep-digging dredge, see Fig 852, 853, Art 128.

Hull is rectangular, with bow and stern corners usually cut off diagonally to increase clearance when maneuvering; a long, narrow, open well extends back from the bow about half the length of hull

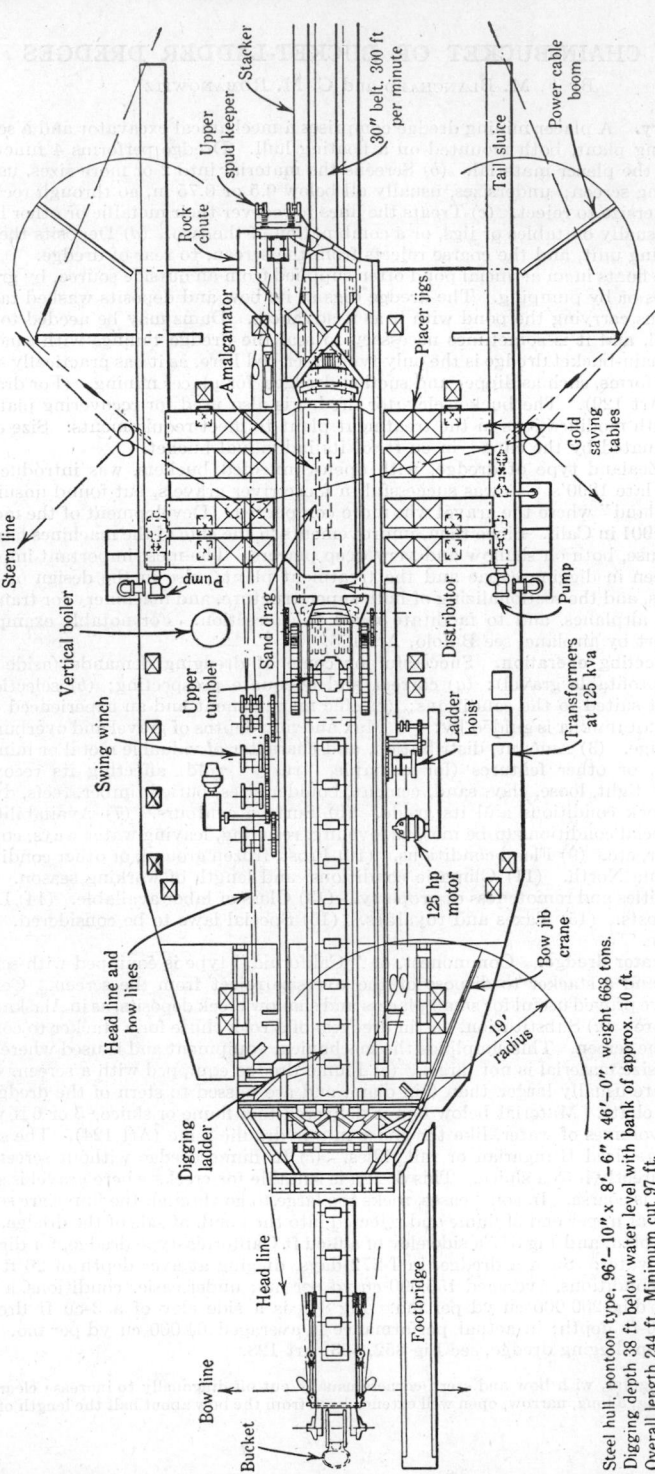

Fig 846. Plan of 6-cu ft Gold Dredge equipped with Placer-type Pan-American Jigs (Yuba Mfg Co)

Steel hull, pontoon type, 96'–10" x 8'–6" x 46'–0", weight 668 tons.
Digging depth 38 ft below water level with bank of approx. 10 ft
Overall length 244 ft. Minimum cut 97 ft.
Installed load 348 hp. Screen 5'–10" dia, 29'–10" long.
Jigs: 8–42" x 42", 2 cell: 1 – 24" x 24" pulsator, 2 cell:
1 – 12" x 12" pulsator, 1 cell.

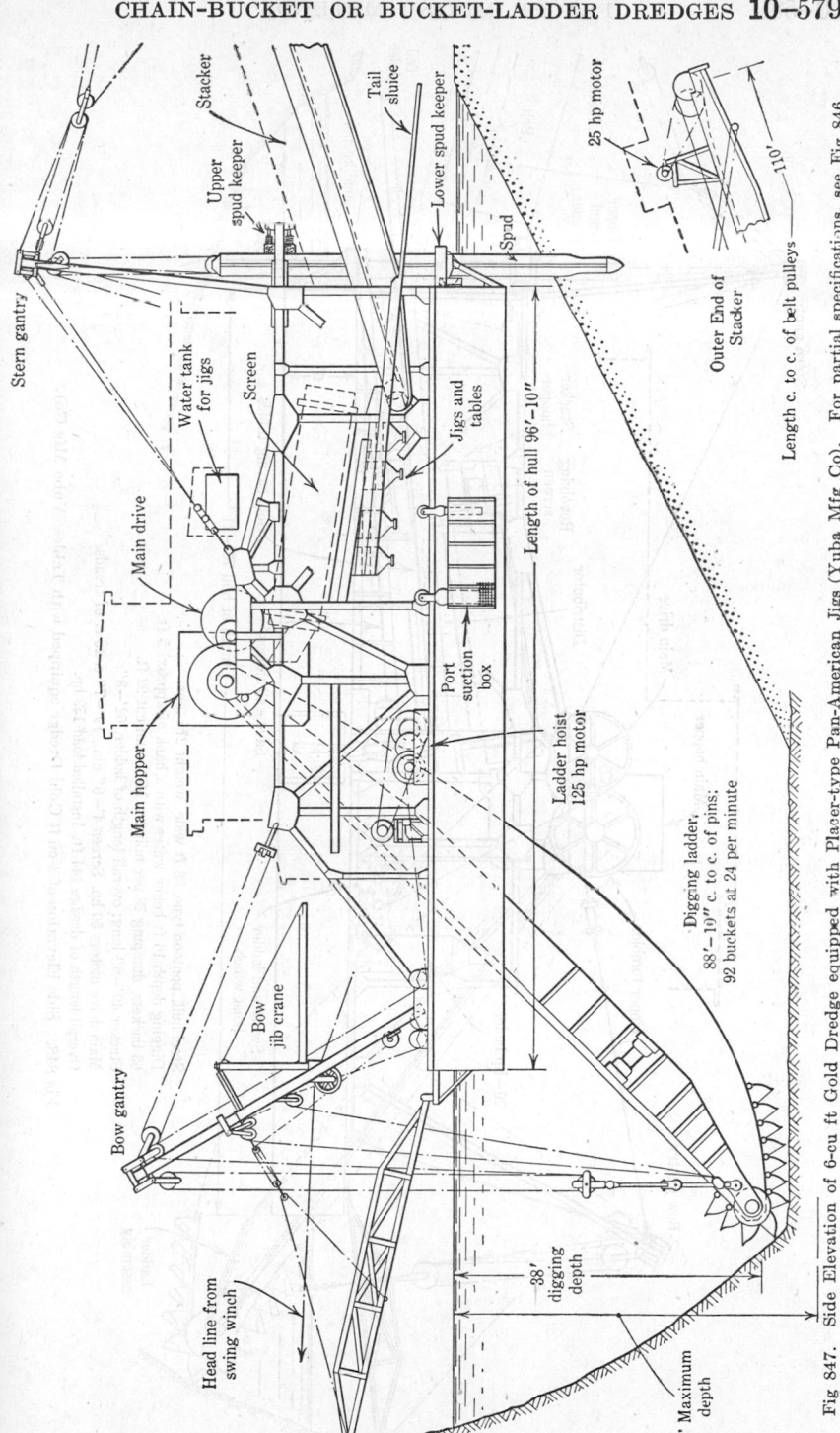

Fig 847. Side Elevation of 6-cu ft Gold Dredge equipped with Placer-type Pan-American Jigs (Yuba Mfg Co). For partial specifications, see Fig 846

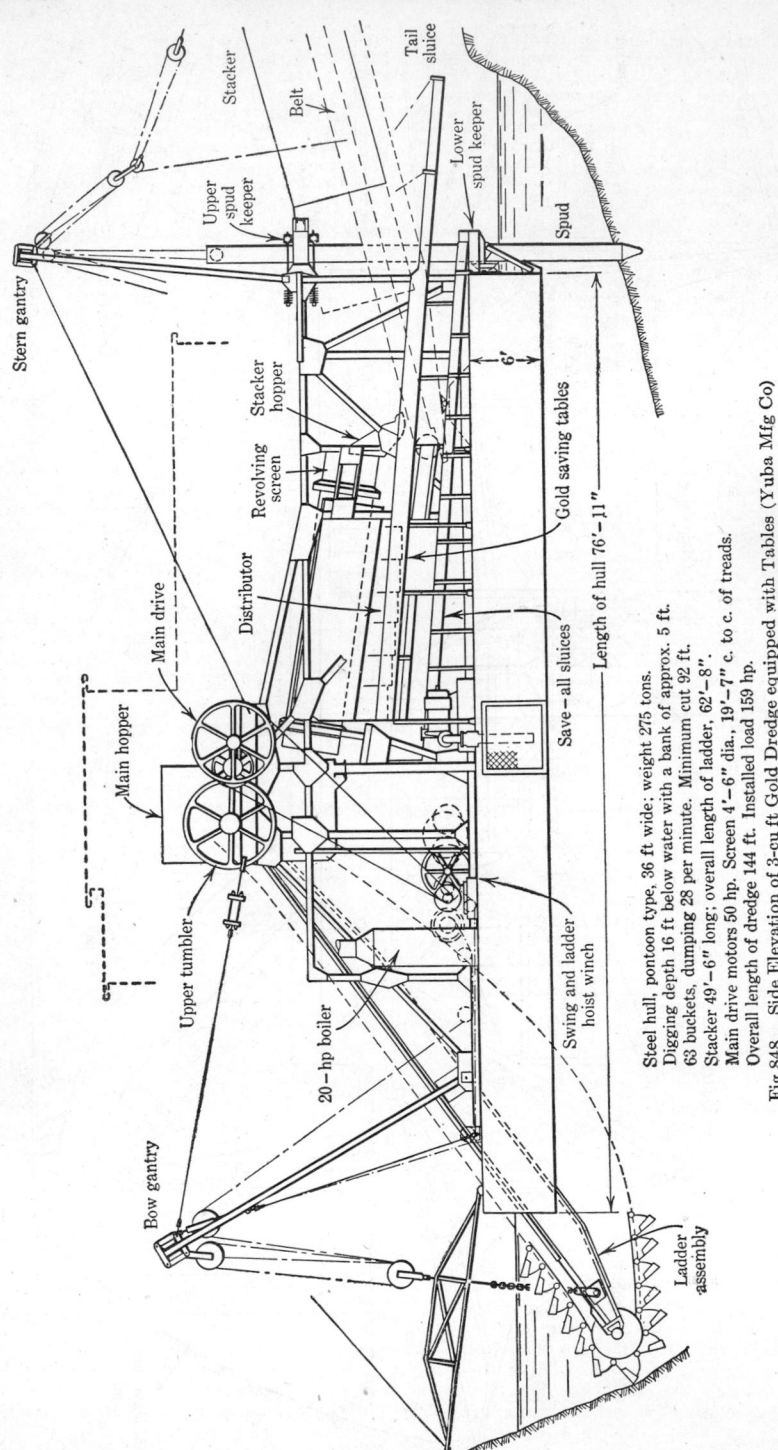

Stern gantry

Stacker

Upper spud keeper

Belt

Tail sluice

Lower spud keeper

Spud

6'

Revolving screen

Stacker hopper

Gold saving tables

Length of hull 76'–11"

Main drive

Distributor

Save–all sluices

Main hopper

Upper tumbler

20–hp boiler

Swing and ladder hoist winch

Bow gantry

Ladder assembly

Steel hull, pontoon type, 36 ft wide; weight 275 tons.
Digging depth 16 ft below water with a bank of approx. 5 ft.
63 buckets, dumping 28 per minute. Minimum cut 92 ft.
Stacker 49–6" long; overall length of ladder, 62'–8".
Main drive motors 50 hp. Screen 4'–6" dia., 19'–7" c. to c. of treads.
Overall length of dredge 144 ft. Installed load 159 hp.

Fig 848.   Side Elevation of 3-cu ft Gold Dredge equipped with Tables (Yuba Mfg Co)

and on its center line, to provide space for the digging ladder. Depth and size of hull depend on weight of machinery and material it has to carry; amount of freeboard, which is usually 2–3 ft, depends on length of hull and change of fore and aft trim occasioned by raising or lowering the digging ladder. Width is usually 0.5 to 1/3 the length, according to area and arrangement of washing equipment. Two longit main trusses, one on each side of center line, extending full length of the hull, provide stiffness and support the heavy machinery mounted on and above the main deck. The trusses are strengthened with additional members where concentrated loads occur, and are side-braced at 3 or 4 points in their length. Hulls are fabricated or assembled in 4 ways: (1) standard steel; (2) pontoon; (3) bolted water-tight compartments; (4) wood.

Standard riveted steel hulls, of steel shapes and plates, are fabricated into convenient shipping sections, set up for inspection in the shop, then dismantled, and finally assembled on the dredging property. This is the commonest type.

Pontoon hull consists of rectangular welded steel boxes, 6 by 6 to 8 by 8 ft in section, and 15–30 ft long, corresponding to width of hull; when assembled crosswise of the hull and bolted together, the structure is practically unsinkable. When properly made, such a hull is as strong as the standard type. The pontoon hull, widely adopted since 1934, has permitted operation of many small properties where the standard dredge would be uneconomical, since this hull can be quickly dismantled and moved to another short-life property; one such dredge was moved to its third placer within 5 years. The pontoon is the only hull that can be assembled in the water, saving expense for foundations and launching; bolt holes below water line are temporarily plugged. There is also a saving in erection time. A standard hull requires 6–8 weeks for erection; the pontoon can be asembled in 4–6 days, and requires no trained mechanics. The same saving occurs in dismantling and re-erection. For example, the time for dismantling a 6-cu ft pontoon was 19 days; for re-erection, 38 days. A standard dredge of same size would take 30 days to dismantle and 100 days to re-assemble. Cost of dismantling the pontoon was $4 000, and of re-erection, $10 000; a standard dredge of this size would cost about $5 000 to dismantle, and $40 000 to re-erect. The main disadvantage of the pontoon is the bulky nature of its components, of especial interest when ocean transport is involved.

Bolted water-tight compartment type is designed to be put together in the field. When assembled, the hull consists of numerous compartments (not pontoons) the max size being adjusted to shipping conditions. As many pieces as possible are combined in the shop into a shipping unit, usually by welding, and all field connections are then bolted. This is economical for field erection and for ocean or other shipment. The hull is as strong as the standard type and practically unsinkable.

Wooden hulls were exclusively used until about 1912, when the first steel hulls were built, but are now rare except in cold northern countries, where wooden hulls deteriorate slowly. In Calif, a wooden hull lasts 10–12 yr. Wooden hulls with steel superstructure have given excellent service in Calif, Ore, and Alaska.

Gantries. At least 3 are required. MAIN-DRIVE GANTRY is centrally located and supports the upper tumbler, the main-drive gearing, the upper end of digging ladder, the main hopper, the save-all, and upper end of the revolving screen. Additional truss legs and heavy top chords with rigid braces are required here to carry both live and dead loads which must be distributed into the entire truss and hull structure. Dead load includes the main-drive gearing and half the wt of the ladder and buckets; live load is that due to thrust of the buckets while digging, and the side movement of the dredge when swinging back and forth across the pond. BOW GANTRY, at forward end of the hull, serves as a cross truss to stiffen the pontoons on each side of the well, and to support the suspension tackle attached to lower end of the ladder. Back guys of cable or steel tension members extend from its top to upper chords of the main truss. STERN GANTRY supports the spuds and the suspension for the stacker. Its lower end is usually pin-connected to top chords of main truss. Large deep-digging dredges usually have 2 stern gantries, a short one for the spuds and a higher one for the stacker suspension.

Digging end of a Calif dredge comprises an endless chain of close-connected buckets passing around tumblers at top and bottom of a ladder, which is pivoted at its top and has rollers to support the chain on the ascending side; the chain is driven by the upper tumbler. The ladder is raised or lowered by tackle hung from the bow gantry.

Digging ladder consists of 2 parallel steel-plate girders with heavy top and bottom flanges, generally of double angles and cover plates, connected by closely spaced plate diaphragms; upper edges of the latter are below the top flanges and covered by a plate, thus forming a trough to catch spillage from the buckets. Ladders are 50–225 ft long and weigh 300–3 000 lb per ft. Rollers, closely spaced along the top of ladder to support the bucket chain, are of high-carbon chrome steel, press-fitted onto forged nickel-steel shafts. Bearings are usually cast steel with replaceable C-I bushings. Different types of seals keep out abrasive substances.

Buckets are in 2 parts, a manganese-steel base and a lip. The 2 front eyes of base are not generally bushed, since the pin is stationary at those points, but the back eye has a manganese-steel replaceable bushing to resist wear at that joint. Manganese-steel lips are either riveted or rivetless, latter now being more common. A riveted lip is fastened with 10-20 large rivets, which frequently loosen and involve loss of time and expense. The rivetless lip (Fig 849) is held in place generally by only 2 bolts, engaging lugs on bucket and lip on both sides of the center. A rivetless lip

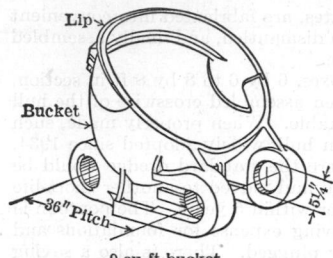

9-cu ft bucket

Fig 849. Manganese-steel Bucket with Rivetless Lip

weighs considerably less than the riveted, thus saving waste of metal when discarded. Bucket pins are forged from high-carbon, chrome, or molybdenum steel, heat-treated for strength and hardness; the "L" head, to prevent rotation, is almost universal.

Upper tumblers are generally of high-carbon cast steel, body and shaft cast integral. The 6 sides of the tumbler are protected against wear by heavy liners of forged nickel-chrome steel or cast manganese steel, and bolted in place. A 2-piece tumbler, with cast-steel body shrunk and keyed to a forged-steel shaft, is often used, especially when transport is a problem.

Lower tumbler, made circular, has a high flange on each side to guide the buckets around lower end of ladder. The body, in a single piece or 2 halves, is of cast manganese steel or high-carbon chrome cast steel, with replaceable manganese-steel wearing plates. The press-fitted shaft is a nickel-steel forging. Bearings are of C I, with rubber seals or other means for excluding abrasive matter.

Idlers. Ladders digging deeper than 75 ft often have the Perry idler (Fig 853). This is suspended in heavy bearings from lower side of ladder at about $1/3$ its length from lower end; it reduces the drag of the buckets on the bottom, due to catenary, when the ladder is at approx 45°, and diminishes the catenary load on tumblers and pins, thereby reducing wear on bucket bushings, pins, and lower tumbler bearings. Dredges digging over 40 ft deep usually have an idler at the aft end of the well on lower deck of dredge, and so located as to engage the chain when the ladder is inclined at 35° or more below horiz. By thus keeping the upper part of the descending chain at a fixed inclination, the clearance between save-all grizzly bars and the buckets may be reduced, affording a more effic save-all arrangement.

Main drive. Small dredges drive the upper tumbler by a single set of reduction gears at one end of tumbler shaft; larger dredges have 2 sets of reduction gears, both ends of the shaft being driven. All gears, pinions, and bearings are of cast steel; shafting, forged nickel steel. A brake wheel on one end of the pulley shaft provides for emergency and for repairs to the bucket line. Recent improvements in drive mechanism: (a) single motor, close-coupled by V-belts to pulley shaft; (b) 2 motors, each driving a pulley shaft by V-belts, have proved advantageous on large dredges requiring a total of 200-600 hp for main drive. Motors are a-c or d-c; advantage claimed for latter is better control of bucket-line speed under variable load, but entailing added expense for motor-generator. Dredges working in easy ground have been speeded up to 40-45 buckets per min, but 24-28 buckets per min for dredges up to 7.5-cu ft capac, and 20-23 buckets per min for larger dredges, is usual practice.

Main hopper receives material dumped from buckets as they pass over upper tumbler; it is of steel plates and angles and has a lining of wear-resistant metal. A short half-round chute directs the material into the screen; it is lined with alloy-steel bars 2-3 in thick. When large boulders are numerous, the hopper back may have a coarse grizzly hinged at one end; on appearance of a boulder, the grizzly is lowered, mechanically or pneumatically, into position to intercept it and then raised to discharge it overboard, *via* chute or conveyer. Spill from buckets is caught on a fixed grizzly surmounting a riffled sluice, the "save-all."

Screens. Roller-mounted trommels have displaced all other types of screen, chiefly because of their vigorous disintegration of clay-bound or partly cemented gravel; disintegration is hastened by adding lifters or other tumbling devices inside the screen. Abundant water at press of 20-40 lb per sq in is supplied through nozzles or spray pipes to aid discharge of fines. Screens are from 4.5 ft diam by 24 ft length for a small, 2.5-cu ft, dredge, to 9 by 52 ft for an 18 or 20-cu ft dredge. Ends of screen are blank plates with replaceable liners; tread rings fastened outside of each plate. Rib bars (6-9-in heavy angles, bars, or channels) connect the end plates and provide longit support. The perforated plates are in sections 2.5-6 ft long and wide enough to span the gap between outside rib bars; sections are small enough for easy handling on replacement; countersunk bolts with spring-lock washers are used for fastening. Material for perforated plates is high-carbon or other abrasion-resistant rolled steel, or cast manganese steel. Thickness is 3/8 in for small to 7/8 in for the largest screens. Diam and spacing of holes depend entirely upon character of material to be washed. To counteract excessive discharge at head of trommel, perforations at this end are often smaller and farther apart than elsewhere. A common size of hole is 5/16 in on the inside, enlarged to 3/8 or 7/16 in on the outside; tapered holes have less tendency to blind. The bridge between holes is from 0.5–1.5 in, diminishing towards discharge end of trommel. Where coarse nuggets occur, the plates at lower end of screen are usually slotted, 5/8 by 3/4 in to 1 by 1 1/4 in. The tread rings on which the trommel rotates are high-carbon or chrome-steel machined castings. The upper ring is carried on 2 idler rollers, the lower on either a central drive roller or on 2 rollers, one of which is driven. As the screen is inclined at 1–1.75 in per ft, thrust rollers are required; these engage a tapered machined face on lower edge of lower ring. The drive roller is actuated by reduction gears direct- or belt-connected to a motor; flat belts have been common at this point, but gear reducers and V-belt drives are now more frequent, occupying less space and giving higher etfic. Peripheral speed of trommels is 150–200 ft per min (6–14 rpm), depending on diam of screen and kind of material being washed.

Stacker hopper. Oversize from the screen falls into a steel-plate hopper, lined, at points of greatest wear, with heavy plates or bars; it delivers to stacker belt through a chute, the discharge end of which is fitted with a mild-steel casting and manganese-steel liner shaped to change the direction and veloc of the stream to correspond with that of the belt, saving wear on the latter, The hopper often has a gate which diverts the material into a sluice discharging over the stern of the dredge; this provides a good footing behind the spud and saves power, since the stacker may be shut down meanwhile.

Stacker. The frame carrying the conveyer belt comprises 2 parallel structural-steel trusses, tied top and bottom and at each panel point with cross-braces. Its lower end is hinged on a shaft permitting the stacker to be raised or lowered. When a swinging stacker is required, an additional vert swivel allows movement of approx 15° to either side of the center line. Inclination of stacker is limited to 20°; in most cases, 15°–18° is satisfactory. Stacker is suspended from the stern gantry cap by 1 or 2 wire-rope tackles fastened at 2 or sometimes 3 points. It is raised or lowered by a line from the swing winch, or preferably from a separate small winch having a self-locking safety device (worm gear or automatic friction) which will necessitate lowering as well as hoisting by power, and thus prevent careless dropping of the stacker. The steel head pulley is lagged with rubber. Length of stacker depends chiefly on digging depth and nature of material. Knowing the swell (usually about 33%), the digging depth, and allowing clearance for outer end of stacker inclined at 18°, the required length can be computed. Due to the extreme length of hull of large deep-digging dredges, the lower end of the screen is so far inboard from the stern that a short auxiliary stacker (Fig 853) may be placed between the screen and main stacker.

Anchorage. For maneuvering dredge by spuds and lines, see "Digging procedure," below. If there are 2 spuds, they are usually placed in line with the main fore and aft trusses; a single spud (as found on many modern dredges) may be near the center line of dredge or in line with the starboard (right-hand) truss.

The SPUD is of plates and angles, or of wide-flanged beam sections with heavy cover plates. Bottom of spud has a massive cast-steel point, and its upper end carries sheaves for the hoisting tackle, which is suspended from the stern gantry cap. Lower spud keeper, acting as cushion between spud and hull, is of steel with a self-adjusting rocker element to accommodate changes in position and maintain a broad bearing against the spud. Resistance to twisting is afforded by heavy brackets fitted with replaceable liners. In the upper keeper, tendency of the spud to move away from the dredge is counteracted by an outside cross-beam connected to the upper truss members by heavy rods and compression springs. A HEADLINE, sometimes replacing a spud in very easy digging, is a wire rope about 1.5-in diam, fastened to a deadman 500–1 000 ft ahead, and held taut by a winch on the dredge. Where the dredge is making a wide cut, a number of "pennant" lines are spaced across the full width, and the headline is attached to these in most convenient positions. SIDELINES, one at each corner of dredge, are anchored ashore, and control lateral movement by winches on the boat.

Winches are for: (a) adjusting inclination of ladder and buckets, the "ladder hoist"; (b) control of side lines (the "swing winch"); (c) hoisting of spuds; (d) adjusting slope of stacker; (e) holding pull on headline; (f) miscel purposes, as handling of heavy machinery. Grouping of winch drums, and their power, vary with size of dredge. SMALL DREDGES, to 5-cu ft capac, have a combination ladder hoist and swing winch, including 2 drums for bow lines, 2 for stern lines, 1 or 2 for spud hoists, 1 or 2 spares, and the ladder-hoist drum. Gearing is so arranged that each may be operated individually, and each drum has expanding-type friction and a band brake. On LARGER DREDGES, the swing winch includes all drums except for the ladder hoist. Either the bow or stern lines, spud, and spare lines may be operated as a unit. Instead of combining all drums in one winch, some dredges have independent bow- and stern-line drums; spud and spare drums are then in another unit, thus requiring 3 motors (usually a-c). Several dredges have had d-c motors for the bow-line winches, with automatic elec control to maintain constant pull on bow lines. LADDER HOIST, on the larger dredges, is a separate unit actuated from the main-drive motor, through pulleys and clutches, or from an additional motor through V-belts or a gear reducer. The drum is divided by a central flange, and 2 ropes lead off to the suspension; on smaller dredges, only 1 rope is required. For DEEP-DIGGING DREDGES, with very heavy ladders and long bucket lines, the ladder winch has 2 separate drums, driven by 400–500-hp motor, direct-connected to a gear reducer, coupled to an intermediate shaft by herringbone gears. A herringbone pinion drives the first drum, the gear of which engages a pinion on an idler shaft driving the second drum. The motor has an elec brake; a heavy wheel with band brake on the idler shaft may be pneumatically controlled from the winch room. An automatic control electrically connected with the motor control is used on many modern dredges, to limit the high and low positions of the digging ladder and the max speed at which the ladder may be lowered.

Pumping equipment usually includes a high-press, a low-press, and a small auxiliary pump, all centrifugals. The high-press pump discharges at 60 to 80-ft head into the screen at both ends, or from a pipe with adjustable nozzles, extending through full length of the screen. The low-press pump discharges at 30 to 40-ft head opposite the head of each cross sluice. Pump sizes depend upon amount and kind of material washed; ratio of water on the tables should be 8–12 times the solids. Auxiliary pump, 2.5 to 4-in diam, at 60 to 80-ft head, is used for washing deck, fire outlets, and priming the larger pumps. In dredging clay or other sticky material, an extra 6 or 8-in pump supplies water at about 120-ft head for nozzles directed against the buckets as they dump into main hopper. Pumps should have liners, as the pond water may contain abrasive matter. Pumps are direct-connected by flexible couplings to motor on same base, each having a suction check valve above water line.

Combination MUD AND MONITOR PUMP is used on dredges digging 80–125 feet deep and with a high bank, where tailing sludge tends to flow out along the bottom of the pond to the bucket line. This pump is about 8-in diam, developing 250-ft head. For extracting mud, the suction extends to a point near the lower ladder tumbler, the discharge pipe passing aft to the end of the stacker. (Fig 853). When serving a monitor, suction comes from the strainer box and the discharge supplies a nozzle at the dredge bow; this washes down a bank which does not cave by itself, to avoid a cave-in which might bury the digging ladder.

Strainers protect suction inlets against floating debris or water-logged material. A frame covered with galvanized wire cloth with 3/8 in openings is usually adequate, but removable perforated plates may save some labor. A self-cleaning, revolving suction box is satisfactory. It consists of a wheel, 10–14 ft diam by 3–4 ft wide, framed of angle-iron and covered with wire cloth. Buckets around the inside periphery are filled from a small nozzle for turning the wheel. Debris outside the screen may be scraped or blown off as the wheel revolves.

Power for elec motors reaches the dredge, from shore, by rubber-covered or steel-armored cable, supported on floats. Voltage, 6 900–2 200; 3-phase, 60-cycle current is usual. Operating voltage on the dredge is 440, delivered by 3 single-phase transformers.

Starters are usually distributed among 3 boards, 1 in winch room for the main drive and swing winch, 1 on main deck for the pumps, and 1 at stern for the screen, stacker, and sand elevators. Pump motors are constant-speed; those for main drive, winches, screen, and stacker, of variable-speed, reversible type. Control is by a breaker and a starter for each motor; the variable-speed motors have C-I resistance grids. Main-drive has a magnetic reversing controller, with line protective, primary, and secondary panels. Motor controls include a thermal overload protection device with a push button for resetting. In isolated places without elec power, dredges have 440-volt Diesel-elec generators. Motor equipment as above.

Digging procedure. Digging starts at top of the ground ahead of dredge. Forward end of ladder is swung slowly from side to side of intended cut by the side lines. At end of a swing, the ladder is lowered for a deeper cut on the return trip; bedrock, when reached, is scraped if its nature permits. On raising the ladder, the dredge is moved ahead for the next cut. To make the forward movement, and maintain position while digging, the dredge may have (a) 2 spuds, (b) 1 spud, (c) headline; side lines are always necessary. For "stepping ahead" with TWO SPUDS, the dredge swings to right of the cut, turning on the "digging" spud as a pivot; the port ("stepping") spud is then lowered and the other raised; after swinging to left, the digging spud is lowered, stepping spud raised, and dredging proceeds.

With a SINGLE SPUD, the stern lines are anchored well ahead of the dredge; by pulling on them, after raising the spud, the dredge is moved. This method is quicker than with 2 spuds, due to fewer operations, but not always applicable. HEADLINE stepping (and digging) is practicable only under easy digging conditions, as in Malayan and other tin fields (Art 132); rarely on gold dredges. When operating from a headline, swinging as usual by the side lines, hard ground offers difficulties in keeping the buckets efficiently at work.

Gold-saving equipment, treating undersize from the screen, includes: (a) distributer; (b) riffled tables; (c) roughing jigs, preceding or following the tables; (d) clean-up box or jig; (e) mercury trap or other form of amalgamator; (f) retort and melting furnaces; (g) sand wheels or elevators sometimes aid disposal of tailings. Fig 850, 851 show alternative flowsheets, with and without jigs.

Distributer is a steel housing enclosing the trommel. Its sloping bottom is partitioned into pockets corresponding in number to the tables; partitions have adjustable gates to equalize distribution; when wide open, the gates facilitate cleaning-down the bottom of distributer. If gold is coarse, riffles are customary instead of partitions, discharging overflow into an outside longit distributing sluice; this has the advantage of spreading the flow more thinly over more tables than could be grouped close to the screen distributer (Fig 850-B). In the usual type of distributer, sand discharges from its bottom, on both sides, by water applied at 15-lb press through 1.5-in nozzles in headers fed by low-press pump;

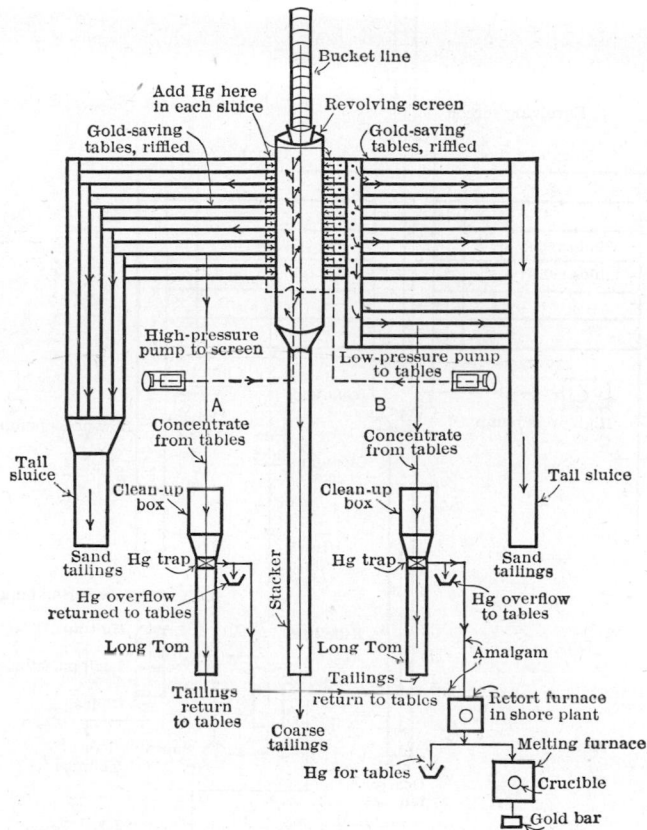

Fig 850. Flowsheets of Gold Dredge equipped with Tables. A—Conventional type. B—Improved Arrangement

a short sluice opposite each nozzle leads to adjoining table or roughing jig; uniform distribution aids effic of recovery.

Tables are rectangular steel sluices, 21–32 in wide, placed crosswise of the hull and sloping 1.25–1.5 in per ft outwardly toward both sides. In Fig 850, 851, the alternative arrangements are only for illustration; a given dredge will be equipped symmetrically. Total table area, in absence of jigs, depends upon size and character of gold, fine gold requiring more area; recent dredges have 200–500 sq ft per cu ft of bucket capac.

Enlarged table area, for large dredges, may be secured without proportionate increase of hull area, in 3 ways: (a) Double-bank tables, having an upper deck permanently fixed 6 ft above the lower, requiring corresponding increases in height of upper tumbler and length of digging ladder and bucket line, entailing added wt. (b) Double-deck riffles; sluice has a false bottom of 10-gage plate, supported from the sides about 8 in above true bottom and similarly riffled. (c) Telescoping or nesting sluices; upper sluice fits between sides of the lower; it is hinged at one end and can be raised by tackle, the 2 decks being similarly riffled; this allows faster clean-up than the false-bottom sluice. Outer ends of all tables discharge into longit sluices carrying tailings to stern of hull and dropping them 15–20 ft overboard; bottoms of tailings sluices are often riffled to catch escaping gold or amalgam.

Wooden Hungarian riffles (Art 125) are almost universal. Common size, 1.25 by 1.25 in, spaced 1.25 in; tops protected by steel or rubber strips $^3/_{16}$ in thick by 1.5 in

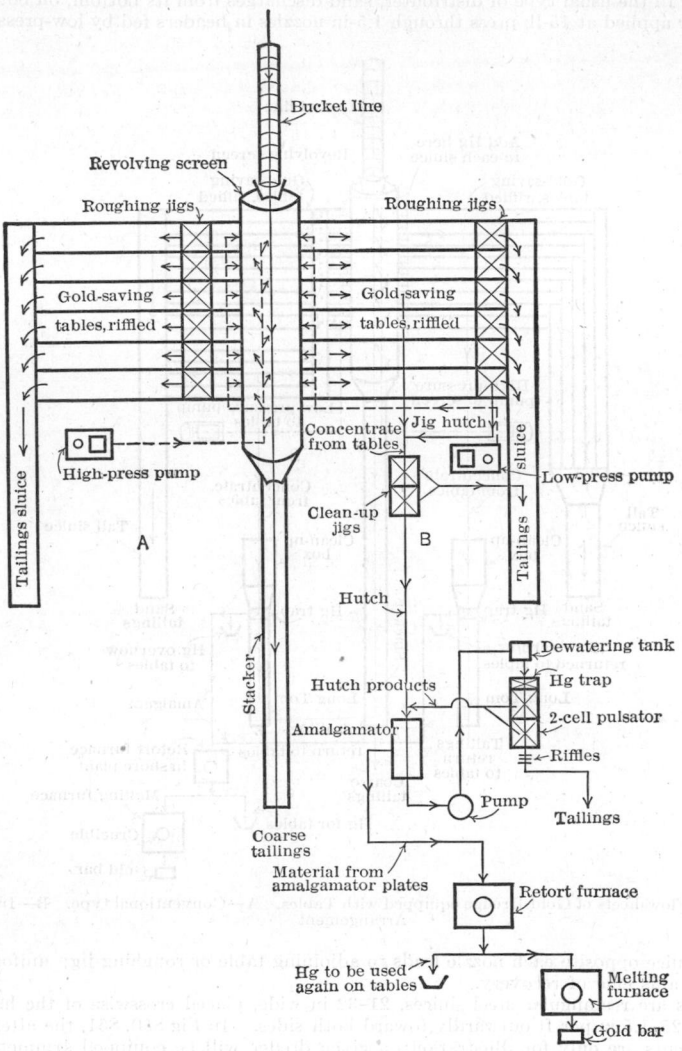

Fig 851. Flowsheets of Combination Jig and Table Dredge. A—Roughing jigs ahead of tables. B—Roughing jigs following tables. Arrangement of cleaning jigs is same in either case.

wide, the 0.25-in overhang being on the downstream side. Riffle bars, usually 6, are made into frames about 13.5 in wide; length corresponding to width of table. The frames are held to bottom by 1.5-in sq battens, wedged under angle-iron brackets riveted along sides of table. Mercury trap riffles are usually placed at intervals along a table.

Jigs are especially useful on gold dredges (common also on tin dredges, Art 132), when gold resists amalgamation or is largely in scales or very fine particles. Jigs are designed for large capac in small space (Fig 846, 847), made possible by the extremely small ratio of concentrate to feed, as compared with ore-concentrating jigs (403).

Fig 851 shows alternative positions of roughing jigs with respect to tables. In either case, the hutch product, and concentrate from riffled tables, is re-treated on 2 cleaner jigs, the second re-treating the hutch from the first, both discharging tailings. Final product may pass through a small ball-mill amalgamator; final recovery of gold is usually on amalgamated plates. Black-sand concentrate containing metals of platinum group, resisting amalgamation, is treated separately.

Clean-up of sluices. After stopping the flow over a table, the riffles are removed, washing any adhering material into the sluice. With a small stream of water the material is washed to the lower end, which is fitted with a wooden stop about 3 in high; here most of the light sand is scraped or washed off; the rest, mostly black sand and amalgam, is shoveled out and transferred to the "clean-up box," a steel or wooden receptacle of about 1-cu yd capac, which collects concentrate for further treatment. From an orifice in lower end of this box, the concentrate is washed, a little at a time, over a sloping plate, to extract heavy foreign matter, and thence into a mercury trap. Excess of free Hg collecting here is tapped off and re-used, the heavier amalgam being removed by hand for subsequent treatment (Sec 33). Sands overflowing the Hg trap then pass through a Long Tom (Art 119), 12–15 ft long, riffled on cocoa matting; discharged sands return to the initial tables, or may be further treated in a ball-mill, or by smelting.

Sand tailings. Tailings sluices usually empty into the pond behind and from both sides of dredge; when working a high bank consisting largely of sand, tailings so discarded may interfere with floating the dredge stern, and must then be disposed via the stacker. In such case, the tailings sluices discharge into sumps, from which water overflows to the pond while sands are lifted by wheel or bucket elevator and delivered by chutes to the stacker. Sand wheels, with light steel frames, are 12–16 ft diam; buckets, 2–3 ft wide; they are chain driven from 7.5–10-hp geared motors. Bucket elevator, of either chain or belt type, occupies less space and permits a higher lift when necessary.

American dredge manufacturers: Bucyrus-Erie Co, So Milwaukee, Wis; Marion Steam Shovel Co, Marion, Ohio; New York Engineering Co, New York; Yuba Mfg Co, San Francisco.

128. GOLD DREDGING

Introductory. Gold dredging is a subject of great detail; for a general discussion, see (385, 403, 409, 437, 438, 614, 627). In the U S, gold dredging began about 1898; by 1927, with price of gold at $20.67 per oz, the known areas suited to dredging were largely worked out, thereby forcing a search by American companies for dredging ground in foreign countries, such as for tin placers in the Malay States (Art 132) and gold placers in Colombia, Central America, New Zealand, and elsewhere. The increase in price of gold to $35 per oz in 1933 stimulated activity in gold dredging in the U S. In recent years, the relatively inexpensive dragline dredge (Art 129) has been widely applied to small and shallow deposits, but the chain-bucket dredge (Art 127) is best for large operations in low-grade gravel. Recent improvements in design have also permitted the chain-bucket dredge to work gravels at much greater depths than were formerly considered accessible.

Requirements and limitations. Deposits suited to dredging are extensive river-bar and gravel-plain placers (Art 117), occurring chiefly in geologically old districts. Requirements as to bedrock, character and size of gravel, effect of boulders, cemented gravel and buried or standing timber, ordinary limits of dredging depth, water for dredge ponds, etc, are summarized in Art 118 and Sec 25, Art 7. Other considerations affecting choice of method and operation and design of dredge are: CHARACTER OF GOLD. Very fine flaky gold, like that on Snake River, Idaho, requires addition of special equipment (usually jigs) to the other gold-saving devices. Coarse gold sometimes modifies the form of apparatus required. "Rusty" gold may entail special methods of recovery. GRADIENTS. Dredging is inherently applicable to large flat deposits, where lack of grade prevents hydraulicking; small topographic irregularities and flat surface or bedrock gradients affect only the height of bank carried above water level. Some dredging has been done on grades as steep as 6%, requiring dams to maintain a pond (431). FROZEN GRAVEL must be thawed before it can be dredged (Art 131). FLOODS. Dredging in beds of torrential streams is precarious, due to danger of being wrecked. CLIMATE determines length of working season and hence the annual output and return on investment for a dredge of a given capac. Min gold content of workable gravel is higher where the season is short than where operation is continuous. Cold climate increases costs, because the dredge must be heated and its equipment protected from accumulations of ice. See Bib (408, 432, 409) for description of successful winter work. TRANSPORT FACILITIES are more important than for other forms of placer mining. Weight of the machinery is large, even for small dredges; attempts to sectionalize a dredge for muleback transport have not been successful, but sectionalizing into units capable of transport by trucks and aeroplanes (see Bulolo) has been accomplished. High first cost where good roads are lacking militates against construction of large boats in remote regions (385, 433). LABOR. A small crew can handle a large yardage; all but a few roustabouts are skilled men. Cheap POWER is essential. TOTAL YARDAGE must be sufficient to amortize the initial investment and yield desired profit. A choice often exists between use of one dredge, or several of different sizes, with corresponding alternatives in first cost, rate of return, and life of property (Sec 25, Art 14). Closer estimates of this kind are possible on well explored dredging ground than on any other form of mining property. An attempt is usually made to adjust the rate of working, and hence life of property, to the LIFE OF DREDGE. This is practically the life of the hull, as the machinery is repaired or renewed as necessary. The machinery is often dismantled, after working out an area, and installed elsewhere at moderate cost on a new hull. Constant running at max capac is essential to low working costs; hence construction and operation of a dredge must be planned to minimize delays. Following examples illustrate dredge work under various conditions.

Central Calif. Data in Table 124, relating to 10 dredges in the Folsom and Oroville districts, were supplied originally by R. G. Smith, Mgr of the Gold Dredging Dept of the Natomas Co, in 1917. Table 124 has been condensed, by F. M. Blanchard, from 4 tables on pp 938–941 in 2d edn of this book (revised only as to history) Mr Smith submits following comments in Feb, 1940, concluding that present aver operating costs per cu yd are slightly lower than in 1917, in spite of increased prices for labor and materials. WAGES per hr on Calif dredges, 1940: winchmen, 82.5¢; oilers, 67.5¢; laborers, 55–60¢; compared with 1917, these wages represent increases of 83% for winchmen, 93% for oilers, 84% for laborers. Total labor charges have increased by 85%, about equal to increase in hourly rates. MATERIALS. Comparison of unit prices is not practicable, but total costs for materials have increased 30% over 1917. POWER RATES to large consumers, equipped to take service at high voltage, have been reduced about 20% since 1917; but total power charges have increased about 23% with longer hours and larger yardage. WATER CHARGES have risen 175% since 1917. GENERAL EXPENSES show apparent increase of about 90% in total, possibly explained in part by changes in accounting methods, some general expenses having formerly been charged to operation. TOTAL OPERATING COSTS have increased by more than 50% since 1917. ANNUAL YARDAGE. Dredges of nearly all sizes have greatly enlarged their yearly output since 1917, through increased speed, longer running times, and improved mechanical effic; increase in yardage, though widely variable, has averaged about 70%. COST PER CU YD. Balancing the above items indicates a slight decrease in operating cost since 1917. TAXES and INSURANCE have increased about 70%, and AMORTIZATION allowance should be 90% greater. Finally, Federal INCOME TAX is an item much more oppressive now than in 1917 (see Sec 24).

Oroville, Calif. Data from C. M. Romanowitz in 1940. Dredging conditions in this field are considered unusually favorable. One 9-cu ft dredge (a frequently adopted size) during a period of 1 363 days averaged 290 000 cu yd per mo from depth of 50 ft. Others of same size, under favorable conditions, have handled 3 500 000 cu yd in a year.

Calif " deep-digging " dredges. Data from C. M. Romanowitz in 1940. Two notable examples of 18-cu ft dredges operate in the Yuba River field, at Hammonton; Yuba No 17 began July 17, 1934, and No 20 on Apl 24, 1939. No 17 has dug 112 ft below water, with bank of 56 ft; No 20 digs at 124 ft below water, with same height of bank as No 17. During a 1 363-day period, No 17 averaged 310 000 cu yd per mo, from aver depth of 110 ft. Usual max depth dug by other dredges in same field is about 80 ft; one such dredge, of 18-cu ft capac and digging in easy gravel at aver depth of 68 ft, handled 415 000 cu yd per mo during a period of 1 287 days. Another, of same size, but with more modern digging facilities, during 704 days averaged 450 000 cu yd per mo from 75-ft depth in tougher gravel. Below 90 ft, the formation at Hammonton is tighter and harder (though not cemented) than at shallower depth. These deep-digging dredges require special design and equipment. Fig 852 and 853 are respectively plan and side elev of an 18-cu ft dredge designed to dig 124 ft below water. The Perry bucket idler and the Yuba mud-pump system (Art 127) give good results. While these dredges are effic, they can not mine as large yardages, in proportion to their bucket capac, as those working at shallower depths, chiefly because the operator can not "get the feel" of the work as well as on smaller dredges. The longer time the buckets take in traveling to the surface makes it impossible to determine promptly whether they are digging to full capac. The unit operating costs of these deep-digging dredges are higher than those of shallower dredges, due to smaller yardage and higher cost of replacements. F. C. van Deinse, V-Pres of Yuba Consol Gold Fields, states that costs for operating the deep-digging dredges are 1.33¢ more per cu yd than for shallower dredges in the same fields.

Table 124. Operating Data and Costs on 10 Dredges, Folsom and Oroville Dists, Calif, 1912-16

Dredge*	A	B	C	D	E	F	G	H	I	J
Hull construction	wood	wood	wood	wood	wood	steel	wood	steel	wood	wood
Started	1908	1908	1908	1905	1908	1913	1911	1912	1908	1911
Dismantled	1917	1918	1918	1917	1921		1921	1924	1922	1925
Rebuilt	1919			1917				1925	†	
Bucket wt, lb	2 390	2 390		2 850	2 830	4 430	4 430	4 430	3 850	4 430
Bucket pos						2	2	2	3	2
Bucket capac, cu ft	8.5	8.5	7.5	9	9	15	15	15	13.5	15
No of buckets	68	72		82	86	83	83	83	60	81
First cost	$135 000	$135 000	$130 000	$160 000	$185 000	$345 000	$330 000	$365 000	$200 000	$320 000
Character of deposit	(a)	(b)	(c)	(d)	(e)	(f)	(g)	(h)	(i)	(j)
Depth, ft	28	29	32	51	48	63	59	45	23	39
Digging below water, ft	35	40	34	50	50	60	60	60	32	50
Digging motor, hp	200	200	150	200	200	400	400	400	300	300
Total hp	463	438	301	528	505	1 119	1 146	1 165	712	757
Ladder length, ft	86	91.5	80.5	97	102	119	119	119	84	110
Table area, sq ft	2 260	2 170	1 680	2 080	2 970	7 500	7 210	7 500	3 940	7 960
Operating data:										
Period	1912-16	1912-16	1912-16	1912-16	1912-16	1913-16	1912-16	1913-16	1912-15	1912-16
Total days worked	1 818	1 819	1 817	1 671	1 747	1 431	1 817	1 453	1 453	1 741.5
Aver hr: min per day	20:30	20:24	20:55	19:26	19:30	19:03	19:47	19:23	19:24	20:28
Aver annual yd	2 061 000	1 725 000	1 449 000	1 677 000	1 588 000	2 251 000	2 382 000	2 550 000	2 963 000	3 181 000
Aver yd per hr	277	232	238	238	224	325	331	362	421	427
Digging range, ft	21-35	26-37	27-35	45-56	40-61	62-67	54-64	37-54	22-24	27-53
Costs per cu yd: (¢ / %)										
Labor	0.92 / 23.3	1.11 / 23.5	0.93 / 28.0	0.84 / 16.5	1.11 / 17.7	0.92 / 16.2	0.81 / 13.8	0.83 / 16.6	0.63 / 17.5	0.67 / 19.9
Supplies	.16 / 4.1	.21 / 4.4	.05 / 1.5	.15 / 2.9	.23 / 3.7	.20 / 3.5	.23 / 3.9	.16 / 3.2	.12 / 3.3	.09 / 2.7
Power	.70 / 17.7	.76 / 16.1	.63 / 19.0	.94 / 18.4	1.03 / 16.4	1.41 / 25.0	1.38 / 23.6	1.13 / 22.6	.68 / 18.8	.90 / 26.7
Water	.08 / 2.0	.08 / 1.7		.08 / 1.6	.12 / 1.9	.10 / 1.8	.12 / 2.0	.10 / 2.0	.08 / 2.2	
Repairs:										
Labor	.19 / 4.8	.20 / 4.2	.12 / 3.6	.36 / 7.0	.31 / 4.9	.28 / 5.0	.27 / 4.6	.21 / 4.2	.19 / 5.3	.08 / 2.4
Supplies	1.27 / 32.7	1.56 / 33.1	.94 / 28.3	1.92 / 37.5	2.56 / 40.8	2.13 / 37.7	2.42 / 41.3	1.95 / 39.0	1.39 / 38.5	1.20 / 35.6
General expense	.54 / 13.7	.69 / 14.6	.47 / 14.2	.67 / 13.1	.78 / 12.4	.56 / 9.9	.56 / 9.6	.56 / 11.2	.44 / 12.2	.24 / 7.1
Totals **	3.95 / 100.	4.72 / 100.	3.32 / 100.	5.10 / 100.	6.28 / 100.	5.65 / 100.	5.86 / 100.	5.00 / 100.	3.61 / 100.	3.37 / 100.

* Dredges C and J in Oroville dist, all others in Folsom dist. Dredges F G, and H were designed for same conditions as D and E. Dredge I, of large capac, was designed for shallow, easy digging; J similar to G, and worked in easier but deeper ground than I. To June, 1914, a suspense acct was carried for large items, as bucket lines, tumblers, etc, these costs being distributed *pro rata* over the life of parts in question. Thereafter, when such parts were put into use, their full cost was charged to operating. Wages on all dredges: winchmen, 45¢ per hr; oilers, 35¢ per hr; laborers, $2.50 per day. Operating costs do not include taxes and insurance, amounting to a yearly charge per dredge of $2740 to $4 970; aver, $3 600 for all dredges but I. For the latter, annual taxes, etc, were $5 500 to $6 760.   † First dismantled and rebuilt in 1916; finally dismantled in 1922.   ** Not exact totals of tabulated items, due to dropped decimals.

(a) Loose sand and gravel on lava bedrock; very easy digging.

(b) Loose sand and gravel, with considerable topsoil, on lava bedrock. Bottom gravel, fair size and generally not easy digging. Considerable drift mining done in former years.

(c) Loose sand and gravel river bar; much sandy soil; easy digging.

(d) Tight clay and gravel, with 5-6 ft topsoil, 4-8 ft hardpan of varying hardness, and soft lava bedrock; similar to (f) and (g).

(e) Tight clay and gravel; some difficult hardpan digging; lava bedrock. Ground like (d), (f), (g).

(f) Tight clay and gravel, with 8-10 ft topsoil; like (d) and (g).

(g) Like (d) and (f). Prospect shafts stand for years with little caving; like (d) and (g).

(h) Worked in 3 benches; much maneuvering; tight clay and gravel, some hardpan. Both soft lava and hard bedrock.

(i) Loose sand and gravel, with 4-8 ft topsoil; soft lava bedrock. Very little clay, and bank not subject to excessive caving.

(j) Very loose sand and gravel on soft lava bedrock; no clay; considerable topsoil.

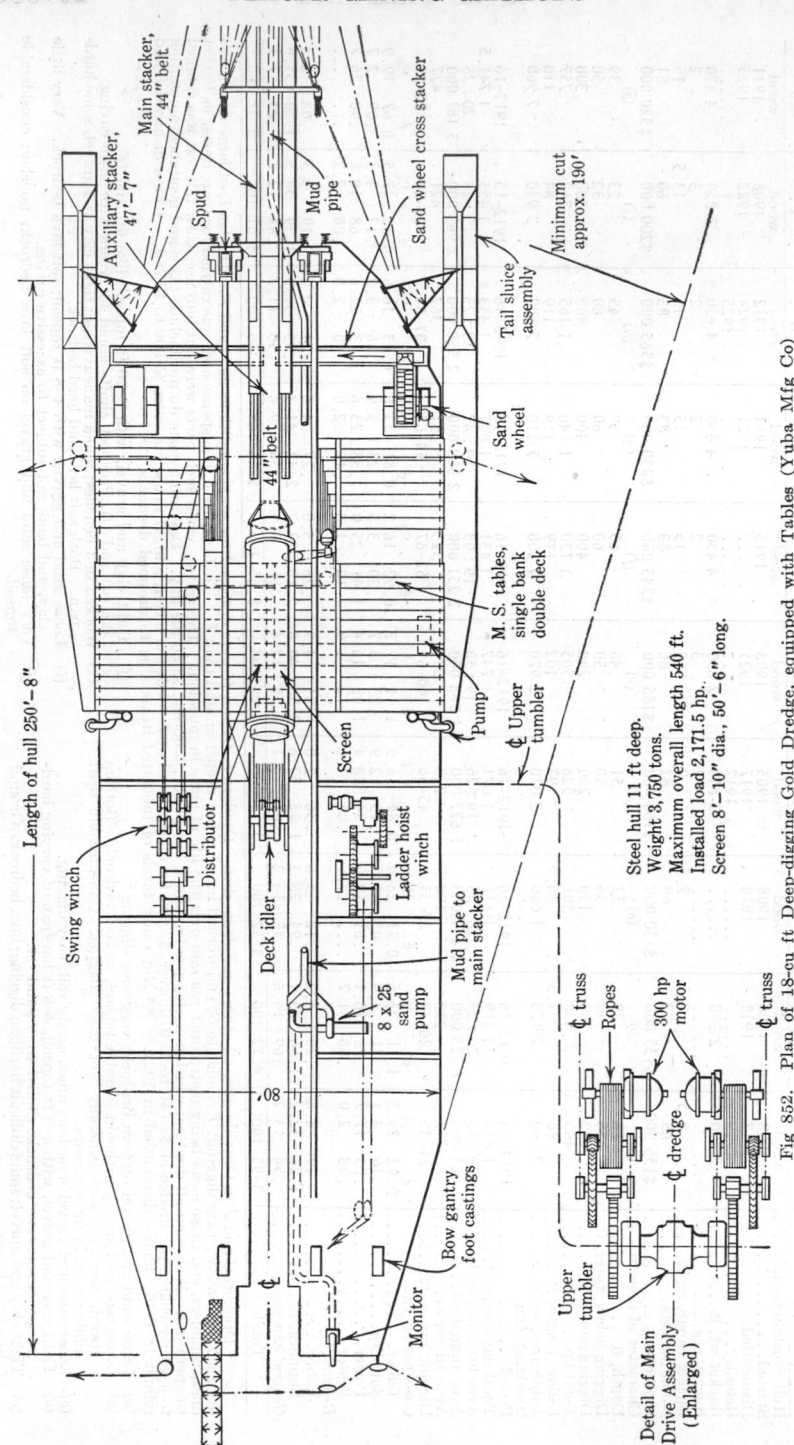

Fig 852. Plan of 18-cu ft Deep-digging Gold Dredge, equipped with Tables (Yuba Mfg Co)

Length of hull 250'–8"

Main stacker, 44" belt
Auxiliary stacker, 47'–7"
Spud
Mud pipe
Sand wheel cross stacker
Minimum cut approx. 190'
Tail sluice assembly
Sand wheel
44" belt
M. S. tables, single bank double deck
Upper tumbler
Pump
Swing winch
Distributor
Deck idler
Screen
Ladder hoist winch
Mud pipe to main stacker
8 x 25 sand pump
Bow gantry foot castings
Monitor

Steel hull 11 ft deep.
Weight 3,750 tons.
Maximum overall length 540 ft.
Installed load 2,171.5 hp.
Screen 8'–10" dia, 50'–6" long.

Detail of Main Drive Assembly (Enlarged)
Upper tumbler
truss
Ropes
300 hp motor
dredge
truss

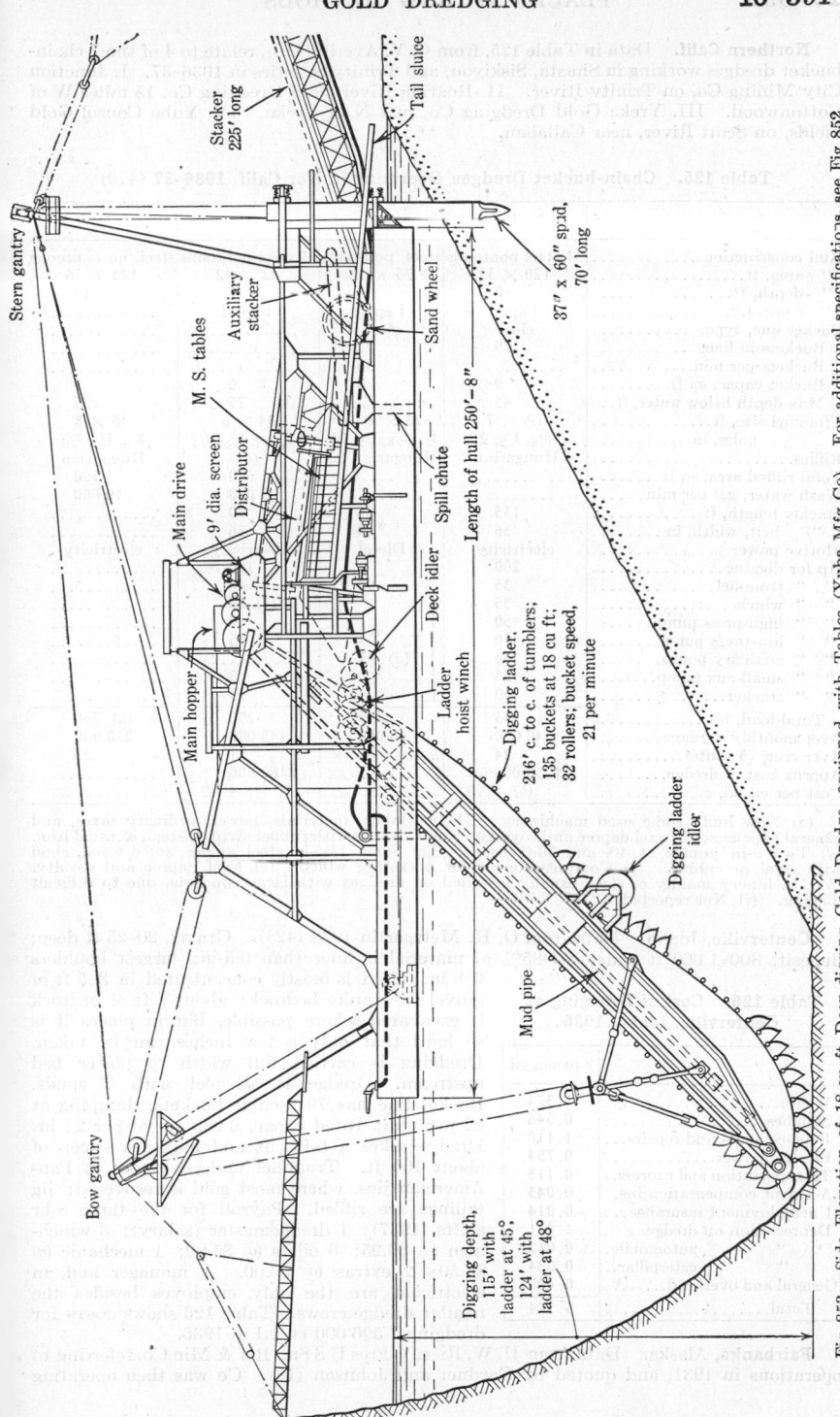

Fig 853. Side Elevation of 18-cu ft Deep-digging Gold Dredge, equipped with Tables (Yuba Mfg Co). For additional specifications, see Fig 852

Northern Calif. Data in Table 125, from C. V. Averill (410), relate to 4 of the 7 chain-bucket dredges working in Shasta, Siskiyou, and Trinity counties in 1936–37. I. Junction City Mining Co, on Trinity River. II. Roaring River Gold Dredging Co, 15 miles W of Cottonwood. III. Yreka Gold Dredging Co, just N of Yreka. IV. Yuba Consol Gold Fields, on Scott River, near Callahan.

Table 125. Chain-bucket Dredges Operating in Nor Calif, 1936–37 (410)

	I	II	III	IV
Hull construction	31 steel pontoons	steel pontoons	19 steel pontoons	steel, no pontoons
" area, ft	120 × 52	75 × 36	82 × 42	123 × 56
" depth, ft	8.1	6	7	10
" control	1 spud	1 spud	1 spud	....
Bucket line, type	close	close	....	....
Buckets in line	79	72	....	....
Buckets per min	....	36	....	....
Bucket capac, cu ft	9 1/2	3	6	9
Max depth below water, ft	45	....	25	35
Trommel size, ft	(i) × 7	23 × 4 1/2	34 × 6	48 × 8
" holes, in	3/8, 1/2, 2	1/4, 3/8, 1/2, 5/8	3/8, 1/2, 5/8, 3/4	3/8, 1/2, 5/8
Riffles	Hungarian	Hungarian (c)	(e)	Hungarian
Total riffled area, sq ft	....	....	1 600	3 500
Wash water, gal per min	....	....	5 000	10 000
Stacker length, ft	135	56	90	....
" belt, width, in	36	24	36	....
Motive power	electricity	Diesel	electricity	electricity
Hp for digging	200	⎫	100	....
" " trommel	35	⎪	40	....
" " winch	35	⎬ 95	(f) 55	....
" " high-press pump	50	⎪	60	....
" " low-press pump	50	⎭	15	....
" " auxiliary pump	50	⎫	....	....
" " small aux pump	25	⎬ (d) 95	3	....
" " stacker	50	⎭	25	....
Total load, hp	495	190	298	(h) 750
Aver monthly yardage	240 000	60 000	145 000	210 000
Aver crew (3 shifts)	24	18	11	23
Approx cost of dredge	$250 000 (a)	....	$160 000	....
Cost per cu yd, ¢	(b) 4.98	....	(g) 4.80	....

(a) New hull; some used machinery. (b) Incl labor, materials, power, ordinary taxes, and general expenses, but excl deprec and royalty. (c) Covered with rubber strips instead of usual iron. (d) Two 8-in pumps at 40- and 60-ft heads. (e) Some 13⁄16-in steel angles, some wood, shod with steel or rubber. (f) Compressing air for operating winch. (g) Excl deprec and royalty. (h) Machinery mainly of sizes usually installed on dredges with larger buckets, due to difficult digging. (i) Not reported.

Centerville, Idaho. Data from O. H. Metzger in 1938 (428). Gravel, 20–25 ft deep; deposit, 800–1 000 ft wide; 80–85% of material is finer than 0.5-in; largest boulders 6–8 in. Gold is mostly concentrated in 3–5 ft of gravel on granite bedrock; about 1 ft of bedrock is excavated where possible, but in places it is so hard that only a few inches can be taken. Dredging is carried full width of placer bed upstream. Dredge is all-steel with 2 spuds. Bucket line has 79 6-cu ft buckets, dumping at 22 per min; rated capac, 6 000 cu yd per 24 hr. Dredge takes a 6-ft cut and makes a sweep of about 100 ft. Trommel undersize goes to Pan-American jigs, where most gold is recovered; jig tailings are riffled. Payroll for the three 8-hr shifts (1937): 1 dredgemaster (salary); 3 winch-men @ $6.25; 6 oilers @ $5.00; 1 mechanic @ $6.50; 2 extras @ $6.00. A manager and an electrician are the only employes besides the regular dredge crews. Table 126 shows costs for dredging 1 596 000 cu yd in 1936.

Table 126. Cost of Dredging at Centerville, Idaho, 1936

	¢ per cu yd
Wages	1.374
Supplies	0.546
Replacements and repairs	1.118
Electric power	0.754
Transportation and express	0.118
Accident compensation ins	0.043
Unemployment insurance	0.014
Depreciation on dredge	1.021
" " automobile	0.012
" " caterpillar	0.084
General and overhead	0.490
Total	5.574

Fairbanks, Alaska. Data from H. W. Rice, V-Pres U S Sm, Ref & Min Co, referring to operations in 1931, and quoted by Gardner and Johnson (18). Co was then operating

3 dredges on Goldstream Cr and 2 on Cleary Cr, respectively 14 and 25 miles from Fairbanks, where the company's steam-driven, elec plant of 8 125 kva capac was situated. Power distributed to dredging areas at 33 000 volts. All the gravels were permanently frozen, and covered with frozen muck to 120 ft depth. Moss, tundra and as much muck as would thaw naturally were stripped hydraulically with water brought 90 miles by ditch, siphons, and a 4 000-ft tunnel; capac of water system was 5 000 miner's in (delivering at press of 80–160 lb), practically all of which was used in stripping. Gravel thawed by cold water (Art 131), between about May 10 and Sept 20. Gravel 35 ft or less in depth was thawed by driven points at 16-ft c-c, requiring about half a season; in deeper gravels, points were set in churn-drilled holes 32 ft c-c, and thawing might not be completed in a whole season. Normally, enough gravel was thawed ahead of each dredge to provide a full season's work, usually about 210 days; re-freezing during winter penetrated only 7–8 ft, which depth thawed naturally early in summer. In season of 1931, stripping amounted to 7 011 000 cu yd, or 52 000 cu yd per day; thawing, 8 133 000 cu yd, or 64 000 cu yd per day; the 5 dredges dug 6 916 000 cu yd of material, or 30 800 cu yd per working day. Gravel contained few boulders over 12 in, and little clay. Gold was mainly close to bedrock, and might penetrate 5 ft into it, if of blocky schist. Table 127 gives construction and operating data on the dredges. Following additional features were common to all: hulls, all-steel, assembled in the field; housings, stacker, and ladder all heated; each hull had 2 spuds in the stern; bucket-chains, close-connected; trommels, pitching 1 5/8 in per ft, had successively 3/8-, 1/2-, and 5/8-in holes in upper 3 segments, followed by 2 segments with 7/8 by 1 1/2-in and 1 1/8 by 1 3/4-in slots; nearly all of gold was finer than 8-mesh, with a few nuggets up to 1 oz; transverse tables sloped 1.25 in, and longit tables 1 1/8 in per ft; Hungarian riffles were 1–1.25 in deep, 1 in wide, 2.25 in c-c.

Table 127. Data, Fairbanks Dredges, in 1931

Dredge No	2	3	5	6	8
Creek	Goldstream	Cleary	Cleary	Goldstream	Goldstream
Aver depth dredged, ft	45.2	46.5	33.5	22.3	18.9
Hull, length, ft	128	148	108	108	99
" width, ft	60	60	60	60	50
" draft	9' 1"	8' 11"	6' 10"	6' 5"	7' 9"
Total depth dug, ft	64	78	53	53	44
of which, under water, ft	48	60	36	36	28
Buckets in line	93	104	78	78	68
Bucket capacity, cu ft	10	10	6	6	6
Trommel, length	44' 7 1/2"	44' 7 1/2"	43' 0 1/2"	43' 0 1/2"	36' 2 1/2"
" diam, ft	8	8	6	6	6
" speed, rpm	6.74	6.74	8.9	8.9	8.9
Tables, total area, sq ft	4 535	4 535	2 125	2 125	1 460
High-press pump, size, in	14	14	12	12	10
press, lb per sq in	27	27	25	25	22
gal per min	5 500	5 500	4 000	4 000	4 000
Low-press pump, size, in	14	14	12	12	10
press, lb per sq in	14	14	14	14	11
gal per min	5 500	5 500	4 000	4 000	3 000
Hopper pump, gal per min	1 000	1 000	....	....	....
Motor hp:					
Digging	250	250	150	150	150
Trommel	75	75	60	60	40
Stacker	50	50	25	25	25
High-press pump	150	150	100	100	75
Low-press pump	75	75	60	60	40
Hopper pump	40	40	....	....	....
Swing winch	40	40	25	25	25
Others (4)	69	69	69	69	69
Total connected load	749	749	489	489	424
Aver load, hp	640	640	360	260	260
Max 3-min peak, hp	925	925	455	360	470
Width of cut, ft	120–190	150–230	100–180	90–170	70–100
No of cuts	2–4	2–3	2–7	2–5	2–3
Aver width of advance, ft	471	349	445	395	310
Distance advanced in season, ft	1 482	3 061	2 302	3 634	5 057
Operating days (3-shift)	204	224	226	225	243
Aver cu yd per day	5 800	8 770	5 990	5 600	5 040

Platinum dredging in Alaska. Data in Table 128, contributed by C. J. Johnston, Treas and Mgr of Goodnews Bay Mining Co, relate to a Yuba 8-cu ft dredge with steel pontoon hull, operating on Salmon River and its tributary creeks, lower Kuskokwim dist.

Table 128. Platinum Dredging, Goodnews Bay Co

	1938	1939
Material dredged, cu yd...........	1 164 098	973 614
Days operated....................	199	184
Aver running time per day, hr : min.	21 : 00	21 : 40
Cu yd per hr running.............	278.8	243.9
Costs, ¢ per cu yd:		
Operating labor.................	4.355	4.772
" supplies..............	0.613	0.341
" power.................	3.366	2.821
Repair labor....................	1.548	1.205
" supplies.................	2.677	3.432
General expense.................	1.670	1.671
Total cost, ¢.................	14.229	14.242

Yukon Consol Gold Corp, Ltd. Data from W. H. S. McFarland, Gen Mgr (434) and G. R. F. Troop, Direc and Sec'y-Treas (435) in 1939. Accompanying statistical and cost tables were contributed personally by Mr. McFarland in 1940,

General. Co, with headquarters at Dawson, Y T, controls about 1 000 sq miles of placer claims and leases distributed along Klondike River and tributaries, and along several north tributaries of Indian River, south of the Klondike. Of 92 000 000 cu yd of gravel (containing gold worth $41 000 000) proved and in reserve at end of 1938, all except 8 000 000 cu yd of hill and bench gravels (to be hydraulicked or draglined) lies in creek valleys adapted for dredging. About two-thirds of the tested area was worked previously by drift or hydraulic mining; of 10 dredges operating in 1939, six were reworking such gravel. Only 2 dredges, those farthest downstream on the Klondike River and Bonanza Cr, worked in naturally thawed gravel; elsewhere, the gravel was almost completely frozen. Gravels in Dawson dist rarely exceed 10-ft depth, except in Klondike valley where max depth is 45 ft (aver, 30 ft). Gold, free and relatively coarse, is mainly in bottom of gravel and upper 4 ft of bedrock; if latter is blocky or slabby, as much as 10 ft of it is sometimes dug. Overburden of frozen, totally barren muck is 10–65 ft deep, usually covered by moss, sod, and brush. Working season is short. Preparatory work on dredges begins about Apl 1; first dredges (usually the larger, or those in richer ground) start towards end of Apl, followed by others as rapidly as increasing water supply develops necessary power at the central hydro-generating plant, until all are operating by mid-May. After Nov 1, diminishing water supply for power, with increasing freezing, lead to suspension, first of the smaller, and later, of the larger dredges; in the exceptionally favorable 1938 season, 2 dredges worked until Dec 24. During the summer, Co employs 600–675 men, of whom only 90 are retained through the winter. Min wages for common labor, 50¢ per hr, plus keep, totaling $7.28 for 10-hr day. Cost of supplies includes freight charges of $55 (for machinery) to $135 per ton from Vancouver to Dawson, *via* Skagway and Whitehorse, plus local transport by truck and tractor, until recently costing about 50¢ per ton-mile.

Stripping of frozen muck is done as in hydraulic mining (Art 123), with water supplied under press from ditches, or by pumping from local streams; suitable press, 50–120 lb per sq in. After providing channels for run-off into nearest natural outlet, a row of 8 or 10 No 2 giants with 3.5-in nozzles is so arranged that consecutive portions of the area can be stripped in rotation, with

Table 129. Data on Stripping by Yukon Consol Gold Corp, Ltd
(From W. H. S. McFarland, Gen Mgr, in 1940)

Dredge No	Year	Cu yd stripped (a)	Water used, in-days (b)	Duty, (c)	Total cost (d), ¢ per cu yd
4	1936	335 910	42 822	7.85	11.85
	1937	202 113	19 320	10.46	10.92
5	1936	666 770	80 862	8.25	6.57
	1937	618 303	74 216	8.33	6.76
	1938	751 927	74 396	10.11	4.53
	1939	896 894	77 331	11.62	....
6	1938	644 067	61 223	10.52	7.84
	1939	576 448	38 545	14.96	....
7	1936	182 700	23 503	7.77	14.07
	1937	266 268	25 232	10.55	10.13
	1938	300 443	24 380	12.32	7.41
	1939	366 991	26 467	13.85	....
8	1937	435 881	35 335	12.34	5.97
	1938	631 500	53 213	11.86	6.80
	1939	954 068	64 236	14.85	....
10	1938	244 820	38 104	6.43	9.81
	1939	408 037	51 257	7.96	....
11	1938	245 511	38 129	6.44	11.31
	1939	394 122	51 729	7.62	....

(a) For depth of muck at those sites where thawing was required, see Table 149. (b) 1 in-day = 1.5 cu ft per min for 24 hr. (c) Cu yd, per in-day. (d) Itemized costs for some examples are in Table 130.

Table 130. Cost of Stripping by Yukon Consol Gold Corp, Ltd
(From W. H. S. McFarland, Gen Mgr; for technical data, see Table 129)

Dredge No	4	5	6	7	8	10	11
Year	1937	1938	1938	1938	1938	1938	1938
Costs, ¢ per cu yd:							
Wag co	4 35	2.10	2.06	2.58	2.55	4.61	4.49
Camp and mess.	2.09	0.95	0.91	1.14	1.15	2.03	1.99
Supplies	0.28	.13	.12	0.05	0.11	0.05	0.38
Shops	.48	.14	.21	.27	.14	.38	.66
Transport	.87	.20	.36	.71	.30	1.10	1.86
Power	2.39	.64	....	.42	.50	.97	.92
Engineering and super.	.46	.14	.19	.32	.19	.46	.75
Ditches	....	....	3.41	1.92	1.36	....	....
Brush cutting	....	.23	.58	....	.50	.21	.26
Total	10.92	4.53	7.84	7.41	6.80	9.81	11.31

little moving of the giants. When the thawed muck has been removed from one portion, the next giant is put into action, leaving the first area to thaw naturally. By the time the last giant in the row has finished its work, the area adjacent to the first will have thawed enough to allow removal of another layer. Distance, in ft, worked from a giant is roughly 1.5 times the water press in lb per sq in. Tailings piles, often complicating the procedure, are removed by a special set-up of a giant before attacking the muck. PUMPS for stripping are 10-in centrifugals, rated at 3 000 US gal per min at 150-ft head, suitable for a 3.5-in nozzle; each is driven by 150-hp 2 300-volt, synchronous motor. Each unit, with starting equipment, is

Table 131. Data on 6 Dredges of Yukon Consol Gold Corp, Ltd
(From W. H. S. McFarland, Gen Mgr, in 1940)

Dredge No	2			3			4		
Built	1911			1912			1912		
Maker	Marion			Marion			Marion		
Hull	Wood			Wood			Wood		
Bucket, cu ft	16			16			16		
Year	1936	1937	1938	1936	1937	1938	1936	1937	1938
Season opened	May 9	May 2	Apr 29	May 4	May 6	Apr 29	Apr 24	July 11	May 3
Season, days	208	216	240	206	203	225	209	145	238
Working time, %	92.92	86.54	86.09	92.21	90.66	89.43	89.57	88.15	88.56
Cu yd dredged	2 032 326	1 811 924	2 071 824	1 864 471	2 721 044	2 045 872	1 891 243	1 089 377	1 756 372
Power, kw-hr	1 986 800	2 060 100	2 262 200	2 092 200	2 036 600	2 446 600	2 147 000	1 610 400	2 599 100
Costs, ¢ per cu yd:							(d)		
Shut-down season									
Direct (b)	1.73	2.46	0.50	1.69	0.60	0.81	1.90	1.71	1.10
Indirect (c)	0.53	0.40	0.48	0.55	0.22	0.34	0.60	0.94	0.45
Working season									
Direct (b)	3.44	4.40	3.88	4.21	2.71	4.33	2.92	5.80	5.00
Indirect (c)	1.14	1.83	1.35	2.99	1.16	1.71	0.73	6.20	11.30
Total	6.84	9.09	6.21	9.44	4.69	7.19	6.15	14.65	17.85

Dredge No	5			6			7		
Built	1937 (a)			1936 (a)			1935 (a)		
Maker	Marion			Bucyrus			Bucyrus		
Hull	Wood			Wood			Wood		
Bucket, cu ft	7			7			5		
Year	1936	1937	1938	1936	1937	1938	1936	1937	1938
Season opened	May 13	Aug 3	Apr 27	June 22	May 4	Apr 28	May 8	Apr 27	Apr 21
Season, days	177	102	209	137	190	196	201	202	214
Working time, %	89.21	90.31	90.40	86.78	88.32	89.64	92.61	92.55	93.11
Cu yd dredged	584 113	310 971	798 890	682 124	579 701	708 768	488 225	508 107	389 936
Power, kw-hr	743 500	474 300	1 018 900	620 400	831 200	854 500	696 100	773 300	640 800
Costs, ¢ per cu yd:							(d)		
Shut-down season									
Direct (b)	3.39	....	0.61	2.02	1.23	0.56	2.81	1.58	1.55
Indirect (c)	2.18	3.56	0.87	1.61	1.05	0.94	2.25	1.39	1.95
Working season									
Direct (b)	5.71	8.31	5.53	4.57	7.88	6.17	8.34	8.60	10.58
Indirect (c)	9.78	9.75	9.70	6.56	7.84	11.35	12.99	7.50	9.67
Total	21.06	21.62	16.71	14.76	18.00	19.02	26.39	19.07	23.75

(a) Rebuilt. (b) Direct charges include: Wages; Mess and camp expense; Repair parts; Other supplies; Machine and electrical shops; Transportation; Power. (c) Indirect charges include: Stripping; Thawing; Prospect drilling; General expense; Bullion expense; Engineering; Supervision; Sundry. (d) Itemized in detail in Table 132.

housed in a portable building, 18 by 10 ft, mounted on skids. Active stripping is feasible only between mid-May and end of Sep; preparatory work begins about a month earlier. Table 129 gives operating data, and Table 130 itemizes costs of such stripping at 7 of the Co's dredge sites.

Thawing is applied to the frozen gravel exposed (as completely as practicable) by removing the muck; the cold-water method is employed. For details and costs, see Art 131.

Dredging. At end of 1939, Co was operating 10 dredges (No 2–11, incl; No 1 was dismantled in 1938 after 33 yr service on 3 sites). All have wooden hulls, and are elec operated. Table 131 gives data and costs for 3 yr on 6 dredges, No 2–7. No 8, a 7-ft Yuba dredge, handled 455 453 cu yd in its 161-day season of 1938, at total cost of 21.72¢ per yd. No 9 is a 5-ft Bucyrus, re-built in 1938; No 10 and 11 are both 7-ft Yubas, built 1939. A new 7-ft dredge in the Klondike costs about $350 000, exclusive of camp buildings, power-line connections, roads, and stripping and thawing equipment; to justify such installation would require about 10-000 000 cu yd (on basis of aver value of present reserves) or a life of 15 yr. Table 132 gives itemized costs for 1938 at 2 dredges selected to represent: (No 3) a large-scale operation in naturally thawed ground on Klondike River; and (No 6) a smaller operation in ground which had to be both stripped and thawed. The 9 dredges working in 1938 dug a total of about 8 500 000 cu yd and produced gold worth $2 131 000 (25.1¢ per yd); 2 of these dredges were working in unproved ground. These 9 dredges, with accessory thawing and stripping equipment, power plant, camps, buildings, and ditches, represent an investment, at cost, of $6 750 000.

Table 132. Itemized Costs at 2 Yukon Consol Dredges, 1938

(From W. H. S. McFarland, Gen Mgr. For operating data, see Table 131)

Costs, ¢ per cu yd	Dredge No 3 2 045 872 cu yd			Dredge No 6 708 768 cu yd		
	Shut-down season	Oper-ating season	Total	Shut-down season	Oper-ating season	Total
Direct Charges						
Wages..............	0.176	1.229	1.405	0.221	2.601	2.822
Mess and camp exp...	.077	.505	.582	.090	1.007	1.097
Repair parts........	.196	.876	1.072	....	.220	.220
Other supplies.......	.042	.394	.436	....	.492	.492
Machine shop.......	.228	.274	.502	.153	.860	1.013
Electrical shop......	.032	.058	.090	.016	.035	.051
Transportation......	.043	.218	.261	.041	.236	.277
Power..............	.020	.772	.792	.042	.715	.757
Total direct.......	0.814	4.326	5.140	0.563	6.166	6.729
Indirect charges						
Stripping..........	....	....	....	....	2.387	2.387
Thawing (by water)..	....	....	....	....	5.244	5.244
Prospect drilling.....	....	.180	.180	....	.499	.499
General exp.........	.277	.717	.994	.800	2.069	2.869
Bullion exp.........	.038	.668	.706	.068	.915	.983
Engineering.........	.006	.064	.070	.028	.168	.196
Supervision.........	.013	.026	.039	.039	.074	.113
Sundry.............	....	.059	.059	....	....	....
Total indirect.....	0.334	1.714	2.048	0.935	11.356	12.291
Total working cost...	1.148	6.040	7.188	1.498	17.522	19.020

Table 133. Yukon Consol Gold Corp; Power Plant Costs

(Data from W. H. S. McFarland, Gen Mgr, in 1940)

Year	1936	1937	1938
Kw-hr distributed...	18 412 308	21 447 648	28 073 088
Cost, ¢ per kw-hr:			
Power plant—			
Operation.......	0.206	0.211	0.114
Improvement....	.....	.....	.021
N Fork ditch—			
Operation.......	.091	.059	.049
Improvement....	.311	.205	.084
S Fork ditch—			
Operation.......	.061	.051	.036
Improvement....	.105	.137	.040
Maint, 33 000-v line..	.069	.057	.057
" secondary lines and sub-stas...	.....	.053	.034.
Total........	0.843	0.773	0.435

Distribution, 1938—Labor, 0.126; camp and mess, 0.060; supplies, 0.037; shops, 0.088; transport, 0.090; engineering and supervising, 0.034; total, 0.435.

Hydro-elec power plant, of 15 000-hp, is situated on Klondike River about 28 miles above Dawson. Its three 5 000-hp turbines, at 220-ft head, drive one 4 690-kva, and two 3 000-kva generators, delivering at 33 000 volts. First water supply came from the North fork of the river, through a 6-mile ditch; added supply of 10 000 miner's in from the South fork was obtained by a 16-mile ditch. The high-tension line is 94.3 miles long; distributing lines, at 2 300 volts, 37.4 miles. Table 133 gives costs of operating and maintaining the power plant.

Bulolo, New Guinea. Contributed by C. A. Banks, Mng Dir, in 1940; for earlier and more detailed data, see Bib (436). Operations are noteworthy because entire equipment of 8 steel dredges and 2 hydro-elec plants delivering 8 000 hp was transported by aeroplane. Beginning in 1931, 30 000 short tons of machinery and supplies were flown up to 1940 without fatal or disabling personal accident, or loss of any equipment. Airline distance from aerodrome at Port Lae to 2 landing fields 5 miles apart on property is only 35–40 miles, but an intervening 5 000-ft range with lowest pass at 4 000 ft, and difficult jungle conditions, made land travel by 110-mile road slow and costly; air transport is estimated to have saved 2 years' time. Flight from Lae to Bulolo takes about 40 min, and the round-trip, incl loading and unloading, about 2 hr. Elev at property is 2 250 ft. TRANSPORT EQUIPMENT includes 3 Junker G–31 aeroplanes, each with three 550-hp Pratt & Whitney Hornet engines. Cargo compartment is 24 ft long, 77 in wide, 69 in high except over the hatch, where height is 82 in; hatch opening, 60 by 141.5 in. Planes were designed for pay-load of 7 000 lb, but 8 000 lb have been carried safely; loads aver about 5 000 lb. Heaviest single pieces (upper-tumbler shafts) weighed 6 950 lb each for the first 4 dredges, and 7 550 lb for No 5. Total capital outlay for air transport was considerably less than would have been required for construction of suitable road and purchase of vehicles. UNIT COST OF AIR TRANSPORT has declined with increasing tonnage and introduction of certain economies. During 54 mos prior to 1937, cost for 14 341 short tons was $49.94 per ton, plus amortization then estimated at $11.85 per ton. During 3 yr to end of 1939, costs on basis of 420 tons monthly were as in Table 134. Gasolene cost about 32.5¢ per Imp gal (27.1¢ per U S gal). Now that the property is fully equipped for

Table 134. Cost of Air Transport at Bulolo

	Per sh ton	%
Loading and unloading..................	$ 0.70	2.01
Operating.............................	16.67	47.96
Maint & repairs on planes................	5.73	16.48
" " " " 'dromes and bldgs.....	1.00	2.88
Management...........................	5.93	17.06
Insurance.............................	4.73	13.61
	$34.76	100.00
Amortization	7.60	
Total per ton....................	$42.36	

Table 135. Costs of Dredging at Bulolo, New Guinea

Fiscal yr ending May 31,	1934	1935	1936	1937	1938	1939	6-yr aver
Cu yd dredged.....	6 674 300	9 920 700	10 915 500	11 197 000	11 222 000	14 688 000	64 617 500
Yield per yd (Au @ $35).............	44.88¢	44.83¢	39.93¢	44.05¢	42.80¢	38.10¢	41.78¢
Costs, ¢ U S per cu yd:							
Jungle clearing...	0.39	0.36	0.29	0.20	0.18	0.22	0.26
Drilling & testing.	0.12	0.07	0.03	0.07	.14	....	.07
Operating wages..	1.60	1.57	1.64	1.44	1.64	1.37	1.53
Supplies.........	.29	.36	.25	.26	.18	.16	.24
Repairs & replacements, incl labor	2.11	1.65	2.00	2.64	2.74	3.78	2.60
Power..........	.87	.76	.34	.38	.40	.34	.48
Servicing........	.27	.23	.34	.42	.45	.34	.35
Gold saving......	....	....	.25	.70	.73	.47	.40
Clean-up........	.16	.12	.13	.14	.16	.14	.14
Bullion frt & refining...........	.27	.20	.19	.18	.17	.16	.19
Bullion postage & insur..........	.12	.13	.12	.12	.12	.12	.12
Gen rep & maint..	.20	.55	.50	.50	.46	.59	.49
General exp.....	.52	.74	.69	.84	.53	.50	.63
Insur & management........	.61	.62	.51	.45	.59	.43	.52
Laboratory......	.18	.08	.04	.04	.08	.07	.07
Travel..........	.24	.20	.24	.17	.12	.11	.17
Medical.........	.18	.17	.16	.12	.12	.11	.14
Lease fees.......	.08	.09	.10	.14	.08	.06	.09
Total working..	8.21	7.90	7.82	8.81	8.89	8.97	8.49
Admin & overhead	.94	.68	.98	1.08	1.05	.87	.93
Royalties.......	2.23	2.29	1.90	2.14	2.09	1.88	2.07
Total expense..	11.38	10.87	10.70	12.03	12.03	11.72	11.49

a life estimated at 16 yr, future transport will be limited to a reduced tonnage of supplies and replacements. Extra cost for design and erection of the dredges, incurred by necessity for sectionalizing, was estimated as 10% for the hulls and 5% for the machinery. DREDGING started in Mch, 1932, with 1 dredge, which was followed by 2 others within the next 2 yr; No 4 began dredging in Aug, 1934. Two more were added at intervals, putting 6 dredges at work by mid-1938. First 4 dredges all had 10.5-cu ft buckets, and dug respectively 29, 35, 52, 59 ft below water; to May 31, 1936, they had handled 32 600 000 cu yd. Costs for 6 fiscal yrs, and aver costs for period, are in Table 135, in U S cents per cu yd. GOLD-SAVING EQUIPMENT on all dredges (as of 1937) includes double-deck tables 21 in wide, 12 ft long, with Hg in wells at top and on riffles. Table tailings go to jigs. Hutch product, 100–150 tons per day, or about 1% of gravel treated, passes through rubber-lined tube-mill 11.75 ft long, 50 in inside diam, loaded with about 1.5 tons of 1.5-in steel balls, and then over amalgamated plates. A flotation cell was installed on 1 dredge, with good saving, but was later found unnecessary when jigging was adopted.

Colombia. C. A. Banks, Managing Director Pato Consol Gold Dredging, Ltd, contributes data on operations of the 3 largest and most typical of Co's 5 dredges, working a property which extends 16 miles along the Nechi River, Zaragosa dist. Equipment includes 2 hydro-elec plants, totaling about 12 000 hp. Table 136 gives costs, in U S ¢ per cu yd, for fiscal yr ended Apl 30, 1939. Each dredge has 13.5-cu ft buckets, and was designed to dig (at 24–26 buckets per min) 3 500 000–4 000 000 cu yd annually; max digging depth is 75–80 ft on Boyacá dredge, 65–67 ft on the others. Jobo dredge has been operating partly on ground covered with 40 ft of barren clay and partly on a bench where a high bank was unavoidable. San Francisco dredge (during yr stated) worked mostly in tailings, with some patches of virgin ground which escaped earlier dredges; digging was relatively easy. Boyacá dredge operated in a low, swampy area, with 50 ft of sand overburden; digging moderately easy. All dredges are equipped with Placer rougher and Pan American pulsator cleaner jigs, treating overflow from riffled tables. Final jig concentrate passes over amalgamated plates, tailings going to a scavenger jig, hutch product of which is ground in a 2 by 4-ft ball mill and returned to the cleaner cells.

Table 136.   Cost of Dredging at Pato, Colombia
(U S ¢ per cu yd: year ended Apr 30, 1939)

Dredge	Jobo	San Francisco	Boyacá	Totals
Cu yd dredged........	3 400 000	3 760 000	3 535 000	10 695 000
Yields per cu yd (Au @ $35)...............	11.48¢	17.27¢	10.14¢	13.07¢
Working costs:				
Wages..............	1.33	0.99	0.87	1.06
Repairs, replacements and supplies.......	1.36	.97	.91	1.07
Power..............	0.43	.30	.39	.37
Clean-up............	.07	.09	.08	.08
Drilling & testing	.17	.12	.13	.14
Total working......	3.36	2.47	2.38	2.72
Bullion realization.....	.23	.36	.19	.26
Office, management, camp, insur, etc.....	1.04	.80	1.52	1.12
Legal, social and agency expenses..........	.65	.65	.65	.65
Total product'n cost.	5.28	4.28	4.74	4.75
Directors, administr, interest, etc..........	.48	.48	.48	.48
Gold tax..............	.63	.94	.55	.71
Income taxes........	.40	.85	.35	.55
Total cost.........	6.79	6.55	6.12	6.49

Bright, Victoria, Australia. H. S. Elford, in 1935, gives mechanical details and operating costs of a steam-driven, flume-type dredge working in gravel averaging about 24 ft deep (439). Buckets are of 7.5-cu ft capac. Ladder has overall length of 78 ft 9 in; wt, 35 tons. Dredge digs 35 ft (max) below water line. Hull, of $5/16$-in riveted steel plate, is 111 ft long, 38 ft 9 in wide and 7 ft deep; draft, 5 ft 3 in. Bucket drive is from a compound, condensing, 125-hp Marshall engine, running at 110 rpm and driving the first-motion shaft through eight 1.75-in manila ropes. By reduction gears, top tumbler is given a speed of 4 rpm, delivering 18 buckets per min.

Steam at 150-lb press is from a wood-fired, multi-tubular boiler, burning 200 cords of eucalyptus per mo; delivered cost of wood, 13 sh per cord. Main winch is driven by a 12-hp, twin-cylinder engine. Dredge buckets deliver into a chute feeding a duplex shaking screen, set at slope of 1.25 in per ft, and making 70 8.75-in strokes per min; holes in upper section are $3/8$- and $1/2$-in; in lower section, $11/16$-in. Oversize material is delivered by "stone chute" 25 ft behind the boat. This chute has semi-circular section, 3.5 ft diam, and is lined with 4 by 0.75-in steel wearing plates. It is suspended by wire ropes from an 8 by 4-in channel 3 ft above bottom of the chute. Screen undersize passes to gold-saving sluices, lined with coconut matting under expanded metal. Most of the gold is caught in the first 6 ft of sluices, the upper 12 ft of which is covered with a steel plate locked in place to prevent theft of gold. Sluice tailings pass into a single launder discharging 42 ft behind the dredge, or 17 ft beyond the stone chute. On cleanup, dredging stops, and expanded metal and matting of all launders are removed. Concentrate is washed out of the matting in a launder and collected behind temporary riffles; then transferred to an amalgamator. Aver capac of dredge is about 16 000 cu yd weekly, from 0.42 acre. Table 137 gives working costs for three 4-week periods in 1935.

Table 137. Costs of Operating Flume-type Dredge, Bright, Victoria, in 1935

Four weeks ending	Jan 19	Feb 16	Mch 16
% full time operating.....	88	90	85
Aver depth, ft............	24	24.1	24.9
Cu yd dug..............	55 600	67 500	65 650
Gold yield, oz............	99.5	124.4	186.0
Cost, pence per cu yd:			
Wages and salaries......	1.219	1.164	1.205
Allowance.............	0.034	0.047	0.040
Stores.................	0.928	0.693	0.798
Fuel...................	0.593	0.458	0.463
Insurance.............	0.032	0.027	0.006
Rent, rates, taxes......	0.019	0.013	0.019
General...............	0.007	0.005	0.002
Total............	2.832	2.407	2.533

Lakekakamu, Papua. Data from J. W. Hinks in 1937 (440). Operation of Tiveri Gold Dredging Co, Ltd, is noteworthy for diminutive size of dredge. Bucket line has 34 buckets of 1.25-cu ft capac, and gross wt of entire plant is only 59 tons; wt of individual parts was limited to permit transport by native carriers; heaviest single part, 725 lb. Bucket ladder can dig 15 ft below water level. Dredge has a steel hull, 50 ft long, 20 ft wide, and 3 ft deep, divided into 6 water-tight compartments.

Power supplied by two 40-60-hp Industrial Marine engines, with clutches permitting either or both to be used. Fuel is producer gas, but engines will operate, without alteration, on benzene or kerosene. Working for 2 yr on producer gas, fuel consumption was 40 lb charcoal per hr; charcoal is from kiln-burning the jungle timber. First recovery is in a sluice 36 ft long by 3 ft wide, with angle-iron riffles and slotted plate over coir matting. Discharge from sluice passes over a grizzly from which the fines return over sand tables covered with expanded metal over coir matting. Oversize discharges behind dredge through a flume. Results for 2 yr ending June 30: In 1936, 154 824 cu yd and in 1937, 158 135 cu yd, cost 8 pence per cu yd.

Resoiling. In normal operation, a dredge destroys the value of land for agriculture, but sometimes, where all conditions were favorable (see below), resoiling has been successful, though at added cost. In most cases, some manual or mechanical work has been needed to complete reconditioning the surface. A dredge operating with headline (Art 127) spreads its tailings more evenly than a spudded dredge, but will still bury the topsoil unless special methods are adopted. A resoiling dredge, with spuds, was developed by the Natomas Co for service in Calif, but proved uneconomical under existing conditions. A similar dredge, by Yuba Mfg Co in 1918, operated satisfactorily in valuable rice lands of Korea, abundant cheap labor being available for final leveling; such land is said to be ready for a crop 6 mos after dredging. C. M. Romanowitz enumerates following conditions for successful resoiling: (a) bedrock fairly smooth and level; (b) bedrock at nearly uniform depth below surface, within area to be dredged; (c) gravel fairly shallow, and water level in pond only slightly below ground surface; (d) deep topsoil; (e) cheap labor, or effic mechanical methods for final leveling; (f) land, or gravel, must be worth enough to justify added cost (above normal dredging) of at least 1¢ per cu yd.

Newstead, Victoria (441). An area of 381 acres on Loddon River, estimated to contain 15 000 000 cu yd of gravel averaging 3.64 grains gold (26.6¢ with Au @ $35 per oz) per cu yd, to aver depth of 24.5 ft, was to be dredged (beginning early 1938) in such manner as to restore surface for farming while avoiding discharge of silt into river. Gravel is covered by 12-13 ft of loam and sandy clay. In its digging, screening, and gold-saving features, the dredge design is conventional. A close-connected chain of 9.5-cu ft buckets is carried on a ladder 72 ft long between centers of tumblers; at 45° inclination, digging depth below water is 27.5 ft; by raising the ladder until bottom tumbler is out of water, a bank 16 ft above water can be dug separately. At 21 buckets per min, output of dredge is 175 000 cu yd per mo. For full details of construction, see Bib (441).

Special features required for resoiling (Fig 854): (a) Receiving end of stacker belt, 42 in wide, is moved forward to a point in front of the high end of the trommel; passing under the latter, the belt rises from the stern at 18° and discharges 25 ft above and 104 ft behind the deck; total length of stacker-conveyer, 160 ft. (b) Chute from bucket-discharge hopper to trommel has a removable bottom segment, under which is another chute which delivers the entire bucket-discharge to the tailings stacker, by-passing the screen; this is done while ladder is working in dry soil above gravel. (c) Chute delivering screen oversize to stacker belt also has a removable bottom segment, through which the coarse tailings can be dropped (*via* another chute) into the pond 15 ft behind the stern. (d) Longit sluice boxes terminate in 4 tail chutes discharging sands 25 ft behind the stern. These modifications reverse the usual order of depositing tailings, the coarse now being on bottom, sands in middle, and soil on top. AVOIDANCE OF SILTING. Tract was prepared in advance by building levees 35 ft wide at base, 4 ft wide at top, and averaging 9 ft high, or 2 ft above highest recorded water

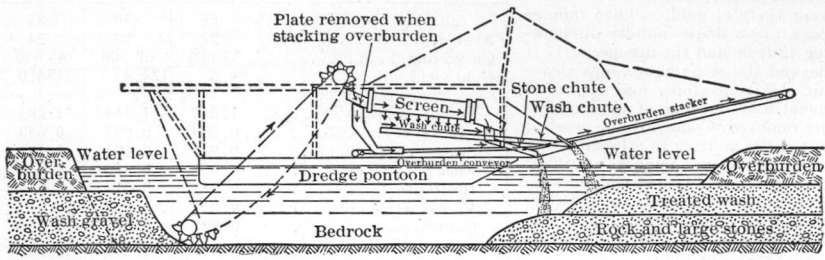

Fig 854. Dredge Equipped for Resoiling, Newstead, Victoria

level of river. A settling dam was provided at elev above highest flood water. To this, dirty water from dredging pond was to be pumped, clarified water returning to pond, makeup water being pumped from river.

129. DRAGLINE DREDGING

By CHARLES WHITE MERRILL, U S Bur Mines, San Francisco

General. The washing plants are mounted on scows or pontoons to which gravel is delivered by dragline excavators standing on dry land; for analogous methods employing stationary or movable washers on land see Art 122. The excavator retreats as it cuts away the bank on which it stands; the washer is floated into the newly-dredged pond. Early installations included a plant built in Siberia by American engineers in 1910; after 2 seasons' operation, the washer was converted into a bucket-ladder dredge. Present practice began in 1933, when 2 plants were built almost simultaneously near Oroville, Calif, and Helena, Mont. Table 138 shows the great expansion of the method in Calif since 1933; many plants are now at work also in Alaska, Ida, Mont, Ore, Colo, Ariz, Nev, and the Philippines. Recent changes in the method and its expanding production have made much of its literature obsolete. The rapid advance of the industry resulted in part from the need for a new method, but the coincident rise in price of gold was a major factor in its widespread acceptance. The special field of the dragline dredge is in working deposits too small to warrant installation of bucket-ladder dredges (Art 127, 128).

Table 138. Dragline Dredging in Calif, 1933–1938. (Minerals Yearbook, 1939, p 235)

Year	Production units		Material treated	Gold recovered		Aver value per cu yd, ¢	% of total Calif placer gold
	Mines	Dredges	Cubic yards	Fine oz	Value		
1933	2	2	11 500	75.26	$ 1 924	16.0	..
1934	4	4	604 000	3 466.04	121 138	20.1	1
1935	24	24	3 906 000	22 191.47	776 701	19.9	6
1936	30	31	10 016 000	49 976.54	1 748 864	17.5	12
1937	51	55	19 364 000	94 142.00	3 294 970	17.0	20
1938	77	80	24 560 000	118 108.00	4 133 780	16.8	21

Requirements for successful operation. (a) Easy-digging gravel, with few boulders (dragline lacks the digging power of a shovel or a bucket-line). (b) Max depth below water, about 30 ft; general aver has been 10–12 ft; ideal digging, 16 ft (working depth of gravels has increased steadily). (c) Fairly smooth, soft, unfissured bedrock; dragline digging under water is less effective in recovering bedrock gold. (d) Gravel of sufficient richness (including in the average such barren gravel as must unavoidably be handled) to pay expenses about 50% higher per cu yd than those of a bucket-ladder dredge. Direct working costs of dragline dredges in the U S in 1937 were 6–15¢ per cu yd (165); aver gold recovery in Calif in 1938 was 16.8¢ per cu yd. (e) Sufficient yardage of profitable gravel to cover amortization of equipment (cost of plants is from $40 000 to $200 000); the whole yardage need not be contiguous, since the plant is readily moved from one deposit to another; provision for moving expenses (Table 139) must be included in cost estimates. (f) Topography not much rougher than for bucket-ladder dredges; if the gravel will hold water, by using bulldozer and dragline on ditches and levees, ponds can be made that enable a washing plant to climb slopes as steep as 5%, but they generally work on much lower gradients.

Table 139. Cost of Moving Dragline Dredges, 1938–39. (Data from U. B. Gilroy)

Equipment......	Lord & Bishop			Sacramento Dredging Co		Table Mt Dredging Co	
	1.5-yd dragline............... 55 tons			1.5-yd dragline... 55 tons		2-yd dragline..... 60 tons	
	1.5-yd washer............... 30 "			1.5-yd washer.... 30 "		2-yd washer..... 35 "	
	Steel pontoons............... 30 "			Steel pontoons... 30 "		Steel pontoons... 35 "	
	Caterpillar bulldozer.......... 22 "			Cat-bulldozer.... 22 "		Accessories...... 5 "	
	Accessories................... 5 "			Accessories...... 5 "			
	Total weight...............142 tons			Total weight...142 tons		Total weight ..135 tons	

	Move No 1	Move No 2	Move No 3	Move No 1	Move No 2	Stage 1	Stage 2
Tons by truck...	87	142	142	142	87	135	......
" by RR....	55	......	......	......	55	......	160 (a)
Locations (b):							
From.........	Butte Co	Grays Flat	Nor Calif	Folsom	Valley Sprs	Hayfork	Redding
To...........	Calaveras Co	Redding	Central Cal	Coloma	Shingle Sprs	Redding	Realito
Distance, miles...	160	155	300	50	90	70	1 600
Cost of haul:							
By truck......	$ 500	$ 900	$ 1 100	$ 1 000	$ 900	$ 1 200	......
By RR.......	475	......	......	......	156	......	$ 5 600
Est cost dismantling and assembling (c).......	620	570	565	545	600		$ 1 200
Total cost of move......	$1 595	$1 470	$1 665	$1 545	$1 656		$ 8 000

(a) At Redding, 25 tons of parts were added before rail shipment.   (b) All in Calif except Realito, Sonora, Mex.   (c) Customary to make convenient repairs during assembly, without segregating their cost; above estimates include no such repairs.

Usual equipment. Dragline EXCAVATORS commonly have 1.5–2.5-cu yd buckets (max to date, 5 cu yd), 45–65-ft booms, and are driven by 125–150-hp Diesel engines (a few have elec or gasolene drive); buckets, especially where gravel is tight, are usually 0.25–1 cu yd less in capac than that for which the rest of the machine is designed. Usual output is 90–125 cu yd per hr of working time. WASHERS (Fig 855) mounted on steel pontoon or wooden scows 25–40 ft wide, 35–50 ft long, and drawing 30–40 in of water, have gold-saving equipment practically identical with that on bucket-ladder dredges (Art 127). Dumping from a dragline bucket, however, requires addition of a hopper, 10 or 12 ft square at top, and about 15 ft above water. The intermittent feed is equalized as far as possible before reaching the tables by: (a) making the hopper with low-sloping sides, on which powerful water jets impinge; (b) by equipping the first section of the trommel as a scrubber; (c) by using screens, retards, lifters, and Archimedean screws in the trommel; failure to equalize the flow of gravel is a prime cause of poor recovery. Recommended total area of tables on a washer receiving 150 cu yd per hr and discarding about 50% of screen oversize is at least 500 and preferably 600 sq ft; width of a single table should not exceed 30 in, due to interference with its smooth flow by careening of the scow when a load of gravel is dumped into hopper. Stackers are 40–60 ft long, with belts 24–36 in wide. Diesel engines of 50 to 100-hp are commonest source of power for driving pumps, trommel, stacker, and jigs; usually the power requirement of the dragline excavator slightly exceeds the total needs of the washing plant. Most plants include tractor with bulldozer, one or more trucks, portable pumping unit for fresh water to pond, a blacksmith shop, and welding outfit (when digging is difficult, the replacing of bucket teeth is a major expense). Stripping barren overburden by scarifier, carryall, and bulldozer is often economical. Table 140 gives data on 6 typical dragline dredges operating in Calif in 1937, from Gardner and Allsman (165). Boulders over 12 in were absent in all cases. Sluices were at grade of 1.25–1.5 in per ft; upper ones had iron-topped wooden riffles (except No VI, which used 1.25-in angles); lower sluices (in all but No VI) were riffled with expanded metal laid on carpet, matting, or burlap.

Cost of dragline dredges. Setting up the outfit is mainly a matter of selecting and assembling large units of ready-built machinery; excavators and buckets, trucks, and bulldozers are always ready-made. Washing plants can be bought ready to assemble or are designed and built at the mine. Table 141 gives prices for 4 typical outfits built in 1939.

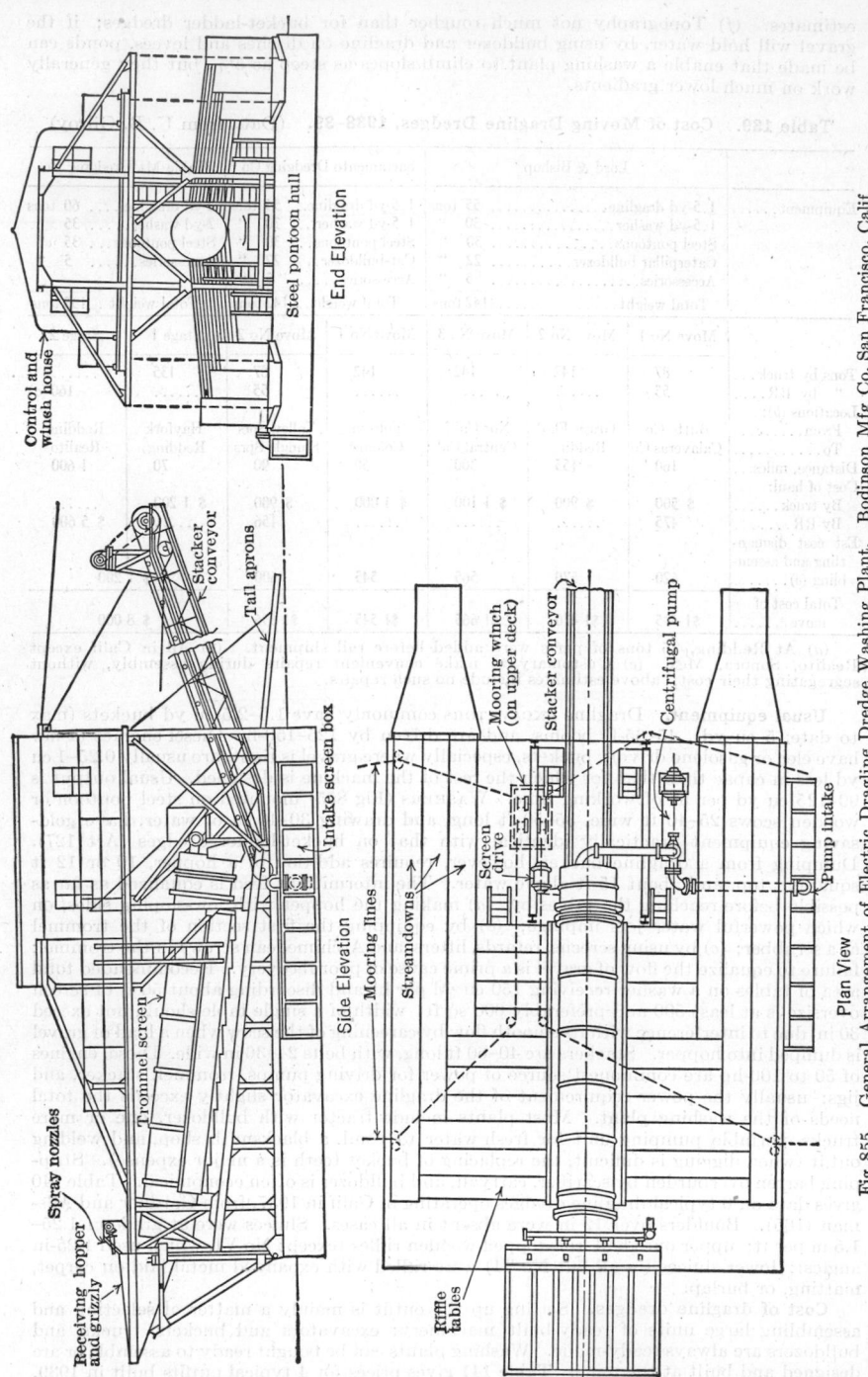

Fig 855. General Arrangement of Electric Dragline Dredge Washing Plant. Bodinson Mfg Co, San Francisco, Calif

Table 140. Data on Calif Dragline Dredges Operating in 1937 (165)

	I	II	III	IV	V	VI
Aver depth gravel, ft	12	10–20	7 1/2	6 1/2	11	4 1/2–12
Digging	easy	med hard	easy	easy	easy	med tight
Clay, %	15	10	small	10	high	10
Bedrock	soft porph	grnstn	hardpan	clay	porph	tuff
Depth scraped, in	12–14	......	6–8	6	18	6
Dragline bucket, cu yd	1 1/2	2 1/4	1 1/4	1 1/2	1 1/2	1 1/2
" boom, ft	50	80	45	50	50	50
" hp	(d) 130	(d) 125	(d)	(d) 95	(d) 120	(e) 121
Washer scow, ft	32 × 42	30 × 40	25 × 40	30 × 40	30 × 40	40 × 35
Trommel size	32' × 54"	27' × 54"	24' × 48"	25' × 54"	30' × 60"	30' × 54"
Scrubber, length, ft	10	5	4	4	12	8
Trommel holes, in	3/8, 1/2	3/8, 1/2	3/8	3/8, 1/2	3/8, 1/2, 11/4	3/8
Cross-sluices, area, sq ft	480	350	324	352	460	432
Longit " " " "	300	320	180	288	250	420
Riffles	(a)	(a)	(a)	(a)	(a)	(a)
Pump, disch diam, in	7 & 4	7 & 5	10	8	8	12
Total washer hp	(d) 85	(d) 65	(d) 80	(d) 50	(d) 100	(e) 185
Clean-up interval, days:						
Cross sluices	10	6	5	6, 12	4	..
Whole plant	20	18	14	18	4	15
Mercury charged, lb	114	150	60	..	60	..
Shifts per day	3	3	2 @ 9 hr	3	2 @ 10 hr	3
Hr operating per day	19 1/2	..	15 1/3	18	19	19
Gravel per hr, cu yd	82	104	122	167	100	100
Total crew per day	13	14	11	13	14	12
Aver rate per hr (weighted)	$0.73	$0.73	$0.71	$0.75	$0.75	......
Fuel oil per hr, gal	8.2	7.3	......	7.8	13	(e)
Wash water, gal per min	......	......	2 800	2 000	1 800	2 500
First cost of plant:						
Excavator	$22 500	$39 600	......	$21 000	$20 270	$18 500
Washer	12 000	16 000	$15 000	14 000	22 800	16 400
Miscellaneous	......	38 900	......	8 600	10 600	3 600
Total	$34 500	$94 500	$40 000	$43 600	$53 670	$38 500
Working cost, ¢ per cu yd:						
Excavating	4	3.32	......	......	......	(f)
Washing	5.6	3.74	......	......	......	(f)
General & miscel	1.5	4.44	......	......	......	(f)
Total	(b) 11.1	11.50	15.0	(c) 9.0	(c) 11.0	(c) 12.5

I—Cinco Mineros, Oroville. II—Penn Dredging Co, Oroville. III—Midland Co, Cottonwood. IV—R. S. Olson, Redding. V—A. C. Mining Co, Redding. VI—Milton Gold Dredging Enterprise, Milton. (a) See text. (b) Excl deprec. (c) Incl deprec. (d) Diesel. (e) Elec. (f) See Table 143.

Table 141. Short Specifications and Prices of Dragline Dredge and Washing Plants
(Bodinson Mfg Co, San Francisco, 1939)

Dragline bucket, cu yd	0.75–1	1.25–1.50	2.5–3	5
Nominal capac, cu yd per hr	75–100	100–125	150–200	300–400
Feed hopper, ft	10 × 8	11 × 10	14 × 10	16 × 16
Trommel, diam and length	48" × 24'6"	54" × 30'	60" × 41'	72" × 50'
Riffle area, approx sq ft	480	780	1 000	1 500
Stacker, width and length	24" × 40'	30" × 50'	36" × 50'	42" × 60'
Stacker, drive motor, hp	5	7.5	15	20
Pump: diam, in; capac, gal per min	8; 2 500	10; 3 000	12; 4 000	14; 6 000
Winches	4 hand power	4 hand power	4 hand power	Elec & drum
Mooring cable	1 200', 3/8" × 8/19	1 200', 3/8" × 8/19	1 200', 3/8" × 8/19	1 600', 1/2" × 8/19
Diesel engine	Cat D-4 600	Cat D-11 000	Murphy, 6-cyl	FM, 225 hp
Auxil generator for light and motor, kw	10	20	25	200
Hull, steel pontoon, width, length, depth	30' × 32' × 42"	34' × 42' × 38"	36' × 48' × 48"	40' × 64' × 54"
Approx export weight, lb	88 000	95 000	200 000	362 000
Approx price washing plant, f o b dock, San Francisco *	$18 900	$25 775	$35 000	$55 000
Add for complete Diesel-elec	2 500	3 000	3 500	(Diesel-elec only)
Approx price of suitable dragline excavator del'd Pacific Coast	14 250	18 400	32 200	70 000
Approx price of suitable bucket	900	1 100	2 000	2 800

* Price includes riffles and Hg-traps, motors, their control apparatus and transmission; not included: lumber, second deck house, or elec wiring.

General procedure. Most gravels worked by dragline dredges are recent stream deposits. If channel is not more than 50–60 ft wide, its full width generally is taken in 1 cut (Fig 856-A), the washer following close behind and discharging tailings behind itself, screen oversize by stacker, and sands into the pond. A wider channel may be worked in successive cuts parallel with the stream, but it is better (Fig 856-B) to take successive 15 to 20-ft cuts back and forth across the channel. (Compare with land dredge at Atlantic City, Wyo, Art 122.) One advantage of latter plan is that the bedrock can be scraped (with improved recovery) in more than one direction. By either method, position of the boat is adjusted by 4 wire ropes anchored to deadmen on shore and held taut by winches on the boat; spuds (Art 127) are usually unnecessary. Following examples illustrate practice as of 1936–1938.

Wyandotte Cr, Oroville. Data from J. F. Magee (442) in 1936. GRAVEL is in 2 beds; upper, loose and easy to dig; lower, slightly harder; both well rounded and of medium size (60% on $3/8$-in). Gold is fine; bright in upper gravel, less so in lower. Depth to false bedrock (decomposed volcanic ash easy to scrape), 4–25 ft, aver 12 ft; max depth dredged, 24 ft; usual working depth 9.5 ft, leaving lower bed intact when necessary. Parts of area have up to 2.5 ft of overburden. DRAGLINE, Lima type 601, caterpillar-mounted; Diesel 102-hp engine; 60-ft boom, 1.25-yd bucket; on aver digging, it delivers 2 heaping buckets per min, or 150 cu yd per hr. WASHER is on a wooden scow drawing 25 in of water when fully loaded (displacement, 65 tons). Hopper, 10 by 10.5 ft at top, has bottom sloping 25°; water jets regulate discharge of gravel. Trommel, 25 ft by 48 in, has 4-ft scrubbing section and 5-ft blind lower end; middle 16 ft has $3/8$-in holes, 1 1/8 in c–c throughout; slope, 1.5 in per ft. Cross-sluices, 7 on each side, are 27 in wide and discharge into a 4-ft sluice on each side; all grades, 1.5 in per ft; total sluice area riffled (iron-topped wooden cross-riffles), 480 sq ft; extensions of side sluices deposit sand tailings 12 ft behind rear of scow. Stacker for screen oversize, 45 ft long, with 24-in belt. Wash water, delivered by centrif pump with 7-in discharge at 1 200 gal per min, is distributed: 84% to trommel sprays, 14% to hopper chute, 2% to skimmer jet to keep the strainer free from floating trash. Purchased water, 40 miner's in. Whole washing plant is driven by 50-hp, 4-cyl Diesel. OPERATION is similar to that in Fig 856-A; pond is 70 ft wide and about 75 ft long. During first 3 mos of operation, all delays amounted to 34.5% of possible time, largest single source of lost time being the moving of dragline, which was then on soft ground. COSTS of Wyandotte operation are compared in Table 142 with those of 2 others (localities not stated), practically identical equip-

Table 142. Costs at 3 Small Dragline Dredge Operations (442)

	Wyandotte	Plant A	Plant B
Period considered	Apr 5–Dec 31, 1935	Apr 12, 1935–Apr 23, 1936	4 1/2 months in 1936
Bucket size, cu yd........	1.25	1.25	1.5
Yardage treated..........	557 764	458 000	689 820
Recovery, ¢ per cu yd.....	21.19	22.88	14.33
Costs: ¢ per cu yd			
Excavating labor.......	1.40	1.67	1.43
" fuel and lubr oil......	.32	1.05	.40
" maintenance	1.60	1.05	.57
Washing labor..........	2.51	4.24	2.16
" fuel and lubr oil	.32	.34	.37
" water..........	.07	.22	.37
" mercury........	.03	.05	.01
" maintenance.....	.90	2.12	.93
General, royalty........	1.83	2.73	1.00
" insurance........	.32	.37	.14
" surveying and prospect'g.....	.24	.18	......
" clearing ground...	.99	....	....
" office and shop...	.06	.10	.15
" marketing gold...	.16	....	....
" transportation....	.12	.09	....
" misc equipment..	....	.34	....
" interest........	....	.05	....
Total (excl deprec)....	10.87	14.60	7.53

ment being employed at all 3 places. Digging and washing conditions differ as follows: At Plant *A*, gravel (9.5 ft deep) is finer (30–40% on $3/8$-in), but harder both to dig and wash; bedrock, of decomposed granite, digs easily but is difficult to distinguish from bottom of gravel. At Plant *B*, gravel (6 ft deep) is loose and sandy, with much coarse (60–75% on $3/8$-in) making for easy washing; bedrock favorable and easily recognized when reached.

Milton Gold Dredging Enterprise, Milton, Calif. For geol, structural, and operating data, see Table 140, col VI; following added information is from Julihn and Horton (57) in 1938. Installation is one of few dragline dredges operated entirely by elec. Trans-

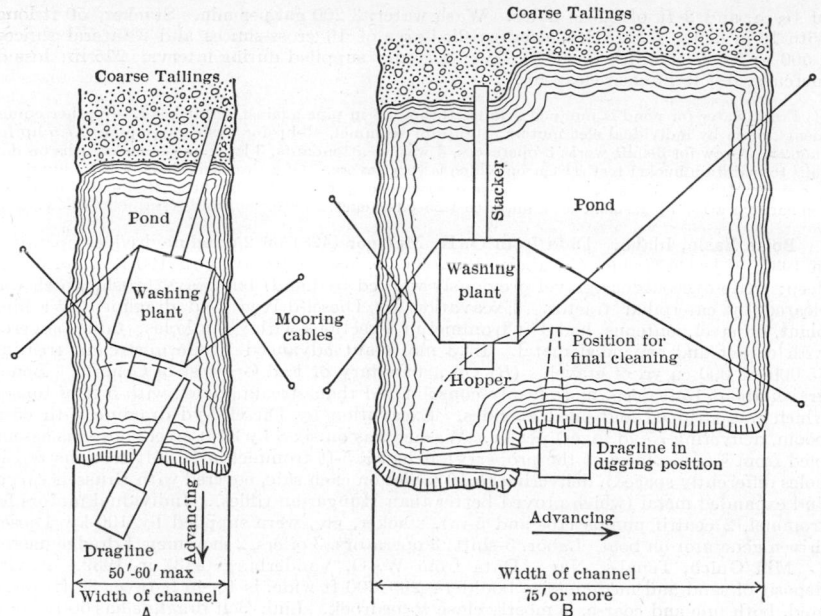

Fig 856.　Two Procedures in Dragline Dredging

formers (4 000–440 volts) are mounted on a wheeled trailer. Ground was carefully prospected with 7 pits to bedrock per acre, each being groove-sampled on up-stream and down-stream sides; no factors to cover bedrock or washing losses were applied. Dredge cuts, surveyed monthly, coincided approx with blocks as used for estimating (Art 11); aver recovery from over 1 000 000 cu yd was 0.2¢ or a little more than 1% above estimate. Crew for 3-shift work comprised 12 men and foreman at (weighted) aver wages of $5.75 per day-in. Water (50 miner's in) cost 11.25¢ per day-in. Power (at 1.1166¢ per kw-hr) for a typical month's operation was 29 500 kw-hr on washer, 20 200 kw-hr on dragline, 900 kw-hr for welding, lights, and shop. During first 2 yr, all time lost (incl several groundings and a sinking of washer) was 30.8% of elapsed time. Aver total cost, on basis of 1 234 908 cu yd (bank measure) handled in 2 yr ending Aug 31, 1937, is itemized in Table 143.

Lilly mine, Camanche, Calif. Data from Julihn and Horton (57) in 1938. Gravel, 4–18 ft deep, is uncemented, and contains no boulders; bedrock, volcanic tuff. Gold fine and flaky. Similar gravel in adjoining tract averaged 16¢ per cu yd in test pits. Dragline, Diesel-powered, has 60-ft boom and 2-yd bucket; normal output, 100–125 cu yd per hr. Washer is on 50 by 36-ft scow, composed of 5 wooden pontoons drawing 2 ft of water. Trommel, 32 by 4.5 ft, has 8-ft scrubber, 18 ft

Table 143.　Cost of Dragline Dredging, Milton, Calif, 1935–37 (57)

(Cents per cu yd, bank measure)

Excavating, labor	2.12	
" supplies	.34	
" power	.62	
" repairs & maint	1.04	
" depreciation	.81	
Washing, labor	1.02	
" supplies	.30	
" power	.48	
" repairs & maint	.85	
" depreciation	.71	
General operating:		
Royalty	1.59	
Prospecting	.09	
Water	.21	
Moving electric lines	.14	
Roads, dams, tailings	.31	
Shop	.11	
Total operating		10.74
General overhead:		
Superintendence	0.58	
Auto transport	.11	
Field office	.09	
Taxes and insurance	.09	
Marketing gold	.08	
Travel	.12	
San Francisco office	.20	
Total overhead		1.27
Total cost, ¢ per cu yd		12.01

of $^3/_8$-in, and 2 ft of 0.5-in holes. Wash water, 3 200 gal per min. Stacker, 50 ft long, with 26-in belt. Total (Hungarian) riffled area of 16 cross-sluices and 2 lateral sluices, 1 500 sq ft. Clean-ups, every 10 days; mercury supplied during interval, 225 lb; loss of mercury, 6–7 lb at each clean-up.

Fresh water for pond is pumped 2 miles through 8-in pipe against 420-ft head. Washer equipment driven by individual elec motors: 30-hp for trommel, 40-hp for wash-water pump, 7.5 hp for stacker. Crew for 3-shift work: 3 operators, 3 washer attendants, 3 laborers; 2 blacksmiths on day shift to maintain bucket teeth, wear on which is very severe. Of 2 close neighbors of the Lilly mine, one suspended operations owing to expense of saving rusty gold, the other because the gravel proved too hard for a 100-hp gasolene dragline with 1.25-yd bucket.

Boise Basin, Idaho. Data from O. H. Metzger (428) on 2 dragline dredges operating in 1937. (*A*) On Grimes Cr, above Pioneerville. Stream gravels 75–100 ft wide, 6–8 ft deep; little overburden (gravel previously worked by hand) but heavy brush, which was cleared by caterpillar tractor. Excavation by Diesel-driven 1-yd dragline. Washing plant, on steel pontoons, had 4-ft trommel in 4 sections with $^3/_8$-in holes; tables covered with carpet and expanded metal. In 3 mo, plant advanced 1 mile upstream, treating 75 000–85 000 cu yd of gravel. (*B*) On a tributary of Fall Cr, west of Granite. Bench gravel about 15 ft deep, more firmly consolidated than stream gravel, with 5 ft of topsoil which was stripped and piled at sides. Excavation by Diesel 3-yd dragline with 65-ft boom, delivering 75 yd (aver) per hr. Washer was on six 8 by 36-ft steel pontoons assembled from $^3/_{16}$-in plates at the property; it had a 5-ft trommel in 10 3-ft sections ($^3/_8$-in holes differently spaced), delivering to 10 tables on each side, covered with Brussels carpet and expanded metal (which proved better than Hungarian riffles). Individual motors for trommel, 2 centrif pumps (10- and 5-in), stacker, etc, were supplied by 100-kw Diesel-driven generator on boat. Labor, 3-shift: 3 operators, 3 oilers, 2 shoremen, 1 dredgemaster.

Mill Gulch, Tenabo, Nev. Data from W. O. Vanderburg (443) in 1939. Ravine deposit of sand and medium-size boulders, 200–300 ft wide, is 10–45 ft (aver 30 ft) deep; gold, both fine and coarse, is mostly close to bedrock. Link-Belt dragline has 60-ft boom and 1.75-yd, heavy-duty bucket. A caterpillar tractor-bulldozer is used for grading. Washer is on wooden scow, 30 by 40 ft, with 3 additional steel pontoons; draft, 40 in. Estimated (3-shift) capac, 1 500 cu yd per day. Trommel, 24 ft by 54 in, is in 2 equal sections; upper, unpunched, has spiral disintegrating flights; lower, $^3/_8$-in holes. Six cross-sluices on each side are 30 in wide by 12 ft long; total (Hungarian) riffled area, 460 sq ft. A 6-in centrif pump circulates wash water, pumped to the pond from a well through 15 000 ft of 8-in pipe against 500-ft head. Stacker is 70 ft long, with 24-in belt. A 160-hp, 8-cyl Diesel supplies all power. Crew, 16 men, 3-shift. Clean-ups daily.

130. DRIFT MINING

Drift mining is the exploitation of placers by underground methods. It was one of the early types of mining in Calif, reaching its peak between 1870 and 1880; thereafter it declined and almost ceased (57). Since 1933, due to higher price of gold, a revival of drift mining has occurred.

Field of use is in mining rich paystreaks of moderate thickness, where open-cut methods are impossible or would yield a smaller net return. Large boulders must usually be blasted; if numerous, they may increase cost to a point which is prohibitive. Drift mining has been practiced chiefly in the ancient buried channels in Calif, the buried beach placers at Nome, Alaska, and the deep leads of Australia (Art 117). Alaska creek gravels, where frozen, are often drifted, especially by small operators. In early Calif and Alaska mining, many placers were drifted for rich streaks by miners with small capital; later the same deposits were profitably hydraulicked or dredged (385). Drift mining costs more than open-cut work, hence requires richer gravels to yield a profit. Ordinary thickness of gravel mined is 5 to 8 ft; up to 10 or 15 ft in rare cases, and down to 3 or 4 ft, which is about minimum for economic work in flat openings.

General plan. The methods of OPENING are the same as for other underground mining (Art 14–16), with emphasis on a mode of entry that will drain the workings and eliminate equipment and costs for hoisting and pumping. But tunnel or drift entries are limited to bench gravels or other elevated deposits like the old Calif channels. Details of LATERAL DEVELOPMENT (Fig 857–859) vary widely with local conditions. In general, a central haulageway is driven from the point of entry close to the long axis of the paystreak, and on or partly in bedrock; in Calif and Victoria, this opening is sometimes entirely in bedrock and connected by chute-raises with the workings in the gravel above. Cross-cuts are driven from the central drift to the RIM of the channel, or limits of the paystreak; auxiliary drifts also are driven in wide deposits. These openings have both a mining and an exploratory function, latter often predominating in fixing the dimensions of the blocks of ground. MINING is done by a form of longwall-retreating (Art 108), called "breasting"; advancing longwall has been used in a few cases. Ground is broken with picks where possible; by hand drilling and blasting where necessary. Frozen gravel is usually thawed before it is excavated; for exceptional case, see Idaho Mining Co, below. The roof of working places is temporarily supported by timber; posts and head boards serve in firm, cemented, or frozen ground; spiling or forepoling may be necessary in loose gravel. Barrows are best for transport in small mines or under low roof; otherwise tracks are laid along the working faces and the gravel shoveled into cars. Tracks are shifted bodily after the face has advanced 6–8 ft. Equipment for haulage, hoisting, and pumping is the same as in metal mines of similar area and output.

Fig 857 typifies early work in Calif in WIDE deposits (456, 457). Main haulageways H are 6 ft by 6 or 7 ft in the clear, often requiring heavy drift-sets and close lagging. Some

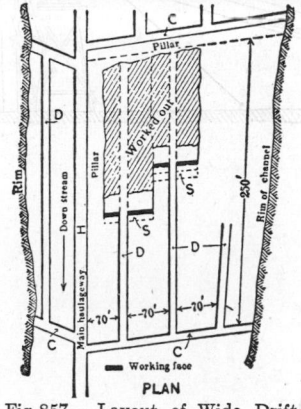

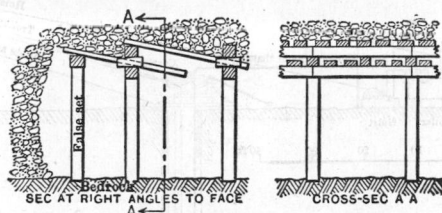

Fig 858. Breast Timbering, Hidden Treasure Mine

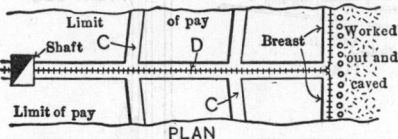

Fig 857. Layout of Wide Drift Mine, Calif

Fig 859. Layout of a Drift Mine in a Narrow Paystreak

of these mines covered large areas, making the maintenance of haulage openings a serious item. Crosscuts C and auxiliary drifts D are 5 by 6 ft or 6 by 6 ft, timbered and lagged in soft ground, but not in as permanent a manner as the main haulageway. Crosscuts C may be driven at an angle to the bedrock slope to secure the desired haulage gradient. Breasting begins at the ends of drifts D, and retreats towards the crosscut from which they were driven. Successive positions of the working faces are indicated by dotted lines S. Short breasts (Fig 857) allow partial control of roof press by regulating speed of advance and distance apart of working faces. In compact gravel requiring blasting, little care was taken to keep breasts "faced-up" evenly; it was cheaper to break from the corners of blocks. Fig 858 shows breast timbering at the Hidden Treasure (457); it is the usual form for soft gravel.

Fig 859 shows a layout for paystreaks 75 to 100 ft wide, typifying early work in Alaska; also that in NARROW paystreaks in Calif. Central drift D may connect with a shaft or an adit; it usually requires timbering even in frozen ground. Prospecting cross-cuts C are driven at intervals; in frozen ground they are generally untimbered. Breasting is carried the full width of the pay, retreating towards the point of entry. Breasts are timbered with sets in heavy ground, with posts and caps in moderately firm ground, or left untimbered in solidly frozen ground.

Fig 860 shows an advancing method of breasting. It has been applied in Alaska and Calif to narrow, irregular deposits where straight haulage drifts, driven

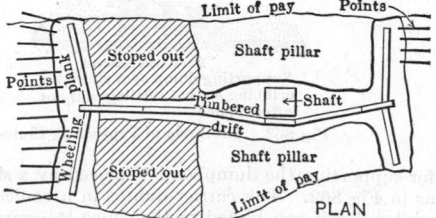

Fig 860. Advancing System (after Ellis)

ahead of stoping, are not feasible. A gangway is kept open through the worked-out area by timbering with light 3-piece sets and tight lagging (459).

Washing gravel. At mines opened by a drift or tunnel, cars are dumped at the portal into a bin feeding a sluice. Sluicing is rarely continuous; bin is flushed out periodically by a small giant working under low head. At shaft mines, gravel is usually hoisted high enough above surface to give headroom for sluices and tailings disposal. Gravel may be dumped directly into a box (Fig 828) at head of an elevated sluice, or into a bin for intermittent sluicing. Latter plan is usual at small mines and where water is scanty or costly. Bins hold a day's output; upper sluice boxes are cleaned up after each run; frequent clean-ups are advisable due to relative richness of gravel. In the far North,

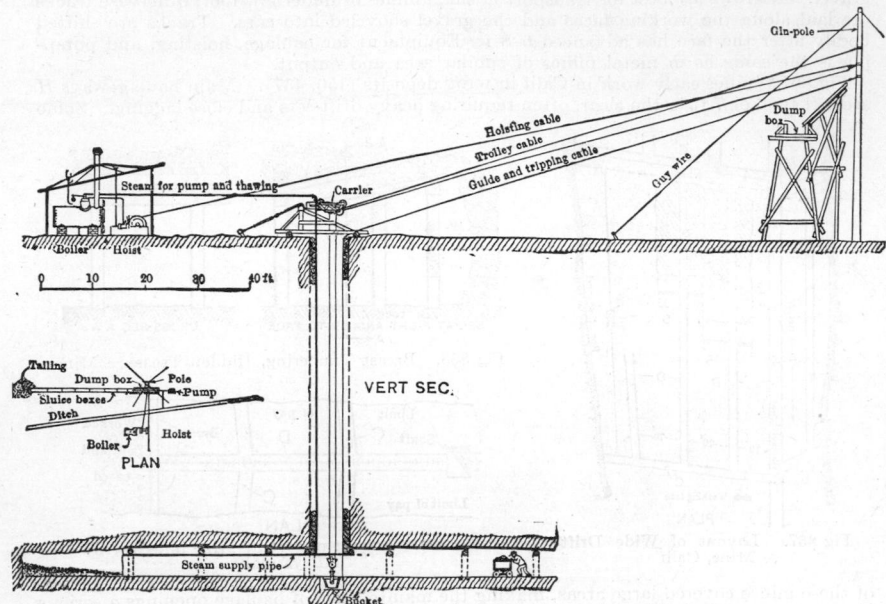

Fig 861. Arrangement of Self Dumper (after Katz)

sluicing is impossible in winter; gravel is stacked on surface and sluiced in spring and summer. In Calif, tough cemented gravel is crushed in stamp mills fitted with coarse screens, and then sluiced. Gravel containing much sticky clay may be passed through trommels or puddled, before sluicing.

Surface plant at Alaskan drift mines is marked by wide use of inclined cableways, the bucket of which descends into the shaft (Fig 861). For winter work, the structure shown

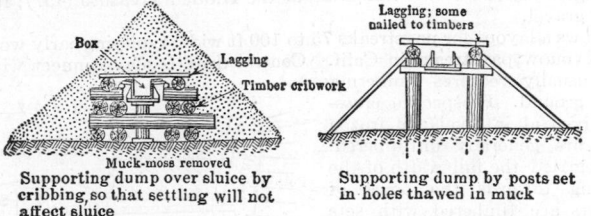

Supporting dump over sluice by cribbing, so that settling will not affect sluice

Supporting dump by posts set in holes thawed in muck

Fig 862. Methods of Protecting Sluice under Winter Dumps (after Ellis)

for supporting the dumpbox is replaced by a sluice, built near the ground, and supported as in Fig 862. The carrier dumps in a conical pile over the sluice; hence, much of the winter dump can be fed to the sluice by gravity assisted by nozzle water in the spring.

Examples of drift mining.

California, EARLY WORK (to 1890). Cost of 6 by 7-ft main haulageways in hard gravel, requiring blasting, $4–$7 per ft; smaller crosscuts and drifts, $3–$5. In ground less difficult to drill, and in picking ground requiring timbering, main tunnels cost $3–$4 per ft; auxiliary openings, $1.75–$3. Table 144 shows effect of local conditions on costs at 4 typical mines (456, 460).

Table 144.   California Drift Mines Operating about 1888 to 1890 (Brown)

	Hidden Treasure	May Flower	Paragon	Red Point
Character of pay gravel	Lo	Hc	Hc	Mc
Aver width breasted, ft	250	75	50	120
Depth of gravel breasted, ft	4–7	2–14	2–7	2–12
Broken gravel left in mine, % (h)	25	35	25	30
Length of channel worked, ft	7 700	3 900	5 400	2 300
Length yielding pay, %	100	66	66	66
Aver grade of channel, ft per mile	70	60	....	75
Method of breaking ground	Pc	Db	Db	Db
Method of treating gravel	Sl	Mi	Mi	Sl
Aver output per 24 hr, ton	275	130	30	100
Labor Timbermen and rock-pilers	12	......	......	......
Miners in tunnels and gangways	12	12	4	7
Miners in breasts	86	44	16	28
Millmen	......	6	2	......
Total men, surface and underground (b)	120	130	27	50
Aver wages per man-day	$2.15	$2.75	$2.70	$2.40
Duty in breasting, tons per man-day (c)	3.20	2.95	1.87	3.57
Milling and sluicing Number of stamps	......	20	10	......
Tons milled per stamp per 24 hr	......	6.5	6.0	......
Water per ton gravel, cu ft	......	325	325	175
Cost of milling: water power (d)	......	$0.25	......	......
steam power (d)	......	$0.35	$0.50	......
Aver total cost, mining and milling (e)	$1.10(f)	$3.25	$3.25	$2.00
Aver gross yield per ton gravel (g)	$1.75	$7.00	$10.00	$2.50

Lo = loose. Hc = hard cemented. Mc = medium cemented. Pc = picking and caving. Db = drilling and blasting. Sl = sluicing. Mi = milling.   (b) Includes surface and underground labor, but not management.   (c) Tons of pay-gravel per man-day computed from table.   (d) Per ton.   (e) Aver cost of labor and supplies for mining and milling (or sluicing) per ton gravel delivered during active operations on aver gravel breast, not including management, improvements, additions to plant, nor dead-work during periods of non-production. See (f).   (f) Includes management. (g) Pay-gravel delivered at surface.   (h) Large stones thrown back from face.

Vallecito-Western mine, Angels Camp, Cal.   Data from C. E. Julihn and F. W. Horton (57) in 1938.   A segment of Central Hill channel, 40–150 ft wide, aver 6 ft (max, 14 ft) deep, is opened by a 153-ft vert shaft and bedrock tunnel extending 4 300 ft upstream.   An abrupt rise of 5 ft occurs in bedrock 300 ft from shaft, beyond which the tunnel, after following bedrock grade of 1.25% for about 2 300 ft, gradually works into and under the bedrock, which thereafter rises at a slightly steeper grade.   The downstream portion, within about 1 700 ft of shaft, and while tunnel was still on bedrock grade, was mined from 2 parallel drifts, one on each rim of

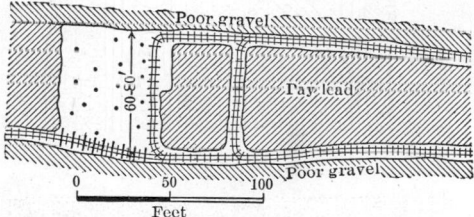

Fig 863.   Development for Breasting, Vallecito Western Mine (18)

channel, connected by crosscuts 100–150-ft apart.   Breasting method (Fig 863) was applied to one 240-ft block in 1932; for details, see Bib (461, 18).

Following notes from Bib (57) relate to subsequent work (1933–36) upstream.   Where gravel lay above tunnel, it was attacked through raises spaced according to the vol of gravel accessible to them; where channel was 100–150 ft wide, spacing might be 50 ft, increasing to 125 ft in narrow parts. Gravel, not cemented but requiring blasting, was well rounded and heavy, with many boulders, some 6–10 ft diam; of ground mined, about 30% consisted of boulders left underground.   Gold was coarse (90% on 20-mesh, with frequent nuggets up to 0.5 oz) and 75% of it was within a foot of bedrock, of which 1 or 2 ft was usually taken up.   Gravel was mined by breasting across full width of channel. Two rows of 6-ft holes, spaced 4 ft horiz, one row 1.5 ft, other 3.5–4 ft, above bedrock, each hole loaded with 3–4 sticks of 40% dynamite, broke to height of 5 ft; another row gave added height, if wanted.   Posts 10–12 ft apart, with headboards, were all the roof support usually required.   Broken gravel loaded into wheelbarrows, dumped down nearest raise, discharged into 1-ton cars, hauled in 4-car trains by storage-battery loco to transfer dump 300 ft from shaft, loaded into other cars, and trammed by hand to 1.5-ton skip in shaft.   Waste, of deep bedrock cuttings and boulders for which storage space was temporarily lacking, amounted to 31% of all material hoisted. Headframe bin discharged directly into 2-ft sluice 12 ft long, with only enough water to move 4 to 5-in stones; larger ones were picked out by hand; this sluice recovered 50–60% of the gold. Discharge from sluice passed into a disintegrator-trommel yielding plus 1.5-in (to dump), 1.5–0.5 in, and minus 0.5-in sizes; 2 latter were washed separately on sluices 12 in wide, at 4% grade, riffled with flat iron cross-bars, 2 in wide, sloping 45° upstream. In Aug, 1936, 25 men on 3 shifts mined and washed 80 tons per day. During 45 mos, ending Aug 31, 1936, hoisting 40 967 tons of gravel and 18 102 tons of waste, direct mining and washing cost was $4.58 per ton of gravel; indirect and marketing, $0.51; total $5.09. Recovered value, $5.68 per ton of gravel.

Calaveras Central mine, Angels Camp, Calif. Data from Julihn and Horton (57) in 1938. Company said to control 3.5 miles along the Tertiary Central Hill channel, and has developed 3 roughly parallel paystreaks of different ages (others known in reserve), lying on slate or schist bedrock and buried to depth of 250–350 ft by alternating beds of gravel and tuffs. Pay gravel is normally limited to 3–4 ft above bedrock (21 ft in one case) and 1–3 ft of the latter is usually taken up. Gravel is coarse, well rounded, and tightly cemented; boulders numerous; gold mainly coarse (over 10-mesh), associated with considerable pyrite and a little black sand. One paystreak (mainly worked in 1932–33) was 50–70 wide; other 2, 150–200 ft wide, of which only one was actively worked in 1934–36. Aver recovery from 138 750 tons of gravel and bedrock washed in 4.5 yr, $4.94 per ton, incl some low-grade gravel moved in exploration; 1935 aver, $5.17 per ton washed. Development is through 3-compt vert shaft 350 ft deep, and a cross-cut tunnel in bedrock passing underneath the 2 channels now mainly developed; another 240-ft shaft affords ventilation.

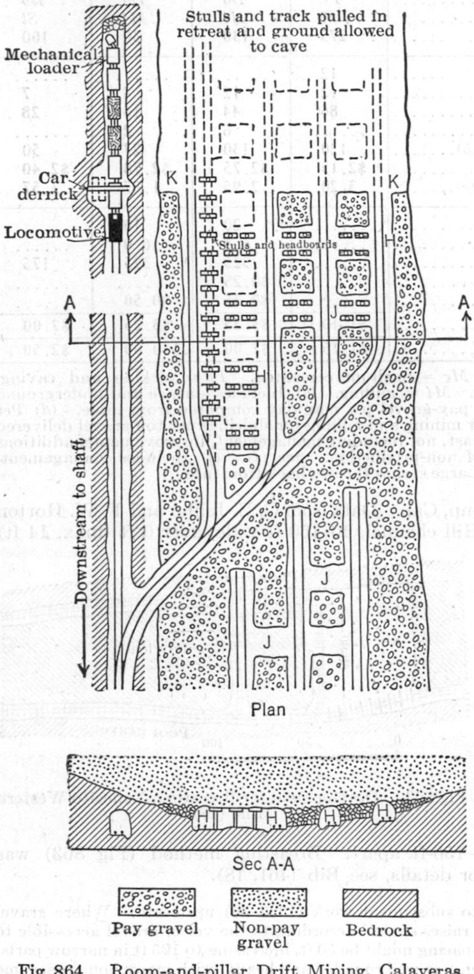

Fig 864. Room-and-pillar Drift Mining, Calaveras Central Mine

Drifts up and down stream from tunnel follow the 2 principal channels, developed (1936) for a total length of 4 000 ft, with about 30 000 ft of workings. Haulage drifts, 7 by 7 ft, on 1% grade, are advanced about 6 ft per shift by 2 men, drilling with light drifters, shooting 8–10 holes with light charges of 40% dynamite, and loading 2-ton cars with Eimco-Finlay loaders. Use of a "car derrick" facilitates movement of cars at face without switches or side tracks. Fig 864 shows one method of mining. Here the haulageway is beneath the rim of the channel. Parallel headings H, 7 by 7 ft, are advanced like bedrock drifts; breakthroughs J divide the long pillars into square blocks: nearly all material from these operations is loaded by Eimco-Finlay loader. Most pillars are recovered on retreat.

For longwall work, as at K, the same type of loader is employed by shifting the track close to the wall before blasting, so that most gravel will be thrown onto the track in better position for the loader. Caterpillar-mounted Nordberg-Butler shovel has also been used with advantage where a train of cars can be placed near the gravel pile. All gravel is loaded, including boulders (except a few of the largest, and these are not piled) since the cost of piling by hand exceeds that of loading, tramming, and hoisting them. Boulders too large for the loaders are sledged or bulldozed. Enough bedrock is taken up and treated as gravel to insure recovery of gold in its crevices. Drag scrapers have been used experimentally, loading into cars through a hole in a raised platform. Under favorable conditions (a large area of well drained and previously broken or caved gravel) scrapers were expected to be advantageous for handling low-grade gravel, provided haulage, hoisting, and washing facilities were adequate for the enlarged output. Trains of 4–6 2-ton cars are hauled by storage-battery locos to shaft pocket, loading into balanced 2.5-ton skips which dump into mill bin. Waste from bedrock drifts, 25–30% of all material hoisted, is handled similarly, but discarded at surface by a 200-ft stacker belt. Mine water, 150 000 gal per day, pumped by 50-hp turbine from shaft to a tank above the mill, supplies an ample quantity for washing. Costs. During 1933–34, gross output (gravel 75%, waste 25%) was 83 419 tons (aver, 114 tons per day) at cost of $1.89 per ton for mining and washing, excl deprec, depletion, and general overhead. Costs per ton varied inversely with monthly output, from $1.40 on 6 507 tons (209 tons per day) to $3.04 on 1 271 tons (41 tons per day). These costs, largely the result of mechanization, compare favorably with those of earlier years when abundant cheap labor was available.

Dakota mine, Rivulet, Mont. Data from E. D. Gardner and C. H. Johnson in 1935 (18). Deposit was only 6–20 ft wide, under 80-ft cover; 7 ft of gravel was mined, of which much was boulders. An adit was started in the face of old hydraulic workings and driven 150 ft through previously drifted ground to reach virgin gravel. Thereafter face was advanced full width of deposit, with round-timber sets, 4 ft c-c. Caps, 12–15-in diam, were usually 10–14 ft long, depending on width of channel; min width of 10 ft was required to stack boulders; posts, 9–12 in; girts, 6 in. Top lagging, 4.5 ft long, of split poles, was driven ahead as ground was picked out. All rock over size of man's fist was stacked on sides of opening, except large boulders for which there was no room; boulders too large to handle were blockholed. Dry walls, built on each side of 18-in gage track, left only enough room for passage of an 8-cu ft car, 3 ft wide. Two men worked on each of 2 shifts, mining and washing 30 cu ft (1.7 tons) per man-shift. Labor cost (@ $4 per shift), $2.35 per ton; total cost, incl supplies, about $2.60 per ton of material trammed.

Alaska. Wimmler (188), in 1927, stated that drift mining had become practically obsolete at Nome and elsewhere in Alaska, except in the Yukon-Tenana valley and a few other interior districts. Formerly, a large drift mine would employ 30–50 shovelers and clean 100 000–200 000 sq ft of bedrock in a season; by 1927 there were less than a dozen mines employing as many as 15–20 men and cleaning 50 000 sq ft; but at numerous places 2–6 men, with old and inefficient equipment and working 1 shift, were cleaning 10 000–30 000 sq ft of bedrock per season. Most drift mining in Alaska has been in permanently frozen gravel, at depths of 25–200 ft. They are developed through shafts, usually 7 by 7 ft, which can be sunk by 2 men at 5–8 ft per shift, after thawing; thawed muck can be bailed out. Cost, if little or no timber, $6–$12 per ft; if close cribbed with round timber, with a framed set at bottom, $10–$20 per ft; some deep shafts in bad ground, $25 or more per ft. (For thawing, see Art 131). Aver duty per man picking, shoveling, and wheeling 200–300 ft from working places to shaft, 75–125 barrow loads in 8 hr; equivalent to 20–40 sq ft of bedrock underlying 5–6 ft of gravel; aver, 25 sq ft (5 cu yd). Cost is often stated on basis of bedrock area cleaned. During chief activity at Fairbanks, some costs were 40¢ per sq ft; a few at Nome, only 25¢; usual costs at Fairbanks in 1927 were 60¢–$1 per sq ft; aver about 75¢. In Tolovana dist, 50¢–75¢; 32¢ at one specially favored mine. In Ruby distr (1922), where channels are narrow (about 75 ft) and other conditions adverse, 60¢–$1.25, aver 85¢ per sq ft or $5 per cu yd, of which 45¢ per cu yd was for thawing and 35¢ for sluicing. Central Alaska and the Yukon are essentially high-cost regions due to high wages, scanty supply and high prices of many supplies (incl large transp costs), and short working season of 3–5 mos. Most mines pay wages plus board; general labor in 1926 ranged from $6.50 in larger and more accessible districts to $12 at more remote; board cost $1–$4 per day. Some mines paid a bonus of 50¢ per shift to men who stayed during a whole season. Old system of lower wages in winter was not in effect in 1926. Underground mines usually worked 2 8-hr shifts.

Nome, Alaska; data by A. Gibson, 1914 (454, 462). Table 145 shows data for 5 successful drift mines in frozen gravel. All thawing was done during night shift; mining, in day shift only. Water for sluicing was pumped by independent distillate engines; mines No 2 and 3 were under same management with a common pumping plant; head on pumps about twice that at mines No 4 and 5. Other conditions affecting costs were as follows. Mine No 1: All mining done in winter; 1.5 ft of bedrock mined. As much as possible of the winter dump (6 520 cu yd) was hydraulicked into sluices, the rest shoveled in; sluice tailing was removed with horse scrapers. Water was pumped day and night for 18 days in larger amounts than necessary. Mines No 2 and 3: All summer work; 1.25 ft of bedrock was mined. Gravel was dumped into bins and sluiced intermittently (about once a day). Mine No 4: Preparatory work was done in early spring; all mining and sluicing in the summer; 1.5 ft of bedrock was mined. Gravel was handled on the surface as at No 3. Mine No 5: Spring and summer work as in No 4. Pay-gravel averaged 2 in above, and 2 ft in, bedrock. Gravel was dumped into a mud-box; sluicing was continuous, hence pumping was continuous on day shift. The bedrock in No 1, 2, 3, and 4 was mica schist; at No 5, black slate. The waste or overburden at No 1, 2, and 3 was coarse sand; at No 4, sand and clay; at No 5, light gravel or sand.

Wild Goose mine, Nome, Alaska. E. E. Fleming (681) describes a system of caving in blocks employed in 1905, after typical Calif method (as at Hidden Treasure) had proved dangerous from caving, and costly, from loss of all timber (@ $60 per M, plus frt from Nome). Channel was 80–110 ft wide and nearly straight; mining took out 1.5–2 ft of mica-schist bedrock and 2 ft of gravel, unfrozen and loose. From shafts 69–140 ft deep, usually 40 ft and never less than 25 ft outside of deeper edge of channel, crosscuts were driven to about center line of channel, and turned both ways

Table 145. Data on Drift Mining, Nome, Alaska, in 1914 (Gibson)

	Mine No.....	1	2	3	4	5
Gen operating data	Depth of shaft, ft	53	81	81	45	50
	Thickness of pay-gravel, ft	2.5	2.5	2.5	3.5	2.166
	Thickness of waste, ft	1.5	2	2	1.5	2.333
	Total height mined, ft	4	4.5	4.5	5	4.5
	Total boiler hp	45	70	70	35	50
	Thawed per day, cu yd	128	205	257	128.6	327.1
	Pay-gravel hoisted per day, cu yd *	80	114	143	90	157.5
	Capac of bucket, cu ft (a)	18	16	24	13.5	13.5
	Aver number of buckets hoisted per day	120	192.4	161	180	315
Thawing data	Length of steam points, ft	7	7	7	6	7
	Number of steam points	40	90	90	25	46
	Steaming time, hr.	9	12	12	8	11
	Hp per steam point	1.12	0.78	0.78	1.4	1.08
	Depth thawed, ft	8	7	9	7.5	7.5
	Sweating time, days	1	2	2	......	2.5
	Duty, cu yd * per point per day	3.2	2.28	2.85	5.14	7.11
Fuel, crude oil	For thawing, gal per day	168	168	168	84	210
	For hoisting, gal per day	52.5	42	42	31.5	52.5
	Per cu yd * thawed, gal	1.3125	0.8195	0.6537	0.6533	0.6419
	Per cu yd * hoisted, gal	0.656	0.368	0.294	0.35	0.333
	Total gal per cu yd * of pay gravel	2.756	1.842	1.469	1.283	1.667
	Distillate per day, pumping sluicing water, gal	132.8	30	30	14	18
	Distillate per cu yd * sluiced, gal	2.73	3.80	4.77	6.43	8.75
	Crude oil per bbl at mine	$2.97	$3.30	$3.30	$2.90	$2.71
	Distillate per gal at mine, ¢	24.25	25.17	25.17	25.5	25.83
Number of men	Thawing: pointmen	3	3	4	2	2
	fireman	1	1	1	1	1
	Mining: manager	1	1/2	1/2	1	1
	foreman	1	1	1	1	1
	engineer	1	1	1	1	1
	laborers	16	17	17	9	20
	Sluicing: engineer	(f)	1/2	1/2	.....	1
	laborer	(f)	1	1	1	......
	Total per day	.....	25	26	16	27
	Duty of labor (cu yd * per man-day)					
	Thawing waste and pay-gravel (b)	32.0	51.25	51.40	42.85	109.04
	Mining waste and pay-gravel (c)	7.11	10.79	13.53	11.69	14.87
	Mining pay-gravel only (d)	4.44	6.0	7.53	8.18	7.16
	Sluicing pay-gravel (sluicing labor)	18.11	76.0	95.33	90.0	157.5
	Thawing, mining and sluicing (e)	.....	4.65	5.61	6.0	6.06

* Loose gravel, not place measure. (a) Bucket of self-dumping cableway (Fig 861). (b) Pointmen and fireman. (c) Foreman, engineer and laborers. Duty, laborers only, 8, 12.06, 15.12, 14.28 and 16.36, respectively, for the 5 mines. (d) Foreman, engineer and laborers. Duty, laborers only, 5, 6.7, 8.41, 10, and 7.87 cu yd, respectively. (e) All labor but manager included. (f) 10 men employed per day while upper part of winter dump was being sluiced; 21 men per day during time it was necessary to shovel-in.

into drifts 300 ft long; a crosscut both ways from end of each drift then divided the channel into sections 600 ft long. Beginning at outer ends of most remote crosscuts, blocks never more than 10 ft square were extracted as in Fig 865, using 8 by 8-in posts at 3 ft c–c, with 3 by 12-in headboards; no headboard was permitted to rest on 2 posts. Runs of gravel from sides were stopped by temporary lagging. When No 1 block was finished and floor cleaned, its 2 gravel faces were close lagged behind posts with 2 by 6-in plank, and all other posts were pulled out; roof usually caved at once, filling block solidly. Block No 2 was then worked back towards No 1, the intervening posts and lagging being drawn before pulling posts in No 2. Successive blocks were mined in the order indicated. A second crosscut had meanwhile been driven 20 ft back, and its 10-ft blocks were removed in same way. This system provided 4 working places at a time, besides crosscut headings, tributary to shaft, keeping hoist busy. Loss of timber in one 600-ft section, full width of channel, was only 5 000 bd ft; shaft timbers were recovered when walls froze in winter.

Fairbanks, Alaska; data from J. F. Newsom; see also Bib (400). 80% of productive deposits are at depths of 40–260 ft; all lie in valley bottoms with flat gradients; most of them solidly frozen. Transport difficult and water supply meager. Work covered by Table 146 was done prior to 1909.

Idaho Mining Co, on Little Eldorado Cr, Fairbanks, Alaska, made successful use of wet jackhammers for working solidly frozen gravel at 165-ft depth (188); mining took 3.5 ft of gravel and 1.5 ft of bedrock. G r a v e l was tight, containing numerous large and hard boulders, but only about 5% of ice. Drilling was applied first to holes for "sweater" pipes (Art 131); 1 man could drill 209-ft holes and put in their sweaters in 8 hr, at cost of 65¢ per hole, whereas (under previous method of point thawing) 2 men could set only 4-6 points in 8 hr, due to difficult d r i v i n g. Thawing for 40-45 hr

Table 146.   Drift Mining, Fairbanks, Alaska (J. F. Newsom)

(a) For 17 claims (b) For 14 claims	Fairbanks Creek			Cleary Creek		
	Max	Min	Aver (a)	Max	Min	Aver (b)
Total depth gravel, ft	55	14	26.7	90	12	45
Width of pay, ft....	450	70	193	350	80	192
Height gravel mined, ft..............	16	2.5	4.9	9	2.5	5.2
Depth bedrock mined, ft........	3	1	1.3	2.5	0.5	1.9
Total boiler hp.....	50	15	....	50	9	....
Hp of hoists.......	48	6	....	38	6	....
Operating cost per sq ft............	$1.30	$0.75	$1.00	$1.30	$0.65	$0.85
Total cost per sq. ft.	$1.40	$0.87	$1.13	$1.51	$0.80	$1.02
Total cost per cu yd.	$7.85	$2.44	$5.40	$9.70	$2.58	$4.50

under steam and 24 hr standing usually reached 18 in beyond end of pipe, or 40 sq ft per sweater. The Co next used drills for blasting unthawed gravel, following typical Calif system of breasting from crosscuts, which (as also the drifts) required no timbering. A man could drill and shoot 150 ft of holes per shift, breaking 100 sq ft or 17 cu yd; cost for explosives (0.4 lb per sq ft) was 60¢ per cu yd. Broken gravel was dragged from faces by 12-cu ft bottomless scraper and loaded into cars. Exceptionally small proportion of ice in this gravel made thawing before sluicing unnecessary.

Victoria " deep leads," Australia, are old river channels under 250-400 ft of alluvium, frequently capped with basalt flows, and sometimes as much as 2 000 ft above level of present streams. Workable gravel, not always in deepest part of channel, is up to 15 ft (aver 3 ft) thick; gold mainly confined to lower 1-1.5 ft of gravel and upper 0.5-1 ft of bedrock, usually kaolinized; bedrock gradient, 20-40 ft per mile. DRAINAGE of channel is first requisite and development is planned accordingly. Shafts are usually in bedrock at side of lead, to avoid costly sinking through loose, wet sand (Fig 866). From shaft bottom, 80-100 ft below channel, a "main reef" crosscut C is driven under the lead. From a point under the middle or deepest part of the lead, drifts D, called "main reef drives," are driven in both directions under center line of channel; they are on an up grade, for drainage and haulage. Main reef drive D is usually timbered with 12-in

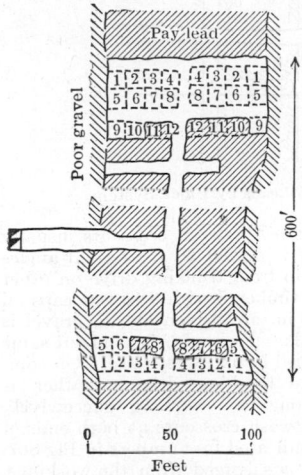

Fig 865.   Block System, Wild Goose Mine

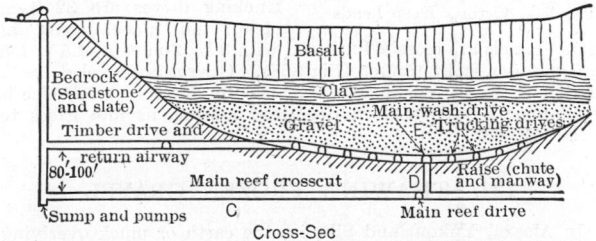

Fig 866.   General Scheme of Development, Victoria Deep Leads

round timber; caps 5.5 ft long; posts, 8.5 ft. At 50-ft intervals along drift D, holes are drilled upward into the water-laden gravel. Later, usually at 300-ft intervals, raises are put up to finish drainage and to serve as orepasses and manways; complete drainage may require 3–5 years, pumping 2–6 million gal per day. Fig 867 shows usual DEVELOPMENT in "wash" (gravel), cutting area into rectangular blocks, drifts and crosscuts being advanced by spiling. Posts in "main wash drive" E are 7 ft long; caps, 4–5 ft. In "trucking drives" F, posts are 5.5 ft long; caps, 3–4 ft. MINING in 1935. Two methods used: (a) "blocking," (b) "paneling." BLOCKING METHOD is adopted where wash is very loose, with large boulders, or where thickness of pay gravel is over 4 ft. Develop-

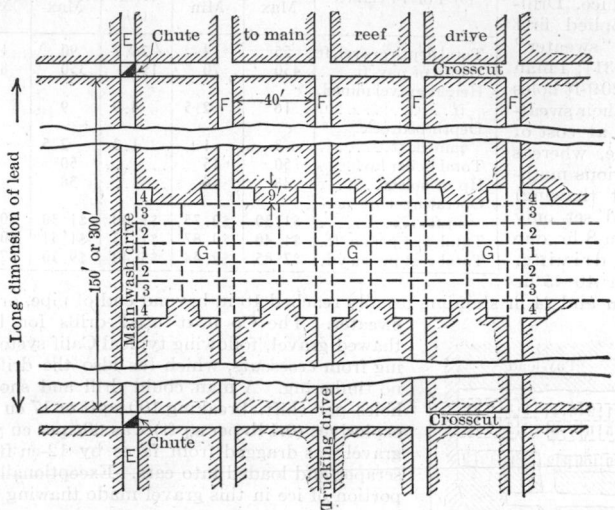

Fig 867. Development and Mining of Victoria Deep Leads by Block System

ment divides wash into strips 40 ft wide (Fig 867); distance between crosscuts, usually 300 ft. Midway between crosscuts, "blocking drive" G is driven 20 ft at right-angles to length of strip. At same time, a similar drive is put in from trucking drive on other side of strip, the two holing at the center. Drives G are timbered with 8 to 9-ft posts on 3.5 to 4-ft posts (6 in round). Spiling "laths," 8 by 2 in, are driven ahead, gravel is dug out, and next set erected; sets are at 4 to 5-ft intervals. Floor of G is at about same elev as that of F. Gravel is shoveled into cars and dumped into nearest raise. On com-

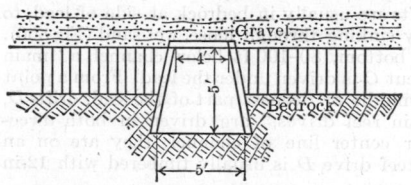

Fig 868. Paneling, Victoria Deep Leads

pleting one blocking drive, another is started alongside, working successively toward the wash crosscuts at both ends of strips, as indicated by numbers in Fig 867. No timber is salvaged from the workings, which soon cave. PANELING is employed where gravel is finer or where gold is confined to bottom 2 or 3 ft of wash. Principle is same as in blocking, but trucking drives are 32 ft apart (instead of 40) and "panel drives" are 4.5 ft wide (instead of 9 ft). Panels are closely timbered with 8 by 2-in caps, 4.5 ft long, supported by props of 2.5 to 3.5-in split timber (Fig 868). Gravel is shoveled back to mouth of panel drive and into car in trucking drive. On "main reef" level, elec locos are customary. Ventilation is important in deep-lead mining, as foul gases tend to exude from the gravels (628, 682, 683).

131. THAWING FROZEN GRAVEL

General. In Alaska, Yukon, and Siberia, the earth or muck overlying most placer deposits, and usually the gravel itself and underlying bedrock, are permanently frozen. Such ground gives little trouble in deposits that can be hydraulicked; the muck is thawed by allowing water to run over the surface; frozen ridges left between channels thus formed thaw naturally, or may be thawed and stripped more quickly with giants. When a pit has been opened, bank and giant water aid in thawing gravel faces and new surfaces are constantly exposed to solar heat. In drift mining (Art 130) no stripping is necessary, but the paystreak must be thawed. In dredging (Art 128) the muck must be thawed and stripped and the entire gravel bank thawed. Adequate (not necessarily perfect) thawing is essential for successful dredging (435) to save excessive wear on machinery, permit effic digging, and to avoid loss of gold encased in frozen lumps rejected by the screen. While most gravel can be sufficiently thawed in a short time to permit dredging, it is best to allow thawed ground to stand several months, during which small isolated frozen patches may continue to thaw.

Thawing methods were developed in drift mining. Early shaft sinking and drifting in Alaska and elsewhere were done with wood fires and hot stones; these are still used by prospectors, but boilers light enough to be carried by 1 or 2 men are now obtainable, and permit steam thawing for prospecting and exploration in remote districts (386, 390, 408, 455). Steam-thawing, introduced about 1898, developed rapidly; steam is carried into gravel through pipes terminating in a bit or "point" (Fig 870); the method was soon applied to thawing frozen ground ahead of dredges. Numerous experiments have been made with hot water instead of steam, but with indifferent success; C. Janin in 1922 traced the development of thawing methods, and summarized available data in Bib (629). Since 1917 cold water has largely replaced steam for thawing dredging ground.

Physical properties of frozen gravel (Table 147). Extensive tests in 1912 by H. M. Payne, on permanently frozen gravel in the Klondike, gave following results; temp (F) of bedrock, 2°–14°; of gravel, 17°–22°; of black muck, 17°–24°; of sandy muck, 19° – 24°. Mean temp of frozen ground depends solely on the kind of material and not on its depth, depth of frost line or water level, nor on presence or absence of muck overburden. A. Gibson states that the temp of perpetually frozen ground on Seward Peninsula is about 28° F, except when near thawed ground; he estimates the sp heat of gravel at 0.2. Nearly all

Table 147. Physical Properties of Frozen Material (393)

Aver of tests on 46 samples		Black, sandy muck	Gravel and sand	Bed-rock
Sp gravity, frozen..............		1.401	2.189	2.590
Sp gravity, thawed and dry....		2.411	2.691	2.655
Sp heat, frozen................		0.196	0.172	0.183
% ice, frozen ground	by vol....	68.2	29.1	9.6
	by wt....	44.7	16.0	4.26
% solids, frozen ground	by vol.	31.8	70.9	90.4
	by wt..	55.3	84.0	95.74
% voids, frozen..............		0.0	1.28	0.0
% voids, thawed..............		6.1	3.97	1.65
Lb ice per cu ft frozen ground..		39.11	22.00	6.96
Lb solids " " " "		48.39	115.50	154.94

the heat required to thaw frozen ground is that needed for converting ice into water; hence percentage of ice in gravel should be determined in estimating probable fuel or water requirements (454, 451, 629).

Comparison of thawing media. Experiments by J. H. Miles, of Alaska Mines Corp'n, in 1917–1918 at Nome, in thawing deep dredging ground with steam, hot water and cold water, are described by W. S. Weeks (644) as follows:

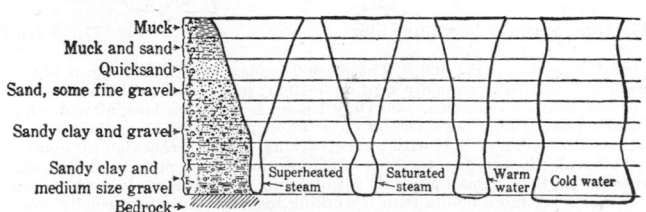

Fig 869. Comparison of Thawing Media

Depth of ground, approx 42 ft; character is shown in Fig 869. Thaws were made with superheated steam, saturated steam, hot water and cold water; in each case the thawing agent was introduced at bottom of a churn-drill hole. In following winter, when surface water was frozen, shafts were sunk on these holes and the thawed volumes computed. Fig 869 shows cross-sec of a thaw of each type. Results (Table 148) show relatively high utilization of heat available for thawing with cold water and very low utilization for steam and warm water. Tests with superheated steam indicated that most of its heat was expended in heating a relatively quiet pool of water around the

Table 148. Tests on Thawing Media, Alaska Mines Corp'n, Nome, 1917 (644)

	Super-heated steam	Satu-rated steam	Warm water	Cold water (a)
Length of test, hr..........	156	98	67	192
Oil burned, gal per hr......	11.25	9	6.04	......
Temp of steam or water at points, deg F............	590	250	105	52
Temp of water at surface...	140	104	70	(c)
Volume thawed, cu yd......	109	83	81	511
Rate of thawing, cu yd per hr.	0.7	0.85	1.21	2.66
Effic of heat utilization, % (b)	3.8	5.80	12.30	57.40

(a) 20 gal per min supplied under 40-ft head. (b) Computed for steam and hot-water tests as: [heat units required to melt the ice in the gravel (about 10% of its wt)] ÷ [heat units in fuel burned × 50% boiler effic]. In cold-water test, the divisor in the above ratio was taken as the heat units available in the vol of water used, between 52° F, the temp of entering water, and 32° F. (c) Temp of outgoing water varied during test; at end of 192 hr it was 36° F (644).

pipe. Also, steam failed to penetrate clay layers appreciably, while clay did not impede action of cold water. Hot water gave uniform thawing, but was inneffic; this test was shorter than the others and its results are not strictly comparable. Miles obtained a patent (U S, No 1 339 036) in 1920 on his cold-water thawing method. Alaska Mines Corp'n made further tests with cold water on a working scale in 1919 and adopted the method; in 1920 this Co thawed 88 807 cu yd of frozen ground with cold water, at aver cost of 11.5¢ per cu yd (629).

Steam points. Fig 870 shows typical head and tips. Steam thawing in drifting (Art 130). The point is pressed firmly against the face, and steam turned on. In a few minutes, the point begins to sink into the face; it is gradually worked in to its full length, being alternately rotated, driven with a hammer, and allowed to stand. Points can not be driven faster than the gravel thaws ahead of them; heavy blows are avoided, except where required by tight ground, as they may injure the point.

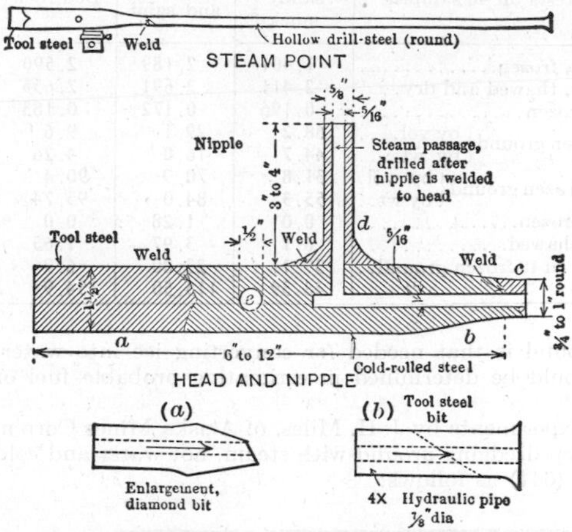

H. I. Ellis gives following data at Fairbanks in 1915 (455). Diamond or square bit (a), Fig 870, is used in easy-driving ground, where stones can be pushed aside. Chisel bit (b) is for hard driving, requiring actual drilling; a cross-bit (as for rock-drills) is used where chisel bit is hard to turn. Steam points are 8, 10, 12, 16 and 20 ft long (some 5–7-ft points are also needed); 8-ft is commonest; deep holes start with short points. For thawing breasts, the points are driven near bottom of face and spaced 2–4 ft apart across it (Fig 860). There are 2 modes: (a) Enough points are driven to thaw required length of face; steam is usually kept on 6–10 hr; points then withdrawn and gravel allowed to "sweat" before being picked down. (b) Only 1 point is used on a face; after driving it home, it is withdrawn and replaced by a "sweater" of 1/4 or 3/8-in pipe (Fig 871). Before turning on steam, the pipe is plugged in collar of hole with gunny sacking. This is repeated for holes over the entire face. Plan (b) is replacing (a); sweaters cost much less than steam points and obstruct shovelers less if gravel settles during thawing and prevents withdrawing the sweaters. In easy ground, 2 men working separately can drive more points than 2 working together; but they usually work in pairs, one striking, while the other rotates the point. Depending on character of gravel, 1–6 pointmen can thaw gravel for 16 shovelers. At Nome good pointmen, working under plan (a), often drove 20 5-ft points in 10 hr.

Steam is distributed in uncovered 3/4-in pipes, carried on posts of haulageway sets and laid on the breast floor about 10 ft back from face. Points and sweaters are connected by crossheads (Fig 872). Ordinary press, 90–100 lb. Thawing time varies with depth of thaw, spacing of points, character of gravel and effective steam press. Ellis says that at Fairbanks a 5-ft paystreak of loose gravel, relatively free from clay or sediment, can sometimes be thawed to depth of 9 ft in 10 hr, using 8-ft points under 100-lb press. W. H. Sirdevan states that at Nome a 5-ft point, thawing for 6–10 hr under 90–100 lb press and followed by a sweating period (without steam) of about 20 hr, will thaw a block

Fig 870. Steam Points (after Ellis)

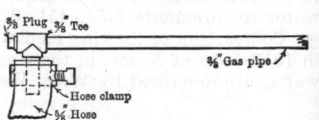

Fig 871. Sweater

of gravel 6 ft long by 3 ft wide by 3–4 ft high, or 2–2.5 cu yd. In drifting in Klondike, 6-ft points aver 3.75 cu yd per 10 hr (408). BOILER CAPAC varies locally, but is about 1 bhp per point. When drift mining on Third Beach at Nome was at its height, the bhp per point was 1–2, aver 1.5; attention to detail reduced this figure. See Art 130, and Bib (390, 408, 451, 455, 454, 629).

Steam-thawing dredging ground. Steam points are driven vertically to bedrock, advancing as fast as thawing ahead of point will permit. Methods of Yukon Gold Co, described by Perry in 1915 and McCarthy in 1914 (451), illustrate good practice at that time. Points, as in Fig 870, were of extra heavy pipe 0.75–1 in diam; driving head was drop-forged; tips, of tool steel, had 5/16-in discharge opening. Points, set in holes made with crowbars to frost line, were alternately struck with a 4-lb hammer, rotated and allowed to stand. Boulders were drilled by a cutting bit on the point, or by withdrawing the point and using a jumper. Aver rate of thawing, about 2 ft per hr; points were driven as deep as 40 ft; points had to be driven 4–6 ft into bedrock; then allowed to steam 12–48 hr. Boiler plants comprised 2 or 3 loco-type 150-hp boilers; the aim was to carry 25-lb press at the points; fuel, wood. Steam lines were asbestos covered and cased in wood boxes packed with sawdust; branch lines were 1.5-in and often several hundred ft long; at 8-ft intervals along them were nipple connections for 5/8-in armored hose, leading to the points. Batteries of 150 or more points formed a unit. Costs varied locally, with depth and character of ground, driving troubles, time of steaming, cost of fuel, etc, from 12 to 20¢ per cu yd. See Bib (629).

N. L. Wimmler (188) gave following data on Alaska practice just prior to 1927. (1) OTTER CR, Iditarod. Gravel, 14 ft deep; 150-hp boiler supplied 95 points; thawing cost, 30–45¢ per cu yd. (2) Same location; 200-hp boiler for 110 points thawed 100 000 cu yd in 1 season; cost 33¢ per cu yd. (3) CANDLE CR, Kuskokwim. Gravel 15–18 ft deep and less than half was frozen; muck removed previously; 100-hp boiler for 80 points spaced 6 ft c–c; fuel per day, 12 cords wood @ $10; employed 10 men per shift and thawed 100 000 cu yd in 1 season, at 25¢ per cu yd.

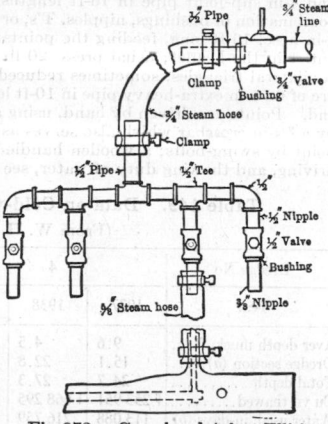

Fig 872. Crosshead (after Ellis)

Cold-water thawing is done by injecting water at normal surface temp and under press (from ditch, if possible, otherwise from pumps) into the gravel through pipes resembling steam points, Fig 870, or sweaters, Fig 871. The water returns to surface through the ground surrounding the pipe; as thawed ground tends to settle, it opens a channel for the rising water along the under surface of still frozen ground, thus promoting effic of operation. Presence of former drift workings often complicates procedure. Water points or sweaters, driven to bedrock like steam points, have been widely used on dredging ground in the North.

Alaska. N. L. Wimmler gives following general information (188) in 1927. Alaskan surface waters reach 50° F or over only during 3.5 summer months; occasionally 65°–70° for short periods; water may be 6°–8° colder at night than in day. Best thawing results when water rises from points at not less than 36°–38°; only about 8°–15° of available temp can ordinarily be utilized; effic is highest at start of thawing. Amount of water varies widely; one case at Nome, thawing 60 ft deep, supplied 1–1.75 miner's in of ditch water per point, at 30–80 lb press; another pumped 1 000 gal per min to supply 100 points at 17.5 lb press; Yukon Gold pumped 3 500 gal per min for 100 points. Excessive press may cause pipes to rise, but 60 lb is more effective than about 40 lb. Water thaws more slowly than steam; hence 2 men can manipulate twice as many water points as steam points, say 10–25 or more, depending on difficulty of ground and temp of water; aver advance of water point, 0.75–1.5 ft per hr.

Water points are usually staggered in straight rows, on 8–16-ft centers; in 60-ft gravel at Nome, with slabby boulders on bedrock, holes at 32-ft centers were churn-drilled in winter and thawed next season. Under aver conditions, points at 8-ft centers finish thawing in 4–8 days; at 10 ft, in 8–12 days; at 16 ft, in 10–14 days; at 32 ft (Nome) in 10–12 weeks. Thawed gravel freezes to depth of only 2–5 ft during a following winter. Water-thawed gravel is easier to work than that thawed naturally or by steam, especially if much clay is present, since circulating water assists in disintegrating clay. In general, water thawing costs 7–15¢ per cu yd; Yukon Gold, having to pump water, thawed for 10–14¢ per cu yd; at Fairbanks Cr, with small and erratic supply of ditch water, cost was 10–12¢ per cu yd.

Yukon Consol Gold Corp. Data from W. H. S. McFarland (434) and G. R. F. Troop (435) in 1939; statistics and costs from Mr. McFarland in 1940. Company aims to gain at least 2 years' reserve of thawed ground ahead of a dredge, requiring operation of 5 or 6 "units" of 400–700 (usually about 600) points each. Thawing season begins about

May 10 (preparation, nearly a month earlier) and ends about Sep 25. Equipment is mainly like that at Nome and Fairbanks.

From its main source (usually a pump), water passes through a 12-in gate-valve into a line of flanged pipe reducing in steps from 11 in to 8 in; this line has 6-in outlets, each with a gate-valve, spaced 27 ft 7 in apart; aver "unit" has 12 such outlets. Header pipes, one for each outlet, are 6-in and 4-in slip-joint pipe in 16-ft lengths, each length having a 2-in threaded outlet at center. By combination of bushings, nipples, T's, or crosses, water is finally delivered through individual cocks to 1-in hose, 16 ft long, feeding the points; usually 2 (occasionally 4–6) points are supplied from each outlet in the header; usual press, 20 lb per sq in. Normal spacing of points is at corners of 16-ft equilateral triangles; sometimes reduced (when much muck remains to be thawed) to 4 ft. Points are of 0.75-in extra-heavy pipe in 10-ft lengths, with a chisel bit of high-carbon steel welded to lower end. Points are driven by hand, using a cyl slotted weight to fit around the point, and kept in place by a 3/8-in crossbar which also serves as handle. The weight strikes a collar firmly clamped to the point by swing-bolts; a wooden handle bolted to the clamp serves to twist the point. For rate of driving, and thawing duty of water, see Table 149. Extra-heavy 1/2-in pipes, without cutting bits,

Table 149. Data on Cold-water Thawing, Yukon Consol Gold Corp, Ltd
(From W. H. S. McFarland, Gen Mgr, in 1940)

Dredge No	4			5				6	
Year	1937	1938	1939	1936	1937	1938	1939	1938	1939
Aver depth muck, ft...	9.6	4.5	7.4	12.8	12.4	6.5	4.5	9.1	5.2
Dredge section (a).....	15.1	22.8	23.9	17.8	17.5	21.3	22.6	28.8	30.2
Total depth...........	24.7	27.3	31.3	30.6	29.9	27.8	27.1	37.9	35.4
Cu yd thawed.........	1 253 951	1 668 295	542 989	2 046 748	1 546 613	206 954	1 057 711	555 159	555 187
Water used, in-days (b)	113 088	216 759	126 279	153 632	132 272	50 622	102 080	99 857	112 242
Aver temp water, °F...	49.6	44.8	47.9	49.0	48.8	48.7	45.9	44.8	47.5
Duty of water (c)......	11.08	7.70	4.30	13.35	11.68	4.08	10.36	5.55	4.94
In-day-deg per cu yd (d)	1.70	1.66	3.70	1.27	1.43	1.75	1.34	2.31	3.13
Total point footage....	138 505	184 713	72 616	234 794	201 069	91 531	128 430	104 580	155 521
Ft driven per man-hr...	5.5	9.0	6.9	13.4	11.0	9.8	10.4	10.9	10.9
Total cost per cu yd (e).	5.53¢	3.92¢	......	2.48¢	4.04¢	(f)14.01¢	......	6.64¢	......

Dredge No	7		8			9		10	
Year	1938	1939	1937	1938	1939	1938	1939	1938	1939
Aver depth muck, ft...	0.2	0.8	14.4	12.5	10.5	16.4	23.6	18.4	15.2
Dredge section (a).....	13.8	14.0	7.0	14.6	10.9	15.6	10.2	8.7	9.1
Total depth...........	14.0	14.8	21.4	27.1	21.4	32.0	33.8	27.1	24.3
Cu yd thawed.........	222 962	215 772	617 663	509 980	495 924	279 296	543 394	400 733	644 103
Water used, in-days (b)	....	....	55 997	124 284	112 672	51 769	110 327	55 348	117 795
Aver temp water, °F...	....	....	43.3	46.3	47.5	44.0	42.6	46.4	46.9
Duty of water (c)......	....	....	11.05	4.12	4.40	5.38	4.92	7.24	5.47
In-day-deg per cu yd (d)	....	....	1.02	3.49	3.52	2.25	2.15	1.98	2.72
Total point footage....	21 486	57 852	75 097	132 170	157 738	60 312	192 451	107 332	198 384
Ft driven per man-hr...	7.0	8.3	20.8	25.0	21.6	25.0	21.2	17.5	17.7
Total cost per cu yd (e)	6.15¢	......	3.02¢	5.76¢	......	9.48¢	......	5.79¢	......

(a) Depth of gravel plus pay bedrock. (b) 1 in-day = 1.5 cu ft per min running 24 hr = 2160 cu ft of water. (c) Cu yd thawed per in-day. (d) 1 in-day-deg = 1 in-day for each deg above 32° F. (e) Itemized costs in Table 150. (f) See footnote (b) Table 150.

are sometimes driven at intermediate positions, but usually not to bedrock. Thawing water has to be circulated, due to scarcity; settling basins are arranged, from which water, after straining through 7-mesh screen, is pumped back into the pipe line. The water from stripping muck (Art 128) can not be sufficiently clarified for use in thawing gravel, and precautions are often required to prevent contamination of the thawing water. Standard pump is a 12-in centrif, rated at 6 000 (US) gal per min under 100-ft head, and driven by 200-hp synchronous motor. Each of the 11 such portable units in service is housed in same manner as those supplying water for stripping (Art 128). A "unit" block of Klondike gravels can usually be thawed by this method in 1–3 mos; progress is examined by driving steel bars into the ground about midway between points. Table 150 gives costs of thawing at 7 of the company's dredge sites, during a period of organization and expansion; lower costs are anticipated. For stripping and dredging on same sites in Klondike distr, see Art 128.

Otter Creek, Iditarod dist, Alaska. Data from N. L. Wimmler (188) on water-thawing in 1923 ahead of a dredge digging 1 500 cu yd, or cleaning 3 000 sq ft, per day. Gravel 15 ft deep; medium size, few boulders, some clay on bedrock; covered 1–2 ft deep with sod and moss, but no muck; about half the vol frozen to bedrock. Water, 150–400 miner's in, from 4-mile ditch, was distributed to as many as needed out of 100 points and 700 sweaters available.

Table 150. Cost of Cold-water Thawing, Yukon Consol Gold Corp, Ltd

(From W. H. S. McFarland, Gen Mgr; for technical data, see Table 149)

Dredge No	4		5			6	7	8		9	10
Year	1937	1938	1936	1937	1938	1938	1938	1937	1938	1938	1938
Cost; ¢ per cu yd:											
Wages.........	2.76	2.14	1.21	1.81	7.95	3.09	2.72	1.35	2.88	4.54	2.77
Camp and mess.	1.30	0.97	0.58	0.86	3.46	1.35	1.13	0.61	1.27	1.99	1.21
Supplies.......	0.10	.04	.07	.21	0.23	0.18	0.46	.17	0.11	0.35	0.23
Shops.........	.08	.05	.11	.12	.38	.09	.27	.11	.14	.26	.52
Transp.........	.36	.17	.12	.29	.70	.35	.67	.14	.38	1.04	.60
Power.........	.87	.42	.36	.69	.91	.71	.57	.51	.74	.63	.27
Supervis.......	.05	.12	....	.04	.26	.26	.25	.11	.19	.20	.14
Engineering.....	.01	.01	.02	.02	.12	.02	.08	.02	.05	.08	.05
Sundry.........	....	....	....	.01	....	(a) .59	....	....	....	.39	....
Totals.......	5.53	3.92	2.48	4.04	14.01(b)	6.64	6.15	3.02	5.76	9.48	5.79

(a) Work on the Australia-Sulphur ditch. (b) Costs high due to necessity for re-thawing much of the 1937 area, for which no credit was allowed in 1938.

Points on 10-ft centers, staggered on rows 10 ft apart, were driven to bedrock under full water press (19–23 lb), then withdrawn, and replaced by sweaters; latter could sometimes be put down without preparation by points. Four men on each of 2 10-hr shifts bottomed 40 points and set sweaters for 4 000 sq ft, each working on 21 points at a time. Temp of inflowing water, usually 42°–44°; max, 69°; usual drop on return, 10°–12°. Thaw finished in 10–12 days (4–5 days when water was warmest). Aver daily labor cost (wages including board @ $3 per day) was: 8 pointmen @ $9, $72; 1 day foreman, $12; 1 night foreman, $10; 1 ditchman, $9; 1/2 blacksmith and helper, $10.50; total $113.50. In 10 days, this crew set 391 points, thawing 21 722 cu yd (39 100 sq ft, 15 ft deep) at 5.25¢ per cu yd for labor and repairs. Former cost by steam thawing was 35–45¢ per cu yd. Equipment (excluding old ditch) cost about $10 000.

Water thawing without points. A different application of cold water for thawing was employed on Candle Cr, Fairhaven dist, Alaska, by E. E. Pearce in 1921 (558). The gravel lay in and alongside a creek, with no muck cover. Length, 1 025 ft; aver width, 60 ft; depth to bedrock, 9 ft; depth to frost line, 3.5 ft. The creek was diverted into 2 parallel ditches, one along each edge of area. A 5 by 5-ft shaft, sunk in middle of the area, about 235 ft from the down-stream end, was timbered tightly to a point 2 ft above bedrock. Timbering extended above surface water; coarse gravel was thrown in at bottom and around the sides of shaft. Water entering shaft bottom was pumped out (at 250 gal per min) by a 2.5-in centrif pump, driven by a 4-hp gasolene engine. Creek water seeped through thawed surface gravel to the shaft, thus creating circulation along the frost line. Aver temp of creek water, 64° F; of shaft water, 48°. Whole area thawed in 15 days; pumping time, 80 hr. Cost, excluding equipment and overhead, 1.4¢ per cu yd. Previous work with water points only, in same type of gravel (water pumped), cost 9.5¢ per cu yd.

132. MINING ALLUVIAL TIN DEPOSITS IN MALAYA

By JOHN BRANNER NEWSOM, Mining Engineer

a. General Conditions

Tin occurs as cassiterite, associated with heavy minerals of Fe, W, etc, over large areas in Malaya. Fig 873 shows types of deposits; alluvials and residuals, occurring separately or in combination, are worked by placer methods and yield the bulk of Malayan tin production. Bedrocks are decomposed granites and soft schist, with areas of very hard irregular limestone. Tin-bearing pay-streaks are locally called "karang"; heavy associated minerals, "amang," correspond to black sands in gold placers. Occasional large pieces of cassiterite occur, but approx 90% of ore grains pass 10 mesh and stay on 150 mesh. Essential differences between these deposits and gold-placer gravels are: (a) sp gr of cassiterite is lower than gold,

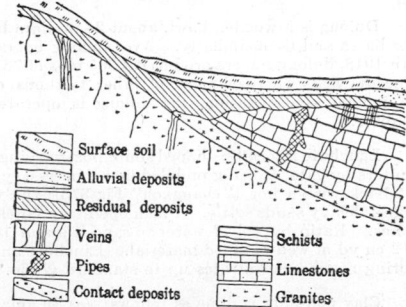

Fig 873. Types of Malayan Tin Deposits.
Ideal Sec

making it more difficult to save; (b) fully 95% of deposit is fine sand and clay, with a few stones and boulders (Table 151); (c) fluctuating price of tin.

Table 151. Sizing Tests of Typical Bank Materials

Screen		Per cent weight on screen	
Mesh	Aperture, mm	A	B
20	0.90	20.5	27.6
40	0.38	19.5	17.8
60	0.21	8.7	8.6
80	0.16	5.2	3.5
100	0.13	2.9	2.0
−100	0.13	42.7	39.7

A. Ampang Selangor. *B*. Sungei Linggi, Negri Sembilan. Note. Voids in alluvials in place vary from approx 38% in pure clay to 23% in material containing 50% sand. Per cent voids in pure clay and sand is higher than in mixtures.

To handle a given vol of material, these conditions require larger areas in sluices and more water than in gold placers; sands in sluices must be agitated artificially to prevent packing; clay puddled, to release included mineral and prevent sluice-robbing; some deposits are worked intermittently, as price of tin varies.

While some ground is very rich, production is mostly from deposits carrying 0.5–1.5 lb tin per cu yd; with prices for tin in 1937, usual open-cut methods operate profitably with Chinese labor where values are 1 lb per cu yd; dredges work profitably under favorable conditions with values as low as 0.3 lb per cu yd; clay and difficult bedrock increase minimum profitable values; normally, 0.5 lb per cu yd is considered good dredging ground. Wages: Chinese common labor, 30–50¢ (U S) per 8-hr day; skilled labor, 75¢–$1.50; much work is on contract and tribute systems. Methods include use of small- or large-scale hand-work, ground sluicing, hydraulicking, hydraulic elevators, gravel pumps, mechanical haulage on inclines, and dredging.

In all cases, a rough concentrate carrying 15–50% tin is made; this is rewashed to the standard grade for the district, which is 73–75% tin and is sold to local smelters. Rough concentrate may contain 50% or more "amang"; finished concentrate is called "ore," a term applying loosely to all kinds of concentrate.

Foreign engineers often fail to recognize the low costs and large outputs attained by Chinese hand methods, through their ingenuity and low cost of labor. A fixed idea of Chinese operators is to avoid expense for equipment wherever possible. Prior to 1900, with possible exception of a few small hydraulic mines, all Malayan placers were worked by hand; still true for certain work involved in present methods using power. In early days, extensive drifting (Art 130) was done by Chinese, but this has almost stopped.

In 1931 the International Tin Control scheme went into effect. Under it, the Malayan quota has varied from low of 25% of rated capac in 1932 to 80% in 1937. In 1936, 87% of world production was controlled and the Straits region, comprising Malaya and Netherlands East Indies, produced 55% of world's tin, valued at $99 000 000 (U S), practically all by placer mining. Malaya furnished 68% of this. Malayan placer mining is the most extensive placer work now being done.

b. Washing Devices

Simple hand-washing devices are important in the industry, being always used to clean rough concentrate. For use of jigs, see Dredging, Art 132g.

Dulong is a wooden bowl, about 24 in diam by 5 in deep, corresponding to the gold miner's pan or batea and used similarly. Aver dulong operator handles 1.25 cu yd of sandy material per 8 hr. In 1918, dulong miners produced 3 365 tons of 73% concentrate, or 8% of total Malay output, but in recent years encroachment of other methods of primary concentration has reduced this figure. For final concentration, the dulong is operated as for rough concentrate, but work is much slower.

Lanchute is a coffin-shaped sluice box, varying from dimensions in Fig 874 to 35 ft long. Material enters by gate *A*, being puddled first if necessary. As the sand streams down the box, a coolie pulls it back with a hoe ("changkol," Fig 875); the water swirling around sides of hoe carries off light sand; heavy sands settle. 1 man operates a lanchute of size shown in Fig 874; 2 or 3 coolies for larger ones. Ratio by vol of water to sand is about 10 : 1; recovery, about 90%. Duty per man-shift, 12 cu yd of well puddled material. Lanchute and changkol are auxiliaries in all large-scale work, to bring rough concentrates up to standard grade.

Clay puddling is done as follows: (a) In small-scale work, with digging changkols (Fig 875), in puddles at lanchutes (Fig 874). A coolie puddles 0.3–0.5 cu yd of tough clayey material per hr. (b) By "stage" working in small open pits. About 60% of water by vol is added to the karang on the pit floor; resultant pulp is scooped across floor with long-handled scoops to the foot of one of the banks, in the face of which a series of small basins or puddles is cut at vert intervals of about 4 ft. Coolies at each puddle dip the pulp, with long-handled dippers holding about 1 gal, from one puddle to the next above, and finally to the lanchute on the surface. Aver duty per coolie is about 16 dippers per min = 2.5 cu yd bank measure per hr on a 4-ft lift. With labor at 50¢ per day, stage working costs approx 0.7¢ per cu yd per ft lifted. As many as 12–14 stages may be used, but such heights are unusual. Stage working, the most effective hand-puddling method, can be used only where karang will form a sludge: mixtures of sand and clay give best sludges. (NOTE. Stages are used for elevating material in opening pits to bedrock for gravel pumps and in working small rich areas.) (c) By power-driven arrastras. A 25-ft diam machine, with 2 drags and 0.5-in discharge screen kept open with a water jet, requires 3 hp at 5 rpm. Capac, 5–15 cu yd per hr; water, 50–75 cu ft per min. At one mine arrastra puddling cost 15¢ per cu yd. (d) By box puddlers similar to

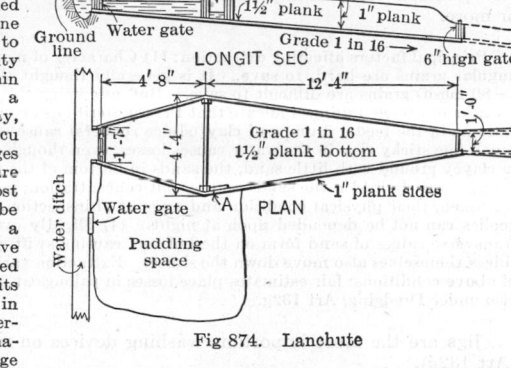

Fig 874. Lanchute

log-washers but run at high speed; this is the usual method. A puddler 12 ft long has 5 sets of steel blades; speed 120 rpm; power, 20–35 hp; water, 10 cu ft per cu ft of dirt. These machines do imperfect work, but have large capacity. (e) Low-speed puddlers, consisting of horiz shafts about 20 ft long with blades extending about 2 ft, the blades tilted so that the clay is moved ahead slightly by each blade as it comes around, were introduced in 1927. They are effic puddlers and are used for final disintegration of clay on some dredges. (Art 132g.)

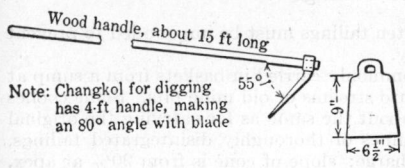

Fig 875. Changkol used in Lanchutes and Palongs

Ground sluices (Art 121) are extensively used in mountainous districts and in hydraulic mines. Capac, about 2 cu yd per hr per ft of width; slope, 4°–8°; water, 15–25 cu ft per cu ft of material washed. They are poor tin savers; recovery often less than 50%. They are cleaned up either by panning the material in the bottom, or by digging it out and concentrating in a lanchute. No blocks or stops are used; the sides are confined and the sand in sluice is allowed to form its own riffles and eddies.

Palong (Fig 876) is a wooden sluice box, in which most of the Malayan tin is recovered. Dimensions vary; typical palong is 120 ft long, 4 ft wide and slopes 3°. Bottom is smooth; transverse baffles A, 4 in high and held in grooves formed by vert cleats B, are usually 10–12 ft apart. Palongs are single or in sets of 2 or more side by side; they are roofed for protection from weather and supported on trestles to give headroom for tailing. Cost of single palong, in 1937, $1 400; cost of moving and re-erection, $1 000. CAPAC, about 1.5 cu yd per hr per ft of width; water, 8 cu ft per cu ft of material washed (see also under Dredging). OPERATION. Material flowing through is stirred by coolies with changkols

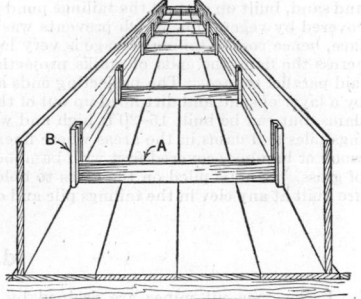

Fig 876. Typical Palong (supports omitted)

(Fig 875) and rakes; 1 coolie per 40 ft of length. As heavy sands accumulate and become difficult to agitate, additional baffles are inserted on top of original 4-in baffles, with no further attempt to stir the bottom layer. In 24 hr, a well managed palong builds up about 1.5 ft of concentrates. CLEAN-UPS, usually one per day, are made with a small stream of clear water. Concentrates are dragged up stream with changkols; each section between baffles is cleaned separately, starting at upper end of palong. Multiple-palongs permit continuous operation, as they are cleaned up one at a time. Final concentrates carry 15–30% cassiterite, depending on amount of amang present. Concentrates are shoveled into buckets and carried to a clean-up house ("tin shed"), where they are brought to standard grade in lanchutes. EXTRACTION. Chinese miners say that an aver palong saves about 80% of tin delivered to it and that 80% of this is caught in first 30 ft. With properly puddled feed, and proper stirring throughout a run, extractionmay reach 90% or more.

Principal factors affecting extraction: (1) Character of material. Water-worn cassiterite is easy, angular grains are hard, to save. It is generally thought that coarse (+ 10 mesh) and very fine (− 80 mesh) grains are difficult to save. But, admitting this in saving minus 60 to 80-mesh grains, samples of dredge tailings indicate that the cassiterite lost comprises grains of all sizes in about same ratio as in the feed. Lumps of clay (sluice robbers) cause serious losses by picking up cassiterite; much fine sticky clay in the water causes losses, even though large lumps are removed. In working in clayey ground with little sand, the sands in bottom of the palong tend to scour out. (2) Stirring is important to loosen the sands and permit concentration; packing causes rapid losses. (3) Skill of workmen, their physical condition and amount of inspection. Continuous stirring is drudgery and coolies can not be depended upon at night. (4) Slightly overloading a palong causes heavy loss; transverse ridges of sand form on the bottom, causing swift currents which prevent settlement; the ridges themselves also move down the sluice. Extraction varies greatly under varying combinations of above conditions; fair estimates place losses in palongs at 5% min, 30% max, 15–20% aver. See also under Dredging, Art 132g.

Jigs are the most important washing devices on modern tin dredges. See dredging (Art 132g).

c.   Disposal of Tailings

Problems resemble those in gold placers; often tailings must be impounded to prevent silting up streams or injuring adjacent property.

In small mines using lanchutes, sands are commonly carried in baskets from a sump at tail of lanchute and stacked, while slimes run into streams or old mine pits. Some coolies load and others carry sands; duty of labor is about the same as for carrying the original dirt (Table 152). Palongs produce large volumes of thoroughly disintegrated tailings, which build up an alluvial cone under the discharge; slope of cone is from 20% at apex, where coarse sands lodge, to 0 at edges, where slimes are deposited. Cassiterite lost in the palong concentrates near apex of cone; resultant deposit of clean sand and ore is in ideal condition for reworking, and such old tailing cones are worked by tributers with royalties up to 40% of tin recovered. If impossible to run tailings into old mine pits, they are impounded by dams. In hydraulic mines and where much water must be restrained and settled, ordinary earth dams are used.

In many smaller mines, impounding dams are made of alternate layers of long grass (lalong) and sand, built up around the tailings pond as the level rises. Slope of dam face, about 45°; it is soon covered by vegetation, which prevents washing by rain. Such dams cost about 1¢ per sq ft of dam face, hence cost of tailing storage is very low. For substantial construction, a layer of grass is laid across the dam, the ends of stalks projecting beyond the face and covered with bundles of grass laid parallel to face. The projecting ends are then doubled back over upper layer and held in place by a layer of sand and dirt hoed up out of the tailings pond. These cost more than simple grass-sand dams, but can be built 15–20 ft high and will hold slimes as well as sand. Drains, provided in tailings piles and dams in the areas where finer material is deposited, comprise long A-shaped frames of wood or bamboo, covered first with bamboo matting with 1/4-in openings and then with a 2-in layer of grass. Sand is piled on the grass to hold it in place until it is covered by tailings. These drains are built at any elev in the tailings pile and drain through the dam face.

d.   Drainage

Large open-cut mines are drained by power pumps; small mines by hand bailers or China pumps worked by hand, foot or water power. Bailers, for lifting water short distances, are made from 5-gal oil-cans; sides braced with light wooden slats. Fig 877 shows operation; the coolies are 15–20 ft apart; each holds 2 light lines attached to can, by which the bailer is swung back and forth and tipped for loading and dumping. Aver lift, 5 ft; coolies aver 20 swings per min; max output, about 80 gal per min. Oil-can bailers are used in lifts to 15 ft; speed of swing varies little with lift, but less water is taken per swing. This is hard work and coolies in a gang spell each other. To bail more than 80 gal per min, 2 crews work in rhythm from the same stands.

China pumps worked by coolies rarely lift more than 4–6 ft; pumps are set on about 30° slope; if power is available, higher lifts are obtained with pumps to 80 ft long. Chief use of China pump is in small workings requiring only intermittent drainage.

Wooden buckets, with a vert pole handle attached to a counterbalanced sweep, are used to bail water to heights of 8–15 ft; they are arranged in batteries of 2–6; men work in rhythm; duty per man,

30–45 gal per min on an 8-ft lift. For lifts over 12–15 ft, batteries of these bailers are arranged on different levels.

Fig 877. Oil-can Bailer

e. Miscellaneous Hand Operations in Open Cuts

Transport in hand-worked open-cuts is by baskets, wheelbarrows, and cars on tracks.

Carrying in baskets, suspended in pairs from a shoulder pole, is practiced in stripping and moving karang: (a) where yardage is too small to warrant cost of barrows and trestles; (b) where carry is less than 50 ft, so that relative cost of loading and dumping barrows is high; (c) where carry is uphill and conditions do not justify or permit mechanical haulage in trucks; (d) in cleaning irregular bedrock. Output is not a serious factor, as large yardage may be moved by increasing number of coolies employed.

Flat rattan baskets are used; capac, 50–60 lb; cost, 17¢; life about 2 weeks. Faces of pits are usually in steps 1–2 ft high; baskets are placed on ground at face and loaded with a changkol. Loading time, 17–80 sec, depending on whether dirt is clay or sand, packed or loose; aver time, 50 sec. A contract coolie carries 2 baskets (aver load, 100 lb); he goes at a trot, which, through the spring of the pole, takes the load off his leg muscles while walking and puts it on when his leg is straight. On up grades, pace is slower, advantage of the spring in the pole is lost, lighter loads are carried and output per hr decreases rapidly. Contract work is usual, with pay based on vol in place; where this is difficult to measure, as in cleaning bedrock, coolies are paid by the trip from the face, regardless of load carried, with resultant lower effic (see Table 152).

Wheelbarrows are used on level leads over 50 ft long, also on long leads where yardage does not justify cost of cars and tracks.

Chinese barrow (Fig 878) is entirely of wood; aver load, 350 lb; cost, $3.50; life, about 2 yr. The projection of the frame in front of the wheel cheapens cost of dumping, etc. Double barrow tracks of 6-in planks are laid at 10-ft intervals along faces. Barrows are loaded with changkols; aver loading time in aver ground, 2 min, 50 sec; dumping time, 3 sec. For duty of labor, see Table 152. Barrow work is usually done by gangs on contract paid by volume in place.

Cars or trucks are V-shaped, steel mine-cars holding 15 cu ft, or about 0.33 cu yd bank measure; they are used on level leads of 600 ft or more and at mines when material is elevated on inclines.

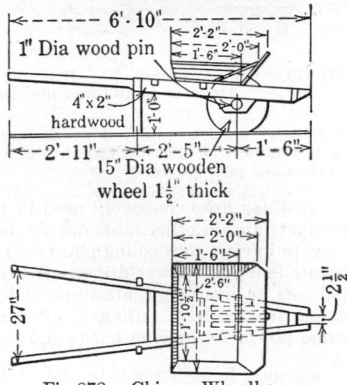

Fig 878. Chinese Wheelbarrow

Track is of 12-lb rails, usually poorly laid; life of cars, 1.5–2 yr. Cars are loaded by 2-handled rattan baskets or trays; area about 18 by 16 in; bottom of tray is curved, with max depth of 6 in. Basket, holding an aver of 63 lb, is loaded with changkols at the face in about 20 sec; it is then picked up and carried to car; hence loading effic depends on distance between car and face (Table 152). Miners do their own tramming; usually 3 coolies per car; with well laid track, 2 coolies per car. Miners paid by truck load.

Duty of labor in above methods of loading and transport is given in Table 152. These data were obtained from typical working places and are averages respectively of 60 time studies of carrying in baskets, 200 of barrow work, and 170 of truck loading.

f. Open-cut Mining

Principal methods: (a) by benches; (b) with inclines; (c) with gravel pumps; (d) by hydraulicking and hydraulic elevators.

Table 152. Cu Yd Bank Material in Place that One Coolie Loads and Moves per Hr

Method			Loading (c)	Distance moved, ft					
				100	200	300	400	500	600
Carrying in baskets	Pd by vol (a)	Sand............	2.42	1.05	0.67	0.47	0.32	0.26	0.22
		Clay.............	0.85	0.5	0.32	0.24	0.18	0.14	0.1
	Pd by trip	Men............	1.5	0.32	0.18	0.12	0.1	0.07	0.06
		Women..........	1.25	0.25	0.13	0.08	0.07	0.06	0.05
Wheelbarrow work (d)		Sand............	2.5	1.75	1.38	1.1	0.94	0.84	0.75
		Clay.............	2.0	1.48	1.18	0.99	0.86	0.78	0.7
Loading cars by baskets		Ft carried in basket.........	0	10	20	30	40	50	.....
		Sand...........	4.6(b)	2.5	1.9	1.5	1.25	1.05	.....
		Clay:..........	1.7(b)	1.25	0.9	0.7	0.6	0.53	.....

(a) Duty of male coolies.   (b) Loading basket.   (c) Loosening and loading.   (d) Contract work.

Working by benches is used in mining large flat alluvial deposits (Fig 873) to 50–60 ft deep. Face is carried in benches (Fig 879); light trestles across the pit provide the shortest possible level distance to dump; max height of benches, limited by danger of caving, is usually about 20 ft.

Overburden is stripped and carried in baskets or moved in barrows over trestles to back of the pit; karang is carried up chicken ladders in baskets to a series of lanchutes set on top of the tailings.

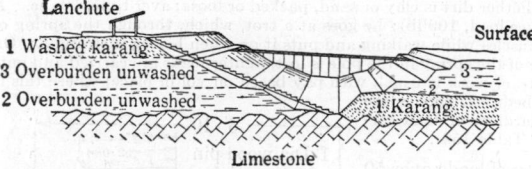

Fig 879.   Open-cut worked by Benches.   Diagrammatic Cross-sec (trestles to lower benches omitted)

The stacked overburden is kept as close as possible to the working face; aver carry or tram from face to dump is approx 150 ft. Drainage of pits is by gravity where possible or by pumps. All digging is done with mining changkols (Fig 875), used as a combination pick, mattock and shovel. To about the year 1900, most large mines were worked by hand in this way; in places faces were 0.25–0.5 mile long, up to 3 500 coolies being employed on one face. Open-cut mines using only hand methods of moving earth generally advance the faces in a fairly straight line; overburden and tailings are dumped in the worked-out pit.

Inclines are extensively used in the deeper mines (to 300 ft) along granite-limestone contacts and in other large open-cuts to depths of 50–60 ft, to hoist waste to dumps, and elevate karang to washing plants. Layouts vary widely with local conditions. Washing plants comprise power-driven arrastras or high-speed puddlers, which feed into elevated palongs or jigs. Pits are drained by centrif pumps, which furnish water for washing; water drained from tailings is often reused. Steam, costing about 2¢ per hp-hour, is the usual power for driving hoists and pumps.

Pits may be advanced in benches (Fig 879), in which case karang is loaded in cars on floor of pit and trammed by hand to foot of incline. At times stripping is handled by cars: (a) hoisted in cars on separate inclines serving each bench; (b) trammed along benches and dumped into the pit at points where it will not interfere with future work; (c) barred down slopes into cars on pit floor and hoisted to surface up main incline. Open pits on contact deposits are usually long and narrow, but in places are circular or elliptical, worked in benches, each served by an incline. In flat alluvials, pit faces are fairly straight, as in bench working (Fig 879). Basins or pockets of karang, occurring too low in bottom of pit for convenient loading into cars, are worked by carrying in baskets to lanchutes on the pit floor. Loading and tramming is done by contract; labor in hoisting, puddling and washing is usually paid by the day.

Gravel-pump mines (see Art 126) are, next to dredging properties, the most important source of tin in Malaya. In 1938, dredges produced 24 550 tons of tin in the Federated Malay States, gravel-pump mines, 20 875 tons, other methods, 9 128 tons.

Usual operation involves: (a) hand work to break material from the bank; (b) ground sluices to carry material to a sump; (c) a pump, usually steam-driven, to elevate materials; (d) palongs for washing. Impounding dams are built around the tailings storage areas, the water running back into the pit and through ground sluices along base of the working face. Clays and sand are broken down into ground sluices with hoes or bars, face slopes being kept steep so that material slides to sluice by gravity. This method, applicable under widely varying conditions in different types of deposit, requires delivery of the entire over-burden and karang to the sump in the pit floor; hence, working faces are continuous from floor to surface and in plan are apt to take a roughly circular shape around the sump as a center. Entire bank is elevated by the pump and must be stored in tailings piles at ends of the palongs. Max lift of pump is about 75 ft; max depth of pit that can be worked is less than this by the elev required for palongs to provide room for tailing-storage. Pumps are usually high enough above pit floor to avoid drowning out during shut-downs. BREAKING GROUND. Some undercutting is done by water in ground sluices, but typical method of excavation is by "steps" (Fig 880). Pit faces slope about 45°; coolies begin at surface and cut a series of steps about 18 in high in face of slope, using bars for cutting and prying off the ground, which rolls down the face to the ground sluice. When the bottom is reached, men work back up the slope, barring off the steps as they go; duty of labor, in stiff clay, 7–8 cu yd per man-day. Work is on a tribute system; men on steps and those working ground sluices receive a percent of ore recovered in ground sluices; owner retains the ore from the palongs. Recovery of over 75% in ground sluices is rare.

Fig 880. Breaking Ground in Steps

The method provides cheap breaking on contract, and delivers low-grade material to palong, thus reducing losses there. Other advantages of gravel pump: (*a*) elevates at fairly low cost; (*b*) delivers material to palong well puddled and with correct ratio of water for washing; (*c*) drains excess water from pit. The large percent of clay and sands and small percent of coarse gravel, combined with necessity of puddling the clay, makes Malayan tin deposits far more favorable for successful gravel-pump operation than most gold-placer deposits. But, liners and impellers are rapidly worn by the sharp sands, and must be cheaply and quickly replaceable; they are renewed about every 6 weeks. Pump intakes are 3–12 in diam; 4 and 6-in are commonest; larger units not usually successful, due to difficulty in keeping their feed steady. Steam costs about 2¢ per hp-hr; power costs are usually about 25% of total working cost. Capac of 6-in pump is approx 16 cu yd of bank material per hr. Pumps can handle up to 25% solids, but this pulp is too thick for palong feed. Under favorable conditions a gravel-pump mine with an 8-in pump can treat 25 000 yd per month.

Hydraulicking and hydraulic elevators are used under same general conditions as in gold placers (Art 123, 126), except that washing is done in ground sluices or palongs.

Monitors are used in a few places in the hills, followed by ground sluices or palongs; tailings go to dumps by gravity. The more important hydraulic mines, of which there are a few, work alluvial deposits that lie too low for gravity tailing disposal; hydraulic elevators or large gravel pumps then elevate the material to palongs built high enough to give tailing room.

In general, the large percent of fine materials in the banks, need for puddling and absence of coarse boulders, are much more favorable conditions for hydraulic-elevator work than are found in most gold placers and elevator efficiencies are higher. The elevator-monitor combination has the great advantages of completely puddling the material, lifting a high percent of solids, and using small labor force. Chief disadvantage: the usual large proportion of tough clays in the banks results in low duty and high water consumption by the monitors. There are few localities in Malaya (except the Gopeng district, Perak), having enough water under head for large hydraulic operations, and, where sandy karang permits undercutting, for caving of banks and large duty. Data on duties and costs are not available.

g. Dredging

General. First dredge started in 1912; it was successful and dredging is now the most important method, as it allows profitable exploitation of low-grade deposits unworkable by hand. All early dredges were sluice type, described below, and had washing capac of 75 000 to 90 000 yd a month. Installation of classifiers and jigs on a Malayan dredge in 1925 focussed attention on better ore-saving methods and led to an enormous increase in the capac of single dredges and the number of dredges in the field. In 1939 there were 126 dredges in Federated Malay States, 20 in Netherlands East Indies, and a few in Siam. Some can dig 130 ft below water level and treat 400 000 cu yd a month. Their high effic is shown by the facts that their ore-saving devices are contained in spaces 90 ft long,

70 ft wide, and 40 ft high, and that they treat 16 000 tons of gravel a day, with less than a value of 0.5¢ a ton left in the tailings.

Types of deposit worked by dredging are the same as in gold placers (see Requirements and limitations, Art 128). Depths now dredged are 20-130 ft. Schist and granite bedrocks are soft and ideal for dredging; limestone bedrocks are hard and always have pinnacles; in some areas most of the karang lies above the pinnacles, making high recovery by dredging feasible; at present, karang lying between pinnacles is left, though there are promising methods for recovering it. Sunken timber sometimes interferes with dredging.

Chain-bucket dredges are used; suction dredges have generally failed. First dredges had open-connected bucket lines, but with development of large-capac washing devices, close-connected buckets are favored. Steam is generally used, with power plant on the boat. Fuel is wood or poor-quality coal mined locally; power costs are high. Some companies operating several dredges have central turbo-electric power plants. Chinese labor is used almost entirely.

Principal factors affecting design and operation of Malayan tin dredges, in comparison with gold dredges, are: absence of boulders, small size of grains composing the deposits, large amount of clay present, and lower sp gr and value of cassiterite. These conditions affect details of dredge design as follows:

Hulls, mostly steel, resemble those of gold dredges; type of washing devices determines whether hull is long and narrow or short and wide. DIGGING MACHINERY is same as on gold dredges; broad, shallow buckets are required to dump clayey ground. As digging is easy, HEAD LINES are used instead of spuds to hold dredge in position. TROMMELS always receive material from the dump hopper; they are the same mechanically as on gold dredges, but of smaller mesh. STONE-CHUTES at tail of dredge are generally used instead of stackers, as there is usually no coarse gravel to handle, hence no stern gantry; tailing piles behind the dredge are level and approx at same elev as original surface. More WATER is needed than on gold dredges of same capac. WASHING DEVICES differ greatly from those for gold (see below).

Types of dredge: (a) sluice dredge, developed from the sluice-type gold dredge, was the first used; (b) classifier-jig dredge, invented by J. F. Newsom, was first used on a commercial scale in 1925; (c) jig dredges without classification, introduced 1927, are an outgrowth of (b); (d) recent clay-working dredges have reached a high state of effic.

Sluice dredges. Trommel undersize is distributed to sluices running fore and aft, which operate like palongs. Many operators prefer wide sluices; 6-ft width is considered a max, due to difficulty of distributing water in wider ones. Capac: 15-20 cu yd bank measure per sq ft of sluice area per month. Grade: approx 2°, when hull is level; trim of dredge is affected by wt of loaded sluices, which operate on slopes of about 3.5°. Common practice uses 1 coolie per sluice for stirring; mechanical rakes working across the sluice are being tried and appear promising. Large dredges have double decks of sluices, and, where steam-operated, require about 100 men for 3-shift work.

Sluices are cleaned up in rotation, like palongs. Bucyrus Co reports that the sluice area of a tin dredge is usually 4-5 times the table area of a gold dredge of the same capac; water for hopper, trommel and sluices is about twice that for the usual gold dredge of same capac. Overcrowding is more apt to occur in dredge sluices than in palongs on shore; dredges take horiz cuts in descending order and adjacent beds in flat alluvials vary from pure sands to pure clays; these conditions tend to increase losses in sluices (see Palongs, Art 132b). Sampling of tailings by some companies indicates a sluice loss of 15-20%. Use of puddlers is rare; clay that is not disintegrated in the trommel goes through rock chute to dump. It is difficult to provide washing capac for more than 100 000 cu yd per month on sluice dredges, although larger digging capacities are easily obtained.

Classifier-jig dredges operate on basis of results of extensive screen tests of bank materials and sizes of ore grains. In general, free- and hindered-settling ratios of sand and ore grains are such that classification discards much of the slimes and finer sands, without serious loss of mineral. Products from classifier spigots are easily concentrated on jigs. A classifier of large capac and good performance has been developed, allowing the whole plant to be erected on a dredge. In 1927, there were 15 dredges of this type in Malaya.

Flow-sheet for handling about 150 000 cu yd per month is typically as follows: material from buckets passes through a trommel with 3/8-in openings; oversize to tailing; undersize to 2 classifiers (Fig 881). Each classifier makes 4 products: Spigot 1, coarse sand, divided between 2 jigs (105 rpm, stroke 1-1 1/4 in); spigot 2, medium sand, to 1 jig (115 rpm, stroke 5/8 in); spigots 3-4, fine sand, to 1 jig (160 rpm, stroke 3/8 in); spigots 5-6 and overflow, very fine sand and slimes, to tailing. All jig tailing goes direct to waste. All hutch products go to a desliming sump and thence to 1 cleaner jig, having 6 compartments, each 2 ft wide by 3 ft long; speed 180 rpm, stroke 1/4-3/8 in. Tailing from the cleaner jig goes to waste; 1st hutch to a final washing plant (lanchute) on shore, while hutch products from other compartments return to the desliming sump. Fig 882 shows jigs and classifiers on a dredge of Rantau Tin Dredging Co; flow-sheet differs slightly from the above; many variations in flow-sheet and arrangement of machines are possible.

Classifier. Fig 881 shows the Newsom double-current classifier; length, 12–16 ft; width, 6 ft; 3 rows of discharge hoppers, each 2 ft sq at top. It has large capac; 1 machine has successfully handled 300 cu yd of sand (without clay) per hr. Water required, 2 500–4 000 gal per min, depending on veloc of currents desired.

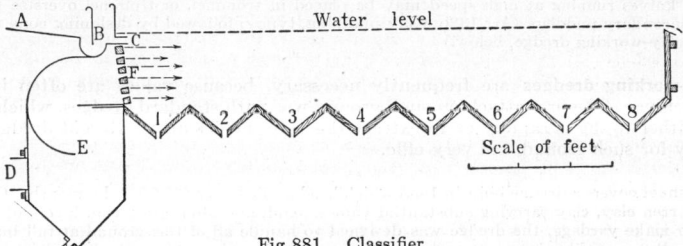

Fig 881. Classifier

Pulp current flows over apron *A*, passes under adjustable gate *B*, and enters classifier through feed slot *C*. Fresh water enters through pipe *D* into pressure-box *E*, thence through grid *F* into body of classifier.

Recovery by classifier-jig system, 90–95%; concentrates run 20–60% cassiterite, depending on kind of ground and skill of operators. The high recovery and large capac of this type of dredge is because the bulk of the cassiterite usually comes down in the classifier with the coarse sands, giving a product that can be jigged rapidly with low loss.

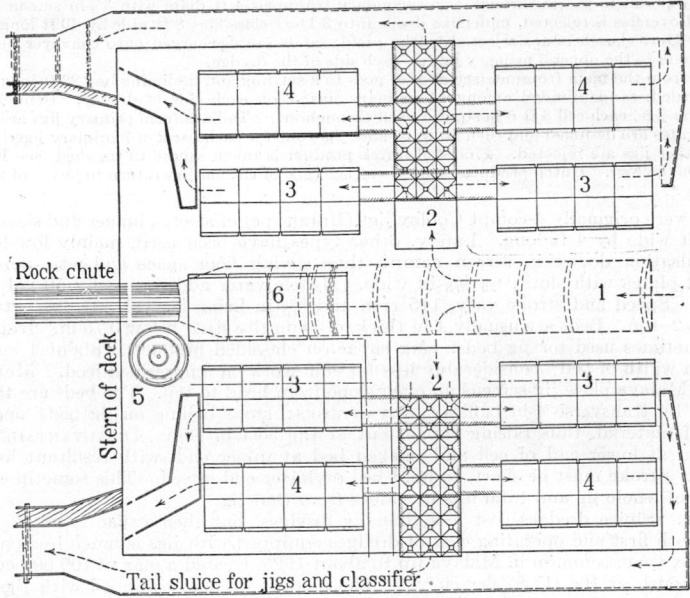

Fig 882. Rantau Classifier-jig Tin Dredge; Outline Deck Plan, showing Arrangement of Equipment. 1, trommel; 2, classifiers; 3, coarse jigs; 4, fine jigs; 5, settling cone to remove water from hutch products; 6, cleaner jig. Classifiers are high enough to feed jigs by gravity. Arrows show direction of flow.

As there is a relatively smaller vol of material discharged from the later spigots, fines can be treated slowly and carefully on a small number of jigs.

Jig dredges without classification have advantage of simpler operation, all jigs being adjusted alike, but yardage treated per jig is lower and tailings losses are higher than for properly operated classifier-jig dredges.

Flow-sheet is typically as follows: Material from buckets passes through a trommel with 3/8-in openings; oversize to tailing; undersize divided equally among 12 jigs (115 rpm, stroke 5/8 in). All jig tailings go direct to waste. All hutch products go to a desliming sump and thence to 1 cleaner jig having 6 compts, each 2 ft wide by 3 ft long; (180 rpm, stroke 1/4–3/8 in). Tailing from cleaner jig goes to waste; 1st hutch to a final washing plant (lanchute) on shore while hutch products from other compts return to desliming sump. Many variations in flow-sheet are used; for example Dorr classifiers to remove slimes, sand from classifiers going to jigs. If ground contains clay, disintegrating knives running at high speed may be placed in trommel, or trommel oversize may pass through secondary puddlers (Art 132b, Clay puddling, type e) followed by desliming cone (see flow-sheet for clay-working dredge, below.)

Clay-working dredges are frequently necessary, because values are often in tough residual clays. The first attack on such ground was with standard dredges, which proved unable either to dig it rapidly or to extract the values efficiently. Recent dredges, built especially for such ground, are very effic.

Flow-sheet covers a dredge built in 1938 which has handled over 400 000 yd a month. Ground is spotty; barren clay, clay carrying substantial values, sand, and alternating thin layers of clay and sand. To make yardage, the dredge was designed to handle all of this ground at full bucket-line capacity. Because of barren spots and occurrence of pure sand in places, the flow-sheet is flexible, with provision to by-pass material when desired and to change the treatment routine in other ways. Buckets of 13.5-cu ft capac, turning 18 per min, deliver the material to primary trommel. When digging clay, an automatic 3-arm clay extractor is swung into place at the upper tumbler, where it scoops the clay out of each bucket as it comes over. The primary trommel is 9 ft diam by 36 ft long, with screen perforations 1/4 by 5/8 in. Undersize goes to settling tank, described below. Oversize may be by-passed to pond behind the dredge or put through the clay disintegrating screen, 9 ft diam by 28 ft long. The walls of this screen are manganese-steel grids with openings 4 by 5 in. Inside is a puddler shaft, 54 rpm, with blades 4 ft long. Oversize from the clay disintegrating screen goes to pond, undersize to two secondary puddlers (Art 132b, Clay puddling, type e). Discharge from the secondary puddlers passes through two secondary trommels 4 ft diam with 3/8-in screen openings. Trommel oversize is rejected, undersize drops into 2 Dorr classifiers 8 ft wide by 30 ft long. Slimes from the Dorr classifiers are rejected to the pond; sands are discharged onto conveyer belts which deliver them to the upper 3 primary jigs on each side of the dredge.

Sand from the main trommel (see above) goes to a settling and desliming box 22 ft long. Slimes are discarded, sands divided among 14 primary jigs, 7 on each side of dredge. Bendelari 4-cell diaphragm jigs, each cell 3 ft 6 in sq, are used throughout. Tailings from primary jigs are rejected. Concentrates are deslimed and then go to cleaner jigs, one for each bank of 7 primary jigs. Tailings from cleaner jigs are rejected. First-cell hutch product is taken ashore to tin shed (see Final concentration, below). Hutch products from the other cells of cleaner jigs return to heads of these jigs.

Jigs were originally 4-compt Cooley jigs (Harz type) of steel; plunger and sieve compts each 3 ft wide by 4 ft long. Lately, other types have been used, mainly low-head jigs with pulsation device in screen compt, thus saving floor space and wt. Screens are punched plates with slots 1/16–1/8 in wide. Hutch water added, usually 50 gal per min per cell. Speed and stroke vary, 115 rpm and 5/8 in being typical. Drops between jig beds are 2–4 in. Beds are usually 4 in thick, of hematite sized below 0.75 in. Iron punchings sometimes used for jig beds. Jig capac on classified product is about 1 cu yd per hr per in width of bed; considerably less for effic work on unclassified feed. Many operators in Malaya place jig screens on even slope from head to tail. The beds are then held in place by transverse 4-in baffles. ADVANTAGES: stops boiling on jig beds, speeds the travel of material, thus raising capac, but at the cost of effic. DISADVANTAGES: very loose bed at lower end of cell and packed bed at upper end, with resultant low-grade product. Stroke must be short, to hold bed on lower end of cell. This sometimes causes packing of whole jig and total loss of values from that jig.

Costs. Sluice dredges cost less than jig dredges, but their capac is much smaller; hence, both first and operating cost of dredges equipped with jigs is much less per cu yd. Sluice-box type, common in Malaya up to about 1925, treated a max of 100 000 cu yd per dredge-month at 10¢ (U S) per cu yd. The modern dredge, equipped with jigs, treats 250 000 to 450 000 cu yd per month at 5¢ (U S) or less per cu yd. This illustrates the great improvement in dredging since 1925, when the first classifier-jig dredge was installed by Yukon Gold Co. Tables 153 and 154 give details of 2 jig-type dredges, fairly representative of current practice in Malaya (G. W. Coffey).

Table 153. Malayan Tin-dredging Data (1937)

Dredge	Time operated		Cu yd mined	Cu yd per aver dredge-month
	Hours	% of total time		
A	7 495	85.6	2 871 100	239 000
B	7 512	85.8	3 470 400	289 000
Total or aver.	15 007	85.7	6 341 500	264 000

Table 154. Distribution of Working Costs during Operations in Table 153

Item	U S ¢ per cu yd	% of total	Item	U S ¢ per cu yd	% of total
European staff............	0.64	12.63	General expense (c)........	0.72	14.22
Native labor..............	0.90	17.95	Auto and truck expense......	0.02	0.37
Power (a).................	1.15	22.82	Transport (employes).......	0.05	0.97
Material and supplies.......	0.84	16.79	Drilling (prospecting).......	0.11	2.24
Replacements.............	0.33	6.57	Miscellaneous.............	0.08	1.51
Ore dressing (b)...........	0.12	2.44			
Land rental...............	0.01	0.28	Total.................	5.03	100.00
Insurance................	0.06	1.21			

(a) Cost of power, approx. 1.0¢ per kw-hr.   (b) Final concentration on shore.   (c) Not including dredge depreciation nor home office expense.

Final concentration. Dredge concentrates are taken ashore and raised to standard grade in lanchutes (built of concrete) and by jigging with hand sieves. This is done by contract; usual pay, 50¢ per picul of clean concentrate. Capac of lanchute in final concentration, 700 lb cassiterite per 8 hr. Jigs are sometimes used to lighten the load on lanchutes. Tables, vanners, etc, often tried, have failed. Lanchute middlings containing pyrite are dried, roasted and rewashed. Magnetite, scheelite, monazite, etc, are sometimes extracted by magnetic separators, but only in small quantities from low-grade ore. Final concentrates are dried, sacked, and shipped to smelter or sold to buyers.

Marketing. Malayan tin smelting industry is concentrated in Singapore and Penang, because refined tin is cheaper to transport than the more bulky cassiterite; also because of heavy export duties on ores shipped outside of Malaya. Smelter contracts usually call for delivery at smelter, but ore is weighed and sampled at the mine. Smelter charges are about $19 per ton of ore, based on 74% tin, with deductions for lower assays. Payment is at market price on day of delivery to smelter agent at mine, or any subsequent day fixed in advance, but within 14 days of delivery. Penalties are charged for S, As, Pb, Cu, Bi, Sb, if in appreciable amounts. Other realization charges are freight, which is very low, and a gov't tax which varies (8–13% *ad val*) with the market price of tin. Total realization cost, including this tax, freight, smelter charges, and ocean transportation of finished product, averages about 15% of New York price.

Malayan weights and money. Many companies report values in "katis" per cu yd, ore production in "piculs," and costs in Straits cents per cu yd. Equivalents are as follows:

Weights

1 kati = 1 1/3 lb
100 katis = 1 picul = 133 1/3 lb
16.8 piculs = 1 long ton = 2 240 lb

Money (at par of exchange)

1 Straits dollar = 100 Straits cts
1 Straits dollar = 2s 4d
1 Straits dollar = 56.776 U S cts

For additional information on Malayan tin mining, see Bib (645, 684, 685, 686, 687).

BIBLIOGRAPHY

(A) *Eng & Min Jour* or *Eng & Min Jour Press*. (B) *Trans A I M E*. (C) *Min & Sci Press*. (D) *Mines & Min*. (E) *Mining Mag*, London. (F) *Jour* Chem, Met & Min Soc of So Africa. (G) *Proc* Lake Superior Min Inst. (H) *Information Circular*, U S Bur Mines.

1. Glossary of Mining and Metallurgical Terms. R. W. Raymond. (B) Vol 9, p 99. Glossary of the Mining and Mineral Industry. A. H. Fay. U S Bur Mines, *Bull* 95 (1920)
2. Treatise on Gold and Silver. W. R. Crane. John Wiley & Sons
3. Ancient Mine-workings. T. L. Carter. (E) Jan, 1913
4. Gold Mining in Matabeleland. G. R. Carey. *Trans* Inst Min & Met, Vol 10
5. Mineral Resources of U S, 1911, Pt 1, p 140, U S Geol Surv
6. Prospecting, Mining, and Washing Alabama Brown Iron Ores. C. Morgan. (B) *Tech Pub* 860 (1937)
7. Iron Ores. E. C. Eckel. McGraw-Hill Book Co
8. Cheap Shaft Sinking. *Sch of Mines Quart*, Vol 3, p 137
9. Hydraulic Stripping of a Stone Quarry. M. Sheppard. (B) Vol 129 (1938) p 26
10. Ore and Stone Mining. C. LeN. Foster. Griffin & Co
11. Prospecting for Phosphate Rock. F. F. Wilson, Jr. (A) Dec 12, 1908
12. Indicative Plants. R. W. Raymond. (B) Vol 15, p 645. Botany Applied to Mining. F. M. Wichman. (A) Dec 11, 1920. E. T. Wherry. (A) June 4, 1921. R. M. Harper. (A) Oct 29, 1921
13. Divining Rod. R. W. Raymond. (B) Vol 11, p 411
14. Divining Rod. W. F. Barrett. *Proc* Soc Psychical Research, Vol 13, 15. A. J. Ellis. *Water Supply Paper* No. 416, U S Geol Surv, 1917
15. Brown Iron Ore of Greenville Dist, Ala. W. B. Jones. *Min & Met*, June, 1938, p 280
16. Placer Mining in Western U S, Part I. E. D. Gardner & C. H. Johnson. (H) No 6786 (1934)
17. Placer Mining in Western U S, Part II. E. D. Gardner & C. H. Johnson. (H) No 6787 (1934)

18. Placer Mining in Western U S, Part III.   E. D. Gardner & C. H. Johnson.   *(H)* No 6788 (1935)
19. Prospecting in Cobalt District.   H. L. Batten.   *App Sci*, Nov, 1910
20. Principles of Mining.   H. C. Hoover.   Hill Pub Co.
21. Application of Descriptive Geometry to Mining.   J. W. Roe.   *(B)* Vol 41, 1910
22. Graphic Methods for Solution of Geologic Problems.   W. S. T. Smith.   *Econ Geol*, Vol 9, 1914
23. Locating Outcrops with a Transit.   W. S. Weeks.   *(A)* Apl 4, 1914
24. Prospecting in Nova Scotia.   W. H. Prest.   *Can Min Jour*, June 15, 1911
25. Gold Mines of the Rand.   Hatch and Chalmers.   Macmillan & Co
26. Prospecting for Brown Iron Ore.   H. S. Geismer.   *(A)* Sept 9, 1911
27. The Ajo Copper District.   I. B. Joralemon.   *(B)* Vol 49, 1914
28. Diamond Drilling at Alaska-Treadwell.   A. Schoenberg.   *(A)* Jan 17, 1914
29. Diamond Drilling at Miami.   F. S. Naething.   *(A)* May 23, 1914
30. Witwatersrand Goldfields.   S. J. Truscott.   Macmillan & Co
31. Methods at Yellow Aster Mine, Randsburg, Cal.   C. L. Cooper.   *(H)* No 6900 (1936).   A. B. Sabin.   *(A)* Sept, 1935, p 444
32. Sampling and Testing a Gold-Scheelite Placer Deposit in the Mojave Desert.   H. W. C. Prommel.   *(H)* No 6960 (1937)
33. Copper Prospecting with Churn Drills in Ariz.   W. G. Weber.   *Wis Engr*, Apl, 1910
34. Data on Miami Churn Drilling.   H. P. Bowen.   *(A)* May 2, 1914; Jan 2, 1915
35. Iron Mining in Minn.   C. E. VanBarneveld.   *Bull* No 1, Minn Sch of Mines, 1912
36. Surveying and Sampling Diamond-drill Holes.   E. E. White.   *(B)* Vol 44, 1912
37. Improved Sludge Box for Diamond Drilling.   G. S. Rollin.   *(A)* Mch 28, 1914
38. Notes on Diamond-drill Sampling.   H. L. Botsford.   *(A)* Jan 4, 1913
39. Diamond-drill Results, Porcupine, Ont.   G. W. Thomson.   *Can Min Jour*, Apl 1, 1912
40. Assaying Diamond-drill Samples.   W. J. Mead.   *(A)* May 6, 1911
41. Prospecting with Churn Drills at Miami, Ariz.   *(A)* Oct 22, 1910
42. Ray Consolidated Mines.   R. L. Herrick.   *(D)* July, 1909
43. Churn Drilling in New Mexico.   I. J. Stauber.   *(A)* Sept 14, 1912
44. Churn Drilling, Wisconsin.   W. F. Boericke.   *(A)* Aug 30, 1913
45. Churn Drills in Ely District.   J. L. Dobbins.   *(D)* June, 1909
46. A 24-inch Alluvial Prospecting Drill.   W. A. Van der Hoff.   *(E)* May, 1934, p 283
47. Prospecting Anthracite Mines by Drill Holes.   F. Lynde.   *(A)* Aug 7, 1909
48. Rack for Drill Cores.   F. N. Turgeon.   *(A)* Oct 21, 1911
49. Mining the Frood Orebody at Depth.   H. J. Mutz.   *(A)* Nov 10, 1930, p 445
50. Use of Geology in Iron Ore Exploration.   C. L. Leith.   *Econ Geol*, Vol 7, 1912
51. Geology of Lake Superior Region.   Van Hise and Leith.   *Monograph* 52, U S Geol Surv. See also *Mon* 19, 28, 36, 45, 46
52. Applied Geology, Michigan Iron Ranges.   P. B. McDonald.   *(A)* Aug 2, 1913
53. Iron Ore Deposits of Moa, Cuba.   J. S. Cox.   *(B)* Vol 42, 1911
54. Exploration of Cuban Iron Ore Deposits.   D. E. Woodbridge.   *(B)* Vol 42, 1911
55. Mining Methods, Southeast Missouri.   H. A. Guess.   *(B)* Vol 48, 1914
56. Hand-drilling Job in the San Juan.   R. B. Dickson.   *(A)* July, 1934, p 310
57. Mineral Industries of Calaveras County, Cal.   C. E. Julihn and F. W. Horton.   U S Bur Mines, *Bull* 413 (1938)
58. Tennessee Phosphate Practice.   J. A. Barr.   *(D)* Oct, 1912;   *(B)* Vol 50, 1914.   See also Bib (338)
59. Sinking Test Pits.   *(A)* Aug 14, 1909
60. Scientific Study of Copper Deposits.   A. J. Sale.   *(D)* June, 1911
61. Mining System, Ray Consolidated.   L. A. Blackner.   *(B)* Vol 52, 1915
62. Copper Deposits, Globe-Kelvin District.   E. Higgins.   *(A)* Apl 23, 1910
63. Mining Practice at the Chino Mines.   H. A. Thorne.   *(H)* No 6412 (1931)
64. Exploration of Mineral Properties.   H. S. Munroe.   *Sch of Mines Quart*, Vol 19, p 9
65. Food Supply, etc.   *(B)* Vol 29, 1899;   *(A)* Mch 21, 1914;   *(A)* Sep 27, 1913;   *(A)* June 29, 1912;   *(A)* Aug 3, 1912;   *(A)* Sept 7, 1912.   See also Bib (326, 327, 328)
66. Top-slicing at Bingham.   D. W. Jessup.   *(A)* Feb 21, 1914, *et seq*
67. Mining Copper at Lake Superior.   C. T. Rice.   *(A)* July 20, 1912, *et seq*
68. Footwall Shafts in Lake Superior Copper Mines.   L. L. Hubbard.   *(G)* Vol 17, 1912
69. Methods at Golden Messenger Mine.   S. H. Lorain.   *(H)* No 6947 (1937)
70. Deep-level Shafts on Witwatersrand.   T. H. Leggett.   *(B)* Vol 30, 1900
71. Three-stage Hoisting System.   *(A)* Sept 6, 1913
72. Notes on Rand Mining Practice.   G. A. Denny.   *Sch of Mines Quart*, Vol 21, 1899
73. Centralized Organization, Crown Mines.   R. C. Warriner.   *Jour So Af Inst Eng*, Vol 11. New Development Method, Randfontein.   G. H. Beatty.   *So Af Min & Eng Jl*, Nov 6, 1920
74. Development System, Lyon Mtn Mine.   H. M. Chance.   *(A)* May 16, 1914
75. Transvaal Gold Mining, Present and Future Methods.   F. H. Hatch.   *Eng Mag*, July, 1912
76. The Newport Iron Mine.   B. W. Vallat.   *(B)* Vol 42, 1911
77. Methods at Magma Mine.   F. W. Snow.   *(H)* No 6168 (1929).   See also Bib (574)
78. Present Mining Conditions on Rand.   T. H. Leggett.   *(B)* Vol 39, 1903
79. Mining Conditions on the Witwatersrand.   W. L. Honnold.   *(B)* Vol 52, 1915
80. Mining Wide Orebodies at Butte.   C. T. Rice.   *Min World*, Aug 2, 1913, *et seq*
81. Rand Gold Mining Industry and its Future.   F. H. Hatch.   *(C)* July 22, 1911
82. Deep Mining Operations on Rand.   R. Gascoyne.   *Min World*, May 23, 1914
83. West Australian Mining Practice.   E. D. Cleland.   Chamber of Mines of West Australia, 1911
84. Costs at Standard Consol Mine.   C. E. Grunsky, Jr.   *(C)* May 31, 1913
85. Costs at Esperanza Mine.   W. E. Hindry.   *(C)* Apl 9, 1910
86. Standards of Work.   A. L. Oke.   *(A)* Feb 11, 1911
87. Chiksan Mines, Chosen.   C. L. Larson.   *(A)* July 25, 1914, *et seq*
88. On fluorescence of minerals.   W. S. Andrews.   *Gen Elec Rev*, 1916, p 317;   Oct, 1917.   R. L. Barrett.   *Am Mineralogist*, Dec, 1934.   W. O. Vanderburg.   *(H)* No 6873 (1935)
89. Hole Directors in Ground-breaking Control.   H. Simon.   *Trans Inst Min & Met*, Vol 40 (1931)
90. Mining Practice at United Verde Extension Mine.   R. L. D'Arcy.   *(H)* No 6250 (1930)
91. Mining Methods at Campbell Mine, Warren, Ariz.   H. M. Lavender.   *(H)* No 6289 (1930)
92. Drifting with a Stoper.   G. E. Wolcott.   *(A)* May 15, 1915
93. Operations and Plants of Internat Nickel Co of Canada.   *Can Min Jour*, Nov, 1937.   Covers Frood, Creighton, Garson, and Levack mines

94. Drifting with Stoping Drill. H. E. Moon. *Mine & Quarry*, Feb, 1911
95. Mining Methods at Lake Shore. L. S. Weldon. *Trans* Can Inst Min & Met, Vol 39 (1936)
96. Rapid Systematic Prospecting in Mountainous Country. N. W. Wilson. (*E*) Jan, 1938, p 9
97. Diamond Drilling at United Verde Mine. M. G. Hansen. (*H*) No 6708 (1933)
98. Testing and Application of Hammer-drills. B. F. Tillson. (*B*) Vol 51, 1915
99. Mining Practice at Morenci, Ariz. McH. Mosier and G. Sherman. (*H*) No 6107 (1929)
100. Methods at New Cornelia, Ajo, Ariz. G. R. Ingham and A. T. Barr. (*H*) No 6666 (1932)
101. Airplane in Mining. Numerous authors. (*A*) Nov, 1935. See also Bib (646, 647)
102. Use of Airplanes in Mining and Petroleum Operations. H. M. Wolflin. (*H*) No 6767 (1934)
103. Aeroplane and the Mining Engineer, II. J. N. Wynne. (*E*) Mch, 1935, p 153. See also Bib (646, 647) and W. E. D. Stokes, Jr, (*B*) Vol 126 (1937) p 582
104. Mining at Homestake. B. C. Yates. Black Hills Min Men's Assn, 1904
105. Treadwell Mines, Douglas Island, Alaska. R. A. Kinzie. (*B*) Vol 34, 1904
106. Unit Costs: Pittsburg-Silver Peak, (*A*) Sept 14, 1912; Erie Consol, (*A*) Sept 28, 1912; Ohio Copper Co, (*A*) Oct 12, 1912; Cananea Consol Cop Co, (*A*) Oct 26, 1912; Mammoth Copper Co, (*A*) Dec 7, 1912; Brit Col Copper Co, (*A*) Dec 7, 1912; North Star, (*A*) Jan 4, 1913; Alaska Treadwell, (*A*) Apl 19, 1914, Liberty Bell, (*A*) Dec 6, 1013
107. Wabana Iron Mines, Nova Scotia. T. Cantley. *Jour* Can Min Inst, Vol 14, 1911. A. K. Snelgrove. Nfld Geol Surv, *Inf Circ* 4 (1938), with bibliog
108. Mucking Costs. (*A*) May 30, 1914
109. Mining Costs at Park City, Utah. F. T. Williams. (*B*) Vol 42, 1911
110. Mining at Tonopah. C. T. Rice. (*A*) Dec 16, 1911
111. Mining of Lead and Zinc Ores, Joplin. C. A. Wright. *Tech Paper* No 41, U S Bureau of Mines, 1913
112. Practices at Elkoro Mines, Jarbidge, Nev. J. F. Park. (*H*) No 6543 (1931)
113. Driving Raises with Stope Drills. A. O. Christensen. (*A*) Sept 25, Nov 6, 1909
114. Mining Bingham Porphyry. *Mines and Methods*, Sept, 1909. Ohio Copper Co. *Mines and Methods*, Dec, 1909
115. Methods at No 1 Mine, Picher, Okla. W. F. Netzeband. (*H*) No 6113 (1929); abs in (*A*) May 18, 1929, p 792
116. Lead Mining Today in S E Missouri. Anon. (*A*) July, 1935, p 326
117. Casing through Overburden to obtain Sample of Bedrock. J. Belknap. *Can Min Jour*, Apl, 1935, p 139
118. Placer-mining Methods of E. T. Fisher Co, Atlantic City, Wyo. C. L. Ross and E. D. Gardner. (*H*) No 6846 (1935)
119. Methods of Utah Copper Co, Bingham Canyon, Utah. A. Soderberg. (*H*) No 6234 (1930)
120. Geology of the Horne Mine. H. M. Butterfield. Mining at Noranda. E. Henderson. *Can Min Jour*, Apl, 1934
121. Mining at Noranda. O. Hall. *Trans* Can Inst M & M, Vol 40 (1937) p 141. *Trans* Inst Min & Met, Vol 46 (1936–37) p 637. O. Hall, R. V. Porritt, and A. D. Carmihael. Inst Min & Met, *Bull* 414, 415 (Mch, Apr, 1939)
122. Underground Mining Methods, Utah Copper Co. T. S. Carnahan. (*B*) Vol 54, 1916
123. Recovering and Interpreting Diamond Core-drill Samples. R. D. Longyear. *Min & Met*, May, 1937, p 239
124. Sampling and Estimation of Borehole Cores and Sludges. D. K. F. MacLachlan. *Trans*. Inst Min & Met, Vol 40 (1931) p 177
125. Drill Sampling, and Interpretation of Sampling Results in Copper Fields of Nor Rhodesia. H. T. Matson and G. A. Wallis. (*B*) Vol 96 (1931), p 66
126. Drifting with a Jackhammer. I. A. Chapman. (*A*) July 25, 1914
127. More Lead from S E Missouri. H. C. Chellson. (*A*) June, 1937, p 283
128. Interpretation of Sludge and Core Assays. J. M. Weller. (*A*) July, 1938, p 36
129. Operating Costs at a Small Mexican Mine. R. H. Allen. (*A*) June 26, 1915
130. Structure Drilling on Western Mesabi Range. H. C. Bolthouse. *Min Cong Jour*, Nov, 1936
131. Notes on Liberty Bell Mine. C. A. Chase. (*B*) Vol 42, 1911
132. Methods and Economies of Mining. C. A. Allen. (*B*) Vol 49, 1914
133. The Blasting of Rock. A. W. and Z. W. Daw, Part 1; Spon & Chamberlain, 1898. Rock Excavation. H. P. Gillette. M. C. Clark Pub Co, 1907. Handbook of Rock Excavation. H. P. Gillette. Clark Book Co, 1916. Theory of Blasting with High Explosives. E. M. Weston. (*F*) Oct, Dec, 1908. Elements of Mining. G. J. Young. McGraw-Hill Book Co
134. Mining Methods at Park City, Utah. J. Humes. (*B*) Vol 51, 1915
135. Mining in Tintic, Utah. L. Palmer. (*D*) Jan, 1912
136. Mining near Negaunee, Mich. M. D. Atkinson. *Jour* Can Min Inst, Vol 7, 1904
137. Jackhammer Supersedes Hand Auger Drill. C. H. Claypool. *Comp Air Mag*, Feb, 1915
138. Conditions and Costs of Mining at Braden. W. Braden. (*B*) Vol 40, 1909. See also Bib (289)
139. Mine Tributing in Rhodesia. W. Anderson. (*F*) Vol 12 (1912), p 513
140. Eiderlinsky Gold Mines. N. T. Truschkoff. (*A*) June 12, 1915
141. Baltic Mining Methods. C. T. Rice. (*A*) Apl 27, 1912, *et seq*
142. Stoping at Cripple Creek. G. E. Wolcott. (*A*) Nov 30, 1907; Jan 11, 1908
143. Methods at Barr Mine, Tri-State Dist. O. W. Keener. (*H*) No 6159 (1929)
144. Mining Methods at Braden. H. R. Graham. (*A*) Nov 20, 1915. See also Bib (289)
145. Mining Methods at Goldfield. C. T. Rice. (*A*) Oct 21, 1911
146. Mining Practice at Kalgoorlie, W Australia. G. W. Williams. (*A*) Jan 25, 1908
147. Methods at Judge Mine, Park City, Utah. G. S. Krueger and E. A. Hewitt. (*H*) No 7003 (1938)
148. Mining Practice in the Florida Pebble Phosphate Field. C. A. Fulton. (*B*) Vol 129 (1938)
149. Government Prospecting for Phosphate in Florida. P. V. Roundy and G. R. Mansfield. (*B*) Vol 129 (1938), p 246
150. Los Pilares Mine, Nacozari, Mex. C. DeKalb. (*C*) June 18, 1910
151. The Cresson Mine. R. L. Herrick. (*D*) July, 1911
152. Copper Mining in Metcalf District, Ariz. P. B. Scotland. (*A*) July 16, 1910
153. Mining without Timber. R. B. Brinsmade. McGraw-Hill Book Co, 1911
154. Stoping at Miami. D. B. Scott. (*B*) Vol 55, 1916
155. Mining Disseminated Lead Ore at a Mine in S E Missouri. C. F. Jackson. (*H*) No 6170 (1929)

156. Mining Zinc and Lead Ore at No 3 Mine, Crestline, Kas. W. F. Netzeband. (H) No 6174 (1929)
157. Methods at Hartley Grantham Mine. O. W. Keener. (H) No 6286 (1930)
158. Sheet-ground Mining in Joplin District, Mo. E. Higgins. (G) Vol 20, 1915
159. Methods of Silver King Coalit Mines Co, Park City, Utah. M. J. Dailey. (H) No 6371 (1930)
160. Handling Sheet Ground. J. H. Polhemus. (D) Nov, 1907
161. Cost of Developing and Equipping a Small or Medium-sized Mine in the Tri-State District. J. R. Reigart. (H) No 6591 (1932)
162. Methods at the Sherritt Gordon Mine. E. L. Brown. Trans Can Inst Min & Met, Vol 36 (1933), p 481
163. Trimming Roofs of High Stopes. C. T. Rice. (A) Oct 5, 1912. See also Bib (155) and (A) Aug, 1932, p 427
164. Lead Mining in S E Missouri. R. D. O. Johnson. (A) Sept 16, 1905
165. Power Shovel and Dragline Placer Mining. E. D. Gardner and P. T. Allsman. (H) No 7013 (1938)
166. Dragline Excavator in Placer Mining. S. R. Fox. (A) Apl, 1935, p 163
167. Limestone Mine in Birmingham District. C. E. Abbott. (B) Vol 129 (1938), p 62
168. Methods of Hanover Bessemer Iron & Copper Co, Fierro, N. M. L. M. Kniffin. (H) No 6361 (1930)
169. Mining Methods in Europe. L. W. Mayer. McGraw-Hill Book Co
170. Mineral Resources of Michigan. R. E. Hore. Mich Geol and Biol Surv. Pub 8, Ser 6, 1911; Pub 19, Ser 16, 1914
171. Story of McIntyre — Development and Mining. D. E. Keeley. (A) Nov, 1933, p 459
172. Cost of Mining. J. R. Finlay. McGraw-Hill Book Co, 1909
173. Mechanized Mining in the Tri-State District. C. W. Nicolson. Min Cong Jour, Jan, 1938
174. Methods at El Potosi Mine, Chihuahua, Mex. H. A. Walker. (H) No 6804 (1934)
175. Methods of American Zinc Co of Tenn, Mascot, Tenn. H. A. Coy. (H) No 6239 (1930)
176. Methods at Wright-Hargreaves Mine. L. B. Smith. Trans Can Inst Min & Met, Vol 37 (1934) p 39
177. Red Ore Mines of Woodward Iron Co, Bessemer, Ala. T. C. DeSollar. (B) Vol 109 (1934)
178. Mining Methods of Arizona Copper Co. P. B. Scotland. (B) Vol 51, 1915
179. A Method of Underhand Stoping. G. A. Laird. (A) Nov 11, 1911
180. Mining Methods of Tenn Copper Co, Ducktown, Tenn. C. H. McNaughton. (H) No 6149 (1929). Reprinted in (A) Vol 128, p 8
181. Suggested Classification of Surface Mining Methods. J. R. Thoenen. (B) Tech Pub 604 (1935)
182. Stoping by Branched Raises. F. W. Sperr. (C) May 20, 1916
183. Methods of Iron Mining in Northern Minn. F. W. Denton. (B) Vol 27, 1897
184. Mining Methods on Marquette Range. H. T. Hulst, G. R. Jackson, W. A. Siebenthal. (G) Vol 19, 1914
185. Granby Mining Methods. C. M. Campbell. Jour Can Min Inst, Vol 11, 1908. Notes on Anyox mining and met. practice. L. R. Clapp. Trans Can Inst of Min & Met, Vol 26, 1923. Granby Consol. R. Dunn. Canad Min Jour, Feb 29, 1924. Hidden Creek Mine. E. E. Campbell. Trans Can Inst Min & Met, Vol 22, 1919
186. Mine Timbering. W. E. Sanders. Min Ind, Vol 8 (1899), p 715
187. Notes on Rand Mining. T. Johnson. (F) Vol 10 (1910) p 276
188. Placer Mining Methods & Costs in Alaska. N. L. Wimmler. U S Bur Mines, Bull 259 (1927)
189. Square-set System of Mining. E. D. Gardner and W. O. Vanderburg. (H) No 6691 (1933)
190. Ore Mining Methods. W. R. Crane. John Wiley & Sons
191. Recent Improvements in Mining Practice of the Tri-State District. C. W. Nicolson. (B) Tech Pub 905 (1938)
192. Example of Prospecting and Valuing a Lead-Zinc Deposit. W. F. Netzeband. (A) June 8, 1929, p 913
193. Methods at Blue Diamond Gypsum Mine, Arden, Nev. W. G. Bradley. (H) No 6615 (1932)
194. Mining in Mexico Today. A. H. Hubbell. (A) Mch, 1936
195. Recent Developments in Mining Practice on the Witwatersrand. R. S. G. Stokes. Trans Inst Min & Met, Vol 45 (1936) p 77
196. Mining Tungsten Ore at Mines of Nevada-Massachusetts Co, Mill City, Nev. O. F. Heizer. (H) No 6284 (1930)
197. Mining Fluorspar at Rosiclare, Ill. E. C. Reeder. (H) No 6294 (1930). Also, on same subj, A. H. Cronk. (H) No 6384 (1930)
198. Latouche System as developed at Beatson Mine, Alaska. Be Van Presley. (B) Vol 76 (1928)
199. The Homestake Enterprise. By the staff. (A) Oct 12, 1931. Mining Methods at Homestake. Ross and Wayland. (B) Vol 72 (1925)
200. Iron Mines of Putnam County, N Y. A. F. Wendt. (B) Vol 13, 1884
201. Masonry Supports at Tilly Foster Iron Mine. L. G. Engel. Sch of Mines Quart, Vol 6, 1885
202. Marquette Iron Region. Sch of Mines Quart, Vol 3, p 112
203. Pyrites Deposits of Huelva, Spain. J. Allan. Trans N of Eng Inst of Min Eng, Vol 37
204. Practical Stone Quarrying. Greenwell and Eldsen. Appleton & Co, 1913
205. Cours D'Exploitation des Mines. H. de la Goupillière. 3rd Ed, Vol 2, Dunod et Pinat, Paris, 1907
206. Planning to Diamond Drill. W. Sack. (A) June, 1938, p 46
207. Methods and Costs, Mother Lode Mine, Brit Col. E. Hibbert. (A) Mch 22, 1913
208. Sublevel Stoping. F. W. Sperr. (A) June 15, 1912; (C) Feb 19, 1916. P. B. McDonald. (C) July 5, 1913. F. C. Roberts. (G) Vol 16, 1911
209. Mine Timbering. Sanders, Parlee, McDonald. Hill Pub Co
210. Mines of Tintic District. R. B. Brinsmade. (D) Jan, 1908
211. Square-set Practice at Bingham. L. S. Cates. (A) Aug 25, 1904
212. Methods of the Bunker Hill & Sullivan Min & Conc Co., Kellogg, Idaho. U. E. Brown. (H) No 6407 (1931)
213. Cost of Square-set Mining. M. J. Elsing. (A) Mch, 1932, p 161
214. Mining and Stoping Methods in Coeur D'Alene. J. Tyssowski. (A) Sept 3, 1910
215. Vertical Face Stoping. (A) Aug 15, 1914
216. Mining at Creighton. R. D. Parker. (A) Nov 10, 1930, p 437
217. Underhand Square-setting for Finishing Stopes. A. Fairweather. (A) Nov 28, 1914

218. Square-set Timbering; Importance and Evolution. C. T. Rice. *Min World*, Dec 14, 1912
219. Timbering in Butte Mines. B. H. Dunshee. (*B*) Vol 46, 1913; discussion by G. E. Moulthrop, p 148
220. Stoping in Calumet and Arizona Mines. P. D. Wilson. (*B*) Vol 55, 1916
221. Square-set Timbers. L. D. Davenport. (*A*) Jan 18, 1913
222. Framing Round Timbers, IV. C. T. Rice. *Min World*, Jan 4, 1913
223. Methods at Hecla and Star Mines, Burke, Idaho. C. H. Foreman. (*H*) No 6232 (1930)
224. Replacing Sills Beneath Square-sets. (*A*) Sept 10, 1910
225. Methods of Square-set Stoping at Bisbee. M. J. Elsing. (*A*) Apl 2, 1910
226. Notes on Square-set Mining. *Mines & Methods*, Jan, 1910
227. Methods at United Verde (underground) Copper Mines. T. W. Quayle. (*H*) No 6440 (1931)
228. Mitchell Slicing System. M. J. Elsing. (*A*) July 23, 1910. C. L. Larson. *Min World*, May 6, 1911
229. Methods at McIntyre Porcupine Mines, Schumacher, Ont. H. G. Skavlem. (*H*) No 6741 (1933)
230. Leaning Stope Sets. (*A*) July 2, 1910. Mining Methods in Mother Lode Dist, Calif. S. L. Arnot. (*B*) Vol 72, 1925
231. Heavy Combination Stope Timber. (*A*) June 13, 1914
232. A Proposed Method of Timbering. A. J. Moore. (*A*) Sept 16, 1911
233. Mining Methods in the Waihi Mine. Gilmour and Johnston. (*C*) Dec 21, 1912
234. Stoping Methods at Nevada Wonder Mine. T. M. Smither. (*C*) May 15, 1915
235. Back-filling at Hollinger Mine. M. E. Williams. *Can Min Jour*, Sept, 1935, p 418
236. Mining Ore from a Caved Stope. J. E. Harding. (*A*) July 10, 1915
237. Methods at Minas de Matahambre, Cuba. G. L. Richert. (*H*) No. 6145 (1929)
238. Resuing in Underground Work. F. C. Roberts. (*A*) Dec 10, 1903
239. Filling System, Minnesota Iron Co. D. H. Bacon. (*B*) Vol 21, 1892
240. Stoping Systems at Broken Hill. A. J. Moore. (*D*) May, 1907
241. Top-slicing, with Filling, at Charcas, Mex. H. Willey. (*B*) Vol 96 (1931) p 51
242. Broken Hill Underground Mining Methods. E. J. Horwood. (*B*) Vol 54, 1916
243. Filling Methods at Sudbury. W. R. Crane. (*A*) June 17, 1911
244. Methods of the Park City Consol Mines Co, Park City, Utah. G. M. Wiles. (*H*) No 6880 (1936)
245. Rock Filling at Rio Tinto. E. Levy. (*B*) Vol 40 (1909) p 893
246. Lectures on Mining. Vol I. J. Callon. Dunod, Paris, 1876
247. Systems of Mining Large Orebodies of Soft Ore. R. P. Rothwell. (*B*) Vol 16, 1888
248. Extraction of Ore from Wide Veins or Masses. G. D. Delprat. (*B*) Vol 21, 1892
249. Working a Wide Gold Quartz Reef at Rezende. J. A. Woodburn. *Trans* Inst Min & Met, Vol 12, 1903
250. Block-caving at King Asbestos Mine, Quebec. J. G. Ross *et al*. *Trans* Canad Inst Min & Met, Vol 37 (1934) p 209. *Ibid*, Vol 39 (1936) p 441
251. Sand Filling on Witwatersrand. E. Pam. (*F*) Vol 10 (1910) p 429; discussion by A. R. Hughes, Vol 11, p 173, and R. Allen, Vol 11, p 123.
252. The Genesis of the Diamond. Alpheus F. Williams. Pub (1932) by Ernest Benn, Ltd, London
253. Mining Practice at the Edwards Mine. J. B. Knaebel. (*H*) No 6586 (1932)
254. Correlation and other Aspects of the Exploited Auriferous Horizons on the Witwatersrand Mining Field. G. Carlton Jones. *Trans* Geol Soc So Af, Vol 39 (1936), p *xxiii*
255. Stoping at Calamon Mine. E. P. C. Sullivan. *Trans* Inst Min & Met, vol 21, 1912
256. Handling Ore in Stopes. D. T. Williams. (*A*) May 5, 1906
257. Rill System of Stoping. J. B. Wilson. (*A*) Nov 18, 1911
258. Methods of Stoping at Kalgoorlie. J. Cheffirs. (*A*) Feb 12, 1910
259. Stope Filling and Caving for Waste. E. K. Hall. (*A*) Aug 31, 1912
260. Shrinkage Stoping, W Aust. F. P. Rolfe. *Trans* Inst Min & Met, Vol 18 (1909) p 291; discussion by O. B. Ward *et al*, p 310
261. Timbering Stopes for Safety. H. H. Hodgkinson. (*A*) May 8, July 10, 1915
262. Ore-drawing Tests at Inspiration Consol. G. R. Lehman. (*B*) Vol 55, 1916
263. Method of Mining Swedish Iron Ores. H. de Rauw. (*A*) Feb 25, 1911, p 409
264. Buffalo Mine, Cobalt. W. J. Dobbins. (*A*) Aug 3, 1912
265. Methods of Mining at Cobalt. R. E. Hore. *Can Min Jour*, Aug 1, 1913
266. Methods at Oceanic Quicksilver Mine, Cambria, Cal. A. W. Frolli. (*H*) No 6950 (1937)
267. Controlling Falls of Ground in Underground Metal Mines. J. V. Claypool. *Min Cong Jour*, Mch, 1937, p 30
268. Transfer Scraper System in Underground Iron Mines on Mesabi Range. Anon. (*A*) Apl, 1934, p 148
269. Blueberry Mine, Marquette Distr, Mich. R. S. Archibald and L. S. Chabot, Jr. (*B*) Vol 126 (1937) p 9
270. Underground Mining on Gogebic Range. P. S. Williams. (*G*) Vol 15, 1910
271. Stoping at Homestake Mine, So Dak. J. Tyssowski. (*A*) July 9, 1910
272. Stoping Without Timber at Homestake. M. Ehle, Jr. (*D*) May, 1908
273. Mining the Treadwell Lode. T. A. Rickard. (*C*) July 18, 1908
274. New Method of Top-slicing at Kipushi, Katanga, Belg Congo. G. VanEsbroeck and M. Van Weyenbergh. (*B*) *Tech Pub* 1078 (1939)
275. Mining Methods, Mesabi Iron Range. Bayliss, M'Neil and Lutes. (*G*) Vol 18, 1913
276. Caving System in Chisholm District. L. D. Davenport. (*A*) Sept 7, 1912, *et seq*
277. Iron Mining on Mesabi Range. A. L. Gerry. (*A*) Oct 12, 1912
278. Top-set Slicing, Mesabi. P. C. Merrill. (*A*) May 10, 1913. L. D. Davenport. (*A*) Feb 1, 1913
279. Top-slicing, Detroit Copper Co. J. R. McLean. Can Soc Civil Eng, Jan, 1915
280. Clifton-Morenci District, II. W. L. Tovote. (*C*) Dec 24, 1910
281. Mining by Top-slicing, with notes on Sub-level Caving. C. F. Jackson. (*H*) No 6410 (1931)
282. Mining Methods at Cananea. M. J. Elsing. (*A*) Nov 5, 1910, *et seq*
283. Miami Copper Co Method of Mining Low-grade Orebody. F. W. McClennan. (*B*) Vol 91 (1930) p 39. See also Bib (601)
284. Cananea Caving and Slicing Systems. R. L. Herrick. (*D*) Aug, 1909
285. Block Method of Top-slicing of Miami Copper Co. E. G. Dane. (*B*) Vol 55, 1916
286. Elements of Mining. G. J. Young. McGraw-Hill, 1916
287. Lake Superior Iron Ore. J. P. Channing. *Min Ind*, Vol 3, 1894

288. Top-slicing at Caspian Mine. W. A. McEachern. (*G*) Vol 16, 1911
289. Mining Practice of Braden Copper Co, Sewell, Chile. J. S. Webb and T. W. Skinner. (*H*) No 6565 (1932)
290. Methods of Mining Ferberite Ore at Cold Springs Mine. W. O. Vanderburg. (*H*) No 6673 (1932)
291. Brown Hematite Mining in Virginia. C. Dixon. (*D*) Apl, 1912
292. Sub-level Caving at the Montreal Mine. R. A. Bowen. (*B*) *Tech Pub* 886 (1938)
293. Marquette Range Caving Method. H. H. Stoek. (*D*) Nov, 1909
294. Practice at Ray Mines of Nevada Consol Copper Co. R. W. Thomas. (*H*) No 6167 (1929)
295. Mercur Mining Methods. G. H. Dern. (*D*) Aug, 1904
296. Mines of Consol Mercur Co. R. H. Allen. (*A*) June 18, 1910
297. Methods at Carson Hill Mine, Calaveras County, Cal. J. A. Burgess. (*H*) No 6940 (1937)
298. Ventilation in Iron Mines of Lake Superior District. E. Higgins. (*G*) Vol 19, 1914
299. System of Mining Orebodies of Uniform Grade. E. F. Brown. (*G*) Vol 5, 1898
300. Caving System on Menominee Range. R. Meeks. (*A*) July 20, 1907
301. Crystal Falls Iron Co, Mich. G. E. Edwards. *Min World*, Oct 19, 1912
302. Caving System at Ohio Copper Mine. C. G. Bamberger. (*A*) Apl 6, 1912; F. S. Schmidt. (*C*) Mch 6, 1915. Recovery of Copper by Leaching, Ohio Cop Co. A. A. Anderson and F. K. Cameron. (*B*) Vol 73, 1925. T. Varley and G. L. Oldright. Utah Metal Min Inst, May 5, 1923. F. E. Wormser. (*A*) July 26, 1924
303. Mining Molybdenum Ore at Climax, Colo. W. J. Coulter. (*A*) Mch 9, 1929, p 394. *Min Cong Jl*, Jan, 1937, p 54
304. Slushing *vs* Gravity Loading at Climax. W. E. Romig. *Min Cong Jl*, Nov, 1937, p 28. (*A*) Oct, 1937, p 57
305. The Utah Copper Mine. C. DeKalb. (*C*) Apl 10, 1909
306. Mining at Hollinger. A. W. Young. *Can Min Jour*, Sept, 1935
307. Mineral Deposits. W. Lindgren. McGraw-Hill Book Co
308. Increasing Brine Output from Salt Beds. E. N. Trump. *Chem & Met Eng*, July, 1936, p 364
309. Golden Queen and Other Mines of Mojave Distr, Cal. C. E. Julihn and F. W. Horton. (*H*) No 6931 (1937)
310. Slot System of Mining at Golden Queen Mine, Mojave, Cal. C. A. Kumke. (*B*) Vol 126 (1937) p 27
311. Mining Salt Through Boreholes. J. H. Merrill. *Bull* 11, N Y State Museum. Evaporated Salt Industry of Kansas. C. M. Young. (*A*) Sept 18, 1909. Salt Industry of Louisiana and Texas. W. M. Weigel. (*B*) Vol 129 (1938) p 405
312. Sulphur—II. W. A. Cunningham. *Jour Chem Education*, Feb, 1935, p 83. See also, Sulphur Operations in South. R. H. Vail. (*A*) Sept 7, 1912
313. Novel Method of Mining Kaolin. A. R. Ledoux. (*B*) Vol 37, 1906
314. Cylindrical Ore Chutes of Wood Staves. A. Fairweather. (*A*) June 6, 1914
315. Ore Chutes of Sheet Steel. J. M. Bridge. (*A*) Jan 31, 1914
316. Opening Ore Passes. W. J. Nicol. (*A*) Dec 28, 1912
317. Handbook of Mining Details. McGraw-Hill, 1912. Details of Practical Mining. McGraw-Hill, 1916. Notes on Underground Transportation. C. F. Jackson. (*H*) No 6326 (1931) Underground Chute Gates in Metal Mines. C. F. Jackson and J. B. Knaebel. (*H*) No 6495 (1931). (*B*) "Mine Plant" (1938), p 249
318. Systematic Timbering at Morenci, Ariz. (*A*) Jan 23, 1926
319. Exploration Methods at a Colorado Zinc Mine. H. N. Lary. (*A*) Oct 26, 1931, p 353
320. Mining Quicksilver Ore at New Idria Mine. W. R. Moorehead. (*H*) No 6462 (1931)
321. Deep-hole Prospecting in Roseberry Mine, Tasmania. I. D. Cameron. *Proc* Austral Inst Min & Met, Sept 30, 1930; abstr in (*E*) May, 1931, p 309
322. Methods at No 8 Mine, St Louis Sm & Ref Co. R. H. Poston. (*H*) No 6160 (1929)
323. Methods at Hartley Mine, Tri-State District. C. N. Anderson. (*H*) No 6656 (1932)
324. Borehole Estimation. C. E. Temperley. (*A*) Dec 28, 1931, p 528
325. Method & Cost of Exploring and Developing Central Patricia Claims, Nor Ontario. A. J. Keast and C. F. Jackson. (*H*) No 6681 (1933)
326. Mining Practices at Small Gold Mines. E. D. Gardner and C. H. Johnson. (*H*) No 6800 (1934)
327. Prospecting for Lode Gold on Public Domain. E. D. Gardner. (*H*) No 6843 (1935)
328. Food Requirements. D. J. Williams. (*A*) Oct 9, 1930, p 326
329. Hydraulic Sand Filling on Rand: Caldecott and Powell. (*F*) Vol 14, 1914, and discussion. B. C. Gullachson. *Trans* Inst Min Engrs, Vol 48 (1914–15) p 122. R. E. Sawyer. *Trans* Inst Min & Met, Vol 22 (1913) p 59. W. A. Caldecott. (*F*) Vol 14 (1914) p 486
330. Cost and Extraction in the Selection of a Mining Method. C. E. Arnold. (*B*) Vol 55, 1916
331. Sand Filling at the Homestake Mine. A. J. M. Ross. (*B*) *Tech Pub* 1075 (1939)
332. Premier Diamond Mine. R. Stokes. (*E*) Nov, 1912. "Diamond Mines of So Africa," Vol 1, chaps 8, 11. Gardner F. Williams. B. F. Buck & Co, N Y, 1906
333. Removing Overburden at a New Guinea Mine. E. B. Jensen. *Proc* Austral Inst Min & Met, NS No 96 (1934); abs (*E*) May, 1935, p 306
334. Summaries of Results from Geophysical Surveys at Various Properties. D. H. McLaughlin. (*B*) Vol 97 (1932), p 24
335. Long-hole Prospect Drilling at Ray, Ariz. M. Brown. *Min Cong Jl*, Dec, 1930, p 925
336. Mining at Grass Valley and Nevada City. G. E. Wolcott. (*A*) Feb 20, 1909
337. Stoping Methods at North Star Mine. L. O. Kellogg. (*A*) Nov 29, 1913
338. Recent Developments in the Tenn Phosphate Industry. P. M. Tyler and H. R. Mosley. (*B*) *Tech Pub* 1053 (1939). See also Bib (58)
339. Slopes in Steam-shovel Mining. E. E. Barker. (*C*) Mch 4, 1911
340. Prospecting and Mining of Copper Ore at Santa Rita, N M. D. F. MacDonald, C. Enzian. *Bull* 107, U S Bur of Mines, 1909
341. Glory-hole Mining at Bisbee. G. J. Young. (*A*) Sept 8, 1930, p 232
342. Proposed Top-slicing with Scraping in Wide Veins. G. T. Harley. (*A*) Jan 23, 1926
343. Methods at the Morning Mine, Mullan, Idaho. C. E. Wethered and L. J. Coady. (*H*) No 6238 (1930)
344. Methods of Cananea Cons Copper Co, Sonora, Mex. W. Catron. (*H*) No 6247 (1930)
345. Anthracite Stripping. J. B. Warriner. (*B*) Vol 57, 1917
346. Mining in Oriente Province, Cuba. J. T. Singewald, Jr, and B. L. Miller. (*A*) Apl 1, 1916
347. Drag-line Stripping and Mining, Balkan Mine. C. E. Lawrence. (*G*) Vol 20, 1915
348. Hydraulic Stripping on Cuyuna Range. E. P. M'Carty. (*G*) Vol 20, 1915

349. Stripping with a Harbor Dredge. L. O. Kellogg. (A) Mch 7, 1914
350. Modern Pebble Phosphate Mining Plants. H. D. Mendenhall. Eng News, Oct 15, 1908.
  Florida Phosphate Practice. J. A. Barr. (D) Dec, 1912. Origin, Mining and Preparation of Phosphate Rock. E. H. Sellards. (B) Vol 50 (1915) p 907
351. Notes on the Milling System of Mining. A. H. Fay. (A) Nov 6, 1909
352. Quarrying Shale by the Tunnel System. D. T. Farnham. (B) Vol 50, 1914
353. A Great Rock Excavation. Eng News, Apl 20, 1889, p 354
354. Creighton Mine. L. Stewart. Jour Can Min Inst, Vol 11, 1908
355. Coal Miner's Pocket Book, 11th Ed. McGraw-Hill, 1916
356. Size of Rooms and Pillars. (D) Oct, 1905, p 108
357. Mining Methods for Maximum Recovery of Coal. H. V. Hesse. (A) Feb 6, 1909
358. Systematic Exploitation in Pittsburgh Coal Seam. F. Z. Schellenberg. (B) Vol 41, 1910
359. Mechanized Retreat Mining (at Mona mine). Anon. Mechanization, May, 1938
360. Pocahontas Region, Mining Methods. H. H. Stoek. (D) Apl, 1909
361. S. O. Andros. Bull 2, 4, 6, 7, 9, and 12; Ill Coal Mining Invest, 1914–15
362. Mining Coal in Southern Indiana. F. W. Parsons. (A) Oct 29, 1909
363. Textbook of Coal Mining. H. W. Hughes. 5th Ed. C. Griffin & Co, 1904
364. Steep Pitch-mining of Thick Coal Seams. W. G. Whildin. (B) Vol 50, 1914
365. Colliery Working and Management. Bullman and Redmayne. C. Lockwood & Son
366. S. O. Andros. Bull 5, Ill Coal Mining Invest, 1914
367. Modern Practice in Mining, Vol III. R. A. S. Redmayne. Longmans, Green & Co
368. Chamber Pillars in Deep Anthracite Mines. D. Bunting. (B) Vol 42, 1911
369. Coal Face Conveyors. J. Jackson. Iron & Coal Tr Rev, Mch 24, 1916. A. E. Booth.
  Col Guard, Mch 10, 1911. H. H. Ridsdale. Iron & Coal Tr Rev, Dec 22, 1911
370. Lectures on Mining. W. Galloway. So Wales Inst of Engrs, 1900
371. Method of Working a Steep Coal Seam. A. Y. Hoy. (A) June 25, 1910
372. Hydraulic Filling as a Roof Support. G. Knox. Coll Eng, Nov, 1913
373. Modern Developments in Hydraulic Stowing. J. D. Paton. Trans Inst Min Engrs, Vol 47,
  1914
374. On support of coal-mine roadways by steel arches or cambered girders. Trans Inst Min Engrs
  (London): Vol 75 (1928) pp 93–135; Vol 82 (1931), pp 243–289, 343. Coll Guard, Nov. 27,
  Dec 4, Dec 11, 1931 (same data as preceding). Iron & Coal Tr Rev, Feb 5, 1932, p 233.
  Trans Canad Inst Min & Met, Vol 31 (1928) p 438
375. Experiments with Steel Roof Supports in Nemacolin and Dehue Mines of Buckeye Coal Co.
  A. W. Hesse. Coal Age, May, 1939, p 34
376. Tesla Coal Mines. F. J. Horsewill. (D) Nov, 1898
377. Genesis and Classification of Placers. A. H. Brooks. Bull 328, U S Geol Surv, 1908
378. The Gold of the Klondike. J. B. Tyrrell. Can Min Jour, May 1, 1913. Types of Canadian
  Gold Deposits. F. C. Lincoln. (A) Mch 4, 1911
379. Origin and Classification of Placers. H. L. Smythe. (A) June 1, 1905, et seq
380. Law of the Paystreak in Placer Deposits. J. B. Tyrrell. Trans Inst Min & Met, Vol 21, 1912
381. Paystreaks at Nome. T. M. Gibson. (C) Mch 25, 1911
382. Investigations of Black Sands from Placers. Day and Richards. Bull 285, U S Geol Surv,
  1906. Black Sand of the Pacific Coast. H. Lang. (C) Dec 2, 1916. Yakataga Beach
  Placers. A. G. Thompson. (A) May 1, 1915
383. Mineral Resources of Alaska, 1913. A. H. Brooks. Bull 592, U S Geol Surv, 1914
384. Third Beach Line at Nome. T. M. Gibson. (C) Apl 25, 1914
385. Mining of Alluvial Deposits. N. B. Knox and C. S. Haley. (E) Feb, 1915, et seq
386. Prospecting Methods at Fairbanks. H. I. Ellis. (A) May 8, 1915
387. How to make a Rocker. W. H. Storms. (A) June 24, 1911
388. Hydraulic and Placer Mining. 2nd Ed. F. B. Noian. J. Wiley & Sons, 1907
389. Conservation of Water in Placer Prospecting. S. O. Andros. (A) June 29, 1912
390. Methods and Costs of Gravel and Placer Mining in Alaska. C. W. Purington. Bull 263,
  U S Geol Surv, 1905
391. Practical Treatise on Hydraulic Mining in California. 10th Ed. A. J. Bowie, Jr. Van
  Nostrand Co, 1905
392. Alluvial Mining in the Urals. J. P. Hutchins. (E) Jan, 1914. Prospecting and Washing
  for Diamonds. W. J. Dick. Jour Can Min Inst, Vol 16, 1913. Gold Dredging in Siberia.
  J. B. Landfield. (C) Sept 25, 1909. Native Methods in Siberia. F. L. Lowell. (C)
  Nov 5, 1910. Prospecting for Tin in Nigeria. J. T. Keating. (E) Nov, 1912. Gold
  and Platinum Alluvial Deposits in Russia. L. Perret. Trans Inst Min & Met, Vol 21,
  1912
393. Development Problem of the Yukon. H. M. Payne. Trans Can Min Inst, Vol 16, 1913
394. Hydraulic Mining. C. C. Longridge. Pub by Mining Journal, London, 1910
395. Principles of Hydraulic Mining. H. L. Mead. Sch of Mines Quart, Vol 34, 1913
396. Tin Mining and Ore Dressing in South Africa. E. M. Weston. (A) Feb 19, 1910, et seq
397. Hydraulic Tin Mining in Swaziland. J. J. Garrard. Trans Inst Min & Met, Vol 26, 1917
398. Mining Methods of the North. T. A. Rickard. (C) Dec 12, 1908, et seq
399. Minister of Mines of Brit Columbia, Ann Rep 1937, p E-43
400. Fairbanks District, Alaska. F. J. Katz. Bull 525, U S Geol Surv, 1913
401. Opportunity in Placer Mining. C. Hartley. (A) Jan 23, 1915. A Dry Land Dredging
  Machine. L. H. Eddy. (A) Dec 16, 1911
402. Mining in Atlin, B C. R. W. Young. Jour Can Min Inst, Vol 13, 1909
403. Jigging applied to Gold Dredges. P. Malozenoff. (A) Sept, 1937. Trend in Dredging.
  H. A. Sawin. Min Cong Jl, Aug, 1937
404. Hydraulicking at Beauce Co, Que. F. Cirkel. (A) June 1, 1912
405. Control of Hydraulic Mining. W. W. Harts. Trans Am Soc Civil Eng, Vol 32, 1906. A Novel
  Debris Dam. L. A. Palmer. (C) July 10, 1915. Plan for Reviving Hydraulic Mining.
  C. S. Haley. (C) Dec 12, 1914
406. Examining and Fitting up a Hydraulic Mine. H. A. Brigham. (A) Dec 26, 1908, et seq
407. Auriferous Gravels of California. J. H. Hammond. Ann Rept Cal State Mineralogist, 1889
408. Yukon Territory, History and Resources. Pub Minister of Interior, Ottawa, 1916
409. History and Development of Gold Dredging in Montana. H. Jennings. Placer Mining Methods and Operating Costs. C. Janin. Bull 121, U S Bur Mines, 1916
410. Gold Dredging in Shasta, Siskiyou, and Trinity Counties, Cal. C. V. Averill. Cal Jour
  Mines & Geol, Apl, 1938
411. Hydraulic Mining at Atlin. A. D. Hughes. (C) Apl 24, 1915

412. Solution of Some Hydraulic Mining Problems on Ruby Creek, B C. Lee and Daulton. (B) Vol 55, 1916
413. Hydraulic Mining at Circle, Alaska. H. I. Ellis. (A) Dec 19, 1914
414. Sluicing Methods at Fairbanks. H. I. Ellis. (A) Dec 18, 1915
415. Comparative Hydraulic Mining Methods. L. H. Eddy. (A) Mch 13, 1915
416. Hydraulicking on Klamath River. J. H. Theller. (C) Mch 28, 1914
417. Manual of Hydraulic Mining. T. F. Van Wagenen. Van Nostrand Co, 1914
418. Textbook of Geology. A. Geikie. Macmillan & Co
419. Transportation of Debris by Running Water. G. K. Gilbert. Prof Paper 86, U S Geol Surv, 1914
420. Study of Riffles for Hydraulicking. P. Bouery. (A) May 24, 1913
421. Hydraulic Mining in British Columbia. (C) Mch 15, 1913
422. Hydraulicking at Waldo, Ore. W. H. Wright. (A) Aug 7, 1915
423. Undercurrents. Construction of Undercurrents. C. S. Haley and others. (C) May 1, 1915, et seq. Burlap Tables, Idaho. J. M. Hill. Bull 620, U S Geol Surv, 1916. New Design of Undercurrent Grizzly. F. H. Hazard. (A) Jan 23, 1912. Losses in Hydraulic Mining. C. S. Haley. (C) Jan 21, 1911
424. The Saving of Fine Placer Gold. F. H. Hazard. (A) Aug 26, 1911
425. Report of New Zealand Minister of Mines, 1902, p 21. H. W. Young
426. The Black Sand Problem. F. Powell. (A) Aug 10, 1907
427. Metallurgy of Alluvial Mining. J. M. Nicol. (C) May 29, 1915. Gold Recovery at Placer Mines. D. F. Carver. (A) Sept 18, 1915
428. Placer Mining in Boise County, Idaho. O. H. Metzger. (H) No 7028 (1938)
429. Geologic Reconnaissance of Circle Quadrangle, Alaska. L. M. Prindle. Bull 538, U S Geol Surv, 1913
430. Mechanical Elevator. T. A. Rickard. (C) Mch 20, 1909
431. Dredging at Iditarod, Alaska. (C) May 2, 1914
432. Winter Dredging in Idaho. J. H. Miles. (C) Mch 14, 1914
433. Dredge Construction in Portuguese E Africa. C. Janin. (C) Aug 1, 1914
434. Operations of Yukon Consol Gold Corp. W. H. S. McFarland. Trans Canad Inst Min & Met, Vol 42 (1939) p 537
435. Gold Dredging in the Klondike. G. R. F. Troop. Mine & Quarry Engng, June, 1939
436. On Dredging at Bulolo, New Guinea. C. A. Banks. Trans Inst Min & Met, Vol 41 (1932) p 616; Vol 46 (1937) p 803
437. Gold Dredging in California. C. Janin and W. M. Winston. Bull 57, Cal State Min Bur, 1910
438. Dredging for Gold in California. 1st Ed. D. Weatherbe. Min & Sci Pr, 1907
439. The Adelong Dredge. H. S. Elford. Chem, Eng & Min Rev (Melbourne), Apl 8, 1935. Abstr in (E) June, 1935, p 371
440. Tiveri Gold Dredge. J. W. Hinks. Chem, Eng & Min Rev (Melbourne), Jan 8, 1937
441. Resoil Dredging. Chem, Eng & Min Rev (Melbourne), May, 1937, p 304. Also Indust Austral & Min Std (Melbourne) Feb 15, 1939, p 43
442. Successful Dragline Dredge. J. F. Magee. (B) Vol 126 (1937) p 180
443. Mining Districts in Lander County, Nev. W. O. Vanderburg. (H) No 7043 (1939)
444. Dry Concentration of Placer Gold. F. J. H. Merrill. (C) July 13, 1912, p 50
445. Dry Blowers in Australian Gold Placers. Abstr from B. Dunstan. (A) Oct 11, 1902, p 482
446. Elementary Placer Mining Methods and Gold-saving Devices. C. McK. Laizure. Ann Rep Calif State Mineralogist, Vol 28, Pt 2 (Apl, 1932) p 112
447. Recovery of Gold in Dredging. C. Janin. (C) Nov 7, 1914
448. Mining Gold Gravels in Sierra Leone. (A) Apl, 1932, p 203
449. Tin Placer Mining in Nigeria. W. E. Sinclair. (A) Feb, 1933, p 55
450. Gold Mining in New Mexico. O. H. Metzger. (H) No 6987 (1938)
451. Stripping Frozen Gravel. E. E. McCarthy. (E) Apl, 1914. Development of Dredging in Yukon Terr. O. B. Perry. Trans Can Min Inst, Vol 18, 1915
452. Alluvial Deposits of West Australia. T. A. Rickard. (B) Vol 28, 1898. Dry Placers in Ariz, Nev, N M, and Cal. V. C. Heikes and C. G. Yale. Mineral Res U S for 1912, part 1, pp 254–263
453. Elevating Ten-cent Gravel at a Profit. C. S. Haley. (C) Apl 13, 1912
454. Thawing Frozen Ground for Placer Mining. A. Gibson. (C) Jan 17, 1914
455. Thawing Methods at Fairbanks. H. I. Ellis. (A) July 3, 1915
456. Drift Mining in California. R. L. Dunn. 8th Ann Rept, State Mineralogist, Cal, 1888. Ancient River Beds of the Forest Hill Divide. R. E. Brown. 10th Ann Rept State Mineralogist, Cal, 1890
457. Timbering in Deep Placer Mining. H. T. Power. (C) Aug 11, 1917
458. Undercurrents for Recovery of Fine Gold. Chem, Eng & Min Rev (Melbourne) Oct 10, 1938
459. Development Methods at Fairbanks. H. I. Ellis. (A) June 12, 1915. See also (A) Sept 25, 1915; Oct 30, 1915
460. Drift Mining. T. Egleston. Sch of Mines Quart, Vol 8, 1887
461. Methods at Vallecito-Western Mine, Angels Camp, Cal. D. Steffa. (H) No 6612 (1932)
462. Drift Mining in the Frozen Gravel of Cape Nome. A. Gibson. (C) Mch 7, 1914
463. Gold Placers of Fortymile, Eagle, and Circle Distrs, Alaska. J. B. Mertie. U S G S Bull 897–C (1938)
464. On hydraulic-mine debris in Calif. L. A. Palmer. (A) Oct, 1937, p 29. W. W. Bradley. (B) Tech Pub 673 (1936)
465. Subsidence Resulting from Mining. Young and Stoek. Bull 91, Eng Exp Station, Univ of Ill, 1916
466. Subsidence in Underground Mines. A. Richardson. (A) Aug 3, 1907
467. Sur les mouvements de terrain provoqués par l'exploitation des mines. M. Fayol. Bull de la Soc de l'Industrie Min, II série, Tome 14, 1885. Partial translation by H. F. Bullman. Coll Eng, May, 1913, et seq
468. Sampling and Exploration by Hammer Drills. J. B. Knaebel. (H) No 6594 (1932)
469. Rep of Sub-committee on Coal Mining to Committee on Ground Movement and Subsidence. (B) Vol 74, 1926
470. Some Observations on Mining by the Opencast or Stripping Method. R. E. Palmer. Trans Inst Min & Met, Vol 30, 1926
471. Factors Affecting Bank Slopes in Steam-shovel Operations. L. S. Cates. (B) Vol 74, 1926
472. Some Problems in Ground Movement and Subsidence. G. S. Rice. (B) Vol 69, 1923

473. Earth and Rock Pressures. H. G. Moulton, and discussion by J. C. Meem. (*B*) Vol 63, 1920
474. Mining Formulas. T. A. O'Donahue. Wigan, 1907
475. Engineering Geology. H. Ries. Wiley & Sons, 1914
476. Report of Commission to Investigate Frank Slide, Alberta. *Mem* 27, Geol Surv of Canada, 1912
477. Mining Conditions under the City of Scranton. Griffith and Conner. *Bull* 25, U S Bur of Mines, 1912
478. Ultimate Crushing Strength of Coal. Daniels and Moore. (*A*) Aug 10, 1907
479. Prospecting, Past and Future. T. A. Rickard. (*C*) Apl 23, 1921
480. Technical Operations on the Suan Concession. A. R. Weigall and J. F. Mitchell-Roberts. (*C*) Oct 11, 25, 1919
481. Vertical and Inclined Shaft Sinking at North Star Mine. A. B. Foote. (*B*) Vol 91 (1930)
482. Mechanical Underground Loading in Metal Mines. C. E. Van Barneveld. *Bull* Missouri School of Min & Met, Vol 7, No 3, 1924
483. Driving a Mines Drainage Tunnel in Nor Wales. J. L. Francis. *Trans* Inst Min & Met, Vol 41 (1932) p 234
484. Tunnel Driving Methods at Ojuela, Mex. J P. Savage. (*H*) No 6480 (1931)
485. Prospecting. S. A. Knapp. (*C*) May 28, 1921
486. Michigan Copper Mining Practice. O. Potter, S. Richards, and H. Vivian. *Min Cong Jl*, Oct, 1931, pp 482, 487, 496
487. Mining Methods in Mich Copper Mines. W. R. Crane. U S Bur Min, *Bull* 306 (1929)
488. Mining Methods at Champion Mine. A. Mendelsohn. (*B*) Vol 102 (1932) p 43. (*H*) No 6515 (1931)
489. Deep Mining Methods, C & H Conglomerate Mine. H. Vivian. (*H*) No. 6526 (1931)
490. MacAlpin Coal Co No 4 Mine. *Mechanization*, Sept, 1938
491. Peabody Coal Co Mine No 8. *Mechanization*, Aug, 1938
492. Mining Methods of Molybdenum Corp of America at Questa, N M. J. B. Carman. (*H*) No 6514 (1931)
493. Mining Practice at Vipond Mine. R. E. Dye. (*H*) No 6525 (1931)
494. Iron Ore Mining at Scrub Oak. H. M. Roche and R. E. Crockett. (*A*) Apl, 1933, p 164
495. Method of Mining in Mineville Dist, N Y. A. M. Cummings. (*H*) No 6092 (1928)
496. Tunnel Driving at Stan Trg Mine, Yugoslavia. D. J. Rogers. *Trans* Inst Min & Met, Vol 42 (1933) p 266
497. Driving a Long Crosscut. W. F. Brown. *Can Min Jour*, Nov, 1936, p 579
498. Mining at Britannia Beach, B C. C. V. Brennan. (*H*) No 6815 (1935)
499. Method of Mining Hematite at Eureka-Asteroid Mine. O. M. Schaus. (*H*) No 6348 (1930)
500. Mining Methods at Mt Isa, Queensland. J. Kruttschnitt and V. I Mann. (*H*) No 6978 (1937)
501. Roan Antelope Mining Practice. R. M. Peterson. (*A*) Nov, 1932, p 557
502. Desert Prospecting. L. A. Palmer. (*A*) Oct 30, 1920
503. Diamond Drilling in El Potosi Mine. H. A. Walker. (*A*) Nov 18, 1922. (*H*) No 6804 (1934)
504. Prospecting in the Quebec Gold Belt. K. W. Fritzsche. *Trans* Can Inst Min & Met, Vol 28 (1925). An Excursion into Rouyn. A. B. Parsons. (*A*) Oct 30, Nov 6, 1926
505. Air Photography and Aeroplane as Aids for Prospecting. C. MacLaurin. *Bull* Can Inst Min & Met, Aug, 1922. Use of Aircraft in Mineral Exploration and Development. G. C. Mackenzie. *Bull* Can Inst Min & Met, Oct, 1924
506. Prospecting for Gold and Other Ores in Western Australia. C. M. Harris. *Trans* Inst Min & Met, Vol 29, 1919
507. Iron Mining in Muscoda No 6. E. M. Ball and A. W. Beck. (*A*) Sept, 1937, p 29; Oct, 1937, p 35
508. Cobalt, Its Past and Future. C. W. Knight. (*A*) May 6, 1922
509. Deep-hole Prospecting at Chief Consol Mines. C. A. Dobbel. (*B*) Vol 72, 1925
510. Diamond Drilling as a Means of Intensive Development. P. S. Couldrey and F H S. Sampson. (*A*) Sept 25, 1920
511. Underground Scraping Practice (at Miami). A. J. McDermid. (*A*) Oct 23, 1930, p 390
512. How to Calculate Tonnage and Grade of an Orebody. J. E. Harding. (*A*) Sept 15, 1923
513. Sampling and Estimating Copper Deposits. I. B. Joralemon. (*B*) Vol 72, 1925
514. Sampling and Estimating Lake Superior Iron Ores. J. F. Wolff, E. L. Derby, W. A. Cole. (*B*) Vol 72, 1925
515. How to Select Prospecting Equipment. G. J. Young. (*A*) Sept 22, 1923. Reducing Cost of Prospecting Isolated Mining Properties. F. A. McLean. *Bull* Can Inst Min & Met, Aug, 1924
516. Scheme for Working City Deep Mine at a Depth of 7000 ft. E. H. Clifford. *Trans* Inst Min & Met, Vol 30, 1921
517. Mining Methods in Morro Velho Mine. A. G. N. Chalmers. *Proc* Inst Civil Engrs (British) Vol 226 (1928) p 189. See also (*C*) Oct 2, 1920
518. Mining Methods in Mineville District. E. C. Henry. (*B*) Vol 72, 1925. Also Bib (495)
519. Standardized Crosscut Rounds. H. Drullard. (*A*) Jan 3, 1920. Applying the Blueprint Round. C. H. Waters. (*A*) Feb 7, 1920. Standard Rounds in Metal Mines. C. S. Hurter, *Bull*, Dupont Explos Serv, Nov, 1924
520. Standardization of Mining Methods. C. A. Mitke. (*A*) Nov 16, 1918
521. Hanging Scaffold for Taking Down Loose Back in High Ground. I. H. Cornell. (*A*) June 3, 1922. Also Bib (155) and (*A*) Aug, 1932, p 427
522. Zinc Mining at Franklin, N J. C. M. Haight and B. F. Tillson. (*B*) Vol 57, 1917
523. Powder Allowances in Mining. G. L. Schmutz. (*A*) May 8, 1920
524. Mining Methods and Costs at United Verde Mine. H. DeWitt Smith and W. H. Sirdevan. (*B*) Vol 66, 1921. C. E. Mills. (*B*) Vol 72, 1925. G. J. Young. (*A*) Mch 7, 1925. Drilling and Blasting Underground at United Verde. C. E. Mills. (*A*) May 29, 1926. Also Bib (227)
525. Leaching Copper at Ray Mines, Ariz. R. W. Thomas. *Min & Met*, Nov, 1938, p 481
526. Mining Rock Salt in Michigan. H. D. Keiser. (*A*) July 10, 1930, p 16
527. Methods at Ground Hog Mine, Asarco Mining Co, Vanadium, N M. F. W. Richard. (*H*) No 6377 (1930)
528. Mining at N'Kana. A. R. Harrison and K. E. Mackay. (*A*) Dec, 1935, p 591
529. Methods at Mt Hope Mine. J. R. Sweet. (*H*) No 6601 (1932). Also F. M. Radel. (*A*) July 24, 1930, p 75

530. Mining Methods of Alaska Gastineau Mining Co. G. T. Jackson. (*B*) Vol 63, 1920, p 464
531. Standardizing by North Butte Mining Co. R. Linton. (*B*) Vol 66, 1921
532. Equipment and Operation of Inspiration Porphyry Shaft. G. H. Booth. (*A*) Mch 21, Apl 18, 1925
533. Methods at Tezuitlan, Mex. E. P. Herivel. (*H*) No 6736 (1933)
534. Mining Methods in Butte Dist. W. B. Daly *et al.* (*B*) Vol 72, 1925. Advantages of Using Timbered Rill Stopes. H. L. Bicknell. *Comp Air Mag*, Aug, 1921. Butte System of Square-set Stoping. H. L. Bicknell. *Comp Air Mag*, Apl, 1922. Rill Stoping in the Butte Dist. H. L. Bicknell. *Comp Air Mag*, July, 1921
535. Mining Sulphide Ore at Fresnillo, Mex. J. H. Ashley. (*A*) June, 1936, p 279
536. Driving and Timbering Drifts. F. D. Lane. Copper Queen Practical Min Course, 1920. Breaking Ground in Drifts. J. McGarry. *Ibid*, 1919. Standard Raises. J. S. Stewart. *Ibid*, 1919. Breaking Ground. F. D. Lane. *Ibid*, 1920
537. Working Obuasi Reef of Ashanti Goldfields Corp. G. W. Eaton Turner. *Trans* Inst Min & Met, Vol 38 (1929) p 62
538. Assoc of Mine Managers of the Transvaal. "Papers and Discussions," 1931–36. Pub by Transvaal Chamber of Mines
539. A Study of Shoveling as Applied to Mining. G. T. Harley. (*B*) Vol 61, 1919
540. Methods at the Pilgrim Mine, Chloride, Ariz. E. F. Hastings. (*H*) No 6945 (1937)
541. French Creek Iron Mine. A. H. Hubbell. (*A*) Dec 24, 1921
542. Red Iron Ore Mining Methods in Birmingham Dist. W. R. Crane. (*B*) Vol 72 (1925) p 157. Roof Support in Red Ore Mines of Birmingham Dist. W. R. Crane. *Ibid*, p 187
543. Mine Fires and Hydraulic Filling. H. J. Rahilly. (*B*) Vol 68 (1923) p 62
544. Methods at United Verde Open Pit Mine, Jerome, Ariz. E. M. J. Alenius. (*H*) No 6248 (1930)
545. Sub-stoping at Amasa-Porter Mine. M. E. Richards. (*G*) Vol 21, 1917. Sub-stoping Method of Mining Used at Chatham Mine. F. J. Smith. (*G*) Vol 21, 1917. Mining Methods in Florence Dist. J. M. Riddell. (*G*) Vol 21, 1917. Mining Methods at Magpie Iron Mine. A. Hasselbring. *Trans* Can Inst Min & Met, Vol 20, 1917. Spies Open-stope System of Mining. S. R. Elliott. (*B*) Vol 68, 1923
546. Improvements in Underground Trolley Conveyers. E. M. Weston. (*A*) Aug 30, 1913
547. Transport of Ore by Electrically Oscillated Trough Conveyer in Ottange 2 Mine, Moselle. L. Jacob. VII Internat Cong of Mining, Paris, 1935; Memoirs of Min Sec, Vol 2, p. 605
548. Geology and Mining Methods of Kennecott and Beatson Mines. S. Birch. (*B*) Vol 72, 1925
549. Underground Methods of Mining Wide Pyritic Orebodies. A. V. Reis. *Trans* Inst Min & Met, Vol 31, 1921
550. Slate Mining in North Wales. M. I. Williams-Ellis. *Jour* So Af Inst of Eng, Vol. 20, 1922
551. Salt Mining in Louisiana. A. G. Wolf. (*A*) July 2, 1921
552. Mining Copper in Baja Calif. M. Bellanger. (*A*) Nov 9, 1931, p 394
553. Low-Cost Salt. H. B. Cooley. (*A*) May, 1932, p 256
554. Moving Ore in Flat Stopes. E. M. Weston. (*A*) Oct 23, 1915
555. Mining Methods at Copper Range Co. W. H. Schacht. (*B*) Vol 72, 1925
556. Assoc of Mine Managers of the Transvaal. "Papers and Discussions," 1937–38. Pub by Transvaal Chamber of Mines
557. Methods at Black Rock Mine, Butte, Mont. D. B. McGilvra and A. J. Healy. (*H*) No 6370 (1930)
558. Cold-water Thawing of Frozen Gravel. E. E. Pearce. (*C*) Feb 4, 1922
559. Mechanical Scrapers on the Rand. C. L. Butlin. (*A*) Apl 24, 1930, p 389
560. Mine La Motte. H. D. Keiser. (*A*) Aug 9, 1930, p 110
561. Mining Methods at Fresnillo, Mex. A. Livingston. (*H*) No 6661 (1932)
562. Handling and Breaking Ore in Bulldozing Chambers. C. W. Wright. (*B*) Vol 126 (1937) p 111
563. Mining Limestone with Shrinkage Stopes. A. B. Parsons. (*A*) Oct 18, 1924. Mining Limestone at Shingle Springs, Calif. G. J. Young. (*A*) June 20, 1925. Mining Practice at the Bell Limestone Mine. S. M. Shallcross. (*B*) Vol 126 (1937) p 46
564. Development, Mining and Transportation at Alaska Juneau. L. H. Metzgar. (*A*) Sept, 1932, p 466
565. Slushing Total Mine Production (at Flin Flon) with Electric Hoists. M. A. Roche. *Can Min Jour*, June, 1931, p 579
566. Methods in the Underground Mine at Flin Flon. M. A. Roche and J. P. Caulfield. *Trans* Can Inst M & M, Vol 38 (1935) p 97
567. Mining Methods of the Flin Flon Mine. W. J. Marshall. *Bull* Can Inst Min & Met, Jan, 1938, p 31
568. Some Aspects of Mining at Depth. J. Thorlund. (*F*) Vol 29 (1928) p 42. Abs in *Can Min Jour*, Nov 30, 1928, p 988
569. Prospecting with the Long-hole Drill in Tri-State District. W. F. Netzeband. *Min & Met*, June, 1930, p 295. Also (*B*) Vol 75 (1927) p 35
570. Panel System of Stoping at the Herman Mine. S. H. Brockunier. (*A*) Dec 6, 1919
571. Method of Support of Hanging Wall in the New States Areas, with Special Reference to Concrete Columns. J. Richardson. (*F*) Vol 27, July, 1926
572. Support of Workings in the Van Ryn Deep. A. E. Payne. (*F*) Vol 27, 1926
573. Mechanical Scrapers in Modderfontein B Mine. C. L. Butlin. *Proc* Third Empire Min & Met Cong, Johannesburg, 1930, Part 2, p 424. Stoping Operations on Witwatersrand. A. E. Payne *et al.* *Ibid*, p 389. Development in West Rand Consol. C. S. McLean. *Ibid*, p 370. Development on Far East Rand. B. D. Bushell. *Ibid*, p 349. Preceding, and other, papers reviewed with comments by C. B. Brodigan in *Trans* Inst Min & Met, Vol 40 (1931) p 350
574. Geol and Operations of the Magma Mine. W. C. Browning and F. W. Snow. (*A*) Jan 31, 1925. Also Bib (77)
575. Mining Methods at Bunker Hill & Sullivan. H. M. Childs and S. A. Easton. (*B*) Vol 72, 1925. U. E. Brown and S. W. McDougall. (*A*) Aug, 1939, p 43. Also Bib (212)
576. Supporting Excavations on the Witwatersrand. A. G. Boyden. (*A*) July 13, 1931
577. Methods at Block P Mine, St Joseph Lead Co, Hughesville, Mont. W. O. Vanderburg. (*H*) No 6416 (1931)
578. Mining Methods in Grass Valley Dist, Cal. J. A. Fulton and A. B. Foote. (*B*) Vol 74, 1926
579. Mining by Briggs Underhand Square Setting. R. H. Dickson. (*A*) Jan 6, 1923. Timber Frame for Underhand Square Setting. G. J. Young. (*A*) July 11, 1925. Mining by Ratterree Modification of Underhand Square Setting. R. H. Dickson. (*A*) Jan 27, 1923

580. Mining Methods of United Verde Extension Mining Co.   C. A. Mitke.   (*B*) Vol 61, 1919. Also Bib (90)
581. Recovering Caved Stopes in Narrow Veins.   C. T. Rice.   (*A*) June 15, July 6, Aug 10, 1918
582. Replogle Iron Mine, Wharton, N J.   A. H. Hubbell.   (*A*) Oct 2, 1920
583. Development of Scraper Loading in the Tri-State District.   S. S. Clarke.   (*B*) *Tech Pub* 1115 (1939)
584. Methods of Alaska Juneau Gold Mining Co.   P. R. Bradley.   (*H*) No 6186 (1929)
585. Preservation of Structural Timber.   H. F. Weiss.   Methods and Cost of Treating Mine Timber. Tracy & Tolsh, Carnegie Inst Tech, *Bull* 33.   Wood Preservation, G. M. Hunt & G. A. Garratt.   Preservative Treatment of Mine Timbers, J. F. Harkom, *Trans* Canad Inst Min & Met, 1930, p 550.   Wood Preservation, A. W. Jones.   (*E*) July, 1937, p 19
586. Timber Treating at Inspiration.   A. C. Stoddard.   *Min Cong Jl*, Aug, 1931, p 381
587. Timber Treating at United Verde Mine, Jerome, Ariz.   C. E. Mills.   *Min Cong Jl*, Apl, 1934
588. Timber Treatment Plant at Hollinger Mine.   W. H. Pritchard.   *Can Min Jour*, Sept, 1935
589. Sand Filling through Pipes and Boreholes.   L. Eaton.   (*B*) Vol 102 (1932) p 33
590. Filling Stopes with Mill Tailing.   G. L. Richert.   (*A*) Mch 2, 1929, p 348.   Rubber Pipe Lining (for sand filling).   D. D. Homor.   (*A*) Oct 26, 1931, p 367
591. Sand Filling at Hodbarrow Hematite Mine, So Cumberland.   A. A. Jones.   *Trans* Inst Min & Met, Vol 41 (1932) p 303
592. Mining Methods at Britannia, B C.   J. I. Moore, Jr.   *Trans* Canad Inst Min & Met, Vol 31 (1928) p 280.   Producing Copper at Britannia Beach, B C.   J. B. Huttl.   (*A*) July, 1938
593. Methods of Mining Copper in Ariz.   G. J. Young.   (*A*) Mch 13, 20, 1926.
594. Inclined-slicing Method as Applied to Large Orebodies.   J. P. Hodgson and J. Kiddie. (*A*) May 27, 1922
595. Inclined Top-slicing Method.   W. G. Scott.   (*B*) Vol 59, 1918.   Coronado Top-slicing Method.   P. B. Scotland.   (*A*) Apl 7, 1917
596. Long Slope Mining at Anyox, B C.   F. S. McNicholas.   (*A*) Nov, 1932, p 567.   Mining under Caved Areas.   F. S. McNicholas.   (*A*) Mch, 1933, p 112
597. Cramp Chain Gate.   *Can Min Jour*, May, 1934, p 241.   U S Pat 1869547, Canad Pat 319759
598. Estimation of Ore Reserves and Mining Methods in Alaska Juneau Mine.   P. R. Bradley. (*B*) Vol 72, 1925
599. Mining under Fire Conditions.   W. G. Scott and S. A. McWhirter.   (*A*) July 21, 1923
600. Mining Methods at Morenci.   M. Mosier and J. Martin.   (*A*) Dec 26, 1925
601. Mining Methods of the Miami Copper Co.   J. H. Hensley, Jr.   (*B*) Vol 72, 1925.   Also Bib (283)
602. Branch-raise System at Ruth Mine.   W. S. Larsh.   (*B*) Vol 59, 1918
603. Mining and Milling at Silver Dyke Property.   G. J. Young.   (*A*) Feb 5, 1927
604. Method of Mining at Loretto Mine.   C. H. Baxter.   (*G*) Vol 21, 1917
605. A Chilean Gold-panning Operation.   L. W. Strauss.   (*A*) Dec 12, 1925
606. Mining Methods in Pittsburgh Dist.   (*B*) Vol 74, 1926
607. Pocahontas Coal Field and Operating Methods of U S Coal and Coke Co.   E. O'Toole. (*B*) Vol 72, 1925
608. Coal Mining by the V-System.   G. B. Southward.   (*B*) Vol 70, 1924
609. Mining a Steeply-pitching Anthracite Vein by Successive Skips.   J. S. Miller.   (*B*) Vol 72 (1925) p 730.   Simultaneous First and Second Mining on Steep Pitches.   D. C. Ashmead. *Ibid*, p 735
610. Systems of Coal Mining in Western Washington.   S. H. Ash.   (*B*) Vol 72, 1925
611. Coal-Pillar Drawing Methods in Europe.   G. S. Rice.   (*B*) Vol 66, 1921
612. Mechanical Mining of Anthracite.   H. D. Kynor.   (*B*) Vol 66, 1921
613. Drilling and Blasting in Some American Coal Mines.   T. Marvin.   *Explos Engr*, Oct–Dec, 1926
614. Gold Dredging in the U S.   C. Janin.   U S Bur of Mines, *Bull* 127, 1918
615. Mechanical Loading in Butte Mines.   H. M. Courtney.   (*A*) Dec, 1938, p 31
616. Diamond Drills for Stoping at Noranda.   F. S. Dunn.   (*A*) Jan, 1939, p 38
617. A Mechanical Rocker.   H. W. Turner.   (*A*) Aug 25, 1920
618. Sluice Boxes.   W. A. Newman.   (*A*) May, 1937, p 229
619. Blasting of Hanging Ore Columns in Chutes and Drawing Raises.   E. D. Gardner.   U S Bur of Mines, *Rep of Invest* No 2790, Jan, 1927
620. Economic Aspects of Bituminous Coal Losses.   J. D. Sisler.   (*B*) Vol 94 (1931) p 196
621. Mine Subsidence in Red Iron Ore Mines of Birmingham Dist, Ala.   W. R. Crane.   (*B*) Vol 72 (1925) p 182
622. G. S. Rice, Dept of Mines of Brit Col, *Bull* No 2, 1918
623. Surface Subsidence in Ill, Resulting from Coal Mining.   Ill Geol Surv, *Bull* 17, 1916
624. Examples of Subsidence in Two Oklahoma Coal Mines.   J. J. Rutledge.   (*B*) Vol 69, 1923
625. Subsidence at Miami.   J. P. Channing.   (*B*) Vol 69, 1923.   Also F. W. Maclennan.   (*B*) Vol 85 (1929) p 167
626. Placer Mining by Centrifugal Pump.   W. E. Sinclair.   (*A*) May, 1933, p 184
627. Gold Dredging in Calif, and Methods for Increasing Recovery.   E. S. Leaver and J. A. Woolf. (*B*) *Tech Pub* 792 (1937).   Operation of Gold Dredges.   R. S. Lewis.   *Canad Min Jour*, Mch, 1935.   Modern Tendencies in Alluvial Dredge Design.   S. A. Westrop. *Min Jour* (London) Mch 4, 1939
628. Deep-lead and Drift-mining.   M. T. Taylor.   (*E*) Oct, 1916
629. Recent Progress in the Thawing of Frozen Gravel in Placer Mining.   C. Janin.   U S Bur of Mines, *Tech Pap* 309, 1922
630. On sand filling in So Africa.   *Min & Indust Mag of So Africa*, Mch 2, 1932, p 26
631. Steam-shovel Mining.   R. Marsh, Jr.   McGraw-Hill, 1920.   Recent Developments in Open-pit Mining.   R. Marsh, Jr.   (*A*) Apl 18, 1925
632. Steam-shovel Mining on the Mesabi Range.   L. D. Davenport.   (*A*) Mch 2, 16, 30, 1918
633. Methods at Washington, N J, Magnetite Mine.   C. H. Loux.   (*B*) Vol 109 (1934) p 51
634. Rubber-tired Haulage at Moffat Mine, Sparta, Ill.   *Mechanization*, Nov, 1937
635. Saxton Coal Mining Company's Modern Mine.   *Mechanization*, July, 1938
636. D. O. Clark Mine, Superior, Wyo.   *Mechanization*, Jan, 1939
637. Mining and Milling Tungsten Ores.   W. O. Vanderburg.   (*H*) No 6852 (1935)
638. Liquid Oxygen Blasting at Chuquicamata.   H. C. Schultz and F. K. Hunter.   (*B*) Vol 76 (1928).   Mining at Chuquicamata.   C. Bellinger.   (*A*) Aug 24, 1929.   Electrification at Chuquicamata.   E. H. Robie.   (*A*) Dec 21, 1929
639. Wheeling Township Coal Mining Co's No 2 Mine, Adena, Ohio.   *Mechanization*, Oct, 1938

640. Glory-hole Mining at Fresnillo. T. C. Baker. (B) Vol 72, 1925. Quarry Mining Methods at Fresnillo. D. B. McAllister. (A) May 7, 1921. See also Bib (561)
641. Estimates of Mesabi Range Orebodies. (A) Aug 21, 1920
642. Practice at Inspiration Mine, Ariz. A. C. Stoddard. (H) No 6169 (1929)
643. Mine Development and Underground Construction of Andes Copper Mining Co, at Potrerillos, Chile. I. L. Greninger. (B) Vol 85 (1929) p 144
644. Thawing Frozen Gravel with Cold Water. W. S. Weeks. (C) Mch 13, 1920
645. Tin Mining in Malaya. L. G. Attenborough. Trans Inst Min & Met, Vol 34, p 118
646. Aerial Prospecting in Nor Canada. E. Hanson. (A) Oct 12, 1929, p 574. Air Transport of Mine Equipment. A. Dresel. (A) May, 1933, p 201. Transportation of Gold Dredges in New Guinea. C. A. Banks. Trans Inst Min & Met, 1932, p 616; 1937, p 803. Aeroplane and the Mining Engineer. J. N. Wynne. (E) Feb, 1935, p 73, Also Bib (505, 647)
647. Aerial Geologizing. L. T. Eliel & W. H. Meyer. (B) Vol 126 (1937) pp 560, 575. Geological Interpretation of Aerial Photographs. J. J. Van Nouhuys. (B) Vol 126 (1937) p 607. Aerial Photographs in Geological Mapping. W. Loel. (B) Tech Pub 890 (1938). Air Survey in relation to Economic Geology. D. Gill. Trans Inst Min & Met, 1933, p 81 (contains long bib)
648. Ore Deposits of Western U S. Am Inst Min Eng, 1933. Chaps III, IV, IX, X
649. Replacement Deposits and Criteria for Recognition. J. D. Irving. Econ Geol, Vol 6 (1911)
650. Treatise on Sedimentation. W. H. Twenhofel. Williams & Wilkins, 1932
651. Geology of Non-metallic Minerals—Principles of Salt Deposition. A. W. Graham. McGraw-Hill, 1920
652. Enrichment of Ore Deposits. W. H. Emmons. U S Geol Surv, Bull 625 (1917)
653. Leached Outcrops as Guides to Copper Ore. A. Locke. Pub Williams & Wilkins, 1926
654. Copper Resources of the World. 16th Int Geol Cong, Washington, 1935, Vol 2
655. New Undercut Caving Method at Inspiration. G. J. Young. (A) Sept 21, 1929, p 474. Also Bib (642)
656. Open-pit Mining at United Verde, Jerome, Ariz. E. M. J. Alenius. Min Cong Jl, Apl, 1930, p 338. Also Bib (544)
657. Phosphate Rock Mining, 1880–1937. A. P. Haskell, Jr, and O. E. Kiessling. W P A Report E-7 (1938)
658. Metal-mine Accidents in U S. W. W. Adams. U S Bur Mines, Bull 374, 377, 398, 410. Also Bull 362 for earlier data. See also Bull 422, 428
659. Iron Ore Mining in Austria. F. Strauss. Min & Quarry Eng, Jan, 1937
660. Recent Developments in Open-pit Mining on Mesabi Range. E. E. Hunner. (B) Vol 91 (1930) p 106
661. Open-pit Mining. A. H. Hubbell. (A) Nov 23, Dec 14, 1931; Mch, 1932
662. Progress at Open-pit Mines on Lake Superior Iron Ranges. M. H. Barber. (B) Tech Pub 487 (1932)
663. Efficient Technique for Drilling and Blasting (at Tilden mine). W. R. Meyers. (A) Jan, 1932, p 30
664. Open-pit Transport on the Mesabi Range. L. C. Moore. (A) Serial beginning Oct, 1938
665. Recent Improvements in Mining (transport) Practice on the Mesabi Range. A. E. Anderson, J. M. Riddell, and G. J. Holt. (B) Tech Pub 968 (1938)
666. New Method of Mining Mesabi Open-pit Ore. W. F. Schwedes. Min Cong Jl, Dec, 1938
667. Truck Haulage on Mesabi and Cuyuna Ranges. W. R. Whitney and G. J. Holt. (A) Jan, 1939, p 29
668. Preliminary Stripping of Morenci Open-pit, Ariz. W. C. Lawson. (B) Tech Pub 980 (1938)
669. Flin Flon Open Pit. M. A. Roche. Trans Canad Inst Min & Met, Vol 36 (1933) p 371. Mining Methods and Problems at Flin Flon. M. A. Roche and J. P. Caulfield. Ibid, Vol 38 (1935) p 87. Open Pit Blasting at Flin Flon. M. A. Roche. Can Min Jour, June, 1933, p 219; Nov, 1933, p 421
670. Asbestos Mining in Quebec. W. A. Rukeyser. (A) Jan, 1932, p 17; also Apl 15 and 22, 1922
671. On anthracite strip-mining. H. H. Otto. (B) Vol 94 (1931) p 181. R. D. Hall. Coal Age, Jan, 1935, p 25. H. N. Eavenson. Ibid, Oct, 1936, p 412. Anon. Ibid, Aug 1934, p 299; Feb, 1935, p 60; Dec, 1935, p 495; June, 1937, p 242
672. Mechanical Loading and Cleaning (of coal) in 1936 and 1937. L. N. Plein, R. L. Anderson, and J. J. Gallagher. Supp to NBCC weekly coal report No 1085, Apl 30, 1938
673. Subsidence and Ground Movement in the Copper and Iron Mines of the Upper Peninsula, Mich. W. R. Crane. U S Bur Mines, Bull 295 (1929)
674. Essential Factors influencing Subsidence and Ground Movement. W. R. Crane. (H) No 6501 (1931)
675. Observation on Ground Movement and Subsidence at Rio Tinto Mines, Spain. R. E. Palmer. (B) Vol 91 (1930) p 168
676. Ground Movement from Mining in Brier Hill Mine, Norway, Mich. G. S. Rice. (B) Vol 109 (1934) p 118
677. Ground Movement and Subsidence at the United Verde Mine. C. E. Mills. (B) Vol 109 (1934) p 153
678. Subsidence resulting from the Athens System of Mining at Negaunee, Mich. C. W. Allen. (B) Vol 109 (1934) p 195
679. Footwall Shafts in Lake Superior Copper Mines. L. L. Hubbard. (G) Vol 17 (1912) p 144
680. Strip Mining of Bituminous Coal in Central and South Central States. A. L. Toenges and R. L. Anderson. (H) No 6959 (1937)
681. Block Stoping and Timbering in Deep Placer Mining. E. E. Fleming. (C) Sept 15, 1917, p 378; quoted in (H) No 6788, p 75
682. Victorian Deep Leads. A. R. O. Williams. (E) Mch, 1935, p 137
683. Mining a Deep Lead (in B C) by Australian Method. D. C. Mackenzie. (A) Apl, 1938, p 39
684. Mining in Malaya. H. G. Harris and E. S. Wilbourn. Malayan Information Agency, London
685. Sketch of Malayan Mining. J. B. Scrivenor. Salisbury House, London, 1928
686. Internat Tin Research and Development Council, London and N Y. Statistical and technical pubs
687. Quarterly Bull of Statistics relating to Mining Industry. Senior Warden of Mines, Kuala Lumpur, F M S
688. Diamond Drilling at Lake Athabaska. N. W. Byrne. Trans Can Inst Min & Met, Vol 40 (1937) p 165

SECTION 10-A

GEOPHYSICAL PROSPECTING *

BY

FREDERICK W. LEE

CHIEF, SECTION OF GEOPHYSICS, U S GEOLOGICAL SURVEY

Note. Numbers in parentheses in titles of Tables and illustrations refer to Bibliography at end of this section.

* Published by permission of the Director, U S Geological Survey.

GEOPHYSICAL PROSPECTING

Geophysical prospecting aims to establish the existence, position and boundaries of mineralized areas and geologic structures, or obtain other information of economic or scientific value. It utilizes the gravimetric, magnetic, electric, seismic, and thermic properties of rocks and minerals, natural to the ground in question, or produced artificially. Under either condition, properties of different materials relative to one another are significant. Two factors, applying to both country rock and mineral deposits, are most important: (a) kind and amount of material; (b) its geometrical form.

1. GRAVIMETRIC SURVEYS

General. Purpose of these surveys is to measure small local variations (ANOMALIES) in the force of gravity, as caused by salt domes, dikes, faults and anticlines. Differences in density of the formations, as well as their geometrical forms, control the size of these anomalies. Since the geol features are very small compared with the earth's volume, the anomalies are correspondingly small. The gravimetric field unit is the GAL (Galileo), the strength of a gravitational field that will act upon a mass of 1 gram with a force of 1 dyne. Thus the earth's field is equal to about 980 gal, whereas the anomalies are of the order of 1 milligal, or approx a millionth of the earth's field. The limit of accuracy is 0.1 milligal; constantly changing celestial and terrestrial disturbances mask smaller anomalies. Most surveys are made with pendulums and gravimeters. PENDULUMS are used at single locations in connection with crystal clocks for determining absolute values; for differences in gravity, they may be spaced several miles apart. GRAVIMETERS determine change of gravity directly from measured changes in their spring extensions. Observations take about 20 min per station. Measurements start at a base station, preceded by pendulum observations. Base stations are about 25 miles apart, and serve to tie in larger areas.

Gravity fields. Older methods called for use of the Eötvös torsion balance, measurement of gravity gradients being in terms of Eötvös UNITS, one unit representing a change of one millionth of a milligal per centimeter, equivalent to 0.1 milligal in 1 km. In the equation of the gravity field, certain coefficients permit evaluation of the change in gravity field.

If v is the gravity potential, then $\frac{\delta v}{\delta z}$ is the gravity component in the z or vert direction. Also $\frac{\delta\left(\frac{\delta v}{\delta z}\right)}{\delta x} = \frac{\delta^2 v}{\delta z \delta x}$ is the change of the vert component horizontally in the x direction; and $\frac{\delta^2 v}{\delta z \delta y}$ is the change of the vert component horizontally in the y direction. The resultant value $\frac{\delta^2 v}{\delta s^2} = \sqrt{\left(\frac{\delta^2 v}{\delta z \delta x}\right)^2 + \left(\frac{\delta^2 v}{\delta z \delta y}\right)^2}$, the rate of change of the vert component horizontally in direction of the max rate of change. The function $\tan\theta = \frac{\delta^2 v}{\delta z \delta y} \div \frac{\delta^2 v}{\delta z \delta x}$ gives the direction of this horiz gradient. These values are determined from the torsion balance deflections in various azimuthal positions.

A second function, the CURVATURE FUNCTION, has the form $\frac{\delta^2 v}{\delta y^2} - \frac{\delta^2 v}{\delta x^2} = g\left(\frac{1}{\rho_1} - \frac{1}{\rho_2}\right)$, where g is the value of gravity and ρ_1 and ρ_2 are the max and min radii of curvature of the equipotential surface at point of observation. Dimensions of this unit are the same as for the potential gradient. It is sometimes referred to as the H D T ("horiz directing tendency"). The value of this function bears somewhat the same relation to the vert gradient as the horiz magnetic variation bears to vert magnetic variations; increase in its value shows the proximity of an anomaly. Fig 1 shows anomalies for simple configurations; the full line gives the gradient values, or vert variation of gravity per unit of horiz distance; the dotted line, the H D T, or curvature function.

The geol interpretation of gravity anomalies is made by comparing observed curves with theoretic curves for ideal bodies. Such anomalies may be defined by the rate of change of the vert component, horizontally and in direction of the max rate of change $\frac{\delta^2 v}{\delta s^2}$ (the full line in Fig 1); the dotted line shows the value of the curvature function $g\left(\frac{1}{\rho_1} - \frac{1}{\rho_2}\right)$ for the same anomaly indicated by the hatched cross-sec. These cross-sections resemble the geol formations and the observed gravimetric gradient and curvature functions in Fig 2.

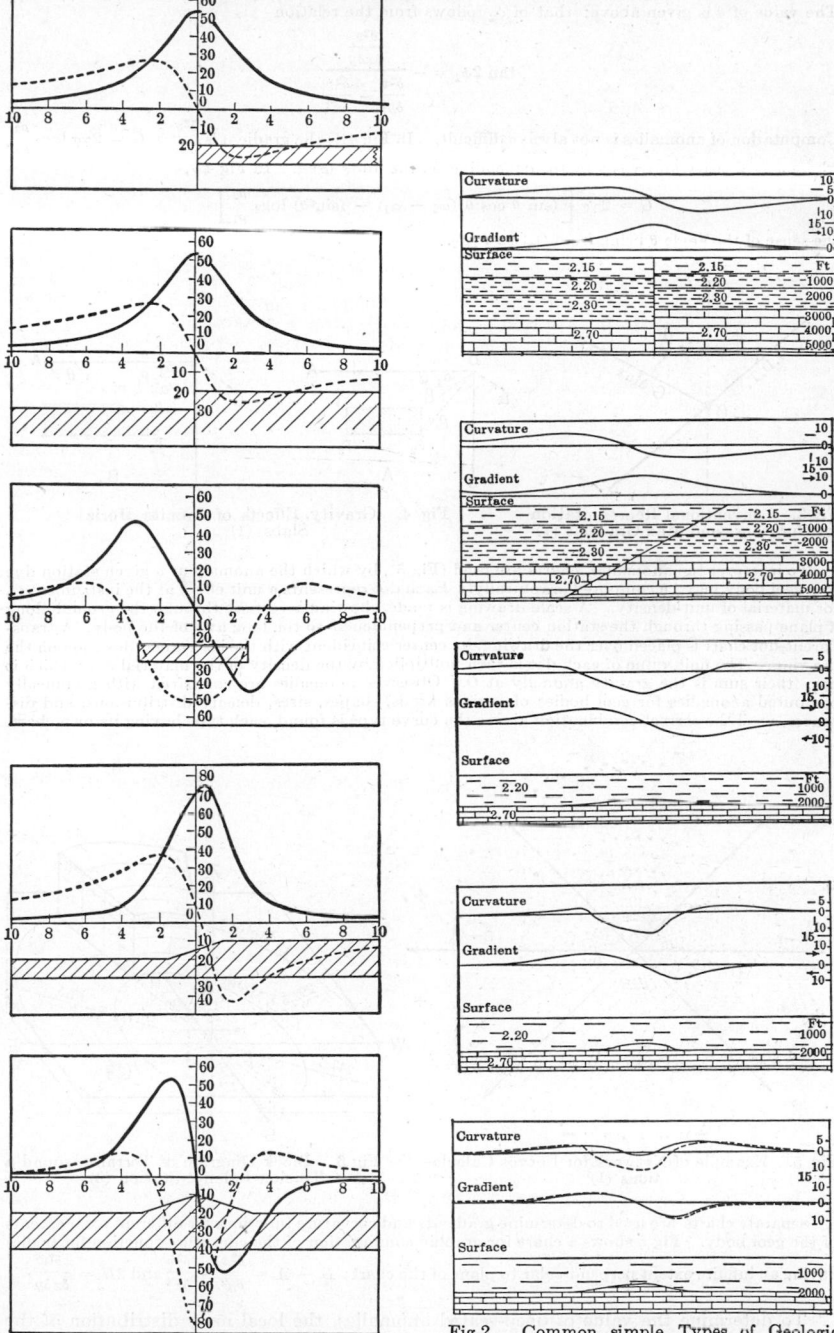

Fig 1. Theoretical Gradient and Curvature Anomalies caused by Geologic Conditions (1)

Fig 2. Common simple Types of Geologic Structure and Their Gradient and Differential Curvature Profiles (2)

Vector relations of gradient and curvature (Fig 3) are connected by the values of angles θ and ϕ_2. The value of θ is given above; that of ϕ_2 follows from the relation

$$\tan 2\phi_2 = -\frac{\dfrac{\delta^2 v}{\delta x \delta y}}{\dfrac{\delta^2 v}{\delta y^2} - \dfrac{\delta^2 v}{\delta x^2}}$$

Computation of anomalies is not always difficult. In Fig 4A, the gradient is $\dfrac{\delta^2 v}{\delta s^2} = G = 2\gamma\sigma \log_2 \dfrac{\rho_2}{\rho_1}$, where σ = density and γ is a factor depending on the units used. In Fig 4B,

$$G = 2\gamma\sigma \left[(\sin\theta\cos\theta)(\alpha_2 - \alpha_1) - (\sin^2\theta) \log_2 \frac{\rho_2}{\rho_1} \right]$$

the sense of the angle θ being from OA to P_1P_2.

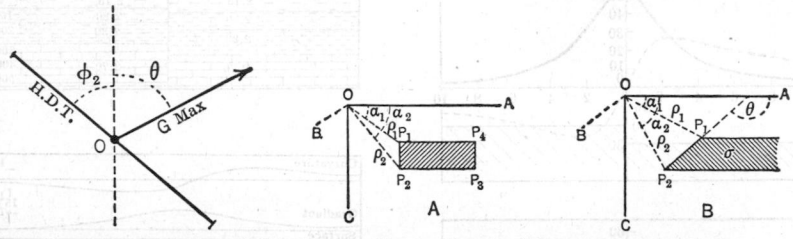

Fig 3. Conventional Representation of Curvature and Max Gradient (1)

Fig 4. Gravity Effects of Infinite Horiz Slabs (1)

To interpret the anomalies, charts are used (Fig 5), by which the anomaly at a given station due to a geol body may be computed graphically. Each dot represents a unit effect at the instrument O, for material of unit density. A scale drawing is made, showing a vert sec through the ground along a plane passing through the station center and perpendicular to the long axis of the body. A transparent-dot chart is placed over the drawing, its center coincident with the instrument location on the drawing. The unit value of each dot is then multiplied by the density of the material over which it lies; their sum is the gravity anomaly at O. Observed anomalies are compared with graphically computed anomalies for geol bodies of various kinds, shapes, sizes, density distributions, and distances, until the correct combination giving the curve type is found, each type having its own chart.

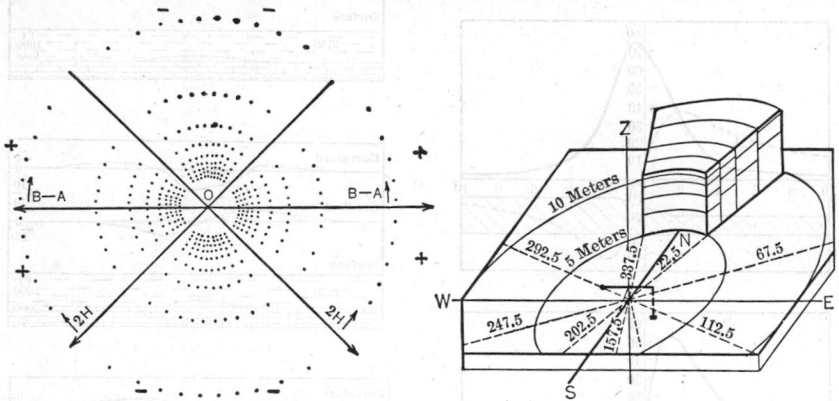

Fig 5. Example of Network for Eötvös Calculations (1)

Fig 6. Block Diagram of Terrane around a Torsion Balance Station (3)

Separate charts are used to determine gradients and curvature functions for different axial extents of the geol body. Fig 5 shows a chart for graphic computation of the curvature function for bodies having an infinite extent perpendicular to plane of the chart; $B - A = \dfrac{\delta^2 v}{\delta y^2} - \dfrac{\delta^2 v}{\delta x^2}$ and $2H = \dfrac{\delta^2 v}{\delta x \delta y}$.

To determine the value of deep-seated anomalies, the local mass distribution of the ground must be corrected. Correction factors for sectors immediately around the torsion balance (Fig 6) must be computed, by a chart like that in Fig 7. The ground is surveyed as in Fig 8, and the chart applied to each sector. The corrected results are charted as in Fig 9, which shows a gravity anomaly over a salt dome capped with anhydrite. The gradient arrows around the margins of the dome point towards the center; farther away, the direction is reversed, since the density of salt is less, and that of the cap rock greater, than that of the surrounding material. The lines without arrows represent direction and magnitude of the curvature.

Apparatus for gravity measurements. The torsion balance was first used to measure gravity anomalies. The observations require a long time, since 5 azimuthal positions must be observed at each station; shortened to 3 by using a double balance; 2 stations

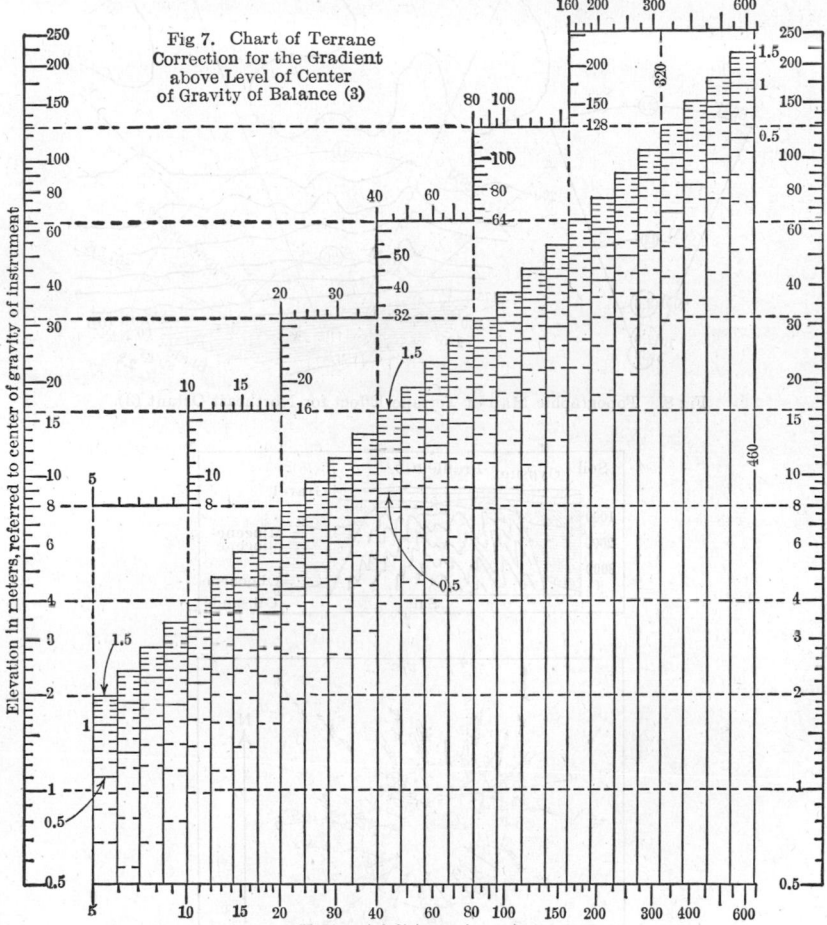

Fig 7. Chart of Terrane Correction for the Gradient above Level of Center of Gravity of Balance (3)

per day for 2 men are usually the max. With gravimeters, readings can be taken every 20 min, measuring the change of the vert component of gravity $S = \dfrac{\delta v}{\delta z}$; level data are needed for each station, accurate to less than 0.5 ft to preserve the limiting accuracy of 0.1 milligal, since a 1-ft difference of elev corresponds to 0.2 milligal in the vert component of gravity.

Pendulum stations at intervals of 25 miles are probably most accurate for measuring differences in the vert component. By using photoelectric cells and wireless to transmit the pendulum's position to a common station for oscillographic recording, with a timing interval on the record of **1 cm per 1/500 sec**, differences of 0.1 milligal can be measured, each measurement requiring about 50

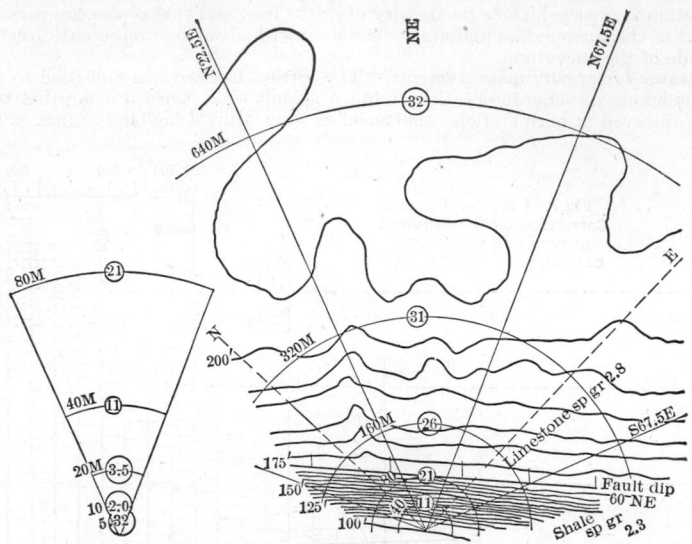

Fig 8.   Topographic Map of Terrane Effect for Northeast Octant (3)

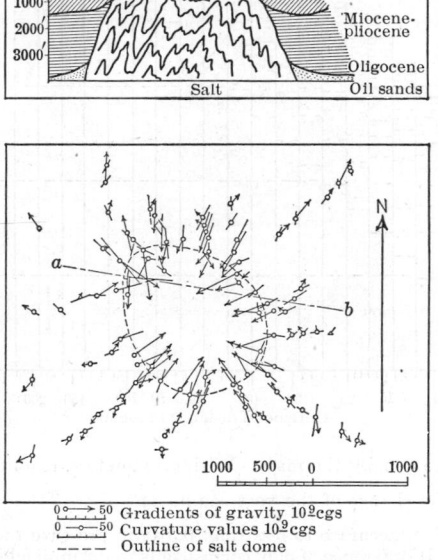

Fig 9.   Gravimetric Anomalies due to a Salt Dome (4)

min.   Charts of equal gravity differences, plotted in iso-gals, give a clear picture of salt domes and other geol formations.

2. MAGNETIC SURVEYS

General. Magnetic exploration is the oldest geophysical method, dating to the 17th century; it is based almost exclusively on measurements of the earth's natural magnetism. Origin of the earth's magnetism is unknown, although its lack of constancy, which bears no relation to geologic bodies, has been explained. Magnetic surveys employ the ordinary compass, together with more precise magnetic instruments. The 2 factors measured are:

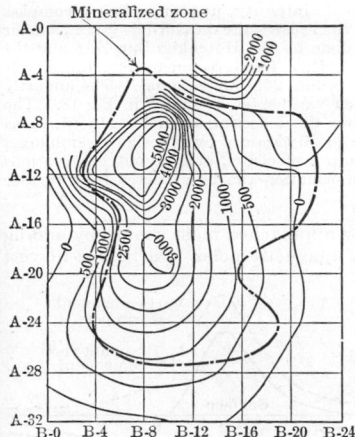

Fig 10. Correlation of Vert Isograms with Zone of Mineralization (5)

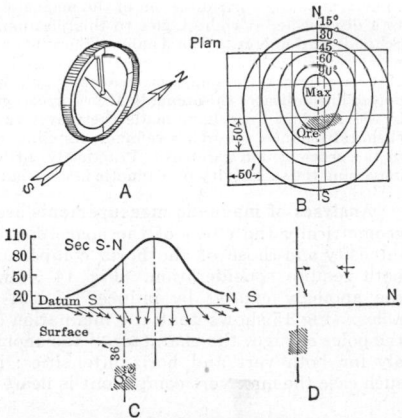

Fig 11. Dip Needle parallel with Magnetic Meridian (6)

change in direction and intensity of the magnetic field. Change of direction in a horiz plane is a change in DECLINATION; that in the vert plane is a change in INCLINATION. Declination measurements can be made with an ordinary compass, to which sights are attached for maintaining a constant direction. Inclination can be measured with a balanced needle swinging vertically in the plane of the magnetic meridian, as determined by compass. This instrument may be called a dipping needle. The balance is tested by turning it at right angles to the magnetic field; the needle then assuming a vert position and deviating equal amounts from the vert for equal displacements in opposite directions from this right-angle position. The results are charted as profiles, or as iso-declination, or iso-inclination lines, connecting points having same deviations.

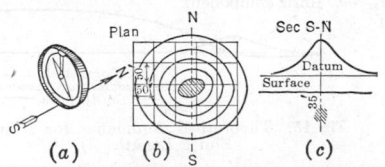

Fig 12. Dip Needle perpendicular to Magnetic Meridian (6)

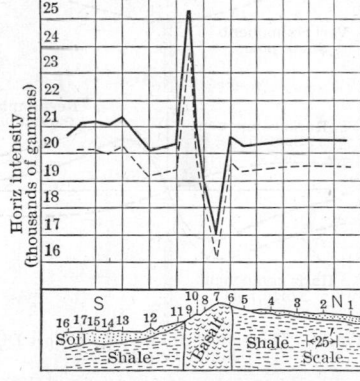

Fig 13. Survey of Horiz Magnetic Intensity, Valmont Dike Extension (7)

To measure changes in intensity of magnetism, the unit is the GAMMA, or 10^{-5} cgs units. The old-type dipping needle is sensitive to about 2 000 gammas per degree; improved instruments to about 200 gammas per degree. The dip needle outlines satisfactorily a magnetite deposit, as that in Fig 10, where the anomalies are large.

Dip needle. Two methods are followed. (a) That shown in Fig 11 places the plane of swing of the needle in direction of the magnetic field. The vert component of the field, governed by a single pole, has a max directly over the magnetic pole, whereas the max of the horiz component, having a value less than that of the vert max, lies to one side of the pole. Hence, the needle's deflection is not always directly over the poles, but is offset so that the ore lies under the more gently sloping side of the magnetic profile, Fig 11. (b) If observations are made with the needle swinging in a plane at right-angles to the magnetic meridian, only the vert component is effective, and the max deflection will coincide with the position of the magnetic anomaly (Fig 12). A non-magnetic tripod, which permits proper orientation of the needle, is best.

Magnetometer, for measuring variations in vert magnetic intensity, uses an ordinary compass to determine the horiz direction of the magnetic field, and then places the measuring system, similar to a dip needle, at right-angles to this position. This is done by the Hotchkiss Superdip and the Schmidt variometer. The Thalen-Tiberg magnetometer and its simplification by Brunton permit measurement of variations in horiz magnetic intensity exceeding 200–300 gammas. The anomaly of a basaltic dike in shale, as measured by a horiz Thalen variometer, is shown in Fig 13. The dotted line indicates the anomaly after correction for length of the deflecting magnet. Modifications by the Askania Corp have made the movement sensitive to 20 gammas by a design resembling a chemical balance. Further refinements eliminate the temp coefficients, and permit observations to the order of 3–5 gammas. Practically, little added information can be expected from further increasing the sensitivity of magnetic instruments.

Analyses of magnetic measurements are probably approached most simply by adding geometrically the effect of the space distribution of magnetic poles. Variations in vert intensity and those of the horiz component both require consideration. Fig 14 shows the anomaly caused by induced N and S poles. Fig 15 shows that the inclination of the poles changes the character of the anomaly for both vert and horiz intensities; in such case the max vert component is nearest

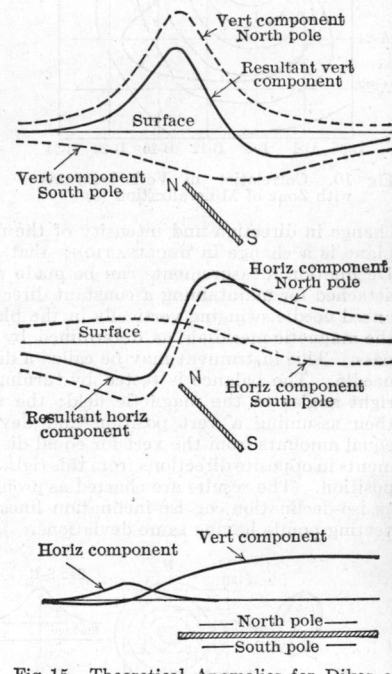

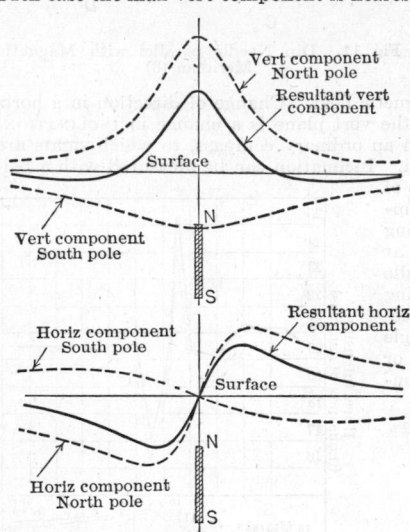

Fig 14. Theoretical Anomalies for Vert Dike of Finite Length (5)

Fig 15. Theoretical Anomalies for Dikes of Finite Length (5)

the source of the anomaly, whereas the max horiz component is not directly over the pole.

The character of the function representing magnetic intensity depends on polarities and strength of the induced poles, and their distribution over the body producing the anomaly. If the body parallels the earth's field and has infinite vert extent, as a narrow dike in the magnetic meridian or a volcanic pipe paralleling the magnetic resultant, only the magnetic poles induced on top of the body need be considered, since the poles on the bottom are so distant as to be negligible. Magnetic intensity of a narrow dike is represented by an inverse first-power function. In case of the volcanic pipe, the poles on top are regarded as a point source, the magnetic intensity being represented by an inverse-square function. If the body is a sheet of finite thickness, so that poles of opposite polarity induced on upper and lower surfaces of the body are both at finite distances from the surface and hence both effective in determining the intensity, the function is an inverse-cube. Generally, the intensity function is complicated by geometrical and intensity factors having no common relation.

Fig 16 shows that the elements causing the 3 functions do not produce different types of anomalies, but only different intensities. Unless the form of the body is known, correct interpretation is difficult. Fig 17 shows the magnetic profile across a nickel orebody, striking E–W. The theoretical vert anomaly indicates the function to be less than

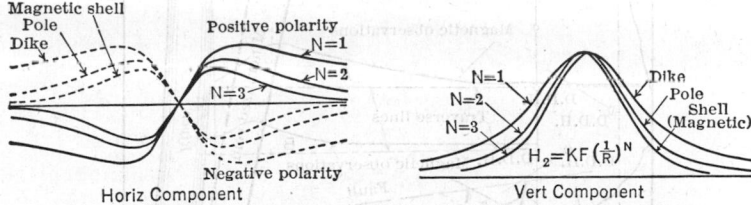

Fig 16. Variation in Magnetic Components for Dikes, Poles, and Shells (8)

$1 \div d$, because the poles are distributed over the sides separated by the dike's width. If the strike of the dike were N–S, the top only would enter the computation, which would be for a simple inverse function. The horiz component, measured by a variometer, shows the general anomaly at about 100 ft N of the pole. The incongruent portion of the horiz magnetic curve south of the dike indicates another of smaller size, which could not have been found by the vert magnetometer alone.

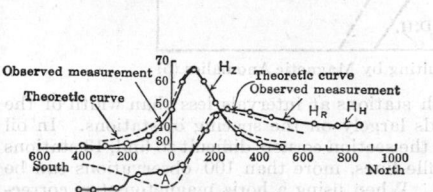

Fig 17. Comparison of Observed and Computed Curves of Vert and Horiz Magnetic Intensity Variations (8)

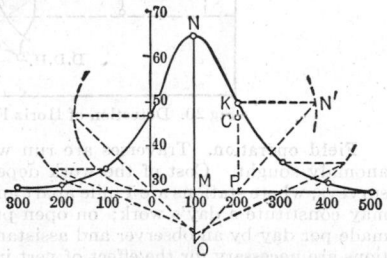

Fig 18. Approximation of Depth of Dike from Vert Magnetic Profile (8)

To ascertain the shape and depth of the source of magnetic anomalies requires knowledge of magnetic field theory. In case of a dike, relatively simple relations can be used (Fig 18). At any point P of the traverse, erect PK, passing through the anomaly curve. About a center C on PK pass circle PN', with radius CP equal to 0.5 MN, through point P and tangent to the base line. Through K pass line KN' perpendicular to PK and MN, intersecting circle PN' at N'. Extend $N'P$ through P to line NM extended; intercept MO gives the depth. Similar construction starting at other points on the magnetic profile should check at same depth. An understanding of magnetic theory is necessary to determine the mode of analysis best suited to any particular case.

If the country rock is magnetic and the orebody is not, the body is defined by a reverse anomaly. Fig 19 shows a hematite body bordered by magnetite in slate. The magnetite causes the vert components to show a max on each side of the body and a magnetic low over it. In some places, faulting has caused the loss of a vein (Fig 20). Here, surveys of the vert magnetic variations indicate the displaced position of

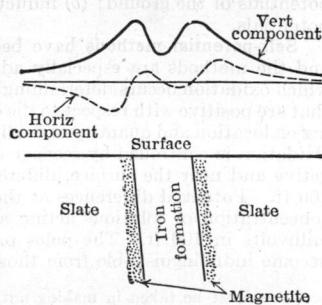

Fig 19. Typical Magnetic Anomalies for Conditions as shown (5)

the orebody, and the amount of shift along the fault; a magnetic high on the edge of the vein characterizes the formation. Local measurements often show features of an area definitely outlining magnetically different rocks related to the vein.

Magnetic variations sometimes reflect changes of elev of the crystalline basement. In such surveys, very small but important anomalies exist; great care is needed to avoid false observations, since the measurement involves differences of only a few gammas. As diurnal variations are often far greater than the anomaly, a base station is used with a second instrument to give the proper correction for the time of each observation. Magnetic storms often prevent such work. Horiz sedimentary formations free from folding may contain considerable magnetite without greatly altering the picture of the underlying basement rock, if the magnetite is uniformly distributed over the area.

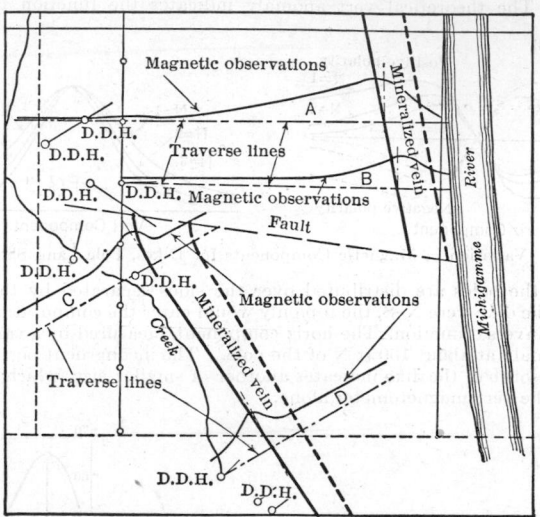

Fig 20. Detection of Horiz Faulting by Magnetic Anomalies (5)

Field operation. Traverses are run with stations at intervals less than width of the anomaly sought. Cost of the work depends largely on the spacing of stations. In oil surveys, where stations are 1 mile apart and the section corners difficult to find, 13 stations may constitute a day's work; on open profile lines, more than 100 observations can be made per day by an observer and assistant. When using a horiz magnetometer, corrections are necessary for the effect of vert intensity. Fig 21 is a chart for this purpose, prepared by U S Coast and Geodetic Survey.

3. ELECTRICAL METHODS

These methods are in 2 main groups: (a) Self-potential methods measure the natural potentials of the ground; (b) induction methods measure artificially-applied currents and potentials.

Self-potential methods have been widely used. The elec field is of chemical origin and the methods are especially adapted to oxidizing sulphide deposits, the manner in which oxidation occurs determining the polarity. Oxidation at the top produces solutions that are positive with respect to the ore. Ore at depth may be positive or negative, depending on location and quantity of oxidized substances in the material at the point of reference. Oxidation is controlled by seepage of meteoric waters containing O. Where deposits are active and near the surface, differences of 500 millivolts may occur over an interval of 100 ft. Potential differences at the surface are common and often due to differences of concentration of solutions acting as concentration cells. These are of the order of 20 millivolts in 100 ft. The poles produced by deposits at increasing depths eventually become indistinguishable from those present from other sources.

Care must be taken in making natural-potential surveys to avoid variable ground potentials, which may originate in auroral discharges, artificial sources, or magnetic storms. Fig 22 shows a section across a sulphide deposit undergoing oxidation from the top. Ground contacts are made at e and e' by non-polarizing electrodes, and the potential difference is measured by potentiometer P; conductor L completes the circuit.

Field surveys. There are 2 methods: (a) using a comparatively short distance between e and e' (Fig 22), most useful where the terrain is difficult; (b) keeping 1 electrode

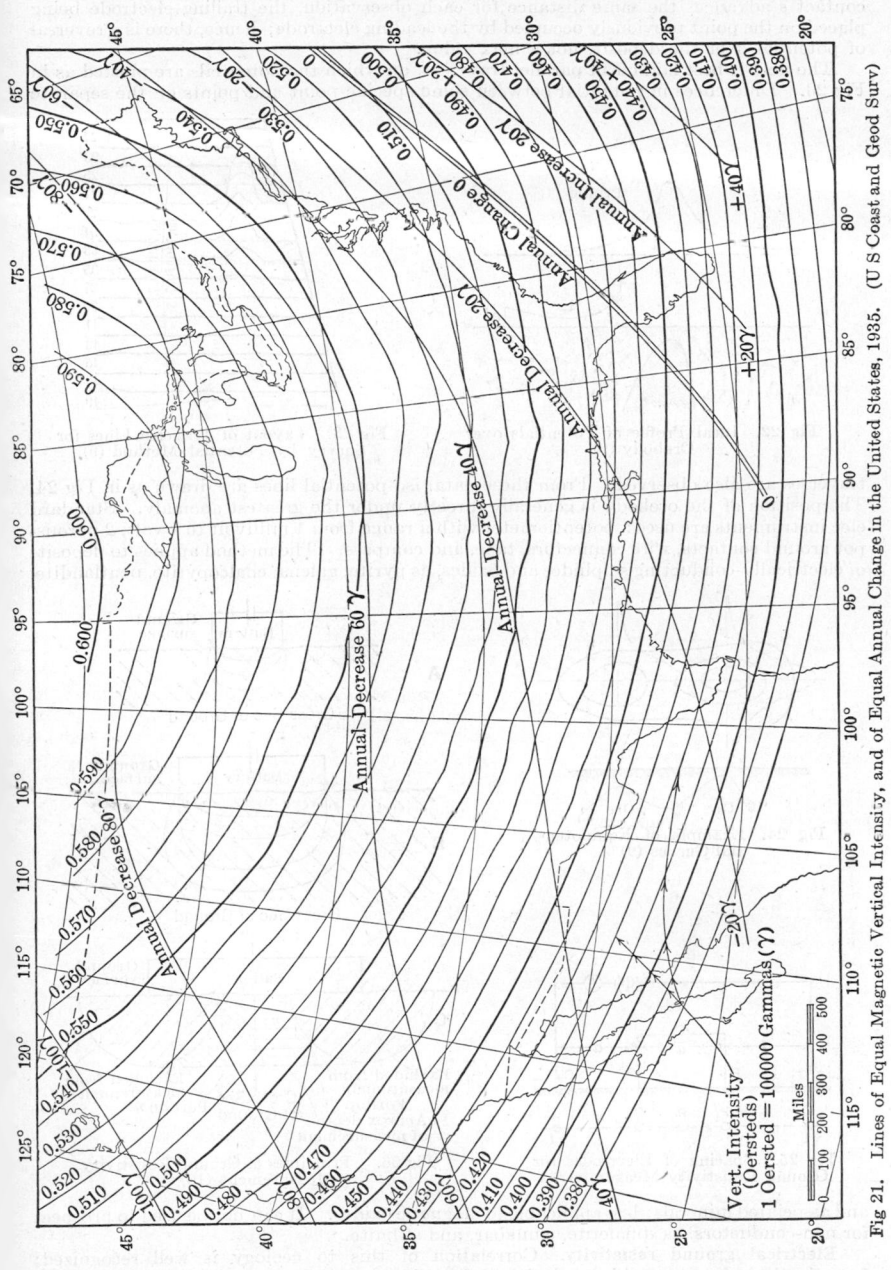

Fig 21. Lines of Equal Magnetic Vertical Intensity, and of Equal Annual Change in the United States, 1935. (U S Coast and Geod Surv)

e' fixed and gradually increasing interval L.   In Fig 22 L is short, and the leading ground contact e advances the same distance for each observation, the trailing electrode being placed on the point previously occupied by the leading electrode; hence, there is a reversal of potential over the deposit, not a max value.

The field is best laid off in parallel traverses, on which the potentials are plotted as in Fig 23.   Differences in potential between some specific point and points on the separate

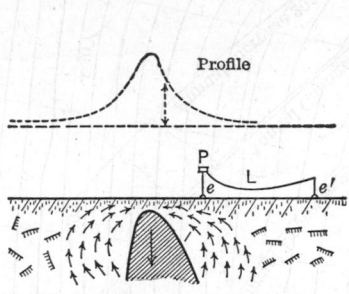

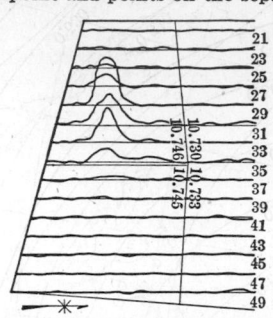

Fig 22.   Ideal Profile of Potentials over Orebody (9)

Fig 23.   Layout of Traverse Lines for Survey by Potential Method (9)

traverses are also observed.   From these data, iso-potential lines are drawn as in Fig 24. The position of the orebody is generally directly under the greatest anomaly.   Standard elec instruments are used: potentiometer with a range from 1 millivolt to 1 volt, 2 porous-pot ground contacts, wire connectors, tape, and compass.   The method applies to deposits of electrically-conducting sulphides and oxides, as pyrite, galena, chalcopyrite, pentlandite,

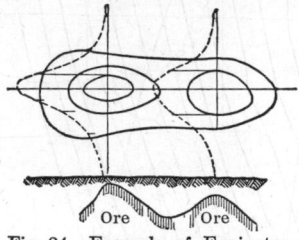

Fig 24.   Example of Equipotential Curves (9)

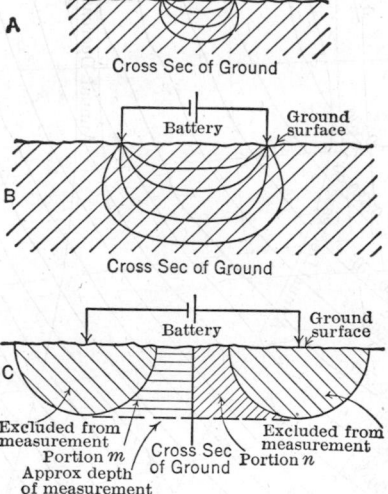

Fig 26.   Principles of Ground Resistivity Measurement (10)

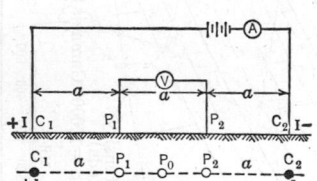

Fig 25.   Spacing of Electrodes for Ground Resistivity Measurements

and associated minerals; less applicable to magnetic oxides.   It can not be used to prospect for non-conductors, as sphalerite, cinnabar, and stibnite.

Electrical ground resistivity.   Correlation of this to geology is well recognized; investigations have provided solutions of problems relating to geol formations and structures, even where few surface indications were available.

In this method, the earth is regarded as a medium having ohmic resistance, and much work has been done regarding the distribution of currents and potentials.   Practical results often give enough information for the purpose. It has been found that certain factors so complicate the laws of ohmic conductivity as to put theoretic conclusions at variance with physical observations. Such factors are the non-uniformity of resistivity with current density, anisotropy, the combination of electrolytic activity associated with ohmic conductivity, and the channeling of the current instead of a uniform distribution through the medium. Hence, a simple number, neither exact nor aver, called APPARENT GROUND RESISTIVITY, is taken as an index and computed on the assumption of a simple distribution of currents and voltages in a uniform isotropic medium.

Two methods for measuring the apparent ground resistivity are: (a) Schlumberger places the current electrodes in the ground very far apart and measures the earth resistivity near one of the contacts, neglecting the effects of the distant electrode; (b) a method first used by Wenner makes equal spaces between current and potential electrodes (Fig 25). This has been modified by Lee, who introduces a third potential electrode P_0, midway between P_1 and P_2, permitting ground comparisons, determination of geol continuity, and elimination of surface resistivity anomalies not related to deeper formations. Fig 26 shows the general principle of the modified Wenner method. The effective field penetrates deeper into the ground when the battery contacts are moved farther apart. The ground around the electrodes is excluded from measurement and the mid-section divided into 2 parts m and n for comparison. Deeper observations are made by gradually separating the electrodes, keeping point A fixed (Fig 27B). As new material is encountered (Fig 28, a, b, c) the apparent resistivity

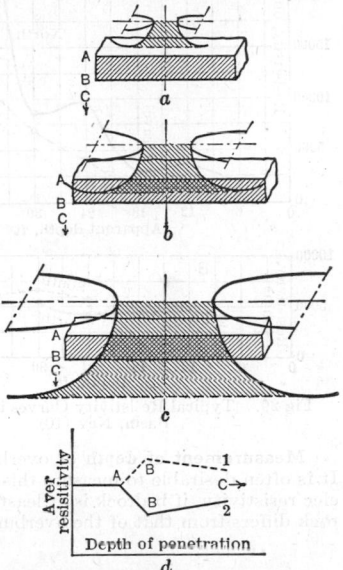

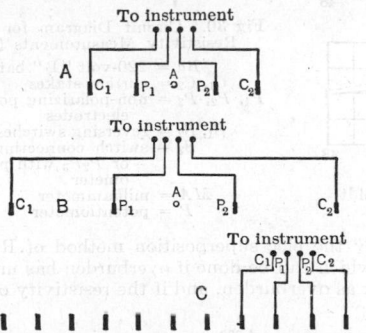

Fig 27. Stake Layout for Measuring Resistivity. A and B, for increasing depths at one point. C, for constant depth along a line (11)

Fig 28. Effect of Increasing Depths on Resistivity Curves (11)

varies with the elec resistivity of the deeper material. It may often be preferable to maintain a fixed spacing and move the whole elec configuration along a line, as in Fig 27C, for discovering lateral changes of ground material.

Fig 29 shows application of this method for determining gravel beds, illustrating the changes in apparent ground resistivity with depth. The gravel has high resistivity, causing the curve (Fig 29A) to rise rapidly after it is encountered at a depth of 18 ft on the N side of the instrument. Similar conditions exist on the S side, except that the resistivity is lower, indicating more silt. The bed extends to depth of 36 ft before meeting clay. The second pair of curves (Fig 29B) indicate uniform ground, containing no gravel to depth of 48 ft. In the method of ground measurements shown in Fig 30, the current contacts can be made regardless of polarization, whereas the potential contacts are best made with non-polarizable electrodes. Reversing switches in both the current and potential circuits are needed to eliminate natural ground potential. If variable ground currents are present, commutating devices operating simultaneously on both current and potential circuits, as used by Gish, are preferable; but commutated current is disadvantageous, owing to the small amount of current used on high-resistance ground, compared to the charging current. Also, for great depths, the skin effect, or lack of current penetrations, is a limiting and disturbing factor.

Simple mathematical relations. For a simple isotropic medium the relation between potential and current is (see Fig 25):

$$V = \frac{I\rho}{2\pi}\left[\frac{1}{r_1} - \frac{1}{r_2} - \frac{1}{r_3} + \frac{1}{r_4}\right],$$ where V = voltage between the potential electrodes, P_1 and P_2; I = current in amperes applied to the ground; r_1 = distance P_1 to C_1, cm; r_2 = distance P_1 to C_2, cm; r_3 = distance P_2 to C_1, cm; r_4 = distance P_2 to C_2, cm; π = 3.1416; ρ = resistivity in ohm-centimeters (ohms per cubic cm).

In the Wenner configuration, $C_1P_1 = P_1P_2 = P_2C_2 = a$, and the above formula reduces to $\rho = 2\pi a \dfrac{V}{I}$ ohm-centimeters.

In the Lee configuration, $C_1P_1 = 2\,P_1P_0 = 2\,P_0P_2 = P_2C_2 = a$, and the above formula reduces to $\rho = 4\pi a \dfrac{V}{I}$.

If a is measured in ft, $\rho = 191.5\,a\,\dfrac{V}{I}$ ohm-centimeters for the Wenner configuration; $\rho = 383\,a\,\dfrac{V}{I}$ ohm-centimeters for the Lee configuration.

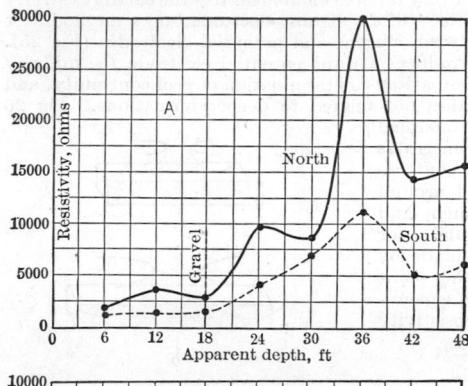

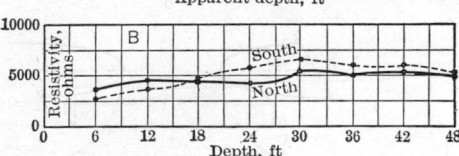

Fig 29. Typical Resistivity Curves in Humboldt Basin, Nev (10)

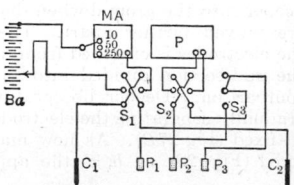

Fig 30. Circuit Diagram for Earth Resistivity Measurements (12)

Ba = 220-volt "B" battery
C_1, C_2 = current stakes
P_1, P_2, P_3 = non-polarizing potential electrodes
S_1, S_2 = reversing switches
S_3 = switch connecting P_1P_3 or P_2P_3 with potentiometer
MA = milliammeter
P = potentiometer

Measurement of depth of overburden by the elec superposition method of Roman. It is often desirable to measure this depth, which can be done if overburden has uniform elec resistivity, if bedrock is at least as thick as overburden, and if the resistivity of bedrock differs from that of the overburden.

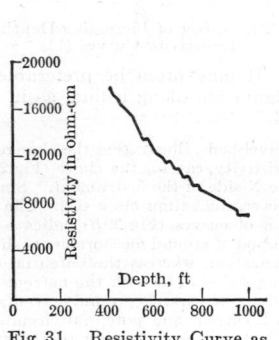

Fig 31. Resistivity Curve as Measured (13)

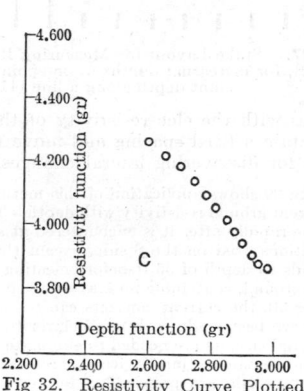

Fig 32. Resistivity Curve Plotted from Conversion Table (13)

Details for an example of sand and gravel on clay are as follows:

(A) Using the Wenner or other suitable electrodes, obtain a resistivity-depth curve (Fig 31) by changing the spacing.

(B) Replot this curve logarithmically (Fig 32) from Table 1 for both axes; GR is mantissa of the log of the number NO. In Fig 31, depth 400 ft and resistivity 18 000 are coordinates of first point; corresponding logs, from Table 1, are 2.602 and 4.255, where .602 and .255 are the mantissas in the table; 2 and 4, the characteristics for 3 and 5 digit numbers respectively. If the curve rises to the right, the underlying bed is an insulator; if the curve falls, a conductor.

Table 1. Plotting Table

NO	GR	NO	GR	NO	GR	NO	GR	NO	GR	NO	GR	NO	GR	NO	GR	NO	GR
100	000	200	301	300	477	400	602	500	699	600	778	700	845	800	903	900	954
105	021	205	312	305	484	405	607	505	703	605	782	705	848	805	906	905	957
110	041	210	322	310	491	410	613	510	708	610	785	710	851	810	908	910	959
115	061	215	332	315	498	415	618	515	712	615	789	715	854	815	911	915	961
120	079	220	342	320	505	420	623	520	716	620	792	720	857	820	914	920	964
125	097	225	352	325	512	425	628	525	720	625	796	725	860	825	916	925	966
130	114	230	362	330	519	430	633	530	724	630	799	730	863	830	919	930	968
135	130	235	371	335	525	435	638	535	728	635	803	735	866	835	922	935	971
140	146	240	380	340	531	440	643	540	732	640	806	740	869	840	924	940	973
145	161	245	389	345	538	445	648	545	736	645	810	745	872	845	927	945	975
150	176	250	398	350	544	450	653	550	740	650	813	750	875	850	929	950	978
155	190	255	407	355	550	455	658	555	744	655	816	755	878	855	932	955	980
160	204	260	415	360	556	460	663	560	748	660	820	760	881	860	934	960	982
165	217	265	423	365	562	465	667	565	752	665	823	765	884	865	937	965	985
170	230	270	431	370	568	470	672	570	756	670	826	770	886	870	940	970	987
175	243	275	439	375	574	475	677	575	760	675	829	775	889	875	942	975	989
180	255	280	447	380	580	480	681	580	763	680	833	780	892	880	944	980	991
185	267	285	455	385	585	485	686	585	767	685	836	785	895	885	947	985	993
190	279	290	462	390	591	490	690	590	771	690	839	790	898	890	949	990	996
195	290	295	470	395	597	495	695	595	775	695	842	795	900	895	952	995	998
199	299	299	476	399	601	499	698	599	777	699	844	799	903	899	954	1000	000

(*C*) Template curves, Fig 33, 34, best plotted on transparent sheet, are provided. Two groups of master curves are given, one for high-resistance or insulator beds and one for low-resistance or

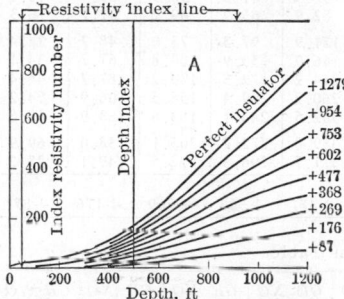

Fig 33. High-resistance Bed (13)

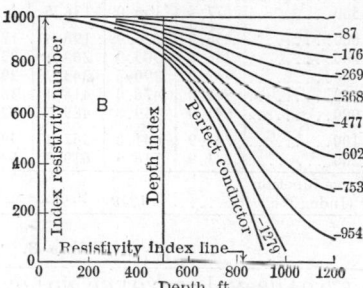

Fig 34. Low-resistance Bed (13)

conducting beds. Table 2 gives values from which the master curves of Fig 33, 34 are plotted, and serves for plotting the templates on a larger scale. Care must be taken in plotting the observational curve (Fig 32), to see that the scale for a logarithmic cycle is the same as that on the template master curves.

(*D*) Slide the template over the curve of Fig 32, as in Fig 35, until the observational curve coincides approx with a master curve. In Fig 35, the curve falls along the conducting-bed master curve, having curve index number −753.

(*E*) Depth index line of the template shows a value of 2.500 in observational curve sheet *C* (Fig 35). Using Table 3 for *GR* = 500, the corresponding number is 316 and, as the characteristic is 2, the depth is 316 ft.

(*F*) Overburden resistivity is obtained from the resistivity-index line intercept on curve sheet *C*, (Fig 35), in this case 4.440. The anti-log of this number being 27 500, the overburden resistivity is 27 500 ohm-cm.

(*G*) Logarithm of resistivity of the bedrock equals the resistivity-index intercept, plus curve-index number, or $4.440 - 0.753 = 3.687$, the antilog of which is 4 860 and the resistivity of bedrock is 4 860 ohm-cm.

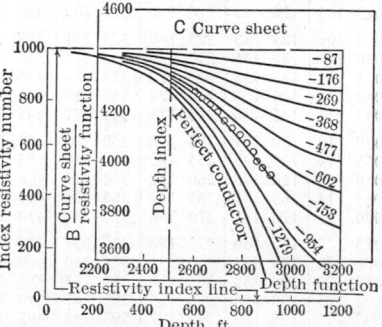

Fig 35. Resistivity Curve plotted from Conversion Table. Low-resistance Bed

Table 2. Master Chart Data

Low-resistance Bed

Depth	Resistivity index numbers									
100	983.8				981.2					
200	969.7				966.1		977.1		988.3	
300	944.8		955.3		966.1		977.1		988.3	
400	902.6		921.8		941.0		960.4		980.0	990.0
500	834.6	851.8	868.7	885.5	902.1	918.6	935.0	951.3	967.5	983.7
600	730.2	760.7	790.1	818.5	846.0	873.1	899.4	925.1	950.4	975.3
700	577.3	631.7	681.9	728.7	772.8	814.6	854.4	892.6	929.5	965.2
800	362.5	461.5	545.8	620.0	686.6	747.5	803.8	856.6	906.5	954.2
900	70.1	256.8	394.4	504.9	598.4	680.4	754.1	821.6	884.5	943.7
1 000		45.9	253.2	402.9	522.4	623.4	712.0	792.0	865.6	934.5
1 100			151.3	330.7	468.4	582.4	681.2	769.9	851.3	927.5
1 200			94.6	289.6	436.3	557.0	661.3	755.0	841.4	922.5
Curve function (Index No.)		−1279	−954	−753	−602	−477	−368	−269	−176	−87

High-resistance Bed

Depth	Resistivity index numbers									
0	11.3									
100	21.4				11.7					
200	39.2				21.5					
300	68.9		52.4		38.0		24.7		12.1	
400	114.3	100.3	87.5	75.4	63.8	52.5	41.6	30.9	20.4	10.1
500	177.4	156.0	136.5	118.0	100.2	82.9	65.9	49.2	32.7	16.3
600	256.3	226.0	198.4	172.2	146.7	121.9	97.3	73.0	48.7	24.4
700	346.6	305.9	269.1	234.2	200.3	166.9	133.9	100.8	67.7	34.1
800	443.0	390.5	343.7	299.4	256.4	214.2	172.3	130.2	87.7	44.4
900	542.0	476.0	418.1	363.8	311.5	260.2	209.4	158.5	106.9	54.2
1 000	641.9	559.8	489.7	424.7	362.8	302.5	243.1	183.8	123.9	62.8
1 100	741.9	641.0	557.1	480.7	409.0	339.8	272.2	205.1	138.0	69.9
1 200	841.9	718.9	619.9	531.5	449.6	371.7	296.3	222.5	149.1	75.2
Curve function (Index No.)		+1279	+954	+753	+602	+477	+368	+269	+176	+87

Table 3. Interpretation Table

GR	NO	GR	NO	GR	NO	GR	NO	GR	NO	GR	NO	GR	NO	GR	NO	GR	NO	GR	NO
000	100	100	126	200	158	300	200	400	251	500	316	600	398	700	501	800	631	900	794
005	101	105	127	205	160	305	202	405	254	505	320	605	403	705	507	805	638	905	804
010	102	110	129	210	162	310	204	410	257	510	324	610	407	710	513	810	646	910	813
015	104	115	130	215	164	315	207	415	260	515	327	615	412	715	519	815	653	915	822
020	105	120	132	220	166	320	209	420	263	520	331	620	417	720	525	820	661	920	832
025	106	125	133	225	168	325	211	425	266	525	335	625	422	725	531	825	668	925	841
030	107	130	135	230	170	330	214	430	269	530	339	630	427	730	537	830	676	930	851
035	108	135	136	235	172	335	216	435	272	535	343	635	432	735	543	835	684	935	861
040	110	140	138	240	174	340	219	440	275	540	347	640	437	740	550	840	692	940	871
045	111	145	140	245	176	345	221	445	279	545	351	645	442	745	556	845	700	945	881
050	112	150	141	250	178	350	224	450	282	550	355	650	447	750	562	850	708	950	891
055	114	155	143	255	180	355	226	455	285	555	359	655	452	755	569	855	716	955	902
060	115	160	145	260	182	360	229	460	288	560	363	660	457	760	575	860	724	960	912
065	116	165	146	265	184	365	232	465	292	565	367	665	462	765	582	865	733	965	923
070	117	170	148	270	186	370	234	470	295	570	372	670	468	770	589	870	741	970	933
075	119	175	150	275	188	375	237	475	299	575	376	675	473	775	596	875	750	975	944
080	120	180	151	280	191	380	240	480	302	580	380	680	479	780	603	880	759	980	955
085	122	185	153	285	193	385	243	485	305	585	385	685	484	785	610	885	767	985	966
090	123	190	155	290	195	390	245	490	309	590	389	690	490	790	617	890	776	990	977
095	124	195	157	295	197	395	248	495	313	595	394	695	495	795	624	895	785	995	989
099	126	199	158	299	199	399	251	499	316	599	397	699	500	799	630	899	793	999	998

Alternating-current and inductive methods, formerly confined exclusively to mineral prospecting, are now used also for oil. They aim to measure the reaction of a geol body to the change of a magnetic field passing through it. Usually they employ alternating magnetic fields with frequencies of 500 cycles per sec. The measured distortion of the original field, in phase and amplitude, is related to the body causing the anomaly. Since the resultant magnetic field is always plane and elliptically polarized, the position of the plane in space and the axes of the ellipse must be determined; hence the measurements of the complete field distribution are slow, and restricted to certain components directly related to the anomaly, but are not contained in the main exciting field, thereby simplifying interpretation.

An inductive method, of NUNIER, permits measurement of resistivity to increasing depth, without losing geol continuity, by placing on the ground a coil the diameter of which is proportional to depth desired. The coil is excited with an alternating current. A small exploring coil in the center

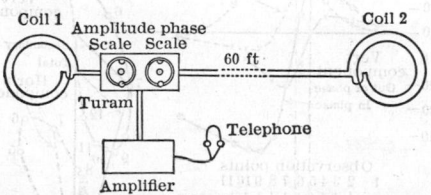

Fig 36. Apparatus used in Turam Method (14)

is adjusted to measure the magnetic field from the induced current in the ground. Various frequencies are used to avoid errors from skin effect. A curve, plotted between depth of penetration and the resistivities observed, is the inductive counterpart of the Wenner system. POTENTIAL RATIO method applies a c to the ground, and measures the ratio between 2 pairs of points in the field by a bridge circuit in which the potential differences of the earth circuits are 2 arms in the bridge, while

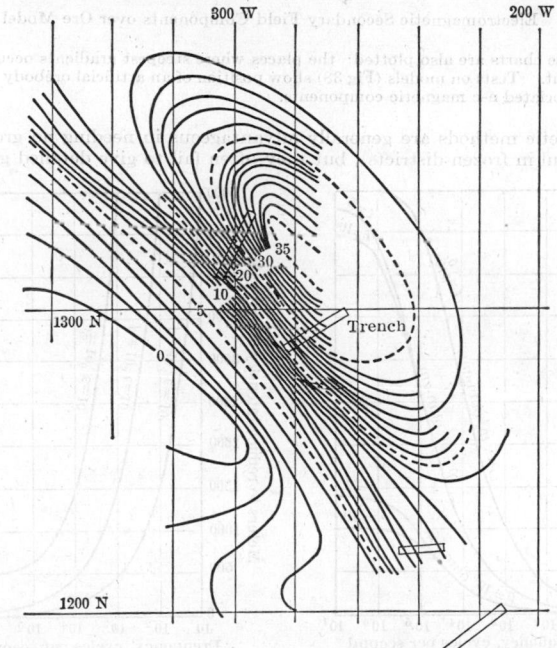

Fig 37. Equiphase Curves in Electromagnetic Field over Orebody discovered Electrically (14)

the other 2 arms are in the measuring set and adjustable for making a balance. Measurements are made along profiles with a definite spacing. Changes of impedance and impedance ratios are correlated with the geology. In the BIELER-WATSON method, a large coil of about 600 by 1 200 ft is placed on the ground and excited by a 500-cycle a c. Induced voltages are measured in a 2-coil system, adjusted in the resultant plane of vibration, and balanced against each other through circuit arrangements; the ratio of minor to major axis of the polarization ellipse is entered on the charts, and iso-anomaly lines are drawn. The TURAM method employs a long, straight conductor, laid on the ground, grounded at each end, and supplied with a c. Two coils (Fig 36), a fixed distance apart, are used to run traverses at right angles to this wire, and changes of phase and amplitude are measured between the induced voltages in each coil. Iso-phase curves are then charted as in Fig 37;

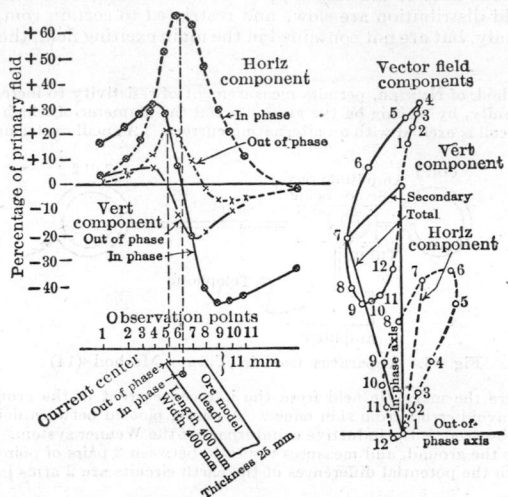

Fig 38.   Electromagnetic Secondary Field Components over Ore Model (14)

iso-phase-difference charts are also plotted; the places where steepest gradients occur on the charts are the areas sought. Tests on models (Fig 38) show position of an artificial orebody and the change of the various associated a-c magnetic components.

Electromagnetic methods are generally advantageous in needing no ground contacts (especially helpful in frozen districts), but they often fail to give detailed geol definition,

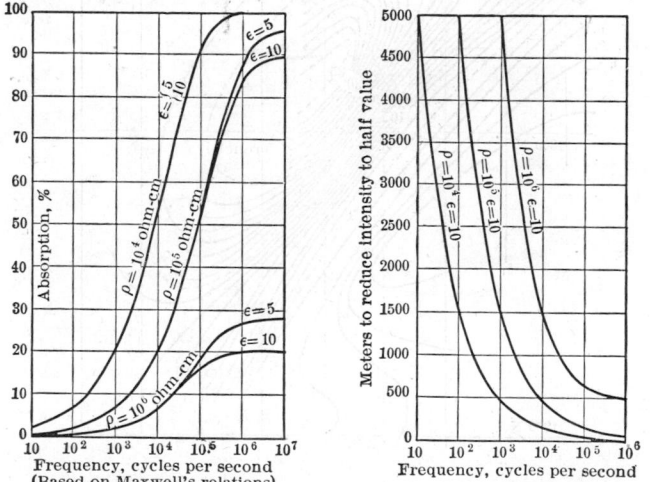

Fig 39.   Absorption of Plane-polarized Electromagnetic Waves in Homogeneous Media (15)

and often do not permit restriction of vert or lateral boundaries to certain limits. The theoretic values of current and potential distribution, even under simple assumptions, are difficult to calculate, especially if the orebody is imbedded in an electrically conducting medium. These methods now rest on a quasi-scientific basis. Changes in amplitude of electromagnetic waves when passing over dikes and faults are noticeable for certain frequencies and can be used for mapping them.

High-frequency radio waves are not well adapted to geophysical work. There is a lack of penetration, due both to skin effect and to absorption of the waves by the rocks. Since the dielectric constant of water is 80, and that of rocks much less, geol anomalies are difficult to identify by using high

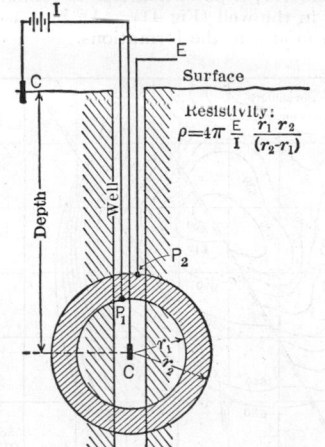

Fig 40. Resistivity about a Single Electrode. Adapted from E. R. Shepard (12)

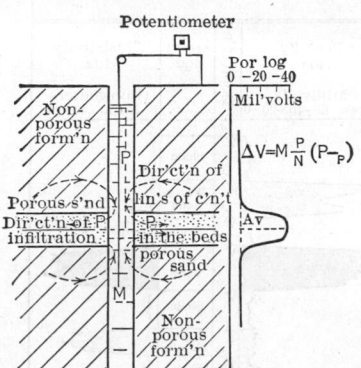

Fig 41. Recognition of Porous Beds by Resistivity Measurements (16)

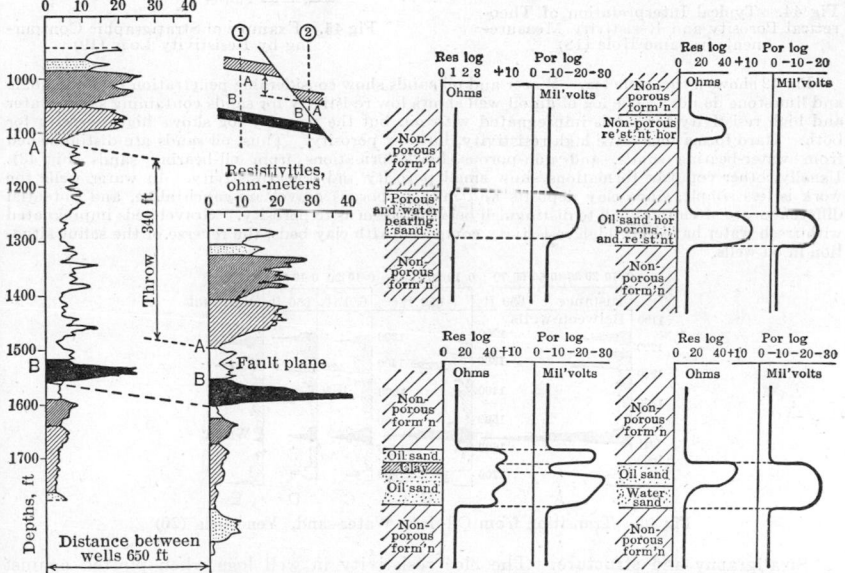

Fig 42. Solution of a Fault by Resistivity Measurements in Boreholes (17)

Fig 43. Interpretation of Resistivity Measurements in Boreholes (16)

frequencies, as they are often concealed by effects due to water in the rocks. The percentage absorption of a plane-polarized magnetic wave, and the depth in meters required to halve the intensity, are shown in Fig 39.

Electrical well logging, according to Schlumberger, comprises measurement of elec resistivities of the formations penetrated by drill hole or well, and charting the values at successive depths, and includes elec observations related to porosity of the formations. To measure RESISTIVITY, a set of electrodes, $(P_2, P_1, C,$ Fig 40) is gradually lowered into the well; current I is held constant and the potential E is registered on a recording chart. The resistivity is proportional to the measured potential, since $\rho = 4\pi \dfrac{E}{I} \dfrac{r_1 r_2}{r_2 - r_1}$ in which all factors except E are constant. To measure POROSITY, a potentiometer is connected from one electrode at top of the well and a second in the well (Fig 41). An increase in potential indicates a wider spreading of the drilling mud into the formations.

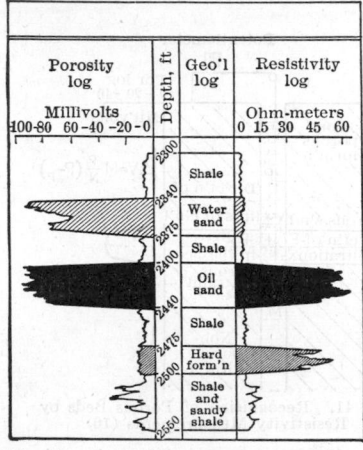

Fig 44. Typical Interpretation of Theoretical Porosity and Resistivity Measurements in Same Hole (18)

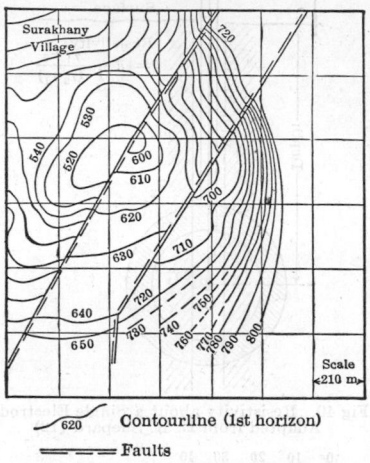

Fig 45. Example of Stratigraphic Contouring by Resistivity Logs (19)

Fig 42 shows a theoretic log. Water and oil sands show considerable penetration of mud; shale and limestone do not. The log of an oil well shows low resistivity for sands containing saline water and high resistivity for sands impregnated with oil, but the porosity log shows high porosity for both. Hard formations have high resistivity, but low porosity. Thus, oil sands are distinguished from water-bearing sands, and non-porous, hard formations from oil-bearing sands (Fig 43). Usually, other compact formations show small porosity and high resistivity. In water wells the work is less simple, since clay deposits and mud in porous gravel are much alike, and potential differences are often too small to distinguish between them as to porosity. Gravel beds impregnated with fresh water have very high resistivity compared with clay beds, the reverse of the saline situation in oil wells.

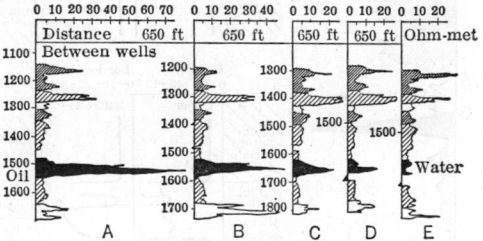

Fig 46. Transition from Oil- into Water-sand, Venezuela (20)

Stratigraphy and structure. The elec resistivity in well logs when plotted against depth forms well defined profiles. By comparing these (Fig 44), and identifying corresponding sequences, faults may be located and their throws measured. To contour the elev of certain identifiable beds, resistivity logs from dry wells are valuable for both stratigraphic and structural information (Fig 45). Resistivity logs of wells are also useful for determining the salt-water boundary of oil pools (Fig 46). Resistivities of oil beds are high, gradually tapering towards the water-impregnated boundaries. Fig 47 shows 3 producing horizons; also an anticlinal structure continuing up into comparatively shallow beds.

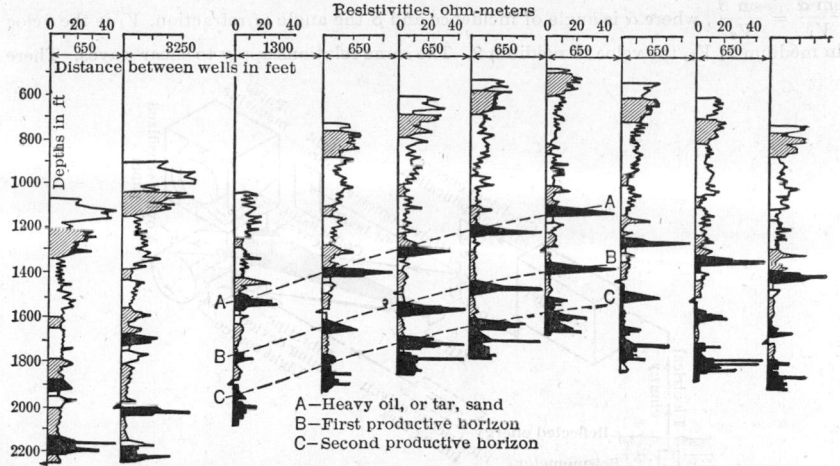

Fig 47.   Example of Oil Structure disclosed by Resistivity Logs (17)

A—Heavy oil, or tar, sand
B—First productive horizon
C—Second productive horizon

4. SEISMIC PROSPECTING (20-22)

General. Seismic prospecting utilizes waves artificially generated in the ground, and examines their path, veloc, time, and character from their origin to their destination. Waves in a homogeneous medium are: (a) dilatational or compressional, similar to sound waves; (b) transverse or shear waves, like light or electromagnetic waves.

Certain combinations of physical constants of the medium determine the veloc of elastic waves. With simplifications due to Macalwain, the factors are:

1. Young's modulus, $E = \dfrac{Fl_0}{A_0 \delta l}$, where F is the stress; l_0, the original length before stress was applied; A_0, the original area before stress was applied; δl, the change in length in direction of the stress.

2. Poisson's ratio, $\sigma = \dfrac{\delta d / d_0}{\delta l / l_0} = \dfrac{l_0 \delta d}{d_0 \delta l}$, where l_0 and d_0 are the original length and diam of the material before stress; δl and δd are the changes of length and diam after stress.

3. Sum of the principle stresses, $X + Y + Z = \dfrac{E\theta}{1 - 2\sigma}$, where X, Y, and Z are the components of the stress F in the x, y, and z directions, and θ is the cubic or volume dilatation; the latter has the value $\theta = \dfrac{\partial V' - \partial V}{\partial V}$, where ∂V and $\partial V'$ are volumes of an element of constant mass δm before and after application of stress F.

4. Lame's constant, $\lambda = \dfrac{\sigma E}{(1 + \sigma)(1 - 2\sigma)}$.   5. Coefficient of rigidity, $\mu = \dfrac{E}{2(1 + \sigma)}$.

6. Bulk modulus, $K = \dfrac{E}{3(1 - 2\sigma)}$.   7. Coefficient of incompressibility, $1 \div k$.

8. Longitudinal veloc, $P = \sqrt{\dfrac{2\mu + \lambda}{\rho}} = \sqrt{\dfrac{K + 4/3\,\mu}{\rho}} = \sqrt{\dfrac{E(1 - \sigma)}{\rho(1 + \sigma)(1 - 2\sigma)}}$, where ρ is the density.

9. Shear-wave veloc, $S = \sqrt{\dfrac{\mu}{\rho}} = \sqrt{\dfrac{E}{2\rho(1 + \sigma)}}$; also: $\sigma = \dfrac{\frac{1}{2}\left(\dfrac{P}{S}\right)^2 - 1}{\left(\dfrac{P}{S}\right)^2 - 1}$.

If an impulse is applied to homogeneous ground, the first arrival is a longit or P wave; followed by a shear or S wave, and then by surface (Rayleigh) waves, the origin of which is controlled by surface boundary conditions.

Seismic prospecting methods, now current, utilize the first arrival of the P or compression waves, which are similar to sound waves and reflected and refracted at surfaces of discontinuity. For reflection, angle of incidence = angle of reflection. For refraction,

$$\frac{\sin \alpha}{V_1} = \frac{\sin \beta}{V_2}$$, where α is angle of incidence and β the angle of refraction, V_1 is the veloc in medium 1; V_2, the veloc in medium 2. The same relations apply to shear waves. There

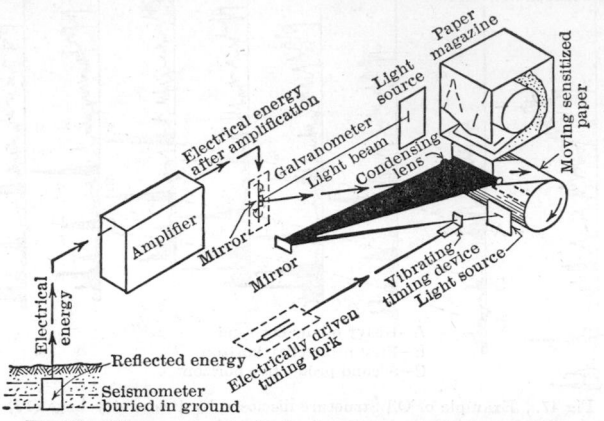

Fig 48. Diagram showing Reflection Seismograph System (21)

is a difference in seismic waves, as they can carry both compressional and shear stresses at boundaries of mediums, because a compressional wave will generate not only the usual reflected and refracted ray, but also a reflected and refracted shear wave. This difference is analysed best by considering the differential coefficients for both dilatation and shear on boundary conditions. The relations at such a contact surface of an impinging compression wave are (Macalwain):

$$\frac{\sin \alpha}{P'_1} = \frac{\sin \gamma}{P'_1} = \frac{\sin \delta}{S'_2} = \frac{\sin \eta}{P'_2} = \frac{\sin \zeta}{S'_2},$$

where P'_1 and P'_2 are velocities of compressional waves P_1 and P_2 in medium 1 and medium 2 respectively, and S'_1 and S'_2, are the velocities of shear waves S_1 and S_2 in mediums 1 and 2; α = angle of incidence of P_1; γ = angle of reflection of P_1; η = angle of refraction of P_1, $i\,e$, the direction of P_2 in medium 2; δ = angle of the shear wave generated in medium 1, and ζ that of the generated shear wave in medium 2. Similar analysis can be made of an impinging shear wave. The veloc of the waves in mediums 1 and 2, and the sine of the angle of incidence of the original wave, control the directions of generated waves. The equation shows that under certain conditions the sine is greater than 1, indicating that no such wave is possible. In seismic reflections, a series of waves are generated at such surfaces of discontinuity and internally reflected.

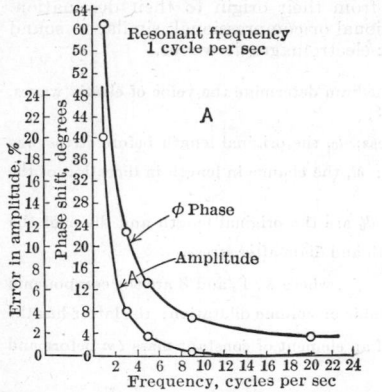

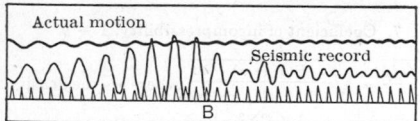

Fig 49. A. Error in Amplitude and Phase. B. Phase Reversal below Critical Frequency; Frequency increasing (22)

Apparatus for refraction and reflection prospecting is similar, except that the seismic "pick ups" need higher sensitivity for recording reflected vibrations (Fig 48). The wave impinges on the seismometer, usually buried in the ground to avoid wind and other disturbance. The seismometer transforms the mechanical into an elec impulse. The latter is amplified by automatic volume control for weak waves near the end of the record, and the output of the amplifier passes through an oscillographic element, the light beam from the latter passing through a condensing lens, to focus the image on sensitized paper. A second light beam is flashed across the paper every 0.01–0.05 sec by a tuning-fork to show elapsed time. The instant of the explosion furnishing the impulse is recorded by interruption of current in a wire wrapped around the explosive. Accuracy of vibration measurement is modified by the motion of the seismometer, when it begins to vibrate. Fig 49*A* shows the error which may occur in phase and amplitude, especially when nearing the resonant frequence, an operational condition to be avoided. Fig 49*B* shows a complete reversal of phase in recording on opposite sides of the instrument resonance point.

Shallow refraction is the simplest application of seismic prospecting as used to determine the bedrock depth for dam sites and depth of glacial drift. Fig 50 shows such a

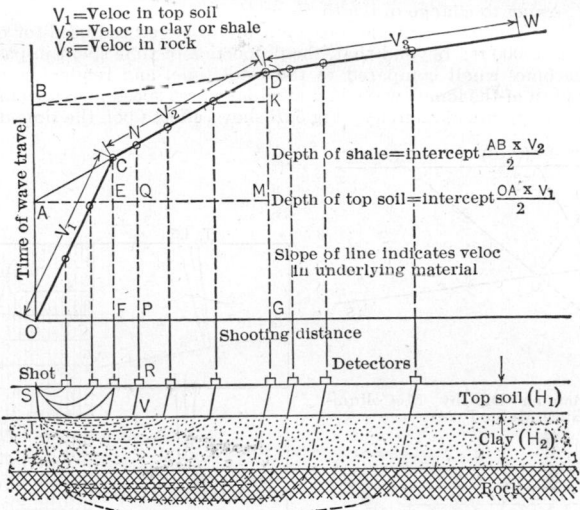

Fig 50. Time-distance Curves for First Arrival of Waves. Adapted from E. R. Shepard (12)

survey. The shot point is at *S*, from which seismic waves travel as indicated. The paths to the first detectors remain in topsoil; those to the second group pass through the soil twice and through the clay; those to the third group pass twice through both topsoil and

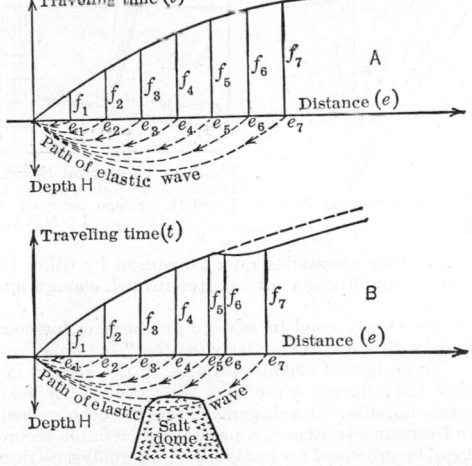

Fig 51. Mintrop Geological Testing Method. Adapted from Mintrop (23)

clay, and through the rock. Charting a travel-time curve shows that the curve consists of nearly straight lines, with a slope in each section inversely proportional to the wave speed in the lowest medium involved. If the angle of entrance is taken as 90°, an assumption usually introducing only a small error, the depths of the respective layers of topsoil, clay, and rock are as in Fig 50. When the contrast in speed between the beds is great, this method is very effective where alluvium rests on hard rock, but if water-soaked gravel rests on a comparatively slow-speed bed, as shale, the contrast is small and its recognition difficult. Where the bedrock is decomposed, seamed or chemically altered, or has an indistinct boundary, causing a gradual increase in speed through considerable depth or thickness, the method is not applicable. Faults are recognized by the offset of lines parallel to DW, owing to change of depth H_1 or H_2.

Deep seismic refraction. Seismic refraction waves have been used for exploration to depths as great as 3 000 ft; beyond that, the proportion of time spent in passing through the anomaly becomes small compared to the total time, and renders results doubtful. Fig 51A shows path of the longit wave in a medium where speed increases uniformly with depth; this path is the arc of a circle. Fig 51B shows effect upon the time-distance curve

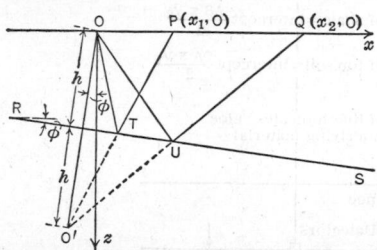

Fig 52.   Determining Dip by McCollum-McGhee Method (24)

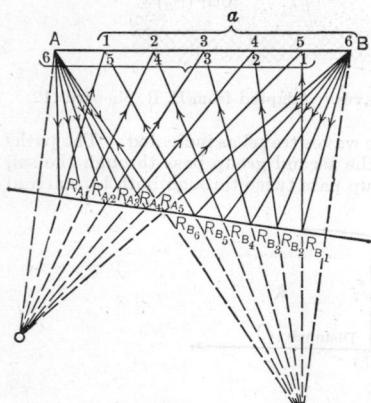

Fig 53.   Seismic Paths in Continuous Profiling (25)

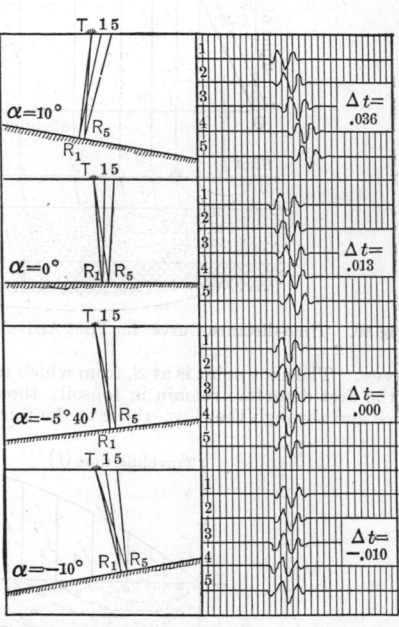

Fig 54.   Theoretical Seismograms for varying Dips.   Aver veloc, 6 000 ft per sec.   Depth, 7 000 ft.   Space between geophones 1 and 5, 1 000 ft (21)

caused by salt-domes; similar anomalies may be caused by other lenticular high-speed beds like slate. Phase and amplitude control often furnish enough information for proper interpretations.

Reflection surveys are chiefly used in seismic prospecting for contouring deep-seated formations. Beds greatly differing in elasticity, as the " big lime " in northern La, cause excellent reflections. The origin of seismic impulse in the ground is the detonation of a charge of dynamite, but the reflected wave from the various beds bears only slight resemblance to the form of this impulse. Impingement sets the echoing bed into vibration with its own characteristic frequencies; hence, a permanent, reliable record is important, such as a sound track that can be produced for analysis. The analysis is interpreted by selecting from the record certain frequencies having direct correlation with the echoes and depths in question. Fig 52 shows the reflection paths of a wave at the border of 2 media; O is the shot point; RS, the reflecting surface; OT and OU are 2 wave paths impinging on the reflection surface at T and U and returning to surface at P (x_1, O) and Q (x_2, O). Draw a line from O perpendicular to the surface RS and extend below to the image point O'.

Let OZ be a vert line and ϕ the angle it makes with OO' (same as dip of bed RS). Know-

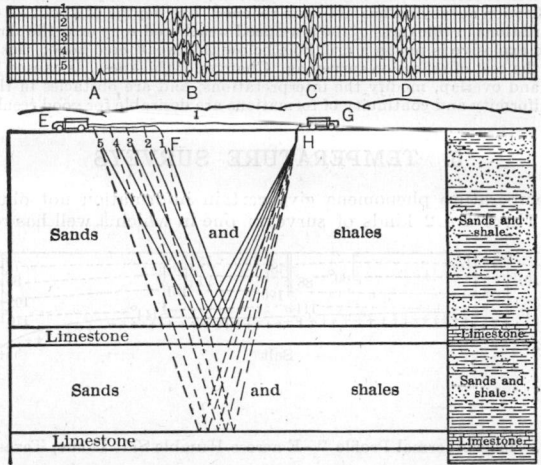

Fig 55. Observation Points, and Theoretical Seismograms for Two Limestone Horizons (21)

ing the speeds of the beds in the region, h and ϕ are computed. To determine bed RS, a number of receptors (Fig 53) are kept in position while the shot point is changed from A to B. Fig 54 shows effect of changes in angle α (dip of bed) upon the reflection records. Fig 55 shows reflections from 2 limestone beds as received at 1, 2, 3, 4, and 5, the source being at H. The echoes C and D refer to the 2 beds. Record B is the time of first arrival of the waves and bears no relation to the reflecting beds. To make a reflection survey, the ground is laid off as in Fig 56 for the shot points. The important factor is the closure of the contour of a reflecting bed.

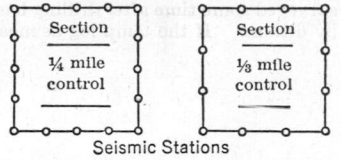

Fig 56. Individual Spreads of Seismograph Stations (25)

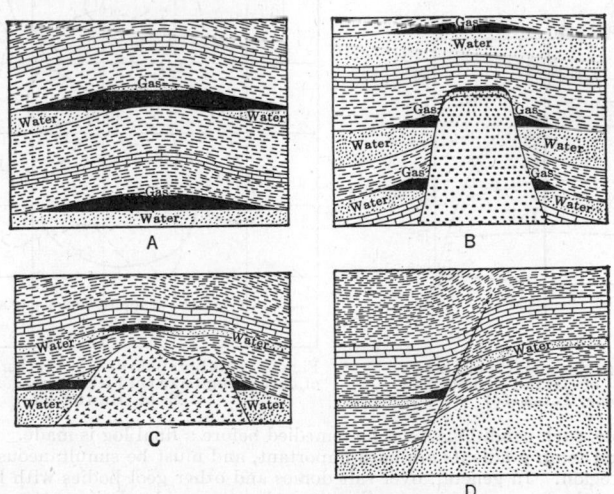

Fig 57. Four Typical Occurrences of Oil (21)

Fig 57 shows a few of the formations and geologic structures to which reflection seismic surveys have been applied. A is a simple anticline with 2 productive oil horizons. B is a salt dome with shallow oil and gas, and an impervious cap rock, oil and gas being entrapped on the flanks of the dome. *C* shows possible reservoirs on a granite ridge; *D*, the oil trapped on a fault.

The limit of reflection surveying has not been reached, but depths of about 20 000 ft have been recorded. Since variations in thickness of the low-speed weathered zone near the surface lead to false interpretations, the explosive is put in a drill hole below this weathered zone; this procedure takes time and increases the cost of reflection surveying. Changes of thickness, as caused by lensing, interfingering, erosion, and overlap, modify the interpretations, and are obstacles in the application of these methods; uniformity and continuity of formations are desirable for good results.

5. TEMPERATURE SURVEYS

General. Temperature phenomena give certain information not obtainable in any other manner. There are 2 kinds of surveys: one in which a well has reached thermal

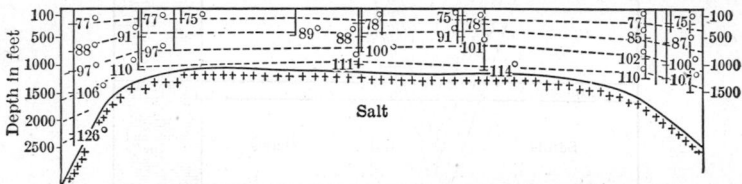

Fig 58.   Isogeothermal Profile W–E across Humble Salt Dome, Texas (26)

equilibrium, the other where a temp transient (see below) is important. A temperature-depth curve shows temp gradually increasing with depth; that near the surface of the ground should be a little above the mean annual temp of the area. The well should be surveyed some time after drilling has stopped, to permit dissipation of local heat generated by drilling. If the temp log as measured is abnormal, owing principally to escape of gas

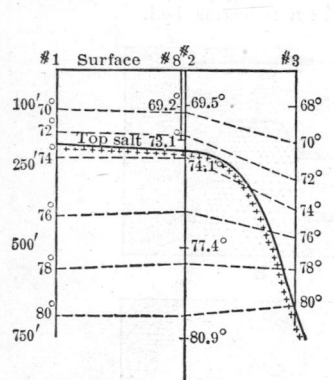

Fig 59. Isogeothermal Profile across South Edge of Grand Saline Salt Dome, Texas (26)

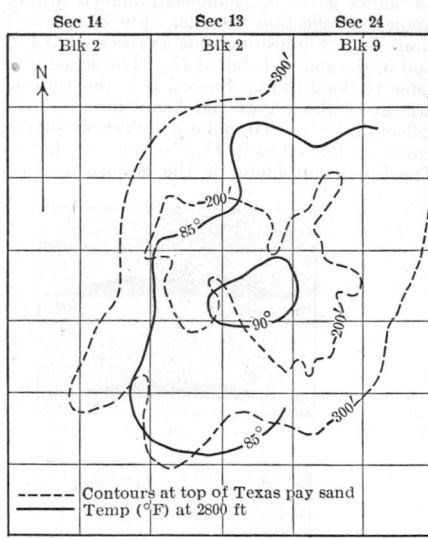

Fig 60.   Stratigraphic and Isogeothermal Contours of Part of Big Lake Oil Field, Texas. Adapted from E. M. Hawtof (26)

from the hole, such conditions must be remedied before a final log is made. Actual temperatures and temp gradients are both important, and must be simultaneously examined in a given region. In general, over salt domes and other geol bodies with high thermal conductivity, the temp and temp gradient are above normal. It is customary to use the number of ft per deg instead of the temp gradient or the degrees per ft.

Fig 58 shows the temp profile over the Humble salt dome; Fig 59, that at edge of the Grand Saline salt dome. Owing to the better heat-conductivity of salt domes, the temp at top of the

Humble dome is higher than along the margins, whence the number of ft per deg over the dome is less. According to Van Orstrand, the number of ft per deg F 'over salt domes is 20–50. Using well-temp measurements as a guide, the direction showing least number of ft per deg generally points towards the top of a dome or anticline. Fig 60 shows the constant-temp contours over the Big Lake field, Texas, at depth of 2 800 ft. Another way of showing temp distribution is to contour the elevations at which a given temp is encountered. Regional temp charts are valuable for large structural features (Fig 61).

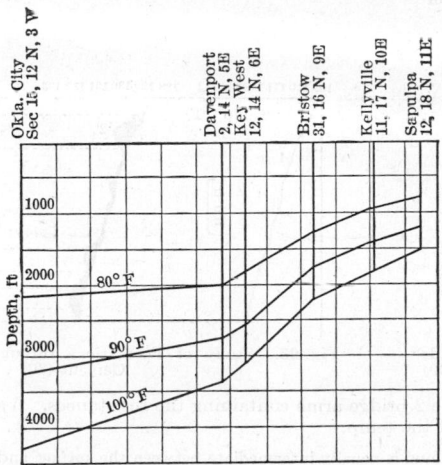

Fig 61. Temperature Profile, Oklahoma City to Sapulpa (27)

Temp measurements in wells are made by maximum thermometers, lowered into the well. For more detailed temp data, other apparatus, as elec resistance thermometers, is necessary.

Ground-temperature transients. The measurement of these, especially in wells, has value for obtaining information upon formations differing greatly in their ability to

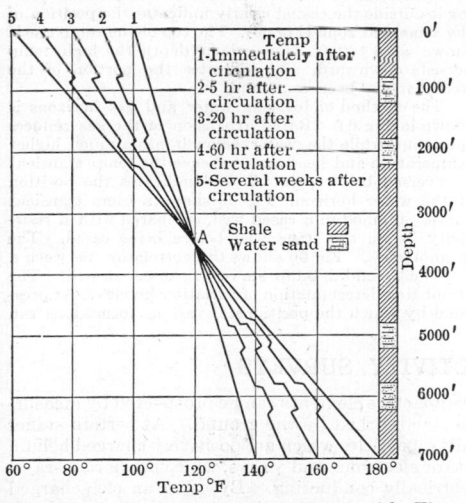

Fig 62. Probable Variation of Temp with Time Elapsed from Moment Circulation Ceased. Deep Wells (28)

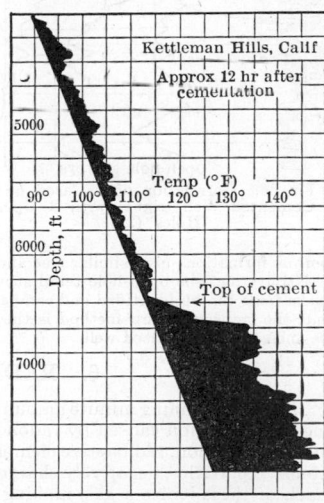

Fig 63. Temperature Survey 12 Hr after finishing Cementation around Casing in a Calif Well (29)

transfer heat. Such measurements also serve to locate cemented zones in wells, even when cased. Another advantage of these observations is that they furnish information on changes in distribution of fluids around wells in operation. Measurements can be made by observing changes in elec resistivity of a resistance element inserted in the well. As the instrument is lowered, the leads also introduce a temp effect. The use of 2 resistance elements (one having a zero temp coef), connected to form 2 arms in a Wheatstone bridge, is therefore recommended. The effect of the leads can then be compensated by a variable

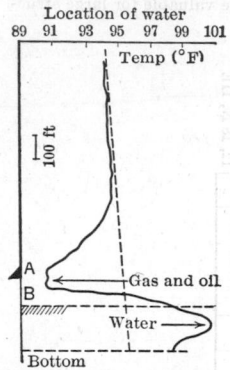

Fig 64. Location of Sands having produced water (30)

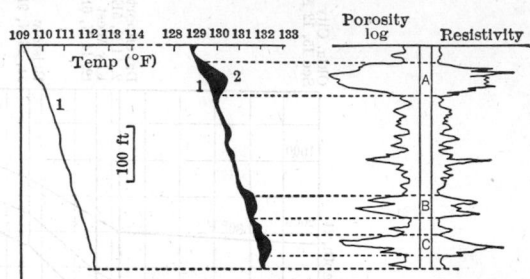

Fig 65. Study of Formations through Casing and "Old" Cement (30)

resistance in one of the 2 bridge arms containing the resistances. Variation in resistance is a simple function of the temp.

The temp of drilling mud is usually intermediate between the surface and bottom temperatures. When the mud circulation is stopped, the mud temp will drop at top of the well and rise at bottom. Fig 63 shows an idealized temp graph made after different time intervals. The important feature is that the changes of mud temp occur faster opposite water sands than opposite shale or limestone. Such beds therefore introduce temp fluctuations in the well indicating both the thickness and position of the horizon. The temp rise caused by the setting of cement within a few hours after placing it outside the casing clearly indicates the position of the cemented zone (Fig 63). The top of the temp rise is shown at 6 400 ft, from which depth the high temp persists downward, and indicates the portion of the well that has been cemented.

Fig 66. Correlation of 1 Cased and Cemented Well (right) with 2 Open Holes (29)

The method of locating water and gas horizons is shown in Fig 64. Rapid expansion of the gas reduces the temp, while the water below it has a much higher temperature and heat capac; hence the temp transient is reversed below point B, and indicates the position of the water horizon. Fig 65 shows a temp transient curve, obtained in a cased well, compared with a resistivity log in the same well before being cased. The porous formations give similar elec and temp anomalies. Fig 66 shows the correlation between a resistivity log, the open-hole temp survey of 2 wells, and a temp survey in a cased well. The formations can be identified and compared, permitting determination of variations in elev. At present, the transient temp method is the only one by which the positions of various formations can be measured in a cased well.

6. RADIOACTIVITY SURVEYS

Rocks containing minute amounts of radioactive elements can be prospected by measuring the ionization caused by radon in the air absorbed by the ground. At certain stages of decomposition, radioactive elements emit α particles which are positively charged helium atoms, β particles, negatively charged units or electrons, and γ rays, which are hard X-rays. Each of these ionize a gas, making it electrically conducting. By using an elec-charged condenser, and recording the rate of decay, the variation of radioactivity can be measured. Unit of measurement is the MACHE UNIT, the amount of radioactive emanation in 1 liter of gas which will produce a saturation current of 0.001 electrostatic unit. In an electroscope, let V_1 = voltage (electromagnetic units) before discharge; V_o = voltage at end of discharge; t = time in sec; C = electrostatic capac, centimeters, of condenser system being discharged, I = amperes (electrostatic units) of saturation current. Hence,

$I = (V_1 - V_o)C \div 300\ t$; and since the number of Mache units (M U) $= 1\ 000\ I$, the formula per liter of gas is: $M\ U = {}^{10}/_3\ (V_1 - V_o)C$, where $V_1 - V_o$ is the change of voltage per sec.

The ground is laid off on traverse lines, and the number of M U are plotted at measured points. If the traverses are sufficiently close, iso-radioactive lines are contoured. This method, useful in locating faults through which radioactive gases are flowing, can be used for prospecting for radio-active ores, as carnotite and pitchblende. Due to small amounts of zirconium and other weakly radioactive elements in the soil, a certain amount of radioactivity is always present, bearing only an indirect relation to the geologic structure.

7. MICRO-GAS SURVEYS

Analysis of soil and of its gas content, for the presence of hydrocarbons, as an indication of gas seepage, has had much attention. According to Rosaire, this seepage is greatest at edges of a pool. By charting the hydrocarbon and gas content along a profile, the presence of oil deposits is indicated. No details are yet available as to methods for dif-ferentiating between methane and ethane in small amounts. Methane is often generated by vegetable decomposition and then bears no relation to oil or gas deposits, whereas ethane, propane, and butane generally occur in natural gas.

8. CHOICE OF GEOPHYSICAL METHOD

In planning the surveys several methods should be applied to the same problem, especially if these methods are not related, and depend upon different properties of the same geol anomaly. Thus, oil prospecting in unknown territory would combine gravi-metric methods with seismic reflection; or, when drilling on known structures for the boundary of discovered fields, elec well logging and well-temp methods are preferable. Mining problems combine magnetic with elec methods. Water investigations use elec, magnetic, and shallow seismic methods. On dam sites and excavations use the shallow seismic, together with the elec resistivity methods. Gravimetric methods are relatively more expensive, because the instruments are large and costly, and because subsidiary parties are necessary to measure elevations. Seismic reflection entails considerable aux-iliary expense for drilling through weathered zones. Elec resistivity methods require many helpers to " run wire " and brush out lines. Less expensive are shallow refraction and magnetometer surveys, which usually require 2 men (operator and assistant). While well-logging and temp surveys do not require much field personnel, the technical equip-ment is costly and suffers rapid depreciation. Table 4 summarizes the principal applica-tions of the several methods.

Table 4. Summary of Geophysical Prospecting Methods

Class	Method	Principal Application	Geologic Units
Gravity	Torsion balance.... Pendulum......... Gravimeter.......	Oil..................	Intrusive bodies, salt domes, faults Anticlines, synclines Buried ridges
Magnetic	Dip needle......... Horiz magnetometer. Vert magnetometer..	Mining............... Mining............... Mining, oil, water......	Magnetic rocks and minerals Contouring crystalline basement, dikes, faults, intrusive bodies
Electrical	Self potential....... Earth resistivity..... Induction..........	Mining............... Mining, oil, ground water. Mining..................	Sulphide and oxide orebodies Stratigraphy, formations and struc- tures. Depth of overburden Faults, dikes, salt water, gravels, channels Electrically conducting veins
Seismic	Shallow refraction... Deep refraction..... Reflection..........	Road excavations, dam sites, ground water Oil.................. Oil..................	Bedrock surface, buried channels Salt domes Salt domes, faults, anticlines, syn- clines
Thermic or temperature	Steady condition.... Transient condition..	Mining Oil Oil	Igneous and sedimentary forma- tions, salt domes, anticlines, syn- clines, faults
Radioactive	Gamma radiation.. Gas ionization.....	Mining................	Faults, radioactive material

9. TABLES OF PHYSICAL PROPERTIES

For determining physical properties of rocks or geol bodies there are 2 methods: laboratory measurements on specimens or samples, and field measurements of material in place. In general, measurements on formations in place are preferable to those on samples. The measurements often involve modifying factors, as the averaging of samples, effect of moisture, and solution factors, which can not be retained in the laboratory samples. As a rule, some information is better than none, and all geophysical tables should be viewed from this standpoint.

Density. Since rocks are usually a complex of minerals, some of which may not be identical in properties from one locality to another, and rocks from different areas may have different degrees of weathering or alteration, many different values may be assigned to the density of the same rock type. Differences in porosity may also appreciably affect densities of similar rocks. Following tables therefore show different densities for like rocks, depending upon their origin and the kinds and degrees of alteration to which they have been subjected. Densities are calculated in c g s units; hence the values for density and spec grav are identical. Spec grav is a numeric and has no dimensions, whereas density is defined as mass per unit volume ($M \div L^3$). Table II, III show effects of certain modifying factors, which may materially alter the density or spec grav. For spec grav of minerals, see Descriptive and Determinative Tables, Sec 1; also Table 3, Sec 25.

Table I. Density of Rocks. After H. Reich (31)

Type of rock	Specific gravity	Type of rock	Specific gravity
I. Igneous Rocks		II. Metamorphic	
A. Plutonic		Orthoclase gneiss..	2.70 } (2.59–3.0)
Nepheline syenite....	2.62 (2.53–2.70)	Plagioclase gneiss..	2.84 }
Granite............	2.65 (2.56–2.74)	Granulite........	2.64 (2.57–2.73)
Anorthosite........	2.73 (2.64–2.94)	Quartz schist......	2.68 (2.63–2.91)
Syenite............	2.74 (2.60–2.95)	Mica schist.......	2.73 (2.54–2.97)
Quartz diorite......	2.79 (2.62–2.90)	Phyllite..........	2.74 (2.68–2.80)
Diorite............	2.86 (2.72–2.99)	Marble..........	2.78 (2.63–2.87)
Norite............	2.93 (2.70–3.24)	Chlorite schist.....	2.87 (2.75–2.98)
Olivine gabbro.......	2.95 (2.85–3.06)	Serpentine........	2.95 (2.80–3.10)
Essexite............	2.95 (2.69–3.14)	III. Sedimentary	
Amphibolite.........	3.00 (2.91–3.04)	A. Consolidated	
Gabbro............	3.00 (2.89–3.09)	Greywacke.......	2.69
Augite diorite.......	3.01 (2.99–3.08)	Sandstone........	2.65 (2.59–2.72)
Hornblende gabbro...	3.05 (2.98–3.18)	Limestone........	2.73 (2.68–2.84)
Peridotite..........	3.06 (2.78–3.37)	Argillaceous shale..	2.78 (2.72–2.83)
Pyroxenite and dunite	3.22 (2.93–3.34)	Calcareous shale...	2.67 (2.56–2.75)
Eclogite............	3.35 (3.20–3.54)	Rubbly marl......	2.66 (2.60–2.71)
B. Hypabyssal and Volcanic		Chert............	2.76 (2.70–2.86)
Quartz porphyry.....	2.63 (2.55–2.73)	B. Unconsolidated	
Quartz porphyrite....	2.63 (2.55–2.73)	Humus soil........	1.45 (1.22–1.68)
Porphyry..........	2.67 (2.60–2.89)	Surface soil — 13	
Porphyrite.........	2.74 (2.62–2.93)	tests...........	1.73 (1.55–1.95)
Melaphyre.........	2.77 (2.63–2.95)	Clayey sand, sandy	
Diabase...........	2.94 (2.73–3.12)	clay..........	1.93 (1.65–2.15)
Rhyolite...........	2.5 (2.35–2.65)	Gravel, very damp.	2.00 (1.95–2.05)
Phonolite..........	2.56 (2.45–2.71)	Dry, loose, arable	
Trachyte..........	2.58 (2.44–2.76)	soil............	1.13 ......
Dacite............	2.59 (2.35–2.79)	Brown coal, lignite.	1.12–1.3 ......
Andesite..........	2.62 (2.44–2.80)	Very fine sandy al-	
Basalt............	2.90 (2.74–3.21)	luvium..........	1.33 ......
Picrite............	2.97 (2.73–3.35)	Carbonaceous loam	1.51 ......
Obsidian...........	2.35 (2.21–2.42)	Clayey sandy soil..	1.6–1.7 ......
Pitchstone.........	2.40 (2.36–2.53)	Marl............	1.96 ......
Andesitic and porphyritic pitchstones....	2.56 (2.50–2.66)	Very wet quartz sand...........	2.25 ......
Basaltic glass........	2.81 (2.75–2.91)	Moulding sand....	2.63 (2.54–2.63)
		Loess............	2.64
		Clay............	2.58

Magnetic properties. While much work has been done on the magnetic properties of rocks and solutions, as to their diamagnetic, non-magnetic, and para-magnetic properties, their susceptibilities remain probably their most important characteristics (Table IV–VI).

The ability to measure very small differences of magnetic intensity by variometers has enhanced the value of magnetic prospecting and the importance of magnetic properties of earth materials. Since susceptibility of rocks is not constant, but varies with the magnetic field strength at which observations are made, the intensity of the earth's field is the most desirable intensity at which to determine the susceptibility of rocks.

In rare cases, the magnetic field around certain iron deposits may exceed the normal earth's magnetic field. About 90% of all magnetic prospecting concerns areas where there are only slight differences in magnetic susceptibility of the materials involved. The magnetite content of rocks appears to be the chief source of higher susceptibilities. Table IX shows percentages of magnetite and ilmenite in some igneous rocks, and Table X gives corresponding data for other rocks.

Table II. Effect of Water on Spec Grav of Rocks. After H. Reich (31)

Type of Rock	Normal spec grav		Authority
	Dry	Wet	
Granite...........	2.58	2.60	C. Moore
Dolerite...........	2.89	2.90	"
Basalt.............	2.87	2.88	"
Serpentine.........	2.71	2.71	Kusakabe
Mica schist........	2.65	2.67	"
Sandstone........	2.23	2.35	"
Permian and Triassic sandstone.........	2.07	2.27	C. Moore
Porous limestone...	1.91	2.20	"

Table III. Effect of Shattering on Spec Grav of Rocks. After H. Reich (31)

Type of rock	Unshattered	Artificially shattered
Trap rock......	2.99	1.7
Granite........	2.72	1.5
Sandstone......	2.41	1.3

Table IV. Magnetic Susceptibility of Igneous Rocks. After H. Reich (31)

Type of rock	Locality	Suscepti- bility, $S \times 10^6$	Field strength, gammas	Authority	Remarks
1. Plutonic					
Granite............	Mount Sorrel	600–650	47–96	E. Wilson	Whole piece
Basic streaks in granite..............	" "	400–1 810	47–67	"	" "
Granite, basic border	" "	220	124–157	"	" "
Hornblende diorite..	" "	120	156–200	"	" "
Camptonite........	Nuneaton	210	128–483	"	" "
Augite granophyre..	Groby Quarry	40	200–440	"	" "
Basic granophyre....	Newhurst Wood	82	137–241	"	" "
Olivine gabbro,.....	Skye	5 610	....	A. W. Ruecker	4 tests
Gabbro............	Deer Forest	4 200	....	"	4 "
"	Skye	2 370	....	"	11 "
"	Mull	1 730	....	"	2 "
"	Cumberland	230	....	"	
"	Hatton Hill	70	....	"	
"	St. David's Hill	nearly 0	....	Ruecker & White	
Tourmaline granite..	....	240	....	" "	
Syenite............	....	1 040	....	" "	
Tourmaline aplite...	L. Iset	40–100	51.3	J. Bahurin	
Gabbro............	"	3 500	10.3	"	
Pyroxenite........	"	4 000	10.3	"	
Dunite............	L. Taghill	40–100	51.3	"	
Gabbro............	Wisconsin	430	Earth's field	L. B. Slichter	0.15% magnetite
"	"	680	" " "	"	0.24 "
Granite............	Harz	8	About 5	J. Koenigsberger	
Granite (Aar).......	Gotthardgebiet	23–34	" "	"	
" (Cristallina)	"	20–30	" "	"	
" (Gotthard)..	"	17–45	" "	"	
2. Hypabyssal and volcanic					
Dolerite............	Nottinghamshire	4 340–4 720	22–49.5	E. Wilson	Rim..... ⎫ of the same
"	"	88–130	132–248	"	Center... ⎭ specimen
"	Leicestershire	3 910–4 080	23–39	"	
"	Nottinghamshire	2 790	19.8	"	
Basalt.............	Derbyshire	125	40–69	"	
Trachyte..........	....	390	....	A. W. Ruecker	
Phonolite.........	....	700	....	"	
Melaphyre.........	....	390	....	"	
Aver of 45 dolerites and basalts.......	British Isles	2 550	....	Ruecker & White	
Quartz dolerite.....	Whin Sill	2 630–5 410	....	" "	
" "	St. Davids	nearly 0	....	" "	Various high values

Table IV.—*Continued*

Type of rock	Locality	Suscepti-bility, $S \times 10^6$	Field strength, gammas	Authority	Remarks
Basalt dike.........	Northumberland	10 090	....	Ruecker & White	
Intrusive basalt.....	Antrim	13 900	....	" "	
Basalt dike.........	"	190	....	" "	Various low values
Basalt.............	"	310	....	" "	
Nephelite basanite...	Tetschen	6 070–7 170	....	F. Pockels	17.7% magnetite
Nephelite basalt....	Lobauer Berg	8 100–9 200	....	"	6.6% magnetite, coarse grained
" "	Tharandt	8 560–10 840	....	"	24.5% magnetite
Weathered basalt...	Balatonsee	1 326	Very high field	L. Steiner	
Dense basalt.......	"	300	" " "	"	
Melaphyre........	Tholey	4 860	8.7	A. Turcev	4.27% mag-netite
		1 120	26.1	"	
		1 670	522	"	
Basalt.............	Owen	1 500	478.7	"	About 4.2% magnetite
		800	8.7	"	
"Pillow" lava	Karadagh	636	17.4	"	3.55% magnetite
		4 365	26.1	"	
		6 300	438.1	"	

(S computed from permeability μ)

Table V. Susceptibility of Sedimentary Rocks.   After H. Reich (31)

Type of rock	Locality	Suscepti-bility, $S \times 10^6$	Field strength, gammas	Authority	Remarks
Dense limestone........	Leicestershire	3, 8	300–515	E. Wilson	
Dolomite.............	Nottinghamshire	1, 8	605	"	
Fine-grained dolomite...	Leicestershire	4, 7	603	"	
Blue clay.............	Irthlingborough	20	94–375	"	
Blue clay shale.........	Charnwood Forst	39	245–355	"	
Hornfels.............	Mount Sorrel	32	332–342	"	Contact-metamorphic rock
"	" "	61	237–240	"	
Tertiary beds.........	Balatonsee	42	Field very weak	L. Steiner	
Dolomite.............	"	14	....		
Ferruginous sandstone..	Switzerland	100	....	J. Koenigsberger	
Black Portland beds....	"	80	2 500	"	
" " "	"	16	5	"	
Miscellaneous sediments.	"	<10	....	"	
Rock salt.............	North Germany	− 0, 4	....	"	Estimated
Country rock of the Salz-horst...............	" "	40	....	"	
Coal.................	Waldenburg	<2	5	"	

Table VI. Magnetic Susceptibility of Metamorphic Rocks.   After H. Reich (31)

Type of rock	Locality	Suscepti-bility, $S \times 10^6$	Field strength, gammas	Authority	Remarks
Ferruginous quartzite.	Krivoj Rog	550	10.3	J. Bahurin	
Hornblende-magnetite schist	" "	9 000	10.3	"	
Hornblende schist	Urals	8 000	10.3	"	
Talc schist..........	"	3 000	10.3	"	
Hornblende schist....	Malvern Hills	1 390	....	A. W. Ruecker	Magnetite—rich
" "	" "	1 130	....	"	Magnetite less abundant
" "	" "	300	10.3	"	Little magnetite
" "	" "	120	....	"	Magnetite very scarce, titano-ferrite?
" "	" "	nearly 0	....	"	Magnetite very scarce, only titanoferrite
Basic para schist.....	Gotthardgebiet	17–180	very weak fields	J. Koenigsberger	
Clintonite phyllite...	"	90			
Injection gneiss......	"	12–25			
Various gneisses......	Bellinzona	10–260			
Serpentine..........	Gotthardgebiet	3 600–6 000			
"	Urals	550	110.3	A. Turcev	
"	"	14 100	30.5	J. Bahurin	Metamorphosed volcanics

Table VII. Magnetic Susceptibilities of Minerals. According to N. H. Stearn (32)

	$S \times 10^6$
Ferromagnetic	
Iron (Fe)	80 000
Magnetite (Fe$_3$O$_4$)	32 122
Paramagnetic	
Hematite (crystals) (Fe$_2$O$_3$)	426.00
Manganosite (MnO)	349.44
Hausmannite (Mn$_3$O$_4$)	318.07
Alabandite (MnS)	177.28
Pyrolusite (MnO$_2$)	131.22
Pyrite (FeS$_2$)	120.00
Hematite (amorphous) (Fe$_2$O$_3$)	107.12
Melanterite (FeSO$_4$·7H$_2$O)	80.00
Bieberite (CoSO$_4$·7H$_2$O)	68.00
Limonite (2Fe$_2$O$_3$·3H$_2$O)	57.00
Platinum (Pt)	26.00
Morenosite (NiSO$_4$·7H$_2$O)	18.00
Chalcanthite (CuSO$_4$·5H$_2$O)	14.30
Cuprite (Cu$_2$O)	4.38
Rutile (TiO$_2$)	0.28
Brookite (TiO$_2$)	0.262
Octahedrite (TiO$_2$)	0.257
Air	0.024

Diamagnetic	$S \times 10^6$
Epsomite (MgSO$_4$·7H$_2$O)	0.63
Soda-niter (NaNO$_3$)	0.70
Water (H$_2$O)	0.72
Niter (KNO$_3$)	0.72
Covellite (CuS)	0.74
Calcite (CaCO$_3$)	0.75
Chalcocite (Cu$_2$S)	0.78
Copper (Cu)	0.80
Halite (NaCl)	0.82
Sulphur (S)	0.85
Sassolite (H$_3$BO$_3$)	0.89
Sylvite (KCl)	0.91
Kalinite (Al$_2$K$_2$[SO$_4$]$_4$·24H$_2$O)	1.00
Calcite (CaCO$_3$)	1.00
Berzelianite (Cu$_2$Se)	1.01
Anhydrite (CaSO$_4$)	1.12
Villiaumite (NaF)	1.12
Quartz (SiO$_2$)	1.20
Lead (Pb)	1.30
Cotunite (PbCl$_2$)	1.31
Silver (Ag)	1.50
Bromyrite (AgBr)	1.53
Cerargyrite (AgCl)	1.55
Iodyrite (AgI)	1.66
Arsenic (As)	1.70
Diamond (C)	1.80
Zincite (ZnO)	1.85
Fluorite (CaF$_2$)	2.00
Graphite (C)	8.00
Bismuth (Bi)	14.00

Table VIII. Magnetic Susceptibilities of the Elements. According to N. H. Stearn (32)

	$S \times 10^6$
Paramagnetic	
Praseodymium	163.17
Erbium	130.36
Cerium	106.06
Manganese	80.00
Palladium	66.00
Uranium	60.96
Platinum	26.00
Chromium	26.00
Vanadium	13.20
Rhodium	13.00
Ruthenium	11.01
Niobium	10.80
Tantalum	9.40
Barium	6.90
Titanium	6.65
Molybdenum	5.13
Iridium	4.90
Tungsten	4.76
Aluminium	1.80
Calcium	1.67
Magnesium	1.44
Osmium	1.35
Thorium	0.89
Strontium	0.86
Potassium	0.52
Sodium	0.50
Zirconium	0.39
Tin	0.35
Lithium	0.23
Oxygen (O$_2$)	0.146
Rubidium	0.126
Hydrogen (H$_2$)	0.008
Nitrogen (N$_2$)	0.001

Diamagnetic	$S \times 10^6$
Helium	0.002
Chlorine	0.007
Argon	0.01
Caesium	0.188
Silicon	0.29
Indium	0.57
Germanium	0.62
Copper	0.80
Sulphur	0.85
Zinc	1.00
Lead	1.12
Bromine	1.26
Selenium	1.30
Gallium	1.34
Arsenic	1.40
Silver	1.5
Phosphorus	1.60
Boron	1.66
Iodine	1.73
Beryllium	1.87
Tellurium	2.10
Mercury	2.50
Thallium	2.73
Gold	3.10
Antimony	4.70
Carbon	8.00
Bismuth	14.00
Cadmium	15.23

Table IX. Magnetite-Ilmenite Content of Igneous Rocks.
According to N. H. Stearn (32)

	Magnetite, %			Ilmenite, %			Combined, %		
	Min	Max	Usual	Min	Max	Usual	Min	Max	Usual
Quartz porphyries.....	0.0	1.4	0.82	0.0	0.5	0.3	0.0	1.6	0.94
Rhyolites.............	0.2	1.9	1.00	0.0	0.8	0.45	0.2	2.2	1.10
Granites.............	0.2	1.9	0.90	0.6	0.8	0.7	0.2	2.5	1.15
Trachyte-syenites......	0.0	4.6	2.04	0.0	1.2	0.70	0.2	5.8	2.74
Eruptive nephelites....	0.0	4.9	1.51	0.0	3.7	1.24	0.0	8.3	2.75
Abyssal nephelites.....	0.0	6.6	2.71	0.0	2.0	0.85	0.0	8.4	3.56
Pyroxenites..........	0.9	8.4	3.51	0.0	1.5	0.40	2.1	8.4	3.91
Gabbros..............	0.9	3.9	2.40	0.0	6.4	1.76	1.9	8.7	4.16
Monzonite-latites......	1.4	5.6	3.58	0.9	2.6	1.60	2.3	7.3	5.18
Leucite rocks.........	0.0	7.4	3.27	0.5	4.1	1.94	0.5	8.9	5.21
Dacites, quartz-diorites	1.6	8.0	3.48	0.0	3.4	1.94	2.1	11.4	5.43
Andesites.............	2.6	5.8	4.50	0.5	1.8	1.16	4.1	7.8	5.66
Diorites..............	1.2	7.4	3.45	1.1	5.4	2.44	2.3	9.7	5.89
Peridotites...........	1.6	7.2	4.60	0.0	7.1	1.31	1.6	13.1	5.91
Analcite rocks.........	1.9	9.0	5.54	0.0	2.5	1.05	2.0	10.8	6.59
Basalts..............	2.3	8.6	4.76	1.1	3.1	1.91	3.4	11.7	6.67
Diabases.............	2.3	6.3	4.35	1.2	4.3	2.70	4.7	8.8	7.05
Basaltic rocks *......	2.8	7.0	4.80	0.0	5.1	2.80	3.4	12.1	7.60
Femic syenites........	4.2	6.0	5.24	1.4	3.7	2.74	6.5	9.7	7.98
Basic and titaniferous rocks..............	3.5	49.9	27.99	1.1	59.0	35.11	25.11	75.3	53.10

* Leucite, nephelite, or melilite basalts.

Table X. Magnetite and Ilmenite Content of Average Rock Types.
According to N. H. Stearn (32)

Rock	Magnetite, %	Ilmenite, %	Combined, %
Aver granite.............	1.72	0.31	2.03
Aver basalt..............	5.80	0.73	6.53
Aver igneous rock (65% granite; 35% basalt)....	3.15	1.45	4.60
Aver sandstone...........	0.58	0.25	0.83
Aver sedimentary rock (82% shale; 12% sandstone; 6% limestone)..............	0.07	0.02	0.09
Aver rock (95% igneous; 5% sedimentary)...........	2.95	0.001	2.951

Resistivity of rocks forms the basis for almost all elec prospecting methods. The degree of resistivity measured in the field differs materially from that measured on laboratory specimens, due to changes in moisture content or salinities of solutions impregnating the rocks, and to variations in constitution of rocks from different areas or geol formations. Differences in resistivity of rocks or members of formations in a specific locality are much more important than the resistivities *per se.* The mode of occurrence of rocks is of great importance; for example, magnetite has a very low elec resistivity, but if each crystal is imbedded separately in quartz, the resistivity will be controlled entirely by the quartz, which has a very high resistivity. In other districts, rocks containing magnetite may be undergoing alteration, and therefore should have extremely low resistivity. Very small amounts of solutions carrying salts will often noticeably modify the resistivity of rocks. In general, non-porous igneous rocks have higher resistivity than sedimentaries; of the latter, especially limestones, older beds have higher resistivities than the younger.

Table XI. Electrical Resistivity of Rock Types. After H. Reich (31)

Type of rock	Place of investigation	No of tests	Resistivity, ohm-centimeters (a)			Remarks	Authority
			Usual	Min	Max		
I. Igneous and Metamorphic Rocks							
Granite.............	Washington	....	>500 000	....	....	....	W. J. Rooney
Traprock...........	Michigan	12	236 000	185 000	390 000		
Traprock, parallel to contact..........	"	8	214 000	185 000	250 000		
Traprock, perpendicular to contact....	"	2	279 000	....	....	Different	
Greenstone.........	"	8	113 000	85 000	133 000	speci-	
Greenstone.........	"	9	159 000	125 000	210 000	mens	W. J. Rooney
Greenstone.........	"	2	310 000	306 000	314 000	of the	
Traprock...........	"	4	141 000	109 300	174 000	same	
Traprock...........	"	11	89 000	43 700	148 000	rocks	
Amygdaloid.........	"	4	90 900	59 000	128 000		
Amygdaloid.........	"	4	45 300	39 200	50 600		
Amygdaloid.........	"	4	16 100	11 900	19 830	Salty ground water	W. J. Rooney
Traprock...........	"	2	27 200	21 050	33 300		
Porous portion of a traprock flow.....	"	5	22 500	18 350	25 700	....	W. J. Rooney
Dense portion of a traprock flow.....	"	5	55 500	43 100	49 450	....	"
Granite porphyry....	New Mexico	....	about 1 000 000				K. Sundberg, Irving, Crosby and Leonardon
Pre-cambrian crystalline rocks.........	Northern U S	....	300 000–400 000	....	....		
Crystalline basement rocks............	Sweden	....	300 000–600 000				
Quartz porphyry....	Germany	....	40 000	....	....	In damp pit	J. Koenigsberger
II. Sedimentary Rocks							
A. Consolidated							
Great conglomerate..	Michigan	7	109 200	103 400	117 000	....	W. J. Rooney
Western sandstone...	"	10	25 650	17 900 (deeper layers)	41 400 (higher layers)	....	"
	"	14	9 830	8 830	11 780	....	"
Eastern sandstone...	"	13	4 300	3 500	7 750 (greater depths)	....	"
Nonesuch argillite...	"	9	15 700	12 300	18 100	....	"
Limestone..........	Spain	....	12 000	....	....	....	"
Dense Jurassic limestone............	Switzerland	....	250 000–350 000	....	....	....	J. Koenigsberger
Marly Jurassic limestone............	"	....	140 000	....	....	....	"
Ferruginous sandstone............	"	....	400 000	....	....	....	"
Carbonaceous sandstone.............	Lower Silesia	....	25 000–51 000	....	....	....	"
Shale..............	" "	....	77 000	....	....	....	"
Cannel coal........	" "	....	15 000–60 000	....	....	....	"
Rock salt, pure......	Lower Rhine area	....	$10^6–10^7$	....	....	....	"
Rock salt, impure...		....	$3\times10^3–5\times10^5$	....	....	....	"
B. Unconsolidated							
Humus soil..........	Switzerland	2	11 000	4 000	18 000	....	"
Glacial deposits.....	Northern U S A	....	18 000–50 000	....	....		Irving, Crosby and Leonardon
Clayey soil.........	"	....	10 000–40 000	....	....		
Sandy soil..........	"	....	110 000–180 000	....	....		
Dry sand...........	Western Australia	....	....	2.5×10^5	4×10^6	....	W. J. Rooney
Damp sand.........		....	....	1×10^5	1×10^6	....	"
Clay, rich in Mg salts		....	....	100	250	....	"
Damp loam.........	Spain	....	....	500	5 000	....	"
Broken rock	"	....	....	75 000	500 000	....	"
Glacial deposits.....	Northern U S A	....	....	825	396 000	....	"

(a) Resistance, in ohms, of a cube 1 cm square.

Table XII.   Resistivities of Rock Samples (Laboratory Tests).   After H. Reich (31)

Type of rock	No of samples	Dry		Damp		Authority
		Usual value	Limiting values	Usual value	Limiting values	
Diabase....	1	3×10⁵	....	2×10⁴	....	K. Sundberg, H. Lundberg, and J. Eklund
Dolomite...	2	over 5×10⁶	....	4.6×10⁵	3.7×10⁵–5.5×10⁵	
Granite....	4	1.1×10⁷	8×10⁶–1.7×10⁷	3.6×10⁴	7×10³– 7×10⁵	
Porphyry...	4	7×10⁸	1×10⁸– 16×10⁸	5.5×10⁷	2×10⁵– 2×10⁸	
Porphyrite..	8	7.6×10⁷	2.8×10⁶–3.2×10⁸	3.8×10⁶	2.2×10⁴– 3×10⁷	According to D. Murashov E. Berengarten A. Etcheistova L. Kudiakova
Sandstone..	8	7.7×10⁷	5×10⁶– 2×10⁸	6.5×10⁵	3.5×10⁴–3.5×10⁶	
Clay shale..	2	1.4×10⁸	1×10⁸–1.7×10⁸	9×10⁵	1×10⁵–1.7×10⁵	
Limestone..	5	1.3×10¹⁰	8×10⁷–3.5×10¹⁰	4.2×10⁷	1.4×10⁶– 1×10⁸	
Hornfels....	6	3.9×10¹⁰	4×10⁷– 2×10¹¹	1.1×10⁶	2.6×10⁵– 6×10⁷	
Chlorite-sericite schist	6	3×10⁹	9.7×10⁸–1.2×10¹⁰	9.8×10⁶	5×10⁵–2.8×10⁷	

Table XIII.   Resistivities of Ores.   After H. Reich (31)

Samples	No	Resistivity, ohm-centimeters			Remarks
		Usual	Min	Max	
(a) According to Murashov, Berengarten, Etcheistova and Kudiakova					
Ores (sulfides) with over 50% of high-conductivity ores	18	128	6	700	A 90% pyrrhotite-pyrite ore has been reported as high as 10 000 ohm-cm.
Ores (sulfides) with 20–50% of high-conductivity ores	26	3 425	1	20 000	A 40% lead ore reported as high as 7×10⁹ ohm-cm.
Ores (sulfides) with 5–20% of high-conductivity ores	14	85 520	8	520 000	A quartz with 10% pyrite reported as high as 4.7×10⁷ ohm-cm.
Rocks with less than 5% of high-conductivity ores	11	30 000×10⁵	8×10⁵	190 000×10⁵	
(b) According to K. Sundberg, H. Lundberg, and J. Eklund					
Pyrite ore..................	8	1 613	0.1	10 500	
Lead-zinc ore..............	1	......	0.1	36 000	
			Parallel to selvage	Perpendicular	
Polybasite ore..............	1	......	0.1	400	
Graphitic shale.............	3	120	0.5	350	
Shale with pyrrhotite.......	2	30	6	53	
Limestone with chalcopyrite..	1	16×10⁶			
Sericite with pyrite.........	1	3.5×10⁶			

Table XIV.   Resistivities of Sodium Chloride Solutions. According to H. Reich (31)

NaCl content, %	Resistivities, ohm-centimeters
1	57.0
5	14.9
10	8.25
15	6.08
20	5.11
25	4.68
26	4.65

Seismic properties. The application of seismic waves for determining geological horizons and structures utilizes primarily the longit wave, the speed of which varies in different rocks. In general, the heaviest, most crystalline rocks give the highest speeds. Cemented sedimentary rocks are next in order, followed by broken or shattered sedimentaries, talus and landslide material, and unconsolidated sedimentary deposits. Speed of propagation is measured: (a) in the laboratory, by determining the density and moduli of elasticity on rock samples; (b) in the field, from the formations in place; the second is preferable. Tables XV–XIX give the longit wave speeds and the elastic moduli.

Table XV. Modulus of Elasticity and Speed of Transmission of Longitudinal Waves in Rocks. After H. Reich (31)

Type of rock	Number of tests	$E \times 10^{-11}$, cgs units (a)	V, meters per sec (a)	Authority	Remarks (b)
I. Igneous rocks					
A. Plutonic rocks					
Granite.................	16	3.47	4 000	Kusakabe	K
"	6	3.71	4 100	Bauschinger	L
"	7	5.05	4 800	Adams and Coker	L
"	3	6.6	5 600	" " Williamson	HC
3 samples of the same...	..	7.5	6 000	" " "	VC
Nepheline Syenite......	..	6.29	5 300	Adams and Coker	L
Essexite................	..	6.71	5 400	" " "	L
Anorthosite.............	..	8.25	5 900	" " "	L
Gabbro.................	..	6.61	5 300	Kusakabe	K
"	..	10.8	6 900	Adams and Coker	L
"	..	10.2	6 700	" " Williamson	HC
"	..	12.0	7 300	" " "	VC
Peridotite..............	..	5.94	4 900	Kusakabe	K
Pyroxenite..............	..	8.27	5 500	"	K
Dunite.................	..	16.4	7 900	Adams and Gibson	HC
"	..	17.5	8 400	" " "	VC
B. Volcanic and hypabyssal rocks					
Rhyolite...............	5	2.0	3 100	Kusakabe	K
Andesite...............	10	3.2	3 900	"	K
Diabase................	..	9.5	6 400	Adams and Gibson	L
" (same sample)...	..	10.1	6 700	" " Williamson	HC
" " " ...	..	11.4	7 100	" " "	VC
" (different sample)	..	7.64	5 800	" " "	HC
" " "	..	10.1	6 900	" " "	VC
Basalt.................	..	10.15	6 400	O. Graf	LC
" (different sample)	..	5.68	4 900	Adams and Williamson	HC
" "	..	8.12	5 900	" " "	VC
Obsidian...............	..	4.82	4 900	" " "	HVC
Pitchstone.............	..	5.54	5 300	P. W. Bridgman	HVC
Basalt glass............	2	8.90	6 400	"	HVC
"	1	9.52	6 500	Adams and Gibson	HVC
II. Metamorphic rocks					
Mica schist.............	3	2.85	3 700	Kusakabe	K
Gneiss.................	..	4.50	4 700	"	K
Graphite schist.........	3	4.76	4 800	"	K
Marble.................	5	6.12	5 300	Adams and Coker	L
Quartz schist...........	3	6.65	5 500	Kusakabe	K
Chlorite schist..........	8	7.00	5 400	"	K
Quartzite..............	..	7.34	5 800	O. Graf	L
Graywacke.............	..	7.6	5 900	Bauschinger	L
Marble.................	1	9.9	6 600	Adams and Williamson	HV
III. Sedimentary rocks					
Glauconitic sandstone.......	3	0.8	2 100	Bauschinger	L
Bunter sandstone..........	..	1.02	2 300	O. Graf	L
" "	8	1.67	3 000	Bauschinger	L
Ohio sandstone...........	..	1.58	3 000	Adams and Coker	L
Sandstone...............	12	1.40	2 800	Kusakabe	K
Tuffaceous sandstone........	6	1.88	3 200	"	K
Soft clay shale............	17	4.69	4 800	"	K
Sandy shale.............	..	6.09	5 300	"	K
Dense shale.............	10	6.39	5 300	"	K
Chalk..................	..	0.795	2 160	Maurin and Eble	L
Chalky limestone..........	3	1.93	3 560	E. Marcotte	L
Fine grained limestone......	8	4.32	4 680	"	L
Crystalline limestone........	4	6.5	5 500	"	L
Dense limestone and marble.	12	5.8	5 100	Kusakabe	K
Jurassic limestone..........	2	3.93	4 600	Bauschinger	L
" dolomite...........	..	5.34	4 900	"	L
Leitha limestone............	..	5.02	4 900	"	L
Nummulite limestone.......	..	6.05	5 200	"	L
Shell limestone............	..	5.8	5 300	"	L
" "	..	7.25	5 800	O. Graf	L
Clymenia limestone.........	..	8.15	6 000	Bauschinger	L

(a) Aver value for a number of observations.
(b) E determined as follows: L, H, or V = by press experiments, in which: L = at low press (about 1 000 megabars); H = at high press (about 2 000 megabars); V = at very high press (about 10 000 megabars); HV = press varying between 2 000 and 10 000 megabars. C = by compressibility tests. K = kinetically.

Table XVI.   Speed of Propagation, V, of Longitudinal Waves in Rocks
After H. Reich (31)

Type of rock	V, meters per sec	Authority
I. Consolidated rocks		
Igneous rocks; metamorphic rocks; massive unstratified rocks; limestone; dolomite; gypsum; anhydrite; rocksalt	5 000–5 600	H. Salfeld
Cambrian (Villanueva de las Minas)............	4 800	J. G. Sineriz
Salt dome cap rocks...........................		Fr. Rieber
Texas salt dome rocks (anhydrite, gypsum, limestone, rock salt).............................	4 500 to 5 500	M. Hannemann
Shell limestone (Rudersdorf)...................	4 300	W. Schweydar and H. Reich
Gypsum beds (Sperenberg)...................	3 500?	W. Schweydar and H. Reich
Zechstein beds (salt, anhydrite) Juterbog........	4 500	G. Angenheister
Carboniferous coal measures (Dobrilugk)........	3 800	H. Reich
Carboniferous coal measures (Villanueva de las Minas).......................................	3 400	J. G. Sineriz
Calcareous marl, calcareous sandstone, slates....	3 200–3 800	H. Salfeld
Siliceous sandstone, slightly calcareous sandstone	2 200–2 400	H. Salfeld
Middle Bunter sandstone (Jena)...............	2 000–2 800 aver 2 500	O. Meisser and H. Martin
Chalk (Germany)............................	2 380	H. Reich
Chalk (France)..............................	2 140	Ch. Maurin and L. Elbe
II. Unconsolidated rocks		
Coastal plain formations (Texas)..............	1 800–2 100	Fr. Rieber
Septaria clay and middle Bunter sandstone (?) (Juterbog)...............................	1 900	G. Angenheister
Miocene (Villanueva de las Minas)............	1 950	J. G. Sineriz
Clay, clay sandstone, slightly calcereous marl....	about 1 800	H. Salfeld
Tertiary and clayey Quaternary (Germany).....	1 630–1 800	H. Reich
Damp Quaternary sand (Sperenberg)...........	855–1 011	H. Reich and W. Schweydar
Broken rock, gravel, sand, loess...............	600–800	H. Salfeld
Same materials, very wet.....................	1 200	H. Salfeld
Alluvium (Villanueva de las Minas)...........	600	J. G. Sineriz

Table XVII.   Longitudinal Wave Speeds in Other Media.   After H. Reich (31)

Material	V, met per sec	Authority	Material	V, met per sec	Authority
Air...............	330.8–0.66t(a)	....	Salt solution 10%..	1 470	
Fresh water.......	1 435	Colladon	" " 15%..	1 530	Dorsing
		Sturm	" " 20%..	1 650	
Glacial ice, neve....	3 140	H. Mothes	Sea water........	1 480–1 490	W. Speiser
" " flowing..	3 570–3 600	....	Petroleum..........	1 326–1 395	Martini

(a) In the formula for V in air, t is the temp in deg C.

Table XVIII.   Compressibility and Longitudinal Wave Speeds in Minerals. After H. Reich (31)

Mineral	Compressibility, cgs $\times 10^{12}$	Speed of longit waves, meters per sec
Sylvite.......	5.62	3 900
Rock salt.....	4.13	4 400
Gypsum......	2.49	5 450
Anhydrite....	1.83	5 650

Table XIX.   Poisson's Ratios. After H. Reich (31)

Type of rock	Limiting values, σ
Various marbles............	0.25–0.28
Various granites............	0.20–0.26
Other igneous rocks.........	0.22–0.28
Ohio sandstone.............	0.26

Porosity depends on the origin of the rock, and its subsequent modification by tectonic, chemical, and physical processes; it is a factor often modifying other physical properties of rocks. Bureau of Standards has compiled porosity data on building stones, notably marble, sandstone, and slate (see publications by D. W. Kessler).

Table XX. Porosity of Rocks. After H. Reich (31)

Type of rock	Number of samples	Porosity, per cent of volume		Authority
		Usual value	Limiting values	
I. Igneous rocks				
Granite	9	0.76	0.23–1.75	Gary
Syenite	...	0.5–0.6	to 1.38	Hofer-Heimhalt
Diorite	...	0.25	....	" "
Gabbro	...	0.6–0.7	....	" "
Porphyry	5	2.66	0.38–6.73	Gary
Phonolite	5	1.65	1.17–3.89	"
Basalt	8	0.95	0.07–2.30	"
Trachyte	1	9.0	....	Hofer-Heimhalt
Pumice	2	63.9	....	C. Moore
Amphibolite	1	0.90	....	"
II. Metamorphic rocks				
Serpentine	1	0.56	....	Hofer-Heimhalt
Marble	4	0.3	0.11–0.59	" "
Argillite	8	2.69	to 10.0	C. Moore
Slate	59	3.8	1.16–10.28	Hirschwald
Graywacke schist	11	3.6	1.28–7.74	"
Graywacke	2	2.3	0.41–4.2	Gary
Quartzite	1	1.91	....	C. Moore
III. Sedimentary rocks				
A. Consolidated				
Carboniferous sandstone	9	3.61	1.09–7.09	Hirschwald
Devonian sandstone	11	4.4	1.36–12.98	"
Crystalline limestone	3	4.54	3.07–6.9	Gary
Bunter sandstone	30	17.7	7.7–27.72	Hirschwald
Lower Cretaceous sandstone	17	18.4	8.81–23.26	"
Various sandstones	17	18.1	6.85–27.3	Gary
Oölitic limestone	...	13.6–16.93	....	Hofer-Heimhalt
Calcareous tufa	...	20.2–32.2	....	" "
Chalk	...	14.4–43.9	....	" "
Limestone	3	28.78	to 42.8	C. Moore
Jurassic oölite	5	14.58	....	"
Shell limestone	9	11.6	0.8–27.6	Hirschwald
Jurassic limestone	3	28.0	24–34	"
Calcareous tufa	2	24.9	24.1–25.7	"
B. Unconsolidated materials				
Uniform spheres in cubic arrangement	...	47.6	....	Theoretical values according to various authors
Uniform spheres in tetrahedral arrangement	...	26.2	....	
Oil sands	84	17.5	3.4–37.7	Meinzer, Melcher
Sand of variable grain size	several	35.0	26–47	" King
Sand of uniform grain size	"	38.0	35–40	" "
Clay	several	45.0	44–47	" "
Various soils	"	55.0	45–65	" U S Dept of Agriculture
Dune sand	...	24.0	....	Hofer-Heimhalt
Sand and gravel	...	36–42.0	....	" "
Loess	...	41–46.0	....	" "
Clay	...	31–34.0	around 45–50	" "
Clay	...	44–50.0	....	" "
Marl	...	47.5	....	" "
Turf	...	81.0	to 85.2	" "
Infusorial earth	...	91.6	....	" "
Rubble marl	...	40.1	35–51	Pfeiffer, Dienemann

Other physical properties of rocks, which have not yet been carefully measured and tabulated, include their heat capac and thermal conductivity. THERMAL CONDUCTIVITIES of certain rocks and minerals are given in Table XXI. These values represent heat transferred (calories) through an area of 1 square cm and thickness of 1 cm in 1 sec, for a temp difference of 1° C. DIELECTRIC PROPERTIES of rocks have been proposed as a basis for prospecting by the use of radio waves. The constants usually range from about 1 to 7, when measured with d c or low-frequency a c; according to Dostovalow, the dielectric constant is much greater when measured at radio frequencies of 300 000 cycles (Table XXII); also the resistivities at high frequencies differ from those at low. Since the constant of quartz is usually greater than that of country rock, the possibility of employing these methods on quartz veins is obvious; but, since the constant of water is 80, presence of moisture would overshadow such observations, rendering interpretation difficult. Since electromagnetic waves involve 3 systems of constants (electrostatic, electromagnetic, and Heaviside-Lorentz values), conversions for these factors are given in Table XXIII.

Table XXI. Thermal Conductivities of Rocks and Minerals (31, 33)

Rock or mineral	Heat conductivity (See text)	Rock or mineral	Heat conductivity (See text)	Rock or mineral	Heat conductivity (See text)
Granite......	0.0058	Feldspar.......	0.006	Coal.........	0.0007–.0012
Gneiss........	0.0051	Mica..........	0.0009	Clays.........	0.0025
Quartz.......	0.01–.03	Limestone.....	0.0036–.0055	Slates.........	0.0033–.0056
Rock salt......	0.0128	Marble........	0.0053–.0064	Water.........	0.0014
Graphite.......	0.01–.03	Chalk.........	0.0022	Air............	0.000057
Magnetite.....	0.01–.03	Sandstones.....	0.0025–.0067		

Table XXII.   Dielectric Constants and Resistivity at 300 Kilocycles
After B. N. Dostovalow (34)

	ϵ, dielectric constant	ρ, resistivity, ohm-cm
IGNEOUS ROCKS		
Plutonic:		
Granite....................................	10.2–18.9	460×10^3–50.3×10^3
Granitite.................................	14.9	82.5×10^3
Granite-porphyry..........................	27.1	17.3×10^3
Astrophylite nepheline syenite	6.93	2.34×10^6
Micaceous nepheline syenite..................	8.47	1.51×10^6
Small-grained nepheline syenite..............	9.55	0.514×10^6
Coarse grained nepheline syenite.............	11.7	....
Miascite...................................	9.97	1.40×10^6
Marinpolite................................	12.1	0.213×10^6
Hornblende-foyaite.........................	7.45	2.07×10^6
Foyaite....................................	8.32	0.262×10^6
Feldspar-urtite............................	11.9	1.37×10^6
Urtite containing sphene....................	12.8	0.508×10^6
Essexite...................................	9.2	....
Khibinite..................................	10.43	
Tawite....................................	14.8	0.717×10^6
Gabbro, southern Urals	12.8	1.44×10^6
Gabbro, solid..............................	16.7	0.732×10^6
Gabbro, fine grained.......................	60.8	1.86×10^6
Gabbro, medium grained....................	28.2	42.6×10^3
Gabbro, coarse grained.....................	42.1	23.7×10^3
Norite.....................................	61.4	6.03×10^3
Proterobase................................	13.7	279×10^3
Hypabyssal and Volcanic:		
Quartz-keratophyre.........................	15.0	....
Albite diabase.............................	18.1	150×10^3
Quartz diabase.............................	34.5	31.3×10^3
Quartz porphyry...........................	14.2–49.3	101×10^3–21.6×10^3
Liparite...................................	12.5	57.9×10^3
Obsidian..................................	5.8–10.4	8.92×10^6–1.23×10^6
Pitchstone................................	18.7	113×10^3
Dacite.....................................	8.16	0.682×10^6
Liparite-dacite.............................	7.68	4.6×10^6
Porous andesite basalt......................	6.53	0.437×10^6
Andesite basalt............................	7.57	1.38×10^6
Traprock	18.9–39.8	2.46×10^3–54×10^3
Tuff......................................	3.79	1.69×10^6
METAMORPHIC ROCKS		
Quartzite..................................	6.63	0.178×10^6
Sandstone.................................	36.9	....
Marble....................................	15.2	0.173×10^6

Table XXIII. Conversion Factors for Electromagnetic Units (15)

	Elec units	e s u	e m u	H–L u
Charge.................	1 coulomb	3×10^9	10^{-1}	$6\sqrt{\pi} \times 10^9$
Current.................	1 ampere	3×10^9	10^{-1}	$6\sqrt{\pi} \times 10^9$
Potential...............	1 volt	$\dfrac{1}{300}$	10^8	$\dfrac{1}{600\sqrt{\pi}}$
Capacity...............	1 farad	9×10^{11}	10^{-9}	$36\pi \times 10^{11}$
Resistivity..............	1 ohm-centimeter	$\dfrac{1}{9 \times 10^{11}}$	10^9	$\dfrac{1}{36\pi \times 10^{11}}$
Self-inductance...........	1 henry	$\dfrac{1}{9 \times 10^{11}}$	10^9	$\dfrac{1}{36\pi \times 10^{11}}$
Magnetic intensity........	1 gauss	3×10^{10}	1	$\dfrac{1}{\sqrt{4\pi}}$
Dielectric constant........	1 practical unit	1	1	1
Permeability..............	1 practical unit	1	1	1

e s u = electrostatic units.   e m u = electromagnetic units.   H − L u = Heaviside-Lorentz units.

Radioactive rocks contain radium and thorium, and emit radon, a gas which diffuses in the ground but can be detected, even when extremely diluted, owing to its radioactive power. According to Petraschak and Krusch, the amounts of radioactive elements per gram of rock for various rock types are as in Table XXIV.

Table XXIV. Radioactive Contents of Typical Rocks

Acid rocks:
    Volcanic origin........ 3.1×10^{-12} gram radium
    Plutonic origin........ 2.7×10^{-2} " "
Intermediary rocks:
    Volcanic origin........ $\begin{cases} 2.1 \times 10^{-12} & \text{" radium and} \\ 3.5 \times 10^{-5} & \text{" thorium} \end{cases}$
    Plutonic origin........ 1.9×10^{-12} " radium
Basic rocks:
    Volcanic origin........ $\begin{cases} 1.1 \times 10^{-12} & \text{gram radium and} \\ 1.7 \times 10^{-5} & \text{" thorium} \end{cases}$
    Plutonic origin........ 1.9×10^{-2} " radium
Sedimentary rocks:
    Clay................. $\begin{cases} 1.5 \times 10^{-12} & \text{gram radium and} \\ 1.3 \times 10^{-5} & \text{" thorium} \end{cases}$
    Sandstone............ $\begin{cases} 1.4 \times 10^{-12} & \text{" radium and} \\ 0.5 \times 10^{-5} & \text{" thorium} \end{cases}$
    Limestone and dolomite $\begin{cases} 0.9 \times 10^{-12} & \text{" radium and} \\ 0.1 \times 10^{-5} & \text{" thorium} \end{cases}$

BIBLIOGRAPHY

There is no complete index of publications on geophysics. Prior to 1926, the bibliography in Ambronn, "Elements of Geophysics" (McGraw-Hill), is most complete. Later publications, to July 1, 1936, are in *Geophysical Abstracts*, issued by U S Bur of Mines and U S Geol Surv. Abstracts in Annotated Bibliography of Economic Geology emphasize the geol phases. Patent abstracts by U S Bur of Mines, *Inf Circ* 6883 (1936), cover legal aspects; continued in the *Geophysical Abstracts*. Other important publications: Principles and Practice of Geophysical Prospecting, by A. B. Broughton Edge, and T. H. Laby, Cambridge Univ Press. Geophysical Prospecting, volumes 81, 97, 110, 1929, 1932 and 1934 by Am Inst of Min and Met Engs. Applied Geophysics in the Search for Minerals, by A. S. Eve and D. A. Keys, Cambridge Univ Press.

Following are sources to which specific references are made in Figure and Table titles:

1. Theory and Practical Employment of Torsion Balance. H. Shaw and E. Lancaster-Jones. *Min Mag*, June, 1927, p 339
2. Eötvös Torsion Balance Method of Mapping Geologic Structure. D. C. Barton. *Trans A I M E*, vol 81 (1929 Geophysics) p 416
3. Graphical Terrane Correction for Gravity Gradient. D. C. Barton. U S Bur Mines, *Tech Paper* 444 (1929)
4. Torsion Balances for Use in Geophysical Prospecting. American Askania Corp. Catalog, 1929
5. Magnetic Study of Some Iron Deposits. E. F. Stratton and J. W. Joyce. U S Bur Mines, *Tech Paper* 528 (1932)
6. Simple Magnetic Method for Ore Prospecting. H. Lundberg. *Bull* Canad Inst Min & Met, July, 1929, p 843

7. Improved Brunton Pocket Transit. W. Ainsworth & Son, Catalog
8. Results of Some Magnetic Measurements on Dikes. F. W. Lee. U S Bur Mines, *Tech Paper* 510 (1932)
9. Exploring for Ore by Potential Methods. E. G. Leonardon and S. F. Kelly. *Eng & Min Jl,* Jan 14, 1928, p 47
10. Geophysical Prospecting for Water in Desert Areas. F. W. Lee. U S Bur Mines, *Inf Circ* 6899, Aug, 1936
11. Measuring Variation of Ground Resistivity with a Megger. F. W. Lee. U S Bur Mines, *Tech Paper* 440 (1928)
12. Subsurface Exploration by Earth Resistivity and Seismic Methods. E. R. Shepard. *Public Roads* (U S Dept Agric) June, 1935, p 57
13. Superposition Method.   Irwin Roman   U S Bur Mines (in press, 1939)
14 Phase Measurements in Electrical Prospecting.   H. Hedstrom.   A I M E, *Tech Pub* 827 (1937)
15. Electromagnetic Absorption by Rocks. J. W. Joyce.   U S Bur Mines, *Tech Paper* 497 (1931)
16. New Technique in Geological Exploration. Parfenov, Melikian, and Nikitine. *Azerbaidjan Oil Industry*, Jan, 1932.   Trans in English by Soc de Prospection Electrique (Schlumberger), Paris, under title "Application of Electrical Coring in the Russian Oil Fields"
17. Electrical Exploration of Drill Holes.   A. Deussen and E. G. Leonardon.   Am Pet Inst, *Drilling and Production Practice*, Tulsa Meeting, May 16, 1935
18. Schlumberger Well Surveying Corp, Houston, Tex. Catalog
19. Results of the Application of Electrical Coring in the Ordjonikidze Distr (Sourakhany). D. Jabrev and K. Emilianov.   See also Bib (16)
20. Electrical Logging Technique as applied to Petroleum Production and Engineering Problems. L. W. Storm and R. T. Wade.   *Petroleum Engineer*, Nov, 1936, p 66
21. Method of Seismic Prospecting by Reflection.   S. J. Pirsson.   *Bull* Soc Belge des Ingrs et des Indust, 1935, No 4, p 385
22. A Study of Some Seismometers.   G. A. Irland.   U S Bur Mines, *Tech Paper* 556 (1934)
23. Geological Testing Method.   L. Mintrop.   U S Pat 1 599 538, Sep 14, 1926
24. Method of Making Dip Determinations of Geological Strata   E. V. McCollum and G. C. McGhee.   U S Pat 2 001 429, May 14, 1935
25. Continuous Profiling Method of Seismographing for Oil Structures. S. J. Pirsson.   A I M E, *Tech Pub* 833 (1937)
26. Results of Deep Well Temperature Measurements in Texas.   E. M. Hawtof.   Am Pet Inst, *Production Bull* 205, Oct, 1930, p 62
27. Determination of Geothermal Gradients in Oklahoma.   J. A. McCutchin.   *Bull* Am Assoc Petrol Geologists, May, 1930, p 535
28. Economic Utility of Thermometric Measurements in Drill Holes.   E. G. Leonardon.   *Geophysics*, Jan, 1936, p 115
29. Use of Temperature Measurements for Cementation Control and Correlations in Drill Holes. A. Deussen and H. Guyod.   *Bull* Am Assoc Petrol Geologists, June, 1937, p 789
30. Temperature Measurements in Oil Wells.   M. Schlumberger, H. G. Doll, and A. A. Perebinossoff.   *Jour* Inst Petrol Technologists, vol 23 (1937) p 11
31. Handbuch der Experimentalphysik, vol 25, part 3.   H. Reich
32. Background for the Application of Geomagnetics to Exploration.   N. H. Stearn.   *Trans* A I M E, vol 81 (1929 Geophysics) p 315
33. Thermo-coring of Boreholes.   Diakonov.   *Neftianoe Khoziaistvo*, vol 19, No 6, 1938
34. B. N. Dostovalow.   Acad Sci, U S S R, Inst Petrog, *Travaux* No 10, p 161.   Moscow, 1937
35. Geophysical Delineation of Structure in Mining Explorations.   S. F. Kelly.   *Trans* Amer Geophysical Union, 1939

SECTION 11

UNDERGROUND TRANSPORT

BY

EDWIN C. HOLDEN

CONSULTING MINING ENGINEER

Note.—Numbers in parentheses (except numbers of equations) refer to Bibliography at end of this section.

UNDERGROUND TRANSPORT

1. GENERAL CONSIDERATIONS

Underground transport of mineral, waste and supplies is a vital function in mine operation. Reports from 41 metal mines using various standard mining methods (1) show that underground transport costs averaged 37.44¢, or 17.22% of total underground cost, varying from 11.35¢ to 59.9¢ per ton hoisted, or 12.77% to 26.30% of total, depending on mining methods (Art 20 and correspondence). In many mines, if first cost and maintenance of workings used primarily for transport were so charged, the total cost of transport would be shown to exceed all other mining costs.

Centralization. If the output can be brought to one level or gangway, transport may sometimes be so concentrated that hand tramming can profitably be replaced by animal haulage, or the latter by mechanical haulage. Even in shaft mines, where, due to shape of deposit or distribution of workings, the output of several levels is lowered to one main haulageway, the increased cost of hoisting may be more than offset by the saving from a centralized haulage system.

Transport method is decided by comparing the total capital and operating costs of systems considered. If these involve changes in mine development, it is necessary to determine what saving in development and maintenance costs may result from adopting a centralized system, which reduces the number, length or size of sub-levels, crosscuts, shaft stations and trackage otherwise required. Such saving must be balanced against cost of installing and maintaining the proposed haulage system.

General formulas. Let D = useful duty per shift, mineral-ton-miles; G = gross duty per shift, ton-miles; d = distance mineral is to be moved, ft; s = aver speed when moving, ft per min; t = time loading and discharging per trip, min; T = mineral handled per trip, tons; T' = tare per trip, tons; C = time of 1 complete cycle, min; m = actual working time per shift, min.

$$D = \frac{m}{\frac{2\,d}{s} + t} \times \frac{dT}{5\,280} = \frac{mdT}{5\,280\,C}, \quad \text{and} \quad G = D + \frac{m\,2\,dT'}{5\,280\,C} = \frac{md\,(T + 2\,T')}{5\,280\,C}$$

Useful duty D varies directly with distance, speed and wt of mineral per trip, and inversely as the time required at terminals. If the gross duty limit has been reached, the useful duty will vary inversely as $(T' \times 2)$. These principles apply to all kinds of transport, from shoveling to locomotive haulage. Despite the rule that cost per ton-mile, other things being equal, varies inversely as the unit load, underground conditions usually require small-scale equipment. But many large-tonnage installations exist in coal, iron and copper mines, varying from the most primitive to standard R R equipment.

2. PRIMITIVE TRANSPORT METHODS (30)

Packing. Mineral is carried in sacks, skins or baskets on backs or heads of men and women, in primitive countries, or occasionally in narrow, tortuous workings, or in emergency work. Unit load is usually 60 to 150 lb, but, in Latin America and the Orient, peones and coolies carry more. Duty varies widely, but approximates 12 to 14 man-hr per ton-mile. Boxes or hand-barrows, holding 200 to 700 lb, and carried by 2 or more men, are slightly more economic, but if there is room for such practice better methods are usually feasible.

Shoveling (Sec 3). Transport by carrying or casting with shovels is proper only as a last resort. One man can move 1 ton 100 ft in about 2.5 hr, equivalent to 125 to 160 man-hr per ton-mile. Long-handle, round-point No 2 shovels are standard for underground mucking; 1938 price, $12–$14 per doz. MUCKING is a common term for underground shoveling. In stopes, with chutes 30 ft apart, the standard duty is commonly 20 cars (17 to 20 tons) per shift, including sledging or blockholing lumps, and stowing filling. If chutes are advantageously placed, shovelers have time to assist miners, but if much sorting is done, their output may be greatly reduced. The stoping method greatly affects cost of shoveling; good shoveling floors and slides are as important as chute spacing. (For mucking in connection with tramming, see Art 10.)

Wheelbarrow transport (Sec 3), exclusive of loading, costs at least 1 man-shift per ton-mile, and is justified only in temporary work, or where first cost of track and equipment is not warranted. Short exploratory workings and small, irregular stopes, where the only alternative is shoveling, are the only proper fields for the barrow in mining work.

Best mining barrow has 3 cu ft capacity, No 14 to 16 B & S gage pressed steel tray, handles, frame, and wheel guard of steel pipe; max height 21 in, wt 70 to 80 lb, price $70–$100 per doz, fob factory. For surface work in very hot or cold climates, wood handles are preferable. For thin seams a flat barrow without legs is used.

Examples. BUTTE, Mont. For periods of 4 years in the larger mines, comparative costs of shoveling for different stoping methods were: square-set, 100; rill, 75; timbered rill, 85; back-fill stoping, 120 (40). UNITED VERDE, Ariz. All mucking in drifts is now done by mechanical loaders (Sec 27). In stopes, broken ore and waste are handled by scrapers. Except for minor track cleaning, no shovels are used (H. M. Lavender, 1938). NORTH BUTTE, Mont (Linton). Classification of underground labor showed: shovelers 26.8%, and trammers 18.9%, as against 15.7% miners, indicating importance of shovel and transport labor. MASCOT, Tenn (42, p 67). 1923 contract shoveling, 23¢ per car of 1.7 ton; aver duty over 6 mo, 16.8 ton per man. NATION No 2 MINE, Mo. 2 yr aver shoveling, company account, 15.46 ton per man-shift; contract, 22.23 ton. SOUTHEAST Mo. Aver for lead district, 1922: company account, 14–18 ton; contract, 19–22 ton. See Sec 10, for comparison with mechanical loading.

3. MINE CARS (1 to 11)

Standard design. The importance of the underground car justifies great care in design or selection. If possible, a single design suited to local conditions should be adopted. This cannot be done where hand-trammed, stope-filling or sub-level cars and larger mechanically hauled main-level or adit cars are all used, and in large mines several designs and sizes are employed. But, if a compromise design is feasible, standardization is advantageous in simplifying repairs and the stock of repair parts.

Car body is of wood, steel or composite construction. Wooden cars are bulky, become very heavy in wet mines, are less durable, but more easily repaired than steel. They are obsolescent in metal mining, and in collieries the number of composite and steel cars is rapidly increasing. Composite cars usually have wood stringers for the truck, and wood lining. The body is rigid, or is hinged on its truck for dumping in one direction, or has a king-pin or turn-table connection to truck to dump in any direction. When conditions permit, the body should be centered over the wheelbase, to equalize wheel loads and avoid accidental head-on dumping. Steel bodies are now generally used.

Rigid-body, flat-bottom cars are simpler and usually lower than others of equal capacity. Advantages: ease of loading because of the low sides, simplicity, cheapness, and

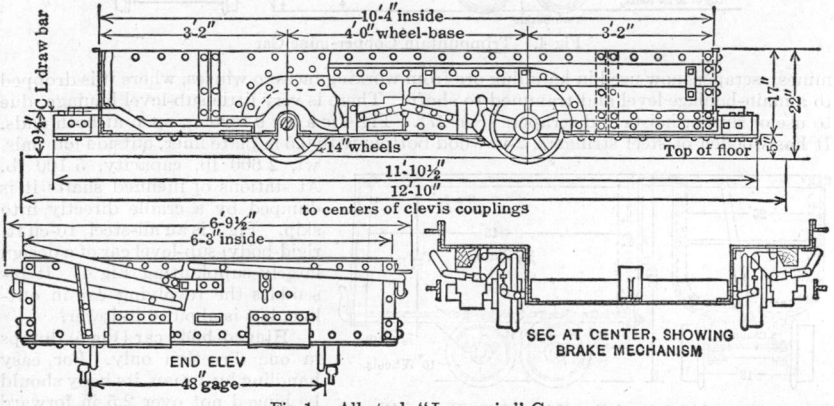

Fig 1. All-steel, "Low-vein" Car

high ratio of capacity to wt. Disadvantage: they can be dumped only at tipples or on track dumps at fixed places. Most colliery cars are of this type. Fig 1 shows an all-steel, "low-vein" car (3) of 100-cu ft level capacity, with bottom below the axles and no door; used with rotary dump at Lynch colliery; approx wt, 4 000 lb. Fig 2 is a standard car of Connellsville, Pa, district; wt, 2 200 lb, capacity 40 cu ft. Fig 3 is a wooden car used in sub-levels in the Mesabi iron range; simple, cheap and easily repaired. This sub-level car has been discontinued by Oliver Iron Mining Co in all but 2 underground

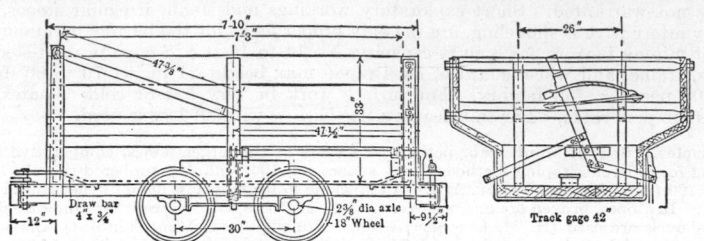

Fig 2. Hockensmith Standard Wooden Car

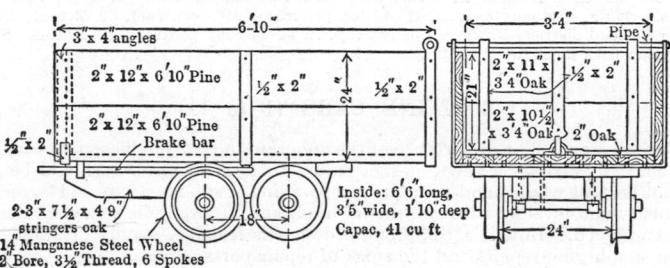

Fig 3. Sub-level Car, Mesabi Iron Range

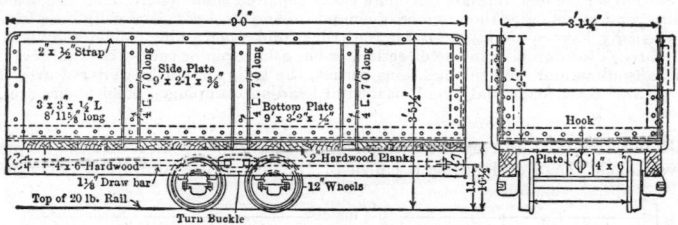

Fig 4. Trimountain Copper-mine Car

mines; scrapers now used in handling ore from working faces to winzes, where it is dropped to a main-haulage level and trammed to shaft. There is very little sub-level haulage, due to use of slusher hoists and scrapers (Sec 27). Fig 4 is a car 9 ft long, open at both ends. It has wooden or steel stringers, 2-in wood bottom with 0.5 in plate liner, outside journals,

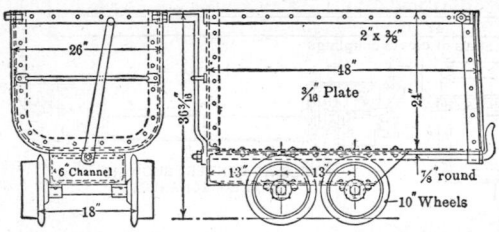

Fig 5. All-steel, Sub-level Car (Lake Shore Engine Works)

wt, 2 600 lb, capacity, 5 100 lb. At stations of inclined shafts it is dumped by a cradle directly into skip. Fig 5 is an all-steel, 16-cu ft, rigid-body, sub-level car of a design largely supplanting Fig 4. It resembles the revolving car in outline, but is about 6 in lower.

Hinged-body car (Fig 6) dumps in one direction only. For easy handling by 1 man, its body should be hinged not over 2.5 in forward of load center line.

Fig 7 (Mich copper mine) is open at both ends; capac, 40 cu ft. Side-dump car, Fig 8, is heavily reinforced, for taking 2-ft lump ore from chutes, at Anyox and Alaska Gastineau. V-BODY, supported on trunnions, may be single or double side-dumping (Fig 9). It is little used underground, but for soft, fine ore, discharged at the side, it may be better than the revolving type. The V can be made high and narrow, or low and wide as required by gangway and chute clearances. It has no doors and can readily be made water tight. Fig 9a is a V-bottom, rolling side-dump car of 45 cu ft, used together with gable-bottom cars of 47 cu ft capac for main-level haulage by Oliver Iron Mining Co (1938).

Revolving dump-car can dump in any direction, and hence is useful for metal mines. Body must be high enough for the bottom to clear the wheels when side dumping. To avoid danger of overturning, the car body should not exceed 4 ft long when handled by 1 man. The car is therefore rather high and short. Wheels are seldom over 12 in. Fig 10 is a typical Butte car; wt, 965 lb; capac, 1 700 to 1 900 lb. Fig 11 is a 30 cu-ft car for both hand tramming and train haulage. Scoop car (Fig 12) is usually of the

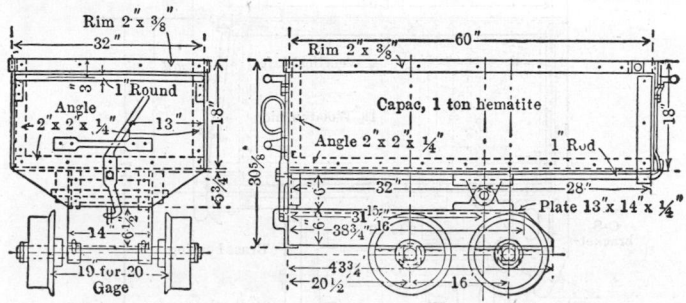

Fig 6.   Standard Hinged-body Car

revolving dump type. Like the V-body car, it is simplified by omitting the door, and can then be made water-tight. It is good for discharging into a chute, but may require a clearance below track level, and it is more liable to upset when side dumping.

Hopper-bottom cars are unusual underground, but are good for transfer service, large unit loads and motor haulage. In the Sanford-Day car, bottom doors are automatically successively released as they reach the storage bin, and are closed and latched by passing over a knuckle on the exit side, the train dumping without stop.

Saddle-back cars, holding 1.5 to 5 tons, are common on main levels in motor-haulage mines. Discharging from both sides they keep tracks clean and fill pockets evenly. Fig 13 is a 6-ft car of 2.75-ton capac, with 16-in wheels and pocket couplers, used by Oliver

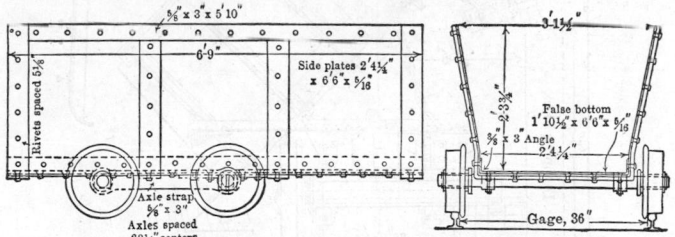

Fig 7.   Open-end Dumping Car (Mich Copper District)

Iron Mining Co with the V-body car of same capac (Fig 9a). Fig 14 shows end of a similar 45-cu ft car, at Miami, Ariz; it has an improved door latch. This is now (1938) replaced by a car of similar design, of 86 cu ft capac.

Special bodies are required for drinking water, toilet and man cars. Standard trucks with removable frames are best for drill steel, wedges and powder, and with side stakes for timber, drills and large supplies.

Steel cars continue to displace wooden and composite cars (Fig 2, 16), which, however, will long be used, especially when they have anti-friction bearings. When new, rigidity of steel cars often causes derailments, if the bearings are not self-alining and are without springs. Sizes of colliery cars: up to 120-cu ft level capacity and 14 ft long. Fig 15a is a Pittsburgh Coal Co all-steel car, for 40-in track, of 176 cu ft capac, 14-in wheels with Tyson roller-bearings and inside spring journals (L. E. Young, 1938).

CAR TRUCKS. Wheels, axles, bearings and frame make over 0.5 the wt and $2/3$ the cost of most mine cars. The frame may be the car bottom itself (Fig 1, 2), a pair of wooden stringers (Fig 3, 4), a built-up steel truck (Fig 5, 6, 9, 10, 12), or single rolled shape, usually a channel, forged into a U (Fig 11). The design in Fig 2 insures perfect alinement of axles, when a wooden car bottom carries journal boxes. On the other hand, cars at a Mich iron mine have the axle boxes carried flexibly by light diagonal straps, and it is claimed that one wheel will climb over a 3-in obstacle on the track without derailment. DOUBLE-TRUCK, 8-wheel car may be used for large loads; it reduces the load per wheel for light rails, and can run on sharper curves than a car of same capac with rigid wheel base.

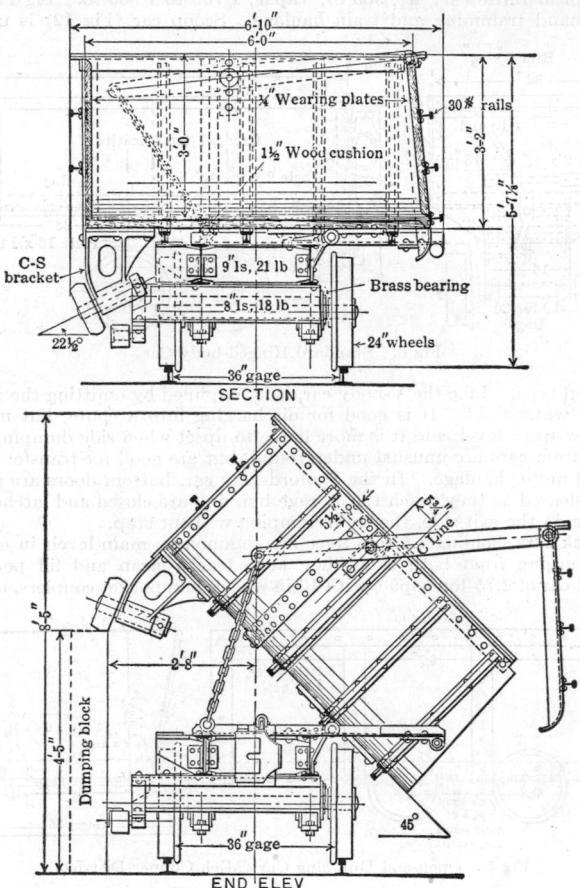

Fig 8.　Side-dump Car, 130 cu ft, Granby Mining Co, Anyox, B C

Fig 17 is a 12-ton car. Large unit loads are economic, and the use of double-truck cars will increase (see *E & M J*, Vol 95, p 276; 96, p 1170). WHEEL BASE. For the sharp curves of mine track the wheel base must be short; rarely more than the track gage. Exceptions: locomotives, because their drivers are of large diam, and cars for overhead rope haulage, since long wheel base tends to prevent derailments. For relation of wheel base to radius of outer rail on curves, see Track gage, Art 5.

Fig 17a is an all-steel, 6-cu yd double-truck coal car; wt 5 300 lb, using dumping cylinder (Fig 17b) which returns to at-rest position by gravity. Each pair of wheels (running on same rail) swivels about a king post for taking curves. Wheels have vert play on king post for uneven track. Fig 17c has gable-bottom for sticky lead-silver ore; wt 4 500 lb, 57 cu ft, with double truck, allowing minimum-radius track curve of 20 ft.

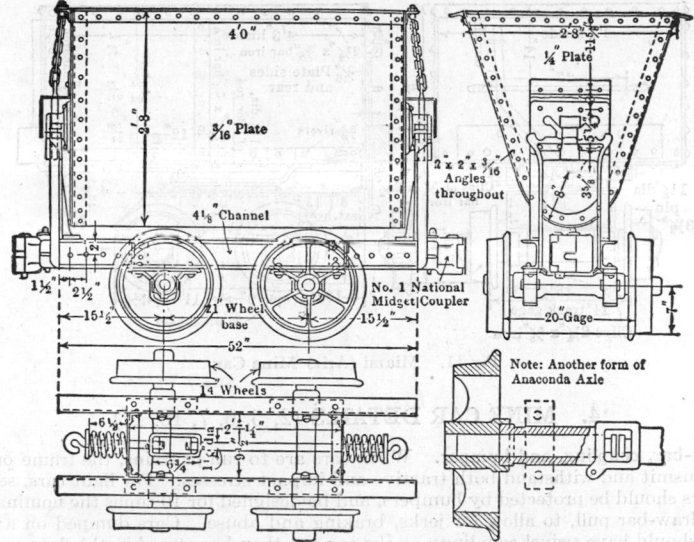

Fig 9. V-body Mine Car, with Anaconda Truck (Copper Queen Mine)

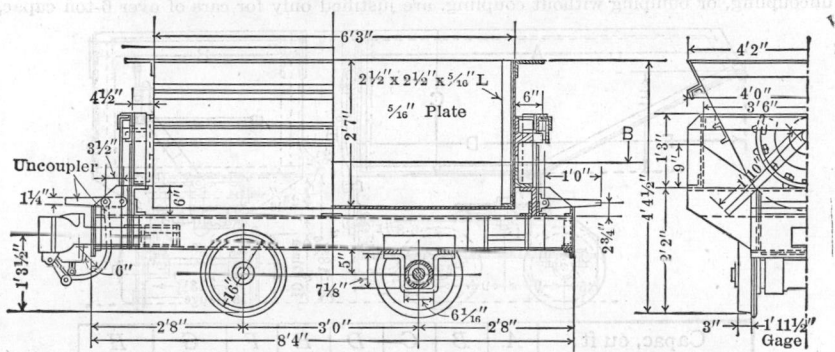

Fig 9a. V-bottom, Side-dump Car, 45 cu ft Capac (Oliver Iron Mining Co)

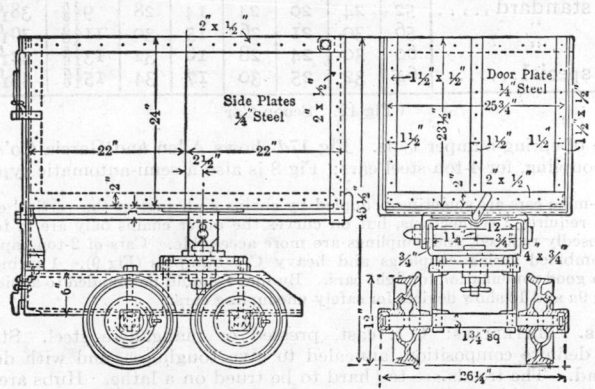

Fig 10. Revolving Dump-car, Butte, Mont

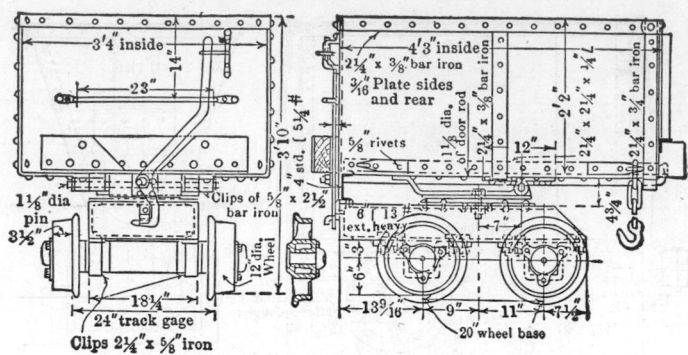

Fig 11.   Miami (Ariz) Mine Car

4.   MINE CAR DETAILS (2, 5, 6, 7, 10, 11)

Draw-bar, coupling, and bumper.   When cars are to run in trains, the frame or body must transmit and withstand both tractive and impact stresses.   For light cars, separate draw-bars should be protected by bumpers, and be designed for 10 times the nominal loco-motive draw-bar pull, to allow for jerks, braking and abuse.   Cars dumped on a rotary dumper should have swivel couplings, as the car can then be rotated in the dump without uncoupling from train (Art 9).   Automatic couplings, due to their cost and difficulty of uncoupling, or bumping without coupling, are justified only for cars of over 6-ton capac,

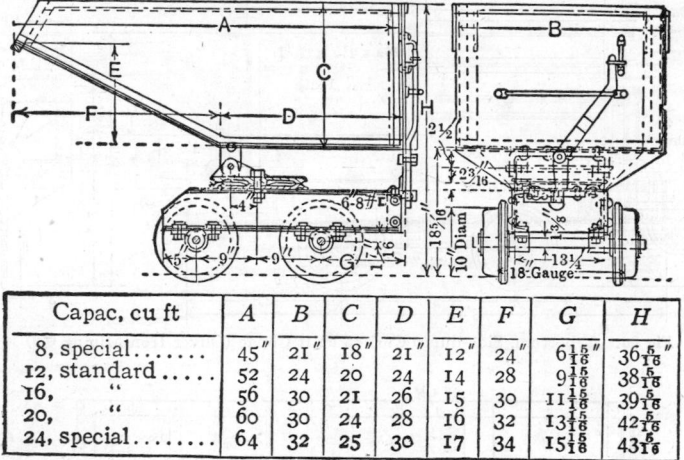

Capac, cu ft	A	B	C	D	E	F	G	H
8, special.......	45″	21″	18″	21″	12″	24″	$6\frac{5}{16}$″	$36\frac{5}{16}$″
12, standard.....	52	24	20	24	14	28	$9\frac{15}{16}$	$38\frac{5}{16}$
16, "	56	30	21	26	15	30	$11\frac{15}{16}$	$39\frac{5}{16}$
20, "	60	30	24	28	16	32	$13\frac{15}{16}$	$42\frac{5}{16}$
24, special.......	64	32	25	30	17	34	$15\frac{15}{16}$	$43\frac{5}{16}$

Fig 12.   Scoop Car

and should be of spring-bumper type.   Fig 17d shows Allen and Garcia Co's semi-auto-matic spring coupling, for 4-ton steel cars; Fig 8 is also a semi-automatic type.

Small metal-mine cars are sometimes coupled by chains and rings at the vertical edges of body (Fig 11).   This requires 2 connections, but on curves the outer chains only are in tension, curve friction is supposedly reduced, and couplings are more accessible.   Cars of 2-ton capacity or over should have combined spring couplings and heavy C-I bumpers (Fig 9).   1 spring and 1 rigid coupling make a good combination for light cars.   Bumpers should be rounded to avoid interlocking on curves.   Fig 9a and 15 show devices for safely uncoupling cars.

Car wheels.   MATERIALS: C I, cast, pressed or manganese steel.   Standard C-I wheels are of definite composition, annealed to give toughness, and with deep chill on flange and tread.   The treads are too hard to be trued on a lathe.   Hubs are soft, easily worn, but readily machined and bushed.   When scrapped they are salable to local foundries. Cast-steel wheels are at least 30% lighter than C I; are tougher, not breaking under

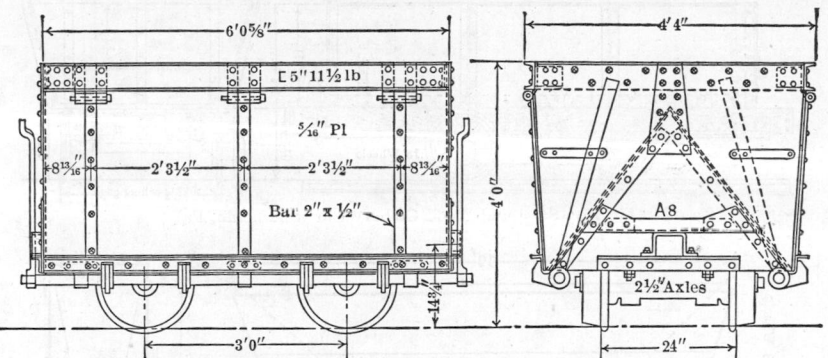

Fig 13. Gable-bottom Car, 47 cu ft Capac (Oliver Iron Mining Co)

impact (as iron wheels may), wear more rapidly on the tread, but are easily machined. In remote regions they are worth less per lb as scrap. Wheels of pressed-steel plate are tougher and lighter than cast steel, easily machined, but can not be made in one piece with self-oiling recesses. Some mines give satisfactory reports of them. Manganese-steel wheels are hard and tough, and outwear any others of the same design. They cost more, can not be machined with tool steel, and in many mining districts make unsalable scrap. Hard, smooth wheel tread gives lowest track friction. DESIGN. Diam, 8 to 20 in; tread, 2.5 to 3.75 in, coned $1/16$ to $3/16$ in (M C B standard coning is 1 in 20). When treads become grooved, wheels should be trued on a lathe or discarded; grooving causes derailment on frogs and increases tractive resistance, especially on curves. Flanges are from $7/8$ to $1 5/8$ in deep. WHEEL BEARINGS. LOOSE WHEELS are held on axle by cotters or linch-pins (Fig 18a, 19c), by bolts or key blocks engaging annular grooves in axle

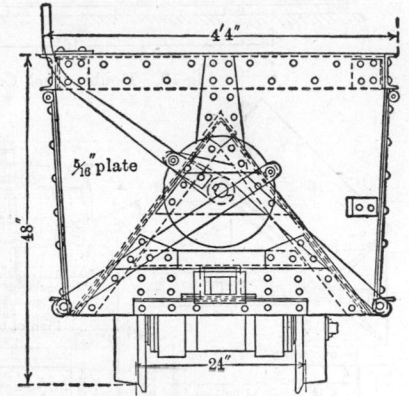

Fig 14. Saddle-back Car, Rear Elev (Miami Mine, Ariz)

(Fig 18), or have outside pedestal boxes and inner axle collars (Fig 4). With finished

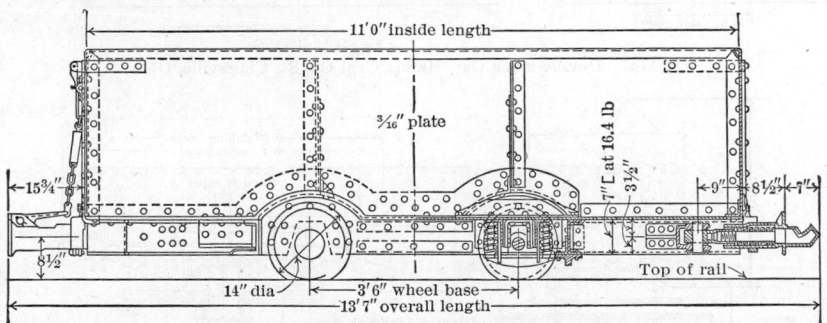

Fig 15. Colliery Car, Pittsburgh Coal Co, 1936.
Width overall, 6 ft; height, 3 ft 3 7/8 in; gage, 3 ft 3 1/2 in.

collars, hubs should be counter-sunk to fit. Hub bore may be machined, or left rough for babbitting, or reamed out for a soft steel, brass or bronze bushing (Fig 19). TIGHT WHEELS

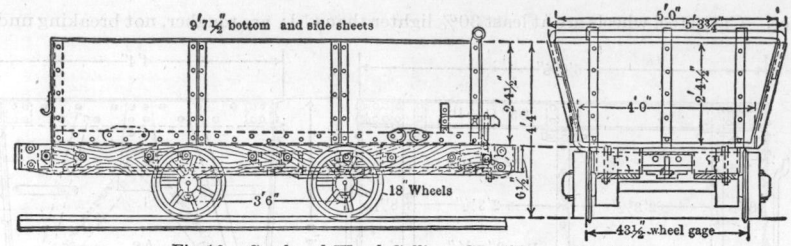

Fig 16.   Steel and Wood Colliery Car (Shamokin, Pa)

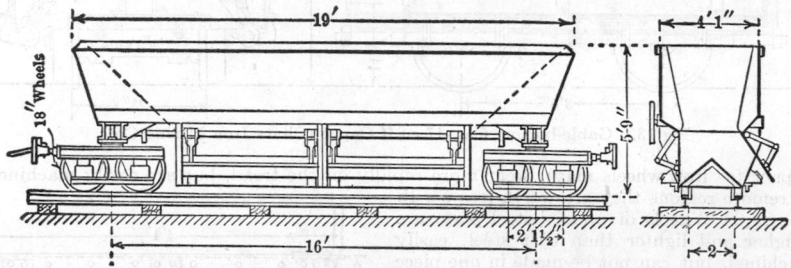

Fig 17.   Double-truck Car (Crown Mines, Transvaal)

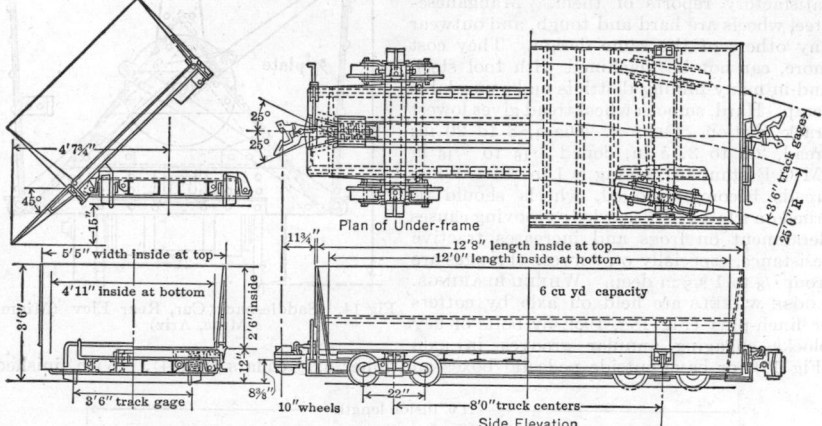

Fig 17a.   Double-truck Car, Hanna Coal Co, St. Clairsville, Ohio

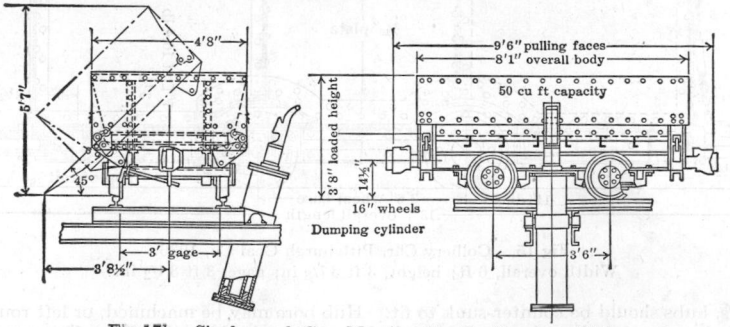

Fig 17b.   Single-truck Car, Marting Ore Co, Caspian, Mich

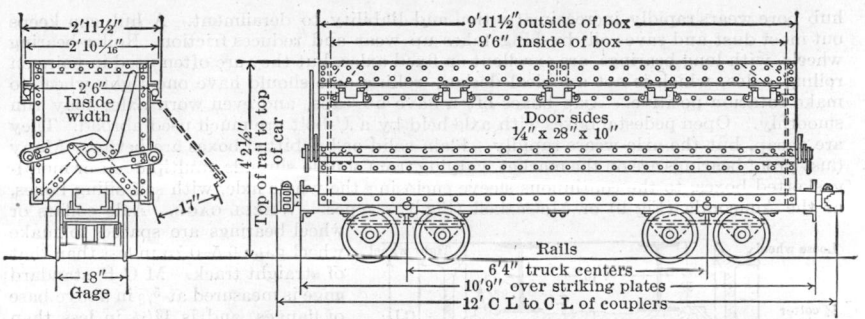

Fig 17c.　57-cu ft, Gable-bottom Car, Park–Utah Consol Mines Co, Park City, Utah

may be keyed or bolted through grooves in the axle; but a close fit is better, wheel being forced on axle by hydraulic press. SELF-OILING WHEELS, of numerous designs, have hub

caps, thus making an oil reservoir (Fig 18), or cast with reservoirs in the hub; they have spokes or wheel disks with oil-feed holes to the journal and screw plugged or spring capped supply hole (Fig 10 and 18a). For large mines, plain and bushed wheel bearings are becoming obsolete, because of the higher effic of roller and ball bearings. ROLLER-BEARING WHEELS are heavier and cost more, but so greatly reduce tractive resistance that they are rapidly replacing the cruder types in both coal and metal mines. Flexible and solid cylindrical rollers,

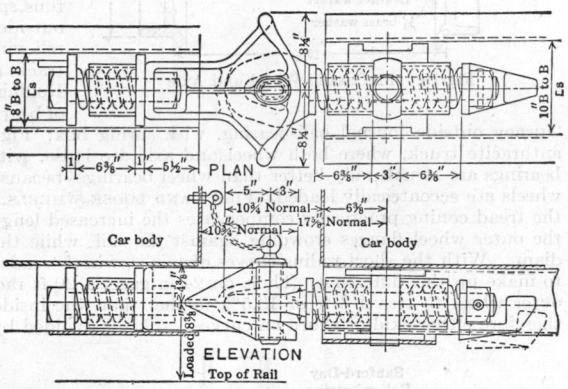

Fig 17d.　Semi-automatic Spring Coupling (Allen & Garcia)

tapered rollers and ball bearings are all in use. Fig 19a, b and c show 5 types of these bearings. For performance of different bearings, see Art 8. AXLES may be fixed or

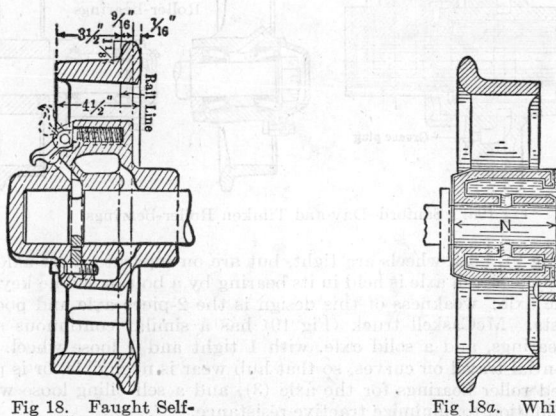

Fig 18.　Faught Self-oiling Wheel

Fig 18a.　Whitney Self-oiling Wheel

rolling. Simplest and cheapest is a square axle bolted to truck frame or car bottom with outside loose wheels (Fig 10). Having no protection against dust or oil leakage, the hub bore wears rapidly, increasing friction and liability to derailment. A hub cap keeps out most dust and saves oil; bushing takes up wear and reduces friction. Roller-bearing wheels, with long bearings, are excellent on fixed axles, but they are often used in pairs on rolling axles, which is not a logical design; rolling axle should have one tight wheel to make rotation positive. Axle boxes often have no caps, and even worn axles may run smoothly. Open pedestal boxes with axle held by a U-bolt are much used abroad. They are cheap, but the axle wears rapidly. Plain solid or babbitted boxes are better. Many dust-proof bearings are on the market, varying from simple shrouds, multiple felt or metal-gasketted boxes, to the continuous sleeve enclosing the whole axle, with self-oiling boxes, as the Anaconda (Fig 9) or McCaskell (Fig 19) types.

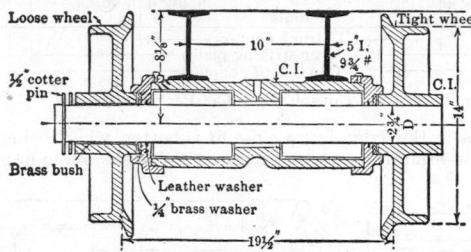

Fig 19.   McCaskell Wheel and Axle

WHEEL GAGE. Axle collars or wheel bearings are spaced to make wheel gage 0.5–0.75 in less than that of straight track. M C B standard gage is measured at $5/8$ in above base of flanges, and is $13/16$ in less than the straight track gage. AXLE BEARINGS. Fixed axles require no anti-friction bearing, except at wheel hubs. Where axle loads exceed 2.5 tons, spring pedestal boxes, preferably outside the wheel, should be used, relieving shock on both car and track and minimizing derailments. Rolling axles have the same variety of bearings as for wheels. Fig 19c is a Gurney outside journal ball-bearing, with spring box; Fig 19a, part of a Sanford-Day anthracite truck, where both wheel and axle are loose, with outside spring box. Axle bearings are structurally better than wheel bearings, because on curves or poor track the wheels are eccentrically loaded. TIGHT AND LOOSE WHEELS. In standard R R practice, the tread coning practically compensates the increased length of the outer rail on curves, while the outer wheel flanges crowding against the rail, while the inner travel on their small diam. With the short-radius curves of mines, wheel treads can not be sufficiently coned to make up this difference. Thus, on 24-in gage, a 20-ft radius curve of 90° requires the outer wheel to travel 3 ft or 10.5% farther than the inside wheel. Fixed wheels must therefore either skid or churn on curves. This is avoided by loose wheels. Or, as in the

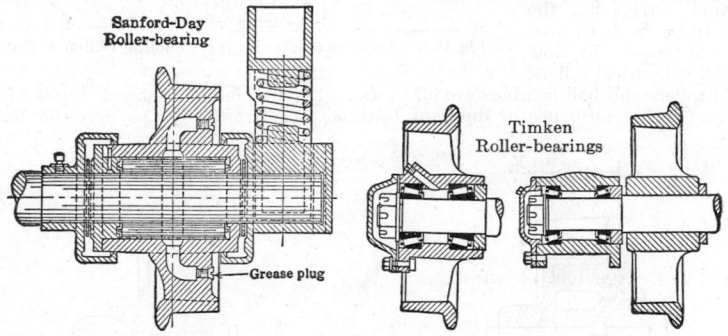

Fig 19a.   Sanford–Day and Timken Roller-bearings

Anaconda truck (Fig 9), both wheels are tight, but are on separate short axles, in a continuous sleeve journal. Each axle is held in its bearing by a bolt or saddle key, riding in a slot cut around the axle; weakness of this design is the 2-piece axle and poor provision to meet end thrusts. McCaskell truck (Fig 19) has a similar continuous oil reservoir shroud between bearings, and a solid axle, with 1 tight and 1 loose wheel. The loose wheel gives differential travel on curves, so that hub wear is negligible, or is provided for by bushing. Cased roller bearings for the axle (3), and a self-oiling loose wheel, would give an ideal combination to minimize tractive resistance.

Lubrication of wheels (25, 27). Thorough lubrication is essential for low tractive resistance. An oil bath on a standard R R axle reduces friction from 10 to 15% of what it is with oiled waste on one side of the journal. Open, unprotected pedestal boxes may require lubrication every trip, and, when used, there should be oil reservoirs beside or between rails, with revolving brushes or cams to oil or grease the axles automatically as they pass. Plain covered bearings should be oiled once or twice each shift. Self-oiling, dust-proof bearings (see above) may not require attention once a week. Best roller bearings run 3 to 12 months with one charge of grease, and makers claim a saving of 80% in

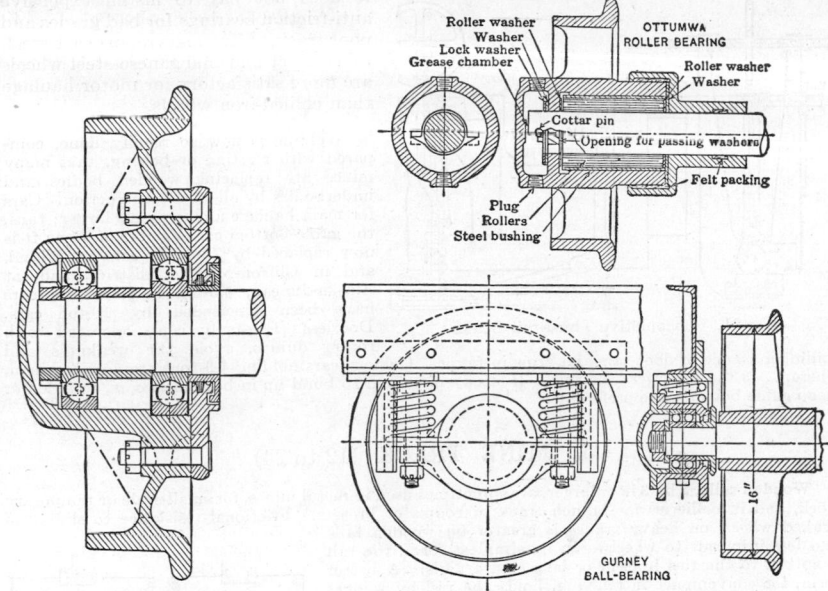

Fig 19*b*. S K F Ball-bearing   Fig 19*c*.   Types of Roller- and Ball-bearings

cost of lubricant over plain bearings (27). Bearings are lubricated by a grease gun, attached to the grease-plug hole; grease is forced in by a screw piston displacing the old grease. Hand guns are customary, but for large mines a grease tank with 100-lb air pressure, and pressure hose lines to both sides of track is better. Mode of lubrication can be advantageously varied with size of wheel, as indicated by Fig 51*b* from the Pittsburgh tests (4, 6). Non-hardening cup grease should be used, and roller bearings should also be oiled sparingly at intervals with a good car oil. In winter use zero-test oil. For effect of lubrication on traction, see Art 8.

Brakes. The simplest brake is a hardwood sprag, thrust between spokes and forcing the wheel to slide. It causes flat wheels and is usually applied to but 1 wheel at a time. A lever with wood block between wheels brakes 2 wheels on one side. A simpler steel-bar brake is shown in Fig 3. Brake shoes of wood or steel, in chairs, with toggle gear cross-connected under body to engage all 4 wheels, are best (Fig 1, 2). Brakes should have a ratchet, latch

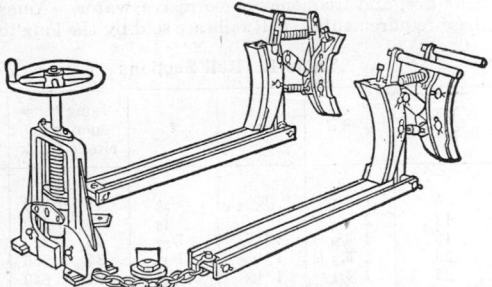

Fig 20.   Vertical Screw Brake

or counterweight, to set or hold them. Fig 20 shows brake system on a Gen Electric Co's trolley locomotive. For locomotives on steep tracks a special rail brake is sometimes provided to grip both sides of a third brake-rail to control train (Fig 21). It is said this brake will stop within 100 ft a 100-ton train and locomotive running 8 miles per hr down 8% grade.

Making vs buying cars. Special cars, as for drill-steel, timber, water, toilet or men, can advantageously be made in the mine shops during dull periods, at nominal labor cost;

but, for standard cars, only large mines with good shops can compete with mine car makers, either in cost or quality of product. Freight rates on manufactured cars are usually higher than on lumber or knocked-down car parts.

Present tendencies. Well-managed mines are standardizing car designs. The various roller and ball bearings are properly replacing plain and bushed bearings, though it does not pay to install expensive anti-friction bearings for bad grades and poor track. Mine mgrs report cast-steel, rolled-steel and manganese-steel wheels are more satisfactory for motor haulage than chilled-iron wheels.

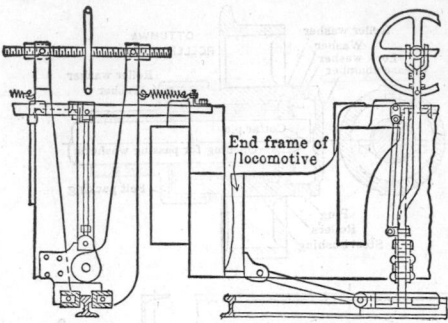

Fig 21. Locomotive Third-rail Brake

Welding is now so readily done, compared with riveting or bolting, that many mines are replacing wooden bodies and underbodies by all-steel construction. Cars for main haulage are becoming larger; thus, the gable-bottom car (Fig 14) of 45-cu ft is now replaced by 75-cu ft cars at Miami, and in Clifton-Morenci district, and, at Alaska-Juneau, 5.5-ton gable-bottom cars have been superseded by 10-ton cars. Doorless rigid-body cars, operated with rotary dumps, avoid the weakness and spilling nuisance of door cars and grow in favor. Colliery cars holding 4-6 tons are now common, where 1.5-3 ton cars were the rule. If sticky ores tend to build up in bottom of cars, rounded or steep gable bottoms are preferable.

5. MINE TRACK (12 to 24)

Wooden rails, 2 by 3 in or larger, are sometimes used in metal mines, for small-scale or temporary work, and in collieries for branch track in rooms or breasts. Frictional resistance to sliding of braked wheels on heavy grades is greater on wooden rails and less injurious to wheels. In its simplest form, the rail is spiked to the ties by 4-in or larger wire nails. A better form, for convenience in relaying, holds the rail by wedges in daps in the ties (Fig 22). Facing wooden rails with strap iron increases their life, but reduces sliding friction practically to that of the T-rail. Straps are 3/8 or 1/2 by 2 in, fastened by countersunk spikes or screws.

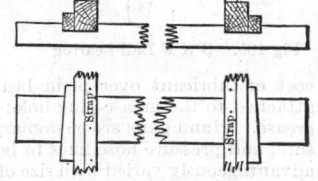

Steel rails are made in 3 standard series of sections, the Amer Soc C E, and A and B series of Amer Ry Assoc; also in many special shapes. For mine track thick web and broad base are best, because of use of light ties, and frequency of corrosive water. Amer Soc C E sections most nearly meet these requirements. R R rails are sold by the long ton, specifications usually calling for 30

Fig 22. Wooden Rails

Table 1. Rail Sections (Amer Soc Civ Eng Standard)

Wt, lb per yd	b = d	c	t	Long tons per mile single track		Lb per 100 ft	Size of hole, in	F, in	L' or L, in
				ton	lb				
8*	1 9/16	13/16	5/32	12	1 280	267	5/8	2	16
12	2	1	3/16	18	1 920	400	5/8	2	16
16	2 3/8	1 11/64	7/32	25	320	533	3/4	2	16
20	2 5/8	1 11/32	1/4	31	960	667	3/4	2	16
25	2 3/4	1 1/2	19/64	39	640	850	13/16	2	16
30	3 1/8	1 11/16	21/64	47	320	1 000	13/16	2	16
35	3 5/16	1 3/4	23/64	55	000	1 167	13/16	2	16
40	3 1/2	1 7/8	25/64	62	1 920	1 333	7/8	2 1/2	20
45	3 11/16	2	27/64	70	1 600	1 500	7/8	2 1/2	20
50	3 7/8	2 1/8	7/16	78	1 280	1 667	1	2 1/2	24
55	4 1/16	2 1/4	15/32	86	960	1 833	1	2 1/2	24
60	4 1/4	2 3/8	31/64	94	640	2 000	1	2 1/2	24
65	4 7/16	2 13/32	1/2	102	320	2 167	1	2 1/2	24
70†	4 5/8	2 7/16	33/64	110	000	2 333	1	2 1/2	34

Letters refer to Fig. 23.   * Few mills roll this size.   † Heavier rails, up to 150 lb, are rolled.

or 33-ft lengths, with not over 10% of shorts down to 24 ft. Shorter lengths (18 to 27 ft) are often necessary for mine track, especially at shaft stations. Relaying-rails, 56-lb and heavier, are usually on the market at reduced prices.

Spacing of holes in rails and splice bars varies with different makers for rails below 40 lb, and should be specified when ordering; b, c, d, G, H and t, refer to Fig 23. $G = 2\,F$; $H = 2\,F + 1/8$ in; L' for 4-bolt joints, up to 65-lb rail; L for 6-bolt joints, for 70 lb and heavier.

Weight of rail. FOR STRENGTH: Fig 24 shows minimum wt of rail and max single-wheel load recommended for 1 1/2 and 3-ft tie spacings, to give reasonably low stresses. Heavier rails than indicated for given loads will reduce track resistance and maintenance costs, while lighter rails should be used only for temporary work. For locomotives, rails

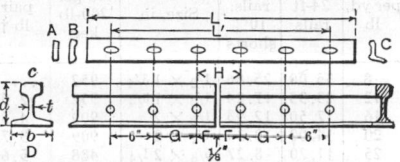

Fig 23.   Rail Section and Splice Bars

lighter than 25 lb will not keep alinement, and should not be used on main lines. FOR CONDUCTIVITY: rails for heavy traffic are usually amply large for return circuit for electric haulage, but with light equipment the size of rail for economic conductivity, rather than the wheel loads, may be the limiting factor in determining wt of rail. Rails carrying 0.25% Cu are reported by J. O. Greenan (15) as being ten times more resistant to acid mine water than non-cuprous rails.

Bonding. The contact resistance of ordinary rail joints is so great as to be equivalent to an open circuit. The best of bonds should be used under splice bars, and rails should be cross-bonded at about every third length, the rail circuit being connected to the negative pole to minimize corrosion. (For rail bonds, see Sec 16.)

Rail joints should have as nearly as possible the same strength and stiffness as the solid rail. Expansion is allowed for by leaving spaces between rail ends, using splice-bars with slotted bolt holes, and drilling the rail holes 1/8 to 1/4 in larger than the bolts. Flat fish-plates (Table 2, and Fig 23, A and B) are made for rails up to 40-lb, but for rails over 25-lb the angle-bar splice (Fig 23, C) is better. ELECTRIC WELDING is the best modern method of bonding, and is becoming standard practice for main-line track, for both bonds and joints.

Track spikes, to have the greatest holding power, should be straight, smooth, of uniform cross-sec, and with a sharp cutting edge beveled back 2 diams. Spikes of different makers vary over 10% in wt; number per keg should be verified when ordering and allowance made for extras. Spikes are staggered on opposite sides of the rail, and the stagger reversed for the other rail, the inside spikes being near the same side of tie. If ties are first bored with holes 1/8 in smaller than the spike, the holding power is greater, but to follow the hole, spikes must be pointed instead of beveled.

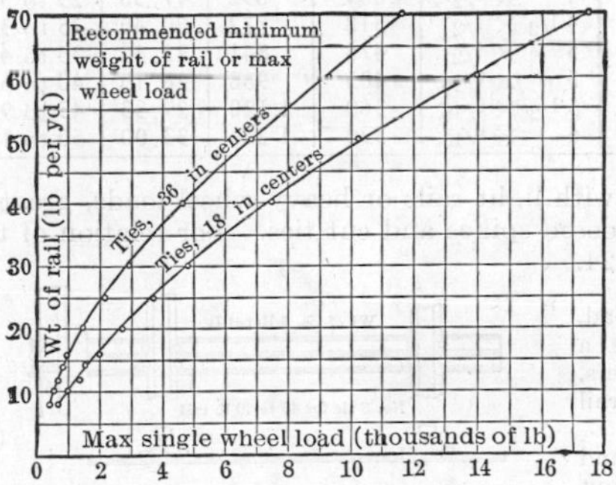

Screw spikes increase life of ties, are more effective, but cost more. Though much used abroad, and almost indispensable for tropical hardwood, they are not yet common in U S, but are replacing driven spikes on some R R lines. Holes must be bored for them.

Wood ties for standard-gage track are 8 to 9 ft long, not less than 6 in thick, flattened to at least 6 in face, or, if sawed, minimum cross-sec is 6 by 8 in. For narrow-gage track, length of ties should be twice the gage, at least 1/4 in thicker

Fig 24.   Weight of Rail for 1 1/2 and 3 ft Tie Spacing

than spike length, and 1 3/8 times spike length in width. But for light or temporary work, or prospecting, ties are often no thicker than the spike length, and but 4 in longer than distance between outside spikes.

Steel ties of pressed and rolled steel, have the advantages of lightness, strength, durability (where mine water is not acid), and of requiring less depth or headroom. They should have flanges along all edges, extending into the roadbed to hold them in place. Rails are fastened to them by bolts, or clips and wedges, or combinations of these. Fig 26 shows some of the numerous designs.

Spacing of ties. Average for standard gage is 24-in centers. Underground ties are spaced from 16-in, on some main haulage ways with soft bed, to 4 and even 6-ft centers in

Table 2.   Rail Joints   (Cambria Steel Co)

Wt of rail per yd, lb	No of joints per long ton		Track bolts *		Splice bars, wt per pair, lb †	Wt of rail per yd, lb	No of joints per long ton		Track bolts *		Splice bars, wt per pair, lb †
	24-ft rails	33-ft rails, 10% shorts	Size, in	No per 200-lb keg			24-ft rails	33-ft rails, 10% shorts	Size, in	No per 200-lb keg	
8	35.00	25.86	1/2 × 1 3/4	952	......	40	7.00	5.17	5/8 × 3	417	16
12	23.33	17.24	1/2 × 1 3/4	952	2.58	45	6.23	4.60	3/4 × 3	278	18.6
16	17.50	12.93	1/2 × 2	909	4.53	50	5.60	4.14	3/4 × 3 1/4	267	25.3
20	14.00	10.34	1/2 × 2	909	3.71	55	5.09	3.76	3/4 × 3 1/2	256	29.2
25	11.20	8.27	5/8 × 2 1/4	488	5.60	60	4.67	3.45	3/4 × 3 1/2	256	32.3
30	9.34	6.89	5/8 × 2 1/2	465	9.10	65	4.31	3.18	3/4 × 3 3/8	247	35.4
35	8.00	5.91	5/8 × 2 3/4	435	11.1	70	4.00	2.95	3/4 × 3 3/4	247	54.6

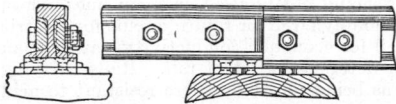

Fig 25.   Offset Fish-plate

* Track bolts of different makers may vary over 10% in wt. Those in the table have square nuts; for hexagon nuts, add 5% to No per keg. Length does not allow for nut-locks.

† For 65-lb rail and lighter, 4-bolt joints; others, 6-bolt. Fish-plates for 25-lb and lighter (see A and B, Fig 23); angle splice bars (C, Fig 23) are for 30-lb and heavier. To join rails of different wts, as may be required in passing from main to branch track, special offset fish-plates and step-chairs are used (Fig 25).

Table 3.   Track Spikes

Size under head, in	No per 200-lb keg	Ties 2 ft centers 4 spikes each		Suitable rail, lb per yd	Size under head, in	No per 200-lb keg	Ties 2 ft centers 4 spikes each		Suitable rail, lb per yd
		Spikes, lb per 1 000 ft, single track	Kegs per mile, single track				Spikes, lb per 1 000 ft, single track	Kegs per mile, single track	
2 1/2 × 5/16	2 230	179	4.74	8 to 12	4 1/2 × 7/16	690	580	15.45	20 to 30
2 1/2 × 3/8	1 650	243	6.40	12 to 16	4 × 1/2	605	652	17.58	25 to 35
3 × 3/8	1 380	290	7.96	12 to 20	4 1/2 × 1/2	518	772	20.40	25 to 35
3 1/2 × 3/8	1 250	320	8.70	12 to 20	5 × 1/2	475	841	22.30	35 to 40
4 × 3/8	1 025	390	10.22	16 to 25	5 × 9/16	405	988	26.15	40 to 56
3 1/2 × 7/16	890	450	11.88	16 to 25	5 1/2 × 9/16	360	1 120	29.33	45 to 90
4 × 7/16	780	515	13.65	20 to 30	6 × 9/16	320	1 250	33.00	50 to 100

room or stope tracks.   An excessive span, with light rails or heavy wheel loads, greatly increases resistance, and the bending rails loosen spikes and cut ties.   For relation of tie spacing to wt of rail to be used, see Fig 24.

Track stringers.   For soft roadbeds, broad, close-spaced ties are used, but in some mines a satisfactory track is made by using heavy stringers, 4 by 8 or 5 by 10 in, laid on the flat under each rail and omitting ties.

Tie plates are used to protect ties under rails and at spike holes.   They are seldom used in mines, but are justified under heavy traffic, or with treated ties.   RAIL BRACES, to reinforce outer rail on curves and switches, are advisable for high-speed haulage.

Life of ties.   In R R service, hemlock, tamarack and white pine ties aver at least 5 yr; cypress, chestnut, white oak, and cedar, 7 to 15 yr.   Generally, the timber most cheaply obtained locally is used for ties, as their life, except where animal haulage is used, is usually longer than that of the mine working.   Preservative treatment is economical only in main entries or long adits.   Soft ties are oftener worn out by SPIKE-KILLING and rail-cutting than by decay; in narrow-gage work, it is

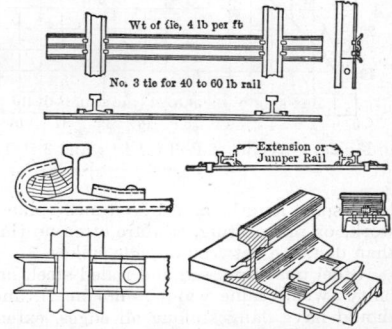

Fig 26.   Steel Ties and Rail-fastenings

well to use long ties, so that they may be shifted longitudinally when relaying, to afford new places for spiking. For frequent relaying, as in room work, wood ties are spike-killed in from 1 to 5 relayings; steel ties, barring corrosion or accident, last indefinitely.

Track ballast may be of broken stone, gravel, tailing, waste, cinders or slag. The standard of Amer Ry Engs & Maintenance of Way Assoc, for Class C R Rs, is a 6-in layer of gravel and chert under 8-ft ties, with 3 to 1 slopes beyond the ends and filled to the tops at center; or, with ties at 24-in centers, 1 180 cu yd per mile. Special ballast is rarely needed for mine track. The floor is generally hard, and care of the drainage ditches will usually remedy soft spots. Ballast will not help a swelling or heaving floor. With animal haulage, roadbed and ties are worn by the hoofs and require more frequent renewal than for other haulage systems.

Track gage should not be less than half the extreme width of car or locomotive. Max gage is limited by the roadway clearance and sharpest curve.

A crude empirical rule, where wheel-base does not greatly exceed gage, is: Gage $< \sqrt{R \div 4}$, where R is the shortest radius. Gages range from standard, 56.5-in, down to 12-in. In metal mines, 18 to 24-in are commonest; in collieries, 36 to 42-in. ADVANTAGES OF BROAD GAGE: stability, large-capacity cars, lower total cost of rolling stock and lower operating cost per ton. ADVANTAGES OF NARROW GAGE: lower first cost of entries and track, and the shorter-radius curves which are made possible. GAGE ON CURVES must be increased, to prevent binding of wheel flanges. In R R practice, for each 2° over 8° of curvature, the gage is $1/8$ in wider, to a max increase, including wear, of 1 in. For sharp curves of narrow-gage track, wheels may require all the extra play that their width of tread will allow. The increased gage is obtained by starting the curve of inner rail before the " point of curve " is reached (Sec 17).

6. LAYING OUT CURVES, SWITCHES, AND CROSSINGS
(12, 13, 14, 23, 24)

Track curves. Simple circular curves fill all speed requirements of underground tracks, and easement or transition curves are unnecessary. DEGREE OF CURVATURE D is the angle at the center subtended by a chord of 100 ft; but curves of less than 200-ft radius are best designated by length of radius R. Trigonometric relations between the elements of circular curves, and modes of laying them out, are given in Sec 17.

Layout of curves is done by transit methods, or in various ways requiring no instrument work. They should not be left, as they often are, to the unguided judgment of trackmen. A reasonably accurate curve layout can be made without a transit by means of offsets, by using a rod ab (Fig 27) 10 ft long, and with a right-angle offset dc at center d, of a length = M, as given in Table 4 for curve of required radius. The curve is started with the rod laid in prolongation of the tangent from the P C (Sec 17, Art 32) in the position ab'. Offset $d'c$ will then indicate the first point c on the curve. Subsequent points will be indicated by point b when rod ab is laid inside the curve. When the P C and P T are within sight of each other, the middle and quarter-ordinate method is most convenient. When workings are driven by directions from the engineer's office, blueprints should be furnished for placing timbering and track as indicated in Fig 28, 29, with a minimum of instrument work.

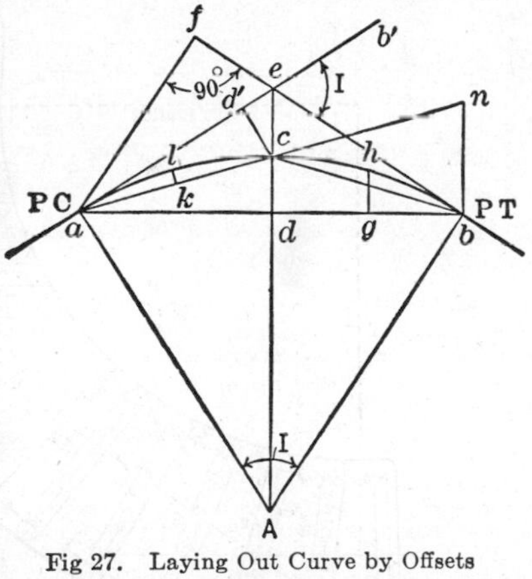

Minimum-radius curve is limited by length of wheel base, diam of wheels and flange clearance. Fig 30, from an empirical formula (Baldwin Locomotive Wks data), gives safe values for curves of same gage as on straight track. With liberal spread for gage on curves, 10 to 25% may be added to wheel-base dimensions.

Fig 27. Laying Out Curve by Offsets

Bending rails. The common rail bender, the "Jim Crow" (Fig 31a), is made in 4 sizes for different wt of rail, the span between claws being 16 to 24 in. Roller bender is a convenient modification, and hydraulic or pneumatic benders (Fig 31, b) are made for heavy rails. Rails are bent to fit curves of given radius by the middle and quarter-ordinate method (see above); or, for short radii, by laying out the curves of both rails in chalk on the shop floor, the value of M for same length of rail being greater for the inner rail (Table 4). If bent in the shop, the max length of a curved rail is limited by size of shaft compartment. Difference in length of inner and outer rails, D = gage $\times$ length of curve $\div$ radius of curve.

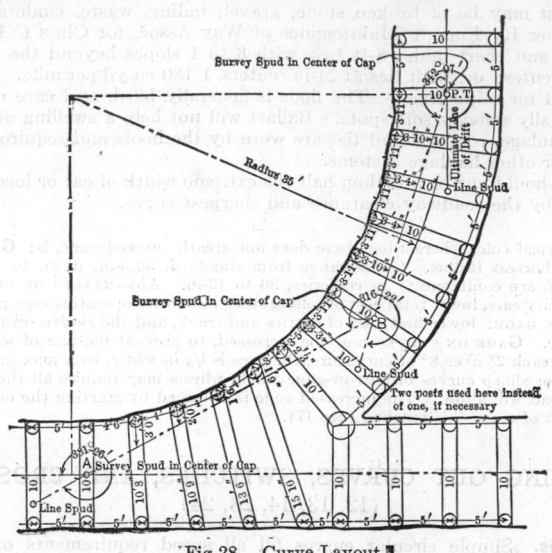

Fig 28.   Curve Layout

Superelevation of outer rail, to balance centrifugal force, is $e = dV^2 \div gR$, where e = elevation of outer rail, in; d = distance between centers of rails, in; V = velocity, ft per sec; g = acceleration of gravity, ft per sec per sec = 32.2; R = radius of curve, ft.

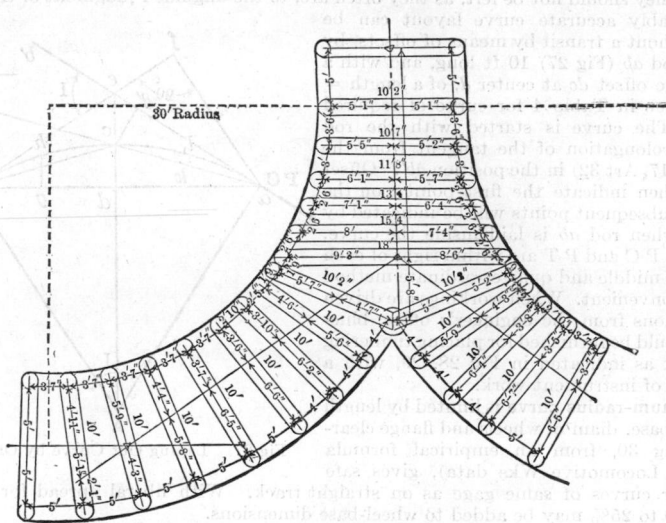

Fig 29.   Layout for Double Turnout

On grades, these elevations should be reduced. With rope haulage, the cross pull of the rope on curves modifies conditions, and may even require that the inner rail be elevated (Art 18). On self-acting planes, track on curves can not satisfy requirements for travel

Table 4. Middle Ordinates *M*, in Inches, of 10-ft Chords

Radius, ft	Center line ord, in	Correction, + for inner, − for outer rail, in *					
		Gage, 15	18	24	30	42	56 1/2
7	25.2	+3.8 −2.8	+4.8 −3.3	....	....	....	....
8	21.1	+2.6 −2.0	+2.9 −2.2	....	....	....	....
9	18.2	+1.7 −1.4	+2.0 −1.6	....	....	....	....
10	16.1	+1.2 −1.1	+1.5 −1.3	....	....	....	....
12	13.1	±0.7	+1.0 −0.9	+1.2 −1.0	....	....	....
15	10.3	0.5	+0.6 −0.5	+0.8 −0.7	....	....	....
20	7.6	0.3	±0.3	±0.4	....	....	....
25	6.1	0.1	0.2	0.3	+0.4 −3	....	....
30	5.0	0.1	0.1	0.2	±0.2	....	....
35	4.3	0.1	0.1	0.1	0.2	±0.2	....
40	3.8	....	0.1	0.1	0.2	0.2	....
45	3.3	....	....	0.1	0.1	0.1	....
50	3.1	....	....	....	0.1	0.1	....
60	2.5	....	....	....	....	0.1	....
75	2.1	....	....	....	....	....	±0.2
100	1.5	....	....	....	....	....	0.1

* Corrections are for ordinates of 10-ft rail chords, not for chords taken radially from 10-ft center-line chord.

in both directions, and level ties, guard rails and slow speed are the compromise. Fig 51a shows tests.

Fitting track for temporary work without cutting rails. For headings or track gaps, a loose rail is laid on its side along inner side of each track rail, with loose rail head against web of track rail. The wheel flanges then run on web of loose rail, which need not be fastened or match track joints. To put in a curve without cutting main rails, spread end rails and fasten right and left beveled switch points at required P C inside main rails.

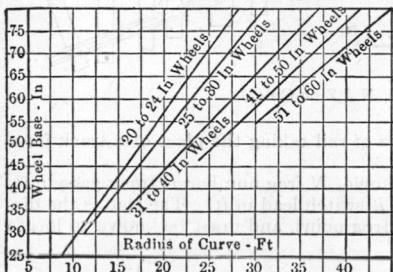

Fig 30. Minimum-radius Curve

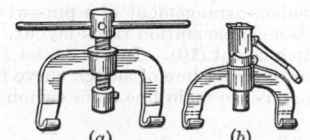

Fig 31. Rail Benders

Switches (10). Standard point and stub switches and many other devices are used in mines to transfer cars from one track to another. The point or split switch (Fig 32) consists of 2 "points" or latches, lead and follower turnout rails, and frog with guard

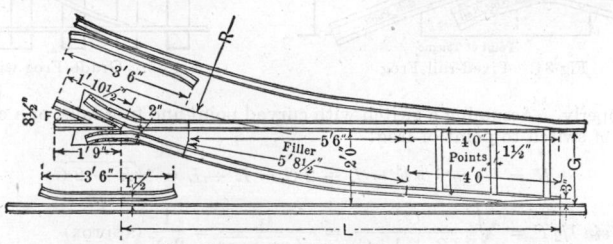

Fig 32. Point or Split Switch

rails opposite frog. On blunt switches the toes of the frog and heels of the point rails meet, otherwise filler rail lengths are inserted. Facing a switch, it is passed from the point end; trailing, from the frog end. Standard formulas for switches and turnouts are given by American Mining Congress, May, 1932 (12).

Frogs. The rail crossing may be a single casting (Fig 33), preferably of manganese steel, or be built up of rails. Fixed-rail frogs may be filled and bolted, for heavy track, or riveted on plate for light track (Fig 34). Spring-rail frogs have one wing rail movable, but held by a spring against the frog point so that wheels on the main track pass over

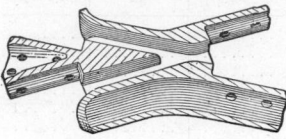

no gap. Standard frogs have straight rails, but, for narrow-gage blunt turnouts, curved frogs are better, though they are not interchangeable for right- and left-hand turnouts, and a turnout guard-rail should be provided. FROG NUMBER is the distance (Fig 34) from the point of frog to any point at which the spread between gage lines is measured, divided by that spread; or it is the total length of frog C divided by total spread $A + B$.

Fig 33.   Cast Frog

For curved frogs the spread is measured to tangents from the frog point. Grade frogs may be avoided by raising the lead rail, and carrying the wheel-flange over the unbroken main rail by a latch (Fig 35). The sharp rise of the lead rail, and the latch closing the main rail are objections. Some mines use a reversible frog block to fill the flangeway of the closed track rail. It is effective, but causes derailments if misplaced and should be unnecessary with proper design. Fig 33a shows

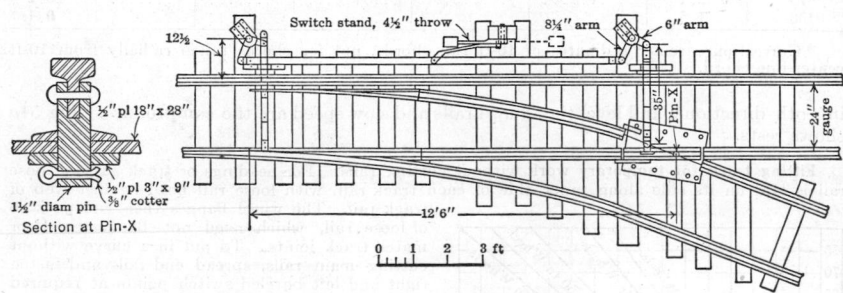

Fig 33a.   Frogless Switch, N J Zinc Co (2)

an ingenious arrangement of a pin-swiveled piece of rail taking the place of a track frog. Fig 49 is a simple station track layout.

Switch layout (10). In Fig 32, let F be frog angle, N frog number, G track gage in ft, R radius of center line of switch curve in ft, and L switch lead in ft. The lead is the distance parallel to main line from switch point to frog point, and must be known to locate

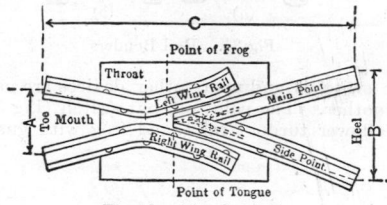

Fig 34.   Fixed-rail Frog

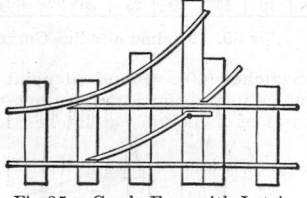

Fig 35.   Grade Frog with Latch

the frog properly. Assuming a switch with curved point and frog rails, or a circular curve from point of switch to point of frog:

$$N = \tfrac{1}{2} \cot \tfrac{1}{2} F = L \div 2\,G = R \div L = \sqrt{R \div 2\,G}$$

$$\sin \tfrac{1}{2} F = \sqrt{\frac{G}{2\,(R + \tfrac{1}{2}\,G)}} = \frac{G}{\sqrt{G^2 + L^2}} = \frac{1}{2\,N} \text{ (approx)}$$

$$L = 2\,GN = R \div N = (R + 0.5\,G)\,\sin F = \sqrt{2\,GR}$$

$$R = LN = L^2 \div 2\,G = 2\,GN^2 = (L \div \sin F) - 0.5\,G$$

Total length of lead rail from point of switch to point of frog = wing rail + point rail $+$ filler $= \pi R$ $(F \div 180)$. With straight frog and point rails, values of L and R are modified:

$$R = \frac{G - w \sin F - h}{\cos \alpha - \cos F} - 1/2\, G$$

$$L = (R + 0.5\, G)\, (\sin F - \sin \alpha) + w \cos F + p$$

in which α is angle of point rails, $w =$ length of wing rail, $h =$ heel distance, and $p =$ length of point rail. For a DOUBLE TURNOUT or 3-way switch (Fig 36), let F_m be the center frog; then, $vers\ 1/2\, F_m = \dfrac{G}{2\,(R + 1/2\,G)} = 1/2\ vers\ F_l = 1/2\ vers\ F_r$. and distance $aF_m = R \div 2\,N_m$.

Stub switch (Fig 37) is simpler than the point switch, and cheaper if both are made at the mine; if supplied by manufacturers, the stub saves little. If the switch has no locking lever, derailments may be caused by the rear wheels throwing the switch rails. This danger is reduced by making the turnout stub rails parallel to the main rails for a distance equal to the car wheel base. Special tie plates or chairs (Fig 38) should be used for stubs. A modified form of stub (Fig 39) eliminates the frog, and is good even for motor haulage, if there is enough room for the rods.

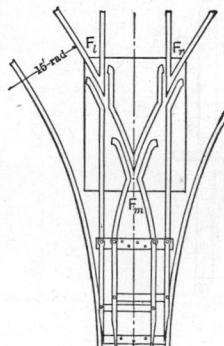

Automatic switches have their latches or points normally held by a spring to clear one track; facing trains must follow

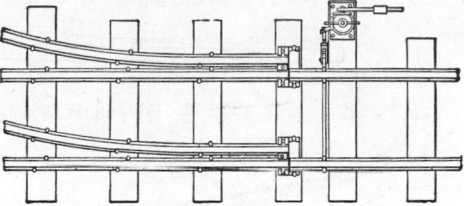

Fig 36. Double Turnout

Fig 37. Stub Switch

that track, but trailing trains may pass from either track, the wheel flanges forcing the point over against the spring when coming from closed track. These switches may have a lever to engage a projection on motor or car for flying-switch work, but head tie bar should then have a spring connection to the throwing lever to reduce impact. The automatic switch is especially serviceable for by-passing at tipples, shaft stations and sidings. In Fig 40, a is a simple automatic switch; b, combined with lever throw.

Finger or single-latch switch, a modified point switch, omits one point rail and the frog. The turnout is an angle instead of a curve, but it is a cheap and good switch for light, narrow-gage work. Fig 41 shows its application to a 3-way switch; Fig 43 to a crossover.

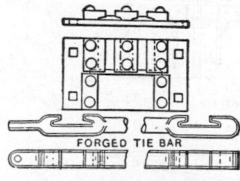

FORGED TIE BAR

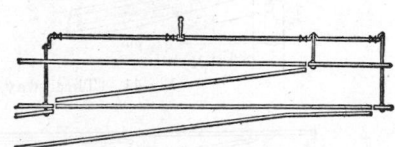

Fig 38. Stub-switch Fixtures
for Light Rail

Fig 39. Stub Switch Without Frog

Fixed switch (Fig 42) is suitable only for hand tramming or animal haulage. All rails are fixed, but with liberal flange clearances at the points, and cars are crowded toward the turnout or against the unbroken main rail to take or pass the switch. Lowering the outer rails slightly at the turnout helps to protect main-line traffic.

Double crossover or diamond switch is the standard for tipples and shaft bottoms. Fig 42, 45, show cases where distance between tracks is greater than the gage, and Fig 44 where the distance is less.

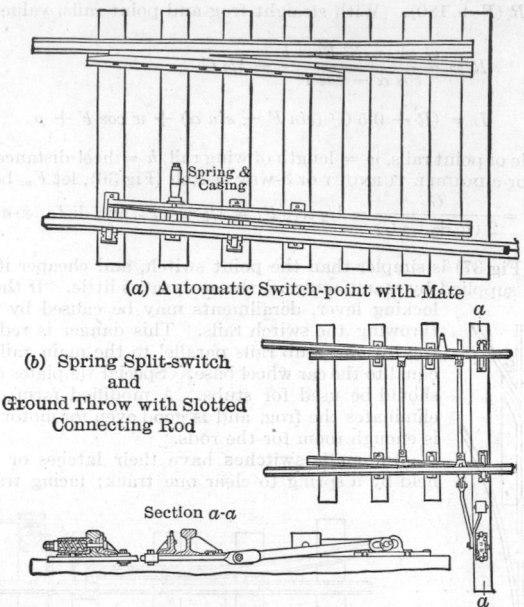

(a) Automatic Switch-point with Mate

(b) Spring Split-switch
and
Ground Throw with Slotted
Connecting Rod

Section a-a

Fig 40.   Automatic Switches

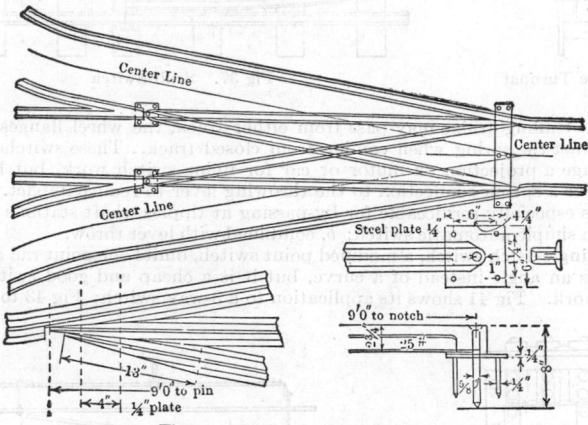

Fig 41.   Three-way Finger Switch

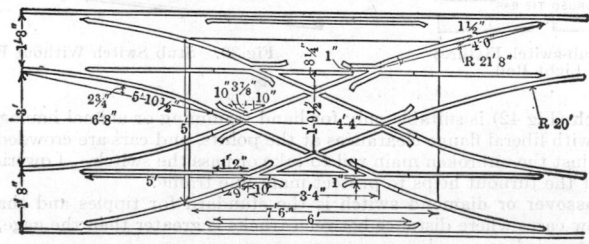

Fig 42.   Diamond Fixed Switch

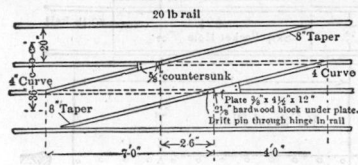

Fig 43.   Crossover Finger Switch

Fig 44.   Diamond Switch

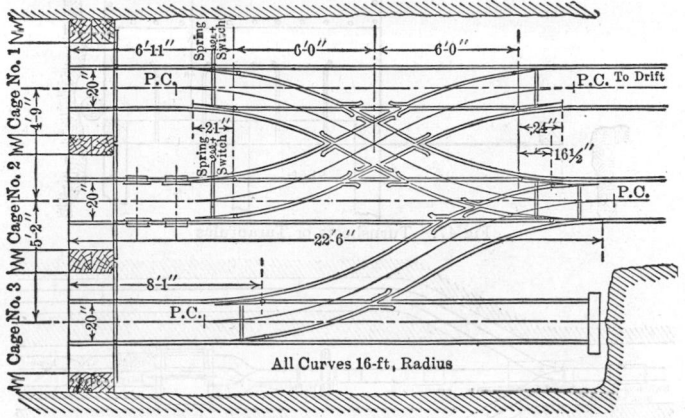

Fig 45.   Double Crossover or Diamond Switch

Track crossing may be an assemblage of frogs, or a built-up riveted plate (Fig 46). A crude crossing which avoids cutting for flange-ways is made by running 1 track higher than the other by the depth of the rail, and carrying it across by one long pair or two short pairs of latches. One track is thus always blocked.

Turnsheets (tarantulas), of $1/4$-in or heavier plate, fastened to sills by countersunk wood screws or drift bolts, are the simplest switching device; suitable at shaft stations, turnouts and crossings, when the gross wt per car does not usually exceed 3 000 lb. Sheets should bo finished on edges and supported by planking or concrete unless the sills are closely spaced. Flared tread POINTS or rounded guards are riveted to plates to guide wheels onto tracks. Fig 47 shows a turnsheet shaft station; Fig 45, a track-laid station.

Turntables are for cars or motors too heavy to handle on a turnsheet, where there is not room for a track switch, or where ground is too heavy for the long caps over turnout curves. Construction: a pair of rails on a swivel platform of plank or steel, or a circular C-I plate, with ball or roller bearings, on a base ring, as furnished by makers of industrial track.

Transfer carriage, a low-truck car on a sub-grade cross-track, carrying rails to fill corresponding gaps in the main or side tracks by moving the carriage, thus transferring

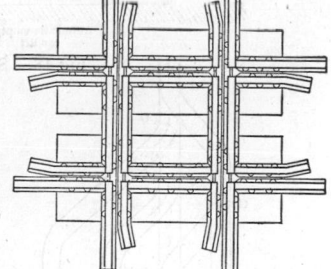

Fig 46.   Riveted Plate Crossing

cars from one track to another. It is much used in industrial plants, and sometimes at shaft tops for loading into bins.

Shaft bottom or station track layout (13) must provide for rapid handling and minimum interference of empty with loaded cars. Standard colliery shaft bottoms have a wide through entry across wall plates, with double crossover on both sides and grades in favor of traffic, so that empties will run to the switch when pushed off the cage by loaded cars. A by-pass track returns empties, when production from both sides is not balanced. A through station with a blind end should have kick-back and spring switch in place of a double crossover. A power lift (Fig 48), to raise empties to top of return grade, makes handling rapid and automatic. Fig 49 is an end-on shaft station with 8 spring switches

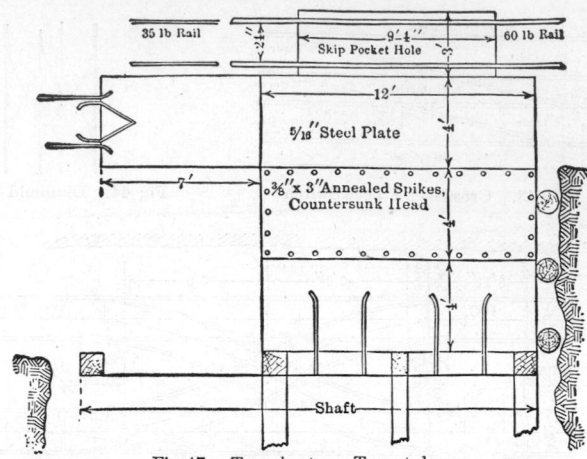

Fig 47.   Turnsheets or Tarantulas

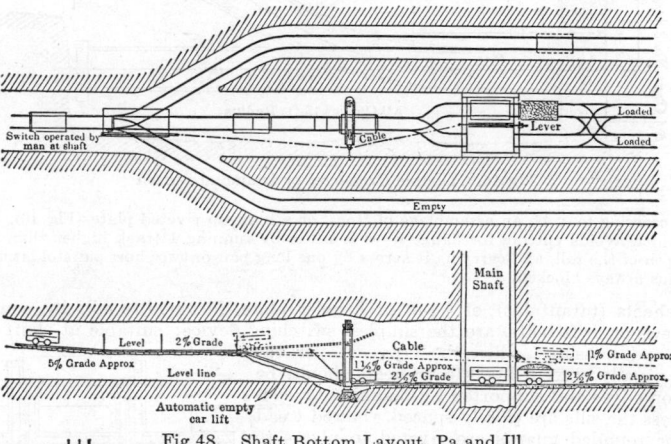

Fig 48.   Shaft Bottom Layout, Pa and Ill

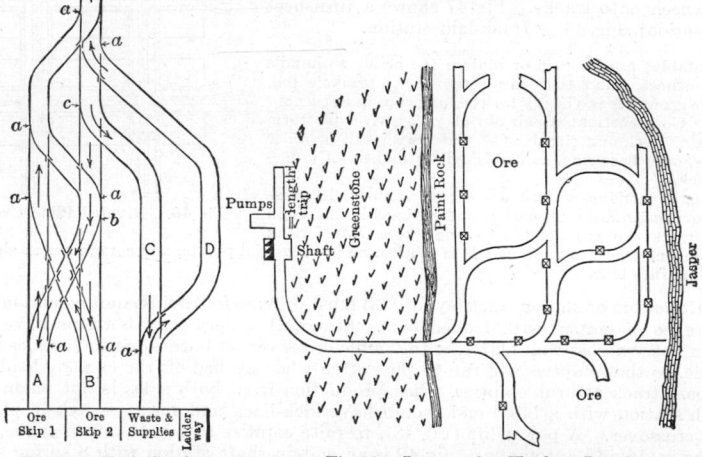

Fig 49.   Shaft Station Layout

Fig 50.   Locomotive Haulage Level, Ely, Minn

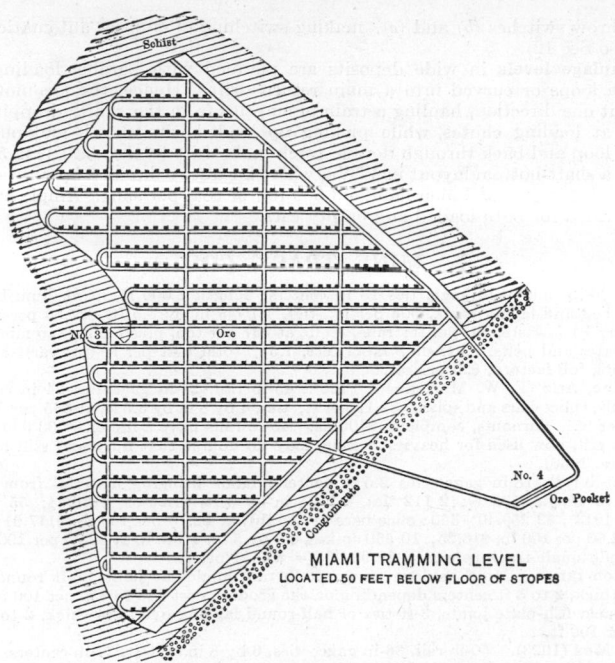

Fig 50a. Tramming Level, Miami Copper Mine, Ariz (see Sec 10)

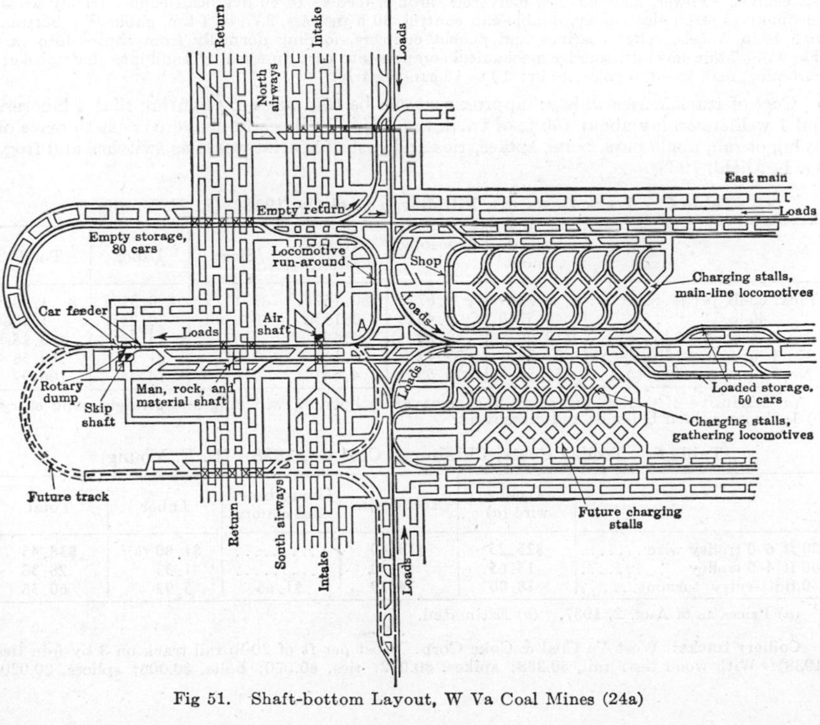

Fig 51. Shaft-bottom Layout, W Va Coal Mines (24a)

(a), and 2 throw switches (b) and (c), making switching of empties automatic to track *A* or *D* (see also Sec 12).

Main haulage levels in wide deposits are planned with parallel loading crosscuts, connected in loops or curved into a main return drift. Hence, the locomotive usually travels in but one direction, hauling a train of empties from the shaft, dropping the rear cars singly at loading chutes, while picking up loaded cars ahead, and pushing them around the loop and back through double-track main drift to the shaft (Fig 50, 50a, 51).

Fig 51 is a shaft-bottom layout in W Va, where 2 cars are dumped by a rotary dumper; using battery locomotives, 3 men handle 3 500 ton of coal per shift. Ample storage space must be provided for both loaded and empty cars.

7. MINE TRACK COSTS

Arizona. 30-lb rail, 24-in gage, ties 18 in centers; length 7 000 ft, in medium hard ground: labor digging bed and laying track, 50¢ per ft; ties, 4 by 8 in by 3.5 ft, $27.50 per M bd ft, fob mine, including 10% waste, 13¢ per ft; rails, 30 lb, at $37 per ton, plus haulage to mine, 39¢ per ft; spikes, fish-plates and bolts, 7.5¢; shop labor, etc, 1.5¢; total cost per ft (prewar), $1.11. Turnouts and points, fob factory, $20 per set.

Miami mine, Ariz (F. W. Maclennan, 1925). 45-lb rail, 24-in gage, ties 24 in centers: labor, 25¢ per ft; rails, splice-bars and spikes, $1.17 per ft; ties, 4 by 8 in by 3.5 ft, at $35 per M, 16¢ per ft; total, $1.58 per ft. Turnouts, complete, $100 ea. 45-lb rails have a life of 6 000 000 tons hauled, whereas 70-lb rail, now used for heaviest traffic, may do double that duty and still be serviceable (R. W. Hughes, 1936).

Idaho. 35-lb rail, 18-in gage, ties 2.5 ft centers: labor bringing material from surface and laying 1 mile of track, $591.00; 2 112 ties, 4 by 8 in by 3 ft, 11.2¢ ea, $236.54; 55 tons rails, at $41.08 (July, 1913), $2 259.40; 360 splice bars (4 356 lb), at $2.70 per 100 lb, $117.61; 1 440 bolts (625 lb), at $2.60 per 100 lb, $16.25; 10 560 spikes, 0.5 by 5 in, 4 140 lb at $2.75 per 100 lb, $113.85; total cost 1 mile single track (prewar), $3 334.65 = $0.631 per ft.

Mesabi iron range. Main haulage track, 40-lb rail, angle-bar joints, 4-ft round timber ties faced to 6 in thick, 2 to 3 ft centers depending on the ground, cost $45 to $50 per 100 ft. Sub-level drift, 12-lb track, fish-plate joints, 3-ft ties of half-round lagging over 3 in thick, 2 to 3 ft centers, $18 to $22 per 100 ft.

Fresnillo, Mex (1923). 50-lb rail, 36-in gage; ties, 6 by 8 in by 6 ft, 24-in centers. Cost per ft: labor, $1.66; supplies, $1.76; exclusive of rails and splice bars, which were charged to equipment.

Oliver Iron Mining Co. Tramming tracks, 60-lb rail, min radius of turnout 25-ft, with No 3 curved frogs; grade 1/2 to 1% favoring loads; ties, pine or tamarack, 6 by 6 in by 6 ft, spaced 2-ft centers. Power, 250-volt d c, delivered through feeders to 40 overhead copper trolley wires. Locomotives 6-ton elec trolley, double-end control, 30 h p; cars, 2.75 to 4-ton, gable or V bottom, with 16-in wheels, roller bearings and pocket couplers, loading normally from chutes into cars (Fig 9a). Main-level drifting by mechanical scrapers into cars dumped by hand into shaft pocket; tramming, max speed, 5 miles per hr; 10 to 15 cars per trip.

Cost of track varies widely; approx cost can be computed by figuring that 4 laborers and 1 welder can lay about 150 ft of track in 8 hr. To this add delivered cost to place of laying of rail, angle bars, bolts, spikes, ties and cost of special work, as switches and frogs (G. E. Diehl, 1938).

Table 5.   Track Costs (a), Pittsburgh Coal Co, 1938   (L. E. Young)

	Rail or turnout	Creosoted ties	Accessories (b)	Slag	Labor	Total
Track, 60-lb, per ft.........	$ 0.7249	$ 0.6720	$0.1624	$0.1125	$ 0.3117	$ 1.9835
" 40-lb, " ".........	0.5280	0.4620	0.1330	0.0900	0.2558	1.4688
1 No 4 turnout, 60 lb.......	110.00	40.80	4.44	3.42	24.58	183.24
1 No 3 turnout, 60 lb.......	93.50	39.12	4.11	2.61	21.24	160.58
1 No 3 turnout, 40 lb.......	59.50	23.55	4.44	2.02	14.46	106.97

(a) Exclusive of trolley, entry grading, excavating bottom, widening and straightening entry.
(b) Includes welded U-bonds and crossovers.

Table 6.   Trolley Costs, Pittsburgh Coal Co, 1938   (L. E. Young)

	Trolley wire (a)	Accessories	Guard board and clamps	Labor	Total
100 ft 6–0 trolley wire.......	$23.25	$13.40	....	$1.80 (b)	$38.45
100 ft 4–0 trolley "	13.65	13.40	....	1.33	28.38
4–0 butt-entry turnout......	18.00	34.79	$1.65	5.92	60.36

(a) Prices as of Aug. 2, 1937.   (b) Estimated.

Colliery tracks: West Va Coal & Coke Corp. Cost per ft of 20-lb rail track on 3 by 5-in ties (1938): With wood ties: rail, $0.368; spikes, $0.012; ties, $0.070; bolts, $0.006; splices, $0.020.

Total $0.476 per ft. With steel ties: rail, $0.368; splices, $0.020; ties, $0.200; bolts, $0.006. Total $0.594 per ft. Labor cost of 20-lb room and entry track, about 10¢ per ft; for bonding with 2/0 bonds, 20¢ per ft.

8. TRACK AND CAR RESISTANCES (25–29)

Tractive resistances comprise rolling resistance between rails and wheels, bearing or journal friction, inertia or resistances of starting and acceleration, and resistances due to grades, curves, and atmospheric friction. COEFFICIENT of tractive resistance is commonly measured in terms of lb pull per ton gross load.

Rolling resistance factors are not well determined. Resistance does not increase proportionately to wheel loads; it depends greatly on condition of track and roadbed; perfectly uniform track eliminates most impact and oscillating resistances. JOURNAL FRICTION per ton is a minimum: (a) with heavy wheel loads; (b) with minimum diam axles and max diam wheels; (c) with car speeds from 10 to 20 miles per hr for standard R R, and probably half that speed for mine equipment; (d) with perfect lubrication; (e) with ball bearings. According to line-shaft tests by Thomas and Maurer (Amer Soc Mech Engrs), roller bearings consume 2.2 to 3 times the power of ball bearings, and babbitt bearings 3 to 4.5 times. STARTING RESISTANCE is usually 1.5 to 3 times the running resistance; on dirty track, after long standing, or in cold weather, it may be 5 times as much. This peak load may be greatly reduced in train work by first backing and then picking up the cars one by one; this is aided by spring couplers. INERTIA (resistance to acceleration) may be computed from $P = 70 \ (V_2{}^2 - V_1{}^2 \div S$, or $P = 95.6 \ (V_2 - V_1) \div t$; where $P = $ force, lb per ton, required to increase veloc from V_1 to V_2 miles per hr, in S ft or t seconds. If starting from rest, $V_1 = 0$. A good empirical formula (T. Robson) allowing for rotary accel of wheels is: $P = 107 \ V$; where $V = $ increase per sec of speed in miles per hr. In R R service, $V = 0.2$ to 0.5.

Track resistance. Baker's tests on perfectly clean track gave 19 lb tractive resistance per ton; same track, coated with $1/8$-in fine dust, 28 lb; with $1/8$-in powdered stone, 40 lb. Fies (38, p 769) reports coal cars slide with spragged wheels on damp steel rails on 12° pitch; that wood rails are used in rooms of 12° pitch and over.

Grade resistance = wt $\times$ sine of grade. For grades under 10%, there is no appreciable error in assuming grade resistance at 20 lb per ton of moving wt for each percent of grade. At 10%, the error is $+ 1$ lb.

Gradient of equal traction is the grade at which the resistance of an ascending empty car is equal to that of a descending loaded car. Drifts and adits should be driven at this grade, unless drainage or other considerations prevent. Exceptions: In hand tramming with poor track or cars, it is wise to keep the grade 0.1 or 0.2% above that of equal traction, so that the loaded car will move easily, and the trammer can give due attention to preventing derailments. With motor haulage, this grade may also prevent overheating motors by light running in one direction. Formula for grade of equal traction is, $\sin g = fM + (f - f') \ c + (M + 2 \ c)$, where $g = $ angle of grade in favor of load; $M = $ net wt of mineral, tons; $c = $ wt of car, tons; $f = $ coeff of tractive resistance for the loaded car on level track; $f' = $ coeff for empty car. Table 7 shows that the difference between f and f' may be considerable. An approx formula for grade of equal traction, assuming $f = f'$, is % grade = $(fM \times 100) \div (M + 2 \ c)$. Practical determinations of f and f' are scanty. Prevailing grades in important adits are $0.4 - 0.6\%$.

Angle of rolling friction, $A_f = $ angle at which car will continue at rest or in uniform motion. $Tan \ A_f = $ coeff of rolling friction of car = % grade of repose, and varies from below 1% for large roller-bearing loaded cars on straight heavy rails to over 4% for plain bearings on straight wooden rails, and higher on curves. F. E. Brackett reports tests of a colliery car with loose 18-in wheels, wheel base 24 in, gage 42 in, wt loaded 6 400 lb. Grade of uniform gentle descent: on 4 by 4-in wood rails, $A_f = 4.23$ to 4.35%; on wood rails, with 0.5 by 2.5-in straps, $A_f = 1.83$ to 2.03%; on steel T-rails, $A_f = 1.62\%$.

Angle of inertia, starting car or train from rest, = $A_f + sin^{-1} \ (107 \ V \div W)$, where $V = $ accel in miles per hr per sec and $W = $ gross moving wt, tons. ANGLE OF SLIDING FRICTION = angle at which cars with brakes set or wheels spragged will continue to coast. On grease-covered rails it may be as low as 6 to 8% for loaded cars, while with clean rails, steel-tired wheels may hold above 14%. It is usually unsafe to trust brakes alone on grades of over 6% on steel rails; on clean, dry, wooden rails, the coeff of friction is greater.

Curve resistance for standard-gage track varies from 0.5 to 1.72 lb; generally taken as 0.8 lb per ton per deg of curve. On short-radius curves used in narrow-gage tracks, the factor is variable and with worn wheel treads is considerably higher. Norris's tests (Trans A I M E, Vol 18, p 514) showed 21 lb per ton friction due to curve for a single car on 85-ft radius curve, and 7 lb per ton for a 20-car train moving at 1 000 ft per min on curve of 350-ft radius. For effect of flat and banked curves, with different car-wheel bearings, see Fig 51b, also (26).

Air resistance varies approx with end area and length of train, and the square of its veloc, and is independent of train tonnage. It is usually unimportant in mine haulage, but because of the piston effect of cars in small-section gangways, it should be taken as equivalent to a wind veloc double that of the train.   With a 20-car train at 10 miles per hr, the total air resistance may be 50–100 lb.

Coefficient of traction (ratio of draw-bar pull to wt of moving load kept in uniform motion on a straight level track = $tan\ A_f$) may be obtained from Table 7 and Fig 51a These are the best available data, but conditions as to road-bed, track, diam, hardness and smoothness of wheel treads and lubrication are factors, so that for any given case the data must be applied only as approx, unless all conditions are as specified.

Liebermann's tests (Table 7), on Hyatt-Hockensmith bearings, showed 48% saving. Coaldale Colliery tests were with new equipment, 9-car trains, on perfect surface track; starting effort determined on "almost level track." Greensburg tests were for 20-car trains, under working conditions. The Virginia Iron, Coal & Coke Co's tests, for 3 trips of 20 cars with 3.1 tons coal each, haul 3 250 ft, averaged: for trip with solid-hub wheel, 14.9 min, 21.0 kw-hr = 0.55 kw-hr per coal-ton-mile; for trip with Whitney Wonder solid-roller bearings, 7.5 min, 8.8 kw-hr = 0.23 kw-hr per coal-ton-mile = 50% saving in time and 58% in haulage power. Makers claim resistances as low as 9 lb per ton for roller-bearing mine cars; probably under working conditions 15 to 18 lb per ton on straight level track is often realized. It is the practice of mine locomotive builders to assume 30 to 40 lb average resistance in mines unless otherwise advised.

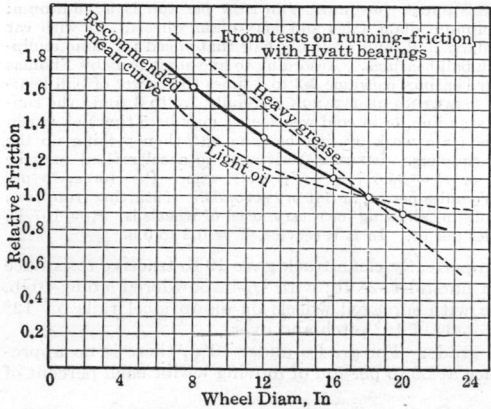

Fig 51a. Relative Friction for Different Wheel Diam, Compared with 18-in Diam (6)

Tests at Pittsburgh Experiment Station, U S Bur Mines, on mine car friction are summarized in Fig 51a and 51b (27). Note that in Fig 51b tests were on 1 car of each type, under 3.5 ton gross load, using light oil lubrication for ball and roller bearings, and semi-fluid grease for plain bearings; track, 42-in gage; curve, 16 ft rad; elev of banked rail, 3 in. Differences shown are not wholly due to different bearings, but partly to variation in rolling friction. Results with truck A are significant in showing effect of rough wheels, as actual bearing friction is probably less for ball bearings than for any other. These tests were apparently not fair to ball-bearings. Tests reported from the Charbonnages de Mariemont, France,

Table 7.   Tractive Resistance of Mine Cars on Straight Level Track

Type of car	Wt, ton	Bearings	Speed, ft per min	Resistance, lb per ton	Gage, in
Coal mine, empty*	1.12	plain open	starting	89.20	42
" " " *	1.07	" "	1 000	57.80 } single	"
" " loaded*	3.44	" "	"	66.40 } car	"
" " empty*	1.07	" "	"	44.00 }	"
" " loaded*	3.44	" "	"	39.00 } train	"
" " empty*	1.21	self oiled	starting	62.00	"
" " loaded*	4.56	" "	"	49.00	"
" " empty*	1.21	" "	1 000	30.40	"
" " loaded*	4.08	" "	"	38.60	"
" " " †	3.57	" "	492	24.30 train	40
" " " †	"	flexible roller	526	12.79 "	"
" " " **	7.00	babbitted	{ starting	129.0 "	"
			380	16.75 "	"
" " " **	"	brass	{ starting	81.10 "	"
			450	7.4 "	"
" " " **	"	flexible roller	{ starting	55.0 "	"
			480	3.9 "	"
" " " ††	3.57	plain	490	24.3 "	"
" " " ††	"	flexible roller	530	12.8 "	"

* Norris, *Trans* A I M E, Vol 18, p 514.   † Liebermann, March, 1916.   ** Edwin Ludlow. Tests by Hyatt Roller Bearing Co at Coaldale Colliery.   †† Edwin Ludlow. Tests at Greensburg Colliery.

Table 7a.   Relative Friction of Mine-car Bearings (25, 27, 29)

Type	Wt, cwt	Bearings	Speed, ft per min	Resistance ratio
Wooden pit car, empty............	4.5	plain, poor lubrication	150	1 : 30
" " " "	"	" good "	150	1 : 68
" " " "	"	" aver "	starting	1 : 20
Steel car, empty................	"	self oiling	....	1 : 60
" " "	"	ball bearing	....	1 : 135

Wheels in these tests were 9–12-in diam; axles, 1 1/8–2 in.

showed the economy of cars with ball-bearings over those with plain bearings, of 85% when loaded and 41% when empty.
At the Big Five mine, Colo, the draw-bar pull of trucks, lb per ton, were reported by SKF Mfg Co: starting, straight track, plain bearings, 77.80, ball-bearings, 34.33; 4 miles per hr, straight track, plain bearings, 31.13, ball-bearings, 15.02; 4 miles per hr on switch, plain bearings, 37.75, ball-bearings, 18.43.

At the Cie de Mines de Courrières (29) the tractive resistance of new cars with roller-bearings was 13.4 to 20.2 lb per ton, compared with 27 to 35.5 lb per ton of old cars with journal bearings. General conclusions are: plain-bearing, loose wheels, well worn, have 1.7 times aver friction of ball and roller bearings, at 5 miles per hr, and 3 times when starting; for all types, 3 times greater on banked curves and 5 or 6 times on flat curves. Fig 52 gives resistance per ton of R R freight cars of different gross wt and at various speeds; also starting resistance of light, narrow-gage locomotives and passenger cars. Starting resistance curves for freight cars should be similar.

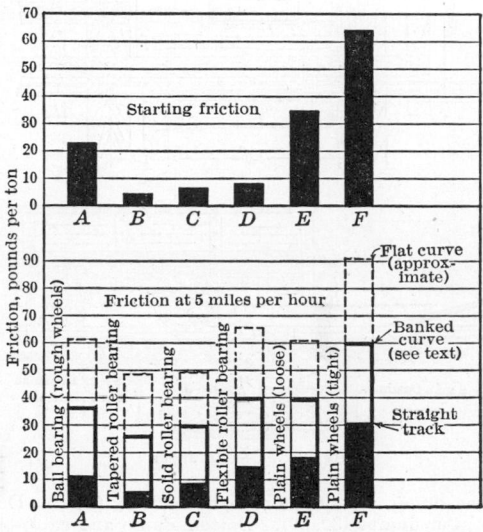

Fig 51b.   Relative Friction of 6 Mine Cars (27)

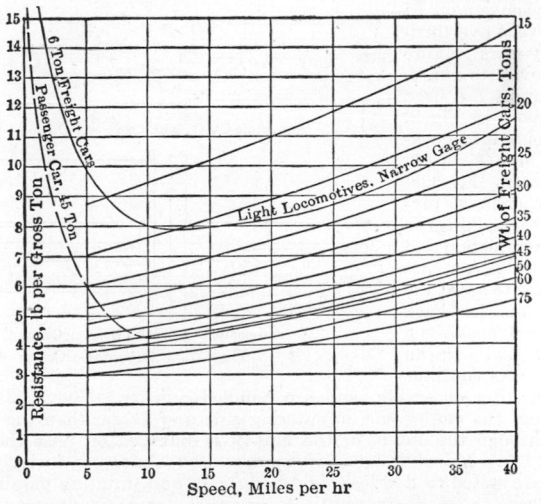

Fig 52.   Tractive Resistance of R R Equipment (Baldwin Locomotive Works)

9. HANDLING CARS, CAR DUMPS (31–34)

Rapid handling of cars. For SIMULTANEOUS LOADING OF TRAINS from chutes, spacing of chutes must be exact multiple of length of car. For SWITCHING CARS IN HEADINGS, replace track switch by horiz extension bar close under roof, carrying an air-lift crawl. This lifts empties off the track, allowing loaded cars to pass; bar is quickly set and kept within 100 ft of face. See Sec 6.

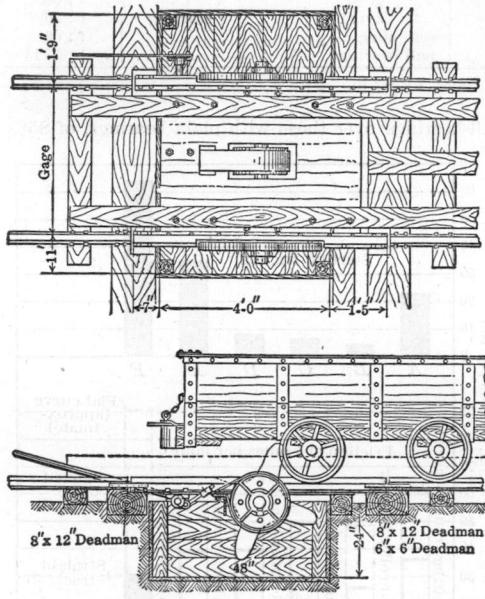

Fig 52a.   Car Spragger

Car stops are usually required when dumping. Simplest stop for track ends on dumps and at ore pockets is a timber clamped across the rails. For small cars, a 1 by 8-in plank, resting on the cross timber and sloping back to the ties, acts as a brake engaging the axle and reducing impact. SAFETY STOPS are advisable at shaft stations, besides the usual gates, to prevent cars from running into the shaft when cage is not at the landing. A simple stop is a horn, normally raised to engage the car axle or bumper. It is connected by crank arms and a rod to a tappet projecting into the cage compartment; spotting of the cage lowers the horn and allows car to pass onto cage. There are many more elaborate mechanisms for spragging and feeding cars onto cages or tipples. Fig 52a shows a manual car spragger; Fig 52b, an automatic cager in continuation with a cross-over dump, and with a cage, as made by the Car Dumper and Equipment Co.

Car dumps (32, 33). Bottom-dump and gable-bottom cars require only a projecting door latch for dumping at bin, chute or station; they are automatically tripped by an inclined guide, which lifts the latch as car passes. Cars with doors, and bodies hinged to the truck, rarely need a dumping device; but if the mineral is sticky or frozen, an anchor rope should be hooked on at the dump to prevent overturning. Rigid-body cars require some external device to dump. Simple track dumps are used with cars like those in Fig 2, 4, 7, 8, for dumping into pockets and skips. CRADLE, HORN, OR KICK-BACK DUMPS (Fig 52c) are horned track ends, so pivoted that loaded car striking the horns tilts the track section and is thus emptied. Automatic forms have springs to assist the returning dump to kick back the empty car. CROSS-OVER DUMPS (Fig 52b, 52d) are an improvement, as cars continue

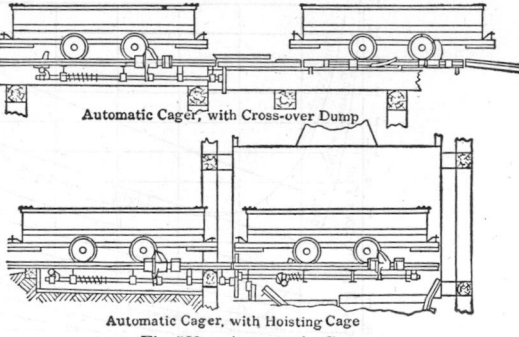

Automatic Cager, with Cross-over Dump

Automatic Cager, with Hoisting Cage

Fig 52b.   Automatic Cagers

across the dump after emptying, and are handled quicker. They are essentially see-saws, heavier than the empty car on entering side and lighter than the loaded. Track is down grade through the dump, or the empty is bumped on past the dump by the following loaded car. Many designs are made; used almost exclusively by collieries. ROTARY DUMPS are suited to doorless rigid-body cars and, rotating parallel to the track, can dump one car, or, made in multiples, a whole train simultaneously. They are operated by gravity, hand or power. By shields and aprons, the mineral may be discharged with sliding contact and minimum of dusting and breakage, especially attractive in coal handling. One to 4-car dumps are now common in coal and metal mining. Fig 52e shows a simple type for 1 car. Other designs are available, as that of Pittsburgh Coal Washer Co.

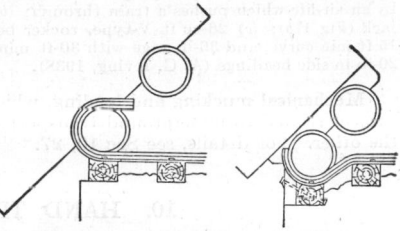

Fig 52c. Cradle or Kick-back Dumps

Examples. MIAMI MINE, Trains of 25–30 gable-bottom, 86-cu ft cars run over 1 000-ton ore pockets and dump without stop; train speed, about 2 miles per hr while dumping (R. W. Hughes). INSPIRATION COPPER MINE. Trains of 20 box-body, 120-cu ft cars dump in 5-car rotary tipples, at 2 shafts. Tipples are revolved in 15 sec by 35-hp motor. At Live Oak shaft, a 6-car air-operated tipple was replaced by using 3.4-ton side-dump cars, with a bridge over ore pocket (42). SNOWDEN COKE CO, PA, has a 26-car rotary dump, 120 ft long, and H. C. FRICK CO, one for 35 cars, 400 ft long, weighing 150 tons; dumping

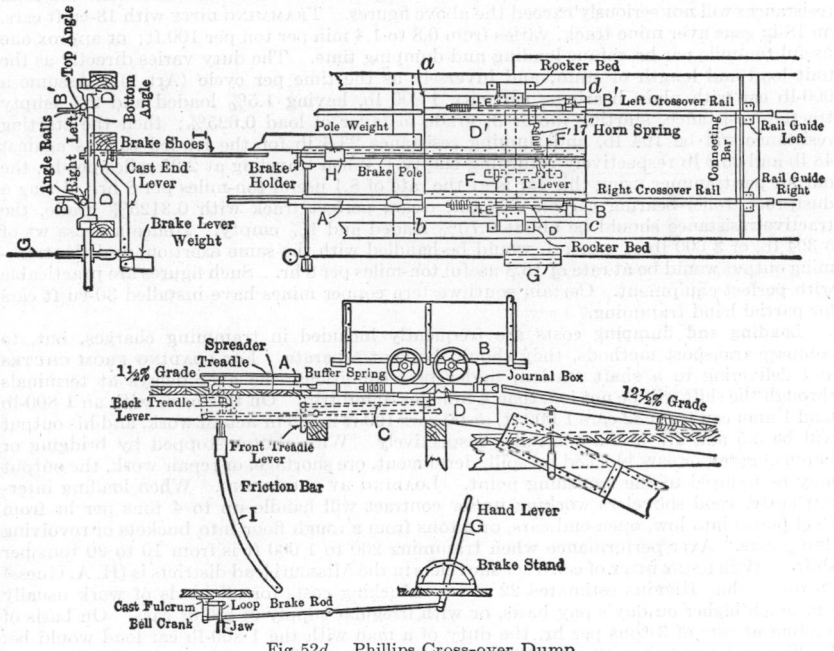

Fig 52d. Phillips Cross-over Dump

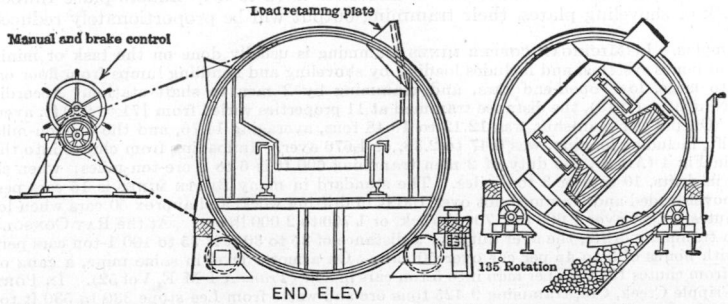

Fig 52e. Gravity Rotary Dumper, Hand-operated Car (Car Dumper and Equipment Co)

130–150 ton of coal; net wt of 35 cars, 60 ton; both made by Car Dumper and Equipment Co. HOLLINGER MINING CO uses 3 types of car: (a) 3-ton solid-body, dumped by rotary air-operated tipples of 2 kinds, one dumping 4 cars at once, the other, single cars, self-feeding and operated by an air-lift which pushes a train through; (b) 3-ton rectangular side-dump cars, operated by air jack (Fig 17b); (c) 26-cu ft V-type, rocker bottom side dump cars. Track is 18-in gage, with 15 ft min curve, and 36-in gage with 30-ft minimum curve; 35-lb rails on main haulage line and 20-lb in side headings (A. G. Irving, 1938).

Mechanical mucking and loading, which have become important in recent years, is a subject related to underground transport on the one hand and to methods of mining on the other. For details, see Sec 10, 27.

10. HAND TRAMMING (30–34)

Strength of trammer. A man pushing a car can readily exert about 20 lb aver horiz push; with frequent intervals of rest, about 50 lb; when starting, or on short spurts, over 150 lb. His useful output will depend on weight and capacity of car, which in turn are limited by character of car bearings, track, and gradients, to such amounts that the total resistances will not seriously exceed the above figures. TRAMMING DUTY with 18-cu ft cars, on 18-in gage aver mine track, varies from 0.8 to 1.4 min per ton per 100 ft; or approx one useful ton-mile per hr, minus loading and dumping time. The duty varies directly as the unit load and length of tram, and inversely as the time per cycle (Art 1). Assume a 900-lb car with plain bearings, capacity 1 800 lb, having 1.5% loaded and 2% empty tractive resistance, starting factor 3, grade in favor of load 0.625%; then the starting resistance will be 104 lb, and running resistance 23.6 lb for the loaded car, as against 48 lb and 23.6 lb respectively returning empty. When traveling at 2.25 miles per hr, the output per trammer using this car is at the rate of 8.1 useful ton-miles per 8 hr. Using a dustproof, roller-bearing car on straight, clean, perfect track with 0.3125% grade, the tractive resistance should be about 0.75% loaded and 1% empty. Hence a gross wt of 5 394 lb, or 3 600 lb of mineral, would be handled with the same exertion, and the tramming output would be at rate of 16.3 useful ton-miles per 8 hr. Such figures are practicable with perfect equipment. Certain southwestern copper mines have installed 30-cu ft cars for partial hand tramming.

Loading and dumping costs are frequently included in tramming charges, but, to compare transport methods, they should be kept separate. For LOADING FROM CHUTES and delivering to a shaft station, under best conditions, the aver delays at terminals through the shift will be not less than 4 min per round trip. On this basis with an 1 800-lb load 1 man can tram 32 cars 1 000 ft, or 90 cars 100 ft in 7.5 hr actual work, and his output will be 5.5 and 1.7 useful ton-miles respectively. With chutes stopped by bridging or jammed gates, or cars blocked by spill, derailment, ore shortage, or repair work, the output may be reduced to the vanishing point. LOADING BY SHOVELING. When loading intermittently, good shovelers working under contract will handle up to 4 tons per hr from steel plates into low, open-end cars, or 2 tons from a rough floor into buckets or revolving dump cars. Aver performance when tramming 200 to 1 000 ft is from 10 to 20 tons per shift. AVER DAILY DUTY of contract shovelers in the Missouri lead districts is (H. A. Guess) 18 tons, while Higgins estimates 22 tons. Mucking costs for all kinds of work usually run much higher on day's pay basis, or with irregular supply of ore or cars. On basis of loading at rate of 3 tons per hr, the duty of a man with the 1 800-lb car load would be: loading and tramming 19 cars 100 ft = 0.32 ore-ton-miles, or 14 cars 1 000 ft = 2.39 ore-ton-miles per shift. If trammers or shovelers have to help miners place timbers, or lay track or shoveling plates, their tramming output will be proportionately reduced.

Examples. In MICHIGAN COPPER MINES tramming is usually done on the task or minimum-wage and bonus systems, and includes loading by shoveling and handling lumps from floor or foot-wall into large, low, open-end cars, and tramming by 2 men to shaft station. According to J. MacNaughton (1913), the distance trammed at 11 properties varied from 171 to 900 ft, averaging 609 ft. Output per man-shift was 12.12 to 19.48 tons, averaging 14.76, and the ore-ton-miles per man-shift, including loading, was 0.47 to 2.38, or 1.676 aver. In loading from chutes into the cars shown in Fig 4 (Art 3), the duty of 2 men tramming 600 ft is 6 to 9 ore-ton-miles; when shovel-loading in drifts, 10 cars or 3 ton-miles. The standard in many BUTTE MINES is 15 cars per shift to be shovel-loaded and trammed not over 100 ft in drifting work, and approx 50 cars when loading from chutes. Cars aver 1 600 to 1 700 lb rock, or 1 700 to 2 000 lb ore. At the RAY CONSOL MINE, Ariz, on tramming drifts, the aver duty for a distance of 25 to 30 ft is 75 to 100 1-ton cars per man-shift, with bonus of 3 to 4¢ per car over 50 cars. On a motor level in same mine, a gang of men loaded from chutes 150 tons per man into 5-ton cars in 8 hr (*Trans* A I M E, Vol 52). In PORTLAND MINE, Cripple Creek, Col, tramming 9 425 tons ore and waste from Lee stope 330 to 530 ft to shaft or waste chute cost 15.4¢ per ton, or $1.568 per ton-mile; duty was about 2.2 ton-miles per trammer shift. In the Captain stope, 35 365 tons ore and waste were trammed an aver of 975 ft, at cost of 12.48¢ per ton, or 98¢ per ton-mile, or 3.2 ton-miles per shift. UTAH COPPER (1915, Carnahan). In loading 1-ton cars from chutes and tramming 90 ft aver to a raise, 2 men handled 65 ton per shift.

11. ANIMAL HAULAGE (35 to 38)

Duty. Mules and horses at underground work travel 3 to 15 miles per shift. With enough cars, and grades not over 2% against the empties, they often average 7 to 12 miles on main haulage lines, and usually below 9 miles on gathering work. Many records show duties from 50 to 100 gross ton-miles (total loaded and empty haul) per animal, or 25 to 66 mineral-ton-miles per shift. To justify animal haulage as against tramming, a minimum of about 15 mineral-ton-miles should be done on a given level or entry per shift, unless there are adverse grades. The economy of animal haulage increases with tonnage. Using tandem or spike teams, and longer trains, increases effic of both animals and drivers, though more cars and longer sidings are required. For duties below 200-mineral-ton-miles per day on grades less than 1.25%, it has been claimed that no mechanical system can compete in economy with animal haulage using a string team of four. The exact dividing line depends upon local conditions, and costs of labor, power, and feed.

Cost of animals. Good mules cost $150-$300 (pre-war), depending on wt, age, and general condition. Their underground working life in the U S is 3-7 yr.

Horses and ponies used in English collieries average 7 to 10 yr. It is false economy to keep an animal in the mine after it has begun to deteriorate. It should still be worth $40 to $75 for surface use. An annual deprec of 20% of first cost should prove conservative.

Cost of feed per day for mules varies from 18¢ in farming regions to 50¢ in cities, and correspondingly more in isolated mining districts. Shoeing and medicine average $1 to $2 per month, interest and deprec on mule and harness $35 to $80 per year; hence, when stable attendance and full time maintenance are charged against working time, mule service per working days costs 60¢ to $1.25, exclusive of driver and stable rental, when working 6 days per week; except for reduced use of feed when idle, the cost will be proportionately higher when time is lost by illness or shut-down.

Feeding (35–38). Horses will dangerously overfeed if permitted, especially when idle. Feed them no more than they will finish at a meal, as damp grain left in feed boxes ferments, causing illness. For same reason, and because of fire hazard, not more than 3-days' feed supply should be taken underground at one time. Allowance of hay for work horses should generally be not over 1 to 1.5 lb per 100 lb live wt. Horses of 1 200–1 300 lb, have worked hard for 8 months on 8 lb hay per head per day, plus sufficient allowance of grain (Morrison).

Ration should vary with the condition, weight, and work of the animal. Table 8 gives the ratio of protein to other food fuels for the important U S feed stuffs. Table 9 gives quantities of the various digestibles required, per 100 lb live wt of animal when idle, and at different kinds of work. With these tables and local prices of feed, the most economic balanced ration can be calculated, just as metallurgical furnace charges are determined. To provide the proper bulk, about 10 to 18 lb of the daily feed should be concentrates, the remainder roughage, the proportion and quantity of roughage decreasing and of concentrates increasing with the severity of work. Most of the roughage should be fed at night, and 1/2 to 2/3 of the concentrates in the morning. The mineral requirements take care of themselves for animals not in foal, except that about 0.25 lb salt should be supplied weekly. On Saturday nights, or when the animal is to be laid off, replace grain by bran and roughage. Regularity in DRINKING is more important than the time. A thirsty animal will not feed well, and it is better to allow it to drink moderately before feeding and again after.

Care (36). Most animals will respond to good treatment, and will make the best average if not over-pushed. A " bad " mule is often made so by abuse.

Some animals are not intelligent or quick-footed enough, or are too nervous or high-strung for mine work, and purchases should be made with a trial option clause. Stable boss, not the drivers, should do the feeding; he should inspect animals coming off shift, report cases of abuse, and see that harness fits well and is kept clean. Especial care should be taken of the feet, and cuts and sores should be given antiseptic dressing (21). Underground stables are always drafty, and sweaty animals should be blanketed until dry. For bedding, 100 lb straw or 350 lb sawdust per month per animal are reasonable allowances.

Underground stables (36) must be well ventilated; a separate split with direct return to the upcast is required by law in most coal mining states. Stalls should be dry, not less than 5 by 10 ft, with not more than 2 in grade to the rear for drainage, and little or no cross grade. There should be a passageway both behind and in front of stalls for handling supplies and refuse, and a raised platform for feed storage. Roof over stalls and feed storage should be watertight. There should be a pressure water supply; tracks should be flush with floor, and partitions raised above it, so that the whole floor may be hosed out.

Table 8. Average Digestible Nutrients in 100 Lb of Typical Feeding Stuffs *

Feeding stuff	Total dry matter, lb	Digestible crude protein, lb	Total digestible nutrients, lb	Nutritive ratio, 1 : —	Wt per bushel, lb
Concentrates					
Dent corn........................	89.5	7.5	85.7	10.4	56
Oats..............................	90.8	9.7	70.4	6.3	32
Wheat............................	89.8	9.2	80.1	7.7	60
Barley............................	90.7	9.0	79.4	7.8	48
Kafir.............................	88.2	9.0	80.0	7.9	56
Linseed meal......................	90.9	30.2	77.9	1.6	35
Cottonseed meal, choice...........	92.5	37.0	78.2	1.1	48
Wheat bran........................	89.9	12.5	60.9	3.9	16
Dried brewers' grains.............	92.5	21.5	65.7	2.1	19
Field peas........................	90.8	19.0	76.2	3.0	67
Roughages					
Corn fodder, medium dried.........	81.7	3.0	53.7	16.9	....
Corn stover, medium...............	81.0	2.1	46.1	21.0	....
Timothy hay.......................	88.4	3.0	48.5	15.2	....
Prairie hay.......................	93.5	4.0	47.9	11.0	....
Alfalfa hay.......................	91.4	10.6	51.6	3.9	....
Red clover hay....................	87.1	7.6	50.9	5.7	....
Oat straw.........................	88.5	1.0	45.6	44.6	....
Green dent corn fodder, glazed....	26.2	1.1	17.8	15.2	....
Green alfalfa.....................	25.3	3.3	14.6	3.4	....
Corn silage, well-matured.........	26.3	1.1	17.7	15.1	....

* Abridged from Henry and Morrison, "Feeds and Feeding," 1919.

Table 9. Modified Wolff-Lehmann Standards for Work Horses or Mules

(Henry and Morrison)

	Daily per 100 lb live weight			Nutritive ratio
	Dry matter, lb	Digestible crude protein, lb	Total digestible nutrients, lb	
Idle....................	13–18	0.8–1.0	7.0– 9.0	1 : 8.0 to 1 : 9.0
Light work.............	15–22	1.1–1.4	10.0–13.1	1 : 8.0 to 1 : 8.5
Medium work............	16–24	1.4–1.7	12.8–15.6	1 : 7.8 to 1 : 8.3
Heavy work.............	18–26	2.0–2.2	15.9–19.5	1 : 7.0 to 1 : 8.0

Horses vs mules. Mules average smaller, require less headroom, endure heat and neglect better, and are less liable to foot lameness than horses. They will eat roughages which horses refuse, but are less apt to overeat, and hence less subject to colic or founder. Horses are heavier, better built draft animals than mules, average more reliable, haul larger loads, and require little or no more feed per 100 lb live wt than mules on similar work. They are more spirited than mules, and a nervous horse is apt to rear and injure his head against roof. Mules are more generally used underground than horses, but, where haulage ways are large enough and the duty sufficient for heavy horses, the advantages of mules are debatable, and where there is headroom many coal operators now use large horses in preference to mules.

Examples. According to the Illinois State Co-operative Reports for 1914, 1 100-lb mules costing $175 to $275, used for gathering colliery cars for locomotive haulage, are worked at high speed, and the underground working life has been reduced to 3 years, the mules then selling at about $40. Cost of feed, shoeing and harness repair is 75¢ to $1 per day. In the best managed mines, cost of feeding mules with corn @ 60¢ per 100 lb and hay @ $15 per ton averages $10 per month, some exceeding $14 per month. At one mine, 1 300-lb mules haul 75 loaded trips 700 ft on 2% grade in favor of the load. Each trip consists of 4 1 000-lb cars, with 3 500 lb coal each, or 18 000 lb gross. Gross daily ton-mileage per mule is 54.67, or 34.80 coal-ton-miles, equivalent to about 10¢ per coal-ton-mile. At another mine, 1 mule on gathering work on 0.5% favorable grades, hauls a trip of 3 cars 1 000 ft, with a duty of 24.43 coal-ton-miles, total cost being 17.6¢ per coal-ton-mile. At another mine, with 2% favorable grade, a 3-mule spike-team handles a trip of 17 1 800-lb cars, each holding 2 100 lb coal, or 22 100 lb gross per mule, corresponding to a tractive effort on the return trip of at least 300 lb per mule.

In Alabama-Tennessee mines, aver for 500 mules in 6 mines: feed and care, 34.9¢ per mule; int on cost, 3.3¢; deprec, 7.0¢; total, 45.2¢ per day; working 276 days = 59.8¢ per working day.

Shoeing and harness 3 to 6¢ (aver 4.3¢) and drivers $1.762 per working day. Aver duty 3.9 to 33.2 net ton-miles per mule, as follows:

Haul, mile	Ton-miles per mule		Cost per net ton-mile, cents	Conditions
	Gross	Net		
0.32	12.4	6.9	35.7	Unfavorable
0.37	24.8	13.8	17.9	Aver
0.78	41.8	23.0	10.7	Best
0.64	35.5	21.4	11.5	Aver

In a Somerset Co, Pa, colliery, following haulage costs were reported: feed, harness, and shoeing for 10 mules, $6 per day; deprec, 20% per annum, 24 days per month, on $200, $1.38; 8 drivers at $2.25, $18; int on investment at 6%, $0.41; total, $25.79. The haul was 2 640 ft down a max grade of 2.5% and against empties 5%; aver duty, 400 tons per working day or 12.9¢ per coal-ton-mile. Total daily cost per mule on gathering work, $3.17 to $3.28, or 2.2 to 2.6¢ per ton.

In West Va, for 211 000 ton handled in 1 year, on 0.75 to 2% grades, aver haul 1 300 ft, aver travel 6 miles per day: drivers, $8 169; keep of 16 mules, $2 302; deprec, $392.50; killed, $400; int 6% on $3 020 value of 16 mules, $181.20; aver cost per ton, 5.496¢, or 22.324¢ per coal-ton-mile.

At Butte, Mont (1922), a good mine horse costs $100–$150, harness $35, collar $8, and should be shod monthly if worked daily. Cost per day: shoeing at $3 per month, 10¢; stable boss for 12 horses, 50¢; feed, 50¢; total, $1.10 per horse.

Feeding mules at metal mines (35, 38): aver for 14 mules, pulling 2 16-cu ft cars, 11 mile per shift; aver tram, 1 000 ft. Per mule per mo: hay, 440 lb; oats, 5 bu; corn, 2 bu. Aver for 22 mules, aver tram, 1 450 ft, with grades and curves, 645 lb hay, 9.1 bu oats, 3 bu corn per mule per mo.

At an Idaho silver-lead mine, mule haulage with 1 800-lb cars; 2 500 lb ore, grade 5 in per 100 ft in favor of load, and aver distance 1 400 ft, cost 16.5¢ per ton for labor, and 1¢ for supplies, feed and harness, or 66¢ per ore-ton-mile, exclusive of int and deprec.

12. LOCOMOTIVE HAULAGE (39–49)

Motive power. Steam and internal-combustion locomotives are independent; compressed air and storage-battery types require intermittent, and trolley, constant connection to outside sources of power. For special service, trolley and storage-battery, or adhesion and rack-rail drives, are combined in a single locomotive. CONDITIONS. Locomotive haulage is justified at mines with easy track grades and large output. Compared with hand tramming or animal haulage, the high speed, large tonnage per trip and few men required, may balance the larger interest and deprec charge on installation. Compared with rope haulage, especially if there are branches or many curves, it is more flexible, and easier to extend and maintain. It requires less headroom, but heavier rails and easier curves (Art 6), than animal haulage and can not compete with it in thick seams on daily output of less than about 175 net ton-miles on grades below 1.25%, or with rope haulage on grades averaging over 4% against or 5% in favor of loads. Short grades, that can be taken by momentum, may be 1 to 3% steeper. Geared locomotives can work up to 12% grades in gathering cars.

Hauling capacity of a locomotive is determined by its draw-bar pull, speed, and the resistance per ton of loaded cars. If it has enough power to make its driving wheels slip,

Table 10. Approx Coeff of Adhesion (Baldwin Locomotive Works, 43)

Condition of rails	Chilled C-I wheels		Steel-tired wheels	
	Without sand	With sand	Without sand	With sand
Covered with dry snow..............	0.10	0.15	0.10	0.15
Covered with sleet..................	0.15	0.20	0.15	0.20
Greasy, moist.....................	0.15	0.25	0.15	0.25
Outdoor, moist....................	0.18	0.22	0.18	0.22
Thoroughly wet, clean..............	0.20	0.25	0.25	0.31
Clean, dry........................	0.20	0.25 to 0.30	0.25	0.31 to 0.37
Best condition, max values........	....	0.38 to 0.42	....	0.47 to 0.52

its max drawbar pull is limited by the adhesion of driving wheels to the rails. COEFF OF ADHESION is the tractive force required to slip drivers ÷ wt on drivers. Table 10 gives approx values for mine locomotives. Makers' tables are usually based on 20 and 25% adhesion, and 20 to 40 lb per ton resistance for train on the level.

General formulas applicable to all types of adhesion locomotives: Let A = coeff of adhesion; C = force required to move complete train, including locomotive, lb; D = drawbar pull, lb; E = fric resistance of locomotive, lb; F = fric resistance of train, lb per ton; G = grade resistance, lb per ton; H = dynamometer or drawbar hp of locomotive; L = wt of locomotive on drivers, tons; S = speed, miles per hr; T = gross wt of train, tons. Then:

$$D = T\,(F \pm G) \dots\dots\dots\dots (1) \qquad C = D + E \pm (L \times G) \dots\dots (3)$$
$$L = D \div (2\,000\,A - G) \dots\dots (2) \qquad H = D \times S \div 375 \dots\dots\dots (4)$$

Total dynamometer hp-hr for M miles, @ aver drawbar pull D, $= DM \div 375$ (5)
From (1) and (2), $T = L\,(2\,000\,A - G) \div (F + G) \dots\dots\dots\dots\dots (6)$

Effect of grade on locomotive capacity. Assuming a max tractive effort on the level of 25% of wt on drivers in Eq (6), then locomotives can move per ton wt on drivers the gross train tons given in Table 11. Multiply these weights by tonnage on drivers for the locomotive under consideration, and for satisfactory running deduct approx 25% from the total to allow for acceleration and contingencies. For greatest effic in power haulage, the grade should be that of equal traction (4, 5) (Art 8). The rapid loss in effic with increasing grades makes the economic grade limit for locomotives usually below 3%. There is also liability of runaway accidents on steeper grades.

Table 11.   Tons Hauled per Ton on Drivers, Besides Wt of Locomotive, when Drawbar Pull on Level = 25% of Wt on Drivers

Resistance of trip, lb per ton	10	15	20	25	30	40	Factor for $D = 0.2\,L$
On level track	50.0	33.0	25.0	20.0	16.6	12.5	0.80
Up 0.5% grade	24.5	19.6	16.3	14.0	12.2	9.8	0.79
" 1% "	16.0	13.7	12.0	10.7	9.6	8.0	0.79
" 2% "	9.2	8.4	7.6	7.1	6.6	5.7	0.78
" 3% "	6.3	5.9	5.5	5.2	4.9	4.4	0.77
" 4% "	4.6	4.4	4.2	4.0	3.8	3.5	0.76
" 5% "	3.6	3.4	3.3	3.2	3.1	2.8	0.75
" 6% "	2.9	2.8	2.7	2.6	2.5	2.3	0.74

Rack-rail locomotives have much better effic on grades than others, because the draw-bar pull with ordinary drivers can not exceed the adhesion, and while the power output of a locomotive, $D \times S$, is not constant for varying speeds, the rack-rail type, being geared to the track, can, by decreasing S, increase D above the adhesion limit, or for a given value of D can decrease locomotive wt below the adhesion requirement. Rack rail is advantageous on long moderate grades, or in rolling seams; it is the only practical type on grades over about 6%, and can be safely but not economically used up to 15 or 16%. These locomotives are little used. Rope haulage is their alternative.

13. STEAM LOCOMOTIVES (43)

Steam locomotives are usually impossible underground because of their exhaust gases and vapor, but may be used in adit mines having large entries and abundant ventilation. Oil burners are preferred to coal burners, because of better control of combustion. Theoretical MAX TRACTIVE FORCE of a steam locomotive is $C = (d^2 \times l \times p \times B) \div W \dots (7)$; where, d = diam cyls, in; l = stroke, in; B = boiler press, lb; W = diam driving wheels, in; p = 0.85 for simple, 0.6 for cross-compound, or 1.2 for Mallet compound engines, d being for high-press cyls. Substitute for C its value from Eq (3) in Eq (7), Art 12, to determine sizes of cyls and drivers. MACHINE FRICTION E = loss between cyls and draw-bar; it increases with the ihp, but its ratio decreases with increasing load. Tests on a consolidation locomotive show E = 10% of ihp with heavy load and 22% with light (*Bull* 82, Ill Exp Sta).

Fuel and steam consumption of simple R R locomotives aver approx 4.5 to 8 lb coal, or 2 to 5 lb fuel oil and 27 to 32 lb water per hp-hr. Superheaters save approx 5 or 6% for every 110° superheat. Compounding saves 10 to 20% over simple engine, if in good condition, but advantage may be more than balanced by poor repair. The overall consumption of locomotives, including stops and roundhouse delays, is approx 50 to 100% more than above figures.

Examples. State Coal Reports of Pa (1912) showed 45 steam locomotives underground in anthracite and 5 in bituminous mines. Many were oil burning and some were being converted from coal to oil.

On Mesabi iron range, 25 6-wheel switch locomotives, with 62 tons on drivers, were used in stripping ore. Following are aver results for 3 yr: round trip, 4.5 miles; grade against loads, 2.25%; trains, 4 16-cu yd 49 000-lb cars = 90 tons material per trip; 18 trips per double shift handled 12 563 gross or 3 645 net ton-miles. Daily cost of operation per engine: coal, 6 tons; water, 48 tons; oil, 5.32 pints; grease, 4 oz; waste, 1 lb; wages (engineer, fireman, and brakeman), $9.95 per shift; locomotive maintenance, $50 to $70 per month, and $900 per year for tires, boiler, machinery, and painting.

14. GASOLENE LOCOMOTIVES

Gasolene locomotives have the flexibility of steam locomotives in radius of travel, and for mining work are geared for speeds of 3 to 12 miles per hr. They have no open fire, consume no fuel when idle, and are less dangerous than steam engines in gaseous mines. The exhaust gases and cost of gasolene are the limiting factors in competing with other types. The max volume of CO produced when feeding gasolene to the explodible limit is 5.75% of the piston displacement, and, under the worst conditions of carburation, 13.5% of the exhaust gases are CO as against 4 to 6% normally. CO should be diluted by 2 000 volumes air for continued breathing and should never exceed 0.01%. Hood therefore concludes that gasolene locomotives require from 7 840 cu ft of air per min for 4-cyl, 5 by 5-in motors, to 35 140 cu ft per min for 6-cyl, 8 by 7-in motors, to maintain the 0.01% dilution. Stopping in dead air, or traveling with the air current or behind a motor, may be dangerous. The exhaust should be washed and cooled by passing through a spray deodorizer before discharging, which does not, however, eliminate any of the CO. Size of motor should be limited by the available air current. Precautions should be taken against leakage at the carburetor and when charging tanks.

Rating of the Assoc Licensed Automobile Manfrs for gasolene motors is: brake hp $= d^2 n \div 2.5$, where d = diam cyl, in; n = number of cyls, with piston speed assumed at 1 000 ft per min. This formula is conservative for automobile motors, but the simple carburetor unfortunately used in many mine locomotives makes them less efficient than

Table 12.   Gasolene Locomotives *

Wt, ton	Cylinders	Draw-bar pull, lb	Wheels, in		Speed, miles per hr	Overall dimen, in			Price, factory
			Diam	Base		Length	Width	Height	
2.5	....	....		....	....		....	....	$1 250 (1914)
3.5	4 1/4 × 5 1/2	1 500	24	36	4 and 8	113	44	62	....
4	....	1 600	16	36	4 " 8	120	48	40	....
5	5 × 6	2 250	18	42	3.5 " 7	144	50	46	3 500 (1916)
6	....	2 400	18	......	4 " 8	132	48	46	....
7	5 1/2 × 7	2 600	30	48	4 " 8	146	54	72	3 500 (1915)
8	7 × 6	3 200	20	50	4.3 " 8.5	180	60	48	5 000 (1916)
10	....	4 000	22	48	5 " 10	150	56	50	....
12	8 × 7	4 800	24	51	5 " 10	156	56	52	4 500 (1915)
15	....	6 000	25	54	6 " 12	171	60	54	....

* Baldwin, Milwaukee, Vulcan and Whitcomb, 4-cyl, 4-cycle engines.

good automobile motors. The uncertainty of the products of combustion of lower distillates or fuel oils prohibits their use for underground locomotives. Makers claim fuel consumption to be 0.1 gal gasolene per hp-hr. Hood's tests (Bureau of Mines, *Bull* 74) show 0.73 to 1.2 lb gasolene per brake hp-hr for full load and full speed, 1.2 to 2.2 at half load and half speed, and 3.5 to over 6.0 lb at one-eighth load and half speed.

Examples. Righter Coal & Coke Co, Lost Creek, W Va. 6-ton Vulcan locomotive; 25-lb rails; undulating grades of 1 to 2.5%; sharp curves; trains, 12 cars, each 0.5 ton empty, 3 tons loaded; haul, 1 800 ft one way; output, 23 trains = 687 tons per 9-hr day. Operating cost: 1 motorman, $2.50; coupler, $2.00; 10 gal gasolene, $1.60; oil, $0.30; total, $6.40 per day = 0.93¢ per ton or 2.72¢ per coal-ton mile, to which add repairs, deprec, and int.

Herbert mine, Pa (*Coal Age*, Vol 8, p 415). 5-ton Milwaukee locomotive, 44-in gage; 400 cars, wt 2 000 lb, coal 4 000 lb; daily output = 2 × car capacity. Operating cost per motor per day: 2 men, $5.35; 11 gal gasolene, $1.32; oil and waste, $0.11; total, $6.78 for 500 tons coal hauled 2 700 to 3 000 ft, showing saving of $8.64 per day over horse haulage.

Shinnston, W Va. 6-ton Whitcomb locomotives; 25-lb rails; 36-in gage; 20 trips of 17 cars each, gross 52.6 tons; haul 3 100 ft. Cost per month of 10-hr days: gasolene, 629 gal; oil and waste, $10.99. Aver cost per ton for year 1914: labor, 1.44¢; gasolene, 0.66¢; oil, 0.08¢; repairs, 0.40¢; total, 2.58¢ per ton = 4.92¢ per coal-ton-mile.

Shade Coal Co, Pa. 7-ton, 4 4-in cyls, 4-cycle Milwaukee locomotive, 36-in gage; 30-lb rails; haul, 3 400 ft one way; max grade, 6% in favor of loads, 5% against empties, aver 2% and 2.2% respectively; daily output, 375 tons. Cost: motorman and trip tender @ $2.75, $5.50; 16 gal gasolene @ 15.5¢, $2.48; oil, grease, and waste, $0.41; repairs @ $35.81 per month, $1.50; int and deprec @ 16% per annum, $1.94; total cost per day, $11.83; cost per ton, 3.15¢, or per ton-mile, 3.79¢. Under similar conditions, but hauling only 145 tons per day, so that equipment was idle about 40% of total working time, cost was 11.73¢ per ton-mile.

Eagle Mining Co, Canton, Ill. 5-ton Milwaukee locomotive, 36-in gage, hauls 20 to 22 cars; loaded wt, 3 500 lb each; train is split at a 3% grade against loads near shaft; duty, 500 tons per

8-hr day; round trip, 6 000 ft or 284 coal-ton-miles. Operating cost, including runner, trip rider, gasolene, oil, and grease = $7.25 per day = 2.6¢ per ton-mile.

Shiloh, Ill. 6-ton Whitcomb locomotives; 42-in gage; 20-lb rails; 0.5% grade in favor of load. Duty per motor per 8-hr day, 36 trips of 16 cars = 42.4 tons gross, 8 tons empty, haul, 2 436 ft. Cost per motor per mo of 110 working hr: gasolene, 194 gal, $25.05; oil, waste, and repairs, $11.46; 2 men, $85.52; total, $122.03 = 1.5¢ per coal-ton mile (approx).

Cleveland Co, Wis, zinc mine. 4-ton Whitcomb locomotive; tonnage (1913), 123 150; total distance traveled, 6 970 miles; cost, labor, supplies, and maintenance, 2.0¢ per ton.

Trojan Co, S D. 7-ton Milwaukee locomotive; 18-in gage, wet track; 4% grade in favor of loads; bad curves limiting return to 8-car trips. Cost for 25 days: engineer, $106.50; gasolene, 382 gal; engine oil, 16 gal; lubricating oil, 10 gal; total, $76.97. Total miles, 612; ton-miles, 3 516; cost per ton-mile, 2.2¢ not including int or repairs.

Huerfano Co, Colo. 6-ton locomotive; 15-car trips, of 41.25 tons gross; 3 000-ft haul; max grade, 5.5%, using engine plane to pull locomotive and train. Cost, 4.94¢ per coal-ton-mile.

Joplin, Mo. 6-ton gasolene loco was most popular for long hauls. Cost, 4 mo, 1917, for 1 750 ft, 7¢ per ton; against mule haulage, 700 ft, 4.58¢.

Ill coal mines, 1921, used 18 gasolene locos on main haulage.

15. COMPRESSED-AIR LOCOMOTIVES (44, 45)

Characteristics. They carry their own power supply, are flexible in operation within the radius of travel from charging stations for which they are designed, require no fire, do not spark nor emit noxious exhaust, but aid ventilation, and are the safest type for gaseous, dry timbered, or poorly ventilated workings, inflammable buildings, or magazines. (For data on air pressure, tank capacity, reheating air, tractive force, storage, pipe lines, charging stations, see Sec 15 and Bib (45).

Operating requirements: (a) a multi-stage compressor to furnish air at the aver rate of consumption and at approx 200 lb greater press than the locomotive requires; (b) stationary storage tanks, or a transmission line large enough to act as storage, near charging station; (c) one or more charging stations so located that the locomotive can always return to a station before its charge is exhausted; (d) a locomotive heavy and powerful enough to exert the max required drawbar pull and with sufficient tank capacity and press to make a round trip at full load to the point most distant from the station. Because of the high press, the ordinary mine compressor can not be used, except that it would be economic for the multi-stage compressor to takes its supply from a cool receiver at the mine press, rather than from the atmos.

Required wt of locomotive is determined as in Art 1, and size of cyl by Eq (7) Art 13, substituting the auxiliary tank press for B and 0.95 to 0.98 for p, because the air at full stroke does not lose heat by radiation as steam does. REQUIRED TANK CAPACITY of locomotive is determined by the total work done per max load and longest round trip. RADIUS OF TRAVEL can be increased by adding an air-tank tender, together with corresponding increase in vol of stationary storage (45).

Table 13. Compressed-air Haulage Plants

Compressor, 3-stage		Air line		Locomotives			Total cost	Round trip, ft	Train, tons		Cost, ¢ per net	
Cu ft free air per min	Press, lb per sq in	Length, ft	Diam, in	No cyl	Size cyl, in	Wt, tons			gross	net	ton	ton-mile
(a) 375	700	9 600	4	2	7×14	8	$13 673	5 100	62.4	42	......	1.875
(b)	......	4 200	5	2	......	.....	13 701	{ 3 200 } { 5 200 }	....	.....	3.6	.....
(c)	700	4 100	......	1	9×14	.....	....	9 000	87.7	.....	......	1.25*
(d) 296	600	7 500	5 & 3	2	7×14	8	15 156	{ 8 000 } { 4 200 }	147.0	.....	···· {	1.39 3.05
(e) 450	1 000	5 000	4	2	......	.....	15 800	....	......	.....	......	2.17

* Gross. (a) *Mines & Min*, Vol 18, p 538. (b) Baldwin Locomotive Wks. (c) Peele, Compressed Air Plant. (d) Morris, *Trans* A I M E, Vol 30, p 566. (e) Two-stage locomotive, operating cost, int and deprec, 2.17¢ per ton-mile, as against 2.56¢ for single-stage, with coal @ $3 per ton (estimates by H. K. Porter Co).

Coal mines of western Pa and West Va were using 150 compressed air locos in 1921 (38). In U S metal mines, the only important compressed air haulage plants now operating are at Homestake mine, S D, and Inspiration mine, Ariz (42).

16. STORAGE-BATTERY LOCOMOTIVES (39, 41, 46, 48, 49)
(See also Sec 16)

Characteristics. They are flexible prime movers, cheaper to install than trolley or air locomotives, simple to operate and safer than any type except compressed air. Suitable for short hauls in temporary workings, as in gathering, or for infrequent long hauls where trolley lines are not warranted or low-roofed wet workings make them dangerous. Grades must be easy; max speed per hr, 5 miles. They require 1 man on gathering work, while cable-reel locomotives (Art 17) need 2. Wt of locomotive is greater than $D \div A$ (Art 12), because of the necessary battery wt; hence it has lower useful load capacity on grades than other types, and is limited to low speed by battery output rate.

Battery capacity depends on: (a) max rate of current discharge required; (b) the kw-hr required to operate on 1 charge. For details, see Sec 16. Storage-battery locomotives usually develop 4 hp max per ton of wt, and 3.5 mile per hr at rated drawbar pull; as against 10 hp per ton and 6 mile per hr for trolley type. With recent improvements in batteries, they are being more widely adopted, replacing the trolley system in heavy ground, where maintenance of track-bonds and trolley wire and its dangers are excessive.

Examples. In COPPER QUEEN tests (*Trans* A I M E, Vol 48, p 295) a storage-battery locomotive required 1.6 kw-hr at power station per useful ton-mile, or 1.28 at locomotive, as against 1.1 and 0.875 for trolley locomotive. BIG FIVE TUNNEL, Col, two 17-hp, 4-ton locomotives and tenders; full-load speed, 4.5 miles per hr; train, 20 to 30 cars, each 2.5 tons gross; 20 and 12-lb rails; grade, 0.25%. Storage battery was used underground and trolley on surface. Operating costs for 6 months: labor, $1 098; material, $113; repairs, $33; power at 1.2 to 5.5¢ per kw-hr, $306; total, $1 551; duty, 18 914 ton-miles, at 6.5 to 12.2¢; aver, 8.2¢ per ton-mile. STERLING COAL Co, O. 11 2.5-ton storage-battery locomotives are used for gathering cars from 12 to 15 rooms, each handling 96 cars per 8 hr. 4 trolley locomotives are detailed to serve 11 entries, requiring 19 men. 11 reel locomotives (Sec 16) could do the work, saving 4 locomotives (approx cost $7 200) but requiring 22 men to operate. GRANT MINE, Ind. A 5-ton locomotive, with 63 Edison cells, averages 75 volts @ 60 amp normal discharge; train of 16 cars of 1 600 lb each, carrying 3 000 lb coal, used 90 amp on level, 160 up 1% grade and 220 on curve up 1.5%. Some CŒUR-D'ALENE mines, and others with conditions favorable to trolley haulage, have adopted storage-battery haulage, because of casualties from trolley current. HECLA MINE, Idaho. Cars weigh 4 040 lb, 8 wheels, 5.2 ton capac; trains of 5 cars make 7 trips per 8-hr, but can make 10; grade against empties, 0.75% speed 4 mile per hr; loaded trains, 6 mile per hr; using Baldwin-Westinghouse storage-battery locomotive, 7 000-lb chassis, 2 000–3 000 drawbar pull; track, 24-in gage, 35-lb rail. ALASKA GASTINEAU MINE (1919). Six-ton storage-battery locomotives haul 8–10 4-ton cars, aver 590 ft. Operating cost per ton-mile: maintenance locomotive, 3.19¢; charging station, 0.22¢; power, 0.89 kw-hr, or 0.132¢; total, 3.54¢. CRIPPLE CREEK, Colo. Three-ton storage-battery locomotives have long been used satisfactorily; crew of 2 men haul 125 16-cu ft cars per shift 2 500 ft and dump at shaft pocket for 7–8¢ per car for labor. EUREKA STANDARD, Utah (E. D. Gardner, 1935). Storage-battery locomotive on main haulage levels; aver train, 10–12 cars of 0.9 ton (18 cu ft); dump with turntable; track, 18 in, 12-lb rails, steel ties 4 to 5 ft centers; tramming labor, 17¢ per ton.

17. ELECTRIC TROLLEY LOCOMOTIVES (40–42, 46, 48, 49)
(See also Sec 16)

Characteristics. These are the prevalent type in mines. They are compact, simple to operate, have high effic and usually the lowest power cost of all types. Disadvantages: cost and danger of the trolley circuit; danger from sparking at commutator or trolley wheel; necessity for wired and bonded track.

About 80% of all mining trolleys use 250-volt d c, which is slightly more economic in design of motors and control and less dangerous than same nominal a-c voltage. A few 500-volt circuits are used, and there is at least 1 3-phase 2-wire underground installation in U S. MOTORS are of approx 10 hp per ton wt of locomotive. MAIN HAULAGE LOCOMOTIVES weigh 3 to 30 tons. GATHERING LOCOMOTIVES are 2 to 8 ton (approx), and can enter rooms 200 to 400 ft off trolley line by using a reel of single or double cable to hook on trolley and track. For rapid work and to prevent overrunning the cable, reel should have a gear to feed out and rewind cable as the locomotive moves. CRAB LOCOMOTIVE has a flexible wire rope on a geared drum, and hauls cars from rooms without entering. COMBINATION GATHERING LOCOMOTIVES have both cable-reel and crab attachments, to serve rooms driven on either dip or rise.

Power plant and transmission requirements for a number of locomotives are found by correction factors similar to those used for compressors, but each case demands special study. Fig 53 gives Oliver Iron Mining Co practice under conditions stated.

Examples. Duty of electric locomotives on main haulage in 18 ILLINOIS COAL MINES (condensed from State Reps) is given in Table 14. Most cars have wood body, with plain bearings. Differences in length of haul, grades, curves, coal or car supply, and in ratio of empty to loaded car from 20% to 46%, account for varying results. BUNKER HILL & SULLIVAN MINE, Idaho. Haulage

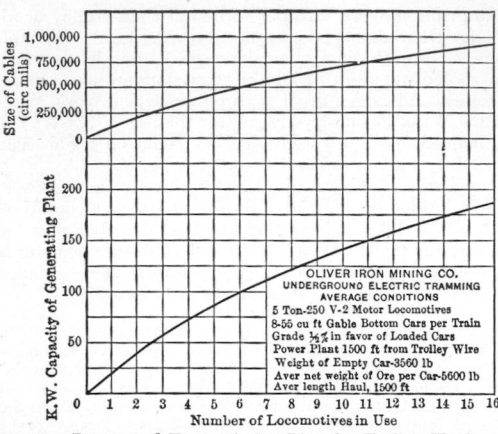

Fig 53. Power and Transmission Line for Trolley Haulage

through Kellogg Mill adit 11 000 ft (1937), of 386 576 ton ore by trolley locomotives; total cost, $40 015, or 10.4¢ per ton, principal items being, trammers $17 343, repairs $7 550, supplies $6 061 (Stanly A. Easton). ZINC MINES OF TENN (66). Main haulage at Mascot and Newmarket mines: 4- and 6-ton trolley locomotives, powered by 250-volt dc double unit motors; trolley wire of figure 8 type supported by insulated hangers spaced 10 ft. Track 24-in gage, 40-lb rails, 0.5% grade in favor of load, min radius curve, 50 ft; electric welded track bonds replacing flexible bonds; Mascot box cars are 40-cu ft, of extra heavy steel with railway type journals, 14-in wheels, steel incased oak bumpers, hook couplings with spring cushioned draw-bars. Newmarket cars are 80-cu ft, Granby type. MORENCI, Ariz (67). 10-ton cars are hauled on a 20-in track, in 300-ton trains by Jeffrey 12-ton tandem locomotives. Cars are 200 cu ft capac, with 24-in wheels; empty wt, 9 700 lb; M C B journals; rail, 60 lb; 100-ft radius curves; grade, 0.4% with load. ALASKA-JUNEAU. 10-ton cars are assembled in trains of 40 cars and hauled to the mill 2 miles distant by 18-ton articulated trolley locomotives, on 30-in track of 75-lb rails (P. A. Bradley, 1938). HOMESTAKE. A new waste haulage system has 30-in track, 50-cu ft Granby cars and 10-ton Goodman trolley locomotive (E. G. Ross, 1938).

Table 14. Trolley-motor Main Haulage (Illinois Mines)

Locomotive wt, tons	Miles traveled per shift	Ton-mileage		Locomotive wt, tons	Miles traveled per shift	Ton-mileage	
		Coal	Gross (excluding loco)			Coal	Gross (excluding loco)
4 (rack rail)	35	690	1 556	10	22.7	568	977
5 " "	40	823	1 593	10	32.5	683	1 366
6	21.8	319	575	12	36.0	2 203	4 095
7.5	41.7	835	1 337	12	15.9	444	730
7.5	47.4	829	1 598	12	23.0	667	1 127
8	42.3	475	888	12.5	26.5	716	1 432
10	10.6	468	875	13	20.3	908	1 560
10	14.2	709	1 167	15	29.8	848	1 509
10	18.0	450	675	15	34.1	1 107	1 823
10	15.1	534	920	Aver 10	28.3	743	1 358

Power consumption tests: OLIVER IRON MINING Co, for 1 week of 17 8-hr shifts, with 4-ton, 250-volt electric locomotives. Cars, 55 cu ft, gable-bottom, weigh 3 560 lb (Fig 13); aver net wt ore per car, 5 600 lb; prevailing grade, 1% in favor of load; total, 890 trips, 5 544 cars, 15 523 tons of ore; aver haul, 1 488 ft = 4 375 ore-ton-miles = 10 943 gross ton-miles, including locomotive. Total tramming energy, 2 423 kw-hr, aver = 0.554 kw-hr per ore-ton-mile, including empty return haulage. At a SOUTHWESTERN COPPER MINE, the current per useful ton-mile was 0.875 kw-hr at the motor. COPPER MINE IN ARIZ. 10-ton trolley locomotives, making 10 trips per 8-hr day, hauled 18 cars, each of 101 cu ft, or gross load of 108 tons (empty, 30.6 tons including motor); aver haul one way, 2 900 ft; power, 3 066 kw-hr per locomotive per month of 240 working hr, at 0.97¢ per kw-hr; total operating cost per motor per month, $212; aver repair cost, $20 per motor per month; aver total operating and repair cost, 4.5¢ per ore-ton-mile, not including trolley line maintenance and repairs. COPPER MINE IN ARIZ: 3.5, 6, and 7.5-ton electric locomotives hauled aver distance of 3 000 ft (max, 8 475 ft) at cost, for 67 700 ore-ton-miles, of 13.9¢ per ton of ore, or 21.78¢ per ore-ton-mile, including repairs on locomotive track and ditch. At BISBEE, ARIZ (1912), cost for 408 000 useful ton-miles, in cents per ton-mile, was: for maintenance of locomotives, 2.95¢; cars, 1.64¢; track, 5.24¢; trolley, 3.60¢; power, @ 1.1 kw-hr, 1.6¢; total, 20.03¢. COPPER MINE IN MICH. 4-ton locomotives hauled 15.4 tons gross, 2 000 ft one way, 7.8 ton return round trip in about 30 min; 420 working hr per month, 1 040 kw-hr per locomotive, repair costs, aver $6. IRON MINE ON GOGEBIC RANGE; track gage, 24-in; 30-lb rail; 1% grade; 5-ton locomotive; gross trip, 42 tons; empty, 20 tons; aver haul one way, 1 450 ft; 12 trips in 8 hr; monthly cost per locomotive, 200 working hr, 1 854 kw-hr at 1.5¢; oil and waste, $2.25; motorman and trip tender, $122.50; aver repairs (approx) per locomotive, $12.50; per car, $0.91. Aver total cost, 81.8¢ per ore-ton-mile. Mine operating on half time for period reported. IRON MINE IN MICH. 4 and 6-ton locomotives; track gage, 24-in; 30-lb rail; grade, 1% aver in favor; reverse, 4%. 8 trips of 8 cars, weighing gross 37.3, empty, 11.3 tons; haul, 900 ft one way; 3 750 kw-hr per locomotive per month of 200 hr; operating and repair cost, $124.75 = 14.06¢ per ton-mile. Motor haulage costs in ANTHRACITE COLLIERIES (Gen Electric Co) are given as follows, deprec @ 5% for 200 working days:

Company	Cost per day		Duty, tons	Cost per ton, ¢
	Operating	Deprec		
Glen Ridge, Scranton, Pa...	$7.96	$1.90	288	2.76
N Y & Scranton (Sturges)..	5.05	1.52	250	2.62
" " (Tunnel)..	4.67	1.75	600	1.07
Hillside, No 2 shaft........	16.47	5.20	989	2.19*
" F C slope........	9.37	2.60	541	2.21*

* Actual operating costs (140 days, approx) were 4.56 and 4.65¢ per ton.

BUTTE, MONT. About 200 trolley locomotives are in use, 4-ton size being standard. Since about 1920, use of storage-battery locomotives has increased. U S COAL AND COKE CO'S MINE NO 6, PA. Usually, a 13-ton trolley locomotive gathers from mouth of working places and delivers 600–700 ton coal per day; round trip not over 4 mile; 5–7 men and 7–10 mules gather coal hauled by 1 locomotive. RAHN COLLIERY, PA. Aver, 6 mo: 2.474 kw-hr per ton are used for transport of coal. UNITED VERDE MINE, ARIZ (1919). Six-ton trolley locomotive, hauling 35-ton trailing load of 20 18-cu ft cars, 18-in gage, a distance of 850 ft to skip pockets, costs 10.79¢ per ton, against hand-tramming 200 ft @ 12.7¢ per ton, and storage-battery locomotive, 9.6¢. ILLINOIS. In 1921, 280 shipping coal mines used 1 424 trolley locomotives on main haulage lines, handling over 71 million ton.

18. ROPE HAULAGE (50–52)

Systems: (a) self-acting or gravity plane; (b) engine plane; (c) tail-rope; (d) endless-rope. Of these, (b) and (c) are commonest, (d) being obsolescent. CONDITIONS: large tonnage, and grades which make locomotive haulage inefficient (Art 12, Table 9). Straight haulways and uniform grades are desirable, but not necessary.

Ropes, sheaves, and rollers. ROPES on flat grades, or wherever especially subjected to abrasion, as in dragging on the ground or over track ties, should have 7 or 12-wire strands. The small-gage wires of standard 19-wire hoisting rope wear too fast (Sec 12). A short length of chain at the coupling protects rope from damage by sharp bending, if the cars overrun. Horiz SHEAVES or vert ROLLERS on curves should be properly alined, and of large diam, to reduce bending stresses; 1 large sheave is better than several small ones. Where rope crosses the rail on curves, guide strips should be provided, to minimize friction (Fig 56, b). Track rollers aver 5 in diam by 12 to 18 in long, spaced 15 to 25 ft on straight track; closer on curves. At points of special wear, C-I rollers are used (often made of a pair of car wheels, bolted together with flanges outside).

Self-acting or gravity plane. Descending loaded cars raise the empties. It is often used on the surface, is effective in slopes or long rooms on pitches too flat for mineral to run in chutes by gravity, and in general serves to transfer cars to a lower level, on main haulage lines, or from a blind level to main level.

Angle of flattest self-acting slope. $Sin \; \alpha = $ (total friction F, lb) ÷ (wt of mineral − wt of unbalanced portion of rope R, lb), in which $F = $ [(wt loaded and empty cars + wt rope on both tracks, lb) × $cos \; \alpha + f'$ (wt rollers + drums, lb)] × f; where $f' = 0.1$ approx, $f = $ coeff rolling friction $= 0.012$ to 0.025. Friction is often figured on basis of cars and rope only, in which case f should be larger. This equation shows that profile of plane should be concave, and that heaviest trip, highest ratio of useful load, shortest distance, and lowest coeff of friction, give flattest workable slope. Use of a tail-rope cancels unbalanced R, but increases F. Flat slopes are steepened at top, or "knuckle," so that the grade exceeds angle of inertia (Art 8) for starting trip promptly. Acceleration $a = (T_l - T_e)g$ $\sin \alpha \div T_l + T_e + R = $ approx $(P_d - P_a) g \div T_l + T_e + R$, where a = accel, ft per sec per sec; P_d = descending pull, lb = $T_l (\sin \alpha - f \cos \alpha)$; P_a = ascending pull, lb = $(T_e + R) (\sin \alpha + f \cos \alpha)$; T_l and T_e = wt loaded and empty trips, lb; α = slope angle. If slope changes, take value for α at top for T_l, at bottom for T_e, and aver for R. Length of slope l (ft) required to attain veloc v ft per sec is $l = v^2 \div 2 a$. Max tension R_s in rope will occur when starting or stopping with a jerk, otherwise $R_s = (T_l + R) (\sin \alpha - f \cos \alpha)$. Number of cars per trip to operate a self-acting plane is

$$N = \left[\left(\frac{\sin \alpha}{f} + \cos \alpha \right) R \right] \div \left[\left(\frac{\sin \alpha}{f} - \cos \alpha \right) W_1 - \left(\frac{\sin \alpha}{f} + \cos \alpha \right) W_2 \right],$$

where α = slope angle R = wt rope, lb; W_1 and W_2 = wt of 1 loaded and 1 empty car respectively; f = coeff of rolling friction.

Arrangement of tracks (Fig 54, a to i). It is best to avoid switches on planes by double tracks as in (b) and (c). In (d) a simple automatic switch is used at L, as shown in detail at (i); steel-faced timbers pivoted at KK are thrown by the descending car for either track. At (e) is shown a track plan for narrow slopes, avoiding switches and saving

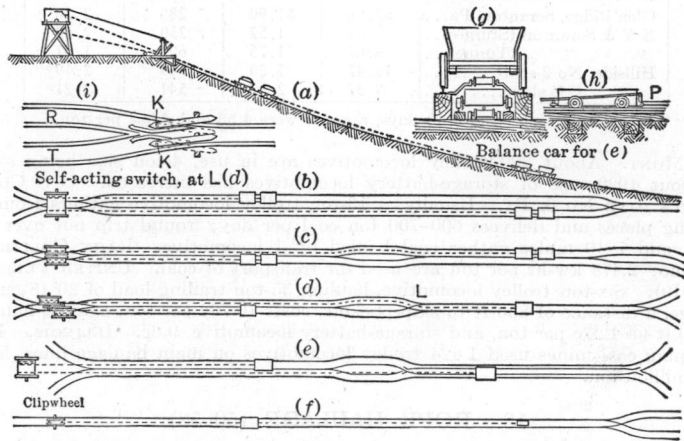

Fig 54. Track System for Self-acting Planes (Hildenbrand, except e)

room below turnout. Fig 54 (f, g, h) illustrate a single main track, with inner counter-wt track, the counter wt being heavy enough to haul up the empty car and unbalanced rope. The balance car (h) has a bell-crank "growler" or safety pin P, to stop car if rope breaks.

Engine plane. Loads are raised or lowered on a slope by a stationary engine and wire rope, as in an inclined shaft. Simple engine planes require single track, with 1 rope = length of plane, and use power only for raising load. The plane may have curves, and varying grade (if all are against the load), provided minimum grade is greater than the angle of rolling friction; it may serve different levels or entries by switches from main slope, with rollers or sheaves to guide rope around turns (Fig 55). On a straight surface plane, 5 000 ft long, under aver conditions, trains of 25 to 30 loaded cars ran at satisfactory speed on 1.75% grade, while empty cars required 2.25% (22). Small British colliery cars (tubs) require 3.5%. A double engine plane has double track, or 3 rails and turnout; the descending trip assists engine to raise ascending trip, thus eliminating dead load, except rope. With engine at head of plane, the max rope pull at drum is: (a) for single track, $D = (T_l + R) (\sin \alpha + f \cos \alpha + P)$, where P = coeff of accel = 0.1 to 0.25; (b) for double-track plane, $D = (T_l - T_e + R) \sin \alpha + (T_l + T_e + R) (f \cos \alpha + P)$. With engine at foot of plane, D is the same as in (a), but rope is balanced and engine pull is $D = T_l \sin \alpha + (T_l + 2R) (f \cos \alpha + P)$. For signification of factors, see under Gravity Plane, above.

Tail rope, the commonest rope haulage system, is applicable on straight, curved, inclined, level or undulating tracks, to a single main line, or including branches (50, 52). MAIN ROPE hauls loaded trip of 1 to 75 cars, with attached TAIL ROPE, to shaft bottom or surface, and tail rope, passing around a large RETURN SHEAVE, returns empties. The engine should be reversible, with separate drums, clutches and brakes, and may be placed anywhere on the line, or on the surface with ropes run through a shaft, slope, adit, or bore-hole. If main and tail-rope drums and engines are at opposite ends of run, each rope = length of run; or, with a double-drum engine at one end, the tail rope = 2 × length, and both ropes = 3 × length of run. Trips are run 8 to 16 miles per hr. When main rope is hauling a loaded trip, the tail-rope drum clutch is loose, and with light braking the train can be kept in tension, to prevent cars from bumping or over-running on grades. The return run of tail rope, from tail sheave to drum, is carried on small sheaves, 10 to 16-in diam, spaced 25 to 60 ft apart, and attached to roof or timbering. MAX TENSION on haul-age rope is: $D = Tl \, (sin \, \alpha + f \, cos \, \alpha) + r \, (h + f \times 2 \, l) + (T_l + 2 \, rl) \, P$, where α = max slope angle; h = total drop of line, ft; l = length of line, ft; r = wt of rope per ft, lb; T_l = wt of loaded trip, lb; P = coeff of accel. Fig 56 (a) shows the Sherrard mine tail-rope system; sheaves and rollers for curves in detail (b). BRANCH ROADS have separate tail ropes = 2 × length of branch, with tail sheaves at ends, and couplings to connect to trip and to main tail rope (Fig 57).

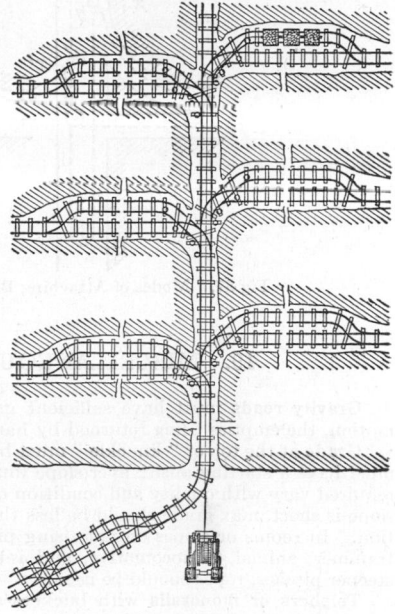

Fig 55. Engine Plane (Leschen)

Endless-rope system. Rope is driven by a grip wheel or pair of multiple-groove sheaves at engine, passes around a return sheave at end of line, and may be over or under the cars. Cars are attached singly, or in short trains, by grips or lashings. On double track, this is done without stopping rope, which is in constant motion. Aver speed, 4–5 miles per hr; max, 10 miles. Length of rope is 1/3 less than for tail rope. Chain, instead of rope, occasionally used for short hauls (catalogs Jeffrey Mfg Co, Robins Conveying Belt Co, and Link Belt Co). This system has almost disappeared in the U S.

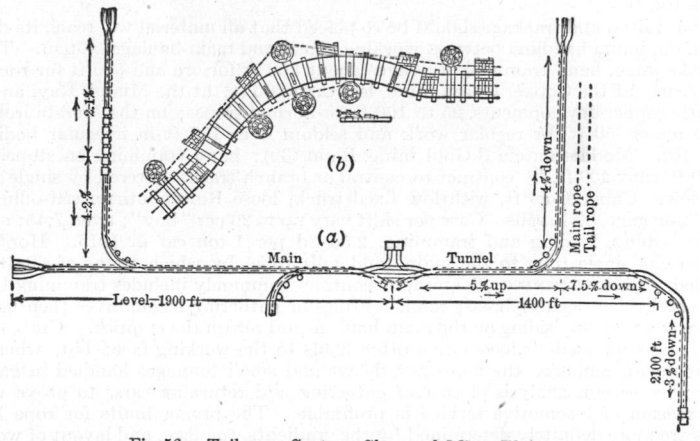

Fig 56. Tail-rope System, Sherrard Mine, Ill (part)

Rope-haulage costs. All types of rope haulage are obsolescent, as indicated by the fact that, in Ill in 1908, 32 mines used rope for main haulage, as against only 1 mine in 1921.

At Sherrard colliery, Ill (Fig 56), when hauling by tail ropes 700–800 ton per day, aver haul 4 000 ft, max 2.25 miles, the cost, including maintenance of track, wear of ropes and sheaves for rope and auxiliary mule haulage, was 14¢ per ton; rope speed, 10–16 miles per hr.

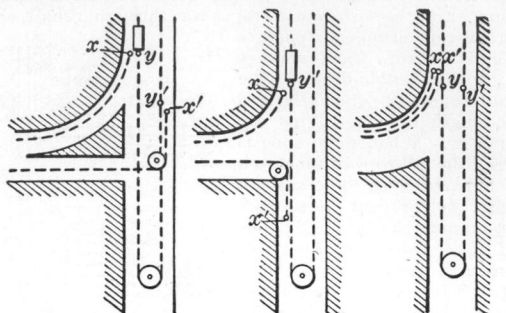

Fig 57.   Modes of Attaching Branch Ropes x, x' to Main Rope y, y'

19. MISCELLANEOUS HAULAGE METHODS

Gravity roads must have sufficient grade in favor of loaded cars to keep cars in motion, the empties being returned by hand, animal haulage, or power.

Grade at the top or " knuckle " must be greater than angle of inertia (Art 8), or the car must have a starting push; aver slope must exceed the angle of rolling friction.   Grades required vary with quality and condition of rolling stock and track; for safety, unless the slope is short, max grade should be less than the probable minimum angle of sliding friction.   In rooms or slopes on flat rising pitch, cars can be delivered to loading point by trammer, animal, or locomotive, and returned to the drift or entry by gravity.   On steeper pitches, ropes should be used.

Telphers or monorails with buckets are used occasionally where tracks or cars are impracticable.   CONVEYER HAULAGE in recent years has developed rapidly, and is suitable for large tonnages.   See Sec 27 for details.

Composite methods.   It is seldom practicable entirely to eliminate hand tramming underground, but development and exploitation should be planned to minimize use of manual labor.   IN METAL MINES, tramming is usually the only possible method of handling ore, waste, and timber in flat-back or slice stopes, sub-levels, and short, temporary workings (Sec 10).

Chutes, raises, and trackage should be so placed that all material will reach its destination with minimum handling between working places and main-haulage system.   Thus, at Homestake mine, hand tramming averages about 300 ft for ore and 500 ft for rock from development; at the Copper Queen mine, less than 200 ft; at the Miami, Ray, and other systematic copper developments, 25 to 100 ft for normal stopes; on the Mesabi iron range top-slice mines, 50 ft for regular work and seldom over 150 ft in irregular bodies (see also Sec 10).   Modderfontein B Gold mine, Rand (39); hand tramming on stope tracks: aver 200 ft, max 400 ft, by contract to central or branch track; lowered by single rope to level below.   Cars, 20 cu ft, with low fixed truck, loose Rowanbotham self-oiling 15-in wheels, 30-in gage, 30-lb rails.   Cars per shift vary up to 20 per "boy"; aver, 7.45; contract price for lashing, loading and tramming, 2.5d–3d per 1-ton car in 1915.   Horses take cars from the single rope to the main (and tail) rope, by which trains of 60–100 cars are hauled.   In COAL MINING, the miners' contract commonly includes tramming between the face and room neck or breast road.   Mules or gathering locomotives then haul cars to the nearest make-up siding on the main haulage and return the empties.   Crab, storage-battery, or compressed-air locomotive often hauls to the working face; but, where there is headroom for animals, the necessary delays and small tonnages handled in gathering work require careful analysis of cost of gathering and returning cars, to prove whether such extension of locomotive service is profitable.   The proper limits for rope haulage systems are more definitely determined by the gradients, tonnage, and layout of workings, than when the more flexible prime movers are used.   In undulating coal seams, frequent examples are found of alternating animal and rope haulage, and there are unusual cases where locomotives with their trains are taken up grades by rope haulage.

20. TRAMMING COSTS

Table 15. Tramming Costs

Company		Year	Tonnage	Cents per ton
Alaska-Gastineau	Alaska	1915–18	6 523 873	6.661 (a)
Alaska-Juneau	"	{ 1923	2 476 240	8.17 } (b)
		{ 1937	4 442 760	8.30 }
Alaska-Treadwell	"	1914	910 000	11.6 (c)
Bawdwin	Burma	1924	175 000	72.9 (c)
Britannia: East Bluff mine	B C	Before 1933	398 664	6. }
Victoria mine	"	....	133 195	13.4 } (d)
Fairview mine	"	....	1 268 234	7.7 }
Bunker Hill & Sullivan	Colo	1937	386 576	10.4 (e)
Cold Springs	"	1931	1 125	71. (f)
Cresson	"	1931	54 747	63. }
"	"	1932	61 914	52. } (g)
El Potosi	Chihuahua	1932	441 094	2.3 (h)
Eureka Standard	Nev	1933	....	17. (i)
Fresnillo:	Zacatecas	1930	......	...... (j)
Hill Top		....	3 858 688	4.32
Others		....	5 111 414	13.95
Grand Republic	Colo	1935	28 515	87.9 (k)
Hartley	Kan	1930	180 212	15.17 (l)
Hollinger	Ont	1937	2 998 240	8.97 (m)
Homestake	S D	1937	4 000 daily	18. (n)
McIntyre	Ont	1931	557 104	13.5 (o)
Miami	Ariz	1931	4 438 808	3.515 (p)
Mt Hope	N J	1930	176 474	45.9 (q)
New Cornelia	Ariz	1930	3 417 374	6.6 (r)
Tezuitlan	Zacatecas	1930–1	66 764	26.9 (s)

Abbreviations in following notes are same as in the Bibliography.
(a) (A) Vol 63, p 483. (b) including loading and tramming, P. R. Bradley. (c) includes proportion of general charges and hoisting. (d) I C 6815. (e) Haulage 11 000 ft, through Kellogg mill adit with trolley locomotives. Stanly A. Easton. (f) high grade ferberite. I C 6673. (g) I C 6806. (h) I C 6804. (i) I C 6851. (j) I. H. Ashley. (E) 1931, p 279. (k) I C 6976. (l) I C 6656. (m) tonnage includes ore, waste and sand, cost per ton milled, 12.9¢; track labor and material, 3.4¢ per ton hauled, or 5.93¢ per ton milled. (n) includes motormen, trackmen, motor, car and track repairs, lubricants and power. E. G. Ross. 1937. (o) I C 6741. (p) figures for 1931 are not Miami's lowest, but are more representative, as they cover the last year of nearly normal production. R. W. Hughes, 1937. (q) I C 6601. (r) I C 6666. (s) I C 6735.

21. HAULAGE ACCIDENTS (72–80; also Sec 23)

Underground haulage accidents in all kinds of mines and underground quarries in 1935 and in 1936 were as follows in accompanying table.

See also Sec 23	Fatalities		Non-fatal injuries	
	1935	1936	1935	1936
Anthracite mines	30	26	1 909	1 914
Bituminous mines	198	202	10 950	12 097
Metal and non-metal mines, except coal	9	13	897	1 445
Underground quarries	......	2	29	35
	237	243	13 785	15 491

Haulage accounted for 20.7% of all fatal and 23.36% of all non-fatal underground accidents in 1935, and 17.12% of fatal and 20.8% of non-fatal accidents in 1936.

To reduce accidents: (a) illuminate haulage ways, so that men will not need individual lights on motor tracks; (b) have head light on motor and on rear car of train; (c) standardize equipment, so that bumpers, couplings, etc, are alike on all cars, with handles so that the hand can not be caught; (d) have safe clearance between cars on one or preferably both ribs of entry (a close rib is better than one with unsafe clearance); Bull 75, U S Bureau of Mines, recommends refuge bays with 2.5 ft clearance at not less than 300-ft intervals; (e) keep track tamped and clean, to prevent derailment; (f) timber and supplies, stored alongside, should be at least 2 ft from rail; (g) transport long tools and material only on special trucks, not on locomotive or ore cars; (*h*) use block fillers to top of rail-web in flangeways and wedge spaces in frogs and switches; (*i*) use low-voltage trolley current; support wire at short distances, so that sag will not exceed 3 in, and, when less than 8.5 ft above rails, guard with boxing 3 in lower than wire; do not run wire over footway side of track; avoid trolley system for low-roofed, wet workings; (*j*) have gong on all motors, and start locomotive only on signal from trip rider and after giving warning bell, and sound bell before all junctions; (*k*) keep car doors and latches in repair and inspect reclosing; an open side door is especially dangerous; (*l*) keep record of haulage delays, and offer bonus to driver having minimum derailments and locomotive repairs. In mines of large output, where many trains operate on main levels, a dispatching and block-signal system are essential (75, 77–80).

BIBLIOGRAPHY

(*A*) Trans A I M E.   (*B*) Mining Congress Journal.   (*C*) Coal Age.   (*E*) Eng & Mining Journal. (*I C*) Information Circular, Bur of Mines.   (*M*) Mining and Met.   (*R I*) Report of Investigation, Bureau of Mines

General

1. Notes on Underground Transport. C. F. Jackson.   (*I C*) 6326 (Revised)
2. Mine Plant. B. F. Tilson.   (*A*) 1938
3. Mine Haulage. A. Crawford.   *Bull* Dept of Mining, Univ West Va, 1925
4. A Study of Coal Mine Haulage in Illinois. H. H. Stoek and others.   Univ of Ill Exper Sta, *Bull* 132 (1922)

Mine Cars

5. Catalogs: Atlas Car & Mfg, Austin-Western Road Mchy, Enterprise Wheel & Car, Fairmont Mining Mchy, Hockensmith Wheel & Mine Car, Hyatt Roller Bearing, Kilbourne & Jacobs, Koppel Div Pressed Steel Car, Mt Vernon Car Mfg, Sanford-Day, Watt Mining Car Wheel
6. Mine Cars. A. H. Hubbell.   (*E*) General discussion of types and sizes, Vol 128, p 400; Granby type, Vol 130, p 225; rocker dump and gable bottom, p 332; rigid body, rotary dump, p 560; bottom and end-dump, Vol 131, p 162
7. Colliery Car Designs. (*a*) Lynch Ky. H. B. Eavenson.   (*A*) Vol 66, p 680; (*b*) New Orient, Ill. A. Allen.   (*A*) Vol 72, p 810
8. Notes on Mine Cars. J. McCrystle.   Coal Mining, Vol 7, p 580.   (*a*) Bigger and Better Cars Needed in Modern Mines. G. A. Richardson.   (*C*) Vol 35, p 668; (*b*) Bigger Cars Cut Cost. F. S. Folansbee.   (*C*) Vol 36, p 628
9. New Mine Cars Raise Mine and per Man Output at Summerlee Shaft.   (*C*) Vol 41, p 20
10. Capacity and Design of Mine Cars. C. E. Watts.   (*B*) Vol 14, p 608
11. Mine Car Couplings.   (*M*) Vol 30, p 474 (see also 1, 2, 3)

Mine Track

12. American Recommended Practice, Frogs, Switches and Turnouts for Coal Mine Tracks.   (*B*) 1936
13. Location and Construction of Mine Track. J. McCrystle.   (*C*) Vol 12, serial, p 146
14. Track Charts. S. C. Mifflen.   (*E*) Vol 130, Track Turnout Chart, p 179.   Track Curvature Chart, p 237
15. Copper Bearing Steel Rails for Mine Use. J. C. Greenan.   (*E*) Vol 134, p 364
16. Treated Ties at Royalton Energy Mines Show Savings.   (*C*) Vol 40, p 245
17. Treated Ties and Timbers at Ziegler a Real Economy.   (*B*) Feb, 1938, p 15
18. Economy of Steel Ties Proved at Scarbro Mine. A. R. Long.   (*C*) Vol 36, p 483
19. Permanent Haulways at Clyde Mines, Pa.   (*C*) Vol 41, p 362
20. Track shifting Machine. Gail Martin.   (*E*) Vol 123, p 571; Vol 125, p 743
21. Hanna Mine Proves Efficiency of Welded Track. J. H. Edwards.   (*C*) Vol 41, p 137
22. Track Welding at New Monarch Mine, Ill. C. C. Conway.   (*C*) Vol 41, p 275
23. Aligning Short Radius Curves. J. Edwin.   (*E*) Vol 131, p 25
24. Modern Mine Tracks. G. A. Richardson.   (*B*) Vol 15, p 295
24a. Shaft- and Slope-bottom Lay-outs at Coal Mines. R. L. Anderson.   (*I C*) 6949

Tractive Resistance

25. Effect of Anti-friction Bearings. P. B. Liebermann.   (*A*) Vol 55, p 24; Vol 57, p 486
26. Curve Resistance and Track Spread on Sharp Turns. J. D. Martin.   (*C*) Sep 6, 1923
27. Mine Car Friction as Influenced by Wheel Diameters and Bearings. U S Bur Mines tests. M. D. Hersey and others.   Mining and Met Investigations, Carnegie Inst of Tech, *Bull* 13, 20
28. Speeding the Wheels of Production, a Symposium of Roller and Ball Bearings.   (*B*) July, 1937, p 49
29. Low Tractive Resistance of Roller-Bearing Mine Cars. *Revue de l'Industrie Minerale,* Sep 15, 1934, p 465

Hand Loading, Tramming and Dumping

30. A Study of Shoveling as Applied to Mining. G. T. Harley.   (*A*) Vol 61, p 147
31. Hints on Equipping for Hand Tramming. L. Eaton.   (*E*) Vol 134, p 369
32. Rotary Dumps.   (*C*) Vol 25, pp 86, 776.   Catal Car Dumper & Equipment Co, Chicago
33. Car Dumpers. Allen & Garcia.   (*A*) Vol 66, p 382
34. See Bib 2, pp 291–295

Animal Haulage
35. Mine Mules and Their Care. J. C. Newhard. *Mines & Minerals*, Vol 28, p 56
36. Underground Stables. *Mines & Minerals*, Vol 26, pp 149, 444
37. Mule Haulage in Metal Mines. W. F. Boericke. (*E*) Vol 112, p 853
38. Feeds and Feeding. Henry and Morrison. Book, 20th edition

Locomotive Haulage
39. Mine Locomotive Catalogs: Atlas Car & Mfg, H. K. Porter, Jeffrey Mfg Co, Whitcomb Locomotive, Baker Raulong, Elwell-Parker Electric, Goodman Mfg Co, Mancha Storage Battery Locomotive Co, Vulcan, Gifford Wood
40. Locomotive Charts. S. C. Mifflen. (*E*) Loco Wt Chart to find trailing load any loco will handle, Vol 126, p 505; H P Chart, p 599; Battery Loco Chart, Vol 133, p 269
41. Cost of Storage Battery, Compressed Air and Gasoline Loco Transport. M. J. Elsing. (*E*) Vol 134, p 191; of Trolley Transport, p 145; of Mine Transport, p 101
42. Modern Methods of Loco Traction in Mines. *Mine & Quarry Eng*, Nov, 1936, p 203
43. Locomotive Data. Baldwin Locomotive Works, Phila
44. Compressed Air Haulage. H. K. Porter Co, Pittsburgh
45. Compressed Air Plant. Robert Peele, Pub John Wiley & Sons N Y, 5th ed, 1930
46. Storage Battery Locomotive Haulage. C. E. Stuart. (*A*) Vol 68, p 153
47. Centralization of Ore Delivery at the Compañia de Real del Monte y Pachuca, Mex. H. I. Altshuler. (*A*) Vol 109, p 78
48. Battery *vs* Cable Reel Locomotive Haulage. B. F. Grimm. (*C*) Vol 40, p 327
49. Storage Batteries in Illinois Mines. (*C*) Vol 36, pp 355, 475

Rope Haulage
50. Underground Haulage of Coal by Wire Rope. W. Hildenbrand. Trenton Iron Works
51. Multiple Rope Haulage in the Tri-State District. S. S. Clarke. (*B*) Feb, 1938, p 18
52. Rope Haulage. L. Eaton. (*E*) Vol 134, p 424

Haulage Operations
53. Mine Haulage Systems. (*M*) Vol 30, p 260
54. Centralization of Ore Delivery at the Compañia de Real del Monte y Pachuca. H. I. Altshuler. (*A*) Vol 109, p 78
55. Electric Haulage in Butte Mines. C. D. Woodward. (*A*) Vol 68, p 101
56. Ore Transport at Alaska-Juneau mine. (*M*) Vol 31, p 94
57. Transport at Consolidation Coal Co. (*C*) Vol 35, p 585
58. Development of Mine Transport in Clifton-Morenci District. N. Carmichael and J. Kiddie. (*A*) Vol 70, p 826
59. Haulage Record at Lehigh Navigation Collieries. I. A. Given. (*C*) Vol 40, p 403
60. Haulage and Hoisting Practice, Miami Copper Co. R. W. Hughes. (*B*) Sep, 1936, p 64; also F. W. Maclennan. (*A*) Vol 1930, p 66; J. J. Luchessa and W. G. Wilson. (*M*) Vol 15, p 365
61. Mining Methods and Costs at McIntyre-Porcupine Mine. H. G. Skavlem. (*I C*) 6741
62. Underground Transport at Morenci. T. W. Maclellan. (*A*) Vol 1930, p 66
63. Mining Methods and Costs at Tezuitlan Copper Mine, Puebla, Mex. E. P. Heriod. (*I C*) 6735
64. Recent Developments in Underground Transport. B. F. Tillson. (*M*) Vol 8, p 209
65. Underground Haulage and Power Distribution at United Verde mine. E. W. Fredell. (*B*) Vol 16, p 335
66. Transport in Zinc Mines of East Tennessee. H. A. Coy. (*E*) Vol 130, p 48
67. Hauling Morenci's Muck. M. C. Pellish. (*B*) Vol 17, p 389
68. Fast and Efficient Haulage. Size of trolley locos and H P per ton wt doubled since introduction. *Jour* Am Mining Cong, July, 1938, p 18
69. Trip Dispatching at Hamilton Mines, Ala. *Jour* Am Mining Cong, May, 1938, p 34
70. Automatic Block Signals for Mine Haulage Systems. C. E. Watts. *Jour* Am Mining Cong, Vol 14, p 608
71. Moving Crippled Mine Cars at St Joe Lead Co. (*E*) Vol 138, p 38

Safety
72. Coal-Mine Accidents in U S, 1935. *Bull* 409, U S Bur Mines
73. Metal-Mine Accidents in U S, 1935. *Bull* 410, U S Bur Mines
74. Hauling Coal Safely with Permissible Storage-battery Locomotives. C. W. Owings. (*R I*) 3031
75. Safety in Utah Coal Mine Haulage. D. J. Parker. (*I C*) 6242
76. Safety with Haulage Practice in Alabama Coal Mines. F. E. Cash. (*I C*) 6243
77. Some Suggestions on Safety in Coal Mine Haulage. C. A. Herbert. (*I C*) 6969
78. See also under Haulage Operations (also Bib 4 to 6)
79. Mine Haulage on Schedule. A. F. Brosky. (*C*) Vol 28, p 555
80. Safety Requirement booklets published by Anaconda Copper Co, Oliver Iron Mining Co and others

SECTION 12

HOISTING PLANT, SHAFT POCKETS AND ORE BINS

BY

WILLIAM M. WEIGEL

REVISED FOR THE THIRD EDITION

BY

PHILIP B. BUCKY, E M,

ASSOCIATE PROFESSOR OF MINING,

SCHOOL OF MINES, COLUMBIA UNIVERSITY

Note.—Numbers in parentheses in text refer to Bibliography at end of this section.

HOISTING PLANT, SHAFT POCKETS AND ORE BINS

1. HOISTING SYSTEMS

Unbalanced hoisting is done in one-compartment shafts, where there is no descending wt of empty car and cage to help lift the ascending cage, car and contents. It is the simplest form of hoist, and is used for prospecting, handling men and supplies, and for mines with small outputs.

Balanced hoisting is done in two-compartment shafts, where the wt of ascending skip, or cage and car, and material is offset by empty skip, or cage and car, descending in the other compartment. It may be used with all shapes of drum or reels, and is the commonest method. With cylindrical drums it is very flexible. For hoisting from one level, 1 or 2 drums are keyed to the shaft. For hoisting from several levels, 2 drums are necessary, one of them clutched and the other keyed or clutched. Advantages: simplicity, low first cost, and adaptability to variation in hoisting conditions. Disadvantage is the large variation in rope load in deep shafts.

Slack-rope hoisting (3), practiced in a few coal mines for self-dumping cages, consists in operating with a certain amount of slack rope, so that one cage strikes bottom and its empty car is uncaged, and a loaded car is caged while the cage in the other compartment is dumping its load, the hoist being at rest only momentarily. The motor must therefore start the loaded cage without the counterbalancing effect of the empty cage and car after landing at the bottom, thus requiring a larger motor and greater power. Its purpose, to increase the tonnage output per unit time, is questionable, since time for retardation is longer. It is not recommended.

Static hoisting moment is the product of load on rope in lb and the drum radius in ft, at the point where the rope leaves the drum. Resultant static moments for balanced hoisting are equal to the difference of the moments for each rope. STATIC MOMENT DIAGRAMS show resultant static hoisting moments for definite positions of cage or skip in a shaft (see Fig 14). Serving to compare hoisting systems from standpoint of balance, they are not always indicative of relative power requirements, because equalization of hoisting load may be obtained by using additional weights in drums and tail-rope, requiring large h p for acceleration. If W = wt of skip or cage and car; w = wt of load; wr = wt of rope; and R = radius of cylindrical drum; then for balanced hoisting with cylindrical drums:

$$\text{Static moment, load at bottom} = (W + w + wr - W)\,R = (w + wr)\,R$$
$$\text{Static moment, load at top} = (W + w - wr - W)\,R = (w - wr)R$$

Tail rope, used with cylindrical drum, gives perfect equalization throughout the hoist. It hangs in a loop in the shaft, its ends being attached to bottoms of cages. The cages can not move independently, as for hoisting from different levels, whence its chief use is in shafts where hoisting is from one level only (2). A large sheave, resting in the bight of the tail rope, and supported in sliding bearings below bottom landing, steadies the rope.

While theoretically good, the tail rope has been rarely used in the U S. There are a few in South Africa (1), but they are not favored, due to difficulties of inspection, cost (due to short life), lashing and vibration, and extra weight and space required for bottom sheaves (Fig 1, 2, 4).

Counterweight hoisting. The skip, or cage and car, in a one-compartment shaft is counterbalanced by a weight sliding in guides at one side of the shaft. Advantages: it eliminates one compartment, increases efficiency, decreases size of engine required, but requires a reversible engine, since power is necessary to lift the counterweight.

Design. As ordinarily designed, the static hoisting moment diagrams for lowering empty and raising loads are the same. Hence, the resultant static moment with load at bottom must equal that with counterweight at bottom. If C equals wt of counterweight and other symbols are as for static moments, then

$$\text{Static-moment, load at bottom} \qquad = (W + w + wr)\,R - CR \qquad (1)$$
$$\text{Static-moment, counterweight at bottom} = (C + wr)\,R - WR \qquad (2)$$

Equating Eq 1 and 2 gives $C = W + \dfrac{w}{2}$, which means that if the wt of counterweight equals wt of skip (W) plus $1/2$ wt of load $\left(\dfrac{w}{2}\right)$, then the hoisting and lowering diagrams will be equal.   COUNTERWEIGHT PLUS TAIL ROPE give perfect equalization of rope load. If the counterweight is equal to $W + \dfrac{w}{2}$ then the unbalanced load, whether hoisting load or counterweight and, in all positions of hoist, is $\dfrac{w}{2}$ or one half the weight of the ore.   This therefore is an economical hoisting method from the power standpoint and has application for small capacities.   COUNTERWEIGHT PLUS CHAIN HOISTING is intended to do away with tail-rope.   A chain, attached to the counterweight, piles up on the shaft bottom as counterweight is lowered.   It has merit in reducing hoisting power required, but adds to stress in hoisting rope, and is not used at present.

Koepe system of hoisting (Fig 1).   In this old European system, which has not been used in America, the drum is replaced by a large, single-groove driving sheave.   A single rope passes around 190° to 200° of sheave circumference, with cages attached to the ends.

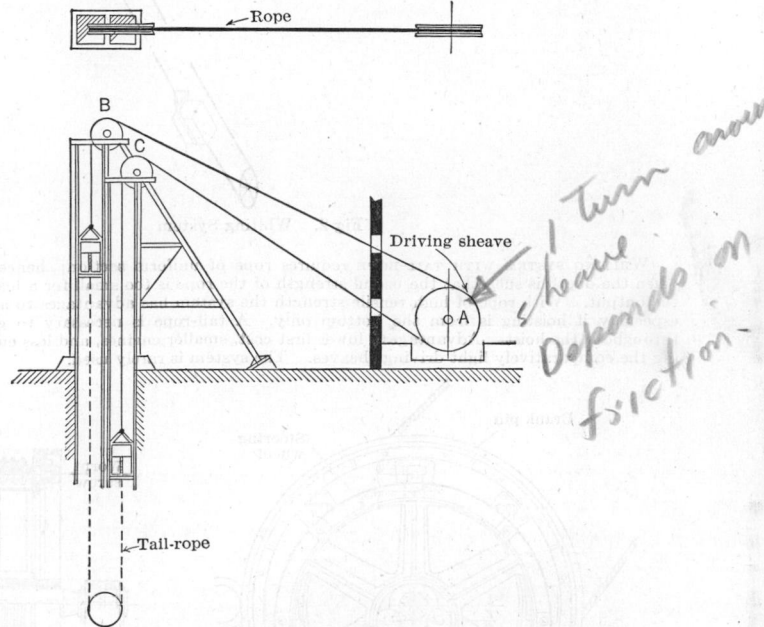

Fig 1.   Diagram of Koepe Hoist

The system is suited only to mines of one level, and a tail-rope is essential.   Head sheaves are placed tandem, so that both parts of hoisting rope are in same vertical plane.   To prevent slippage of rope on driving sheave, the wt on loaded side plus its accelerating force must not exceed wt on empty side minus its accelerating force by more than a certain percentage, depending on arc of contact on driving sheave and coef of friction.   Ratio of the greater to the smaller pull must not exceed e^{fa}, in which e is the base of Nap log (2.71828), a the angle of contact on driving sheave, and f the coef of friction (0.18 to 0.25).   Advantages: since in the sheave there is less mass to be accelerated and retarded than in a drum, more rapid accel and retardation are possible, smaller foundations and buildings are required, and wear on rope due to bending is minimized.   Disadvantages: cages can not move independently; if rope breaks both cages fall, and drag of rope over the head sheaves is likely to prevent operation of safety catches.   The system is best suited to electric hoists, which have constant torque (4).

Whiting system (Fig 2), designed to overcome the disadvantages of the Koepe system, has three 3 to 5-grooved driving sheaves, placed tandem and coupled to engine by connecting and parallel rods.   The rope has ample frictional grip by passing several times around both sheaves.   To adjust or change distance between cages, or let out rope as shaft is deepened, a slow-motion geared fleeting engine is used.   Abnormal stresses, due to creep of rope on sheaves and to unequal wear of grooves, are compensated by steel rings in the grooves of one sheave. The rings slip under unusual stress, but are tight enough to resist the ordinary rope pull. Advantages: tail-rope is unnecessary to prevent slipping; can be used for sinking and for shafts that are periodically deepened.

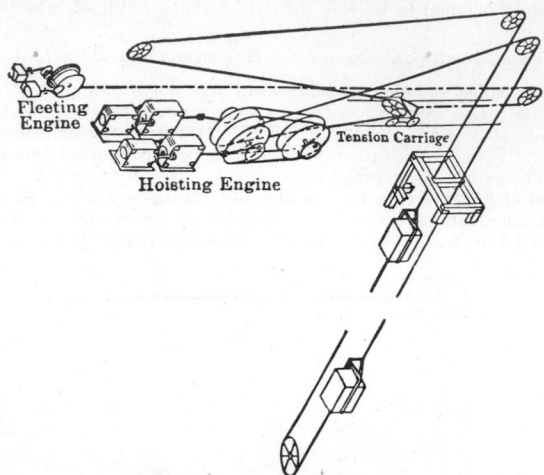

Fig 2. Whiting System

WHITING SYSTEM WITH TAIL-ROPE requires rope of uniform section; hence is not applicable when the depth is such that the useful strength of the rope is too small for a load required to give the output. With rope of high tensile strength the system has advantages to a depth of 6 000 ft, especially if hoisting is from the bottom only. A tail-rope is necessary to give constant load throughout the hoist. Advantages: lower first cost, smaller engines, and less energy for accelerating the comparatively light driving sheaves. The system is rarely used.

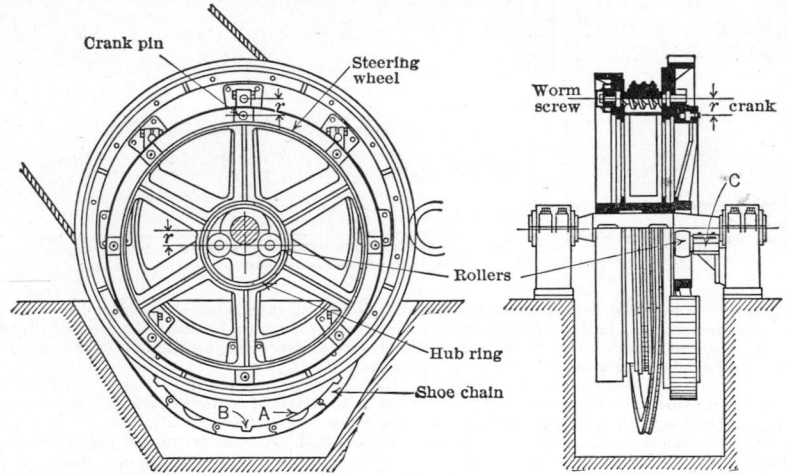

Fig 3. Ohnesorge Driving Sheave with Endless Shoe Chain. (*E & M Jour*)

Koepe hoist with Ohnesorge sheave (Fig 3) (5). This recent modification provides for a number of rope wraps on the driving sheave; the rope is kept in the center line of the sheave, and travels in a vertical plane over the head sheaves. There is a set of independent, semicircular grooves in the form of an endless shoe-chain, set spirally in a number of turns on the sheave face. For 1 1/2 rope turns, there are 3 chain turns on the sheave; for 2 1/2 rope turns, 4 chain turns. Inside projections A (Fig 3) of the chain links fit in threads of worm-screws, and rectangular recesses B fit on a rectangular cleat on sheave face, which keep the chain from slipping. A number of worm-screws on sheave periphery engage inside the face with certain links of the chain. Pitch of worm equals width of chain link, and one side of each worm-shaft ends in a crank of radius r. A single eccentric steering wheel, hanging freely from the ends of this crank, revolves with main sheave about its own axis, and is kept in position by small rollers, revolving in bearings c, which are integral parts of main sheave bearings. As the worm-screws thus make one complete revolution in a direction opposite to that in which the rope would tend to travel, due to direction of rotation of main sheave, there is no fleet angle.

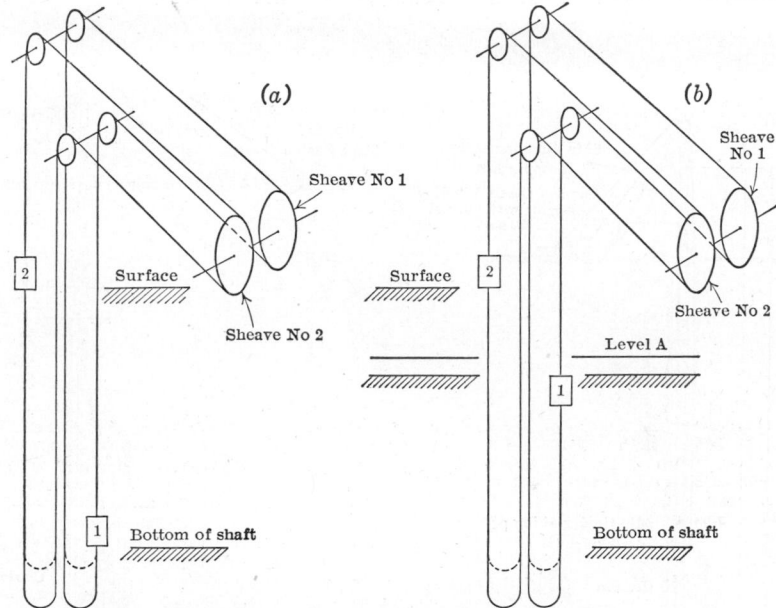

Fig 4. Diagram of Ohnesorge System for Hoisting from Different Levels. (*E & M Jour*)

Advantages. Since the frictional grip of rope on the Ohnesorge sheave may be varied at will by controlling the number of rope turns, it permits: (1) high-speed hoisting; (2) greater acceleration; (3) elimination of tail-rope, if desirable; (4) hoisting of light or heavy loads; (5) perfect rope lubrication; (6) a smaller sheave than the regular Koepe; (7) hoisting from different levels, as in Fig 4, where 2 Ohnesorge sheaves are clutched on the same shaft. [Skip 1 is at the bottom, skip 2, at top. Counterclockwise sheave rotation causes skip 1 to rise and 2 to descend. To hoist in balance from an intermediate level, place skip 2 on rope of sheave 2 and unclutch sheave; then pull skip 1 to level desired. Clutch sheave 2 and proceed to hoist in balance]; (8) permits occasional cutting off a piece of rope near cage or skip, for testing; (9) may be operated with 2 or more ropes, making it also suitable for elevators. Costs in Germany, 1932: for 40-in diam driving sheave and 1-in rope, with 3 turns of shoe chain, $700; for 8.2 ft sheave and 1.6-in rope, with 3 turns of shoe chain, $2 900. An extra shoe-chain turn on 40-in sheave adds $50 to cost; an extra shoe-chain turn on 8.2-ft sheave adds $150.

Tandem system of hoisting in deep shafts (Fig 5) consists in having 2 skips in the same compartment, the upper skip with a rope equal to half the depth of shaft, the lower with its rope attached to bottom of upper skip. Upper skip receives its load from pockets at middle point of shaft, into which the lower skip dumps. Both are loaded and dumped simultaneously. The upper rope carries its own weight and that of both skips. Both ropes may be tapered. The drums need be only large enough to hold rope equal to half the total depth. With conical drums, the ratio of small to large diam is less than with a single lift, and the moment of inertia of drums is thus reduced. There is a theoretical economy in steam consumption of about 9% over hoisting in a single lift, and the hoist is smaller, with consequent lower first cost. Offsetting this is the cost of extra loading pockets, shaft arrangements and labor attendance.

Two-stage hoisting (Fig 6) requires 2 engines, one hoisting from the bottom and dumping into a bin at an intermediate station, from which the other engine hoists to the surface. The engines may be duplicates, by which first cost is materially reduced. With conical drums (Art 2) this condition may make it necessary to sacrifice equality of static moments. The two lifts must overlap by about 65 ft. This system gives better steam economy than the single lift, by about 10.5%, but against this is increased cost of shaft construction and extra attendance at surface and intermediate station.

This is the commonest system for deep hoisting, especially where the shaft changes from vert to inclined. Engine for the lower lift is usually placed in an underground station, and driven by elec, sometimes by compressed air, steam being out of the question. Even with elec hoists special ventilation is necessary, due to the heat generated.

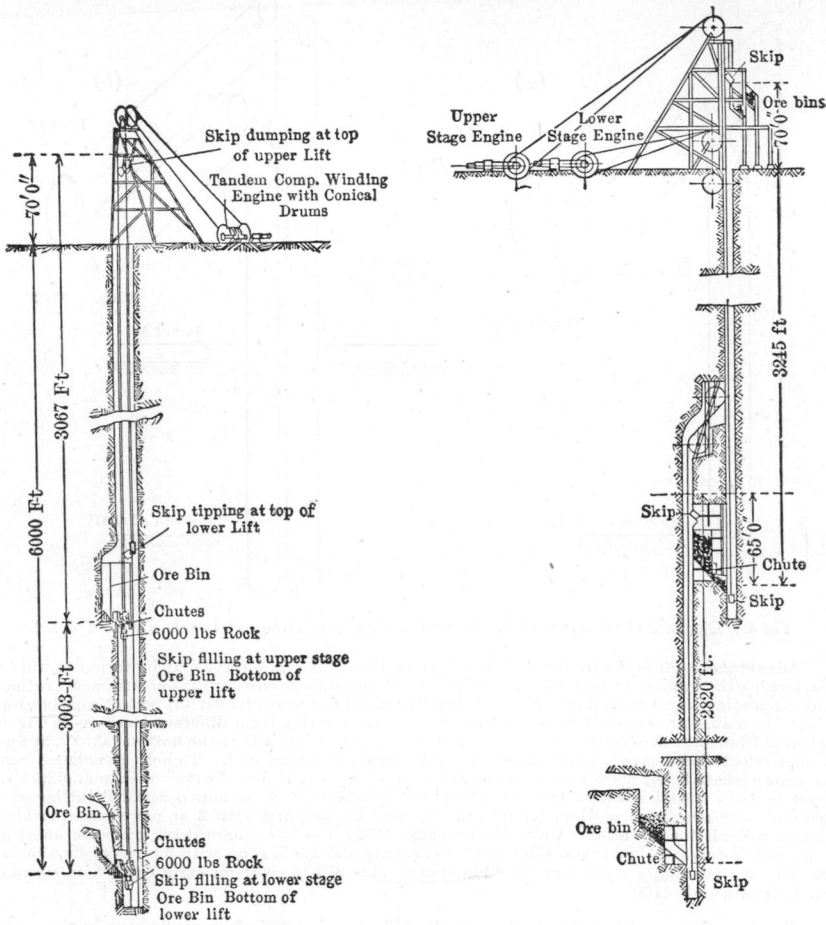

Fig 5. Hoisting in Tandem

Fig 6. Two-stage Hoisting

Single-lift, tandem, and two-stage systems compared. SINGLE LIFT. Advantages: simplicity, flexibility, absence of attendance at intermediate station and elimination of cost of this station. Disadvantages: high first cost, on account of large engines and drums; excessive ratio of end diameters; danger of whipping of the ropes; increase in cost of headframe; engines are proportionately less economical when handling men, tools, and supplies. TANDEM SYSTEM. Advantages: smaller size of engines and very much better ratio of end diameters of drum, thus reducing first cost; engines more economical; no whipping of ropes; may be used for greater depths than single-lift system; steam demands on boilers are more equally distributed than in single-lift system. Disadvantages: extra first cost of, and attendance at, intermediate station; high cost and size of headframe; lack of flexibility, so that the system is not suited to sinking, or hoisting from different levels. Two-STAGE SYSTEM. Advantages: greater flexibility than the single lift; favorable drum proportions (equal to the tandem system); tail ropes could be used in both upper and lower stages; use of brakes is attended with less loss of energy; is suitable for sinking; hoisting may be done by either stage from intermediate levels, without interfering with operation of other stage; first cost of 2 small engines is probably not much greater than 1 large engine, for a single lift; engine for upper stage could be installed first, and second

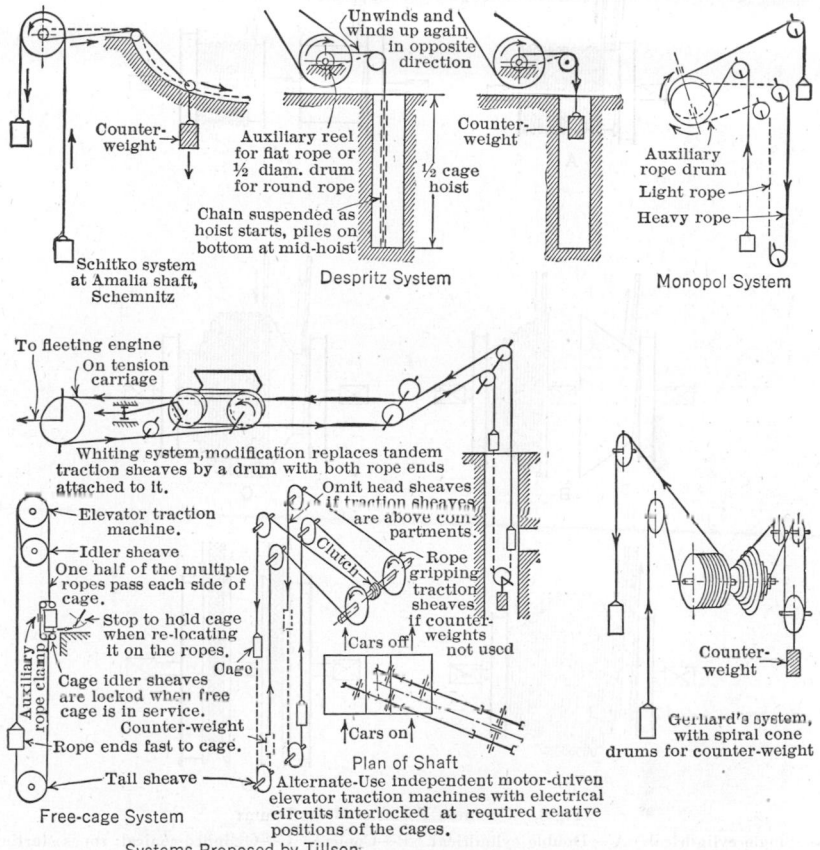

Fig 7. Miscellaneous Hoisting Systems (37)

engine not purchased until needed; steam demand on boilers is more uniform, requiring smaller boiler plant.

Other hoisting systems (37), the Schitko, Despritz, Monopol, Gerhard and Tillson, are modifications of the preceding; diagrammatically shown in Fig 7.

2. HOISTING DRUMS

Drums (3) may be cylindrical, conical, cylindro-conical, or reel (Fig 8).

Cylindrical-drum hoists may have: (*a*) one drum, keyed to driving shaft; (*b*) two drums, both keyed to shaft; (*c*) two drums, 1 clutched and 1 keyed; (*d*) two drums, both clutched. Keyed drums are used for single-level mines; clutched drums, for hoisting from more than one level and for adjusting rope stretch. (A novel design is shown in Fig 9 (6). The drums are bi-cylindro-conical, mounted on parallel shafts geared together and driven by motors coupled to the gear pinions.) Drums have flanges to prevent rope running off end. Winding surface may be smooth, grooved, or lagged with wood. A smooth surface causes rope to chafe and wear. With wood lagging, there is less wear, as rope makes its own groove. Grooved metal drums are best. The winding of rope on itself (in more than one layer) is poor practice, and rarely admissible. BRAKE SURFACE forms part of the drum, and is of a diam and width sufficient for the hoisting load. MINIMUM DRUM

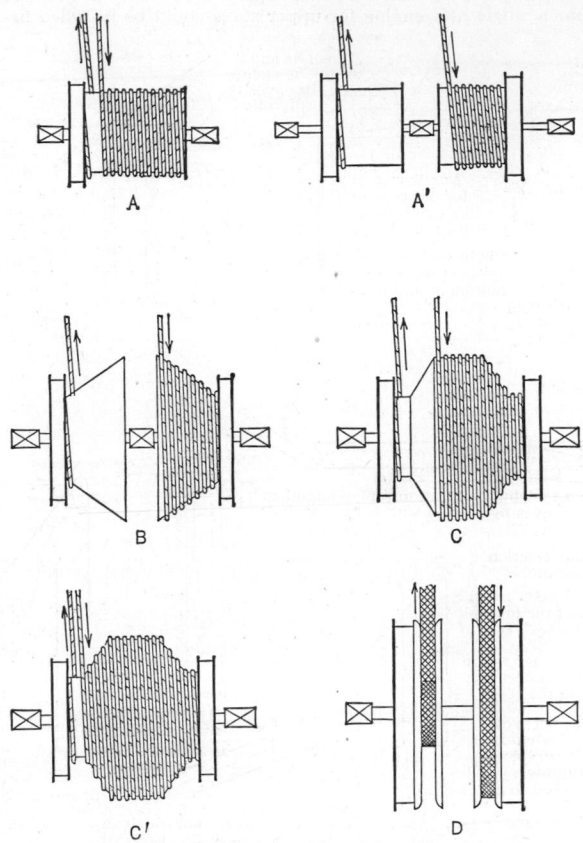

Fig 8.   Common Forms of Hoist Drums

A—Single cylindrical. A'—Double cylindrical. B—Conical. C—Cylindro-conical; ropes starting on different diams.   C'—Cylindro-conical; ropes starting on same diams.   D—Reels

DIAMETER, D, is at least 60 times rope diam r (in) ; general ratios are: 70 in coal mines and 85 in metal mines.   If $L =$ length of rope, and N the number of turns of rope on drum,

$$N = \frac{L}{\pi(D + r)} \tag{3}$$

Allow 2 extra turns to protect rope fastenings, and 2 turns against overwinding; then, length (W) of a smooth-face drum between flanges $= (N + 4) \times r$ $\tag{4}$

For a grooved drum, allow $1/4$ in between adjacent coils of rope; then,

$$W = (N + 4) \times (r + 1/4 \text{ in}) \tag{5}$$

Conical drum.   In theory, the varying radius of a conical drum should be such that the static hoisting moment is constant.   But this is true only when the element of the conoidal surface is a curved line.   Curve-faced drums are costly and difficult to make, and are not used.   A single, straight-faced cone gives perfect equalization only at beginning and end of hoist (Fig 10); moments at all intermediate points exceed the end moments.   A pair of cone drums (in double compartment shaft) equalize also at passing point of cages (Fig 11); at all other points, equalization is only approximate.   To design a conical drum, depth of shaft, weight of cage, car, ore, and size and weight of rope

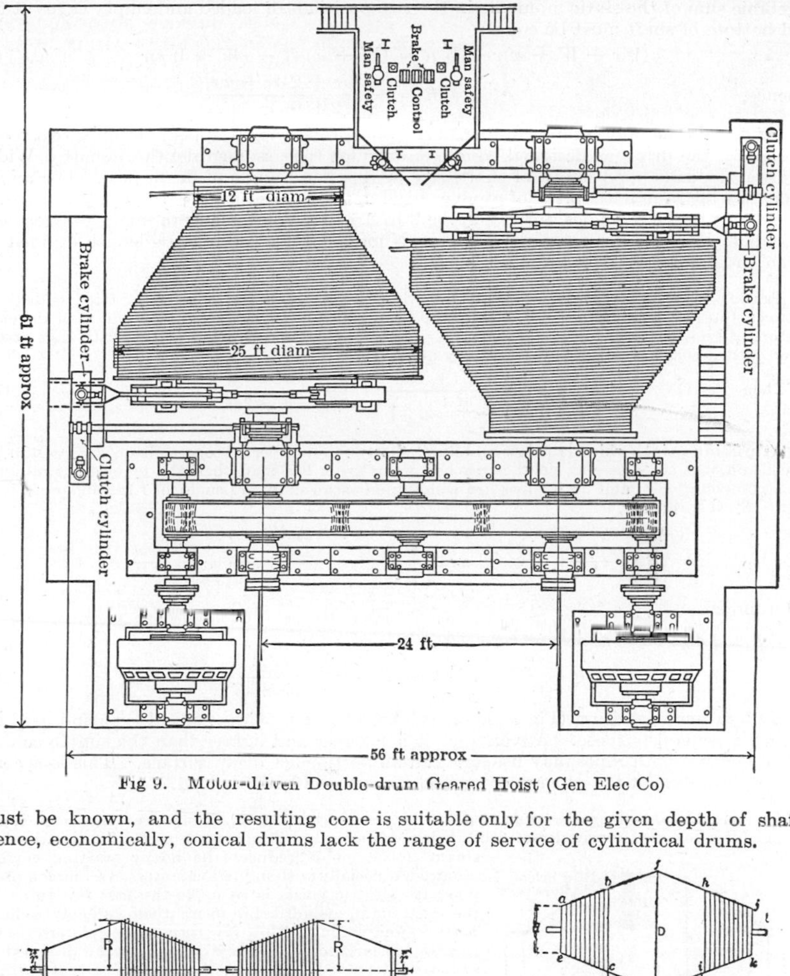

Fig 9.   Motor-driven Double-drum Geared Hoist (Gen Elec Co)

must be known, and the resulting cone is suitable only for the given depth of shaft. Hence, economically, conical drums lack the range of service of cylindrical drums.

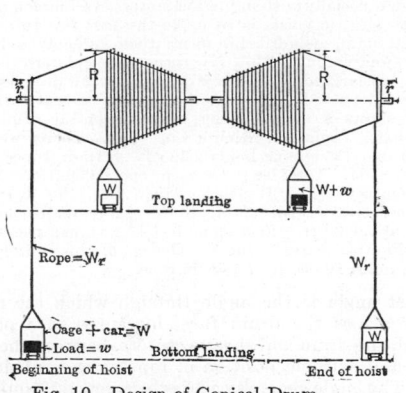

Fig. 10   Design of Conical Drum

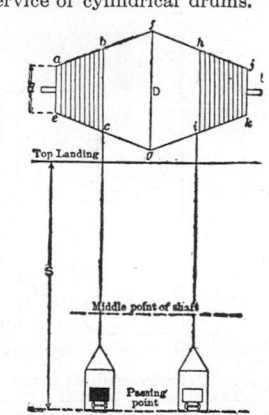

Fig 11.   Passing Point of Cages

Design.   Assume small diam of drum, which should generally be not less than 60 times diam of rope (Art 5 and 7).   Let R = radius large end of drum, ft; r = radius small end of drum, ft; Wr = wt of one rope between top and bottom landings, lb; W = wt of cage and car, or skip, lb; w = wt of ore, lb. From Fig 10, to fulfill the conditions, the algebraic sum of the static moments in the two positions of loaded and empty cages at top and bottom of shaft must be equal:

$$(Wr + W + w)r - WR = (W + w)R - (W + Wr)r \tag{6}$$

whence,
$$R = \frac{r(2Wr + 2W + w)}{2W + w} \tag{7}$$

in which R is the only unknown quantity. Since rope weight appears in only two terms of Eq (6), the drum as designed equalizes only for the assumed depth of shaft. Width of drum depends upon depth of shaft, size of rope, and angle of drum face. For angles under say 30°, the horiz pitch of grooves need not be more than $1/8$ to $1/4$ in greater than rope diam; for large angles, pitch may be 2 to 2.5 times rope diam, to make grooves deep enough to prevent displacement of rope. Number of grooves = rope length divided by mean circumference of drum.

Passing point of cages. Let S = distance of passing point below surface, ft; l = distance between top and bottom landings, ft; d and D = respectively small and large diam of drum at bottom of groove, ft; a = rope diam, ft; n = number coils of rope on one drum with cage at top (2 or 3 extra coils at each end being usually allowed).

Then (Fig 11)
$$n = \frac{l}{\pi\left(\dfrac{D+d}{2} + a\right)} = \frac{2l}{\pi(D + d + 2a)} \tag{7a}$$

At passing point (which is below middle of shaft) the number of rope coils on $abce$ = number of coils on $bfgc$, since passing point is reached when drum has made half the revolutions required for a complete hoist, and both ropes are winding on mean diam. Length of rope unwound from $bfgc$ = S, whence:

$$S = \frac{\pi(bc + fg)}{2} \times \frac{n}{2} \quad \text{and} \quad \frac{bc + fg}{2} = \frac{\dfrac{d+D}{2} + D}{2} + \frac{3D + d}{4}$$

Substituting,
$$S = \frac{\pi n}{8}(3D + d) \tag{8}$$

If D and d be taken as diam of rope coils,

$$n = \frac{2l}{\pi(D + d)}, \quad \text{whence,} \quad S = \frac{l}{4}\frac{(3D + d)}{(D + d)} \tag{9}$$

Cylindro-conical drum (Fig 8, 9, 12) is a modification of the conical type and used for the same general purpose. Advantage: it is cheaper and lighter than the simple conical drum, because both ropes may use any and all portions of drum surface. This is accomplished, however, at the expense of true equalization of hoisting load.

To increase rate of acceleration, and attain max speed sooner, drums are sometimes coned steeply for a few rev, remainder of drum being cylindrical. This is more useful for electric than steam hoists, as it reduces the heavy starting current required, especially with induction motors. Common practice with electric hoists is to make the first few turns, at the small diam, cylindrical in form; then a steeply-inclined portion, and ending with a few turns on a cylindrical surface at the large diam. Each drum must be designed to suit conditions of load, speed and electric current factors. Fig 12 shows a steam-driven cylindro-conical drum at No 5 shaft, Tamarack Mining Co, Mich. Drum weighs 300 000 lb. Each cone holds 2 125 ft of 1.5-in rope; the center, 3 875 ft. Total length of each rope, 6 000 ft. At No 2 shaft, Quincy mine, Hancock, Mich (23), the drum is cylindro-conical, small diam, 16 ft; large diam, 30 ft; length, about 30 ft. Each cone has 42.5 turns; the common cylindrical part, 76 turns. One cone, plus cylindrical surface, holds 10 000 ft of 1 5/8-in rope.

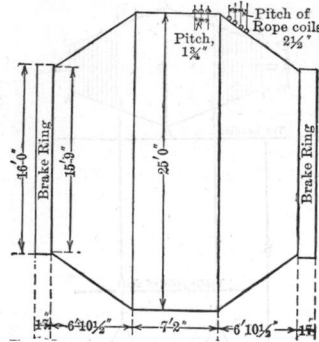

Fig 12.   Cylindro-conical Drum, Tamarack No 5 Shaft

Fleet angle is the angle through which the rope travels across the drum face, measured in a plane through the drum and sheave centers, between sheave center and extreme position of rope at ends of drum face. The angle generally varies between 1.5° and 4°; when excessive, it increases wear on rope and makes even winding on drum difficult. Methods of decreasing fleet angle: (a) increase drum diam, with consequent decrease in length; (b) increase horiz distance between drum and head-sheave; (c) wind rope on drum in more than one layer, or use reels; (*d*) increase height of headframe; (*e*) use Koepe hoisting system, with or without Ohnesorge wheel (Art 1); (*f*) end-lift sheave and drum arrangement (Fig 13). Most common methods are *a* and *b*; *c*, *d*, and *f* are used only under severe topographic conditions; *e*, with Ohnesorge sheave, is used in Europe, but not in U S.

Fleet-angle determination. If *d* = horiz distance between sheave and drum-shaft centers (ft), *h* = vert distance between sheave and drum-shaft centers (ft), *w* = width of drum covered by rope (ft), and *F* = fleet angle, then

$$\tan \frac{F}{2} = \frac{w}{2} \div \sqrt{d^2 + H^2} \qquad (10)$$

Drum and head-sheave arrangements, Fig 13, are referred to as front and end lift. End lift (drum in line with shaft compartments) is used to reduce the fleet angle when required by topographic conditions around collar of shaft.

Reels for flat rope have same effect as conical drums in tending to equalize static hoisting moment. Advantages: small space occupied; smaller cost; due to absence of

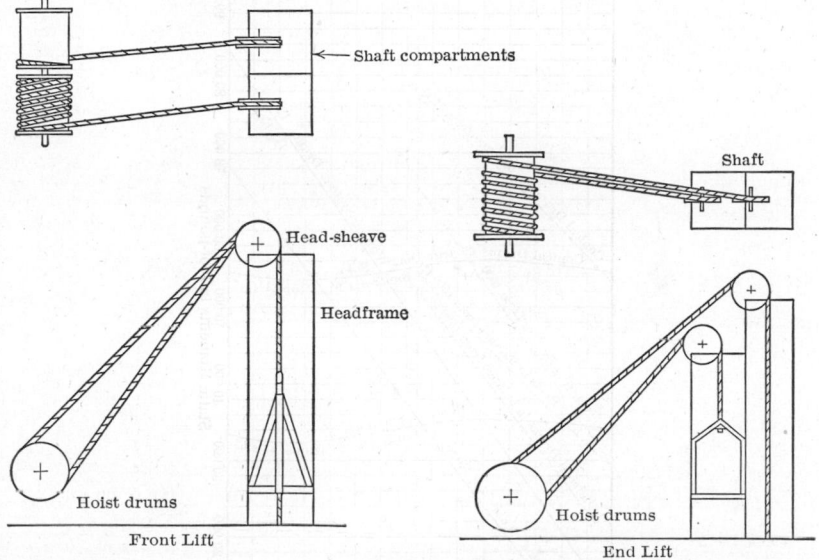

Fig 13.   Diagram of Two Arrangements of Hoist with Reference to Headframe

fleet angle, hoist may be placed close to shaft; weighing less than drums, less power is required for acceleration. Disadvantages: flat rope costs more, is heavier and has shorter life than round rope of same strength. A few reel hoists are still used, but no new installations are being made.

Flat rope (Art 6, 7) increases winding radius at each rev by an increment equal to rope thickness; hence, the result is theoretically the same, and same calculations apply, as for round rope and conical drum. But in making flat rope, practical considerations fix its thickness for a given width, thus modifying the winding increment, so that equalization is even more imperfect than with conical drum. Disadvantage: lack of steadying effect on engine produced by heavier drum (4). Also, rope troubles are serious (Art 7).

Design. Diam of reel hub *d* should be at least 60 times the rope thickness. Having selected rope of proper strength, following are the relations between small and large winding diam *d* and *D*, length of rope *l*, and its thickness *t*, all in in. Annular area between inner and outer surface of coiled rope = *lt*; whence,

$$lt = 0.25 \, \pi \, (D^2 - d^2) \qquad (11)$$

and, if $D = xd,\quad lt = 0.25 \, \pi \, d^2 \, (x^2 - 1)$

whence, $d = \sqrt{\dfrac{lt}{0.25 \, \pi \, (x^2 - 1)}} \qquad (12)$

in which *x* = *D* ÷ *d*, found from Eq 8.   Knowing *d*, *D* = *xd*.

Example. Rope, 2 000 ft = 24 000 in of 4 by 3/8 in, 2.65 lb per ft = 5 320 lb. Ore, 6 000 lb; skip, 3 000 lb. Then $x = (2 \times 3\,000 + 2 \times 5\,320 + 6\,000) \div 2 \times 3\,000 + 6\,000) = 1.88$. Substituting in Eq 13:

$$d = \sqrt{\frac{24\,000 \times 3/8}{0.7854\,(1.88^2 - 1)}} = 67.2 \text{ in} = 5.6 \text{ ft} \qquad (13)$$

Hence, $\qquad D = 1.88\,d = 1.88 \times 67.2 \text{ in} = 10.52 \text{ ft}$

Comparison of systems of equalization. Fig 14 shows static moments for different depths, based on calculations for a 3 000-ft shaft, skip 3 000 lb, ore 8 000 lb; hoisting in balance. Working stress in rope, including bending stresses, is taken at 50 000 lb per sq in of steel section, as near as standard size can be selected. Conditions: Cylindrical

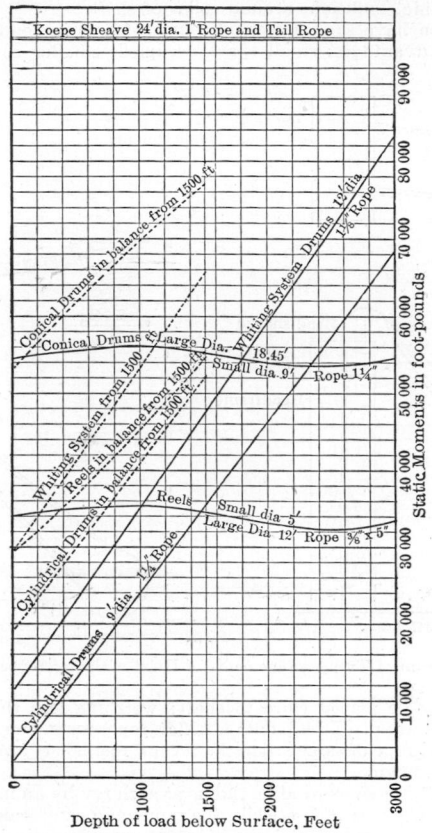

Fig 14. Static Hoisting Moments

drums, 9 ft diam, rope 1.25 in @ 2.45 lb per ft. Conical drums, 9 by 18.45 ft, rope 1.25 in, 69.6 coils. Reels, small diam 60 in, large diam 144 in, rope 3/8 by 5 in @ 3.25 lb per ft, 112.4 coils. Whiting sheaves, 12 ft diam, rope 1 1/8 in @ 2 lb per ft. Koepe sheave, 24 ft diam, rope 1 in @ 1.58 lb per ft, with 1-in tail rope. Thus the Koepe sheave, because of its large diam, requires largest engine; its static moment is greatest, but is uniform. Curves for conical drums and reels show good equalization when hoisting from shaft bottom; but the dotted lines, giving moments when hoisting in balance from half the depth, show that larger engines are necessary for hoisting from intermediate levels in balance than for hoisting from bottom only.

Drum construction. Small drums are cast in one piece, with brake ring and clutch surfaces. Large drums are cast in parts, to prevent shrinkage stresses and for convenience of transport. The shell and flanges may be cast in one piece and each spider separately, or shell itself cast in segments. To reduce wt, the shell may be of steel plate (Fig 14a), and large drums (especially when conical) may be of cast steel instead of iron. If drums are loose on shaft and controlled by clutches the hubs are bushed with brass or bronze.

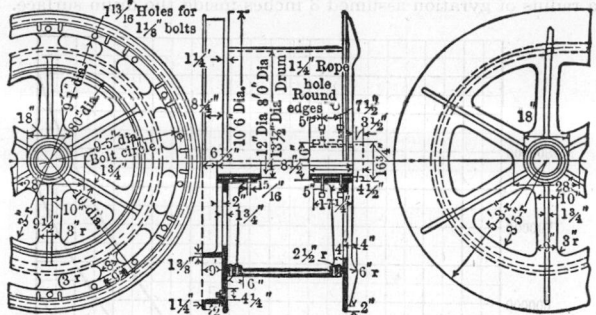

Fig 14a. Drum, 8 ft Diam × 4 ft Face

Main drum may have a small internal drum, on which is wound extra rope to be let out as shaft is deepened. Rope life is increased by grooving the drum.

Drums at Belmont Mine, Butte, Mont (9) are steel plated cylindrical, 12 ft diam by 93 in face. The shells are grooved, fitted on the inside with 3 expandable wedge rings and bolted to CI spiders provided with removable bushings. Drum shell, end rings and spider are made in halves and split

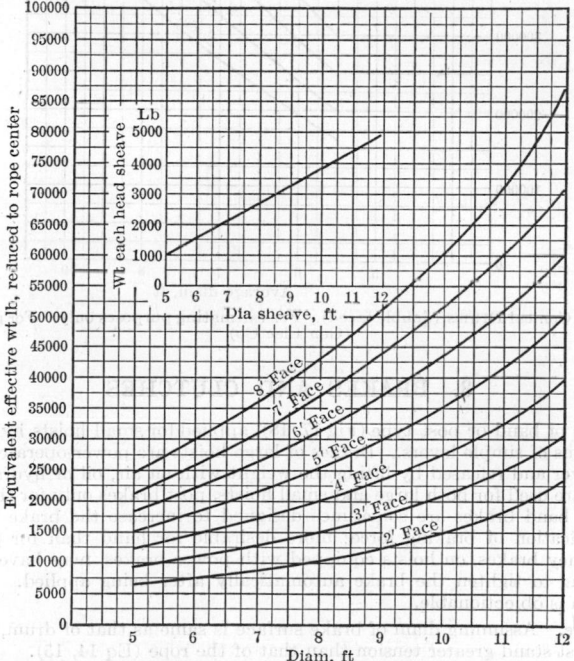

Fig 15. Effective Weight of Drums (Single-cylinder) and Head Sheaves, for Estimating Purposes Only (Gen Elec Co). For gears, add 10%; for double drums, add 100%

parallel to drum-shaft axis. The iron brake and clutch rings are cast integral and bolted to drum end flanges, which are of cast steel. The drum holds 5 500 ft of 1 7/8-in rope in 3 layers.

Inertia effect (3) of the drum, important in calculating duty cycles, is influenced by design and varies with different makers. Hence, for final calculations, the inertia effect

I—35

is determined by the maker. For estimating purposes, Fig 15, 16 are included here, but it should be remembered that the accuracy may not be better than 1 to 2. G. Bright (8) suggests obtaining the inertia of a cylindrical drum by allowing 200 lb per sq ft of drum surface with a radius of gyration assumed 3 inches inside the drum surface.

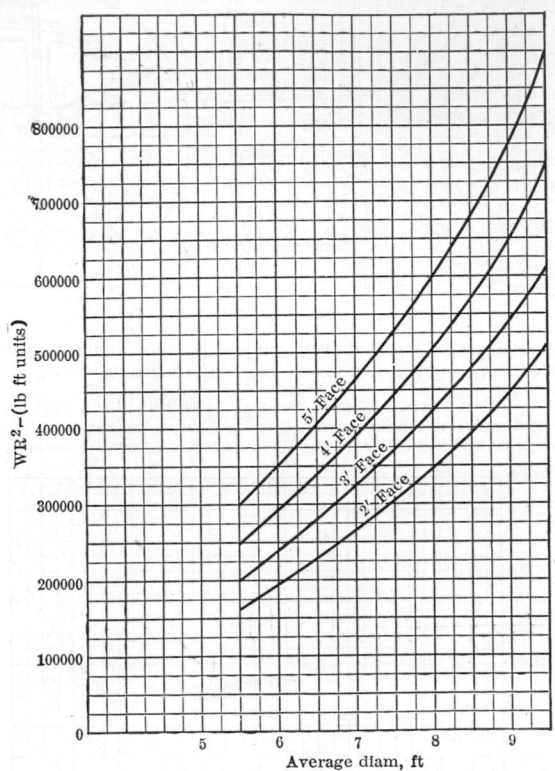

Fig 16. WR² of Conical Drums (double faced). For estimating purposes only. For gears, add 10%. (Gen Elec Co)

3. BRAKES AND CLUTCHES

Brakes are of band or post type (Fig 17, 18), applied for small hoists by hand or foot, through systems of simple levers. Brakes of large hoists are power-operated; applied by a weighted lever and released by lifting the weight with an air, oil or hydraulic cylinder. Band brakes are used for both large and small hoists, post brakes only for the larger sizes. The levers of band brakes are sometimes designed to increase the brake pressure by a constant application of braking force; more desirable for hand than for power brakes. Hand emergency brakes, on hoists equipped with power brakes, may have a differential motion tending to tighten the brake automatically after being applied. Their instantaneous action is objectionable.

Band brake. Assuming diam of brake surface is same as that of drum, the band and anchorage must stand greater tension than that of the rope (Eq 14, 15).

Let W = friction between band and brake surface = pull on rope,

T_1 and T_2 = tension respectively at anchorage and at end of brake band,

e = base of Naperian system of logs = 2.71828,

f = coefficient of friction, wood on iron = 0.30,

c = ratio of length of arc of contact of brake to radius of brake surface,

a = angle of arc of contact, deg.

Then $$W = T_1 - T_2 \tag{14}$$

But
$$T_2 = T_1 \div e^{fc}, \qquad \text{or} \qquad \frac{T_1}{T_2} = e^{fc} = e^{\left(f\frac{\pi}{180}a\right)}$$

and
$$\log_{10}\left(\frac{T_1}{T_2}\right) = f\frac{\pi}{180} a \log_{10}(2.71828) = \frac{\pi}{180}(0.4343)fa$$

or
$$\frac{T_1}{T_2} = 10^{\frac{\pi}{180}(0.4343)fa} = 10^{0.00758fa}$$

When
$$a = 270° \quad \text{and} \quad f = 0.30, \quad \frac{T_1}{T_2} = 10^{0.6139} = 4.11 \tag{15}$$

Substituting in Eq (14), $W = 0.757\,T_1$; whence, T_1 is about 1.3 times the rope pull under best conditions and with drums nearly at rest. If braking surfaces are in poor condition, f is reduced and T_1 increased. If brakes are applied suddenly, with hoist in motion, T_1 may be doubled or tripled, if tension T_2 be sufficient. Hence, with heavy loads, the limit of hand braking with practical leverage ratios is soon reached. If hoisting in balance, with over and under ropes on one drum, brake band should be in halves (Fig 17), so that the anchorage will always take the load due to either rope, otherwise one rope will pull against the brake lever.

Post brake requires a smaller movement for necessary clearance from brake ring. Also, the load is always carried by the anchorage, regardless of direction in which the rope winds upon drum. Frames of post brakes should

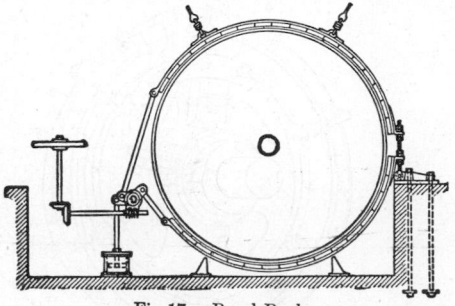

Fig 17. Band Brake

have PARALLEL MOTION, to secure uniform pressure over entire surface of brake shoe. This is done by supporting the frames on swinging links (Fig 18, in which the weighted lever for applying the brake is not shown). Post brakes increase first cost of hoist 4-8%, but are now used on nearly all large hoists.

Clutches are of jaw or friction type. JAW CLUTCH is simple and safe, but, because of its positive action, both drum and engine must be at rest, or nearly so, when clutch is thrown in gear, and the two parts of clutch must be in certain relative positions before they will mesh. It is suitable where hoisting is generally in balance and from one level. Simple jaw clutch is used only on the pinion shaft of geared hoists. Multiple-tooth clutch, with large number of teeth in a circle near periphery of drum, and a sliding member on shaft, is sometimes used. Nearly as close adjustment can be had as with friction clutch. FRICTION CLUTCH is preferable where relative positions of cages are changed frequently, or a nice adjustment of distance between them is neces-

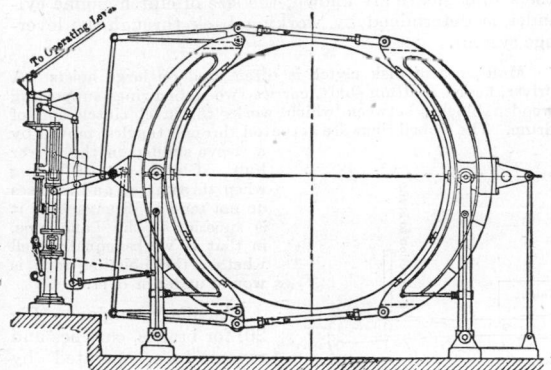

Fig 18. Parallel-motion Post Brake, Operated by Comp-air Cylinder (Nordberg)

sary. It is best suited to general mining purposes. CONE FRICTION CLUTCH is satisfactory for drums up to 48 in diam, and may be used on larger drums. But, with large drums, heavy loads, or high speeds, the end thrust on drum-shaft bearings and friction on thrust pin cause trouble. Cone friction is always operated by hand power. BAND FRICTION CLUTCH costs more, but is otherwise preferable. It is readily inspected and adjusted for wear. Fig 19 shows the Lane type. It comprises a cast-iron spider a, keyed to drum shaft, and fitted with fixed arm b, and movable arm c, pivoted at d. The arms carry steel band e, lined with wooden blocks. Inner end of c is connected to sliding sleeve f by toggle g. When the sleeve is moved toward drum the band tightens on the friction ring j. When released the band is prevented from sagging by the lifters k. On drums 8 ft diam and over, the band is usually made in halves. As toggle levers g approach the normal the tensile strain in the band becomes very great, with risk of excessive stresses if clutch is set too early. Since clutch path may be greasy, coeff of friction is assumed at 0.2. With the rope pull reduced to its equivalent at periphery of clutch path, the tension at ends of band may be calculated as for band brakes. The rope should be so wound on drum that the greatest pull is on fixed end of band; less tension is then required in the clutch. It is

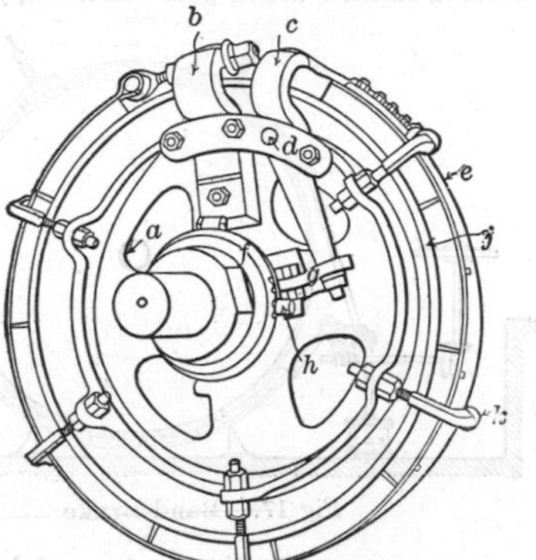

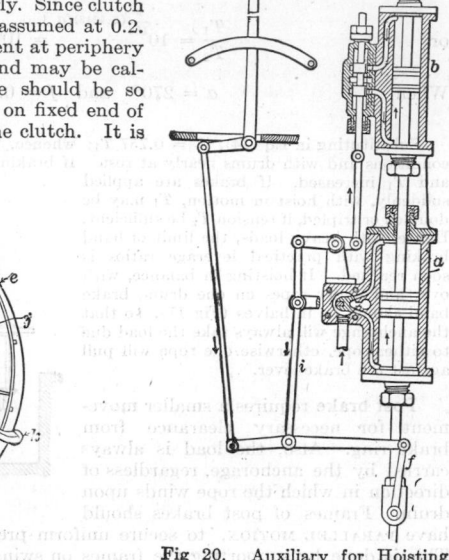

Fig 19. Lane Band Friction Clutch

Fig 20. Auxiliary for Hoisting Engine Control

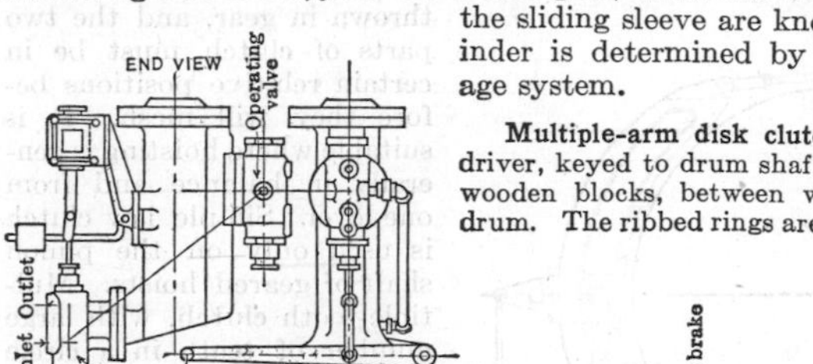

recommended that the leverage between end of band and the sliding sleeve be 20 to 1. Assuming effic of 50% for the clutch gear, when the band tension and force required on the sliding sleeve are known, the size of clutch-engine cylinder is determined by working back through the leverage system.

Multiple-arm disk clutch is often used on large hoists. A driver, keyed to drum shaft, carries two ribbed rings supporting wooden blocks, between which works the steel clutch-ring of drum. The ribbed rings are actuated through toggles, moved by a sleeve sliding on the driver hub. Clutch is self-locking when thrown in, and stresses do not tend to disengage it; it is superior to the Lane type, in that it works equally well whether the hoisting rope is wound under or over.

Auxiliary engines (Fig 20) for brakes, clutches and reverse are operated by steam, air or oil under pressure. Brakes should always be applied by a weight and released by power, so that they are set automatically if power fails. In steam hoists the same form of engine often operates brake, clutch and reverse.

Fig 21. Oil-operated Brake Engine, with Automatic Stop, for Electric Hoist

Steam and air operate expansively. Because of cylinder condensation of steam, operator can not definitely control motion of piston of auxiliary engine; hence, a cataract cylinder (See Sec 40) is placed tandem with steam cylinder. Valves of both cylinders are controlled by one hand lever with a "floating lever" motion. Opened by hand, the ordinary valves are automatically closed by motion of the pistons. Fig 20 shows valve motion of auxiliary engine; a is steam cylinder and b, oil cataract cylinder. Hand lever opens steam and cataract valves, and motion of piston rod, acting through f and i, closes them after a movement proportional to that of hand lever has taken place.

Auxiliary engines operated by oil (Fig 21), under pressure from an accumulator or oil-pressure reservoir, do not require a cataract cylinder, as the liquid is non-expansive and only one cylinder needed. Control is by a floating lever, to make motion of piston coincident with that of operator's lever, so that any pressure can be applied and held. Recent types have auxiliary valves for applying brakes automatically, in connection with safety devices against overwinding (Art 34), or failure of steam pressure, or current in case of electric hoists.

4. MOTOR AND HOIST CONNECTIONS (3)

First-motion or direct-acting hoists have the engine or armature shaft directly connected to drum shaft, through rigid flanged couplings keyed to or forged on the shafts, or the armature is pressed on an extension of drum shaft. First-motion steam hoists are used for large outputs, or depths requiring high hoisting speeds. First-motion electric hoists always use D C motors, because of the poor electrical characteristics and high costs of induction motors for these purposes. In the DUAL-MOTOR DRIVE, sometimes used for large hoists, half the motor capacity is coupled at each end of drum shaft. This better distributes the shaft stresses, lessens rotor inertia effects, and insures against complete interruption of service.

Second-motion hoists have one gear reduction. With herringbone gears, which permit high tooth speeds and large gear reduction (15 to 1), double reduction is rarely needed except for small capacities. This type is well adapted to an A C high-speed motor or a steam engine. The motor has two bearings, and the armature shaft is connected to pinion by a flexible coupling.

Conversion of steam hoists to elec drive may be made by bolting a gear to the crank disk, and coupling the motor to the shaft of a pinion meshing with the gear. The drag-link connection has been used in So Africa. The link connects the engine crank to a similar crank on the motor or to an intermediate gear shaft.

5. HOISTING SHEAVES

Sheaves are generally of the bicycle spoke type; of C I in one piece, a C I-rim with W I spokes, or of a welded structural-steel skeleton type (10). Tread or bottom of groove must be true, with a radius slightly larger than the rope. Voigtlander (11) recommends:

Diam of rope	Tolerance of groove diameters
1/2 in and smaller	+1/32 in minimum to +3/32 in max
9/16 in to 1 in	+1/16 in minimum to +1/8 in max
1 1/16 in to 2 in	+3/32 in minimum to +3/16 in max
Over 2 in	+1/8 in minimum to +1/4 in max

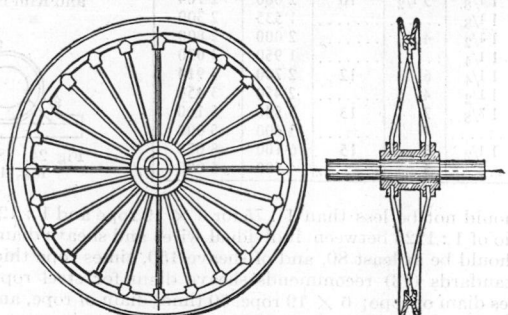

Fig 22. Wrought-iron Spoke Sheave

Sheave grooves may be lined with wood blocks, grain on end, or steel liners. Depth of groove and width at rim are 3.5 to 4 times rope diam. Sheaves of minimum wt should be used to reduce the inertia effect on rope when engine stops, which causes a scrubbing action and wear on the rope. Spokes of W-I sheaves are cast into rim and hub (Fig 22 and 23), making an angle of about 7° with plane of sheave. Sheave shaft or arbor is solidly keyed in the hub, and supported in heavy bearings. Hub is sometimes held between 2 collars on the arbor, one being turned solid on arbor, the other split, fitting in an annular groove in arbor, and bolted to hub (11).

Bearings are of the post type (Fig 24), with the cap at 45° to plane of base, or of the ordinary horiz type, depending on design of headframe (Art 23). Post bearings may be used in either vert or horiz position, having the advantage that the resultant of the rope pull always falls approx in bottom of bearing. Journals should be so proportioned that the unit press does not exceed 200 lb per sq in, to permit proper lubrication.

Costs of sheaves may be computed at 10 to 12¢ per lb for weights in Table 1.

Table 1. Sheaves for Round Rope

Diam, in	Type	Max diam of rope, in	Journals Diam, in	Journals Length, in	Wt, sheave only, lb	Wt complete, with shaft and boxes, lb
16	Cast iron	5/8	1 1/2	....	58	92
18	"	1/2	....	....	86	120
20	"	5/8	1 1/2	....	85	139
24	"	5/8	....	....	115	190
24	"	3/4	1 3/4	....	115	165
24	"	5/8	....	....	150	220
30	"	5/8	....	....	165	315
30	"	7/8	2	....	150	200
30	"	3/4	....	....	175	300
36	"	1	3 1/2	8	350	607
36	"	7/8	....	....	275	400
36	"	7/8	....	....	155	225
36	"	7/8	2	....	271	321
42	"	3/4	....	....	440	665
42	"	7/8	....	....	272	375
42	"	7/8	....	....	470	690
48	"	1	4	8	600	961
48	"	7/8	....	....	460	750
48	"	7/8	....	....	368	460
48	"	7/8	....	....	565	690
60	"	1	....	....	900	1 200
60	"	1	4 1/2	8	1 050	1 467
60	"	1	....	....	540	725
60	W-I arms	1 1/4	3 3/8	....	....	1 200
72	Cast iron	1 1/8	....	....	1 200	1 800
72	W-I arms	1	4 1/2	10	1 500	1 973
72	W-I arms	1 1/4	3 3/8	....	1 440	2 040
84	Cast iron	1 1/8	....	....	1 530	2 400
84	W-I arms	1 1/8	5 1/2	10	2 000	2 764
84	Cast iron	1 1/8	....	....	1 535	2 300
84	W-I arms	1 1/2	4	....	2 000	2 800
96	Cast iron	1 1/4	....	....	1 950	3 030
96	W-I arms	1 1/4	6	12	2 700	3 914
96	"	1 1/2	4	....	2 450	3 450
120	"	1 3/8	7	13	3 500	5 160
120	"	....	4	....	3 600	5 000
144	"	1 1/2	8	15	6 100	8 070
144	"	....	5	....	4 500	6 000

Diameter of sheave, measured at bottom of tread, depends upon diam and type of rope. It should be as large as conditions will permit, considering economy of first cost with respect to life of rope. Makers' lists advise a minimum ratio of diam of rope to diam of sheave of 1 : 48 for 6 × 19, and 1 : 84 for 6 × 7 cast- and plow-steel rope. With these ratios, bending stresses are approx 10% of ultimate strengths of rope for crucible cast steel, and 8% for plow steel. For economical

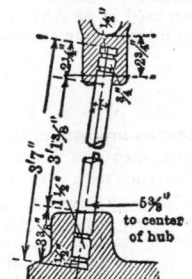

Fig 23. Wrought-iron Spoke Sheave. Hub and Rim Ends of Spoke

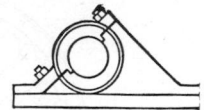

Fig 24. Sheave Bearing, 45° Type

wear, the ratios should not be less than 1 : 75 for 6 × 19 rope and 1 : 125 for 6 × 7 rope; equivalent to a ratio of 1 : 1125 between individual wires and sheave diam. For flat ropes, diam of reel hub should be at least 80, and of sheave 150, times rope thickness.

U S Bur of Standards (13) recommends sheave diam for steel rope as follows: **for** 6 × 7 rope, 85 times diam of rope; 6 × 19 rope, 50 times diam of rope, and never less than 20; 6 × 37 or 8 × 19 rope, 30 times diam of rope.

6. VEGETABLE-FIBER ROPE

Materials, in order of strength: manila hemp, or fiber from *abaca* plant (sometimes erroneously called aloe), Baden split hemp, Russian and Italian hemp, American hemp, sisal, and cotton. Many grades of each material are used, price depending upon strength, length of fiber, and care in cleaning.

Construction. Hemp rope is of 3, sometimes 4 or more, strands, each composed of many fibers; which may be individual fibers, for very small rope, or yarn spun from a number of fibers. Original fibers rarely average over 3 ft long, so that strength of rope depends upon the binding action of the twisted fibers under tension, and friction between them. For same diam, 4-strand rope has greater wearing surface and strength than 3-strand. Manila rope is 25% stronger than sisal.

Strength. Following formulas (C. W. Hunt) give the relations between strength, size, and weight of rope:

$$T = 720\,C^2 = 7\,106\,d^2 = 22\,500\,W = 9\,048\,A$$
$$W = 0.032\,C^2 = 0.316\,d^2 = 0.000044\,T = 0.402\,A$$

T = ultimate strength, lb; C = circumference, in; A = nominal area, sq in; d = diam, in; W = wt, lb per ft.

C. Bach gives modulus of elasticity of rope as follows:

New manila, 1.97 to 2.17 in diam, loosely twisted,   113 806 lb per sq in
"   "   "   "   "   "   hard   "   135 145 "   "
New Baden split hemp 1.97 to 2.17 in diam, loosely twisted 149 371   "   "
"   "   "   "   "   "   hard   "   177 822 "   "

Table 2. Ultimate Strength and Weight of Best Manila Rope (av of different makers)

Diam, in	Wt per 1 000 ft, lb	No of ft and in in 1 lb	Ultimate strength, lb	Diam, in	Wt per 1 000 ft, lb	No of ft and in in 1 lb	Ultimate strength, lb
1/4	23	48–0	450 to 620	1 1/2	746	1–6	17 000 to 17 600
3/8	42	25–0	1 000 " 1 600	1 5/8	826	1–2	19 500 " 20 000
1/2	74	12–0	1 760 " 2 400	1 3/4	1 000	1–0	23 700 " 25 000
5/8	132	7–3	3 140 " 4 000	2	1 291	0–10	30 000 " 33 000
3/4	167	6–0	3 970 " 4 700	2 1/4	1 620	0–7.5	37 000 " 44 000
7/8	250	4–3	5 900 " 6 500	2 1/2	2 000	0–6	43 000 " 55 000
1	297	3–7	7 000 " 7 500	2 3/4	2 380	0–5	53 000 " 63 000
1 1/8	405	2–6	9 600 " 10 500	3	2 983	0–4	62 000 " 70 000
1 1/4	465	2–2	11 000 " 12 500	3 1/4	3 300	0–3 5/8	75 000 " 78 000
1 3/8	597	1–9	14 000 " 15 400	......	......	......	....

Uses. For mining in America fiber rope is used chiefly for windlasses, whims, and light crane and derrick work. Chief advantage for prospecting is that the rope is uninjured by kinks, which would destroy wire rope, and there are no projecting broken wires to injure workmen's hands. For same strength a 6-strand, 19-wire cast-steel rope is as flexible and weighs less than manila. The only advantage of tarring a rope is prevention of contraction and expansion in wet and dry weather. Tarring increases wt 20 to 25%, and decreases strength. Some makers apply a dressing of graphite and tallow or fish oil to the fibers, as the rope is made, to act as lubricant and prevent excessive internal wear, when rope runs over sheaves. In Belgium, flat vegetable fiber ropes are used for hoisting from deep colliery shafts. These taper in both width and thickness; ratio of width to thickness is constant, and is from 6.4 : 1 to 8 : 1. Manila rope is now rarely used, except for prospecting, winze hoisting, etc. Steel rope is always employed in shafts.

7. WIRE ROPES (14, 22, 24–29)

Materials are charcoal iron, Swedish iron, and various grades of cast steel. Iron ropes are still used for special purposes, but steel is practically universal for mining. General trade names are: "iron" (commonly meaning low-carbon steel), "cast steel," "extra strong cast steel," "plow steel," and "extra plow steel." Makers have various trade names for their extra plow-steel quality. Different tensile strengths are due to methods of manufacture and treatment of wire. Plow steel is lower in P and S, and higher in C and Mn, than crucible steel. Toughness of wire is obtained by tempering, and tensile strength is increased by repeated drawings, so that from same grade of steel the finer wires are stronger than the larger.

Modulus of elasticity in tension is 28 500 000 to 30 000 000 lb per sq in. Experiments with nickel and vanadium steel and other alloys for rope wire have not been successful.

Table 3. Ultimate Tensile Strength of Rope Wire, lb per sq in

Size of wire	Charcoal iron	Crucible steel	Plow steel
No 6 to No 8	80 000 to 85 000	120 000 to 160 000	200 000 to 240 000
No 9 to No 16	85 000 " 95 000	130 000 " 180 000	220 000 " 280 000
No 16 to No 18	95 000 " 98 000	150 000 " 190 000	240 000 " 300 000
No 18 and finer	98 000 " 115 000	180 000 " 200 000	260 000 " 320 000

Structure, or number and arrangement of wires in a rope, depends upon use for which it is intended. It is usually designated numerically by stating number of strands and number of wires per strand. Thus, 6-strand rope with 19 wires per strand is called a 6 × 19 rope, and one with 6 strands of 7 wires per strand, a 6 × 7 rope. Except for special purposes, the strands of all hoisting and running ropes are laid around a HEMP CORE, which absorbs and holds lubricant, and acts as a yielding cushion in which the strands may embed, thus preventing frictional wear when bending on sheaves and drums. The hemp center adds no appreciable strength. Ropes with a wire center are suitable only for standing ropes, lacking the flexibility necessary for hoisting or running ropes. Wire core adds about 10% to wt and cost, but less than 10% to strength. ORDINARY TYPE comprises 6 strands of either 7 or 19 wires, with hemp center. In 6 × 7 rope each strand has 6 wires twisted around 1 wire (Fig 26). In 6 × 19 rope each strand has 12 wires around 6 wires around 1 wire (Fig 25). A modification known as "three-size wire," or WARRINGTON STRAND, has the 7 inside wires of one size, the outer 12 being alternately larger and smaller (Fig 27). This increases area of metal and strength about 10%. For same diam of rope, the 6 × 7 has wires of about 64% greater diam than the 6 × 19, and hence better withstands surface wear; but is less flexible, requiring larger sheaves and drums. Thus, 6 × 7 rope is used for slopes and inclined planes, where surface wear is great; 6 × 19 is best for vert shafts, and wherever flexibility is important. A 6 × 16 two-size wire rope is often used on slopes, as it wears better than a 6 × 19 and is more flexible than a 6 × 7. TWIST or LAY of the strands in a rope may be either right- or left-hand, right-hand lay being standard (Fig 28); Fig 29 shows left-hand lay. ORDINARY LAY rope has the strand wires twisted in opposite

Fig 25   Fig 26   Fig 27

direction to twist of strands in the rope. In a LANG LAY (sometimes called "Albert" lay) the strand wires are twisted in same direction as the strands (Fig 30), giving larger area to resist wear than ordinary lay rope. The latter is more elastic and resists shocks better, does not tend to untwist so much as Lang lay, and is preferable for hoisting with buckets, where spinning is objectionable. (A rope which no longer spins is termed "dead.") With Lang lay a broken wire may project farther and do more damage than in ordinary lay, but

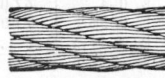

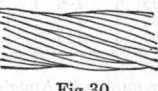

Fig 28   Fig 29   Fig 30

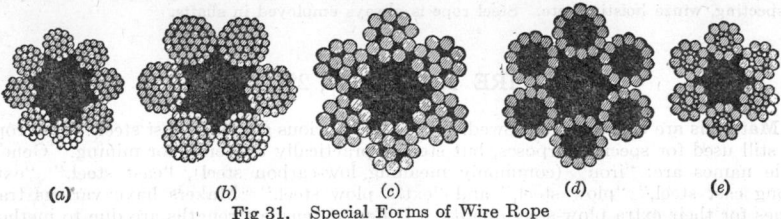

(a)   (b)   (c)   (d)   (e)

Fig 31. Special Forms of Wire Rope

the rope is more easily inspected for internal wear and corrosion. LENGTH OF LAY (pitch of helix) of wires in a strand is 8 to 12 times the diam of strand; lay of strands is 7 to 9 times the rope diam. Long-lay rope wears better than short-lay, but short-lay is more flexible and elastic, and broken wires can not project so far. In 6 × 7 rope the diam of individual wires is 1/9 diam of rope; in 6 × 12 and 6 × 19 rope the diam of individual wires average $1/12$ and $1/15$, respectively, of rope diam. This is for new rope; after use, the rope wears smaller, and strands pack into the core, so that the ratio is increased.

Special ropes. EXTRA FLEXIBLE, 8 strands of 19 wires, with hemp core (Fig 31, a). SPECIAL FLEXIBLE, 6 strands of 37 wires, with hemp core, for use on small drums and sheaves (Fig 31, b); also 6 strands of 12 wires (Fig 31, c). TILLER ROPE, 6 strands, each being a complete 6 × 7 hemp-center rope; for use where extreme flexibility is necessary and where there is but little abrasion. STEEL HAWSER, 6 strands, of 12 wires in a single layer about a hemp center (Fig 31, d); usually galvanized, and suitable only for standing rope or tow lines. SEALE LAY rope (Fig 31, e), 6 or 8 strands of 19 wires, each having an outer layer of 9 wires, about an inner layer of 9 smaller wires, about 1 central wire; wears well, and is intermediate in flexibility between 6 × 7 and 6 × 19 standard rope. FLATTENED-STRAND ropes are of two forms: one has 5 strands about a hemp core, each strand having 1 oval center wire, surrounded by 8 wires (Fig 32, c), or 2 layers aggregating 27 wires (Fig 32, a), the outer wires being the larger; the oval wire is sometimes replaced by 3 small wires. The other forms in Fig 32 have 6 strands, each composed of a central triangular wire, surrounded by 7 wires (d), or an outer layer of 12 wires, on an inner layer of 12 smaller wires (b). These ropes are as flexible as 6 × 7 and 6 × 19 standard rope of same diam. The center or "form" wires in the strands are of soft metal, and no account is taken of their strength. The shape of these strands exposes a larger wearing surface than the ordinary lay, with probable increase in durability. Flattened-strand ropes are always Lang lay, and about equal in strength to standard rope of same quality of wire.

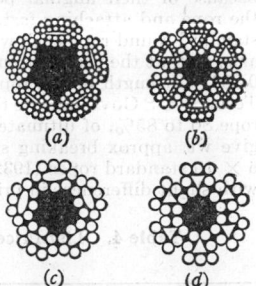

Fig 32. Flattened-strand Wire Ropes

Flat ropes have been used to some extent for equalizing load in deep shafts (Art 2), but few are now in service. They consist of a number of 4-strand, 7-wire round ropes, without cores, side by side, and sewed together with soft iron wire. Ratio of width to thickness depends chiefly on number of component round ropes. The latter are alternately right and left lay, to counteract tendency to twist. The lay of their strand wires, and of the strands themselves, is longer than in standard round rope. Flat ropes are usually ripped apart, cleaned, and re-sewed 1 to 4 times before being discarded; records at a mine in Montana show 3 to 4 re-sewings in a total life of 2 years.

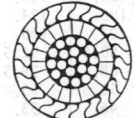 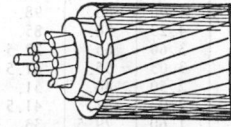 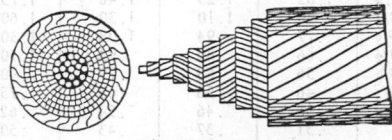

Fig 33. Locked Coil Track Cable   Fig 34. Locked Coil Hoisting Rope

Locked-coil rope (Fig 33, 34) has no strands, the specially shaped wires being in layers, having alternately opposite lays, about a wire core. The rope in Fig 34 has the larger number of wires, of smaller gage; hence more flexible than that in Fig 33. The surface wires interlock, so that if one breaks its ends can not project. But, when outer wires are worn slightly smaller by abrasion, broken ends begin to project, and the rope is rapidly destroyed. Entire surface of the rope is available for resisting wear. Inspection of condition of interior wires is practically impossible. These ropes are not suitable where exposed to action of acid mine water, and have rarely been employed for shaft hoisting in the U S; chief use is for track cables of aerial tramways (Sec 26). In So African shafts they sometimes serve as guide ropes.

Taper ropes, formerly used to some extent in Europe and So Africa, are now rare. In the U S a few have been employed in drilling deep bore holes; none for shaft hoisting. There are two forms: in one the rope has same number of wires throughout, the taper being effected by brazing on wires of smaller diam, no two brazes coming at same point; in the other, one or more wires at a time are cut off, at regular distances.

Preformed wire rope (15, 16) consists of preformed strands. Advantages claimed are: resistance to kinking, no spinning, broken wires lie flat, ease of splicing (as it will not untwist), and use of processed fittings, small initial stresses in the rope. John A. Roebling's Sons claim no material increase in strength for their preformed rope.

Tests of rope wire are for tensile strength, per cent of elongation at rupture, torsion and flexure. Bending of a wire through 90°, and back to original position, around a radius equal to diam of the wire is considered one flexure. U S Govt specifications give following test for torsion (13): Steel wire when uncoated shall

Material	Min number 360° turns
Cast steel...............	2.6
Extra strong steel.......	2.4
Plow steel...............	2.2
Extra plow steel.........	2.0

$\div$ { diam of wire, in

not break when one end is held and the other rotated the number of complete 360° turns stated in table. Distance between jaws of testing machine, 8 in. For importance of fatigue and wearing tests see (12), and Boomsliter (14) states that the ability of steel to withstand repeated stress decreases greatly when stress exceeds elastic limit. Adams (22) states that a high fatigue limit is not the most important property of hoisting rope wires, because they are destroyed by overstressing and wear.

Strength of wire rope can not be taken as the sum of strengths of individual wires, because of their angular position with respect to rope's axis, and difficulty of making the rope and attaching fastenings so that each wire will take its proportionate load. In standard round rope each wire at some point makes an angle of about 28° with the rope's axis, so that the useful strength of the wire is its actual strength multiplied by cos 28°, or 0.883. Strength of the rope is therefore about 88% of aggregate strength of the wires. Tests by U S Govt indicate that ultimate strength of 6 × 7 rope is 90 to 92%, and of 6 × 19 rope 80 to 85%, of ultimate strength of the wires. Tables 4 and 5 (American Cable Co) give wt, approx breaking strength, list price and minimum sheave diam for 6 × 7 and 6 × 19 standard ropes (1932). Data from John A. Roebling's Sons are approx the same, with slight differences in prices.

Table 4. List Prices per Foot of Hoisting Rope with 6 Strands of 19 Wires, American Cable Co, 1932

Diam	Cast steel	Mild plow steel	Plow steel	Improved plow steel	Approx wt per ft, lb	Approx strength, ton of 2 000 lb			
						Cast steel	Mild plow steel	Plow steel	Improved plow steel
2 3/4	$2.10	$2.55	$3.00	$3.45	12.10	212.	234.	256.	294.
2 1/2	1.75	2.10	2.50	2.80	10.	176.	195.	214.	246.
2 1/4	1.44	1.70	2.00	2.50	8.10	144.	160.	176.	202.
2 1/8	1.30	1.52	1.79	2.15	7.22	128.	143.	157.	181.
2	1.16	1.34	1.58	1.85	6.40	114.	127.	140.	161.
1 7/8	1.02	1.25	1.46	1.75	5.63	100.	112.	123.	142.
1 3/4	.90	1.10	1.30	1.60	4.90	88.	98.	108.	124.
1 5/8	.77	.94	1.08	1.30	4.23	76.	85.	94.	108.
1 1/2	.66	.80	.93	1.10	3.60	65.	72.5	80.5	92.5
1 3/8	.56	.68	.79	.90	3.03	55.	61.5	68.	78.5
1 1/4	.46	.56	.65	.75	2.50	46.	51.	56.5	65.
1 1/8	.38	.46	.54	.62	2.03	37.	41.5	46.	53.
1	.31	.37	.43	.50	1.60	29.5	33.	36.5	42.
7/8	.25	.29	.34 1/2	.39	1.23	22.8	25.4	28.	32.2
3/4	.20 1/2	.24	.28	.31	.90	16.8	18.7	20.6	23.7
5/8	.15 3/4	.18	.21	.22 1/2	.63	11.8	13.1	14.4	16.6
9/16	.13 3/4	.15 3/4	.18 1/4	.19	.51	9.6	10.6	11.7	13.5
1/2	.12	.13 3/4	.16	.17	.40	7.7	8.5	9.4	10.8
7/16	.10 1/2	.12	.14	.15 1/2	.31	6.	6.6	7.3	8.4
3/8	.09 1/2	.11	.13	.14 1/2	.23	4.5	5.	5.5	6.3
5/16	.09 1/4	.10 3/4	.12 1/4	.13 1/2	.16	3.2	3.5	3.9	4.5
1/4	.09	.10 1/2	.12	.13	.10	2.1	2.3	2.5	2.9

Note—For galvanized rope, add 25% to list price; for rope with wire-strand center, add 10%; for independent wire center (any construction), add 15%.

Stresses in hoisting rope are due to dead load, accelerating force, starting factor for slack rope, friction and bending stresses, depending on sheave diam, kind of construction, kind and size of wire.

Dead-load stresses. Let W = wt of 1 cage and empty car or 1 skip; w = wt of ore; Wr = wt of 1 rope; a = acceleration, ft per sec per sec; F_1 = accelerating force in ascending rope; F_2 = accelerating force in descending rope; g = acceleration due to gravity; then

$$\text{Dead-load stress} \quad = \quad W + w + Wr \tag{16}$$

$$\text{Accelerating stress in ascending rope,} \quad F_1 \quad = \quad \frac{(W + w + Wr)}{g}\, a \tag{17}$$

$$\text{Accelerating stress in descending rope,} \quad F_2 = \frac{W\,a}{g} \tag{18}$$

Boomsliter (14), Perry & Smith (23), Hogan (24), and others show that acceleration stresses in hoisting are much larger than usually assumed, because the elastic properties

Table 5. List Prices per Foot of Haulage Ropes with 6 Strands of 7 Wires, American Cable Co, 1932

Diam, in	Iron	Cast steel	Mild plow steel	Plow steel	Improved plow steel
1 1/2	$0.51	$0.60	$0.75	$0.90	$1.05
1 3/8	.43	.51	.64	.76	.88
1 1/4	.36	.43	.53	.62	.72
1 1/8	.30	.36	.44	.51	.58
1	.24	.29	.35	.41	.48
7/8	.18 1/2	.23	.27	.32 1/2	.37
3/4	.14	.18 1/2	.22	.26	.28 1/2
5/8	.10	.13 1/2	.16	.19	.20 1/2
9/16	.08 1/4	.11 1/2	.13 3/4	.16 1/4	.17
1/2	.06 1/2	.09	.10 1/2	.12 1/2	.13 1/2
7/16	.05 1/2	.07	.08 1/2	.10 1/2	.11 1/2
3/8	.04 1/2	.05 3/4	.06 3/4	.08	.08 3/4
5/16	.03 3/4	.04 1/2	.05 1/2	.06 1/2	.08 1/4
9/32	.03 1/4	.04 1/4	.05 1/4	.06 1/4	.07 1/2
1/4	...	.04	.05	.06	.07

Diam, in	Approx wt per ft, lb	Approx Strength, in tons of 2 000 lb				
		Iron	Cast steel	Mild plow steel	Plow steel	Improved plow steel
1 1/2	3.38	29.7	62.5	68.7	75.	86.5
1 3/8	2.84	25.2	53.	58.2	63.5	73.5
1 1/4	2.34	21.	44.5	48.7	53.	61.
1 1/8	1.90	17.2	36.4	40.	43.6	50.
1	1.50	13.7	29.	31.9	34.8	40.
7/8	1.15	10.5	22.4	24.6	26.8	30.8
3/4	.84	7.86	16.5	18.1	19.8	22.8
5/8	.59	5.52	11.5	12.6	13.8	16.
9/16	.48	4.49	9.4	10.3	11.3	13.
1/2	.38	3.57	7.5	8.2	9.	10.3
7/16	.29	2.76	5.8	6.3	6.9	7.9
3/8	.21	2.05	4.3	4.7	5.15	5.9
5/16	.15	1.43	3.1	3.35	3.65	4.2
9/32	.12	1.17	2.52	2.72	2.95	3.4
1/4	.094	.....	2.	2.15	2.35	2.7

Note—See under Table 4.

of rope introduce considerable periodic acceleration stresses. Doomsliter gives following formulas:

$$S\,(\max) = W\left[1 + \frac{a}{g} + \frac{\sqrt{a^2 + 2ag\,(m+1)}}{g}\right] \qquad (19)$$

S (max) = greatest stress in rope when upper part is uniformly accelerated; m = ratio of slack or stretch in rope to its stretch under wt of cage; W, a and g, as above. If no stretch or slack is assumed, then

$$S\max = W\left[1 + \frac{a}{g} + \frac{\sqrt{a^2 + 2\,ag}}{g}\right] \qquad (20)$$

Compensation for slack rope by the use of springs is of little value. Following dynamometer tests show effect of slack; total length of rope below sheave not stated.

(1) Empty cage, 4 000 lb	Aver stress, lb	(2) Cage and 4 empty cars, 6 375 lb	Aver stress, lb	(3) Cage and loaded cars, 11 300 lb	Aver stress, lb
Lifted gently........	4 030	Lifted gently........	6 725	Lifted gently........	11 400
" with 2.5 in slack	5 600	" with 3 in slack	11 200	" with 3 in slack	19 025
" " 6 in "	8 950	" " 6 in "	12 250	" " 6 in "	24 600
" " 12 in "	12 300	" " 12 in "	15 675	" " 9 in "	26 850

Bending stress. Its effect and amount is a controversial question, on which authorities differ (12, 17). Practice tends to as large sheaves and drums as possible. With ample safety factor, the computed bending stresses and other more or less indeterminate factors are often disregarded. Reasons for uncertainty respecting bending stresses are: differences of opinion as to whether modulus of elasticity of the rope or of the wire should be used (although that of the rope is generally conceded to be correct); and doubt as to correctness of published data on moduli. Assuming that the modulus of elasticity of the rope should be used, and that published values are correct, then bending stress is expressed by: $S = E_R(d \div D)$, in which S = stress in wires due to bending, lb per sq in; E_R = modulus of elasticity of rope; d = diam of largest wire, in; D = diam of bend over sheave or drum on center line of rope, in. If A be aggregate area of wires (sq in), and S_R bending stress in rope (lb), then for any rope the total bending stress is:

$$S_R = E_R \times (dA \div D). \tag{21}$$

Table 6 gives values of A for standard 6×7 and 6×19 rope. American Steel and Wire Co give $E_R = 12\,000\,000$ maximum for new 6-strand rope. Various authorities give $E_R = 35\%$ of the modulus of elasticity of steel wire = 10 150 000. According to A. W. Brown (18), 11 180 000 is a good aver of E_R for the entire rope, after it has been in use long enough for the strands to bed into the core; 19 000 000 being modulus for old rope. Boomsliter (14) states that stressing wire rope to $2/3$ of the ultimate strength results in modulus reaching values between 14 000 000 and 18 000 000.

Table 6.   Approximate Diameters and Areas of Wire in Wire Rope

Diam of rope, in	6 × 19 hoisting rope			6 × 7 haulage rope		
	Diam of wire = $\dfrac{1}{15.52}$ diam of rope, in	Area of 1 wire, sq in	Aggregate area of wires, sq in	Diam of wire = $\dfrac{1}{9}$ diam of rope, in	Area of 1 wire, sq in	Aggregate area of wires, sq in
3/8	0.0241	0.00045	0.0513	0.041	0.00132	0.0554
1/2	0.0320	0.00080	0.0912	0.055	0.00237	0.0995
9/16	0.0360	0.00102	0.1162	0.062	0.00302	0.1268
5/8	0.0404	0.00128	0.1456	0.069	0.00374	0.1571
3/4	0.0480	0.00181	0.2063	0.083	0.00541	0.2272
7/8	0.0564	0.00250	0.2850	0.097	0.00739	0.3104
1	0.0644	0.00325	0.3705	0.111	0.00968	0.4065
1 1/8	0.0720	0.00407	0.4640	0.125	0.01227	0.5153
1 1/4	0.0805	0.00509	0.5802	0.139	0.01517	0.6371
1 3/8	0.0890	0.00622	0.7090	0.153	0.01838	0.7720
1 1/2	0.0970	0.00739	0.8400	0.167	0.02190	0.9198
1 5/8	0.1045	0.00857	0.9769	....	....	....
1 3/4	0.1130	0.01003	1.1434	....	....	....
2	0.1290	0.01307	1.4900	....	....	....

In Eq 21, $A = 42 \times 0.25\,\pi d^2$, and if d_R = diam of rope, then $d = d_R \div 9$ for 6×7 rope. Substituting, and taking $E_R = 12\,000\,000$ for 6×7 rope, $S_R = 542\,880\,(d^3_R \div D)$.

For 6×19 rope, $A = 114 \times 0.25\,\pi d^2$, $d = d_R \div 15.50$ and $S_R = 288\,000\,(d^3_R \div D)$.
For 6×37 rope, $A = 222 \times 0.25\,\pi d^2$, $d = d_R \div 21.7$ and $S_R = 204\,000\,(d^3_R \div D)$.
For 8×19 rope, $S_R = 172\,500\,(d^3_R \div D)$.

Fig 35 (American Steel and Wire Co) shows bending stresses in 6×19 rope, as calculated by above formulas.

Frictional stresses F may be assumed as 1% of sum of dead load and acceleration stresses and are often neglected.

Total rope stresses may now be expressed as follows, wl being wt of rope:

$$P = S_r + \left[W + wl + a \times \left(\frac{W + wl}{g} \right) \right] \tag{22}$$

Factor of safety. Past practice has been to use safety factor of 3.5 to 4 for hoisting ore and 6 for men, when stresses are determined as in Eq 22. U S Bur of Mines (19) recommends a factor depending on LENGTH of rope (Table 7). Mining Regulations of Transvaal require factor of 6, bending and accel stresses being disregarded, but Vaughan (1) recommends making exception to this for deep shafts, especially if "capacity factor" (breaking load of rope ÷ load at lower end of rope) is above 12. R. B. Greer (20) recommends a sliding-scale factor of safety for depths exceeding 2 500 ft, since the elasticity of a long rope in part compensates the stresses due to starting with slack rope, the wt of cage and contents and bending stresses being practically constant for all depths. Conference on Wire Rope (21) brought out the fact that rope with a safety factor of 2.1 had a 6-month life as against 7 years with a 10.7 factor. It is evident that the relation of safety factor to life of rope should be seriously considered.

Rope design. Present practice is to determine values of W, a, and L for working conditions. Assume a rope size and drum diam. Then from makers' tables (or Tables 4, 5) and Eq 21 determine wl and S_r. Apply these in Eq 22, and determine P, total stress in rope. Multiply by safety factor required, and compare with ultimate strengths in tables, selecting rope of a strength nearest that calculated. With this size rope, recalculate bending stress and wt of rope, and check result. There is no fixed economical ratio between bending stress and load. In shallow shafts, the bending stress may economically be 0.33 to 0.40 of total rope stress; but in deep shafts such a ratio leaves too little of the rope's strength for net load, after wt of rope is deducted.

Table 7. Hoisting Rope Safety Factors for Various Depths of Shaft

Length of rope, ft	Minimum factor, new rope	Min factor when rope is discarded
500 or less.......	8	6.4
500 to 1 000.....	7	5.8
1 000 to 2 000....	6	5.0
2 000 to 3 000....	5	4.3
3 000 and more...	4	3.6

Boomsliter (14) recommends rope design based on the empirical formula:

$$S \text{ (max)} = W (1.5 + 0.1 \, a) \tag{23}$$

Example. Assume wt of load $W = 21\,600$ lb; wt of 1 3/4-in rope $wl = 2\,160$ lb; acceleration $a = 8$ ft per sec per sec. Then, from Eq 23, S (max) $= 21\,600\,(1.5 + 0.1 \times 8) = 49\,700$ lb

Friction (approx)... 500
Bending stress, 1 3/4-in rope on 8-ft sheave......................... 14 960
Total stress... 65 160 lb

With safety factor of 4, 260 640 lb is the ultimate strength of rope required; satisfied with a 1 3/4-in extra strong plow-steel rope. Using Eq 22 and the same values:

$$P = 14\,960 + \left[21\,600 + 2\,160 + 8 \left(\frac{21\,600 + 2\,160}{32.2} \right) \right] = 44\,660 \text{ lb.}$$

With safety factor of 4, the ultimate strength of rope required is 188 600 lb, a smaller figure than obtained from Eq 23. In view of evidence as to increased life of rope with large safety factor formula 23 should be seriously considered.

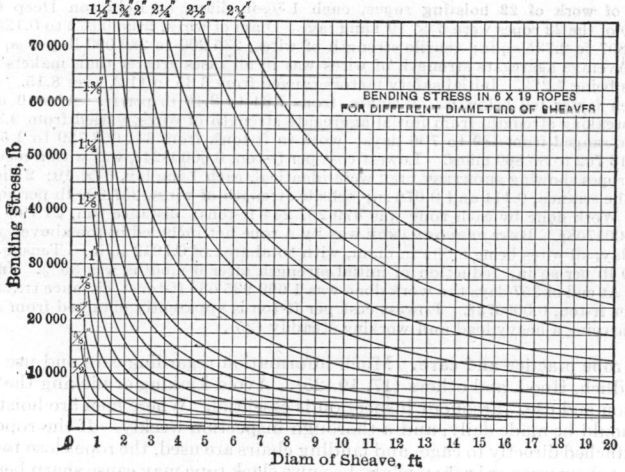

Fig 35. Bending Stresses in Hoisting Ropes

Choice of rope requires knowledge of the working conditions. Steel is always better than wrought iron, and plow or extra crucible steel preferable to ordinary steel. For same strength, a plow-steel rope may be used on smaller sheaves than wrought-iron rope, and on sheaves of same diam as for ordinary steel rope. For the same ultimate strength, plow-steel rope costs 10 to 12% more than cast steel; while, for same wt, plow steel is stronger by from 10% for small sizes to 35% for the larger. Hence, for heavy loads and deep shafts, where rope wt is a large part of total load, plow- or extra plow-steel rope should be used, bending stresses being the same for cast- and plow-steel rope of the same diam.

For slopes, inclines, and rope haulage, 6 × 7 rope wears better than 6 × 19, and Lang lay is preferable for endless-rope haulage where car grips are used. For vertical shafts, 6 × 19 ordinary lay is standard U S practice. In shafts where men are hoisted it is psychologically desirable to use rope not smaller than $3/4$ in, regardless of the actual strength required.

Ropes of special construction (Fig 31, 32) are rarely used for mine hoisting in the U S, though present practice seems to tend toward round, preformed rope. Flat rope is obsolescent here, although retained where original reel hoists are in operation. In Butte District, Mont, 9 out of 24 hoists listed (34) use flat rope. Present tendency in the Transvaal is towards ordinary round rope (30). In England the tendency in 1922 was to replace Lang-lay rope by flattened-strand or locked-coil (32).

Wear and durability of rope depend upon diam of sheaves and drums, speed, conditions causing wear or abrasion of the outside wires, and conditions causing corrosion. These qualities are practically independent of the load, so long as it is within elastic limit of the wires. Large diam of drum and sheave increases life of rope; when too small, the rope's outer wires break sooner. High speed causes rapid wear; excessive vibration causes fatigue and crystallization of the steel. If sheaves have rough grooves, and if fleet angle is large, wear on surface wires is severe, due to chafing of the rope on sheave flanges and between the rope coils on ungrooved drums. Internal wear and corrosion depend upon efficiency of lubrication, and whether the mine water is acid. In dry shafts, if rope is well lubricated, and sheaves and drum are of proper size, corrosion and wear of interior wires is negligible. In wet shafts, where water is acid, corrosion of wires determines the rope's life. Rope life may also be increased (24, 30) by: (a) using electric hoisting engines, with Ward-Leonard control (Art 13), to insure smooth acceleration and retardation with consequent small increase in kinetic stress; (b) having braking electrically controlled and mechanically governed, to minimize stresses.

Precautions should be taken to prevent abrasion and reverse bends. Plow steel resists abrasion, fatigue and severe shocks better than the lower grades of cast steel, and is always best for heavy service or where great strength is necessary, as in deep shafts. Deflecting sheaves and rollers on slopes and haulage ways should be properly alined, free running and as light in wt as is consistent with strength. Soft rubber makes good wearing surface for rollers. Diam of turn-sheaves and rollers should be at least: 0.8 × deflection angle × diam of rope (19).

Summary of work of 22 hoisting ropes, each 1 3/8-in diam, at Robinson Deep Gold mine, Transvaal; 19 of the 22 ropes were 6 × 19 Lang lay. Diam of wires, from 0.072 to 0.125 in; aggregate area, 0.6897 to 0.735 sq in; tensile strength of wires, 235 200 to 280 000 lb per sq in, average 259 500 lb. Average aggregate strength of wires was in all cases greater than makers' guarantee, average excess being 7.2%. Initial safety factors ranged from 6.35 to 11.2, aver 8.15. Ropes were discarded when factor fell below 6. Weights, from 2.84 to 3.16 lb per ft. After 6 months' use reduction in breaking strength, from initial aggregate strength of wires, varied from 9.3 to 33.5%. Working life ranged from 139 to 706 days; work in ft-tons, from 341 058 789 to 1 551 805 722; distance run, 13 702 to 80 860 miles. Lowest cost per ft-ton, 0.0000824¢, was with a medium priced rope. The 2 ropes showing shortest life were identical, each Lang lay, 6 × 19; 2 diams of wire were used in the strands, 0.114 and 0.076 in; tensile strength of wires, 257 600 lb per sq in; safety factor, 11.2. Work done by each rope was 479 297 244 ft-tons; distance run, 21 790 miles; cost per ft-ton, 0.0001708¢. Best performance was by a rope not included in the above. This was a 6 × 19 Lang lay, all wires being 0.094 in diam, with total area of 0.7912 sq in. Tensile strength of wires, 274 000 lb per sq in; reduction of initial strength after 6 months was 35%. Initial safety factor, 7.08. At end of 357 days the work done was 1 669 935 634 ft-tons; distance traveled, 57 488 miles; cost per ft-ton, 0.000073¢. Lowest cost per ft-ton is apparently obtained from a high-class heavy rope, carrying a heavy load and working steadily (25).

Hoisting rope practice and care. Much information regarding care and use of ropes is given by Kudlich, Hood, and others (17, 19, 25). Avoid kinking or nicking the wires during installation and use. Frequent inspection is essential. Where men are hoisted, a brief inspection should be made daily, and a thorough inspection weekly. If the rope socket or capping is attached directly to cage, and landing chairs are used, the rope close to the socket will often first show wear or broken wires, because slack rope may cause sharp bends at that point. When this occurs, a few feet of rope should be cut off at regular periods, and a new socket joint made. If there is enough headroom, a few feet of chain between rope socket and cage draw-bar is advantageous, and in some cases required by law. Changing the rope end for end, at the expiration of half its useful life, is also recommended, so that if wear occurs at any particular point, it will be distributed over a greater length of rope.

Lubrication must be efficient, to prevent wear and corrosion of wires and to minimize surface abrasion. In severe service proper lubrication will lengthen a rope life's 75 to 100% (26, 27, 28, 29). The core should never be allowed to become dry enough to absorb moisture. A good lubricant should be chemically neutral, and of such character and consistency that it will penetrate the strands to the core; it should not run nor drip off, nor be so thick and sticky as to form lumps on the rope or in sheave grooves. Some lubricants, apparently good at first, soon harden and flake off, especially in cold climates. Raw linseed oil is good, but runs off easily. More body is given by adding lampblack or fine flake graphite. Mixtures of pine tar and tallow, or coal tar with slaked lime to neutralize acid, are sometimes used. But all tar mixtures are objectionable, because in cold climates they do not penetrate the rope for lubricating interior wires, and tend to form a hard, gummy coating, likely to strip off. Petroleum jelly or vaseline mixed with fine flake graphite and applied hot is good. Rope makers have rope dressings for different conditions. Lubricant should be applied at intervals of say 1 to 3 weeks, depending on conditions; the rope being first cleaned of dirt and gummed lubricant, by passing it through a bath of hot kerosene and scrubbing with stiff-wire brushes (Fig 35a).

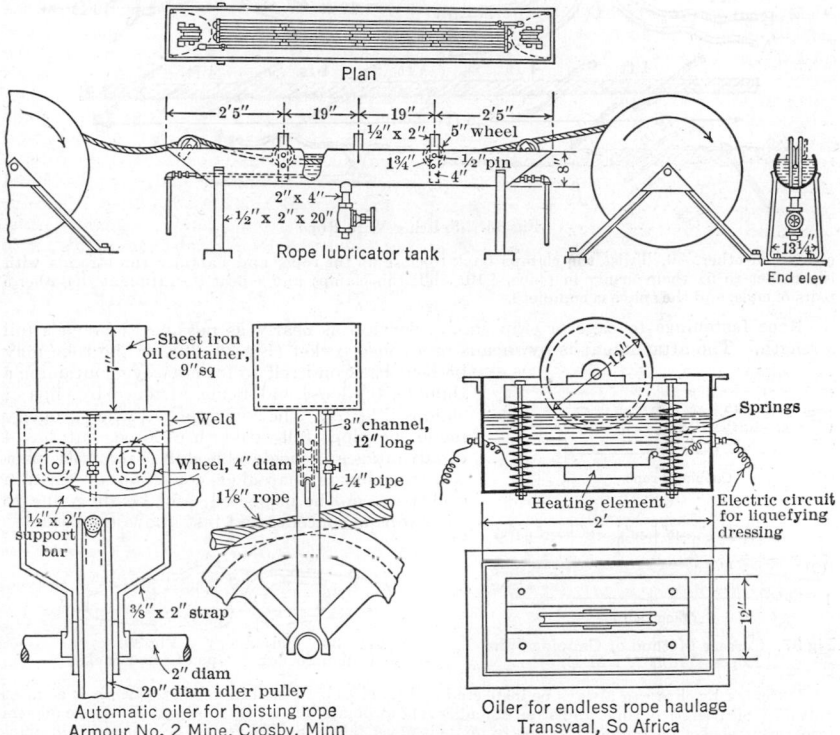

Fig 35a. Lubricating Devices for Wire Rope (37)

Splices are not permitted in hoisting ropes used for raising or lowering men; but for haulage, aerial tramway, and power transmission rope, splices may be made practically as strong as the rest of the rope (Fig 36)

For running rope, the splice should be at least 20 ft long for 0.5-in rope, increasing to 30 or 40 ft for 1.25 and 1.5-in rope. Tools required are: hammer and sharp cold-chisel, pair of strong nippers, steel marlin spike, 2 rope clamps (or small hemp rope slings with sticks, Fig 36, e), a knife and a pair of 2-lb copper or lead mallets. A bench vise is convenient. To splice (Fig 36): 1. Overlap the rope 20 ft or more, and mark center of lap on each end with string or chalk (a). 2. Unlay each end to center mark, and cut off hemp core (b). 3. Interlock the 6 unlaid strands of each end alternately, and draw together until center marks meet (c). 4. Unlay a strand A from one end, and follow it closely with opposite strand 1 of other end, laying it into the groove left open by A, and proceeding thus until all but 12 in of strand 1 are laid in (c); then cut off A an equal length and tie the strands temporarily in place. 5. Treat similarly strands 4 and D, and so on for each pair of opposite strands, stopping each pair about 1/5 of the length of splice short of the preceding pair (d). 6. Bend the rope back and forth until all strands are set in place and have equal tension. 7. Wrap ends of strands with friction tape, or strips of sheet lead, and straighten them. 8. With the vise and clamps, untwist and open the rope at one strand of the end pair; cut the hemp core at the center, draw it out slowly and follow it up with the strand until the latter occupies the center (*f*). Cut off core at end of this strand. Tuck in the other strand of the pair, being careful that their ends do not

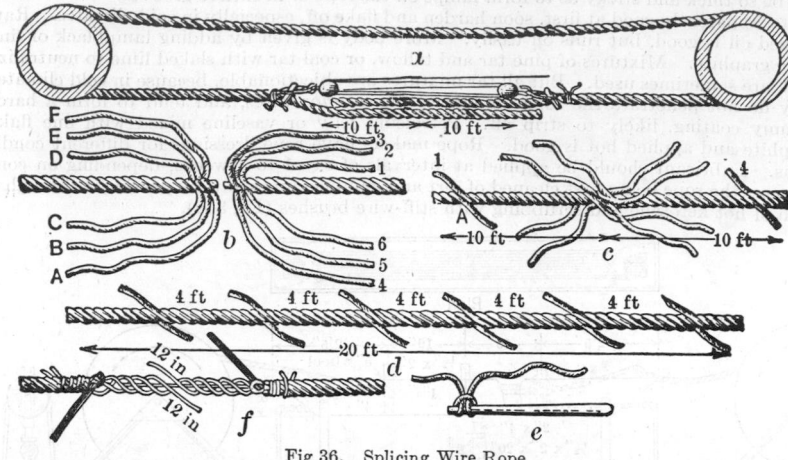

Fig 36. Splicing Wire Rope

cross each other. 9. Twist the clamps back to close up the rope, and hammer the strands with the mallet to fix them firmly in place. 10. Shift the clamps and repeat operation at the other 5 pairs of ends, and the splice is complete.

Rope fastenings to cage or skip should develop as nearly as possible the rope's full strength. The attachment is by means of a coned socket (Fig 38, 39), or the rope may be bent back on itself to form an eye containing a thimble, the loose end being fastened by clips or clamps (Fig 37). The coned socket, when properly made, develops full strength of rope, but has 4 disadvantages: considerable skill is required, poor workmanship is concealed, condition of wires in socket can not be inspected, and bending due to slack rope is concentrated just above the socket.

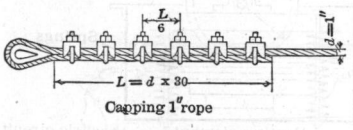

Capping 1″ rope

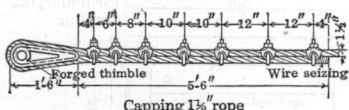

Capping 1½″ rope

Fig 37. Correct Method of Capping Wire Ropes (*Trans* A I M E)

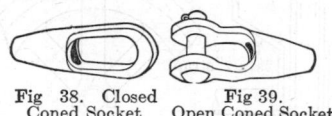

Fig 38. Closed
Coned Socket

Fig 39.
Open Coned Socket

Fastening by clips can always be inspected and requires little skill in making, but gives at most only 85% of strength of rope, and often damages rope at points where clips are applied. Rope makers recommend socket fastening; if properly made it never fails. Special forged or cast-steel thimbles or eyes, instead of usual pressed steel, should always be used for clip attachment of hoisting ropes.

Coned socket is of 2 types, closed (Fig 38) and open (Fig 39). They should be of best W-I or steel forgings, without welds, and accurately bored.

Details of attaching ropes. Bureau of Mines recommends following methods (23). CONED SOCKET: The rope is securely seized at end with soft iron wire, before end of rope is cut square; with another seizing a distance back equal to length of socket from the end. After rope is trimmed off, the end seizing is removed, the rope opened down to second seizing, hemp center cut out and wires broomed out; that is, they should be untwisted but not straightened. Then the wires are thoroughly cleaned in benzene or gasolene, as far as they are to be inserted in socket, and dipped in commercial H_2SO_4 for 30–60 sec, to clean the wires. Next, the rope end is dipped in boiling water, containing a little soda to neutralize the acid. Rope end is then inserted in socket and warmed, if temp is below 65° F, to prevent cooling the zinc-filling too rapidly. Finally, the socket is placed with its axis vert and coinciding with axis of rope, the bottom is sealed with clay or putty, and molten zinc or spelter, heated to a temp that will just char wood, is

Diam of rope, in	No of clips	Length of wrench, in	Effic, %
3/4	5	18	77.39
7/8	5	18	79.13
1	5	24	77.89
1 1/8	5	24	80.00
1 1/4	6	24	82.15

poured into the socket until full. CLAMP ATTACHMENT: The rope is bent back over the thimble, and loose end clamped with proper number of clips. Crosby type of U-bolt-and-drop-forging clip is most satisfactory. Clips are spaced a distance equal to 6 times the rope diam, the forging being against long end and the U-bolt against loose end of rope. Number of clips to develop approx 80% effic of the rope, and proper length of wrench to tighten bolts, are given in above table. Clips must be carefully inspected each day, and tightened if they show signs of loosening by stretching of the rope.

Wire rope clamps, for attaching bridle or safety chains to rope, above socket, are more commonly used at coal than at metal mines; laws of most coal districts require them. Vulcan Iron Works makes the clamps shown in Fig 40. They are usually of cast steel, but forgings are better. They are grooved to fit the rope closely, and the bolts should be finally tightened after the rope is under tension. Tests on such clamps show the ultimate strength against slipping to be about 10 000 lb per sq in of area of the bolts.

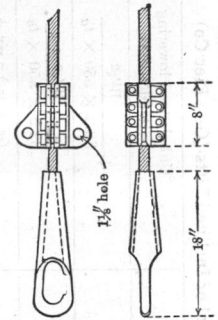

Fig 40. Rope Clamps for Bridle Chains

8. DATA FOR CALCULATING HOISTING-DUTY CYCLE (3, 33, 35)

(1) Weight and kind of material per trip.

(2) Wt of cage or skip (plus man-cage if used), cars hoisted per trip and weight of car.

(3) Diam and wt of rope (Art 7).

(4) Max tonnage per hr and per shift; number of hr per hoisting shift and number of shifts per day. Approx distribution of tonnage between levels.

(5) To select rope speed, determine the max number of trips per hr required from stated level, also time for loading and dumping. If a cage hoist, state whether the cage is landed at collar and car run off, or car is dumped by a self-dumping platform cage.

(6) Is the "slack-rope system" of hoisting used (Art 1)? If so, give length of slack and working details.

(7) Present and ultimate length of travel from loading levels to the dump or to uncaging position. Estimated time before shaft will be sunk deeper.

(8) Shallowest and deepest levels, that is, length of travel as in (7), from which hoist may be required to operate at full load for an hour or more consecutively.

(9) If shaft is inclined, give angle of inclination with horiz, or per cent grade. If it varies, give inclination and length of each stretch. Per cent grade is generally taken as: vert rise ÷ length along incline.

(10) Is hoist balanced or unbalanced? If normally balanced, when will operation be necessary with cages out of balance? Can rope speed or load, or both, be reduced for unbalanced operation if desirable? Number of unbalanced trips required in succession?

(11) To what extent and for what reasons will partial speed operation be necessary? At what loads and speeds? Duration and frequency of such operation.

(12) Will men be handled? If so, at what speed? Always in balance or sometimes out of balance?

(13) Double or single drum, fixed or clutched?

(14) Diam of drums. Width of face or number of layers of rope? If not cylindrical, furnish sketch of drum, with working diameters and number of active rope turns on each part of drum. If reel, give minimum working diam and thickness of rope.

(15) If an existing hoist, give WR^2 (Fig 16) of drums, or equivalent wt at a stated radius. If a new hoist, state makers' name, or give WR^2.

(16) Is motor or engine geared or direct connected to drum? If geared, how many reductions?

(17) For elec drive, state voltage, frequency and number of phases of supply.

(18) Capacity and character of generating station or system.

(19) Is flywheel equalization required, and for what reason? If power is purchased, obtain a copy of all clauses of proposed contract covering reservation and kw-hr charges.

(20) If hoist is to be installed underground, give dimensions and wt of largest piece that can be lowered in mine shaft and drifts.

(21) Is location dry, damp, or wet?

(22) If above 3 000 ft elev, give altitude of hoist house above sea level.

(23) If an old hoist is to be electrified, give full details; also drawings or sketches of hoist, and photographs if possible.

(24) If overwind protection is contemplated, state max rope travel above top landing or dump before damage can occur.

Table 8. Formulas for Calculating Hoist Load Diagrams. Cylindrical Drum Hoists for Vertical or Inclined Lifts (Gen Elec Co)

Period		Symbols (Fig 40a)	Balanced hoisting	Unbalanced hoisting	Unbalanced lowering (loaded)*
Hp acceleration (max)		(1)	$+\dfrac{Wv^2}{32.2 \times 550 \times t_a}$	$+\dfrac{W'v^2}{32.2 \times 550 \times t_a}$	$+\dfrac{W'v^2}{32.2 \times 550 \times t_a}$
Hp retardation (max)		(2)	$-\dfrac{Wv^2}{32.2 \times 550 \times t_b}$	$-\dfrac{W'v^2}{32.2 \times 550 \times t_b}$	$-\dfrac{W'v^2}{32.2 \times 550 \times t_b}$
Hp at beginning of accel (equiv power)		(3)	$+\dfrac{(w+w_r)v\sin\phi}{550}$	$+\dfrac{(w+w_r+w_s)v\sin\phi}{550}$	$-\dfrac{(w+w_s)v\sin\phi}{550}$
Hp at full speed at end of accel		(4)	$+\dfrac{(w+w_r-2w_a)v\sin\phi}{550}$	$+\dfrac{(w+w_r+w_s-w_a)v\sin\phi}{550}$	$-\dfrac{(w+w_s+w_a)v\sin\phi}{550}$
Hp at full speed at beginning of retard		(5)	$+\dfrac{(w-w_r+2w_b)v\sin\phi}{550}$	$+\dfrac{(w+w_s+w_b)v\sin\phi}{550}$	$-\dfrac{(w+w_s+w_r-w_b)v\sin\phi}{550}$
Hp at end of retard (equiv power)		(6)	$+\dfrac{(w-w_r)v\sin\phi}{550}$	$+\dfrac{(w+w_s)v\sin\phi}{550}$	$-\dfrac{(w+w_s+w_r)v\sin\phi}{550}$
Hp friction (aver) for vert lifts		(7)	$+7a$	$+7a$	$+7a$
Hp friction (aver) for inclined lifts		(7)	$+7a+7b+7c$	$+7a+7b+7c$	$+7a+7b+7c$

Friction Components

Period		Symbols (Fig 40a)	Balanced hoisting	Unbalanced hoisting	Unbalanced lowering (loaded)*
Hp mechanical friction	Vertical	(7a)	$+\dfrac{wv}{550}\left(\dfrac{1-E}{E}\right)$	$+\dfrac{(w+w_s+0.5w_r)v}{550}\left(\dfrac{1-E}{E}\right)‡$	$+\dfrac{(w+w_s+0.5w_r)v}{550}\left(\dfrac{1-E}{E}\right)‡$
	Inclined	(7a)	$+\left(\dfrac{wv\sin\phi}{550}+7b+7c\right)\times\left(\dfrac{1-E}{E}\right)‡$	$+\left(\dfrac{(w+w_s+0.5w_r)v\sin\phi}{550}+7b+7c\right)\times\left(\dfrac{1-E}{E}\right)‡$	$+\left(\dfrac{(w+w_s+0.5w_r)v\sin\phi}{550}-7b-7c\right)\times\left(\dfrac{1-E}{E}\right)‡$
Hp rolling friction, inclined only		(7b)	$+\dfrac{(w+2w_s)\times 0.02\,v\cos\phi}{550}$	$+\dfrac{(w+w_s)\times 0.02\,v\cos\phi}{550}$	$+\dfrac{(w+w_s)\times 0.02\,v\cos\phi}{550}$
Hp rope friction, inclined only		(7c)	$+\dfrac{w_r\times 0.10\,v\cos\phi}{550}$	$+\dfrac{w_r\times 0.10\,v\cos\phi}{550}**$	$+\dfrac{w_r\times 0.10\,v\cos\phi}{550}\times**$

* For lowering empty unbalanced cage, omit w throughout.   ** At bottom of incline only.   Value is zero at top.
‡ For normally balanced hoists operating out of balance use approx 70% of 7a.

(25) Give full information as to local conditions, and unusual requirements or details not covered by the foregoing.

9. CYLINDRICAL DRUM HOIST

A typical load diagram for hoisting in balance with cylindrical drums is shown in Fig 40a. For the power components, see Table 8, the symbols corresponding with those

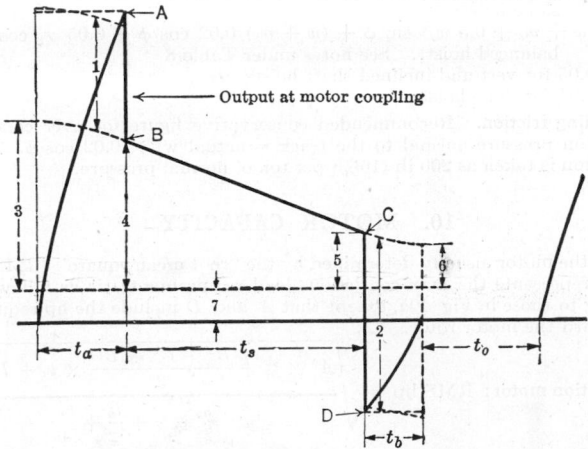

Fig 40a. Load Diagram for Cylindrical Drums and Balanced Hoisting. Horiz broken line at A shows aver motor torque required during acceleration and retardation (Gen Elec Co)

in Fig 40a. The resultant power values for each point of the diagram are obtained by combining the components listed in Table 8 as follows:

$$\text{Hp at } A = (1) + (7) + \frac{(4) + 2 \times (3)}{3}; \quad \text{Hp at } B = (4) + (7); \quad \text{Hp at } C = (5) + (7);$$

$$\text{Hp at } D = (2) + (7) + \frac{(5) + 2 \times (6)}{3}; \quad (2) \text{ is always negative, and } (7) \text{ always positive.}$$

If D is negative, motor or brakes must absorb power during retardation. If D is positive, motor must deliver power during retardation. Power requirements during retardation may be positive, negative, or zero, depending on relative values of dead load, inertia of moving parts, and time assigned for retardation.

The above calculations may be checked as follows:

    a. Ratio of net work done during the lift (in hp seconds) to net work represented by the output duty cycle (in hp seconds) should equal the mechanical efficiency.

    b. The hp seconds for acceleration and retardation should be equal.

List of Symbols in Table 8:

w = wt of material handled, lb

w_s = wt of one skip (or cage and car), lb

w_r = wt of rope per side, lb

w_a = wt of rope per side wound on during accel = $0.5 - (vt_a \times \text{wt per ft})$

w_b = wt of rope per side wound on during retard = $0.5 \, (vt_b \times \text{wt per ft})$

w_{ro} = w_r + wt dead rope turns + wt rope between drum and skip

W_o = equiv wt of revolving parts (for balanced or unbalanced operation, as case may be), reduced to drum radius, including gears, drums with clutches, head-sheaves, but not including motor armature (Fig 40a)

W = $w + 2w_s + 2w_{ro} + W_o$ (balanced hoisting)

W' = $w + w_s + w_{ro} + W_o$ (unbalanced hoisting)

v = max rope speed, ft per sec

    = $\dfrac{L}{t - 0.5(t_a + t_b)}$

t = time of one-way trip, excluding stops (found from hourly tonnage) = $\dfrac{L}{v} + 0.5$ $(t_a + t_b)$

t_a = accelerating time, seconds

t_s = full speed time, seconds

t_b = time of retardation, seconds

t_o = time at rest

L = total travel of cage or skip, ft

ϕ = angle of slope with horiz

E = mechanism effic, expressed as a decimal, includes drums, gears, sheaves and guides for vert shaft, but not including rolling or rope friction on slope or inclined shaft

Effic of hoisting mechanism, in per cent, is as follows:

First motion   Second motion   Third motion

$$E = \frac{w}{w+kW''} = \frac{0.95\,w}{w+kW''} = \frac{0.90\,w}{w+kW''}$$

where $W'' = (w + 2w_s + w_r) \sin \phi$ (for balanced vert and inclined shaft hoists)

$= (w + w_s + 0.5\,w_r) \sin \phi$ (for unbalanced vertical and inclined shaft hoists)

$= (w + 2w_s + w_r) \sin \phi + (w + 2w_s)\,0.02 \cos \phi + 0.10\,w_r \cos \phi$ (for balanced slope hoist)

$= (w + w_s + 0.5\,w_r) \sin \phi + (w + w_s)\,0.02 \cos \phi + 0.05\,w_r \cos \phi$ (for unbalanced hoist).   See notes under Table 8

$k = 0.05$ for vert and inclined shaft hoists

$k = 0.04$ for slope hoists

Car or rolling friction.   Recommended conservative figure for aver conditions is 2% or 40 lb per ton pressure normal to the track = actual wt $\times 0.02 \cos \phi$.

Rope friction is taken as 200 lb (10%) per ton of normal pressure.

10. MOTOR CAPACITY

Rating of the motor, usually determined by the "root mean square" (RMS) of the duty cycle, which represents the max continuous load requirements, is as follows, the letters corresponding to those in Fig 40a, except that A and D include the hp required to accelerate and retard the motor rotor.

For induction motor: $\text{RMS hp} = \sqrt{\dfrac{A^2 \times t_a + \dfrac{B^2 + C^2 + BC}{3} \times t_s + D^2 \times t_b}{\dfrac{t_a}{2} + t_s + \dfrac{t_b}{2} + \dfrac{t_o}{4}}}$ (24)

For direct-current motor: $\text{RMS hp} = \sqrt{\dfrac{A^2 \times t_a + \dfrac{B^2 + C^2 + BC}{3} \times t_s + D^2 \times t_b}{\dfrac{3t_a}{4} + t_s + \dfrac{3t_b}{4} + \dfrac{t_o}{2}}}$ (25)

Since the RMS of the duty cycle, which together with the overload requirements establishes the rating of the motor, can not be accurately worked out until the inertia of the armature (rotor) is known, it is customary to estimate this after a preliminary determination of the motor rating, either by inspection of the cycle or from the RMS calculated with the armature effect omitted.   It is impossible to devise any general rule by which the motor-rotor inertia can be accurately predetermined for every case, but in absence of actual values, the following is offered for estimating.

Max hp required to accelerate motor rotor in 1 second: For induction motors and, geared d-c motors, hp = 150% to 180% of normal rating.   For direct coupled d-c motors, hp = 80% to 125% of normal rating.   In general, the lower values apply to lower speed motors and vice versa, but in individual cases these values may vary considerably from the actual.   When the WR^2 of the armature is known the max hp to accelerate is:

$$\text{hp} = \frac{WR^2 \times \text{rpm}^2 \times 0.62}{1\,000\,000 \times t}$$ (26)

t being time of acceleration in seconds.

11. CONICAL DRUMS AND REELS

Factors for computations:

w = wt of material hoisted, lb

w_s = wt of one skip (or cage and car), lb

w_r = wt of rope per side, lb (Art 9)

w_h = wt of one head-sheave, lb (effective)

r_1 = smallest working radius of drum, ft

r_2 = largest working radius of drum, ft

r_{ua} = radius of up side at end of accel = $r_1 + pT_a$

r_{da} = radius of down side at end of accel = $r_2 - pT_a$

r_{ub} = radius of up side at beginning of retard = $r_2 - pT_b$

r_{db} = radius of down side at beginning of retard = $r_1 + pT_b$

p = radial pitch per rev, ft (for reels = thickness of flat rope)
T = total active turns on drum (one side)
T_a = revolutions during accel = $0.5 t_a \times rps$
T_b = revolutions during retard = $0.5 t_b \times rps$
T_s = revolutions during full speed run = $T - (T_a + T_b)$
w_{ua} = wt of rope wound on during accel = $\pi T_a (r_1 + r_{ua}) \times$ lb per ft
w_{da} = wt of rope wound off during accel = $\pi T_a (r_2 + r_{da}) \times$ lb per ft
w_{ub} = wt of rope wound on during retard = $\pi T_b (r_2 + r_{ub}) \times$ lb per ft
w_{db} = wt of rope wound off during retard = $\pi T_b (r_1 + r_{db}) \times$ lb per ft
L = total travel of cage and skip, ft
rps = max drum speed in rev per sec = $T + (t - 0.5 (t_a + t_b))$
WR_2 of drums include gears (if any), but not motor armature
Other symbols have same significance as for cylindrical drums

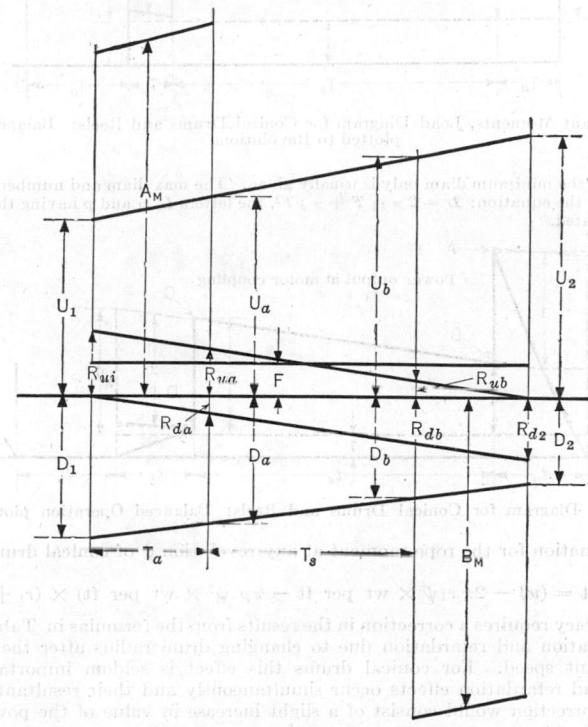

Fig 41. Component Moments, Load Diagram for Conical Drums and Reels, plotted to Revolutions

Load diagrams for conical drums and reels are readily calculated by the moment method. Formulas for component and resultant moments at different points in the cycle are given in Table 9, and moments are shown graphically in Fig 41, 42, 43 (Gen Elec Co). The hp required at motor coupling is derived as follows from Fig 43, the numbers in small parentheses referring to Table 9, column 4:

$$\text{Hp at } A = \left((1) + (7) + \frac{(4) + 2 \times (3)}{3} \right) \times \frac{2\pi \times rps}{550}$$

$$\text{Hp at } B = ((4) + (7)) \times \frac{2\pi \times rps}{550}$$

$$\text{Hp at } C = ((5) + (7)) \times \frac{2\pi \times rps}{550}$$

$$\text{Hp at } D = \left((2) + (7) + \frac{(5) + 2 \times (6)}{3} \right) \times \frac{2\pi \times rps}{550}$$

Conical-drum hoists are rarely required to operate unbalanced, but from the formulas given unbalanced diagrams may readily be calculated. The large and small working diameters of conical drums are usually known (Art 2), and the number of rope turns is directly obtained from the aver

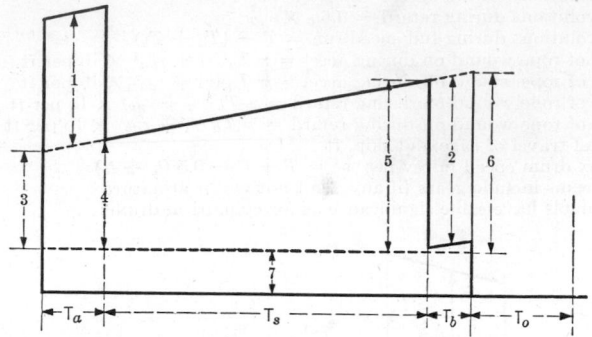

Fig 42. Resultant Moments, Load Diagram for Conical Drums and Reels; Balanced Operation plotted to Revolutions

diam. For reels the minimum diam only is usually given. The max diam and number of rope turns is obtained from the equation: $L = 2\pi r_1 T + \pi pT^2$, the letters L, r_1 and p having the significance previously indicated.

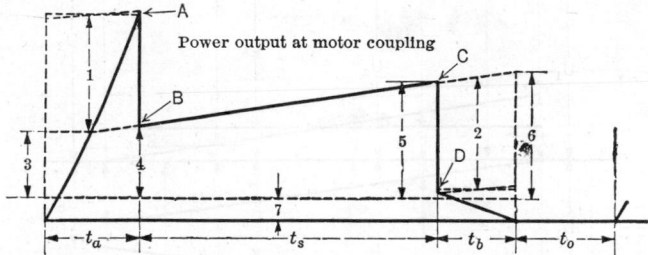

Fig 43. Power Diagram for Conical Drums and Reels; Balanced Operation plotted to Time

General equation for the rope moment at any revolution ψ of conical drums and reels is:

$$\text{Moment} = (w_r - 2\pi r_1\psi \times \text{wt per ft} - \pi p\,\psi^2 \times \text{wt per ft}) \times (r_1 + p\,\psi)$$

Strict accuracy requires a correction in the results from the formulas in Table 9, to take care of acceleration and retardation due to changing drum radius after the drum itself reaches constant speed. For conical drums this effect is seldom important, because acceleration and retardation effects occur simultaneously and their resultant is of small value. The correction would consist of a slight increase in value of the power required at A and B (Fig 43).

Example of load-cycle calculation for conical-drum hoist (3). Conditions assumed: Coal-mine hoist, vert shaft; output, 2 500 short ton per 8-hr day:

Total lift	410 ft
Wt of self-dumping cage	11 000 lb
Wt of car (one car per cage)	3 000 lb
Wt of coal per car	6 000 lb (3 short ton)
Size of rope	1.5 in diam
Wt of rope per side = (3.55 × 410)	1 420 lb
Working radii of drums, $r_1 = 4$ ft; $r_2 = 5$ ft	
WR^2 of drums	700 000 (ft-lb units)
Wt of each head-sheave	3 300 lb
Number active turns of rope = 410 ÷ 9π	14.5
Accelerating time chosen	6 sec
Retarding time chosen	5 sec
Assumed net operating time per shift	7 hr
Dumping and loading time per trip (rest period)	6 sec

Table 9. Formulas for Calculating Load Diagrams, Conical Drums and Reels, Balanced Vert Lifts (Gen Elec Co)

Period	Symbols Fig 41	Component moments	Symbols Fig 42	Resultant moments
Acceleration force (max)	A_M	(See last column)	(1)	A_M
Retardation force (max)	B_M	(See last column)	(2)	B_M
Beginning acceleration			(3)	$U_1 + R_{u1} - D_1$
Up load	U_1			
Up rope	R_{u1}	$w_r + r_1$		
Down load	D_1	$w_s \times r_2$		
Down rope		zero		
End of acceleration			(4)	$U_a + R_{ua} - D_a - R_{da}$
Up load	U_a	$(w + w_s)\, r_{ua}$		
Up rope	R_{ua}	$(w_r - w_{ua})\, r_{ua}$		
Down load	D_a	$w_s \times r_{dc}$		
Down rope	R_{da}	$w_{da} \times r_{da}$		
Beginning retardation			(5)	$U_b + R_{ub} - D_b - R_{db}$
Up load	U_b	$(w + w_s)\, r_{ub}$		
Up rope	R_{ub}	$w_{ub} \times r_{ub}$		
Down load	D_b	$w_s \times r_{db}$		
Down rope	R_{db}	$(w_r - w_{db})\, r_{db}$		
End of retardation			(6)	$U_2 - D_2 - R_{d2}$
Up load	U_2	$(w + w_s)\, r_2$		
Up rope		zero		
Down load	D_2	$w_s \times r_1$		
Down rope	R_{d2}	$w_r \times r_1$		
Friction	F	$\dfrac{w(r_1 + r_2)}{2} \times \left(\dfrac{1-E}{E}\right)$	(7)	F

Moment of acceleration force, A_M

Up load, Up rope, head sheave:
$$\frac{(w + w_s + w_r + w_h)\, 2\pi r^2{}_{ua} \times rps}{32.2 \times t_a}$$

Down load, head sheave:
$$\frac{(W_s + W_h)\, 2\pi r^2{}_{2} \times rps}{32.2 \times t_a}$$

Down rope $= \dfrac{w_r \times \pi\,(r_1{}^2 + r_2{}^2) \times rps}{32.2 \times t_a}$

Drum $= \dfrac{W R^2 \times 2\pi \times rps}{32.2 \times t_a}$

Total $= A_M =$ sum of above components

Moment of retardation force, B_M

Up load, head sheave:
$$\frac{(w + w_s + w_h)\, 2\pi r^2{}_{2} \times rps}{32.2 \times t_b}$$

Up rope $= \dfrac{w_r \times \pi\,(r_1{}^2 + r_2{}^2) \times rps}{32.2 \times t_b}$

Down load, Down rope, head sheave:
$$\frac{(w_z + w_r + w_h)\, 2\pi r^2{}_{db} \times rps}{32.2 \times t_b}$$

Drum $= \dfrac{W R^2 \times 2\pi \times rps}{32.2 \times t_b}$

Total $= B_M =$ sum of above components

The procedure is as follows (refer to Tables 8 and 9):

$$\text{Trips per min} = \frac{2\,500}{7 \times 3 \times 60} = \ldots\ldots\ldots\ldots\ldots\ldots\ldots\ldots\ldots\ldots\ldots \quad 2$$

$$\text{Time per trip} = {}^{60}/_2 = \ldots\ldots\ldots\ldots\ldots\ldots\ldots\ldots\ldots\ldots\ldots\ldots\ldots\ldots \quad 30.0 \text{ sec}$$

$$\text{Equivalent full-speed hoisting time} = \left(30 - 6 - \frac{6+5}{2}\right)\ldots \quad 18.5 \text{ sec}$$

$$\text{Max drum speed} = 14.5 \div 18.5 = 0.784 \ rps = \ldots\ldots\ldots\ldots \quad 47.0 \text{ rpm}$$

$$t_s = 18.5 - \frac{6+5}{2} = 13 \text{ sec} \qquad\qquad T_a = \frac{6 \times 0.784}{2} = 2.35 \text{ rope turns}$$

$$p = \text{radial pitch} = \frac{5-4}{14.5} = 0.069 \text{ ft.} \qquad T_b = \frac{5 \times 0.784}{2} = 1.96 \text{ rope turns}$$

$$T_s = 14.5 - (2.35 + 1.96) = 10.19 \text{ rope turns}$$
$$r_{ua} = 4 + 2.35 \times 0.069 = 4.162 \text{ ft}$$
$$r_{da} = 5 - 2.35 \times 0.069 = 4.838 \text{ ft}$$
$$r_{ub} = 5 - 1.96 \times 0.069 = 4.865 \text{ ft}$$
$$r_{db} = 4 + 1\,96 \times 0.069 = 4.135 \text{ ft}$$
$$w_{ua} = \pi \times 2.35 \ (4 + 4.162) \times 3.55 = 214 \text{ lb}$$
$$w_{da} = \pi \times 2.35 \ (5 + 4.838) \times 3.55 = 258 \text{ lb}$$
$$w_{ub} = \pi \times 1.96 \ (5 + 4.865) \times 3.55 = 216 \text{ lb}$$
$$w_{db} = \pi \times 1.96 \ (4 + 4.135) \times 3.55 = 178 \text{ lb}$$

$$E = \frac{0.95 \times 6\,000}{6\,000 + 0.04\,(6\,000 + 6\,000 + 22\,000 + 1\,420)} = 76.0\% \ \text{(2nd motion)}$$

Calculation of moments:

$$
\begin{aligned}
U &= (6\,000 + 3\,000 + 11\,000) \times 4 &&= 80\,000 \text{ ft-lb} \\
R_{u1} &= \qquad\qquad\qquad\quad 1420 \ \times 4 &&= 5\,680 \text{ ''} \\
D &= \qquad (3\,000 + 11\,000) \times 5 &&= 70\,000 \text{ ''} \\
U_a &= (6\,000 + 3\,000 + 11\,000) \times 4.162 &&= 83\,240 \text{ ''} \\
R_{ua} &= \qquad (1420 - 214) \times 4.162 &&= 5\,019 \text{ ''} \\
D_a &= \qquad (3\,000 + 11\,000) \times 4.838 &&= 67\,732 \text{ ''} \\
R_{da} &= \qquad\qquad\qquad\quad 258 \ \times 4.838 &&= 1\,248 \text{ ''} \\
U_b &= (6\,000 + 3\,000 + 11\,000) \times 4.865 &&= 97\,300 \text{ ''} \\
r_{ub} &= \qquad\qquad\qquad\quad 216 \ \times 4.865 &&= 1\,051 \text{ ''} \\
d_b &= \qquad (3\,000 + 11\,000) \times 4.135 &&= 57\,890 \text{ ''} \\
r_{db} &= \qquad (1\,420 - 178) \times 4.135 &&= 5\,136 \text{ ''} \\
u_2 &= (6\,000 + 3\,000 + 11\,000) \times 5 &&= 100\,000 \text{ ''} \\
d_2 &= \qquad (3\,000 + 11\,000) \times 4 &&= 56\,000 \text{ ''} \\
r_{d2} &= \qquad\qquad\qquad\quad 1\,420 \ \times 4 &&= 5\,680 \text{ ''}
\end{aligned}
$$

$$F = 6\,000 \times \frac{(4+5)}{2} \times \frac{(1-0.76)}{0.76} \quad = 8\,500 \text{ ''}$$

Acceleration moment "A_M":

Up load, up rope, and head sheave =

$$\frac{(6\,000 + 3\,000 + 11\,000 + 1\,420 + 3\,300)2\pi \times \overline{4.162}^2 \times 0.784}{32.2 \times 6} = 10\,950$$

$$\text{Down rope} = \frac{1\,420 \times \pi(4^2 + 5^2) \times 0.784}{32.2 \times 6} \ldots\ldots\ldots\ldots\ldots\ldots = 743$$

Down load and head sheave =

$$\frac{(11\,000 + 3\,000 + 3\,300)2\pi \times 5^2 \times 0.784}{32.2 \times 6} = 11\,050$$

$$\text{Drums and gears} = \frac{700\,000 \times 2\pi \times 0.784}{32.2 \times 6} \ldots\ldots\ldots\ldots\ldots = 17\,900$$

$$\text{Total ``}A_M\text{''} = 40\,643 \text{ ft-lb}$$

Retardation moment "B_M":

Up load and head sheave =

$$\frac{(6\,000 + 3\,000 + 11\,000 + 3\,300)2\pi 5^2 \times 0.784}{32.2 \times 5} = 17\,850$$

Up rope = $\dfrac{1\,420 \times \pi(4^2 + 5^2) \times 0.784}{32.2 \times 5}$ . . . . = 892

Down load, rope and head sheave =

$$\frac{(11\,000 + 3\,000 + 1\,420 + 3\,300)2\pi \times \overline{4.135}^2 \times 0.784}{32.2 \times 5} = 9\,800$$

Drums and gears = $\dfrac{700\,000 \times 2\pi \times 0.784}{32.2 \times 5}$ . . . . = 21\,500

Total "B_M" = 50\,042 ft-lb

Resultant moments (see Table 9):

(1) =			40 643 ft-lb
(2) =			50 042 "
(3) =	80 000 + 5 680 − 70 000		= 15 680 "
(4) =	83 240 + 5 019 − 67 732 − 1 248		= 19 279 "
(5) =	97 300 + 1 051 − 57 890 − 5 136		= 35 325 "
(6) =	100 000 − 56 000 − 5 680		= 38 320 "
(7) =			8 500 "

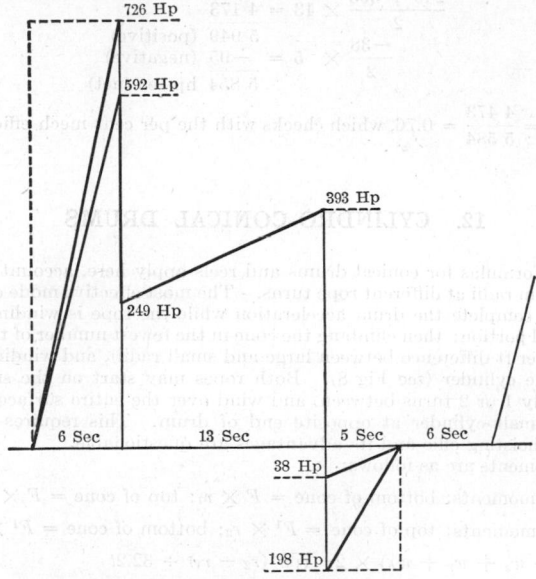

Fig 44.   Power Diagram for Conical Drum (Gen Elec Co)

Power diagram (Fig 44):

$$\text{Hp at } ``A'' = \left[40\,643 + 8\,500 + \frac{19\,279 + (2 \times 15\,680)}{3} \right] \times \frac{2\pi \times 0.784}{550} = 592 \text{ hp}$$

$$\text{Hp at } ``B'' = [19\,279 + 8\,500] \times \frac{2\pi \times 0.784}{550} = 249 \text{ hp}$$

$$\text{Hp at } ``C'' = [35\,325 + 8\,500] \times \frac{2\pi \times 0.784}{550} = 393 \text{ hp}$$

$$\text{Hp at } ``D'' = \left[-50\,042 + 8\,500 + \frac{35\,325 + (2 \times 38\,320)}{3} \right] \times \frac{2\pi \times 0.784}{550} = -38 \text{ hp}$$

Estimating the *rms* of this cycle by inspection to be 500 hp for induction-motor drive, and assuming the max power to accelerate the armature in one sec to be 1.6 times the assumed rating, the acceleration peak = 592 + 134 = 726 hp, and retardation peak = $-38 - 160 = -198$ hp.

$$\text{The } rms = \sqrt{\frac{\overline{726}^2 \times 6 + \dfrac{(\overline{249}^2 + \overline{393}^2 + 249 \times 393)}{3} \times 13 + \overline{198}^2 \times 5}{{}^6/_2 + 13 + {}^5/_2 + {}^6/_4}} = 486 \text{ hp}$$

Selecting a standard 500-hp, 450-rpm motor and checking back, using the actual WR^2 of its rotor, to accelerate requires 127 hp, to retard 152 hp, and the *rms* is 482 hp. The motor selected should be capable of operating continuously at the *rms* output, with a temp rise not exceeding 40° C. As full speed of drum is 47 rpm, single-reduction gearing will be suitable, for the motor speed selected.

Applying the checks mentioned:

$$\text{Net work done in shaft} = \frac{6\,000 \times 410}{550} = 4\,473 \text{ hp-sec} \qquad (a)$$

Area under load diagram is computed as follows:

$$\frac{592}{2} \times 6 = 1\,776$$

$$\frac{249 + 393}{2} \times 13 = 4\,173$$

$$\begin{array}{rl} & \underline{5\,949} \text{ (positive)} \\ \dfrac{-38}{2} \times 5 = & \underline{-95} \text{ (negative)} \\ & 5\,854 \text{ hp-sec (net)} \end{array} \qquad (b)$$

Ratio (a) to $(b) = \dfrac{4\,473}{5\,584} = 0.76$, which checks with the per cent mech effic E, used in the calculations.

12. CYLINDRO-CONICAL DRUMS

The general formulas for conical drums and reels apply here, account being taken of the changing drum radii at different rope turns. The most effective mode of arranging the rope turns is to complete the drum acceleration while the rope is winding on the small-radius cylindrical portion; then climbing the cone in the fewest number of turns (minimum being one turn per ft difference between large and small radii), and winding remainder of rope on the large cylinder (see Fig 8). Both ropes may start on the small cylindrical portion, with only 1 or 2 turns between, and wind over the entire surface, finishing with both ropes on small cylinder at opposite end of drum. This requires a large motor, results in lower hoisting effic and its advantages are questionable.

The force moments are as follows:

Accelerating moments: bottom of cone $= F \times r_1$; top of cone $= F \times r_2$.

Retardation moments: top of cone $= F^1 \times r_2$; bottom of cone $= F^1 \times r_1$

where $F = (w + w_s + w_r + w_h) \times 2\pi \overline{\text{rps}} \ (r_2 - r_1) \div 32.2t$

and $F^1 = (w_s + w_r + w_h) \times (2\pi \overline{\text{rps}}) \times (r_2 - r_1) \div 32.2t$,

where r_1 = radius small cylinder (ft) r_2 = radius large cylinder;

t = time during winding (or unwinding) on cone, sec;

w_r = wt of rope hanging at bottom of cone + 1/2 wt of rope wound on cone. Other symbols have meanings given at beginning of Art 11.

Example of load-cycle calculations for cylindro-conical drum (3). Following are calculations for a hoist where conditions are the same as for the preceding conical-drum problem:

Small diam...................	8 ft	Time for acceleration.........	6 sec.
Large diam...................	10 ft	Time for retardation..........	5 sec.
Active turns on conical portion.	4	Time at full speed...........	13 sec.
WR^2 of drum................	800 000 ft-lb^2		

First determine distribution of rope turns on drum:

Let Z = rps of drum at full speed.

$$8\pi \times \frac{6Z}{2} = \text{rope wound on during acceleration} \dots\dots\dots\dots\dots\dots\dots\dots\dots \quad (1)$$

$$10\pi \times \frac{5Z}{2} = \text{rope wound on during retardation} \dots\dots\dots\dots\dots\dots\dots\dots\dots \quad (2)$$

$$\frac{10+8}{2} \times \pi \times 4 = \text{rope wound on cone} \dots\dots\dots\dots\dots\dots\dots\dots\dots\dots\dots\dots \quad (3)$$

$$10\pi(13Z - 4) = \text{rope wound on large cylinder during full speed} \dots\dots\dots\dots\dots \quad (4)$$

The sum of (1), (2), (3), and (4) is 410 ft of rope, which gives $Z = 0.75$ rps = 45 rpm

$$\text{Turns on small cylinder} \quad = T_a = \frac{6 \times 0.75}{2} = \quad 2.25 \text{ turns}$$

$$\text{Turns during retardation} = T_b = \frac{5 \times 0.75}{2} = \quad 1.88 \text{ turns}$$

$$\text{Turns on large cylinder} \quad = T_b + 13Z - 4 = 7.63 \text{ turns}$$

$$\text{Total turns on drum} \qquad\qquad\qquad = 13.88$$

(Also note $13.88 \div 18.5$ sec = 0.75 rps)

$$\text{Energy lost in friction} = \frac{4\,475 \times 1 - 0.76}{0.76} = 1\,415 \text{ hp-sec}$$

$$\text{Aver hp friction} = \frac{1\,415}{18.5} = 76.5 \text{ hp}$$

$$\text{Aver hp friction torque} = \frac{76.5}{2\pi \times 0.750 \div 550} = 8\,900 \text{ ft-lb}$$

$$\text{Hp load} = \text{moment} \times \frac{2\pi \times 0.750}{550} = 0.00856 \times M$$

Summation of moments:

Time-sec	0	6	6	11.34	11.34	13.19
No turns	0	2.25	2.25	6.25	6.25	7.63
Up load	80 000	80 000	80 000	100 000	100 000	100 000
Up rope	5 680	4 880	4 880	4 150	4 150	3 400
Friction	8 900	8 900	8 900	8 900	8 900	8 900
Acceleration	39 950	39 950	2 670	3 180	....	....
Total (+) M	134 530	133 730	96 350	116 230	113 050	112 300
Down load	70 000	70 000	70 000	70 000	70 000	70 000
Down rope	0	1 225	1 225	3 400	3 400	4 150
Retardation	....	....	....	....	....	....
Total (−) M	70 000	71 225	71 225	73 400	73 400	74 150
Net M	64 530	62 505	25 125	42 830	39 650	38 150
Horsepower	553	535	215	366	340	327

Time-sec	13.19	18.53	18.53	19	19	24
No turns	7.63	11.63	11.63	12.01	12.01	13.88
Up load	100 000	100 000	100 000	100 000	100 000	100 000
Up rope	3 400	1 225	1 225	1 000	1 000	0
Friction	8 900	8 900	8 900	8 900	8 900	8 900
Acceleration	....	....	....	....	....	....
Total (+) M	112 300	110 125	110 125	109 900	109 900	108 900
Down load	70 000	56 000	56 000	56 000	56 000	56 000
Down rope	4 150	4 880	4 880	5 040	5 040	5 680
Retardation	2 450	2 000	....	....	49 730	49 730
Total (−) M	76 600	62 880	60 880	61 040	110 770	111 410
Net M	35 700	47 245	49 245	48 860	− 870	− 2510
Horsepower	306	405	422	418	− 7.5	− 21.5

Fig 45 shows component and resultant moments, plotted against rev of drum, and Fig 46 is the power diagram, plotted from the values of hp and time calculated above. The rms value of this cycle is somewhat less than that for the simple conical drum (Fig 44), and the overall effic of hoisting is greater, due to lower values of power required during acceleration and retardation.

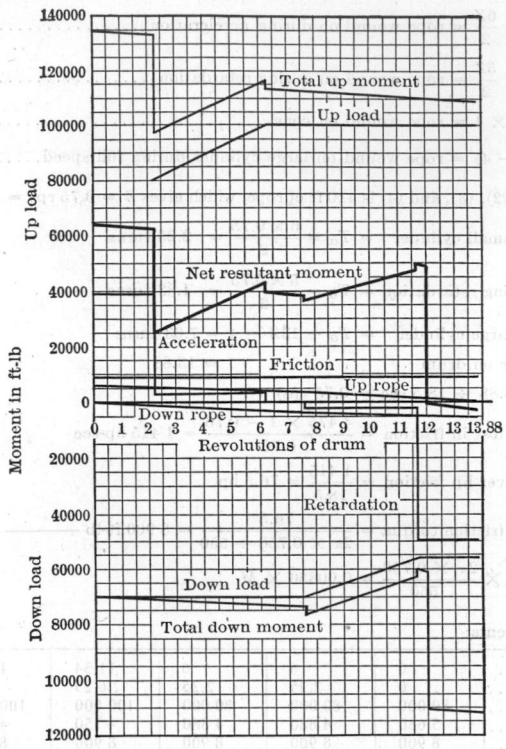

Fig 45. Component and Resultant Moments, Cylindro-conical Drum, Plotted to Revolutions (Gen Elec Co)

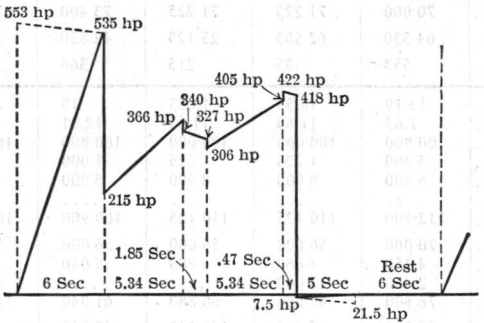

Fig 46. Power Diagram, Cylindro-conical Drum, Plotted to Time

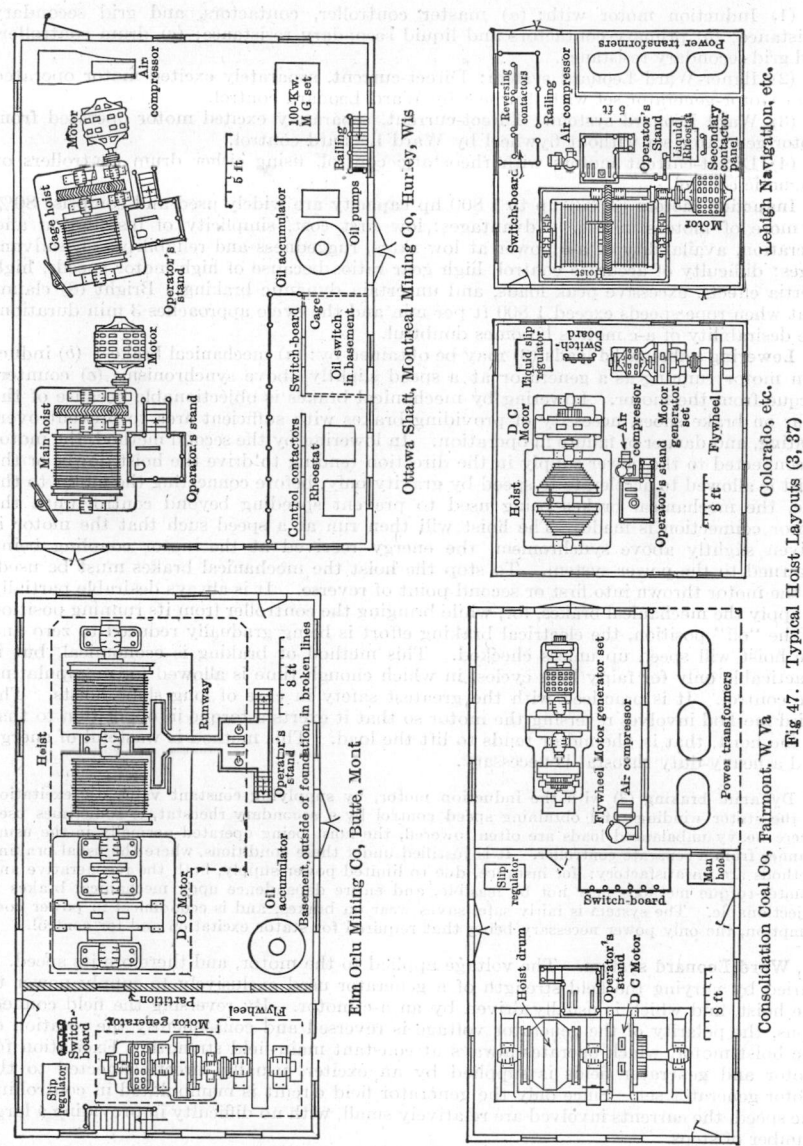

Fig 47.   Typical Hoist Layouts (3, 37)

13. ELECTRIC HOISTS

Electric drives (3) now in use are:

(1) Induction motor with: (*a*) master controller, contactors, and grid secondary resistance; (*b*) primary contactors and liquid secondary resistance; (*c*) drum controllers and grid secondary resistance.

(2) Ilgner-Ward Leonard system: Direct-current, separately excited motor operated from motor-generator set with flywheel by Ward Leonard control.

(3) Ward Leonard system. Direct-current, separately excited motor operated from motor-generator set without flywheel by Ward Leonard control.

(4) Direct-current motors with rheostatic control, using either drum controllers or magnetic control.

Induction motors (3, 33) up to 1 800 hp capacity are widely used and comprise 80% or more of motors in use. Advantages: low first cost, simplicity of installation and operation, availability of a-c power at low rates, ruggedness and reliability. Disadvantages: difficulty of accurate control, high gear ratios because of high motor speeds, high inertia effects, excessive peak loads, and uncertain dynamic braking. Bright (8) claims that when rope speeds exceed 1 800 ft per min and the cycle approaches 3 min duration, the desirability of a-c motors becomes doubtful.

Lowering unbalanced loads (3) may be obtained by: (*a*) mechanical brakes; (*b*) induction motor running as a generator at a speed slightly above synchronism; (*c*) counter-torque from the motor. Lowering by mechanical brakes is objectionable because of the wear on brake shoes, necessity of providing brakes with sufficient area to prevent overheating, and danger of failure in operation. In lowering by the second method, the motor is connected to the power supply in the direction tending to drive the hoist down, or the hoist is allowed to accelerate to speed by gravity only, before connecting the motor to the line, the mechanical brakes being used to prevent speeding beyond control until the motor connection is made. The hoist will then run at a speed such that the motor is driven slightly above synchronism, the energy received at the motor coupling being returned to the power system. To stop the hoist the mechanical brakes must be used, or the motor thrown into first or second point of reverse. It is always desirable partially to apply the mechanical brakes, for, while bringing the controller from its running position to the "off" position, the electrical braking effort is being gradually reduced to zero and the hoist will speed up unless checked. This method of braking is economical, but is practicable only for fairly long cycles, in which enough time is allowed for manipulating the control. It is practiced with the greatest safety in case of long slope hoists. The third method involves reversing the motor so that it exerts a torque in opposition to that of the hoist, that is, the motor tends to lift the load. This method is wasteful of energy and a heavy-duty rheostat is necessary.

Dynamic braking (3) with the induction motor, by supplying constant value d-c excitation to the stator windings and obtaining speed control by a secondary rheostat, is sometimes used where heavy unbalanced loads are often lowered, the hoist being operated normally in the usual manner from a separate controller. It is justified under these conditions, where the usual braking methods are unsatisfactory; for instance, due to limited power supply, both the regenerative and counter-torque methods may not be feasible, and entire dependence upon mechanical brakes is objectionable. The system is fairly safe, saves wear on brakes, and is economical in power consumption, the only power necessary being that required for stator excitation and for control.

Ward Leonard system. The voltage applied to the motor, and therefore its speed, is varied by varying the field strength of a generator used exclusively to supply power to the hoist, and which is usually driven by an a-c motor. By reversing the field connections, the polarity of the generator voltage is reversed and consequently the rotation of the hoist motor, which operates always at constant main-field strength. Excitation for motor and generator fields is supplied by an exciter, usually direct-connected to the motor-generator set. Since only the generator field circuit is manipulated in controlling the speed, the currents involved are relatively small, with no difficulty in providing a large number of steps.

Principal factors justifying Ward Leonard control are: (*a*) accuracy of control (desirable for high-speed hoists, rapid rate of hoisting or frequent shifting); (*b*) increased safety in operation; (*c*) higher effic on certain duty cycles; (*d*) equalization of power demands; (*e*) possibility of elimination of gearing.

Ilgner-Ward Leonard system. A flywheel, mounted on the motor-generator shaft, acts as an equalizer, cutting down the peak power demand. It is desirable where high peaks are liable to disturb an electrical system, or a heavy charge is made for peak demands.

Comparison of results of different electric drives. See (3) and Tables 10, 10a.

The data for the coal hoist are as given in Art 11; Data for metal-mine hoist (Table 10a) are:

Lift, max.	2 000 ft
Skip	6 000 lb
Ore per trip	8 000 lb
Rope speed	1 765 ft per min
Time for acceleration	15 sec
Time for retardation	8 sec
Time at full speed (2 000-ft lift)	56.5 sec
Rest period	15 sec
Rope, round for cylindrical drums	1 3/8 in
Rope, flat for reels, 4 to 11 ft diam	1/2 by 6 in
Cylindrical drums	9 ft diam
Mechanical effic, 2nd motion a-c motor	80%
Mechanical effic, 1st motion d-c motor	85%

For the coal hoist, the conical drum shows some advantage over the cylindrical in effic, peak-power demand, and size of motor. For the ore hoist, reels would show a decided advantage over cylindrical drums if it were unnecessary to hoist from shallower levels. When so operating, reels are disadvantageous both as to effic and peak load, and the driving motor required is therefore as large as for cylindrical drums. The effic for the aver lift is about the same as for cylindrical drums. For the coal hoist, the d-c equipments show higher effic than the induction. In a measure this is also true of the ore hoist without flywheel, there being some advantage in effic of the induction motor over the Ilgner equipment, although the latter very greatly reduces the peak load. The adoption of these d-c systems is most often justified by considering the advantages of control and reduced power demand, rather than the question of increased effic.

Table 10. Coal-mine Hoist (Gen Elec Co)

	Cylindrical drums, 540 ft lift			Conical drums, 540 ft lift		
	Induction motor	Ward Leonard (no flywheel)	Ilgner-Ward Leonard (with flywheel)	Induction motor	Ward Leonard (no flywheel)	Ilgner-Ward Leonard (with flywheel)
Net work	6 880 hp-sec	6 880 hp-sec	6 880 hp-sec	6 880 hp-sec	6 880 hp-sec	6 880 hp-sec
Hoist friction	1 720 hp-sec	1 210 hp-sec	1 210 hp-sec	1 720 hp-sec	1 210 hp-sec	1 210 hp-sec
Loss in driving apparatus*	1 576 hp-sec	5 910 hp-sec	7 910 hp-sec	1 296 hp-sec	4 910 hp-sec	6 910 hp-sec
Rheostatic loss	10 404 hp-sec			6 249 hp-sec		
Total energy consumed	20 580 hp-sec	14 000 hp-sec	16 000 hp-sec	16 145 hp-sec	13 000 hp-sec	15000 hp-sec
Over-all effic	33.5 per cent	49.2 per cent	43.0 per cent	42.6 per cent	53.0 per cent	46.0 per cent
Peak-power demand	2 200 hp	2 100 hp	560 hp	1 750 hp	1 550 hp	520 hp
Motor rating	1 100 hp	900 hp	900 hp	850 hp	700 hp	700 hp

* Includes losses in slip regulator for Ilgner system

Table 10a. Metal-mine Hoist

	Cylindrical drums, 2 000 ft lift			Reels, 2 000 ft lift		
	Induction motor	Ward Leonard (no flywheel)	Ilgner-Ward Leonard (with flywheel)	Induction motor	Ward Leonard (no flywheel)	Ilgner-Ward Leonard (with flywheel)
Net work	29 100 hp-sec	29 100 hp-sec	29 100 hp-sec	29 100 hp-sec	29 100 hp-sec	29 100 hp-sec
Hoist friction	5 170 hp-sec	4 825 hp-sec	4 825 hp-sec	5 170 hp-sec	4 825 hp-sec	4 825 hp-sec
Loss in driving apparatus*	8 290 hp-sec	19 075 hp-sec	27 075 hp-sec	8 730 hp-sec	26 075 hp-sec	27 075 hp-sec
Rheostatic loss	17 440 hp-sec			7 000 hp-sec		
Total energy consumed	60 000 hp-sec	53 000 hp-sec	61 000 hp-sec	50 000 hp-sec	50 000 hp-sec	61 000 hp-sec
Over-all effic	48.5 per cent	55.0 per cent	47.8 per cent	58.3 per cent	58.3 per cent	47.8 per cent
Peak-power demand	1 800 hp	1 670 hp	615 hp	1 550 hp	1 250 hp	615 hp
Motor rating	900 hp	750 hp	750 hp	900 hp	750 hp	750 hp

* Includes losses in slip regulator for Ilgner system

Costs of electric drive (36), 1938:

Wound-rotor induction motors for geared drive. (*a*) 200-hp, 600 rpm, 2 200-volt, 3-phase, 60-cycle motor with magnetic control and switch board, $22.50 per hp. Same as

Table 10b. Recent Electric-hoist Installations

	1	2	3	4	5	6
	International Nickel Co	Ottumwa Iron Wks	Homestake Mining Co	Ottumwa Iron Wks	Anthracite Mine in Penna	Northern Iron Ore Mine*
Maker	Nordberg	Ottumwa Iron Wks	Nordberg	Ottumwa Iron Wks	Allis Chalmers	Allis Chalmers
Type of drive	Ward Leonard	a-c motor	Ward Leonard	a-c motor	a-c motor	Ward Leonard
Motor voltage		440, 60-cycle		2 200, 60-cycle	440, 60-cycle	
Hp of motors	two 1 200 d-c	one 1 000	two 1 500 d-c	250	600	2 250 d-c
No of gear reductions	1	1	1	1	1	direct
Peak horse power	3 250	1 300	3 050	450	985	4 200
Power per shaft h-p hr		5.2 kw-hr per trip		1.56 kw-hr per trip	1.45 kw-hr per trip	1.42 kw-hr per trip
Drums	2-cylinder	1-cylinder—conical	2-cylinder—conical	2-cylinder	2-cylinder—conical	2-cylinder
Size of drums, diam × face	14' × 8'	6 1/2' and 11' diam	12' and 25' diam	7' × 4'	9' to 15' diam × 9', 4"	12' × 7' 6"
Keyed to shaft or loose	1 keyed, 1 loose	keyed	loose	keyed	1 keyed, 1 loose	1 keyed, 1 loose
Type of brake	post	post	post	post	post	post
Power for auxiliaries	oil press	oil press	oil press	oil press	oil press	oil press
Unbalanced rope pull, lb	45 000	16 000	56 900	6 000	27 220	49 100
Aver hoisting speed, ft per min	1 638	1 140	2 100	770	1 350	
Max hoisting speed, ft per min	2 250	1 600	2 750	900	1 785	2 200
Depth of shaft, ft	2 000	550	5 400	410	1 728	450
Inclination of shaft	90°	90°	90°	90°	90°	90°
Time for caging, sec		4	6	8	8	5
Size of rope, in	1 3/4	1 5/8	1 1/8	1 1/2	1 1/2	1 3/4
Skip or cage and wt, lb	13 000	skip 13 000	12 500	cage and car 22 700	13 000	9 200
Weight of ore, lb	21 000	16 000	14 000	6 000	8 000	17 900
Tons hoisted and time	3 300, 7 hr	870 per hr	1100, 7 hr	141 per hr	1 800, 7 1/2 hr	1 200, 8 hr
Hoisting time per trip	80.33 sec	29 sec in motion	161 sec	32 sec in motion	100 sec	140 sec
Time of accel, sec	20	6	15	5	10	15
Time of retard, sec	20	6	15	5	10	10
Wt of hoist, lb	92 000	175 000 †	1 100 000	97 000†	358 000	450 000
No of levels served		one †		one	4	several
First cost, fob factory		$41 000†		$19 500†	$85 000	$96 800

* Change from 1 000 hp, 2 200-volt a-c hoist.   † These weights and prices include motor and control equipment.

above, but with liquid-rheostat secondary control, $31.50 per hp. (b) 600-hp, 459 rpm, 2 200-volt, 3-phase, 60-cycle motor, with magnetic control, $15 per hp; with liquid rheostat, $17.50 per hp. (c) 1 300-hp, 360 rpm, 2 200-volt, 3-phase, 60-cycle motor, with magnetic control or liquid rheostat, $14.50 per hp.

D-c motor, geared to drum, with motor-generator set and Ward Leonard control: (a) 800-hp, 350 rpm, 550-volt d-c motor, 700-kw motor-generator, with 500-kva synchronous motor, $35 per hp; (b) same as (a), but with 600-hp induction motor and 18 000-lb flywheel, Ilgner control, $48 per hp.

D-c motor, direct-connected to drum, with motor-generator set and Ward Leonard control: (a) 950-hp, 93 rpm, 550-volt d-c motor, 700-kw motor generator, with 500-kva synchronous motor, $43.50 per hp; (b) same as (a), but with 600-hp induction motor and 18 000-lb flywheel, $53.50 per hp. Table 10b gives makers' data and costs of recent installations.

Automatic hoisting (42) at Emma Nevada shaft is obtained by a push button at skip loader's station of either of two mine levels. Pushing the button starts the hoist, automatically controlling acceleration, full-speed running, retardation, final stop at dumping point and the setup for reversing rotation on the next cycle. A third button is used for test purpose. Provision is made for manual operation of the master controller, when changing the drum adjustment for the two levels, or for hoisting men. The hoist is of the balanced cylindrical-drum type, with Ilgner-Ward Leonard drive, and operates at depths of 646 and 826 ft, with a 12-ton load and 10 1/2-ton skip. Similar hoists are used at Miami (43), Inspiration Copper Co, and Butte.

14. HOISTING ENGINE CALCULATIONS

Factors for general case: 1. Daily output required governs number of hoists per day or shift. This, in turn, depends on load per trip, as determined by size of car (or other local conditions), depth of shaft, type of plant, and allowances for delays and handling men and supplies. 2. Gross load = wt of ore + car + cage + rope. 3. Size of rope is determined by wt of ore, car and cage, multiplied by starting factor of 2 to convert dead into live load, plus weight of rope. Rope weight must first be assumed, and one or more approximations made. (For Bending Stresses in hoisting ropes, see Art 7.) 4. Max unbalanced load, when hoisting in 2-compartment shaft, equals wt ore + rope. 5. Total time for a complete hoist. These five factors must be harmonized for selecting type and power of hoist, suitable for conditions; geared hoist for low, direct-acting for high, hoisting speeds.

Total time per load. For SINGLE-COMPARTMENT SHAFT, this covers down trip + up trip + delays at bottom and top, for caging cars; or, with skips, for loading and dumping. This also holds good, in general, for double-compartment shaft, with independent drums operated by clutches. For DOUBLE-COMPARTMENT SHAFT, hoisting in balance with fixed (keyed) drums, or single drum with over and under rope, the total time per load is the elapsed time from the moment cage stops at bottom on down trip until it stops at top on up trip.

Delays. Caging car, with best track arrangements, takes 5 to 10 sec, which may be greatly exceeded when loading facilities are poor. With skips and power-operated loading chutes, loading time may be reduced to 3 to 9 sec (10). When hoisting in balance, delays at top and bottom are coincident and only the longer one needs to be allowed for. If hoisting capacity permits, larger allowances should be made; preceding figures are not obtainable with hand caging or hand loading of skips. If men and supplies are handled with ore hoist (usually requiring 20–40% of each shift), it is best to allow total time for them and compute delays on net time.

Hoisting time and speed. Time per trip includes periods of acceleration, uniform speed, and retardation. Acceleration and its period vary widely. For shafts exceeding say 600 ft depth, acceleration is from 2 to 8 ft per sec per sec (11); for shallow shafts and large tonnages, it may be 6 to 12 ft. At latter rate acceleration period may run into retardation period, with practically no time of uniform speed (as with conical drum or reel). Uniform speed period varies with depth of shaft and hoisting speed. With geared hoists max speed rarely exceeds 1 000 ft per min. With direct-acting hoists, 4 500 to 5 000 ft per min is sometimes attained. Speeds of 2 000 to 3 000 ft are common. Tendency is to obtain increased capacity by increasing load rather than speed, which conduces to safety and less wear and tear.

Let a = accel, ft per sec per sec; v = mean veloc, ft per sec; v_1 = max veloc, ft per sec; t = hoisting time, sec; t_1 = time of accel, sec; t_2 = time of max speed, sec; h = depth of shaft, ft; s = distance passed over during accel, ft. Then, $t_1 = v_1 \div a$, and $s = v_1^2 \div 2a$; and if time and distance of accel and retardation be assumed equal,

$$t_2 = \frac{h - 2s}{v_1} = \frac{h}{v_1} - \frac{v_1}{a}$$

also,
$$t = 2t_1 + t_2 = \frac{2v_1}{a} + \frac{h}{v_1} - \frac{v_1}{a} = \frac{v_1^2 + ah}{av_1}$$

But
$$v = \frac{h}{t} = \frac{ahv_1}{v_1^2 + ah}, \text{ whence } a = \frac{vv_1^2}{h(v_1 - v)} \tag{27}$$

Examples. Tamarack No 3 shaft, Mich, 4 800 ft in 75 sec, or 3 880 ft per min aver, with max about 5 000 ft per min. Whiting shaft, Calumet & Hecla mine, from 4 900-ft level at aver speed of 3 500 ft. Kimberley diamond mines, South Africa, from 1 560 ft depth, aver speed 2 230 ft, max 3 770 ft; acceleration period 16 sec, retardation 13 sec, constant speed 13 sec, total 42 sec. Hence, acceleration is about 3.5 ft per sec per sec. Loading skip requires 5 sec. Quincy No 2, Mich, 10 000 ft in 250 sec; max speed, 3 200 ft per min; accel, 36 sec; retardation, 26 sec (7). Orient shaft, Ziegler Coal Co, Ill, 600 ft, 5 sec to cage, 5 sec accel and retard; total time for complete hoist, 17.12 sec; max speed, 5 070 ft per min. Dowlais shaft, Cardiff, Wales, 2 220 ft in 52 sec, an aver of 2 562 ft per min. Rosebridge Colliery, England, speed of 5 100 ft per min is on record. Usual speeds are: SMALL GEARED HOISTS, 450 to 500 ft per min; large, 900 to 1 200 ft. SMALL DIRECT-ACTING HOISTS, 1 000 to 1 500 ft per min; large, 2 500 to 3 500 ft.

Table 11. Acceleration in Various Mines (National Safety Council) (46)

Shaft		Aver length of hoist	Max hoisting speed, ft per min	Accel, ft per sec	To reach max speed, ft	Time to reach max speed, sec
N J Zinc Co, Franklin, N J	Inclined	915	3 000	3.33	375	15
Inter Nickel Co, Creighton, Ont	"	1 600	1 100	2.33	260	15
Witherbee-Sherman, Mineville, N Y	"	1 000	1 200	1.33	150	15
Copper Range Co, Painesdale, Mich	"	1 500	2 360	2.48	130	10
Republic Iron & Steel Co, Birmingham, Ala	"	5 400	2 200	1.47	459	25
Sulphide Corp, N S W, Australia	Vertical	825	3 650	5.06	300	15
Calumet & Arizona, Warren, Ariz	"	1 500	1 600	5.33	70	5
United Verde Copper Co, Clarkdale, Ariz	"	850	2 000	4.70	115	10
North Butte Co, Butte, Montana	"	3 600	2 700	2.53	400	17
Great Boulder Prop, Boulder, W Australia	"	2 000	2 000	5.85	95	6
Old Ben Coal Corp, Frankfort, Ill	"	475	3 600	12.00	150	5

With fixed output, speed and load are dependent upon each other. If V = average hoisting speed per min; T = output, tons per hr; W = net load, tons; h = depth of shaft, ft, and t = caging time, min; then,

$$V = \frac{ht}{60W - Tt} \tag{28}$$

15. STEAM HOISTS

Engine details. Minimum diam of drum depends on diam of rope (Art 2 and 7); maximum diam, on hoisting speed required and piston speed of engine. RATIO OF GEARING, from 1 : 3 to 1 : 6. PISTON SPEED rarely exceeds 650 ft per min; for small engines 500 ft. RATIO OF CYL DIAM to length of stroke varies for geared hoists from 1 : 1.2 to 1 : 1.67; ratios of 1 : 1.25 to 1 : 1.33 are common. For direct-acting hoists ratios are usually from 1 : 1.3 to 1 : 2.66.

Friction allowance for engines, sheaves, and shaft guides is generally lumped to cover all these items, including windage. McCulloch and Futers (4) assume starting friction of engine as 25% of wt of one cage + contents + rope; running friction as 0.6 of this or 15%, and shaft friction and windage as 10%. But, since all these items are not effective until after starting, it is customary to take friction allowance at 20% for direct-acting and 25% for geared hoists. Following frictional resistances were measured at three Butte (Mont) shafts, when hoisting from depth of 2 200 ft, at max speeds of 3 000 to 3 500 ft per min (47, p 837):

	In balance	Out of balance
Speculator shaft	21.1%	13.0%
High Ore shaft	23.0	17.5
Diamond shaft	29.0	10.0

These percentages are in terms of indicated work of the engines, the difference between values when hoisting in and out of balance showing that shaft friction at high hoisting speed is much greater than engine friction. In these cases the engine friction alone was probably less than 6% (47).

Effective crank radius is taken at 0.58 of full crank radius for engines cutting off at 87.5% of stroke, which is about as late as is practicable. This enables one cylinder to start the load, when cranks at 90° apart are in their most disadvantageous positions.

Steam pressure. INITIAL PRESS for small hoists is assumed in makers' lists at 80 to 100 lb. For simple, non-condensing hoists, assume 100 lb; for compound, 125 to 150 lb.

(NOTE.—Hoist should be designed to start under a lower pressure, to take care of emergencies.) MEAN EFFECTIVE PRESS (m e p) does not affect size of cylinder necessary to start the load, but must be considered when engine is up to speed and running with shortened cutoff. In absence of indicator cards, approximate m e p may be calculated by:

$$p = 0.9 \left[c \left(p_i + 14.7 \right) - b \right] \qquad (29)$$

in which: p = m e p (gage); p_i = initial steam press (gage); b = absolute back press (for hoisting engines = 17 to 19 lb); c = constant depending on point of cutoff; 14.7 = atmos press at sea level, and 0.9 is the diagram factor.

Table 12. Values of "c" for Engines with 7% Clearance

Point of cutoff, % of stroke	Ratio of expansion	c
100	1.00	1.000
83.3	1.18	0.986
75.3	1.30	0.969
62.5	1.54	0.925
50.0	1.88	0.860
37.6	2.40	0.766
25.0	3.35	0.637

Force required to accelerate load and moving parts can be disregarded for slow hoisting speeds, and in general for geared hoists, but must be determined for rapid hoisting.

Let M = mass of one cage and empty car, and W their weight: M_1 = mass of ore and w its weight; M_2 = mass of one rope and W_r its weight; F_1 = accelerating force in ascending rope; F_2 = accelerating force in descending rope.

Then $F_1 = a \left(M + M_1 + M_2 \right)$, and $F_2 = aM$.

During period of acceleration, load on ascending rope is $W + w + W_r + F_1$, and on descending rope, $W - F_2$, assuming empty cage at surface. Unbalanced load during acceleration, neglecting changing lengths of ropes, is:

$$L = \left(W + w + W_r + F_1 \right) - \left(W - F_2 \right) = w + W_r + a \left(2 M + M_1 + M_2 \right) \qquad (30)$$

Engines must also accelerate the masses of drums, sheaves, and reciprocating parts. Weight of drum is assumed as concentrated at its equivalent radius of gyration, taken at 0.7 r. Then, if M_d is mass of drum, and neglecting sheaves and other parts, the accelerating force required is $F_d = 0.7 M_d a$, since surface of drum is moving at same velocity as the rope. Weight of drum is calculated, or estimated from known weight of a similar one. A drum 8 ft diam by 8 ft long weighs about 20 000 lb.

Hoisting-engine formulas.

Let P = total press on one piston, due to initial steam press,
p_i = initial steam press, lb per sq in,
l = length of stroke, ft,
d = diam of cylinder, in,
e = starting efficiency or factor, to allow for starting friction of engine, sheaves and cages, assumed at 0.7 to 0.83,
D = diam of drum, ft,
A = area of piston, sq in = 0.7854 d^2,
L = unbalanced load, lb,
k = ratio of stroke to diam = 12 $l \div d$,
m_L = moment of unbalanced load about center of drum,
m_P = moment of steam press on one piston about center of crank shaft, in least advantageous position of cranks.

Then $\qquad m_L = LD \div 2$, and $m_P = 0.58 Pl \div 2$

To start the load, $e m_P$ must be equal to or greater than m_L, or $0.58 ePl \div 2 = LD \div 2$, whence

$$d^2 = 2.19 \frac{LD}{e p_i l} \qquad (31)$$

Substituting for l its value in terms of d, $\qquad d^3 = 26.3 \frac{LD}{e p_i k} \qquad (32)$

Eq 31 and 32 neglect area of piston rod. For a geared hoist, if q be the gear ratio,

$$d^3 = 26.3 \frac{LD}{e p_i k q} \qquad (33)$$

These formulas give cylinders amply large unless rapid acceleration and high speed are necessary. Assuming uniform acceleration, the engines develop greatest power just at end of acceleration period.

Let V = maximum rope speed, ft per min; p = m e p, lb per sq in; N = revs of drum per min; L_T = total unbalanced load, lb, including wt of ore and rope, and total force necessary to accelerate load, cages, ropes, and drums. Then the required h p = $L_T V \div 33\ 000$, and h p of both cylinders = $2\ eplAN \div 33\ 000$. Equating and reducing to same form as Eq 31,

$$d^2 = \frac{L_T D}{e p l} \qquad (34)$$

and $\qquad d^3 = 12 \frac{L_T D}{e p k} \qquad (35)$

Table 13. Examples of Hoisting Engines (McCulloch and Futers)

Case	I	II	III	IV	V and VI	VII	VIII
Type of engine	Non-condensing, duplex cylinders. Cyl drums, no tail rope	Non-condensing, duplex cylinders. Conical drums	Non-condensing, duplex cylinders. Cyl drums, tail rope	Non-condensing compound. Cyl drums, no tail rope	Compound condensing. Cyl drums, no tail rope	Compound condensing. Conical drums	Compound condensing. Cyl drums, tail rope
Diam of drums	8 ft	6 × 14 ft	8 ft	8 ft	8 ft	6 × 14 ft	8 ft
Cylinders	21 5/8″ × 48″	22″ × 48″	16 1/4″ × 48″	18 5/8″ × 30 1/4″ × 48″	18 5/8″ × 32 1/4″ × 48″	6 × 14 ft	8 ft
Distance during acceleration	211½ ft	......	411½ ft	As in Case I	As in Case I	As in Case II	As in Case III
No revs during acceleration	7/8	1.13	1.66	"	"	"	"
Time of acceleration, sec	1.87	3.1	3.6	"	"	"	"
Distance during retardation	200 ft	......	43½ ft	"	"	"	"
No revs during retardation	8	2.1	1.74	"	"	"	"
Time of retardation, sec	25	7.3	4.8	"	"	"	"
Max shaft velocity, ft per sec	18.5	24.5	17.34	"	"	"	"
Max hp at full speed	365	190	170	"	"	"	"
Min hp at full speed	48	190	170	"	"	"	"
Steam consumption, acceleration period	36 lb	38 lb	20 lb	36 lb	36 lb	38 lb	20 lb
Steam consumption, full speed period	278 "	252 "	200 "	218 "	143 "	126 "	123 "
Total steam	314 "	290 "	220 "	254 "	179 "	164 "	143 "
Steam per shaft hp-hr, entire trip	61.6 lb	56.8 lb	43 "	50 "	35 "	32 "	28 "
Safety factor of rope	10	10	10	10	10	10	10
Per cent of economy, compared with Case I		8%	30%	19%	43%	48%	55%
Per cent extra rope stress due to accel	43%	18%	25%	43%	43%	18%	25%
Starting crank radius	0.58 r	0.58 r	0.58 r	0.8 r	*0.8 r	*0.8 r	*0.8 r
Condensation loss factor, full speed period	1.6	1.48	1.4	1.25	1.3	1.3	1.28

* In these cases starting crank radius is taken as 0.8 r, for cross-compound engines. For tandem-compound, this point is immaterial.

Table 14. Examples of Direct-acting Hoisting Engines

	I	II	III	IV	V	VI	VII	VIII
	Boston & Montana Mining Co, Butte, Mont	Inverness Coal & Ry Co, Nova Scotia	Chief Consol Mining Co, Eureka, Utah	Newport Mining Co, Mich	Maryland Coal Co, Penna	No 5 shaft, Tamarack Min Co, Mich	New Jersey Zinc Co, Franklin Furnace, N J	No 2 shaft, Quincy Mining Co, Mich
Maker	Allis-Chalmers	Nordberg	Wellman-Seaver-Morgan	Nordberg	Wellman-Seaver-Morgan	Nordberg	Allis-Chalmers	Nordberg
Cylinders	32"×72"	34"×72"	20"×48"	20" and 37"×66"	32"×48"	4 cyls, 34"×60"	22"×48"	32"×60"×66"
Simple, compound or condensing	Simple, N C	Simple, N C	Simple, N C	Compound, condensing	Simple, N C	Simple, N C	Simple, N C	Compound, condensing, 4 cyl
Initial steam press	140	125	125	150-100° superh't	100-140	100	140	160
Valves	Corliss	Corliss	non-detaching Corliss	Corliss	piston valves	Corliss	non-detaching Corliss	Corliss
Cutoff at start and at full speed	0.85-0.25						0.85-0.25	
Steam consumption, shaft hp-lb-hr		45 lb		28 lb		45 lb	39 lb per i hp hr	
No and type of drums	2 cyl	2 cyl	2 cyl	2 cyl	1 cyl	1 cylindro-conical	2 cyl	1 cylindro-conical
Size of drums, diam × face	12'×5.5'	10'×6.5'	6'×3.5'	10'×5.5'	12'×6'	(a)	10'×5.5'	16'×30'
Keyed to shaft or loose	loose post	loose post	loose post	1 keyed, 1 loose post	keyed 2 post	keyed post	1 keyed, 1 loose post	keyed 2 post
Type of brake	steam	steam	steam	oil under press	steam	steam	(b)	oil under press
Power for auxiliaries	both	both	both					
Unbalanced rope pull, lb	34 000	40 680	19 000	26 000	11 000-16 000	42 200	14 800	52 700
Balanced or unbalanced	both	both	both	balanced	balanced	balanced	balanced	balanced
Aver hoisting speed	2 300	1 500	1 000	3 000	2 100	5 000	2 700	2 400
Max hoisting speed	3 500	same	1 900		3 000	6 000	3 000	3 200
Depth of shaft	3 500	6 000	1 800	2 700	700	5 300	1 610	7 000
Inclination of shaft	90°	15°-35°	90°	68°	90°	90°	47.5°	36°-54°
Time for caging	8 sec	10 sec		5 sec		2 min	5 sec	
Size of rope, in	1.5	1.5	1 1/8	(c)	2	1.5	1 1/8	1 5/8
Skip or cage and weight, lb	skip 7 200 cage 3 400	12 cars, 1 150 each	cage 2 630, 2 decks	skip 4 500	cage {2 decks, 7 750; 3 decks, 9 700}	cage, 6 200; 2 decks	skip, 5 500	skip, 10 000
Weight of ore	10 000	26 880	3 000	13 440	(d)	12 000	12 200; ore 3, men 6	20 000
No of levels served	several	3	4			8		
Tons hoisted and time		1 100 gross, 9 hr	400, 16 hr			19 hr	1 650, 8 hr	
Time of complete hoist, min	1 min from 2 400	7		1		1	35 to 50 sec	
Weight of hoist, lb	520 000	540 000	153 000	550 000	248 200	1 122 000	250 000	1 765 000
First cost, fob factory			$15 000		$20 000	$75 000	$26 500, erected	

(a) 15.75' and 25' (Fig 1). (b) Reverse and clutch; air; brake; gravity and air. (c) 1 3/8" flattened strand. (d) 2 cars, 8 000; 3 cars, 12 000 lb.

By substituting for L_T the unbalanced load only, at uniform speed, the m e p for any given engine may be determined, and minimum point of cutoff found for constant speed.

In Eq 34 and 35, e is the factor for running engine friction, shaft friction, and windage, and may be assumed as having same value as in Eq 32, since increase in shaft resistance offsets the reduction from starting engine friction to running engine friction.

Comparison of performance of different types of hoisting engines is given in Table 13. These engines are designed for max depth of 3 000 ft; load of ore, 3 360 lb; skip, 2 240 lb; initial steam press, 150 lb; output, 25 ton per hr; balanced hoisting. (NOTE.—"Shaft horsepower-hour" denotes net load in lb of ore only × total aver depth in ft hoisted per min ÷ 33 000.)

Examples and costs of hoisting engines. Table 14 gives data of large direct-acting hoists, with approx costs in 1914. Present costs (1938) are about double those quoted. Large hoists are all especially designed and costs vary greatly. Table 15 gives approx 1926 costs (in eastern U S) of ordinary geared hoists.

Table 15. Geared Hoists, Single Friction Drum, Reversible Link Motion

Rated hp	Cylinders, in	Drum, in	Wire rope on drum in single coil	Aver hoisting speed, ft per min	Bed-plate, in	Weight hoisted	Shipping wt complete	Approx price, factory
		diam lgth	ft		width lgth	lb	lb	
10	5 by 6	16 by 20	150	225	57.5 by 41.5	1 500	2 300	$ 890
16	6.25 " 8	24 " 24	240	265	66.5 " 50	2 000	3 800	1 000
30	8 " 10	29 " 25	276	350	73.5 " 59.5	3 500	6 500	1 250
50	10 " 12	42 " 34	426	400	89.75 " 68.75	4 500	9 400	1 650
75	12 " 16	48 " 40	500	450	105.25 " 81.5	7 000	18 500	2 650
100	14 " 18	54 " 48	602	450	117 " 92.25	9 000	27 000	3 300
150	16 " 18	60 " 60	754	450	120 " 94	10 000	31 000	5 700

Note.—For double-drum hoists add 50% to weight and 45% to price.

Small geared steam-driven hoists for prospecting, development, or mines of small output and depth, are self contained and of simple design (Table 16). Gear ratios, 1 : 4, to 1 : 6. Lowering is usually by brake, but reversing gear may be had for 10% added cost. Total cost, approx 18¢ per lb.

Table 16. Lidgerwood Portable Hoists, Single Cone-friction Drum

Rated h p	Cylinders		Drum		Average hoisting load, lb	Average hoisting speed, ft per min	Bed plate		Approx total wt, lb
	Diam, in	Stroke, in	Diam, in	Length, in			Width, in	Length, in	
12	6.25	8	24	26	1 500	250	49	59	3 600
20	7	10	29	26.5	2 000	275	54	72	5 500
30	8.25	10	34	32	3 000	350	55	74	7 500
35	9	10	41	40	3 500	350	72	74	9 000

Portable column- or stope-hoists, for handling timber and ore in stopes and winzes, are usually operated by compressed air or electric motor. Air motor is some form of rotary engine, mounted at the end or inside the drum, and has double-reduction gearing. These hoists have 1 or 2 drums, and are especially convenient in narrow workings, as they may be mounted on a column, or temporary timber foundation. Their most useful applications are in operating underground scraper loaders (2) (See 27), and in hoisting and erecting heavy timbers in stopes. Capacity, 1 000-2 000 lb, at 50-300 ft rope speed; wt, 450-700 lb; air consumption, 200-250 cu ft per min; over-all dimensions, 14 by 18 by 23 to 15 by 20 by 38 in.

Medium-size geared hoists are suitable for more extensive development work, or mines of small tonnage, to say 500 ft in depth. They are especially adapted for hoisting with buckets, light cages or skips, at speeds of 450 to 700 ft per min (Table 17).

Large geared hoists may be self-contained, or with engines and drums supported on independent bed-frames. They are especially suited to hoisting heavy loads at moderate speeds, up to say 1 500 ft per min; hence, are advantageous for slopes or inclines, where high speeds are not permissible. Under these conditions, geared engines give better steam economy, due to higher piston speed and ability to use drums of large enough diam to prevent undue bending stresses in rope. Geared hoists are useful where economy of floor space and foundation is an object. Their cost is 35 to 50% that of direct-acting hoists for same hoisting load.

Table 17. Single- and Double-drum Geared Hoists, Band Friction Clutches

Rated h p	Cylinders		Engine speed, r p m	Drums			Gear ratio	Unbalanced load, lb, with 100 lb steam	Rope speed, ft per min	Weight		Over-all dimensions		
	Diam, in	Stroke, in		Diam, in	Face, in	L'gth of rope in 1 layer				Single drum	Double drum	Width, single drum	Width, double drum	Length
												ft in	ft in	ft in
85	9	12	250	42	30	410	1 : 5.5	4 700	480	8 700	15 000	7– 8	12–0	7– 6
92	10	12	230	48	30	450	1 : 5.5	5 000	520	10 200	17 500	7– 8	12–0	7– 6
130	11	15	200	54	36	540	1 : 6	7 300	490	17 300	28 600	9– 0	13–6	9– 4
140	12	15	180	60	36	540	1 : 6	7 800	470	19 000	30 000	9– 0	13–6	9– 4
160	13	15	180	60	36	540	1 : 5	7 800	550	26 400	40 000	10– 8	15–6	10– 7
200	14	18	175	60	36	480	1 : 4.5	8 700	610	37 000	51 100	10–10	17–3	11–10
200	14	18	175	72	36	570	1 : 4.5	7 200	730	39 000	56 600	11– 0	17–3	11–10
230	15	18	175	72	36	570	1 : 4.5	8 300	730	44 500	60 800	11– 0	17–3	11–10

Note.—Specifications of different makers vary. For preliminary estimates, cost may be taken at 25¢ per lb at factory.

First-motion or direct-acting hoists are useful for large output, or for depths requiring high hoisting speeds. Besides the advantage of eliminating gearing, their relatively slow speed of stroke permits use of Corliss or other variable-cutoff valve motion. Though usually designed for greater economy in steam consumption, their first cost is higher, and they should not be used for depths less than 500 ft, unless output is large.

Compound hoisting engines have limited application. Their high cost is justified only where fuel is expensive, and large loads are hoisted in rapid succession from deep shafts. When not operated condensing (condensers often work unsatisfactorily in hoisting service), their economy is but little better than that of simple engines, taking into account the intermittent running. They are either cross-compound or twin tandem-compound. Though more costly, the latter design is preferable, because in the cross-compound the high-press cylinder must be large enough to start the load when low-press cylinder is on center. This prevents an economical ratio of cylinder volumes. Throttle and valve gear must be designed so that, in starting and until full speed is reached, the l-p cyl receives steam at such press as will give a starting effort equal to that of h-p cyl. Cylinder ratios can be proportioned to best advantage in the twin tandem-compound.

Examples of compound cylinder ratios. Old Dominion Copper Co, Ariz, twin tandem condensing, 17 and 31 by 48 in, ratio of areas 1 to 3.4; 20 and 37 by 66 in, ratio 1 to 3.45. Copper Queen Consol Mining Co, Ariz, twin tandem condensing, 16 and 28 by 48 in, ratio 1 to 3.08. Homestake Mining Co, So Dak, duplex cross-compound condensing, 28 and 52 by 42 in, ratio 1 to 3.47. Randfontein, Transvaal, cross-compound condensing, 22 and 40 by 48 in, ratio 1 to 3.3. Village Deep shaft, Transvaal, twin tandem condensing, 17 and 28 by 60 in, ratio 1 to 2.73; duplex cross-compound geared hoist, 14 and 21 by 20 in, ratio 1 to 2.25. Cambria Steel Co, Johnstown, Pa, cross-compound condensing, 28 and 50 by 48 in, ratio 1 to 3.2. Grand Central Mining Co, Mexico, twin tandem, 16 and 24 by 42 in, ratio 1 to 2.25.

Table 18 shows test of a Nordberg twin tandem-compound condensing hoist; cyls 16 and 28 by 48 in, Corliss valve gear; 2 clutched drums, each 7 ft diam, holding 2 100 ft of 1.25-in rope; total rope pull, 19 000 lb.

Valve gear of hoists should be as simple as is compatible with good construction, and economy in steam consumption; with minimum number of parts, and all motions positively controlled when possible.

Three types used in American engines: slide, piston, and Corliss valve. SLIDE VALVES are always used for small and generally for large geared hoists, and for many direct-acting hoists. In small engines, valves are unbalanced; in large, balanced valves should be used. PISTON VALVES are used in the simpler forms of heavy-duty direct-acting hoists; they are balanced as to steam pressure, and are well adapted to high pressure and speed and also to long-stroke engines, because each end of cylinder has its own valve, thus reducing length of ports. But, since the piston valve is not held on seat by steam pressure, it is liable to leakage from wear. High cost of CORLISS GEAR is justifiable when fuel is high, and when saving in this and in decreased maintenance cost exceeds the added first cost within life of mine. It is especially suited to large output from depths of 1 000 ft or more. Its economy results mainly from the automatically controlled variable cutoff, which is more easily applied to Corliss than to other valves. Variable cutoff is operated by ball governor (which also prevents excessive speed), or by an auxiliary lever to throttle, by which cutoff is shortened as throttle is opened. With slide and piston valves, cutoff may be shortened by "linking up," but this interferes with exhaust. Corliss valves with non-detaching gear are now used, having advantage of separate steam and exhaust valves with quick opening and closing. Variable-expansion gear must automatically return to position of latest cutoff with the stopping or slowing down of hoist. As Corliss gear is limited to speed of about 125 rev per min, it is rarely applied to geared hoists.

Reversing gear, when hoisting is in balance, or if lowering is done by steam when not balanced, is commonly of link-motion type, or a modification of it. Both open and crossed eccentric rods are used, but open rods are best as they increase lead of the valve as cutoff is shortened, giving more compression and earlier admission of steam for cushioning when running at full speed. On large Corliss hoists, valve rods are sometimes driven from a crank on an auxiliary shaft inclosed by a hollow shaft geared from main shaft. Inner shaft is driven from hollow shaft, but may be rotated independently by the reverse lever, through an angle sufficient to reverse the engine. Medium size direct-acting and geared hoists are reversed by hand; large hoists by an auxiliary engine (Art 3).

Table 18. Test of Sacramento Hoist, Copper Queen Consol Mining Co

April 19, 1911. (Charles LeGrand, Cons Eng)

	A M 7–11:30	P M 12–3:30	Total shift 8 hr
Steam press (at boiler, corrected)......................	144	144.5	144.25
" " (at hoist, corrected).......................	137	137	137
Steam temp at boiler, deg F...........................	430	430	430
Vacuum..	19.7	19.9	19.8
Ore hoisted No 4 level, lb...........................	337 700	199 000	536 700
" " " 8 " "...........................	79 100	....	79 100
" " " 10 " "...........................	248 900	312 900	561 800
" " " 14 " "...........................	177 700	280 900	485 600
" " " 16 " "...........................	104 500	28 200	132 700
Total pounds hoisted................................	947 900	821 000	1 795 900
Work done, hoisting ore, shaft hp-hr..................	435.88	418.20	854.08
" " " men and skip, shaft hp-hr..........	23.33	20.05	43.38
Total shaft hp-hr.................................	459.21	438.25	897.46
Average shaft hp.....................................	102.05	125.21	112.18
Mean hoisting depth..................................	910	1 010	968
Steam charged to hoist, including condensation in pipe line, lb..	13 942	12 158	26 100
Steam to condenser, lb...............................	1 215	945	2 160
Total steam, lb..................................	15 157	13 103	28 260
Steam per shaft hp, excluding condenser, lb...........	30.36	27.74	29.08
Steam per shaft hp-hr, including condenser, pipe-line condensation, and steam for oil pump, lb................	33.00	29.90	31.49

Notes.—Aver load of ore per skip for 232 skips hoisted, 3.81 tons. Wt of empty skip, 5 400 lb. Wt of 1.25-in rope, 2.5 lb per ft. Condensation in pipe line from boilers, 625 lb per hr, with steam on line and hoist not running. Steam for condensing plant charged at 30 lb per kw-hr, an aver of 9 kw being used.

Steam economy of hoisting engines is necessarily poor, due chiefly to intermittent operation. A hoist must start under full load and have rapid acceleration, thus requiring uneconomical admission of steam during nearly full stroke. Also, intermittent work involves loss of stored energy near end of trip if heavy braking is done, and the large variation of load within the short hoisting period prevents economical operation. The frequent stops and periods of idleness allow cylinders to cool and increase condensation loss. Superheating reduces condensation, and is justifiable for large hoists. Hoisting engines cut off at about 0.85 stroke in starting, and with slide or piston valve this is not changed as engine comes up to speed, when hoisting from shallow shafts. Though indicator cards are useful for determining condition of valves and pistons, their results are comparative, rather than absolute, because with varying speed and load no two engine strokes give the same card. Hence, steam consumption as calculated from hoist indicator cards is an approximation at best. Steam consumed per unit of work may be obtained very closely by measuring water supply to boilers, if plant is so arranged that one or more boilers supply the hoist independent of auxiliaries. Such tests should last several hours, useful work being calculated from tonnage hoisted.

Steam consumption varies between wide limits. Small hoists at a distance from boiler require 150 to 175 lb per shaft hp-hr; for large compound condensing hoists, winding from deep shafts, 25 lb per shaft hp-hr is obtainable; for moderate size, simple, non-condensing hoists, with slide or piston valves, 50 to 75 lb.

16. COMPRESSED AIR HOISTS (See also Sec 15)

Compressed-air hoists have same general construction as steam hoists. For small-scale work portable " column " or " stope " hoists (Art 15), or small geared hoists (Table 17) are used. For economy, large expansive-working engines require cylinders of special design. Cutoff is later, clearance volume is reduced to minimum, and larger admission ports are required, since at same pressure the density of air exceeds that of steam. SMALL HOISTS, running intermittently, give no trouble from freezing of moisture in exhaust ports, as cylinder walls and passages have time to regain normal temp. But, for economy, the air should be reheated. For starting and acceleration, air is admitted at practically full stroke, and power controlled by throttle. In LARGER HOISTS, with expansion gear, expansion is only partial, because, since there can be no condenser, the terminal press must be sufficient for proper exhaust. Owing to rapid drop in temp of expanding air, the work done is less than with steam; that is, the adiabatic curve of air is below that of steam, with corresponding decrease in mean effec press. Hence, for same m e p, cutoff must be later (Sec 39). On the other hand, the theoretical final temp of expansion is never reached in practice, because of transmission of heat by cylinder walls, compression in clearance spaces, and presence of moisture in the air. Loss in efficiency due to incomplete expansion can be reduced by two-stage expansion. With cutoff in high-press cyl at 0.9 stroke (minimum practicable starting cutoff), and reheating between cylinders to initial temp, the loss in compound cylinders is about one-half that of a simple cylinder, or a saving of 25% of the energy in the air entering high-press cyl.

Work done by compressed air. See Sec 39 for theory, and results of work with partial and complete expansion. Table 19 gives relations between initial and terminal press and temp for different

Table 19. Theoretical Ratios of Pressures and Temperatures Due to Expansion of Compressed Air in a Motor Cylinder

Point of cutoff	Ratio of expansion = 1 ÷ cut-off	Ratio of mean to total abs press, for entire stroke	Ratio of mean to total abs press, during expansion only	Ratio of initial to final temp	Ratio of initial to final abs temp, due to expansion only	Ratio of initial to final abs press for ratio of expansion
0.10	10.00	0.249	0.166	0.513	0.513	0.039
0.15	6.67	0.348	0.233	0.460	0.578	0.069
0.20	5.00	0.436	0.295	0.518	0.627	0.104
0.25	4.00	0.515	0.353	0.568	0.669	0.142
0.30	3.33	0.585	0.408	0.612	0.705	0.184
0.35	2.86	0.647	0.460	0.652	0.737	0.228
0.40	2.50	0.706	0.510	0.688	0.767	0.275
0.45	2.22	0.757	0.558	0.722	0.794	0.325
0.50	2.00	0.802	0.604	0.754	0.818	0.378
0.55	1.81	0.842	0.649	0.784	0.841	0.433
0.60	1.67	0.877	0.692	0.812	0.862	0.487
0.65	1.54	0.907	0.734	0.839	0.882	0.545
0.70	1.43	0.932	0.774	0.865	0.902	0.605
0.75	1.33	0.954	0.814	0.889	0.920	0.667

points of cutoff (48). Corrections are necessary for clearance volume, the actual effect of cutoff being found by dividing the sum of cutoff plus clearance, by cylinder volume plus clearance. Thus, if stroke is 5 ft, with cutoff at 0.2 and clearance of 5%, total volume of cylinder plus clearance is (5 × 0.05) + 5 = 5.25; the sum of cutoff plus clearance is 1 + 0.25 = 1.25, and actual cutoff is 1.25 ÷ 5.25 = 0.23. Table 20 is thus calculated. As volume of air at cutoff is increased by the clearance, the mean press is greater than if calculated on basis of nominal cutoff.

(Tables 19 and 20 are adapted from G. D. Hiscock, "Compressed Air, Its Production, Uses and Applications," 1901. Also, see Peele's "Compressed Air Plant," 5th edn, Chap 16.)

Cylinder volume. Work per stroke is calculated from ft-lb of work to be done and revolutions of engine. This, with initial and final pressures is substituted in formula for partial or for complete expansion (Sec 39), which is solved for initial volume of compressed air per stroke = theoretical cylinder volume. This is corrected for clearance, according to type of engine, and the proper ratio of stroke to diam is determined. Initial vol of air ÷ vol at end of expansion = per cent of cutoff.

Volume of compressed air required = volume of air per stroke (calculated above) × number of strokes, remembering that there are 4 strokes per revolution in a duplex hoist. Volume so found is reduced to free air (Sec 39). Table 21 gives volume of free air per min per indicated hp, for different cutoffs, without reheating, and at 60° initial temp. These values do not include the volume corresponding to piston clearance (see above).

Table 20. Actual Cutoffs Due to Clearance, for Nominal Cutoffs in Column 1

Point of nominal cutoff	Percentage of clearance						
	0.03	0.04	0.05	0.06	0.07	0.08	0.10
0.10	0.126	0.135	0.143	0.151	0.159	0.167	0.182
0.15	0.175	0.184	0.191	0.198	0.206	0.213	0.227
0.20	0.223	0.231	0.238	0.245	0.252	0.259	0.273
0.25	0.272	0.279	0.286	0.293	0.299	0.305	0.318
0.30	0.320	0.327	0.333	0.340	0.346	0.352	0.364
0.35	0.368	0.376	0.380	0.387	0.392	0.398	0.409
0.40	0.417	0.423	0.429	0.434	0.439	0.444	0.455
0.45	0.465	0.471	0.477	0.481	0.486	0.490	0.500
0.50	0.514	0.519	0.524	0.528	0.533	0.537	0.546
0.55	0.564	0.568	0.571	0.576	0.580	0.585	0.591
0.60	0.612	0.615	0.619	0.623	0.626	0.630	0.637
0.65	0.660	0.664	0.667	0.670	0.673	0.676	0.682
0.70	0.709	0.711	0.714	0.717	0.720	0.722	0.727
0.75	0.758	0.760	0.762	0.764	0.766	0.768	0.772

Table 21. Cubic Feet of Free Air per Minute per Engine I H P (F. C. Weber)

Point of cutoff	Gage pressures, lb									
	30	40	50	60	70	80	90	100	110	125
1	23.3	21.3	20.2	19.4	18.8	18.42	18.10	17.8	17.62	17.4
3/4	18.7	17.1	16.1	15.47	15.0	14.6	14.35	14.15	13.98	13.78
2/3	17.85	16.2	15.2	14.5	14.2	13.75	13.47	13.28	13.08	12.9
1/2	16.4	14.5	13.5	12.8	12.3	11.93	11.7	11.48	11.3	11.1
1/3	17.5	15.2	12.9	11.85	11.26	10.8	10.5	10.21	10.02	9.78
1/4	19.6	15.6	13.4	13.3	11.4	10.72	10.31	10.0	9.75	9.42

Quantities of free air in Table 22 are based on actual running time of geared hoists. As such engines seldom run more than 1/4 to 1/2 the time, a compressor of 1/4 to 1/2 the volume given is sufficient, provided there is ample storage capacity, and the time per trip is short.

Table 22. Volume of Free Air for Duplex Hoists (@ 60 lb gage)

Diam of cyl, in	Stroke, in	Rev per min	Normal hp	Actual hp	Wt lifted, single rope, lb	Free air per min, cu ft
5	6	200	6	11.8	1 000	300
5	8	160	8	12.6	1 650	320
6.25	8	160	12	19.8	2 500	500
7	10	125	20	24.2	3 500	604
8.25	10	125	30	33.6	6 000	680
8.50	12	110	40	37.8	8 000	952
10	12	110	50	52.4	10 000	1 320
12.25	15	100	75	89.2	. . . .	2 250
14	18	90	100	125.0	. . . .	3 174

Reheating (theory and results given in Sec 39 and 15) reduces volume of air required proportionally to the ratio $T_2 \div T_3$, where T_2 = absolute normal temp, and T_3 = absolute temp to which the air is reheated. Or, the increase in volume is expressed by:

$$T_2 : T_3 = 1 : V_3 \tag{36}$$

V_3 being the volume at temp T_3. The added volume is obtained at $1/4$ to $3/8$ of the cost of producing the same volume in the compressor itself (15, 5th edn, Chap 18).

Practicable increase of temp is up to 400° F; higher temp makes cylinder lubrication difficult and loss in heat between heater and cylinder becomes excessive. Reheating to 400°, and allowing a transmission drop to 300°, produces theoretical gain of 43%; in practice, say 20 to 30%. Using dry reheaters, a fair average fuel consumption per added hp-hr due to reheating is 0.2 lb coke. Experiments on an 80-hp Corliss engine, with air at 95.5 lb abs, reheated to 338° F, gave a coke consumption of 0.176 lb per added hp-hr. At Anaconda Copper Co's plant, the air is reheated by steam at 200 lb pressure to 250° to 350° F. At Miami, Ariz, the reheating temperature is 350° to 375° F. For hoists, a reheating gain of 20% is generally practicable.

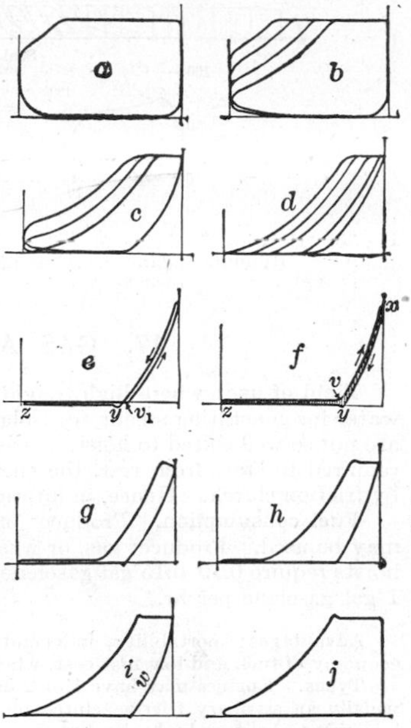

Anaconda valve gear. In modifying the large hoists at the Anaconda mine, and in designing other plants for using compressed air, the aim has been to utilize energy stored in moving parts during retardation to compress air back into the storage system, instead of wasting power in braking. This is done also when lowering instead of hoisting.

Cylinders and valve gear of Anaconda air hoists perform the following functions (47, p 868). In starting, the throttle is opened wide; air is admitted during 0.9 of stroke and exhausted during entire return stroke, giving the card a, Fig 48. After making 1 to 3 rev, the governor takes control, cutting off the air at different points as speed increases (card b). On reaching about 0.6 full speed the point of closure of exhaust valves is advanced to such point as will cause the clearance air to be compressed to full initial press. As speed increases the cutoff is further shortened by the governor (cards c), the last card of series c representing the air expanded to atmospheric press, and engine theoretically working at its best efficiency. To maintain this efficiency and eliminate loops in the card (due to expanding below atmos press) free air is admitted to cylinder at all points of cutoff shorter than last card in

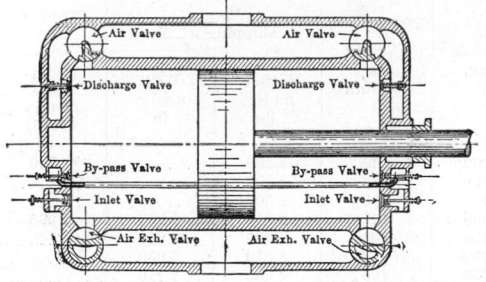

Fig 48. Air-hoist Cards,
B. V. Nordberg (47)

c. This stage is shown in cards d. In card e, the last of the group, air is cut off practically on center, and expanded to atmos press, which is then maintained to end of stroke. Also, atmos press is maintained on return stroke to the point where recompression begins. This card corresponds to work of ± 0. At this point maximum speed is attained, and the hoist runs by momentum of the moving masses.

To retard without applying brakes, the regulating lever is moved to retarding position, causing admission valve to remain closed during forward and return strokes, as in card e. Exhaust valve now opens, air is ejected during return stroke, and the process of producing cards e and f is the same. The regulating lever con-

Fig 49. Anaconda Air-hoist Cylinder, B. V. Nordberg (47)

trols point of closure of exhaust valves during the exhaust stroke, resulting in the shaded area of f, which represents negative work. By further movement of the lever from its neutral position, cards g, h and i are made successively, i representing compression of a full cylinder of air. The effect of the gear is to exhaust all air not to be compressed, and then compress the remainder. By moving the lever to its extreme position, an auxiliary valve opens communication between ends of the cylinder, while the piston passes its center with both exhaust valves closed. The compressed air then flows to other side, which is filled with free air, causing increase of several pounds press in front of piston, the disappearance of the re-expansion line w in card i, and a much higher mean effec press of compression, which stops the hoist. Card j is produced at this time. Fig 49 is a diagrammatic section of the cylinder and valves. The poppet inlet valves prevent air in cylinder from expanding below atmos press. Discharge valves operate automatically when air is compressed back into the system; by-pass valves are opened positively and closed automatically. Fig 50 shows the operation of this gear. For first 5 strokes, cylinders are completely filled; next 5 strokes are made with gradually shortened cutoff, after which the clearance compression gear comes into action.

No air is admitted during last 6 strokes, air being compressed back into the system. Work repre-sented by this compressed air is shown by the area below atmospheric line.

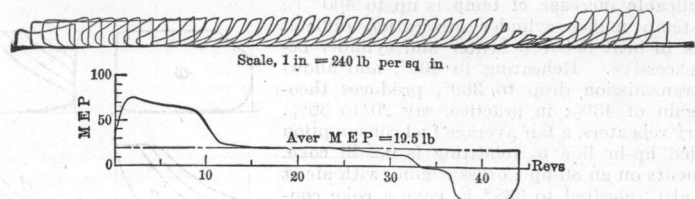

Fig 50. Hoisting Card (Leonard Shaft, Butte) from Head End of 34 × 72-in Air Hoist, 12-ft Drum, Running Balanced. Hoisting Speed, 1 800 ft in 45 sec (B. V. Nordberg, 47)

17. GAS AND GASOLENE HOISTS

Field of use: where high freight rates make coal expensive, where there is scarcity of water for generating steam, for isolated mines, or for temporary work. Small gas engines are not so well suited to hoisting as steam or air hoists of same capacity. Because of time required to start from rest, the engine must run continuously, the drum being operated by friction clutch. Hence, in intermittent hoisting, economy is low.

Fuel consumption. Producer or city gas, gasolene, distillate, kerosene, or crude oil, may be used. Producer gas, or waste gas from coke ovens, furnishes a cheap fuel. Small hoists require 0.10–0.15 gal gasolene per hp-hr; a standard 4-cyl, 20-hp engine uses about 1 gal gasolene per hr.

Advantages: portability, independence of steam or electric plant, low cost of attendance, economy of fuel, and low first cost, when power plant for steam or electric hoists is considered.

Types. Engines may have 1 or 2 drums, with friction clutches. For the larger hoists there is usually an auxiliary friction clutch on engine shaft. They are usually non-reversible, requiring lowering to be done by brake, but there may be special gearing between engine and drums, similar to an automobile gear-shift, to reverse direction of rotation of drum, thus permitting hoisting in balance. Sometimes designed for 2 speeds. Engine is 4-cycle, and varies from single horiz cyl to vertical 6-cyl, rated as 60–80 hp. Larger multiple-cyl units may have self-starters.

Table 23. Single Friction-drum Gasolene Hoists (Fordson units used on 20-hp sizes)

Horse power	Drum		Hoisting capac, lb	Speed, ft per min	Approx shipping wt, lb		Approx price with motor, f o b factory (1926)
	Diam, in	Length between flanges, in			Without motor, lb	With motor, lb	
5	8	18	1 000	100	1 200	....	$ 700
10	10	18	1 500	150	2 200	....	....
15	10	20	2 500	150	2 800	....	....
20	12	20	4 000	125	3 750	4 900	1 095
20	18	20	2 500	200	3 800	4 950	....
20	24	20	2 000	250	3 850	5 000	....
20	24	20	1 250	400	4 000	5 150	....
35	12	26	6 000	160	4 200	....	1 260
50	14	27	8 500	160	6 200	....	....
60	14	27	10 000	160	6 500	....	2 500

Rating and capacity. Rating is usually on basis of indicated hp. Lifting capac and hoisting speed depend on quality of engine and care in maintenance. Let L = load or lifting capac; HP = rated hp of engine; e = mech effic of hoist; S = hoisting speed, ft per min; then,

$$L = 33\ 000\ eHP \div S \qquad (37)$$

Up to 10 hp, e may be assumed as 0.5 to 0.6; for larger engines, 0.6 to 0.7.

Costs vary widely with type and make of motor. A Middle-west manufacturer quoted (1926) on single-cyl hoists: 3 hp, 9 to 12-in drum, $368; 6 hp, 6.5 to 12-in drum, $520; 10 hp, 9 to 16-in drum, $845. For other costs, see Table 23.

18. HAND WINDLASS

Windlass has low efficiency and small capacity; hence, limited to prospecting, sinking winzes, beginning shafts, and small-scale development work. For prospecting, economical limit of depth is, say, 75 to 100 ft.

Principal dimensions for ordinary windlass (Fig 51): Diam of barrel, 6 to 9 in; length, to suit size of shaft; crank arm, 14 to 16 in; length of handles, 15 to 18 in; height, center of barrel above platform, 42 in.   Cost, $20 to $35 complete, varying more with cost of labor than of materials.

Capacity and cost of operation. An average man can do 2 500 ft-lb of work per min, applying force of 20 lb at crank.   Hence, crank velocity is 125 ft per min; which, with 15-in crank, gives 16 rpm, or a hoisting speed of 33.5 ft per min with 8-in barrel.   At 75 lb gross load per man (125 ×

20 ÷ 33.5 = 75, nearly), allowing half the time for filling, dumping, and lowering bucket, 2 men can hoist 7 200 lb from 100 ft in 8 hr. Fig 52 shows cost and capacity, for different depths, with 2 men and 1 bucket, wages 20¢ per hr, 3 min being allowed for filling, dumping, and lowering (1915).

Manila rope, 0.75 to 1 in diam is best for windlass; wire rope tends to kink and is not suited to small diam of barrel.

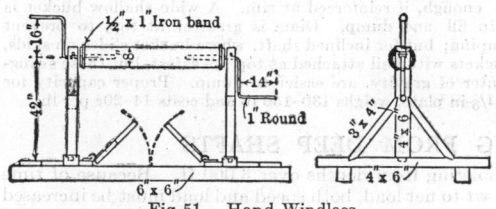

Fig 51. Hand Windlass

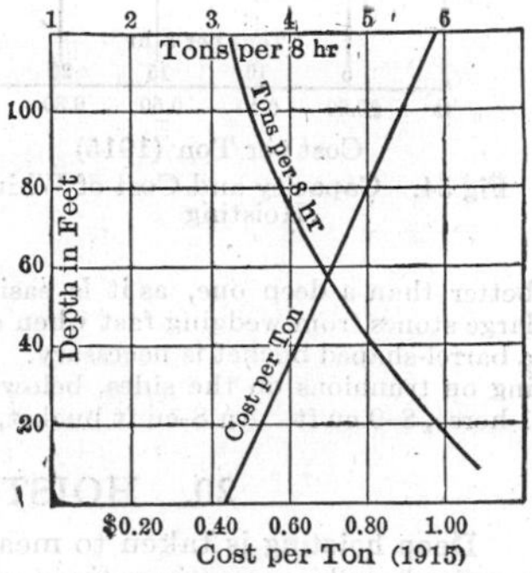

Fig 52. Hoisting with Windlass

Buckets may be of heavy sheet iron, or made from half of an oil barrel, with iron bands top and bottom. Bail, 0.75-in round iron, with eye at center; ears for bail are the ends of a 0.25 by 1.25-in strap, passing down each side and under bottom of bucket, with 3 or 4 rivets on a side. Wt of bucket, 60 to 75 lb (Art 28).

19. HORSE WHIM

Uses. For sinking when depth and capacity required are too great for a windlass; for preliminary or small-scale development work, not warranting a power hoist; or for beginning a shaft while installing steam or electric hoist.

Construction. When made at the mine, whim is entirely of wood except bolts and small quantity of bar iron (Fig 53) (49). This design is called "malacate" in Spanish-American countries. Axis of drum is vertical, and arm or sweep is attached at top or bottom of drum. If at bottom, the horse passes under rope leading to head sheave; if at top it steps over rope, which is then led off in a covered trench. DETAILS of Fig 53: Foundation a of rough logs, drift bolted and filled with

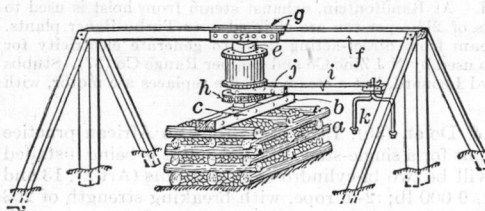

stone. Footstep bearing for drum is of two 10 by 12-in by 8-ft timbers b. Spindle e, 12 by 12 in, cut down at ends c to 6 in diam and capped with 6-in pipe couplings. Drum, 3 ft 6 in diam by 2 ft 6 in high, of 3-in plank bolted together and lagged with hardwood strips. Sweep i, 6 by 12 in, is mortised to spindle and reinforced with 3 by 6 in by 5-ft pieces j. Crosspiece f, 10 by 10 in by 30 ft, is reinforced at center with 3 by 10 in by 5-ft pieces g, and supported by 12 by 12-in posts, braced to suit direction of pull of hoisting rope.

Fig 53.   Whim for Sinking Shaft at Mineville, N Y

Yoke k is of 3 by 0.75 in by 6-ft steel, swedged to 2 in diam at top and swiveled in end of sweep, so that horse can turn sharply and travel in either direction. Brake ring h, of 3-in planks, may be added for safety.   With this whim a 1 100-lb horse raised a gross load of 2.5 tons at 27 ft per min. Instead of a timber crib base, the bottom bearing may be made by a socket in a large stone or in a timber imbedded in the ground. Cost of whim (1915), $70; (1926), $125–$150.

Length of sweep should not be less than 12–14 ft, as a horse does not work when traveling a circle of less than 24–28 ft diam. Decrease in hoisting speed due to a long sweep is counteracted by increasing drum diam; and this increases life of rope. Length of sweep should be 5–7 times radius of drum, when gearing is not used.

Ready-made whims are obtainable in a number of forms. They are occasionally used, but have been largely displaced by small gasolene hoists (17).

Capacity and cost of whim hoisting, for a given depth, depends on power of horse (21 000 to 25 000 ft-lb per min), time required for filling, dumping, and lowering bucket and rate of wages.

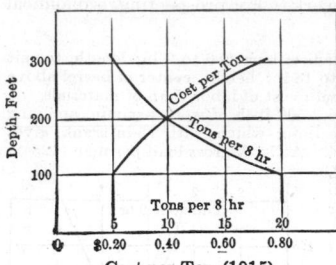

Fig 54. Capacity and Cost of Whim Hoisting

Fig 54 shows cost per ton and capacity for whim hoisting from depths of 50 to 300 ft, under following conditions: One horse, @ 25 000 ft-lb per min; hoisting speed, 50 ft per min; gross load, 500 lb; wt of bucket, 125 lb; wt of 5/8-in wire rope, 0.62 lb per ft; 2 men and 1 horse at surface, $1.25 per hr; time for dumping and changing buckets, 1 min (requiring good arrangement at shaft mouth); lowering with brake, 200 ft per min. For depths of 50 to 100 ft the duty and cost are constant, because tonnage handled is all that 4 shovelers (maximum number that would be employed under the conditions) could load in time required for each hoist. (Note.—Manufacturers' rating of whims is sometimes equivalent to 2 or 3 times the average work of a horse.)

Rope for whims is sometimes hemp, but is better cast steel, of ordinary lay, 1/2 to 5/8 in diam. (For wire rope data, see Art 7.)

Buckets should be light; 1/8-in plate is thick enough, if reinforced at rim. A wide shallow bucket is better than a deep one, as it is easier to fill and dump. Diam is greatest at top, to prevent large stones from wedging fast when dumping; but for inclined shaft, where bucket slides on skids, a barrel-shaped bucket is necessary. Buckets with bail attached at top are safest, but those swinging on trunnions on the sides, below center of gravity, are easier to dump. Proper capacity for 1 horse, 8–9 cu ft. An 8-cu ft bucket, of 1/8-in plate, weighs 130–150 lb and costs 14–20¢ per lb.

20. HOISTING FROM DEEP SHAFTS

Deep hoisting is taken to mean hoisting from depths over 3 000 ft. Because of time required, and increase in ratio of rope wt to net load, both speed and load must be increased to maintain a given tonnage. Long ropes require large drums, presenting special design problems. Best grades of steel rope are requisite and the tendency is towards round rope of constant cross-section. Bi-cylindro-conical drums are used to decrease load on motors, and are of such dimensions that rope does not wind on itself, thus increasing rope life (6, 30). Cylindrical drums are sometimes used, but in each case the choice must be an adjustment of operating cost, effic and capital outlay.

Methods in use and proposed (Art 1) are: (a) balanced hoisting in a single lift, with conical drums and ropes of uniform section or tapered; (b) Whiting system, with tail rope; (c) Koepe system, with tail rope; (d) hoisting in tandem with 2 skips on each rope, one suspended at half the depth and one at full depth, for loading and dumping simultaneously, lower skip discharging into bins from which upper skip is filled; (e) hoisting in 2 or more stages, with lower stage hoist either on surface or underground.

Types of drive on the Witwatersrand (1923). Out of 72 winding engines serving 39 deep shafts, there were 50 steam, 10 Ward Leonard and 12 induction plants (1). Present practice is towards Ilgner-Ward Leonard drive, in both U S and So Africa (6, 30). A. L. G. Tindley (39) recommends direct-acting steam hoists as economical, when hoisting plant is considered in relation to compressor and haulage capac required. At Randfontein, exhaust steam from hoist is used to give 30 000 cu ft of air per min. Savings of 2 1/2¢ per ton are claimed over Turbo-Ilgner plants. Donk Bros Coal Co, Ill, use exhaust steam from direct-acting hoist to generate electricity for underground haulage and coal cutting; also used by N J Zinc Co and Copper Range Co (37). Stubbs Perry plant (39) resembles the Ilgner-Ward Leonard, but a steam turbine replaces a-c motor, with an eddy-current brake, all on same shaft.

Hoisting in a single lift. Elsdon & Dolan (30), 1935, state that So African practice favors stage hoisting, but that equipment for a single-stage lift of 6 300 ft is being installed at the Simmer & Jack mines. There will be two bi-cylindro-conical drums (Art 2), 13 and 35 ft diam. Ore load, 8 ton; skip wt, 9 000 lb; 2-in rope, with breaking strength of 203 to 210 ton; rope speed, 3 000 ft per min; a Ward Leonard drive, with 2 d-c motors, each of 1 800 hp at 225 rpm. Rope safety factor, 5 for men, 4.7 for ore.

21. EXAMPLES OF HOISTING PRACTICE

Ross shaft, Homestake Mining Co, S Dak (6). Max vert lift, 5 275 ft; wt of skip, 12 500 lb; wt of ore per skip, 14 000 lb; 1 7/8-in rope. Drums, double bi-cylindro-conical, 12 and 25 ft diam, with parallel shafts, cross gear connected, both clutched, Ilgner-Ward Leonard drive. With two 1 500-hp, 300-rpm, 600-volt motors, two 1 250-kw, 720-rpm, 600-volt generators, one 1 750-hp, 720-rpm a-c motor, one 40-kw, 720-rpm, 125-volt exciter, and one 44-ton flywheel, the hoisting capac is 3 225 ton in 15 hr, at 5 275 ft, and 5 475 ton in 15 hr, at 2 200 ft.

Simmer & Jack shaft, So Africa. Stage hoisting (30); vert lift, 6 300 ft; double bi-cylindro-conical drums; wt of ore, 16 000 lb; wt of skip, 9 000 lb; 2-in rope. Rope speed, 3 000 ft per min; Ward Leonard drive, 2 d-c motors, one for each drum, rated at 1 810 hp, at 225 rpm.

No 4 shaft, City Deep mine, So Africa (41). Stage hoisting; max vert lift, 4 500 ft; 2¼-in rope; rope speed, 3 100 ft per min; wt of ore per trip, 8 ton; capac 250 ton per hr, Ward Leonard drive; 2 cylindrical shafts, 50½ ft between centers.

New Orient coal mine (45, 46), Ill, normally hoists 10 000 ton in 8 hr from 500-ft depth. It has hoisted 15 000 ton and equipment was designed for 12 000 ton per 8 hr. Ilgner-Ward Leonard drive, with a 2 200-hp, 2 200-volt a-c motor; two 1 650-kw, 600-volt d-c generators; one 50-kw, 250-volt d-c exciter, 90 000-lb flywheel at 575 rpm. Hoist motors, d c, are cooled by washed air, each being 2 000 hp, at 75 rpm. Cycle: acceleration, 5 sec; full speed 6 sec; retardation, before entering dumping horns, 3 sec; retardation at dump horns, 3 sec; rest period, 9 sec. Total cycle, 26 sec. Depth of shaft, 607 ft; wt of coal per trip, 22 000 lb; wt of skip, 15 100 lb.

Red Jacket shaft, Calumet, Mich, is equipped with Whiting hoists. Shaft is vert, 4 900 ft deep (91). Two driving sheaves, 19 ft diam, driven by a pair of inverted vert, triple-expansion condensing engines. High-press and intermediate cylinders of each engine act on one crosshead, low-press cylinder on another. The crossheads are attached by connecting rods to opposite ends of a triangular walking beam, pivoted between the crosshead guides. From third point of the beam, a connecting rod goes to crank of first driving sheave. Cranks are 90° apart, connected by parallel rods to cranks of second sheave. Cylinders, 20.5, 31.75, and 50 in, by 72-in stroke. Steam press, 180 lb. Max speed, 50 rev per min. Use of a tail rope greatly reduces swaying and vibration of hoisting rope. Main rope, 1.75 in, tail rope, 1.375 in.

No 5 shaft, Tamarack mine, Mich, is 5 309 ft deep. Hoist has 2 simple, non-condensing Corliss cylinders, each 34 by 60 in (see Table 14, No VI). Cylinders are set at 45° to horiz, so that the two at each end have center lines at right angles, and are connected to a common crank pin. Hence, when one cylinder is on center the others act at 45°, 90° and 135° from this position, giving ease of starting and uniform torque (Fig 12).

Turf shaft, Village Deep mine, So Africa. Vert depth, 6 600 ft. There are 3 stages: upper, about 4 100 ft vert, the two lower stages being inclines (8).

San Juan Del Rey mine, Brazil. Vert depth, 6 726 ft. Hoisting is in 5 stages; in upper stage, 2 264 ft deep, hoist is driven by Pelton water wheel; next 3 stages are each 1 200 ft, with compressed air hoists; lowest stage has an electric hoist.

Quincy No 2 hoist (installed 1920) has probably the greatest single lift: 10 000 ft on the incline; 6 600 ft vert depth. It has a cylindro-conical drum, grooved for 15/8-in rope. Skip weighs 10 000 lb; rope, 10 000 ft, 41 500 lb; ore, 20 000 lb.

North and South vert shafts of Randfontein Central Gold Mining Co, So Africa. Two Ward Leonard electric hoists, installed 1922, are designed for 5 000 ft vert depth, at max speed of 4 000 ft per min. The cylindrical drums are 12 ft diam by 6 ft wide; rope, 1.75 in. A steam hoist, designed for same duty, has 39- by 78-in cylinders; cyl drum, 14 ft diam by 5.5 ft wide, to hold 4 layers of 2-in rope; max unbalanced load, 60 000 lb. On the Rand, cyl drums are preferred to cylindro-conical (8). Conical drums can not be constructed for full equalization of rope load, as angle of drum face becomes dangerously steep for deep shafts, or length of drum prohibitive.

For hoisting 50 tons per hr from 5 000 ft, McCulloch and Futers (4, p 142) calculate an engine of following dimensions: small diam of drum, 9 ft; large diam, 24 ft; cyls, 38 by 48 in; max speed, 60 ft per sec; time for loading and dumping skip, 30 sec; net load, 6 100 lb; taper rope in 4 sections, lowest 1 800 ft being 0.9375 in diam, the other 3 of 1 400 ft each being 1.0625, 1.1875 and 1.25 in diam, respectively; total wt of one rope 11 600 lb, with safety factor of 7. If a uniform-section rope were used, diam would be 1.4375 in; total wt, 30 000 lb. Steam press is assumed at 150 lb. For same output, steam consumption is about 4 times that required for 3 000 ft. H. C. Behr (50) shows that hoisting engines more than 3 times as large are required for a given hourly output from 6 000 ft as from 3 000 ft.

22. COSTS OF HOISTING

Table 24. Segregated Hoisting Costs, in Cents Per Ton (44)

Mine	Labor	Power	Supplies	Repairs	Total
Joplin district.............	3.3	2.0 (a)	1.0	0.2	6.5
No 8, Missouri.............	3.1	0.4	....	1.0	4.5
Acme, Tri-State...........	7.1	1.2	0.8	....	7.1
Mineville, N Y.............	10.3	6.3	4.7	....	21.3
Montreal, Wis.............	6.6	10.2	0.2	....	17.0
Montreal, Wis.............	7.2	5.3	1.7	....	14.2
85-Mine, N M..............	9.8	8.3	6.4	....	24.5
Copper Queen.............	2.6	1.9 (a)	0.2	2.4	7.1
United Verde.............	18.1	20.8 (b)	0.4	3.7	43.0
United Verde.............	2.1	0.9	0.1	0.3	3.4
United Verde.............	6.0	3.3	0.7	5.4	15.4
Smuggler Union...........	7.9	1.3	0.1	5.6	14.9
United Eastern...........	18.4	5.0	1.4	2.7	27.5
Argonaut..................	25.3	10.9	15.7	....	51.9
Ray......................	0.8	0.7	0.3	0.2	2.0

(a) Steam.   (b) Operating boiler plant.

Table 25. Hoisting Costs per Ton (44)

Mine	Year	Tonnage per year	Max depth, ft	Cost per ton, cents	Remarks
Joplin district, Mo..........	1917	136 272	250	6.5	Vert, cans (b)
Acme, Tri-State............	1917	364 285	300	9.1	" "
No 8, S E Mo..............	1928	168 089	568	4.5	" skips
Mascot....................	1923	212 990	582	4.3	" "
Montreal, Mich............	1928	700 000	2 700	14.2	Incl and vert skips
Montreal, "	1928	500 000	2 700	17.0	" skips
Mineville, N Y............	1927	770 000	4 200	21.3	" and vert skips
United Verde Extension, Ariz	1928	275 212	1 700	15.1	Vert, skips
United Verde..............	1918	530 470	1 050	43.0	" cars
United Verde..............	1919	110 487	1 050	3.4	" skips
United Verde..............	1926	1 387 397	2 350	15.4	" "
Copper Queen (Sacremento shaft)....................	1914	659 102	1 550	7.1 (a)	" " (steam)
Copper Queen..............	1914	659 102	1 550	18.9 (a)	" cars
Bunker Hill & Sullivan......	1930	445 475	2 000	11.5	Incl, skips
85-Mine, N M..............	1930	7 220	1 650	24.5	Vert, "
Smuggler Union, Colo.......	1928	71 521	796	14.9	Incl, "
Elko Prince...............	1917	21 674	300	19.6	" "
United Eastern............	1917–24	732 000	1 298	27.5	Vert, "
Mogollon, Ariz............	1922	50 144	500	30.1	Incl, "
Argonaut, Calif............	1929	7 800	7 800	51.9	" "
Beatson...................	1922–26	1 682 079	200	5.1	Vert, "
Miami, Ariz...............	1925–29	16 556 296	811	3.3	" "
Ray......................	1928	3 243 159	465	2.0	" "
Nevada Consol............	1924	694 476	700	5.2	" "
Lucky Tiger...............	1924	60 000	400	16.0	Incl, "

(a) Cost of hoisting ore at Sacremento shaft was 7.1¢ per ton; at 8 other shafts, which delivered ore to the Sacremento hoist, 18.7¢ per ton, making a total cost of 26¢.   (b) Local term for hoisting buckets.

Table 26. Kilowatt-hours Per Ton Ore Hoisted (44)

Mine	Reference	Max dist, ft	Car or skip	Vert or inclined	Kw-hr per ton
No 1, Tri-State...........	L C 6113	200	"Cans"	Vert	2.8
No 2, "	I C 6121	300	"	"	2.4
No 3, "	I C 6174	200	"	"	2.8
Hartley, "	I C 6656	250	"	"	1.6
S E Missouri..............	I C 6170	245	Cars	"	0.5 (a)
Daisy, Ill................	I C 6384	640	Skips	"	6.2
Hillside, Ill..............	I C 6294	550	"	"	1.2
No 1, Marquette..........	I C 6138	1 000	"	"	1.8
No 2, "	I C 6179	1 650	"	"	2.1
No 4, "	I C 6390	1 060	"	"	1.6
No 5, "	I C 6380	1 200	"	"	2.5
No 1, Menominee........	I C 6180	1 200	"	"	3.3
Mineville, N Y...........	I C 6092	4 200	"	Both	4.2
Mineville, N Y...........	A I M E Vol 72	4 200	"	"	4.8
Montreal, Wis...........	I C 6369	2 700	"	Vert	4.0
Page, Idaho.............	I C 6372	1 200	"	Incl	2.7
Hecla, Idaho.............	I C 6232	2 000	"	Vert	4.4
Cortez, Nev.............	I C 6327	240	"	Incl	9.4
Copper Range...........	A I M E Vol 72	2 000	"	"	4.1
Homestake, S D..........	A I M E Vol 72	2 300	"	Vert	2.1
Mascot, Tenn............	I C 6239	582	"	"	1.1
United Verde............	A I M E Vol 72	1 500	"	"	1.1
United Verde............	M C J Sept '27	2 350	"	"	0.8
Old Dominion, Ariz.......	I C 6237	2 600	"	"	9.8
Argonaut, Calif..........	I C 6311	5 800	"	Incl	9.9
Plymouth, Calif..........	A I M E Vol 72	3 000	"	"	10.7
Mary, Tenn.............	I C 6397	900	"	Vert	12.2 (b)
Black Rock, Butte.......	I C 6370	3 000	"	"	10.3
Bunker Hill & Sullivan....	A I M E Vol 72	2 000	"	Incl	13.1
Tintic Standard..........	I C 6360	1 300	Cars	Vert	15.4 (c)
Miami, Ariz.............	A I M E Vol 72	796	Skips	"	1.3
Morning, Idaho..........	I C 6238	2 250	"	"	4.4

(a) Questionable; too low. (b) Estimated from 81.1 lb coal per ton ore hoisted. (c) Distribution on direct labor basis. I C = Information Circular, U S Bur Mines.

23. DESIGN OF HEADFRAMES

Types. Headframes are of the A-type or modifications of it (Fig 56 and 65), or of the 4- or 6-post type (Fig 64 and 59). The A-type is more economical in material, and the stresses are all determinate. The 4- or 6-post type is necessary when the shaft com-

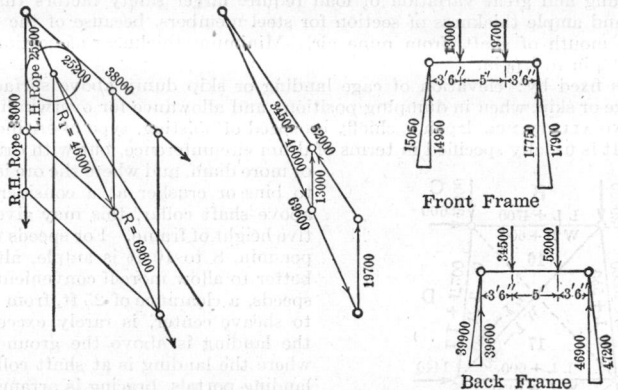

Fig 55. Rope Load Resolution

partments are not in line with engine; that is, when axis of drum is normal to long dimension of shaft. They are common in the Penn coal fields, where the compartments are large and so require considerable overhang of sheave to line up its circumference with center of shaft, and where there are often 4 compartments in a row. Where a rock-house or tipple

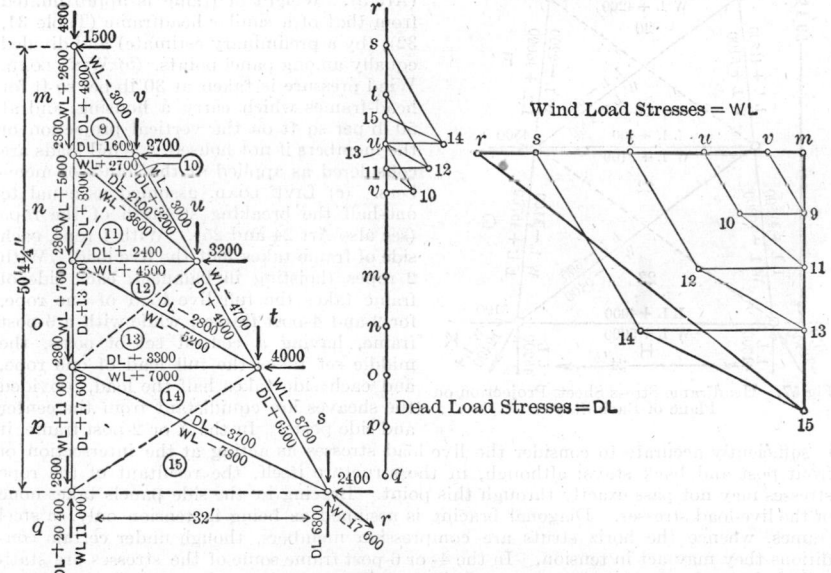

Fig 56. Headframe Stress Sheet, Side Elev

is combined with the headframe, the 4- or 6-post type lends itself a little more readily to the construction.

Special structures, falling within the above two classes, are sometimes erected to meet unusual conditions; for example, the concrete headframe (Fig 80), and the rock-houses of the Mich iron and copper districts (51, 52). Also, frames like those of Allen and Garcia (Fig 74), with single or narrow back-brace, are sometimes advantageous. The main frame may usually be classified as of the A or 4-post type, or combinations of these, as where two or more hoists serve several shaft compartments not symmetrically placed, thus requiring back bracing on more than one side; or where the headframe is built into the tipple or crusher house.

General principles of design are the same as for any framed structure. Severe conditions of mining and great variation of load require larger safety factors than ordinary structures, and ample thickness of section for steel members, because of the exposure to corrosion at mouth of shaft, from mine air. Minimum thickness of section is usually specified as $1/4$ in to $5/16$ in.

Height is fixed by: elevation of cage landing or skip dump above surface; over-all height of cage or skip, when in dumping position; and allowance for overwinding (Art 34). OVERWINDING ALLOWANCE depends chiefly on speed of hoisting, type of engine, and drum diameter. It is usually specified in terms of drum circumference, but with drums of 20 ft or more diam, and where the ore is discharged to bins or crusher at a considerable height above shaft collar, this may give a prohibitive height of frame. For speeds above 500 ft per min, 8 to 10 ft is ample, although it is better to allow more if convenient. For high speeds, a clearance of 25 ft, from rope socket to sheave center, is rarely exceeded, where the landing is above the ground, and 35 ft where the landing is at shaft collar. At the landing portals, bracing is arranged to allow ample room for handling.

Calculation of stresses. For A or 2-post frames, all stresses are determinate and are conveniently found graphically. Total stresses are due to: (a) DEAD LOAD, or weight of the structure and sheaves with their bearings (Art 5). Weight of frame is approximated from that of a similar headframe (Table 31, 32), (by a preliminary estimate) and divided equally among panel points. (b) WIND LOAD. Wind pressure is taken at 30 lb per sq ft for head-frames which carry a housing, and at 50 lb per sq ft on the vertical projection of the members if not housed. Wind loads are considered as applied at the joints of members. (c) LIVE LOAD, assumed as equal to one-half the breaking strength of the rope (see also Art 24 and 25). With 1 rope, each side of frame takes half the live load. With 2 ropes (hoisting in balance), each side of frame takes the full live load of one rope, for 2-and 4-post frames, while with a 6-post frame, having a central set of posts, the middle set takes the full load of one rope, and each side takes half the load, provided the sheaves are equidistant from the center and side posts. In the A or 2-post frame, it

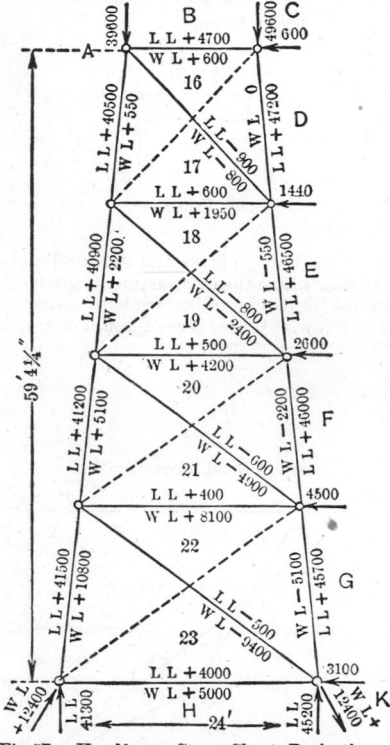

Fig 57. Headframe Stress Sheet, Projection on Plane of Back Stay

is sufficiently accurate to consider the live-load stresses as acting at the intersection of front post and back stays; although, in the structure itself, the resultant of the rope stresses may not pass exactly through this point. Bracing in the side panels takes none of the live-load stresses. Diagonal bracing is assumed as being in tension only, in steel frames, whence the horiz struts are compression members, though under certain conditions they may act in tension. In the 4- or 6-post frame some of the stresses are statically indeterminate, and for accurate design reference may be made to standard works on the subject (53). Fig 60 shows a method meeting ordinary requirements. The frame and its bracing are assumed to carry all the wind and dead load, excepting the wind stresses in transverse bracing of back stays. Since diagonals are considered as tension members only, redundant diagonals are omitted in calculations.

It is to be remembered that the frame as a whole must be sufficiently stable to resist overturning by wind pressure. For this it is usually best to depend on width of base, rather than on anchor bolts, which may be weakened by corrosion. Maximum overturning effect of wind will be in a direction parallel to the shortest dimension of the base area. The total area in sq ft of all members exposed to wind, *on both windward and leeward sides* of frame, multiplied by assumed maximum horiz press per sq ft, gives total press in lb. This may be taken as a concentrated horiz load, acting at the center of figure of the frame. It is resisted by the wt of structure, including sheaves and bearings, multiplied by half the width of base.

The position of the center of figure can be closely approximated in any given case. In proportioning the width of base, sufficient allowance should be made to cause the

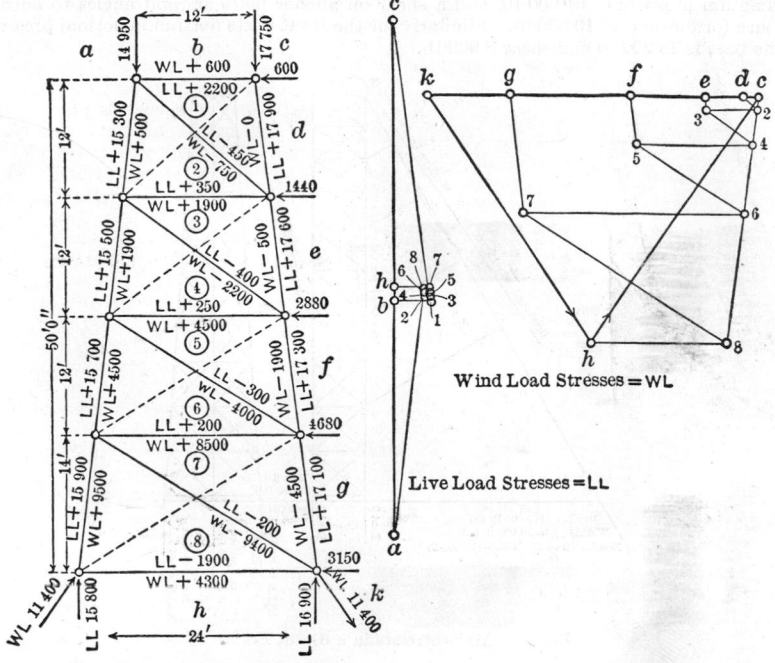

Fig 58. Headframe Stress Sheet, Front Elev

diagonal resultant of wind press and wt of frame to fall well within the base area. The calculation is similar for a structure with housing attached to the frame.

Graphic determination of stresses for an A or 2-post frame is shown in Fig 55, 56, 57, 58, in which the loading on one rope is assumed as half the rope's breaking strength and on

Table 27. Maximum Stresses in Headframe Members

Member	Maximum tension	Maximum compression	Member	Maximum tension	Maximum compression
Front posts	0	+45 700	11–12	0	+ 6 900
Back brace posts	−3 000	+63 000	12–13	− 8 000	0
1–2	−1 200	0	13–14	0	+10 300
2–3	0	+ 2 250	14–15	−11 500	0
3–4	−2 600	0	16–17	− 1 700	0
4–5	0	+ 4 750	17–18	0	+ 2 550
5–6	−5 200	0	18–19	− 3 200	0
6–7	0	+ 8 700	19–20	0	+ 4 700
7–8	−9 600	0	20–21	− 5 500	0
8–9	−1 900	+ 4 300	21–22	0	+ 8 500
9–10	0	+ 4 300	22–23	− 9 900	0
10–11	−5 700	0	23–H	− 4 000	− 5 000

the other double the weight of skip, contents, and rope. Shaft, 1 200 ft deep; skip, 2 500 lb; ore, 4 500 lb; 1-in plow-steel rope, 1 896 lb; breaking strength of rope, 76 000 lb; sheave, 6 ft diam. In Fig 58, the wind load on side of frame, combined with the live load, gives the maximum stresses in front posts and bracing. Bracing in front and back elevations takes none of the dead load. Weight of frame is estimated as 50 400 lb, and stresses due to dead load, and wind pressure from the rear, as shown in Fig 56, give maximum uplift at foot of back brace if the ropes should at any time be removed from the sheaves. Fig 57 shows stresses in back brace due to live load and to wind pressure on one side. Bases of posts are usually made normal to plane of front and back of frame. Combining the reactions at foot of one back post gives maximum uplift normal to the base of 10 500 lb, a maximum pressure of 61 900 lb, and a shear on anchor bolts at right angles to normal pressure (or tension) of 10 000 lb. Similarly for the front posts maximum normal pressure on the base is 48 200 lb and shear 8 900 lb.

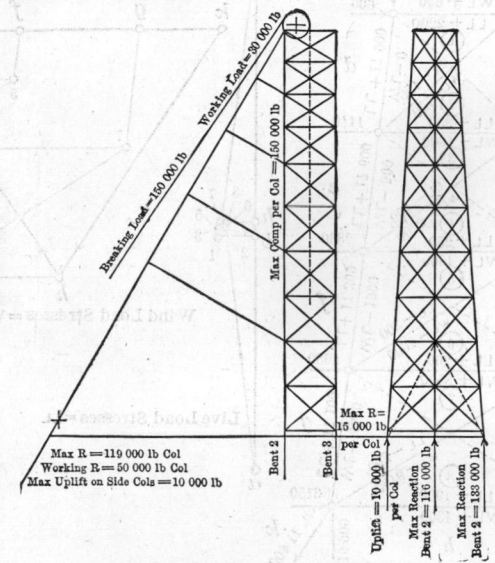

Fig 59. Main Stresses in a 6-post Frame

Four- and six-post headframes. In these, since live and wind-load stresses are indeterminate in some members, either the tower, or the A-frame made by the middle bent and back brace, may be considered as carrying all wind load from front or back. In first case, diagonal bracing between back brace and tower is superfluous, because the struts transmit wind pressure from back brace to tower; in second case, struts between front and middle bents transmit wind pressure from the front. Wind pressure from the side is carried by each bent and its bracing in proportion to the surface supported by each, and the stresses are determinate in a 4-post frame. In a 6-post frame the center post is redundant, and wind stresses may be assumed as transmitted to the outside posts and the bracing between them.

Approximate determination of live-load stresses (Fig 60). 1. Resolve resultant of rope stresses at sheave center into its horizontal and vertical components. 2. Determine equivalent reactions due to total vertical component at front and middle bents. 3. Combine vertical reaction at middle bent with total horizontal component, thus making a new resultant through intersection of middle bent and back brace. 4. In these, determine stresses due to new resultant, as in case of an A-frame.

Fig 60 shows this resolution of stresses in the plane of one rope and sheave. Taking a 6-post frame, and considering both ropes loaded with 100 000 lb, vertical reactions at top of each post are shown in (b) and (c), and in plane of back brace in (a). If back brace is placed near resultant, this method gives less stress due to live load in middle bent than in the front, but in practice the middle bent is usually made of same size members as the front. Dead and wind-load stresses with wind from the side are greatest in middle bent. As exact calculation of stresses in statically indeterminate structures depends on rigidity of the structure, this approximate method may be used to determine the sections of members, and on basis of the sections so found, stresses are exactly calculated. If the section of any member is unsuitable, recalculate by the "method of least work." Stress and design features of Eureka Standard headframe are shown in Fig 61, 61a (37).

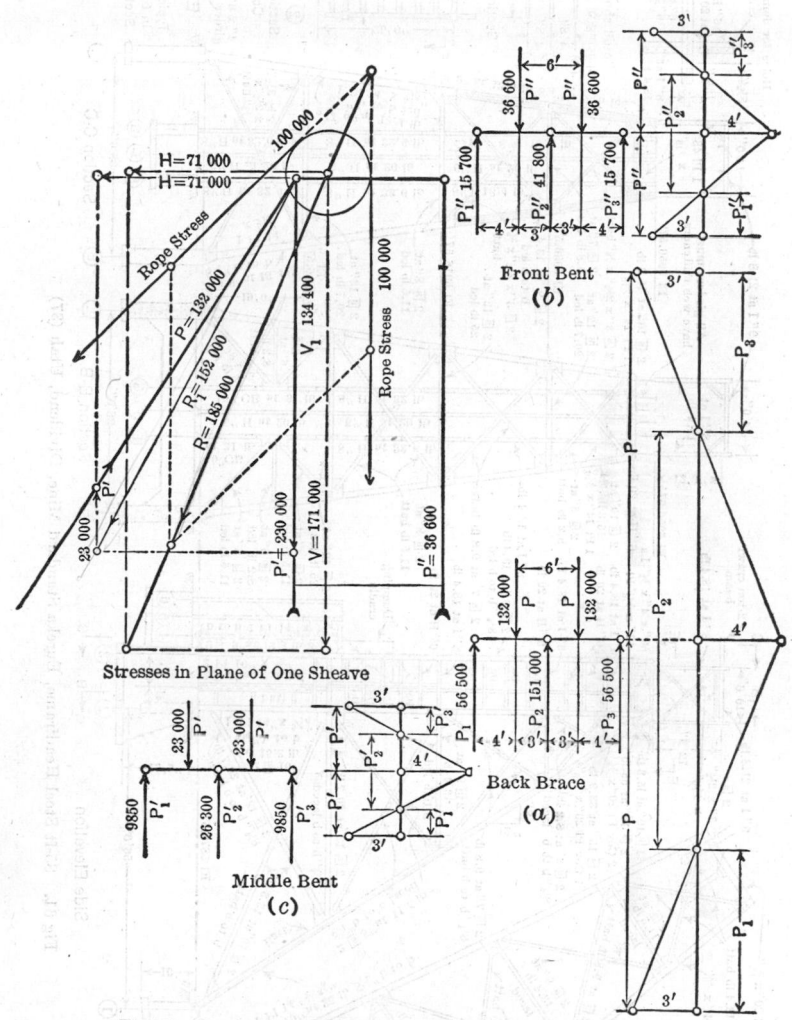

Fig 60. Resolution of Stresses in Plane of One Rope and Sheave

24. WOODEN HEADFRAMES

Temporary headframes for development and shaft sinking are of wood, which costs less, is usually readily obtained and quickly erected. Height depends upon method of disposal of the rock, and size of ore bucket. Simplest form, suitable for a whim in sinking test pits, is a tripod of 3 light posts. A small frame used in Joplin district (Fig 62) has 4 equally inclined posts, without a back brace; the hoist being placed close to shaft mouth, so that the resultant of the rope pull falls well within the base. Fig 63 shows the Montana type, which may be modified for almost any condition; Fig 64, a 4-post and back-brace frame. Fig 65 shows an A-frame, for an inclined shaft at West Dome mine, Porcupine, Ont (54), combined with an ore bin; height, 40 ft; hewed posts,

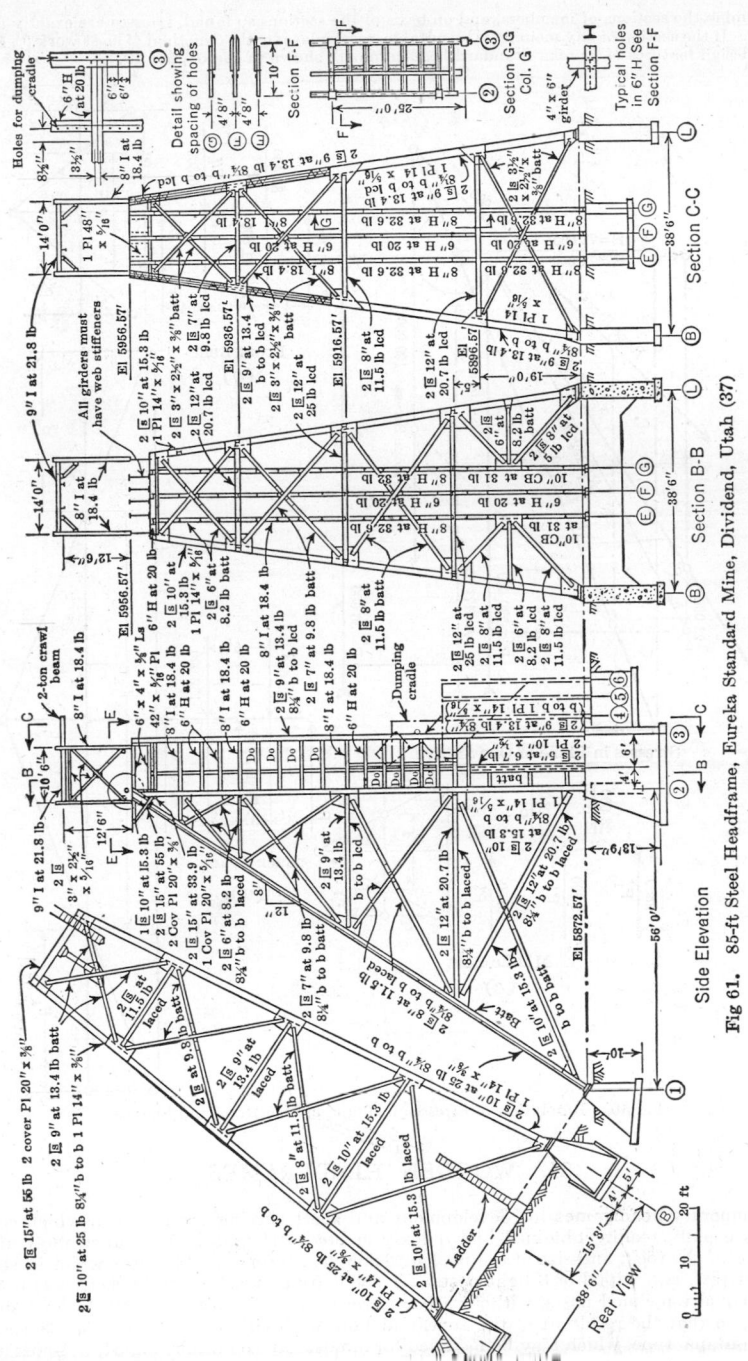

Fig 61. 85-ft Steel Headframe, Eureka Standard Mine, Dividend, Utah (37)

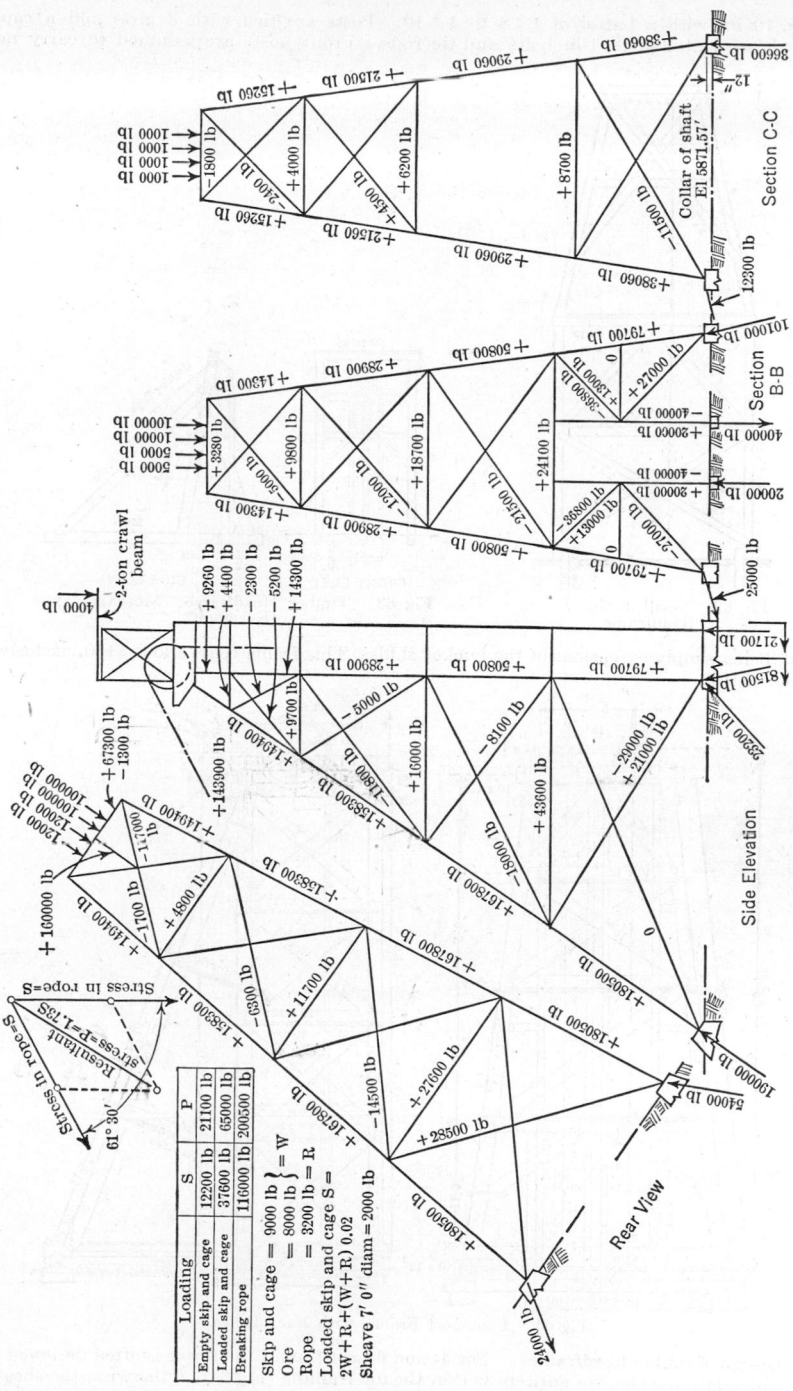

Fig 61a. Stress Diagram for 85-ft Steel Headframe, Eureka Standard Mine, Dividend, Utah (37)

10×10 in, with a batter of $1 : 8$ to $1 : 10$. Posts are tied with 3 girts and a cap, back brace with 2 girts, 1-in bolts and tie rods. Front posts are assumed to carry no

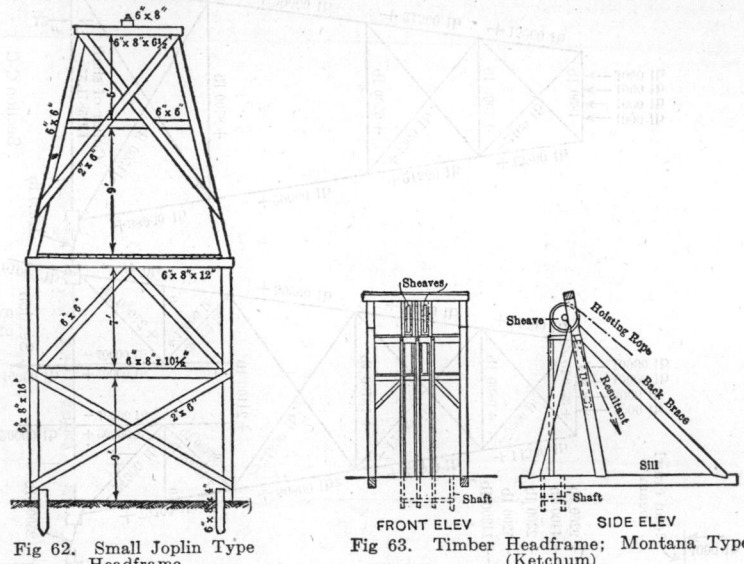

Fig 62. Small Joplin Type Headframe

Fig 63. Timber Headframe; Montana Type (Ketchum)

load, being simply extensions of the bucket skids. This frame costs about $150, exclusive of bin (1913).

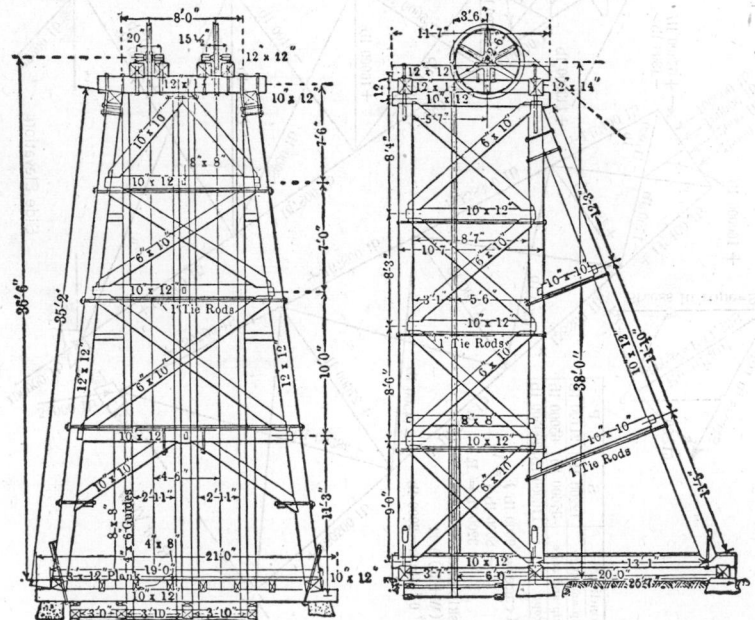

Fig 64. Four-post Frame, with Back Brace

Design of timber headframes. For 4- and 6-post frames the tower is often designed to accommodate the sheaves entirely within the top framing (Fig 64). Otherwise, the sheave girders are carried on short posts set on a girt in plane of middle bent. For 2-post frames the sheaves are supported as in steel frames (Art 25). Fig 67 shows top of 2-post frame, for single-compartment shaft, and working load of 8 000 lb.

Fig 68 shows details of a timber headframe, with tandem sheaves, working load 9 000 lb on each rope. Mortise and tenon trenailed joints, with tie rods, make neat construction, but reduce strength of timbers, and labor cost is greater than for gained joints with bolt connections. For the latter, the braces are gained 1 to 2 in on the posts, with plenty of bolts. Strength of tension members

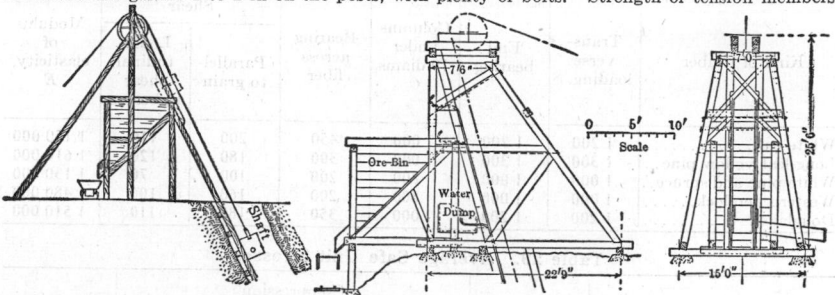

Fig 65. Frame for Inclined Shaft,   Fig 66. Headframe and Orebin for Development
        Porcupine, Ont   (*Mines & Min*)

depends more on bearing area of the bolts than sectional area of timber. Malleable or steel castings at joints make strong connections. Steel-plate brackets are not so good as castings. Columns standing directly on the foundation are anchored by angles on opposite sides of the post and bolted through. If resting on sills, columns are similarly anchored to the sill, which in turn is bolted to foundation. A cast pedestal, recessed to receive foot of post, is also recommended. Solid timber is best for main posts, but built-up columns may be used. Allowance for reduction of section by mortises and bolt holes must be made.

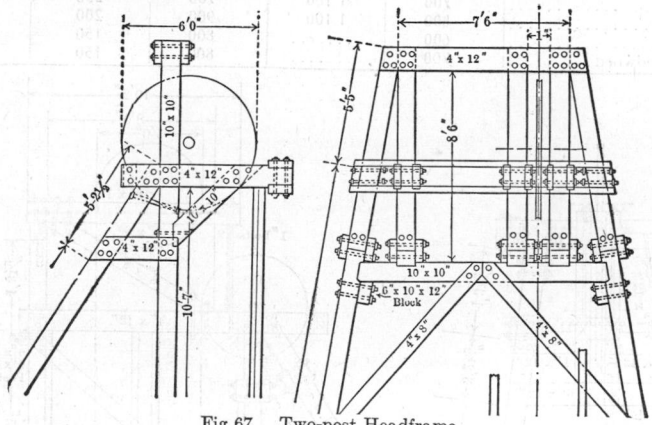

Fig 67. Two-post Headframe

Factor of safety should be double that allowed for ordinary structures, taking into account total rope load from all causes. Or, since headframe should be stronger than the rope, ultimate strength of frame is made twice breaking strength of rope (Art 25).

Allowable unit stresses and strength of members. For timber headframes M. S. Ketchum (53) gives Table 28. Formula 38 gives allowable stresses for dead load, which applies to live load when properly converted to dead load (Art 14). Length of columns should not exceed 45 times least dimension. Unit stress for lengths of more than 10 times least dimension is found by:

$$P = C - (Cl \div 100d), \tag{38}$$

where C = unit stress for short columns (Table 28); P = allowable unit stress, lb per sq in; l = length of column, in; d = least side of column, in. Assoc of R R Superintendents of Bridges & Buildings recommended (1895) the safe unit stresses in Table 29.

Formula 39, for wooden columns, is based on that of the Division of Forestry, U S Dept of Agriculture:

$$P = F \times \frac{700 + 15\,C}{700 + 15\,C + C^2} \tag{39}$$

in which P = ultimate strength, lb per sq in; F = ultimate crushing strength of timber; $C = l \div d$; l = length of column, in; d = least diam, in; F = 5 000 lb for white oak and long-leaf yellow pine, 4 500 lb for Douglas fir and short-leaf pine, 4 000 lb for red pine, spruce, hemlock, California redwood, and 3 500 lb for white pine and cedar.

Table 28. Allowable Working Unit Stresses for Dead Loads, lb per sq in

| Kind of timber | Transverse loading, S | End bearing | Columns under 10 diams, C | Bearing across fiber | Shear | | Modulus of elasticity, E |
					Parallel to grain	Longitudinal shear in beams	
White oak............	1 200	1 200	1 000	450	200	110	1 150 000
Long-leaf yellow pine..	1 300	1 300	1 000	300	180	120	1 610 000
White pine and spruce..	1 000	1 000	800	200	100	70	1 130 000
Western hemlock......	1 000	1 000	800	200	160	100	1 480 000
Douglas fir..........	1 200	1 200	1 000	350	180	110	1 510 000

Table 29. Average Safe Unit Stresses

| Kind of Timber | Tension with grain, lb | Compression | | | Transverse extreme fiber stress, lb |
		End bearing, lb	Columns under 15 diams, lb	Across the grain, lb	
Factor of safety........	10	5	5	4	6
White oak...............	1 200	1 400	1 000	500	1 200
Long-leaf yellow pine.......	1 200	1 400	1 000	350	1 200
White pine...............	700	1 100	700	200	700
Douglas fir...............	800	1 100	900	200	800
Hemlock.................	600	....	800	150	600
California redwood.........	700	....	800	150	750

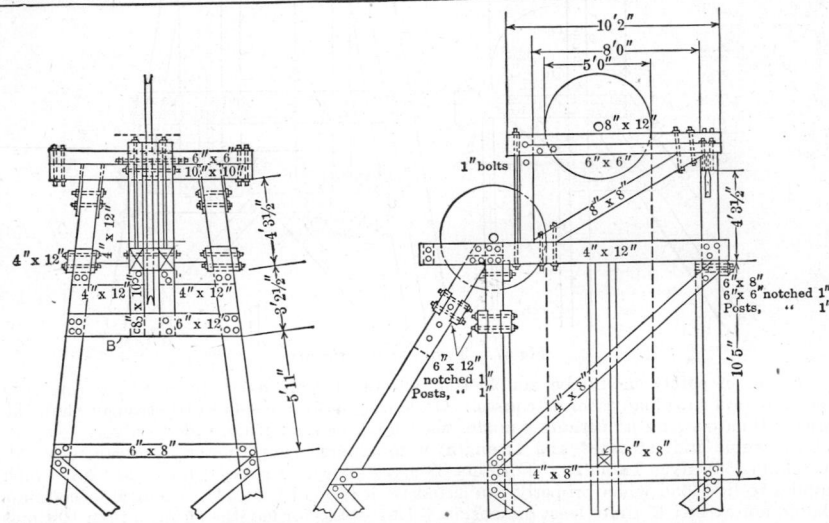

Fig 68. Headframe with Tandem Sheaves

Cost of wooden headframes (Table 30) varies more widely than for steel, due to variation in cost of timber, which ranges from $35 to $100 per M bd ft. With carpenters at $6 per day, cost of erection will be from $40 to $50 per M bd ft. Cost of ironwork, bolts and nails, depends on design, averaging say $20 per M bd ft of timber used.

Comparisons between wood and steel headframes can be sharply drawn for special cases only. Wooden frames are cheaper in first cost and total erection time, considering time required to obtain the material, while steel frames are fireproof and much more durable. Unless given preservative

Table 30. Examples of Timber Headframes

Mine and location	Year erected	Inclination, deg	No hoisting compartments	Depth, ft	Weight of cage (or skip) and contents, lb	Size of rope, in	Diam of sheave, ft	Type	Height to sheave center, ft	Posts: Tower	Posts: Back brace	Bracing: Horizontal	Bracing: Diagonal	Total bd ft timber	Wt of iron work, exclusive of sheaves, lb	Base Width	Base Length	Height of landing above collar	Distance from center of shaft to center of drum	Cost: Lumber	Cost: Iron work	Cost: Labor	Total cost, exclusive of sheaves and foundations
Rose Mohawk, Nev								A	36	10X10	10X10	6X10	6X10							443	123	123	$686
Gold Field, Nev								4 post	36	10X10	10X10	6X10	6X10							404	133	393	927
N Am Sm Co, Ont	1913	90	1	275		7/8	6	A	73	10X10	10X10	10X10	4X8	7 500	2 650	35	47	45	60	280	135	253	665
Park City, Utah	1902	90	1		6 500	2 1/4	6	4 post	40	12X12	12X12	10X10	10X10	7 900	2 200	17	35.5	at surface	56				
Joplin type, Mo								4 post	30 and up	6X8 or 8X8	none	6X8	2X6	1 500 and up		12	12	12 to 35		20 and up	5 and up	20 and up	50 and up
Kanopolis, Kansas	1895	90	2			1 1/4	12	A	96	4 pcs 6X8	2 pcs 6X8	6X6 and 8X10	6X6 and 8X10	26 470		40	72	55				250	750
Stratton's Independence, Colo.			2				6	4 post	52	16X16	16X16	12X12	8X10			26	59	at surface					
Portland, Colo.		90	2				6	4 post	60	14X14	2 pcs 10X14 spaced 10 in	10X10 and 8X14	10X10 and 8X14			16	56	21	60				
Tesla Mine, Cal.		60	3				6	A	44	16X16	16X16	14X14	6X12			20	60						
East Brookside, near Pottsville, Pa	1907	90	2	1 800			14	6 post	front 78, back 103	16X16	16X16	12X12	14X14			35	60	at surface					
Hiawatha Shaft, Iron River, Mich	1909	90	1			1 1/4	8	4 post	80	12X12	12X12	12X12 10X10 1 1/4-in rods	12X12 8X8 6X8 4X8			30	51		84				
Cons Coal Co, No 17, Collinsville, Ill		90	2				8	4 post	65.5	2 pcs 6X12 4" space	same	6X12	6X10			17	57	44					

treatment, wooden frames decay rapidly, and are a source of danger in case of fire. They are now seldom built, except for temporary work or short lived mines; for large tonnage, and when life of mine will exceed that of a wooden frame (say 8–20 yr, depending on climatic conditions), the greater first cost of steel is justified. The difference in cost is less than formerly, due to increased cost of timber. As the strength of steel is known within much closer limits than that of wood, the design can be made with more certainty as to safety of the structure. Large allowances must be made for the variable strength of even the same kind of timber. It is difficult to retain full strength of a timber member at joints, without use of special ironwork which may make the cost approximate that of an all-steel structure. Damage to a wooden frame can usually be quickly repaired by materials and tools at hand. Since joints of wooden frames tend to loosen, from the action of moisture, and from seasoning, steel makes a more rigid structure for high frames. A wooden frame can be erected by local carpenters, while a steel frame requires services of expert erectors.

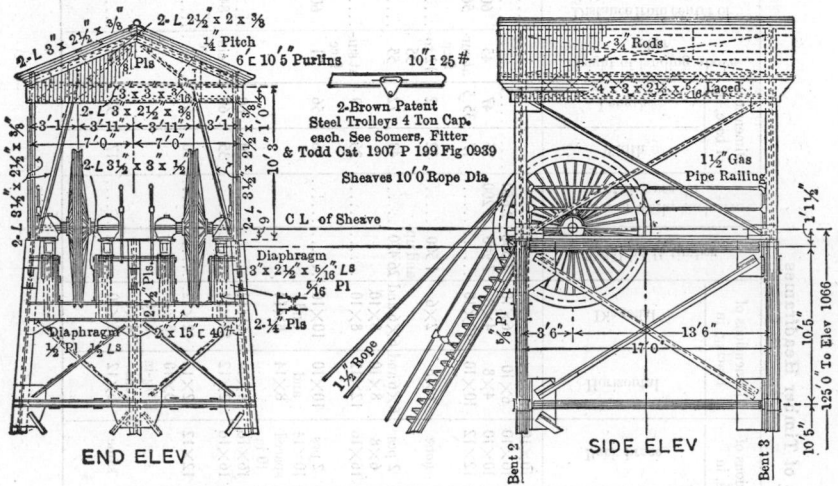

Fig 69. Design of Sheave Supports, Ralph Shaft, H. C. Frick Coke Co

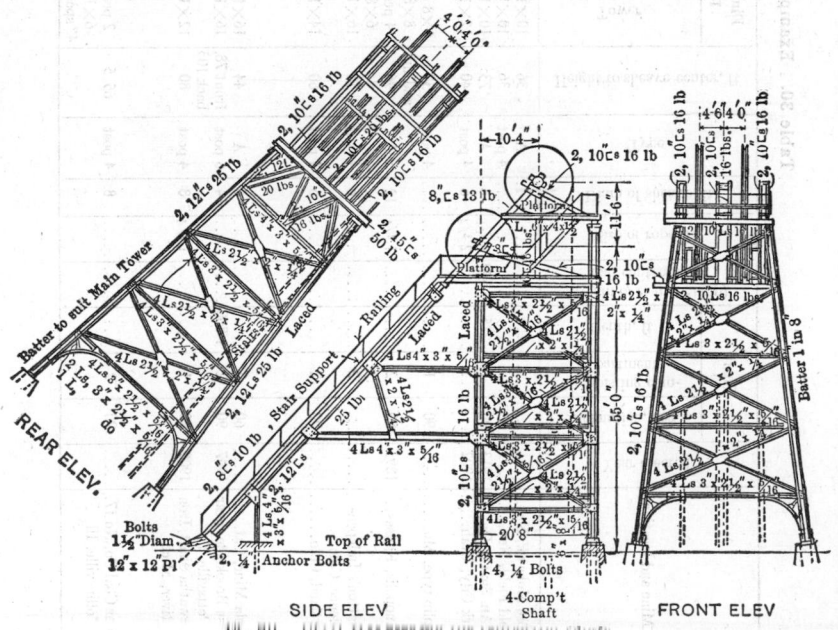

Fig 70. Steel Headframe for Gilberton Shaft

25. STEEL AND CONCRETE HEADFRAMES

Details of design. Cross-sections of posts and main bracing are determined as in Art 23; then sheave girders, post bases and guide supports are designed (see Sec 43). Table 31 gives types of sections of members; angle or H-sections often used for posts

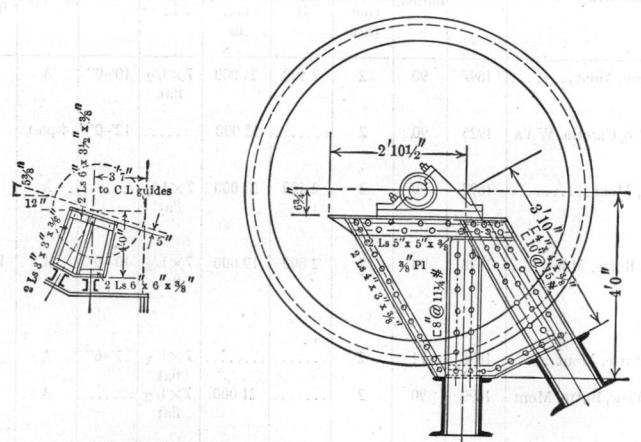

Figs 71 and 72. Sheaves Supported by Diaphragms

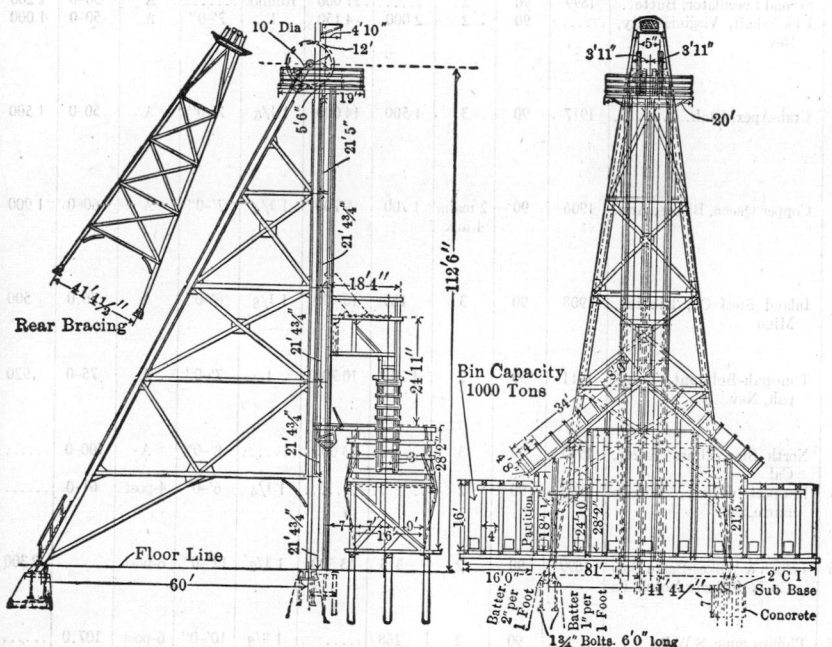

Fig 73.   Steel Headframe, Orig Mine, Butte, Mont.   (*E & M Jour*)

of small frames.   For 4- and 6-post frames, sheave bearings are usually supported by I-beams.   Two shallow beams give a broader and more stable support than one deep beam. They are designed for the bending moment due to vertical component of total rope load on

Table 31.   Examples of Steel

Number	Name and location	Year erected	Shaft			Weight (of cage or skip) and ore, lb	Diam of rope, in	Diam of sheave	Type	Height to sheave center, ft and in	Hoisting speed, ft per min
			Inclination, deg	No hoisting compartments	Depth, ft						
1	St Lawrence, Mont........	1897	90	2	2 100	21 000	7×1/2 flat	10'–0''	A	97–0	2 200
2	Con Coal Co, Caretta, W Va	1925	90	2	....	35 000	....	12'–0''	4-post	91.6	....
3	Anaconda, Mont..........	1898	90	2	2 400	21 000	7×1/2 flat	....	A	58–8	2 200
4	High Ore, Butte, Mont.....	1898	90	2	2 800	19 000	7×1/2 flat	10'–0''	A	100–0	2 200
5	Stewart, Butte, Mont......	1898	71	2	......	....	7×1/2 flat	7'–6''	A	55–0	......
6	Montain View, Butte, Mont	1899	90	2	......	21 000	7×1/2 flat	......	A	80–0	2 200
7	Basin & Bay State, Basin, Mont	1899	90	2	......	....	......	10'–0''	A	70–0	......
8	Second Speculator, Butte...	1899	90	2	......	21 000	Round	......	A	50–0	2 200
9	Union shaft, Virginia City, Nev	....	90	2	2 000	4 150	1	7'–0''	A	50–0	1 000
10	Utah-Apex, Utah..........	1917	90	3	1 500	14 000	1 1/8	7'–0''	A	50–0	1 500
11	Copper Queen, Bisbee, Ariz.	1906	90	2 main, 1 aux	1 700	9 700	1 1/4	7'–0''	A	60–0	1 900
12	Inland Steel Co, Hibbing, Minn	1908	90	3	185	10 400	1 1/8	6'–0''	A	76.0	500
13	Tonopah-Belmont, Tonopah, Nev	1911	90	2	1 700	10 700	1	7'–0''	A	75–0	920
14	North Star, Grass Valley, Cal	1915	90	3	....	13 000	......	8'–0''	A	100–0	......
15	Prospect colliery, Wilkes-Barre, Pa	1898	90	2	......	....	1 1/4	6'–0''	4-post	61–0	......
16	Lehigh & Wilkes-Barre Coal Co, No 9, Sugar Notch, Pa	1899	90	2	315	13 500	1 1/2	12'–0''	6-post		2 300
17	Phillips mine, S W Pa......	....	90	2	268	....	1 3/8	10'–0''	6-post	107.0	......

Headframes, with Costs

Vertical posts	Back brace	Side horizontal struts	Side diagonals	Front and back horizontal struts	Front and back diagonals	Distance, back post to brace, ft	Height, landing above collar, ft	Distance, center of shaft to center of drum	Weight, without sheaves, lb	Cost erected without sheaves and foundations
4 Zs, 6× 7/16; 1 Pl, 15 1/2×7/16	Same	2 12 in ⌷s	2 9 in ⌷s	2 12 in ⌷s	2 9 in ⌷s	......	......	......	117 000	$3 920
4 Ls, 3×4×5/16	2 12 in ⌷s; 1 4×3/8 Pl	1 10 in ⌷s	L s, 5×3 1/2 to 2 1/2×2 1/2	......	......				......	......
4 Zs, 6× 3/8; 1 Pl, 8 × 3/8	Same	2 9 in ⌷s	2 L s, 5×3×5/16	2 9 in ⌷s	2 L s, 5×3×5/16	......		......	74 700	2 755
1 cover Pl, 2 web Pls, 4 Ls, 3 1/2 ×3 1/2×3/8	20×7/16, 18×7/16, 3 1/2×3 1/2 ×1/2	2 ⌷s, 15 and 12 in×1/2				61	38	......	292 000	8 940
2 9 in ⌷s	2 9 in ⌷s	2 8 or 9 in ⌷s	2 6 or 7 in ⌷s	2 6, 8 or 9 in ⌷s	2 6 or 7 in ⌷s	......	......	83	45 000	2 327
2 Pls, 20×3/8; 2 15 in ⌷s	Same	2 9, 10, 12, or 15 in ⌷s				......	......	......	183 000	7 320
2 9 in ⌷s	2 10 in ⌷s	2 7 in ⌷s	2 6 or 7 in ⌷s	2 7 in ⌷s	2 6 or 7 in ⌷s	44	31	110	79 000	3 857
2 7 in ⌷s Pl, 12× 5/16; 4 Ls, 3 1/2×3 ×5/16	2 8 in ⌷s Pl, 18× 5/16; 4 Ls, 4×3×5/16	2 5 in ⌷s None	Same None	Same Front 1 L, 4×3×5/16; Back 2 Ls, 3 1/2×2 1/2 × 5/16	Same 1 L, 3×2 1/2 ×5/16	30 / 30	......	75	42 200 / 42 000	2 500 / ......
2 10 in ⌷s	2 12 in ⌷s; 1 Pl, 16×1/4	2 8 in ⌷s	2 8 and 6 in ⌷s	Same	Same	50	......	......	......	15 000 including foundations
2 8 in ⌷s	2 10 in ⌷s	2 6 in ⌷s	2 Ls, 3 1/2×2 1/2 ×1/4	Front, 2 ⌷s, 10 or 6 in; Back, 2⌷s, 6 in	2 Ls, 3×2×1/4	34	15	100	35 250	......
2 10 in ⌷s	2 10 in ⌷s	2 ⌷s, 5 or 6 in	2 Ls, 4× 3×5/16 or 3 1/2×2 1/2 ×5/16	2 6 in ⌷s	2 Ls, 4×3×5/16 or 3 1/2× 2 1/2×5/16	34	39	150	79 000	5 000
2 9 in ⌷s	2 12 in ⌷s	2 6 in ⌷s or 2 Ls, 2 1/2×2 1/2 ×1/4	2 Ls, 2 1/2×2 1/2 ×1/4	Front 2 Ls, 5×3×5/16; Back, 2 6 in ⌷s	2 Ls, 2 1/2×2 1/2 × 1/4	39	40	100	65 000	6 920
2 10 in ⌷s	2 12 in ⌷s	2 6 or 8 in ⌷s	Same	2 6 or 9 in ⌷s	Ls or ⌷s	55	......	......	96 000	......
2 Is, Pl 10×5/16; 4 Ls, 4×3×1/2	......	2 Ls, 6×4×7/16	Same	Same	Same	......	20	116	......	......
2 Ls, 5×3×3/8	2 Ls, 6×6×1/2	⌷s	1 L, 6×3×3/8	⌷s,	1 L, 6×3×3/8	41	67	60	350 000 including trestle	16 175 including trestle
4 Zs, 3×2 11/16 ×3/8 Pl, 6×3/8	Same	2 Pls, 8×3/8; 4 Ls, 3× 2 1/2×3/8 battened	2 Ls, 3×3×3/8	Same as side	2 Ls, 3×2 1/2 ×3/8	75	80	84	......	......

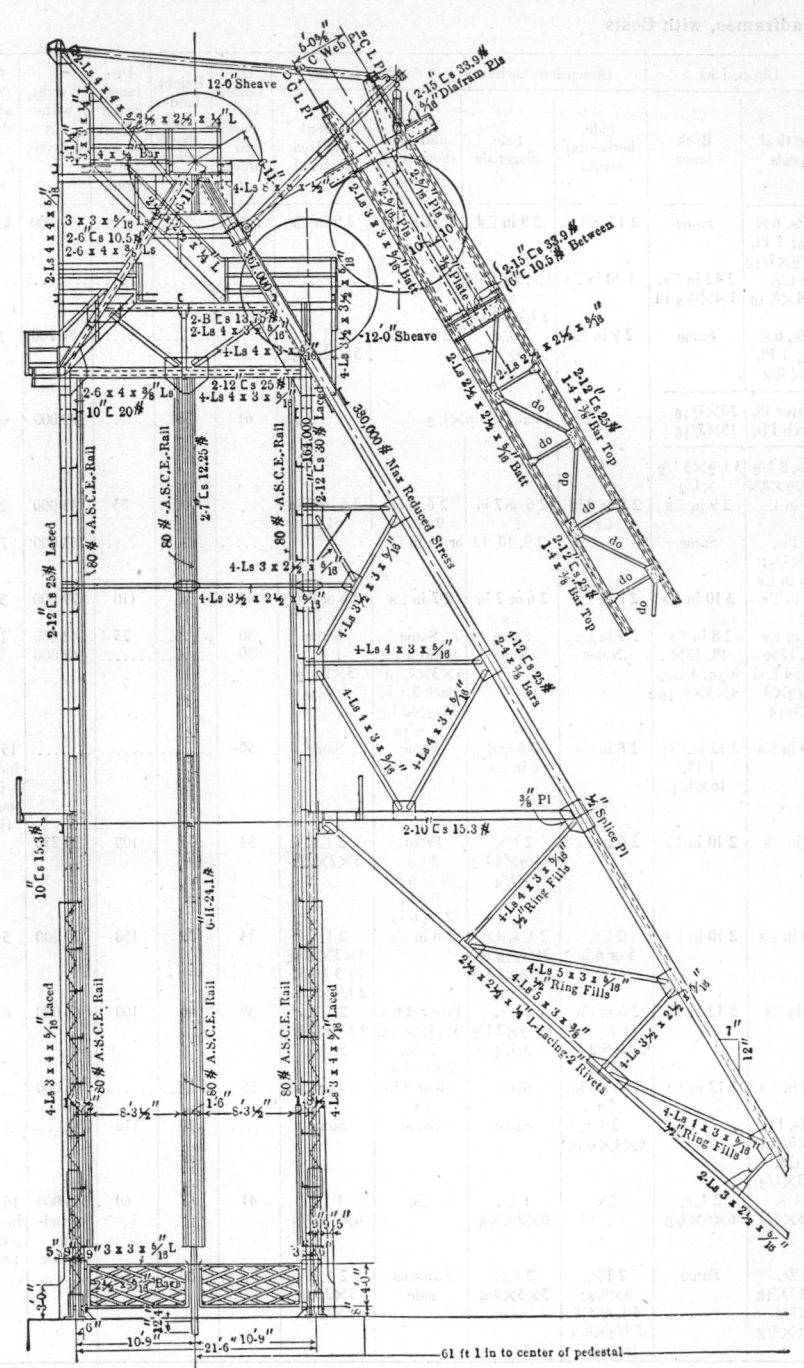

Fig 74.   Steel Headframe, Consol Coal Co, Carretta, W Va

sheave (Art 14), plus wt of sheave. For the front and back cross girders supporting sheave girders, channels work best into the design. Sheave girders and top of frame are often covered by a steel-plate floor, in which case the horiz component of rope load goes to intersection of back brace and posts, and cross girders on back brace are omitted (Fig 69).

Table 32. Statistics of Headframes in Butte District (37, 56)

Shaft	Weight, lb		Capacity of skip, ton	Depth of shaft, ft	Ore hoisting speed, ft per min	Height of headframe, ft	Weight of headframe, lb	Diam of sheaves, ft	Size and type of hoisting rope
	Cage	Skip							
Anaconda..........	4 000	8 500	5	2 800	2 200	58.82	74,700	10	7 1/2″ × 1/2″, flat
Badger State........	4 000	10 500	7	3 500*	2 800	129.5	256 000	12	1 7/8″ diam, rd
Belmont.............	4 000	10 500	7	3 400*	2 600	129.5	256 000	12	1 7/8″ diam, rd
Belmont (old).......	3 800	8 900	5	3 400	2 250	114	timber	10	7 1/2″ × 1/2″, flat
Berkeley...........	3 900	8 500	5	3 200	2 600	80	timber	10	1 1/4″ diam, rd
Black Rock No 1....	3 800	10 000	10	2 800	2 600	152	250 000	10	1 1/2″ diam, rd
Black Rock No 3..	3 800	10 000	10	2 800	2 600	152	250 000	10	1 1/2″ diam, rd
Diamond...........	3 850	8 960	5	3 400	2 800	100	318 000	10	6″ × 1/2″, flat
Elm Orlu...........	4 000	10 000	7	3 300	2 600	94	65 000	10	6″ × 1/2″, flat
High Ore...........	3 850	8 960	5	3 400	2 600	100	292 000	10	6″ × 1/2″, flat
Leonard...........	3 800	8 500	5	2 800	3 000	141	346 425	12	1 1/2″ diam, rd
Mountain Con......	4 000	10 500	7	3 600*	2 800	129.5	256 000	12	1 7/8″ diam, rd
Mountain Con (old).	3 850	8 900	5	3 500	1 000	100	timber	10	1 1/4″ diam, rd
Mountain view.....	4 000	11 000	5	2 600	2 200	80	183 000	7 1/2	7″ × 1/2″, flat
Never Sweat.......	3 200	5 700	3 1/2	2 800	2 600	100	315 000	10	1 1/4″ diam, rd
Original...........	3 900	7 800	4	3 800	2 600	112	318 000	10	1 1/2″ diam, rd
Orphan Girl.......	3 050	no skips	....	1 000	1 500	70	79 000	7	1″ diam, rd
Pennsylvania.......	3 500	8 500	5	3 400	2 800	100	315 000	12	1 1/2″ diam, rd
Pittsmont..........	1 250	3 875	5	1 600	2 600	58.5	41 500	8	6″ × 1/2″, flat
St Lawrence........	3 900	7 000	7	2 100	1 000	97	117 000	10	7″ × 1/2″, flat
Speculator.........	2 100	11 000	5	2 800	2 200	50	42 200	10	1 1/2″ diam, rd
Stewart............	3 800	8 500	5	3 800	2 800	100	292 000	10	1 1/2″ diam, rd
Tramway...........	3 850	8 500	5	2 800	2 800	100	315 000	12	1 1/2″ diam, rd
West Colusa...... {	3 500 } 2 200 }	no skips	....	2 200	2 800	50	43 000	10	4″ × 3/8″, flat

* Hoisting installation, designed for depth of 5 100 ft.

Support of sheaves. With large sheaves, projecting over back of frame, back cross girder must be dropped to clear sheave, and sheave girders then rest on plate diaphragms, with angle stiffeners extending up from cross girder. Fig 69 shows details of this standard design, for Ralph shaft, H. C. Frick Coke Co, by American Bridge Co. Other designs are in use, probably with no increase in wt of material, but at increased cost for shop work. Instead of I-beams, deep plate girders sometimes support sheave bearings, resting directly on the cross girders, but with no special advantage. When sheaves must be in tandem, upper sheave girders are carried at the back by auxiliary posts in plane of back brace (Fig 70); or, upper sheave is supported on an auxiliary tower on main frame. Fig 74 shows an A-frame, designed by Allen & Garcia, with tandem sheaves, the back brace being extended to bearings of upper sheave, and the lower one carried on brackets on back brace. This frame is built into the tipple, and lower half is concreted. As upper half is braced by tipple frame, its width (5 ft) is much less than would otherwise be possible for stability.

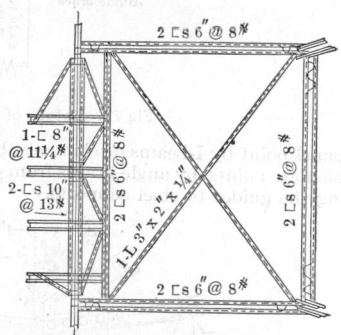

Fig 75. Horiz Sec of Frame, showing Guide Supports

For A- or 2-post frames, sheaves may be supported by plate-girder diaphragms, carried on cross girders on front posts and back brace. If diam of sheave permits, its bearings are bolted to front of diaphragms; if not, they are placed on top. In first case, diaphragms may be braced to the posts by front and back plates. Another cross girder connects front posts above the sheaves, and the diaphragms are extended to it. In second case (Fig 71 and 72), the front posts need not extend above sheave bearings, unless they are to carry brackets for crab rail for changing sheaves. Fig 71, 72 refer to headframes No 7, 12, and 11, Table 31. Fig 73 shows a typical A-frame, Butte, Mont.

Guides for 2-post frames are generally bolted to flanges of I-beams, or other sections, running from shaft collar to top of frame; supported in line by braces of I-beam,

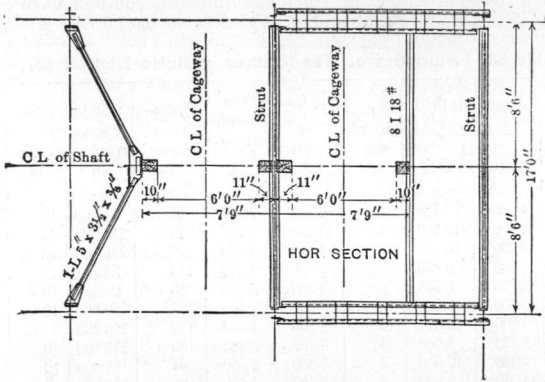

Fig 76. Guide Supports

channels or angles, from horizontal struts of front bent; they are more rigid if carried back to an auxiliary girt across the frame between 2 side struts (Fig 75). In 4- and 6-post frames, wooden guides are not commonly backed by steel sections, but supported at each

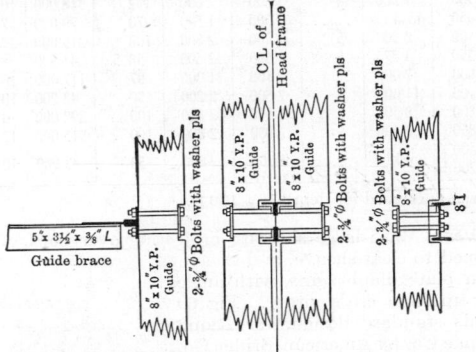

Fig 77. Details of Fastening Guides to Steel Supports

panel point by I-beams or channels, between the bents; and, if support is needed at intermediate points, by angle braces from corner posts (Fig 76). Fig 77 shows details of fastening the guides to steel supports.

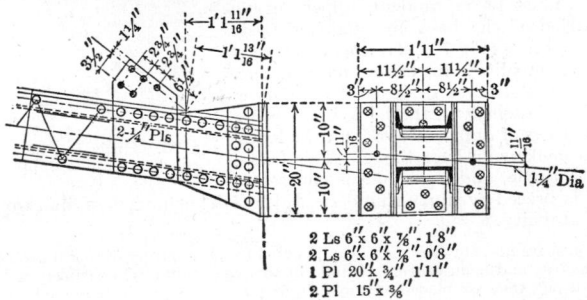

2 Ls 6″ x 6″ x ⅞″ - 1′8″
2 Ls 6″ x 6″ x ⅞″ - 0′8″
1 Pl 20½ x ¾″ - 1′11″
2 Pl 15″ x ⅜″

Fig 78. Base of Headframe Post

Bases of posts must transmit load to the foundation within the allowable safe unit stress for the type of foundation. This, for best Portland cement concrete, is about 500 pounds per square inch limestone masonry, 400 lb per sq in. There should be at least 2 anchor bolts at foot of each post. Fig 78 shows details of base for a column of two 10-in latticed channels, for a back brace, and Fig 79 an anchorage for front post and back brace. Sometimes a C-I footing is placed between base and foundation, but without advantage for steel frames.

Safety factor must be larger than for ordinary structures, because of varying load and indeterminate stresses (Art 23). Ketchum (53) recommends a factor of 4 for dead and wind load, and 8 for live load (live load being taken as twice the wt of cage and contents, plus wt of rope, plus load due to cage and rope friction); or, a factor of 2.66, if breaking strength of rope or ropes be used instead of live load. If unit stresses for wind,

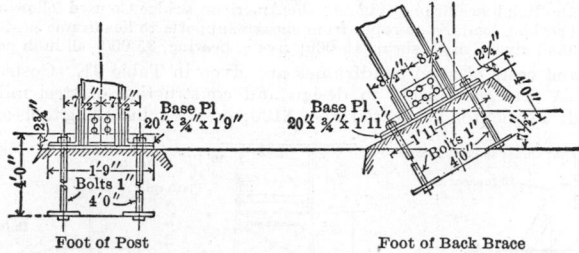

Fig 79.   Anchorage for Headframe

dead and live loads, are added the total unit stress should not exceed the allowable unit stress for dead load by more than 25%; that is, the combined safety factor should not be less than 3.2. If the basis of breaking strength of the rope be used, wind-load stresses may be neglected, except as regards overturning of the frame.

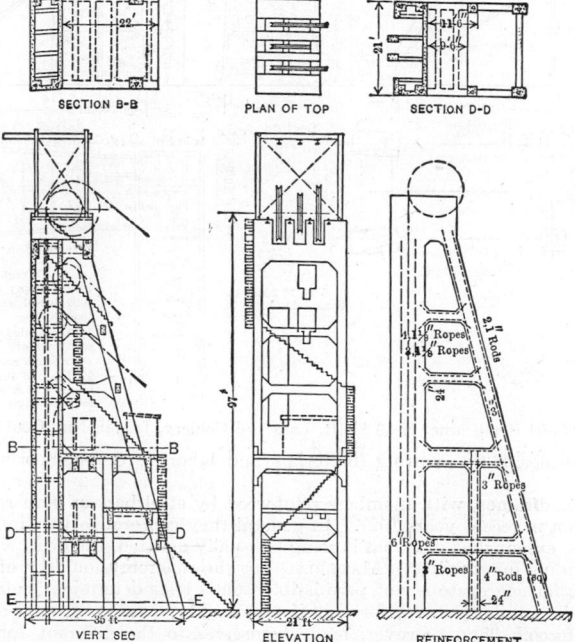

Fig 80.   Concrete Headframe, Curry Shaft, Penn Iron Mining Co, Vulcan, Mich *(E & M Jour)*

A rational method is to design for an ultimate strength equivalent to twice breaking strength of rope. Then, by assuming the live load as half the rope's breaking strength, with a safety factor of 4 for all stresses, the live, dead, and wind loads may be combined. This is convenient in selecting proper size of member from structural steel handbooks, the tables of which are usually calculated with a safety factor of 4.

Allowable unit stresses, with a safety factor of 4 (live load being converted to equiv dead load) are: for tension, 16 000, and for compression, 16 000 − 70 ($l \div r$), both in lb per sq in; where l = length of member, in, and r = least radius of gyration, in. Length of compression members should not exceed 100 r for main members, nor 140 r for secondary members. Following values recommended:

Rivets and pins, bearing................... 22 000 lb per sq in
Rivets and pins, shear.................... 11 000 "   "   "   "
Pins, bending, on extreme fiber........... 24 000 "   "   "   "
Plate girder webs, shear on net section..... 10 000 "   "   "   "

In designing the Ralph headframe (Fig 69), the American Bridge Co used following unit stresses for transferring breaking load of the ropes from sheave supports to headframe posts: tension and compression, 25 000; rivets, single shear, 15 000; rivets, bearing, 35 000; all in lb per sq in.

Examples and costs of steel headframes are given in Table 31. Costs apply to the year erected. A firm specializing in design and construction of steel mine structures recently quoted: Per net ton fabricated steel, $100; erection, including tools and insurance,

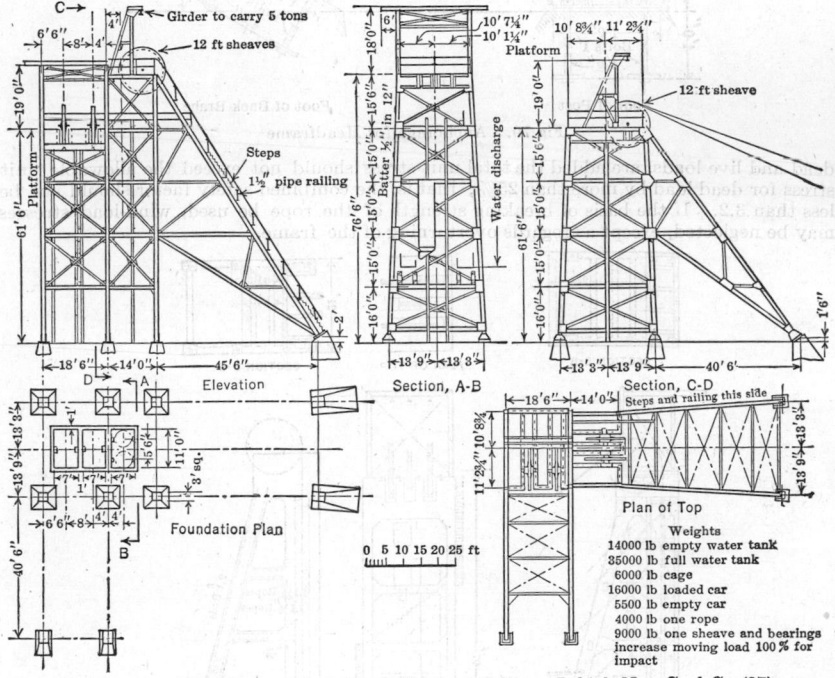

Fig 81. Steel Headframe, No 6 Shaft, Lansford Colliery, Lehigh Nav Coal Co (37)

$45; shop drawings, $30; painting (materials and labor), $10; engineering, $15; total, $200 per ton.

Concrete headframes, with members reinforced by steel bars or wire rope, have had some application in recent years (52). In general they conform to the lines of steel and wooden frames, except that diagonal bracing is usually omitted, the dead wt and massive structure providing for stability. MATERIALS for the concrete should be of the best; use of mill tailings for aggregate is not permissible unless tests determine their fitness. Old hoisting rope is suitable for reinforcing, if thoroughly cleaned of rust and lubricant. Standard reinforcing bars, however, lend themselves to the different forms and their properties are fully known. DESIGN, as in steel and wood, depends on local conditions. After computation of stresses in usual way, taking into account that dead load usually exceeds rope load, the members are designed as for reinforced concrete structures. ADVANTAGES are permanence, non-combustibility and resistance to atmospheric conditions or corrosive gases from the shaft. Absence of diagonal bracing (Fig 80) leaves more room for portals, and permits most desirable arrangement of bins and tracks. Rigidity and mass of the structure prevent vibration from dumping skips or cars, or swaying from wind and

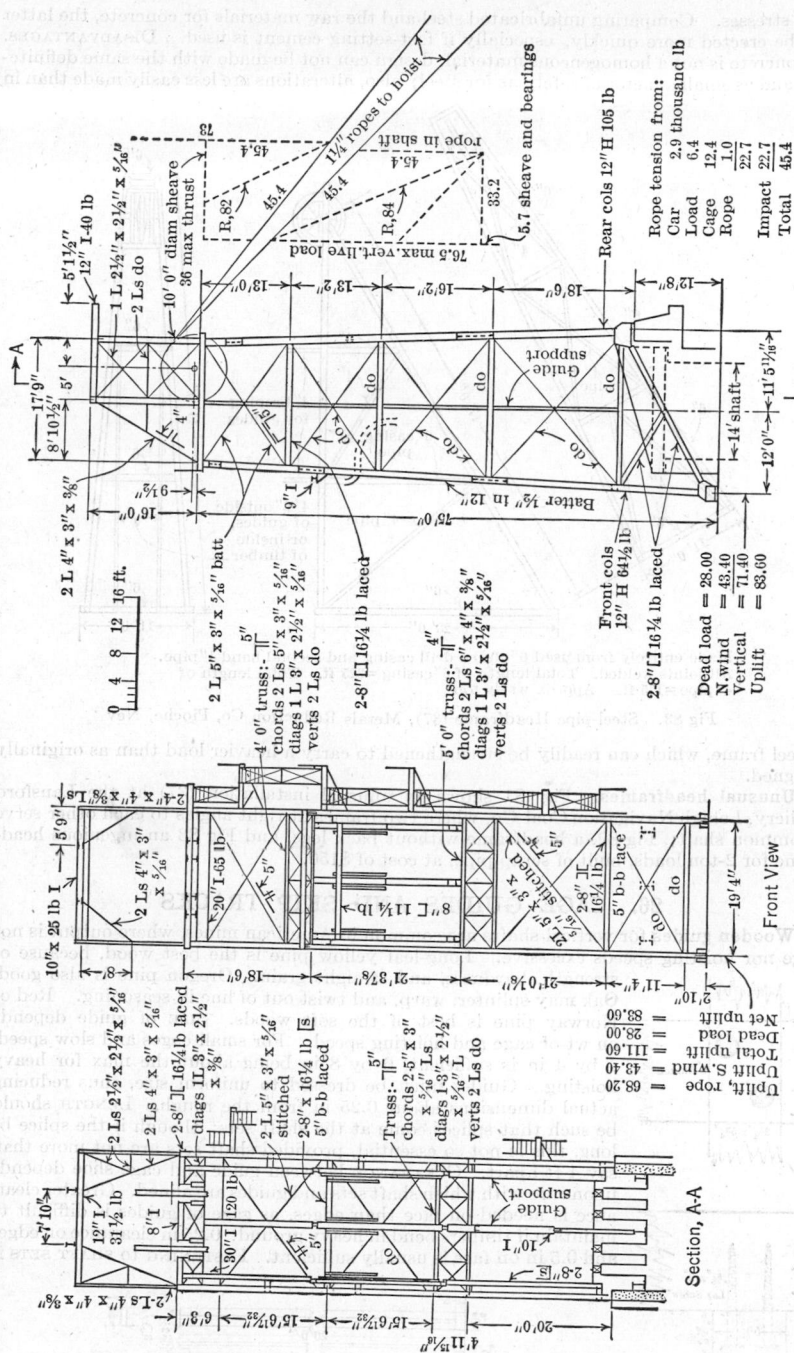

Fig 82. Steel Headframe without Back Legs, Bellevue Breaker, Glen Alden Coal Co, Scranton, Pa (37)

rope stresses. Comparing unfabricated steel and the raw materials for concrete, the latter can be erected more quickly, especially if fast-setting cement is used. DISADVANTAGES. As concrete is not a homogeneous material, design can not be made with the same definiteness and as small a factor of safety as for steel; also, alterations are less easily made than in

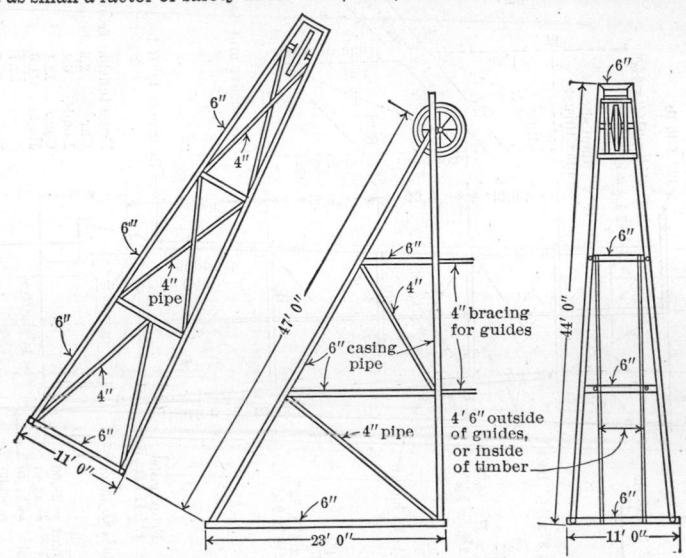

Made entirely from used 6″ churn drill casing and second hand 4″ pipe. All joints welded. Total length of 6″ casing = 325 ft. Total length of 4″ pipe = 175 ft. Approx wt = 6 ton

Fig 83. Steel-pipe Headframe (37), Metals Reduction Co, Pioche, Nev

a steel frame, which can readily be strengthened to carry a heavier load than as originally designed.

Unusual headframes. Fig 81 shows an unusual installation (37) at the Lansford Colliery, Lehigh Navigation Coal Co, where two frames at right angles to each other serve a common shaft; Fig 82, a headframe without back legs, and Fig 83 an ingenious headframe for 2-ton loads, built of scrap pipe, at cost of $150.

26. CAGE GUIDES AND SKIP TRACKS

Wooden guides for vertical shafts are common in American mines, where output is not large nor hoisting speeds excessive. Long-leaf yellow pine is the best wood, because of

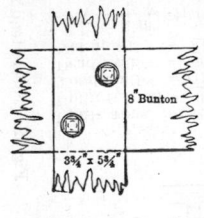

strength, hardness, and straight grain. Oregon pine is also good. Oak may splinter, warp, and twist out of line in seasoning. Red or Norway pine is best of the soft woods. SIZE of guide depends on wt of cage and hoisting speed. For small cages and slow speed, 4 by 4 in is sufficient, 6 by 8 in being about the max for heavy hoisting. Guides must be dressed to uniform size, thus reducing actual dimensions about 0.25 in from the rough. LENGTH should be such that splices come at the shaft sets; though if the splice be long, this is not so essential, provided shaft sets are not more than say 4 ft apart. CLEARANCE between guide and cage shoe depends upon care with which shaft sets and guides are alined. Greater clearance is needed on face than edges, as gage of guides is difficult to maintain if timbers bend in heavy ground; 0.25 in clearance on edges and 0.5 in on face is usually sufficient. FASTENING TO SHAFT SETS is

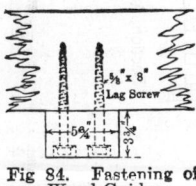

Fig 84. Fastening of Wood Guides

Fig 85. Slotted Guides

commonly by 1 or 2 lag screws, with countersunk heads (Fig 84). The penetration of lag screw into bunton should be at least equal to thickness of guide. Use of galvanized lag screws facilitates removal and replacement of guides. Iron angles may be used for fastenings, bolted to both guide and shaft timber (Fig 87).

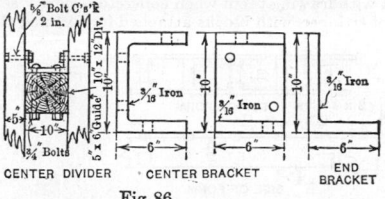

CENTER DIVIDER · CENTER BRACKET · END BRACKET

Fig 86

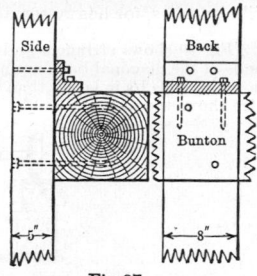

Fig 87

Examples of wooden guides. At No 2 shaft, Hancock Consol Mining Co, Mich, guide face is slotted with lag screw heads countersunk in slot (Fig 85); if a screw becomes loose it will work down this slot, instead of sticking between guide and show. These guides are backed by studdles between the dividers. Fig 87 shows fastening for guides at Tobin & Dunn mines, Mich. Lag screws are 5/8 in. The 3 by 3-in angle is placed every 10 to 15 ft, bolted to guide by 0.5 by 6-in bolts, and to divider by 0.5-in lag screws. Fig 86 shows method at Indiana mine, Mich. Guides are 5 by 6 in, in 32-ft lengths, with butt joints; brackets, 3/16 by 5 in. On the Rand, So Africa, the standard wooden guide is 4 by 8 in (1).

Guide joints. Fig 89 shows joints used on the Rand and elsewhere, for 4 by 8, 5 by 6, 4 by 6, and 4 by 5-in guides. At Butte, Mont, guides are usually 4 by 9 and 5 by 9 in, fastened by two 7/8 by 8 or 7/8 by 9-in lag screws at each shaft set.

Steel guides are rapidly coming into use for heavy hoisting, especially in concrete-lined shafts. They wear better than wood, have better alinement, and are non-combustible; safety catches, if of correct design, work satisfactorily. As steel guide dimensions are not changed by moisture, clearance between cage shoe and guide may be smaller.

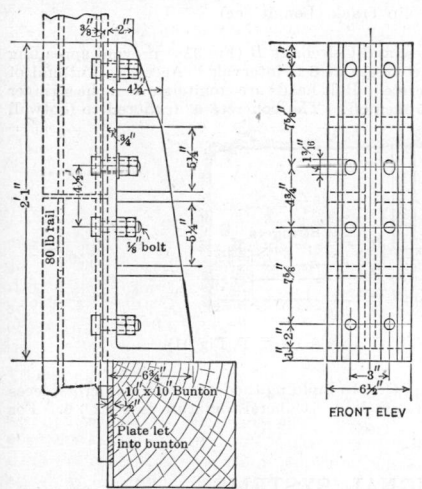

Fig 88. Bracket Support for Steel Rail Guides, Rand (Vaughan)

FRONT ELEV

Different forms of rolled sections are used, but standard T-rail is common. Rails are bolted to buntons and connected by standard splice bars, since only the rail head serves as a guide. Wt of rail, 60–100 lb per yd. In a concreted shaft, Rosedale mine, Cambria Steel Co, Pa, 100-lb T-rail guides are carried by 8-in channels (57). Fig 88 shows bracket support for 80-lb rail guides, in No 4 shaft (cylindrical), of City Deep mine, Rand (1).

Wire-rope guides, preferably of locked-coil type, are often used in Europe for shafts of circular section. At Dalton collieries, Rotherham, England, the shaft is 21 ft diam and 2 238 ft deep. Cages are 3-decked, 18 ft high, and carry 7 tons of coal. At each corner of the

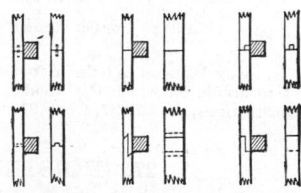

Fig 89. Joints for Wooden Guides

cage is a locked-coil rope guide, under 14 tons tension; and between the cages, to prevent collision at passing point, hang 2 rubbing guide ropes under similar tension.

Skip tracks for inclined shafts, if at a pitch not exceeding 30°, are built like surface tracks, except for measures to prevent downward creep of the rails. Notching rail flanges for spikes at 2 or 3 places in a rail length is generally sufficient. If shaft timbering includes sills, rails rest on these with 1 or 2 intermediate ties, and are lined up with wedges. In absence of timbering, every third or fourth tie must be "hitched" into side walls of the shaft. Rails not lighter than 30-lb should be used, even for light skips and slow speeds; 45 and 50-lb rails for heavier work. Concrete stringers for skip tracks are replacing sills and ties, for heavy service and when the life of the mine warrants added cost.

Fig 90 shows stringers and mode of fastening rails at Mohawk and Wolverine mines. Upper ends of the diagonal bolts are not exposed to injury by derailment of skip. Bolt holes are made by inserting rods 1/8 in larger than the bolt, and withdrawing them when concrete is partly set. Fig 90 also shows the form for molding upper part of stringer, with blocks attached for forming the recesses

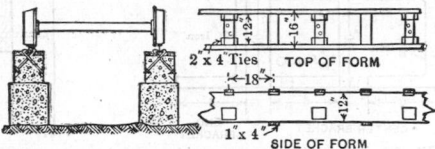

Fig 90. Skip-track Concrete Stringer and Form (*E & M Jour*)

for nuts and washers. 2 by 4-in creosoted blocks are set in the concrete, 1 in deep and 18 in apart, to cushion the rail. Concrete of 1 : 2 : 5 is mixed on the level above, and poured down troughs to desired point. In 24 hr 6 or 8 men can build 100 ft of double-track stringer. On steep slopes it is difficult to hold the rail. At Copper Range shafts, pitching 70°, the method shown in Fig 91 and 91a was devised. The rail rests on a 6 by 10-in longitudinal stringer, set in the concrete base.

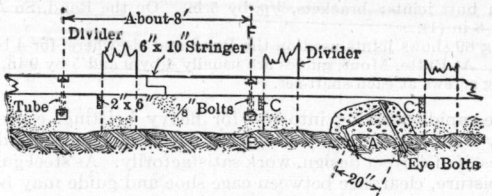

Fig 91. Copper Range Skip Track (Longit Sec)

Three notches on each side of rail receive the spikes, and C-I chairs B (Fig 91a) prevent spreading of rails. The wooden stringers are bolted to the concrete at 8 ft-intervals. Access to nut end of bolts is through 3 by 4-in iron boxes, set in the concrete. Bolt heads are countersunk in the stringer and covered by the rail, so that they can not be broken off. The concrete is anchored to footwall

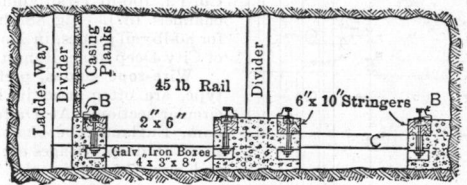

Fig 91a. Copper Range Skip Track (Cross-sec on E–F, Fig 91)

every 25 ft, by eyebolts set in holes in foot wall (Fig 91). In building the forms 2 by 6-in crosspieces C are set to grade, on which the wooden stringers are laid. Concrete mixture is 1 : 2 : 6. For further illustrations, see Bib 37, Chap 21.

27. HOISTING SIGNAL SYSTEMS

Signals in use and recommended for metal mines (58) are shown in Table 33; signals in use and recommended for coal mines (59), Table 34. Modifications to provide for hoisting or lowering from and to different levels are generally made by the local management or by telephonic communication with hoistman.

Bell wire and gong operated by hand is cheap and positive for a few levels, or depths not exceeding 400 or 500 ft. Beyond this the springs or weights to counterbalance wt of bell wire require a heavy pull; and the man giving the signal is not sure it has been properly received or understood by the engineer. Light galvanized guy strand, 0.156 to 0.25 in diam makes the best bell wire, though it is quite stiff, and changes of direction should be made by bell cranks, not by sheaves. Wooden cleats are better than iron staples to hold the bell wire to shaft timbers. Fig 92 shows usual arrangement.

Table 33. The More Important Signals (No of Bells) Prescribed by Law or in Common Use in Metal-mining Districts (58)

	Ariz (a)	Mich (c, b)	Mich (d, b)	Mich (e)	Mich (f, b)	Mich (g)	Minn (h, b)	Minn (i, b)	Mont, SD (a)	N Y (j)	N Y (k)
Hoist............		3	3	3	3	3		3		2	
" or stop......	1 (l)								1		1
" men on cage.		1–3	6	8–6 (m)		5	6		3		
" slowly......		6		5				6		4	
" skip, slowly..							6				
" slowly to collar.......				6				5			
" ore (n).....							3				
" rock.......					1–3		5				
Stop...........		1	1	1		1	1	1		1	
Lower..........	2	2	2	2	2	2	2	2		3	2
" men.......		1–2	4	8–4 (m)		4	4		2		
" slowly......		4		4				4		5	
" skip, slowly..							4				
Men on.........	3				6						3
Blasting........	5				6				4		
Steam on.......	4						7		5		
" off........	4						7		6		
Air on..........	6						8	7	7		
" off........	6						8	9	8		
More air.......								8			
For shaft men (o)..										6	
Danger.........	7						9		9		
Fire...........							10				

	Calif (a)	Colo (a)	Idaho Nev (a)	Mo (p, b)	Ore (a)	Utah (b)	Wyo (a)
Hoist or stop........	1	1	1		1	1	1
" men or stop......				1			
" men						3	3
Lower	2	2	2	2	2	2	2
" tools...........	5				5	5	
" timber.........	6				6	6	
Pull steel..........				4			
Move slowly........					4		
Men on.............	3	3	3		3		
Call conveyance for men...				3			
Blasting............	2–2–1	3–2–1	4		3–2–1	3–2–1	3–2–1
Start or stop pump....	4					4	
Foreman wanted......	7						
Accident............		7 (q)			7	7 (q)	7 (q)
Danger.............			9				

(a) State code. (b) Common use. (c) Dickinson Co. (d) Gogebic Co. (e) Iron Co (recom by comm of mgrs). (f) Keweenaw Co. (g) Marquette Co (leading company). (h) Crow Wing Co. (i) St Louis Co. (j) Salt company. (k) Large iron company. (l) Or release shaft conveyance. (m) Where repeating system not used. (n) Or empty cage. (o) As during repair. (p) Joplin dist. (q) And move by verbal orders only.

Table 34. Standard Signals for Hoisting and Lowering in Coal Mines (59)

Signal from shaft to engineer:

1 Bell—Hoist; or stop if hoist is in motion.

2 Bells—Lower.

3 Bells—Men to be hoisted. If men can be hoisted, the engineer signals to cager with one bell, who then admits men to the cage, and gives signal to hoist, one bell.

4 Bells—Hoist slowly—danger.

5 Bells—Accident in mine; send in stretcher.

Signals from engineer to shaft:

1 Bell—Men can get on cage.

2 Bells—Send up empty cage.

Other signals as needed may be arranged by mine officials with approval of mine inspector. They must be added to the list posted at landings and in engine room.

Pneumatic signals are largely used in collieries in eastern and middle states. Ordinary pipe and fittings are used between stations. A stroke of the hand plunger in cylinder *A* (Fig 93) slightly compresses air in the pipe, causing all the gongs of the system to ring, and the whistles to blow. The pipe may also be used as a speaking tube.

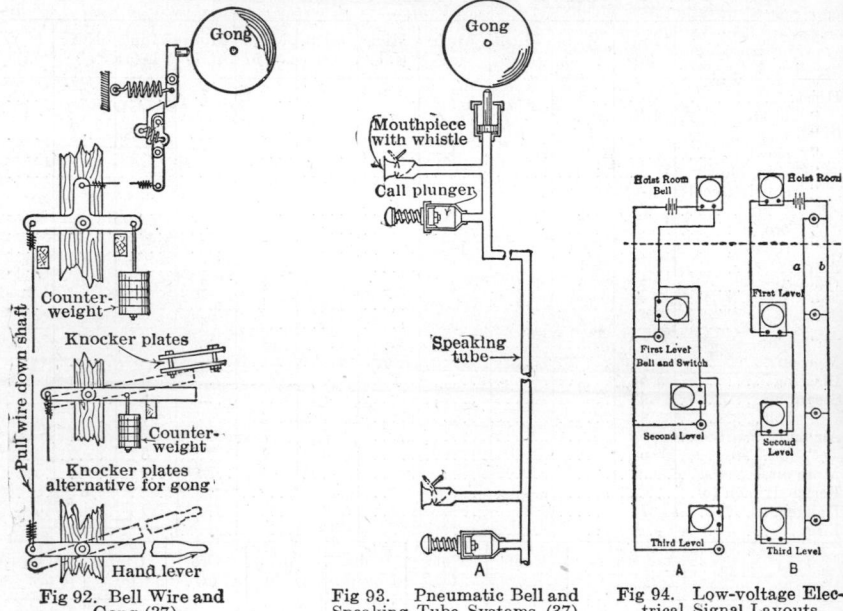

Fig 92. Bell Wire **and** Gong (37)

Fig 93. Pneumatic Bell and Speaking Tube Systems (37)

Fig 94. Low-voltage Electrical Signal Layouts

This method is reliable, with practically no maintenance expense; not affected by water, and accidental signals can not be given as in some electrical systems. No indicator can be used, as in electrical systems, to supplement bell signal. Cost for each station outfit (Fig 93), not including piping between stations, is approx: 300 ft signaling distance, $30; 800 ft, $35; 1 500 ft, $45; 2 000 ft, $60. In Missouri lead district, a small whistle is often placed on the air line at top of shaft, and blown by a hand wire from the shaft stations; a bell in engine room is sounded from the shaft mouth.

Electric signal systems are of general application, but for reliability require careful installation and maintenance. There are 3 classes:

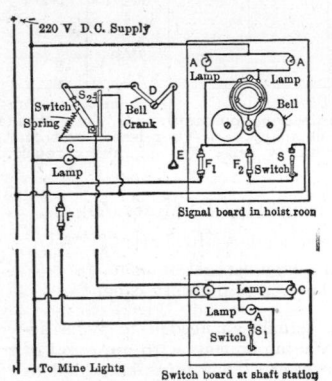

Fig 95. Shaft Signal System, Rosiclare, Ill

A. Low-voltage direct current, operated by wet, dry or storage batteries. Annunciator bells should be iron clad and waterproof, and heavier and more durable than house bells. Only the best rubber-covered double-braided wire should be used, and all wiring carried down the shaft in metal conduit. Double-conductor twisted wire is good. Small single-throw knife switches are better than push-buttons; or specially designed contacts, protected from dirt and water, may be used.

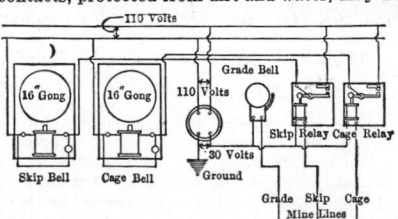

Fig 96. Signal System, Penn & Republic Mines, Mich

All the bells should be on one circuit (Fig 94, *B*), so that the signal sounds at all stations and in the engine room. If only the sending station and engine room bells ring (Fig 94, *A*), confusion may be caused by two stations attempting to signal simultaneously. Engine room and station bells are in series, so that the signal may be repeated from engine room. If necessary to signal from the cage at any point in the shaft, wires a and b (Fig 94, B) may be bare and carried on insulators on shaft timbers, the signal being made by making contact with a piece of iron or by pressing the wires together. In wet shafts this plan gives trouble, and the batteries are rapidly exhausted.

B. Bell-ringing magnetos are excellent, as they do not become exhausted like batteries; though the cost of installation is much higher. Loud-ringing weatherproof bells should be used. Equipment for one installation, consisting of one station outfit of 1 magneto and 1 bell with two 6-in gongs, with a similar engine room outfit so that engineer can return signal, 1 extra bell at shaft mouth, and 200 ft of double-braid rubber-covered No 16 conductor wire, cost $35. Besides this, 150 ft of 0.75-in pipe was used for conduit, the shaft being very wet; also a few insulators on the surface. Labor cost of installation, about $17 (1912). The 3 gongs and 2 magnetos were connected in series.

C. Power or lighting circuits (direct current) not exceeding 220 volts, where fairly constant power is assured, may be utilized for arranging signal systems, both bells and visual signals being used. Alternating current, of 220 volts, is dangerously high, and should be stepped down to 55 volts.

Fig 95 shows a layout at Rosiclare, Ill. All wiring is double braid, rubber covered, and carried down shaft in metal conduit. For signaling, S_1 is closed, ringing engine room bell and lighting lamps A. Signal is returned by pulling E, thus closing switch S_2, which lights lamps C until switch is opened. One lamp is at the engineer's stand. F and F_1 are 5-ampere fuses. To test or adjust the bells, F_1 is removed and placed at F_2, and switch S is closed. This rings the bell and lights lamps A, but not C. Lamps are 50-watt, on 220-volt direct current. Bells are weatherproof ironclad, having a resistance of 30 ohms and consuming 0.3 ampere.

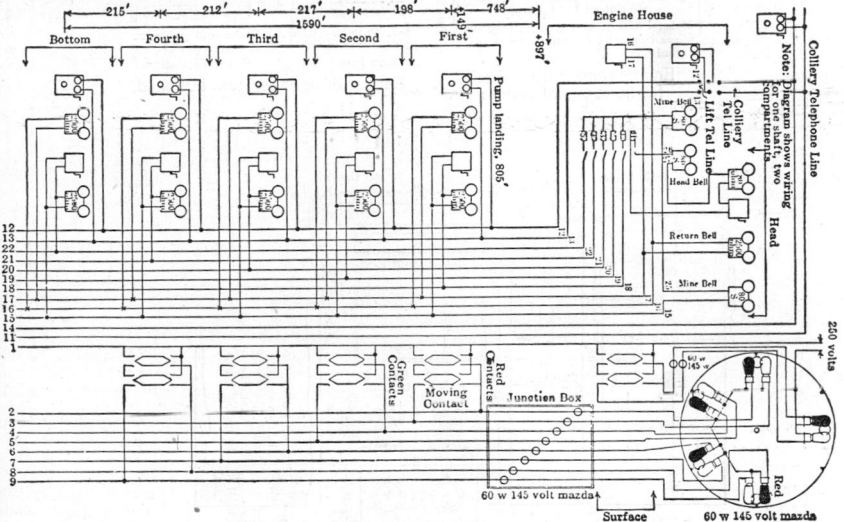

Fig 97. Electrical Signal System, Lykens, Pa

At the Penn and Republic iron mines, Mich, 110-volt alternating current is used (90), stepped down to 30 volts (Fig 96). It is grounded on one side, the other leading to a relay for each bell in engine house, and skip, cage and one side of a grade bell, in shaft house. The other side of each relay and the grade bell are connected to one of 3 No 4 bare copper wires, supported on insulators in the shaft. By grounding any one of these wires a current will flow through the grade bell or the relays in engine room. The relay then rings the 16-in gong, through the 110-volt circuit. A heavy single blow is struck by the a-c solenoid, an indicator registers number of bells, and a lamp is lighted. The signal wires may be grounded from the cage at any point in shaft.

D. Combined magneto and power circuits are sometimes used where both bell and lights are desired. At No 1 shaft, Lykens, Pa (Susquehanna Coal Co), is a magneto circuit for bells and power circuit, to indicate by lights the position of cage chairs at shaft stations. Fig 97 shows wiring for 4 intermediate levels and bottom of this shaft. Five-bar, open-circuit magnetos and 6-in bells are used throughout. Each station has a magneto, two 2 500-ohm extension bells and a phone. One bell is for return signal from engine room; the other is connected across the magneto, so that the man giving signal can hear it. A signal from a station rings the bell there, at top of shaft and in engine house, and records the ring on an a-c operated annunciator. Then topman signals, ringing bell at top and in engine house, the signal being recorded on annunciator. The station bells have different tone from that at top. Telephones connect to a common line between engine room and stations. If necessary, shaft phones may be connected to outside lines. Annunciator has a battery reset (not shown), wired to a brush contact on the dial indicator and is automatically cleared after each hoist. The system is so arranged that the engineer has full control of signals from stations by operating a series of switches, which are all kept open except the one at station from which hoisting is being done. Each station has landing chairs; attached to each is a switch in a C-I box, wired to light a green lamp on indicator in engine room, if both chairs are free of the shaft, and a red lamp if one or both chairs are thrown in. This facilitates handling the cage when stopping or starting. In the indicator, 1.25-in holes are drilled at points corresponding to the levels and covered by frosted glass. Back of these holes are 1 red and 1 green bulb, to indicate position of chairs at landings.

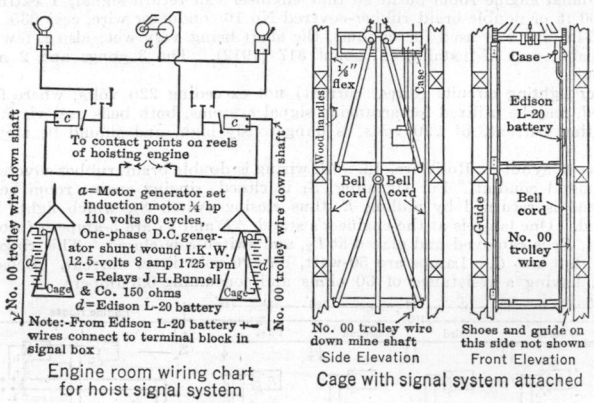

Engine room wiring chart
for hoist signal system

Cage with signal system attached

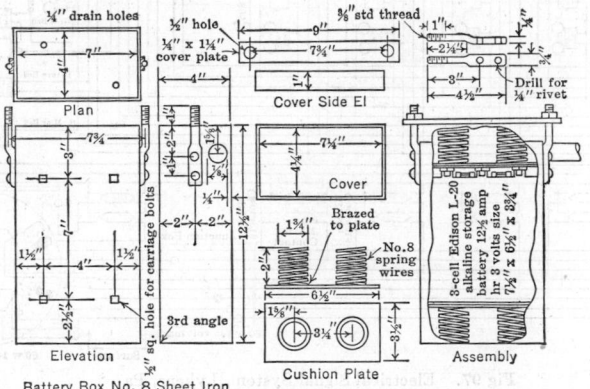

Details of Edison L-20 battery

Fig 98. Cage-pull, Shaft-conductor Signal System, Park Utah Cons Mines Co, Keetley, Utah (60, 37)

Desirable features of a hoisting signalling system: 1. In the hoistroom visual or sound devices should indicate: (*a*) cage or skip position; (*b*) landing chair position; (*c*) station where signal originates; (*d*) also provision for hoistman to repeat signals to sender, or signal all levels. 2. Each signalling station should have (*a*) devices for signalling hoistman, and visual or sound devices to indicate whether (*b*) cage or skip is in motion, (*c*) hoistman is being signalled, or (*d*) hoistman is signalling. 3. A communication system between all signalling stations and engine room on an independent circuit, to be used in case of failure of signalling system, and for general communication. 4. A signalling and/or communicating system between man-cage and hoistman, to operate while in motion or at rest, is desirable for shaft repair work and when hoisting men.

Special signalling systems (60). Fig 98 shows detail of signalling between cage and hoistman. At Park Utah Consol Mines, source of power for signals is a battery on the cage. Essentials: (1) a sensitive telegraph relay in engine-room, connected to the hoisting rope and a bare copper wire in the shaft; (2) an Edison battery on the cage, one terminal being permanently connected to the hoisting rope; (3) a contact-maker, operated by pulling a chain which completes contact between the battery on cage and bare copper wire in the shaft. With this device a man on cage has full control of its operation, a desirable feature when hoisting men or doing shaft work.

The signalling system (61) of Oglebay Norton Co, Gogebic range mines (Fig 99), provides for giving signals from cage whether at rest or in motion, and makes conversation possible between cage tender and hoistman at all times. These features are particularly desirable for shaft work. An interesting feature is a safety switch connected with the rope in cage bonnet and normally open. Slack on the cable, due to cage sticking when lowering, closes the switch and signals hoistman to stop. Cost of equipment, 1931, was $250.

Ross shaft, Homestake, S D, signalling system (62), designed for a deep shaft (5 200 ft) and in operation since 1934, has distinct modes of wiring for each of two skip compts.

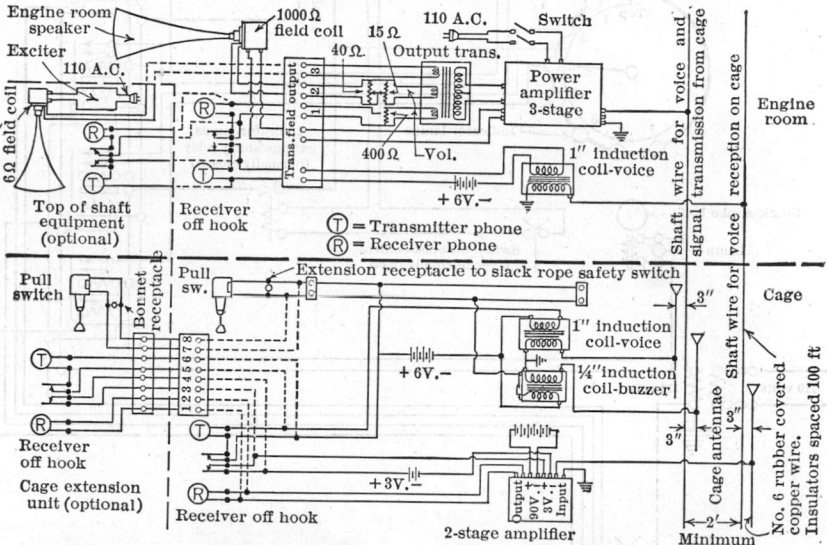

Fig 99. Wiring Diagram of Radio Cage-signalling System, Oglebay, Norton & Co, Ironwood, Mich (37, 61)

When hoisting men, skips are removed and cages substituted. Fig 100 is the diagram for one compartment, showing only 4 of the numerous stations. The annunciator is part of the skip or cage position-indicator. Receptacles for holding indicating lamps are placed radially outside the station numbers or names, and correspond to respective switches. The shaft part operates with a ground return; ropes and conduits have a return circuit wire, so that if the ground return causes too much induction the entire circuit may be made metallic and carried in the same sheath. The return wire is indicated by the broken line. OPERATION. When the pull switch is operated, a circuit is closed in the ground through one winding of a relay, then through one of two wires to the bell and lamp, and finally through the secondary of the transformer to the ground. The first impulse, caused by closing a switch, closes a connected relay which locks itself in position through a contact and second coil, and lights the indicator lamp through a second contact on the relay. The engineer may extinguish this lamp by a device attached to the hoist control-lever, operating a relay that in turn opens the relay holding circuit, and relay contacts. The bell sides of the relay coils, in series with the pull switches, are connected alternately to one of two wires connected as a single wire to the bell. SIGNAL ROPES. Fig 100 shows two pull ropes attached to each switch. One rope is short; the other long enough to reach the next switch. The long rope is a small, galvanized-steel cable, with a chain insert at the switch and chain at lower end. It is used for station and shaft-inspection work only, and is attached to the switch, so that it does not move when the short rope is pulled. The ropes may be reached by the cageman when cage is at the station. They are of light manila and attached to the switches with harness snaps. PULL SWITCHES are housed in cast-iron boxes, and ruggedly built. The insulating parts, of bakelite, provide long creeping distances, so that moisture within reason does not cause appreciable leakage. Switch mechanisms, held in the boxes with only one bolt, can easily be replaced. CALL HORNS for signalling cagemen, operated at any station by a convenient pull switch are placed in the shaft at 100-ft intervals down to the 1 100-ft level; below that, at the level stations, 150 apart. They are placed under timbers, for protection from falling rocks. The horn boxes have small heaters to keep the air in them slightly warmer than the surrounding air, because high humidity damages the coil. Each heater consumes 6 watts. Fig 101 shows connections for the horns. At present, power is received at the top end, but, when the shaft reaches its ultimate depth of 5 200 ft, it may be necessary to supply power to the system at its midpoint, to prevent excessive voltage drop. Wiring is rubber-covered, in a galvanized-steel conduit. A fourth wire (dotted in the diagram) was installed as a precaution, so that if the number of horns became too great for one circuit they could be sounded on several

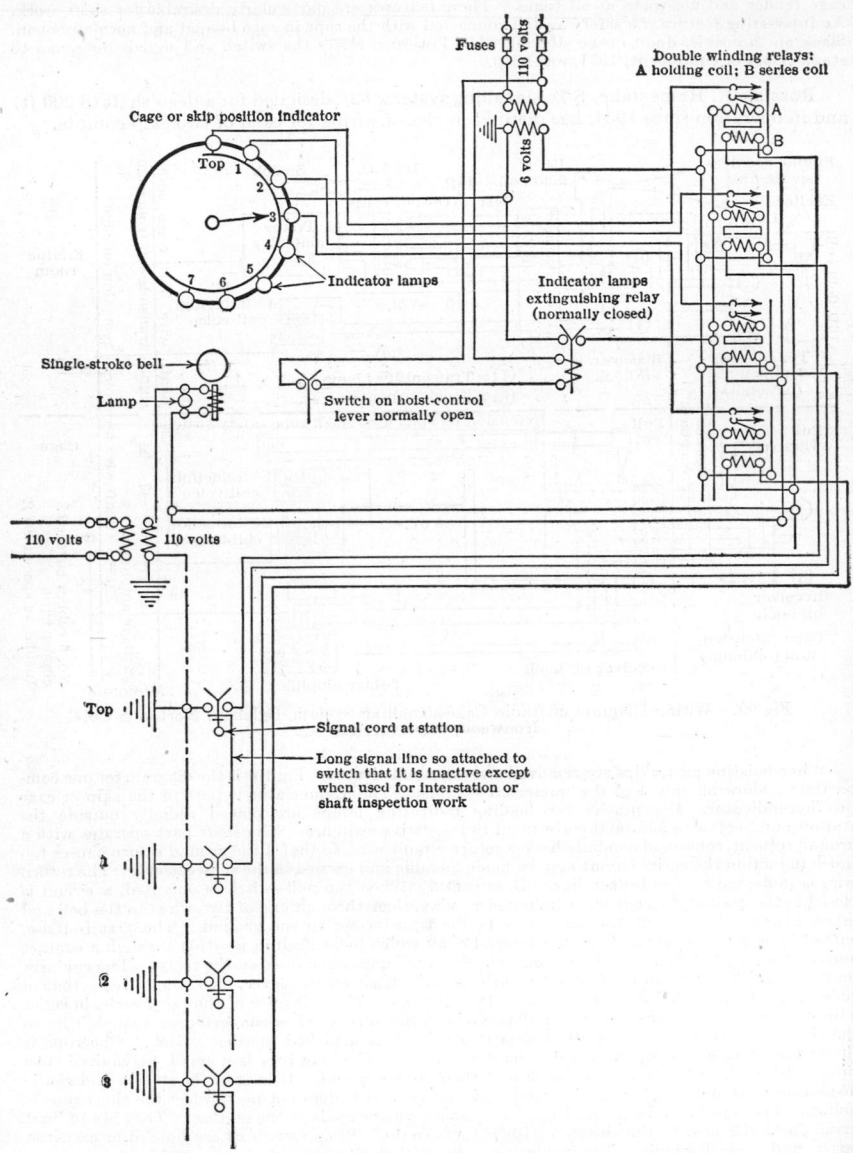

Fig 100. Electric Signalling System, One-compartment Ross Ore Hoist

circuits by relays operated by this fourth wire. Probably this wire will not be required for the shaft depth contemplated. The third wire is a ground connection, so that men will not receive shock when handling the cover and attached mechanism while changing units, if a wire is grounded to a live part.

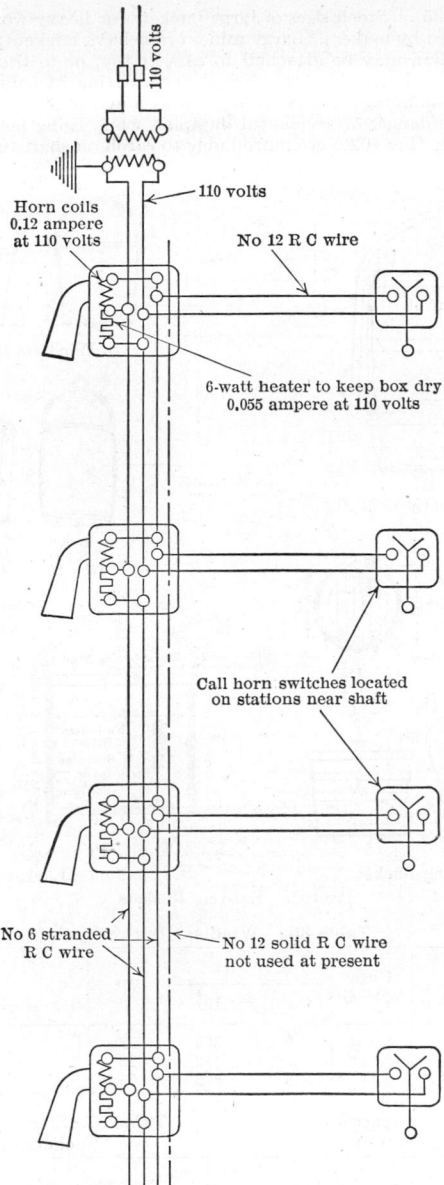

Fig 101.   Call-horn System for the Ross Shaft

28. BUCKETS AND CROSSHEADS

Ore buckets, unless made at the mine, are of steel (see also Art 18, 19). Fig 102a shows a bucket made from three-quarters of an oil barrel; capac, 4.5 cu ft. Band B is 0.25 by 2.5 in, riveted to bottom and sides, and forged into bail pins C. Rings A and lugs D prevent accidental overturning. This bucket is too large for a windlass; it requires a horse whim, or power hoist. Fig 102, b to e, shows light steel windlass buckets, as made by mining supply houses (Table 35). Stock sizes of large buckets for heavy work, with capacities of 1 ton or more, are listed by makers. Large mines often have buckets for sinking and winzing made to order. Bail may be attached to ears at top, or to trunnions a little below center of gravity. The bottom is best dished, with a ring at center for attaching the dumping hook. Self-dumping buckets are more convenient to dump and clean themselves better, but with some danger of accidental dumping while being hoisted. Buckets with straight or flaring sides (Fig 102b) are more liable to catch on shaft timbers.

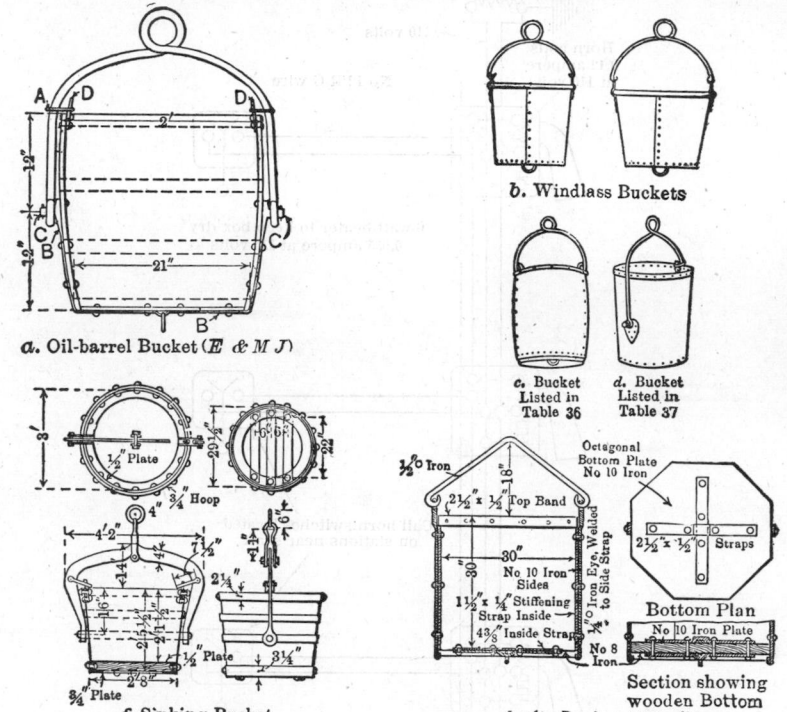

a. Oil-barrel Bucket (*E & M J*)

b. Windlass Buckets

c. Bucket Listed in Table 36

d. Bucket Listed in Table 37

f. Sinking Bucket

e. Joplin Bucket ("Can")

Fig 102.   Hoisting Buckets

Table 35.   Windlass Buckets

Height, in	Diam, in		Gage of steel	Capacity		Wt	Cost per lb
	Top	Bottom		Cu ft	Lb		
16	16	14	No 16	1 3/4	200	28	18 to 20¢ for
15	19	14	16	2	250	28	smaller sizes,
23	22	17	14	3	375	55	14 to 16¢ for larger

Table 36. Sizes and Capacities of Buckets (Fig 102c)

Diam, in			Height, in	Wt, lb	Capacity, cu ft
Top	Center	Bottom			
18	24	16	30	270	5
20	22	18	30	270	5.5
21	24	18	30	280	6
21	26	18	33	300	7.5
24	30	22	30	340	8.5
25	26	24	36	350	10
28	30	26	36	400	12.5

Table 37. Sizes and Capacities of Buckets (Fig 102d)

Diam bottom, in	Diam top, in	Depth, in	Wt, lb	Capacity, cu ft
18	24	26	260	5
20	26	28	300	7
22	28	32	350	9
24	30	36	400	12
28	34	36	450	16

Examples. At Joplin, Mo, buckets (locally, "cans") are used commonly for both regular hoisting and development work. Largest size is 34 by 34 in, called a "1 600-lb can," but usually loaded with about 1 200 lb. Other sizes: 30 by 30, 30 by 28, and 28 by 30 in, diam being the first dimension. Smaller sizes: 26 by 28 and 24 by 28 in. Fig 102c shows typical Joplin bucket: ears are welded

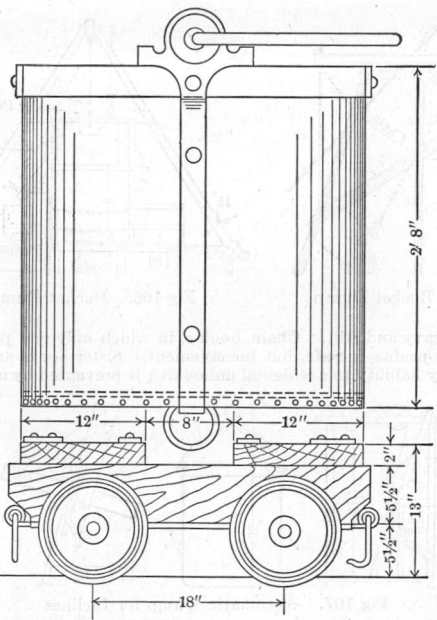

Fig 103.   Ore Bucket on Truck.   Hartley Mine, Interstate Zinc & Lead Co, Baxter Springs, Kan,
(63, 37)

to side straps, which generally hook under bottom flange (72). Fig 102f shows a heavy shaft-sinking bucket. At iron mines of Mineville, N Y, a heavy 1-ton bucket was used for sinking. It had flaring

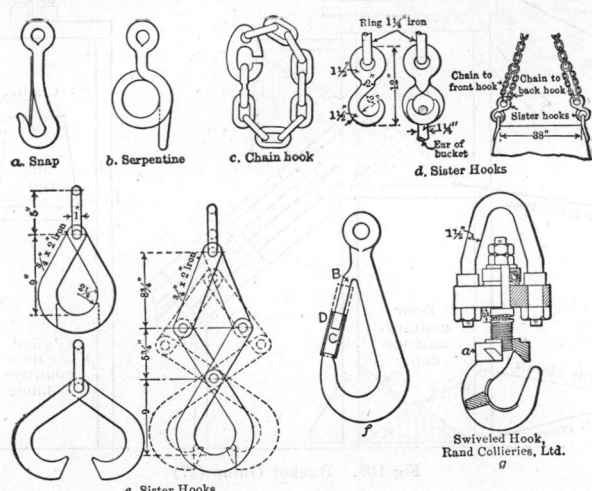

Fig 104.   Bucket Hooks

sides, with bail pivoted on side trunnions. Fig 103 shows ore bucket and truck as used in many lead and zinc mines in the U S (63, 37) for both hoisting and haulage.

Bucket hooks should be designed to prevent accidental unhooking, due to slack rope, spinning, or striking shaft timbers. They are best made of Norway iron.

Ordinary snap hook (Fig 104a) is safe, but, with a spring strong enough to be safe, it is difficult to unhook. Serpentine hook b is safe and convenient for rope up to 0.5 in diam, but difficult

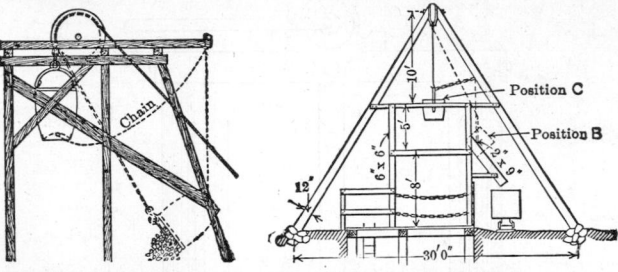

Fig 105. Bucket Dump   Fig 106. Bucket Dump

to unfasten if rope is heavy and stiff. Chain hook c, in which only one part of the last link will pass through the hook opening, is safe, but inconvenient. Sister hooks are both safe and convenient (Fig 104d, e). Any liability to accidental unhooking is prevented by a ring around both hook

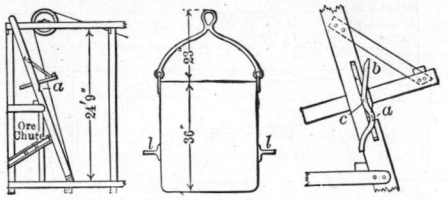

Fig 107.   Automatic Dump for Inclines

shanks, which must be raised before hooks will separate. Fig 104d shows use of 2 pairs of sister hooks and chains, instead of a bail, for a sinking bucket at Hancock No 2 shaft, Mich. Two forms used

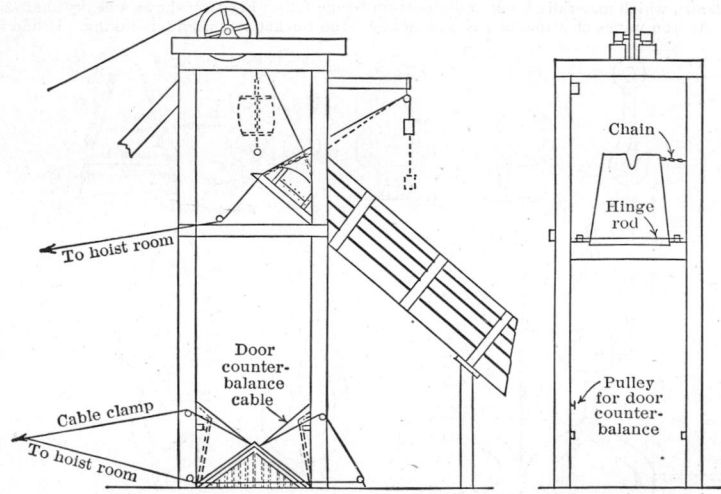

Fig 108.   Bucket Dump (37)

in Canadian mines are shown in Fig 104e. Fig 104f shows a simple safety hook. Gap C, large enough to pass the bucket bail, is closed by thimble D, made of heavy pipe, or a piece of-shafting bored out. COMBINED HOOK AND SWIVEL, used at the Rand Collieries, Ltd, So Africa, is shown in Fig 104g. Dimensions given are for a 2-ton bucket. Locking nut a has a large-pitch thread, so

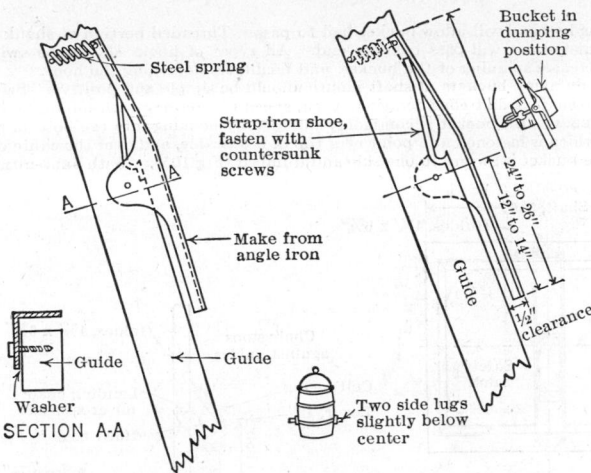

Steel spring

Strap-iron shoe, fasten with countersunk screws

Make from angle iron

Guide — Guide

Washer
SECTION A-A

Bucket in dumping position

Guide

24' to 26'
12" to 14"

½" clearance

Two side lugs slightly below center

Fig 108a.   Bucket Dump for Sinking Inclined Shafts (37, 64)

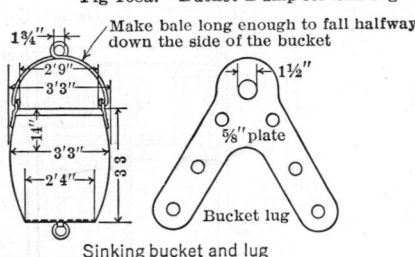

Make bale long enough to fall halfway down the side of the bucket

1¾"
2'9"
3'3"
4"
3'3"
2'4"
3'3"

1½"
⅝" plate

Bucket lug

Sinking bucket and lug

3'9"   4¼"
5"
5'9½"   2'5¾"   2'5⅞"
5"
Plan A
Two ¾" chains
20 cu ft bucket
1" chain
A
10' x 10'
3" boards

Note: These doors operated by air lifts

5'9½"
7'7"   6'8"
4¼"   5'
10' x 10'
10' x 10" post
5½" x 7½" Guide
5½"
5'9½"
2'5⅛"   1¾"
7'7"   7'7"

Fig 108b. Sinking Bucket and Shaft Doors, Granby Consol Min Co (65)

that 3 or 4 turns by hand will allow bucket bail to pass. Threaded portion of shank of hook must be upset, so that the nut will pass over its end. All types of hooks should be swiveled to rope socket; this decreases spinning of the bucket, and facilitates detaching the hook.

Devices for dumping buckets at shaft mouth should be simple and positive. Safety from rock falling down the shaft is first consideration; then, speed of handling with minimum labor. WHEN BAIL IS ATTACHED AT RIM, bucket is commonly dumped by hooking into the bottom ring the lower end of a chain which is fastened at a point near top of headframe, and over the chute or bin. Then, by lowering, the bucket is swung to one side and dumped (Fig 105). With SELF-DUMPING BUCKET,

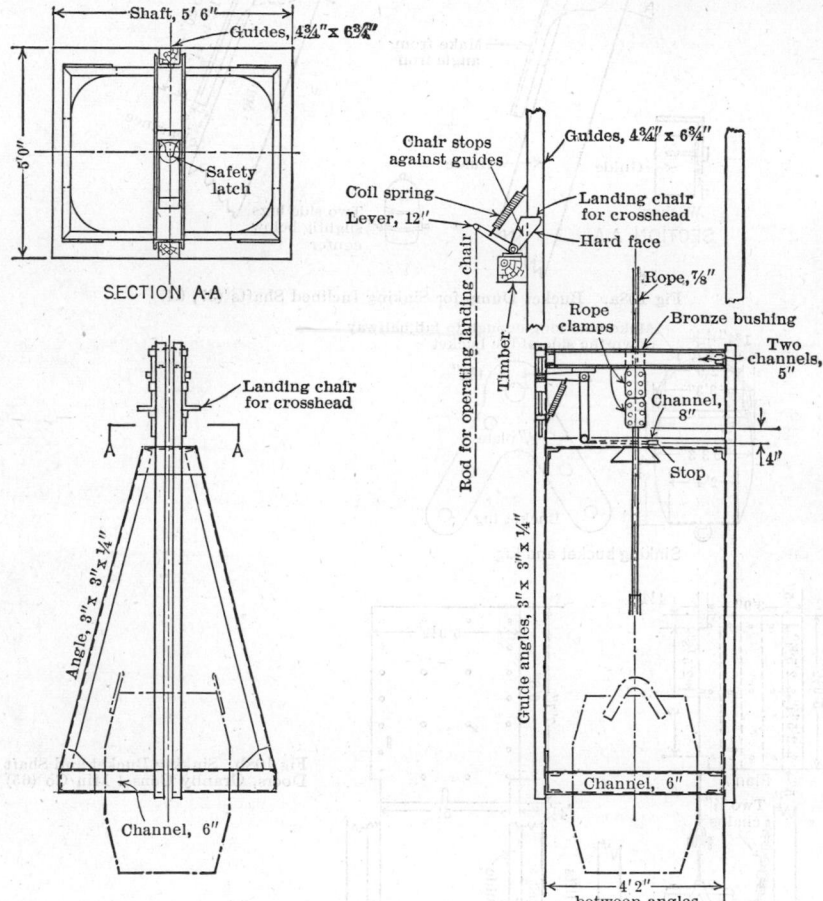

Fig 109. Crosshead for Bucket Sinking, Macassa Mines, Kirkland Lake, Ont (37, 65)

after hoisting to position *C* (Fig 106), the chain is hooked into bail ring; then, by lowering, bucket is swung to position *B*, for dumping and the latches are released. AUTOMATIC DUMP, for inclines with skids (Fig 107), is used at several Ontario mines. Bail is fastened to rim of bucket, and lugs *l* are below center of gravity. Lugs slide on skids until they drop into notches *a* above chute, when, by lowering, bucket is dumped. Bucket is then raised until lugs are above pivoted curved arms *b*; and on lowering again these arms cover the notches and allow bucket to slide down shaft. After bucket has passed the arms, they swing back by gravity to their original position. At the notch, skids should be edged with 0.5 by 2-in iron; curved arms are of 5/8 by 3-in iron, pivoted at *c* on a 1-in bolt. At dumping point, skids should have a slope not exceeding 72°. CROSSHEADS, to prevent bucket from swinging, are required by law in some states and countries. As there is danger of serious accident if crosshead sticks in its guides, and then falls after bucket has been lowered some distance, the crosshead should be held positively to the rope socket, until it reaches the stops at lower end of guides. To prevent jamming in the guides, the height of crosshead should exceed distance between guides. *Examples.* Fig 109 shows crosshead for bucket shaft sinking at Macassa Mines, Kirkland Lake, Ont (66). Similar crossheads of this general type made of aluminum have also been used in Ontario (67, 37). BRYANT CROSSHEAD (73) has safety gear to prevent crosshead and bucket from falling if rope breaks, and to hold the crosshead if it should stick in the guides. It has a bonnet. Crossheads with safety catches are justified in large or deep shafts; they are usually entirely of steel. Fig 110 shows a design recommended by U S Bur of Mines (74); *a* is safety-dog spring; *d*, 1/2 in less than distance between guides; *g*, not less than distance between guides; *j*, rope button. Frame and connecting angles, all 3- by 3- by 5/16-in. In the BERRY SAFETY CROSSHEAD (Fig 110a), designed in the Transvaal, springs, instead of gravity, keep the bucket attached to crosshead until guide stops are reached. In descending, levers *a* strike stops *b*; and, through rod *c*, the latches *h* are thrown outward against springs *e*, thus disengaging rope socket and allowing bucket to descend. When crosshead is raised from the stops, springs *e* again cause latches *h* to engage the rope socket. In the headframe is a device to hold crosshead and release the bucket for dumping.

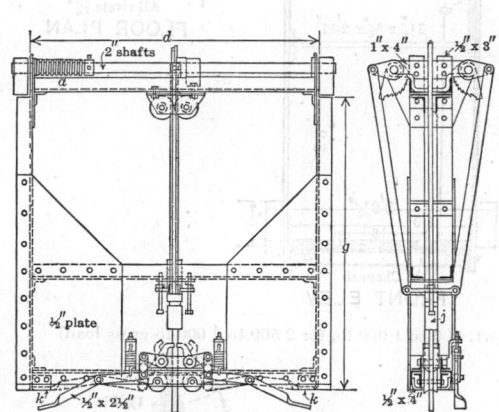

Fig 110. Safety Crosshead for Sinking Buckets (U S Bur Mines, *Tech Pap 276*)

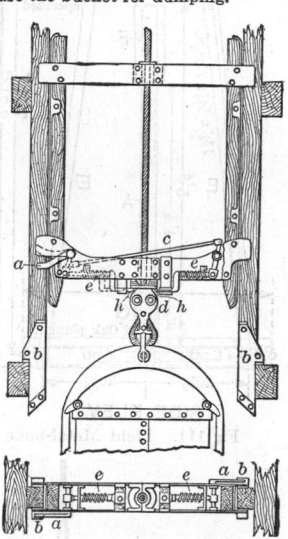

Fig 110a. Berry Safety Crosshead

29. CAGES

General features. Since the cage is a dead load, its weight should be as small in proportion to the useful load as is consistent with safety. Platform frame is of flat bars, or structural shapes (channels or heavy angles for side members and I-beams or channels for crosspieces). For LIGHT METAL-MINE CAGES (Fig 111) center suspension member *A*, carrying guide shoes *G*, may be a flat, welded to forging *B*, for the jackshaft (*S*) bearings. To *B* is bolted or riveted the triangular forging *C*, with a socket for draw-bar *D*. Inclined members *E*, from *B* to the cage deck, are of light angles, or flat or round bars. If members are narrow bars, bolted joints are best; if wide (structural shapes), rivets are used, with at least 2 rivets for each joint. For HEAVY COLLIERY CAGES (Fig 112) the center suspension member on each side is a single channel, or a pair of angles, riveted to a plate carrying jackshaft bearings and pins for bridle chains. In this case, upper cross member is made of structural shapes.

Multiple-deck cages are used more in Europe than in America, although they are employed to some extent in Western U S for increasing hoisting capacity of shafts of small cross-sec, or where skips are not feasible. In Butte, Mont, and in S W Ariz, there are cages of 2 to 4 decks. Their DISADVANTAGE is the loss of time in handling cars, as each deck must be shifted to the landing to receive or discharge its load. To save time there may be multiple landings, so that only 1 shift of cage is required for 4 decks; but this adds largely to expense of installation, and complicates car handling arrangements. Multiple-deck cages are sometimes used for handling men, when ore is hoisted in skips. These are usually in separate compartments, or the skip is removed and cage substituted at beginning and end of each shift.

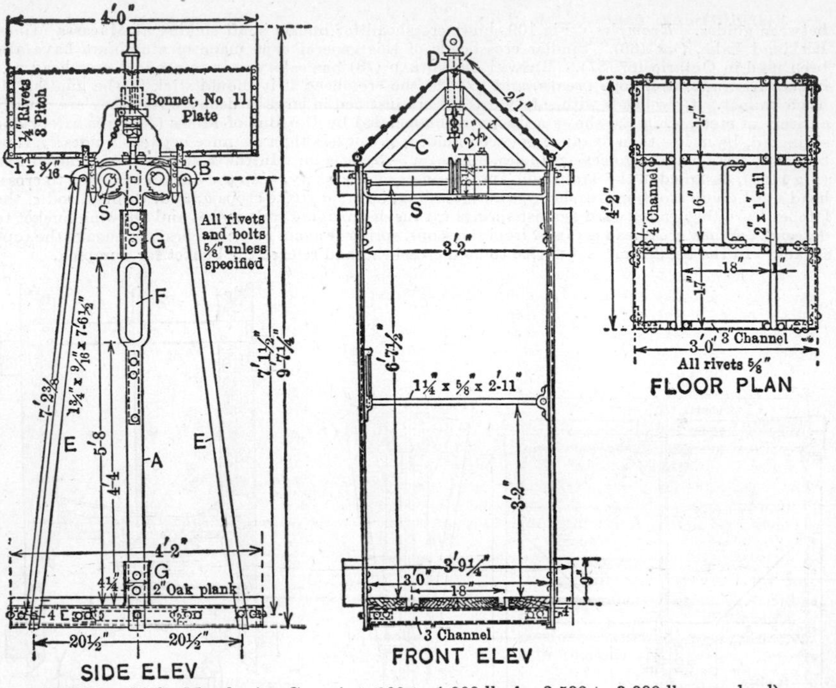

Fig 111. Light Metal-mine Cage (wt, 800 to 1 000 lb, for 2 500 to 3 000-lb gross load)

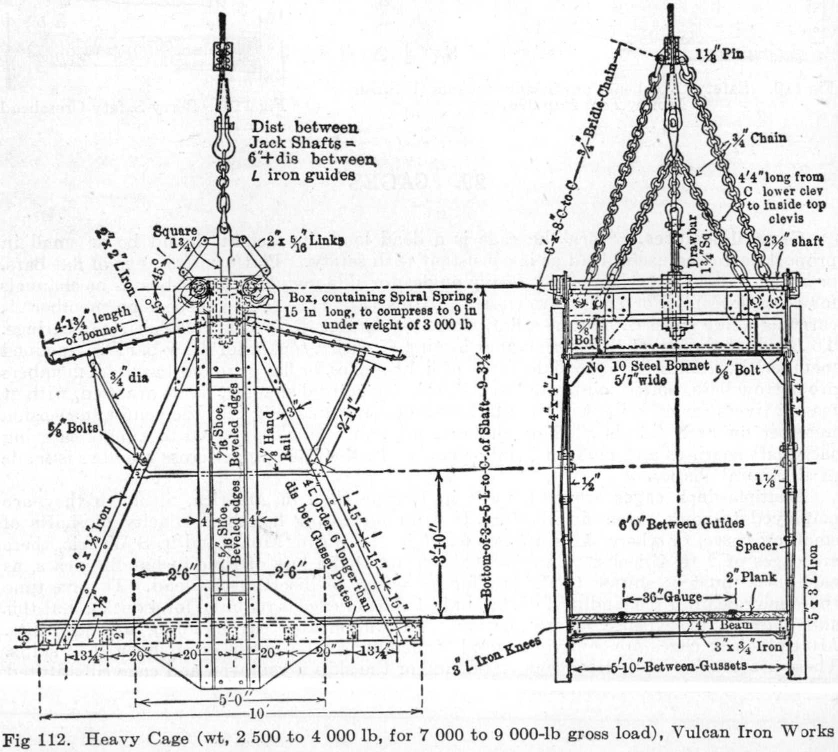

Fig 112. Heavy Cage (wt, 2 500 to 4 000 lb, for 7 000 to 9 000-lb gross load), Vulcan Iron Works

Self-dumping cages (Fig 113, 114) are often used in bituminous and sometimes in anthracite coal districts; rarely elsewhere.

Cage consists of 2 frames (Fig 113). The outer runs in the shaft guides; pivoted to this at bottom is an inner frame and platform, on which car is held fast by a locking device. At dumping point, inner frame is swung outward, by roller a engaging in curved guides, thus supporting car at a dumping angle. Meantime, the outer frame runs up on main guides. Catch b, to prevent accidental tipping of inner frame before dumping point is reached, is not common. Sometimes, pivot c is at one side of center line of cage, while center of gravity of car is on opposite side. Wheel a may run in an auxiliary guide, passing out of the guide through a gap at dumping point.

Where utmost capac is necessary, cage is wide enough to take 2 cars side by side; as at Cloverdale mine, Pittsburgh Terminal R R and Coal Co, where each cage carries 2 2.5-ton cars, 4 000 tons being hoisted in 8 hr; total lift, 405 ft (75). In some self-dumping cages the platform and car only are tilted, by rollers mounted near front end of platform and running in dumping guides. When closed-end (no door) cars are used, an overturning cage may be employed; cage platform and car are rotated endwise through 135° (78) by a pair of rollers at top, as in most dumping cages. In this case, special arrangements are necessary, due to greater movement of platform and car. ADVANTAGES of self-dumping cages: (*a*) reduced labor cost and attendance at top landing, and increased capac; (*b*) less wear on car than with most stationary dumps. DISADVANTAGES: (*a*) increased cost and wt; though, when hoisting in balance, extra wt is objectionable only in adding to total rope load, which also must be accelerated each trip; (*b*) larger rope and stronger headframe are required.

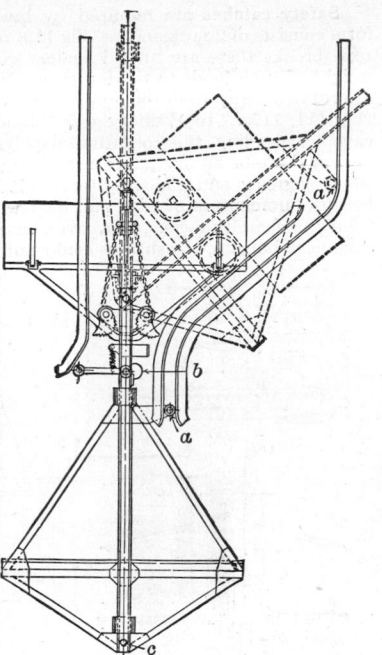

Fig 113.   Self-dumping Cage

30.   CAGE DETAILS

Structural details. For light cages the platform frame may be one W-I bar, say 0.75 by 4 in or 0.5 by 6 in, bent to a rectangle. Crosspieces, 2 for a small cage, are of same size, their ends being bent at right angles and riveted to frame. Rails may be of bar iron not less than 1 in wide, or T rail. Ends of VERTICAL SIDE MEMBERS should be bent under bottom frame (Fig 111). Opening F in side member is for access to guide bolts. SHOES are of short bent plates; or 2 angles back to back, or a channel, extending from platform to bonnet. Edges of shoe are rounded to prevent cutting the guides; rivets are countersunk and their heads chipped flush. Width of shoe is 0.5 in greater than width of guide; length, 2 to 3 times the width. If UPPER MEMBER of frame is a triangular forging (Fig 111), flats are welded to the lower angles, to give rivet or bolt space for attaching suspension members. If a straight horiz member is used, 2 channels back to back are structurally convenient. DRAWBAR is of best Norway iron; of square section, or sometimes round with a spline, to prevent rope from twisting. Area at root of thread determines its strength (Art 31). When VERTICAL SIDE MEMBERS are flat bars, they are widened at the head to receive the cam shafts, as in Fig 111, or riveted to a piece of heavy plate; when of angles or a channel (Fig 112), these serve as shoes; but in any case liners or wearing pieces, of thin plate, should be provided. With the construction shown in Fig 112, cage is usually attached to rope by CHAINS of such length that they take the weight of the cage when the drawbar operating the safety catches is in its highest position. Auxiliary or safety chains (Fig 112) are required by law in some states. These are fastened to a clamp on rope above the socket (see Art 7), and should be just slack when load is on the chains. An incidental advantage of the chain connection is that, when slack rope has been paid out after cage has been landed, the rope is not bent sharply at socket. Large cages are braced at corners with GUSSET PLATES, to keep cage square, and to reinforce connection of horizontal member to side gussets. For small cages, the BONNET is hinged at sides (Fig 111); for large cages the hinge is at center (Fig 114). By raising the bonnet, long timbers, rails, or pipe, can be stood on platform and lashed to hoisting rope. Bonnet is of No 10 or 12 steel for light work, up to $5/16$ in for heavy work.

Safety catches are required by law where men are hoisted or lowered. Standard form consists of 2 JACKSHAFTS (Fig 112) on which are keyed TOOTHED CAMS or dogs. When rope breaks these are turned against guides by springs, and after they grip the guides, weight of cage tends to tighten them still more. When cage is supported by rope, cams are rotated away from the guides by chains, or link and arm connections, to the drawbar (Fig 111, 112). Ideal safety gear should bring cage to rest gently. If rope breaks when cage is ascending, this condition may be realized, as the cams have time to grip guides during the momentary pause before cage begins to fall. But, if cage is descending, the shock is great; and if moving rapidly it is doubtful whether any safety device could hold, because momentum of cage and load would either break the safety gear, or strip guides from the shaft timbers. Moreover, in a deep shaft, if rope should break near top, with cage near bottom, the springs could not quickly overcome inertia of the rope, and falling

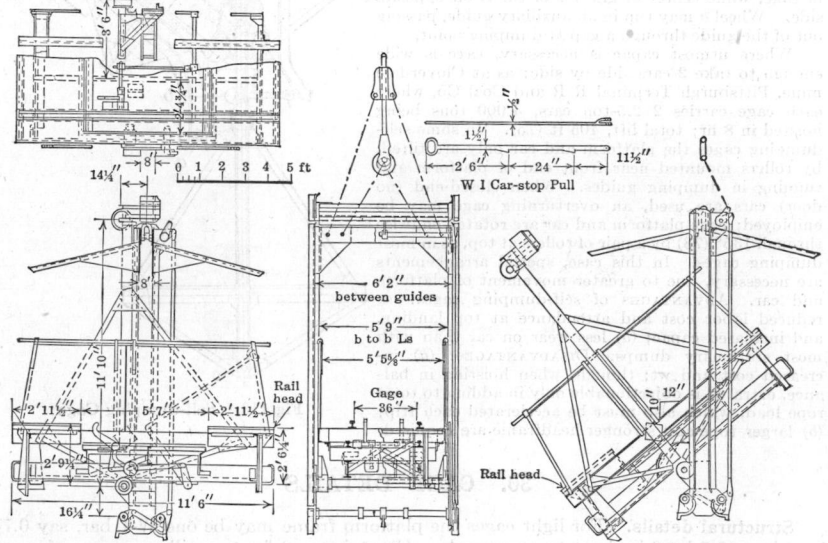

Fig 114. Drop-bottom, Self-dumping Car Cage, Lehigh Valley Coal Co, Wilkes-Barre, Pa (37)

cage would attain too high a velocity for the cams to be effective. Also, if hoisting engine fails, the springs could not overcome the drag exerted on the rope by the drum. Fatal accidents from these causes have occurred.

Details of safety gear. All parts are of steel or W I except the cams, which are of C I or cast steel. CAM CURVE is usually involute of a circle, but is often modified. Teeth should be sharp and deep enough to bite well into guide, with an angle at the end of not less than 45°. Width of cam is about 2 in for small, to 3.5 in for large, cages. Chain connection between drawbar and chain wheel on jackshaft (Fig 111) is simplest construction for light cages. In coal districts the cams are sometimes placed at sides of cage, 2 or 3 ft above platform, and connected with jackshafts by levers and long links (Fig 115, a). Several designs of flat spiral or helical SPRINGS, encircling the jackshafts or drawbar, are used. When on jackshaft, one end of spring is fast to a collar keyed on shaft, the other end to the side of cage; or, short levers keyed on each shaft are connected across by helical springs. For heavy cages, a powerful spring encircling the drawbar (Fig 112) is effective, and incidentally eases the shock when starting to hoist. An objection to operating both jackshafts by one spring or set of springs is that, if one shaft sticks or the cam happens to act against an unusually hard or smooth place on the guide, the other shaft can not bring it into action. They are best operated by independent springs.

Fig 115 shows designs of typical safety catches: a, sometimes used in Penn anthracite mines, has chisel-pointed levers thrown against guides by action of springs (said to be effic); b is for a 3-by 4-ft metal mine cage; c, for a cage about same size as b; d, for a light coal mine cage. One type of catch consists of a pair of toothed wedges, working between edges of guide and angles on the side plates, which are set at an angle equal to that of the wedge. They are thrown in by spring-operated levers, as in other forms, and are automatically tightened by wt of cage. It is stated they are difficult to release, sometimes requiring cutting away of guide. For STEEL GUIDES, the cams are either not toothed or have much smaller teeth; because, as the increment of the cam spiral is less, they grip the guide more strongly.

Safety gear should frequently be inspected and tested. Present tendency is to rely more on careful inspection of rope and to use rope of better quality. Many mines have discontinued safety catches on cages and skips which hoist ore only. Where men are not raised or lowered, the law does not require them. For description and tests of other safety devices, see Bib 37, 76, 113.

Weight and cost of cages. Plain steel colliery cages, for a gross load of 6 000 lb, weigh 3 000 to 4 000 lb; for heavier loads, up to 6 000 lb. A combined wood and iron cage, in anthracite district, weighs 5 600 lb, has a deck 6 ft by 11 ft 6 in, carrying a 2 500-lb

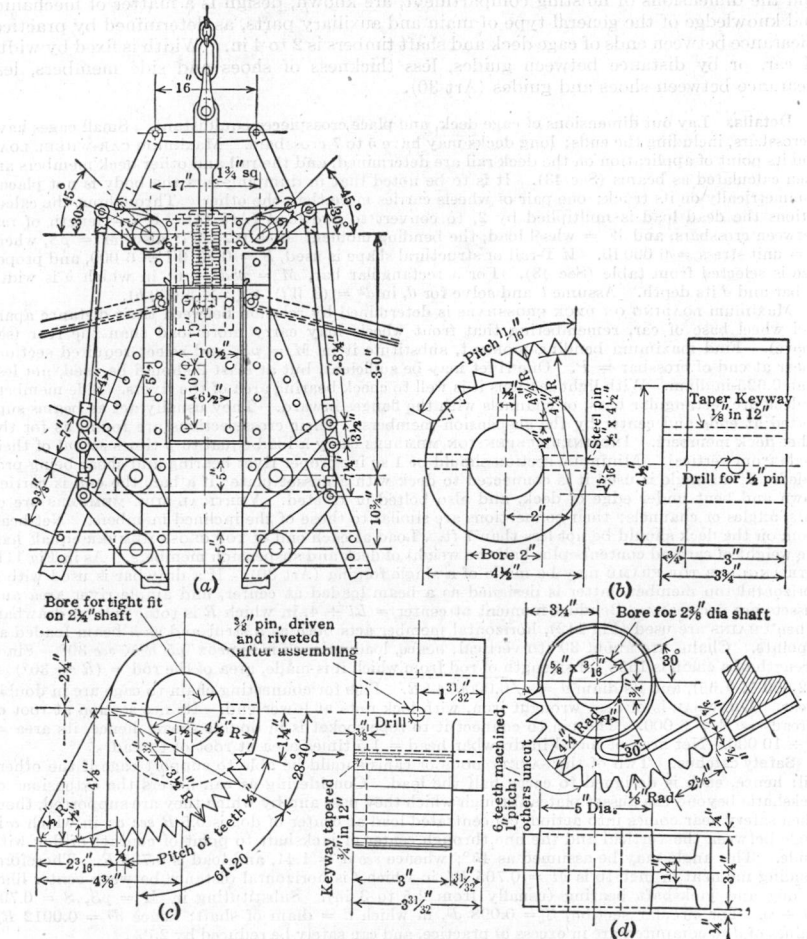

Fig 115. Types of Safety Catches

car and 6 000 lb of coal. Cage at Sugar Notch No 9 colliery, Pa, weighs 5 000 lb, car 2 500 lb, and contents 6 500 lb. Drop-bottom cage in Fig 114 weighs 2 680 lb, car 1 270 lb, contents 2 000 lb. Large colliery drop-bottom cages weigh 6 000 to 8 000 lb. Single-deck cages, with 4 by 5-ft decks, for 1-ton gross load, weigh 900 to 1 400 lb; for 3 000-lb load, 1 400 to 1 800 lb; for heavier loads, up to 2 800 or 3 000 lb. Each additional deck adds 50 to 60% to the weight. Self-dumping cages are 30 to 40% heavier than plain cages. Light cages of standard design cost 16 to 24¢ per lb; heavy cages, 14 to 20¢. If made from special designs requiring new patterns, cost is increased 20 to 25% (1935).

31. DESIGN OF CAGES

Factor of safety should be 10, whence allowable unit stresses for iron and steel are: tension, 6 000 lb; and for compression, $S = 6\,000 - 70\,(l \div r)$; where l = length of member, and r least radius of gyration, both in inches. Rivets and pins: single shear, 5 000 lb; double shear, 10 000 lb. Bolts, when used in place of rivets or turned pins, single shear, 3 500 lb, double shear, 7 000 lb. If size and gross weight of car and contents, and the dimensions of hoisting compartment, are known, design is a matter of mechanics and knowledge of the general type of main and auxiliary parts, as determined by practice. Clearance between ends of cage deck and shaft timbers is 2 to 4 in. Width is fixed by width of car, or by distance between guides, less thickness of shoes and side members, less clearance between shoes and guides (Art 30).

Details. Lay out dimensions of cage deck, and place crosspieces equidistant. Small cages have 4 crossbars, including the ends; long decks may have 5 to 7 crossbars. Maximum CAR-WHEEL LOAD and its point of application on the deck rail are determined, and the rail and other deck members are then calculated as beams (Sec 43). It is to be noted that in dumping-cars the body is not placed symmetrically on its truck; one pair of wheels carries more than the other. Throughout the calculations the dead load is multiplied by 2, to convert to live load (Art 14). If l = length of rail between crossbars, and W = wheel load, the bending moment $M = 0.25\,Wl$; also, $M = pS$, where p = unit stress = 6 000 lb. If T-rail or structural shape is used, $S = 0.25\,Wl \div 6\,000$, and proper size is selected from table (Sec 43). For a rectangular bar, $M = pbd^2 \div 6$; in which b is width of bar and d its depth. Assume b and solve for d, in $d^2 = (3\,Wl) \div (2 \times 6\,000\,b)$.

Maximum LOADING ON DECK CROSSBARS is determined by relation between their distance apart and wheel base of car, remembering that front wheels may carry more load than the rear (see above). Find maximum bending moment, substitute it in $M = pS$, and select required section. Shear at end of crossbar = P. One rivet may be sufficient, but at least 2 should be used, not less than 0.625-in diam. With light sections it is well to check bearing area of the rivets. Side members of deck are rectangular bars, or channels with the flanges inward. They usually act as beams supported at ends and center by the suspension members. Their cross-sections are found as for the other deck members. INCLINED SUSPENSION MEMBERS carry a load equal to p times *secant* of their angle from vertical. Minimum section should be 1 sq in, proper rivet bearing and shear being provided. If an angle is used it is connected to deck with a gusset plate; if a bar, the end is carried down and bent under edge of deck, and also bolted or riveted. VERTICAL SIDE MEMBERS are of flats, angles or channels; their connections are similar to those of the inclined members. Net head room on the deck should be not less than 7 ft. Load at each end of TOP CROSS MEMBER equals half the weight of car and contents plus half the weight of deck and suspension members. As in Fig 111, a TRIANGULAR TOP FRAME may be made of a single forging (Art 30). If a drawbar is used with a horizontal top member, latter is designed as a beam loaded at center, and ample rivet area and gussets are necessary. Bending moment at center = $Rl \div 4$, in which R is total pull on drawbar. When CHAINS are used (Fig 112), horizontal member acts both as a strut and as a beam loaded at 2 points. Chains are about 30° to vertical; hence, load on each is approx $0.5\,R \times sec\,30°$. Since strength of a chain is 165% of strength of rod from which it is made, area of the rod = $(R\,sec\,30°) \div (12\,000 \times 1.65)$, and its diam $d = \sqrt{0.0000742\,R}$. Pins for connecting chain to cage are in double shear. DRAWBAR is of best wrought iron, with lock nuts at lower end. Its net section at root of threads = $R \div 6\,000$. The pin to connect it to rope socket is in double shear; hence, its area = $R \div 10\,000$. Net area of metal in drawbar head = 1.5 times area at root of thread.

Safety catches. Two of the SAFETY DOGS or cams should be able to support cage if the others fail; hence, each is designed to carry half the load. Considering as cantilevers the extensions of jackshafts beyond the gusset plates through which they pass and by which they are supported, then, when safety gear comes into action, concentrated load at center of dog is $0.5\,R\,sec\,\alpha$; in which α is angle between the vertical and the line through center of jackshaft to point of contact of dog with guide. This angle may be assumed as 45°; whence $sec\,\alpha = 1.41$, and load is $0.705\,R$. Therefore, bending moment in inch-lb is $M = 0.705\,Rf$, in which f is horizontal distance between center lines of dog and jackshaft bearing (usually from 2.5 to 3 in). Substituting in $M = pS$, $S = 0.705 \, Rf \div p$. For circular section, $S = 0.098\,d^3$, in which d = diam of shaft; hence $d^3 = 0.0012\,Rf$. Values of d so computed are in excess of practice, and can safely be reduced by 25%.

SPRINGS FOR SAFETY CATCHES must be strong enough to act promptly, and yet be deflected by weight of empty cage, with sufficient margin to prevent lashing of hoisting rope from causing the dogs to grip the guides. Total supporting power of springs is from 0.33 the weight of cage for small cages to 0.10 the weight for large ones. Number of coils in the spring depends upon deflection required, or the angle through which the shaft must turn to engage dogs with guides. Cross section of rod composing spring depends upon load, and radius R of crank arm or chain wheel by which rope pull rotates the jackshafts against spring pressure. For FLAT SPIRAL SPRINGS:

$$P = \frac{S}{6}\frac{bh^2}{R}\,; \qquad f = R\theta = 12\frac{PlR^2}{Ebh^3} \qquad (40)$$

in which, P = force applied at radius R, or assumed load on chain or link connecting drawbar with chain wheel or arm on cam shaft; θ = angular motion of R, in radians; S = allowable max unit ▮▮▮▮▮▮ ▮▮ ▮▮▮ ▮ ▮ ▮ ▮ ▮ ▮▮ modulus of elasticity in tension = 30 000 000; l = developed length of spiral; b = width of spring and h = thickness. For large cages R may be taken as 7 in;

for small cages, 2.5 in.   Angle of rotation should be from 60 to 90°.   For HELICAL SPRINGS, WRAPPED AROUND SHAFT:

$$P = \frac{S\pi d^3}{32\,R}\ ; \qquad f = R\theta = \frac{64\,PlR^2}{\pi E d^4}\ ; \qquad \frac{f}{R} = \frac{2\,Sl}{Ed} \tag{41}$$

where, besides the values given above, d = diam of the spring rod.   If HELICAL SPRINGS are used IN TENSION OR COMPRESSION (Fig 100) following formulas by J. W. Cloud apply:

$$P = \frac{S\pi d^3}{16\,R}\ ; \qquad f = \frac{32\,PR^2l}{\pi Gd^4} \tag{42}$$

in which, P = load on each spring; S = max unit stress = 80 000 lb; R = radius of center of coil; l = developed length of coil; G = modulus of elasticity in torsion = 12 000 000; d = diam of spring rod; f = deflection of spring in inches under load P.   In this case, the pull from drawbar to chain wheel or lever must be converted into component load in direction of axis of the spring. (See also Sec 41, Art 10.)

32. CAGING DEVICES AND LANDING CHAIRS

Caging of small cars is nearly always done by hand.   Large cars are also often caged by hand; but mechanical devices are common, especially in collieries, and increase capacity and safety.   For hand caging, where station layout permits tracks on both sides of shaft, the track approach to cage is laid with 1.5 to 2% grade, so that cars will run on by gravity, the loaded car pushing off the empty on opposite side.   Car checks, placed at a safe distance back from the shaft, are controlled by a lever worked by the station tender.   They should be so far automatic that, after a car passes, the check is raised into position to hold the following car.   At surface landing, if point of dumping be some distance from cage, loaded car may be pushed off by the empty; but, with hand caging, this is not satisfactory, because more effort is required than at shaft stations.

Mechanical cagers.   Rams, operated by steam or compressed air, are often used at collieries.   They act against the empty car, which pushes loaded car off the cage.   Throttle for the ram should be operated by levers interlocking with car check and landing chairs, so that it can not be opened unless cage is at landing and car check down.

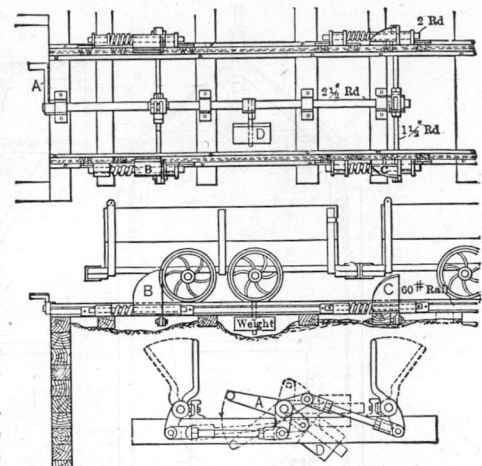

Fig 116.   Automatic Cager

Fig 116 shows an apparatus made by the Mining Safety Device Co.   When cage reaches station landing, its weight turns crank A and opens horns B.   This allows first car to run onto cage, and at same time closes horns C, thus holding back second car.   When cage is raised, horns C are opened and B closed by weight D.   For intermediate levels, the cage-operated crank is replaced by a hand lever, which is locked in position unless cage is at that level.

Car stops, to hold car on cage, may act on the body, wheels, or axles.   Commonest stops are: (a) hook attached to side of cage, which drops into an eye on side of car; (b) pair of bent bars, 0.375 or 0.5 by 1.5 in, hinged on vertical side members of cage, and resting in brackets on the diagonals.   These bars drop with a small clearance over ends of car body.

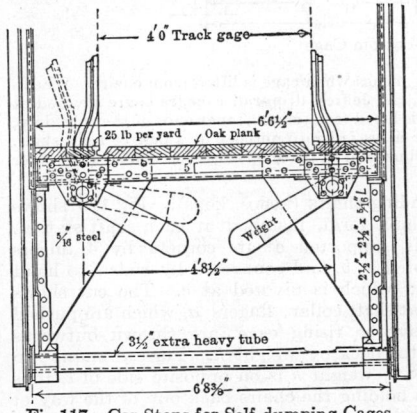

Fig 117.   Car Stops for Self-dumping Cages, Jed Coal and Coke Co

Automatic stops applied to car wheels or axles, whenever cage is not on the chairs, permit more rapid caging.   They are of 2 kinds: (a) HORNS raised in front of wheels or between them, and operated by weight and levers when cage leaves landing. Fig 117 shows stops for a self-dumping cage. For ordinary cages, the horns are often operated by a lever at corner of cage, within reach of cage tender at landing. (*b*) DROP-BOTTOM CAGE. In this an independent transverse section of

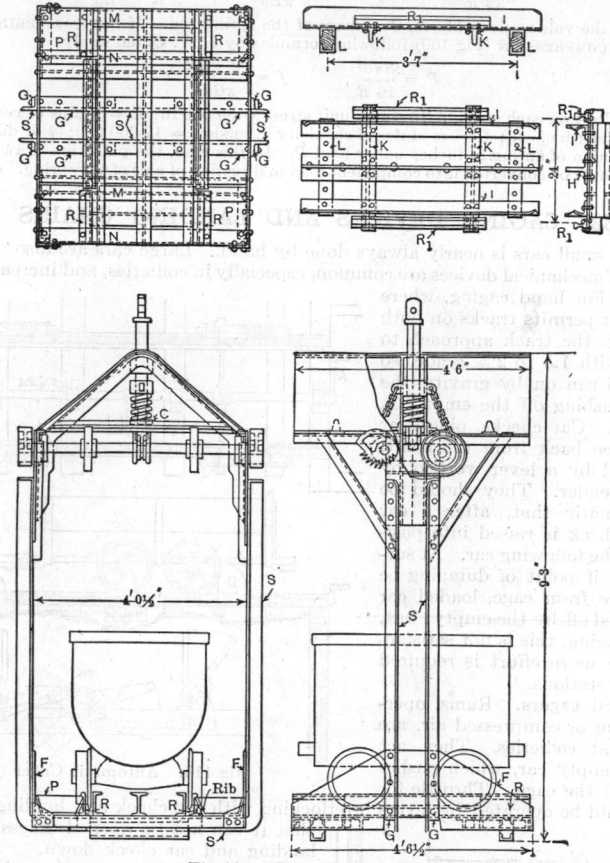

Fig 118. Drop-bottom Cage

deck and rails, on which the car stands, drops a few inches when cage is lifted from chairs. Wheels are thus blocked by the fixed rail ends (Fig 118). In Jeffrey drop-rail cage, rails are pivoted at outer ends and divided in the middle. When cage is lifted from chairs, inner ends of the rails drop, and car axles fall into notches in a pair of rigid skids. Car is thus held in place until cage is landed at another station.

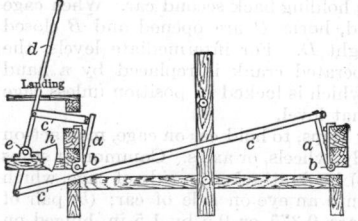

Fig 119. Chairs for Surface Landing

Landing chairs (keeps, keps). Fig 119 shows a common form, installed at each shaft station. Cage is supported at its corners by 4 fingers *a*, pivoted at *b*, and connected by rods *c* to hand lever *d*; which is pivoted at *e*. The cut shows chairs at shaft collar; fingers *a*, which are pushed back by the rising cage, are thrown outwards under the deck by weight *h*. For UNDERGROUND LANDINGS, weight *h* is on opposite side of *e*, thus always holding the chairs back out of the way of a passing cage. To support cage at a given landing, the station tender pushes lever *d* into the position shown. A spring may be used instead of a weight. Especially designed chairs, with 8 fingers instead of 4, are required for drop-bottom cages.

Fig 120 shows chair supported by steel construction at mouth of Annabelle shaft,

Four States Coal and Coke Co. Fig 121 shows a simple design used by Desloge Consol Lead Co, S E Missouri. Parallel rails are caused to slide in and out by links and levers, serving both compartments. CHAIRS ATTACHED TO CAGE DECK (Fig 123) have advan-

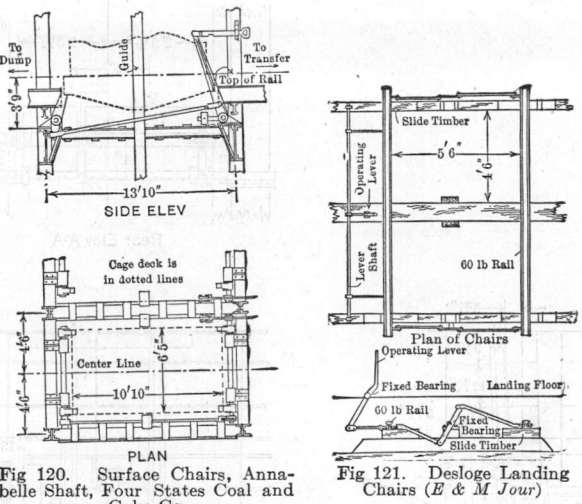

Fig 120. Surface Chairs, Annabelle Shaft, Four States Coal and Coke Co

Fig 121. Desloge Landing Chairs (*E & M Jour*)

tages for shafts with many levels, since only one set of chairs is required for each cage. Fig 123 (37) shows method at Horne Copper Mine.

Man cages should be fitted with gates, about 6 ft high. If same cage is used for ore, the gates are detachable, and removed when not needed. Cages especially for men have

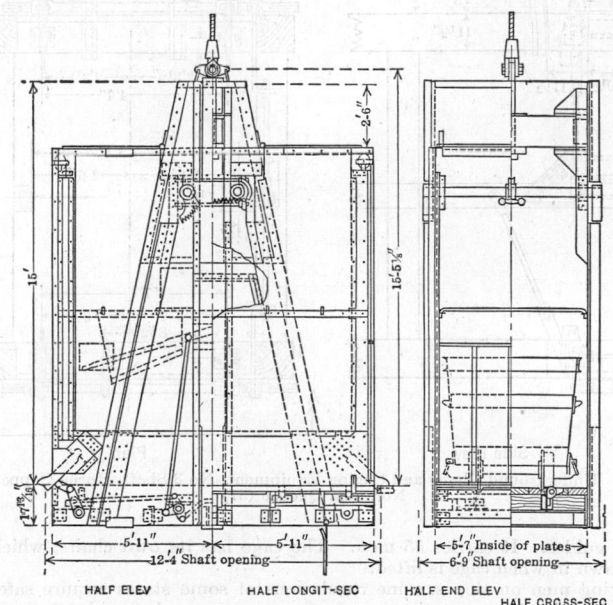

Fig 122. Man and Material Cage, Inspiration Mine, Ariz (*E & M J*)

hinged gates, opening inward, or of pantograph form as for elevators, and are lined on sides with sheet steel, or strong closely-woven wire mesh. Hand-holds should be provided;

usually horiz rods attached to cage frame under the bonnet. Fig 122 shows the man and material cage of Inspiration Consol Copper Co (77), with counterweighted gates moving

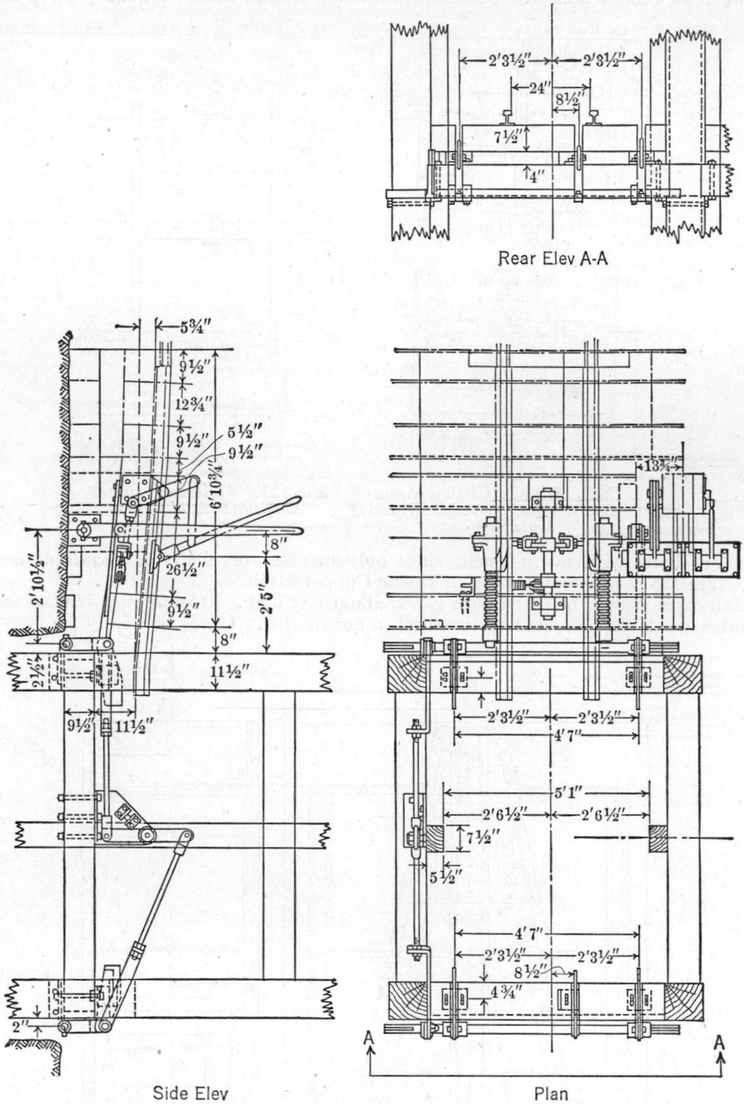

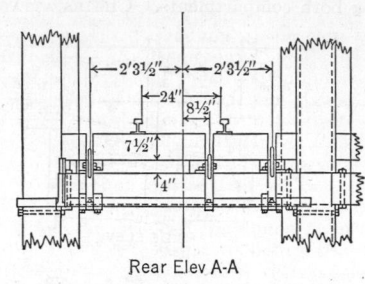

Rear Elev A-A

Side Elev   Plan

Fig 123. Underground Chairs and Caging Equipment, No 3 Shaft, Horne Copper Mine, Noranda, Quebec (37)

vertically in guides. It carries 55 men. The cage has its own chairs, which are automatically drawn in when cage is lifted.

For hoisting men on slopes, mine regulations of some states require safety catches, working on a third rail, on a stationary wire rope, or on wooden guides as for cages.

33. SKIPS

Skips may be used in either vertical or inclined shafts (as employed for colliery slopes they are called "gunboats"). ADVANTAGES over cages: less time required for loading and dumping; large capacity in shafts of small cross-section; less labor for dumping at shaft top; weigh less than combined cage and car. Less dead wt means smaller rope, drums and engine, or greater useful load. DISADVANTAGES: difficulty in keeping separate different grades of ore, or ore and waste; impossible to distribute output into a long storage bin without additional handling; men can not be so conveniently raised or lowered; while loading or dumping, there is more danger of ore dropping down shaft. With well designed skips, breakage of coal is very little or no greater than with self-dumping cages (78). When skips are used, MEN ARE CONVEYED: (a) on a cage permanently fixed above skip; (b) on a man car, replacing the skip at end of shifts; (c) on a cage in a special shaft compartment. When a skip is hung below a cage, increased height of headframe is necessary.

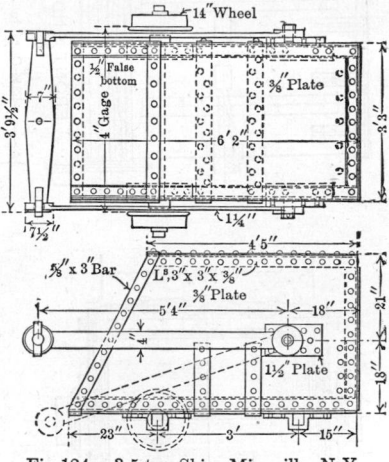

Fig 124.   3.5-ton Skip, Mineville, N Y
(E & M J)

Inclined-shaft skips. Fig 124 and 126 show skips of heavy construction, for iron and copper mines. Skips similar in design to that of Fig 127 are built for Michigan copper mines up to capacities of 7 and 10 tons. For convenience of loading, the angle at forward end is made approx equal to dip of shaft.

Where inclination of shaft is low, the skip body has no top and becomes a modified car. Fig 127 shows such a design, of the Tenn Coal, Iron and R R Co, Birmingham, Ala (1925), for hoisting

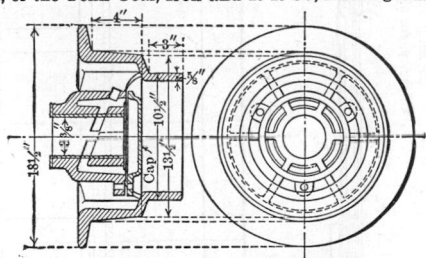

Fig 125.   Rear Wheel, Mineville Skip

iron ore. Front end is hinged at top, and held closed until the dumping point is reached by the front crossbar of the bail, which is in contact with 1-in plates, faced with angles extending from the

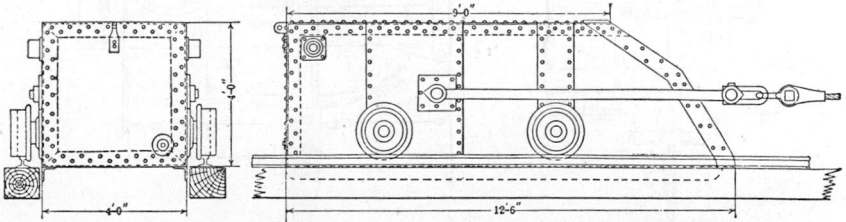

Fig 126.   8-ton Skip, Hancock No 2 Shaft, Quincy Copper Mine, Mich;   Weight, 4¾ Tons

door. As skip goes into dumping position the front end drops, while the bail maintains its position, allowing the door to be opened by the wt of ore. For safety, a loop of wire rope passes around the skip body, and through the hoisting rope thimble.

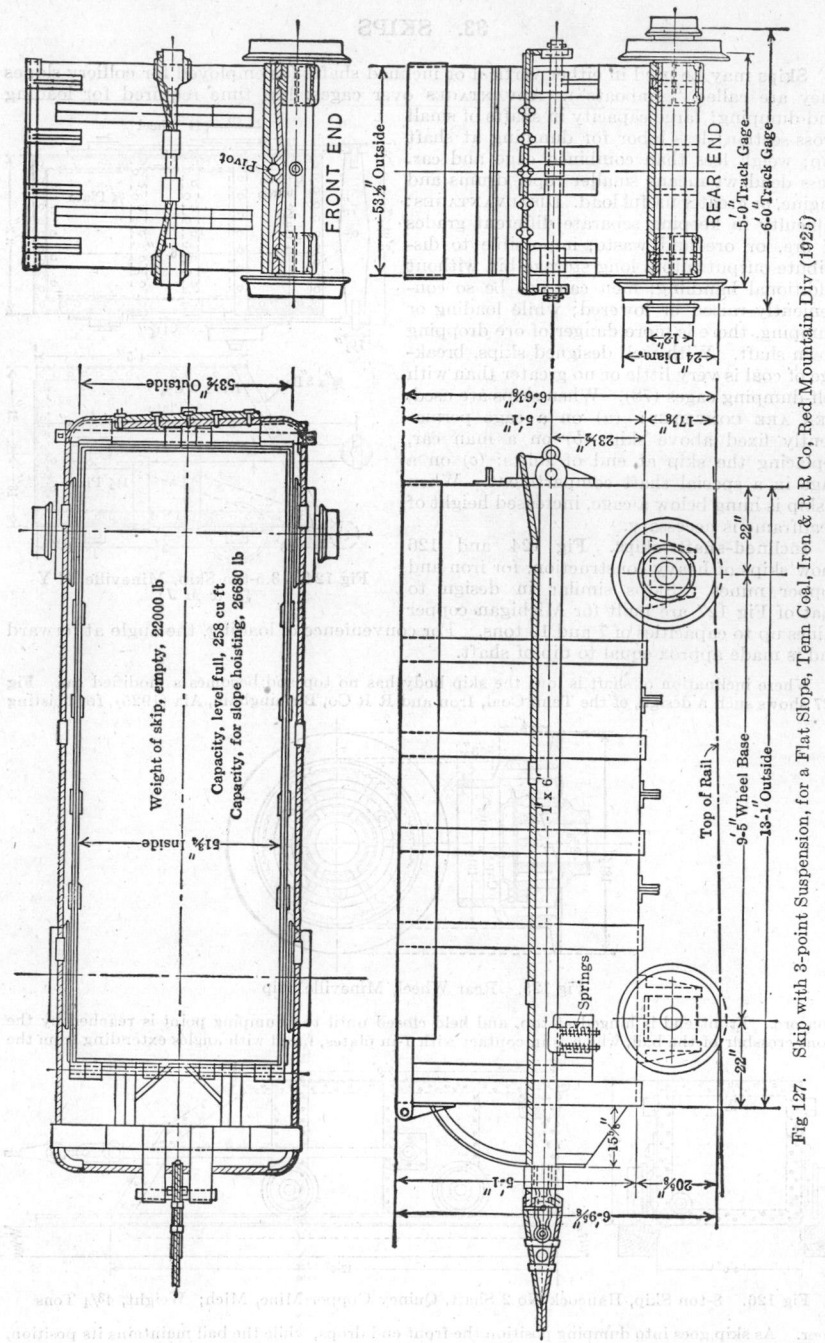

Fig 127. Skip with 3-point Suspension, for a Flat Slope, Tenn Coal, Iron & R R Co, Red Mountain Div (1925)

Weight of skip, empty, 22000 lb
Capacity, level full, 258 cu ft
Capacity, for slope hoisting, 26680 lb

Details. WHEELS are on axles under the body (Fig 124), or on trunnions set in heavy plates or castings bolted to sides (Fig 126). They must be in accurate alinement. Side trunnions cost more, but reduce headroom required in shaft compartment; and if body extends below rail heads, derailment is almost impossible. Axles, when worn, are more readily replaced than trunnions. Wear on

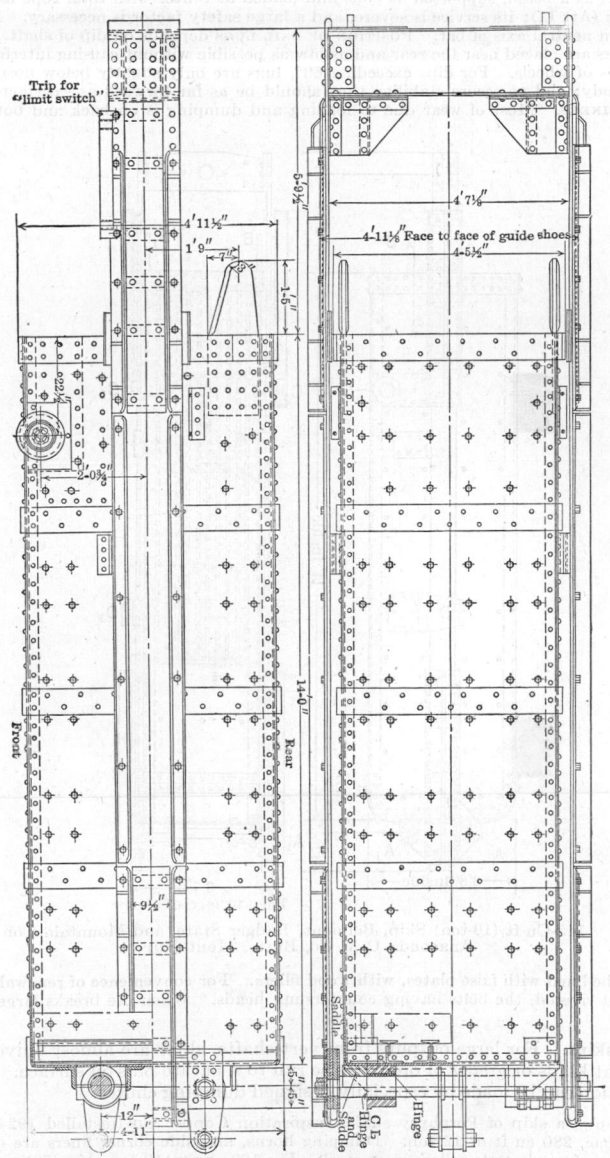

Fig 128.   12-ton Skip, Inspiration Mine, Ariz (77)

wheels and axles is severe, due to grit and frequent presence of acid mine water; hence, end of axle should be capped and liberal lubrication provided for. These features are shown in Fig 126, illustrating rear wheel of skip in Fig 125. Manganese steel wheels are good; or a steel or chilled tread, with soft center bored for a bronze bushing. Front wheels have treads of standard width; rear wheels are extra wide (5 to 6 in) for dumping the skip (see below). BAIL side bars are attached to lugs bolted to side plates, as shown; or better, to pins supported in double shear by a flat bar, passing around back of body. Pins should have ample bearing value. Sectional area of metal through center of eyes of bail bars should be 35 to 40% greater than that of the bar. Length of side bars should be such that crossbar will not interfere with loading, as skip hangs on the rope. Cross-bar is designed as a beam, supported at ends and loaded at center with total rope load, including starting factor (Art 14); its service is severe, and a large safety factor is necessary. Hole for rope clevis is best in neutral axis of bar. Position of bail lugs depends on dip of shaft. For dips of 30° or less, lugs are placed near the rear and as low as possible without causing interference of side bars with hubs of wheels. For dips exceeding 60°, lugs are only slightly below horizontal center line of skip body; and to secure stability they should be as far forward as satisfactory dumping will allow. Liners. Most of wear due to loading and dumping is on back and bottom of skip,

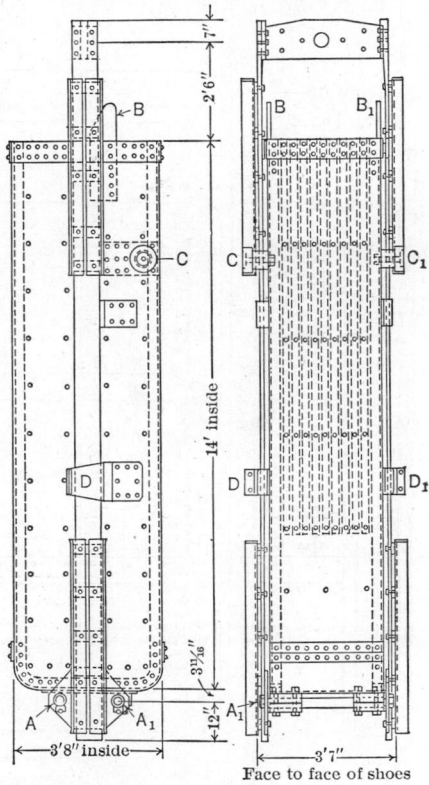

Fig 129.   145-Cu ft (10-ton) Skip, Belmont, Badger State, and Mountain Con Mines, Anaconda C M Co, Butte, Mont (79)

which should be lined with false plates, with wood fillers. For convenience of renewal, these plates are bolted, not riveted, the bolts having countersunk heads. When ore breaks large, the wear is great.

Vertical skips. For large outputs from vert shafts, skips are almost universal, except when different kinds or grades of ore must be run to separate bins on surface. Even then, some separation can be made by especially designed dumping chutes.

Fig 128 shows a skip of Porphyry shaft, Inspiration Copper Co (installed 1924); wt empty 14 000 lb; capac, 280 cu ft or 12 ton. Dumping horns, and side corner liners are of manganese steel; trunnions, forged steel; rollers, cast steel. Fig 129 shows 10-ton skip (79) used at Butte; Fig 130, a Kimberley type skip in Wisconsin (37, 80).

Ore sticking to bottom of steel skips at mines of the Randfontein Gold Mining Co, So Africa, resulted in decreased skip load and increased spillage. See Fig 131 (37). It was found that tendency to expand of a rubber (linatex) bottom caused skip to empty itself completely. Rubber lining may be applied to mine cars used in rotary dumps, where bottom pounding is used to clear muck.

Design of vert skips is largely a matter of experience and good practice, load stresses being usually more than taken care of by proper allowance for heavy wear and tear of operation. Unless required capac cannot otherwise be obtained, LENGTH of body should not exceed twice the least cross-sectional dimensions; otherwise the skip is slow in dumping, especially if the ore is sticky. Safety gear, if employed, must be high enough above body to be out of danger of injury, and not to obstruct loading from chute or car.

Combined cage and skip are useful in providing transit for men and supplies; also, for sinking operations when the shaft is to be deepened, provided height of skip body is small. Fig 132 shows a design for regular hoisting, Federal Lead Co, Flat River, Mo; capac, 125 cu ft, or about 6 ton,

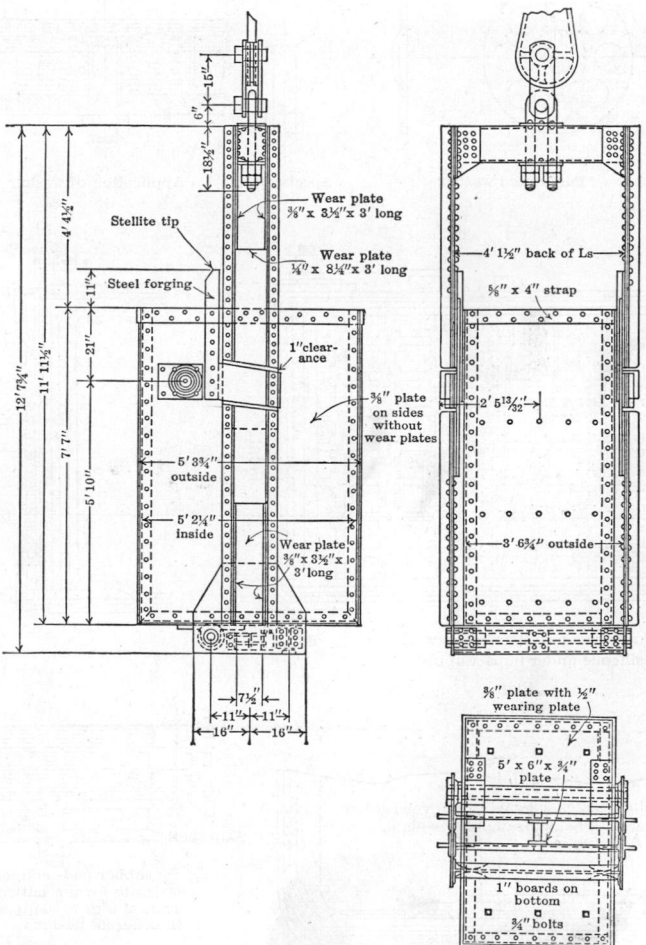

Fig 130.   9-ton Kimberley-type Skip, Montreal Mining Co, Wis (80)

though 5 ton is the ordinary load.   Main vert frame is of 10-in, 20-lb channels, spliced between cage and skip for convenience of handling and renewal of parts.

Coal skips ("gunboats"). Although use of skips tends to cause more breakage of coal, due to additional dumping, improvements in methods of loading and dumping have partly overcome this objection, and they are now common for large output (78). As coal is more bulky than ores, the volumetric capac is much greater than that of ore skips.

There are two types, overturning and bottom discharge. Breakage of coal is lessened: (a) in the overturning skip (Fig 133), by shape of bottom and front side and special arrangement of dumping chute; (b) in bottom-discharge type (Fig 135), by discharging through lower part of front, which opens and forms an apron between skip and chute. In Fig 135, revolving chute 2 is hinged at 4. Toggle links 12 are hinged to shaft 14, across lower end of chute. Rollers 6, on moving into fixed dumping guides *5*, rotate bell-crank *8* about fixed point *9*, thus rotating the chute through 135°. As toggle joint *12-A* is below the line joining *14* and *9*, the gate is self-locking. In each type, the greatest breakage of coal probably occurs during loading.

Loading arrangements. In INCLINED SHAFTS, skips are loaded direct from cars, the skip holding 1, 2 or more carloads; or from a pocket, through a gate controlled from

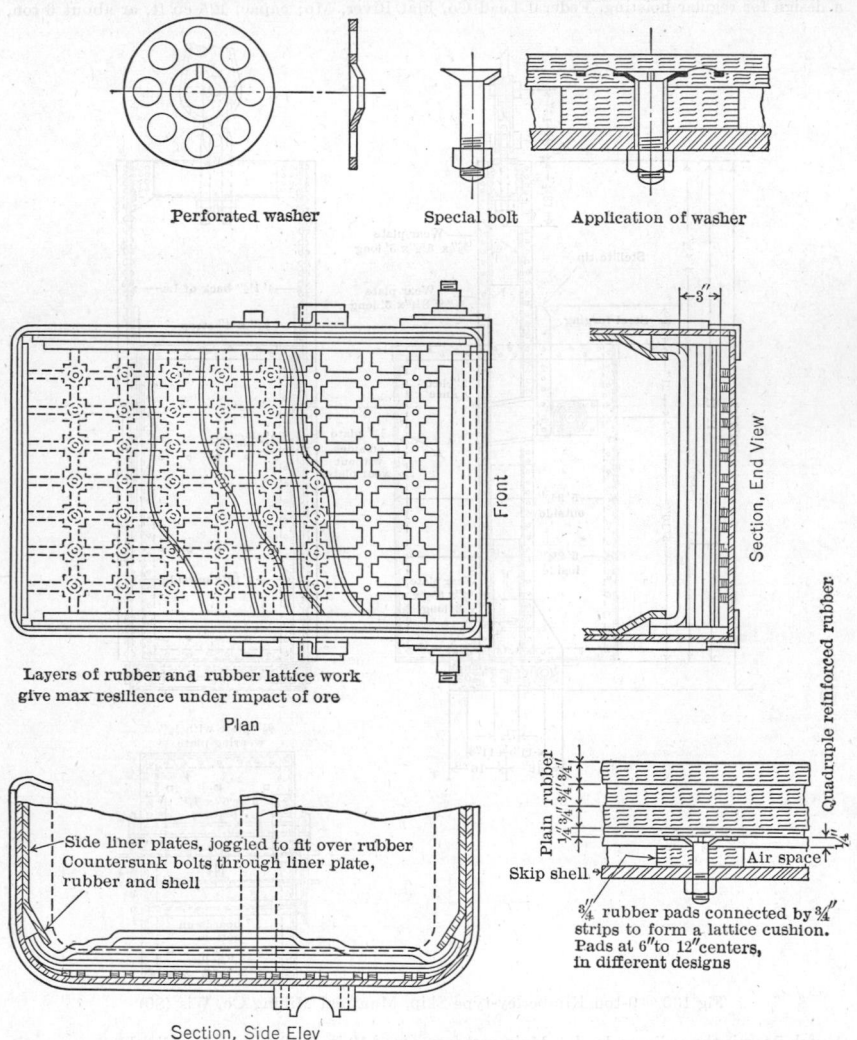

Perforated washer   Special bolt   Application of washer

Front

Section, End View

Layers of rubber and rubber lattice work give max resilience under impact of ore

Plan

Quadruple reinforced rubber

Side liner plates, joggled to fit over rubber
Countersunk bolts through liner plate, rubber and shell

Plain rubber

Skip shell

Air space

¾ rubber pads connected by ¾" strips to form a lattice cushion. Pads at 6"to 12"centers, in different designs

Section, Side Elev

Fig 131. Rubber Skip Lining (37)

landing above. Latter plan is best, since cars and skip are independent of each other, and on reaching shaft station, the skip is loaded promptly, without waiting for cars. In VERT SHAFTS, a skip holding 1 or 2 carloads may also be loaded direct (Fig 135, *a*); but pockets are always preferable (see Shaft Pockets, Art 35).

Arrangements for dumping are more varied than those for loading. For INCLINED SHAFTS, a "knuckle" is formed at dumping point by curving main rails inward to horizontal. The narrow-tread front wheels run forward on these bent rails, while broadtread rear wheels continue up the regular slope on a pair of auxiliary rails set at wider gage, beginning at the knuckle.

Fig 135, *b* shows a modification of this typical dump, as used at Quincy mine, Mich, for an 8-ton skip. By curving upward the broad-gage rails, the skip is brought more quickly to proper dumping angle. Design must be such that, when skip is lowered, it cannot go down the shaft head first. If, as in Fig 127, the whole tread of the wide rear wheels is of one diameter, guard rails may be necessary to prevent rear of the skip from slipping sidewise. Or, as in Fig 126, diameter of outer part of tread may be 2 to 3 in less than that of inner part, the shoulder so formed acting as a flange on the auxiliary rails.

It may be necessary to dump at more than one point, as for putting different grades of ore into separate bins. At Quincy mine, Mich, gaps in main rails at dumping point, through which front wheels pass, are opened or closed by a plate, moved sidewise by an attendant, by rods and levers. ANGROVE DUMP for intermittent service (Fig 136), as used by Copper Range Mining Co, has no

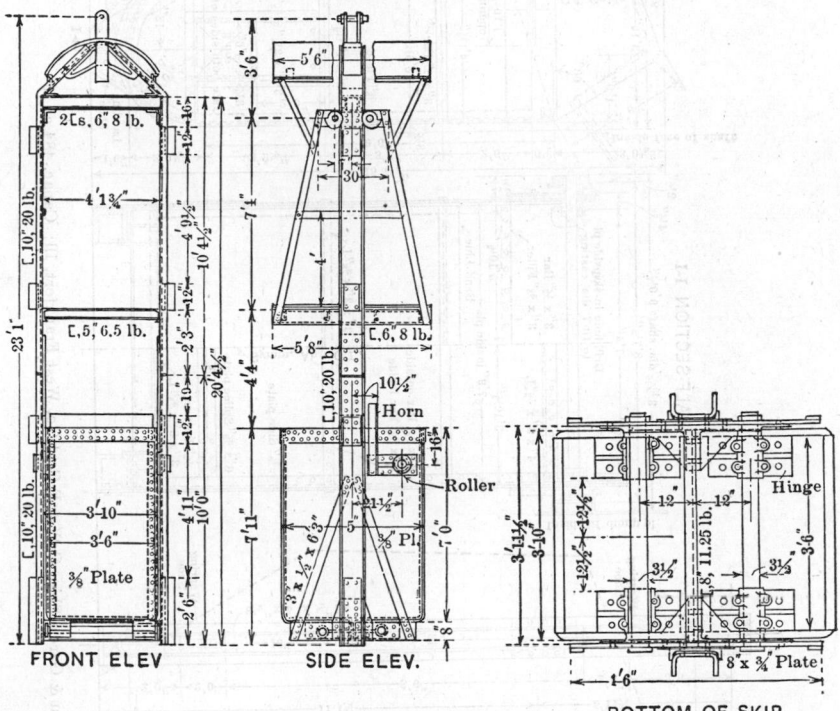

FRONT ELEV   SIDE ELEV.   BOTTOM OF SKIP

Fig 132.   Combined Skip and Cage

break in main rails. The wide-tread rear wheels follow curved auxiliary rails *K*, and when skip reaches a proper dumping angle, the front edge is supported by rollers *L*, otherwise front end of skip would drop. Points *B* of auxiliary rails are hinged at *A*; and, by a system of counterweighted rods and levers, may be raised to dotted position *B'*, if skip is to pass up to a higher dumping point.

For VERTICAL SHAFTS the skip body, which is pivoted at bottom to the rigid guide frame, is thrown outwards and supported at a dumping angle by a pair of small wheels, near upper edge of skip (Fig 137), which run into a curved slot-like track attached to head-frame at the dumping point.

Fig 137 shows dumping track for the skip in Fig 130. The skip body rests on two parallel shafts bolted to the guide frame, and far enough apart to insure stability of the skip while being hoisted. One shaft passes through 2 heavy pillow blocks with caps, bolted to skip body, thus forming a pivot on which the body rotates. The other shaft rests in pillow blocks without caps, also bolted to the skip bottom. Track must be so designed that skip body will not reverse, and go down head first when lowered. Generally, a pair of roller wheels is attached to side plates of dumping track (Fig 137) in such position that the horns (Fig 128, 133) projecting forward from front end of skip body will just slide over them; these rollers thus carry wt of skip while dumping wheels are being lifted across gap to reversed portion of dumping track, and on down trip they insure that skip body will be turned right side up. Instead of 2 rollers, a continuous bar or roller spanning gage of track is

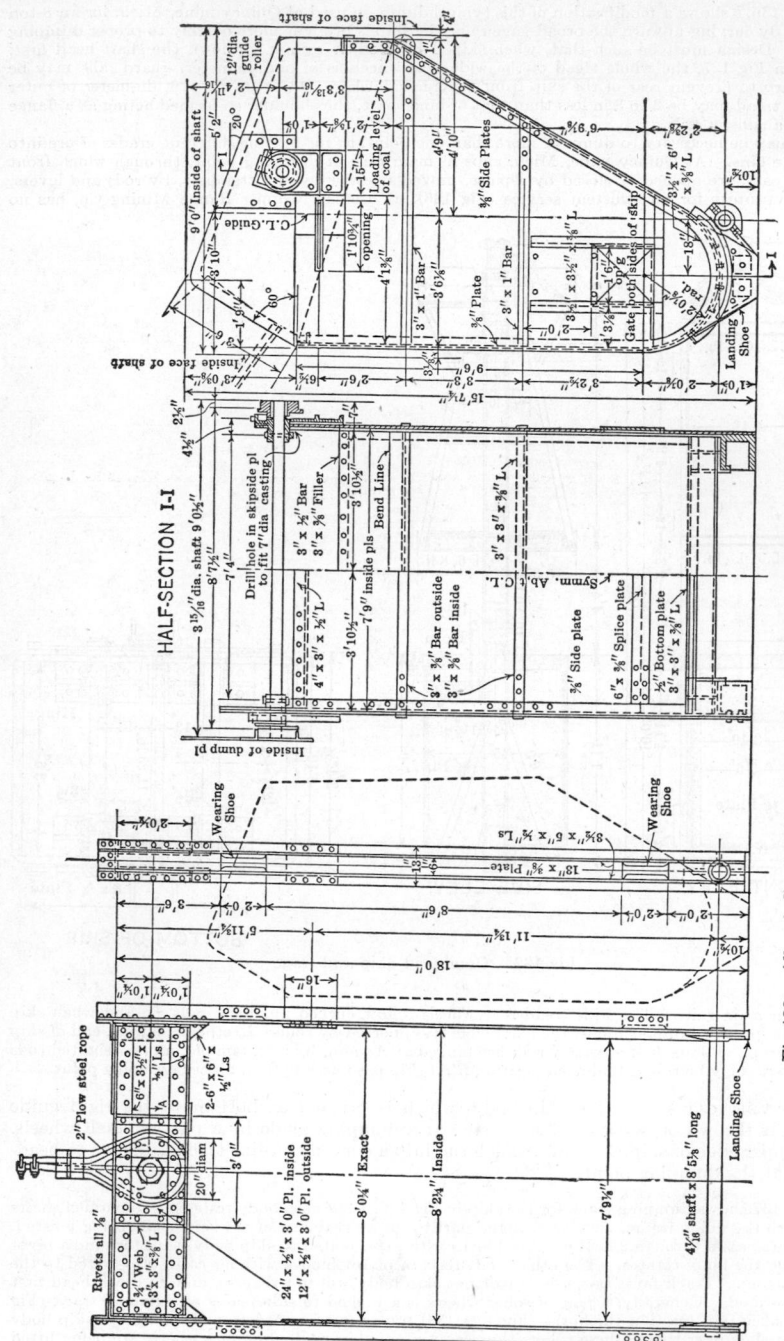

Fig 133. Allen & Garcia Skip, C W & F Coal Co, West Frankfort, Ill; Capac, 484 cu ft

sometimes used, but it may interfere with free dumping. Dumping wheels (Fig 128) should be placed close to dumping side of skip, so that ends of pivoting shaft will have clearance space between the main and dumping guides. The farther this shaft is from center line of skip, the less the liability to accidental overturning, but the greater is the force required to dump skip, thus throwing excessive stresses on guides. Main guides sustain heavy side thrust at dumping point, and must be well

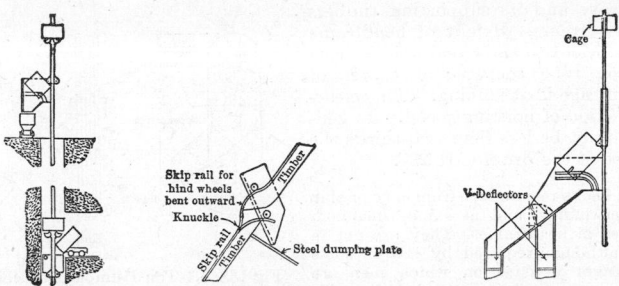

Fig 134. Arrangements for Loading and Dumping Skips

reinforced and bolted to headframe. Pivoting shaft is usually placed at 0.33 to 0.5 the distance from center line to side of body, 0.375 being good practice. For small skips the side plates are 1/4 to 5/16 in; front plate, 3/8 in; bottom plate, 3/8 to 1/2 in. For large skips, sides are 1/2 in, and front and bottom 3/8 to 3/4 in; in some Mich copper mines, even heavier.

Handling men in vertical-skip shafts. For large numbers of men, a double or triple-deck cage is substituted for the skip at end of shift. The change may be made quickly by

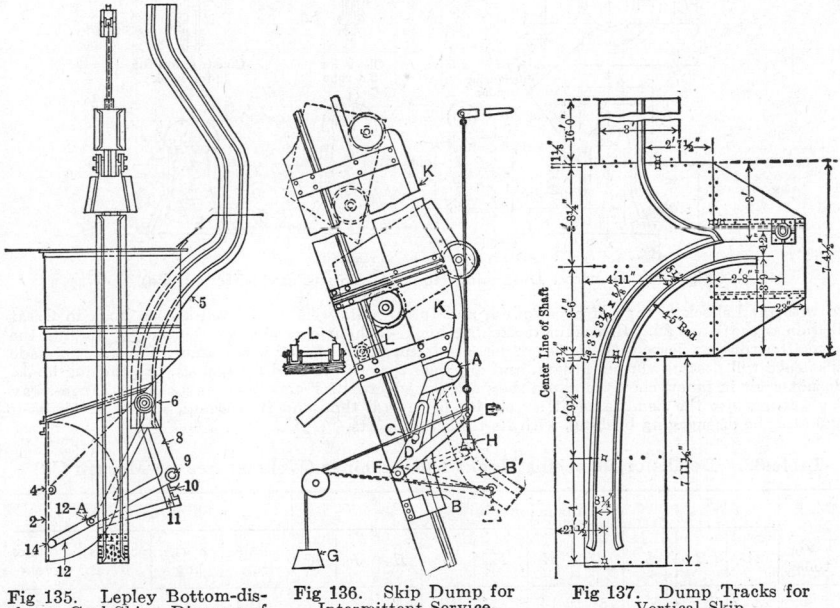

Fig 135. Lepley Bottom-discharge Coal Skip. Diagram of Mode of Dumping

Fig 136. Skip Dump for Intermittent Service (E & M J)

Fig 137. Dump Tracks for Vertical Skip

hinging a section of the guides above shaft collar, and handling skip and cage by a small crane; as at Butte, Mont, and elsewhere (92).

Weight and cost of skips. WEIGHT is commonly 40-60% of wt of ore, reckoned at 110-120 lb per cu ft. COST: usual designs, 10-14¢ per lb at factory; vert skips, with safety catches, 14-16¢ per lb. Dumping guides, with supporting plates and rollers, weigh 2 000-3 000 lb for 30- to 60- cu ft skips, to 4 500 lb for 100-cu ft capac.

34. OVERWINDING

Overwinding occurs when for any reason the hoisting engineer fails to check engine in time to bring cage to rest at surface landing. In such case the cage may rise at high speed into the sheave and its supporting timbers at top of headframe. Height of headframe should be sufficient to allow reasonable clearance between rope socket and center of sheave, when cage is at landing. This clearance is a function of hoisting speed. In general it should not be less than two-thirds the circumference of the drum (Art 23).

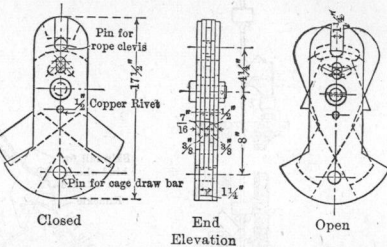

Fig 138. 4-Ton Humble Detaching Hook

Detaching hooks release rope from cage or skip in case of overwinding, and at same time hold cage suspended in headframe. They are not in general use, although required by law in some districts for cages or skips on which men are hoisted. They can be used for vertical shafts only. Original HUMBLE HOOK with 5 leaves or plates, and capacity of 4 tons, is shown in Fig 138. Disengaging plate, into which hook rises, and which opens it for releasing the rope, is bolted to timbers in upper part of headframe. This plate is of C I or steel, with a round opening of a diam about 0.5 in greater than width of hook. Details of the ORMEROD HOOK (a modification of the Humble) with 3 plates instead of 5, and C I-disengaging bushing, are shown in Fig 139 and Table 38. DISENGAGING PLATE OR BUSHING should be placed as high as possible in headframe, and solidly supported

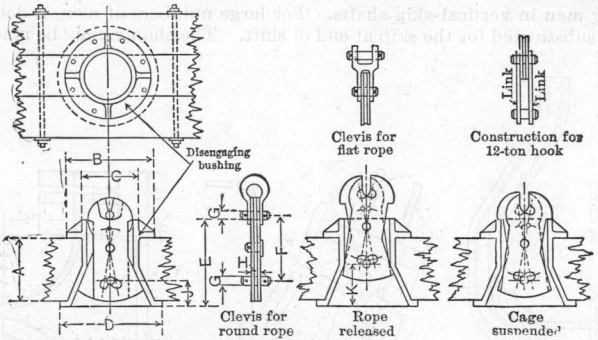

Fig 139. Ormerod Detaching Hook (Wellman-Seaver-Morgan Co)

to withstand shock of cage, if overwound, and to carry its weight. A well-known hook in Great Britain is the WALKER. If a plain detaching hook, without ears or lugs, is used for holding the cage after rope is released, chairs or catches are set in upper part of headframe. They are so made that cage will pass up through them, and are then thrown outward by springs. Detaching hooks do not grow in favor, chiefly because they are not effectual for high hoisting speeds. A run-away cage, rising into the headframe at a velocity of several thousand ft per min, would wreck itself and also the disengaging bushing, with its timber supports.

Table 38. Details of Detaching Hooks and Bushings (Wellman-Seaver-Morgan Co)

Max safe load, tons	Dimensions, in										Shipping wt, lb			
	A	B	C	D	E	F	G	H	J	K	Cast-iron	Forging	Struct steel	Bolts & rivets
4	8 1/2	14	8	18	14	10 1/2	1 1/2	1 3/4	3	7	190	13	39	5
6	12	16 1/2	10 3/4	20 1/2	19	14	1 3/4	1 7/8	4	11	325	13	96	8
8	18	25	16	29	25	29	2	2	6	13	875	32	183	28
12	24	30	20	36	33	23	3	2	9	17	1 325	100	351	67

Safety devices, to prevent overwinding by automatically controlling the engine, generally operate by closing throttle and applying brakes. Some also center the reversing links. Requirements are: (a) simplicity; (b) all parts should be accessible for inspection and testing; (c) derangement or failure of any part should cause the loop to operate; (d) steam should be cut off close to the valve chests; (*e*) steam should be throttled as cage approaches surface, and brakes applied for bringing the engine gradually to rest; (*f*) the apparatus should come into operation automatically, if the engineer fails to check the engine at the proper time; it should also be self-locking, so that engine can not again be started until gear has been thrown off and engine reversed.

Lilly hoist controller (81), largely used in U S for both steam and electric hoists, has a fly-ball governor, working through cams and levers controlled by electrical contacts.

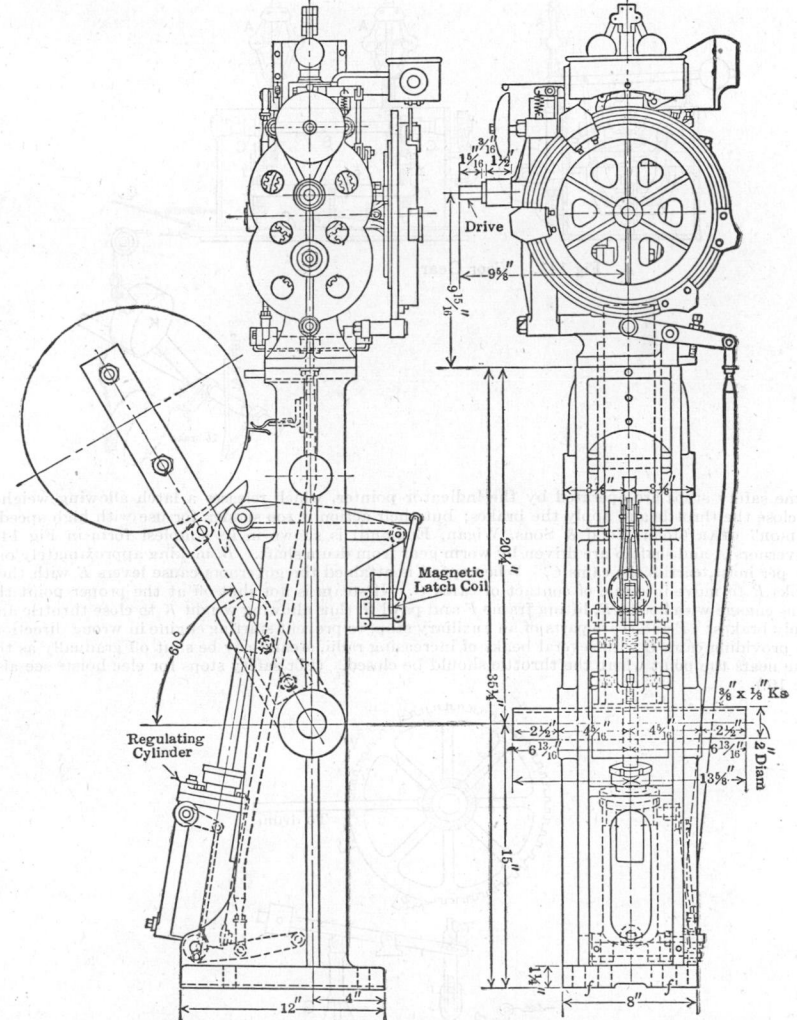

Fig 140.   Lilly Controller for Small Electric Hoists

Controller is operated from the drum shaft, or hub of clutch-operated drums, by a train of gears or sprocket chain.   It guards against overspeeding, overwinding at ends of trip, and warns engineer by a bell when full speed is exceeded; also acts to reduce speed at proper point, if engineer fails to do so, and to prevent starting engine in wrong direction.

For steam hoists, the current is supplied by batteries; for electric hoists, power circuit supplies current.   On steam hoists the controller acts by releasing a wt, which closes throttle; on electric hoists by controlling the power circuit.   If hoist has power-released gravity brakes, they are applied by an auxiliary weight, which operates the brake-engine valve.   For small hoists, hand brakes are applied by a weighted lever, automatically controlled through an oil cylinder having a by-pass and valve to prevent too sudden application of brake except at extreme limit of travel.   For high-speed hoists, the controller has an auxiliary attachment, set to prevent excessive speed when hoisting men. Fig 140 shows a form used for small elec hoists, with hand-brakes.

Futer's safety stop (82) acts directly on the cutoff, shortening it as the cage rises above a fixed point in the shaft, centering the valves at a predetermined point, and gradually applying the brakes. Its best features are; it shuts off steam directly at the cylinders, and gradually applies the brake.

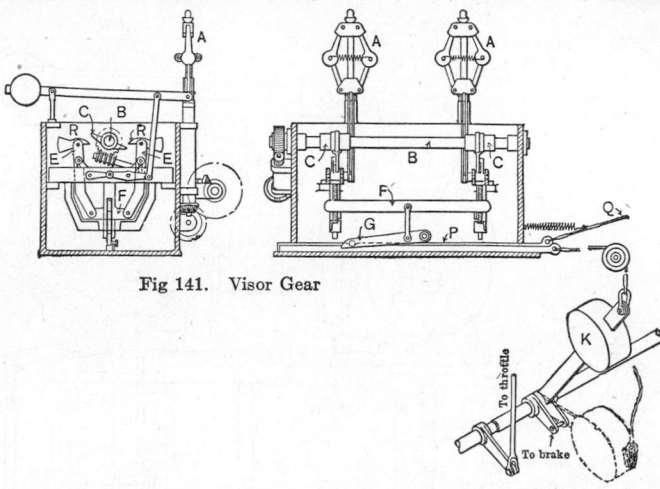

Fig 141.   Visor Gear

Some safety stops are operated by the indicator pointer, which releases a latch allowing weights to close the throttle and apply the brakes; but their action is too sudden for use with high speeds. "VISOR" GEAR (John Wood & Sons, Wigan, England) is shown in its simplest form in Fig 141. Governors A and shaft B are driven by worm gear from drum shaft. B, making approximately one rev per hoist, carries the cams C.   When speed is attained the governors cause levers E with their hooks R to move into line of contact of cams C.   If steam is not shut off at the proper point the cams engage with hooks, R, lifting frame F and pawl G, thus allowing weight K to close throttle and apply brakes. P and Q are parts of an auxiliary stop, to prevent starting engine in wrong direction. By providing cams C with several beaks of increasing radii, steam may be shut off gradually as the cage nears the point where the throttle should be closed.   (For safety stops for elec hoists see also Sec 16.)

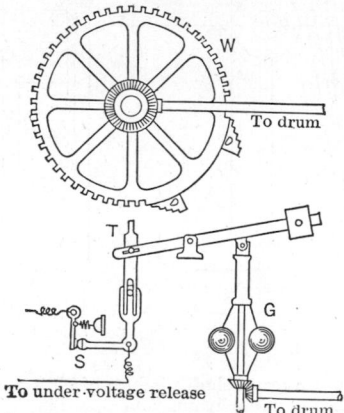

Fig 142.   Diagram of Mechanical Overwind Device for Mine Hoists (3)

Speed governors, in addition to safety stops, are necessary for high-speed hoisting engines.   They are usually of the flyball type.   With Corliss valves they act by shorten-ing the cutoff; with slide and piston valves they throttle the steam.

A system of protection for electric hoists is shown in Fig 142 (3). The notched wheel W, carry-ing an adjustable tripping dog D, is geared to the drum to make not more than one revolution for the max lift. Governor G, also geared to drum, determines the position at which the trip T for the circuit-opening switch S (wired in the "undervoltage" release circuit) is operated by the notches of the dog on wheel W. Dog D is placed to correspond to positions near end of travel and the graduated steps correspond to distances between the point at which slow-down should start and the limit of travel. Opening of switch S is determined by relative positions of T and D; the former governed by speed of drum and the latter by position of cage in the shaft. The last tripping position of D corresponds to an actual overtravel of the cage, and opens S irrespective of the speed. The notches on W protect against overspeeding at any point. These devices may differ considerably in construction. They usually have a hand resetting device. For further protection, it is customary to install in the shaft guides above the landing, a "shaft limit-switch," operated directly by the cage or skip. If the hoist is stopped by either device, means must be provided to prevent starting again in the same direction. This is done by a small double-throw controller, reestablishing the power supply and releasing the brakes, but permitting closure of only that primary contactor which will allow the over-wound skip to be backed down.

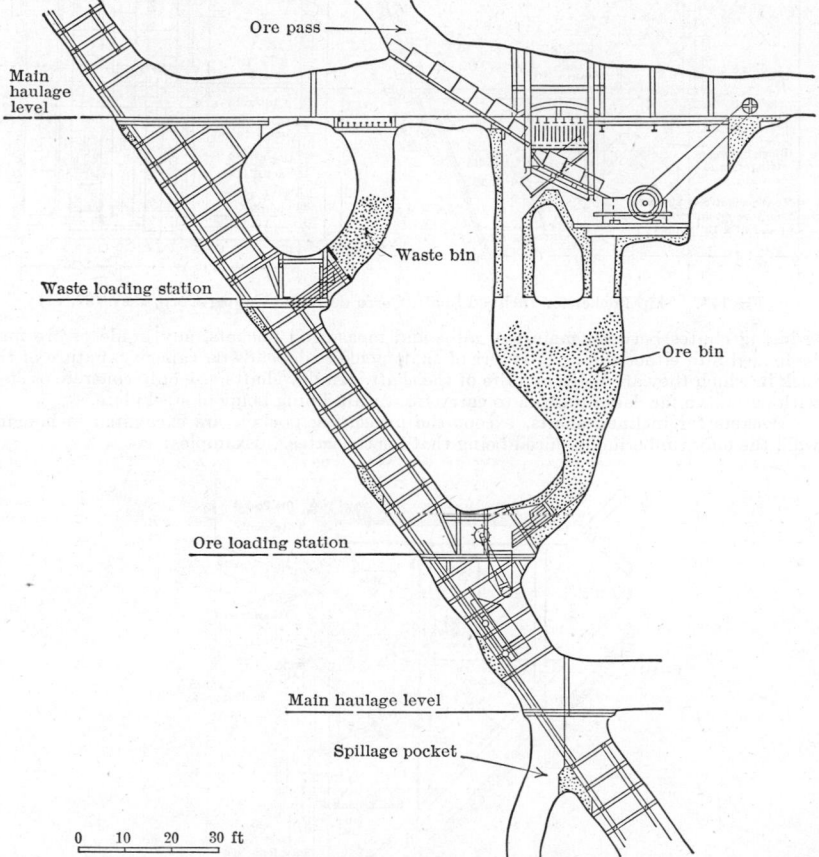

Fig 143.   Loading 9-ton Skips, No 3 Shaft, Creighton Mine, Int Nickel Co, Canada (37, 68)

35. SHAFT POCKETS

Shaft pockets at loading stations decrease time required to load a skip, and furnish reserve ore capacity, so that hoisting and tramming are not directly dependent on each other. Filling a skip from a pocket also involves less likelihood of spilling ore down the shaft. CAPACITY of pockets depends upon tonnage hoisted, size of ore cars or trains of cars, and storage need at the level to take care of ore trammed while hoisting is being done from other levels. It may reach 1 500 tons or more. As a rule, a measuring pocket is placed below the storage pocket. It holds one skip load and is filled from main pocket, thus saving time and avoiding danger of overfilling skip, if gate should stick or break. This also permits dividing main bin into 2 or more pockets for different grades of ore; then, with

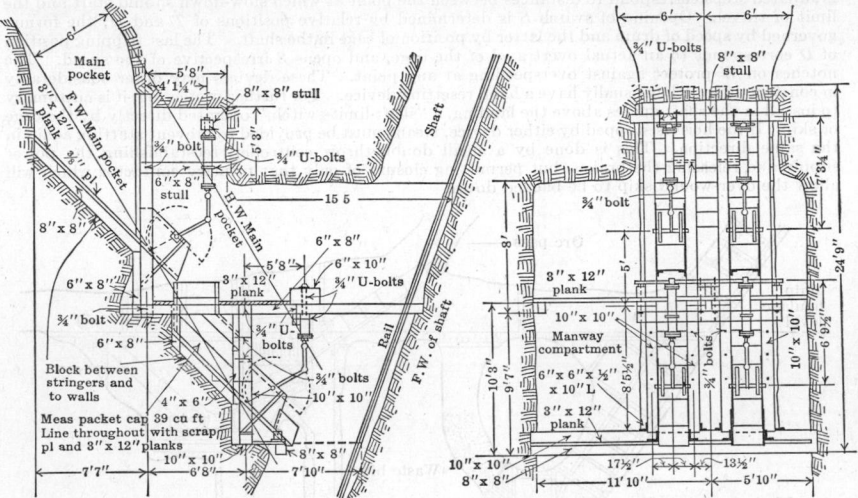

Fig 144. Skip Pocket for Inclined Shaft, Cerro de Pasco Copper Corp, Peru (37, 71)

swinging chutes between main-bin gates and measuring pockets, any grade of ore may be loaded into either skip. Support of shaft pockets depends on capacity, nature of the rock in which they are built, and life of the shaft. In dry shafts, use only concrete or steel with perhaps a few large timbers to carry front wall, lining being of steel plate.

Pockets for inclined shafts, except the measuring pocket, are excavated in hanging wall, the only timbering required being that for the gates. Examples:

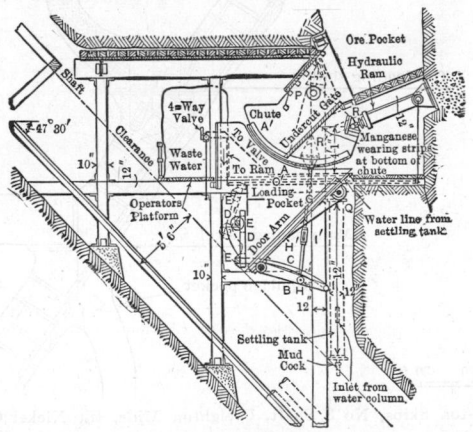

Fig 145. Shaft Pockets, Franklin Furnace, N J (*E & M Jour*)

I. Large pockets at 14th, 20th and 26th levels of No 3 shaft, Creighton Mine, Ontario, are shown in Fig 143. Dip of shaft, 55°. Ore hoisted in 9-ton skips, weighing 12 200 lb. Shaft has 5 compartments, 2 for ore, 2 for men and supplies, and 1 for ladders, pipes and cables. A 30- by 42-in Farrell jaw crusher, with 6-in opening, breaks the ore before it enters pocket. A measuring box of 9 ton capac handles ore from bin to skip (68, 37).

II. At the Francisco Mine, Cerro de Pasco Copper Co, Peru, the skip pocket (Fig 144) has a bottom of 3 by 12-in plank, covered with scrap plate and inclined at 45°. The measuring pocket holds 39 cu ft (one skip load). Gates operated by air cylinders are used in both main and measuring pockets. Gates should shut off ore flow by rising, but with sufficient power they may close from the top. Valves for the 4 gates are operated from a platform in front of main pocket. All gates and signalling are controlled by one man (37, 71).

III. At Palmer shaft, N J Zinc Co, Franklin, N J, both main and measuring pockets are of steel (Fig 145). Main gate and loading chute are moved by a hydraulic ram, taking its water from the column pipe in the shaft. The cut shows the closed apparatus; lower door closed and upper

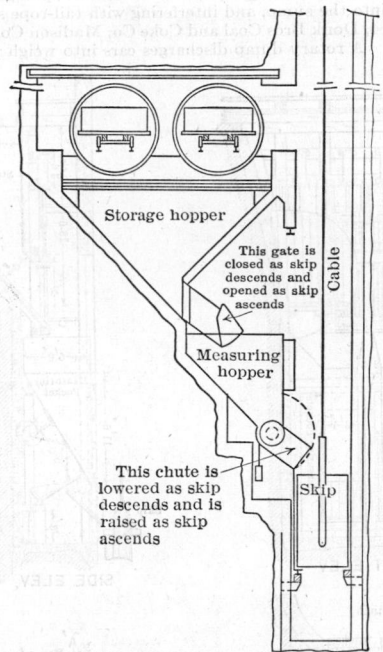

Fig 146. Shaft Bottom Dumping Arrangement, Standard No 2 Mine, Schoper, Ill (37, 69)

undercut gate open, allowing ore to fill measuring bin. When the angle of repose is reached flow stops, with pocket and upper chute full. To load skip, the ram moves out along the arc shown until edge of undercut gate is at A'. At same time rod G moves to position G', moving levers B and C so that pins H and I assume positions H' and I'. Door D, held in position by arms pivoted at Q and E, is forced to position D' by movement of B and C. The advance of cutoff gate A is at first more rapid than that of D, but D closes first, so that the measuring pocket is ready to fill when A has opened. Gate A can not jam, as it cuts upward through the ore. The operation is controlled by one 4-way valve. With 6-ton skips over 2 000 ton have been hoisted in 8.5 hr.

Vertical-shaft pockets. In their construction, concrete is more generally used than for pockets in inclined shafts. Examples:

I. At Standard No 2 coal mine of the Standard Oil Co of Indiana (Fig 146), there are 2 rotary dumps in which cars are dumped singly into a 40-ton hopper, from which coal goes to a 12-ton measuring hopper holding a skip load. The empty descending skip closes discharge gate of storage hopper, and opens that of measuring hopper; ascending skip closes measuring-hopper gate and opens that of storage hopper. Amount of ore discharged into measuring hopper may be varied by a dam in upper part of hopper. This procedure does away with spillage (69, 37).

II. Shaft No 3, Negaunee mine, Mich, is circular in section, with 2 skip compartments (83). Storage pockets (Fig 147) are 12 ft 6 in wide, 18 ft 6 in deep, and 23 ft 3 in long at the top; divided into compartments for 3 grades of ore. Center compartment has 2 gates, for loading into either skip. End compartments have 1 gate, and load into but 1 skip. Front wall of the pocket is supported by horizontal timbers, lined with 5- by 7-in vertical timbers, covered with 0.5-in steel plate near bottom and 0.25-in plate at top. Sides are concreted, and lined with 0.5-in and 0.25-in plates bolted to timbers embedded in the concrete; plates are put in position and concrete poured behind them, thus making forms unnecessary. Bottom is concreted and lined with 2 layers of 3-in hardwood planks, spiked to 5 by 7-in timbers embedded in the concrete. This lining also is placed before concrete is poured, thus serving as forms. Gates are vertical finger bars, about 4 in square, suspended by chains from a crosshead attached to piston of an air cylinder with 3-ft stroke. Each measuring pocket holds a skip load. Their gates, of 2 thicknesses of 0.5-in plate, counterweighted, and opened and closed by an air cylinder, open away from the shaft, so that no part shall project into the hoisting compartments. Ore drops through a stationary chute into skip. Measuring pockets are of steel plate, their fronts being supported by I-beams across the openings in the concrete shaft lining.

III. At No 3 shaft, Village Deep mine, So Africa, an incline from level above, used for ore storage, discharges into a steel measuring pocket, for loading the skip (Fig 148). The gate forms a chute between pocket and skip, and a sloping spill plate diverts spillage into the level below; thus preventing it from falling into the sump, and interfering with tail-rope sheave.

IV. Thermal Mine No 4, Donk Bros Coal and Coke Co, Madison Co, Ill, has no storage pockets, as they increase breakage. A rotary dump discharges cars into weigh pans of scales, one for each

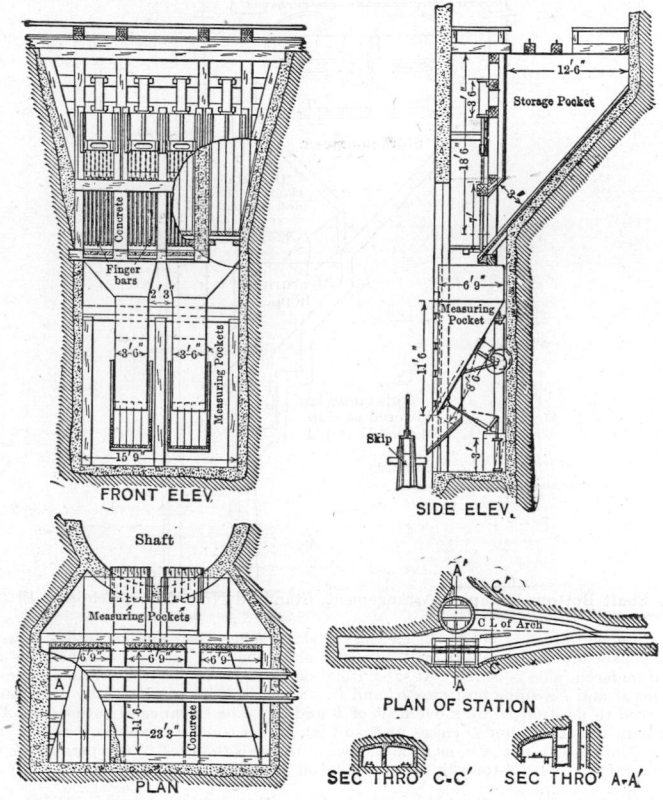

Fig 147. Stations and Storage Pockets, Negaunee No 3 Shaft (83)

compartment (Fig 149). Car loads are weighed separately, 2 cars filling a 6-ton skip (84). Descending skip trips a lever, which opens the rotary gate of chute between scale pan and skip, the same movement opening the discharge of scale pan. Coal may be dumped from scale pan before the skip arrives, as the chute does not open until skip is landed. When skip rises, the gate closes automatically. For very high speeds, mechanical control of the chute is unsatisfactory, and electric control is used. A constant-running motor is connected through a magnetic clutch and gear train with the rotary gate of skip chute. Descending skip makes an elec contact at the proper point, energizing the clutch and opening the gate. As skip rises, current is broken, closing the gate.

V. Skip loading at Porphyry shaft, Inspiration, Ariz (Fig 150), exemplifies extreme mechanical control. Ore is dumped into 2 cylindrical, concrete-lined storage bins, 30 ft diam by 40 ft deep; total capac, 1 600 tons. One gate in bottom of each bin discharges to pan feeders, 48 in by 7.5 ft, which deliver to a 12-ton steel hopper supported on knife edges. When hopper is full, feeder stops automatically. Descending skip, on coming to rest on chairs, opens the gate for loading; it then closes and starts feeder (77).

Stresses in shaft pockets. Pressures on walls are computed as for surface ore bins (Art 36, 37), but, because the service conditions are severe, and construction may not be so carefully carried out as for surface structures, a larger safety factor is advisable.   If bin structure supports also the walls of the excavation, this fact would generally be the deter-

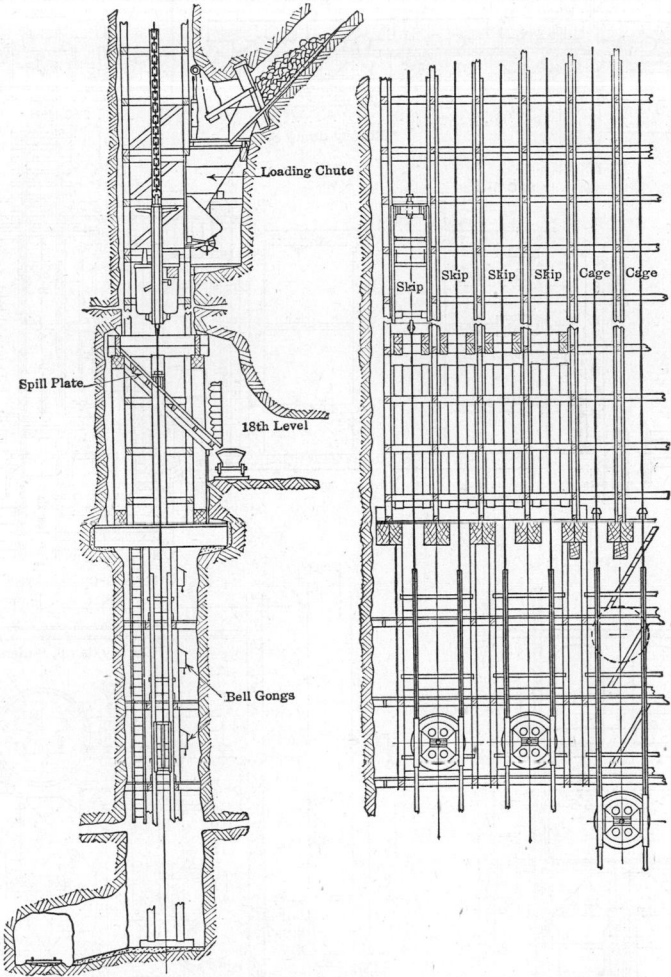

Loading Chute

Spill Plate

18th Level

Bell Gongs

Skip Skip Skip Skip Cage Cage

Fig 148.   Loading Station, No 3 Shaft, Village Deep Mine, Rand

mining factor in design.   For deep pockets, excavated in ore or rock, the gate or chute and its support should be carefully designed, since it may be subjected to unusual loads due to ore bridging above and then falling from some height.

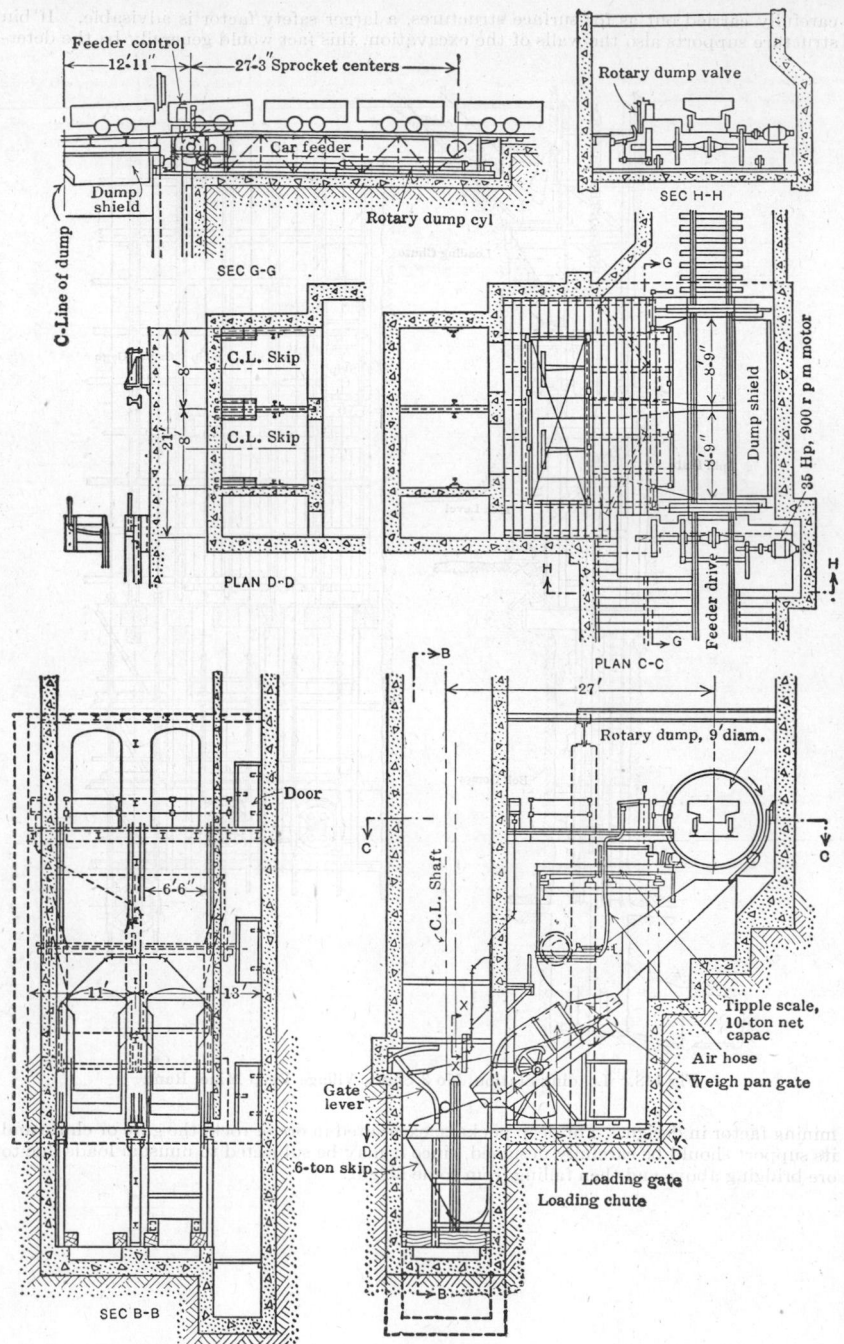

Fig 149.   Shaft Bottom, Thermal Mine No 4, Ill. (*Coal Age*)

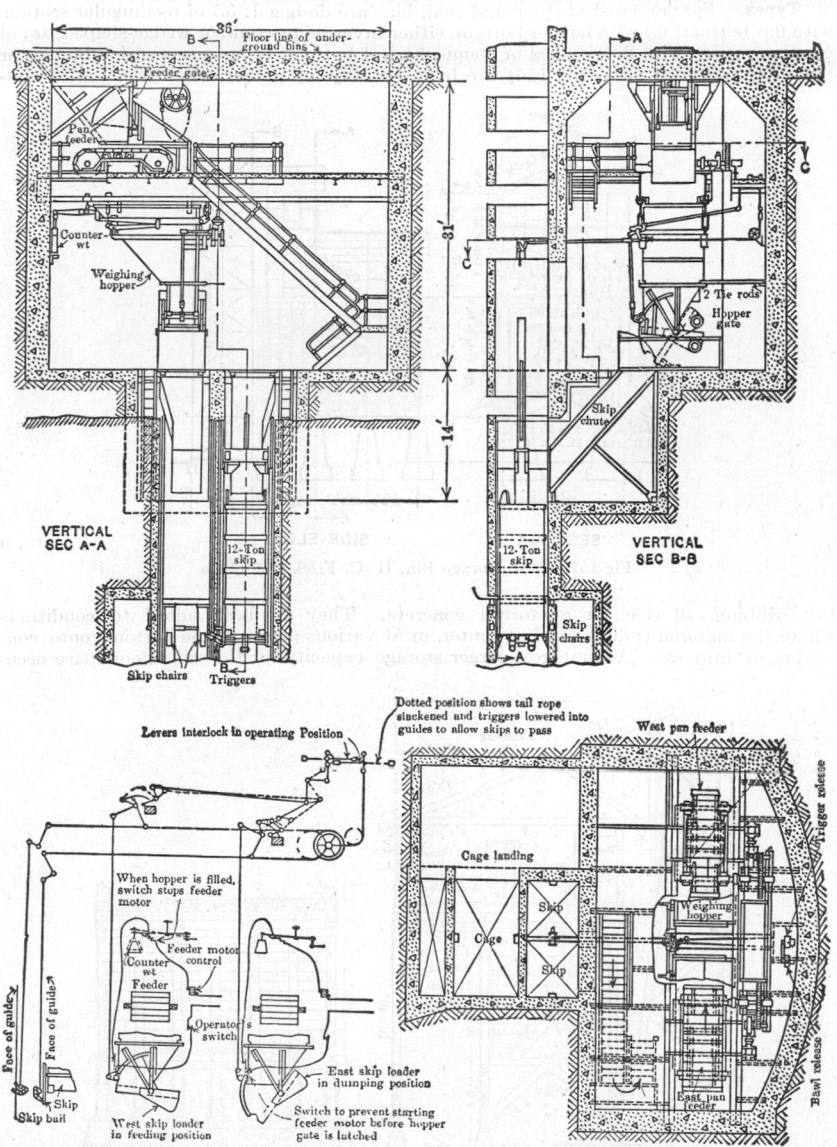

Fig 150. Skip Loading Arrangement, Porphyry Shaft, Inspiration Mine, Ariz (*E & M J*)

36. ORE BINS

Types. For ore, crushed stone and coal, bins are designed: (*a*) of rectangular section, with flat bottom; (*b*) with hopper bottom, either inverted pyramid or wedge-shaped; (*c*) of circular section with flat, conical or hemispherical bottom; (*d*) as a suspension bunker or bin. FLAT BOTTOM BINS (Fig 155) are built entirely of timber, steel frame with tim-

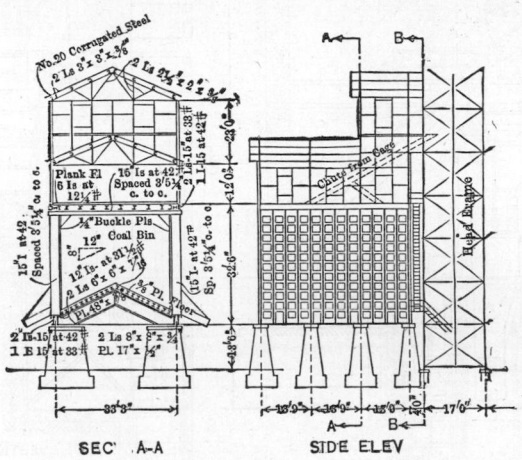

SEC' A-A SIDE ELEV

Fig 151. Coal Storage Bin, H. C. Frick C & C Co

ber cribbing, all steel, or reinforced concrete. They are best suited to conditions where the material is discharged at center, or at various points of the bottom, onto conveyers or into cars. Advantages: larger storage capacity for the same floor space occu-

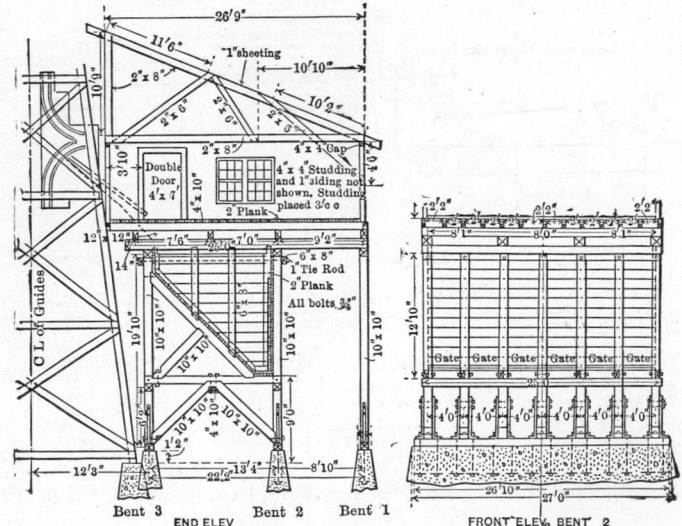

Bent 3   Bent 2   Bent 1
END ELEV   FRONT ELEV, BENT 2

Fig 152. Small Timber Bin

pied; simplicity of construction; the ore forms its own bottom and there is no wear on the floor, except around the discharge spouts. Disadvantage: the bin can not be completely emptied without shoveling the material lying below the angle of repose.

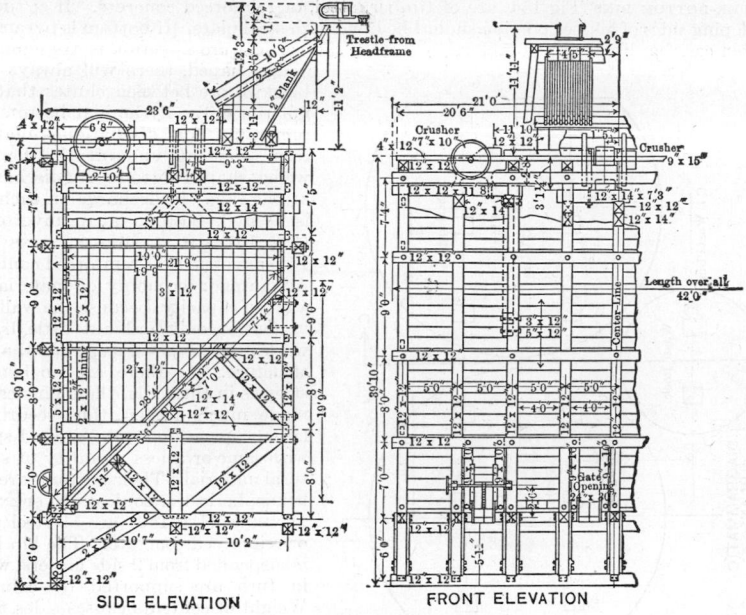

Fig 153. Bin with Grizzly and Crusher

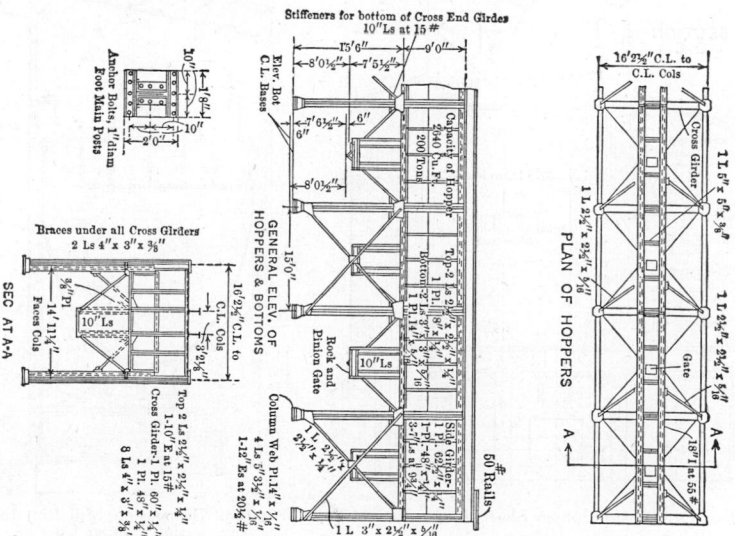

Fig 154. Steel Hopper Bins, Cananea Consol Copper Co (85)

HOPPER-BOTTOM BINS (Fig 154) are of timber, steel, or reinforced concrete. If of timber, the sloping sides of hopper portion should be lined with steel plate. [If bottom is pyramidal, the bin can be discharged completely; but, if the vertical cross-section is triangular or wedge-shaped, there will always be a block of ore between chutes that will not run out. Pyramidal bottoms are preferable for discharging material from a point underneath the bin; wedge-shaped bottoms, for discharging at one side. If discharge on each side is desired, bottom is an inverted V (Fig 151). CYLINDRICAL BINS (Fig 155) are of steel or reinforced concrete. Advantage: economy of material for a given capacity, because the walls are in tension only and but little framework is necessary except for the substructure. As there are no bending stresses in the walls, these bins can be made much deeper, thus securing a larger capacity on same ground space, with same or a less quantity of structural material. Their bottoms are flat, hemispherical or conical. SUSPENSION BUNKERS (Fig 156) are of steel plate or reinforced concrete. The bin body is suspended from 2 side girders, which in turn are supported by columns. Weight of contents causes sides to assume form of the equilibrium polygon

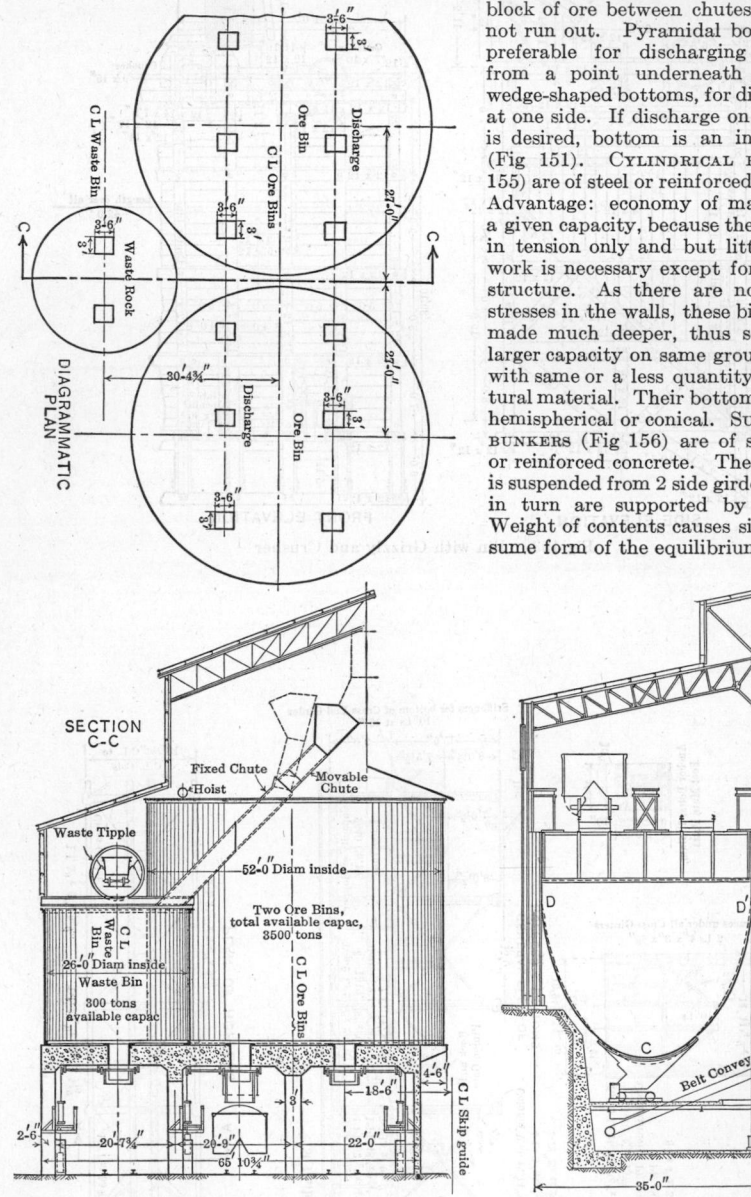

Fig 155. Ore Bins, Porphyry Shaft, Inspiration Mine, Ariz

Fig 156. Suspension Mill Bin, Inspiration Copper Co

(see 66), and when fully loaded, stresses in plates are tension only. As form of the curve changes with different degrees of loading, the plates are slightly distorted; and for reinforced concrete the reinforcing, or steel framework supporting the reinforcing, must carry the load, the concrete serving only to protect the steel.

Examples of this distortion are shown by dotted lines in Fig 156, 159. In Fig 156, the wt of bin contents caused a drawing in of the flanks and lowering of the bottom, sufficient to make the discharge gate interfere with the pan feeder (87). In Fig 159, when bin was full, the flanks moved outward and bottom rose. To prevent such movements from affecting operation of the feeders, these were suspended from the bin; but rigid connection between gates and bin plates was sometimes broken by distortion.

Suspension bins are rarely used at mines for coarse ore, as large pieces may cause unequal stresses in the plates; they are commoner for mill bins, after at least one crushing. Examples:

I. A flat-bottom wooden bin, for loading ore or crushed stone into R R cars, has following dimensions: width, 26 ft; length, 40 ft; depth, 12 ft; bottom of bin, 18 ft above foundations; top of R R ties 22 ft below bin bottom; bin supported on eight 12 by 12-in and eight 8 by 10-in posts.

II. Fig 151 shows steel bins for coal storage, at Phillips mine, H. C. Frick Coal and Coke Co, Pa. Capacity, 800 tons. The coal is discharged into the bins from self-dumping cages. Sides are lined with 0.25-in buckled plates, supported by 15-in, 42-lb I-beams, spaced 3 ft 5 1/4-in centers. Inclined bottom is of 3/8-in plate, its framing consisting of plate girders with 48 in by 3/8-in web and flanges of 6 by 6 by 7/16-in angles. Girders are spaced 3 ft 5 1/4-in centers, and tied together by 2 angles 8 by 8 by 0.75-in and 1 plate 17 by 0.5 in at the bottom and 15-in, 42-lb I-beams at the top. Main side girders consist of two 15-in 42-lb I-beams and one 15-in 33-lb channel. Floor is carried on 12-in I-beams, spaced 1 ft 6 in centers. Coal is discharged through gates in vertical side walls.

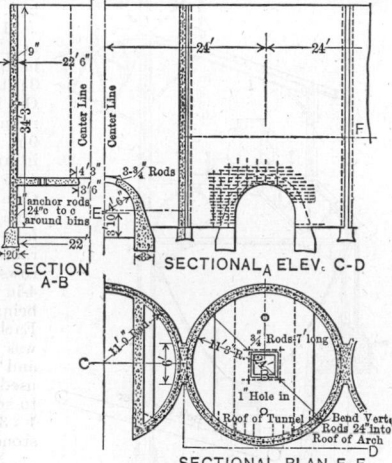

Fig 157. Reinforced Concrete Bins, Croton Iron Mines (88)

III. Fig 152 shows a timber bin, designed for a jaw crusher to be mounted on its top and to receive fine ore from the grizzly. Ore is discharged to carriers of an aerial tramway. Total timber required was 21 700 ft B M; 14 300 ft for the bin proper, and 7 400 ft for crusher floor, roof structure, and siding. Capacity, 2 200 cu ft, or 110 tons of ore weighing 100 lb per cu ft, equivalent to 6.5 ft B M of lumber per cu ft capacity for the bin proper.

IV. Fig 153 shows a timber bin, somewhat similar to, but larger than the preceding. Planking is 5 in thick on bottom and front; 3 in on ends. Bottom and front have a replaceable 2-in lining.

V. Fig 154 shows steel hopper bins of Cananea Consol Copper Co, receiving lump ore from R R cars on top. Ore is drawn off onto a conveyer, through rack and pinion gates in bottom of each hopper. Bin is divided into 8 pockets, approximately 15 ft square; capacity of each 2 640 cu ft, or 200 tons. Side plates are 0.25-in, stiffened with 7-in channels, spaced 4 ft apart. Hopper plates are 3/8-in, stiffened with 10-in channels (85).

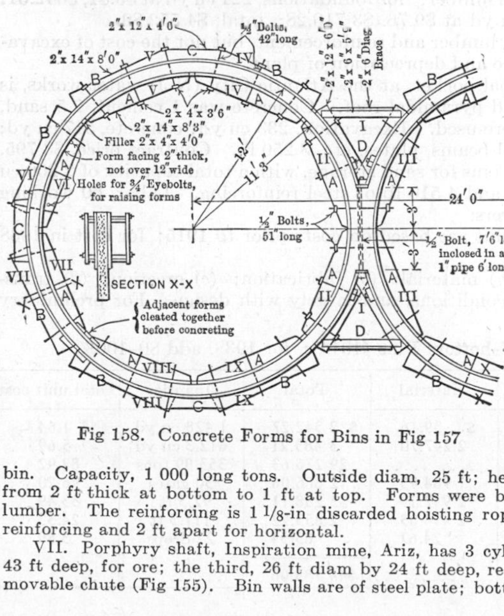

VI. At No 3 Mill, Witherbee, Sherman & Co, Mineville, N Y (86), a cylindrical reinforced-concrete bin is used for mill storage. Ore is magnetite, of 4-in size, delivered by belt conveyers. The flat bottom is carried on a concrete arch, which houses the feeder and conveyer taking the discharge from

Fig 158. Concrete Forms for Bins in Fig 157

bin. Capacity, 1 000 long tons. Outside diam, 25 ft; height, 50 ft. Inside diam is stepped in from 2 ft thick at bottom to 1 ft at top. Forms were built in 6-ft sections, of 7/8-in matched lumber. The reinforcing is 1 1/8-in discarded hoisting rope; coils placed 1 ft apart for vertical reinforcing and 2 ft apart for horizontal.

VII. Porphyry shaft, Inspiration mine, Ariz, has 3 cylindrical bins (93): two, 54 ft diam by 43 ft deep, for ore; the third, 26 ft diam by 24 ft deep, receives waste rock from skips through a movable chute (Fig 155). Bin walls are of steel plate; bottoms, reinforced concrete. Total capac of large bins, 3 500 ton; small bin, 500 ton. Ore is discharged into R R cars, through 6 gates in bottom of each ore bin and 2 gates in waste bin.

VIII. Fig 156 (87) is a section of a suspension-type mill bin, also of Inspiration Consol Copper Co. Width between rows of columns, 35 ft; columns spaced 16 ft 8 in longitudinally. Length, 330 ft; cross-sec area, 800 sq ft; capac, 40 tons per lineal ft. Top of bin plates is reinforced, forming a girder between columns. Discharge gates are in center of each bay.

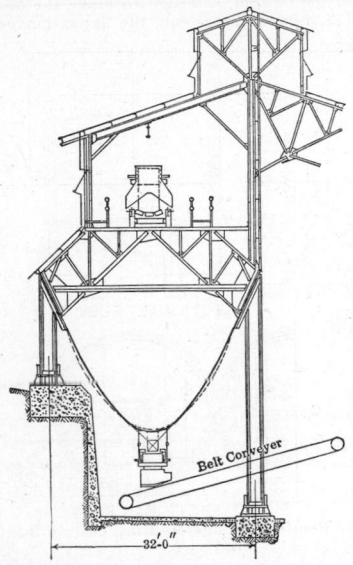

Fig 159. Suspension Bin, New Cornelia Copper Co, Ajo, Ariz (*E & M J*)

IX. A set of 4 cylindrical concrete bins, built 1914, at Croton iron mines, Brewster, N Y (88), are arranged in line (Fig 157). The bins are 22 ft 6 in inside diam by 34 ft 3 in high; capacity of each, 390 cu yd, or 500 tons. Ore is withdrawn through hoppers onto belt conveyers, running in arched tunnels under each bin. Bin walls are 9 in thick, reinforced vertically by 0.5-in round rods 18 in apart, and horizontally by old 0.75-in cable, spaced 4.25 in apart for the first 5 ft, 6 in apart for 10 ft, and then 9 in apart to the top. Forms (Fig 158) were 4 ft high, of rough 2-in chestnut. They were made by nailing face boards (not over 12 in wide) to 2 ribs cut to proper radius. Inner and outer forms were held together by 2 rows of 0.5-in bolts, long enough to pass through 2 by 4-in vertical bolting pieces outside the ribs. These bolts being greased and withdrawn, were used over and over. Each rise of the forms held 25.5 cu yd of concrete, and was filled in 10 to 11.5 hr by 9 men, including engineer and fireman for the hoist. A 0.1-cu yd batch mixer was used, concrete being hoisted at one end of line of bins to scaffolding above the form. Foundation mixture was 1 : 3 : 6; walls, 1 : 2 : 4. Coarse aggregate of 2.5-in stone was used in the 9-in walls, with careful tamping.

X. Mill bin of New Cornelia Copper Co, Ajo, Ariz (87), is of suspension type (Fig 159). Area of cross-sec, about 665 sq ft; length, 300 ft; capac, per lineal ft, 33 ton; width, c to c of columns, 32 ft; columns spaced 20 ft. Top edge of side plates is reinforced, to act as a girder. Six discharge gates, 10 ft apart.

Cost of timber bins. Labor, nails, bolts, and iron work, exclusive of steel plate lining, cost $25 to $35 per 1 000 bd ft, to which is added the timber cost.

Cost of concrete bins. Four bins of the Croton iron mines (Example IX) cost, after crediting the future value of the form lumber: for foundations, 221 cu yd at $3.81, $842.61; structure above foundations, 380 cu yd at $9.76, $3 710.28; total, $4 552.89.

This includes labor and material, lumber and reinforcement, but not the cost of excavation, nor charges for superintendence and depreciation of plant.

A 400-ton reinforced-concrete coal pocket, at the Atlantic City (N J) water works, is 30 ft diam, with conical bottom and pyramidal roof. Concrete was 1 cement, 2.5 sand, 5 gravel. Plain reinforcing bars were used. Excavation, 233 cu yd; concrete, 317 cu yd; steel for reinforcing, 13 700 lb; steel beams, plates, etc, 3 250 lb. Contract price, $3 795.

A group of 4 reinforced concrete bins for sand storage, with a total capacity of 2 200 cu yd, required 680 cu yd of concrete and 4 510 lb of steel reinforcing. Labor, 60 working days for 11 carpenters and 14 laborers.

The above figures on concrete bins are based on costs prior to 1915; for cost in 1938 add 80–100%.

Cost of steel bins comprises: (*a*) material; (*b*) fabrication; (*c*) erection; (*d*) transportation. Cost varies with local conditions, and largely with design. For preliminary

Table 39. Cost of Steel, V-bottom Bins (1914); for 1938, add 80–100%

	Labor	Material	Total	Quantity	Total unit cost
Excavation............	$2 303.11	$ 39.16	$ 2 342.27	1 428 cu yd	$ 1.64
Foundations..........	1 235.51	2 247.70	3 483.21	612.3 cu yd	5.69
Steel structure........	....	....	29 276.63	353.09 tons	82.92
Gates................	901.15	1 984.93	2 886.08	30 gates	96.20
Conveyer No 1........	310.92	2 947.19	3 258.11	97.3 ft	33.49
Conveyer No 2........	355.19	2 498.03	2 853.22	117.3 ft	24.33
Lighting..............	60.87	24.67	85.54	22 drops	3.89
Totals..............	....	....	$44 185.06	....	....

estimates, following figures in ¢ per lb may be used: (*a*) material, 3¢; (*b*) fabrication, including drafting, mill details and shop labor, painting, and transport from mill to shop, 3.5¢; (*c*) erection, 1.5¢; total, exclusive of freight from shop to point of erection, 8¢.

According to M. S. Ketchum (85) the costs of bins of different materials and designs is as follows: Wooden bins cost about half as much as steel or concrete. Suspension bunkers are cheaper than other types, costing 50 to 70% as much as rectangular bins. Cylindrical bins are slightly cheaper than rectangular. Reinforced-concrete bins cost approximately the same as steel bins of same type.

Cost of steel V-bottom receiving bins (Fig 160) at the smelter of the Arizona Copper Co, Clifton, Ariz, is given in Table 39 (89). Bins are in 2 separate structures: coarse-ore bin, 25 by 70 ft, divided into 4 pockets; concentrate bin, 25 by 100 ft, divided into 6 pockets. Fig 160 shows a cross section of bins and gates. Excavation for each pier was 7 by 7 ft, in gravel 16 to 25 ft deep. For foundations only 5% of the concrete required forms. In the bin structure are 11.35 tons of corrugated steel and 341.74 tons of structural steel. Gates are operated by rack and pinion, 12 for the coarse-ore bin cutting upward through the stream, and 16 for the concentrate bin cutting downward. No 1 conveyer, 97 ft centers, has a 30-in belt, and includes traveling feeder, motor for drive, and all accessories except steel frame for supporting the idlers. Conveyer No 2, 117 ft centers, has a 20-in belt, and includes the same items as No 1 conveyer (Table 39).

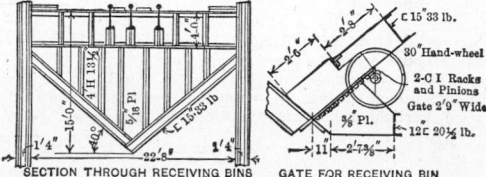

Fig 160. V-bottom Bins, Ariz Copper Co (89)

37. STRESSES IN ORE BINS

Forces acting on bin walls depend upon the weight per unit of volume, angle of repose and moisture content of the bin filling, and angle of friction of the filling on bin walls.

Shallow bins. When the walls are flat, and the plane of rupture cuts the free surface of the contents, the theory and formulas for retaining walls apply. According to Coulomb's theory, the plane of rupture forms with the bin wall a "wedge of maximum thrust," which exerts pressure on the wall. For a vertical wall, without surcharge or heaping of the material above the top, the plane of rupture bisects the angle between the wall and the plane of repose of the filling, provided the resultant thrust is normal to the wall. In this case, the resultant thrust may be assumed as making an angle with a normal to the wall equal to the angle of friction between the filling and the bin wall. Rankine's theory, on the other hand, assumes that the direction of the resultant thrust on a vertical wall is always parallel to the top surface of the filling; so, that the angle between the direction of the resultant thrust and a normal to the wall is never greater than the angle of repose of the bin filling. In both methods of solution the point of application of the resultant stress is assumed at one third the height of wall.

Algebraic methods. Factors in the formulas for pressure on bin walls are: P = resultant pressure per ft of length of wall; N = total normal pressure per ft of length of wall; ϕ = angle of repose of bin filling; ϕ' = angle of friction of the filling on the wall; θ = angle between plane of wall and the horizontal measured on loaded size; δ = angle of surcharge; z = angle between direction of P and a normal to wall; λ = angle between P and the horizontal; h = vertical height of wall; w = wt of bin contents per cu ft.

Rankine's formula, for a vertical wall without surcharge, is

$$P = \frac{1}{2} wh^2 \frac{1 - \sin \phi}{1 + \sin \phi} \tag{1}$$

and for a vertical wall with surcharge δ:

$$P = \frac{1}{2} wh^2 \cos \delta \frac{\cos \delta - \sqrt{\cos^2 \delta - \cos^2\phi}}{\cos \delta + \sqrt{\cos^2 \delta - \cos^2\phi}} \tag{2}$$

If $\delta = \phi$, then

$$P = \frac{1}{2} wh^2 \cos \delta \tag{3}$$

In Eq 1, 2, and 3, the direction of P is assumed parallel to upper surface of the bin contents, and its point of application at one-third of the vertical height.

Coulomb's theory gives the following formulas:

$$P = \frac{1}{2} wh^2 \frac{\sin^2 (\theta - \phi)}{\sin^2 \theta \sin (\theta + z) \left(1 + \sqrt{\frac{\sin (z + \phi) \sin (\phi - \delta)}{\sin (\theta + z) \sin (\theta - \delta)}}\right)^2} \tag{4}$$

If, in Eq 4, z be made equal to zero, $P = N$ and

$$N = \frac{1}{2}\, wh^2 \frac{\sin^2(\theta - \phi)}{\sin^3 \theta \left(1 + \sqrt{\dfrac{\sin \phi \cdot \sin(\phi - \delta)}{\sin \theta \cdot \sin(\theta - \delta)}}\right)^2} \tag{5}$$

For a vertical wall $\theta = 90°$, and Eq 5 reduces to

$$N = \frac{1}{2}\, wh^2 \frac{\cos^2 \phi}{\left(1 + \sqrt{\dfrac{\sin \phi \cdot \sin(\phi - \delta)}{\cos \delta}}\right)^2} \tag{6}$$

For a level top surface $\delta = 0°$, and Eq 6 reduces to

$$N = \frac{1}{2}\, wh^2 \frac{1 - \sin \phi}{1 + \sin \phi} \tag{7}$$

which is identical with Rankine's formula (Eq 1) for a vertical wall, with upper surface of filling material level with the top.

Cain's formulas assume that $z = \phi'$, Eq 8 to 22 applying also to shallow bins. In addition to previous nomenclature, $N' =$ normal pressure on the wall when $\phi = 0$.

(a) Vertical wall, surface of filling level, $z = \phi'$,

$$P = \frac{1}{2}\, wh^2 \frac{\cos^2 \phi}{\cos \phi' \left(1 + \sqrt{\dfrac{\sin(\phi + \phi') \sin \phi}{\cos \phi'}}\right)^2} \tag{8}$$

and

$$N = P \cos \phi' \tag{9}$$

If

$$\phi = \phi', \quad P = \frac{1}{2}\, wh^2 \frac{\cos \phi}{(1 + \sin \phi \sqrt{2})^2} \tag{10}$$

If

$$\phi' = 0, \quad N' = \frac{1}{2}\, wh^2 \tan^2\left(45° - \frac{\phi}{2}\right) \tag{11}$$

(b) Vertical wall, surcharge $= \delta$, $z = \phi'$,

$$P = \frac{1}{2}\, wh^2 \frac{\cos^2 \phi}{\cos \phi' \left(1 + \sqrt{\dfrac{\sin(\phi + \phi') \sin(\phi - \delta)}{\cos \phi' \cdot \cos \delta}}\right)^2} \tag{12}$$

If

$$\delta = \phi, \quad P = \frac{1}{2}\, wh^2 \frac{\cos^2 \phi}{\cos \phi'} \tag{13}$$

and

$$N = P \cos \phi' = \frac{1}{2}\, wh^2 \cos^2 \phi \tag{14}$$

If

$$\phi' = 0, \quad N = \frac{1}{2}\, wh^2 \cos^2 \phi \tag{15}$$

(c) Wall sloping outward, $\theta < 90° + \phi'$, $\delta = 0$,

$$P = \frac{1}{2}\, wh^2 \frac{\sin^2(\theta - \phi)}{\sin(\phi' + \theta) \sin^2 \theta \left(1 + \sqrt{\dfrac{\sin(\phi + \phi') \sin \phi}{\sin(\phi' + \theta) \sin \theta}}\right)^2} \tag{16}$$

$$N = P \cos \phi' \tag{17}$$

(d) Wall sloping outward, $\theta < 90° + \phi'$, surface surcharged,

$$P = \frac{1}{2}\, wh^2 \frac{\sin^2(\theta - \phi)}{\sin(\phi' + \theta) \sin^2 \theta \left(1 + \sqrt{\dfrac{\sin(\phi + \phi') \sin(\phi - \delta)}{\sin(\phi' + \theta) \sin(\theta - \delta)}}\right)^2} \tag{18}$$

$$N = P \cos \phi' \tag{19}$$

(e) Wall sloping outward, $\theta > 90° + \phi'$, $\delta = 0$,

$$P = \frac{1}{2}\, wh^2 \sqrt{\tan^2 \theta + \tan^4\left(45° - \frac{\phi}{2}\right)} \tag{20}$$

$$N = P \cos \phi' \tag{21}$$

In above cases, if T is the component of P parallel to wall, the thrust in plane of wall is

$$T = P \sin \phi' \tag{22}$$

Deep bins. The preceding formulas for shallow bins do not apply when a bin is so deep that the plane of rupture of contents cuts the bin walls. Following formulas are by M. S. Ketchum (85):

$$V = \frac{wR}{k\mu'}\left(1 - e^{-\frac{k\mu'h}{R}}\right) \tag{23}$$

$$L = \frac{wR}{\mu'}\left(1 - e^{-\frac{k\mu'h}{R}}\right) \tag{24}$$

in which, in addition to previous notation: V = vertical pressure of filling, lb per sq ft; L = lateral pressure of filling, lb per sq ft; R = area of bin in sq ft ÷ circumference of bin in ft ÷ "hydraulic radius" of bin; h = depth of filling at any point, ft; μ = tan ϕ = coef of friction of filling on filling; μ' = tan ϕ' = coef of friction of filling on bin walls; k = constant depending on character of filling; e = base of Nap log = 2.71828.

The approximate value of k may be calculated from $k = (1 - \sin \phi) \div (1 + \sin \phi)$.

Constants applying to materials in bins are tabulated from various sources in Table 40.

Table 40.   Constants Applying to Materials Stored in Bins

Material	Wt, lb per cu ft	Angle of repose ϕ, degrees	Angle of friction ϕ' on		
			Steel plate	Wood	Concrete
Bituminous coal............	47–56	35–40	18	35	35
Anthracite coal.............	52–56	27–30	16	25	27
Slaked coal................	53	38–45	....	....	....
Coke......................	23–32	45	25	40	40
Ashes.....................	40–45	40	31	40	40
Ore, soft iron.............	....	35	....	....	....
Ore, various..............	100–140	38–42	15–20	38–40	38–40
Crushed shale.............	90	39	....	....	....
Portland cement...........	103	30–35	....	....	....
Sand......................	90–120	34	18	30	30

Suspension bunkers. The stresses are due to a load which varies from zero at the support to a maximum at the center, and the loading varies nearly as the ordinates to a straight line (Fig 161).

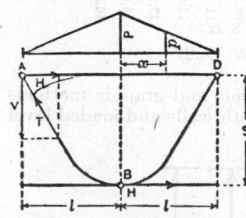

Fig 161. Diagram of Suspension Bunker

P = maximum load at center of bin, lb
l = one-half bin span, ft
S = depth of bin, ft
w = wt per cu ft of bin filling
T = maximum tension in plate per ft of length
C = capacity of bunker in cu ft per lineal ft of bin
B = lowest point of bin and origin of coordinates

The equation of the curve of the bunker is,

$$y = \frac{1}{2}\frac{S}{l^2}\left(3x^2 - \frac{x^3}{l}\right) \quad (25)$$

which shows that the shape of the curve is independent of maximum load and depends only on width and depth of bin.

Capacity of a bunker level full is $C = 5/4\ lS$ (26)

Max pressure P at center is calculated as follows:

$Pl = Cw$, $P = Cw \div l$, and from Eq 26 for a bunker level full, $P = 5/4\ Sw$ (27)

Tension in the plates at supports A and D is

$$T = Cw\sqrt{\frac{1}{4} + \frac{l^2}{9\ S^2}} \quad (28)$$

Length of bin curve is not exactly determinate. If L be the length for one-half the curve

$$L = \int_0^l \sqrt{dx^2 + dy^2}$$

By substituting values of dx and dy from Eq 25, the length of one-half the curve is

$$L = \frac{1}{2\ l^3}\int_0^l \sqrt{4\ l^6 + 9\ S^2\ (2\ xl - x^2)^2}\ dx \quad (29)$$

By using Simpson's rule for approximate integration, with 10 divisions, one-half the length of curve becomes

$$L = \frac{1}{2\ l^3} \times \frac{l}{30}\ [y_0 + y_{10} + 4\ (y_1 + y_3 + y_5 + y_7 + y_9) + 2\ (y_2 + y_4 + y_6 + y_8)] \quad (30)$$

in which $\quad\quad\quad y = \sqrt{4\ l^6 + 9\ S^2\ (2\ xl - x^2)} \quad (31)$

In Eq 30, 31 y_0 = value for $x = 0$; y_1 = value for $x = l \div 10$; y_2 = value for $x = 2\ l \div 10$; and so on.   Ten divisions give sufficiently accurate results for practical purposes.

A diagram due to R. W. Dull for calculating stresses, capacity, and length of curve of suspension bunkers, is given in Fig 162. It is for coal weighing 50 lb per cu ft. For material of different weight multiply the stresses in the diagram, and the capacity per ft of length, by the ratio of the weight of material per cu ft to 50 lb. To use the diagram, assume that a capacity of 5 tons of coal per ft of length is required, and that the bin is to be surcharged. Enter right-hand diagram at 5 tons. Below intersection of horiz line with surcharge curve is depth $S = 11.55$ ft, and width

$L = 19.25$ ft; above same intersection, at top of diagram, is length of curve, 372 in. On left-hand diagram, at same horiz line, is reaction $R = 5\,000$ lb; following this horiz line to intersection with heavy diagonal, and thence through light diagonal to left-hand margin, is $T = 5\,800$ lb; vertically below same intersection is $H = 2\,900$ lb.

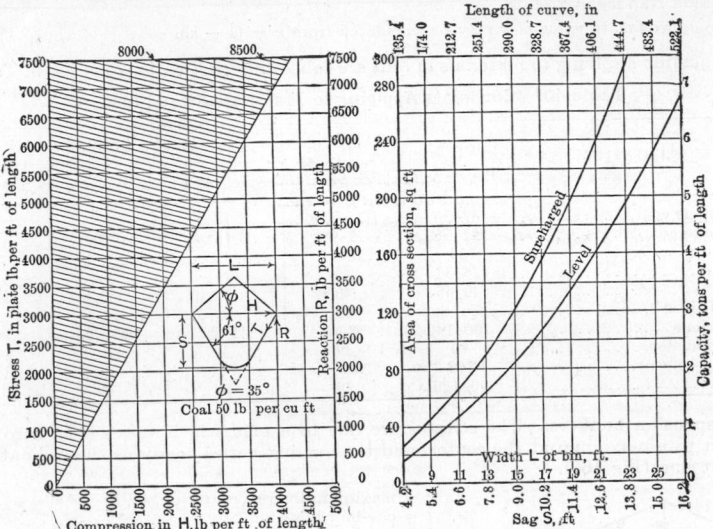

Fig 162. Diagram for Suspension Bunkers (R. W. Dull)

Graphic method. For shallow bins a combination of algebraic and graphic methods gives the simplest solution. In bin $ABCD$ (Fig 163), with smooth walls and loaded level

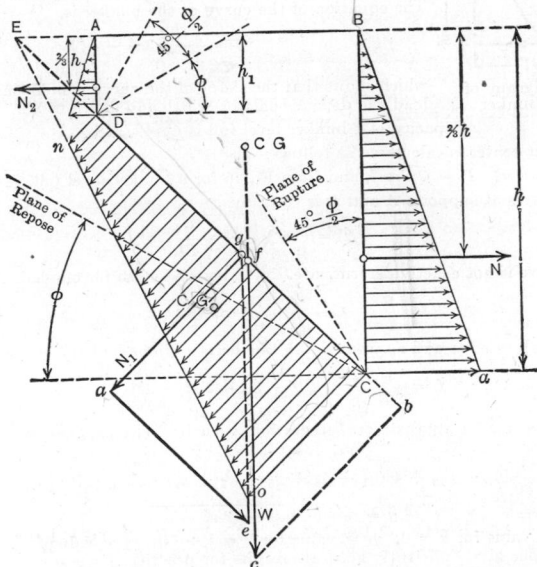

Fig 163. Graphic Solution for Shallow Bins

full, the normal pressure on side BC is $N = \frac{1}{2}\,wh^2\,\dfrac{1 - \sin \phi}{1 + \sin \phi}$. The area of triangle $BCa = N$, unit press at $B = 0$, and the unit press $Ca = (\text{area }BCa) \div \frac{1}{2}\,h$. Total normal press

N_2 and unit pressures on side AD are similarly found. For the bottom DC, continue AB and DC to intersection at E. Weight W of triangle EBC acts through its center of gravity, and by construction the normal press on $EC = cb$, represented by the area of the triangle ECo. The unit normal press Co at $C =$ (area ECo) $\div$ $1/2$ EC. Unit normal press Dn at D is found by construction, and the total normal press N_1 on the sloping bottom CD is represented by area of trapezoid $DCon$. It acts at g through the center of gravity of the trapezoid. The component of the weight of the bin filling acting parallel to the plane of DC is ae. If, in Fig 163, the bin be extended, with a horiz bottom, to such distance that the plane of rupture laid off from C to right of BC (instead of to left, as shown) cuts the surface, the direction of N would be reversed. N would be extended to intersection with W at f, the resultant of N and W laid off acting through f, and a normal from end of resultant to EC extended represents normal press on EC, in a similar manner to cb. With normal press known, the remainder of construction is same as above.

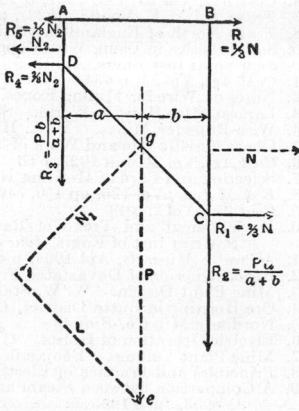

Fig 164. Stresses in Bin Framing

Stresses in the bin framing. Total horiz and vert stresses at the intersection are shown in Fig 164. These are carried by the framework and calculated in ordinary manner.

Trautwine's formulas for the pressure on vertical bin walls are:

(a) Surface horizontal, horiz press per ft of length of bin is

$$\frac{1}{2} wh^2 \tan^2 \left(45 - \frac{\phi}{2} \right) \tag{32}$$

For anthracite coal, total horiz press $= 9.78\ h^2$, and press on lowest foot $= 9.78\ (2\ h - 1)$
For bituminous coal, total horiz press $= 6.37\ h^2$, and press on lowest foot $= 6.37\ (2\ h - 1)$

(b) Surface sloping, $\delta = \phi$, horizontal pressure $= wh^2 \sin^2 \left(45 - \frac{\phi}{2} \right) \tag{33}$

For anthracite coal, total horiz press $= 14.22\ h^2$ and press on lowest foot $= 14.22\ (2\ h - 1)$
For bituminous coal, total horiz press $= 10\ h^2$ and press on lowest foot $= 10\ (2\ h - 1)$

Stresses in circular bins are usually calculated the same as for deep bins. For horiz press on walls at any point, Eq 24 applies. Tensile stress in walls per ft of height at any point $= Lr$, in which $L =$ horiz press, lb per sq ft (Eq 24), and $r =$ radius of bin. If bin is shallow, entire weight will be carried by bottom. If deep, Eq 23 applies. For flat bottoms, press is normal and equal at all points. If conical, tensile stress, at any point in the bottom parallel to an element of cone, is

$$H = \frac{\csc \theta}{2\ \pi r_1} (\pi r_1^2\ V + W_1) \tag{34}$$

in which $\theta =$ angle cone makes with horiz; $r_1 =$ radius of cone at point considered; $W_1 =$ wt of bottom and filling below this point; $V =$ Eq 23, considering radius of bin r_1 instead of r, and $\phi' = \phi$.

Horiz stress at any point in conical bottom is $H_1 = Lr_1 \tag{35}$

in which L is found from Eq 24, using r_1 for r. In spherical bottoms, the tension parallel to any meridian is

$$H_2 = \frac{1}{2} Vr' + \frac{W_1 \csc \theta}{2\ \pi r_1} \tag{36}$$

in which values are same as in Eq 34, $\theta =$ angle of tangent to meridian with horiz, and $r' =$ radius of sphere. The tension normal to a meridian at any point is

$$H_3 = 1/2\ Vr' \tag{37}$$

BIBLIOGRAPHY

1. Notes on Deep Level Winding. J. A. Vaughn. *Jour So Africa Inst of Engrs*, Vol 23, Oct 1924; *Trans Instn Min & Met* (England), Vol 34 (1925), p 164
2. *Mines* and *Minerals*. Vol 24, p 581
3. Electric Drive for Mine Hoists. Russel S. Sage. Gen Elec Co, *Bull* G E T 198
4. Winding Engines and Winding Appliances. McCulloch and Futers
5. Koepe Hoist with Ohnesorge Pulley. Theodore Simons and Gerhard Grassmueck, *E & M J*, Vol 135, Sep 1934, p 387
6. Electric Equipment for Homestake's New Hoist. R. S. Sage. Gen Elec Co, *Bull* G E A 2270
7. Deep Mine Hoisting. H. W. Dow, *E & M J*, Vol 135, May 1934, p 200
8. Determination of the Electrical Equipment for a Mine Hoist. G. Bright, *Trans* A I M E, Vol 66
9. Electric Hoist at the Belmont Mine, Butte. C. D. Woodward, *Min & Met*, Vol 8, p 380
10. Allis Chalmers Co, *Bull* 1830, p 31
11. Study of Stresses and Design of Head Sheaves. *Coal Age*, July 27, 1922, p 127

12. Wire Engineering. *Bull,* J. A. Roebling & Sons
13. U S Bur of Standards, *Circ* 208 (1925)
14. Acceleration Stresses in Wire Hoisting Rope. G. P. Boomsliter, *Trans* A I M E, Vol 75, 1927
15. Wire Rope Users Handbook, American Cable Co
16. *Coal Age,* Vol 31, Feb 1927, p 263
17. *Trans* A I M E, Vol 68 (1923), p 171, 189
18. *Trans* North of England Inst Min & Mech Engrs, Vol 62, pt 1
19. Safe Practice in Using Wire Rope in Mines. U S Bur of Mines, *Tech Pap* 237 (1919)
20. *Jour* So Af Inst Engrs, Apl 1913; *E & M J,* Sep 6, 1913, p 448
21. *Coal Age,* Vol 34, p 654
22. Notes on Wire for Mining Ropes. A. T. Adams, *Coll Guardian,* Vol 139, Sep 1929, pp 991–995
23. Largest Mine Hoist in World. Skillings *Mining Rev,* Dec 19, 1920
24. Wire Rope for Mines. M. A. Hogan. Instn Min & Met (England), Apl 1937
25. Characteristic Life and Work of 30 Hoisting Ropes. *Jour* So Africa Inst Engrs, Jan 1913
26. *Coal Age,* Vol 31, Jan 1927, p 83
27. Selection and Care of Hoisting Rope. David Butchart, *E & M J,* Vol 131 (1931)
28. *E & M Jour,* Vol 125, pp 456, 746
29. *Coal Age,* Vol 2, p 49
30. Development and Trend of Rand Winding Practice. W. Elsdon-Dew and J. J. D. Dolan, S Africa Inst of Engrs, *Jour* 33, 1935, pp 265–279
31. *Mines & Minerals,* Apl 1904, p 413
32. Reconstruction of Devastated French Winding Equipment. Vickers *Gazette,* Jan 1922
33. Mine Plant Design. W. W. Staley, McGraw-Hill Book Co, 1936
34. Ore Hoisting in Butte District, *E & M J,* Vol 129 (1930), p 441
35. Nordberg Mfg Co, *Bull* 43
36. Electric Operation of Hoists. G. Fox, *E & M J,* Vol 126 (1928), p 91
37. Mine Plant Volume. Benjamin F. Tillson, A I M E, 1938
38. Principles and Practice of Electrical Engineering. Gray. 3rd Ed. McGraw Hill Book Co
39. A Comparison between Steam and Electric Winders. A. L. G. Lindley, *Jour* So Af Inst Engrs, Vol 33, June 1935
40. *E & M Jour,* Vol 125, Jan 1928, p 179
41. *E & M Jour,* Vol 126, p 313
42. Automatic Hoist Control at Emma Nevada Shaft. J. E. Borland, *E & M J,* Vol 129 (1930)
43. Miami's Automatic Hoist. F. R. Grant, *E & M J,* Vol 129, Apl 7, 1930
44. Cost of Hoisting. J. Elsing, *E & M J,* Vol 135 (1934), p 59
45. New Orient, an Unusual Coal Mine. G. B. Harrington, *Trans* A I M E, Vol 72 (1925), p 798
46. Safety Practice for Hoisting Rope. *Trans* A I M E, Vol 66 (1923), p 171
47. Compressed Air System at Butte. *Trans* A I M E, Vol 46 (1913), p 826
48. Compressed Air Plant, Robert Peele, 5th Ed, 1930
49. *E & M J,* Vol 83, p 1133
50. Hoisting Plants for Great Depths. *Trans* Instn Min & Met, Vol 11
51. Building Reinforced Concrete Shaft Houses. *Trans* A I M E, Vol 66, p 225
52. Design of Headframes. *E & M J,* Vol 103 (1917), p 611
53. Design of Mine Structures. M. S. Ketchum
54. *E & M J,* Vol 94, p 636
55. Design of Small Wooden Headframes. W. W. Staley, U S Bur of Mines, *Inform Circ* 6943
56. Safety Practice for Hoisting Rope. *Trans* A I M E, Vol 68 (1913), p 171
57. *Coal Age,* Sep 7, 1922, p 351
58. U S Bur of Mines, *Bull* 15
59. Standardization Handbook. American Mining Congress
60. A Practical Safety Signalling System. H. D. Keiser. *E & M J,* Vol 126 (1928), p 137
61. Safety Cage Signalling System. *E & M J,* Vol 131 (1931), p 448
62. U S Bur of Mines, *Inform Circ* 6979
63. U S Bur of Mines, *Inform Circ* 6656
64. *E & M Jour,* July 1930, p 71
65. *E & M Jour,* Aug 1930, p 167
66. U S Bur of Mines, *Inform Circ* 6674 (1932)
67. *E & M Jour,* Nov 1933, p 459–71
68. *E & M Jour,* Nov 10, 1930, p 437–442
69. *Trans* A I M E, Vol 63, p 808–817
70. *Trans* A I M E, Vol 48, p 247
71. *E & M Jour,* Feb 18, 1928, p 304
72. *E & M Jour,* Vol 94, p 254
73. *E & M Jour,* Apr 15, 1911
74. U S Bur of Mines, *Tech Pap* 276
75. *Coal Age,* Nov 30, 1922, p 865
76. Safety Catches and Appliances in Mine Shafts. *Rep* Transvaal Comm on Hoisting Ropes, 1907
77. Inspiration Consol Porphyry Shaft. *E & M J,* Feb 10, 1925, p 265
78. Skip Hoisting for Coal Mines. *Trans* A I M E, Vol 66 (1922), p 370
79. *E & M Jour,* June 7, 1930, p 555
80. *E & M Jour,* May 1932, p 281–4
81. Lilley Hoist Controller. *E & M J,* Nov 30, 1918, p 956; *Coal Age,* Nov 25, 1920, p 1079
82. Mechanical Engineering of Collieries. Futers, Vol 1, p 265
83. *E & M Jour,* Vol 95, p 265
84. *Coal Age,* June 26, 1924, p 935
85. Walls, Bins and Grain Elevators. M. S. Ketchum
86. *E & M Jour,* Vol 96, p 959
87. Design of Large Suspension Bins. H. K. Burch, *E & M J,* Oct 11, 1924, p 566
88. Cylindrical Concrete Bins. *Eng News,* June 4, 1914
89. *Trans* A I M E, Vol 49, p 48
90. *Trans* A I M E, Vol 48 (1931), p 247
91. *Mines & Min* July 1904, p 614
92. *Mines & Min* Jan 1910, p 359
93. *E & M Jour,* Mch 21, 1925, p 477

SECTION 13

DRAINAGE OF MINES

BY

THE LATE ROBERT VAN ARSDALE NORRIS

CONSULTING MINING ENGINEER

REVISED BY

ROBERT E. HOBART

MECHANICAL SUPERINTENDENT, LEHIGH NAVIGATION COAL CO

Note.—Numbers in parentheses in text refer to Bibliography at end of this section.

DRAINAGE OF MINES

1. SOURCES AND CONTROL OF MINE WATER

Surface inflow through outcrops is the chief source of mine water in regions of heavy or moderate rainfall, especially where mines are worked to the outcrop, and large drainage areas are above or tributary to extensive outcrop workings. In such cases, mines may be subject to sudden floods, which usually require definite times to reach the workings. Hence records of quantity and character of precipitation, and time and extent of resulting extra inflow, should be kept for their value in giving warning. Deposits outcropping under water-bearing surface wash, as in alluvial valleys, while not exposed to similar flooding, are subject to continuous percolation through the strata, the amount dependent upon the character of the measures and closeness of mine workings to buried outcrop. In case of a coal seam in contact with a bed of fire-clay, the latter may be washed out over areas sufficient to cause disastrous inflow. Surface flood water may also find its way into mine openings or open crop-falls (1).

Surface water through cracked or broken measures may be more dangerous and troublesome than that from open outcrops. Where a deposit has been extensively worked by open or by shrinkage stopes under fissured rock cover, cracks and crevices may admit large quantities of both surface and ground water, combining serious permanent flow with periodical flooding from rainfall.

Flooding may also come from caves extending into water-bearing wash or water-soaked deposits, from mining under too thin a rock cover, or cutting into " pot-holes " or buried valleys. At Nanticoke, Penn, 26 men were buried in quicksand from a pot-hole over 100 feet deeper than the surrounding rock.

Water from permeable measures is always possible, and in formations like soft massive sandstones may be expected. It may enter as seepage, or under pressure, often from large areas, resulting in persistent inflows. Relief can be obtained only by draining entire basins, or by general lowering of ground-water level. WATER FROM CREVICES OR UNDERGROUND CHANNELS is sometimes encountered in shaft sinking or in mining itself, coming in unexpectedly and in large volume. It may persist to the complete drainage of territory tapped. WATER FROM UNSUSPECTED UNDERGROUND CAVITIES, either natural caves or abandoned workings, is fortunately rare. Its serious aspect, aside from quantity of water, is suddenness of inflow, which may endanger life and quickly flood lower workings.

2. PREVENTION OF INFLOW

Surface. It is generally cheaper to keep water out of mines than to remove it after it has entered. While it may be impossible to prevent the entrance of all water, the amount can usually be decreased by attention to sources of inflow. In impervious soil, entrance of surface water can be minimized by well-planned ditching around outcrop or fractured areas. In permeable soil, ditches should be lined, or wooden or concrete flumes installed. If streams or drainage channels cross outcrops or fractured areas they should be flumed, or diverted by canals, designed to take maximum flood volumes, and located to minimize danger of rupture from surface settlement often occurring during flood periods.

Drainage works are sometimes built through extensive districts by a combination of interests, as in Hazleton region, Penn, where Black Creek has been diverted outside of the coal measures for miles, relieving the drainage situation in a number of collieries, each of which formerly pumped practically the entire creek flow.

Besides diverting surface water, the discharge of mine pumps must be delivered outside of drainage area of mine. This may cause contamination of streams. Some state courts have ruled that discharge of mine water into its natural drainage channels is permissible, but that damages may be recovered for its discharge into streams not reached by gravity in case the mine should fill. Thus, drainage tunnels discharging onto unpolluted watersheds may furnish ground for damages.

Entrance of flood water through openings other than crop-falls or cracked measures should be impossible. If there are openings below flood level, along creeks or in alluvial flood plains, shut-off doors or temporary dams should be installed. In planning new openings flood records should be obtained, and openings placed well above danger line. D u from flooding may be so serious Ii maximum considerable expenditure to avoid it. In case of shafts, the cost of extending waterproof curbs above possible flood level is small, and the shaft spoil may be economically used for filling necessary to raise plant above high-water mark. This has been done at many shafts in the flood plain of Susquehanna River, Penn, shaft curbs being at least 5 ft above highest recorded flood mark; also, provision is made for shutting openings promptly in case of possible higher floods.

Underground. In mining under heavy water-bearing wash or quicksand, it is imperative to leave sufficient rock cover, and to keep workings far enough below buried outcrops to avoid danger. Preliminary exploration of rock surface should be done by borings sufficiently close together for making a fairly reliable contour map of the buried rock surface.

Fig 1 is a map of a small area of the buried valley of Susquehanna River, showing the great irregularities of rock surface revealed by borings. The wash varies from less than 100 to nearly 300 ft deep, and without borings the workings might easily have been extended into unsuspected deep recesses in the rock. In such boring, especially in stratified measures, some holes must be continued into the rock, to determine its nature. These holes should be grouted to the rock surface, to prevent entrance of water through them to subsequent mine workings.

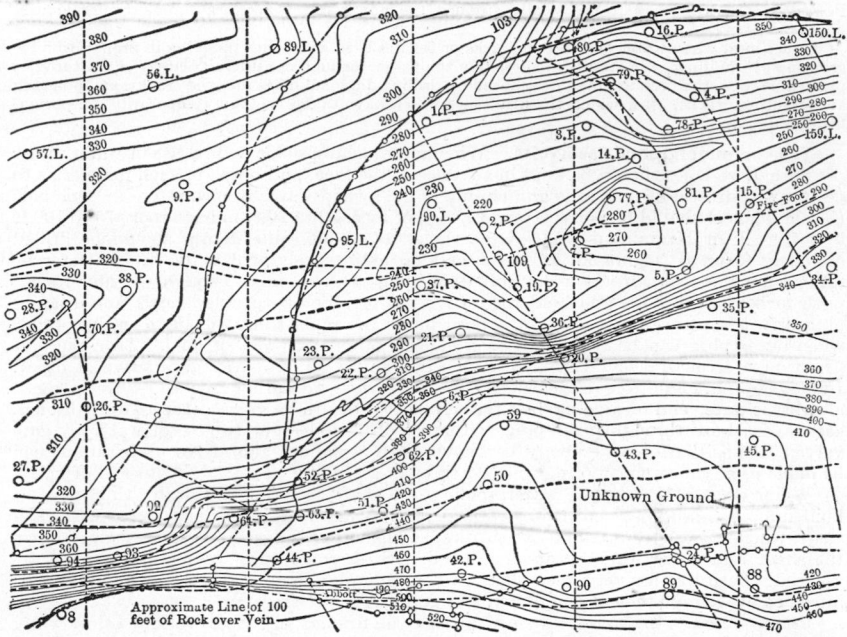

Fig 1. Map of Rock Surface of Buried Valley

Rock thickness required between workings and overlying wash depends so largely on character of deposit, nature of overlying rock and method of mining, that no general rule is possible. In the Wyoming Anthracite Field, Penn, under the Susquehanna Valley and under the river itself, the rock cover varies from 100 to 50 ft minimum; under deeper wash, from 20 to 100% of thickness of wash. Under aver conditions, with sandstones and slates overlying mine openings, and with ample pillars, a rock thickness above workings equal to $1/3$ of total cover is a reasonable minimum. In steeply-pitching measures, thickness of cover is determined by the distance from outcrop required to prevent inflow along bedding planes; best determined by test openings toward outcrop.

Douglas Bunting gives the following relations for 24 ft width of mine openings:
$T = 1.5\sqrt{d} + 5$ (strong measures, rock surface fully explored).
$T = 1.5\sqrt{d} + 15$ (softer measures, liable to disintegration, rock surface fully explored).
$T = 1.5\sqrt{d} + 40$ (strong measures, rock surface imperfectly explored).
$T = 1.5\sqrt{d} + 50$ (softer measures, liable to disintegration, rock surface imperfectly explored).
In these formulas: T = thickness of rock cover, d = depth of surface wash, ft.

Grouting and waterproof linings. Inflow from water-bearing strata is avoidable by waterproof linings of shafts and other openings, or by grouting under pressure into surrounding rocks.

In approaching known or possible OLD WORKINGS, and when mining in limestone where cavities may be expected, drill holes, preferably bored through gate valves previously secured, should be kept well in advance of all workings, to avoid disastrous inrushes of water, and to control flow from any orebody which may be tapped by holes, letting water out only in such quantities and at such times as may be suitable for capacity of the pumps.

No means have yet been devised for materially diminishing the inflow of deep ground water, as encountered in porous formations of some western mines. An adequate pumping plant is the sole safeguard. Grouting in advance of sinking may be done through bore holes surrounding proposed shaft location; or during sinking through radiating drill holes; or subsequently behind shaft lining of steel, brick, stone or concrete (Sec 7, 8).

In case of fissured or broken ground the flow may be reduced and sometimes entirely cut off by cement grouting under pressure through bore holes, or by the Kirby (patented) process, consisting of injection through drill holes or into partly-plugged cracks of chopped straw, sawdust or other finely divided material, followed by clay, slimes or mud (first used at the Flat River, Mo, mines of Federal Lead Co, where it practically stopped the flow from a network of fissures previously unconquerable).

Sometimes, when water pressure in cracks or fissures is so great that plugging in preparation for grouting or mudding only results in spreading the water through considerable areas of fractured or permeable rock, the pressure may be relieved by drilling diagonal holes into the cracks, and plugging and grouting cracks, after which the drill holes which have taken the flow temporarily are permanently closed.

Tapping underground reservoirs. When approaching suspected bodies of water under pressure, bore holes should be kept in advance of the face, and bored in such manner as to permit withdrawal of drill rods and closing of hole when water is encountered. One hole (better 2 holes) should be bored straight ahead of face, 10 to 20 ft in hard rock, 75 to 100 ft in soft rock or bituminous coal. Other holes, of about same depth, should be drilled obliquely forward (about 30° from center line) at intervals of 8 to 12 ft. If water be tapped unexpectedly, insert a dry soft-wood plug of diam small enough to enter freely; push to bottom of hole, and hold there by a rod or pipe of suitable length, and a larger plug driven into neck of hole. In several hours the inner plug will have swollen tight, when outer plug can be removed; then enlarge outer 5 or 6 ft of hole. To a piece of heavy pipe screw a sleeve coupling at one end and a straight-way gate valve at other. Insert coupling end into enlarged hole, and wedge with oakum and dry soft-wood wedges; also brace outer end of pipe against timbering, if pressure be great. Insert drill through gate valve, bore through inner plug, withdraw drill, and regulate flow of water by gate valve. If position of water body be known with certainty, the above preparations can be made in advance, and boring finished through a stuffing box attached to end of valve.

Water rings. If complete waterproofing of a shaft be too costly, water rings may be built into the lining, to lead water entering above them into sumps excavated in sides of shaft, whence it may be pumped to surface, saving a material vertical lift, or piped down the shaft, and power thus obtained utilized. Such rings and intermediate sumps are especially desirable for very deep shafts, where pumping is done in two or more lifts, the intermediate sumps then serving for upper pumps.

Chain pillars. In deposits opened by drift or tunnel, and later worked below water level, a chain pillar sufficient to retain permanently all surface water should be left on the water level. Openings to dip are so arranged that water can be led past them and out through tunnel. A chain pillar ties up part of the mineral, which, however, is recoverable before final abandonment of the property, and by reducing pumping throughout life of mine may pay for itself many times over.

3. SUMPS, UNDERGROUND DAMS, BOREHOLES AND PIPING

Drainage levels. In general, water should be intercepted at as high a point in the workings as possible, to avoid unnecessary height of pumping lift. But this principle is modified by considerations as to the best points for locating sumps and installing pumping plant, even at cost of increasing the head for a portion of the water. The main collection point should be determined early in the development of a mine, and all openings driven from it should have a grade of at least 0.25% (0.5% being sometimes adopted, to make haulage resistance nearly equal for both empty and loaded cars. See Sec 11). Water ditches, excavated below or on one side of track, in entries, drifts or tunnels, should be kept clean and open. If main drainage levels are in broken or fissured ground, ditches should be lined with concrete; or wooden flumes, half-round terra cotta tiles, or even pipe, may be used, to prevent water from percolating into lower workings.

For main drainage, chain pumps should be maintained as long as possible under drainage levels. An exception is where exhausted workings may be allowed to fill with water without detriment to the mine, as in small local basins in a flat deposit. Workings in wet ground should not be extended to the dip, if this would require installation of a number of small, scattered pumps. In such case, water may sometimes be drained off through bore holes to the lower workings. By similar means, water troubles may be avoided in sinking shafts and winzes.

Size of sump is chiefly dependent upon quantity of inflow. It should be large enough to take care of inflow while pumps are stopped for ordinary repairs. A sump capacity of

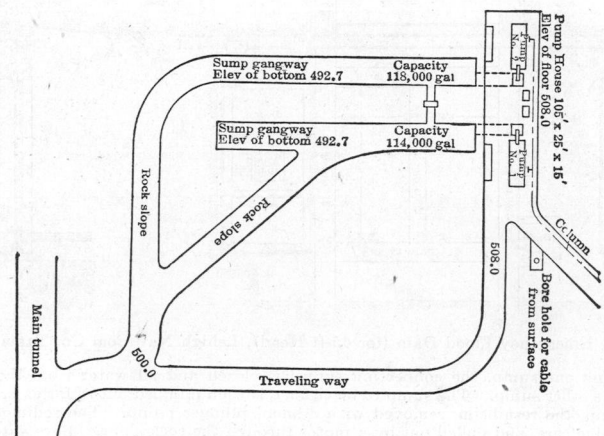

Fig 2. Plan of Sumps and Pump Room, No 6 Mine, Lehigh Nav Coal Co, Lansford, Pa

8 hr max inflow, without submerging the pump, may be considered a minimum; capacities of 24 hr or more are not unusual.

Location of sumps should be carefully considered in layout of mine workings. Since haulage ways, with their drains, gravitate towards shafts, the main sump is usually placed near foot of shaft or slope. Where conditions permit, a good sump is obtained at low cost

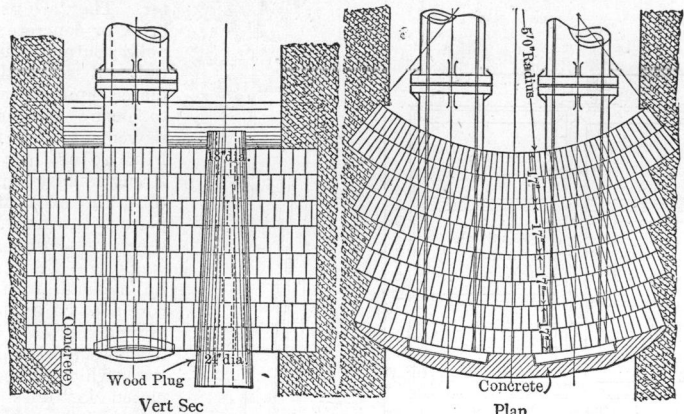

Fig 3. Details of Underground Dam, Hazleton Shaft Colliery

by working out an area of the deposit to the dip, adjacent to shaft station, leaving chain pillars to isolate sump from lower workings. Sumps should be arranged so that they can be easily cleaned out.

In pitching deposits, where several veins are worked, the sump is sometimes placed in main workings and pumps in an overlying or underlying vein, the two being connected on main level by a tunnel closed by a dam (Fig 8). The pipe from dam to pump has a shut-off valve, so that if necessary, main workings can be flooded to considerable depths without affecting operation of pumps.

Fig 2 shows a well designed sump at Lansford No 6 mine, Lehigh Navigation Coal Co. There are two centrifugal pumps, each of 2 000 gal per min, and 2 sumps holding 118 000 and 114 000 gal. The sumps are connected, to maintain same water level in both; this is important, as the pumps operate automatically, and are started and stopped by float switches. Switches are so arranged that when pump No 1 can not alone handle the inflow, pump No 2 starts automatically.

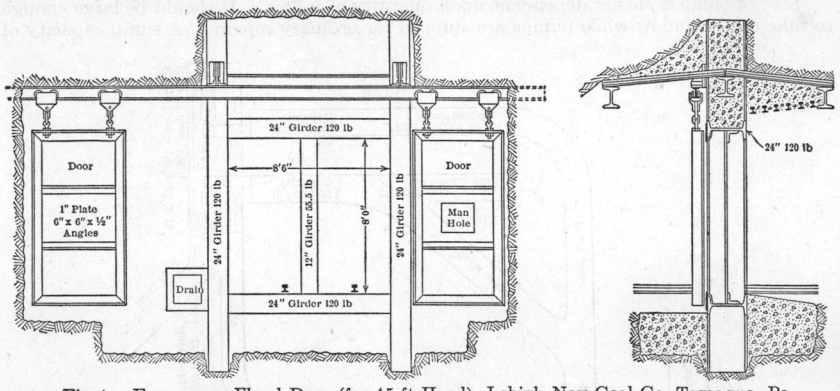

Fig 4.   Emergency Flood Dam (for 45-ft Head), Lehigh Nav Coal Co, Tamaqua, Pa

For cleaning one sump, the connecting tunnel is closed and all water from the main tunnel diverted to the other sump. The sump to be cleaned is then pumped out as far as practicable with the main pump, the rest being removed with a small plunger pump. The sediment removed is loaded into mine cars, and pulled out by a motor through the rock slope. Low-water level in the sump should be not more than 20 ft below center line of pump, and end of suction pipe not less than 2 ft from bottom of sump.

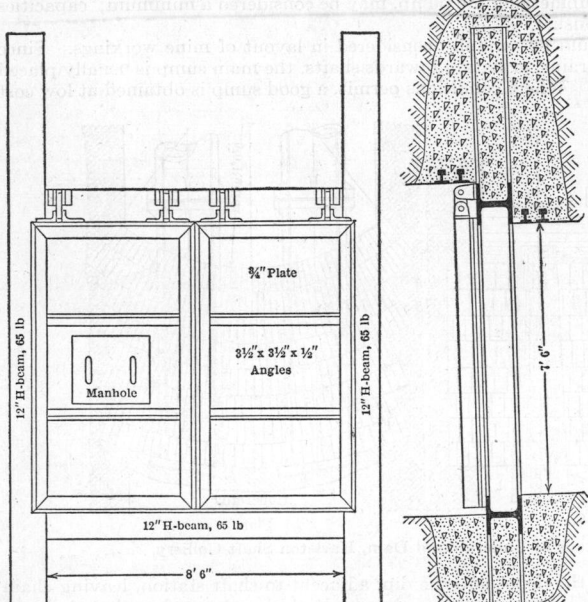

Underground dams (4) must often hold water under heavy heads, and should be backed by masonry, calculated to resist max possible head of water. They are usually of brick or concrete (Fig 3). Solid abutments are essential; all soft adjacent material must be cut away to insure against bodily movement of the dam. Manholes of ample strength must be provided to drain off water and permit entrance and inspection. Timber dams, single, or better double bulkheaded, with a clay core may be used in case of emergency. Fig 4 and 5 show steel emergency dams which can be readily closed in times of high water. A flat rubber $1/4$-in gasket, between frame and door, provides an effective seal.

Fig 5.   Emergency Flood Dam, 35-ft Head

As mine dams are subject to heavy strains, their strength is a vital matter and careful calculations are necessary. The following formula is for arch dams (Fig 3):

$$\frac{\sqrt{0.4\,r - 1}}{4\,s}$$

in which: t = thickness, in; r = shorter or external radius, in; w = width of opening or span, in; p = maximum water pressure, lb per sq in; s = safe compressive strength of material used, lb per sq in; factor of safety, not less than 8.

A. Faulds gives (4), quoting W. S. Aldis, using same notation, but with factor of safety 10:

$$t = r\left(1 - \sqrt{1 - \frac{2\,p}{s}}\right) \text{ for arch dams; } \quad t = r\left(1 - \sqrt[3]{1 - \frac{1.5\,p}{s}}\right) \text{ for spherical dams.}$$

Factors $\dfrac{2\,p}{s}$ and $\dfrac{1.5\,p}{s}$ must be less than unity, or proposed material will be too weak.

A straight or flat concrete dam, necessary where strata will not safely stand thrust of an arch dam, is practically a plate supported on 4 sides, a condition requiring an intricate calculation. For such a plate tests have shown an increase in strength of fully one third over that of a beam supported at both ends. It is safe to calculate a straight dam as a beam having its shortest length loaded uniformly and supported at both ends, using the formula:

$$s = \frac{wl}{2\,bd^2} \quad \text{whence,} \quad d = \sqrt{\frac{wl}{2\,bs}}$$

in which: s = unit stress in extreme fibers; b = breadth, in; d = thickness, in; w = total load, lb; l = length, in. In this case the strength of plain concrete in tension should be taken at not over 50 lb per sq in, whence for a dam with span of 7 ft (= 84 in), built to withstand 500 ft head (= 216.6 lb per sq in):

$$w = 84 \times 216.6 = 18\,208 \text{ lb per linear in, and } d = \sqrt{\frac{18\,208 \times 84}{2 \times 50}} = 126 \text{ in}$$

A saving in material can be made by building a flat dam of reinforced concrete.

If the rock formation be of doubtful strength to stand direct thrust of either arched or flat dam, a larger surface of abutment may be obtained by stepping the notches (Fig 6). In a large Schuylkill County, Penn, colliery, a special method was employed (Fig 7) to drown out a fire in upper levels without

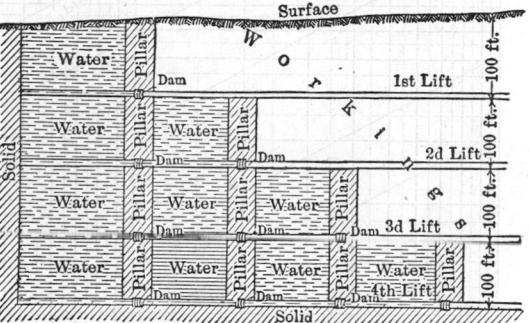

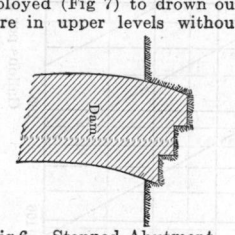

Fig 6. Stepped Abutment, Concrete Dam

Fig 7. Series of Dams, with Counterbalanced Pressures

complete flooding. As the pillars were not considered safe to support the pressure which would be brought on the lower dams, these were relieved by flooding behind auxiliary dams, thus building up a series of counterbalanced pressures. Hence the coal in each pillar took no more pressure than that due to a single lift on any one dam. Fig 8 shows an underground dam and pumping plant in the Hazleton Shaft mine, Lehigh Valley Coal Co.

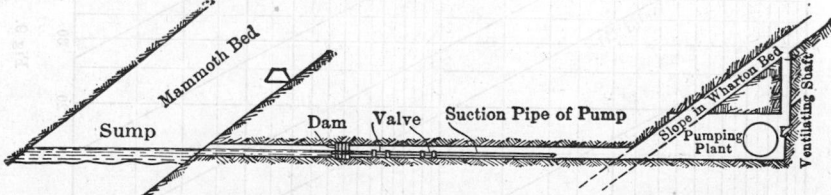

Fig 8. Underground Dam and Pumping Plant, Hazleton Shaft Colliery

Pumping through boreholes is a common practice in both coal and metal mines, the pump delivering directly into holes drilled from surface to mine workings (33). In weak strata the holes are lined with W-I pipe, around which rich cement mortar is poured. If the water is very acid the pipe should be wood-lined, or the boreholes lined with terra-cotta piping. In hard rock no lining is necessary.

By using boreholes the pumping plant can be located to suit the position and shape of the mine openings.   They often reduce the lift, save cost of providing space for and installing column pipe, and avoid possibility of damage to mine workings from broken column pipe.   Boreholes are 8–24 in diam, drilled by churn or shot drill (Sec 9).   Objections to them are the possibility that the holes will be closed by caving or settlement of the strata and the difficulty of renewing worn out pipe lining.   In water-bearing, porous strata, boreholes with use of air-lift pumping have successfully lowered water levels in advance of sinking.

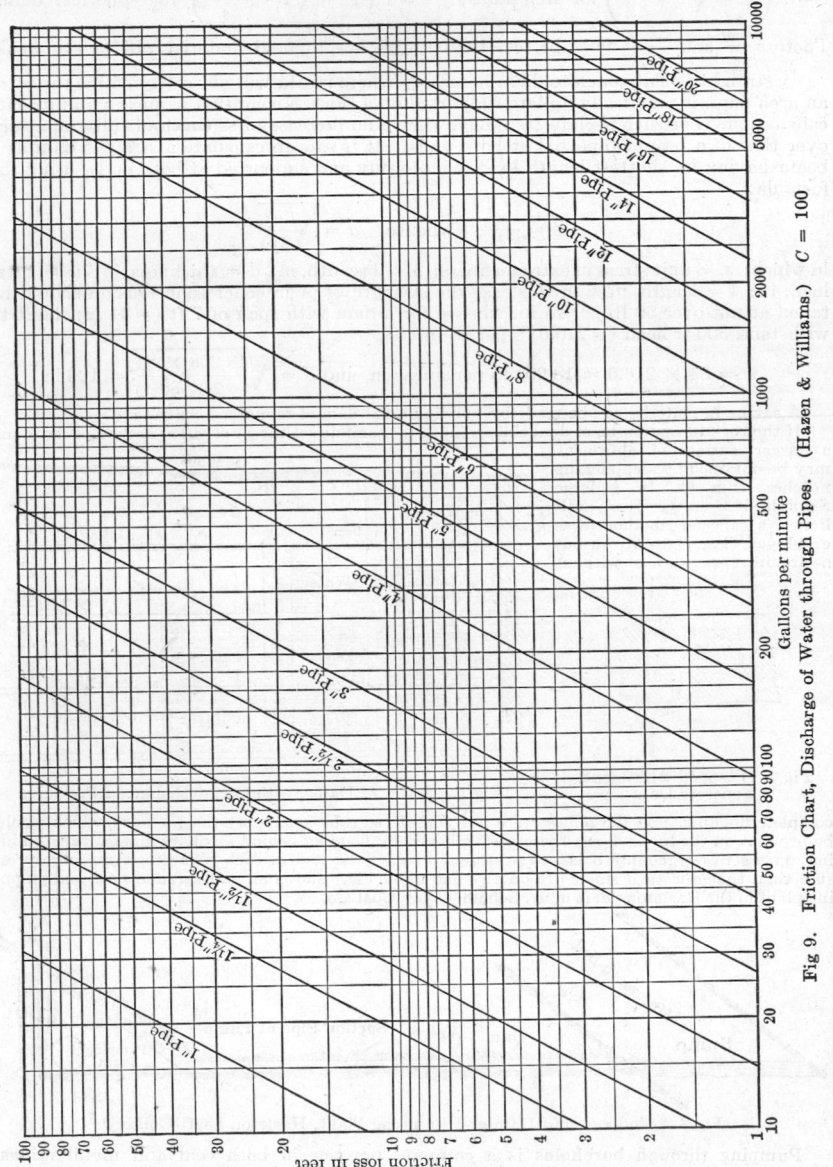

Fig 9.   Friction Chart, Discharge of Water through Pipes.   (Hazen & Williams.)   C = 100

Boreholes are sometimes used for dropping water from an upper to a lower level. Quantity of water discharged can be determined from a friction chart (Fig 9).   If there were no pipe friction, the water would flow through borehole with increasing speed and be discharged at a veloc $V = 2gH$, where H is the vert distance between upper and lower basin. Pipe friction retards flow, which becomes uniform when the total friction in borehole equals the head H; that is, when the friction becomes 100 ft for every 100 ft of borehole. The capacities causing a friction loss of 100 ft per 100 ft of pipe can be taken from the chart.

Example. A vert borehole 3 in diam will discharge approx 500 gal per min, and a 6-in hole, 3 000 gal per min, regardless of their length, providing there is a sufficient head of water over the inlet to produce the veloc required in the pipe and that the borehole is smooth (37).

For a sloping hole or pipe 3 in diam, 100 ft long, on a grade of 1 in 10, the effective head is 100 divided by 10, or 10 ft. The friction loss per 100 ft of borehole or pipe can not, therefore, be more than 10 ft, corresponding to a max flow of approx 150 gal per min. (See Sec 38.)

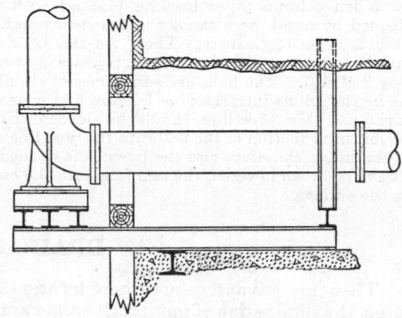

Fig 10. Mode of Supporting Column Pipe in Shaft

Pump piping. SUCTION PIPE should be short as possible, with few bends and should dip directly into the water (Fig 20, Art 11), so that it can be raised from the sump by the crane which should be installed in every pump room. Suction piping must not be wood-lined, as the staves may become loose and block the strainer. For acid water, it is cement-lined, by a mixture of 1 part finely sieved Portland cement and 2 parts sharp silica sand, applied by a long handle trowel, to form a layer about 0.5 in thick; after which, both ends of the pipe are closed with damp canvas to keep out the air until cement has set. If wet cement is exposed to air it will crack. Good cement linings should last for years. DISCHARGE PIPING must be well supported and braced, so that any water hammer caused by closing of the check valve is not transmitted to the pump. Fig 10 shows proper method of supporting column pipe in the shaft. Size of column pipe should be calculated to minimize friction head; increased power due to frictional resistance may cost more than the larger piping.

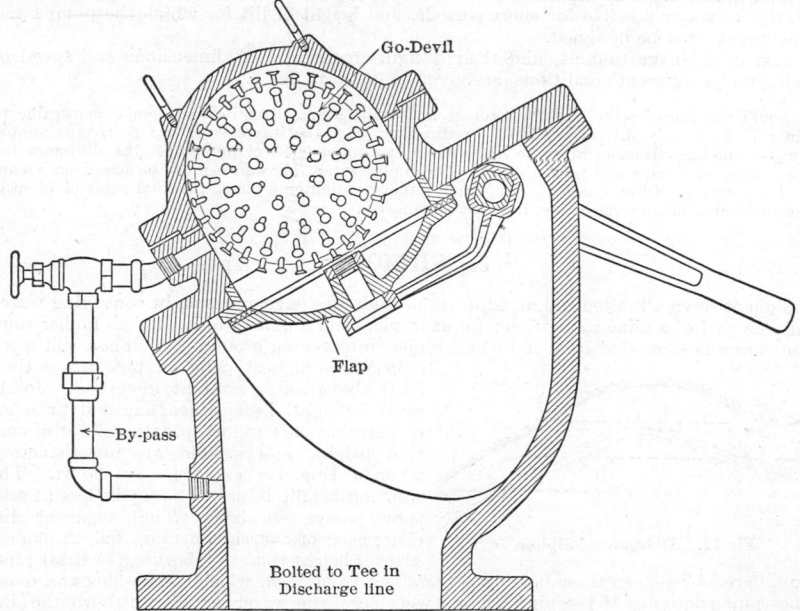

Fig 11. "Go-Devil" and Housing, for Cleaning Column Pipes

As elbows increase resistance, they should be of long radius. Always use Y branches with long bends; avoid tees. C-I flanged pipe is generally in 10- or 12-ft lengths, without male and female joints, as these are troublesome when piping is renewed. Present practice leans to straight flanges, with concentric V-grooves to retain the gasket. A W-I ring, $1/8$-$1/4$ in by 1 in wide, wrapped with tarred hemp, makes a good gasket. Composition fiber gaskets have also been successful. Minor bends in piping may be made with bevel-ring joints (either the iron-ring built-up gasket, or the composition fiber gasket), thus avoiding necessity for lengths of special curved pipe. Column pipe, not otherwise protected, should be coated inside and out by hot asphalt or tar.

Linings for acid water (31, 32). Cement lining for suction piping is satisfactory; lead lining is good, but wears rapidly in gritty water; wood lining is cheap and simple, with excellent wearing and acid-resisting qualities. Wood lining is best of narrow, sawed strips with radial joints, driven dry and swelled with pure water; strips should not be planed, because sawed surfaces, when swelled, interlock and form better joints. For pipes to 8 in diam, liners 0.5 in thick are ample, 3/8-in strips are sometimes used; for 8 to 14-in pipe, 0.75-in liners are sufficient; for over 14 in, usually 1 in.

When column pipes become blocked with incrustations, the sections are disconnected and cleaned by hand, or a cleaner is drawn through the entire line to cut loose the scale. There are various types of cleaners. The " Go-Devil," a wooden ball with a large number of spikes driven into it and protruding 1 to 1½ in, is generally used in the anthracite region for removing " Yellow-Boy " (FeS_2). The balls are sometimes of stainless steel, with spikes or knives welded onto them. As incrustations increase pipe friction and consequently the pumping head, resulting in decreased capac and effic, pipe lines should be cleaned at regular intervals. " Go-Devil " housings (Fig 11) permit introduction of the ball into the pipe line while the pump is in operation. The ball is placed in the upper chamber, and the by-pass is opened, equalizing the pressure on both sides of the flap. The flap is then lowered, the ball falls into the column line and the pump pressure drives it through to the surface.

4. DRAINAGE TUNNELS

These are advantageous where location and topography permit. Though first cost is large, the elimination of pumping charges and freedom from possibility of flooding the mine, due either to accident to pumps or power plant, or to labor troubles, may warrant the investment. In most cases, local conditions are such that only the upper levels of a mine can thus be unwatered by gravity. When workings extend below tunnel level, pumps must be installed. But, drainage tunnels still have the advantage of saving cost of raising the entire volume of water through a height equal to distance below surface at which tunnel intersects deposit. An estimate of length of tunnel justified in comparison with a pumping plant must be made with careful consideration of: cost of driving, maximum quantity of water possible for short periods, and height of lift for which the pumps and power plant must be designed.

Cost of drainage tunnels, and their design, cross-sectional dimensions and speed of driving under different conditions, are given in detail in Sec 6.

Should the tunnel serve also for haulage and ventilation, all of its cost is not chargeable to drainage. To justify driving a tunnel for drainage only, the interest on first cost, plus annual allowance for amortization, must be less than operating expense of pumping, plus allowance for amortization of pumps and power plant. The amortization allowance must be based on a conservative estimate of life of mine. If a tunnel replaces a pumping plant, the final value of plant is its second-hand, or its scrap value, less cost of removal.

5. SIPHONS

Siphons have a limited use as adjuncts of main drainage systems, in conveying water from one part of a mine to another; for example, from a place which, though higher than main sump, is separated from it by still higher intervening ground. A siphon will work only when highest point of pipe is less than 34 ft above water level at inlet end. Joints must be tight, because leakage and presence of entrained air reduce practical limit of suction height, and siphons are unsatisfactory when a (Fig 12) exceeds, say, 20 ft. The working height is proportionately less at altitudes above sea level. The longer or discharge leg of the siphon must fall through a greater height than the short leg, or draft pipe.

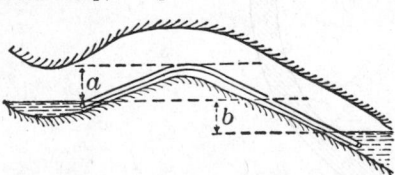

Fig 12.   Diagram of Siphon

The difference between these heights is the effective head, h, which causes flow and overcomes pipe friction. If the pipe friction were zero, the water would run down the discharge pipe at increasing veloc, and have a veloc at the outlet of $V = 2gH$. The pipe friction retards the flow and the chart (Fig 9) should be used for calculating siphons.

Example. For a siphon of 2 in diam, 200 ft long, with $a = 10$ ft and $b = 18$ ft, the effective head $H = b - a = 8$ ft. The friction loss in 200 ft of 2 in pipe, therefore, can not exceed 8 ft, or 4 ft per 100 ft, which, according to the chart, corresponds to a flow of approx 30 gal per min. Actual flow is

20% to 40% less, depending on losses at entrance and in bends, and leakage of air into the draft pipe.   To charge the siphon for starting, a short stand-pipe is placed at the summit and gate valves at each end of the pipe.   The discharge valve is used to regulate the flow if the discharge veloc becomes so great that a vacuum forms at the crown of the siphon.

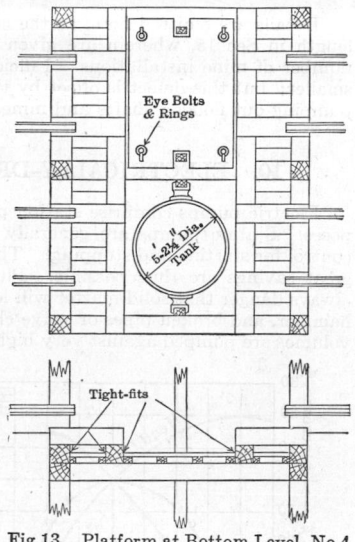

6. HOISTING WATER IN TANKS

Water hoisting, though less economical than pumping with electric or centrifugal pumps, is useful for unwatering flooded mines.   For this emergency service it usually replaces the hoisting of ore or coal, which presumably can not be raised while hoisting water.   The mineral hoist of a shaft subject to sudden inrushes of water should be convertible to a water hoist in the least possible time.   A water tank is designed either to be attached under each cage or is put on in its place.   The shaft should extend at least 30 ft below the bottom level, at which there is a platform with doors (Fig 13).   When water is to be hoisted the doors are removed, thus allowing the tank to be lowered into the sump.   The false bottom should be tight, so that solid matter can not enter, the sump.   A small pump should be installed to pump out the sump occasionally.

Fig 13.   Platform at Bottom Level, No 4 Shaft, Lansford Mine (L Nav C Co)

Readers desiring further information regarding water hoisting by tanks are referred to the previous editions of this book, in which full details of the tanks are given, with costs.   See also Bib 27, 28.

7. STEAM PUMPS (4-7)

Current practice tends toward complete electrification of mines.   Steam pumps are now rarely installed, most of them having been replaced by centrifugals.   But, at mines where there is an excess of boiler fuel and pump and boiler plant are in good condition, it is advisable to maintain steam pumps.   If the boiler plant is near the pumproom, and pumps are of compound condensing type, pumping cost compares favorably with that of the best motor-driven centrifugals.   New steam-driven units are generally centrifugals, driven by steam turbines, with or without speed reduction gearing.   Their advantage over motor drive is that speed can be regulated and capac adjusted to inflow, but they can not be operated safely without an attendant; a decided disadvantage.   See Sec 40 for details of pumps and their design.

8. COMPRESSED-AIR DRIVEN PUMPS (see Sec 15) (20)

Though pumping by compressed air is less efficient than by steam or electricity, its use is sometimes warranted: (a) in gassy collieries, where electricity is dangerous, and pumps are too far from boiler plant for economical steam transmission; (b) in mines where heat from steam pipes is objectionable, or heat combined with moisture would injure roof rock; (c) where there is no electric plant and amount of current required would not warrant an installation.   It is common to use compressed air in pumps built for steam, and in cylinders not properly proportioned for the pressure employed.   Under these conditions it is rare that more than 20% of indicated power at compressor is represented by actual water pumped; with reheated air, the efficiency may rise to about 30%.   The chief difficulties are, that ordinary direct-acting pumps fail to make full stroke, and their clearance volume is too great for compressed-air operation.   Better results are obtainable from larger fly-wheel pumps, designed for the service.   In absence of reheating, trouble from freezing in exhaust ports may be minimized by use of separators and traps in air lines close to the pumps, and by directing a small stream of water, taken under column-pipe pressure, into the exhaust passages below the valves.

9. AIR-LIFT PUMPS (see Sec 15) (Bib, 19–24)

Details are omitted here, as the construction and operation of air-lifts are treated at length in Sec 15, wherein are given also examples embodying results obtained from a number of mine installations. Efficiency is low, rarely exceeding 45% and often much smaller; but this defect is offset by their efficacy under certain conditions, especially for pumping out flooded shafts and mines.

10. ELECTRICALLY-DRIVEN PUMPS (see also Sec 16, 40)

Electric pumps comprise station pumps, and portable pumps used for gathering purposes. Station pumps are generally centrifugals, recent installations having automatic control for starting and stopping. They can be operated safely without an attendant and great savings are thus possible. Plunger pumps must have an attendant, as there is always danger that solid matter will lodge on the valve seats, causing slippage and water-hammer, and broken pipes or valve chambers. Plunger pumps are used only when small volumes are pumped against very high heads; for instance, 100 gal per min against 800 ft.

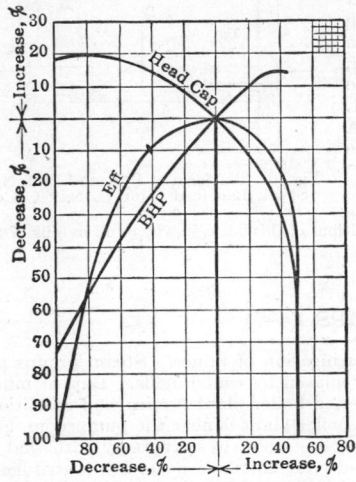

Fig 14. Performance of Volute Pumps

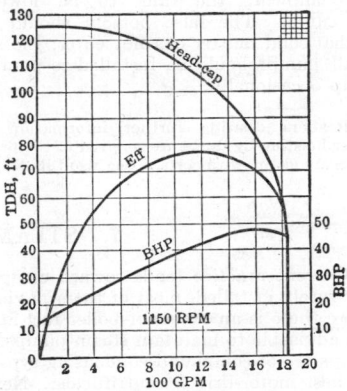

Fig 15. Characteristic Curves of a Centrifugal Pump

This condition would require a high-speed centrifugal, with 6 or more stages and high upkeep cost, especially when the water is acidulous. High upkeep would be somewhat offset by saving in first cost and maintenance of the column pipe, due to the smooth, non-pulsating discharge from a centrifugal pump. Actual figures are lacking, but practice proves that these savings are considerable.

Centrifugal pumps. Operating conditions differ entirely from those of plunger pumps. When the discharge pressure of a plunger pump is reduced, the power required falls off; when the head on a centrifugal is reduced, the power increases. The delivery volume of a plunger pump running at constant speed is invariable, regardless of the lift; whereas a centrifugal at constant speed delivers more water at low heads than at high (14, 15).

Performance. Water entering a centrifugal pump is set in rotation by the impellers and issues at the periphery at high veloc. This veloc is gradually reduced in the pump casing and converted into pressure, which in turn overcomes the resistance in the column pipe. Obviously, the volume delivered increases as resistance decreases. The high veloc at which the water leaves the impeller should be reduced in the casing gradually, without shock, and transformed into press with minimum loss. This is effected in a volute casing, or in one having a diffusion ring between impeller and outer casing. Volute casings are the rule for single-stage pumps, and are common also for multi-stage pumps, especially when the water is acid. To obtain high effic in a diffusion-ring pump, the tips of the diffusion vanes must be rather thin, so that acid water soon destroys them. The volute pump has higher effic over a wider range than diffusion-ring pumps. Fig 14 shows the approx performance of volute pumps. If the head and capac at which a pump is most efficient be taken as unity, by increasing the head 15%, the capac decreases about 40%, power decreases 24%, and effic is reduced 9%. If the head decreases 12%, the capac increases 20%, power increases 10%, while effic decreases 4%. An average pump will deliver no water whatever against a head approx 20% higher than that at which the pump shows its best effic.

Centrifugals are usually driven by constant-speed motors. If driven by variable-speed motors, it should be noted that the capac increases or decreases directly as the speed. Head increases or

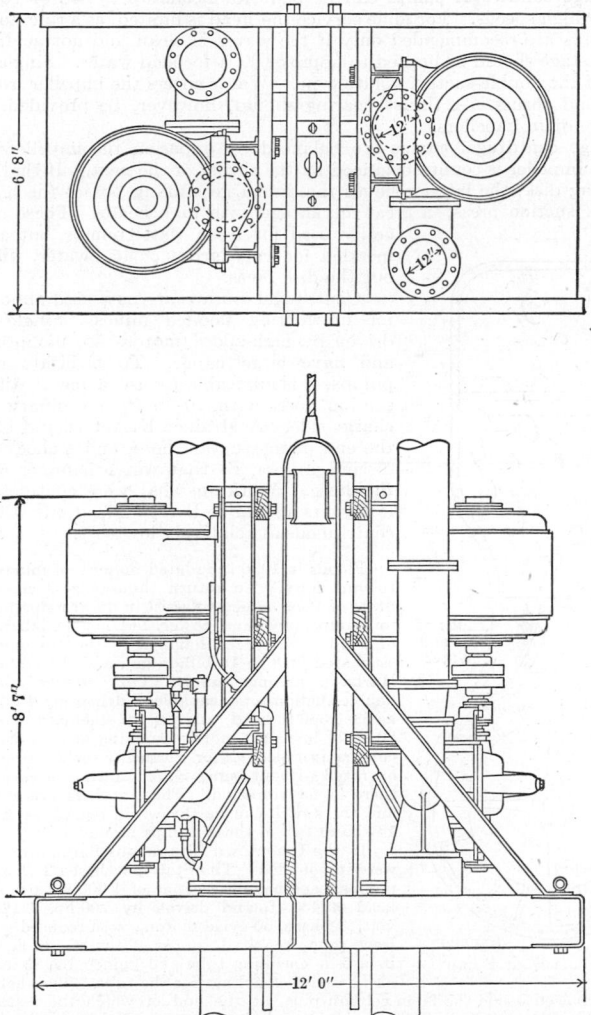

Fig 16. Two 400-hp Hazleton Sinking Pumps, on Cage. (Barrett, Haentjens & Co, Hazleton, Pa)

decreases as the square of this ratio, the hp increasing or decreasing as the third power. Thus, if a pump driven by a 1 200-rpm motor, delivering 1 000 gal against 100 ft head, and requiring 35 hp, were connected to an 1 800-rpm motor, the results would be: capac, $(1\,800 \div 1\,200) \times 1\,000 = 1\,500$ gal per min; head, $(1\,800 \div 1\,200)^2 \times 100 = 225$ ft; power required, $(1\,800 \div 1\,200)^3 \times 35 = 118$ hp.

Before changing speed of a centrifugal pump, the maker should be consulted. Performance curves of different makes vary. If a centrifugal is to work against a fixed head, as in case of a station pump, the shape of the head capac curve and the effic curve are of little importance, and the pump giving highest effic for the specified conditions should be selected. But, if the pump be used for unwatering purposes, or if it may be used in different locations underground, that pump should be selected which gives good effic over a wide range, and does not overload the motor to a dangerous point when the head is reduced. Fig 15 shows the characteristic curves of a pump with effic of 70% and over, for any condition between 700 gal per min against 120 ft head and 1 600 gal against 80 ft head. Max effic occurs when delivering 1 200 gal against 105 ft head.

Single-stage centrifugal pumps can be built for heads up to 600 or 700 ft, but this involves very high speeds. For mine service the head is limited, as a rule, to about 250 ft, and such heads are recommended only if the water is clean and not acid. In general, the head per stage should be limited to approx 100 ft for acid water. Single-stage pumps are usually of the double-suction volute type. Water enters the impeller from both sides, eliminating end thrust. A thrust bearing should, however, be provided, and insisted upon for large-diam impellers.

Multi-stage centrifugal pumps are balanced by opposing the impellers, so that the thrust of one impeller is counterbalanced by the thrust of the next. If they are balanced by a balancing disk, the latter relieves the discharge stuffing box of the high press, and puts it under suction press; a great advantage with high heads. These disks are generally used for fresh water pumps, but are not recommended for very gritty or acid water, which soon cuts out the disk faces.

Centrifugal pumps are now used almost exclusively for unwatering flooded mines. Single-stage pumps driven by high-speed motors are mounted on trucks, and have large capac. To facilitate moving these pumps, it is advisable to use a metal-stiffened rubber suction hose, with 10–15 ft of ordinary hose on discharge side. A strainer basket should be attached to the end of the suction hose, and a check valve on the discharge hose, so that water hammer can not burst the hose. Workings that were considered hopelessly lost years ago, have been pumped out with high-speed centrifugals at relatively low cost.

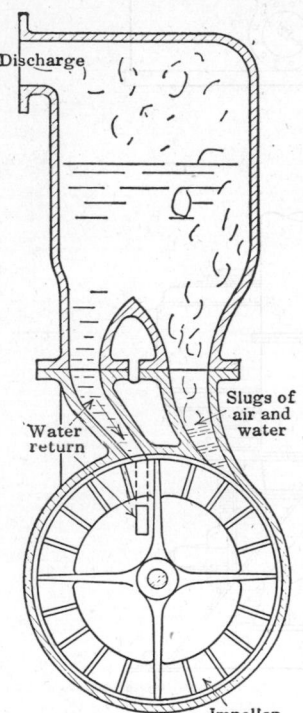

Fig 17. La Bour Pump

Floods in 1936 inundated many coal mines, forcing them to shut down. To return thousands of men to work, the State of Penn agreed to assist in de-watering mines by paying for pumps, pipes and power, but not for labor. The volume of flood water to be handled in the Wyoming Valley was estimated at 8 to 18 billion gal, and the state purchased 18 Hazleton sinking pumps. They were of the single-stage, double-suction type, capable of delivering 4 000 gal per min, against 350 ft head; driven by 400-hp, 4 000-volt, 3-phase, 60-cycle line-start motors, running at 1 750 rpm. The units can be installed either vertically or horizontally and are operated without being bolted down or secured by props, as there is no vibration. The impellers are non-overloading, and the switch can be thrown in regardless of the head. Fig 16 shows two of these pumps mounted vertically on a cage.

In the Uniontown Bituminous Basin, approx 3 billion gal were impounded. The State purchased 3 Deep-well Turbine pumps, each having a capac of 4 000 gal per min, against a head of 450 ft, driven by 700 hp, 1 160 rpm, 2 300-volt, 3-phase, 60-cycle motors, with reduced voltage starters. Each pump required approx 420 ft of 4-in shafting, running in a 6-in enclosing tube and guided by 85 bearings, which also acted as couplings for the tube. The shaft, with enclosing tube, was placed inside the 20-in column pipe, at the end of which the 6-stage pump was mounted. The whole assembly was hung in the shaft and supported by steel beams extending across top of shaft. The entire 20-in column pipe was vulcanized on the inside with rubber compound, and the tube enclosing the shaft was vulcanized on the outside to protect against corrosion.

11. PUMP ROOMS

Fig 20 shows an up-to-date pump room, containing 3 4-stage centrifugal pumps, each of 2 000 gal per min, against a head of 800 ft.   The pumps work automatically, requiring no attendance.

This pump room is provided with an 8-ton traveling crane, to facilitate repairs.   The suction pipes drop directly into the sump, and can be lifted out by the crane.   Each pump has 2 strainers, one near the pump, the other (a "basket") at end of suction pipe.   The basket strainers have liberal openings, but must prevent large floating objects from entering the intake.   Each pump has a check valve, and there is another check valve in the discharge line.   There are also 3 priming pumps of the dry vacuum type (Art 12), each of a capac of 50 cu ft per min.

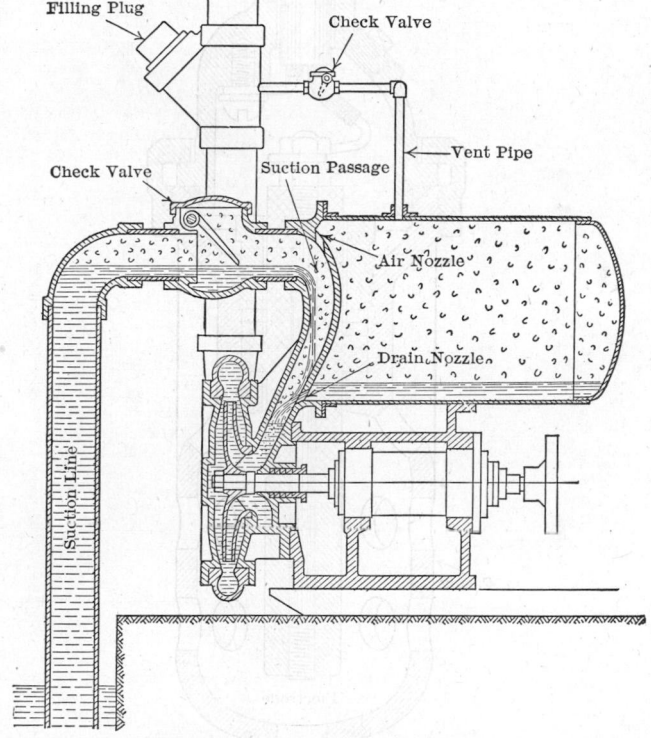

Fig 18.   Hazleton Auto Station Pump

Foundations.   For station pumps, solid concrete foundations are well worth while.   They should be true, of good materials, and only one end of pump bed-frame should be bolted down, the other being left free, to allow for expansion.

Gathering pumps, designed to be moved frequently from place to place, are preferably of the self-priming centrifugal type.   Generally, the types capable of pumping continuously a mixture of air and water are less effic and more subject to wear than those pumping water only.

The La Bour pump (Fig 17) is primed by trapping water within the pump and utilizing the veloc of expulsion of pockets of water discharged by the impeller, which entrain air and carry it out of the casing.   The pump can handle a mixture of air and water, and draw from several sumps simultaneously.

In the Hazleton Station pump (Fig 18) air is trapped in a vessel connected to the suction line, and pushed directly into the discharge line by a return flow of water caused by stopping the pump.   Repeated starts and stops, made automatically, may be required to prime the pump if suction line is long. This pump handles water only and can draw from one sump only. It is started by an electrode (Fig 19), which is suspended over the ditch. When water reaches its high level, contact through the water is established between the electrode and its casing, whereupon the

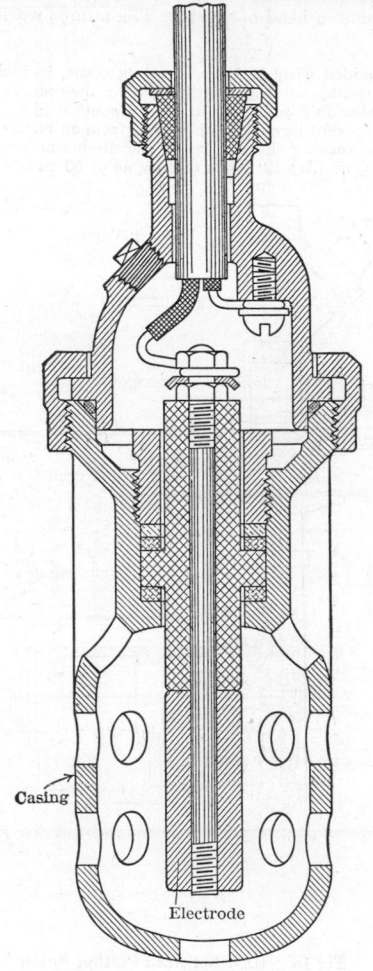

Casing

Electrode

Fig 19. Electrode for Starting Hazleton Pump

pump starts, and runs until the water is pumped down and air enters the suction line. Then the pump stands idle until the ditch has filled again. Power consumption and wear are thus kept at a minimum.

12. CHECK VALVES AND STRAINERS

Check valves should be carefully selected, since their failure may ruin the pump. They are of the single-flap or multiple-flap type. Experience shows that when a single-flap valve is liberally proportioned it will close without shock. Its construction should be simple and all parts exceptionally heavy, as indicated in Fig 21. Noisy seating of a check valve is sometimes caused by breaking (or separating) of the water column in the discharge pipe, when the pump is being shut down. As momentum keeps the water moving in the discharge faster than the pump delivers, the column is broken, resulting

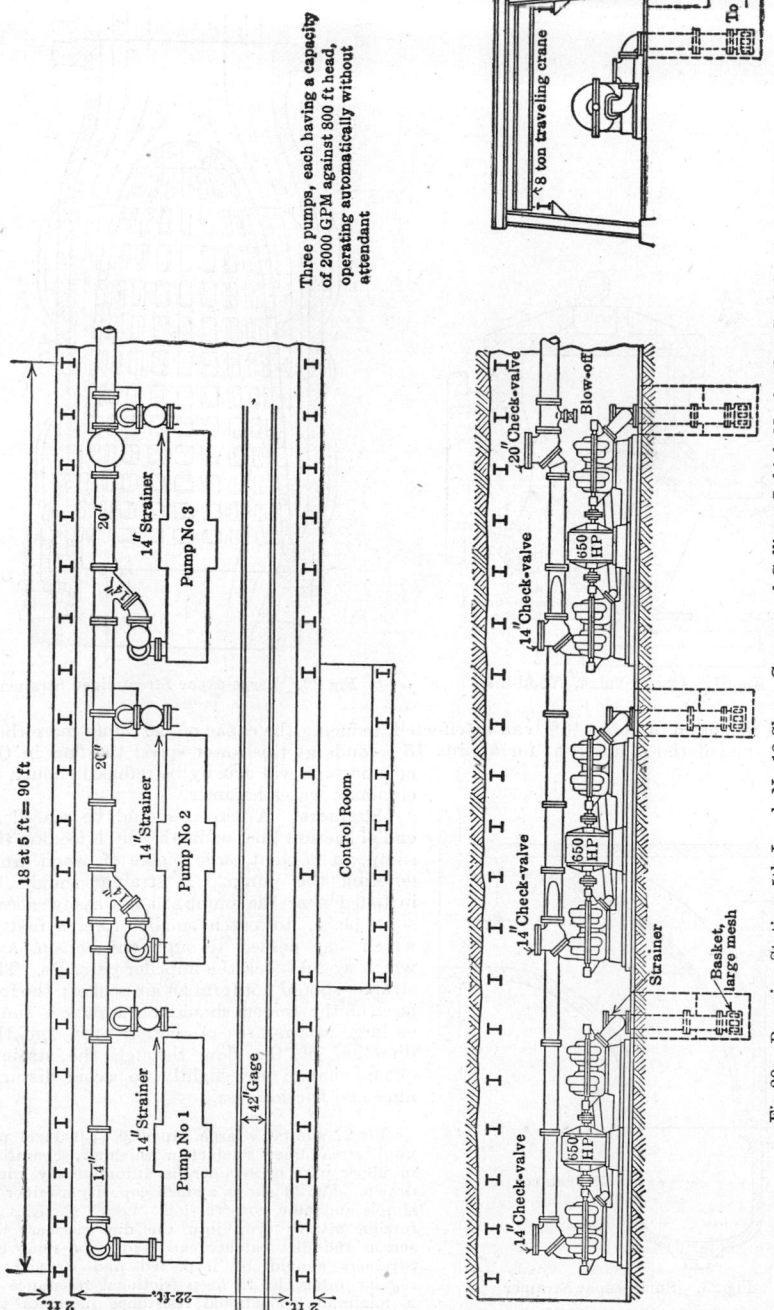

Three pumps, each having a capacity of 2000 GPM against 800 ft head, operating automatically without attendant

Fig 20.   Pumping Station, 5th Level, No 12 Slope, Greenwood Colliery, Lehigh Navigation Coal Co, Lansford, Pa

in a water hammer when the flow is reversed. This can be averted by slowing down the motor before cutting off the current entirely. If the motor is of the slip-ring type, a

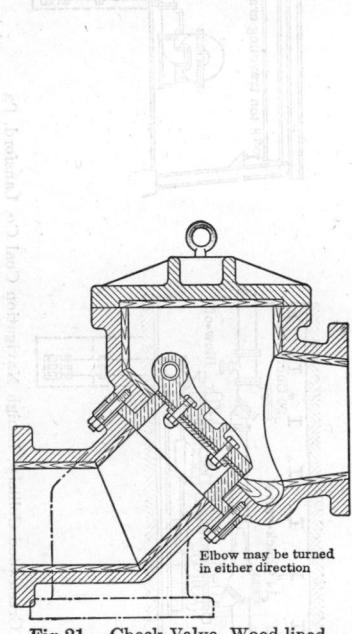

Fig 21. Check Valve, Wood-lined

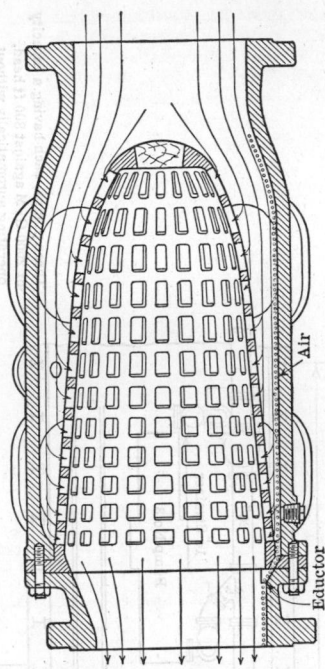

Fig 22. Large-capac Streamlined Strainer

speed reduction of about 10% can be effected, reducing the capac of the pump more than 50%; and if the motor runs for approx 15 seconds at this lower speed the flow in the column pipe will usually be reduced enough to eliminate water hammer.

Strainers. A screen should be placed at end of suction line, or in the ditch feeding the sump, to prevent large pieces of wood from entering the pump. A strainer should be installed near the pump, in an easily accessible place, to catch smaller foreign matter which has passed through the screen, and which would block the impeller passages. The strainer should not form an air pocket; the free area of the screen should be approx 4 times as large as the area of suction pipe, and the direction of the flow through the strainer should change only slightly, to avoid disturbance and friction loss.

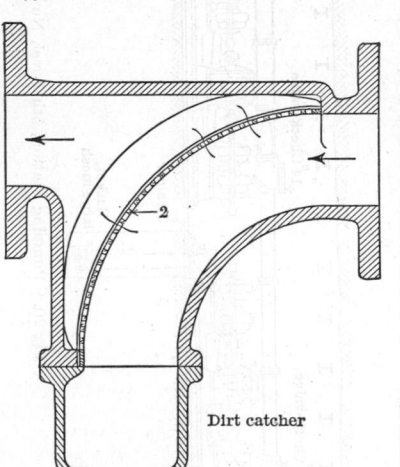

Fig 23. Small-capac Strainer

Fig 22 shows a large capacity (7 000 gal per min), streamlined strainer in which air, separating in upper part of strainer, is automatically withdrawn. Fig 23 shows a small capacity strainer of simple and effic construction. Large particles of foreign matter drop into the dirt catcher; the screen and dirt catcher can readily be removed. Strainers should be inspected and cleaned at regular intervals, to keep frictional resistance at a minimum. Frictional resistance increases the suction lift, which in turn decreases the capac and effic of the pump.

13. AUTOMATIC OPERATION OF CENTRIFUGAL PUMPS

This is rapidly coming into use, and has been so perfected that the largest units can be run with absolute safety without an attendant. Pump runners' wages are thus saved. Automatically controlled pumps keep the water in the sump at a predetermined level; they are protected against accidents caused by loss of water due to air leaks in the suction line, or to choked strainers, and stop automatically in case of breakage of the column.

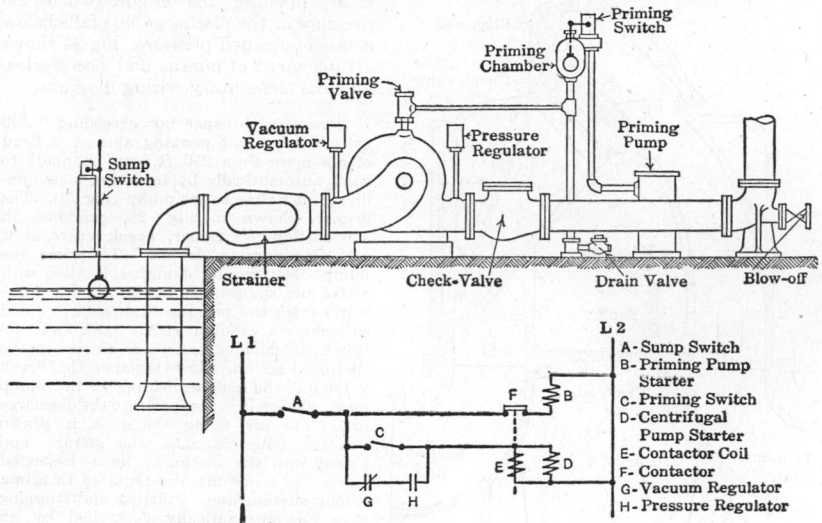

Fig 24. Arrangement of Primer and Accessories for Automatic Control of Centrifugal Pump, with Diagram of Wiring

A - Sump Switch
B - Priming Pump Starter
C - Priming Switch
D - Centrifugal Pump Starter
E - Contactor Coil
F - Contactor
G - Vacuum Regulator
H - Pressure Regulator

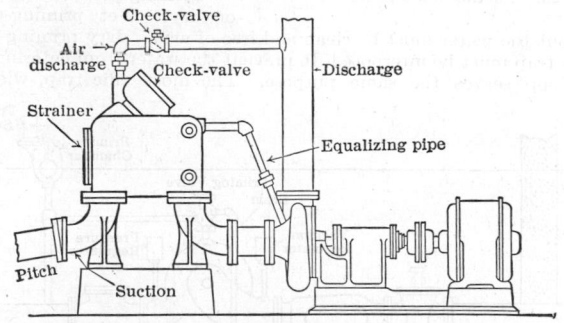

Fig 25. Centrifugal Pump with Suction-line Primer

Priming centrifugal pumps. There are 3 methods: (a) installing a foot valve and filling the suction pipe and pump casing with water from the discharge column; (b) using a vacuum pump, or other means of exhausting air from the suction line and pump casing, and filling them with water from the sump; (c) providing a head on the suction, when a pump takes water from a dam. Foot valves are widely used for small pumps, but are not reliable, as they are apt to leak and wear out rapidly in acid water. A pump with a foot valve will operate automatically with safety, but often fails to start when the valve becomes leaky. Hence, foot valves are not recommended for mine service.

A priming-pump is used for most centrifugals. It is started by a switch operated by a float in the sump, and exhausts the air from the centrifugal, thus drawing water from the sump through the suction pipe and pump casing, and thence through a valve into a priming chamber, which contains a float. When water enters the chamber, the float rises and closes the priming switch, which starts the centrifugal pump motor. The motor having been accelerated a contact is automatically opened, stopping the priming pump. When the centrifugal begins to run, the priming valve is closed by the pressure from the pump, the water from the priming chamber drains out, and the priming switch opens. Protective devices are shunted around the priming switch, and the current flows through them when the switch is open. These devices consist of a vacuum regulator, which opens the circuit if the vacuum exceeds a predetermined value, and a pressure regulator, opening the circuit when the pressure in the discharge line falls below a predetermined pressure. Fig 24 shows arrangement of pumps and accessories, and the elementary wiring diagram.

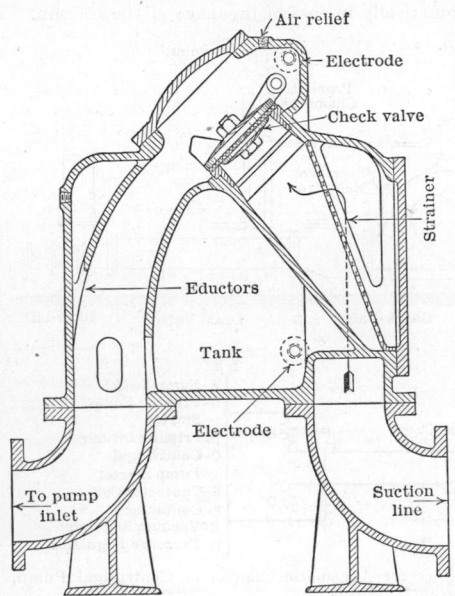

Fig 26. Suction-line Primer

Pumps with capac not exceeding 1 500 gal per min, and working against a head of not more than 250 ft, can be made to work automatically by installing a suction-line primer close to the pump (Fig 25). The primer, shown in Fig 26, combines in one casting a strainer, check valve seat, and air-removing device. To prime the pump, the priming chamber is filled with water and the pump started. It draws the water from the priming tank, and in doing so creates a vacuum in the tank and suction line, which causes water to rise in the suction line and flow through the check valve into the passage leading to the pump inlet, whence it is pumped into the discharge line. The air filling the tank is drawn through eductors into the stream and forced into the discharge line. Repeated starts and stops may be required to prime a long suction line. Starting and stopping may be automatically controlled by an electrode fitted in the tank.

Priming-pumps may be either wet or dry. Wet priming-pumps are in common use, but the water must be clean and free of acid. Dry priming-pumps require less power. A trap must be interposed, to prevent the water from entering the cylinder; a barometric loop serves the same purpose. The most effic trap, widely used with

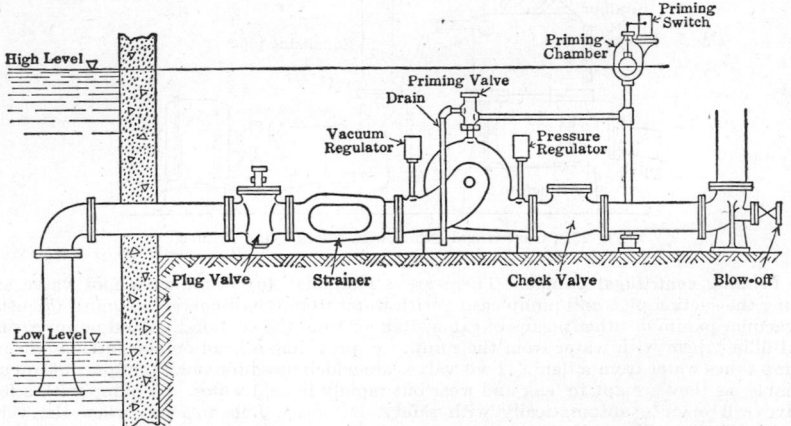

Fig 27. Automatic Control of a Centrifugal Pump Taking Water from a Dam

pumps handling acid water, is a chamber in which a float operates an air valve. This valve opens when the water enters the chamber, causing the vacuum to break, thus preventing water from entering the pump. The chamber is placed above the pump and connected to top of the casing of a single-stage pump, or to top of the first stage of a multi-stage pump. The remaining stages need not be primed.

When a centrifugal takes water from a dam (Fig 27), no priming is required. As the water rises behind the dam, it also rises in the suction line and pump casing, and raises the float in the priming chamber, thus closing the priming switch and starting the pump. The protective devices are shunted as described above. The pump is stopped by the vacuum regulator switch, which opens when the water behind the dam has receded to the low level.

14. NEUTRALIZING ACID MINE WATER (30)

Acid water is sometimes neutralized before pumping, thus avoiding damage to pumps and column pipe. In many mines the quantity of water is so great that it can not be economically neutralized before pumping. Sometimes part of the water used for the preparation of coal is neutralized to prevent rapid wear of the breaker equipment.

A computation based on actual conditions is necessary to determine the advisability of this procedure, dependent as it is on character and quantity of water, type and cost of pumping plant, and price of the alkali required. Milk of lime may be added to sump water in measured quantity at regular intervals, as in coal mines and in metal mines at Butte, Mont, and elsewhere.

BIBLIOGRAPHY

1. Run-off and Mine Drainage. *Trans* A I M E, Vol 66, p 624
2. The Water Problem at Old Dominion Mine, Ariz. *Trans* A I M E, Vol 55, p 35
3. Bulkhead Door for Underground Water Control. *E & M J*, Nov 24, 1928, p 825
4. Mine Dams. *Trans* N of England Inst Min Engs, Vol 32, p 201. *E & M J*, Vol 77, p 965

Direct-acting Pumps
5. *Trans* Am Soc Mech Engs, Vol 20, p 50. *Trans* A I M E, Vol 52, p 532
6. *Min & Sci Pr*, Dec 25, 1920, p 912
7. *Coll Guardian*, Feb 20, 1931, p 669
8. Selection of Type of Pump. *Coal Age*, Jan 3, 1924, p 11
9. Automatic Underground Pumping. *E & M J*, May 11, 1931, p 422; *Min & Met*, July, 1933, p 295
10. Pumping 2 200 ft in One Lift. *E & M J*, June 28, 1924, p 1041
11. A Central Pumping Plant, Berwind-White Coal Co. *Coll Guardian*, Jan 10, 1930, p 124
12. Deep-level Pumping Plants, 2 000 ft. *E & M J*, Sept 8, 1928, p 365
13. Pumping Machinery. A. M. Greene, 1919 (book)

Centrifugal Pumps
14. Loewenstein and Crissey. Daugherty. Two useful books
15. Centrifugal *vs* Reciprocating Pumps. *E & M J*, Jan 14, 1922, p 62; Jan 28, 1922, p 171
16. Efficiencies of Centrifugal Pumps. *E & M J*, Nov 19, 1927, p 813
17. Pumping at Park Utah Mine with Centrifugal Pumps. *E & M J*, Mch 8, 1930, p 253
18. Centrifugal Pumps at Cerro de Pasco, 16 000 gal per min. *E & M J*, May 14 and 21, 1927

Air-lift Pumps
19. Pumping by Compressed Air (book). Ivens (1914)
20. Compressed Air Plant. Peele. (5th Ed, 1930)
21. *Trans* A I M E, Vol 63, p 421
22. *E & M J:* July 10, 1920, p 63; Jan 28, 1922, p 172
23. *Min & Sci Pr*, Nov 19, 1921, p 711
24. Air-lift Pumping for Flooded Mines. *Coal Age*, July 30, 1925, p 143

Miscellany
25. Choice of Mine Pump. *E & M J*, June 28, 1924, p 1041; *Coal Age*, Dec 16, 1920, p 1229
26. Selection of Type of Pump for Mine Drainage. *Coal Age*, Jan 3, 1924, p 11
27. Water Hoisting. *Trans* A I M E, Vol 34, p 106
28. *Coal Age*, June 15, 1918, p 1094; Aug 29, 1918, p 397
29. Acid Water in Mine Drainage. *Coal Age*, July, 1930, p 406
30. Neutralization of Mine Water. *Trans* A I M E, Vol 66, p 609; *Jour* Franklin Inst, Nov, 1928, p 705
31. Acid-resisting Alloys for Pumps. *Coal Age*, Apl 26, 1923, p 665
32. Concrete-lined Pipe for Acid Water. *Coal Age*, Oct 16, 1924, p 548
33. Pumping through Boreholes. *Trans* Instn Min & Met, Vol 41 (1932), p 44
34. Deep-well Pump for Unwatering a Flooded Mine. *Min & Met*, July, 1935, p 294
35. A Submerged Pumproom, with Centrifugal Pumps. *Coal Age*, Dec, 1930, p 713
36. Dewatering Shafts and Mine Workings; mathematical analysis. *So Af Min & Eng Jour*, Oct 4, 1930
37. Gould Pump Co, *Bull No 400* (1930)

SECTION 14

MINE VENTILATION

WRITTEN FOR FIRST AND SECOND EDITIONS

BY THE LATE

F. ERNEST BRACKETT

MINING ENGINEER

REWRITTEN FOR THE THIRD EDITION

BY

GEORGE E. McELROY

SENIOR MINING ENGINEER, U S BUREAU OF MINES

Note.—Numbers in parentheses in text refer to Bibliography at end of this section.

MINE VENTILATION

This section treats of the natural and artificial circulation of air currents in mines and tunnels. For composition and properties of mine air, and physiological effects of its impurities and variations in physical conditions, see Sec 23.

1. MINE ATMOSPHERE

Ventilation of mines is a form of air conditioning by distribution of air currents in underground openings, in quantities sufficient to maintain working places in safe and healthful condition; it is most elaborately developed in coal mines, because of occurrence of explosive gas and dust. In metal mines it is confined largely to combating effect of high air temp on effic of miners, and effect of rock dusts on health.

Mine air may contain a number of impurities, in addition to normal constituents, and may absorb water vapor and heat in passing through workings (Sec 23, Art 1–4). Major impurities: (a) smoke and gases from blasting; (b) gases from the strata; (c) dust from mining operations. Open lights, breathing of men and animals, and chemical oxidation consume O, and (except oxidation of sulphides) produce CO_2. Minor sources of gaseous impurities are: rotting timber, excretions of men and animals, and smouldering mine fires.

Gases from explosives are dangerous mainly on account of CO, which seldom exceeds 0.3 cu ft per lb of explosive, but is variable and dependent on the oxygen-combustible balance. Gases from strata are most important in coal mines, with CH_4, CO_2, and H_2S in order of occurrence. CO_2 is often found in metal mines, CH_4 and H_2S rarely. Smouldering mine fires may produce CO. DUST in coal mines (other than anthracite) is explosive and therefore dangerous; in metal and anthracite coal mines, it may be a health hazard of importance. MINE AIR TEMP approximates that of the walls of air passages, and, as rock temp increases with depth, deep workings may have hot, high-humidity air conditions (Art 17, 18). Abundant ventilating currents, properly distributed, reduce dangers of gases and dusts and alleviate discomfort due to high-temperature air.

2. VENTILATING SYSTEMS

Definition. Any set of connected underground openings and the forces and appliances that cause flow of air through them constitute a ventilating system. Every mine has its own system, taken as a whole; the similarities occur between separate parts of mines. SYSTEMS: controlled and uncontrolled natural and mechanical ventilation.

Control of ventilating currents is required for their effective use and protection of life and property in case of fire or explosion. Uncontrolled currents may produce good air conditions; but lack of control, resulting in unknown conditions of recirculation, adds to natural hazard. Mechanical systems increase natural hazard from fire or explosion, by causing faster travel of gases.

Uncontrolled natural ventilation. Most small metal mines, a few small coal mines, some large metal mines, and near-surface sections of some large coal mines, are ventilated by uncontrolled natural ventilation (Art 12). Where openings are large and numerous, mines have reached great depths without intentional control of natural air flows. Above the lowest adit connection, mines in mountainous country are generally well ventilated by natural draft.

Controlled natural ventilation. Air flow is often partly controlled by natural conditions, or intentionally. In shallow mines, the driving of openings to the surface at intervals is a form of control. Circulation can be improved and direction of flow controlled by doors and bulkheads (Art 12). In large mines on pitching veins, workings should be divided into sections by barriers extending from surface to top of active zones; as in many Mich copper mines (63), where good natural ventilation exists at depths of 3 000–6 000 ft vert and 4 000–9 000 ft on the dip, below a practically level surface.

Mechanical ventilation. Where natural ventilation is inadequate, circulation is produced by fans (Art 13–16), as at most coal and large metal mines; they are always advisable, if only to provide reversible direction-of-flow for emergencies, and increased flow when the surface temp limits natural flow. In most metal mines, the chief objects of mechanical ventilation are to reduce high air temp in depth and rapidly remove the blasting fumes. Other objectives: better control of air currents in fire areas or for fire protection; dilution and removal of strata gases; reduction in amount of comp air used for air cooling; reduction of timber decay; and removal of rock dust.

Application of mechanical ventilation. In bedded deposits, as coal, the outlines of the deposit usually are known, and layout of openings is planned in advance for effective ventilation. Most metal mines rely on natural draft until conditions demand more air and better distribution, as supplied by fans. A large multi-seam coal mine is often divided, between seams or at natural barriers, into separately-ventilated sections. A large metal mine is usually ventilated by 2 or more fans operating in parallel or series on the same ventilating system, without division between circuits. Ventilation by one fan is desirable if it can be arranged economically. In planning a mechanical system, the main factors are volume of flow and effect of layout of openings on pressure requirements.

Air quantity requirements (Sec 23, Art 6) for effective ventilation depend on conditions as to gas, dust and rock temp, and vary from 50 to 1 000 cu ft per min per man on largest underground shift employed. In practice, quantities are adjusted until the air in working places seems good. Usual criterions: movement of smoke after blasting in metal mining; presence or absence of gas accumulations in coal mines; and temp and humidity in hot mines. In some U S coal mines, air quality based on routine air analysis is the control used. LEGAL REQUIREMENTS for metal mines or tunnels in the U S are few; N Y regulates siliceous dust concentrations (24). Legal requirements for coal mines (25), based on number of men and animals underground and position of air measurement, are generally exceeded in practice. Abroad, there is a trend to requirements based on max permissible limits of impurities, temp and humidity (26). MINIMUM REQUIREMENTS IN PRACTICE are about 30 cu ft per min (" c f m ") per man and 3–5 times as much for a horse (12). For small metal mines, with long intervals between shifts, and blasting at end of shift only, 50 c f m per man may be enough, but, with scattered working places and large openings, requirements approach 100 c f m, the general minimum for coal mines. Blasting during the shift, much timbering, production of gas from the strata or by oxidation, or moderately high temp, increase requirements 50–100 c f m per man. General requirements in under-cut-caving, where a veloc of about 100 ft per min is required in grizzly drifts to permit intermittent blasting, are 200–300 c f m per man. Except under extreme gas or high-temp conditions, requirements seldom exceed 500 c f m per man, but may reach 1 000 (9). In Pa non-gaseous anthracite mines the limits are about 100–1 000 c f m; aver, about 300 c f m per man. In Pa gaseous anthracite mines, the limits are about 300–1 000, aver 500 c f m per man (27). In all mines, the quantities necessary for good air conditions are found by trial, but are subject to frequent change.

Total air circulated in gaseous mines often amounts to 10 tons air per ton coal mined; aver, about 6 to 1 (3). In Pa anthracite field, several mines circulate over 1 000 000 cu ft per min; others there and elsewhere, 500 000–900 000 (27); but the aver large mine requires 50 000–250 000 c f m and few exceed 250 000.

Reduction of normal air quantities during idle times, rare in metal mines, is sometimes practiced at intermittently operated coal mines working fairly flat seams, saving much power at moderate sacrifice of safety; usually not practical on pitching seams making much gas, because of gas accumulations.

Pressure requirements. At fixed quantity, power required for circulating air depends on press, which is determined by the airways and their layout. In coal mines, design of airways is usually part of original plan of development (Art 11); in metal mines, it may involve best use of existing openings, with a minimum of " new " work. Press requirements (Art 10, 11) depend on size of airways and how combined in flow circuits; that is, how the flow is split between openings. Main airways, carrying entire flow, demand most attention, as restricted areas or high resistance therein may cripple the whole system. Layout of minor openings, in which split flow occurs, usually has no important effect on press requirements.

Fan pressures at U S metal mines are usually 3–5 in of water gage. In coal mines, economical size of airways is larger and range of fan pressures is usually 0.5–3 in of water. Mine airway conditions may be compared in terms of press required to pass a unit quantity (Art 11). Requirements for 100 000 cu ft per min are: max for small metal mines, 20–30 in; usual for large metal mines, 5–10 in; aver for non-gaseous coal mines, 1–5 in; aver for gaseous mines, 0.2–1.0 in; at a few coal mines, even lower. Aver conditions of fan operation in terms of equivalent orifice (Art 11) are: min for small metal mines, 5–10 sq ft; aver for large metal mines, 15–25; aver for non-gaseous coal mines, 25–40; aver for very gaseous coal mines, 40–90 sq ft.

Major outlines of ventilation systems are determined by the number, size, use and position of shafts, slopes, and adits to surface. DESIRABLE FEATURES: (1) utilization as intakes, or fresh-air outlets, of openings used for transporting men; (2) utilization of all available surface openings, or enough to give low-resistance; (3) coursing of intakes directly to lower levels of active zones, so that currents ascend through them to main outlets; (4) splitting of total flow and uniting separate flows close to surface; (5) minimizing distances traveled; (6) maintaining balanced resistance between main intake and outlet airways, and between separate sections of main airways; (7) minimizing obstructions, as doors and air locks in active openings; (8) avoidance of leakage, recirculation and creation of fog; (9) circulation of air from active zones to caved ground rather than the reverse.

Interventilation of mines is rarely desirable, as cooperation of separate operating staffs is not dependable. It should be a temporary expedient only, except where full control of ventilation in a group of mines is exercised by one official. Connections between adjoining mines are desirable for safety, but should be normally shut off with fire-door air locks.

Exhaust systems of ventilation are preferable, with the fan or fans on the surface at air shafts, slopes or adits; this pays due regard to safety, air is then drawn in and coursed directly to active zones, and the fan is always accessible. Although exhaust systems are general, many blowing systems are in use, especially in eastern U S bituminous mines, except Pa. Main haulage and hoisting openings are then on return air, chiefly to avoid operating inconvenience in cold weather (Art 3).

Location of openings. To decrease distance traveled by air currents, provide safety, and reduce leakage, intake and outlet openings should be so arranged that active workings lie mainly on the line between them. If active workings extend in two or more directions from a downcast shaft, an upcast near the limit of activity in each direction is desirable. If shafts are spaced fairly regularly, as on an extensive pitching vein, alternate shafts should be upcasts and downcasts, to distribute resistances and reach areas that would otherwise receive little flow. Two shafts close together usually serve better when carrying air in the same direction, because few stoppings are required on connections between them, leakage is avoided, and distance traveled by the air is usually minimum.

Ideal lay-out of airways best illustrates desirable major features, as shown in Fig 1 for a typical metal mine. Surface exhaust fans, on outlying and small inactive shafts of a steep vein, draw air in through the centrally located and relatively large operating shaft to the bottom levels, through

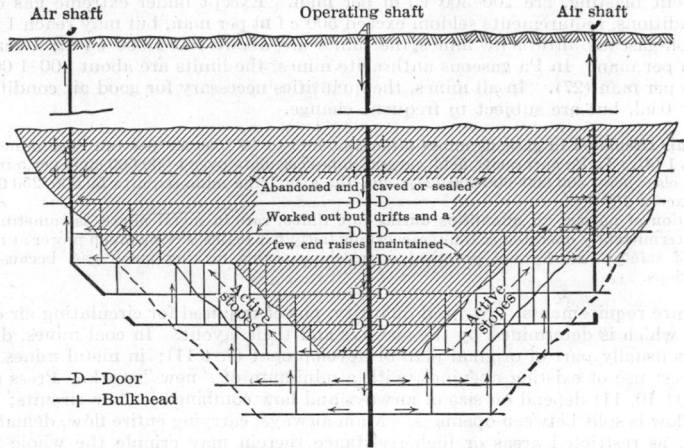

Fig 1. Ideal Layout of Mechanical-ventilation System, Metal Mines (9)

which it passes to active stopes and thence to less active workings connected to upcast. The foregoing nine desirable conditions are fulfilled and a safe and effic system should result. A similar ideal layout for gaseous coal mine workings on moderate to steep pitches is shown in Fig 2. Here the air is more definitely coursed, and main intakes and returns are close to each other, as generally required for coal mines. The same major conditions are met, as well as the following special objectives for gaseous mines: (1) active sections on separate splits; (2) pillar workings on splits separate from advancing first mining; (3) inactive sections ventilated by returns from active sections; (4) development for ventilation is completed before development for extraction is advanced.

Minor outlines of systems are controlled largely by the individual characteristics of mines, even in quite similar deposits. The more important are: degree of concentration of operations; position of active areas; relative ease or difficulty of maintaining openings; location of sources of heat, dust, or strata gases; position of sealed fire areas or areas liable to spontaneous ignition; condition of abandoned and inaccessible workings; and the precooling of zones of warm rock. These and other special conditions may require modification of the major outlines of the system as a whole, but if the major objectives are observed the system should be effective.

Concentration of working places is important in insuring good air conditions at low cost, for gaseous mines and workings in warm rock, as at great depth. Sections should be cleaned up so they can be abandoned in regular order, thus maintaining a uniform size of active zone. If possible, sections temporarily abandoned should be sealed: timber can be preserved by either sealing or thorough ventilation, whereas insufficient ventilation leads to rapid deterioration of timber and extensive sloughing of rock walls.

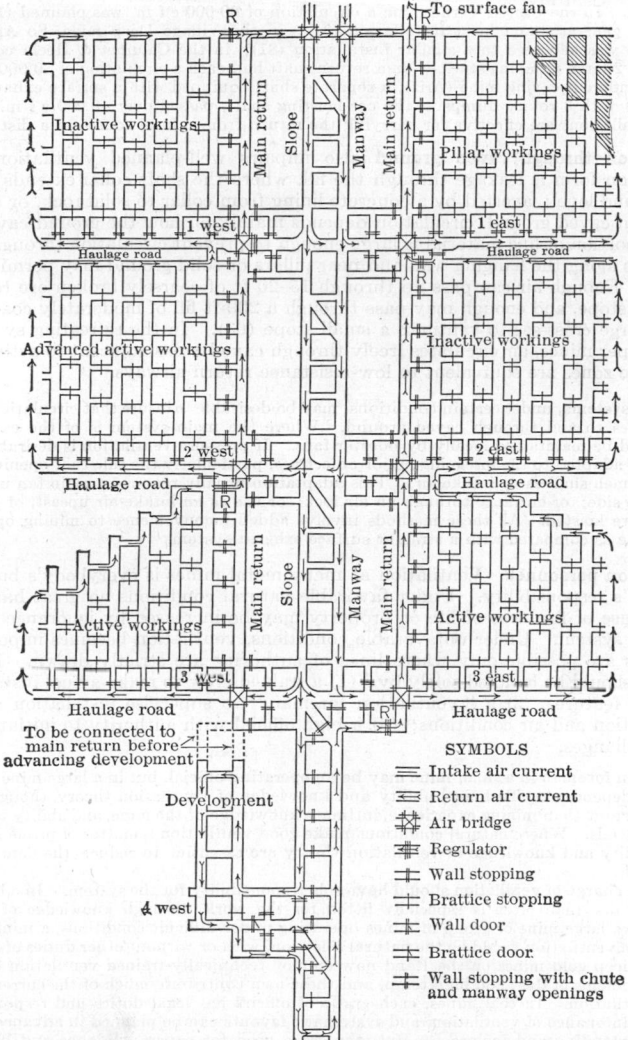

Fig 2. Desirable Method of Ventilating Gaseous Coal Mines on Moderate to Steep Pitches (27)

Extensive operations above the active zone of " first mining," as the reworking of gobbed areas, leasing operations on scattered pillars and lean zones, and retreating pillar extraction, should be on circuits separated from the main circuits below by barriers, natural or artificial. Insistence of mill operators on uniform grade of ore, from sections of non-uniform grade, tends to prevent concentration of active workings in metal mines. Mechanical systems of mining effect this concentration in coal mines.

Local sources of heat, dust, gas, fire hazard, or other conditions interfering with normal arrangement of an otherwise desirable system, are often troublesome and sometimes expensive to handle. A separate intake split usually must be diverted direct to an outlet not used to transport men, or a separate air circuit must be formed. Underground stables in a coal mine require a separate split, as do other possible sources of fire, as elec transformer and pump stations. Sealed fire zones are commonly handled by putting the area under enough press to overcome reverse natural drafts, and providing a small separate split to a main return or to the surface, from a point above the fire zone.

Examples. In the United Verde mine a circulation of 60 000 c f m was planned (1930) for an underground generator and hoist installation (31); in the Village Deep mine, So Af, a split of 75 000 c f m was allocated to a similar installation (81); in the Calumet & Hecla conglomerate mine (Mich), 2 large pumping stations on a return shaft had each a circulation of 30 000 c f m (63); at the Ray undercut-caving mine (Ariz), a separate shaft equipped with a surface exhaust fan connected (1930) with 3 rotary dumps at the ore-hoisting shaft, passed over 40 000 c f m. Auxiliary fan-pipe installations are effective for carrying the return from a local source to a distant airway.

Circulation through caved ground also impairs well-planned ventilation systems. Most common form is leakage through the fill, where the shaft collar extends above the natural ground level; averted by a concrete lining from collar to solid rock, or other tight stratum. In caved ground, circulation depends mainly on how the ground caves. Even though proportion of fine material is large enough to prevent circulation through the mass itself, spaces along the hanging wall and near pillars or solid ground may permit considerable flows. Enough air can pass up through 15–20 ft of coarsely broken ore to ventilate a shrinkage stope, and enough may pass through a 200-ft fill of moderately coarse rock in a raise of large cross-sec to ventilate a small stope (63). In the retreating systems used in Mich copper mines, air circulates freely through caved areas adjacent to active stoping, so that these zones are equivalent to low-resistance return airways.

Pressure systems, under certain conditions, may be desirable to insure that circulation goes from working places to and through caved ground. Where the main system is of the exhaust type, pressure could be maintained locally by booster fans. If pressure ventilation is desirable throughout, it can be adapted to the foregoing major objectives, particularly the rule that openings used for transporting men shall carry intake air. This adaptation usually requires a main fan underground on the intake side; or entrance through an air lock; or use as an intake-air upcast, of the shaft in which men are hoisted. All these methods involve added inconvenience to mining operations or added expense as compared with a straight surface exhaust system.

Ventilation personnel. Ventilation at many metal mines is everybody's business and thus no one's responsibility. Under favorable natural conditions no great harm results, though in case of fire, loss of life or property may be increased by ignorance of the air-distribution system. Under unfavorable conditions, ventilation becomes important, and good results are possible only where lines of authority are strictly drawn. In general, ventilation should be handled solely by: (1) a trained crew to make actual installations of distribution features, (2) a "ventilation foreman" to supervise installation and record the distribution and air conditions; (3) a high official with authority to initiate and control major changes.

Ventilation foreman in a small mine may be an operating official, but in a large mine his position should be independent. Technical ability and knowledge of ventilation theory, though desirable, are less important than mining experience, intimate knowledge of the mine, and ability to work with operating officials. Where natural conditions make good ventilation a matter of prime importance, technical ability and knowledge of ventilation theory are essential to reduce the demands on the higher official.

Official in charge of ventilation should have sole responsibility for the system. In a large organization, some one man often is especially fitted for the work, through knowledge of ventilation theory. For a large mine or group of mines operating under difficult conditions, a mining engineer specializing in ventilation would be the natural selection, with or without other duties of importance. Most large, deep gold mines on the Rand now employ technically-trained ventilation engineers to cope with problems of dust and high temp, and these men contribute much of the current literature on mine ventilation. In coal mines, each grade of official has legal duties and responsibilities in regard to maintenance of ventilation, and systematic layouts can be planned in advance so as to be largely self-extending and foolproof. But, the same need for expert guidance and help exists if operations are to be conducted safely and economically, and the above remarks on metal mining practice apply also to coal mining (3).

Cost of ventilation at many metal mines, where ventilation is wholly "natural," is nil; even where natural circulation is partly controlled, cost is negligible. Mechanical ventilation is expensive and must be effic. Costs vary widely for different operations and conditions, regardless of economy attained or bookkeeping methods used. Few data have been published, particularly for U S coal mines. Briggs (3) estimates that British coal mines circulate about 80 000 000 cu ft of air per min at a cost of about $10 000 000 a year, or 4¢ per ton coal produced, or $122 per year per 1 000 c f m. Davies

(28) gives an aver of about 8.8¢ and a range of 3.2–18.6¢ per ton for 11 So Wales collieries, with power at 2¢ per kw-hr. Cost of ventilation in Northern anthracite field of Pa is estimated (27) as approx $3 500 000 for circulations totaling 25 000 000 c f m, or about 14¢ per ton coal produced. In Western Middle anthracite field of Pa, 10¢ per ton excluding power is said to give good ventilation, 7–8¢ fair, and 4–5¢ poor ventilation. Shallow, easily ventilated, non-gaseous bituminous mines in U S show costs of 1.5–4¢; gaseous operations, 9–14¢ for steady, up to 24¢ per ton for irregular operation. J. A. Saxe estimates that gaseous mines in Pa bituminous fields, of 3 000–5 000 tons per day, with power at 1¢ per kw-hr, should be ventilated for 4¢ per ton; that well-designed new mines could attain 3¢, and new mechanically-operated mines possibly as low as 1.5–2¢ per ton for continuous multiple-shift operation.

Operating and cost data for 14 large metal mines are shown in Table 1, where costs per ton are 0.32–18.7¢, and effect of large-scale concentrated production in reducing per-ton cost can be seen by comparing figures for shallow block-caving operations (first 4 items) with rest of group, which represent normal, deep mine operations.

Distribution of costs between labor, power and supplies depends largely on mine conditions, especially the degree of control of air distribution. With little control, approx percentages are 15–70–15 in the order given; for moderate control, as in the aver deep metal mine or non-gaseous coal mine, 30–50–20; for extensive control, as in gaseous or deep, hot mines, 50–25–25. PERCENT OF TOTAL MINE POWER USED IN VENTILATION at mechanically-ventilated mines is large. For the group shown in Table 1, it is 2–35%; for the small metal mine, it may be 50% or more. A survey of 40 Ill coal mines (29) found an aver of 22.45%. Briggs (3) quotes estimates of 7–40% for British coal mines; probably applicable to U S coal mines, with an aver of roughly 20% for mechanized bituminous and 35% for non-mechanized anthracite mines.

Table 1. Ventilation Costs for Large Metal Mines

Mine	Operating data, 1929				Performance data, 1929					Cost data, 1924–28			Mean yearly unit cost	
	Ore per day, tons	Metal, percent	Total underground employees	No employees on largest shift	Total circulation, cu ft per min	Cu ft per min per man underground	Cu ft per min per h p, main fans	H p per ton	Ventilating power, per cent of mine power	Mean yearly total	Cents per 100 000 cu ft of air	Cents per ton of ore	Cents per lb of metal
Morenci	5 000	2.0 Cu	350	235	168 000	715	1 040	0.045	2.0	$17 647	2.5	1.2	0.035
Ray	10 000	1.3 Cu	800	400	162 000	405	1 430	.011	2.7	11 752	.8	.39	.017
Inspiration	23 000	1.1 Cu	1 760	810	165 000	205	1 440	.005	3.2	16 535	2.0	32	.019
Miami	13 500	.9 Cu	725	470	105 000	225	470	.020	16.6	27 567	4.5	.85	.052
Magma	800	7.0 Cu	400	200	156 000	780	390	.68	23.7	44 601	6.0	18.7	.156
Old Dominion	1 300	2.7	600	300	180 000	600	900	.32	14.0	58 625	7.9	17.0	.266
Copper Queen: Porphyry	2 200	2.1 Cu	295	150	} 100 000	250	540	{ .016	} 30.0	41 018	6.8	{ 6.2	.179
Limestone	850	4.3 Cu	500	250				{ .24				{ 9.5	.092
Calumet and Arizona	1 750	5.0 Cu	680	450	140 000	310	470	.26	13.3	60 335	7.8	12.5	.128
United Verde	2 400	4.0 Cu	900	500	350 000	700	780	.13	35	97 899	4.6	11.8	.147
United Verde Extension	2 200	9.0 Cu	450	330	90 000	270	670	.11	26	33 963	3.7	16.3	.078
Pilares	2 800	2.5 Cu	1 200	600	240 000	400	1 020	.11	35	18 174	1.6	2.3	.044
Bunker Hill Sullivan	1 400	10.01 Pb	580	540	40 000	75	500	.06	24	11 656	6.0	2.6	.....
Morning	1 100	{ 9.11 Pb / 6.0 Zn }	} 450	305	40 000	130	570	.12	22	21 040	11.0	7.4	.022
Hecla	850	10.01 Pb	300	270	70 000	260	470	.19	7	12 865	6.0	4.0	.023

3. DISTRIBUTION OF AIR CURRENTS

Control of air currents. Natural distribution of air is almost always inefficient; for effic distribution, both direction and quantity of flow must be controlled. In a large mine, many conflicting factors are involved, and the system should be planned to care for as many factors as possible in order of importance, first with regard to safety, and second, to service (15).

Mine pressure adjustments. General directions of flow are determined by points in the system at which pressures are generated; quantities of flow, by intensity of these pressures. Both direction and quantity can be controlled by modifying the natural resistances to flow in the mine openings, or by artificial airways. Resistance of an airway may be increased by tight stoppings so as to stop the flow entirely, or by loose stoppings to restrict the flow to leakage, or by regulators to provide a flow under quantitative control. Resistance may be decreased by combining airways or changing their physical conditions; or the equivalent effect obtained by a booster fan. A single airway may be divided by a brattice to make 2 separate airways; or an artificial airway may be constructed within an airway (as in auxiliary ventilation by fan-tubing units), or at a junction of airways to permit air currents to pass each other, as by an overcast.

Direction of flow in a mechanically-ventilated mine is primarily determined by position of main fan or fans. Demands of service and safety sometimes coincide, but usually conflict, in whole or in part. With two surface openings available, one in active use for operating purposes and the other inactive, the planning of ventilation distribution involves 3 decisions: what should be the normal direction with respect to the operating opening; should the fan be on the surface or underground; should the general direction be fixed or subject to reversal in emergency? Actual conditions control these decisions, but usually a reasonable regard for safety of life and property requires a primarily-exhausting reversible fan installed on the surface at the non-operating opening, as discussed below.

Operating openings as intakes. In all mines, the important consideration in determining direction of flow is that the means of exit should be on intake air; hence the operating opening should usually be an intake, actuated by an exhaust fan on a non-operating opening. Other effective means are: making the operating opening a fresh-air outlet, or upcast in the case of a shaft, or putting it under pressure with intake air. Most coal and metal mines are so ventilated, including large mines recently equipped. In a gaseous coal mine or deep, hot mine, it is almost essential to make the operating opening an intake; in the former, to limit elec haulage to intake airways, and in the latter, to permit direct coursing of surface air to active workings. DISADVANTAGES: in cold climates, formation of ice in the opening, freezing of water lines, and discomfort caused by low temp. These difficulties can be largely overcome at moderate expense. Due to effect of rapidly changing temp and moisture conditions on timber and rock, intake openings are subject to higher maintenance costs near the entrance than the returns with their uniform air conditions; return air currents may not only be highly corrosive to equipment, but may also make gangways wet or produce hot, foggy, and smoky air conditions. Where large quantities of dust are raised, on or near an opening that for safety should be an intake, dust should be prevented from entering intake currents.

Location of main fans, in general, should be on the surface, for effic control; legally required for coal mines in some states and in most European countries (26). A fan underground may be wrecked by an explosion or during a fire; the only sure means of control is to cut off the power. However, some normal operating conditions favor underground location, which may actually be more accessible in certain metal-mine layouts than location on surface; but it is then wise to provide also a surface fan for emergencies. Where all surface openings are required for operations, underground location is the usual solution in metal mines; but in English coal mines, location on surface with air locks for passing cars is common. This is relatively expensive where rapid hoisting is done, but operation of main fans underground may be more wasteful of power than is generally realized. Underground installations usually require air locks on main haulage roads that might otherwise be left open; they almost always result in considerable recirculation, dangerous during a mine fire and always undesirable.

Effect of fan location on pressure. In surface installations, greatest press differences between intakes and returns occur in the upper part of the mine, where stoppings can usually be kept in good condition because of infrequent use. In underground installations, greatest press differences are on stoppings and doors in an active zone where, due to frequent use, it is difficult to keep them tight. Surface fans permit air-flow systems of lower resistance than underground fans, as the latter usually must be placed so that flow is confined to less than the full number of airways available.

Arrangement for reversing direction of main flow (Art 13) is required by law for coal mines in some states (25) and in most European countries (26); common at most metal and bituminous coal mines, and at a few mines in the Pa anthracite district. As insurance against emergencies, it should be installed at all mines, regardless of whether its need can be foreseen or not. Lack of reversing arrangements has been held responsible for much loss of life and property in mine-fire disasters. Whether or not to reverse a fan after a mine explosion or during a mine fire is a serious decision, to be made only by the highest officials after consideration of all the factors; the reversing arrangements should therefore be locked unless the attendants are reliable. Time is important, and as it is required to ascertain the need for reversing and make the reversal, not only should smooth operation be insured by occasional trials of the mechanism, but other methods of control should also be planned to effect safe exit of men.

Fireproofing of intake openings is essential. Intake airways usually present a serious fire hazard against which it is difficult or impossible to protect the men underground, except by fireproof construction. But such construction does not overcome the hazard well enough to permit dispensing with the reversible feature of the fan; burning materials in the openings or on stations may give off enough gases to cause danger. Fireproof construction is also desirable in main return airways, though there it is mainly insurance against property loss or interference with operations, since the returns are usually wet throughout.

Fireproofing of installations is customary for main fans; less often for auxiliary fans. These often present fire hazards, particularly the forward-curved-blade centrifugals, which may overload and burn out their motors. Even the backward-curved-blade centrifugals with constant-power characteristic are not entirely safe in this regard, when reversed.

Splitting of the air current. In small mines or sections of a mine, the required quantity of air is best circulated in a single current. In large mines the flow should be split, so that each mine section has its own air current, for effic and safety. The power required for the same circulation is thereby reduced, one section is not necessarily affected by air pollution and hazards of others, and quantities may be adjusted to requirements. For max effic, splits should be taken off the downcast circuit, and returned to the upcast, as close to the surface as possible. Legal requirements as to number of men per split of air make splitting compulsory for all except very small coal mines.

Plan of splitting. In some cases, the main current is divided, say at a shaft bottom, into two or more primary splits, which in turn are divided into two or more secondary splits, and these in turn may be further subdivided. In others, successive splits are taken off the main air current, until it becomes the last split. Splitting should not be carried too far, or veloc of flow will be reduced to ineffectiveness; or, in the case of pitch workings, press may be reduced until natural draft pressures, due to differences in temp or gas content, interfere with circulation.

Natural and controlled splitting. In metal mines, the air generally divides naturally, with minimum regulation, the object being to get as much air as possible through restricted openings. Flow outside the main airways may be through a network of interconnected openings, and little attempt is made to keep the air splits separate. In coal-mining terms, the air is " broadcast " through the active zones of operation. In special cases, a similar procedure is followed at coal mines, but generally the air splits are carefully controlled, with quantities adjusted to requirements by regulators (Art 5). Natural splitting would normally give the least air to the longest working section with the largest requirements. Generally, all splits but one (the " open " split) are throttled by regulators (Art 7).

Average quantities per split vary considerably even for similar mine conditions. Aver figures, to which there are many exceptions, are: 20 000–30 000 cu ft per min for metal mines and longwall coal mines; 10 000–15 000 for flat-pitch room-and-pillar coal mines; and 5 000–10 000 (at higher pressures) for gaseous steep-pitch coal mines.

Booster fans. Control of air currents by regulators is obtained only at expense of increased power requirements, generally accepted as a necessary evil. Where the " open," or unregulated, split has abnormally high resistance, power requirements can be decreased by a booster fan in that circuit, equivalent to reducing circuit resistance. This device is common in metal mines, where irregularity of ore deposits often demands it (Art 13); less often required in coal mines; in gaseous mines, it introduces a hazard and booster fans are prohibited by law in many states and in most European countries, or allowed only for rare conditions (25, 26). Booster fans are also used in special cases to put sections of workings under pressure in mines ventilated by exhaust systems, particularly sealed fire areas or caved areas through which gas or high-temp air would otherwise enter the main circulation.

4. VELOCITY OF AIR CURRENTS

Velocities in passageways. Moderate veloc saves power, by reducing friction and therefore pressure. In airways driven solely for ventilation, veloc should be that for max economy, as determined by balancing construction cost against operating cost (Art 11). In airways for transport and travel, it is limited by considerations of safety and health. High veloc may drive the flame of a safety lamp against the gauze and ignite a surrounding explosive atmosphere (Sec 23). The bonneted, double-gauze lamps now in use are safe to velocities above 2 500 ft per min. Carbide lights can withstand up to about 1 000 ft per min, but for working purposes 500 ft per min should not be exceeded.

In open-light mines, high-veloc exits should be electrically lighted and provided with regulators to permit reducing velocities temporarily in emergency. Max permissible vel in operating shafts in France is 1 500, and in Germany 1 600 ft per min (26). Veloc is not limited in U S coal mines, except occasionally by individual mine inspectors.

Velocities at working faces. In non-gaseous coal mines velocities at working faces are not important. Veloc of 20–30 ft per min moves blasting smoke out of dead ends as a compact cloud. Higher veloc breaks up and diffuses the cloud. In gaseous mines, 100–200 ft per min is sometimes required across faces for rapid dilution of gas emitted. In undercut-caving, 100 ft per min or over is desirable across grizzly levels, to relieve operator of dust from chute-running (31). In hot mines, veloc required for comfort increases about as the square root of the veloc (Fig 59, Art 17), so that the economy of attempting veloc over 100 f p m in local circulations is debatable. (For veloc distributions in airways, see Art 9; for pipe inlets and discharges, Art 6.)

5. DEVICES FOR CONTROLLING AIR DISTRIBUTION

Stoppings. Almost all devices for controlling distribution by introducing obstructions to flow, or artificial division or deflection walls in airways, may be called " stoppings," since materials and conditions of installation are similar.

Note: Space between frame and rock surfaces filled with concrete

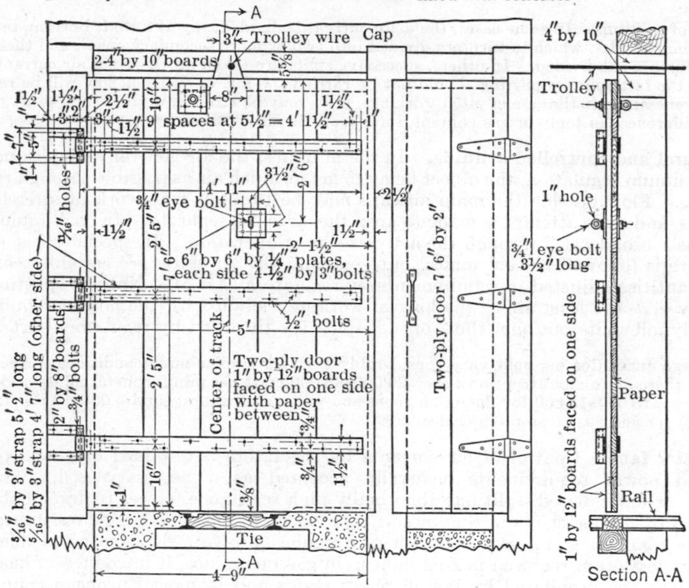

Fig 3.   Ventilation Door used on Motor Haulageway in Metal Mine (31)

Permanent stopping is a tight wall across an airway to prevent flow to adjoining openings; usually designated " stopping " in U S bituminous mines, " wall-stopping " in anthracite mines, and " bulkhead " in metal mines; often used in connections between parallel airways in coal mines. While gob stoppings, usually faced with plaster or cement, are still the rule in many older U S coal mines, concrete-block and brick are now preferred in bituminous, and plain concrete in anthracite mines.

A study by Williams (30) of 80-sq ft main-entry stoppings in Ill (1915) shows aver first costs from $7.20 for dry-wall gob type and $7.34 for rough board stoppings, to $11.57 for 8-in concrete and $17.43 for 8-in brick walls; but under specified conditions, annual costs, chiefly of power wasted in leakage, were $1.53 for concrete, $1.91 for brick, $35.93 for dry-wall gob and $76.99 for rough board stoppings. Permanent stoppings in metal mines, chiefly for sealing off abandoned or fire areas, are usually of heavy wood construction, often luted with clay or gunited with cement for tightness, and erected in ground subject to movement. Aver costs per sq ft of gunited stoppings are estimated (1521) as about 40¢ for small and 30¢ for large isolated stoppings, and 20¢ for large jobs or especially large stoppings. Where the ground is "heavy," packs of short timbers laid endwise, or of alternate layers of rock and timbers, give good service by crushing until practically airtight, in circumstances where a reinforced concrete wall would eventually be demolished.

Temporary stoppings. Where waste material is available, and tightness not essential (as in connections between rooms in room-and-pillar work), temporary stoppings are usually of loosely-packed gob. Otherwise, and for extra tightness, they are of light wood, or brattice cloth on a wood frame, usually called "brattices" (bituminous) or "brattice stoppings" (anthracite mines). Temporary stoppings are infrequent in metal mines.

Doors. Where men or traffic must pass through a stopping, it has a door. In coal mines, the resulting hazard keeps the number of doors to a minimum. In metal mines, they are often used where stoppings would be used in coal mines, and transport and travel are thereby facilitated. Where passage of men is infrequent, doors in gaseous coal mines are about 2 by 3 ft, so arranged that they can not be left open. Otherwise doors are almost as large as the stoppings containing them: 6 by 9 ft aver for coal and 5 by 6 ft for metal mines. In metal, but less often in coal mines, a main traffic door, especially if automatically operated, is supplemented by an adjoining narrow door for passage of men (Fig 3). In metal mines doors are often installed in untimbered sections to control air currents in case of fire.

Type of door, commonest in both coal and metal mines, is single, vertically hung and unpainted, made of 2 plies of 1-in boards, with cloth or paper between plies. Practice favors horiz and vert,

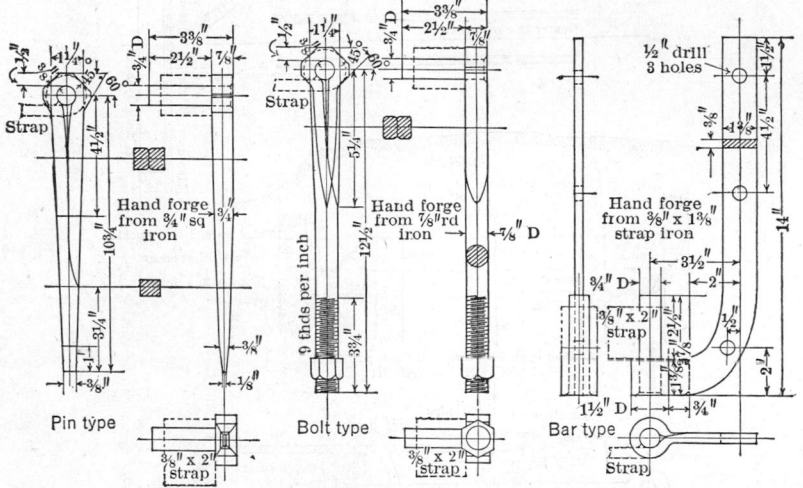

Fig 4.   Door Hooks, or Studs, of Strap-type Hinges (27)

rather than diagonal plies, with vert ply on the "push" side and nails clinched on the "pull" side. Door is set in a timber frame, with posts wedged to roof and floor, and closes flush against the frame rather than on a jamb. Wooden stop blocks are provided at the floor, with clearance for track rails. Doors are swung by long strap hinges on studs, or "hooks" (Fig 4) and arranged to be self-closing with the air current, and stay closed against reversed flow. In coal mines, the frame is erected on a slight batter and lower hinge-stud offset about 1.5 in, the door closing by its own weight. In metal mines, the frame is vert, and door is closed by counterweight. Space between frame and walls is filled with concrete; or, in metal mines, it may be boarded over and gunited; in coal mines, filled with "slate" dry-walls faced with mortar. Various devices reduce leakage where tightness is essential (Art 7). For temporary use, or where leakage is not important, light cross-braced single-ply wooden doors, or doors of canvas and wood, set in light wooden frames, are common in coal mines. Metal-covered and all-metal types are rare. Glass reflector buttons are often set in doors to warn motormen of their location, and small glass panels may be inserted in automatic doors to warn men of approaching motor trips.

Curtains of several narrow, overlapping strips of non-flammable brattice cloth, hung from the roof, often replace doors on entries in bituminous, and on breast manways, in anthracite practice.

Air locks. Where opening a door would seriously interfere with ventilation or create hazard, an air lock is formed of 2 doors, only one of which is opened at a time. Distance between doors is adjusted to the traffic. On main roads in gaseous mines, a third door is often added, to function if either of the others is disabled; required by law in Pa anthracite and some European countries.　In metal mines, an air lock is sometimes used where press-difference is high, to facilitate opening the doors, as the net press tends to distribute over both doors.　Where the press on air-lock doors makes opening difficult, a small shutter may be inserted in each door, to equalize press before opening.

Automatic doors. In gaseous mines, attendants are required, often by law at important doors and air locks.　Sometimes they may be replaced by an extra man on the motor crew, or by automatic doors operated by bell-crank lever connected to a false rail, depressed by wt of approaching car.　Such a device, common in flat and light-pitch coal workings, has been adopted in a few metal mines; but in steep-pitch coal workings and main motor roads of metal mines, doors operated by comp air are preferred.　A motor-operated door, controlled by trolley-wire contacts, is increasing in use for main motor roads of metal mines.

Remote-control doors. Many metal mines use doors operated from a distance by wires attached to the valve of a comp-air cylinder (Fig 5).　The door is opened by the piston, and closed by a counterweight when press is released.　Similar designs operate by water press.

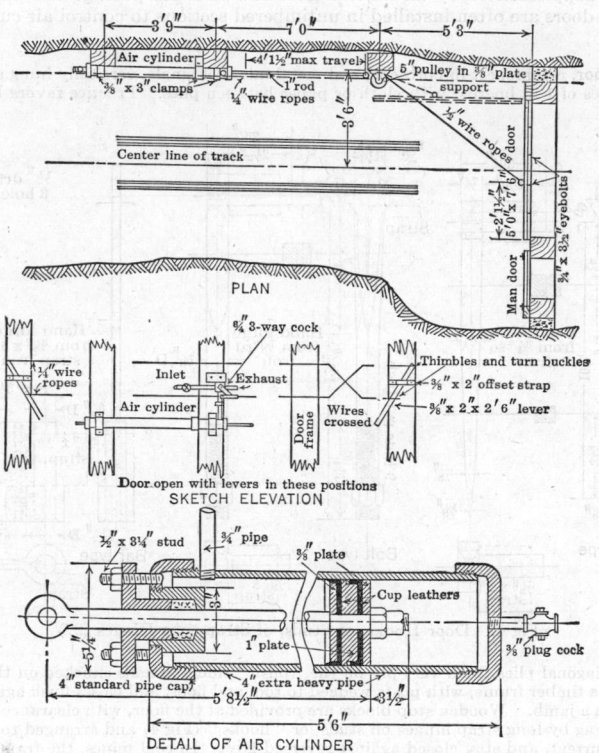

Fig 5.　Device for Operating Ventilation Door by Comp Air, Metal Mines (31)

Fire doors and their control. In case of fire the veloc of certain ventilating currents should be immediately reduced without changing directions of flow.　As stopping the fans does not stop mine air currents, the only sure means is to shut off all main airways with doors.　These are normally blocked open and used only in case of fire.　They resemble ventilation doors, except that those installed in timbered sections are usually of fire-proof or at least fire-resistant construction.　Best position for the main group of fire doors is on all open airways off the main or operating shafts; many metal mines are so provided and some have installed remote control on sets of doors adjacent to particular shafts, so that all may be closed from one or more positions, particularly from surface.　The control utilizes water press, comp air, or elec mechanisms to withdraw a latch, which normally holds the door open against the pull of a counterweight; the device may act by applying press or current, or by removing it. Continual inspection of such mechanisms is important; failures due to ground movement and corrosion are common enough to retard the spread of this useful idea.

Costs of doors. Costs for substantially constructed 4.5 by 6.5-ft doors in Ariz copper mines in 1928 (31) were: door only, $25; door in concrete frame, $50; air-operated door in concrete frame, $175; same, with adjoining narrow man-door, $225. A rail-operated automatic door with adjoining man-door is said to cost approx $300. A temporary type of light wooden door in wooden frame of aver size costs $15–$25.

Line brattice is a lengthwise stopping of light construction (like a temporary stopping), dividing a single opening so as to direct air flow to a gassy working face. It is used in moderately gaseous workings to conduct air from the last crosscut to a development face; also in rooms in very gaseous workings, particularly pitch workings (see Fig 8); usually made of random lengths and widths of 1-in rough boards nailed to each other and to posts of small diam, set on 4 to 6-ft centers; joints are sometimes clayed for tightness. Nonflammable cloth, usually jute but termed " canvas," is often used, especially for room brattices in bituminous mines; it is hung from narrow boards nailed to the posts along roof and floor. Canvas is also used for temporary extensions, and is then hung from small wooden pegs set in roof. Random lengths and widths of light gages of sheet steel " seconds " are used in Ala coal mines at a first cost (comparable to canvas) of 20¢ per sq yd, and last much longer than the 4–5 months aver life of canvas (32). For long extensions of single openings, to make connections in coal mines (" cross-measure tunnels " in Pa anthracite), line brattice is substantial, usually of concrete walls or packed filling between heavy double-plank walls. In rock openings, small pressure-release panels are inserted in the brattice for protection against blasting concussions (27).

Pipe as a substitute for line brattice (common in steep-pitching measures of the Middle Pa anthracite field) is of 24- to 30-in diam, extending to development faces from a board stopping at the last crosscut. This is airtight, and avoids leakage, the major defect of line brattice. In metal mines, auxiliary fan-tubing ventilation replaces line brattice, and is rapidly increasing in coal mines, particularly in deep European mines and U S bituminous mines using mechanical systems of mining (Art 6).

Deflector brattices. A loose stopping for deflecting air current from its normal path is usually termed " deflector brattice " in metal mines, or simply " brattice " or " check " in coal mines. Placed across an airway in a coal mine, it often serves to " hurdle " the air into a high spot in the roof where explosive gas would otherwise collect. Deflector brattices have been tried in metal mines for increasing aver veloc through working zones, by constricting the flow. They are of rough wood construction; canvas brattices are not successful in metal-mine stopes, due to damage by blasting concussions. Deflector brattices are used in hot metal mines to keep convection currents, from dead ends, out of a cooler intake airway, as such currents cause multiple small-temp increases in the cooler air current.

Regulators are stoppings with openings of adjustable size, for adjusting resistance to flow, in series with normal resistance of the airway or mine section, to allow only the vol of flow desired. They should be placed to cause min press-differences on stoppings: on intake side of circuit in a press system, and on return side in an exhaust system. Regulation by adding resistance is common in coal mines, but in most metal mines has been confined to inactive openings, where a small air flow is sufficient to prevent falls or excessive decay of timber. Usually a door is fastened open; if press is high, blocks are placed at both cap and sill to prevent warping. As a regulator is merely an orifice in an airway, its pressure loss and size can be calculated for constant conditions from data on orifice-press losses (Art 10). In practice, the conditions of possible use are largely unknown at time of installation, and a large opening is best, which can be adjusted by trial more accurately than by calculation.

Types of regulator. A door set partly open is sometimes used as a regulator, but the common construction is a stopping with a rectangular opening and adjustable sliding door, often known as a box regulator. Iron slides in concrete stoppings are common on important airways and locked in position; but a wooden slide door in a brattice is more usual, as tightness is not required. The slide is dispensed with on minor airways, and the opening is then adjusted by nailing boards on or ripping them off.

Overcasts. Crossing of air currents without intermingling is effected by overcasts (" air bridges " in Pa anthracite), made by blasting down part of the roof at intersection of airways and building an airtight structure in the space so formed. Although often of wood, more substantial construction is now required; usually of concrete with the floor slab reinforced by old rails (Fig 6). Costs of these range from about $250 where little rock work is required, to $350 for aver flat-pitch bituminous conditions and $500 and over for large structures in moderate to steep-pitch anthracite workings. Undercasts, made by blasting up the floor at intersections, are rarely used on account of the danger of filling with water or debris. Crossings are practically never used in metal mines, as the ordinary layout does not require them. Minor return currents are sometimes passed through intakes in large-diam pipes. Large culvert pipe has been used in coal mines, as well as sectional-steel liner plates. Multi-seam coal mines often substitute rock drives to adjoining seams for overcasts (27).

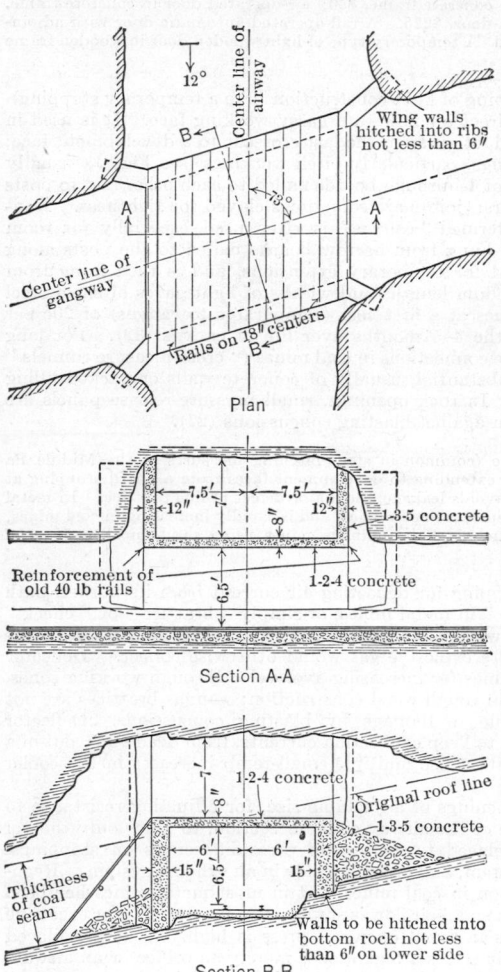

Fig 6. Overcast of Reinforced Concrete (27)

6. AUXILIARY VENTILATION

Fan-pipe installations, whereby air is forced through small-diam pipes to dead-end working faces, or exhausted from them, are common in metal mining and tunnel driving, under conditions of length and high cost of excavation for which line-brattices are not suitable. Although largely used in the Comstock (Nev) mines before 1850 (16), the real development of fan units and piping, particularly canvas pipe (20, 33), started in the U S in Butte about 1915, for combating effects of high temp; then spread to other metal-mining districts with similar problems, and later to coal mines (where permitted), where objectives are reduced leakage due to fewer breakthroughs, and better and cheaper ventilation in mechanized-mining areas. Pipes over 4 miles long have been used in driving tunnels.

Fans of BLOWER TYPE are preferred in both metal and coal mines, because of better cooling effect, better dilution of gases at the face, and in permitting use of canvas tubing. With this type, recirculation should be prevented by placing the fan, or a connection to its inlet, in an intake current at least twice as large as the fan circulation. In coal mining (34), fan inlet should be at least 10 ft from the nearby edge of nearest return current, and fan should not take over 40% of total circulation. EXHAUST and REVERSIBLE FANS are preferred in driving long tunnels. Exhaust units discharge blasting smoke, gases, and dust through the pipe, whereas with blower units these return through the tunnel at very low veloc. Reversible units have special dampered ducts at the fan to secure flow in either direction; usual practice is to exhaust for a time after blasting, otherwise to blow. Advantages of both systems are sometimes secured by using 2 blowers: a large unit near the face, discharging to the main circulation or to surface through canvas tubing; and a smaller unit, just outby the larger, blowing part of the tunnel intake air to the face for ventilation (Fig 7). The fans must be far enough from the face to be uninjured by blasting. DIFFERENCES IN VENTILATING EFFECT between exhaust and blower types depend largely on differences in veloc distribution and convection current effects (Art 12), both of which favor the blower. Air movement is perceptible only a few ft in front of a pipe inlet, but 20–30 ft from a pipe discharge. Actual veloc depends primarily on pipe area at inlet or discharge and is little affected by shape (36, 37). For exhaust units, temp differences between end of pipe-line and face are small, and convection effects negligible. For blower units, temp difference is often large and convection effects important. Anaconda Copper Mining Co (38) uses blower units with narrow-slot discharge, to control direction of discharge so as to produce minimum dust concentration at the breathing level.

Type of fan unit in metal mines is usually the direct-connected motor-driven centrifugal; for elec drive in coal mines, the propeller type. For protection against explosive coal-mine gas, compair drive should be used, and fans operated continuously or not at all. Comp-air units are useful auxiliaries at metal mines for emergencies and fire fighting. Comp-air injectors (Art 14) are used for short pipes on temporary jobs; their effic is low, but so also is first cost.

Pipes may be of wood, iron or " canvas," usually jute treated to render it airtight and resistant to fire and decay. Wood-stave pipe and heavy gages of iron pipe are usually limited to long lines in tunnel driving. Canvas tubing and light-gage galvanized iron pipe of 8–16 in diam, occasionally larger, are common in metal mines; 8 in for lines to 250 ft long, 10–12 in to 500 ft, and 16 in to 1 000 ft or more. Canvas is good for temporary installations and where a straight line is impracticable. It comes in 25, 50 and 100-ft lengths with sewed-in couplings, and is attached to a wire fastened to timbers or to rib or roof pegs. It is more easily handled than iron pipe, stands blasting concussions better, but is often torn in service. Iron pipe is good for more lasting installations and for straight lines; press requirements for straight lines are lower than for canvas tubing, in approx

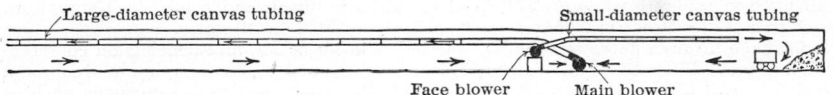

Fig 7. Fan-tubing Installations for Ventilating Long Dead-end Openings with Canvas Tubing (9)

ratio of 3 to 5, and joints can be made tighter. Sections are usually about 10 ft long, made up to 12-in diam of single sheets with crimped seams; over 12-in, of 3 sections with all seams riveted-and-soldered, or longit seams crimped. A small swage, or bead, is often formed near ends of separate sheets, used in assembling sections, for extra stiffness; for single-piece sections, ends are swaged and two or more thin iron bands are spot-welded at intermediate positions.

Pipe lines should be as straight as possible and extend to within 15–25 ft of face for max benefit. Depending on type of rock blasted and pipe material, pipe within 25–200 ft of the face must be removed before blasting. To put blasting sections quickly back in service, use of gas masks is recommended for headings; telescopic sections may be used in shafts (12). Blasting gases are usually blown back to the pipe-end with comp air (35).

Joints in canvas tubing usually permit slight leakage which can not be controlled. Slip joints, with male ends pointing downstream, are common for iron pipe, and since pipe ends are easily deformed, large leakages are frequent; remedy is to wrap joints with asphalt-soaked muslin. Joints may be made tight against mine press by using draw-bands over wrapped joints, with pipe ends and bands swaged. Joints in heavy-gage iron pipe used in long tunnels (up to 5 miles) were formerly equipped with expensive flanges, but now are usually welded in place.

Capacities for mine units vary from 500 to 5 000 cu ft per min, occasionally more, depending on size of opening and heat, gas, or dust conditions. For aver conditions in metal mines, roughly approx sizes (51) for 30–50-sq ft openings in warm rock (85–90°) are: 8-in tubing with fan driven by 3-hp motor to give about 1 000 cu ft per min at 4–5-in press for lengths up to 250 ft; 12-in tubing with fan driven by 5-hp motor to give about 2 000 c f m at 5 to 6-in press for lengths up to 500 ft; 16-in tubing with fan driven by 10-hp motor to give about 3 000 c f m at 6 to 8-in press for lengths up to 1 000 ft; and similar fans in series for lengths much over 1 000 ft. If tubing lines are in aver condition, 40–70% of the air passing the fan will be discharged at end of line.

Pipe costs. A 12-in pipe of aver wt, in 10-ft lengths for iron or 50-ft lengths for flexible tubing, costs approx 75¢ per linear ft in small quantities. Costs for other sizes vary roughly with content of material, that is, with diam. For flexible tubing, cost per ft is about 10% lower for 100-ft sections and 10% higher for 25-ft sections. Under aver conditions, cost of installing flexible tubing is about one-third that for iron tubing. Approx aver figures are 2¢ per ft for flexible and 6¢ for iron pipe.

Costs per cu ft of air delivered at or near the working place by fan-tubing methods vary widely, but an approx total of capital return, power cost, and maintenance is 0.2¢ per 1 000 cu ft, against an aver of say 2¢ for comp air released at the face and 0.05¢ for main-fan circulation.

7. LEAKAGE IN VENTILATING SYSTEMS

Effic of distribution. Proportion of entering air that actually passes through working places, is the real criterion of a ventilating system. It is just as important as effic of fan, and much more difficult and expensive to attain, because leakage in solid ground can be minimized only by substantial construction, and in fissured and pervious ground is difficult to control. Leakage losses are generally large and effic of distribution low. Leakage at stoppings, doors, and fan installations are common causes of poor distribution.

Effic in practice. Williams' tests in 16 Ill coal mines (30) showed that the max per cent of the entering air reaching the last crosscuts of splits was 33.5%, aver about 20%, and in 3 instances less than 10%. Davies (28) says that in high-resistance coal mines in So Wales not more than 20% of the air moved by the fan reaches coal faces. In metal mines where all main fans are underground, it is impossible to avoid large recirculation; usually, such fans handle 1.5–3 times the amount of air entering the mine. However, aver practice is much better than these examples indicate. In the aver coal mine, 30–50% of fan air reaches active workings; in the aver metal mine, 50–60%, since fewer stoppings are involved; in both, max is probably about 85 per cent.

Leakage through permanent stoppings. The bane of coal-mine ventilation is leakage through stoppings between adjoining intake and return airways, whereby air is short-circuited without passing through active workings. Leakage is dependent on construction and press-difference p (see Art 11 for effect of leakage on pressure-loss computations), varying directly as p for very small openings in packed material and as $\sqrt{p}$ for ordinary leakages. Williams (30) gives test averages in Ill coal mines, showing range of 6 cu ft per min for 8-in concrete walls, to 171 c f m for faced gob-wall and good board stoppings. Aver press-differences (not given) were probably 0.1–0.2 in of water.

Leakage through doors is an important factor in all mines, and depends on construction and press-difference p, varying as $\sqrt{p}$. At a press of 1 in, common in metal mines, a good door will often pass as much as 3 000 c f m unless precautions are taken, such as covering the edges with canvas strips. Leakage may thus be reduced to about 1 000 c f m on active doors, and to 500 on inactive doors. In coal mines, aver press-difference, where doors are used, rarely exceeds 0.25 in of water, and the above leakages are halved for the same door conditions. However, canvas flaps are less effective at low press and less common in coal mines, and the ordinary " good " door will usually pass 1 000–1 500 c f m. In good Pa anthracite usage, 1 by 6-in boards are set with one edge against the door, when in the normal closed position, and nailed to inside of frame on top and sides. These are adjusted from time to time, as required by warping of the door, or effect of ground movement on the frame (27). Excessive leakage at doors may be due to lack of a tight seal between frame and walls, lack of water-seal on drainage ditches, and excessively large openings for pipes, tracks, and trolley-wires.

Leakage at fan installations, where max press-difference occurs, requires especially tight construction, for which wood is unsuitable for both effic and safety. Under aver conditions of substantial fireproof construction, leakages of 1 000–2 000 cu ft per min for small installations, to 3 000–10 000 for large installations, can be expected on the basis of available data (9).

Leakage at fan shafts. Collars of fan shafts and portals of fan drifts should be thoroughly sealed to rock, as by concrete construction, to prevent excessive leakage through ground that may appear tight. Shaft collars of waste from sinking operations will " leak like a sieve " and spoil an otherwise good installation.

Leakage through shaft walls. The practice of carrying intake and return currents in adjoining shaft compartments, though generally regarded as obsolete and forbidden by law in some states and most European countries, is still common at many Ind and Ill mines and anthracite mines in Northern Pa field. In the former, excessive leakages through the curtain wall are common; but in anthracite mines, substantial 16-in brick and concrete walls hitched 2 ft into the side walls practically eliminate leakage unless ground movement is excessive.

Leakage through strata is normally negligible, but practically always present, as shown by the usual low pressures on fire-area seals even in " good " ground. Where air must be carried through broken, caved, or filled ground, leakages are often amazing: losses of 90% in only 1 000 ft of travel are not uncommon. The usual remedy is new airways through better ground, with air broadcasted through broken ground to similar returns or to surface. In metal mines, booster fans are sometimes used to minimize press-differences at local areas on airways where leakage would otherwise be excessive. Leakage in airways passing through pervious ground may also be reduced by carrying the air through by low-press fans operated in series to minimize press differences.

8. EFFECT OF MINING METHODS ON AIR DISTRIBUTION

General effect of openings on distribution. Exact conditions of distribution at working places where mineral is extracted depend largely on details of mining method, both as to position and type of openings, and time-sequence in driving them. In general, the larger and more numerous the openings, the better the air conditions at working places. However, the prime need for good ventilation is 2 or more openings to all working chambers, to effect through-circulation. To remove blasting smoke to the main flow, for diluting strata gases, or to provide air-motion cooling in warm atmos, quantity of flow usually is less important than veloc. For the same power load, quantity is increased, but veloc decreased, as openings are increased in number and size, whence openings should be of minimum size at working places, and max size elsewhere in the circuits. Exactly the reverse is the normal result of all mining methods, since working places are large openings, and connections much smaller. Low veloc of flow in working places can be increased

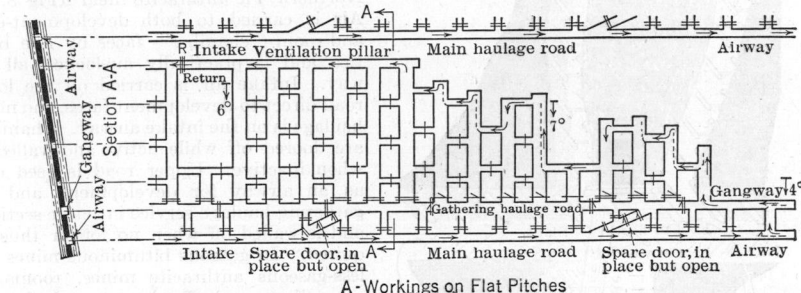

A - Workings on Flat Pitches

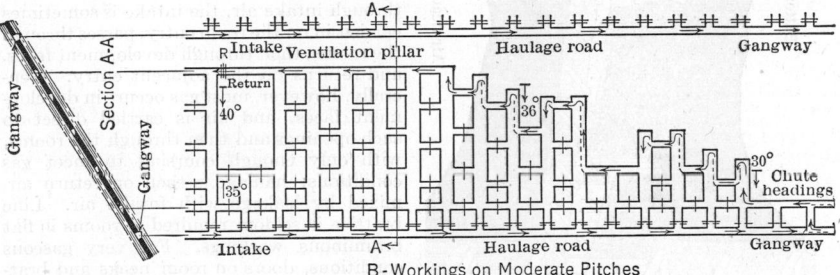

B - Workings on Moderate Pitches

Fig 8.   Methods of Ventilating Gassy Room-and-pillar Workings (27)

by attention to details; but for aver conditions velocity requires little consideration, because even very low veloc on through-circuits, with diffusion and convection currents in openings off through-connections, usually suffice. Veloc is important only in gaseous coal mines and for high temp.

Ascensional ventilation. For inclined working places, the relative elevations of connections are important because of natural-draft and convection-current effects. Essential requirement is that connections be made to airways above and below the working openings, so that ascending through-circulation is possible and max advantage is taken of natural-draft press. To utilize available flow in both inclined and flat workings, the rule of next importance is that through-openings be offset with respect to the working openings, so that the actual working place is not a long dead end off a through-opening.

Room-and-pillar methods are practically standard in U S coal mines, and, although details of layouts of workings differ, the essential features in active working sections are shown in Fig 8. Development is by double-entry, employing 2 parallel openings connected by crosscuts 60–100 ft apart.

In steep-pitch workings, air may be distributed as in Fig 8, B, except that "chutes" connecting haulage-road and airway, also the rooms ("breasts"), are partly filled with broken coal, leaving one manway open in the chute and one along each rib in the room

(Fig 9). These manways are bratticed off below the last open crosscuts, and carry air to the face on one side and back to the open crosscut on the other. Manway and airway brattices and chute stoppings have small canvas-covered openings for passage of men. Chute and manway openings in chute stoppings are small, and are sealed off when the chute is no longer used.

In moderate-pitch gaseous workings, the breasts are carried open, and line brattice is used to convey air to the faces; distance from face to end of brattice, and tightness of brattice, depend on gas conditions at the face. Separate lifts, or sections along the pitch, are usually kept separate by ventilation and drainage pillars, and face-ends are connected (Fig 8, B) to avoid gas accumulations in dead ends extending to the rise.

In flat-pitch gaseous workings occurs the extreme of ventilation control, as in Northern Pa anthracite field (Fig 8, A). Air is carried to both development-ends and room ("chamber") faces by line brattice and is practically air-locked all the way. Intake air is carried on the lower road direct to development faces, and main-haulage is on the intake airway. Chambers are doored off while active and walled off when inactive. Upper road is used only as an airway for development and for gathering-haulage service in active sections, and is walled off when no longer thus required. In gaseous bituminous mines and less-gaseous anthracite mines, rooms are generally turned off only one road of a pair of entries. To bring haulage near the rooms through intake air, the intake is sometimes carried in on the room entry, passes through the rooms, then through development faces, and returns on the adjacent entry. Generally, however, most gas occurs in development faces, and air is carried direct to such openings and then through the rooms, with only enough coursing to meet gas conditions; haulage is then on return air, mixed by leakage with intake air. Line brattice is seldom required in rooms in flat bituminous workings. For very gaseous conditions, doors on room necks and brattices in room crosscuts generally suffice. For less gaseous conditions, the latter are not required; the air is forced to travel through the rooms by check curtain brattices on the entry in the active section, sometimes between all room necks (Arkansas).

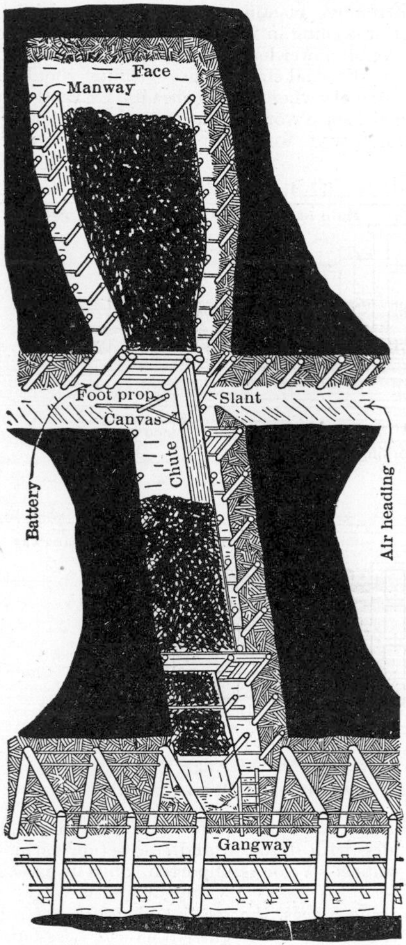

Fig 9. Start of "Full" Breast in Steep-pitch Breast-and-pillar Mining (P & R C & I Co)

Flat non-gaseous workings. In these, only minimum control is needed. A few check curtains on the room entry serve to keep the air "broadcasting" through the rooms. Even these are often omitted, and the only air passing through rooms is that due to natural splitting, occasioned by variable resistances to flow. Interference by cars in entries of small cross-sec forces most of the air to take lower-resistance paths through the rooms and room crosscuts. Rooms are often driven off both entries, so that the intake must necessarily be through one group and the return through another. Often, air requirements are so small that several sections are ventilated by a single split of air, and the return of one section becomes the intake of another, often " sweetened," however, with small additions of intake air direct to each section (see Coal Mining, Sec 10).

Longwall methods used in U S are mostly short-face types with working face comparable to the rib of a room, and air-distribution conditions are like those in room-and-pillar methods. In typical longwall workings (Fig 10) as in Europe, with branching roads from centrally-located downcast and upcast shafts to long working faces, few splits are required and large-volume flows sweep the faces, an important advantage of this system.

Metal mining methods in rare cases are comparable to flat non-gaseous coal mine layouts; usually to multi-seam, steep-pitch, coal operations, but with more variety of

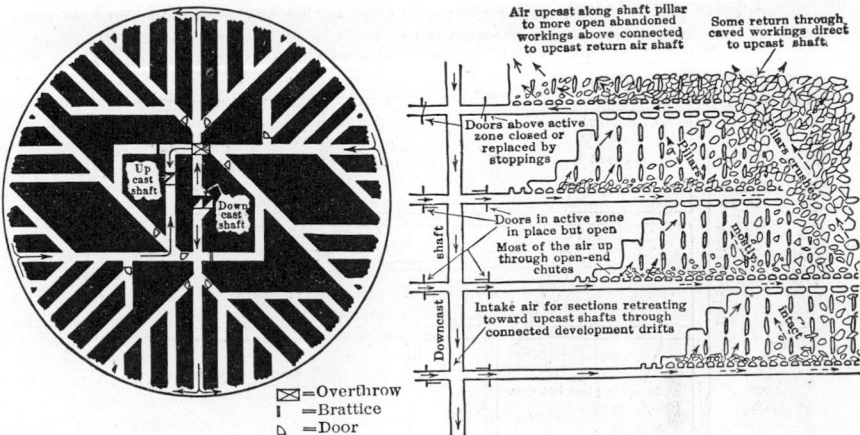

Fig 10.   Ventilating System for Longwall Mining

Fig 11.   Method of Ventilating Retreating Open Stopes (9)

mining method.   Strict coursing of air currents is not required except to cope with high temp.   Larger quantities of explosives are used and blasting smoke is more of a problem than in coal mines.

Open-stope workings are usually large and thus easily ventilated, as air requirements are low. There must be at least one opening from each large working place to the level above.   Veloc of air

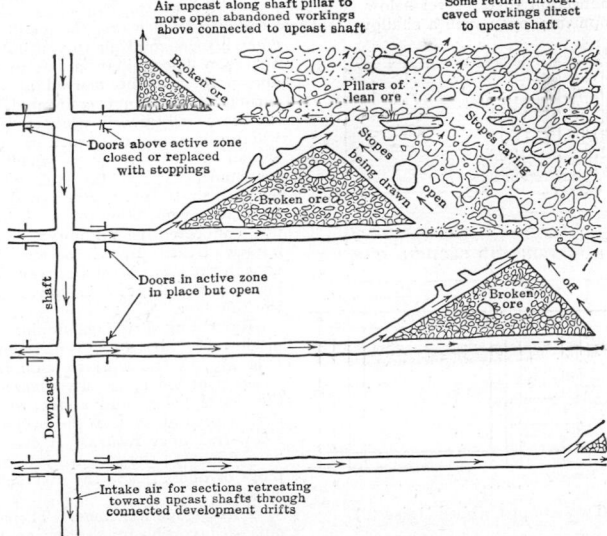

Fig 12.   Method of Ventilating Retreating Shrinkage Stopes (9)

travel is usually very low, but blasting smoke and gases have only a short distance to go before reaching inactive workings, where their slow travel is of little importance.   Depths of mining which involve high rock temp usually also require changes in mining methods (as from advancing to retreating stoping), and openings cave more readily, automatically diverting air flows to active openings.

Recently-caved ground near active openings is usually still fairly permeable to flow and constitutes a second opening of low resistance for retreating working faces (Fig 11). Even after caved areas have become compacted, they will usually pass considerable air, chiefly along pillars and solid boundaries. Eventually, with increased depth, special return airways must be provided.

Shrinkage-stope workings. Ground that can be worked by temporary-fill, or shrinkage-stope methods is also easily ventilated. For safety, each stope should have 2 openings, and for good

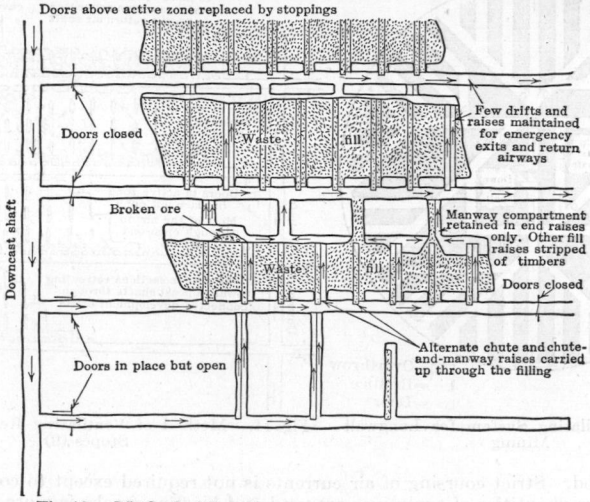

Fig 13.   Method of Ventilating Horiz Cut-and-fill Stopes (9)

ventilation these should connect to the levels below and above. The opening at the working face is restricted, and, with blasting confined to end of shift, the small quantities and low veloc of the normal air flow give good ventilation, sometimes permitting blasting of large slabs during the shift, although such blasting is usually confined to the lunch period or end of shift. In continuous shrinkage stoping, connection to the level below is usually provided by the chute-raises driven during advance development; even with a shallow depth of coarsely broken ore, these will often permit enough seepage of air to ventilate the stope. Where a floor pillar is left under the level above, it must be pierced at intervals. A shrinkage stope not connected to an upper level is usually poorly ventilated, particularly where the stope-wall rock is warmer than the air in the airway to which connections are made. Where the wall rock is colder, natural draft may give good ventilation. Often the ventilation of a shrinkage stope, not connected [to an upper level, could be improved easily by a loose curtain or canvas door in the lower level, between the end openings into the stope, thus hurdling air to the working face.

Retreating shrinkage stoping on moderate pitches provides good ventilation conditions (Fig 12), as the working chamber is a relatively confined space with large openings to the levels below and above, and the slowly caving ground back of the broken ore makes a low-resistance return. If desired, flow can be confined to the stopes by temporary stoppings or doors inside the last active drawing chute.

Filled-stope workings. Their natural layouts are favorable for ventilation, because they require connections to the levels below and above. However, ground conditions often limit the size of passages, so that air flows are small, even with mechanical ventilation. The larger compartments of raises are usually full of ore or fill, so that circulation depends on the manway compartments, of which two are always kept open for safety. In a stope in its early stage, both manways run off the lower level; in later stages the only one maintained may lead to the upper level. Or a single manway may go directly from level to level; stope ventilation then depends largely on eddy cur-

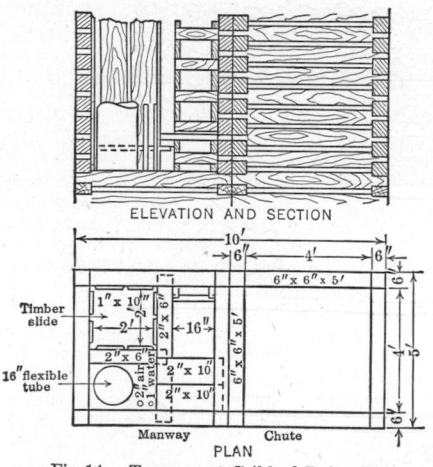

Fig 14.   Two-compt Cribbed Raise (9)

rents off this manway. For good air conditions, the layout should provide ascensional flow, with air coursed through the working area (Fig 13). Manway design is important; a good design used in many western metal mines is shown in Fig 14. As veloc must increase in high-temp ground, the cross-sec of openings must be minimized, and filling should closely follow extraction. Rill stoping and filling, especially when retreating, favor stope ventilation.

Top-slicing provides poor natural conditions for ventilation, due to dead-end workings and to heat from decaying crushed timber in the mat. For good results, special openings for air must often be made. There are 3 general methods: "hurdling" from the level below by well-arranged stoppings and doors; connecting each floor in succession to a raise in an adjoining section, connected to the return airway; and connecting, to a return airway, the open space above a thin mat and fill. Miami Copper Co, Ariz (1918), using mechanical ventilation, employed a ventilation level of closely spaced openings, with numerous doors and stoppings to force air through closely spaced raises to large top-slice operations; results were so good that continuous blasting was possible in the stopes. In general, the hurdling method (Fig 15) is applicable to aver top-slice conditions, the other two applying only to special conditions of advancing or retreating methods, or of mining small sections or pillars in ground that stands well.

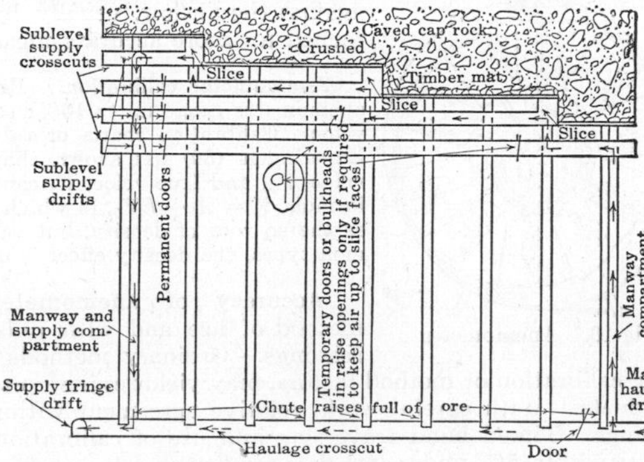

Fig 15. Hurdling Method of Ventilating Top-slice Stopes (9)

Undercut caving involves many development openings without upper connections (unless made to old prospect openings); but the many openings between undercut and grizzly levels usually induce convection currents, with enough circulation for 1-shift work. Mechanical ventilation is always used, and provides quick clearance of smoke from working places and grizzly drifts, where intermittent blasting is required. In general, intake air along the main-haulage level is carried to the grizzly level through raises driven for new development, and passes thence, through active drawing drifts, to fringe-drifts connected to the returns. Due to difficulty of keeping other raises (in drawn and drawing sections) blocked off with waste or ore, control is uncertain, but some control is possible by using doors or stoppings at fringe-drifts, to close all but the active drawing drifts. Actual layouts often preclude simple methods, and in 1929 the Miami mine was considering a special ventilation level for a new section, for better control of ventilation (31). Good ventilation of boundary-caving shrinkage workings usually requires a well-planned system of connected openings.

9. VENTILATION MEASUREMENTS

Quantity of air passing in an airway is expressed in cu ft per min (c f m); not determined directly, but calculated by multiplying the airway area in sq ft by the aver veloc of flow, ft per min.

Measuring current veloc. Usual methods are smoke-clouds for low veloc, anemometers for moderate to high, and pitot-static tubes or special anemometers for very high veloc. Measurements should be made where the cross-sec is regular and preceded by as long a straight section as possible. The observer should not obstruct or disturb the air current, by causing local increases of veloc around his person; his best position is in the plane of measurement at arm's length, or farther, from point of measurement.

Velocity distribution. As veloc is variable over any section, areas must be traversed by multiple readings. One-point observations, if exactly the same point is used, will show relative changes. Max veloc in a straight airway of uniform cross-sec occurs at middle of section and is about 1.2 times the mean veloc. At a constriction in a straight airway, side velocities are increased and mean veloc approaches, or may exceed the center veloc. At an enlargement, side velocities are decreased, and center veloc may be as much as 1.4 times the mean veloc.

Smoke-clouds may be used to determine direction and approx magnitude of flow at velocities below the usual anemometer range. More accurate instruments, including special anemometers and the (dry) kata-thermometer, are available, but their use in mines is limited. Smoke-clouds may be generated with an aspirator bulb blowing puffs of air through a glass tube containing granulated pumice, saturated with anhydrous tin or titanium tetrachloride. Clouds generated to travel at the quarter points of cross-sections give results averaging about 10% high. Variations in flow are easily detected and observations may be limited to periods of normal flow, a decided advantage where velocities are low.

Biram vane anemometer having a range of 150–2 000 ft per min is usual for moderate to high veloc. It is a small windmill (Fig 16) with oblique blades connected through clutch and gearing to one or more dials, which record the velocity of air passing the blades. Observations must therefore be timed: difference between the final and initial readings divided by time in minutes gives veloc in ft per min. Recent designs have a zero reset, giving the total reading directly. Common size is 4-in diam. Side opposite the dial is held against the airflow, usually by hand; but a rod can be attached for more accurate measurements and greater reach.

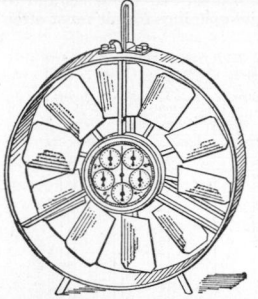

Fig 16. Anemometer

Anemometer calibration. Errors in single readings by Biram anemometer range up to 10%: too high at high veloc, too low at low veloc. Calibration charts or tables are furnished by the maker. Experiment (39) has shown that the relation between registered veloc, V_o, and true veloc, V, can be expressed by the straight-line formula $V = A + BV_o$, in which A and B are constants. A varies as the sq root of density, but values of A being about 30 for common types, the density effect is negligible.

Accuracy of anemometer measurements varies with method of use and with pulsating flow, which causes high readings. Ordinary methods of traversing by hand, without using calibration or method factors, may yield results up to 20% high for high veloc, as in fan ducts. With careful work, relative agreement within 2% is possible for successive readings. Timed hand traversing and use of calibration and method factors (9), give results within 5% under aver flow conditions. In precision traversing, with anemometer shaft guided by a frame, results accurate within about 2% are possible, and relative agreement of successive observations within 0.1% has been obtained (40) when flow is uniform. Holding the instrument by hand increases the reading about 10%.

Other anemometers. HIGH-SPEED INSTRUMENTS of the Biram type usually have half as many blades as the standard, but are otherwise similar. INDICATING ANEMOMETERS, although sensitive and convenient, are little used in mines, because: oscillation of the pointer prevents accuracy; many readings must be averaged to attain accuracy; and observations often involve interference with air currents. Common forms are: windmill types with devices similar to speedometers; and pivoted vanes, indicating veloc by the angle to which the vane is set. VELOMETER is a swinging-vane anemometer, in which the vane is enclosed in a housing with inlet and outlet openings, to which attachments are fitted for measuring veloc and press over a wide range of flow conditions. Impact press of the veloc (and press-differences) cause proportional flow of air through the instrument; and the momentum of this flow actuates the vane. In impact-vane instruments, veloc reading varies directly as the sq root of air density (end of Art).

Pitot tube apparatus is more practicable for measuring very high velocities than are special anemometers, as measurements are often made inside pipes and tubing where an anemometer cannot be used. It consists of a double-walled pitot-static tube (Fig 17) and manometer for measuring difference in press, transmitted through tubing from the two component parts. This press difference is equal to veloc press of the flow (see below). The apparatus is a primary device for air measurement, accurate in most designs to within 1% (39).

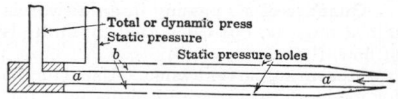

Fig 17. Pitot-static Tube

APPLICATION. With V = veloc in ft per min; H_v = veloc press, in of water; w = wt of 1 cu ft of air (approx 0.075 for usual mine conditions), $V = 1\,098 \sqrt{\dfrac{H_v}{w}}$

or $H_v = \dfrac{8\,310\,w}{10^{10}} V^2$

If $s = \dfrac{w}{0.075}$ = sp density of air, based on standard wt of 0.075 lb per cu ft,

$$V = 4\,008 \sqrt{\frac{H_v}{s}}, \text{ and for } s = 1, H_v = \left(\frac{V}{4\,008}\right)^2 = \frac{623}{10^{10}} V^2$$

For careful work, aver veloc must be the mean of computed velocities, not that derived from the mean of veloc pressures. Accuracy also requires precision traversing, and, for moderate to low veloc, very sensitive manometers; press is approx 1 in at 4 000, but only 0.25 in at 2 000 ft per min. Under mine conditions of high-veloc flow, the common vert U-tube manometer or "water-gage" is sufficiently accurate, and merely approx methods of traversing are justified.

Other pressure-difference methods, wherein veloc or quantity of flow is measured by the press change caused by an obstruction, such as an orifice plate, or by difference in cross-sec area, as in a venturi-shaped section, are rarely used in mines, although applicable to certain phases, as tests of fan-pipe installations.

Accuracy of air-flow measurements. Considering the normal variations in air quantities in mines, particularly on the split flow, accuracies of individual measurements of the order of 10% for low veloc and 5% for moderate to high veloc are satisfactory. For fan tests, and other purposes where care is justified, accuracy within about 2% is obtainable in absence of marked pulsations. Effect of pulsations in causing high readings can be allowed for if their amplitude and period are known (39); not the case in mine flow. Considering the aver inaccuracy of measurement, the reporting of flows below 20 000 c f m to the nearest 500 c f m, and over 20 000 c f m to the nearest 1 000 c f m, is sufficiently precise.

Absolute pressure of the atmosphere is usually measured by aneroid barometer, chiefly to determine air density (end of Art). Approx values are obtainable from tables of altitudes and temperatures (4), but as the abs press at any point may vary 1 to 2 in of mercury during the year, actual observations are better.

Aneroid barometer is a flat, circular, corrugated vacuum capsule with one side attached to a case and the other to an index mechanism carrying a pointer over graduated circles on front of case. Air pressures distort the capsule and thus actuate the pointer. Best aneroids are compensated for temp by a bar in the linkage, composed of two or more metals. Scales may be graduated to read inches of mercury, or approx equivalent ft of altitude, or both. Mine instruments usually have both, and should always have the mercury scale. For mines at very high altitudes and deep mines at sea level, instruments with special scale ranges are required. Small rugged types are better for mine work than larger and more accurate ones, as they stand sudden and large press and temp changes better without change in calibration. Accurate work requires occasional comparisons with a laboratory-standard vert-tube mercury barometer. With the best instruments there is considerable lag in press and compensation for large changes. PAULIN ANEROID (12) is a special design, in which distortion of the capsule is prevented by changing a spring tension, adjusted by turning a ring on the dial until a secondary pointer comes to zero position, whereupon the main pointer indicates pressure. Several concentric dials are used to indicate very small press changes.

Absolute-pressure surveys. Methods and instruments **(41)** for measuring abs press closely enough to determine small press-differences due to air flow are in the development stage. Approx results have been secured in main airways of flat-pitch mines, but difficulties in steep-pitch mines have led to a preference (42) for direct press-difference methods. High-precision standard aneroids are popular in England, where a special vert-tube barometer, the " contrabarometer," also finds some use. In Germany, the Askania Statascope (43) is favored; it is an aneroid, in which the base press can be set and small differences from it are measured. In the U S, the Paulin is most used, with graduations in ft of altitude only; and in coal mine practice, density differences are ignored by making direct corrections for differences in altitude, usually without material error. More precise instruments are required for use in minor airways.

Measurement of small pressure differences due to air flow is usually made on liquid manometers (U-tubes partly filled with liquid), by connecting each press to a separate leg of the U and measuring the vert difference in height of liquid due to difference in press. If a liquid other than water is used, its sp gr is determined and press-difference is expressed in inches of water at 60° F; 1 in of water equals 5.2 lb per sq ft or 0.0361 lb per sq in. Kerosene and alcohol are often used in more sensitive types; kerosene in permanent set-ups, because it does not vaporize or change sp gr; alcohol in the laboratory, as it does not cling to glass nor affect rubber tubing. Toluol is used in some high-precision gages.

Manometers. VERTICAL TYPE (water-gage) is so widely used in mine ventilation that press differences are usually termed "water-gage." Its simplest form is a U-shaped glass tube, partly filled with water and with scale attached. Where mine pressures are separated by a brattice, no tubing connections are needed, the gage being applied as in Fig 18. To facilitate reading differences in level in the two legs, the scale is adjustable to bring an even inch mark opposite one liquid level.

Precautions: (1) connections should be tested for air tightness by observing if the gage will hold a press when the ends are sealed; (2) where differences of elev are involved, composition and temp of air in connections should be the same as in the air current, so that small pressures due to unbalanced air columns do not affect the reading; (3) tube and tubing ends should be in quiet air to avoid small errors due to veloc effects on orifices. Where used in moving air currents, tubing should terminate in a plate or tube, like the static terminal of a pitot tube, having a small burr-less orifice in a surface parallel to the flow. INCLINED MANOMETER, or U-tube with both legs in an inclined plane, magnifies the reading and measures to 0.001 instead of 0.01 in of water; used for greater sensitivity, as in research or with pitot tube. Angle of inclination, accurately known and maintained, is deter-

mined by the magnification desired and sp gr of liquid used; its sine is found by dividing the recipro-
cal of the sp gr by the magnification ratio, or length (in) of slanting scale for 1 in of vert displacement of water. Instruments with fixed magnification and mounted on a leveled base are usual.
For mine work, Weeks (12, 44) has designed a transit-mounted adjustable-slope instrument (Fig 19)
suitable for measuring small press changes in short sections of airways. DRAFT GAGE, for fixed
positions in power plants, is a manometer with one leg of large and one of small bore, proportioned
so that over 95% of the vert displacement of liquid occurs in the smaller tube, which has a graduated
scale; readings are made on this leg only. One reading only is required, whereas both levels of a

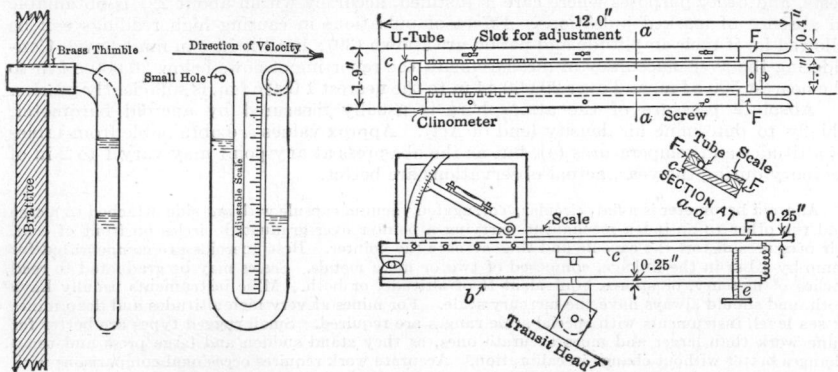

Fig 18. Water Gage   Fig 19. Weeks Manometer (*Min & Met*, Jan, 1923)

uniform-bore U-tube gage must be read for fluctuating press-diff; but calibrations are required for
accuracy. MICROMANOMETERS are precision manometers, for great accuracy, as in measuring low
velocities by pitot-tube press methods, and for calibration of ordinary manometers. They resemble
draft gages, with micrometer measurements of magnified scale readings and scales set to zero at
the level in the large bulb in which, due to large area ratio, only an infinitesimal part of the total
displacement occurs. Most types commercially

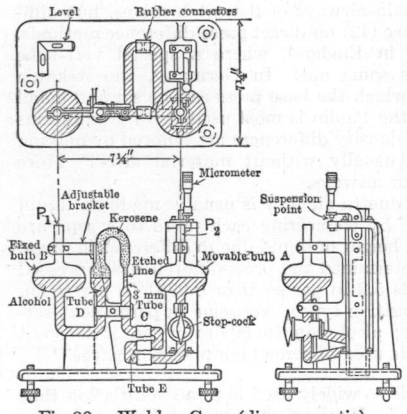

Fig 20. Wahlen Gage (diagrammatic)

available are of German make, as Prandlt's precision manometer (3) and Askania Minimeter (43).
WAHLEN GAGE (45) is a precision manometer of a
two-liquid, tilting gage (Chattuck) type, accurate
to 0.0001 in of water (Fig 20). It consists of 2
unequal-bore U-tubes half filled with alcohol
colored red with aniline, connected by a third
U-tube which is inverted and filled with clear
kerosene of a sp gr about 0.01 less than the alcohol.
In one U-tube the large bulb is movable vertically
by a micrometer. Junction of the liquids is in a
tube of capillary size. A zero reading is obtained,
with both bulbs open to the air, by adjusting
height of bulb A to bring the junction to an etched
mark. Then with the greater press connected to
bulb B, vert displacement of the junction is
neutralized by raising bulb A. The difference of
final and zero readings measures the press-difference, in inches of alcohol. A scale etched on the
capillary is useful where press fluctuates (49).
Due to the large amount of exposed glass, this
instrument is greatly affected by small temp
changes, and can be used properly only under
laboratory conditions.

Recording pressure gage is useful for continuous records. Common design for fan
pressures is like a clock, the face consisting of a 24-hr circular paper chart, with radial hour-
lines. An index pen describes a line varying in radial distance according to air press.

Indicating and recording quantity gages are little used in mine ventilation, due to expense and
necessity for special calibration. As recording designs are based on measurement of small press
differences, the small forces involved require expensive construction. In the BACHARACH QUANTITY
RECORDER, veloc press is multiplied by venturi devices 2 to 3 times, and recorded on a drum chart,
graduated for quantity if desired. Multiplication of press is not exact and calibration is required.

Power of a ventilating current in ft-lb of work per min = press (including veloc press)
in lb per sq ft, × veloc in ft per min, × area of air course in sq ft = pVa,   wherein

Q = quantity of flow in cu ft per min. Hp of current = $pQ \div 33\,000$. Example: hp of ventilating current passing 100 000 cu ft per min at press (including veloc press) of 2 in of water = $(100\,000 \times 2 \times 5.2) \div 33\,000 = 31.6$ hp.

Air density (see Sec 23, 39). Press of water vapor is determined by its dew-point (temp) (Sec 23). Both this temp and relative humidity, the ratio of vapor press at dew point to that at dry bulb temp, are determined, from observed wet- and dry-bulb temp and abs press, by psychrometric formulas, tables (57) or charts (9). "Standard atmosphere" is dry air weighing 0.08072 lb per cu ft at 29.922 in barom press at 32° F (at Paris).

Density formulas. Wt of dry air in 1 cu ft of moist air at temp t, barom press b, and press of water vapor f in of mercury, is:

$$w_a = 0.08072 \, \frac{491}{459 + t} \cdot \frac{b - f}{29.922} = \frac{1.325}{459 + t} \, (b - f)$$

Wt of water vapor in 1 cu ft, at press f, is: $w_v = 0.622 \, \dfrac{1.325}{459 + t} \, f$. Combined wt of air and vapor in 1 cu ft of moist air is:

$$w = w_a + w_v = \frac{1.325}{459 + t} \, (b - 0.378 f)$$

If relative humidity is r and vapor press corresponding to air temp is F, then $rF = f$. For dry air f = zero, and press = b.

Weight of gaseous mixtures can be computed when proportions of the constituents are known. Wt of moist air is found as above, and the mixture of air and aqueous vapor is treated as a single element; not quite correctly, except when humidity is determined before the air is polluted with mine gases. This is seldom possible, because mine conditions usually increase humidity, but the error is negligible.

Example. To find wt of mine atmos containing 1% CO_2 (sp gr 1.529) and 1% CH_4 (sp gr 0.5545), at 29 in barom, 75% relative humidity and 50° F (at which, press of saturated aqueous vapor is 0.362 in of mercury). Weights per cu ft are as follows:

For moist air, $\dfrac{1.325}{459 + 50} \, (29 - 0.378 \times 0.75 \times 0.362) = 0.07519$

For CO_2, $1.529 \, \dfrac{1.325}{459 + 50} \, 29 = 0.1154$

For CH_4, $0.5545 \, \dfrac{1.325}{459 + 50} \, 29 = 0.0424$

For the mixture:

0.98 cu ft moist air	@ 0.07519	weighs	0.07369 lb
0.01 " " CO_2	@ 0.1154	"	0.00115 "
0.01 " " CH_4	@ 0.0424	"	0.00042 "
1.00 " " of mixture weighs			0.07526 "

10. AIR FLOW IN MINE OPENINGS

Air flow conditions. When air is flowing in a duct, the wall surfaces, and their position with respect to the flow, cause interference of one airstream with another, whereby part of the kinetic energy of flow is converted to heat; hence, to maintain kinetic energy, it must be constantly renewed from total energy of flow. The flow therefore causes continuous decrease in total energy of air current in the direction of flow, and automatically adjusts itself as to quantity, so that total energy used in a circuit equals total energy generated therein. Energy losses occurring in straight ducts of uniform cross-sec are called *friction losses*; those due to deflections and change of cross-sec are *shock losses* (9). Both energy losses and energy gains (as by natural or mechanical means) are evaluated in terms of press.

Pressure forms. Theoretically, total energy of flow is measured by abs static press and velocity press. Abs static press depends on flow and also on difference of elev. But, as changes due to elev are almost balanced in any inclined or vert flow circuit, changes are conventionally considered as though the flow were horiz, and small changes due to unbalanced weights of air columns, as naturally generated press, or "natural draft" (Art 11). The absolute nature of static press is thus ignored, and only changes in absolute press due to flow are considered.

Pressure changes. The sum of static and veloc pressures is the TOTAL PRESS, which remains constant except as depleted by friction and shock. (For positive and negative pressures, see Art 12.) Changes in veloc of flow, due to varying areas of cross-sec, cause corresponding changes in static and veloc pressures, which are mutually convertible; but conversion is always accompanied by some shock loss, depending on abruptness of change in area. Veloc pressures in mine airways usually are so small that practice commonly ignores them and considers only static press, or "water gage," which is usually, but not always, the difference between the abs static pressures in an air stream and in the atmosphere outside.

Pressure losses. Both friction and shock losses depend primarily on dimensions of the airway. Roughness of wall surfaces is a determining factor of friction losses, whereas relative positions of wall surfaces largely determine shock losses. Friction press losses in straight sections of approx uniform cross-sec comprise most of the total press loss in a mine ventilation system. In deep metal mines, main airways alone often account for 70 to 90% of the total press requirement.

Friction formulas. The generally-accepted formula, or law, for press required for flow in mine airways, as developed (12) from an old hydraulic formula for turbulent flow, is

$$p = \frac{kPLV^2}{A} = \frac{kSV^2}{A}$$

where p = difference in total press between ends of airway, lb per sq ft; k = experimental factor (Table 2); S = rubbing surface, sq ft = P, perimeter, ft, $\times$ L, length, ft; V = veloc, ft per min; A = aver cross-sec, sq ft. A more convenient form for direct application is

$$H_F = \frac{kPLQ^2}{5.2\,A^3}$$

where H_F = press difference due to friction losses, in of water; Q = cu ft per min.

Laws of proportion. Proportional changes in press requirements due to variations in airway and air-flow conditions are deduced from the basic formulas above, using the first for constant-veloc assumptions, the second for constant-quantity assumptions, which are of more practical importance. For constant quantity through similarly-shaped airways, press difference varies as the 5th power of a side or diam.

Effect of shape of cross-sec on pressure requirements, for same quantity and area (9), can also be deduced from the formula. Multiply the value for circular cross-sec by: 1.13 for a square, 1.15 for a 1 to 1.5 rectangle, 1.20 for a 1 to 2 rectangle, 1.30 for a 1 to 3 rectangle; in shafts with square compts by 1.60 for a 2-compt, 1.95 for a 3-compt and 2.26 for a 4-compt shaft; in shafts with rectangular compts, with 1 : 2 ratio of sides, by 1.69 for 2-compt, 2.07 for 3-compt, and 2.39 for 4-compt shaft.

Value of friction factor k depends chiefly on character (roughness) of sides of airway, and varies directly with air density (Art 9); also affected to a lesser extent by size, and possibly form, of cross-sec and veloc of air current; and may be adjusted to include minor shock losses due to curvature, sinuosity, or obstruction. Formulas, based on experiments on pipes and small ducts, have been developed for effect of size and veloc on k for straight, unobstructed, smooth-lined ducts; but not for rough-surfaced ducts, as mine airways, where these effects are relatively unimportant for usual sizes and velocities, in comparison with character of walls, irregularity of section, curvature and obstructions. Table 2, based on existing data and original experiments in coal and metal mines by the Bureau of Mines, applies to velocities of 300–2 000 ft per min, and values of $A \div P$ between 1 and 2 ft.

Table 2. Friction Factors for Mine Airways (40) (9)

| Type of airway | Values of $k \times 10^{10}$ for air at 0.075 lb per cu ft * | | | | | |
| | Straight | | Slightly sinuous or curved | | Highly sinuous or curved | |
	Clean	Moderately obstructed	Clean	Moderately obstructed	Clean	Moderately obstructed
Smooth lined........Min...	10	25	20	35	35	50
Max...	20	35	30	45	45	60
Sedimentary rock....Min...	30	45	40	55	55	70
Max...	70	85	80	95	95	110
Timbered..........Min...	80	95	90	105	105	120
Max	105	120	115	130	130	145
Igneous rock........Min...	90	105	100	115	115	130
Max...	195	210	205	220	220	235

* For air density w (other than 0.075 per cu ft) corrected value $k' = kw \div 0.078$.

Mean radius of duct, $r = A \div P$ (used in some air-flow formulas), is a term borrowed from hydraulics to designate comparative sizes of cross-sec.

Effect on k of included shock losses. Investigation (40) has shown that intermittent shock losses, due to sinuosity and crookedness of airways and minor obstructions in them, may be computed as friction losses by adding constants to friction factors. Values of increments depend on value of r. Thus, in Table 2, the factors for clean, straight airways are base values; increments, based on $r = 1.5$ ft, are 10 for slightly curved, 25 for highly curved, and 15 for moderately obstructed airways.

Effect on k of both veloc and mean radius. Experimental data on smooth ducts have been correlated (50) in terms of a dimensionless constant, the "Reynolds Criterion," or diam × velocity × density ÷ viscosity, largely restricted to interpreting results of tests on models (Sec 38). Experimental results are often expressed by formulas including a constant k, but with fractional exponents for diam, r, or V; facility in application then requires use of special charts. It is better to maintain the general form of the friction-loss equation and relate variations in k to r and V, as done by Goodenough for tests on smooth concrete ducts for the N Y–N J Vehicular Tunnel Commission (48).

His formula for frictional resistance for veloc of 1 000–6 000 ft per min is: $p = w \left[B + \dfrac{C}{v^2 r^2} \right] \dfrac{S v^2}{2 g A}$

wherein for smooth ducts, $B = 0.0035$ and $C = 0.02867$; $v =$ velocity in ft per sec; other notation as before. Value of k, deduced from the above for $g = 32.16$ and $w = 0.075$, is:

$$k \times 10^{10} = 11.337 + \frac{334\ 300}{r^2 V^2}$$

If multiplied by 3, to allow for variation in roughness, results by this formula agree closely with those of the Bur Mines (49) on a 6.2 by 9.2-ft straight butt-heading in a coal mine: value of $k \times 10^{10}$ at 300 ft per min by formula and by the Bureau, 37.3; at 900 ft per min, 35.1 by formula, 34.9 by the Bureau. Hence, the formula seems of wide utility.

Friction factors for fan pipes. Tests by Bur Mines (51) on straight sheet metal and canvas tubing, 8–16 in diam, showed aver values of $k \times 10^{10}$, at velocities of 1 000–4 000 ft per min, of 15 for sheet metal and 20–23 for canvas; for aver mine conditions of "straight" lines, values of 20 for metal pipes and 25 for canvas are recommended. Leakage usually prevents accurate application of these factors (Art 11).

General formula for shock losses. Bends, changes in area of cross-sec, and obstructions cause changes in area of air flow; the resulting press losses are independent of roughness of walls, and bear a practically constant ratio to veloc-press of mean veloc of flow. General formula is:

$$H_s = X H_v$$

where $H_s =$ shock press loss due to change of veloc, in any units; $X =$ empirical factor; $H_v =$ veloc press at mean veloc, in same units as H_s, or $\dfrac{V}{4\ 008}$ in of water at $w = 0.075$, varying directly as w.

Shock losses expressed as equivalent friction losses, that is, in terms of equivalent lengths in ft or diameters, or as increments to friction factors, are commonly used in reporting and applying experimental results, especially on bends. Equating shock loss to friction loss (53); Equivalent length in ft $= \dfrac{3\ 240}{k \times 10^{10}} \dfrac{A}{P} X$; equivalent length in diam $= \dfrac{810}{k \times 10^{10}} X$; increment for $k \times 10^{10} = 3\ 240 \dfrac{A}{P} \cdot \dfrac{X}{L}$. *Example.* For $k \times 10^{10} = 20$, $A \div P = 1.5$, and $X = 1$, equiv length is 243 ft or 40.5 diameters; increment for $k \times 10^{10}$ ($X = 1$ per 1 000 ft) is 4.86.

Characteristics and types of bends. General flow conditions at bends or deflections of air current are as shown in Fig 21. Experiments indicate (53, 9) that press loss is due to abrupt one-sided expansion from the contracted area at departure end, to full area beyond. Characteristics used in specifying bends are shown in Fig 22, and designations of the more common types in Fig 23.

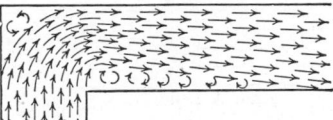

Fig 21. Air Flow at Bend (9)

Shock-loss factor X for bends (53, 9). Data are fragmentary and apply only to airways of uniform area before and after bend. There is no general formula for areas not thus uniform, nor are effects of V, $A \div P$, or roughness of lining known. Approx shock factor X for a NORMAL BEND (Fig 23A), with notation as in Fig 22, is $X = \dfrac{0.25}{r^2 a^{\frac{1}{2}}} \left(\dfrac{i}{90} \right)^2$. When $i = 90°$, $X = 0.25 \div r^2 a^{\frac{1}{2}}$ for rectangular airway and $X = 0.25 \div r^2$ for round or square airway; max $X = 1$ for square inner corner ($r = 0.5$); there is no practical advantage in exceeding $r = 2$, for which $X = 0.06$. For a SQUARE BEND (Fig 23B), $X = \dfrac{0.60}{r a^{\frac{1}{2}}} \left(\dfrac{i}{90} \right)^2$. When $i = 90°$, $X = 0.60 \div r a^{\frac{1}{2}}$ for rectangular airway and

$x = 0.60 \div r$ for round or square airway; max $X = 1.20$ for square inner corner ($r = 0.5$); low values of X practically require changing to a normal bend by rounding outer corner. For other bends, calculation of X is less precise. For a CROWDED BEND (Fig 23C), X for a similar normal bend is arbitrarily increased: e g, by 40 per cent when outer radius at bend = 0.75 of the normal. INNER BEVEL and SEGMENTAL BENDS (Fig 23D, E) may be treated as normal bends with radii circumscribing the segments; but X for a segmental bend is slightly increased to allow for " crowding " on the outer radius. VENTURI BENDS (Fig 23F) may be treated as normal bends with $r = 0.8$ to 0.9. For a BLADE BEND (Fig 23G), X may be taken as for one of the equal sections only, with a small increase for excess rubbing surface. RADIAL VANES divide bends into sections having different values of r and a. Aver factor is determined by weighting factors of separate sections according to area, and increasing result slightly for edge effect and excess rubbing surface. Best position for single vane is about 1/3 width from inner corner. Straight extensions beyond radius in either direction cause increased press loss and should not be used.

Special bend conditions. Bends discharging directly to atmos involve 50–80% more loss than interior bends, due to greater differences in veloc involved in shock loss. Tests on CLOSELY SPACED BENDS show that close spacing affects press losses, probably by its effect on veloc distributions, but data are meagre.

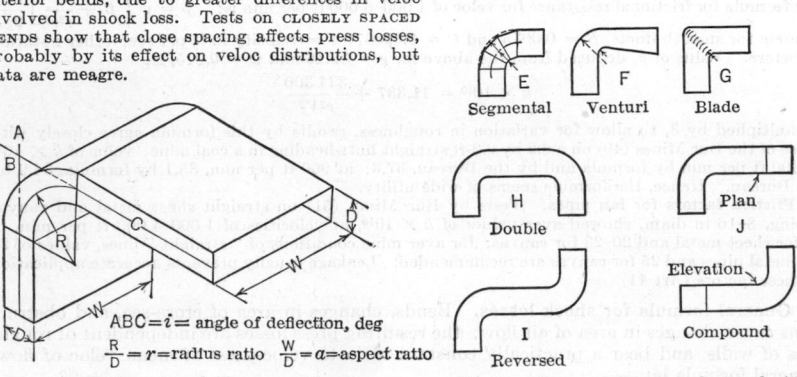

Fig 23. Types of Right-angle Bends (9)

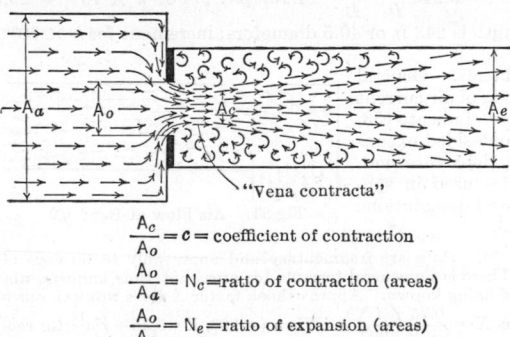

$ABC = i =$ angle of deflection, deg

$\dfrac{R}{D} = r =$ radius ratio $\dfrac{W}{D} = a =$ aspect ratio

Fig 22. Bend Characteristics

Sinuous and crooked airways. Airways often have bends and curves, wherein shock losses are too small for calculation individually, though a rough approx of total shock loss is desired. Tests by Bur Mines in metal mines (40, 9) gave following range: For a large-radius curve, or sharp bend of about 15°, or a wall line close to center line, not oftener than once every 100 ft; or a small-radius curve, or sharp bend of about 30°, or a wall line crossing center line not oftener than once every 200 ft, $X = 0.2$ per 100 ft. For a continuous large-radius curve, or continuous curve of repeated small deflections of 10°–15° every 20–30 ft, or bends of 20°–30° every 50–100 ft, or a wall line crossing center line about every 50 ft, $X = 0.5$ per 100 ft.

Splits and junctions of air currents cause shock losses due to bends and area changes, for which exact data are lacking. Split loss may be approximated as a bend loss based on veloc of diverted stream. Junction loss is (very roughly) 1.5 times bend loss based on veloc of entering stream.

Characteristics and types of area changes and general conditions of flow threat are shown in Fig 24. Contraction of the flow to pass a smaller opening causes it to occupy a still smaller area immediately beyond the opening, the so-called "vena contracta."

Pressure losses are primarily shock losses due to abrupt expansion from a smaller section and higher veloc (that of the "vena contracta," where contraction precedes expansion) to a larger section and lower veloc. Types of area changes common to airways and ducts are shown in Fig 25.

$\dfrac{A_c}{A_o} = c =$ coefficient of contraction

$\dfrac{A_o}{A_a} = N_c =$ ratio of contraction (areas)

$\dfrac{A_o}{A_e} = N_e =$ ratio of expansion (areas)

Fig 24. Flow Conditions and Characteristics of Expansion and Contraction (9)

Shock-loss formulas for abrupt expansion. Carnot-Borda equation or Borda formula (56) shows that loss of head, due to abrupt expansion of a faster to a slower stream, is equivalent to the veloc press corresponding to difference of aver veloc involved; or loss of head h in ft of air $= (v_1 - v_2)^2 \div 2g$, velocities being in ft per sec. At $w = 0.075$ lb per cu ft, with velocities V_1 and V_2 in ft per min, loss H_s, in of water $= \left(\dfrac{V_1 - V_2}{4\,008}\right)^2$. Since $Q = A_1V_1 = A_2V_2$,

$V_1 = (A_2 \div A_1)V_2$, and $H_s = \left(\dfrac{A_2}{A_1} - 1\right)\left(\dfrac{V_2}{4\,008}\right)^2 = \left(\dfrac{A_2}{A_1} - 1\right)H_{v_2} = X_2H_{v_2}$. Similarly, $H_s = X_1H_{v_1}$, where X_1 and X_2 are shock factors, or loss in terms of ratios of veloc press, corresponding to veloc before and after expansion respectively; H_{v_1} and H_{v_2} are veloc heads, in of water. In cases of contracted flow, shock loss is due to expansion from the "vena contracta," whose area is c times the actual area preceding expansion, where c (Fig 24) is termed the "coeff of contraction." Where c is known, V_1 can be determined from $c \times A_1$ and applied directly in the preceding formulas.

Shock factors for expansion and contraction (53, 9). More generalized formulas, using the notation of Fig 24, are the following:

$$X_o = \left(\frac{1}{c} - N_e\right)^2 ; \quad X_e = \frac{\left(\frac{1}{c} - N_e\right)^2}{N_e^2} ; \quad \text{and} \quad X_a = \frac{\left(\frac{1}{c} - N_e\right)^2}{N_c^2}$$

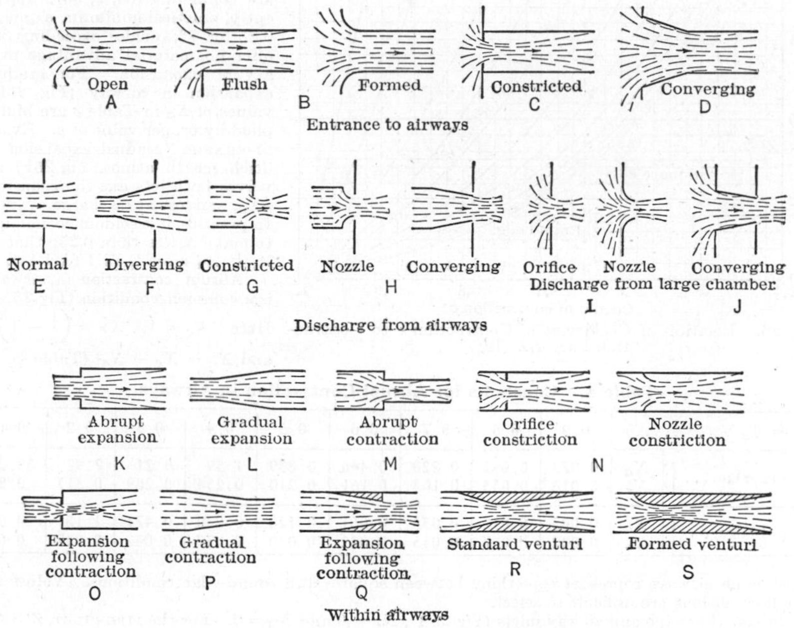

Open A / Flush B / Formed C / Constricted / Converging D
Entrance to airways

Normal E / Diverging F / Constricted G / Nozzle H / Converging
Orifice I / Nozzle / Converging J
Discharge from large chamber
Discharge from airways

Abrupt expansion K / Gradual expansion L / Abrupt contraction M / Orifice constriction N / Nozzle constriction

Expansion following contraction O / Gradual contraction P / Expansion following contraction Q / Standard venturi R / Formed venturi S
Within airways

Fig 25. Common Types of Area Changes in Airways (9)

In particular cases, c, N_e or N_c may be equal to 1 or 0, simplifying the formulas. References cited contain tabulated values and charts for graphical determination.

Coeff of contraction c depends on: N_c, or ratio of contraction of areas (Fig 24); the edge condition at contraction, represented by "contraction factor" Z; and conditions of symmetry.

A sufficiently accurate relation for c and Z for symmetrical conditions is: $c = \sqrt{\dfrac{1}{Z - ZN_c^2 + N_c^2}}$ as plotted in Fig 26.

Value of contraction factor, Z. If contraction occurs symmetrically against wall surfaces (normal condition), Z is approx 1.05 for a bell-mouth, 1.5 for a round edge like a mine timber, 2.0 for a smooth edge, as of thin sheet-iron, 2.5 for square edges common to mine forms, 2.8 for very sharp thin edges as in orifice plates for air measurement, and 3.8 for free contraction to a sharp edge (as at entrance to a pipe). Meager data on obstructions in airways, as mine cars or timbers, where contraction occurs along the perimeter of the obstruction, indicate that normal contraction factors should be about doubled; that is, 5.0 for square edges, 3.0 for round edges. For unsymmetrical contraction in ducts (56), press losses and values of c are much greater than for same ratio of symmetrical contraction.

Abrupt expansion. For discharge to atmosphere (Fig 25E), $X = 1$. For expansion in airway (Fig 25K), $c = 1$ and $A_o = A_a$ (Fig 24). Table 3 gives shock loss factor X_a, and change $H_{v_a} - H_{v_e}$ in veloc press, in terms of veloc press H_{v_a} before expansion; also the ratio of these quantities.

Table 3. Constants for Abrupt Expansion in Airways

$N_e = A_a/A_e$	0.9	0.8	0.7	0.6	0.5	0.4	0.3	0.2	0.1
X_a	0.01	0.04	0.09	0.16	0.25	0.36	0.49	0.64	0.81
$\dfrac{H_{v_a} - H_{v_e}}{H_{v_a}}$	0.19	0.36	0.51	0.64	0.75	0.84	0.91	0.96	0.99
Ratio of X_a to $\dfrac{H_{v_a} - H_{v_e}}{H_{v_a}}$	0.05	0.11	0.18	0.25	0.33	0.43	0.54	0.67	0.82

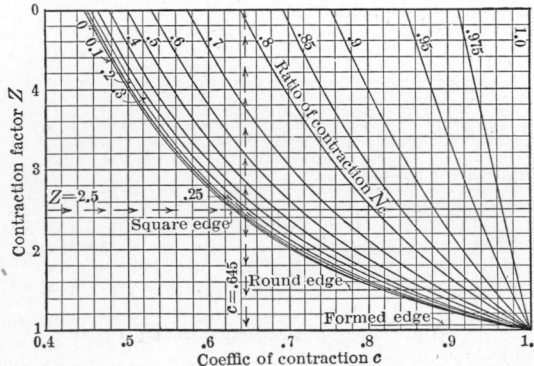

Fig 26. Relation of Coefficient of Contraction c to Contraction Factor Z (19)

Gradual expansion diminishes shock loss by a constant ratio y, depending on included angle; $X' = yX$, where X' is the shock factor for gradual, and X for abrupt expansion. Test values of y are conflicting (53, 9, 56); apparently, practical minimum is approx 0.25 for 7°; angles exceeding 30° offer no material advantage over abrupt expansion. For gradual expansion in airway (Fig 25L), values of X_a in Table 3 are multiplied by proper value of y. EVASÉ DISCHARGE (gradual expansion at discharge to atmos, Fig 25F) involves both loss due to expansion, yX_a, and loss at discharge, $X_e = 1$. In practice, it is seldom economical to make N less than 0.25; that is, $A_e \div A_a$ more than 4 (Art 14).

Abrupt contraction in airways is a common condition (Fig 25M). Here $N_e = 1$, $X_e = \left(\dfrac{1}{c} - 1\right)^2$, and $X_a = X_e \div N_c^2$ (Table 4).

Table 4. Constants for Abrupt Contraction in Airways

$N_c = A_a/A_e$		0.9	0.8	0.7	0.6	0.5	0.4	0.3	0.2	0.1
Square edge....	X_a	0.022	0.091	0.220	0.446	0.839	1.59	3.21	7.92	33.2
	X_e	0.018	0.058	0.108	0.161	0.210	0.254	0.289	0.317	0.33
Round edge....	X_a	0.003	0.012	0.030	0.061	0.120	0.230	0.471	1.18	4.96
	X_e	0.002	0.007	0.015	0.022	0.030	0.037	0.042	0.047	0.05

Most mine airways represent something between square- and round-edge conditions. Values for rough conditions are difficult to select.

Inlets. For pipe and airway inlets (Fig 25A), $N_c = 0$ and $N_e = 1$. For the PIPE INLET, $Z = 3.8$ and $X_e = 0.95$. For the AIRWAY INLET, X_e is approx 0.34 for square edge, 0.05 for round or beveled, and 0.0006 for a formed or bell-mouth opening (Fig 25B). CONVERGING INLET (Fig 25D) is also a low-loss type, but has both abrupt and gradual contraction. For a RESTRICTED INLET (Fig 25C), $N_c = 0$; then c is 0.633, 0.817 and 0.976 for square, round and formed edges, in the formula for X_e.

Orifices. RESTRICTED DISCHARGE to atmos (Fig 25G, $N_e = 0$) is often used in fan testing with square-edged orifice plates, for which $Z = $ approx 2.5. For FLOW THROUGH A SMALL HOLE in thin wall (Fig 25I), $N_e = 0$ and $N_c = 0$; then $X_e = Z = 2.5$, 1.5 and 1.05 for square, round and formed respectively. CONSTRUCTION IN AIRWAY (Fig 25N) involves abrupt contraction followed by abrupt expansion. General formulas apply, but in duct or airway of uniform area, $N_c = N_e = N$. Edge of orifice plates used for air measurement approximates $Z = 2.8$.

Regulator is a restrictive device to cause shock loss. Solution by trial and error of

$$X = \left(\frac{1}{c} - N\right)^2 \div N^2,$$

or use of chart (55), is required for N greater than 0.2; $N = $ ratio of regulator- to airway-area; X is desired press loss divided by veloc press in airway; c is selected from Fig 26 for $Z = 2.5$ and corresponding value of N. In practice, N is usually less than 0.2, and value of c practically constant; hence approx size can be found by

$$N = \frac{1.6}{\sqrt{X} + 1} \quad \text{(approx for } N > 0.2\text{)}.$$

Solutions by "equivalent orifice" formula, $A = 0.0004 \, Q \div \sqrt{H_s}$, are 10% too high for $N = 0.1$, to 30% too high for $N = 0.3$.

Example. For $Q = 10\,000$ c f m, required area of regulator in a 50-sq ft entry to cause press loss H_s of 0.25 in of water: $V = \dfrac{10\,000}{50} = 200$ ft per min; veloc press $= \left(\dfrac{200}{4\,000}\right)^2 = 0.0025$ in;

$X = \dfrac{0.25}{0.0025} = 100$; $\sqrt{X} = 10$; $N = \dfrac{1.6}{11} = 0.145$; regulator area $= 50 \times 0.145$ or approx 7.3 sq ft.

Regulator would be made at least 2 by 4 ft and have a slide. Same solution can be used for size of opening in a door-regulator, but results are less reliable.

Gradual contraction in an airway (Fig 25P) is followed by abrupt expansion from the "vena contracta" to the area following contraction; $N_e = 1$. Values of Z and c are influenced by the included angle and edge condition. Univ of Ill found values equivalent to $Z = 1.51$ for 60° and 1.34 for 30° smooth edges, approximating $Z = 2$ in abrupt contraction (56). Shock losses for included angles less than 30° are practically negligible. GRADUAL CONTRACTION FOLLOWED BY ABRUPT EXPANSION (Fig 25Q) presents the same flow conditions, except that N_e is less than 1. CONVERGING DISCHARGE FROM AN AIRWAY has the special condition that $N_e = 0$. CONVERGING INLET (Fig 25D) and CONVERGING DISCHARGE FROM A LARGE CHAMBER (Fig 25J) involve both abrupt and gradual contraction and require special test values to find press loss.

Contraction followed by gradual expansion, the contraction being either abrupt or gradual: multiply factors for abrupt expansion by y (see gradual expansion). VENTURI ORIFICE, OR NOZZLE (Fig 25R) is a common form of gradual contraction followed by gradual expansion, designed to give large press change with small press loss. The general formulas, with appropriate values of y and Z, are required for solution. With a formed entrance, as in the "standard" orifice, Z may be 1.05, and c determined from Fig 26.

Obstructions in airways cause shock losses due to contraction of flow along the perimeter, followed by abrupt expansion. Bur Mines tests (9) show $Z =$ approx 5 for square edges of timbers and cars, so that Z factors for wall contraction should be doubled for aver conditions of contraction against perimeter of an obstruction. MINE CARS cause shock losses at front and rear and increased friction loss. Abrupt contraction at front end, and expansion at rear, may be computed from foregoing data, using $Z = 5$. Friction loss in constricted area is approx $(2 - N) \div N^3$ times normal loss. For area ratio of $N = 0.2$, resistance of car = approx 100 ft of coal-mine entry or 40 ft of rough rock drift; for $N = 0.4$, these values are 400 and 160 ft (9). CLOSELY SPACED CARS do not allow length required for full expansion downstream and shock loss is less than the above. A trip of cars is therefore treated as a single obstruction.

Intermittent obstructions, causing minor losses, too small or irregular for separate calculation, may be estimated per unit of length. Tests by Bur Mines (40) gave following range: for trolley box, water box, large flanged pipe, occasional falls of roof, hangers and props, $X = 0.1$ per 100 ft; for combinations of the above, large roof falls, piles of timber or pipe, closely set crossbars, props or constrictions, $X = 1.0$ per 100 ft.

11. MINE RESISTANCE

Mine pressure. Total press to circulate air through a system of mine openings is press required to overcome all friction and shock losses along any continuous path from inlet to outlet, regardless of changes in the distribution of total quantity in different parts of that path. Press for circulating a definite quantity depends on whether natural or controlled splitting is used.

Controlled splitting. General procedure in coal mines is to regulate, or add resistance artificially to, all paths from inlet to outlet except one, this being termed the "open split" throughout the section occupied by divided flow. In calculating mine press, quantities are assigned to the various branch splits and press requirements are calculated for each. The path of highest resistance is then determined and the summation of its press losses, from inlet to outlet, is the press required for the total quantity. Regulators placed in all splits and branch splits, other than the open split, bring their press requirements for assigned quantities up to that for the corresponding part of the open split.

Mine characteristics. If press required to circulate one quantity Q is known, press required to circulate any other quantity Q' is easily calculated, since press varies as $(Q' \div Q)^2$, whether for a single airway, or system of airways. Corresponding values of press and quantity may be plotted to show the press-quantity relation, or CHARACTERISTIC, of the airway or mine (Art 12, 15).

Pressure-quantity relation (1) may be expressed as $H = rQ^2$, or as $Q = c\sqrt{H}$, where H is press, and r and c constants; because both friction and shock losses vary directly as the square of veloc, or quantity, for constant airway conditions. For unit quantity, $H = r$, so r is a constant designating specific resistance to flow. For unit press, $Q = c$, so c is a constant designating specific capac for flow. Many expressions equivalent to these, as "equivalent orifice," "press potential," and "Atkinson," are in use.

Equivalent orifice. Since flow through an orifice follows the same law as flow through a mine, the resistance through a mine or a fan may be represented by the size of orifice in a thin plate, that would pass same amount of air with same press loss (for a fan, "orifice of passage") (10). The usual formula is $a = 0.0004Q \div \sqrt{H}$, where a is area of orifice in sq ft. Its derivation (55) assumes constant density, a coeff of contraction of 0.625 (or 0.65 if coeff of Q is 0.000385), and that all veloc press in the contracted stream from the orifice is lost. These conditions hold only for a small hole discharging air to atmos from a large chamber, for which the formula gives a close approximation. Although this conductance constant has been widely used, its restricted theoretical application has caused some confusion, especially in calculating size of regulator openings (Art 10). In form, it is equivalent to $Q = c\sqrt{H}$, where $c = a \div 0.0004$.

Pressure potential. The standard friction formula (Art 10) may be transposed to: $Q = \left(A \sqrt{\dfrac{A}{kS}} \right) \sqrt{p}$, in which $A \sqrt{\dfrac{A}{kS}}$, termed "pressure potential" by Beard (2), has often been used in solving theoretical problems of natural splitting or parallel flow. With p constant, Q varies directly as the press potential, whence, for splits beginning and ending together, total quantity is divided between splits in proportion to their respective press potentials. The formula is equivalent to $Q = c\sqrt{H}$, where $c = A\sqrt{\dfrac{A}{kS}} \times \sqrt{5.2}$. But, as it does not provide for shock losses and is not suitable for summations of pressure losses in series, involving variations in A, k or S, it serves only for rough solutions.

"**Atkinson.**" A committee of the Inst Min Engrs, London, recommended use of the form $p = R_A \left(\dfrac{q}{1\,000} \right)^2$, which is the standard resistance form with press in lb per sq ft and quantity expressed in the "cusec," or 1 000 cu ft per sec, equivalent to 60 000 cu ft per min (3). Hence, an "Atkinson" (commonly used in England) is the press in lb per sq ft required to pass 60 000 cu ft per min $= R_A = \dfrac{2\,800}{a^2}$, where a is equiv orifice in sq ft.

Resistance factor. Most convenient form, much used in U S and Gt Britain, is $H = R \left(\dfrac{Q}{100\,000} \right)^2$, wherein the quantity unit is 100 000 cu ft per min. R has been termed (9) "resistance factor," specified as the press required to pass 100 000 cu ft per min. This large quantity unit gives values close to unity for mine circuits and facilitates computations of R involving friction factor k. For problems of small flows in ducts, values of R are large, and a smaller quantity unit is better.

Determination of R for an airway or a mine may be made directly from measurements of press and quantity. As R is affected by air density, values thus derived are corrected to standard density by multiplying by $(0.075 \div w)$. R may be calculated for friction losses, by inspection of friction formula: $R = \dfrac{k \times 10^{10}\, PL}{5.2\, A^3}$; for shock losses, $H_s = X\, H_v$, where $H_v = \dfrac{623}{10^{10}} V^2$ for $w = 0.075$ lb per cu ft (Art 9) ; whence $R = \dfrac{H_s}{\left(\dfrac{Q}{10^5} \right)^2} = \dfrac{10^{10}\, H_s}{Q^2} = \dfrac{10^{10}\, X\, H_v}{Q^2} = 10^{10}\, X\, \dfrac{623\, V^2}{10^{10}\, A^2 V^2}\, \dfrac{w}{0.075} = \dfrac{623\, X}{A^2}\, \dfrac{w}{0.075}$.

For known equiv orifice, $R = \dfrac{1\,600}{a^2}$; for known Atkinsons, $R = 0.535\, R_A$.

Series flow. Resistance constant r (any unit), for an airway, is the sum of r-factors for the friction and shock-loss conditions involved; r for a system of airways is the sum of the separate r-factors of successive parts through which the same total quantity flows ($r = r_1 + r_2 + r_3 + \ldots$).

Parallel, or split flow. Where flow occurs in 2 or more splits in parallel, beginning and ending together, press diff H is the same on all paths, and total quantity is the sum of the separate quantities, or $Q = Q_1 + Q_2 + \ldots$. Then by the general equation for resistance, $H = rQ^2$, or $Q = \sqrt{\dfrac{H}{r}}$, where $\sqrt{\dfrac{H}{r}} = \sqrt{\dfrac{H}{r_1}} + \sqrt{\dfrac{H}{r_2}} + \ldots$ and $\dfrac{1}{\sqrt{r}} = \dfrac{1}{\sqrt{r_1}} + \dfrac{1}{\sqrt{r_2}} + \ldots$; also $\dfrac{Q_1}{Q} = \dfrac{\dfrac{1}{\sqrt{r_1}}}{\dfrac{1}{\sqrt{r}}} = \dfrac{\sqrt{r}}{\sqrt{r_1}}$, and $\dfrac{Q_2}{Q} = \dfrac{\sqrt{r}}{\sqrt{r_2}}$. That is, the separate quantity through each split bears the same ratio to total quantity as its $1 \div \sqrt{r}$ value bears to the same value for the group in parallel.

Conductance Factor. In the foregoing expression, $1 \div \sqrt{r}$ is a conductance constant, and, in solving problems in free splitting, is conveniently given a separate designation. Since $r = \dfrac{H}{Q^2}$ and $c = \dfrac{Q}{\sqrt{H}}$, then $c = \dfrac{1}{\sqrt{r}} = C$ ("conductance factor") when H is in of water and Q is 100 000 cu ft per min (9). C is quantity of flow resulting from a press difference of one in of water, and measures capac for flow of an airway, or system of airways. It can be determined directly from quantity and press measurements, or calculated separately for friction and shock losses; but, as it does not provide for combining press losses, it is useful only for the specific case of split flow. Hence, it is simpler to derive C values from R values ($C = 1 \div \sqrt{R}$) and use them for deriving R values to represent split flow, or resistance to flow where the total is divided between 2 or more paths.

Laws of parallel or split flow: (1) the conductance constant for a group of splits with ends in common is the sum of the conductance constants of its parts; (2) total quantity is divided between the parts in proportion to their conductance constants.

Natural splitting. In metal mines, air currents are usually allowed to divide naturally, without use of regulators. Calculations of mine press are then less precise, as working zones are usually a network of airways. Approximations can usually be made by ignoring networks and treating main airways as a series of branching splits. A diagram of the usual metal mine, or section of a coal mine, resembles a ladder, somewhat as shown in Fig 27, in which series-flow in main airways often accounts for 80–90% of total resistance. In attempting a summation for split flow, begin at the bottom, or innermost, split. Calculations are made in terms of corresponding resistance and conductance constants, adding resistances for flow in series and conductances for flow in parallel, and converting from one to other as required, until a single resistance value for split flow is obtained; to which are added resistances of airways carrying the total flow, to obtain the mine resistance in terms of r in $h = rQ^2$. Actual mine press is then obtained for any particular quantity of flow. Proportionate distribution remains constant with change in quantity, except as affected by natural draft (Art 12). In computing the resultant resistance for split flow, networks are avoided by ignoring cross connections and approximating resistances for a group of N similar airways as equal to $1 \div N^2$ times that for a single airway. Charts for finding resistance values and converting them to corresponding conductance values facilitate this analysis (9).

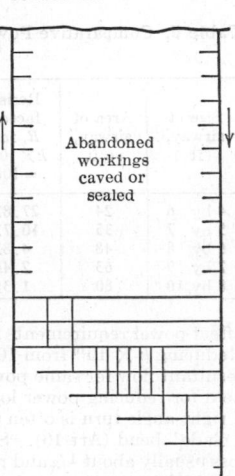

Fig 27. Diagram of Main Airways of a Typical Metal Mine (9)

Networks. Calculation of division of flow in a network of openings is possible, though tedious. The square relation for quantity practically prevents (12) solutions by Kirchoff's laws, as applied to electrical networks, but solutions may be made by trial and error (58).

Allowances for leakage. Indeterminate leakages cause discrepancies between computed and actual resistances. Each leakage path is a high-resistance path or separate split. Approx solutions for effect of leakage may be made for given conditions by assuming variations in quantities; but accurate solutions for known conditions involve networks. Mathematical solutions for 2 common forms, leakage at stoppings between airways and leakage at joints in pipe lines, would greatly aid computation. Where leakage and percolation exist, values of k or r may be assumed at about 60% of normal values for airtight airways.

Allowances for density changes. Computations are easier if based on standard density for which measured values may be corrected; with final result corrected to aver prevailing density. Minor variations from standard density are usually ignored, as in mines near sea level. For deep mines or at high altitudes, aver density is generally used, without regard to seasonal variation. Change in quantity Q, due to greater density in depth, is usually ignored, although excessive allowances are often made for change due to aver temp difference between main intake and return. Only the weight flow is constant. Press varies directly as density for constant Q, but Q varies inversely as density for constant weight flow; and, since press varies as Q^2, the net result is that, in terms of flow at surface, resistance at depth varies inversely as density, rather than directly. Density-increase with depth at constant temp is between 3 and 4% per 1 000 ft for aver temp and press. If H is press required at 0.075 density, H_f fan press, w_f density at surface fan, and w_m mean density of flow,

$$H_f = H \, \frac{W_f}{0.075} \, \frac{W_f}{W_m} \quad \text{and not} \quad H \, \frac{W_m}{0.075}.$$

The second form is often used, but gives results too high by 2–3% per 1 000 ft of depth for deep mines.

Power-quantity relation. As rQ^2 may be substituted for H in the formula for horsepower (Art 9), hp $= \dfrac{pQ}{33\,000} = \dfrac{5.2\,HQ}{33\,000} = \dfrac{rQ^3}{6\,350}$; that is, for constant mine resistance and constant density, hp required to circulate air varies as Q^3 (Art 14). Since $H = R$ $(Q \div 10^5)^2$, above formula in terms of resistance factor R is: hp $= 15.75\,R(Q \div 10^5)^3$.

Economics of air flow. Minimum total cost for air flow depends largely on design of main airways for proper balance between power costs and capital construction charges.

Since power varies as Q^3 for constant resistance, small increases in Q require large increases in power, and large increases in Q are obtained practically only by reducing resistance to flow through physical changes in the airways. Data on friction and shock losses (Art 10) indicate procedure. CHANGES IN AREA A are important, since resistance and power, for constant quantity, vary as $A^{5/2}$ for friction losses, and as A^2 for shock losses. In coal mines, construction of new return airways to permit use of old ones as additional intakes, is a common expedient for increasing area. The large range in possible power costs as affected by quantity and area is indicated in Table 5. CHARACTER OF WALL SURFACE may

Table 5. Comparative Power Costs Due to Friction Pressure Losses for 1 000-ft Lengths of Straight Timber-lined Airways

Size of airway, ft	Area of airway, sq ft	Resist factor R, for $k \times 10^{10} = 100$	Air h p for			Annual power cost at 60% overall effic and at 1¢ per kw-hr, for		
			25 000 c f m	50 000 c f m	100 000 c f m	25 000 c f m	50 000 c f m	100 000 c f m
4 by 6	24	27.82	6.85	54.8	438	$746	$5 965	$47 716
5 by 7	35	10.77	2.65	21.2	170	289	2 308	18 472
6 by 8	48	4.87	1.20	9.6	77	131	1 044	8 353
7 by 9	63	2.46	0.61	4.8	39	66	528	4 219
8 by 10	80	1.35	0.33	2.7	21	36	290	2 316

affect power requirements in the ratio of 10 : 1, as indicated by variation in friction factors. Reducing $k \times 10^{10}$ from 100 to 20, by smooth-lining timbered airshafts, more than doubles resultant flow for same power consumption (20). REDUCTION OF SHOCK LOSSES is a fertile field for reducing power loss. A special case is the top of a fan shaft, where press loss at a right-angle turn is often 0.2–0.3 in of water. Long life justifies a long-radius curve or "blade" bend (Art 10). Short life justifies a short 45° connection, which decreases power loss usually about $1/3$ and puts fan out of direct line, as it should be at a coal mine, and as required for emergency hoisting at a metal mine. A "blade" turn in a square bend at such locations is found at a few coal mines, and normally decreases power loss of a plain square bend by 75–80%. SHAPE OF AIRWAY slightly affects power requirements, in a range of 2–1 for normal conditions. Minimum is for circular shape, with octagon and square as close competitors (Art 10).

Allowable costs for reducing resistance. Costly changes in airway conditions must be justified by economic advantage, which may be computed with fair accuracy. Comparatively short life involved in mine installations usually justifies crude rather than elaborate types of design. For rough estimates, it is convenient to remember that 100 000 cu ft per min at 1-in press costs $1 000 per year, at overall effic of 51.5% with power charge of 0.5¢ per kw-hr; corrections for specific cases are then a matter of direct proportion. For shock losses, veloc press is approx 1 in at 4 000, $1/4$ in at 2 000, and $1/16$ in at 1 000 ft per min.

Economic size of airway may be determined by computing capital charges and power costs for a small number of specific sizes and finding the minimum. Careful investigation is justified where large quantities are involved. Weeks (12) cites a case where handling 100 000 cu ft per min through 1 000 ft of 8-ft diam circular shaft for 12 years would represent an increased cost of $57 000 over a 10-ft diam shaft. Mathematical investigation of friction losses in airways (59) shows that $A = Y^{2/7}Q^{3/7}$, where A is area for max economy; Y is resultant of many separate factors, involved in capital charges and power costs. Area for economy is thus mainly a question of Q. Results of one set of computations as above can be solved for $Y^{2/7}$; areas for other quantities may then be determined by the above equation.

Economic velocities. Above equation, confirmed by computation (59), indicates that the range of economic velocities ($V = Q \div A$) is limited. For aver conditions, safe approximations are: 600–1 000 ft per min in unlined airways, 1 000–1 500 in timber-lined, and 2 000–2 500 in smooth-lined airways.

12. NATURAL VENTILATION

Natural draft. Press differences, required to cause air flow, may be produced by natural or mechanical forces. Flow caused by unequal densities, or weights, of air columns in or near the openings (due mainly to temp differences) is "natural-draft" flow, and resulting pressure differences are "natural-draft" pressures. The relatively feeble currents forming complete flow circuits in undivided single openings, also due to unequal densities, are separately termed "connection currents." Many metal mines, and some small coal mines, are ventilated by natural draft alone, which also acts in conjunction with fan pressure in mechanically-ventilated mines; where its importance largely depends on depth of workings and mine resistance (Art 14).

Natural-draft pressures, or density press, are differences in total wt of air columns of unit cross-sec and same difference of elev or vert height. They are computed by assuming the air to move in closed circuit from intake opening, through the mine to the outlet, and thence over the surface at insensible veloc back to the intake. This circuit is divided by its highest and lowest points into 2 columns; and difference in wt of these columns tends to create flow from the heavier to the lighter. Where currents in inclined workings split, each split is a similar complete circuit, which includes the main airways, or 2 connections to surface. Each separate circuit, although it may overlap others, develops its own natural-draft press, which is dissipated by resulting flow in the circuit. Pressures on split-flow circuits in multi-level mines may be opposed in direction; in summer, flow on upper circuit, may be from upcast to downcast, due to temp changes in downcast. Usually one column is partly or entirely outside the mine; for tunnels, both are outside. Surface components are seldom important, because they usually involve only small differences in elev as compared with underground components.

Seasonal and daily changes. Weights of downcast columns and surface components depend largely on surface-air temp. Major effect is usually confined to relatively shallow depth of downcast, depending on veloc of flow. With high veloc, variation in temp at 3 000 ft may be as much as one-tenth the surface variation. Due to seasonal variations in surface-air temp, seasonal reversal of flow, or of press operating in series with fan press, occurs in mines having large surface components, or in relatively shallow mines, or upper parts of deep mines. In the latter, directions of main flows remain constant; seasonal effects are reflected in variations of press and quantity of flow. Where reversal of flow occurs, circulation may be sluggish or lacking for hours, days, or weeks; the time depends largely on elevations of surface openings. In 2 such periods, late spring and late fall, the flow may reverse daily, due to difference between day and night temp.

Currents started artificially in deep mines, when mine atmos is in equilibrium, may determine permanent direction of flow, due to temp changes caused by the flow. In deep naturally-ventilated mines, operating shafts are usually upcast because a slight excess production of heat in them starts feeble upcast flow, which in turn increases temp differences and increases flow. Many would stay reversed permanently when a fan is used.

Quantity of flow. Except in deep mines, or those having many large openings, natural flows are small because temp differences are small, or act only on short columns; the flow usually ranges from say 5 000 to 20 000 c f m. In deep mines, depending on depth and size and number of openings, flows from 50 000 to 150 000 c f m are found. Aver temp of mine air is higher than that of surface air, due to increase of rock temp with depth (Sec 23). In a naturally-ventilated mine, circulation is normally better in winter than summer; in a mechanically ventilated mine, natural press acting with fan press is normally greater in winter than in summer, causing similar, but smaller, variations in flow.

Intensity of natural pressures in shallow mines usually ranges from a few hundredths to a few tenths inches of water; in deep mechanically-ventilated mines, max is about 1 in for winter and $1/3$ in for summer, per 1 000 ft of column depth underground (9). Max is larger for surface columns: at the 6-mile Moffat Tunnel in Colo, under a 3 000-ft peak, measurements over a year showed max of over 5 in of water in winter and 2 in in summer, with more rapid variation than would occur at mines.

Measurement of natural pressure. If a stopping, or door, can be so placed as to stop the flow on a total-flow circuit temporarily, the press-difference on the stopping approximates the natural press causing the flow (12), as underground temp changes very slowly. If impracticable to stop the flow, a similar procedure may be applied to various splits in a multi-level mine, but analysis of resulting press and flow measurements is involved (60).

Calculation methods. Wt per cu ft of moist air (Art 9) depends on temp, abs press, vapor content, and impurities present, all varying too much to justify precise calculation, which involves logarithmic means for temp (4) and abs press (12). Accuracy within 2-3% is possible by using weighted averages for separate sections of a column of variable temp, to obtain its aver density. Difference in aver densities of the 2 columns gives their aver difference in wt, lb per sq ft; this multiplied by ft of air column gives total press in lb per sq ft, which is divided by 5.2 to obtain press in in of water. The small variations in aver barom press and vapor content are usually neglected except in deep mines. Results within 5-10% are obtainable by the following approximation: $H_n =$
$$\frac{1.325 \; BL}{5.2}\left(\frac{1}{T_1} - \frac{1}{T_2}\right) = 0.255 \; BL\left(\frac{1}{T_1} - \frac{1}{T_2}\right),$$ where H_n is natural-draft press, in of

water; B is aver abs press, in of mercury, obtained approx by direct measurement near center of columns, or from measurement at any elev, corrected for difference in elev from center at the rate of 1-in change per 1 000 ft (more closely if rate of change is known); L is vert height of air columns, ft; and T_1 and T_2 are aver abs temps of the columns, deg F, weighted with lengths of separate sections if column temp varies. Natural press may be estimated as 0.03 in of water per 10° F difference per 100 ft difference in elev, at standard air density of 0.075 lb per cu ft.

Application of natural-pressure measurements and calculations. Data on natural drafts and separate components are required to calculate approx changes in quantities and distribution, that would result from changes in either a natural or a mechanical ventilating system. Calculated resistances may be checked against resistances determined by calculated natural drafts and measured flows (60), when installing a fan at a naturally-ventilated mine. Intensities of natural press are necessary to calculate power requirements for changes of fan speed for mechanical ventilation, and for distribution calculations.

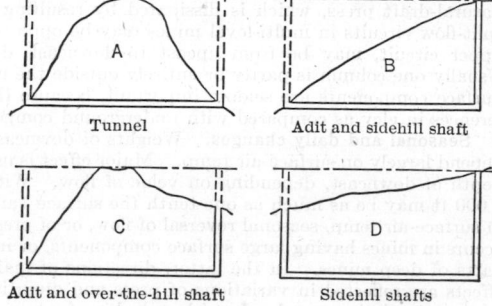

Tunnel   Adit and sidehill shaft

Adit and over-the-hill shaft   Sidehill shafts

Fig 29.   Natural-draft Columns for Simple Flow Circuits (9)

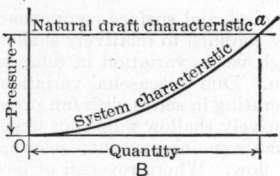

Fig 28.   Pressure-quantity Characteristics for Natural-draft Flow (9)

Characteristic of natural-draft flow is taken as a straight line, that is, press (at any one time) remains constant with change in quantity, if such change is produced otherwise than by change in natural press. If the natural-draft characteristic (straight line) and mine characteristic (parabola) are plotted to the same scale (Fig 28), the crossing point, a, indicates quantity that will flow.

Natural-draft distribution. Solutions are relatively simple for flat workings with 2 openings to surface, as only one press is involved, which may be considered as a single fan press. With more than 2 openings, separate pressures apply between each individual pair, and the resulting distribution is as though a fan were operating between each pair of openings. For inclined workings, distribution is as though a fan were on each cross-connection. For all except the first condition (fortunately usual in most U S coal mines) distribution calculations as between shafts and levels require either trial-and-error methods or solution of simultaneous equations (61).

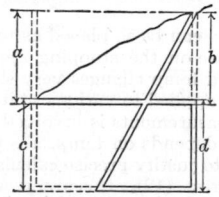

Fig 30.   Simple Metal-mine Type of Split-flow Circuits

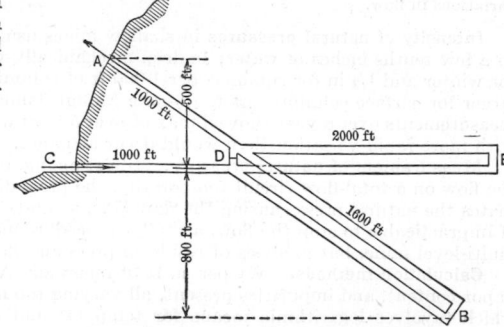

Fig 31.   Simple Coal-mine Type of Split-flow Circuits

Simple flow circuits. Natural-draft generation in flat-seam workings may be represented by the simple flow circuits of Fig 29, with 2 columns of equal height. The single horiz connection represents the multiple openings of actual workings. In case A, winds are usually given credit for flow actually caused by the natural press difference of the 2 columns shown by dotted lines.

Split-flow circuit of the simplest type is represented by an interior shaft to surface from a tunnel, equivalent to a fan acting at each portal; here, 1 shaft is better than 2 or more, as flow between interior shafts is practically nil, due to small temp differences. A simple type often found in metal mines is shown in Fig 30, and its counterpart in coal mines in Fig 31. In the usual metal mine there would be no bypass, or separation of currents, at junction of adit and inclined shaft, hence some recirculation would occur on the inside loop. In the coal mine there would be 2 splits, separated by a stopping at D.

Example. In Fig 31 let AB be a slope, and CDE a level, with connecting air courses. Cross-sec of all passages is 6 by 8 ft, and coeff of friction is $0.8 \div 10^8$. Average barom press between A and B is 30 in. Temp of outside air, 32° F, and its humidity 50%. Aver temp and humidity of the slope from A to B, 55° F and 95%. Under these conditions the mine air will be lighter than outside air, and a current will flow in at C and out at A. Part of the air will pass into the level by first circuit, $CEDAC$, and part by the second circuit $CDBAC$. As CE and DE are level, the density of the air in them is of no effect. Influence of incoming air makes the aver temp and humidity of slope DB, 50° F and 90%. Neglecting impurities, weights of air under these conditions are (Art 9):

At temp 32° F, humidity 50%, barom 30 in, 0.081 lb per cu ft
" " 50° " " 90% " 30 " 0.078 " " " "
" " 55° " " 95% " 30 " 0.077 " " " "

Then for the press of the air columns of the first circuit:

500 ft of outside air @ 0.081 lb per cu ft = 40.5 lb per sq ft
500 " " inside " @ 0.077 " " " " = 38.5 " " " "
Difference = motive press p' = 2.0 " " " "

Similarly, for the second circuit:

500 ft of outside air @ 0.081 lb per cu ft = 40.5 lb per sq ft
800 " " inside " @ 0.078 " " " " = 62.4 " " " "
Total weight of column = 102.9 " " " "
1 300 ft of inside air @ 0.077 lb per cu ft = 100.1 " " " "
Difference = motive press p'' = 2.8 " " " "

If Q be total cu ft of air circulating per min, and q' and q'' be the parts in first and second splits, respectively, the velocities are: $Q \div 48$, $q' \div 48$, and $q'' \div 48$. The surface rubbed by total current in CDA equals 56 000 sq ft; by air in first split DED, 112 000 sq ft, and by air in second split, DBD, 89 600 sq ft. If both splits are open (without regulators, Art 5), the simultaneous equations to determine Q, q', and q'' are (neglecting velocity head):

$$p' = \Sigma \frac{ksV^2}{a} = \frac{k \times 56\,000}{48} \times \left(\frac{Q}{48}\right)^2 + \frac{k \times 112\,000}{48} \times \left(\frac{q'}{48}\right)^2 = 2.0$$

$$p'' = \Sigma \frac{ksV^2}{a} = \frac{k \times 56\,000}{48} \times \left(\frac{Q}{48}\right)^2 + \frac{k \times 89\,600}{48} \times \left(\frac{q''}{48}\right)^2 = 2.8]$$

Putting $k = 0.8 \div 10^8$, these equations reduce to:

$$5.6\, Q^2 + 11.2\ q'^2 = 2.76 \times 10^9$$
$$5.6\, Q^2 + 8.96\, q''^2 = 3.86 \times 10^9$$
$$Q = q' + q''$$

whence, $Q = 20\,100$, $q' = 6\,700$, and $q'' = 13\,400$ cu ft per min.
The friction press in different parts of mine are:

From C to D (or D to A), $\dfrac{ksV^2}{a} = \dfrac{0.8}{10^8} \times \dfrac{28\,000 \times 17.6 \times 10^4}{48} = 0.82$ lb per sq ft

" D to E (or E to D), " $= \dfrac{0.8}{10^8} \times \dfrac{56\,000 \times 1.95 \times 10^4}{48} = 0.18$ " " " "

" D to B (or B to D), " $= \dfrac{0.8}{10^8} \times \dfrac{44\,800 \times 7.8 \times 10^4}{48} = 0.58$ " " " "

The head produced by the different densities between A and level CE = 2.0 lb per sq ft. Of this, the air moving in CD and DA absorbs 1.64 lb, leaving 0.36 lb per sq ft, equivalent to water gage of 0.069 in, read on an instrument placed in the stopping in the crosscut at D. Also, this pressure measures the friction in level DE ($2 \times 0.18 = 0.36$ lb per sq ft). The split in the slope is assisted by a difference of density in the two legs, amounting to 0.8 lb per sq ft. As the ventilating press at $D = 0.36$ lb, the total press in DBD is $0.36 + 0.8 = 1.16$ lb per sq ft, which equals the friction head, 2×0.58.

Workings to dip or rise. The essential features of natural ventilation of openings above or below a through current are shown in Fig 32. These may be termed " shunt " circuits, as one branch leaves, and returns to, a main airway, through which the flow is dependent on outside sources. Natural press generated by columns a and b causes flow far different from that due to natural splitting, without such local natural draft. Temp increases, and addition of lower-density gas, such as CH_4, cause natural draft that opposes flow in a shunt above an airway, and acts with it in one below an airway. Cooling air currents and presence of heavy gases cause the reverse. In developing hot or very gaseous mines, it is often cheaper or safer to drive development openings to the dip rather than the rise, although the latter may otherwise be cheaper and more convenient. Gas-air mixtures in pitch workings are difficult to move down the pitch, as relatively short columns of air and methane-air mixtures generate large natural-draft press.

Multi-level split-flow circuits of common type are shown in Fig 33, where a and b are vert projections of either slopes or shafts, adjoining or separated. Here there are 4 overlapping circuits, acb, adb, aeb, and afb, in each of which the total press losses must

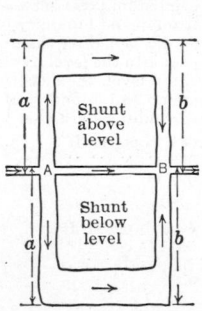 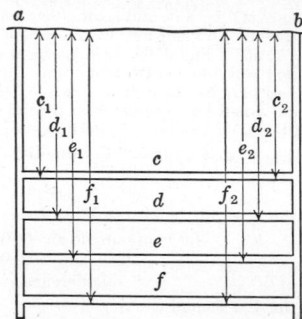

Fig 32.   Shunt Type of Split-flow Circuits   Fig 33.   Multi-level Type of Split-flow Circuits

equal the difference in wt of the air columns c_1 and c_2, d_1 and d_2, e_1 and e_2, f_1 and f_2, respectively. With resistances and pressures known, quantities are determined by solving simultaneous equations, of which 4 are obtained by equating the natural press for each circuit to the sum of its separate resistances, the first being: $H_c = r_{c_2}Q_{c_2}{}^2 + r_cQ_c{}^2 + r_{c_1}Q_{c_1}{}^2$. Also, total quantity equals the sum of the separate quantities, giving 5 equations. Resistance and conductance factors (Art 11) facilitate calculations, which are very tedious.

Recirculation due to 2 general conditions may be visualized by referring to Fig 33: (1) high-temp air entering the downcast shaft a, but cooling quickly in length c, may cause flow in the c level opposite to flow in levels below; (2) natural press difference is normally greater in each successive level below; hence, where cross-flow resistances are less than those of the upcast, air is often forced from upcast to downcast rather than to surface. Consequently, large quantities may circulate underground, where only small quantities pass to and from surface (9).

Control of natural ventilation (Art 2). Natural-draft pressures give rise to many variations of flow conditions in both naturally- and mechanically-ventilated mines. In

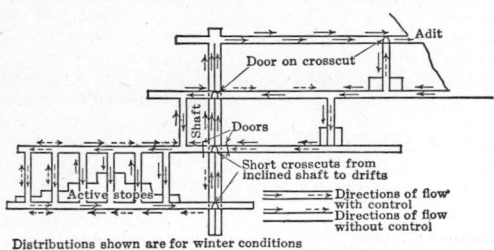

Fig 34.   Controlled Natural-draft Distribution (9)

both, however, natural drafts can be partly controlled and used to max advantage permitted by existing conditions. The beneficial effect of a few doors in a typical small metal mine is shown in Fig 34. Seasonal reversal of natural flows is undesirable, both for ventilation, operation, and safety. Reversals are reduced by eliminating large differences in surface elev between inlets and outlets; by coursing intake downcast air at low veloc close to the surface, so that surface-air temp variations affect only a relatively small part of downcast air columns; and by coursing return air at high veloc, to conserve relatively high temp in upcasts. For application of these methods to a medium-sized metal mine in mountainous country, see Fig 35.

Artificial aids to natural draft (62, 6). Before the common use of fans, natural draft was supplemented by furnaces, stacks, air-, water- and steam-jets, and falling water. Furnaces are particularly dangerous. All these devices are inefficient and have been displaced by fans, except for remote prospect openings and occasional emergency use in controlling natural draft currents (see 2nd ed of this book, Sec 14, Art 11, 19).

Effect of wind. Wind may exert press on mine openings by impact, or increase pressure losses of a mine system by deflecting discharge currents. On a high-press system, the effects are usually variable and small; becoming important only on low-resistance systems, unless winds are very strong. Not more than 80% of wind-veloc press (measured some distance away) is actually exerted on a building of cubical shape, and the same relation is assumed for effects on mine openings. Deflectors, or wind cowls, on mine openings would be a doubtful economy and hardly practicable.

Convection currents are natural draft currents circulating in a single undivided opening. Unequal densities, as between columns in such openings and those in adjacent atmospheres, generate pressures that are used up by flow to keep abs press everywhere in equilibrium. Such currents, sometimes traveling at insensible veloc and hard to detect even by smoke clouds, sometimes strong enough to be easily perceptible, are the major factors in natural ventilation of "dead-end" openings.

In horiz openings, the colder air travels along the floor, the warmer along the roof, with a "neutral" zone between the flows, which expands vertically in the direc-

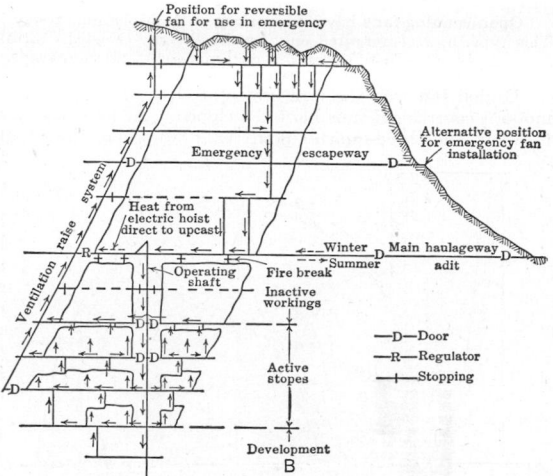

Fig 35. Natural-draft Distribution Controlled to Prevent Seasonal Reversal (9)

tion of flow until temperatures are finally equalized by action of the wall rock, and flow terminates. In one case, such currents maintained an air temp of 90° F saturated at the face of a 5 by 7-ft crosscut in rock at 115°, and 120 ft from an airway carrying 66° saturated air; in another, a 43° F differential caused currents that could be traced about 1 000 ft (9)

13. MECHANICAL VENTILATION

Definition. Mechanical ventilation produces underground air currents by press differences generated by fans, the pressures acting in conjunction with each other and with natural-draft press. Most coal mines and many metal mines are thus ventilated.

Development of fans. Early types consisted of a rotating drum, with vanes mounted on the open rim and with a central opening in one side, opposite the mine opening, whence air was drawn into the fan and discharged into the atmosphere. With the addition first of a side casing, and later of complete casing with expanding discharge opening, the present centrifugal fan was developed, in which the air is discharged at right angles to direction of entry. Axial-flow fans, in which air is driven axially by the oblique stroke of vanes or blades set at an angle to plane of rotation, have been limited to light duty until quite recently, when propeller designs, suited to all mine service, became available. Positive-displacement machines (Art 14) are used only for ventilating long tunnels. Injectors (Art 14) have a very limited use in fan-pipe auxiliary ventilation.

Designations. Fans are termed "main" fans when they handle the total flow of the mine or of a major circuit; "booster" fans when installed to aid distribution in one section of the workings, "auxiliary" fans when used with pipe or tubing to ventilate single openings. Position of the fan with reference to the airway circuit determines the common designations: "pressure" or "blower fan" for intake position; "exhaust" or "suction fan" for discharge position; and "booster fan" for intermediate positions. Position of fan determines press difference between the atmosphere and a particular point in the air circuit, but does not affect the press difference generated by the fan, or, for the same direction of flow, the press losses due to flow (71) (Art 14).

Centrifugal fan is a low-press large-quantity machine, producing a difference in total press between its inlet and outlet. It is essentially a drum or wheel, composed of a number of blades on a frame keyed on a shaft, inclosed in a casing with parallel sides and gradually-expanding periphery. Air entering at center of one or both sides is caught up by the blades, and given a rotatory motion while being thrown toward the periphery. Centrifugal force is developed, which generates static radial press from center to circumference (12). Also, pressure is developed by impulse effect through conversion of velocity press (in excess of that required at discharge) to static press in the expanding housing. Some of the press developed is lost in the fan itself, by friction against casing and blades, and by shock losses at entrance and in passage through the fan. (See Art 14 for performance, Art 15 for application, and Art 16 for selection of fans.)

Open-running fans have side casings only, discharging freely to atmosphere from the periphery. This type, now represented only by the Waddle (English) (3, 6), can be used only as an exhaust fan. A few were installed at U S coal mines, but are now rarely used.

Guibal fan was the forerunner of closed fans with expanding discharge, from which modern centrifugal fans have developed. At first, the casing was circular and extended to about the three-quarter point (Fig 36) where the expanding outlet or evasé started.

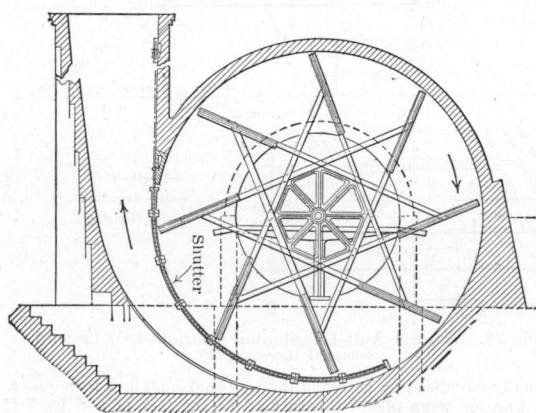

Blades were flat, but laid back at about 45° from radial position, and supported on braced bars bolted to parallel "spiders" keyed to fan shaft. At first, all were single-inlet. Later designs included more or less complete expansion scrolls, double inlets and backward-curved blade tips, though with many variants; they are slow-speed fans, of diam up to 40 ft. Many are still operating with fair effic in Pa anthracite mines, and a number in the bituminous districts. A modification of the Guibal, the Walker "Indestructible," is still made in England (3). INTERMEDIATE TYPES of deep-bladed backward-curved radial-vane centrifugals, mostly smaller and of higher speed

Fig 36.   Early Type of Guibal Fan (12)

than Guibals, were installed (1895–1910) in U S bituminous mines, the Capell fan (73, 6) being the best known.

Multiblade, or "Sirocco," fans. Modern designs in U S are almost all of the multiblade type, wherein the drum-shaped rotor has a large number of shallow blades (the original Davidson or Sirocco had 64, forward-curved blades). Designs differ mainly as to shape and position of blades. Although types with radial, forward-curved, backward-curved and composite-curved blades were developed simultaneously, 1900–1905, the forward-curved blade types, due to greater capac for equal size and speed, have dominated the U S mining field. Practically all main fans at metal mines, most fans at bituminous coal mines, and many at anthracite mines, are of this type.

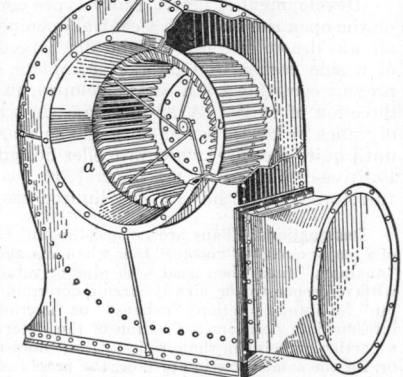

Fig 37 shows a typical Sirocco fan in an old-style, single-inlet, industrial type of casing. Late designs have a higher cut-off with top of fan discharge about on center-line, thus reducing overall height; mine designs have evasé discharge. Most metal-mine and many coal-mine fans in U S have this type of rotor. A commoner type at coal mines is the Jeffrey stepped multiblade rotor shown in Fig 38. BACKWARD-CURVED MULTIBLADE FANS, on account of certain desirable characteristics for mine use (Art 16), were introduced in a number of designs about 1925. Many have been

Fig 37.   "Troy" Sirocco Fan (6)

installed, particularly in metal mines for secondary services, but there are few main-fan installations of this type, probably because of size and speed limitations.

Variations in design. Available designs vary in number of inlets, width, degree of completeness of housing, and direction of rotation and discharge. Basic design of standard single-width fan may have single or double inlets. A double-width fan always has

2 inlets and is virtually 2 single-width fans with rotors on a common shaft. Double-width fans are popular as main fans for mines, especially underground, because both fan and installation costs of large units are usually lower than for single-width. The latter generally give lower total costs for small units and sidehill surface locations. The double-width fan passes about twice as much air at same press as the standard single-width of same design. Fans of special width occasionally are used for operating conditions not conveniently met by standard designs. Standard design has a complete metal housing (" full-housed "). The purchaser builds foundations according to plans supplied with the fan; since he must erect a building to house the fan drive and ducts to connect the fan to the mine, he may also build part of the fan housing, for which the maker furnishes plans; the fan is " half-housed " if the buyer builds the lower half, " three-quarter housed " if he builds the lower quarter of the housing. Where the casing extends below ground level, it is important to provide for draining the pit.

Reversing arrangements. Air flow through axial-flow fans is reversed by reversing direction of rotation. In centrifugal fans, direction of rotation is constant, and flow is reversed by reversing the connections of fan to atmosphere and mine respectively, by adjustment of doors in the housing (Fig 39). The doors permit considerable leakage, and resistance to flow through the connections is greater for reversed than for normal flow; hence design should be governed by the primary duty. In a surface installation, the reversing feature represents up to 20% of cost; underground, up to 50%.

Fig 38. Rotor of Jeffrey Mine Fan (6)

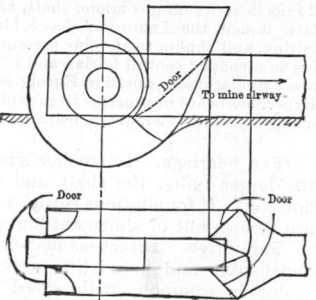

Fig 39. Setting for Reversible Fan

Direction of rotation and discharge. Direction of discharge is designated by the relation of center line of discharge to position of fan shaft, when viewed from the drive side (in a single-inlet fan, the side opposite the inlet, regardless of position of drive). From this viewpoint the normal rotation and discharge are clockwise, and vice versa. If the line or discharge is horiz and above the shaft, the discharge is top horiz; if below the shaft, bottom horiz. If the discharge is vert, it is either upblast or downblast, according to whether above or below the shaft. Discharge in any other direction is angular discharge, and specified in degree as top or bottom angular, up or down discharge.

Disk fan is an axial-flow fan with plane or curved vanes, attached to a shaft through a central hub or disk. It is easily erected, operates at high speeds, is cheaper than a centrifugal for the same duty, permits reversal of flow by simple reversal of rotation, and is only a little less efficient than a centrifugal; but it is adapted only to a low resistance system. Many are installed at coal mines, a few at metal mines. Usual types have iron or steel wheels, 1.5–10 ft diam, with 5–12 vanes with tips at about 30° to plane of rotation, corresponding to a peripheral screw pitch of about 1.8 diam. Casing is cylindrical and serves merely to protect blades and give a surface to seal to. To increase effic by preventing eddies, late designs have the central part, to 0.5 diam, blanked off with a disk or cone. Limiting tip speed is 2 000 ft per min for large, to 12 000 ft for small fans. Pressures rarely exceed 1.5 in water-gage, but greater press is obtainable from especially strong wheels. Larger sizes pass 100 000–150 000 cu ft per min.

Propeller fans (7) of axial-flow type, with propeller-shaped blades attached to a central hub on a shaft, are refined types of disk fans, developed in aeronautical research. They generate high veloc at low press differential, at the same time imparting a spin to the air.

For high effic, an expanding discharge (diffuser or evasé) is required to convert veloc to press, and guide-vanes are required to take the spin out of the air after it leaves the propellers, or to put the proper spin in the air as it enters them (Fig 40). Advantages of modern designs are: cheapness and easy flow-reversal of the disk fan, non-overloading power characteristic (Art 16) of the backward-curved multiblade centrifugal, and higher effic than present-day centrifugals. They are therefore rapidly supplanting centrifugals in mine service, where their chief drawback, noisiness, is rarely important.

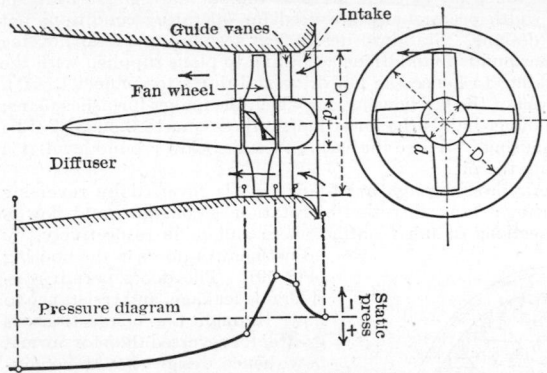

Fig 40. Propeller Fan (7)

An early Coppus design found use in Western metal mines for auxiliary and booster service. Steart in Australia (66) showed that airplane-type propellers, mounted in series on a common shaft, give effic comparable to that of centrifugal fans and can be adjusted to variable duties by changes in number and pitch of blades. A number of Steart fans have been installed in So Africa and in England, where one at the Grange colliery (67) has 14 10-ft diam, 2-bladed propellers. In the Jeffrey Aerovane (1931), 12 airplane-type blades are mounted in a single hub, and 2 stages, or 2 fans in series on a common shaft, are used for press much exceeding 2 in, depending on diam. A later design, the Aerodyne, has 8 blades of typical propeller-fan design, operating in a streamline fairing, and applies to all mine pressures in a single stage. Ladel-Troller fan has 4 blades operating in a shaped central fairing and is also designed for the whole range of mine press in 1 stage, as are 2 similar designs used in Europe and So Africa, the Belgian " Aeroto " and English " Aerex." Experiments are in progress to provide for changing pitch of blade, so as to maintain max effic with changing mine resistance, a feature of the Steart fan omitted in later designs.

Fan bearings. In smaller sizes, shaft bearings are supported by the housing, but in the larger units, the shaft and wheel are supported on pedestals independent of the housing. If foundations settle, as they often do around mine workings, wheel and casing are thrown out of alinement and performance is seriously affected.

Fan drive. Direct-connected steam drive is preferred at gaseous mines, as most dependable and permitting easy change of speed. Belt drive by constant-speed a-c motor is common, with speed adjusted by changing belt pulleys. Variable-speed motors are sometimes advantageous, but seldom used because of higher cost. Direct-connected units are best for auxiliary fans, occasionally for boosters; their speeds are limited by the phase and cycles of the elec current; 3-phase, 60-cycle predominates, but 25-cycle current is sometimes used. Short-center V-belt drives are favored, as flat-belts often give trouble underground. Squirrel-cage induction motors are common, although synchronous motors may be used on large units for power-factor correction, and other types for multiple-speed control. At gaseous mines, either 2 units with different sources of power, or 2 different types or sources of power for a single unit are required for absolutely dependable service. Steam and elec drive for close-in fans, and elec and gasolene-engine drive for outlying fans, constitute good practice in anthracite mines. Auxiliary fans of several types are made for comp-air direct drive by a turbine attached to the fan; small comp-air motors are also obtainable. These are less effic than elec drives, but useful when current fails, as at time of a mine fire, and for temporary service, since comp air is generally available in metal and anthracite mines.

Booster fan position, in active areas underground, requires provision for trips and men to pass without disturbing the flow. If 2 openings exist at desired location, fan is placed to discharge through a stopping in one, with an airlock in the other; if there is only one opening, fan may be placed in a short run-around drift, and the original opening is air-locked. In firm ground it is generally cheaper to widen the opening and provide an airlocked passage alongside the fan (Fig 41). With passage limited to men and single cars, a small fan may be placed at one end of a short air-lock, with the discharge carried through the doorframes in pipe of same area as fan discharge. Installations should be fireproof, or at least fire resistant. Fans with non-overloading power characteristics (Art 16) are best for this duty. Confining flow to one airway in itself increases the normal resistance, which is often further increased by design of installation. Direct drive is preferable to belt for all underground installations.

Cost of fan installations. Total costs of complete main-fan installations (1925–30) range from $5 000 to $15 000; booster fans, $2 000–$5 000; auxiliary fans, $300–$1 000.

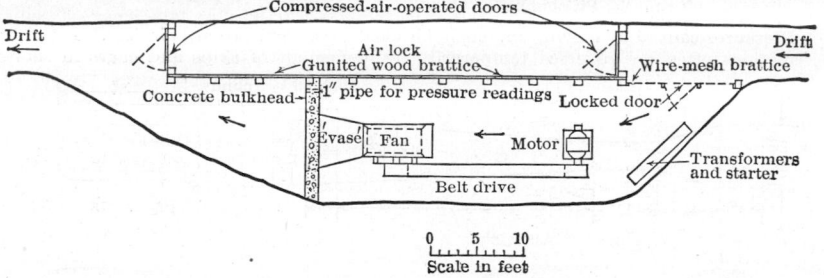

Fig 41.   Booster Fan Installation (9)

Cost of centrifugal fans, wheel and casing only (with evasé), f o b factory, is approx 40 D^2 dollars for single-width, single-inlet, non-reversible fans of width 0.5 D; and 60 D^2 for double-width, double-inlet, reversible fans of width D, where D is diam of wheel in ft.   Side drifts for reversing add $500–$1 500 for the ordinary large double-inlet, double-width fan, for which shaft hoods aver $500 and airlocks $150 extra.   Total costs of non-reversible installations aver about 3 times, and of aver double-width reversible installation about 4 times, the cost of fan alone.   Approx costs f o b factory (1936) of centrifugal fan and motor for auxiliary ventilation:

> 8-in diam pipe,   8-in diam fan wheel,   1-hp motor, $140
> 12-in "   "   16-in   "   "   "   5-hp   " $320
> 24-in "   "   28-in   "   "   "   15-hp   " $900

Cost of disk fan, without motor, f o b factory in 1936 was approx 80 + 6 D^2 dollars, where D is diam in ft.

Centrifugal compressors are sometimes used for auxiliary ventilation in tunnel driving, where press requirements of long pipe lines are 1–3 lb per sq in.   They have same characteristics as centrifugal fans (Art 16), but the large density changes involved at compressor and in the line must be considered (68).   For given speed and inlet volume, ratio of abs discharge press to abs inlet press is constant for fixed resistance (12).

Volumetric, or displacement, ventilators. The rotary positive-press blower (Fig 42) is the only one in common use for forcing or exhausting air through long pipe lines under press differences of say 1–3 lb per sq in.   Theoretically, they pass a fixed volume per rev; actually some air trapped at each rev leaks from discharge to inlet side ("slip").   The amount of slip depends on press and clearances, and is specified as "slip speed," required to maintain a definite press at no delivery.   Variations in air density must be taken into account for pipe line press and blower performance (68).

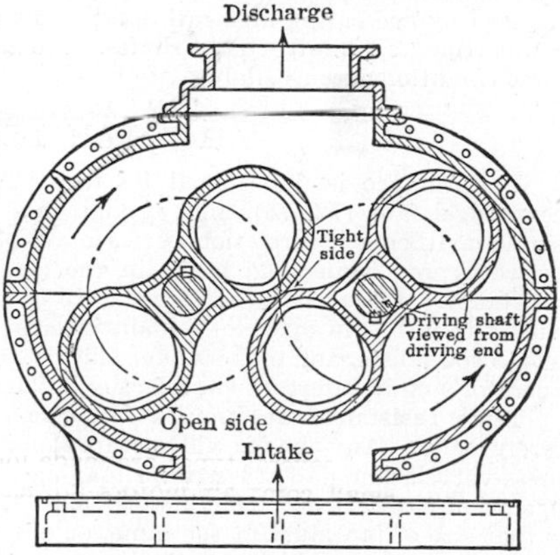

Compressed-air injectors are useful in emergencies; they are cheap and easily installed, but very ineffic.   They depend on conversion of the energy of a high-veloc jet into press required for the desired flow.   For low-resistance flows, where only discharge veloc is desired, a jet discharging along the axis of a pipe is sufficient.   Where flow against resistance is required, venturi designs are used to convert veloc press to static press.   Most home-made designs are patterned after the "Modder" (Fig 43); much used in German and So African, to some extent in U S metal mines, but very little in coal mines.   Performance may be closely approximated by theory (69).   Effic increases with proper design of venturi, as resistance of line increases and as air press decreases.

Fig 42.   Root Blower (9)

Saccardo system uses a low-press injector for ventilating tunnels, by which streams of high-veloc air are discharged from nozzles, or wall openings, at a slight angle to axis of tunnel.   Performance (70) varies mainly with ratio of nozzle area to airway area. Effic is max for one condition only, as for fans, and may possibly reach 50%, but overall effic is less than half that of direct fan ventilation, and veloc restricts use to low-resistance (smooth-lined) systems. Example, Liberty vehicular tunnels, Pittsburgh.

Pressures caused by moving objects in air passages assist or retard air flow. Large-vol circulations often are reversed temporarily by movement of skips and cages in shafts.

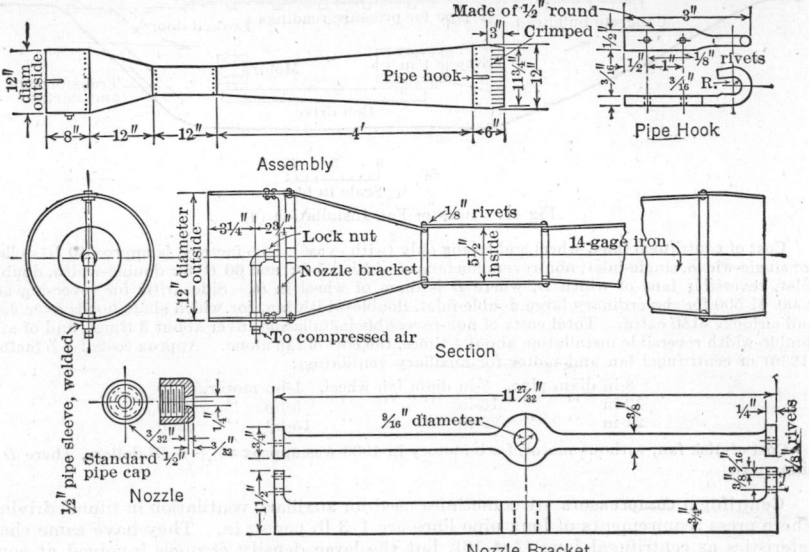

Fig 43.   Modder Type of Comp-air Injector (9)

Effect depends mainly on shape of object and ratio of its area to area of airway, and is reduced by decreasing area ratio and by frequent openings between adjoining airways or compartments of multi-compt shafts. No authentic data for computation of effects under mine conditions are available.

14.   FAN PERFORMANCE

Performance is determined by test. Theory gives only rough approximations for centrifugal fans (72, 73), and, though more precise for recent propellers (74), offers no simple mathematical relation between vol of flow and press, due to the variable balance between press gains and losses in the fan itself, when operating against varying flow resistance. Formerly, when fans were specially constructed for each mine, largely by rule-of-thumb, the operator's main interest was in design. Now, when construction is left to specialists, and makers offer effic designs in a range of sizes for all requirements, the operator's main interest is in selecting a fan suitable for his needs.

Mine resistance determines fan size. Special sizes (except very large ones) are rarely made. Any one fan will operate at max effic against only one resistance condition, or press-vol relation, and at less than max against all others; but a size may be selected for operation close to max effic against any resistance. Primary condition for effic service is that size of fan must fit the mine, or position of fan in the circuit. Not quantity, but resistance to flow, which practically means size of airways, determines size of fan. Low-resistance requires large fans; high resistance, small fans.

Tests. Makers determine performance by laboratory tests, as prescribed by the Standard Test Code of Nat Assoc of Fan Manufacturers and the Amer Soc of Heating and Ventilating Eng (75). Measurements of 5 factors are required: speed, density, quantity, press, and power; repeated, with speed practically constant, for 8 or more different resistance conditions, by varying the resistance added at discharge or inlet end of a test duct. Similar tests are sometimes made on fans in place at a mine, to determine performance, or data on operating conditions and mine resistance. Conditions in field tests are usually unfavorable for accuracy, and results are approx only.

Characteristic curves. Results of tests, corrected to constant speed and standard air density (see below), and plotted against quantity as a base, give a series of " characteristic " curves that specify fan performance (Fig 44). The total-press variation with quantity is the basic characteristic that shows results when the fan is applied to a mine, and is therefore the true " fan characteristic "; point of operation is determined (Art 15) by the intersection of the mine characteristic (Art 11) with the fan total-press characteristic. Point of operation a (Fig 44), determines quantity Q, and this in turn determines the total press H, rated static press S, mechanical effic E, and power P.

Fan laws. Changes in performance have been found by experiment to obey certain laws closely enough to permit general use of the laws over a large range of variation in flow. Hence, from one set of constant-speed tests against variable resistance, fan-performance characteristics can be computed for other speeds and sizes. Actually, a slight increase in effic accompanies increase in speed, but is ignored. Also, fan performance differs slightly, depending on whether the fan takes air at zero veloc, as in the blower position, or at definite veloc, as in exhaust or booster positions, since the shock-press loss in the fan entrance is larger for the first case. With coned or rounded inlets, the difference is negligible. A slight increase in effic also accompanies increase in size of fan, important enough in the smaller sizes to require separate characteristics for different size groups. The larger sizes, for main fans, can usually be placed in one group with little error. With these qualifications "fan laws" are: (1) If speeds of a fan operating against fixed resistance are changed: (a) effic remains constant; (b) quantity varies directly as s; (c) press maintained varies directly as s^2; (d) power required varies directly as s^3. (2) If geometrically similar fans, with diam in ratio m, are operated at the same speed, then, for constant effic: (a) quantities vary directly as m^3; (b) pressures maintained vary directly as m^2; (c) powers required vary directly as m^5. (3) If density of air is changed: (a) quantity and effic remain unchanged; (b) press and power vary directly as the change in density.

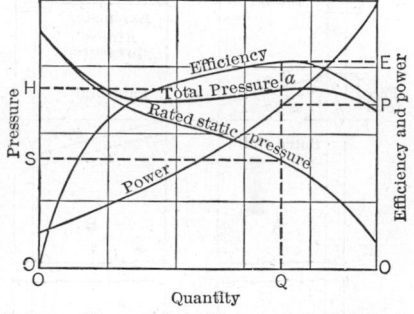

Fig 44. Characteristic Curves of Fan Performance (9)

Pressures and ratings (9) are confusing because press difference, measured directly against atmos press, does not correspond directly to the total-press difference generated by the fan. To avoid confusion, most makers rate their fans on a static-pressure basis. Fan performance has therefore come to be based almost entirely on static-pressure measurements, to which it has no direct relation, but by which it is approximated closely enough in most cases to obviate serious error, since the veloc press involved in the usual installations is small. Static-press rating must refer to a definite area and operating position. Ordinarily, it is based on area of the discharge connection, and the blower position of operation. Fans for use only for exhaust are sometimes given static-press ratings based on area of inlet connection; then ratings may refer to a fan with free discharge, but usually to a fan having evasé discharge integral in the design.

Pressure graphs (71). The best way to avoid confusion, in correlating field test results to fan ratings, is to chart the press changes, which are changes in abs press, though charted from atmos as a base. Then: (1) difference between aver total press at fan inlet and discharge is the only constant value for all operating positions, and is the value to be used in determining rated static press, which customarily is one discharge-veloc press less; (2) aver total press at any cross-sec of a ventilating system is the algebraic sum of 2 mutually convertible components, static press and aver veloc press, the ratio of which depends only on area of cross-sec; (3) aver total press and static press may be positive or negative in relation to atmos press, but veloc press is always considered positive; (4) aver abs total press always decreases in direction of flow; but (5) is always increased in this direction by a fan. Relations of fan and ventilating-system pressures to atmos are shown graphically in Fig 45 A, B, and C, for 3 fan positions in the same circuit assuming uniform resistance and veloc throughout. In each position, total press developed is the same, and the fan's static-press rating equals this total press, minus veloc press at discharge; that is, it is based on discharge area of the fan operating as a blower. For the exhaust position (Fig 45 B), negative total press at the inlet is equal to static-press rating (blower position) and is independent of area of duct; it is therefore used as an alternative rating for fan in exhaust position. Aver total press over a mine section can be observed directly only by a traverse; hence, is usually computed from measured static press and calculated mean veloc press. Use of such different pressures for rating in different fan positions leads to confusion, increased by still another mode of rating required for a fan in booster position. The basic facts are: position of operation is immaterial; true performance is the total press difference generated; rated static press is an arbitrarily determined figure that has a direct relation to the press generated.

Pressures underground. Where flow for fan in booster position underground is through mine airways, the graph of press change is as in Fig 45 C, but atmos press is not available as a base. Basic measurement is the difference in static press between a point close to the inlet, such as X, and a point close to the discharge, such as Y. If quantity of flow and the areas at X, Y (fan inlet and fan outlet) are known, velocity press can be computed and the graph followed to determine the fan total press and rated static press.

Evasé discharge, or gradually expanding section (Art 10) added to fan discharge, increases both total and static (negative) press at inlet of exhaust fan (Fig 45 D), and thus increases proportion of press difference generated that is usefully applied, but without effect on the total press difference. When added to blower-fan discharge, it reduces shock loss at discharge by reducing difference in veloc, which is also its true effect with exhaust or booster fan position. (See paragraph above on "Pressure graphs.") Evasé is really part of the airway system, but is usually supplied by manufacturer to assure effic use of veloc of discharge of fan proper.

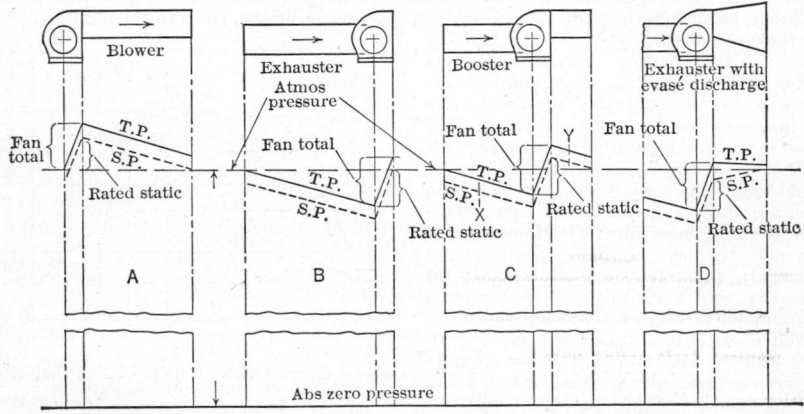

Fig 45. Pressure Changes in Ventilating Systems (71)

Mechanical effic. All of the energy supplied to a fan is not applied to useful work. Part of it, varying with the resistance against the fan, is required for flow through the fan itself; the rest represents useful work, the hp in the air. Useful work per unit of time divided by corresponding power input is the mech effic of the fan. Useful work is computed from total press of the fan and vol of flow. In data on fan performance, "mechanical effic" refers to effic based on total press, even though the fan's press rating is given on a static-press basis. Occasionally, for convenience of application with rated static press, a "static effic" (calculated from rated static press) is given. This bears the same ratio to effic that rated static press does to total press, and can thus be used directly with rated static press to calculate power requirements.

15. APPLICATION OF FANS TO VENTILATING SYSTEMS (12, 9)

Constancy of fan duty. Fans may act singly or in combination with other pressure-generating sources. In a ventilating system there are usually natural-draft pressures acting in series with or against the fan press, and often 2 or more fans acting in series, parallel, or series-parallel combinations with each other and natural-draft press. When a fan is the only pressure source, its required duty is constant, and controlled by the resistance; but when it operates with other pressure sources, all combine to overcome the resistance, and the duty of a fan operating at any one point is variable and determined by its position and by intensity of the other sources acting with it.

Fan as only source of pressure. A fan running at constant speed can produce only the combinations of press and quantity of flow indicated on its characteristic curve (Art 14) for that speed. Press losses in a ventilating system vary with quantity of flow, and the possible combinations are indicated by the characteristic curve of the system (Art 11). Only one combination of press and quantity will satisfy both fan- and system-characteristics; this is indicated graphically by the intersection of fan- and system-characteristics at *a* in Fig 46, which determines press as *H* and quantity as *Q*.

Fan in series with natural-draft press. Except in auxiliary service, fans rarely are the only source of press. Components of natural-draft press always act either with or against fan press. If of small intensity they may be neglected, but in a deep mine they are important in determining both fan duty and quantity of flow. If all workings are on one level, there is but one component of natural draft, developed between the highest surface opening and the level of the workings, and this press acts in series with a fan passing the total flow. In a multi-level mine, the components of natural-draft press act like a group of constant-press fans operating in parallel, and with the resultant of the group operating in series with fans on the main flow. Although problems of distribution require different treatment (Art 12), the resultant of the components acting in series with a main fan may be treated as approx the natural-draft press developed between the highest surface opening and the uppermost mine connection carrying an appreciable part of the total flow. Such pressures developed below the uppermost main cross-connection have little effect on the duty of a fan in the total-flow part of the circuit, but act mainly

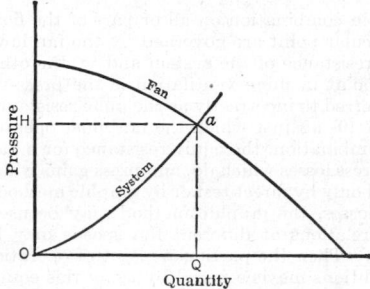

Fig 46. Fan as only Pressure Source (9)

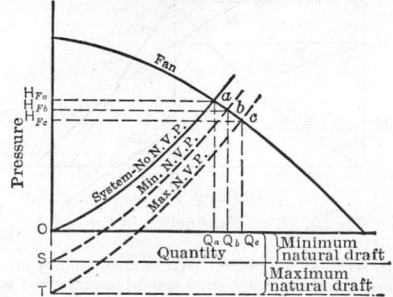

Fig 47. Natural Draft acting with Fan (9)

to change the distribution below this level from that which would result with the fan acting alone (9).

Natural draft acting with fan (Fig 47). The combined press characteristic of both fan and natural draft is obtained by adding the pressures for equal volumes. Flow conditions are indicated by intersection of the combined press characteristic and the system characteristic at a, which determines total press as H and quantity as Q. The latter determines the operating position of the fan for this condition, as at b on its characteristic, and the fan press as H_{Fb}. With natural-draft press H_N acting alone on the system, the intersection of the natural-draft and system characteristics at c indicate the quantity of flow as Q_N. With the fan acting alone on the system, the intersection of characteristics at d indicates its operating position and determines the pressure as H_{Fd} and quantity of flow as Q_F. Practical result of natural draft acting with the fan is a decrease in resistance and an increase in quantity of flow over what would be produced by the fan acting alone.

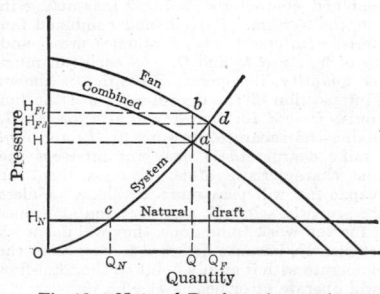

Fig 48. Natural Draft acting against Fan (9)

Fig 49. Fan Characteristic used as Combined Characteristic for Fan and Natural Draft (9)

Natural draft acting against fan (Fig 48). The combined characteristic, obtained by subtracting natural-draft press from fan press for the same vol, crosses the system characteristic at a and determines press and quantity of flow as H and Q. Q determines the operating position at b and the fan press as H_{Fb}. With natural draft H_N acting alone, the characteristics cross at c for quantity Q_N, and flow would be in the opposite direction. With the fan acting alone, the characteristics cross at d, and quantity would be Q_F, and fan press H_{Fd}. The duty of the fan is changed, through the action of natural draft, from d to b. Practical result of natural draft acting against the fan is to increase resistance and reduce vol of flow.

Variation in fan duty. If the limits of variation in natural-draft pressures acting in the same or opposite directions are known, combined characteristics can be laid off for each condition, and range of variation in fan duty determined by the quantity intercepts on the fan characteristic, the quantities being determined by intersections of the combined press characteristics with the system characteristic. A more convenient method is to plot the same system characteristics to separate press bases, as at O, S, T (Fig 49), the intercepts OS and OT representing min and max natural-draft pressures on the same scale. The corresponding conditions of fan performance are then determined directly by intercepts of the separate system curves with the fan curve, since the latter, in relation to the proper press base, is equivalent to the conbined press curve of Fig 47 or 48. The 3 operating positions of a constant-speed fan, when (1) operating alone, (2) acting in conjunction with minimum natural draft, and (3) with max natural draft, are indicated in Fig 49 by the intersections a, b, and c on the fan characteristic.

Equivalent resistance. When pressures act in combination on all or part of the flow, the characteristics of a fan operating at a particular point are governed by the fan laws, but the operating point is determined both by resistance of the system and by the other pressures acting on the flow. As the major point in mine ventilation is the press-vol relation at the main fan, this relation often is referred to incorrectly as the mine resistance. It is better termed the " equivalent resistance " (9) against which the fan must operate. Since, in a system acted upon by pressures in combination, the equiv resistance for a particular pressure source is determined partly by press losses which do, and press gains which do not, follow a definite law, it can be determined only by direct test or by graphic methods. For known characteristics of press gains and losses, the graphic method may be used. When these are unknown, the press-quantity relations at different fan speeds may be plotted as the characteristic of equiv resistance. Then the particular point of operation of the same or a different fan for the same conditions may be found by using this equiv-resistance characteristic as a system characteristic, and solving graphically for the point of operation, as though the fan were the only press source.

Fans in series. Although generation of press at one point in a system is generally cheaper, sometimes more effic distribution and better operating conditions may be obtained by generating press at more than one point, particularly where resistance to flow is abnormally high or leakage circuits are unavoidable. Fans operate in series when working on the same flow circuit, each handling total circuit flow and each generating part of the total press required. Any number of fans can be so used. Flow conditions are determined by the intersection of the system characteristic and the combined press characteristic of the fans, the latter being the combined fan pressures plotted against quantity.

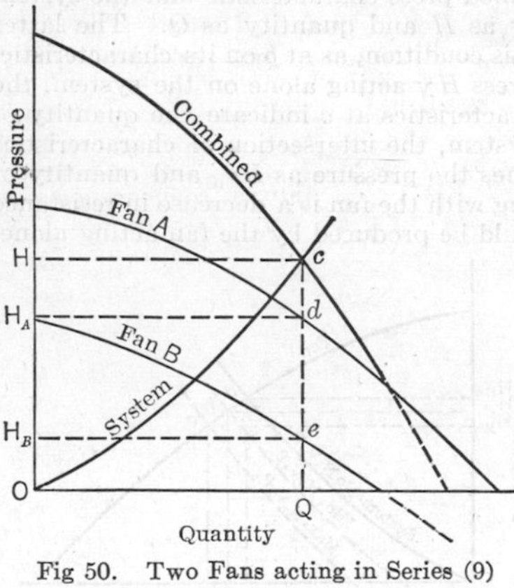

Fig 50. Two Fans acting in Series (9)

Series diagram. Fig 50 shows the separate and combined characteristics for 2 fans acting in series on the system. System and combined fan characteristic intersect at c, whence press and quantity of flow are H and Q. As each fan must pass this quantity, its operating position is shown by the intersection of the Q ordinate with the fan characteristic, at d for fan A and at e for fan B, determining the separate pressures as H_A and H_B. If the mine characteristic does not intersect the combined characteristic of the 2 fans, then the larger-capac fan will pass more air alone. Unless fans are properly selected, and operated at proper speeds for the work to be done, they will not work in series at max effic. Where a single fan operates inefficiently, because designed for less than the resistance encountered, a second fan may be installed to operate with it at any point on the total-flow part of the system, and be so selected that both fans will operate at or near max effic.

Fans in parallel may be used to take full advantage of the layout of airways available, to provide for effic operation within certain limits of change in resistance, or to increase the effic of a fan that by itself would be operating against a resistance lower than that for which it was designed. The fans may be placed to operate on the same or separate airways. FANS ON THE SAME AIRWAY act together, and a simple graphic solution is available, like that for fans in series. Their combined press characteristic is obtained by plotting pressure against combined quantity. In Fig 51, intersection c of the system and combined fan characteristic determines press H; and, since press must be the same for both fans, the H abscissa determines the relative fan quantities, Q_A and Q_B, by intersections d and e. If the mine characteristic does not intersect the combined characteristic, then the higher-press fan *A* will pass more air alone than the 2 fans together, and if an attempt is made to operate them in parallel, *A* will blow air back through the lower-press fan *B*. If intersection *c* is at a press higher than any press on the characteristic of fan *B*, the same reversal of flow will occur. Fans having steeply sloping press characteristics act together well in parallel; those that have characteristics combining a comparatively flat part and a steeply sloping part must be operated on the steeply sloping part, at a sacrifice of effic, else a sudden change in the equiv resistance of the system may cause the higher-press fan to take all the load, with danger of burning out a motor. Where forward-curved-blade fans are so installed, various precautions are taken, such as use of fans exactly alike, operated at the same speed or from a common drive shaft; arrangements for speed regulation on one or both

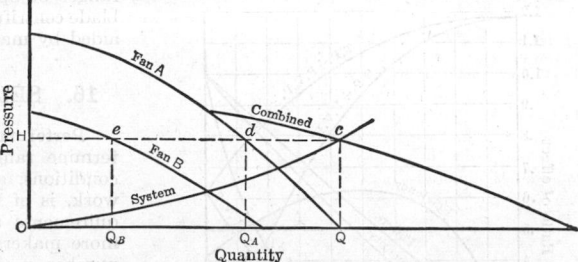

Fig 51. Two Fans acting together in Parallel (9)

fans; or an "equalizing" tube connecting the fan inlets or discharges. FANS ON SEPARATE AIRWAYS constitute the more usual layout for operation in parallel. Where the resistances of the separate airways are comparatively large, very little trouble is experienced, but it is difficult to determine the equiv resistance against which fans so installed must operate for a fixed speed. Resistances of the separate airways, and of the

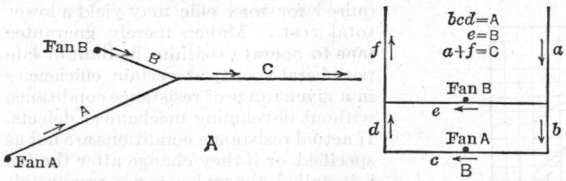

Fig 52. A, Analysis of Flow Conditions for Fans acting in Parallel on Separate Airways; B, Sketch Diagram (9)

system beyond their junction, must be considered, and flow conditions and fan performances must be solved graphically by trial and error.

Where fans in parallel are the only sources of press, distribution may be represented by fans discharging into separate branches into a common duct (Fig 52 A), although actual conditions might be as in Fig 52 B, where the series resistance $b + c + d$ would be equivalent to *A*, that for *e* equivalent to *B*, and that for $a + f$ equivalent to *C*. Primary condition: vol of flow in each branch must be such that press generated by fan, less pressure-drop between fan and junction, shall equal the common press at the junction, which is the press required to pass the total flow through the rest of the system. Fan characteristics and the 3 mine-section characteristics are plotted in Fig 53, and the flow conditions solved graphically by successive trials. A total quantity of flow, Q_C, is assumed; the intersection of its ordinate with system-characteristic *C* determines press H_C, that would be required in the total-flow section *C* (Fig 52, 53). The excess of each fan press over H_C is available for flow through its respective branch, and the broken curves are special fan characteristics, each based on such excess press (fan press minus H_C); the intersections of these curves with system characteristics *A* and *B* (of the branches) determine the quantities of flow through branches Q_A and Q_B, and the press required as H_A and H_B, under the assumed condition of total quantity Q_C. If $Q_A + Q_B$ is more or less than Q_C, then a larger or smaller total quantity is assumed in the next trial.

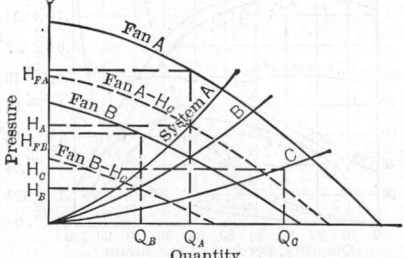

Fig 53. Solution by Trial and Error for Fans acting in Parallel on Separate Airways (9)

When quantities are found that agree, the intersections of ordinates Q_A and Q_B with the characteristics of their respective fans (solid curves) indicate the equiv resistances against which the fans must operate and the corresponding pressures H_{FA} and H_{FB}.

Complex combination of pressure sources. In large metal mines fans may operate at various points in conjunction with natural-draft press. The layouts sometimes may be resolved into equivalent simple-flow systems, but often the fan pressures act on only part of the flow in series, parallel, or series-parallel combinations with each other and natural drafts; many leakage circuits are involved, with resultant changes in quantities of flow in addition to those caused by density changes and use of comp air underground. Solutions are therefore complex and only approximate. The important condition is, that the press losses on any complete circuit, regardless of changes in quantity, are equal to the press generated on that circuit, whether by natural draft or fans. If the pressure source may be considered to have a constant-press characteristic, as for natural draft and for limited ranges of operation of forward-curved-blade centrifugal fans, solutions may be aided by mathematics.

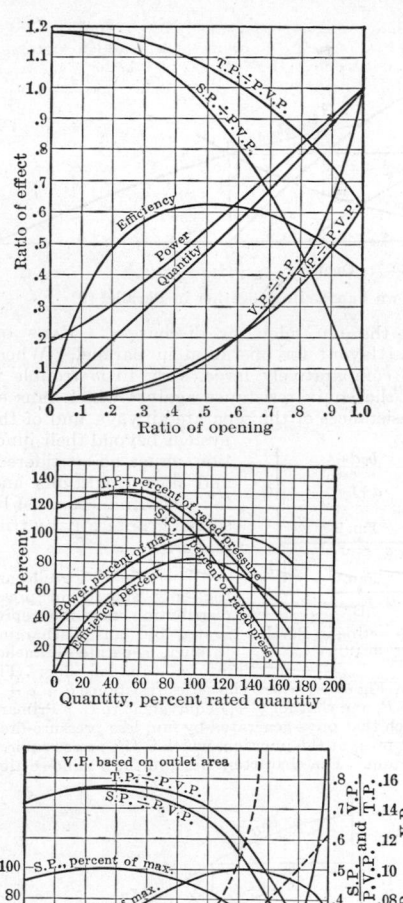

16. SELECTION OF FANS

Performance guarantees. To determine range of duties or resistance conditions, against which a fan must work, is of first importance. The requirements are submitted to one or more makers, who quote on a limited number of sizes and types, from which selection is made on basis of satisfactory performance throughout expected life, at minimum total installation and operating cost. Max effic is not the sole criterion, since, for conditions of limited life, low power requirements, or low power cost, a size smaller than that required for max effic may yield a lower total cost. Makers merely guarantee fans to operate (within the limit of safe peripheral speed) at certain efficiencies in a given range of resistance conditions, without developing mechanical defects. If actual resistance conditions are not as specified, or if they change after the fan is installed, the maker is not responsible for resulting lower effic.

Tables of performance data. For catalog and general use, fan-performance data are tabulated in 3 forms. The first shows rated performance only, for press-quantity combinations that permit max effic; one table represents a complete line of sizes of the same design. In the second and third forms, a separate table gives data for each size over a limited range of high-effic operation: in one of these forms, rated performances are listed in bold-face type; in the other they must be calculated from power, press, and quantity data. Data for performances intermediate between those listed are determined approx by interpolation, or accurately by calculations based on the fan laws (Art 14).

Characteristic-ratio charts. Constant-speed tests against variable resistances on a single size of fan give the maker enough data to determine the

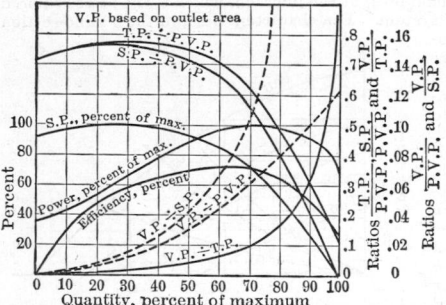

Fig 54. Three Types of Characteristic-ratio Charts

operating characteristics of a group of similar fans for any speed. Such characteristics for one size at constant speed (Fig 44) or at a number of speeds, cover the usual service requirements; but in selecting a fan for special requirements, more general methods of representing performance are needed. The basic method is to plot the characteristics as ratios and percentages, rather than actual values; the graphs, in a variety of forms, present a concise conception of the relative changes in performances for the particular design, but their practical use for fan selection is limited. Fig 54 shows 3 types of characteristic-ratio charts.

Constant-effic coefficients. For homologous fans running at constant effic, the fan laws (Art 14) may be combined to show relation of quantity (Q) and press (H) to diam (D) and speed (N), as $Q = k_1 N D^3$ and $H = k_2 N^2 D^2$, where k_1 and k_2 are coefficients. These equations may be combined algebraically to yield many pairs of formulas (76), embracing quantity, press and size, and either quantity or press and peripheral speed, with a coeffic varying with effic in each.

In certain forms the coefficients are dimensionless, that is, independent of the units used (3). Coefficients are plotted against effic in what might be termed effic-coeffic charts, which serve as a base for calculating size and speed requirements for high effic, or for calculating effic for a given size and speed required to pass desired quantity. Coefficients expressing relation of size and speed for max effic only, have had more general use, particularly in the forms: $D = k_3 \sqrt{\dfrac{Q}{\sqrt{H}}}$ for size, and $N = \dfrac{k_4 \sqrt{H}}{D}$ for speed, in rpm, where D = diam in ft, Q = cu ft per min, and H = press in inches of water, either total or rated-static, usually the latter. Values of k_3 and k_4 vary over a limited range; k_3 depends chiefly on ratio of width (W) of wheel to D, whereas k_4 is practically independent of the width ratio. Aver values of k_3 and k_4, based on rated static press, are in Table 6.

Table 6. Size and Speed Coefficients of Fans at Max Effic

	k_3 (size)	k_4 (speed)
Multiblade centrifugals:		
Double-width, $W = D$, forward-curved-blade	0.020	900
Single-width, $W = 0.5\,D$, forward-curved-blade	0.028	900
Single-width, $W = 0.5\,D$, backward-curved-blade	0.031	1 600
Disk fans	0.024	3 500
Late-type Guibals, $W = D \div 3$	0.067	1 100
Early-type Guibals, $W = D \div 3$	0.116	1 200

Fan-selection charts (76). Properly prepared graphic charts, based on constant-effic coefficients, facilitate fan selection and solution of fan problems, particularly if so constructed that size, effic and speed may be determined directly from quantity and press. Fig 55 shows a simple chart in general use; Fig 56, a proposed, more compact, chart.

Effect of blade shape on performance of fans. General performance characteristics, attributable to blade shape, are shown by the 5 sets of characteristic-ratio curves of Fig 57, 58, representing types rather than particular designs. The characteristics are plotted in terms of resistance to flow, that is, percent r in the general resistance relation $H = rQ^2$ (Art 11), as these are the factors to be coordinated in service. Against percent r, percentage values of power, total press, rated static press, quantity, and effic are plotted for 3 types of centrifugal

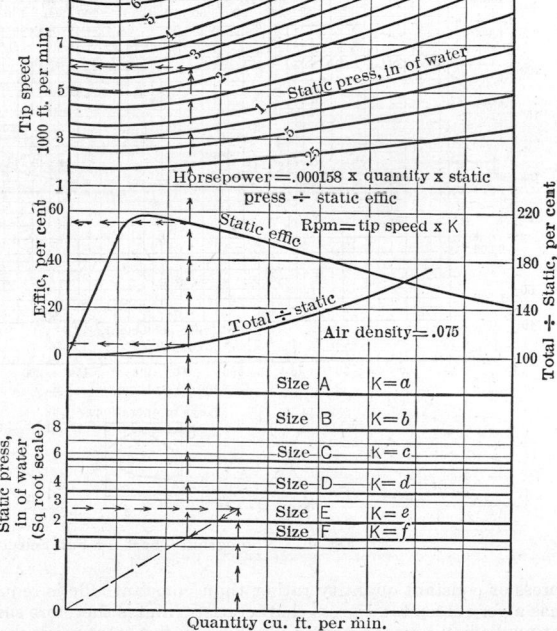

Fig 55. Performance Chart, B. F. Sturtevant Co (9)

and for disk fans. Recent propeller designs have characteristics similar to those of the backward-curved-blade centrifugals.

Power characteristics are decisive for mine application. Having power requirements practically constant at, or lower than, the rated power, backward-curved centrifugals and some propeller designs are said to have a "non-overloading" power characteristic and are therefore suitable where resistance fluctuates widely. As both radial- and forward-curved-blade types have rising power characteristics, they are subject to large overloads if resistance is greatly reduced, as by short circuits through doors left open or tubing disconnected from an auxiliary fan. They require motors of excess capac, up to 50%, to guard against possible overloads from fluctuating resistance.

Pressure characteristics have had much attention, being related directly to blade shape. They determine suitability of type for operation in parallel, and where constant

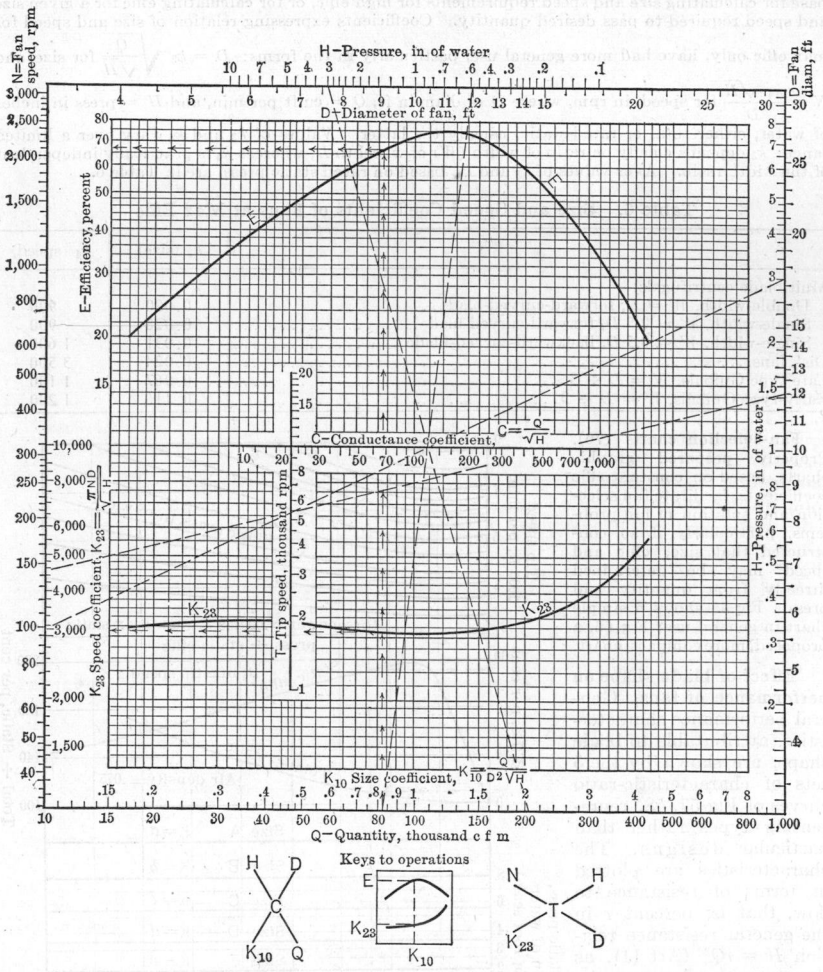

Fig 56.　Nomogram Chart for Fan Selection (76)

press or constant quantity rather than constant effic is required: backward-curved-blade has a very steep total-press characteristic and is therefore suitable for operation in parallel at max effic; forward-curved-blade has a flat total-press characteristic near max effic and requires large sacrifice in effic for operation on the sloping part of the characteristic, as required when operating in parallel (Art 15); radial-blade has a gently sloping characteristic, requiring only small sacrifice in effic for parallel operation. Press characteristics may be modified by design of housing, as in certain forward-curved-blade types for auxiliary service, which have a steeply sloping press characteristic similar to that of the backward-curved-blade. Forward-curved-blade types are good for constant-press, and backward-curved-blade for constant-quantity requirements.

Effect of roof falls or short-circuit on water gage. Whether changes in main airway conditions, as a fall of roof or short-circuit, may be inferred from fan press depends on the press characteristics. Water gage for the fan in blower position follows the rated static-press characteristic, and any increase or decrease in it generally indicates change in resistance, though not necessarily the degree of change. Water gage of a fan in exhaust position follows the total-press characteristic (Fig 45); change in press generally indicates a similar change in mine airway and resistance conditions, except for the forward-curved-blade centrifugal, the characteristic for which is so flat over the usual operating range that no such inferences can be made. Most coal- and metal-mine fans have forward-curved-blades, operating in the exhaust position on the flat part of the press characteristic, where water-gage records serve no useful purpose other than to show the constancy of fan speed.

Efficiency characteristics. Economy of operation is not only a question of max effic but also of range of resistance possible at high effic. The flatter the effic characteristic near its max, the more suitable the fan for operation against changing resistance. Effic characteristics in Fig 58 indicate that the backward-curved-blade has a slight advantage over the forward-curved-blade.

Comparative mechanical effic of the various types is fairly well established by consensus of opinion. Virtually all designs can give equally high effic if cost is disregarded, but the designs now on the market have the following comparative ranges of max effic: radial-blade and auxiliary-ventilation centrifugals, and disk fans, 50–60%; forward-curved blade and straight-side backward-curved blade centrifugals, [and propeller fans with airplane blades, 60–70%; backward-curved blade centrifugals with coned sides (limited in diam by mechanical design), 70–80%; and late propeller designs, 80–85%. These are actual or total-press efficiencies. Effic based on static press averages about 10% lower. In general, the lower efficiencies apply to smaller, and the higher to larger sizes. Max variation for designs of the same type apparently is limited to about 5%.

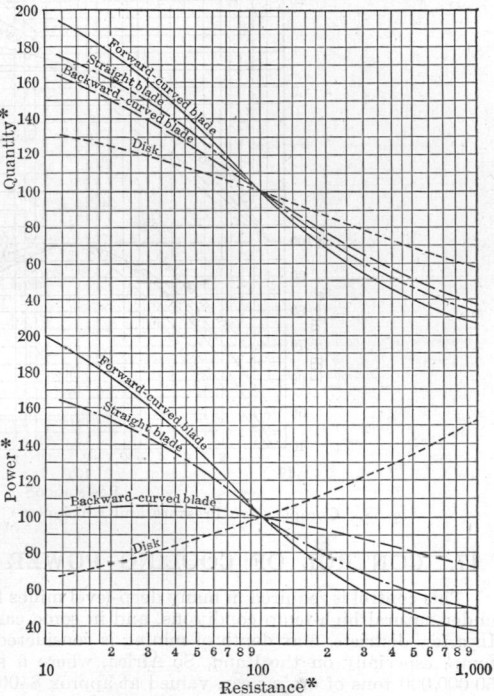

*Each scale, Fig 57 and 58, represents values expressed as percentages of value at max effic

Fig 57. Comparative Quantity and Power Characteristics of Mine Fans (9)

Other operating characteristics. For the same resistance, SPEED of rotation (Table 4) of the backward-curved-blade centrifugal is almost double that of the forward-curved-blade, with speed of the radial-blade type intermediate. The speed of the ordinary disk fan is about twice that of the backward-curved-blade centrifugal. High speed is a definite advantage in direct-connected motor-driven units, as high-speed motors cost less than low-speed. QUIETNESS of operation is usually unimportant in mine ventilation. Although conversion of veloc press to static press in the housing is mainly responsible for noise, speed of operation and details of design of both fan and connecting ducts also contribute. Propeller fans are very noisy, forward-curved-blade types of centrifugals moderately, and backward-curved-blade types least noisy. Uniform intensity of noise indicates constancy of performance. Cases of unstable performance are rare; probably caused by turbulence effects at the inlet, due to "wild" turbulence or excessive shock-press losses in inlet passages.

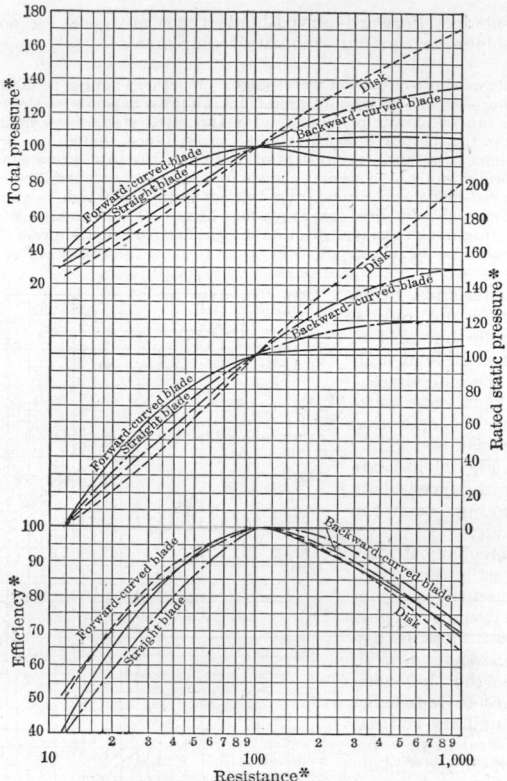

Fig 58. Comparative Pressure and Efficiency Characteristics of Mine Fans (9)

17. CONTROL OF COOLING POWER OF AIR IN HOT MINES

This control is required in many deep-level mines for maintaining effic of manual labor under natural high-temp conditions, and in some cases is of great economic importance. In a few districts, max depth of mining is considered to depend largely on control of air temp, especially on the Rand, So Africa, where a series of deep mines produce about 50 000 000 tons of ore a year, valued at approx $400 000 000, and the recovery of about $3 000 000 000 in gold (77) depends largely on air conditioning at depths of 6 000–12 000 ft. Since 1935, large air-conditioning plants (Art 18) have been installed on the Rand, whence comes much of the literature on the subject.

Limiting air conditions (Sec 23). Comfort depends on rate at which the body loses heat, which in turn depends on wet-bulb temp, air veloc, and dry-bulb temp. Conditions may be compared in terms of kata-thermometer (Sec 23) cooling powers (rate of cooling from 100 to 95° F of large-bulb alcohol thermometer with or without wet sack on bulb) or "effective temp" (temp of still, saturated air that gives same feeling of warmth). Approx empirical relations of Kata cooling powers to temp and air velocity are:

For velocities under 200 ft per min: $K_d = (0.111 + 0.016 \sqrt{V})(97.5 - t_d)$ and $K_w = (0.194 + 0.08 \sqrt[3]{V})(97.5 - t_w)$. For velocities over 200 ft per min: $K_d = (0.072 + 0.019 \sqrt{V})(97.5 - t_d)$ and $K_w = (0.056 + 0.011 \sqrt[3]{V})(97.5 - t_w)$, where K_d and K_w are dry and wet Kata cooling powers, in milli-calories per sq cm per sec, t_d and t_w are dry- and wet-bulb temp, and V is veloc in ft per min. Effective temp is determined from charts (Fig 59). Limit of cooling is at effective temp equal to body temp. Effective temp of 85° F (about 7.0 wet-Kata) is about the limit (81) for a fair amount of physical effort by an acclimatized miner stripped to the waist. This corresponds to working face conditions of 87° saturated air with aver veloc of 100 ft per min, and to development face conditions of 93° saturated air with aver veloc of 1 000 ft per min.

Sources of heat underground: (1) heat transmitted from rock to air in workings, and 'n passage from surface to workings; (2) heat due to auto compression of downcast air caused by change of abs press; (3) heat from men and machinery underground; (4) heat from oxidation, timber decay and use of explosives; (5) heat due to air passage through fans and friction of air currents; and (6) heat due to ground movement.

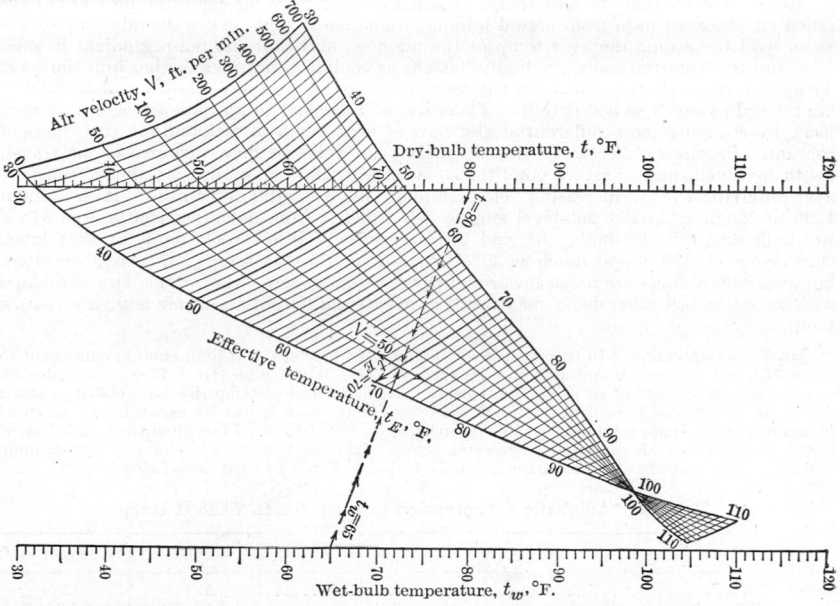

Fig 59. Effective-temp Chart for Men at Rest and Stripped to the Waist (9)

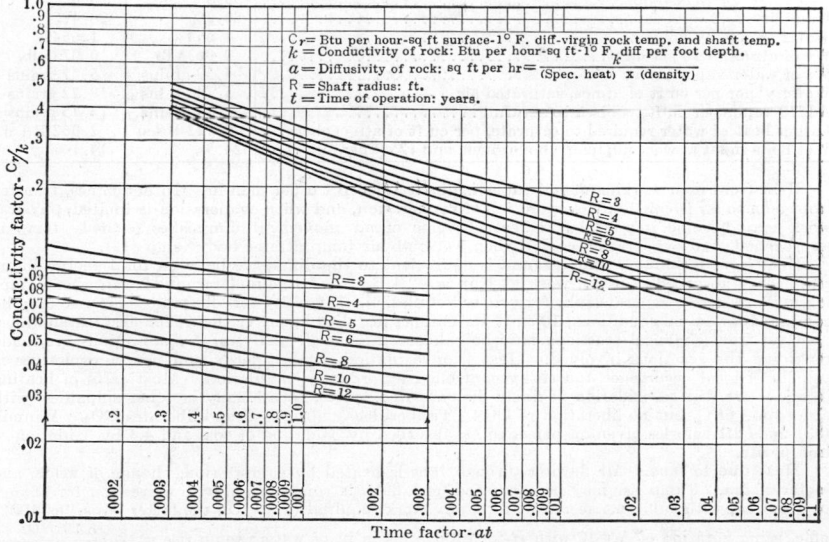

Fig 60. Chart of Heat Flow in Mines (79)

Heat flow from rock. Theoretic computation of heat flow from rock walls into air currents is complex (78), and of qualitative, rather than quantitative interest, due to difficulty of adjusting to actual conditions. Carrier (79) has developed a chart for constant-temp assumptions (Fig 60) from which the heat-transfer coeffic may be determined from time of cooling, and conductivity and diffusivity coefficients of the rock. The latter, for granite, limestone, sandstone, and slate are much alike (Sec 39); aver for conductivity, in B t u per hr per sq ft per ft of thickness, is about 1.25, and for diffusivity (conductivity ÷ [sp heat × density in lb per cu ft]), about 0.038.

Relation of air temp to rock temp. Estimates of duty of air-conditioning plants have relied on observed data from actual mining, which show that rock walls adjacent to airways tend to assume the aver temp of the air flow, and that the temp gradient in solid rock, inward from the walls, gradually flattens as cooling penetrates farther into the rock. Temperatures in deep boreholes in the walls of intake airways have shown cooling extending inward as much as 350 ft (80). These cooled zones act to insulate airways from rock heat, by reducing temp differential and flow of heat between rock and air at surfaces of contact. Practical differentials depend mainly on veloc of flow, distance of air travel, depth involved, and moisture conditions. Constant flow maintains an almost constant aver differential (81); increasing veloc gradually increases the differential. Aver temp in 1936 in Magma (Ariz) 3 200-level stopes, 500–1 500 ft from downcast shafts, was 84° F wet-bulb and 90° dry-bulb, 43° and 37° respectively below rock temp at that level. Other cases of air temp as much as 30°–40° below virgin rock temp (127°) could be cited, but aver differentials are much lower and range down to zero. Low veloc flow combined with oxidation or timber decay may result in negative differentials, or air temp above rock temp.

Heat of compression. In theory, 1 lb air falling D ft develops D ft-lb of energy, equivalent to $(D \div 778)$ B t u, which is sufficient to raise the temp of 1 lb of dry air $[(D \div 778) \div 0.24$ deg F], wherein 0.24 is sp heat of air at constant press. Then theoretical temp rise for 1 000 ft is about 5.4° F, or 1° per 185 ft of depth. Heat added by compression is lost by expansion in an equal height of upcast, hence total heat in mine is unchanged; but change in location of the heat is important for its effect on air conditions in working zones. Increase in wet-bulb temp depends on temp and abs press; approx range for mine shafts is 1.5°–2.5° F per 1 000 ft (see Table 7)

Table 7.   Adiabatic Compression in Ideal Shaft, 7 123 ft Deep

	At surface	At foot of shaft
Barometer.	25 in	32 in
Corresponding elev above tide.	5 059 ft	− 2 064 ft
Temperature: Dry bulb.	60.0° F	98.9° F
Wet bulb.	55.9	73.6
Humidity.	80.0%	28.4%
Water vapor, by volume.	1.654%	1.654%
Wt of atmosphere per cu ft.	0.0633 lb	0.0755 lb
Wt of water vapor per cu ft of atmos.	4.59 grains	5.47 grains
Water vapor per cu ft of atmos, saturated air.	5.74 grains	19.22 grains
Added vapor per cu ft required to saturate.	1.15 grains	13.75 grains
Latent heat of water required to saturate, per cu ft of atmosphere.	0.172 B t u	2.062 B t u
Wet Kata index at wet bulb temp above given, and 125 ft per min veloc	24.5	14.1

Heat from men working at full capac is about 1 000 B t u per man-hr. In hot mines, transfer from man to air is chiefly by evaporation of perspiration, and when evaporation is limited, physical work may become impossible. Effect of veloc of air movement diminishes as body temp is approached, and evaporation ceases when wet-bulb air temp attains body temp (12).

Heat from machinery underground is equivalent to the difference between total energy input and energy absorbed in useful work at 1 hp = 42.4 B t u. Large underground hoisting or pumping units require a separate split for proper ventilation. Quantity for allowable temp rise may be computed for actual conditions; 10 cu ft per min per installed hp is aver figure for elec installations.

Heat from chemical reactions may be calculated from air analyses, if assumptions are made regarding the reactions involved. Heat from oxidation, timber decay and use of explosives is usually of local occurrence and easily controlled by ordinary ventilation. Most cases of heating in mines are due to oxidation of finely disseminated pyrite, occasionally of other sulphides, with absorption of O, but no liberation of CO_2. Timber decay absorbs O and liberates CO_2. Winmill (83) finds 2.1 calories given off per cc of O_2 absorbed by oxidation of coal and 4.3 by oxidation of iron pyrite.

Heat due to fans. Air flowing through fans is heated by compression, change of veloc, and ineffic of fan. Temp rise may be computed for adiabatic compression, with correction for change of veloc, or, with sufficient accuracy, for equiv work required (84). On the latter basis, for 100% effic, using notation of Art 10 with H for total press in in of water: temp rise = $\dfrac{5.19\,HQ}{778 \times 0.24 \times Qw}$ = $\dfrac{0.0278}{w} H$. Due to inefficiency of the fan, actual temp rise is $\dfrac{0.0278}{w} \times \dfrac{H}{\text{effic (as ratio)}}$. For $w = 0.075$, temp rise $= 0.37\,H \div$ effic.

Friction and shock losses in air currents develop heat equivalent to the energy change. Assuming that all the heat enters the air current, derivation is same as above; temp rise is $0.37\,H$ for standard air density and varies inversely as density. Energy changes correspond to total press changes, but may be approximated by using static press, both for temp rise at fan and in air currents. Veloc energy existing at fan discharge is not converted to heat until dissipated in the airway as friction or shock loss, or as shock loss at discharge to the atmos.

Ground movement produces heat, but effects are not important. Local increases in temp have been noted at active faults (85), but in crushed areas the heat can usually be traced to increased rates of oxidation, from increased area of exposure to oxidation.

Effects of circulating air through mine workings, in order of importance, are: (a) reduction of natural temp of rock along intake airways and in deep workings; (b) reduced humidity, (c) increased veloc of air currents. Daily changes in surface air temp and humidity have little effect on downcast air currents except close to the surface, and seasonal effects in slow moving currents at depths of several thousand ft are small. Reduction in amplitude of temp variations largely depends on time of contact: at 10 min only seasonal effects are detectable and at 20 min even these are negligible.

Cooling and drying effects. Downcast air currents absorb heat from warmer rock walls, and absorb water, by evaporation, from walls of intake airways and workings. Cooling power of the air is large in winter, and the lower temp stored in ground near the surface warm intake air in summer. Walls of intake airways over a period of years are cooled to great depths, serving to insulate airways from higher-temp rock. Heat and moisture thus absorbed are largely redeposited along upcast airways of deep mines, only a part being discharged to atmos. Where mean cooling power of surface air is limited, or the economic limit of cooling by circulating air currents has been reached, the air must be artificially cooled to permit mining at great depths (Art 18). Continuous absorption of moisture from mine workings by comparatively dry intake air tends to reduce the moisture available, until workings become noticeably drier and relative humidities are decreased. With increased ventilation, mines that were damp to wet have become almost dry in appearance, even though the amount of moisture absorbed in intake shafts and workings remains quite large. Small increases in the normally low veloc of air currents through working places are effective in increasing comfort conditions, even though the same small increase in main-airway veloc would have no detectable effect.

Temperature, heat and moisture changes in air currents involve: dry-bulb, or sensible temp of the air; wet-bulb, or temp of adiabatic saturation; and dew-point, or temp at which condensation would occur upon sufficient cooling. Total heat changes in moist air are measured by changes in: sensible heat of the air, latent heat of the moisture by evaporation or condensation, and sensible heat of the moisture. The latter is negligibly small. Changes in latent heat are most important in air conditioning problems. Dry-bulb temp determines rates of heat transfer, but otherwise represents only the relation of sensible to latent heat in the air. At constant press, the wet-bulb temp represents total heat changes and the dew-point temp changes in absolute moisture content. Both wet-bulb and dew-point temp are affected by changes in abs press. These changes may be ignored in the case of shallow mines at or near sea-level, for which the ordinary constant-press psychrometric charts and tables at 29.92 in of mercury suffice. But, changes in psychrometric characteristics with change of abs press must be taken into account in deep mines, and special charts or tables (86, 79, 9) are required to compute temp change in terms of heat and moisture changes. Also, change in quantity of flow accompanying change in press makes it desirable to use flow rates in terms of lb of air rather than cu ft as in ordinary practice.

Thermal data. Sp heat of air at constant press is 0.2389, usually taken as 0.24. Sensible heat change for 1° F for standard air of 0.075 lb per cu ft is 0.0179 B t u per cu ft. Latent heat of evaporation or condensation is about 1 050 B t u per lb of water, or 0.15 B t u per grain of water (Sec 39). In refrigeration terms, 1 ton refrigeration is 200 B t u per min, or approx 1.05×10^{10} B t u per year.

Cooling with air currents. Within limits, the cheapest way to obtain added cooling at deep levels is by increasing the quantity Q of ventilating air (77, 87); limits are imposed by power cost, since fan hp increases about as Q^3. Increase in airway capac may be gained through additional shafts to depth, but as cost often exceeds $100 per ft, this solution may not be economical, especially as shafts have no salvage value, whereas air-conditioning plants are removable. Thus artificial cooling may give the same result more economically, or produce results not possible with unconditioned surface air. Cooling by ventilating air has been the main reliance of hot deep mines to date, and only a few have supplemented it by artificial cooling.

Effect of increasing veloc of air travel in intakes is to spread the heat and moisture absorbed over more air and thus heat it less. General result is a lowering of aver temp in working zones, accompanied by increases in seasonal effect.

Examples. At Village Deep, So Africa (88), workings were advanced 800 ft in vert depth from about 6 500 ft, to a 3.3° F higher rock temp, without increase of temp in intakes or splits (shaft to stopes) when air flow was increased approx 50%; but stope temp gradually increased at a somewhat lesser rate than rock temp, as did temp at development faces, except when machines were drilling, at which times approx the same temp existed as at levels 800 ft higher. At the Magma mine, Ariz (31), monthly records of stope temp in the central block adjacent to downcast shafts show little change in mean yearly temp in 8 years, while the lowest stoping zone progressed from the 2 550 to the 3 200 level, where virgin rock temp was approx 10° F higher. During this time air circulated gradually increased 60–70%. However, the seasonal ranges of aver stope temp were increased from about 82–89° F wet-bulb and 86–90° dry-bulb to 79–90° wet-bulb and 85–93° dry-bulb. During this period, the mine workings became perceptibly drier and gradual improvement in comfort was noted, except at the max summer condition, which remained about the same.

Dry vs wet shafts. Evaporation of water in downcast intake shafts lowers dry-bulb temp and thus increases the differential between air and virgin rock temp, with more rapid transfer of heat and cooling of walls. But cooling of the walls also reduces rate of heat flow for the same virgin-rock temp differential, and the relative merits of dry and wet shafts have been much debated. Observations (89) indicate that, although wet-bulb temp and total heat are about the same at the bottom of dry or wet deep shafts, dry-bulb temp is much higher in the case of dry shafts, and the air is therefore in better condition to travel from shaft to working place with minimum accession of heat from the walls. As air absorbs moisture, the dry-bulb temp decreases and heat flow into the air is increased. Every effort should therefore be made in hot mines to keep evaporation of moisture at a minimum to the last working place on the circuit, where, however, reduction of the dry-bulb to the wet-bulb temp by evaporation of moisture slightly improves comfort conditions.

Fan-pipe auxiliary ventilation delivers air long distances at high veloc without change in moisture content, and therefore provides optimum conditions for minimum increase in total heat and wet-bulb temp. Final temp of air is largely determined by temp of slow-moving return air along the pipe line, which is reduced as air quantity is increased. In high-temp rock, wet-bulb depression at discharge at development faces is often 15–20° F, but usually is not more than half as much at working faces 10–20 ft from the discharge. Fan-pipe ventilation is practically a method of maintaining the cooling power of mine air, auxiliary to all general methods of cooling, whether by ventilation or air conditioning. Small, hot mines sometimes use fan-pipe ventilation for all working places (9) and secure better working conditions than would be possible for the same layout with general ventilation. McIntyre (90) has proposed that the total intake be carried from surface to depth in a similar air-insulated pipe.

Control of development return air. Currents from fan-pipe-ventilated development faces in hot mines usually have max temp of the mine, often 95° to over 100° wet-bulb. These are usually added to intake currents of active workings and thus increase temp in working zones. Each small current of 2 000–4 000 c f m is equivalent to at least 15–30 tons of refrigeration. An important step in combating high temp, therefore, is to carry return air shafts to the bottom, rather than the top, of active zones, so that development returns can be directly coursed to them without traversing active stopes.

18. AIR CONDITIONING IN MINES

Definition. As generally applied to mines, air conditioning refers to artificial or mechanical cooling of air currents for control of the cooling power of the air. Other forms of air conditioning are applied to mine air (Sec 23), but are not thus specifically designated.

Cooling and drying methods, other than refrigeration, have been proposed for local use in mines, but high costs of production and transport generally rule them out (87), and only a few have been used regardless of cost.

Examples. Use of cool water from surface, sprayed directly on the men at hot faces, has been a last resort in some hot mines. Ice has been used, particularly in So Africa, where the Village Deep used blocks of ice on trays in fan-pipes for development faces, and, by spraying ice-chilled water into stope intake air, secured a 5° reduction in wet-bulb temp. Surface water, run to waste, was used experimentally (1931) at the Mountain Con mine, Butte (91), to determine design data for conditioning plants installed later. Similar smaller plants were occasionally used later at other Butte mines; in the winter of 1938, 6 fan-pipe cooling units were in use and 12 more contemplated, each using 20 gal per min of city water discharged between closely spaced plates in the pipes. In an aver case, wet-bulb temp in a development face was reduced 10° F (A. S. Richardson).

Drying agents, aside from high cost, have the disadvantages of heating the air with latent heat released by change from vapor to liquid, and of requiring heat for regeneration. Silica gel has been proposed (E. C. Holden, 1926) for drying comp air on surface, so as to increase its cooling effect underground when expanded in air drills, but has not been used although devaporizing comp air is now the essence of comp-air refrigeration methods. Absorption materials might be used at the bottom of wet shafts to change latent to sensible heat to condition the air for minimum heat absorption in further travel.

Lowering vapor tension by using solutions of magnesium chloride (92), a cheap waste product, and of calcium chloride has been proposed, to reduce moisture absorbed by air in passing through wet workings. Expected difficulties due to corrosion and effect on milling methods have retarded large-scale trials. In deep Mich copper mines (63), waters in lowest levels are concentrated calcium chloride solutions, and wet-bulb depressions of 3° to 11° F are found in places where depression in similar water-wet workings would not exceed 1°.

Mechanical refrigeration involves both cooling and drying, as changes in heat content are affected by changes of temp and of moisture content. Both air and its vapor are cooled. Vapor cooled to the dew-point temp condenses and drops out, but liberates latent heat of condensation, which is the principal load on a plant dealing with air near saturation, or air cooled through a large range. A refrigeration system merely transfers heat from the cooled medium to some other medium from which it can be dissipated without reaffecting the cooled medium. Safe refrigerants for underground service have been developed in recent years; the major difficulty and cost is in dissipating the heat (93).

General requirements for large-capac plants in commercial service are said to be about 0.2 ton refrigeration per 1 000 c f m per deg wet-bulb cooling, 2 gal condenser water per ton, 2.5 gal spray water per ton, and 1.0 hp per ton of refrigeration. At high-temp level of heat exchange underground, about 0.4 ton refrigeration is required, and estimates of condenser water, spray water, and hp are about 50% higher than above.

Methods for mine air-conditioning have been: (1) vapor refrigeration of air at surface, or underground; (2) cooling of liquids on surface, by evaporative cooling and by vapor refrigeration, both surface and underground, for use in underground heat exchangers; and (3) dehumidification of comp air on surface, by over-compression-and-expansion, for use underground in air motors and drills.

Surface air refrigeration. The largest plants so far installed, Morro Velho (Brazil), Robinson Deep (So Africa), and Kolar (India), are surface vapor-refrigerating plants. Advantages of surface plants: easy disposition of waste heat, absorbed from the air, plus heat due to work performed; max safety, reliability and operating convenience; and increase of summer natural draft to approx winter conditions. Disadvantages: low positional effic (about 0.4 the first year for 7 500 ft on the Rand (77) with probable increase in time to 0.55), due to increased flow of heat from walls of downcast; operation at aver of approx 60% capac, requiring larger plant; and limited capac, due to limited temp range available above freezing, and to lower heat capac of air at lower temp. Reduction of 1° in wet-bulb temp requires about 3 times as many heat units per lb of air at 90° as at 40°.

Morro Velho mine, Brazil, (94) was the first to be artificially cooled. A surface plant was installed in 1920 and an underground plant in 1929. The mine is very dry and in a warm moist climate; surface elev, 2 768 ft. Aver dry-bulb temp (t_d), 68° F; max wet-bulb (t_w) in rainy season, 75°; aver max t_w, 72°. Rock temp increases 1° per 140 ft from surface to 6 400 ft, but 1° per 119 ft from 5 300 to 6 400 ft and is 123° at 7 000 ft. Monthly output from a pitching gold reef by cut-and-fill methods was about 14 000 tons in 1922, with aver of 290 men underground per shift (3 shifts). Stopes are 6–12 ft high, 8 ft wide and over 1 000 ft long; one per level, off 5 active levels spaced 300 ft vertically (active zone of 1 500 ft). Hoisting is in relatively shallow stages through offset interior shafts. Advance in depth per year is approx 150 ft. In 1926 lowest stoping operations were on 24th level, about 7 000 ft (E. Davies).

Surface plant. Ammonia-vapor refrigeration, divided into 6 stages (with provision for 3 more). Reciprocating compressors and rotary-plate water coolers are installed at portal of the 850-ft main adit at elev 2 444 ft. Cooled air is blown in by fans, with pressures adjusted to prevent admixture of surface air, and no airlock is required. A safety door is placed in the adit, with remote control from plant and shaft. Rated capac, 100 600 B t u, or 503 tons refrigeration, equal to reduction of t_w from 72° to 43.2° F for 5 040 lb dry air per min, or 80 000 c f m. (Condition of cooled air approximates aver climatic condition in England.) Design based on reducing moisture of surface air to a content estimated to hold max t_w on 22nd level (12 500 ft of travel) at 81° and max in 21st level stope, 85°. When plant started, an underground fan, in series with the surface fan, doubled the pressure and increased the quantity in circulation 40%. Both together lowered max wet-bulb temp 9.4° during first 16 mo. In the same period, the fatality accident rate was reduced two-thirds and cases of heat cramp three-fourths; and production increased 12% with the same force. In 1926, the lowest stoping level was the 24th, where aver cooling was 8° t_w (Davies). The plant cost $455 000, and expenditures for power supply made total cost about $630 000. Max requirements for 6-stage operation, 700 hp for 21 motors. UNDERGROUND PLANT (95), in series with surface plant on the 5 800-ft level, above the active mining zone and 6 000 ft from lowest stopes, consists of 2 centrifugal compressors using Carrene (CH_2Cl_2) as refrigerant, which boils at 104° (sea level) and permits operation at pressures below atmos. Capac is said to be 150 tons, cooling a shunt circuit (to avoid excessive lowering of t_d) of 50 000 c f m from 75 t_w — 100 t_d to 64 t_w — 74 t_d. This gave an aver temp of 82 t_w — 100 t_d at lowest level. Temp as high as 126° t_d are known, but corresponding t_w is about 80° and men can work at good rate. Condenser water is cooled by spray tower in upcast air of 82 t_w — 102 t_d at plant horizon, with only 0.5% loss by evaporation (79). Added resistance of cooling tower is compensated by increased natural draft.

Turf Shaft, Robinson Deep, So Africa (96, 97) has the second surface installation (1935), the largest of its kind. Mine is dry, except for water to wet down timbered shafts and combat dust hazard; climate warm and dry; surface elev, 5 600 ft. Mean t_d, 60° F; mean t_w, 52.5°. Rock-temp gradient (80) is 1° per 185 ft; temp at 8 000 ft, 101.5° F.

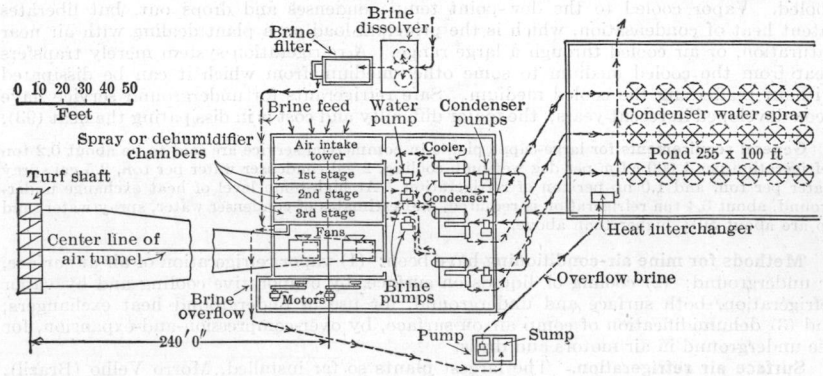

Fig 61. Sketch-plan of Robinson Deep Refrigeration Plant (79)

Monthly output of Turf Shaft section is about 40% of total tonnage. In 1933, with production at 117 000 tons per mo, mine employed aver of 390 whites and 6 100 natives. Uniform-grade, narrow reefs dipping about 33° are mined by cut-and-fill (resuing) methods, with stopes 5-ft high off rock drifts on levels spaced 300 ft along the dip and extending up to 1 mile from shafts. Aver depth of stoping zone was 6 700 ft in 1933; max depth of development, 8 000 ft; advance in depth, about 200 ft per yr. The 7-compt Turf shaft goes to the 4 060-ft level, the 6-compt Main Incline shaft thence to the 6 200 ft level (3 775 ft slope), and two 3-compt sub-inclines 80 ft apart thence to bottom. Max air travel is 2 miles as intake, and 5 miles in all.

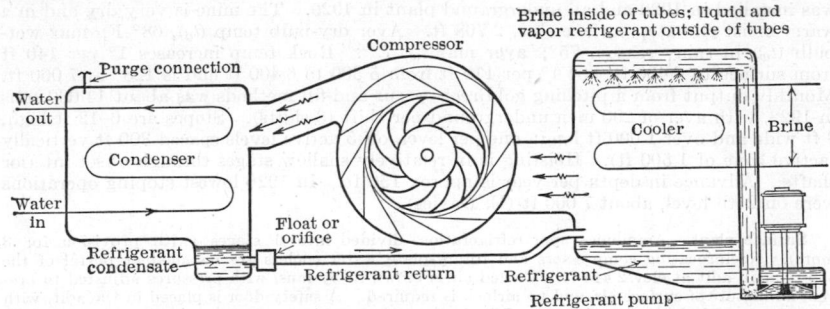

Fig 62. Arrangement of Centrifugal Refrigeration System (79)

Plant (Fig 61, 62) is in separate units, using Carrene No 2 (monofluorotrichloromethane), boiling at 75° at sea level. Each unit has a 750-hp 2-stage centrifugal compressor, shell-and-tube cooler and condenser, 150-hp 2 300-gal per min spray pump and 75-hp 2 000-gal per min condenser pump. Plant rated at approx 2 100 tons refrigeration; designed to cool 407 000 c f m from 65° F t_w to 38°, actually cools approx 360 000 c f m from 65° t_w to 33.5°. Water is used for first stage and brine for others. Cooled air is blown by fans through spray-type dehumidifiers, and through a 12 by 36-ft duct on 27° slope, entering shaft 100 ft below collar. Fan pressures are adjusted to permit small upcast of cooled air to surface. Main fan is on the 33rd level (6 204 ft), between main incline and sub-incline shafts, and downcasts air from surface duct to the lowest levels. Return air is broadcast through old workings to shallow surface shafts. Lack of an upcast shaft was important in deciding on a surface rather than underground plant. First year of operation prevented normal summer rise of 6° t_w in stopes, and summer max t_w was subsequently lowered 8°–9°, or an aver reduction of stope temp of 4°–4.5° t_w (79). Notwithstanding depth and aver distance air has to travel, results are considered satisfactory, and sufficient to warrant deepening of workings at least 1 500 ft beyond 1935 limits. Positional effic at 7 500 ft depth at shaft in 15 mo was 75%. Plant cost approx $500 000, including winze connection to shaft, and requires about 3 000 hp at capacity. Operation is at aver of 55% of capac. Initial operating cost of about $7 320 per month is expected to decrease gradually to aver of $6 200.

Kolar Goldfield, So India (Pryor, 77) has its third large surface air-refrigeration plant, approaching completion on a mine 8 200 ft deep in 1938. Plant, of standard ammonia-compression type using brine in pipe coils, has capac of 1 140 tons refrigeration, to cool 150 000 c f m (10 000 lb) from 73° to 40° F.

Underground air refrigeration. The underground plant at Morro Velho (above), was the first thus installed. A second has been placed in an East Rand mine. Advantages: high positional effic, operation at full capac, and practically unlimited heat capac due to high temp range. Disadvantages: difficulty and cost of disposing of heat abstracted; high cost of required excavation; deduction of heat radiated by machinery from net cooling effect; and no increase of natural ventilation except where condenser water is cooled by heating upcast currents.

East Rand Proprietary Mine, So Africa (95). A Freon vapor refrigerating plant of about 500-ton capac was installed on 46th level, 6 400 ft deep and 1 000 ft below sea level, in 1936. It cooled 157 000–176 000 c f m from 81° t_w − 83° t_d to about 72° and 71° saturated. Heat to condenser water represents about 630 tons actual refrigeration. Mine water is used for condensing and pumped to surface; but an estimated return of 400 000 c f m at about 3 000 ft depth could cool condenser water for 1 400 tons actual refrigeration with increase of 10° t_w.

Surface refrigeration of liquids used underground. Plants for this purpose have been installed at mines in Germany and Butte, Mont. Use of a liquid rather than air to transport cooling has often been advocated in discussions of mine air-conditioning (77), but the heavy piping required to withstand press at great depths, or alternate necessity of stage heat exchangers, has retarded use of this system. Main advantage over surface air refrigeration is less loss in transfer of cooling to working places; hence better positional effic, and smaller space required for transporting same volume of cooling in aver ratio of 1 for water to 3 500 for air. Main disadvantages: cost of piping; finding place for piping in already crowded pipe compts of shafts; and danger in case of pipe failure by corrosion.

Zeche Radbod mine, Ruhr, Germany (81). A small surface ammonia plant was installed about 1923 for temporary cooling of water in pipe radiators on the 3 150-level, pending sinking of another shaft and increase in ventilating quantity. Coal is mined at depths between 2 600 and 3 250 ft. Rock temp gradient, 1° per 50 ft; max rock temp 111° F, expected to reach 136°. At temp above 82.5° t_w, miner works shift of 5 instead of 6 hr. Short shifts increased to 83% and production fell to 0.51 ton per man by June, 1921. Ventilation was increased from 350 000 to 700 000 c f m and by Feb, 1922, short shifts had decreased to zero and production rose to 0.68 ton per man. But in summer of 1922 short shifts were up to 25% and production down to 0.64. A new shaft was sunk to increase ventilation, and trials of cooling were made pending its completion. At first, city water, 61° at surface, cooled 250 000 c f m on 3 150 level, an aver of 1° t_w. Then water was cooled by ammonia plant to 34° at surface, rising to 41° at 3 150 level in 1.5-min travel in insulated pipe, and 22 c f m heated to 61° (138 ton refrigeration) at discharge. Radiator of 340 ft of pipe with 19 000 sq ft surface cooled 250 000 c f m 5.5° t_d (est as approx 2° t_w) from 73° t_d. Plant (second-hand) cost $17 000 to build and $107 per shift to operate, with increase of $170 output per shift.

Mountain Con Mine, Butte, Mont (98) has adopted A. S. Richardson's new method of evaporative cooling of water to a temp about halfway between t_w and dew-point, whereas ordinary cooling in spray towers leaves water 5°–7° above t_w of air. Mine is damp to dry (but damp to wet without intensive ventilation), in exceptionally cool, dry climate. Mean annual temp (1922) at approx 6 000 ft elev, 36.9° F t_d; precipitation 12.8 in; aver temp, Jan 12°, July 62° t_d; aver t_w 10° below t_d for 4 summer months. During warmest part of day, t_w is usually 15°–30° lower than t_d, and dew-point 10°–20° lower than t_w; dew-point is often below freezing in hottest months. Rock temp gradient for Butte mines is probably nearer 1° per 55–60 ft, than per 100 ft as usually stated. Rock temp at Mountain Con 3 500-ft level, over 100° F. Ore, copper sulphides in granite country rock; veins dipping 70°–90°. Levels, approx 135 ft apart, extend 1 000–2 000 ft from a downcast shaft carrying 120 000 c f m for approx 100 working places.

Plant (Fig 63): (1) surface plant of fan, low-press heat absorber and spray tower; (2) high-press pipe columns in shaft, carrying sump water and forming closed circuit from surface to underground plants and return; (3) high-press underground heat absorbers on 3 500- and 3 600-ft levels. Shaft

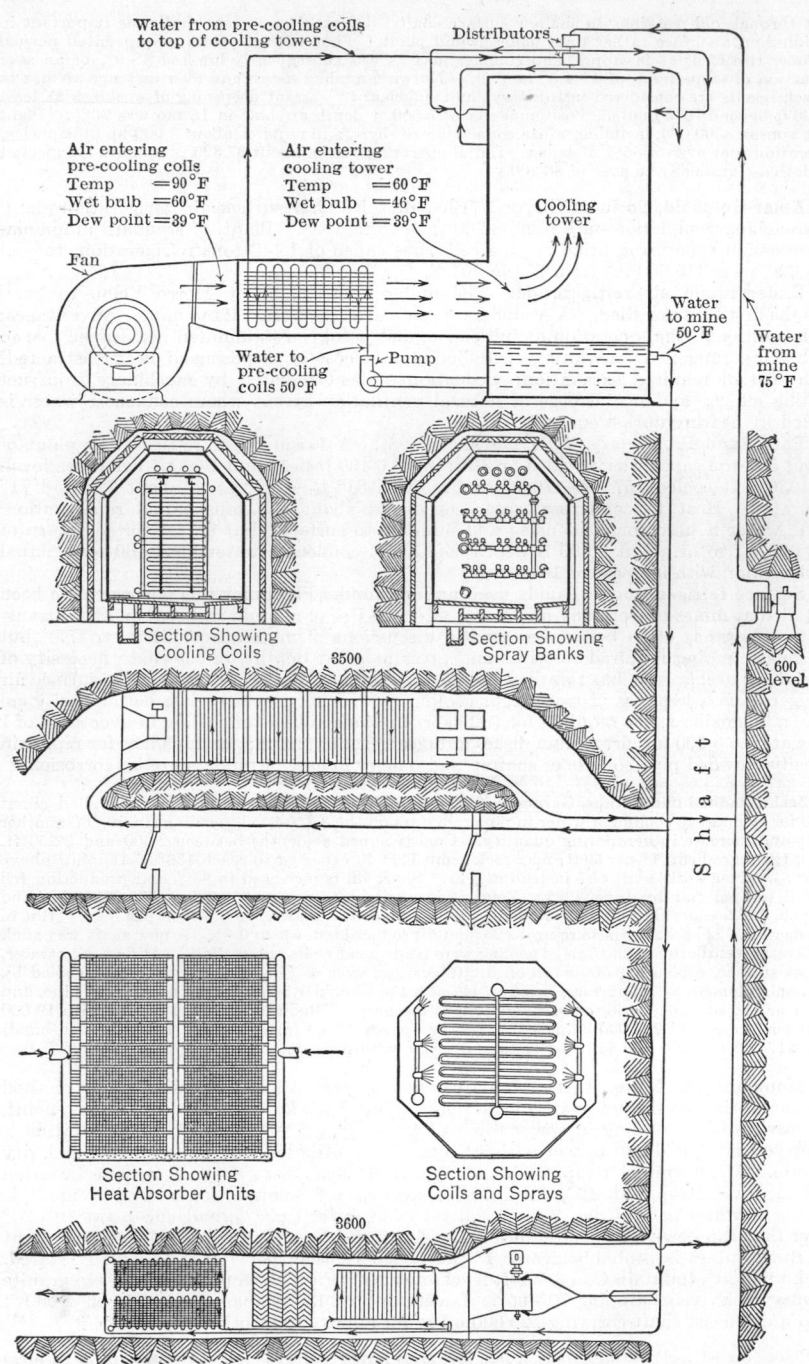

Water from pre-cooling coils
to top of cooling tower

Distributors

Air entering
pre-cooling coils
Temp = 90 °F
Wet bulb = 60 °F
Dew point = 39 °F

Air entering
cooling tower
Temp = 60 °F
Wet bulb = 46 °F
Dew point = 39 °F

Cooling
tower

Fan

Water to
pre-cooling
coils 50 °F

Pump

Water
to mine
50 °F

Water
from
mine
75 °F

Section Showing
Cooling Coils

Section Showing
Spray Banks

600
level

3500

Shaft

Section Showing
Heat Absorber Units

Section Showing
Coils and Sprays

3600

Fig 63.　Evaporative Cooling System devised for Butte Mines (63)

pipe columns, **1 000** gal per min capac, are $85/_8$-in steel tubing, tested to withstand 2 000 lb per sq in with safety factor of 4; branch lines, 6-in and smaller; all insulated with 1.5 in of mineral wool. Small pump near surface overcomes friction in balanced circuit. In surface plant, air is blown through an extended surface pipe-coil absorber, which circulates sump-water countercurrently; the cooled exit air, of same vapor content as at entrance, rises through cooling tower against heated sprays from (a) same absorber coils, (b) underground absorbers. The latter, using sump water piped from cooling tower comprise high-press plain coils with closed-circuit spray water, to wash the air and assist heat transfer; also (3 600-ft level), high-press extended-surface coils of special design that, for equal capac, require only $1/_{12}$ as much excavation as plain coils with sprays. Of 4 units planned (total capac, 1 200 tons refrigeration), 2 are installed, with shaft piping for four. Water was the cooling medium to 1938, but brine or non-freezing solutions are contemplated. Results have varied with operating conditions and location of working places. The 3 600-level unit lowered t_w of the 14 working places (to 3 800 level) for which it was installed, an aver of 14° (max 30°); in 5 mo, aver temp of 100 working places decreased from 83.7° t_w to 75.3. Seasonal effect being estimated at about 2°, conditioner effect was about 6° plus. Costs of plant and operating cost are low, but have not been revealed.

Underground refrigeration of liquids, although a logical selection, is used in but one plant (Magma). Main advantage over surface cooling of liquids is avoidance of high-press pipe and high-press heat absorbers. Main disadvantages lie in providing condenser water and disposing of heat abstracted, which may require as much pipe as surface cooling. As liquids cooled at a central plant may be used in one or more semi-portable units, positional effic is higher than for cooling air directly.

Magma Copper Co, Ariz (99). Mine, in hot, dry climate, is normally damp, but dried by intensive ventilation. Elev of 500 level (main-operating adits), 3 050 ft. Mean surface t_d, 72.4°; mean t_w, 57.4°; mean relative humidity, 38%. Mean annual precipitation, 18.7 in. Rock temp gradient, 1° per 67 ft; rock temp 140° F at 4 000 ft (lowest level in 1939). Deposit, high-grade copper sulphides in a steep-pitching orebody; also, small bodies of copper and zinc ore. Method, rill cut-and-fill stoping with raises through, before mining, on 105-ft centers; levels 200 ft apart. Advance in depth, about 100 ft per yr. Main orebody is 1 000–1 500 ft long. Production, 1 300 tons a day with about 420 men underground on 3 shifts, 200 on largest shift. Of total ventilation of 240 000 c f m, about 145 000 passes up through main orebody, intaking on bottom levels from vert shafts. Initial development is by footwall drifts between shafts in comparatively dry rock, with mining off drifts in the vein.

Plant: 2 vapor units, with a capacity of 140 tons refrigeration each, are installed in a 20 by 62 by 12-ft chamber on 3 600 level, with space for an additional unit. Rated performance lowers the t_w of 60 000 c f m 12° from 85°, but capac decreases with decrease of exit temp at cooling coils. Refrigerant is Carrene No 2 (as at Robinson Deep). Chilled water is pumped through extended-surface cooling coils, set in crosscuts before 30 000-c f m booster fans; initially placed on 3 600 level near plant and vert above on 3 400 level, but coils can be placed over 1 000 ft below plant if required in future. Water condensed on cooling coils keeps them clean. Condensers heat 400 gal per min of mine water (from distant part of mine on opposite side of orebody) from 90° to 113°; 7 929 ft of pipe, mostly 6-in, was required for these lines, with 2 000 ft of return line, insulated in passing through the footwall drift to a pipe column in intake shaft on opposite side of orebody; 1 650 ft of 4-in pipe was required for cooling-coil connections. A new return shaft in the hanging wall now carries the mine pump column, and possible use of future cross-cuts to this shaft for cooling condenser water were under consideration. Operation of the plant greatly speeded development and start of stoping on the 3 400 and 3 600 levels. Results for only 4 mo of operation have been reported; inconclusive, due to large seasonal range of temp in shaft-stations, stopes and development faces. Aver decreases of 7°–8° t_w on 3 600 and 3 400 levels, and of 1°–2° t_w on 3 200 and 3 000 levels are indicated. Effect on aver stope temp can not be large, as only 43% of ventilation air is cooled not more than 10° t_w aver over the year. But, effect of plant will increase with time, and will be reinforced by connecting development direct to new return shaft, instead of to intakes. Total cost of plant, $86 538, exclusive of fans and crosscuts normally required for ventilation; $24 351 was for condenser pipe lines and pump. In May 1939 (C. B. Foraker), power requirements were 229 646 kw-hr, divided about 62–24–14% between compressors, fans, and condenser pumps (to sump on 3 600 level at new shaft); operating cost, exclusive of power, $547. Plant is operated 6 days a week. For development of 4 000 level, a 25-ton vapor-refrigeration plant was installed there in Jan, 1938, for conditioning the air intake of 2 fan-pipe units.

Use of devaporized compressed-air. One large group of mines on the Rand has installed (and on order) a number of special compressors for producing practically dry air, which greatly increases coldness of exhaust (to −80° F) of underground machinery without freezing troubles. This method has max positional effic, max flexibility in use, permits gradual expansion of plant, introduces no new factor into mine operations, and the main plant is on surface. Chief objection is cost, estimated to be at least twice that of vapor refrigeration. Also, capac is limited unless all machinery underground is converted to comp-air drive.

Anglo-American Corpn, Rand, So Africa (77) had devaporizing compressors of 10 000–20 000 c f m free air capac installed at 6 mines in 1938, and four 20 000-c f m machines on order, a total capac of 198 000. Those on order are elec driven, with over-compression and expansion stages built in. Earlier types have separate devaporizing units, or, in case of steam turbine drive, extra stages mounted on same shaft.

Devaporizing method is shown diagrammatically in Fig 64. Normal comp air at 90 lb is over-compressed to 130 lb, cooled (in cooler and heat-exchanger), expanded back to normal press and 32° F, and then restored to normal temp in heat exchanger, where cooling is transferred to over-compressed air before expansion. Water is removed between stages, so that final product is dried to moisture content at normal press and 32° F. Control of temp in expansion stage is either automatic or manual. For producing similar results at lower cost, a regenerative system (100) has been proposed, but not yet applied.

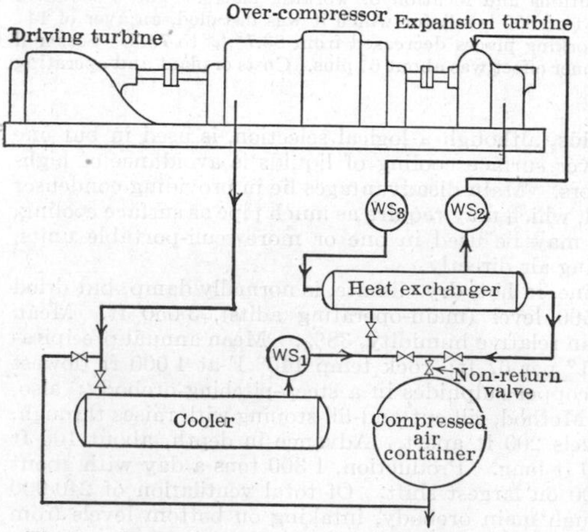

Comparative costs of cooling B t u's (87, 90). Aver cost by ventilation, where feasible, is 0.00001–0.00002¢ per B t u. McIntyre estimates cost of piping air from surface at about 0.000025¢. With capital charge of 10%, and power at 1¢ per kw-hr, comparative costs per B t u for full-capac operation of cooling plants may be calculated from available data as approx 0.00018¢ for Morro Velho (surface plant only), 0.00013¢ for Robinson Deep, and 0.00015¢ for Magma (without charge for pumping condenser water from 3 600 level). On the same basis, the cost of Richardson's system is estimated not to exceed 0.00005¢

Fig 64. Devaporization Method for Comp Air (77)

at Butte, though impracticable for most mining districts. Actual costs would be reduced by lower power rates and increased by under-capac operation (surface plants). Actual cost for 1st-yr operation at Robinson Deep, at less than 1/3 capac (97), was about 0.00019¢ on basis of 10% capital charge. Estimates for devaporized comp air are usually 0.0001–0.0002¢, and for free discharge of comp air from nozzle 0.001–0.002¢. Minimum for ice, with ice at 5¢ per 100 lb, is 0.003¢ plus transport; and for liquid air at 1.7¢ per lb, 0.008¢ plus handling charges.

BIBLIOGRAPHY

1. Atkinson, J. J. Theory of the Ventilation of Mines. *Trans* N of Eng Inst M E, Vol 3, 1853, p 73, 321
2. Beard, J. T. Mine Gases and Ventilation of Mines, 1920
3. Briggs, H. Ventilation of Mines, 1929
4. Carrier, W. H. and Madison, R. D. Fan Engineering. Buffalo Forge Co, 2nd ed, 1925
5. Haddock, M. H. Mine Ventilation and Ventilators, 1924
6. Internatl Corresp School Staff. Mine Ventilation, 1930
7. Keller, C. Axial Flow Fans. Transl by L. S. Marks, 1937
8. Mauchline, R. Mine Foreman's Handbook, revised by F. E. Brackett, 1905
9. McElroy, G. E. Engineering Factors in Ventilation of Metal Mines. U S Bur Mines, *Bull* No 385, 1935
10. Murgue, Daniel. Theories and Practice of Centrifugal Ventilators, transl by A. L. Steavenson, 1883
11. Redmayne, R. A. S. Ventilation of Mines, 1911
12. Weeks, W. S. Ventilation of Mines, 1926
13. Ventilating Mines and Removing Gas. J. J. Rutledge. *Coll Eng*, Sept, 1913, p 81
14. Ventilation in Flat Coal Seams. A. H. Stow. *E & M Jour*, Jan 26, 1907, p 191
15. Pressure vs Exhaust Fans. A. H. Stow. *Trans* A I M E, Vol 40, p 398
16. Ventilating System at the Comstock Mines, Nev. G. J. Young. *Trans* A I M E, Vol 41, p 3
17. Ventilation in Metal Mines. C. A. Mitke. *E & M Jour*, Nov 30, 1918, p 939
18. Dust-Ventilation Studies in Metal Mines. D. Harrington. *Trans* A I M E, Vol 66, p 272
19. Metal-Mine Ventilation in the Southwest. C. A. Mitke. *Trans* A I M E, Vol 69, p 377
20. Ventilation of Butte Mines of Anaconda Co. A. S. Richardson. *Trans* A I M E, Vol 68, p 33
21. Underground ventilation at Butte. D. Harrington. U S Bur Mines, *Bull* No 204, 1923
22. Mine Ventilation. Committee Report. *Proc* Amer Min Cong, Sept, 1923, p 599
23. Ventilation Problems at Champion Reef Mine, Kolar Gold Fields, India. C. F. Heathcote. Trans Inst Min & Met, Vol 00, p 160

24. Control of Silica Dust in Rock Drilling. N Y Dept of Labor, *Industrial Code Bull* 33, 1937
25. State Coal Mining Laws Concerning Ventilation. J. A. Garcia. *Trans* A I M E, Vol 74, p 409
26. Coal Mining in Europe. G. S. Rice and I. Hartman. U S Bur Mines, *Bull* No 414, 1939
27. Ventilation at Anthracite Collieries of Northern Pennsylvania Field. G. E. McElroy. U S Bur Mines, *Inf Circ* No 6965, 1937
28. Observations on Mine Ventilation. D. F. Davies. *Proc* So Wales Inst Eng, Vol 43, p 471
29. Power Studies in Illinois Coal Mining. A. J. Hoskin and T. Fraser. Univ Ill Exp Sta, *Bull* 144, 1924
30. Mine Ventilation Stoppings. R. Y. Williams. U S Bur Mines, *Bull* No 99, 1915
31. Ventilation of Copper Mines of Arizona. G. E. McElroy. U S Bur Mines, *Bull* No 330, 1931
32. Brattice Cloth in Coal Mines. G. S. Rice and C. W. Owings. U S Bur Mines, *Rept Inv* No 2872, 1928
33. Canvas Tubing for Mine Ventilation. L. D. Frink. *Trans* A I M E, Vol 59, p 326
34. Recirculation Caused by Auxiliary Fans in Coal Mines. H. P. Greenwald and H. C. Howarth. *Trans* A I M E, Vol 76, p 164
35. Experiments on Ventilation in Development Work. E. J. Laschinger. *Trans* Chem Met & Min Soc, So Af, Vol 21, p 76
36. Design of Local Exhaust Hoods. J. M. Dallavalle and T. Hatch. *Trans* A S M E, Vol 54
37. Air Flow from Grills. A. L. Greenlow. *Heat Piping & Air Cond*, Vol 10, pp 387, 452
38. Health Conservation of the Metal Miner. W. B. Daly. Min Cong *Jour*, Apl, 1939, p 64
39. Measurement of Air Flow. E. Ower, 1927
40. Resistance of Metal Mine Airways. G. E. McElroy and A. S. Richardson. U S Bur Mines, *Bull* No 261, 1927
41. How to Make Air Pressure Surveys. J. N. Williamson. *Coal Age*, Aug-Sept, 1932, p 297, 331
42. Use of Inclined Gage for Determination of Pressure Losses. R. Clive and J. G. Bromilow. *Trans* Inst Min Eng, Gt Britain, Vol 90, p 91
43. Pamphlet. American Askania Corp, Houston, Texas
44. Precise Manometer for Ventilation Measurements. W. S. Weeks. *Min & Met*, Jan, 1923, p 19
45. Wahlen Micromanometer. L. W. Huber. *Coal Age*, Apl 26, 1923, p 669
46. Friction of Air in Mines. F. E. Brackett. *E & M Jour*, Apl 22, 1911, p 822
47. Application of Kutter's Formula to Flow of Gases. F. E. Brackett. *Trans* A I M E, Vol 74, p 313
48. Report N Y State Bridge and Tunnel Commission. N Y Legislature, 1923, *Doc* 108
49. Coal Mine Ventilation Factors. H. P. Greenwald and G. E. McElroy. U S Bur Mines, *Bull* No 285, 1929
50. Mine-Air Flow. G. E. McElroy. *Trans* A I M E, Vol 74, p 297
51. Friction Factors for Fan Piping. G. E. McElroy and A. S. Richardson. U S Bur Mines, *Rept Inv* No 2540, 1923
52. Friction Factors in Ventilating Pipe. W. S. Weeks and others. *E & M Jour*, June 10, 1922, p 1001
53. Pressure Losses due to Bends and Area Changes. G. E. McElroy. U S Bur Mines, *Inf Circ* No 6663, 1932
54. Experimental Study of Fan Evasées. H. Briggs and J. N. Williamson. *Trans* Inst Min Eng, Gt Britain, Vol 68, p 323
55. Air Current Regulator. W. S. Weeks. *Trans* A I M E, Vol 76, p 136
56. Pressure Losses Resulting from Changes in Area. A. P. Kratz and J. R. Fellows. Univ Ill Exp Sta, *Bull* No 300, 1938
57. Psychrometric Tables. C. F. Marvin. U S Weather Bureau, *Bull* No 235, 1915
58. Flow in Networks of Conduits or Conductors. H. Cross. Univ Ill Exp Sta, *Bull* No 286, 1936
59. Economic Size of Metal Mine Airways. G. E. McElroy. U S Bur Mines, *Inf Circ* No 6585, 1932
60. Determining Resistance of Small Mine by Natural Draft. G. E. McElroy and A. S. Richardson. Bur Mines, *Rept Inv* No 2890, 1928
61. Direct Solution of Problems Involving Natural Ventilation. W. S. Weeks. A I M E, *Tech Pap* No 957, 1938
62. Mine Ventilation. F. E. Brackett. Sec 14, 2d Edition of this Handbook, Art 11, p 1211 (furnace ventilation); Art 19, p 1233 (Emergency ventilators)
63. Natural Ventilation of Michigan Copper Mines. G. E. McElroy. U S Bur Mines, *Tech Pap* No 516, 1932
64. Features of Fans at 164 Mines. D. Harrington and M. W. von Bernewitz. U S Bur Mines, *Rept Inv* No 2637
65. Operating Regulations to Govern Coal Mining on Leased Lands of the Public Domain. U S Bur Mines, *Pub* No 146
66. Application of Air Screws to Mine Ventilation. F. A. Steart. *Trans* Inst Min Eng, Gt Britain, Vol 68, p 310
67. Testing a Steart Fan at Grange Colliery. G. Lindley and D. Hay. *Trans* Inst Min Eng, Vol 76, p 101
68. Theory and Practice in Ventilation of Long Tunnels. W. S. Weeks. *E & M Jour*, Nov 17, 1928, p 779
69. Air Injector for Auxiliary Ventilation. W. S. Weeks. *E & M Jour*, Apl, 1937, p 196
70. Ventilation of Tunnels by Saccardo's System. *Bull* Internatl R'y Cong, Vol 13, p 447
71. Experiments on Mine Fan Performance. G. E. McElroy and A. S. Richardson. U S Bur Mines, *Tech Pap* No 447, 1929
72. Mine Ventilation. F. E. Brackett. Sec 14, 2d Edition of this Handbook, Art 12–16, pp 1215–1232 (Theory and design of fans)
73. Developments in the Theory of Centrifugal Fans. H. Briggs. *Coal Age*, Apl, 1923, p 601
74. Propeller Type Fans for Mine Ventilation. T. H. Troller. A I M E, *Tech Pub* No 712, 1936
75. Standard Test Code for Centrifugal and Axial Fans. Natl Assoc Fan Mfrs, *Bull* No 103, 3rd Ed, 1938
76. Charts for Determining Performance of Centrifugal Fans. G. E. McElroy. U S Bur Mines, *Rept Inv* No 3298, 1936
77. Engineering Problems Associated with Improvement of Temperature and Humidity Conditions in Mines. J. H. Dobson and W. J. Walker. *Proc* Instn Mech Eng (London), Vol 139, p 185
78. Heat Flow in an Infinite Solid Bounded Internally by a Cylinder. L. P. Smith. *Jour* App Physics, Vol 8 (1937), p 441

79. Air Cooling in Gold Mines on the Rand. W. H. Carrier. A I M E, *Tech Pub* No 970, 1938
80. Borehole Temperatures at the Turf Shaft, Robinson Deep. E. C. Whittaker. *Jour* Chem Met & Min Soc, So Af, Vol 36, p 234
81. Rock and Air Temperatures in Deep Level Mines. M. O. Tilliard and E. C. Ranson. *Jour* Chem Met & Min Soc, So Af, Vol 26, p 184; discussion, Vol 26 and 27
82. Factors Affecting the Condition of Mine Air. F. J. Tromp. *Jour* Chem Met & Min Soc, So Af, Vol 36, p 338
83. Absorption of Oxygen by Coal: Part III, Thermal Value of Absorption. T. F. Winmill. *Trans* Inst Min Eng, Gt Britain, Vol 48, p 508. Atmospheric Oxidation of Iron Pyrites, Vol 51, p 500
84. Efficiency of a Fan. J. W. Whitaker. *Trans* Inst Min Eng, Gt Britain, Vol 72, p 43
85. Heat due to Strata Movements. H. Briggs and others. *Trans* Inst Min Eng, Vol 67, p 355
86. Review of Existing Psychrometric Data. W. H. Carrier and C. O. Mackey. *Trans* A S M E, Vol 59, PRO, p 33
87. Review of Engineering Aspects of Improving Mine Atmospheres at Great Depths. J. H. Dobson. *Jour* So Af Inst Eng, Vol 25, p 23; discussion, Vol 25, 26
88. Comparative Temperatures with Varying Air Movements Underground. E. C. Ranson. *Jour* Chem Met & Min Soc, So Af, Vol 31, p 68
89. Effect of Wet and Dry Ducts on Air Condition and Acquisition of Heat from Walls. E. C. Ranson. *Jour* Chem Met & Min Soc, So Af, Vol 36, p 85
90. Review of the Difficulties of Air Conditioning and Suggested Methods for Improvement. J. T. McIntyre. *Jour* So Af Inst Eng, Vol 31, p 84
91. Experimental Air Conditioning for Butte Mines. W. B. Daly and A. S. Richardson. *Trans* A I M E, Vol 109, p 231
92. Proposal for Conditioning Air in Hot Mines. P. Hirschfelder. *Jour* Chem Met & Min Soc, So Af, Vol 34, p 400
93. Air Conditioning in Deep Mines. R. W. Waterfill. A I M E, *Tech Pub* No 206, 1929
94. Air-Cooling Plant at Morro Velho Mine, Brazil. E. Davies. *Trans* Inst Min Eng, Gt Britain, Vol 63, p 326
95. Heat Balance Diagrams for Underground Air Cooling Plants. J. J. P. Dolan. *Jour* So Af Inst Eng, Vol 35, p 154; discussion Vol 35, 36.
96. Some Special Features of Deep Mining on the Witwatersrand. W. C. Coe and J. P. Rees. *Jour* So Af Inst Eng, Vol 31, p 192
97. Surface Refrigeration at Turf Shaft of Robinson Deep. K. J. MacWilliams and J. T. McIntyre. *Jour* Chem Met & Min Soc, So Af, Vol 37, p 438
98. Air Conditioning for Ventilation of Butte Mines. A. S. Richardson. *E & M Jour*, Oct 1938, p 29
99. Ventilation and Air Conditioning of Magma Mine. C. B. Foraker. A I M E, *Tech Pub* No 979, 1938
100. Analysis and Design of Regenerative Compressed-Air Scheme for Mine Cooling. W. J. Walker and R. L. Straszacker. *Jour* So Af Inst Eng, Vol 37, p 22

INDEX

1